FIRE
PROTECTION
HANDBOOK
FOURTEENTH EDITION

FIRE
PROTECTION
HANDBOOK
FOURTEENTH EDITION

Gordon P. McKinnon, Editor

Keith Tower, Assistant Editor

NATIONAL FIRE PROTECTION ASSOCIATION

Boston, Massachusetts

First Impression, January 1976
Forty-five Thousand Copies

Previous Editions

First	1896
Second	1901
Third	1904
Fourth	1909
Fifth	1914
Sixth	1921
Seventh	1924
Eighth	1935
Ninth	1941
Tenth	1948
Eleventh	1954
Twelfth	1962
Thirteenth	1969

Library of Congress Catalog Card Number: 75-34683
NFPA Number: FPH1476
Standard Book Number: 87765-062-4
The National Fire Protection Association,
470 Atlantic Avenue, Boston, MA 02210
Copyright © 1976 by the National Fire Protection
Association. All rights reserved
Printed in the United States of America

Cover Design: Frank Lucas

Dedication

This Fourteenth Edition of the FIRE PROTECTION HANDBOOK
is dedicated with respect, admiration, and gratitude
to Paul C. Lamb who throughout a long career
in fire protection engineering has
contributed most generously of his time
and great abilities to the advancement of
the National Fire Protection Association
and its worthy objectives.

In the long history of the Association
few men have matched his service
as a member and chairman of technical committees,
as a Director, as Chairman of the Technical Advisory
Committee and of its successor, the Standards Council,
since that body came into being in 1974.

These and many other contributions,
together with the personal attributes of sound judgment,
persuasive leadership, and great tact
make Paul C. Lamb a most worthy recipient
of any honor the Association can bestow.

Paul C. Lamb

Contents

CONTENTS

Preface

A handbook, no matter the discipline or technology it represents, is a living document. If it has a history of previous editions, and expectations of editions to come, it must never represent itself as a definitive work. Rather, it should present itself as a contemporary summation of the state of the art in the field with which it is involved.

Thus, the Fourteenth Edition of the NFPA FIRE PROTECTION HANDBOOK is presented in the tradition of fulfilling the needs of the fire protection community for a single-source reference book on good contemporary fire protection practices. And in that tradition it is hoped that it will be as successful in meeting the information needs of its users as has been its thirteen predecessors to generations past, starting with the first slim volume in 1896. It continues, too, in the tradition of recognizing that while firesafety is, on one hand, increasingly complex because of scientific and technical advances, it continues, on the other hand, as a relatively simple matter more related to human acts of commission and omission than to technology. It is facetiously said, but so heartbreakingly true, that men, women, and children continue to be the three principal "causes" of destructive fires.

This edition represents a sharp departure from the traditional physical format of its predecessors. A new and larger trim size, double-columned text pages, new type faces, and a somewhat slimmer overall thickness contribute to a design that will make the HANDBOOK a much easier resource to use. But the physical format is only the vehicle for carrying what the NFPA staff and HANDBOOK editor feel is a much more comprehensive and useful content.

Those familiar with the Fourteenth Edition's immediate predecessor will note numerous changes from a comparison of the Table of Contents of the two volumes. Some sections have disappeared, others have had chapters added, while still others have been greatly modified as to the information they contain. The reorganization and additions were articulated to make the HANDBOOK a much more comprehensive and efficient text. For example, information on the fire hazard properties of materials and their storage, handling, and use, which previously appeared scattered throughout three different sections, is now consolidated into a single section (Fire Hazards of Materials) for easier reference to information concerning a particular material or commodity. Similar reorganization involving basic fire protection information in other sections of the text was accomplished in the interest of greater efficiency in use of the HANDBOOK.

More important, though, is the scope of new material that has been added in recognition of the many advances made in fire protection technology since the Thirteenth Edition was published in 1969. New fire problems, and the solutions to them, that in the last decade were only then beginning to make themselves known are now deserving of extensive attention. High-rise buildings, for example, received only passing mention in the last edition with no direct reference to their potential as a source of hazard to life. But in the ensuing years tragic fire incidents involving high-rise structures have occurred throughout the world. That, coupled with a growing body of knowledge on the movement of fire and products of combustion throughout tall buildings and the influence of specific design features on their inherent firesafety, have made such structures subjects of concern. Thus numerous references to high-rise structures will be found throughout the HANDBOOK. The same can be said for other facets of fire protection endeavors.

Perhaps a quick section-by-section summary of the contents of this new edition will best illustrate the scope of changes and additions.

Section 1—Introduction to Fire Protection: A thorough revision that more concisely puts into perspective the characteristics of the fire problems through reference to current data on loss of life and property from fire. A new introductory chapter discusses the complexities of the relationships between man and fire and the status of his efforts to control its disastrous effect.

Section 2—Characteristics and Behavior of Fire: The discussion on the characteristics and behavior of fire has been updated. New is a chapter on smoke movement in buildings.

Section 3—Fire Hazards of Materials: A consolidation and updating for easier reference to information on the fire hazard properties of materials and the hazards associated with their storage, handling, and use. Previously this information was spread throughout three sections in the Thirteenth Edition. The text of the fire hazards of fibers and textiles, and of explosives and blasting agents has been greatly expanded.

Section 4—Industrial and Process Fire Hazards: A completely new section devoted to more commonly encountered industrial equipments and processes and the fire hazards associated with them. Protection measures that can be taken to eliminate or reduce hazards are discussed.

Section 5—Special Fire Protection and Prevention Problems: A consolidation into one section of information on a variety of miscellaneous fire protection and prevention problems. While all of the subjects were covered in the previous edition, in recognition of the growing concern with the hazards associated with these subjects separate chapters have been prepared on materials handling equipments, oxygen-enriched atmospheres, medical gases, pesticides, laboratories, wildland fires, and electrical generating systems.

Section 6—Firesafety in Building Design and Construction: A complete restructuring of the presentation on the fire hazard aspects of building construction. New information includes a discussion of the systems approach to analyzing fire protection for structures and a refined step-by-step presentation of the concepts associated with good fire protection practices in building construction.

Section 7—Building Services: An update of the text on the fire hazards associated with building services. It includes a new chapter on refuse handling systems and equipments.

Section 8—The Hazards of Occupancies: A completely new Section that is concerned with life safety in the various classifications of occupancies. The opening chapter discusses fundamentals of human characteristics and behavior that must be considered in providing firesafe environments in buildings based upon predictable responses. Each following chapter identifies life hazard situations and factors contributing to them in the occupancy in question, e.g., residential and health care, and discusses life safety requirements associated with them.

Section 9—Public Fire Protection: The role of public fire protection is explained in terms of its organizational structure, administrative functions and operational procedures, and the facilities and equipment required in fulfilling its missions. A new chapter gives guidance on evaluation and planning of fire service functions.

Section 10—Organization for Private Protection: The responsibilities of the various levels of management in an organization for private fire protection are delineated. This section is essentially an update of similar text from the previous edition.

Section 11—Water Supplies for Fire Protection: Chapters on water supplies and facilities from the last edition were consolidated and revised for more convenient reference.

Section 12—Fire Alarm Systems, Detection Devices, and Guard Services: This text has been substantially revised based on similar chapters from the previous edition. A major change, coverage of alarm systems and detective devices in separate chapters, results in a more comprehensive presentation including more illustrations of alarm and detection systems and devices.

Section 13—Extinguishing Agents: The chapters on foam and halogenated agents have been completely rewritten, while the chapters on other extinguishing agents have been revised to reflect current knowledge concerning their uses and limitations.

Section 14—Water Sprinkler Systems: The chapters on sprinkler protection have been updated to reflect current practices in the installation and use of automatic sprinklers and related sprinkler equipment.

Section 15—Special Fire Protection Systems: Included is a new chapter on standpipe and hose systems that includes information on the specialized nature of installations in high-rise buildings. Another new chapter covers halogenated extinguishing systems while other chapters covering the longer established systems have been either completely rewritten or revised to reflect current state-of-the art in systems application and components.

Section 16—Portable Fire Extinguishers: Material on extinguishers represents a consolidation and updating of similar text from the previous edition. Guidance on the distribution of extinguishers throughout a building now includes diagrammatic representation of how to locate units to meet distribution requirements.

Section 17—Transportation Fire Hazards: A new chapter on rail rapid transit systems reflects the growing concern with fire hazards associated with the growth of urban transit systems. The text on railroad transportation addresses itself more specifically to hazards associated with rolling equipment while the chapter on marine transportation takes recognition of the firesafety concerns associated with small pleasure craft.

Section 18—Miscellaneous Data: Procedures to follow in preparing property inspection reports and plans as well as a series of useful mathematical and conversion tables and tables on the strength and size of materials make up this concluding section.

Appendices: Six appendices contain information that is complementary to the technical material in the main body of the text. Subjects covered include organizations with fire protection interests, fire testing and research laboratories, the role of the federal government in fire protection, and fire protection standards and laws.

In offering the Fourteenth Edition of the FIRE PROTECTION HANDBOOK, the editor solicits suggestions for changes in the interest of making future editions more responsive to the needs of HANDBOOK users. Every effort has been made to make the text consistent with the best available information on current fire protection practices, but the National Fire Protection Association, as a body, is not responsible for its contents, as there has been no opportunity for the association membership to review the HANDBOOK prior to its publication. If readers discover errors, the editor would appreciate their being called to his attention.

Gordon P. McKinnon, Editor

Acknowledgements

A handbook is the work of many individuals. Thus the editor wishes to acknowledge those who have made contributions to the compilation of this Fourteenth Edition of the FIRE PROTECTION HANDBOOK.

As with previous editions, the major share of the work in compiling the text was accomplished by members of the NFPA Executive Office staff. Special appreciation is directed to **Richard E. Stevens,** Assistant Vice President (Standards), for his diligent review of all technical text and to **Keith Tower,** Assistant Editor, for his skilled work in preparing the text for publication. Special thanks also go to **Amy Meterparel,** Secretary, for her help in the lengthy project.

Printing arrangements were under the skillful guidance of **Donald McGonagle** of the Graphic Arts Production Department. Special thanks are due the Editorial Assistants in that Department for their help in processing materials for this HANDBOOK.

NFPA staff members who devoted many hours to the content of this HANDBOOK are listed below alphabetically with the sincere appreciation of the editor.

Chester I. Babcock, Division Director (editorial).
Robert C. Barr, Fire Service Specialist.
Robert E. Benedetti, Fire Protection Specialist.
Peter M. Bochnak, Fire Protection Specialist.
Michael DiMeo, Fire Analysis Specialist.
Martin E. Grimes, Division Director (public protection).
Robert M. Hodnett, Fire Protection Specialist.
George K. Horvath, Special Assistant to the Vice President.
William D. Jordan, Hospital Fire Safety Specialist.
George C. Koth, Engineer.
Paul R. Lyons, Fire Service Editor.
Barbara L. Manning, Standards Assistant.
Ronald K. Mellott, Senior Fire Service Specialist.
John Ottoson, Fire Data Analyst.
Charles S. Morgan, President.
Carl E. Peterson, Field Representative (data systems).
Homer S. Pringle, Staff Counsel.
Kamala Raghavan, Librarian.
Kent M. Savage, Marine Field Specialist.
Arel R. Sessions, Assistant Electrical Field Service Specialist.
Wilford I. Summers, Electrical Field Service Specialist.
Robert J. Thompson, Assistant Director (engineering services).
George H. Tryon, Assistant Vice President (member relations).
Wilbur L. Walls, Engineer, Gases Field Service Specialist.
A. Elwood Willey, Assistant Director (engineering services).
Miles E. Woodworth, Flammable Liquids Field Service Specialist.

Three Former NFPA staff members made contributions to the HANDBOOK. They are **J. Thomas Hughes,** formerly Washington Representative; **Michael J. Slifka,** formerly Fire Protection Specialist, and **Laurence J. Watrous,** formerly Field Representative (fire protection systems). **Joseph J. Worthen,** a summer internist in the NFPA staff counsel's office, was instrumental in the compilation of information on fire protection standards and laws that appears in Appendix D.

While the NFPA staff was deeply involved in preparation of the HANDBOOK, others, to whom the editor is unsparing in his gratitude, shared in the task by serving as authors of new material or of major revisions of selected portions of the text. Those who contributed of their time and talent and the areas in which they made their contributions are:

Donald Belles, P.E., SFPE; Fire Protection Consultant, Hendersonville, Tenn. (egress design and health care occupancies).

Henry P. Beltramine, CSP, Assistant Director for Plant Services Peter Bent Brigham Hospital, (laboratory firesafety).

Samuel Billings, ESA, IBS; U.S. Environmental Protection Agency (retired), (pesticides).

John A. Blair, AIChE, SPE; Senior Consultant, Plastics Department, Technical Services Laboratory, E.I. duPont de Nemours and Company, Inc. (plastics).

J. Ward Bush, SFPE, Industrial Security and Fire Protection consultant, East Peoria, Ill. (private fire protection).

Harold C. Clar, Code Consultant, Los Angeles, Calif. (educational occupancies).

Bert M. Cohen, P.E., SFPE, ASSE; Vice President, Gage-Babcock and Associates (records protection).

W. D. Cook, ASME, LP-Gas Consultant, Silver Spring, Md. (fire hazards of gases).

Glenn H. Damon, ACS, AIC, AIChE; Reemployed Annuitant, Bureau of Mines, U.S. Department of Interior (explosives and blasting agents).

William H.L. Dornette, M.D., ACLM, ASA; Director of Education and Research, Division of Anesthesiology, The Cleveland Clinic (medical gases).

William H. Doyle, SFPE, AIChE, NSPE; Consultant, Simsbury, Conn. (chemical processing equipment).

Robert W. Fitzgerald, P.E., Associate Professor of Civil Engineering, Worcester Polytechnic Institute (building design and construction).

Charles L. Ford, AIChE, Market Manager, Organic Chemicals Department, Fire Extinguishants, E.I. duPont de Nemours and Company, Inc. (halogenated extinguishing agents and systems).

George J. Frankel, AIAA, IES; Group Head, Mechanical Systems Test Engineering, Grumman Aerospace Corporation (oxygen enriched atmospheres).

Walter M. Haessler, P.E., SFPE, ASME, Engineering Specialist, Florida State Fire College (fire and explosion control).

William Hiotaky, AIA, Vice President, The Taubman Co. (mercantile occupancies).

Oliver W. Johnson, P.E., SFPE, ACS; Vice President, GasTech, Inc. (static electricity).

Philip E. Johnson, SFPE, Chief Engineer-Special Hazards, Factory Mutual Research Corp. (dry chemical agents and systems).

Robert L. Jones, Safety Code Coordinator, Carrier Air Conditioning Co. (refrigeration systems).

Helen Kahn, Washington Bureau Chief *Automotive News* (motor vehicles).

Warren Y. Kimball, Fire Service Consultant, Jamestown, R.I. (public fire protection).

Carroll V. Lovett, SFPE, ASSE, Manager-Fire Protection Operations, Xerox Corp. (building services).

Edward H. McCormack, Jr., Chief, Massachusetts Fire Fighting Academy (public fire protection).

Donald N. Meldrum, SFPE, ACS, President, National Foam Systems, Inc. (foam extinguishing agents and systems).

Harry H. McIntyre, Harry McIntyre Associates (identification of hazards of materials).

Harold E. Nelson, SFPE, Chief, Program for Design Standards, National Bureau of Standards (business occupancies).

Eugene P. Nunes, ASSE, Safety Supervisor, Bay Area Rapid Transit District (rapid transit systems).

Marshall E. Peterson, P.E., SFPE, CSP, Fire Protection Engineer, Rolf Jensen and Associates (portable fire extinguishers).

David R. Sayers, Formerly Fire Chemicals Manager, ICI (United States) Inc. (halogenated extinguishing agents and systems).

Joseph F. Schulz, ASHRAE, President, Van-Packer Products Co. (refuse handling systems).

Richard F. Schwab, P.E., SFPE, AIChE; Manager, Loss Prevention, Allied Chemical Corp. (explosions and hazards of dusts).
James M. Simmons, P.E., SFPE, BSCE; Senior Engineer-Industrial Heating, Factory Mutual Research Corp. (ovens and furnaces).
Orville M. Slye, Jr., P.E., SFPE; Associate Engineer, Mobil Research and Development Corp. (industrial occupancies).
C. Walter Stickney, SFPE, Oregon State Fire Marshal (retired), Salem, Ore. (public fire protection).
Richard L. Tuve, AIC, AAS, ACS; Staff Consultant, Johns Hopkins University Applied Physics Laboratory (foam extinguishing agents and systems).
James C. Vonderhaar, Assistant Director of Insurance, Southern Railway System (railroad transportation).
George E. Weldon, Senior Engineer-Nuclear Specialist, Factory Mutual Research Corporation (nuclear reactors and radiation machines).
Francis W. Wischmeyer, ASSE, CSP; Safety Section Supervisor, Eastman Kodak Co. (explosion venting, suppression and prevention systems).
J. Herbert Witte, P.E., Consultant, Lincolnwood, Ill. (heating appliances and systems).
William S. Wood, P.E., ACS, AIChE; Chemical Safety Consultant, William S. Wood and Associates (industrial and emergency waste control).
Calvin H. Yuill, SFPE, Consultant, San Antonio, Tex. (building materials).

Generous in giving of their time in reviewing chapters from the Thirteenth Edition and in offering suggestions for revisions as a prelude to preparing text for the new Edition were the following:
J.C. Abbott, Consultant, Bucks, England; **John L. Abbott,** Chief Systems Engineer, Factory Mutual Research Corporation; **A. Richard Albrecht,** Loss Prevention Specialist, The Dow Chemical Company; **John R. Anderson,** Staff Supervisor, Insurance Services Office, New England Region; **Raynal W. Andrews, Jr.,** Consultant, Pittsburgh, Penna.; **Benjamin B. Aycock,** District Office Supervisor, Insurance Services Office, North Carolina District Office; **Donal M. Baird,** Coordinator, Public Fire Protection Surveys, Insurer's Advisory Organization; **E. Arthur Bell,** Consultant, Stamford, Conn.; **John P. Benedict,** Vice President of Operations, Benedict-Miller, Inc.; **H.C. Bigglestone,** Staff Supervisor, Public Protection, Insurance Services Office, Pacific Region; **C.E. Blome,** Consultant to Metalbestos Systems, Wallace-Murray Corporation; **Deane Boddorf,** Manager, Technical Services, Explosives Division, Hercules, Inc.; **Kenneth J. Carl,** Director of Municipal Surveys, Insurance Services Office; **John D. Coons,** Senior Engineer-Chemical Specialist, Factory Mutual Research Corporation; **Ralph E. Cramer,** Chief Standardization Engineer, American Gas Association Laboratories; **John J. Crowe,** Consultant, Airco Inc.; **A.D. Curl,** Managing Director, Walter Kiddie & Company of Canada, Limited; **Robert C. Davis,** General Administrator-Fire Protection and Safety, General Motors Corporation, Chevrolet Motor Division; **John G. Degenkolb,** Consulting Fire Protection Engineer, Director of Safety, Association of Motion Picture & Television, Inc.; **Donald A. Diehl,** Senior Fire Protection Engineer, Pyrotronics, Inc.; **Donald L. Drumm,** Assistant Director, municipal survey service, Insurance Services Office; **H.W. Eickner,** Research Project Leader, U.S. Department of Agriculture, Forest Products Laboratory.
Also: **Robert Ely,** formerly Assistant Fire Chief, San Diego Calif. Fire Department; **Lawrence M. Engleman,** Fire Protection Coordinator, Washington Metropolitan Area Transit Authority; **Slade B. Gamble,** Projects Manager, Flinn & Dreffien Engineering Co.; **Rudolph H. Golde,** Consultant, London, England; **Scott K. Goodwin,** Executive Engineer-National, Factory Insurance Association; **George J. Grabowski,** Manager, Protection Systems Division, Fenwal, Inc.; **Harvey L. Hansberry,** formerly Chief, Aircraft Safety Division, NAFEC, Federal Aviation Administration; **Charles J. Hart,** Associate Director of Services

Codes and Standards, National Electrical Contractors Association; **Roger E. Hatton,** Technical Services Manager, Monsanto Industrial Chemicals Company; **John E. Heilman,** Director of Engineering, Processing Division, Continental Grain Company; **Harry Hickey,** Professor, Fire Protection Engineering Curriculum, University of Maryland; **Chief Raymond M. Hill,** Fire Prevention Bureau, Fire Department, Los Angeles, Calif.; **George W. Huckeba,** Director, Pollution Control and Chemical Services, Liberty Mutual Insurance Company; **Richard E. Hughey,** Chief Engineer, Insurance Services Office; **Raymond B. Hunter,** American Air Filter Company, Inc.; **Ernest Kaswell,** Director, Fabric Research Laboratories Division, Albany International Corporation; **Haik R. Kazarian,** Manager, Engineering Services, Grinnell Fire Protection Systems Company, Inc.; **Hugh V. Keepers,** Consultant, Dallas, Texas; **Donald J. Kerlin,** Technical Advisor to Chief, Merchant Marine Technical Division, Office of Merchant Marine Safety, U.S. Coast Guard; **Alfred W. Krulee,** Norris Industries, Fire and Safety Equipment Division.

Also: **F. Owen Kubias,** Division Safety Coordinator, Glidden-Durkee Division, SCM Corporation; **Louis E. LaFehr,** Executive Vice President, International Association of Electrical Inspectors; **Paul C. Lamb,** Consultant, Englewood, N.J.; **Robert W. Lassell,** Sales Manager, Radio Communications, Eagle Signal; **Dee L. Lockwood,** Assistant Corporate Insurance Manager, Western International Hotels Company; **Norman R. Lockwood,** Engineering Consultant, Mobil Research & Development Corporation; **Jeremiah R. Lynch,** Assistant Associate Director, National Institute of Occupational Safety and Health; **Clarence A. McCorrison,** Assistant Chief Systems Engineer, Factory Mutual Research Corporation; **Allan J. McQuade,** Chief, Polymers and Organic Materials Branch, U.S. Army, Natick Development Center; **Irving Mande,** Director, Fire Alarm Products, Edwards Company, Inc.; **Frank J. Mapp,** Assistant Engineering Manager, American Telephone and Telegraph Company; **Dr. Charles M. Mason,** Supervising Research Chemist, Pittsburgh Mining and Safety Research Center, Bureau of Mines; **Lewis G. Matthews,** Manager, Safety Affairs, Union Carbide Corporation, Linde Division; **Walter W. Maybee,** Fire Protection Engineer, U.S. Energy Research and Development Administration; **Stephen Mazzoni,** Manager, Santa Clara Office, Underwriters Laboratories, Inc.; **Dr. Emery P. Miller,** formerly Vice President, Ransburg Corporation; **Robert Nespeco,** Staff Engineer, National Oil Fuel Institute; **James W. Nolan,** President, James W. Nolan Company; **Howard O'Drain,** Jr., Assistant Chief, Philadelphia Fire Department; **James F. O'Regan,** President, Feecon Corporation.

Also: **Theodore Pearce,** formerly Executive Vice President, National Fluid Power Association; **Parker Peterson,** Assistant Manager, Protection Systems Division, Fenwal, Inc.; **Patrick E. Phillips,** Senior Fire Protection Engineer, Nevada Operations Office, U.S. Energy Research and Development Administration; **Reuben P. Prichard,** Jr. Director, Safety and Environmental Health, National Aeronautics and Space Administration; **George A. Quandee,** Property Insurance Administrator, ESMARK (Swift): **J. Sharp Queener,** formerly Manager of Safety and Fire Protection, E.I. duPont de Nemours Company, Inc.; **Jack N. Richards,** formerly Chief, Seattle Fire Department; **R. C. Richards,** Fire Safety Research Project Manager, U.S. Coast Guard Research and Development Center; **Dr. John A. Rockett,** Chief, Program for Physics and Dynamics of Fire, National Bureau of Standards; **William M. Rosenfeld,** Director of Association Services, National Association of Engine and Boat Manufacturers; **Anthony Santos,** Assistant Chief Engineer-Special Hazards, Factory Mutual Research Corporation; **George W. Saunders,** Managing Engineer, Burglary Protection and Signaling Department, Underwriters Laboratories, Inc.; **Leon G. Schaller,** Consultant, E.I. duPont de Nemours & Company, Inc.; **Chester W. Schirmer,** President, Schirmer Engineering Corporation; **William A. Schmidt,** Office of Construction, Veterans Administration; **R.W. Shaul,** Assistant Manager Safety Regulations, National Electrical Manufacturers Association; **Dr. Edwin E. Smith,** Director of Chemical Engineering Research, Ohio State University; **Richard B. Smith,** Division of Operational Safety, U.S. Atomic Energy Commission; **Edward C. Sommer,** Senior Engineering Associate, Exxon Research and Engineering Company; **James H. Stannard,** Jr., Consulting Engineer, Basking Ridge, N.J.

Also: **Norman V. Steere,** Minneapolis, Minn.; **Howard H. Summers,** Jr., Assistant Chief Fire Marshal, State Fire Marshal's Office, Richmond, Va.; **Richard L. Swift,** Product Line Manager, portable instruments, Mine Safety Appliances Company; **Nicholas L. Talbot,** Senior Engineer, Improved Risk Mutuals; **George T. Tamura,** Senior Research Officer, National Research Council Canada; **Hugh E. Thompson,** Director of Fire Protection, Hiram Walker & Sons Limited; **James E. Troutman,** Assistant General Manager and Manager of Engineering, Factory Insurance Association; **Theodore A. Ventrome,** Manager of Safety and Loss Prevention, American Cyanamid Company; **Clay B. Wade,** Staff Supervisor-Policy Services, Insurance Services Office-Southeastern Region; **James J. Walker,** Manager, Process Safety and Fire Protection, Chemical and Plastics Division, Union Carbide Corporation; **Abraham A. Willan,** Furnace and Machine Tool Engineer, Pratt & Whitney Aircraft Division, United Technologies Corporation; **Dr. Frederick Williams,** Head, Combustion Section, Naval Research Laboratory; **H. V. Williamson,** Manager, Research & Development, Fire Systems Division, Chemetron Corporation; **Jack E. Gray,** Chief, Fire Prevention and Protection Division, Fort Detrick, Frederick, MD; **Jack A. Wood,** Vice President, The Viking Corporation; **George M. Woods,** HPR Staff Officer, Kemper Insurance Companies; **R.J. Wright,** Section Engineer, Underwriters Laboratories of Canada; **Peter R. Yurkonis,** Consulting Engineer, Rolf Jensen & Associates; **John C. Zercher,** Manager, Chemical Transportation Emergency Center, Manufacturing Chemists Association; **Ben A. Zimmer,** Associate Managing Engineer, Fire Protection Department, Underwriters Laboratories, Inc.

SECTION 1

INTRODUCTION TO FIRE PROTECTION

Chapter 1

FIRE AND MAN'S ENVIRONMENT

The control and use of fire, like the ability to reason and to walk upright, is a characteristic peculiar to human beings. Man has had fire as companion and servant since long before the dawn of recorded history, yet today his mastery is far from perfect and his understanding limited.

There is today scarcely any aspect of our lives to which fire is not a contributing element. Far beyond the human needs for cooked food and heated shelter, fire is essential to a developed society based on technology. As man's environment expanded from the cave, so did his application of fire and so did his need to understand and master the phenomenon.

Fire continues to exact an enormous and dreadful toll from society—a toll measured in pain, suffering, and death; a toll that is also measured in wasteful destruction of property, not sparing irreplaceable historic and cultural treasures, with consequent economic costs tending always to depress the standard of living.

Man's understanding of fire, imperfect though it is, has been sufficient to enable him to develop the technology of control to a reasonably advanced state. Indeed, our failure to minimize the fire threat to life and property lies not in a lack of technology or available means, but rather in social attitudes, in business economics, and in practical politics.

Fire is not perceived by most people as a significant personal threat to themselves. Though they acknowledge the existence of the danger of fire, it is rarely personalized and then only in relation to others. For most persons fire is too remote a possibility to evoke an action response, and the resulting apathetic attitude subverts fire prevention education and obstructs practical application of fire protection knowledge.

The application of fire protection technology to safeguard life or property involves expense, and dollars for safety always come hard. Taking a calculated risk often appears more attractive than the investment of substantial funds in protective facilities, particularly when the penalty of a faulty calculation may be substantially mitigated by insurance. While the economic wastage is equally great whether or not property destroyed by fire is insured, this fact is obscured by the natural effects of the insurance concept itself. The very uncertainty of fire is an everpresent temptation to risk taking and the consequent avoidance of expensive fire protection. These facts lead to business decisions which, in many instances, result in substantial losses of property by fire—losses which could have been averted if an alternative had been sufficiently attractive.

Another variable factor which must be considered is, in nature, political. Laws are enacted by political bodies to require that minimum of provision for firesafety of life and property which society demands. Such laws invariably lag far behind the technology of firesafety. Lawmakers, being elected officials, rarely display leadership in pursuit of safety, an unpopular course, offensive to the property owners affected, and likely to lead to retribution at the polls. Handwringing and lamentation, though unlikely to avert a recurrence of a fire disaster, is safer political behavior than forthright corrective action. Thus is progress toward the firesafe environment slowed to a crawl.

While the material losses from fire are enormous and measurable to a considerable degree, the human losses are not easily calculated. As Dr. Norman R. Bernstein* has described, "The initial shock from a burn is dreadful. . . . The traumatic experience alone can be remembered for a lifetime, but add to this the long siege in the hospital. The separation from family and friends, repeated surgery, repeated anesthesia with the dread of dying each time the patient is forcibly reduced to unconsciousness, the painful treatment, the application of discoloring and hurtful chemicals, and the inevitable time of sadness, dejection, and hopelessness that comes with major burns are all superadded. Families go through parallel reactions, going from shock to dread, to fear for the life of a seriously burned relative, and then the chronic apprehension and burden of concern about how the patient will look and what the different medical procedures will entail. For all members of a family in which someone has been burned, there is a sense of guilt and culpability that can lead to chronic tainting of home life. . . . This is a loss that is not measurable in monetary terms, though it is the most terrible kind of social price that can be paid."

A proper concern for humanity demands an end to conditions which present unnecessary and avoidable possibilities of destructive fire and an intensification of firesafety education employing the most effective methods of motivation. Such an approach to a solution to the fire problem must be supported by a developed technology, and it is a purpose of this HANDBOOK to provide fundamental technical information upon which educational programs may be built.

A. Fire and Research

Understanding fire from inception to flaming combustion and beyond is essential if man is to control the destructive nature of fire. Fundamental to this understanding is the research (both basic and applied) required so that all concerned can better deal with fire.

Since World War II countless millions of dollars have been spent in research on fire. The impetus following the war came from the need to evaluate the effects of atomic and nuclear bombs which not only destroy through the effects of blast and radiation, but also result in multiple ignitions in combustible materials. There was also a need to know more about the combustion process to develop better and more efficient jet engines. From this beginning, further work has been accomplished in understanding the combustion process, which, amongst other benefits, has led to the development of extinguishing agents that interrupt the combustion process rather than extinguish by the conventional process of cooling or smothering.

Further basic research has evolved into studies of thermal columns, flame, the mechanism of flame spread, the composition of smoke and other products of combustion, the mechanism of heat transfer, the effect of ventilation on fire severity, and predicting flashover. These are only typical examples of the many facets that have been explored.

---

* Dr. Norman R. Bernstein, M.D., Chief of Psychiatry, Shriners Burn Institute, Boston.

As new problems arise as a result of new products and techniques, or as inquiring minds prompt reevaluations of existing methods, applied research has been conducted in such diverse areas as corridor tests to study the contribution of wall and ceiling finishes and floor covering to fire spread, room burnouts to study fire spread and flashover, protection techniques for high-piled storage, measuring the rate of smoke production from materials and the obscuration of smoke, and numerous full scale tests to study the burning characteristics of materials and assemblies. Probably one of the most significant series of full scale tests was the series conducted by the Los Angeles Fire Department in condemned school buildings from 1959 to 1961. Those tests, focused national attention on smoke as the initial killer in fires, and led to a reevaluation of many of the fire protection concepts prevalent at that time.

The phenomenon of fire involves an infinite combination of variables. While it may appear to be an impossible task to research and quantify all of those variables, it is vitally important that enough of them be researched to permit the prevention of as many fire incidents as possible, and to permit a reasonably accurate prediction of the outcome should fire initiation occur.

In both the public and private sectors the United States spends about $105 million annually on fire-related research and development. It would be difficult to define an adequate level of investment against which this figure could be compared. But, despite the progress made since World War II, certain deficiencies remain; these run the gamut from imperfect, though growing, understanding of the combustion phenomenon; methods of treatment of burns and smoke victims; and applied research related to product development.

An overriding concern is that throughout the process of studying fire, it is important that there be a continuous dialogue between the researcher and the fire protectionist so that each will benefit from the knowledge and understanding of the other. It is equally important that the fire protectionist use the results of research to upgrade his knowledge of fire and thereby do a better job in reducing the loss of life and property by fire.

B. The Technology of Fire Control

Research, fire experience, and engineering fundamentals provide the tools by which fire problems can be assessed and solutions found. The practitioner uses these tools to make a total assessment of each problem to design the solution and then to plan the method by which the solution will be implemented. Finally, he may supervise the implementation and completion of the solution to the problem and test the result. The problem may vary in magnitude from smoking in theaters to the firesafe design of a large building or complex industrial process. In any case, the assessment and solution must be approached in a systematic manner taking into consideration all the factors affecting the problem and the solution. This is the typical engineering approach. To assist the practitioner in a systems analysis to fire problems, an entire chapter of this HANDBOOK is devoted to that subject and specific guidelines are provided. It will be noted that there are two alternative approaches to a fire problem: prevent ignition or control fire impact.

If ignition is to be prevented, at least within a reasonable probability, and if ignition prevention is to be the sole criterion for firesafety, it would be necessary to know the energy required for ignition to occur, the conditions under which that energy is relevant, and all sources of that required energy. If that knowledge is required for only one substance or material, the knowledge may be available or obtained by research. If, however, there are many substances, materials, and energy sources to be considered (as, for example, in a building), the problem becomes much more complex. Considerable research has been done on the ignition characteristics of many substances and materials, particularly for process hazard control. Obviously there is practically an infinite number of materials, substances, and conditions under which they may exist. Therefore, it would not be correct to say that knowledge in this area is by any means complete. In addition, as technology advances, new substances, new materials, and new conditions develop making the job of the practitioner even more difficult. It is thus essential that research be continued, hopefully at an accelerated pace. Then too, human failure must be considered, since technology has not yet advanced to the point where the human being is not a factor.

If the fire impact is to be controlled, ignition is assumed and several alternate approaches are possible. In assessing these approaches it is necessary to study the rate of fire growth, fire spread, and the products of combustion and how lack of them is related to the means of fire impact control selected. These factors may be assessed by a knowledge of the physical and chemical characteristics of the fuel, its fire characteristics, and its disposition in relation to other fuels of similar or different characteristics. This subject has been researched to some extent, but largely for the purpose of measuring results that simulate conditions known to have been problems in specific fires (e.g., flame spread through corridors, and fire growth and spread in various fuel arrays in warehouses and rooms in certain occupancies). Research on the products of combustion has centered on toxicity, obscuration, and spread of those products in high buildings. This phase of consideration of controlling fire impact has been particularly affected by the introduction of new materials which, although used in what are classified as light hazard occupancies, have very high calorific values, burn with great rapidity, and give off prodigious quantities of toxic and vision-obscuring smoke.

The remainder of the decisions to be made to control the fire impact involve the use of techniques that have been quite thoroughly investigated by basic research, applied research, and fire experience. The decisions involve the use of such fundamental concepts as compartmentation, exposure protection, automatic fire detection, and manual and automatic fire suppression. Each of these concepts are further subdivided to be as sophisticated and all encompassing as the practitioner may require. In addition, codes and standards are available that provide the guidance necessary to assure adequacy of each control feature selected.

C. The Social Organization and Fire Control

Pascal said, "Man is only a reed; but he is a thinking reed." When confronted with a task which requires propositional thought, man—social animal that he is—has always functioned best when that task required him to marshal his intellectual, physical, and social resources into effective patterns of action for the common good. And in this instance the tremendous task of organizing available resources in order to attack the fire waste problem intelligently is of paramount concern.

But sadly the motivation to maintain a concerted attack on the fire problem is shadowed by public ignorance and apathy—ignorance of the true significance of the depth of the fire problem, not only as a threat to personal welfare in a combustible environment but to the material resources of our nation, and apathy toward using intelligently the knowledge already possessed to mitigate fire losses. A peculiarly American quality—an extravagance nurtured by an early American tradition which found our ancestors in a land of apparently inexhaustible resources—has tended to denigrate the magnitude of the irretrievable nature of losses through fire as it has the dangers from wanton use of natural resources. Time is running out, and the attitude of conservation must be enhanced—a massive change in a social attitude deserving increasing attention from the fire community.

The patterns of social movement, brought on by changing economic conditions and an advancing general technology, also have added enlarged facets to the fire problem. One is the increasing trend towards urbanization. Half a century ago, about half our nation's population lived in urban areas; today, about three out of four Americans do. Intensive use of land in urban areas means bigger buildings, clogged streets, and in general a more constant exposure to the perils of fire from a myriad of sources in the physical environment. High-rise buildings, for example, though hallmarks of urban progress, concentrate people in confined areas where they are exposed to fire dangers and elements of risk that only now are beginning to be realized.

Urbanization also has created other unique social problems that have affected the magnitude of fire losses not necessarily measured in monetary terms. The most run-down neighborhoods, where dilapidated buildings are tinder boxes, are where the poor are forced to live. Crowded apartment houses and tenement buildings often reflect total indifference to firesafety because landlords see no profit in decent, long-term upkeep of their properties. Discontent and neglect in the ghettos can breed problems for fire departments in the form of riots, set fires, false alarms, and harassment of fire fighters. Solutions are not easy and extend beyond control and direction by the fire community, but the conditions exemplify how totally enmeshed in the fabric of our social structure are many of the fire problems.

Another social change pertinent to our nation's fire protection is the increased militancy of municipal employees, including the fire service, in demanding higher wages and better working conditions. And this militancy meets, head on, another important change: the increasing financial plight of local governments. Especially in the large cities, but not exclusively there, governments are facing static or declining tax revenues, increasing costs, and hence the need to question all city expenditures and to place greater emphasis on the efficient operation of municipal services. Local governments are demanding better long-range planning and better utilization of manpower and equipment. They are pressing fire departments to produce sophisticated cost-benefit justifications for their expenditures. They are demanding that fire departments operate more efficiently without jeopardizing the public's safety from fire.*

This makes pertinent a further trend: the increasing application of management science to solve these local problems. Local governments are relying more and more on a critical review of municipal services, including cost-benefit ratios in relation to effect on public safety. Thus does the fire service require application of new skills on the part of its members to meet the demands of good management of its affairs.

The educational and intellectual aspirations of the fire service, in terms of technical knowledge and professional goals, is finding increasing response from the academic community. In recent years as the number of community colleges in the nation has grown in response to an expressed need for education at a level heretofore denied to many, so has grown the offerings of fire science curricula to meet the specific needs of the fire service and the fire protection community as a whole. A National Fire Academy, under the aegis of the federal government, where fire service officers and candidate officers can receive advanced training, is soon to be a reality.

Yet there is a dichotomy involved when viewing the growing sophistication of the public fire service and the attendant cost of maintaining it. The fire service is viewed fundamentally as an emergency force that must respond when something somewhere goes awry. It is almost as if it is an accepted right of a person or corporation to create a fire threat to a community and then depend for its control on forces provided from the public purse. Yet as this disquieting attitude prevails, there is available a variety of systems for the prompt detection and rapid extinguishment of fires. This "private" protection, although extensively used in the United States, is still extremely limited in relation to its potential and the need. Again, the technology is available, but the impetus for a change in social attitude comes slowly.

Response to society's changing needs is vital to improving the nation's security against losses from fire. And the response must be in national harmony rather than in cacophonies. If it is the interest of one sector to move ahead with vigor in the direction it sees to be the way to reach the goal, it must be done in unity with other sectors striving for the same goal.

Creation within the federal government of the National Fire Prevention and Control Administration (NFPCA) as an aftermath of a study by the National Commission on Fire Prevention and Control early in this decade is an excellent example in point. The very fact that the NFPCA was created illustrates the burgeoning concern in the public sector with the need to attack the nation's fire problems in concert with other sectors of the national community. The NFPCA is charged with contributing a major effort toward reducing losses of life and property from fire through public education, improved training of the fire service, a technology development program, and a national data center. There is a familiar ring to the NFPCA's goals. They are shared with others, such as the National Fire Protection Association, which has pursued similar goals for more than three-quarters of a century. The important point is, though, that the total effort can be enhanced as resources heretofore not available come into being which hopefully will have a synergistic effect on the total fire protection effort.

The continuing reinforcement of the interrelationships between the public and private sectors, and the academic, professional, and technical communities is necessary if an even more cohesive and intelligent approach to the fire problem is to take place. The adequacy of research, both by government and by private organizations, must be assured; the urgency of the fire protection message must be emphasized with clarity so there is intelligent and far-reaching response to it; and the social problems of our time, both in terms of individuals and institutions, must be recognized fully by the fire protection community which in turn must show its willingness to participate forcefully in the solutions. Short of that would be failure.

---

* *America Burning: Report of the National Commission on Fire Prevention and Control,* U.S. Government Printing Office, Washington, D.C., 1973.

Chapter 2

FIRE CASUALTIES

Throughout the world fire takes a heavy toll of human life. The progress that has been made in controlling this tragic waste has been due primarily to the intelligent application of the principles of fire prevention and protection discussed in other sections of this HANDBOOK.

In this chapter, the present and past record of destruction of life by fires and explosions in the United States is reported, and the factors affecting life safety from fire are discussed. In the other chapters of this Section, property damage is similarly treated, fire investigating and reporting are discussed, and large loss fires and conflagrations are analyzed.

A. Deaths and Injuries by Fire

According to estimates by the NFPA Fire Analysis Department, the annual fire death toll in the United States has averaged about 12,000 per year over the last 20 years. The number increased in absolute terms until 1970. Since then, it has shown a slight decline. (In 1974 the estimate was 11,600, a decline of 100 from the previous year.) In general, the risk of death from fire to a given individual has been declining fairly steadily, as can be seen from the death rate per million population (see Fig. 1-2A).

A high fire death rate seems to be peculiarly an American problem. No other industrialized nation comes close to the American fire death rate (see Fig. 1-2B).

Fire Injuries

Personal injury by fire, always painful and often disfiguring, involves about ten times the number of deaths in the United States. According to estimates by the NFPA at least 123,000 fire-related injuries occurred in the United States in 1974. Every fire injury is a potential fatality,

although improvement in medical techniques has substantially improved the chances of recovery from serious fire injuries.

Nonfatal fire casualties are principally due to burns and to the inhalation of carbon monoxide and other gaseous products of combustion, though many casualties involve various other types of injury.

Trend of Fire Casualties

The principal reason that gradual improvements in life safety have not resulted in a more significant downward trend in the actual number of fire casualties in the rapid growth of population in recent years. From 1964 to 1974 the number of people in the United States increased about 10 percent. During the same period, the annual death rate from fire decreased 2½ percent.

The annual total of fire deaths is continuing, however, at a high level in spite of improvements in building construction, more widespread installation of automatic protection, more effective fire prevention campaigns, and more efficient fire department operation. While these factors have all had their effect in improving life safety from fire, there have been other offsetting factors, particularly the progressive increase in the smoking habit and the general increase in the use of flammable liquids.

B. NFPA Definition of Fire Casualty

The discrepancies among statistics on fire casualties reported by various agencies have been due in large part to

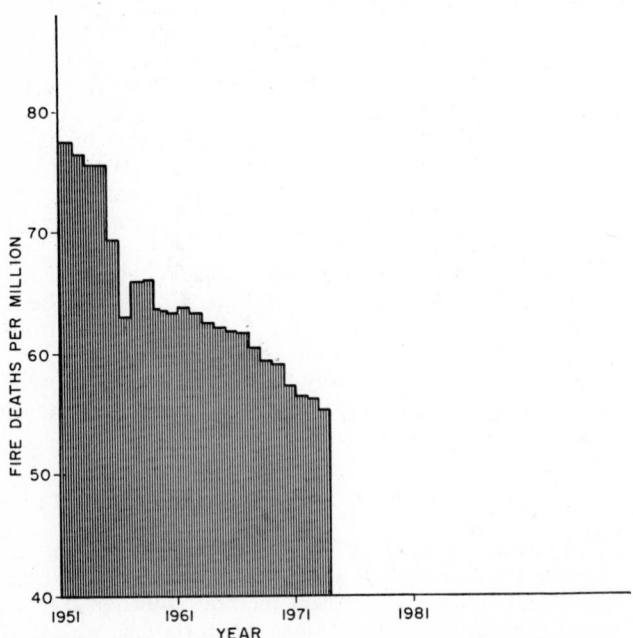

Fig. 1-2A. Trends in fire deaths in the United States.

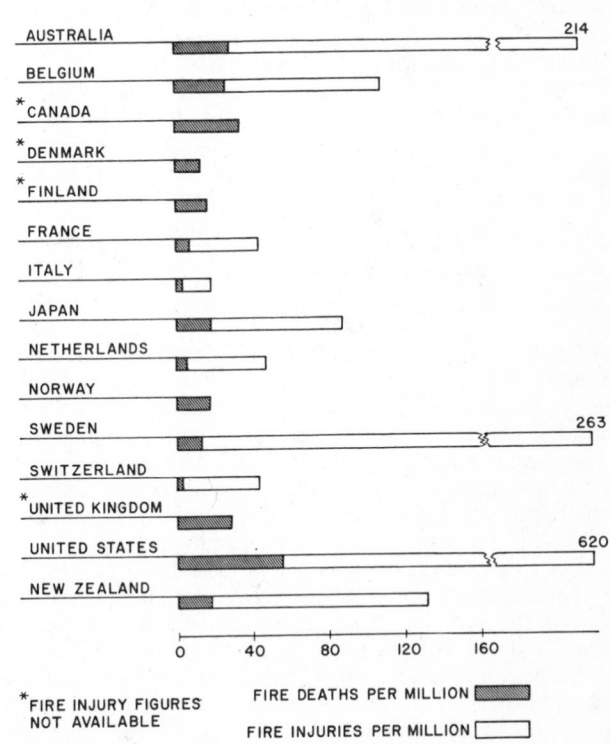

Fig. 1-2B. International fire deaths and injuries per million of population.

lack of agreement as to just what constitutes a fire casualty. In an effort to eliminate this confusion, the NFPA Committee on Fire Reporting developed the following definition of injuries and deaths that should be included in a tabulation of fire casualties:

Fire Casualty: A fire casualty is a person receiving an injury or death resulting from a fire. The causes of fire casualties are classified as direct or indirect. Direct fire casualties are those where injuries or deaths are due to fire. Indirect fire casualties are those where injuries or deaths are due in part to fire, but some other cause is assigned as primarily responsible.

Fire Injury: A fire injury is one suffered as the result of a fire that requires (or should require) treatment by a practitioner of medicine within one year of the fire or explosion (regardless of whether treatment was actually received).

Fire Death: A fire death is a fire casualty which is fatal or becomes fatal within one year of the fire.

More Than One Cause of Death: Where a death may be due to more than one cause, one of which is a fire cause, the classification made by appropriate authorities shall govern, provided this classification is in accord with the *Manual of the International Statistical Classification of Diseases, Injuries, and Causes of Death.*

Indirect Causes of Fire Injuries: These are the injuries which result indirectly from fire and include:

1. Disease contracted due to exposure to weather in time of fire.

2. Injuries due to fire breaking out in vehicles following an accident which is not in itself a fire. If the accident is a fire, the injury is a direct fire injury.

3. Overexertion while escaping from or fighting a fire.

4. Injuries to fire fighters while responding to or returning from a fire.

5. Injuries suffered by fire fighters, while in the execution of their incident-related duties, due to the violence of others.

These definitions are contained in NFPA No. 901, Uniform Coding for Fire Protection.[1] See Chapter 4 of this Section for further information on fire investigation.

C.   Who Are the Victims?

Fire deaths are disproportionately high among the younger and older people (see Fig. 1-2C). The young sometimes are not skillful at tasks which may put them in danger. They are curious to try what they see adults doing —using matches or cigarette lighters, "working" at stoves, tending fireplaces, etc. They are not always able to foresee the consequences of their acts. They may be insubordinate (testing the adult world) and play with matches even though emphatically told not to do so. And, too frequently, they have not been trained in the rudiments of self preservation from fire—rolling on the ground if their clothes ignite and escaping from a burning house.

The elderly may be inattentive to food that is cooking, or a cigarette they are smoking. They may not notice the danger they are in, or may not recognize it as a danger when they see it. Their reactions may be slow and illogical.

There seems to be a correlation between the age of fire victims and the places where their deaths occur. Most fatal fires occur in residences. Again, a disproportionately high percentage of the victims are very young or very old, undoubtedly in part because children and elderly people spend nearly all their time at home.

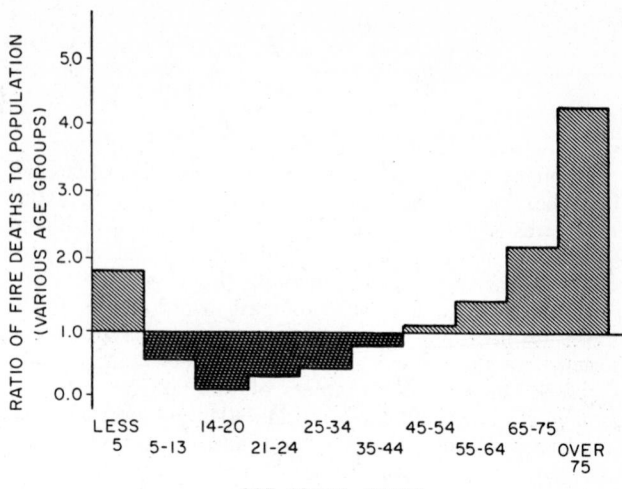

Fig. 1-2C.   *Normalized fire deaths by age versus population by age (United States—1974). ("Normalized" means the percentage of fire deaths divided by the percentage of total populations for a given age group. This technique gives a better indication of risk to a given age group than just the percentage of fire casualties for a particular age group. For example, the elderly have a high risk of fire death. They are relatively few in the total population, so their risk is not apparent in a simple percentage. A 1.0 rating means that a particular age group shows the same percentage of fire deaths as of the total population.)*

Fire Fighter Deaths

An unfortunately large number of fire fighters die in the line of duty each year. The number has ranged from 160 to 175 annually (NFPA estimates) in recent years. Other sources correlate these estimates. For example, the *International Association of Fire Fighters* (IAFF) reported that in 1973, 84 of every 100,000 full-time fire fighters died in the line of duty.[2]

Fire Deaths and Alcohol

A disturbing finding has been the functional relationship observed between fire deaths and the drinking of alcoholic beverages in the young adult and adult age groups. A study found that the primary cause of fire deaths of persons aged 16 to 60 was the ingestion of alcohol.[3] ("Primary cause" is used here in the sense of either the primary cause of the fire that caused the death, or the primary cause of death although not the primary cause of fire; e.g., the primary cause of a smoking-in-bed fire death may be consumption of alcohol. Or the primary cause of a fire death may be consumption of alcohol by way of numbing senses that might have perceived the fire or by inhibiting escape if the fire was perceived although the fire itself may have been caused by, say, defective wiring.) Table 1-2A, taken from the study, shows that of twenty-nine persons aged 16 to 60 who died from fire, twenty-four, or 82.8 percent, were or had been consuming alcoholic beverages at the time of death.

D.   Life Safety and Fire Protection

Prevention of personal injury or loss of life by fire should be the first objective of all fire protection. Life safety, where involved, is considered in all of the fire protection recommendations in subsequent Sections of this Handbook. Every measure for the prevention of fire reduces the probability of personal injury or loss of life by fire, and every measure

Table 1-2A.   Incident of Alcohol in Fire Deaths of Persons Aged 16 to 60[3]

Drinking Status*	Number of Fire Deaths	Percent
.00	5	17.2
.01–.04	0	0.0
.05–.09	2	6.9
.10–.19	4	13.8
.20–up	12	41.4
Positive—Unknown	6	20.7
	29	100.0

Note: Based on a study of fire deaths in Memphis, Tenn., over an 8-yr period.

* Expressed in terms of percentage of blood alcohol content by weight where the level was known and as *Positive—Unknown* where the level was positive but unknown. Source: Records, State of Tennessee Medical Examiner's Office.

for its prompt extinguishment or its control likewise contributes to life safety.

In addition to the general measures for the safeguarding of property, there are certain special provisions which must be taken for life safety. Most important of these are adequate exit facilities (see Sec. 6, Chap. 9). Although there is gradual acceptance of the importance of adequate exit facilities, fire casualty statistics show that there are still many buildings, particularly residential occupancies, where exit facilities are inadequate.

Automatic sprinkler protection is a particularly important factor in safeguarding life from fire (see Sec. 14, Chap. 1). NFPA records show that the loss of life by fire in buildings equipped with automatic sprinklers has been almost negligible. The few deaths that have occurred have been under unusual circumstances where the sprinkler system was shut off for some reason, where the fire was confined to clothing and did not generate enough heat to fuse sprinklers, or where the fatal burns were due to flash fires or explosions. Because of these and other situations where a sprinkler system alone does not necessarily assure life safety, it is not good fire protection practice to neglect other safety precautions even though sprinklers are installed.

Fire resistive construction is an important life-safety measure (see Sec. 6, Chap. 7). However, severe fires may occur in the contents of fire resistive buildings, and highly combustible decorations and interior finish materials may more than offset the value of noncombustible structural materials.

Measures for restricting the spread of fire in buildings are major elements in life safety. Most important is the enclosure of stairways, elevator shafts, and other vertical openings through floors (see Sec. 6, Chap. 8). Thousands of lives have been lost due to the rapid upward spread of fire and smoke through unprotected vertical openings.

Inadequate planning for a fire emergency is frequently responsible for fire deaths. A substantial percentage of the lives lost annually in dwelling fires occurs because families have not taken the time to be sure that each member knows how to escape in case of fire. Escape plans include locating alternate escape routes, arranging for removal of infants and incapacitated persons, training in how to call the fire department, instructing baby sitters, and holding family fire drills.

A considerable proportion of fire casualties occurs in cases where occupants of buildings are unaware of a fire until it is too late to escape, particularly when people are sleeping and fire is not discovered until it has reached

major proportions. Automatic fire detection systems provide an alarm automatically when fire occurs (see Sec. 12, Chaps. 2 and 3). Automatic sprinklers provide an alarm as well as apply water to the fire (see Sec. 14, Chap. 2). Manual fire alarm systems in buildings are designed to be used by a person to notify occupants of a building of the discovery of fire, and, if connected to a fire alarm office, to notify the fire department (see Sec. 12, Chap. 2).

Fires confined to clothing are responsible for many painful, and often, disfiguring and fatal burns. The answer to the wearing apparel burn problem lies in teaching the need for care to prevent ignition, selection of the fabric of lowest flammability when a choice is available, and use of garments that are free from dangerous design features, such as kimono-type sleeves, that increase the possibility of ignition. It is practical to use flame-retarding materials to reduce the flammability of certain garments, particularly costumes (see Sec. 3, Chap. 2).

E.   Fire Casualties in Private Residences

Of particular concern is the record of fire deaths in private dwellings. Fires in private dwellings account for a majority of fire deaths in residential-type occupancies and a majority of deaths in building fires (see Fig. 1-2D). In part this poor record can be attributed to the large number of private dwellings in the country.

Fatal residential fires show characteristics distinct from those of other types of residential fires.[4] They mostly occur at night during hours of sleeping (see Fig. 1-2E). Non-fatal residential fires peak during the afternoon hours when people are more likely to be active and less likely to be sleeping. Fatal residential fires usually start in the living areas (see Fig. 1-2F) where people usually are during the waking hours but where they may be during sleeping hours, e.g., family playrooms, kitchens, basements but not necessarily bedrooms. The majority of these fires originate when smoking materials ignite textiles, such as upholstery and clothing (see Fig. 1-2G).

The victims usually do not sense the fire until it has gained some headway. Heat and smoke make escape difficult. Often, people can be overcome by smoke while trying

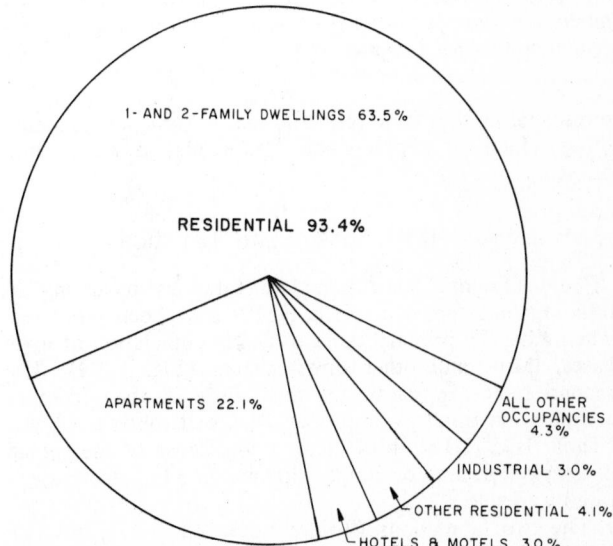

Fig. 1-2D. Occupancies where fire deaths in buildings occur.

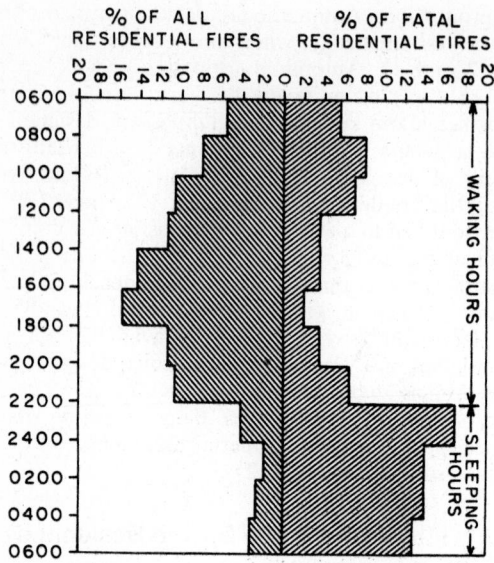

Fig. 1-2E.   Time distribution of fatal residential fires.

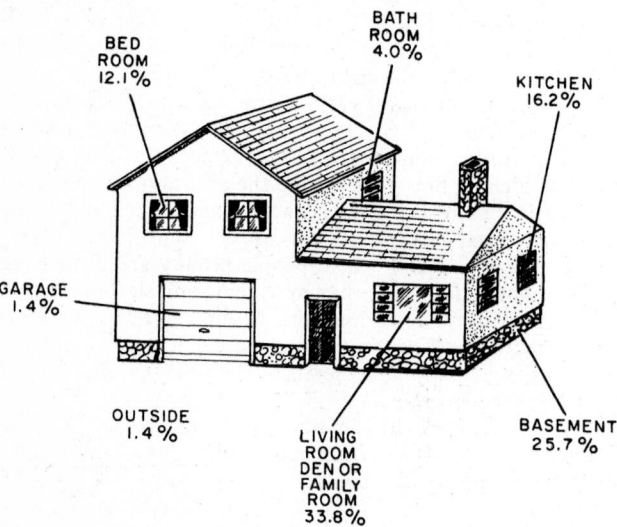

Fig. 1-2F.   Locations where fatal fires start in one- and two-family dwellings (5.4 percent of the locations where fatal residential fires started were unknown.)

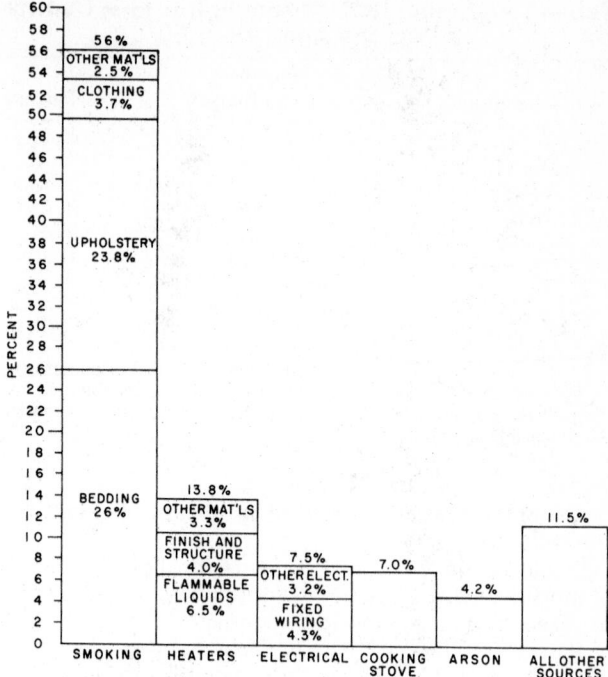

Fig. 1-2G.   Causes of fatal residential fires.

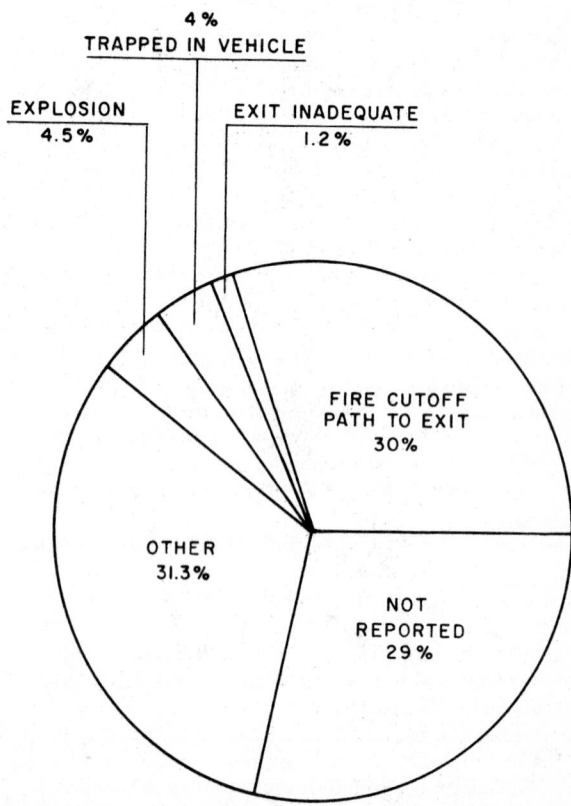

Fig. 1-2H.   The reasons why fire victims do not escape.

to escape, or they may return to rescue someone or something. (Lack of a practicable escape plan is also a hindrance.)

F.   NFPA Loss of Life Statistics

Three factors contributing to fatalities occurring in building fires reported to the NFPA have been tabulated. The first is the primary cause of death—inhalation of toxic gases, burns and other direct causes (Fig. 1-2H). The second factor is reason for the failure of the victim to escape from the fire—improper exits, exits obstructed, etc. (Table 1-2B). The third factor is the cause of the spread of smoke or fire, or both, within a building to cause a fatality (Table 1-2C).

The two tabulations (Tables 1-2B and 1-2C) and Fig. 1-2H are the result of a study of 500 building fire fatalities reported to the NFPA.

Fig. 1-2D shows the classification of deaths by the occupancy in which they occurred. Included are only those reported to the NFPA Fire Analysis Department. The data on which Fig. 1-2D is based is believed to be of sufficient volume and therefore may be used to draw conclusions as to the distribution of the various causes of loss of life.

Table 1-2B.   Factors Responsible for the Failure of Persons to Escape from Fires

(Figures are the number of fires (not number of fatalities) based on data supplied to the NFPA. Where multiple factors are involved in any fire each factor is considered; total number of fires is 500.)

| | Types of Occupancies | | | | | |
| | | | | Institutional | | Other Buildings (Mercantile, Office, Industrial, Storage, and Mixed) |
	Residential (Dwellings[1])	Residential (Other[2])	Public Assembly Buildings	Health and Custodial Care	Restrained Care	
Total Fires Analyzed	311	82	8	8	3	88
Exits:						
Inadequate number	6	6	0	0	0	3
Improperly designed exits	6	5	0	0	0	0
Exits Obstructed:						
Doors swing wrong way	0	0	1	0	0	0
Doors locked	7	0	0	0	0	0
Inadequately marked	0	0	1	0	0	0
Blocked by furnishings or contents	2	0	0	0	0	0
Persons under restraint	0	0	0	0	3	0
Personal Handicaps:						
Too young	76	20	1	0	0	1
Asleep	118	23	0	0	0	3
Intoxicated or under influence of drugs	18	3	0	0	0	1
Bedridden or handicapped	19	5	0	4	0	2
Failed to act properly	12	4	1	0	0	3
Mentally ill or senile	3	2	0	1	0	0
Persons improperly trained in evacuation procedure	3	2	0	0	0	0
Felled by smoke or heat	108	26	3	3	0	15
Trapped in confined areas	0	0	0	0	0	9
Explosion:						
Blocked exits	0	0	0	0	0	4
Injured	9	1	1	0	0	35
Killed	11	2	2	1	0	35
Lack of Adequate Warning:						
No alarm where required	0	0	0	0	0	1
Failed to sound alarm	0	4	0	0	0	0
Automatic detection system failed	3	0	0	0	0	0
Panic	0	0	1	0	0	0

[1] Dwellings are one- and two-family dwellings only plus mobile homes and recreational vehicles.
[2] Other residential includes multifamily dwellings, apartment houses, hotels, motels, dormitories, fraternity houses, etc., excluding institutional properties. Other occupancies classified are as described in the NFPA Life Safety Code (NFPA No. 101).

Table 1-2C.   Factors Responsible for the Spread of Smoke and Fire Resulting in Loss of Life

| | Types of Occupancies | | | | | |
| | | | | Institutional | | Other Buildings (Mercantile, Office, Industrial, Storage, and Mixed) |
	Residential (Dwellings[1])	Residential (Other[2])	Public Assembly Buildings	Health and Custodial Care	Restrained Care	
Total Fires Analyzed	311	82	8	8	3	88
Building Construction						
Vertical Spread:						
Open stairways	126	38	0	2	0	6
Doors blocked open	6	3	0	0	0	0
Elevator shafts open	0	0	0	0	0	1
Utility shafts open	0	1	0	0	0	0
Nonfirestopped walls	49	13	0	0	0	0
Exterior spread	0	3	0	0	0	0
Other openings	2	0	0	0	0	0

(Continued)

Table 1-2C.   Factors Responsible for the Spread of Smoke and Fire Resulting in Loss of Life (Contd.)

	Types of Occupancies					
				Institutional		Other Buildings (Mercantile, Office, Industial, Storage, and Mixed)
	Residential (Dwellings[1])	Residential (Other[2])	Public Assembly Buildings	Health and Custodial Care	Restrained Care	
Total Fires Analyzed	311	82	8	8	3	88
Horizontal Spread:						
Lack of fire walls or fire partitions	1	0	0	0	0	5
Openings in fire walls or fire partitions	0	1	0	0	0.	0
Fire doors blocked open or inoperative	0	0	0	0	0	0
Fire doors of improper design	0	1	0	0	0	0
Smoke barriers not provided	6	2	0	2	0	0
Smoke barriers blocked open or residential doors open	30	3	0	0	0	0
Nonfirestopped ceiling areas or undivided attic	20	8	1	0	0	0
Exterior spread	1	0	0	0	0	0
Interior Finish:						
Combustible ceiling finish	63	7	2	3	0	2
Combustible wall finish	107	13	1	2	3	1
Floors soaked with flammable materials	4	0	1	0	0	1
Building Equipment:						
Air conditioning ducts	5	1	0	0	1	1
Conveyor and machinery openings	0	0	0	0	0	1
Fans	3	1	0	0	0	0
Other	0	2	0	1	0	1
Building Contents:						
Decorations	6	3	2	0	0	0
Furniture and fixtures	4	17	0	1	0	1
Flammable liquids not properly contained or handled	59	3	1	0	0	36
Flammable gases not properly contained or handled	19	3	3	1	0	23
Flammable dust or solid chemicals	0	0	0	0	0	16
Explosives and fireworks	1	1	0	0	0	9
Stored material	2	0	1	0	0	7

[1] Dwellings are one- and two-family dwellings only plus mobile homes and recreational vehicles.
[2] Other residential includes multifamily dwellings, apartment houses, hotels, motels, dormitories, fraternity houses, etc., excluding institutional properties. Other occupancies classified are as described in the NFPA Life Safety Code (NFPA No. 101).

Table 1-2D.   Fires Causing Large Loss of Life

(Significant fires and explosions prior to 1969 in the United States in which there were multiple deaths.)

PUBLIC ASSEMBLY

		Deaths
Dec. 30, 1903	Iroquois Theater, Chicago, Ill.	602
Apr. 23, 1940	Rhythm Club, Natchez, Miss.	207
Nov. 28, 1942	Cocoanut Grove (night club), Boston, Mass.	492
July 6, 1944	The Ringling Brothers and Barnum and Bailey Circus, Hartford, Conn.	168
Oct. 10, 1963	Indiana State Fairgrounds Coliseum, Indianapolis, Ind.	74
Feb. 7, 1967	Dale's Penthouse (restaurant), Montgomery, Ala.	25

EDUCATIONAL

Mar. 4, 1908	Lakeview Grammar School, Collinwood, Ohio	175
Mar. 18, 1937	Consolidated School, New London, Tex. (gas explosion)	294
Dec. 1, 1958	Our Lady of the Angels Grade School, Chicago, Ill.	95

INSTITUTIONAL

May 15, 1929	Cleveland Clinic, Cleveland, Ohio	125
Apr. 21, 1930	Ohio State Penitentiary, Columbus, Ohio	320
Dec. 8, 1961	Hartford Hospital, Hartford, Conn.	16
Nov. 23, 1963	Golden Age Nursing Home, Fitchville Township, Ohio	63

Table 1-2D. Fires Causing Large Loss of Life (Contd.)

(Significant fires and explosions prior to 1969 in the United States in which there were multiple deaths.)

RESIDENTIAL

		Deaths
June 5, 1946	The LaSalle Hotel, Chicago, Ill.	61
Dec. 7, 1946	Winecoff Hotel, Atlanta, Ga.	119
Dec. 29, 1963	Roosevelt Hotel, Jacksonsville, Fla.	22

STORE AND OFFICE

Apr. 5, 1968	Marting Arms (sporting goods store), Richmond, Ind. (gun-powder explosion)	41

BASIC INDUSTRY, UTILITY, DEFENSE

Oct. 20, 1944	East Ohio Gas Co., Cleveland, Ohio (gas explosion)	130
Mar. 25, 1947	Centralia Coal Co., Centralia, Ill. (dust explosion)	111
Dec. 21, 1951	C. W. & F. Coal Company, W. Frankfort, Ill. (gas explosion)	119

MANUFACTURING

Mar. 25, 1911	Triangle Shirtwaist Co., New York, N.Y.	145

SPECIAL

June 15, 1904	Excursion steamer, *General Slocum*, Hell Gate Passage, East River, New York, N.Y.	1,030
Sept. 8, 1934	S. S. *Morro Castle*, off New Jersey Coast	125
Apr. 16, 1947	S.S. *Grandcamp*, Texas City, Tex. (ammonium nitrate explosion)	468

Table 1-2E.   Recent Fires Causing Large Loss of Life: 1969–1974

(Significant fires and explosions in the United States in which there were multiple deaths.)

PUBLIC ASSEMBLY

		Deaths
June 24, 1973	Cocktail Lounge, New Orleans, La. (incendiary fire)	32
June 30, 1974	Discotheque, Port Chester, N.Y. (incendiary fire in adjacent occupancy)	24

INSTITUTIONAL

Jan. 9, 1970	Convalescent Home, Marietta, Ohio (smoke spread throughout building)	31
Jan. 14, 1971	Nursing Home, Buechel, Ky. (lack of automatic fire protection)	10
Oct. 19, 1971	Nursing Home, Honesdale, Pa. (lack of automatic fire protection)	15

RESIDENTIAL

June 3, 1969	Apartment House, Kansas City, Mo. (dumbwaiter shaft spread fire throughout building)	12
June 8, 1969	Dwelling, Parkersburg, W. Va. (arson—gasoline spread as accelerent)	12
Mar. 20, 1970	Ozark Hotel, Seattle, Wash. (spread via stairways; incendiary origin)	20
Aug. 5, 1970	Apartment, Building, Minneapolis, Minn. (doors blocked open; open stairways)	12
Sept. 13, 1970	Ponet Square Hotel, Los Angeles, Calif. (spread via stairways; incendiary origin)	19
Dec. 20, 1970	Pioneer Hotel, Tucson, Ariz. (spread via stairways; incendiary origin)	28
Apr. 25, 1971	Apartment Building, Seattle, Wash. (careless smoking; open stairways)	12
Jan. 16, 1972	Hotel, Tyrone, Pa. (open stairways; nonfirestopped walls)	12
Nov. 30, 1972	High Rise Housing for the Elderly, Atlanta, Ga. (delayed alarm, open apartment door, combustibility of corridor carpeting)	10
Nov. 15, 1973	Apartment House, Los Angeles, Calif. (open stairways)	25
Aug. 25, 1974	Hotel, Berkeley Springs, W. Va. (unsprinklered ordinary construction; open stairways)	12

STORE AND OFFICE

Feb. 25, 1969	Office Building, New York, N.Y. (single exit; fire flashed)	11
Feb. 2, 1973	Department Store, Eagle Grove, Iowa (natural gas explosion)	14

BASIC INDUSTRY, UTILITY, DEFENSE

Dec. 30, 1970	Coal Mine Explosion, Hyden, Ky.	38
May 2, 1972	Silver Mine, Kellogg, Idaho (toxic gases through ventilation system; inadequate breathing aids)	91

MANUFACTURING

Feb. 3, 1971	Chemical Plant, Woodbine, Ga. (violent explosion and fire)	25
Dec. 16, 1972	Steel Plant, Weirton, W. Va. (gas explosion in a coke oven)	21

STORAGE

Feb. 10, 1973	Gas Storage Tank, Staten Island, N.Y. (polyurethane insulation)	40

(Continued)

Table 1-2E.   Recent Fires Causing Large Loss of Life: 1969–1974 (Contd.)

(Significant fires and explosions in the United States in which there were multiple deaths.)

	SPECIAL	Deaths
Feb. 25, 1969	Twin Engine Beachcraft, Port Angeles, Wash. (stalled, crashed and burned)	10
Mar. 20, 1969	DC 3 Charter Plane, Kenner, La. (crashed in heavy fog and burned)	13
Apr. 6, 1969	S.S. *Union Faith*, Mississippi River at New Orleans, La. (collided with oil barges)	25
Nov. 28, 1970	DC 8 Charter, Anchorage, Alaska, (crashed on take off)	47
June 7, 1971	Convair 580, East Haven, Conn. (low landing approach, hit houses)	28
June 24, 1971	Water Project, Sylmar, Calif. (ignition of methane by drill)	16
Nov. 15, 1971	C 130, Little Rock, Ark. (crashed during landing)	11
Dec. 11, 1971	Water Tunnel, Port Huron, Mich. (ignition of methane gas by drill)	21
Feb. 1, 1972	Tank Ship *V. A. Fogg*, Galveston, Tex. (lightning caused explosion)	39
Sept. 24, 1972	Ice Cream Parlor, Sacramento, Calif. (jet plane crashed into structure)	22
July 5, 1973	Rail Tank Car, Kingman, Ariz. (fire during unloading operations)	13
July 31, 1973	Aircraft Crash, Boston, Mass. (instrument landing in fog)	46
Apr. 9, 1974	Oil Tanker, Tinicum Township, Pa. (explosion during unloading)	11

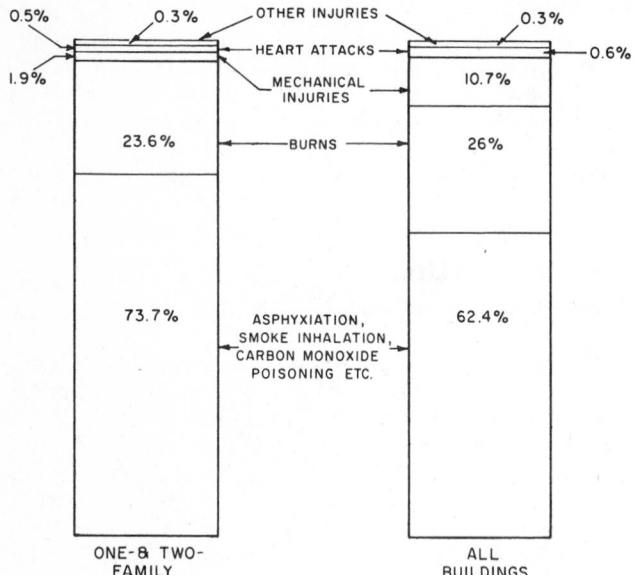

Fig. 1-2I.   Causes of death in building fires.

Deaths and Injuries by Fireworks

Conservative current estimates indicate that possibly 10 deaths and 4,000 injuries are caused by fireworks each year. In 1969 two field studies on fireworks incidents were conducted, one by the NFPA jointly with the Fire Marshals Association of North America and the other by the National Society for the Prevention of Blindness.[5] A total of 2,009 incidents was reported during the survey. They resulted in injury to 1,330 people and 774 cases of property damage from the discharge of pyrotechnic devices. The survey was indicative of the scope of injuries suffered in fireworks mishaps and the types of property that are damaged.

G.   Fires Causing Large Loss of Life

Table 1-2D lists some individual fires and explosions involving major loss of life in the United States prior to 1969 in which significant lessons were learned in regard to firesafe practices and which in some cases led to substantial changes in legislation aimed at preventing further losses from similar sources. Table 1-2E lists more recent (1969–1974) large loss of life fires and the significant factors that contributed to life loss.

The largest loss of life by fire in the United States occurred on October 9, 1871 (also the date of the historically important Chicago conflagration). Isolated fires that had been burning in dried-up peat bogs in the Green Bay area of Wisconsin entered forestland and spread rapidly over 1,280,000 acres. The fire leveled Peshtigo and at least 16 other towns, and caused deaths conservatively estimated at 1,152. (Some estimates were as high as 2,000.)

The largest loss of life in a single building fire occurred in Chicago, Ill., on Dec. 30, 1903, when 602 persons were killed by fire in the new fire resistive Iroquois Theater. The fire started when an arc light ignited nearby combustible scenery on the stage. The asbestos curtain failed to close properly, and doors on the stage and at the top of the balcony that were open to the outside caused a draft to carry fire, heat, and smoke quickly to the balconies.

Bibliography

References Cited

[1] "Uniform Coding for Fire Protection," NFPA No. 901, 1973, National Fire Protection Association, Boston.

[2] "Annual Death and Injury Survey," *The International Fire Fighter* (Nov. 1974) p. 14.

[3] Hollis, Slater W., "Drinking: Its Part in Fire Deaths," *Fire Journal*, Vol. 67, No. 3 (May 1973), pp. 10-11, 13.

[4] A Study of "Fatal Residential Fires," FR 72-1, 1972, National Fire Protection Association, Boston.

[5] "Fireworks Incidents in the United States During 1969," *Fire Journal*, Vol. 64, No. 3, May 1970, pp. 21-29.

Chapter 3

PROPERTY LOSS BY FIRE

Those who use this HANDBOOK are unquestionably familiar, in a general way, with the tremendous annual waste by fire and explosions. To think of this waste as including only the destruction of and damage to property by fire, water, and smoke would be to underestimate grossly its true nature. For also included in our annual fire waste are innumerable indirect and intangible losses that cannot be measured in dollars, such as loss of jobs and income, business failures, and destruction of irreplaceable art objects. The annual fire waste also includes the cost of conducting the fire insurance business, of maintaining fire departments, of manufacturing and installing fire detection and suppression equipment, and the promulgation and enforcement of fire prevention laws and regulations. Much of this expense could well be devoted to more productive enterprise.

The National Fire Protection Association collects estimates of direct property loss by fire. These estimates are based on the cost of replacement of a damaged or destroyed item or building with one of like quality, age, and condition. The cost of repair would be used if it can restore the damaged object or building to its prefire condition for less than the cost of replacement. Business interruption losses and lost profits due to the fire are not considered.

A. Direct Property Losses

Each year the NFPA publishes a summary of fire losses in the September issue of *Fire Journal* (see Table 1-3A and 1-3B). Over the years the losses have been increasing. During the same period, inflation has significantly decreased the value of the dollar. For example, the direct dollar fire loss by occupancy as estimated by the NFPA for 1974 was $3,818,800,000, an increase of $798,000,000 above the previous year. Figure 1-3A shows the increase in fire losses

after the influence of inflation has been removed from the estimates.

The population has also increased significantly. Fire losses per capita on a cost basis are shown in Figure 1-3B. The losses are still increasing, but more slowly. Perhaps the bulk of the increase is due to the greater value and variety of goods available to be destroyed or damaged. For example, if a house were totally destroyed by fire in 1940, the fire would not have destroyed a television set. Today, a fire which totally destroys a home probably also destroys a television set, perhaps a color set. Thus, the increase in constant dollar per capita fire loss may not indicate that the fires themselves are becoming more serious. They are still large enough to show that fires are a continuing threat to our resources.

Another measure of fire losses would be to compare them to Gross National Product, the combined value of all goods and services produced in a country in a year. This comparison would minimize the effects of inflation because both losses and Gross National Product would be measured in the same terms (contemporary currency). A glance at Figure 1-3C shows that fire losses have remained fairly constant since 1950 at about 0.25 percent of the Gross National Product.

The insurance industry also compiles estimates of property loss by fire. Its estimates are not directly comparable to those made by the NFPA; however they usually show the same trends. The insurance estimates indicate various types of casualty claims, such as boiler failure and building collapse. They do not include losses on fires not normally covered by insurance, such as government buildings, standing crops, or timber. They also use adjusted loss figures in cases where the property owner is significantly underinsured.

International Fire Losses

As in casualties, the United States has more fires and more direct property loss than other industrialized coun-

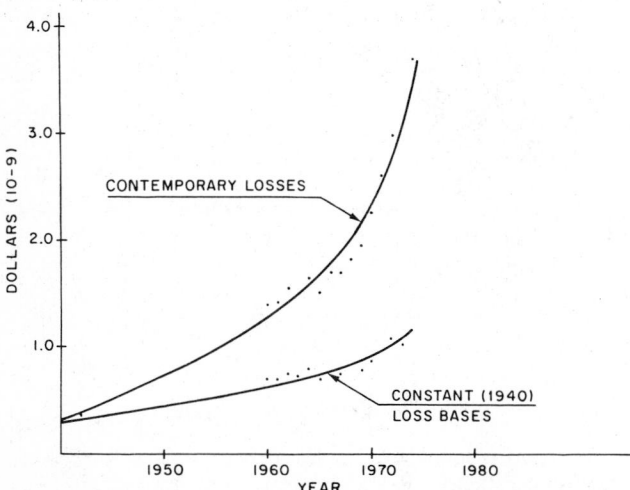

Fig. 1-3A. Fire losses through the years. (These figures were calculated by multiplying the annual loss estimates by the 1940 consumer price index and dividing by the consumer price index for the particular year. Consumer price indices from U.S. Statistical Abstractor for 1974 using 1967 as the base year.)

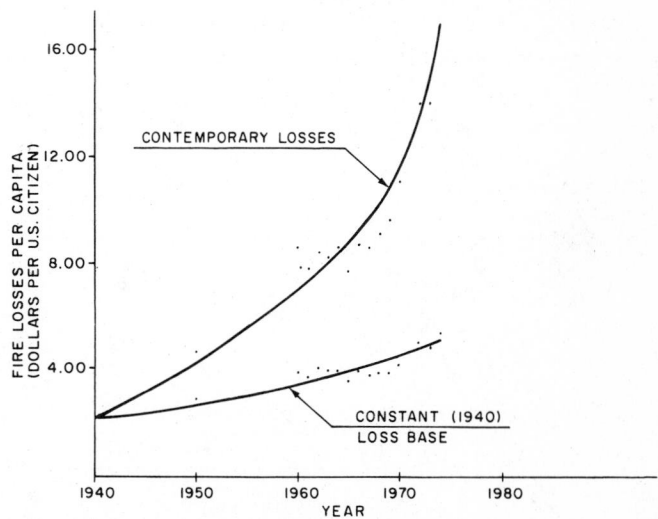

Fig. 1-3B. Per capita fire losses in the United States.

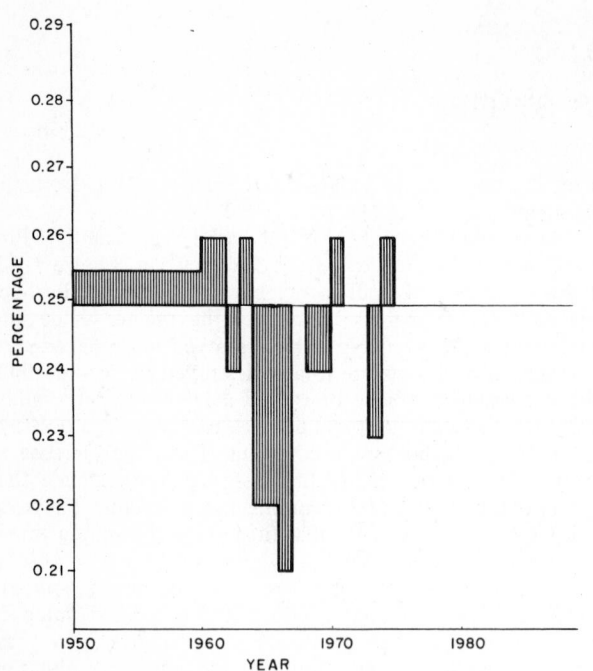

Fig. 1-3C. Fire losses as a percentage of the gross national product (U.S. only).

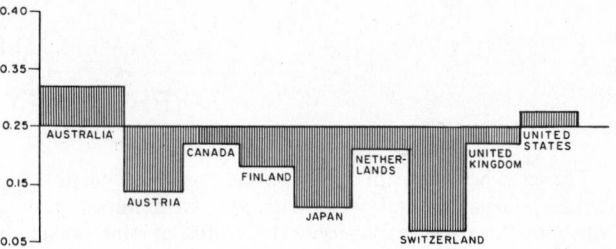

Fig. 1-3E. International fire losses expressed as a percentage of each country's gross national product.

tries. Figure 1-3D shows a comparison between per capita fire loss and numbers of fires per 1,000 population per year for a number of industrialized countries. Figure 1-3E shows fire losses in these countries in relation to Gross National Product.

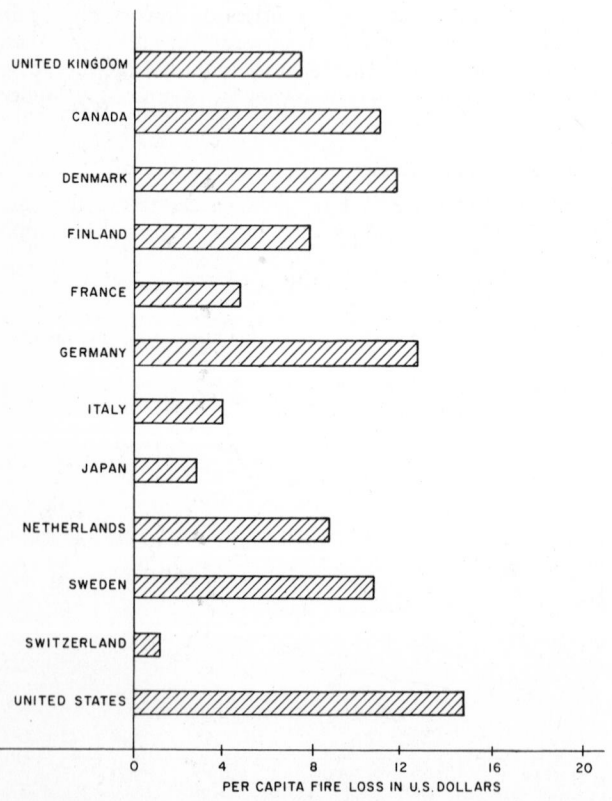

Fig. 1-3D. Fire losses in industrialized countries expressed as per capita loss in terms of U.S. dollars.

B. Large Loss Fires

A small percentage of the building fires in the United States cause a disproportionately large percentage of losses. In 1974, less than 0.2 percent of the fires caused 14 percent of the direct property loss. These large loss fires are a most obvious target for any attempt to make a significant reduction in fire losses. See Chapter 5 of this Section for further information on the analyses of factors contributing to the cause and spread of large loss and other types of fires.

The NFPA defines a large loss fire as one causing $250,000 or more damage to buildings and contents. Each year in the July issue of *Fire Journal*, the NFPA's Fire Analysis Department publishes a study of large loss fires of the preceding year by occupancy (see Table 1-3C). The number of fires has remained approximately constant over the past several years, but the total losses have increased significantly.

Multimillion Dollar Losses

The number of fires which cause over $3,000,000 loss each and over $10,000,000 loss each have been increasing fairly steadily over the past several years (see Table 1-3D). The increase in these fires can be attributed to several causes. First, large values are concentrated within single structures. Huge super plants have been built which have cost over $30,000,000. High-rise buildings, major computer installations, super tankers, and jumbo aircraft all represent sufficient value that a single fire in one of them could cause $10,000,000 or more damage. Large fires in these structures and equipment usually are beyond the capability of private fire protection or public fire protection agencies. For purposes of increased production or cost saving, many large aggregations of real property have not been separated by fire subdivisions or similar means of protection.

These multimillion dollar losses are concentrated in commercial and industrial properties either when they are actively operating or when they are under construction or renovation. Over 84 percent of the large loss fires in 1973 occurred in these occupancies, causing 69 percent in the damage.

C.   Indirect Fire Losses

So far as is known, there is no clear cut and full assessment of indirect losses due to fires. Some are obvious. The enterprise loses income from the normal flow of business. Customers may be forced to go elsewhere, and not come back when normal business is resumed. Temporary expedients as housing, processing, shipping, sales, etc., can cost money and may result in lower profits than anticipated in normal business. Skilled employees may find new jobs.

Table 1-3A. Number of Fires by Occupancy 1970–1974

	1970	1971	1972	1973	1974
Public Assembly Occupancies					
Amusement Centers, Ballrooms	2,300	2,400	2,400	2,300	3,100
Auditoriums, Exhibition Halls	700	700	700	600	800
Bowling Establishments	800	800	900	800	1,100
Churches	3,300	3,400	4,300	3,900	5,400
Clubs, Private	2,900	3,000	3,400	3,000	4,100
Restaurants, Taverns	17,800	18,200	21,700	19,500	26,800
Theaters, Studios	1,000	1,000	1,200	1,100	1,500
Transportation Terminals	600	600	600	500	600
Other Public Assembly Occupancies	1,600	1,600	2,600	2,400	3,600
Total:	31,000	31,700	37,900	34,100	47,000
Educational Occupancies					
Schools, thru 12th grade	13,000	15,700	17,200	18,900	27,800
Other Schools	4,000	4,800	5,200	5,200	7,700
Total:	17,000	20,500	22,400	24,100	35,500
Institutional Occupancies					
Rest & Nursing Homes	3,700	4,800	6,100	6,400	9,300
Hospitals	7,800	10,100	10,500	10,700	15,600
Mental Institutions	500	700	800	800	1,200
Other Institutions	2,000	2,600	3,800	3,700	5,400
Total:	14,000	18,200	21,200	21,600	31,500
Residential Occupancies					
Dwellings, 1–2 Family	547,000	536,000	562,500	587,200	661,400
Apartments	87,700	103,000	109,000	138,000	151,500
Hotels, Motels	13,400	15,200	16,400	21,700	30,200
Mobile Homes	22,600	25,000	27,400	25,100	29,700
Other Residential Occupancies	19,400	19,800	20,300	23,800	28,200
Mercantile & Office Occupancies	74,500	71,000	76,900	76,100	86,800
Appliance, Furniture Stores	4,000	3,800	4,100	4,100	4,700
Clothing Stores	4,400	4,200	4,500	4,500	5,100
Department, Variety Stores	5,200	5,000	4,600	4,500	5,700
Drugstores	3,000	2,900	2,900	2,900	3,300
Grocery Stores, Supermarkets	6,500	6,200	6,900	6,900	7,800
Motor Vehicle Sales, Repair	9,700	9,200	9,700	9,600	11,900
Offices, Banks	14,200	13,500	16,100	15,900	8,100
Service Stations	5,500	5,200	5,400	5,300	6,000
Other Mercantile Occupancies	22,000	21,000	22,700	22,400	24,200
Total:	690,100	699,000	735,600	795,800	901,000
Basic Industry, Defense Occupancies					
Electric Power Plants	3,900	2,900	3,100	3,000	3,100
Laboratories, Data Processing Ctrs.	900	600	800	800	800
Mines, Mineral Products Plants	2,000	1,500	1,600	1,600	1,700
Other Basic Industry Occupancies	1,800	1,300	1,500	1,500	1,600
Total:	8,600	6,300	7,000	6,900	7,200
Manufacturing Occupancies					
Beverage, Tobacco, Essential Oils	1,200	900	900	900	1,300
Drug, Chemical, Paint, Petroleum PL	4,200	3,100	3,800	3,600	4,900
Food Product Plants	5,100	3,700	3,700	3,600	5,700
Laundry, Dry Cleaning Plants	4,400	3,200	3,400	3,300	3,100
Metal, Metal Product Plants	4,700	3,500	4,100	4,000	5,700
Paper, Paper Product Plants	2,400	1,800	3,000	3,100	4,800
Plastic, Plastic Product Plants	1,300	1,000	1,900	1,900	3,700
Printing Plants	1,900	1,400	1,600	1,600	1,400
Textile, Textile Product Plants	3,800	2,800	3,500	3,500	3,900
Wood, Wood Product Plants	3,700	2,700	3,100	3,100	3,700
Other Manufacturing Occupancies	14,900	10,900	12,000	11,800	14,800
Total:	47,600	35,000	41,000	40,400	53,000
Storage Occupancies					
Barns, Stables	19,800	20,600	19,300	14,800	17,900
Bulk Plants, Tank Farms	1,400	1,500	1,500	1,100	1,400
Garages, Residential Parking	26,900	28,000	26,000	20,000	24,800
Grain Elevators	3,000	3,100	2,400	1,800	2,200
Lumber, Building Materials Storage	1,400	1,500	1,300	1,000	1,400
Sheds, Farm Outbuildings	15,000	15,600	14,000	10,800	12,700
Other Storage Buildings	10,600	11,000	10,400	7,800	8,100
Total:	78,100	81,400	74,900	51,300	68,500
Other Buildings	31,100	33,800	33,000	30,200	39,500
Total Building Fires:	992,000	996,600	1,050,200	1,085,900	1,270,000
Nonbuilding Occupancies					
Standing Crops	27,000	22,000	22,000	21,000	22,000
Forests	121,700	111,500	125,000	119,000	127,000
Grass, Brush, Rubbish	908,000	1,076,300	989,900	891,200	920,000
Motor Vehicles	479,700	501,600	550,300	574,000	640,000
Ships, Boats, RR	21,000	20,000	20,000	2,750	2,700
Aircraft, Aerospace Vehicles	150	200	200	250	300
Total Fires:	2,549,550	2,728,200	2,757,600	2,694,100	2,982,000

Table 1-3B.   Estimated Fire Losses by Occupancy

	1970	1971	1972	1973	1974
Public Assembly Occupancies					
Amusement Centers, Ballrooms	9,500,000	10,100,000	10,600,000	10,700,000	12,300,000
Auditorium, Exhibition Halls	5,500,000	5,500,000	5,600,000	5,600,000	7,500,000
Bowling Establishments	7,400,000	8,100,000	9,300,000	9,500,000	10,400,000
Churches	18,500,000	23,300,000	28,100,000	28,400,000	34,200,000
Clubs, Private	13,500,000	12,800,000	14,200,000	14,500,000	19,400,000
Restaurants, Taverns	46,000,000	50,900,000	54,300,000	54,900,000	65,300,000
Theaters, Studios	7,600,000	11,700,000	13,400,000	13,500,000	13,400,000
Transportation Terminals	2,500,000	2,800,000	2,600,000	2,600,000	3,500,000
Other Public Assembly Occupancies	8,900,000	13,700,000	15,100,000	15,300,000	15,400,000
Total:	$119,400,000	$138,900,000	$153,200,000	$155,000,000	$181,400,000
Educational Occupancies					
Schools, thru 12th grade	64,800,000	72,500,000	76,100,000	81,900,000	106,200,000
Other Schools	13,000,000	14,500,000	14,800,000	17,100,000	18,600,000
Total:	77,800,000	87,000,000	90,900,000	99,000,000	124,800,000
Institutional Occupancies					
Rest & Nursing Homes	2,700,000	3,500,000	3,900,000	3,600,000	5,900,000
Hospitals	8,500,000	11,100,000	12,200,000	12,400,000	20,400,000
Mental Institutions	1,000,000	1,300,000	1,500,000	1,500,000	2,500,000
Other Institutions	5,000,000	6,500,000	7,200,000	6,400,000	10,600,000
Total:	17,200,000	22,400,000	24,800,000	23,900,000	39,400,000
Residential Occupancies					
Dwellings, 1–2 Family	603,500,000	608,600,000	638,500,000	700,700,000	808,100,000
Apartments	132,800,000	151,400,000	151,600,000	265,300,000	299,100,000
Hotels, Motels	33,800,000	37,900,000	43,600,000	42,200,000	68,300,000
Mobile Homes	33,000,000	36,500,000	42,000,000	57,800,000	77,200,000
Other Residential Occupancies	38,600,000	39,700,000	42,700,000	37.400,000	50,100,000
Total:	841,700,000	874,100,000	918.400,000	1,163,400,000	1,302,800,000
Mercantile and Office Occupancies					
Appliance, Furniture Stores	26,000,000	24,800,000	28,100,000	27,500,000	32,600,000
Clothing Stores	20,400,000	19,400,000	21,800,000	20,900,000	24,900,000
Department, Variety Stores	37,400,000	35,600,000	41,900,000	40,700,000	53,300,000
Drugstores	11,800,000	11,200,000	11,800,000	11,400,000	12,900,000
Grocery Stores, Supermarkets	33,200,000	31,600,000	36,900,000	35,900,000	40,900,000
Motor Vehicle Sales, Repair	33,300,000	31,700,000	35,100,000	34,100,000	43,800,000
Offices, Banks	43,000,000	41,200,000	48,700,000	47,300,000	55,800,000
Service Stations	11,500,000	10,900,000	11,600,000	11,100,000	14,200,000
Other Mercantile Occupancies	132,000,000	125,800,000	141,800,000	137,800,000	154,200,000
Total:	348,600,000	332,200,000	377,700,000	366,700,000	432,600,000
Basic Industry, Defense Occupancies					
Electric Power Plants	9,500,000	8,600,000	24,700,000	22,900,000	26,900,000
Laboratories. Data Processing Ctrs.	2,500,000	2,000,000	2,800,000	2,600,000	12,900,000
Mines, Mineral Products Plants	44,100,000	39,700,000	44,500,000	41,000,000	40,400,000
Other Basic Industry Occupancies	8,700,000	7,900,000	9,600.000	9,400,000	8,200,000
Total:	64,800,000	58,200,000	81,600,000	76,300,000	88,400,000
Manufacturing Occupancies					
Beverage, Tobacco, Essential Oils	6,600,000	6,400,000	6,700,000	5,100,000	6,800,000
Drug, Chemical, Paint, Petroleum PL	76,000,000	73,700,000	94,900,000	89,000,000	172,000,000
Food Product Plants	41,400,000	40,200,000	42,200,000	39,600,000	58,600,000
Laundry, Dry Cleaning Plants	9,200,000	8,900,000	9,900,000	9,200,000	7,100,000
Metal, Metal Product Plants	46,500,000	45,100,000	54.400,000	51,700,000	82,700,000
Paper, Paper Product Plants	8,400,000	8,100,000	11,800,000	11,000,000	17,000,000
Plastic, Plastic Product Plants	11,500,000	11,200,000	16,500,000	16,700,000	27,600,000
Printing Plants	5,400,000	5,300,000	6,400,000	6,100,000	14,100,000
Textile, Textile Product Plants	16,500,000	16,100,000	18,100,000	15,700,000	32,200,000
Wood, Wood Product Plants	39,800,000	38,600,000	46,500,000	43,600,000	48,600,000
Other Manufacturing Occupancies	81,400,000	98,900,000	82,000,000	76,700,000	118,200,000
Total:	342,700,000	332,500,000	389,000,000	364,400,000	584,900,000
Storage Occupancies					
Barns, Stables	81,600,000	85,000,000	81,000,000	74,400,000	96,600,000
Bulk Plants, Tank Farms	7,900,000	8,300,000	10,300,000	9,300,000	58,700,000
Garages Residential Parking	29,800,000	31,000,000	30,500,000	27,900,000	36,100,000
Grain Elevators	47,800,000	49,800,000	42,800,000	39,300,000	51,300,000
Lumber, Building Materials Storage	20,400,000	21,300,000	20,700,000	18,900,000	29,900,000
Sheds, Farm Outbuildings	30,200,000	31,500,000	30,100,000	27,600,000	36,600,000
Other Storage Buildings	126,400,000	131,800,000	111,800,000	102,600,000	125,100,000
Total:	344,100,000	358,700,000	327,200,000	300,000,000	434,300,000
Other Buildings	52,900,000	62,200,000	53.500,000	48,500,000	71,400,000
Total Building Fires:	2,209,200,000	2,266,000,000	2,416,300,000	2,537,200,000	3,260,000,000
Nonbuilding Occupancies					
Standing Crops	27,200,000	26,000,000	29,000,000	32,000,000	36,200,000
Forests	131,100,000	119,000,000	128,000,000	126,000,000	168,700,000
Grass, Brush, Rubbish	——	——	——	——	——
Motor Vehicles	88,900,000	112,660,000	127,300,000	135,300,000	135,000,000
Ships, Boats, RR	29,000,000	27,600,000	29,200,000	30,300,000	37,900,000
Railroad Rollingstock					
Aircraft, Aerospace Vehicles	145,000,000	192,000,000	198.000,000	150,000,000	181,000,000
Total Fire Losses:	$2,630,400,000	$2,743,260,000	$2,927,800,000	$3,020,800,000	$3,819,100,000

Table 1-3C. Occupancies Where Large-loss Fires Occurred, 1974

Occupancy	No. Large-loss Fires	Loss	No. Large-loss Fires	Loss
Public Assembly			73	$41,649,577
Bowling Establishments	8	$4,345,000		
Churches	15	6,014,875		
Clubs	7	2,460,000		
Restaurants, Night Clubs and Taverns	31	16,656,786		
Other Public Assembly Places	12	12,172,916		
Educational			42	29,831,212
Nonresidential Schools	40	28,571,212		
Other Educational	2	1,260,000		
Institutional			2	1,350,000
Residential			43	19,242,599
Apartments	16	9,483,607		
Hotels and Motels	13	5,423,325		
Other Residential	14	4,335,667		
Mercantile			118	85,830,629
Food Sales	15	8,731,378		
Textile Product Sales	6	2,837,000		
Household Goods Sales	17	8,808,000		
General Item Sales	20	14,123,750		
Offices	18	17,704,727		
Other Commercial	42	33,625,774		
Basic Industry			24	31,244,500
Utilities	10	6,375,000		
Other Basic Industry	14	24,869,500		
Manufacturing			119	132,668,862
Food Processing	15	17,915,470		
Wood and Wood Paper Products	24	35,320,001		
Chemical, Plastic and Petroleum Products	15	33,754,000		
Metal and Metal Products	29	18,986,457		
Other Industrial and Manufacturing	36	26,692,934		
Storage			138	139,909,279
Agricultural Products	15	19,201,660		
Textile Products	11	18,377,617		
Wood and Wood Paper Products	29	13,239,691		
Chemical, Plastic and Petroleum Products	20	13,992,000		
Metal and Metal Products	16	10,350,500		
General Items	21	24,846,480		
Other Storage	26	39,901,331		
Other Occupancies			35	74,207,057
Special Structures	1	$7,500,000		
Unoccupied Properties*	20	9,003,417		
Ships and Other Water Vessels	2	2,180,000		
Rail Vehicles	3	31,250,000		
Road Vehicles	4	6,203,640		
Aircraft	5	24,820,000		
Unclassified Property	21	9,975,696	21	9,975,696
Total			615	$565,909,411

* Includes buildings under construction, renovation and demolition.

Table 1-3D. Large-loss Fires by Size of Loss

Year	No. Fires $250,000 and Over	No. Fires $750,000 and Over	No. Fires $3,000,000 and Over	No. Fires $10,000,000 and Over
1974	615	177	31	8
1973	501	157	22	4
1972	574	158	12	0
1971	499	132	10	1
1970	504	149	21	4

NOTE: See 1974 Large-loss Fires in the United States, *Fire Journal*, pp 13-18, Sep. 1975.

Credit may be more expensive. Return on invested capital may be lower. The cost of replacing buildings and equipment may be substantially greater than the value of those destroyed. Substantial delays may be encountered in obtaining replacement equipment. Demolition and site clearance can be significant expenses. Items whose intrinsic value is greater than their book value may also be destroyed, such as plans, molds, records, memorabilia, etc.

When a going industry is struck by fire, and key processes or equipment sustain damage, serious business interruption can occur. Such business interruption can have one or more of the following effects:

1. Losses to the Fire-damaged Business
   (a) Loss of customers
   (b) Loss of return on capital investment
   (c) Loss of profits on finished goods
   (d) Loss of confidence of stockholders
   (e) Loss of credit standing
   (f) Loss of good will of customers, employees, and the community
   (g) Loss of trained personnel who transfer to other jobs
   (h) Cost of retaining key personnel during shutdown
   (i) Loss of productive services of key personnel retained during enforced shutdown
   (j) Seizure of fire insurance payments by uneasy creditors
   (k) Excessive replacement costs due to overtime, inability to buy at time most advantageous to buyer, etc.
   (j) Cost of demolition
   (m) Cost of replacing depreciated buildings and equipment with new facilities
   (n) Continuance of fixed charges during shutdown.
   (o) Cost of hiring temporary quarters
   (p) Loss of patterns, valuable records, and other items that cannot be replaced or can be replaced only at great cost
   (q) Loss of earning power of patents, trade marks, etc.
   (r) Loss of value of past advertising
   (s) Inability to defend against unjust claims due to loss of records
   (t) Loss of rent from tenants
2. Losses to the Community
   (a) Loss of circulation of employee payroll
   (b) Increased burden on welfare funds

   (c) Loss of business by suppliers of raw materials and services to fire-damaged plant
   (d) Loss of a labor market
   (e) Loss of taxes on destroyed property

In some special cases, a single fire can seriously hamper production in an entire industry. The 1954 fire in an automatic transmission plant, in Livonia, Mich., halted production for several months. Its transmissions were used in six makes of automobile. Their unavailability led to sharply depressed sales for five major U.S. automobile makers. Indirect losses were never accurately estimated.

Another example is a fire in a telephone exchange in downtown New York City in 1975 that disrupted service to 170,000 phones. The impact of such an outage on a major commercial center, such as the Wall Street financial district, is hard to assess, but it must have been substantial.

These two cases indicate the magnitude that indirect losses can assume.

Finally, there are indirect losses of a personal nature. These may be even more difficult to estimate, yet their importance should not be neglected. In addition to financial losses incurred through temporary unemployment and expenses incurred in finding and moving to new housing, there is the destruction of irreplaceable personal belongings.

D. Gains Realized from Fires

It would be unfair to discuss only the fire losses and leave unmentioned possible fire gains. It is obvious that if an obsolete building, obsolete equipment, or obsolete stock is burned, there is no real loss, except perhaps to exposures. This fact is recognized to some extent through taking only the depreciated value of the property rather than the replacement cost in figuring fire loss. It is obviously unsafe, however, to accept a fire in obsolete property as of little consequence, since there is always the chance of spread to other property.

Then, too, recapitalization by insurance may be more than could be funded from individual resources. It has been suggested that some fires have been deliberately caused to get new capital from insurance. Correlation has been noted between major fires and the fiscal calendar which seems to substantiate the contention (see Figs. 1-5B and 1-5C).

In large-scale fires, the value of funds and services provided by insurance and government disaster assistance sometimes may be greater than the value of property destroyed.

Chapter 4

FIRE INVESTIGATION AND REPORTING

The fire problem can be reduced to three basic phases: (1) preventing the outbreak of fire, (2) preventing the serious spread of fire, and (3) preventing casualties from fire. Each phase must receive attention, for the possibility of human or mechanical failure makes it possible for any one of these phases to be significant.

To secure the greatest practical measure of safety and financial return with the least effort, expense, and interference with business frequently requires wide knowledge of past experience. Such knowledge is developed mainly by the investigation of fires and the analysis of accurate information on losses.

A. Purpose of Fire Investigation

Fire investigation is an important function of every fire department. The fire service is present at the vast majority of fires and has firsthand knowledge of the extent and magnitude of such fires; this same service is responsible for fire protection in the community and, therefore, usually has a clear picture of what happened when a fire occurred.

Fire investigations by the public fire service serve three basic purposes:

1. To determine what happened, so that preventative measures can be taken in the future. Too often fire investigations are conducted strictly to affix blame. A fire occurrence generally is a failure of either a code enforcement program or a public education program, except in the case where criminal activity is involved. Fire investigations can lead to better pre-fire activities that exact better control over the ignition sequence, particularly in those areas where the fire investigation shows shortcomings on the part of the fire service.

2. To ascertain whether there was any criminal activity involved. The rate of incendiarism is on the increase, and it is only through proper fire investigation that incendiarism will be detected and the proper evidence secured for conviction of arsonists.

3. To provide accurate information for the fire report. (By definition, the fire report is the legal record of a fire department incident.) The fire service must maintain an accurate report of each fire occurrence, the circumstances surrounding it, and the damage and/or casualties resulting from it. Information for the fire report can only come from an investigation of the fire.

A fire investigation should be conducted following each fire. This investigation may last only a few minutes when the fire is small and all the facts are easily obtained, or it may last many days when the fire is large or complex and details of its ignition and development are difficult to ascertain. The amount of time spent should be governed by how long it takes to fully understand the facts, not by a dollar loss criterion or by some other criteria.

The fire investigation should include at least a survey of the fire scene and a discussion with eyewitnesses or victims as to what they saw or heard. Sometimes it is necessary to have physical or chemical analyses of the debris performed in laboratories, and to review technical specifications on products to determine the condition of materials or equipment prior to the fire. Sometimes it is necessary to have ex-

perts in areas other than the fire service assist in piecing together a sequence of events, or in evaluating certain pieces of debris to ascertain what happened.

Fire Investigation Groups Other Than the Fire Service

Private groups also have reason to investigate fires. Chief among these groups is the insurance industry. Their investigations are initially to determine if there was fraud, but secondarily, they use the information obtained from fire investigations as input for underwriting and property protection programs.

Special interest groups and manufacturers are interested in performance of their product and will often investigate fires when there is a chance to gather information for product improvement or product safety, or to defend themselves in product liability cases.

Federal agencies with regulatory authority over certain hazards, conditions, or operations and code and standards development groups are interested in certain fires, as the information gained will provide input to the adequacy of the regulations or standards. (For other details concerning Fire Investigation, see Part C of Chapter 3, Section 9, this HANDBOOK.)

B. Details Covered by the Investigation

Fire investigations in many communities still revolve solely around arson investigation, or at best determination of "fire cause." A fire investigation should cover a wider range of subject areas. The three most significant areas are: the fire ignition sequence, fire development, and casualties.

The Fire Ignition Sequence: It is important to determine the location within the property where the fire started, and the ignition sequence that caused the fire to start. This ignition sequence consists of identifying three factors. There must be a heat source, a kindling fuel, and an event, human action, or natural act that gets the heat source and the kindling fuel together to start the fire. Each of these three factors must be identified separately if the ignition sequence is to be fully explained.

Fire Development: Once a fire starts, its growth or development is based on a number of factors. Each of these is important in understanding why a fire got as large as it did or stayed as small as it did.

The contents often play an important part in contributing fuel to the fire. These materials can cause intense fire spread or intense fire in concentrated areas. In addition, they can cause smoke and toxic gas conditions which may have affected the fire fighting operations. These materials should be identified and their part in the overall fire development or growth evaluated.

Compartmentation or other subdivision of a building with physical barriers often limit the development of fire and smoke conditions, and their performance should be evaluated after the fire. If fire walls, doors, dampers, or other smoke or fire limiting devices were present and did not perform as they were designed to perform, the reasons for this unsatisfactory performance should be investigated.

The time the fire burned prior to its detection or discovery, and the time between the detection and the transmission of an alarm to the fire department, are often important factors in the ultimate extent of damage from the fire. If there was automatic fire detection equipment in the building or automatic alarm transmission capability, then any delays in the performance of this equipment should be thoroughly investigated. Any other reasons for delays should be evaluated as part of the study of the overall fire development sequence.

If the structure is equipped with any type of automatic fire suppression system in the area where the fire occurred, its performance should be evaluated and any unsatisfactory performance fully investigated.

The tactics of the fire department used at the fire scene often affect the outcome of the fire. A thorough evaluation of the tactics should be made after each major fire to determine whether part of the fire development or spread might have been due to poor tactical procedures. Too often there is an attempt to affix blame on some structural defect or other failure when in fact the fire department did not have the available resources to properly tackle the fire, or it did not properly use the available resources.

Casualties: All injuries or fatalities associated with a fire incident should be thoroughly investigated to determine why they happened and what could be done to prevent future casualties. Casualties should be followed up for a period of time to determine the ultimate outcome of the person's injuries. Sometimes an understanding of the fire development sequence will be necessary to evaluate the reason for the casualties.

C. Responsibility for the Investigation

The initial responsibility for fire investigation must rest with the local fire department. They are the people who must extinguish the fire and are the ones who make an initial determination as to how the fire started.

In many American states and all Canadian provinces, the primary responsibility for investigation of incendiary fires is in the office of a state or provincial fire marshal. In states where there is no state fire marshal's office or where this office has not been delegated the responsibility for incendiary fire investigation, this duty falls to the local police and fire departments. These departments must collect the evidence and present it to the prosecuting attorney. The state fire marshal sometimes has powers beyond those which are customarily given to police. In such cases their function is quasi-judicial in character and similar to that of the coroner. In addition to the ordinary investigation into the circumstances of a fire, the fire marshal may summon persons to an inquest. He may start proceedings to compel testimony under oath and to punish for contempt.

The function of holding an inquest into the causes of fires is assigned by the majority of state laws to the fire marshal and his deputies. About a dozen states, however, give local authorities, such as the head of the fire department or a municipal fire marshal, powers equal to those of the state fire marshal insofar as local investigations are concerned. In nearly all jurisdictions it is possible for the fire marshal to delegate at his discretion certain of his powers to local officials. Numerous cities have specialist fire investigators in the fire department, or an arson squad operated cooperatively by the police and fire departments.

Beyond the investigation of incendiary fires or of all fire causes, the local fire department should train its officers to conduct routine investigations into the ignition sequence, fire development, and reasons for casualties at all fires.

They should have available to them a team of specialists who can assist when circumstances are too complex for the fire officer to handle or when the situation is such that it would be too time-consuming for the fire officer. In any event the fire officer, having been present during the time that the fire was extinguished, should continue to stay involved. The fire officer can lend considerable support to the investigative team in reconstructing the scene and identifying the time sequence when certain events took place.

D. Training for Fire Investigation

A survey conducted in 1972, in which 1,401 fire departments returned survey forms, showed that thorough investigations were mainly conducted on those fires that were suspicious or involved fatalities or major dollar loss. It also showed that fire department line officers are generally responsible for conducting the initial investigation with special investigators responding only if requested. Formal training in investigative procedures is conducted in very few departments. Those having training programs generally rely on the lecture method by an "experienced" fire investigator since printed texts and publications are not widely available except in the limited scope of arson determination. State fire marshals' agencies are heavily relied upon for assistance when special investigators are required, but outside specialists such as engineers, chemists, and others are seldom utilized in fire cause determination.

In an effort to overcome this deficiency, the National Fire Protection Association has developed two training packages—FIFI: Fire Information Field Investigation, Units A and B.[1] The first of these is planned to increase the observation powers of the fire fighters and officers at the scene and to encourage the preservation of evidence on the fire ground. The second package is planned to give the fire officer basic training in determining the ignition sequence and circumstances of a fire. These two packages are designed for training local personnel in the business of fire investigation and should be supplemented to develop the broad levels of expertise needed to thoroughly investigate all factors related to the fire.

Most of the regional seminars held either by colleges or by special groups are aimed at arson investigation and can help enhance that aspect of a fire officer's responsibility.

E. The Fire Report

During the fire investigation and at its conclusion, it is important that all the information gathered be properly recorded for future use. This record, together with other information, is the fire report—the legal record of a fire department incident. The fire report includes the information on the time of the incident, the response to the incident, the action taken, the details of the fire, if any, and the damage or the casualties resulting from the incident. This report must be in the words of the fire officer and must be complete enough to allow some other fire service person to understand what happened even if he was not at the fire scene. The report can be as brief as a partial page or as extensive as a multiple page report with photographers and physical evidence or laboratory test results.

F. Purpose of the Fire Report

There are three basic purposes of a fire report. First, it is the legal record of the fact that the fire occurred and the fire department took some type of action. It reports factors about the property where the fire occurred, why it occurred, how building components and fire protecton devices performed, what damage or casualties resulted, and what action the fire department took. Second, it provides information to superior officers and fire department managers concerning the particular incident, what occurred, and what action was taken. This can be helpful in evaluating the performance of their units at the incident and allow them to talk intelligently with their superiors about the incident. Third, it provides data on the fire problem to fire service management so that they can track trends, measure the effectiveness of fire prevention and fire suppression measures presently in practice, evaluate the impact of new methods, and indicate those areas that may require further attention. It should also provide data to state and national data banks for use in evaluating the scope of the fire problem on a broader basis.

G.   Uniformity in Fire Reporting

For the purpose of providing a legal record and advising superior officers of what occurred at a particular fire incident, it is not necessary to maintain uniformity in fire reporting. However, to provide data on the fire problem and to aggregate this data at state and national levels, it is definitely necessary to have uniform reporting procedures and terminology in use in the fire service.

There has been little uniformity in fire reports either between fire departments or internally in the past. Within a fire department the forms used for collecting data are the same, but terminology, depth of detail, and procedures for reporting often are left to the individual officer, with the result that there is a variety of terminology used to explain the same situation, and the completeness of reports varies from very complete to totally inadequate. Quality control is often lacking, and the volume of reports is such that information cannot be readily aggregated from the reports. Between departments the problem becomes even more difficult. Wide variances seem to exist between fire departments protecting the same type and size of environment. These variances are generally due to differences in reporting terminology and procedures. Aggregation of data at the state or national level has been extremely difficult, and only the grossest of numbers can be captured with any degree of accuracy.

Recognizing this problem, the NFPA established a Technical Committee on Fire Reporting. This Committee has developed Standard No. 901, Uniform Coding for Fire Protection, hereinafter referred to in this Chapter as the NFPA Uniform Coding Standard. This Standard establishes basic definitions and terminology for use in fire reporting systems, and a means of coding data so that it can be aggregated either manually or by automatic data processing means.

The NFPA Uniform Coding Standard provides a common language for many data elements. It is recognized that every fire department will not want to collect every data element; likewise, there may be additional data elements that a fire department wishes to collect. When a fire department finds that it can use the data elements from the NFPA Uniform Coding Standard in its reporting system, it will also find that it is in a position to contribute data to larger data bases and to utilize data from these larger data bases in its municipal management. It will also find that the quality of information and the uniformity within the

fire department will improve. The NFPA Uniform Coding Standard has data elements which provide a classification of practically every type of property whether fixed or mobile, provide elements for assessing the fire risk of a specific piece of property prior to an incident, provide data elements to describe the ignition sequence and the area of origin of the fire, and provide data elements to describe factors surrounding the incident, what was found on arrival, what action was taken, and why the fire got as large or stayed as small as it did. There are also data elements for describing the extent of damage, the loss of property, the investment in manpower provided by the community, and injuries or fatalities to both civilians and fire fighters as a result of the fire incident.

H.   Fire Reporting Systems

There is a major difference between a fire report and a fire reporting system. A fire report has been previously defined. A fire reporting system has three components or operations which must be present for any system to be complete. These are "fact finding", "fact processing", and "fact use". Each of these is discussed as follows.

Fact Finding

The traditional functions can be satisfied with as little as a written narrative of the basic facts of the incident. To serve as input to a fire reporting system, however, an incident report must be clearly structured and must use uniform definitions and terminology. The collection of information on an incident report requires a form or forms on which to record the information desired, instructions for completing the forms so that the information within the reporting area is provided in a uniform manner, and a procedure for forwarding these forms to a central point.

Fact Processing

Once data has been recorded, it must be processed into a record useful for legal, statistical, planning, and management purposes. The first step in information processing involves checking the incident reports for accuracy and completeness, and aggregating information about one incident from several reports into a composite record. The second step involves the creation of a file consisting of all of the records of the reported incidents. This fire fact file will constitute the basic source of information about past incidents. The use to which the incident file is put will determine to a large extent the facts that must be recorded on an incident report.

Fact Use

Once an incident file has been generated, it may have many potential uses. At the least, it should meet the informational needs of all the sectors of the local fire service. These include both information required from a legal standpoint and information needed for periodic statistical reports. A more general use would be to spot trends in fire incidence and to provide data for program evaluation and fire related research.

Even though a small fire department may have an incidence level that is too low for meaningful evaluation, the data collected from several such services may be sufficient to provide information useful to their managers, planners, and analysts. Therefore, it is important that information being recorded by fire services use a uniform terminology and uniform coding so that data from different fire services can be merged.

A vital function of an effective system is to provide input to those designing and marketing new equipment and to those designing and providing interior finshes and furnishings so that the total effort of all concerned can reduce the fire problem.

The Systems Concepts Committee of the NFPA and the "Decision Tree" (see Fig. 6-2A) will count upon the output of fire reporting systems on a continuing basis. Each time a method of fire defense works well and the fire loss and danger are confined to a small area, the "success" will increase the confidence in that particular method of fire defense. Conversely, each time a method of fire defense fails as indicated by an expensive loss or by injuries or death, this failure needs to be recorded so that the confidence in that method of fire defense can be reduced.

Thus, through each incident report, the company officer, the fire service manager, and the chief of the department can work to "manage" the local problem. State and federal authorities can "manage" their interests, and on a broader scale industry, educators, architects, research scientists, and fire protection engineers can work as a team to reduce the fire problem as defined by the basic local fire fact file.

I. Benefits to the Fire Department

A fire department can derive many benefits from a good fire incident reporting system, particularly if it is based on the NFPA Uniform Coding Standard. The data can be aggregated using uniform definitions and coding and analyzed to:

Describe a Community's Fire Problem: It is possible to pinpoint where fires are occurring, what factors are most responsible for ignitions, and what damage and casualties are occurring as a result of fires. With the problem in proper perspective, the most serious aspects of the fire problem can be tackled first.

Support Budget Requests: In this era of increasing tax rates, municipal officials are quick to cut budgets and slow to add new programs. One of the reasons is that fire department managers do not have the data to support their requests for additional funds. Good data will put the fire problem in perspective with other social problems and make community officials realize the consequence of budget cuts or the value of new programs.

Support Code Changes: Building and fire prevention codes are sometimes altered for political purposes so as to neutralize them. In other cases the changing character or complexity of a community requires additions to existing codes. A good data base provides the ammunition to go to the governing body with accurate reports of losses which could have been prevented through code changes. Loss data from other areas with more stringent codes can also be used as a valid comparison.

Evaluate Code Enforcement Programs: It is not sufficient to have codes on the books if they are not being properly enforced. In evaluating loss experience, it is easy to see whether certain classes of losses are occurring because existing codes are not being properly enforced. The reason for the improper enforcement can then be analyzed and corrected.

Evaluate and Guide Fire Prevention Educational Programs: Not all programs can be solved by establishing codes and enforcing them. There are certain aspects of the fire problem which can best be controlled by public edu-

cation programs, making people aware of the dangers and how to prevent them, and how to react when certain situations do arise. Such programs require considerable money and time. It is important to know what the problem is that the educational program is supposed to solve, and to be able to measure whether the program is in fact solving that aspect of the problem.

Plan Future Fire Protection Needs: Many communities are becoming very active in community planning, and fire departments are developing master plans. It is essential that the fire service be involved in such planning. A good data base will allow a fire department to track changing community characteristics and plan for future fire protection needs based on planned community growth. It will also provide input to decisions on what type and level of fire protection a community will provide so that requirements can be established for developers who construct properties which exceed the capabilities of the fire department.

Improve Allocation of Resources: It is not always possible for a fire department to grow at the rate necessary for the changing community needs. Likewise, it may not be necessary for a department to expand. Proper analysis may show where a redeployment of existing resources can provide the same level of protection or even improve the level of protection within a community.

Schedule Nonemergency Activities to Avoid Peak Response Periods: Training sessions, in-service inspections, and other activities are an important aspect of a fire department's function. Fire experience which tracks times and severity of fires will allow a fire department to schedule these activities when they are least likely to be interrupted by emergency calls or when the normal delay from such activities will have the least impact on emergencies.

J. Status of Uniform Reporting Practices

There has been and there continues to be considerable work done in developing fire reporting systems based on the NFPA Uniform Coding Standard. The NFPA Fire Reporting Committee has established a basic system which can be used manually or adapted for automatic data processing. The NFPA also has a sophisticated incident reporting system which is available with the necessary computer programs to process the data and generate reports. Both of these systems are receiving widespread use at the local level. Likewise, a number of communities have developed their own reporting system based on the NFPA Uniform Coding Standard.

At the state level, many states have had legislation for many years requiring fire reports to be filed with the state fire marshal. Many states are now requiring that that report conform to the NFPA Uniform Coding Standard. States are becoming active in processing data for analysis of the fire problem at that level. Many states without such legislation are seeking it and encouraging fire departments to begin basing their reporting on the NFPA Uniform Coding Standard. Others are encouraging or developing reporting systems without the legislation.

The NFPA has used the NFPA Uniform Coding Standard as the basis of its in-house fire data system for many years, and the National Fire Prevention and Control Administration is working toward a national data file based on that Standard. The NFPA Uniform Coding Standard is being widely accepted by the fire service and should produce a much more meaningful picture of the fire problem in the future.

Bibliography

Reference Cited

[1] *FIFI: Fire Information Field Investigation, Units A and B*, National Fire Protection Association, Boston, 1974. (Training package for fire investigation.)

NFPA Codes, Standards, and Recommended Practices (see the latest *NFPA Publications and Visual Aids Catalog* for availability of current editions of the following documents)

NFPA No. 901, Uniform Coding for Fire Protection.

NFPA No. 901AM, Fire Reporting Field Incident Manual.

Additional Readings

"Fire Information Field Investigation Final Report, FIFI Phase 1," Contract No. 1-35928 to National Bureau of Standards, 1972, National Fire Protection Association, Boston.

Kirk, P. L., *Fire Investigation*, John Wiley and Sons, New York, 1969.

Uniform Fire Incident Reporting System, National Fire Protection Association, Boston, 1974. (A series of documents and computer programs for reporting and analyzing fire incident information.)

Chapter 5

ANALYSES OF FIRE LOSSES

As a vital adjunct to a successful fire prevention and protection program, fire record experience serves the fivefold function of: (1) presenting a factual enumeration of the various direct and indirect losses from fire, (2) providing a continuous measure of the progress in reducing fire losses, (3) pointing out the places where the various features of fire prevention and protection have been or can be effectively applied, (4) providing the stimulus for fire research, and (5) being the basis and justification for the recommendations in fire protection standards. Thus, the record of fire experience is essential to the science of fire protection, without which most of the essential features of twentieth-century living, including concentrations of populations in large communities, as well as large-scale industrial and commercial enterprises, would be impossible.

This chapter shows how fire experience, when compiled in statistical form, reveals the weaknesses most frequently encountered in fire losses and other facts vital to a good comprehension of the complex fire protection and fire prevention problems. This chapter also covers in a broader context the analyses of the contributing factors to the start and spread of conflagrations that, while not the problem they were some years ago, nevertheless pose a potential threat to any community where conflagration "breeders" are present.

The fundamentals of good fire investigation, which are the backbone of the statistical data gathering effort, are covered in Chapter 4 of this Section.

A. Analyses of Large Loss Fires

Large loss fires are usually more thoroughly investigated than those causing smaller losses, and consequently they can be analyzed more accurately. Analyses of these comparatively few fires that have resulted in staggering losses give a clear indication of what fire protection and human weaknesses are most frequently encountered in fires. And, too, many of the lessons learned from analyses of large losses can be applied to prevent extensive damage in property where the total value is relatively small, such as dwellings, since the factors influencing fire spread are the same irrespective of the value of the property subject to destruction.

(Fires resulting in individual losses of $250,000 or more are termed "large loss fires" by the NFPA Fire Analysis Department. See Chapter 3 of this Section for a discussion of the annual large loss fire record and the monetary loss it represents.)

The factors that permit fires to develop into large losses fall into four groups: (1) structural defects, (2) improper handling and storage of combustible contents, and (3) private fire protection weaknesses. With very few exceptions, large loss fires are the result of the combined effects of factors from two or more of these groups.

Table 1-5A illustrates statistically the principal factors responsible for large loss building fires. The Table was prepared from a study of selected large loss fires reported to NFPA.

Structural Defects Influencing Fire Spread

Construction deficiencies are major factors in the large loss fire experience. Referring to Table 1-5A, it will be seen that most frequently mentioned as a structural fault was the absence of walls to subdivide large areas where good judgment would have recommended subdivisions. The study also shows that there were frequent instances where a division wall had been installed but was ineffective as a fire barrier because there were no fire doors or other protection for openings in the walls, or fire doors were blocked open (see Sec. 6, Chap. 8).

The analysis also shows that the principal structural weakness responsible for vertical spread of fire is the absence of fire cutoffs at openings between floors. Open stairways and elevator shafts are the most frequent paths for vertical fire spread, but other structural weaknesses that allow fire to spread beyond the floor of origin are conveyor and pipe openings and nonfirestopped walls (see Sec. 6, Chap 8).

When a fire spreads to an exposed building, it is usually because of congested combustible construction, lack of exposure protection (such as wired-glass windows), poorly constructed party walls, and interconnecting passageways. Other factors not relating to construction that have been noted in exposure fires include yard storage between buildings and lack of outside sprinklers (see Sec. 5, Chap. 2, and Sec. 14, Chap. 2).

Combustible interior finish is a recurring cause of fire spread in large loss fires. Combustible acoustical tile ceilings, fiberboard wall panels, plywood, and oilsoaked floors are some common examples of this means of fire spread.

Contents Features Influencing Fire Spread

The most frequent contents factor contributing to large loss fires is improper storage as shown in Table 1-5A. This item includes poor stock subdivision and stock piled too high or against windows. Excessive fire loads due to improper storage may also greatly increase the fire severity.

Flammable and combustible liquids represent the second most frequent contents feature influencing fire spread. The effect of these liquids is felt when through improper storage or protection they escape from drums, tanks, processing equipment, or piping, and intensify the fire. Flammable gases have a similar effect when they escape from cylinders or piping during a fire.

Poor housekeeping, another significant contents feature, is a convenient term to describe a general lack of cleanliness as evidenced by such fire hazardous conditions as dust on structural members and rubbish accumulations.

Private Fire Protection Weaknesses

Only a very small percentage of the large loss fires occurred in buildings equipped with either complete or partial sprinkler systems. If the absence of sprinklers were listed as a "factor responsible for fire spread," as, for example, the absence of vertical fire cutoffs, the number would be in the hundreds. The various reasons for unsatisfactory performance of sprinklers in large loss fires are enumerated in Table 1-5A.

Table 1-5A. Factors Responsible for Fire Spread Involving Property Damage of $250,000 or More to Buildings

The items detailed in this table reflect some of the significant factors responsible for the spread of fire in buildings which resulted in loss to the structure or its contents of $250,000 or more. The data are based on studies of selected fire experiences as reported and analyzed by the NFPA Fire Analysis Department. In any given fire a number of contributing factors might be involved. The purpose of the information presented is to assist in evaluating those features of structures of their contents, private fire protection weaknesses, or public protection handicap which have proven to be significant in these fires. The numbers reflect only the recorded number of instances as reported in the fires studied and should not be taken to reflect the relative importance of each factor in any given property.

A. Principal Structural Defects Influencing Fire Spread

	Public Assembly and Office Facilities	Mercantile Facilities	Industrial Facilities	Manufacturing Facilities	Storage Facilities
Vertical Spread					
1. Stairways and elevators not enclosed by fire walls or partitions	27	9	4	4	3
2. Nonfire stopped walls	14	8	1	4	4
Horizontal Spread					
1. Nonfire stopped areas including floors and concealed spaces above or below floors and ceilings	73	60	3	51	53
2. Interior wall openings unprotected	8	6	2	10	5
3. Exterior finish	4	1	2	7	15
Combustible Framing/Finishes					
1. Structure or framing	62	41	7	56	58
2. Ceilings, walls, floors	8	6	1	2	4
B. Contents Features Influencing Fire Spread					
1. Products in storage	3	19	1	24	53
2. Flammable liquids, gas not properly contained	3	3	1	12	9
C. Principal Fire Protection Defects Influencing Fire Spread					
Automatic Sprinkler Performance					
1. Extinguished/controlled fire	4	3	2	17	9
2. Did not control/extinguish fire	12	4	2	37	34
3. Standpipe/hand extinguisher helped control fire	6	1	10	11	Not reported
4. Standpipe/hand extinguisher did not help control fire	22	2	6	10	Not reported

The Human Element

Underlying all the evidence of tangible protection and prevention weaknesses brought out by fire analyses is evidence of an intangible weakness which was present wherever a fire loss was suffered. That weakness was a failure by someone somewhere to recognize and comprehend the significance of the faults which ultimately combined to contribute to a loss.

Time of Occurrence

Large loss fires generally have been found to occur at night between 8 p.m. and 8 a.m. with fire activity peaking between midnight and 4 a.m. (see Fig. 1-5A). On the other hand, fires which cause little loss show just the opposite characteristics; such fires peak during the daytime, and show a significant decrease during the night. Large loss fires usually occur when buildings are closed for business or have just a few occupants, perhaps a maintenance crew or supervisory staff only.

Large loss fires are also observed to occur in the first part of the month and in the months following the end of the fiscal quarter (see Figs. 1-5B and 1-5C). This pattern is too clear to be chance-occasioned. Such coincidence was first observed in a 1929 NFPA study and has been noted several times since then.

B. Fire Losses by Fire Ignition Sequence

Statistics on fire ignition sequence provide data on ignition sources and on the combustible materials most frequently involved in fires. Fire prevention involves the control of both of these factors. There are situations where more stress should be placed on one than on the other, and fire prevention may be more easily attained in one instance by elimination of an ignition source and in another by removal of combustible material.

For example, the fire ignition sequence referred to as "children and fire" can be controlled by keeping matches away from children. On the other hand, fire ignition sequences from welding and cutting may be prevented in most situations by removal of combustible material from cutting and welding areas.

A third method of fire prevention is to eliminate the oxygen (air) or the oxidizing agent which permits the combustion process to proceed. This technique is employed in various recognized extinguishing systems or methods, and is most simply illustrated by placing a cover over a skillet containing burning grease. This technique is only infrequently practical in fire prevention practices. It is normally employed only with materials which are unstable in air or which are powerful oxidizing agents.

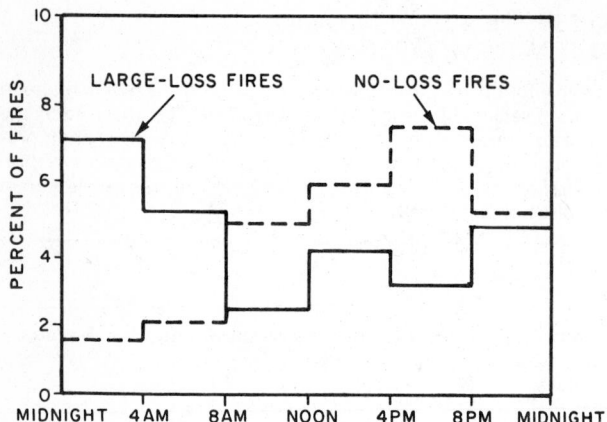

Fig. 1-5A. Time of occurrence of large-loss and no-loss fires. Graph drawn from data in Oregon Fire Marshal Report, 1970.

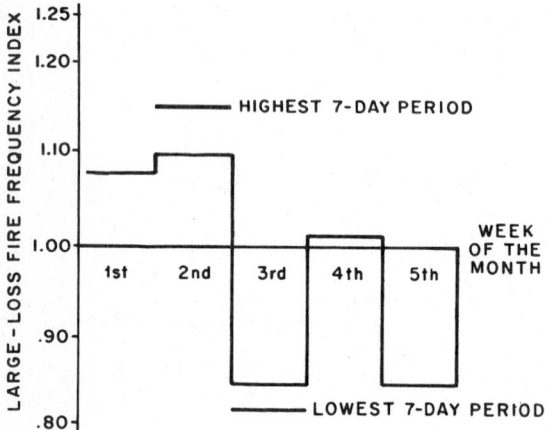

Fig. 1-5B. Large loss fires by the week of the month of occurrence.

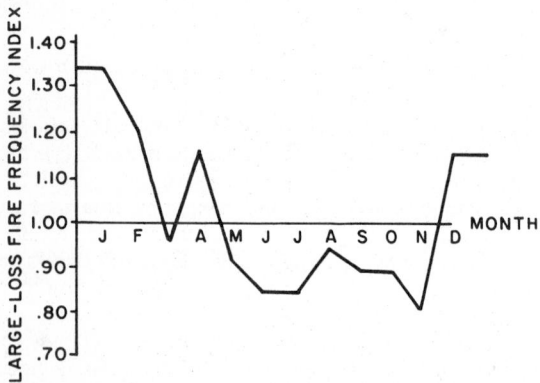

Fig. 1-5C. Large loss fires by the month of occurrence.

Tables 1-5B and 1-5C present statistics on fire ignition sequence compiled by the NFPA for 1970–1974. The average annual number of building fires and amounts of losses in the United States are classified according to the more common fire ignition sequences.

Heating and Cooking Equipment

Defective or Overheated Heating and Cooking Equipment: These conditions account for more than 100,000 fires each year. Included are fires caused by improperly installed, maintained, or operated furnaces, smoke pipes, vents, portable and stationary heaters, industrial and commercial furnaces, domestic and commercial cooking ranges and stoves and other heating devices, and incinerators. Not included are chimney and flue fires, ignition of combustible material placed too near heating and cooking equipment, and fires started by hot ashes or coals, all of which are discussed separately in the following paragraphs (also see Sec. 7, Chap. 3).

Chimneys and Flues: Included are fires commonly referred to as "chimney fires" which involve soot that has been allowed to accumulate in chimney flues or ignition of combustibles having inadequate separation from chimneys or smoke pipes. A soot fire is usually confined to the chimney, but if the flue lining is cracked, if the flue is not lined, or if combustible building materials are in contact with the chimney, a soot fire may spread beyond the chimney (see Sec. 7, Chap. 3).

Hot Ashes and Coals: These materials stored in combustible containers, or in proximity to combustible material, account for most of the fires in this category. Others are caused by mixing combustible refuse with ashes.

Combustibles near Heaters and Stoves: These fires often result from and most frequently involve such materials as rubbish, clothing, furniture, etc., placed too near heat-producing equipment, rather than through any fault with the device or its installation (see Sec. 7, Chap. 3).

Smoking and Related Fires

Fires caused by careless smokers and the careless use of matches and lighters by smokers are grouped together. Among smoking materials the cigarette is the most frequent fire cause due to the greater number smoked. Disposal of burning tobacco or glowing ashes from pipes may have greater potentialities than cigarettes for the ignition of combustible materials under many conditions, but because of the smaller number of pipe smokers, pipes are considered a less serious hazard. Cigars present the least danger.

The continued burning of cigarettes after they have been discarded or left unattended is the principal hazard. Glowing cigarettes reach temperatures high enough, in theory at least, to ignite the great majority of combustible solids, liquids, and gases.[1] However, many variables, such as humidity and draft, affect the results; consequently, ignition by a smoldering cigarette can take place only when certain combinations of these variables permit.

"Rats and matches" was in former years frequently reported as a fire ignition sequence, but experiments have shown that match heads are not attractive to rats or mice.[2] Occasionally, matches are used as nest-building material and are carried into walls and partitions and left near steam pipes or chimneys where their presence may cause a fire ignition sequence.

Ash trays of improper design constitute a hazard, particularly types which allow a lighted cigarette to fall or roll off the tray.

Electrical

Wiring and Distribution Equipment: These fire sources include fixed electrical wiring and associated components, such as fuse boxes, circuit breakers, other overcurrent protective devices, electrical outlets, panel boards, and similar equipment. These installations cause fires by short circuit faults or by arcs and sparks from damaged or defective components (see Sec. 7, Chap. 2).

Motors and Appliances: These include all electrical appliances except fires caused by electrical heating, cooking,

Table 1-5B. Estimated Number of Building Fires by Fire Ignition Sequence, 1970–1974

	1970	1971	1972	1973	1974
Heating and Cooking Equipment					
Defective, misused equipment	79,600	87,800	89,400	97,500	93,300
Chimneys, flues	20,300	22,400	21,800	23,900	14,000
Hot ashes, coals	7,200	8,000	6,800	6,500	12,600
Combustibles near heaters, stoves	35,800	39,500	37,200	37,900	40,100
Total:	142,900	157,700	155,200	165,800	160,000
Smoking Related	107,200	118,400	109,700	115,200	121,600
Electrical					
Wiring distribution equipment	89,500	98,800	101,600	106,700	112,200
Motors and appliances	56,200	62,100	61,000	64,000	52,800
Total:	145,700	160,900	162,600	170,700	165,000
Trash Burning	31,100	34,400	36,000	35,200	177,000
Flammable Liquids	58,800	64,900	65,200	67,300	56,100
Open Flames, Sparks					
Sparks, embers	5,000	5,500	6,200	6,500	13,300
Welding, cutting	8,800	9,700	8,200	9,800	11,600
Friction, sparks from machinery	14,700	16,200	17,000	16,200	11,900
Thawing pipes	5,200	—	5,500	5,500	5,800
Other open flames	33,500	—	35,000	32,000	34,900
Total:	67,200	74,100	71,900	70,000	77,500
Lightning	20,100	22,200	22,700	21,600	16,600
Children and Fire	63,800	70,400	69,200	70,800	59,600
Exposure	21,000	23,200	25,400	25,200	44,200
Incendiary, Suspicious	65,300	72,100	84,200	94,300	144,400
Spontaneous Ignition	14,200	15,700	15,100	14,900	11,000
Gas Fires, Explosions	11,400	12,600	8,700	9,600	11,900
Fireworks, Explosives	3,500	—	4,200	4,300	4,200
Miscellaneous Known Causes	77,800	3,800	65,900	70,500	91,700
Unknown Causes	162,000	166,200	154,200	150,500	159,200
Total Building Fires:	992,000	996,600	1,050,200	1,085,900	1,270,000

Table 1-5C. Estimated Loss by Fire Ignition Sequence

	1970	1971	1972	1973	1974
Heating and Cooking Equipment					
Defective, misused equipment	108,700,000	111,487,000	116,700,000	126,800,000	137,300 000
Chimneys, flues	15,500,000	15,862,000	16,200,000	17,700,000	19,300,000
Hot ashes, coals	4,300,000	4,305,000	3,900,000	3,700,000	2,000,000
Combustibles near heaters, stoves	40,300,000	41,241,000	40,800,000	41,500,000	40,700,000
Total:	$168,800,000	$172,895,000	$177,600,000	$189,700,000	$199,300,000
Smoking Related	95,900,000	98,344,000	95,900,000	100,700,000	136,300,000
Electrical					
Wiring and distribution equipment	184,300,000	188,984,000	203,100,000	213,300,000	253,300,000
Motors, appliances	80,100,000	82,285,000	112,700,000	118,200,000	110,200,000
Total:	264,400,000	271,269,000	315,800,000	331,500,000	363,500,000
Trash Burning	21,100,000	21,754,000	2,400,000	2,400,000	5,000,000
Flammable Liquids	52,600,000	53,931,000	56,900,000	61,200,000	53,200,000
Open Flames, Sparks					
Sparks, embers	5,500,000	5,665,000	6,700,000	7,000,000	7,900,000
Welding, cutting	30,700,000	31,497,000	28,800,000	34,400,000	48,900,000
Friction, sparks from machinery	18,500,000	19,034,000	22,000,000	17,100,000	19,100,000
Thawing pipes	11,500,000	11,783,000	11,900,000	11,100,000	15,300,000
Other open flames	31,400,000	32,177,000	32,800,000	29,900,000	56,400,000
Total:	97,600,000	100,156,000	102,200,000	99,500,000	147,600,000
Lightning	39,300,000	40,335,000	43,300,000	41,900,000	39,100,000
Children and Fire	70,400,000	72,285,000	74,600,000	76,300,000	100,100,000
Exposure	41,200,000	42,148,000	23,400,000	23,200,000	26,200,000
Incendiary, Suspicious	206,400,000	232,947,000	285,600,000	320,000,000	563,000,000
Spontaneous Ignition	24,900,000	25,606,000	25,900,000	25,500,000	41,200,000
Gas Fires, Explosions	41,400,000	26,286,000	23,400,000	23,400,000	41,900,000
Fireworks, Explosives	5,100,000	—	5,200,000	5,200,000	5,200,000
Miscellaneous Known Causes	102,400,000	105,142,000	191,400,000	191,400,000	268,500,000
Unknown Causes	977,700,000	1,002,931,000	992,700,000	1,045,300,000	1,237,000,000
Total Building Fires:	$2,209,200,000	$2,266,000,000	$2,416,300,000	$2,537,200,000	$3,260,000,000

and welding appliances which are listed under other entries in Table 1-5B. Careless use, improper installation, and poor maintenance are responsible for most of these fires. Appliances not constructed in accordance with nationally recognized standards are also a factor (see Sec. 7, Chap. 2).

Trash Burning

Rubbish and waste material is frequently classified as a fire cause, even though, except in the case of spontaneous ignition, such material does not cause fires, but rather furnishes the fuel for ignition sources. In these fires the ignition source is unknown. However, rather than classify them "unknown" it is much more useful to designate them as "rubbish fires, ignition source unknown."

Flammable Liquids

In this category are fires originating from the careless storage and handling of flammable or combustible liquids, and liquid fuel-fired appliances with the exception of heating and cooking appliances. It includes fires involving flammable or combustible liquid-fuel lamps, lanterns, or torches due to leaking fuel, spills while filling, overturns, or ignition of combustible material due to careless handling of such appliances. As in the case of rubbish, flammable or combustible liquids rarely by themselves constitute an ignition source, but they are listed separately as they are a particular fire problem.

Open Flames and Sparks

Sparks and Embers: These include fires caused by ignition of roof coverings by sparks from chimneys, incinerators, rubbish fires, locomotives, etc. Fires due to sparks from exposure fires are separately classified.

Welding and Cutting: These fires may be caused by the arc or flame itself, by heat conduction through the metals being welded or cut, by molten slag and metal from the cut, or by sparks which fly from the work.

Friction, Sparks from Machinery: These include fires caused by friction heat or sparks resulting from impact between two hard surfaces, at least one of which is usually metallic.

Friction heat can result from rolling or sliding in machinery or between two hard surfaces, at least one of which is metallic. Heated bearings on rotating machinery, and belts that become overheated and belts that become overheated due to slipping at pulleys are ignition sources.

Sparks from dropping steel tools on a concrete floor, from falling tools striking machinery or piping from tramp metal in grinding mills, and from shoe nails on concrete floors are examples of friction sparks that are often reported as responsible for fires.

Thawing Pipes: These include fires involving torches, oil-soaked rags, and other open flame devices used in the dangerous practice of thawing pipes with an open flame.

Other Open Flames: These include fires caused by such ignition sources as candles, locomotive sparks, incinerator sparks, and chimney sparks (except when fires originate on roofs). Many of the fires in this classification could probably be included in some other group if more detailed information on the cause were reported. For example, an open flame fire that originated in a laboratory might well have been the flame of a Bunsen burner, in which case the fire should be classified under "gas and appliances."

Lightning

This category consists of all building fires caused by the effects of lightning.

Children and Fire

Fires in this category are the result of children playing with matches or using them carelessly or without realizing the hazard involved.

Exposure

Fires in buildings classified as "exposure" fires are those originating in other than buildings, but which ignite buildings. A fire originating in one building and spreading to another is classified under the original cause of the fire.

Incendiary, Suspicious

This category includes all fires that are known or thought to have been set, fires set to defraud insurance companies, fires set by mentally ill persons, and fires set by malicious persons.

The number of fires known to be of incendiary origin has increased dramatically over the past ten years. Experienced investigators feel that half the fires of unknown origin are actually incendiary, but the completeness of destruction prevents determination of the cause. None of the available statistics on fire losses are based on data reliable enough to indicate more than approximately what proportion of the losses may be considered incendiary. Also it is somewhat hard to classify many borderline cases which may be due to indifference of property owners rather than to deliberate incendiarism. The steady growth in the number of incendiary fires from 1964 to 1974 is shown in Table 1-5D.

Table 1-5D. Incendiary and Suspicious Fires and Losses, 1964–1974

Year	Number	Property Loss
1974	114,400	$563,000,000
1973	94,300	$320,000,000
1972	84,200	$285,600,000
1971	72,100	$232,947,000
1970	65,300	$206,400,000
1969	56,300	$179,400,000
1968	49,900	$131,100,000
1967	44,100	$141,700,000
1966	37,400	$94,600,000
1965	33,900	$74,000,000
1964	30,900	$68,200,000

Spontaneous Ignition

This category is a record of fires resulting from the uncontrolled spontaneous heating of materials.

Gas Fires and Explosions

Fires and explosions that involve gas that has escaped from piping, storage tanks, equipment, or appliances account for most of the fires in this classification. In addition, fires caused by misuse or faulty operation of gas appliances, except heating and cooking appliances and welding and cutting torches, are also included in this category.

Fireworks and Explosives

This category includes explosions that do not fall into established classifications, such as explosions caused by uncontrolled chemical reactions, etc. Also included are explosions where the material that exploded and the ignition source cannot be determined. This category represents only a small percentage of all explosions, as they differ from fires only in the rate of burning and are placed in the same category as fires having the same ignition source. For example, an "explosion" of an oil-fired space heater would be classified with fires caused by defective oil-fired heating equipment.

Miscellaneous Known Causes

This group includes fires of known cause which cannot be classified in any of the other known causes of fires in Tables 1-5B and 1-5C. Fires caused by static electricity, and molten metal are examples of some of the fire causes in this category.

Unknown Causes

Inability to determine the probable cause of a fire or failure to make a careful investigation means that the cause must be classified as "unknown."

C.   Fire Losses by Occupancy

The term "occupancy" as used in fire prevention and protection describes buildings, vehicles, etc., by their use. For example, places where people worship are classified in the occupancy "churches," and places that serve food to the public are classified as "restaurants." Such classifications are important because the fire hazards of most buildings are determined to a large extent by what goes on in the buildings.

Causal factors for fires in the most common occupancy classes are given in Table 1-5E. These causal factors are those of NFPA No. 901, Uniform Coding for Fire Protection. A brief explanation of these terms is given below. A more detailed explanation will be found in the Uniform Coding for Fire Protection Standard. (See also Chap. 4 of this Section for further discussion of the NFPA system for fire reporting.)

Area of Origin: The use of that room or part of a room where the fire started.

Source of Heat of Ignition: The equipment which brings about ignition.

Form of Heat of Ignition: The nature of the heat energy which resulted in the fire.

Type of Material Ignited: The kind or nature of material first ignited, which resulted in the fire. Was it a solid, a liquid, or a gas? A grease? Oil, wood, or paper?

Form of Material Ignited: The shape and use of the material first ignited.

Act or Omission: The act or failure to act (omission) which results in ignition. (Natural occurrences which result in fires are also included.)

D.   Analyses of Conflagrations

There is no universally accepted exact definition of a conflagration. Some list as conflagrations all fires causing more than a specified amount of loss, irrespective of the extent of spread or the number of buildings involved. The best practice is to apply the term only to fires extending over a considerable area and destroying numbers of buildings. A large fire in a group of buildings such as those belonging to a single industrial plant is not considered as a conflagration even though the area and values involved may be considerable. Neither is a fire in a closely exposed group of mercantile or warehouse properties classified as a conflagration unless the fire crosses natural or prepared exposure barriers such as streets and fire walls.

It is best to use the term "conflagration" conservatively.

For certain fires the term "group fire" is more closely descriptive. This includes fires within the limit of an industrial plant property even if several buildings are involved, and fires in a group of mercantile buildings, particularly within a single city block. In both such cases, buildings may be so close together that a fire may spread from some of the buildings to adjoining ones, but it is unlikely to spread outside the plant area, or beyond the block or group of mercantile buildings because of fire wall barriers, streets or other open spaces.

This discussion is limited to the special type of fire regarded as a conflagration and excludes individual and group fires regardless of their magnitude. Forest fires have not been included except in instances where they spread to or destroyed numbers of buildings. Also excluded are wartime conflagrations, such as those that destroyed several German cities in World War II, because of the special conditions that contributed to their start and spread.

Conflagrations have been of five general types:

1. Fires starting in hazardous occupancies or dilapidated and abandoned buildings ("conflagration breeders") in congested sections which spread in one or more directions before effective resistance is organized to bring them under control. These fires usually spread first to nearby properties lacking exposure protection, cross streets by means of radiated heat, and spread chiefly in the direction in which the wind is blowing. Failure to control such fires is due almost entirely to lack of sufficient water application through heavy stream devices by the fire department, and lack of exposure protection. Buildings equipped with automatic sprinklers, adequately supplied by water, have been eminently successful as barriers to the spread of such fires.

2. Fires occurring in primarily residential sections which spread beyond control due to closely built combustible construction and wood-shingled roofs. Such conflagrations may occur where such construction practices are allowed, and where fire protection forces are weak and water supplies are inadequate.

3. Conflagrations resulting from extensive forest and brush fires entering a municipality over a wide frontage.

4. Conflagrations due to explosions with resulting fire over a wide area.

5. Conflagrations evolving from multiple fires started in one area or city, caused by earthquakes or rioters. Either source may hamper or prevent fire fighting.

In many peacetime conflagrations, heated gases of combustion have been known to travel for considerable distances and then burst into flame, spreading the fire. Conflagrations also extend horizontally by means of radiated waves of heat. Exposed buildings ignite before flames reach them directly. Burning brands, such as flaming wood shingles, also start fires well ahead of the flame front. This fact makes exposure protection of utmost importance in combating conflagrations.

Fire Storms

The fundamental characteristics of a fire storm occur in any fire; a column of burning gases and hot air rises over the fire, and air is drawn in at the sides. Normally the air movement in toward the center of a fire is at low velocities and in small fires cannot be felt. But in a fire storm, the movement of air can reach hurricane forces, uprooting trees and destroying buildings at the periphery of the fire.

Fire storms are associated with conflagrations because of the magnitude of the area involved. For example, the destruction of Hamburg and Dresden, Germany, in World

Table 1-5E. Fire Ignition Sequence Factors for Fire Losses by Occupancy

Churches

Area of Origin	Percent
Assembly	18.8
Primary function	1.8
Auxiliary function	29.0
Storage	7.2
Service facilities	—
Service and equipment areas	10.4
Structural areas	12.4
Special	—
Other, unknown	20.4
	100.0

Source of Heat of Ignition	
Heating system	11.7
Cooking equipment	—
A.C., refrigerators	—
Electrical distribution	16.2
Electrical appliances	1.8
Special	—
Process equipment	—
Service and maintenance equipment	—
Other, unknown	70.3
	100.0

Form of Heat of Ignition	
Fuel fire equipment	11.7
Electrical arc short	14.5
Smoking material	4.5
Miscellaneous open flame	24.6
Hot object	6.3
Explosives and incendiary devices	18.2
Heat from natural source	9.4
Exposing hostile fire	4.5
Other, unknown	6.3
	100.0

Type of Material Ignited	
Gas	3.0
Flammable liquid	9.0
Volatile solids	—
Chemical, plastics, paint	3.0
Natural products	—
Rubber, leather	4.0
Wood, paper	53.0
Fabric, fur	16.9
Materials compounded with oil	2.0
Other, unknown	9.1
	100.0

Form of Material Ignited	
Structural component	33.2
Furniture	5.6
Soft goods, wearing apparel	14.0
Adornment, recreational	7.6
Stock, supplies	2.9
Power transfer equipment	4.7
Special gas, liquid escaping container	16.5
Other	15.5
	100.0

Act or Omission	
Incendiary act	35.7
Suspicious	15.2
Misuse of heat of ignition	13.6
Misuse of ignited material	3.1
Mechanical failure	16.7
Electrical equipment too close to container	5.3
Other	10.4
	100.0

Schools and Colleges

Area of Origin	Percent
Assembly	33.4
Primary function	8.1
Auxiliary function	14.5
Storage	16.4
Service facilities	4.9
Structural areas, concealed spaces	8.4
Other	14.3
	100.0

Source of Heat of Ignition	
Heating system	5.0
Cooking equipment	2.5
Electrical distribution	13.5
Electrical appliances	2.0
Special laboratory equipment	1.5
Same as form of heat of ignition	75.5
	100.0

Form of Heat of Ignition	
Fuel fire equipment	4.5
Electrical arc, short	15.5
Smoking material	1.5
Miscellaneous, open flame	47.0
Hot object	3.0
Explosives	24.8
Other	3.7
	100.0

Type of Material Ignited	
Gas	5.9
Flammable liquid	25.0
Chemical, plastics, paint	5.5
Rubber, leather	29.0
Wood, paper	34.6
	100.0

Form of Material Ignited	
Structural component	14.0
Furniture	5.9
Soft goods, wearing apparel	3.9
Adornment, recreational	22.5
Stock, supplies	11.0
Power transfer, equipment	3.4
Gas/fuel escaping container	22.5
Other	16.8
	100.0

Act or Omission	
Incendiary act	61.7
Suspicious	12.8
Misuse of heat of ignition	4.8
Misuse of ignited material	3.1
Mechanical failure	9.5
Other	8.1
	100.0

Hospitals

Area of Origin	
Lounge	6.8
Patient's room	55.2
Dining room	3.4
Lavatory	5.1
Kitchen	1.7
Laundry	5.5
Storage	15.3
Stairways	1.7
Other	5.3
	100.0

Source of Heat of Ignition	
Heating system	2.4
Electrical distribution	14.4
Electrical appliances	7.2
Smoking	2.4
Service and maintenance equipment	73.6
	100.0

Form of Heat of Ignition	
Fuel fired equipment	7.4
Electrical arc, short	19.4
Smoking material	50.8
Miscellaneous open flame	22.4
	100.0

Type of Material Ignited	
Flammable liquid	6.9
Chemical, plastics, paint	9.6
Rubber, leather	4.2
Wood, paper	16.7
Fabric, fur	62.6
	100.0

Form of Material Ignited	
Structural component	2.4
Furniture	11.1
Soft goods, wearing apparel	68.8
Stock, supplies	2.3
Power transfer, equipment	4.4
Gas/liquid, escaping containers	4.4
Other	6.6
	100.0

Act or Omission	
Incendiary act	2.9
Suspicious	10.4
Misuse of heat of ignition	60.5
Misuse of ignition material	19.4
Mechanical failure	—
Other	6.8
	100.0

Apartments

Area of Origin	
Assembly	19.4
Primary function	25.9
Auxiliary function	11.8
Storage	9.8
Service and equipment areas	4.7
Structural areas	6.7
Other	21.7
	100.0

Source of Heat of Ignition	
Heating system	9.9
Cooking equipment	8.7
Electrical distribution	9.1
Electrical appliances	5.0
Same as form of heat ignition	67.3
	100.0

Form of Heat of Ignition	
Fuel fire equipment	14.7
Electrical arc, short	13.0
Smoking material	33.6
Miscellaneous open flame	20.3
Hot object	5.4
Explosives	5.7
Heat from natural source	1.4
Other	5.9
	100.0

Type of Material Ignited	
Gas	8.4
Flammable liquid	8.8
Volatile solids	4.1
Chemical, plastics, paint	2.0
Rubber, leather	3.1
Wood, paper	26.1
Fabric, fur	45.8
Materials compounded with oil	1.7
	100.0

Form of Material Ignited	
Structural component	15.5
Furniture	21.0
Soft goods, wearing apparel	25.4
Adornment, recreational	1.5
Stock, supplies	6.3

Table 1-5E. Fire Ignition Sequence Factors for Fire Losses by Occupancy (Cont'd.)

	Percent
Power transfer equipment	4.3
Special	10.8
Other	15.2
	100.0

Act or Omission
Incendiary act	12.7
Suspicious	7.6
Misuse of heat of ignition	39.7
Misuse of ignition material	6.1
Mechanical failure	17.9
Design installation defect	16.0
	100.0

Hotels

Area of Origin
Assembly	4.6
Primary function	33.7
Auxiliary function	22.0
Storage	19.9
Service facilities	13.3
Structural areas, concealed space	5.5
Other	1.0
	100.0

Source of Heat of Ignition
Heating system	2.8
Cooking equipment	7.0
A.C., refrigeration	1.4
Electrical distribution	9.8
Electrical appliances	4.2
Special	12.5
Process equipment	2.8
Service and maintenance equipment	59.5
	100.0

Form of Heat of Ignition
Fuel fire equipment	11.4
Electrical arc, short	24.5
Smoking material	21.5
Miscellaneous open flame	27.0
Hot object	7.1
Explosives	4.3
Heat from natural source	—
Lightning	4.2
Other	—
	100.0

Type of Material Ignited
Gas	5.8
Flammable liquid	8.8
Chemical, plastics, paint	13.3
Rubber, leather	4.6
Wood, paper	13.2
Fabric, fur	54.3
	100.0

Form of Material Ignited
Structural component	7.0
Furniture	4.0
Soft goods, wearing apparel	45.2
Stock, supplies	6.7
Power transfer equipment	15.3
Other	21.8
	100.0

Act or Omission
Incendiary act	18.2
Suspicious	6.7
Misuse of heat of ignition	32.6
Misuse of ignition material	6.5
Mechanical failure	22.3
Design, installation defect	2.6
Other	11.1
	100.0

Mobile Homes

Area of Origin
Lounge	17.9
Bedroom	14.3

	Percent
Dining room	0.3
Bathroom	1.7
Kitchen	22.0
Closet	2.8
Heating equipment	18.0
Structural areas	9.6
Other	13.4
	100.0

Source of Heat of Ignition
Heating system	26.9
Cooking equipment	11.1
A.C., refrigeration	1.4
Electrical distribution	21.8
Electrical appliances	9.8
Same as form of heat	29.0
	100.0

Form of Heat of Ignition
Fuel fire equipment	27.8
Electrical arc, short	27.6
Smoking material	12.5
Miscellaneous open flame	5.8
Hot object	8.6
Explosives	1.4
Other	16.3
	100.0

Type of Material Ignited
Gas, flammable liquid	14.2
Chemical, plastics, paint	9.0
Rubber, leather	5.4
Wood, paper	5.9
Fabric, fur	37.5
Other	28.0
	100.0

Form of Material Ignited
Structural component	40.9
Furniture	8.5
Soft goods, wearing apparel	6.7
Stock, supplies	2.2
Power transfer equipment	15.5
Gas, liquid escaping container	13.2
Other	13.0
	100.0

Act or Omission
Incendiary act	3.6
Suspicious	3.2
Misuse of heat of ignition	28.9
Misuse of ignition material	4.2
Mechanical failure	43.9
Design installation defect	5.0
Other	11.2
	100.0

Road Transport Vehicles

Area of Origin
Fuel tank, fuel line	24.0
Running gear	10.1
Passenger area	12.9
Load area	24.9
Special	28.1
	100.0

Source of Heat of Ignition
Heating system	1.5
Electrical distribution	3.8
Special engine	8.5
Brakes, etc.	6.0
Same as form of heat	80.2
	100.0

Form of Heat of Ignition
Fuel fire equipment	1.6
Electrical arc, short	6.6
Smoking material	3.2
Miscellaneous open flame	12.4
Hot object from friction	40.4
Explosives	6.1

	Percent
Heat from natural source	3.6
Exposing hostile fire	24.1
Other	2.0
	100.0

Type of Material Ignited
Gasoline	6.9
Flammable liquid (other than gasoline)	62.0
Volatile solids	—
Chemical, plastics, paint	8.5
Natural products	
Rubber, leather	3.3
Wood, paper	5.3
Fabric, fur	4.9
Materials compounded with oil	—
Other	9.1
	100.0

Form of Material Ignited
Structural component	4.4
Furniture	2.4
Soft goods, wearing apparel	2.6
Adornment, recreational	1.4
Stock, supplies	10.4
Power transfer equipment	11.4
Gas escaping container	60.4
Other	7.0
	100.0

Act or Omission
Incendiary act	5.5
Suspicious	1.1
Misuse of heat of ignition	8.3
Misuse of ignition material	7.1
Mechanical failure	5.5
Other, unknown	72.5
	100.0

One- and Two-Family Dwellings

Area of Origin
Means of egress, entry, stairs	1.5
Assembly, sales areas, living room	26.4
Function areas 20–39, bedroom, kitchen	36.5
Storage areas	6.1
Service facilities	0.5
Service and equipment areas, heater room, utility closet	4.4
Structural areas	6.3
Vehicle areas	1.8
Other, undetermined, unreported	16.5
	100.0

Source of Heat of Ignition
Heating systems	20.8
Cooking equipment	9.7
Air conditioning, refrigeration	0.4
Electrical distribution equipment	8.5
Appliances	8.7
Special equipment	0.1
Process equipment	0.6
Service and maintenance equipment	0.5
Other, undetermined, unreported	50.7
	100.0

Form of Heat of Ignition
Heat from fuel-fired object	27.4
Electrical arc or overload	13.2
Heat from smoking materials	25.9
Open flame or spark	13.1
Heat from hot object	8.1
Explosives, fireworks	5.5
Heat from natural source	0.8
Heat from another hostile fire	5.8
Other, undetermined, unreported	0.2
	100.0

Table 1-5E.   Fire Ignition Sequence Factors for Fire Losses by Occupancy (Cont'd.)

Act or Omission	Percent
Incendiary act	4.6
Suspicious	1.9
Misuse of heat of ignition	43.4
Misuse of material ignited	17.5
Mechanical failure, malfunction	22.2
Construction design or installation deficiency	2.6
Operational difficulties	0.0
Natural conditions	0.0
Other, undetermined, unreported	7.8
	100.0

Type of Material Ignited	
Gas	5.5
Flammable or combustible liquid	17.5
Volatile solid	4.3
Chemical, metal, plastic	5.9
Natural product	2.8
Wood or paper	19.2
Textile	44.1
Material compounded with oil	0.5
Other, undetermined, unreported	0.2
	100.0

Form of Material Ignited	
Structural component, finish	13.9
Furniture	19.8
Soft goods, apparel	26.1
Decoration, recreation material	1.5
Supplies, stock	1.5
Fuel, power equipment	5.9
General forms	19.6
Special forms	0.0
Other, undetermined, unreported	11.7
	100.0

Industrial

Act or Omission	
Incendiary act	5.1
Suspicious	4.0
Misuse of heat of ignition	14.3
Misuse of material ignited	5.6
Mechanical failure, malfunction	52.1
Construction design or installation deficiency	5.8
Operational difficulties	—
Natural conditions	—
Other, undetermined, unreported	13.1
	100.0

Form of Material Ignited	
Structural component, finish	7.9
Furniture	0.9
Soft goods, apparel	1.5
Decoration, recreation material	0.4
Supplies, stock	15.0
Fuel, power equipment	13.1
General forms	33.4
Special forms	—
Other, undetermined, unreported	27.8
	100.0

Type of Material Ignited	
Gas	6.4
Flammable or combustible liquid	22.1
Volatile solid	5.4
Chemical, metal, plastic	15.7
Natural product	9.6
Wood or paper	27.9
Textile	10.3
Material compounded with oil	2.2
Other, undetermined, unreported	0.4
	100.0

Form of Heat of Ignition	
Heat from fuel-fired object	19.0
Electrical arc or overload	21.0

	Percent
Heat from smoking materials	4.2
Open flame or spark	10.4
Heat from hot object	29.1
Explosives, fireworks	2.2
Heat from natural source	11.0
Heat from another hostile fire	2.8
Other, undetermined, unreported	0.3
	100.0

Source of Heat of Ignition	
Heating systems	6.9
Cooking equipment	1.1
Air conditioning, refrigeration	0.4
Electrical distribution equipment	13.2
Appliances	5.2
Special equipment	2.5
Process equipment	35.6
Service and maintenance equipment	3.7
Other, undetermined, unreported	31.4
	100.0

Area of Origin	
Means of egress	0.5
Assembly, sales areas	0.2
Function areas 20–39	57.2
Storage areas	16.4
Service facilities	3.3
Service and equipment areas	9.5
Structural areas	4.6
Vehicle areas	1.8
Other, undetermined, unreported	6.5
	100.0

Storage

Form of Material Ignited	
Structural component, finish	12.0
Furniture	1.0
Soft goods, apparel	0.8
Decoration, recreation material	54.0
Supplies, stock	3.4
Fuel, power equipment	18.2
General forms	—
Special forms	0.0
Other, undetermined, unreported	10.6
	100.0

Type of Material Ignited	
Gas	4.7
Flammable or combustible liquid	11.1
Volatile solid	1.3
Chemical, metal, plastic	8.3
Natural product	18.1
Wood or paper	47.1
Textile	7.4
Material compounded with oil	1.5
Other, undetermined, unreported	0.5
	100.0

Form of Heat of Ignition	
Heat from fuel-fired object	6.8
Electrical arc or overload	15.4
Heat from smoking materials	10.8
Open flame or spark	24.0
Heat from hot object	10.8
Explosives, fireworks	9.8
Heat from natural source	10.0
Heat from another hostile fire	11.9
Other, undetermined, unreported	0.5
	100.0

Source of Heat of Ignition	
Heating systems	7.0
Cooking equipment	0.1
Air conditioning, refrigeration	0.5
Electrical distribution equipment	12.7
Appliances	2.4

	Percent
Special equipment	1.3
Process equipment	2.5
Service and maintenance equipment	5.7
Other, undetermined, unreported	67.8
	100.0

Area of Origin	
Means of egress	0.9
Assembly, sales areas	0.8
Function areas 20–39	6.7
Storage areas	57.4
Service facilities	0.4
Service and equipment areas	4.0
Structural areas	7.4
Vehicle areas	6.2
Other, undetermined, unreported	16.2
	100.0

Restaurants

Area of Origin	
Means of egress	4.9
Assembly, sales areas	1.7
Function areas 20–39	50.1
Storage areas	11.4
Service facilities	4.6
Service and equipment areas	3.2
Structural areas	9.7
Vehicle areas	0.0
Other, undetermined, unreported	14.4
	100.0

Source of Heat of Ignition	
Heating systems	4.6
Cooking equipment	37.6
Air conditioning, refrigeration	1.8
Electrical distribution equipment	17.9
Appliances	1.8
Special equipment	0.9
Process equipment	0.5
Service and maintenance equipment	0.0
Other, undetermined, unreported	34.9
	100.0

Form of Heat of Ignition	
Heat from fuel-fired object	31.9
Electrical arc or overload	25.6
Heat from smoking materials	8.1
Open flame or spark	12.4
Heat from hot object	4.8
Explosives, fireworks	11.4
Heat from natural source	1.0
Heat from another hostile fire	3.8
Other, undetermined, unreported	1.0
	100.0

Type of Material Ignited	
Gas	2.9
Flammable or combustible liquid	17.1
Volatile solid	36.0
Chemical, metal, plastic	2.0
Natural product	2.0
Wood or paper	35.1
Textile	2.9
Material compounded with oil	2.0
Other, undetermined, unreported	0.0
	100.0

Form of Material Ignited	
Structural component, finish	23.2
Furniture	4.3
Soft goods, apparel	1.7
Decoration, recreation material	0.9
Supplies, stock	7.3
Fuel, power equipment	2.6
General forms	16.3

Table 1-5E. Fire Ignition Sequence Factors for Fire Losses by Occupancy (Cont'd.)

Percent

Special forms — 0.0
Other, undetermined, unreported — 43.7
——— 100.0

Act or Omission
Incendiary act — 21.4
Suspicious — 9.4
Misuse of heat of ignition — 20.5
Misuse of material ignited — 5.6
Mechanical failure, malfunction — 37.1
Construction design or
   installation deficiency — 2.1
Operational difficulties — 0.0
Natural conditions — 0.0
Other, undetermined, unreported — 3.9
——— 100.0

Nursing Homes

Area of Origin
Means of egress — 1.5
Assembly, sales areas — 10.3
Function areas 20–39 — 67.6
Storage areas — 14.7
Service facilities — 0.0
Service and equipment areas — 1.5
Structural areas — 2.9
Vehicle areas — 0.0
Other, undetermined, unreported — 1.5
——— 100.0

Source of Heat of Ignition
Heating systems — 3.7
Cooking equipment — 0.0
Air conditioning, refrigeration — 1.9
Electrical distribution equipment — 11.1
Appliances — 7.4
Special equipment — 0.0
Process equipment — 0.0
Service and maintenance
   equipment — 0.0
Other, undetermined, unreported — 75.9
——— 100.0

Form of Heat of Ignition
Heat from fuel-fired object — 3.7
Electrical arc or overload — 16.7
Heat from smoking materials — 53.6
Open flame or spark — 20.4
Heat from hot object — 3.7
Explosives, fireworks — 0.0
Heat from natural source — 0.0
Heat from another hostile fire — 1.9
Other, undetermined, unreported — 0.0
——— 100.0

Type of Material Ignited
Gas — 0.0
Flammable or combustible liquid — 3.6
Volatile solid — 1.8
Chemical, metal, plastic — 3.6
Natural product — 7.1
Wood or paper — 14.3
Textile — 67.8
Material compounded with oil — 0.0
Other, undetermined, unreported — 1.8
——— 100.0

Form of Material Ignited
Structural component, finish — 3.4
Furniture — 11.9
Soft goods, apparel — 59.2
Decoration, recreation material — 0.0
Supplies, stock — 3.4
Fuel, power equipment — 8.5
General forms — 6.8
Special forms — 0.0
Other, undetermined, unreported — 6.8
——— 100.0

Percent

Act or Omission
Incendiary act — 3.2
Suspicious — 9.7
Misuse of heat of ignition — 59.6
Misuse of material ignited — 6.5
Mechanical failure, malfunction — 17.8
Construction design or
   installation deficiency — 0.0
Operational difficulties — 0.0
Natural conditions — 0.0
Other, undetermined, unreported — 3.2
——— 100.0

Offices and Banks

Area of Origin
Means of egress — 4.4
Assembly, sales areas — 2.3
Function areas 20–39 — 32.2
Storage areas — 14.1
Service facilities — 1.4
Service and equipment areas — 13.0
Structural areas — 14.1
Vehicle areas — 1.1
Other, undetermined, unreported — 17.4
——— 100.0

Source of Heat of Ignition
Heating systems — 10.4
Cooking equipment — 1.1
Air conditioning, refrigeration — 1.1
Electrical distribution equipment — 21.3
Appliances — 2.2
Special equipment — 2.7
Process equipment — 1.6
Service and maintenance
   equipment — 1.6
Other, undetermined, unreported — 58.0
——— 100.0

Form of Heat of Ignition
Heat from fuel-fired object — 8.4
Electrical arc or overload — 26.8
Heat from smoking materials — 8.4
Open flame or spark — 18.4
Heat from hot object — 9.5
Explosives, fireworks — 13.4
Heat from natural source — 5.0
Heat from another hostile fire — 10.1
Other, undetermined, unreported — —
——— 100.0

Type of Material Ignited
Gas — 12.9
Flammable or combustible liquid — 15.5
Volatile solid — 0.0
Chemical, metal, plastic — 3.9
Natural product — 1.3
Wood or paper — 53.6
Textile — 7.7
Material compounded with oil — 3.9
Other, undetermined, unreported — 1.2
——— 100.0

Act or Omission
Incendiary act — 26.7
Suspicious — 7.6
Misuse of heat of ignition — 13.3
Misuse of material ignited — 4.3
Mechanical failure, malfunction — 30.4
Construction design or
   installation deficiency — 2.9
Operational difficulties — 0.0
Natural conditions — 0.0
Other, undetermined, unreported — 14.8
——— 100.0

Percent

Hospitals

Area of Origin
Means of egress — 2.8
Assembly, sales areas — 4.2
Function areas 20–39 — 38.9
Storage areas — 23.6
Service facilities — 12.5
Service and equipment areas — 2.7
Structural areas — 12.5
Vehicle areas — —
Other, undetermined, unreported — 2.8
——— 100.0

Source of Heat of Ignition
Heating systems — 3.4
Cooking equipment — 6.9
Air conditioning, refrigeration — —
Electrical distribution equipment — 10.3
Appliances — 5.3
Special equipment — 12.1
Process equipment — 3.4
Service and maintenance
   equipment — 1.7
Other, undetermined, unreported — 56.9
——— 100.0

Form of Heat of Ignition
Heat from fuel-fired object — 8.8
Electrical arc or overload — 24.5
Heat from smoking materials — 26.3
Open flame or spark — 22.8
Heat from hot object — 8.8
Explosives, fireworks — 3.5
Heat from natural source — 5.3
Heat from another hostile fire — —
Other, undetermined, unreported — —
——— 100.0

Type of Material Ignited
Gas — 6.1
Flammable or combustible liquid — 8.2
Volatile solid — 6.1
Chemical, metal, plastic — 14.2
Natural product — 4.1
Wood or paper — 8.2
Textile — 53.1
Material compounded with oil — —
Other, undetermined, unreported — —
——— 100.0

Form of Material Ignited
Structural component, finish — 3.3
Furniture — 3.3
Soft goods, apparel — 45.9
Decoration, recreation material — —
Supplies, stock — 8.2
Fuel, power equipment — 18.0
General forms — 9.8
Special forms — —
Other, undetermined, unreported — 11.5
——— 100.0

Act or Omission
Incendiary act — 18.0
Suspicious — 6.6
Misuse of heat of ignition — 32.8
Misuse of material ignited — 6.6
Mechanical failure, malfunction — 24.5
Construction design or
   installation deficiency — 3.3
Operational difficulties — 0.0
Natural conditions — 0.0
Other, undetermined, unreported — 8.2
——— 100.0

Table 1-5F. Principal Factors Contributing to Conflagrations in the United States and Canada: 1900–1967

(Not including combustible construction or contents that contribute to every fire)

Factor		Number of Times Contributing	
	1901–1925	1926–1967	1901–1967
1. Wood-shingled roofs	45	24	69
2. Wind velocity in excess of 30 mph or "high"	22	41	63
3. Inadequate water distribution system	23	32	55
4. Lack of exposure protection	18	29	47
5. Inadequate public protection	23	24	47
6. Unusually hot or dry weather conditions	4	23	27
7. Delay in giving alarm	5	13	18
8. Congestion of hazardous occupancies of difficult access for fire fighting	5	13	18
9. Delay in discovery of fire	4	16	20
10. Forest or brush fire entered town	2	10	12
11. Failure of water pumps or breakage of pipes	5	6	11
12. Ineffective fire fighting	4	6	10
13. Private fire protection failed or inadequate	1	9	10
14. Fire department at other fires	4	3	7
15. Fire spread through inaccessible spaces under pier or building	2	4	6
16. Winter conditions severe	2	3	5
17. Earthquake, floods, hurricane, etc.	1	3	4
18. Hose couplings or hydrant connections not standard	2	1	3
19. Cotton rags, etc., stored outside of buildings	2	1	3
20. Burning brands from lumberyard	0	2	2
21. Dry vegetation adjacent to buildings	0	2	2
22. Explosion of liquefied natural gas holders	0	1	1
23. Explosion of ammonium nitrate aboard cargo vessel	0	1	1
24. Slow response of fire department	0	1	1
25. Fire alarm failed	1	0	1
26. Explosion of explosives truck	0	1	1
27. Riots prevented or hampered fire fighting	0	2	2

War II was accompanied by massive fire storms. The fire storm phenomenon was observed at the Chelsea, Mass., conflagration of Oct. 14, 1973.[3]

In fire storms destruction is usually complete within the area. In a conflagration some buildings escape due to irregular convection currents, fire barriers, or fire fighting efforts.

Factors Responsible for Conflagrations

The factors listed in Table 1-5F are derived from a study of reports of the conflagrations which occurred from 1900 to 1967. Table 1-5G identifies more recent conflagrations in the United States (1969–1975) and the contributing factors to their cause and spread. Conflagrations are seldom due solely to any one factor and the summary in Table 1-5F indicates the number of fires to which each factor has contributed rather than one outstanding factor for each fire. No attempt has been made to list all the minor factors responsible for the spread of these fires, but the principal ones have been determined as accurately as possible from analyses of reports in NFPA files.

The changes in order of frequency of the contributing factors during the two time periods given in Table 1-5F are significant. Wood-shingled roofs, for example, dropped from No. 1 position to share position No. 4 with inadequate public protection in the more recent period.

High winds comprise the leading factor in the 1926–1967 period. Inadequacy of water distribution systems is now the second most frequent contributing factor, an indication that the development of public fire protection has not kept pace with structural growth in many communities. A new factor, riots, appeared in 1965, during which fire fighters

were shot at (some killed) and otherwise prevented or hampered from fighting fires that had been set.

Inferior and combustible construction is the predominant factor in the development of conflagrations and is a particularly vital matter where large areas of closely built wood-framed structures exist in congested sections. Combustible construction and contents of buildings have obviously contributed to every conflagration and, for this reason, have not been specifically listed except where the factors of congestion and inaccessibility have been involved.

Prevention of Conflagrations

A number of factors have contributed to reducing the frequency and severity of conflagrations in recent years; however, the threat of them will never be entirely eliminated. Wood-shingled roofs are prohibited by ordinance in many areas, although there has been a resurgence of interest in them, particularly in isolated areas. (The 1961 Los Angeles conflagration involved one of these areas.[4]) Water distribution systems by and large have been vastly improved, although inadequate systems, with small or dead-ended mains and no auxiliary supplies, still continue to be a factor in conflagrations that occur.[3] More fire departments have been organized and equipped in urban areas and alarm and signaling systems have been vastly improved. Building codes and zoning and fire prevention ordinances have become more widely adopted, more stringent, and more effectively enforced. Urban renewal, open area concepts of land use, and swaths for multi-laned highways have combined to create firebreaks in metropolitan areas.

Other means of reducing the conflagration threat are:

1. Adequate exposure protection wherever communicat-

Table 1-5G. Conflagrations, 1969–1974

Date	Location	Property Destroyed	Reported Loss
May 22, 1964 (Delayed discovery, closely located combustible structures, hot, dry, windy day)	Boston, Mass.	17 buildings	$750,000
October 29, 1969 (50 mph winds, warm, dry weather, inadequate water)	Los Angeles County, Calif.	5,000 acres/5 homes	
February 7, 1972 (Volatile chemicals (MEK), high winds, severe cold, congested and aging buildings)	Wakefield, Mass.	6 buildings	$1,500,000
May 27, 1973 (Explosions damage sprinklers, broken water mains)	Chicago, Ill.	5 buildings involved	$25,000,000
June 12, 1973 (Explosion, flammable liquids)	Philadelphia, Pa.	4 buildings and 4 dwellings 2 fire fighters killed	Over $5,000,000
October 14, 1973 (Poor water supply, dry weather, high winds, closely stored combustibles, narrow streets, no fire breaks, delayed reporting)	Chelsea, Mass.	300 buildings involved	$1,313,650
November 5, 1973 (Delayed detection, tremendous radiant heat, sprinklers out of service)	Indianapolis, Ind.	5 buildings (2 high-rise)	$5,321,000
April 9, 1974 (Broken water main, high winds)	Grand Junction, Col.	8 buildings	$2,594,000
April 9, 1974 (Towns of Sacramento and Weed and natural forest)	Cloudcroft, N.M.	14,500 acres	$16,000,000
May 22, 1974 (Inadequate water supply, large closely located combustible buildings, flammable liquids helped spread, chemical explosions, hot and dry weather)	Chelsea, Mass.	6 buildings	$3,592,326.91
September 8, 1974 (Delayed detection, inadequate water, combustible movie sets and stages closely constructed)	Burbank, Calif.	7 structures involved	$5,826,832
December 13, 1974 (Frame construction, delayed detection, inadequate water for sprinklers)	Middleboro, Mass.	4 buildings	$500,000

ing fires are likely, including openings in fire resistive buildings.

2. Removal of conflagration breeders.

3. General use of automatic sprinklers, particularly in high value districts and hazardous occupancies.

4. Improved fire department efficiency, including ample heavy stream equipment, better training of fire fighters for large operations and increased manpower where necessary.

5. Complete municipal fire alarm and radio systems to provide for the handling of all alarms and the dispatching of apparatus without the necessity of dependence upon public telephone facilities, which are invariably severely taxed during emergencies. Automatic fire alarm installations in hazardous properties with arrangements for the prompt response of the fire department will contribute to the control of fires before they reach a stage where they may overtax available fire protection equipment (see Sec. 9, Chap. 4).

Bibliography

References Cited

[1] Yockers, J. R. and Segal, L., "Cigarette Fire Mechanisms," NFPA *Quarterly*, Vol. 49, No. 3, Jan. 1956, pp. 213–222.

[2] "Rats, Mice, and Matches," NFPA *Quarterly*, Vol. 31, No. 1, July 1937, pp. 30–32.

[3] "The Burning of Chelsea," *Fire Journal*, Vol. 68, No. 3, May 1974, pp. 17–23.

[4] Wilson, R., "The Devil Wind and Wood Shingles: The Los Angeles Conflagration of 1961," NFPA *Quarterly*, Vol. 55, No. 3, Jan. 1962, pp. 241–288.

NFPA Codes, Standards, and Recommended Practices (see the latest *NFPA Publications and Visual Aids Catalog* for availability of current editions of the following documents)

NFPA no. 901, Uniform Coding for Fire Protection.

SECTION 2

CHARACTERISTICS AND BEHAVIOR OF FIRE

Section 2

Chapter 1

CHEMISTRY AND PHYSICS OF FIRE

This chapter presents basic definitions for certain physical properties, and some of the chemical terms applicable to the chemistry and physics of fire; it also discusses the principles of fire, heat measurement, heat transfer, and heat energy sources.

The material contained herein does not attempt to offer a comprehensive course of instruction in the chemistry and physics of fire, but is intended to present a source of basic background reference materials applicable to this and other sections of this HANDBOOK.

A. Basic Definitions and Properties

Atoms: The basic particles of chemical composition are called atoms. Atoms are extremely minute. Substances composed of one type of atom are called elements. An atom has a compact core or nucleus around which electrons (negatively charged units of matter) travel in orbit. The nucleus is made up of protons (positively charged) and neutrons (no charge). The total number of protons is the atomic number of the element. Substances which have loosely bound electrons are good electrical conductors. Those with rigidly bound electrons (so that no easy transfer of heat is possible) are good insulators.

Molecules: Combined groups of atoms are called molecules. Molecules composed of two or more different kinds of atoms are called compounds.

Chemical Formula: The chemical formula shows the number of atoms of the various elements in the molecule, and gives an indication of their arrangement. The chemical formula for propane is $CH_3CH_2CH_3$. (See Table 2-1A for symbols of the various elements.)

Atomic Weight of an Element: The atomic weight of an element is the weight of an atom of carbon, arbitrarily assigned as 12.011. Table 2-1A gives the atomic weights of elements.

Molecular Weight of a Compound: The molecular weight of a compound is the sum of the weight of all atoms in its molecule. The subscripts following an element's symbol indicate the number of atoms of that element present.

Gram Molecular Weight: The weight of a substance in grams equal to its molecular weight is called the gram molecular weight.

Specific Gravity: The ratio of the weight of a solid or liquid substance to the weight of an equal volume of water is called the specific gravity. The scales of the most commonly used hydrometers are based on a specific gravity of 1 for water at 4°C (1cc of water at 4°C weighs 1 g).

Vapor Density: As commonly used in fire protection, vapor density is the weight of a volume of dry air at the same temperature and pressure. A figure less than 1 indicates that a gas is lighter than air, and a figure greater than 1, that a gas is heavier than air. If a flammable gas with a vapor density greater than 1 escapes from its container, it may travel at a low level to a source of ignition. In order to calculate the vapor density of a gas, the following formula may be used:

$$\text{Vapor density of a gas} = \frac{\text{Molecular weight of a gas}}{29}$$

In the formula, 29 is the composite molecular weight of air. The formula gives reasonably accurate estimates of relative vapor density only when there is no dissociation of molecules in the gas and when it is at a standard temperature and pressure (0°C and 1 atm). Carbon dioxide, with a molecular weight of 44, is denser than air, and when discharged from an extinguisher, might accumulate near ground. The higher the temperature of a gas, the less dense it is. Thus, hot products of combustion rise.

Vapor Pressure and Boiling Point

Because molecules of a liquid are always in motion (with the amount of motion depending on the temperature of the liquid), the molecules are continually escaping from the free surface of the liquid to the space above. Some molecules remain in space while others, due to random motion, collide with the liquid.

If the liquid is in an open container, molecules (collectively called vapor) escape from the surface, and the liquid is said to evaporate. If, on the other hand, the liquid is in a closed container, the motion of the escaping molecules is confined to the vapor space above the surface of the liquid. As an increasing number strike and reenter the liquid, a point of equilibrium is eventually reached when the rate of escape of molecules from the liquid equals the rate of return to the liquid. The pressure exerted by the escaping vapor at the point of equilibrium is called vapor pressure. Vapor pressure is measured in pounds per square inch absolute (psia), millimeters of mercury (mm), or torr.*

As the temperature of a liquid increases, its vapor pressure approaches atmospheric pressure. At the temperature at which vapor pressure equals atmospheric pressure, the opposition to evaporation exerted by the atmosphere is neutralized and boiling takes place. The boiling point of a liquid is the temperature at which its vapor pressure equals the atmospheric pressure.

Although the vapor pressure of a liquid varies with the temperature of the liquid, a great many variables affect the rate at which a liquid actually evaporates when exposed to air. These variables include atmospheric temperature and pressure, air movement, specific heat, and latent heat of evaporation.

Vapor-air Density (vad): Vapor-air density is the weight of a vapor-air mixture resulting from the vaporization of a flammable liquid at equilibrium temperature and pressure conditions, as compared with the weight of an equal volume of air under the same conditions. The density of a vapor-air mixture thus depends upon the ambient temperature, the vapor pressure of the liquid at the temperature, and upon the molecular weight of the liquid. At temperatures well below the boiling point of a liquid the vapor pressure of the

---

* Absolute pressure equals the total pressure exerted against a unit of area. It is measured in pounds per square inch, or dynes per square centimeter. It is expressed in fractions or multiples of atmospheric pressure, or in terms of the height of a column of liquid (usually mercury) which will balance the absolute pressure. In situations where pressure gages are used, absolute pressure is determined by adding gage pressure to atmospheric pressure. Atmospheric, or ambient, pressure equals 14.7 psia, 760 mm of mercury, or 760 torr.

liquid may be so low that the vapor-air mixture, consisting mostly of air, has a density which approximates that of pure air. As the temperature of the liquid increases, the rate of vaporization increases and the vapor displaces the surrounding air.

A vapor-air mixture with a density significantly above that of air at the ambient temperature will seek lower levels. On the other hand, diffusion and mixing by convection will limit the distance of travel of flammable mixtures having densities near 1.

The vapor-air density of a substance at ambient temperature may be calculated as follows:

Let P equal the ambient pressure, p the vapor pressure of the material at ambient temperature, and d its vapor density. Then,

$$\text{vad} = \frac{pd}{P} + \frac{P - p}{P}$$

The first term $\left(\dfrac{pd}{P}\right)$ is the contribution of the vapor to the density of the mixture; the second term $\left(\dfrac{P - p}{P}\right)$ is the contribution of air.

EXAMPLE: find the vapor-air density at 100°F (37.8°C) and atmospheric pressure for a flammable liquid whose vapor density is 2 and whose vapor pressure at 100°F (37.8°C) is 76 mm,

$$\text{vad} = \frac{(76)(2)}{760} + \frac{760 - 76}{760} = 0.2 + 0.9 = 1.1$$

Endothermic and Exothermic Chemical Reactions

Heat of formation is the energy that is added or lost when a given reaction takes place. In endothermic reactions the substances formed contain more energy than the reacting materials, whereas exothermic reactions produce substances with less energy than was in the reacting materials. While energy may appear in many different forms, it is usually added to, or released from, a chemical reaction in the form of heat.

Table 2-1A. Chemical Elements

Based on the assigned relative atomic mass of $C = 12$.

Elements with atomic weights in parentheses are unstable isotopes.

The value given is that of the most stable isotope.

Element	Symbol	Atomic No.	Atomic Weight	Element	Symbol	Atomic No.	Atomic Weight	Element	Symbol	Atomic No.	Atomic Weight
Actinium	Ac	89	(227)	Hafnium	Hf	72	178.49	Praseodymium	Pr	59	140.9077
Aluminum	Al	13	26.9815	Helium	He	2	4.0026	Promethium	Pm	61	(145)
Americium	Am	95	(243)	Holmium	Ho	67	164.9303	Protoactinium	Pa	91	231.0359
Antimony, stibium	Sb	51	121.75	Hydrogen	H	1	1.0080	Radium	Ra	88	226.0254
Argon	Ar	18	39.948	Indium	In	49	114.82	Radon	Rn	86	(222)
Arsenic	As	33	74.9216	Iodine	I	53	126.9045	Rhenium	Re	75	186.2
Astatine	At	85	(210)	Iridium	Ir	77	192.2	Rhodium	Rh	45	102.9055
Barium	Ba	56	137.34	Iron, ferrum	Fe	26	55.85	Rubidium	Rb	37	85.4678
Berkelium	Bk	97	(247)	Krypton	Kr	36	83.8	Ruthenium	Ru	44	101.07
Beryllium	Be	4	9.0122	Lanthanum	La	57	138.905	Samarium	Sm	62	150.4
Bismuth	Bi	83	208.980	Lawrencium	Lr	103	(257)	Scandium	Sc	21	44.9559
Boron	B	5	10.81	Lead, plumbum	Pb	82	207.2	Selenium	Se	34	78.96
Bromine	Br	35	79.904	Lithium	Li	3	6.941	Silicon	Si	14	28.086
Cadmium	Cd	48	112.40	Lutetium	Lu	71	174.97	Silver, argentum	Ag	47	107.868
Calcium	Ca	20	40.08	Magnesium	Mg	12	24.305	Sodium, natrium	Na	11	22.9898
Californium	Cf	98	(251)	Manganese	Mn	25	54.9380	Strontium	Sr	38	87.62
Carbon	C	6	12.011	Mendelevium	Mv	101	(256)	Sulfur	S	16	32.06
Cerium	Ce	58	140.13	Mercury, hydrargyrum	Hg	80	200.59	Tantalum	Ta	73	180.9479
Cesium	Cs	55	132.9055	Molybdenum	Mo	42	95.94	Technetium	Tc	43	98.9062
Chlorine	Cl	17	35.457	Neodymium	Nd	60	144.2	Tellurium	Te	52	127.60
Chromium	Cr	24	51.996	Neon	Ne	10	20.179	Terbium	Tb	65	158.9254
Cobalt	Co	27	58.9332	Neptunium	Np	93	237.0482	Thallium	Tl	81	204.37
Columbium, see niobium				Nickel	Ni	28	58.71	Thorium	Th	90	232.0381
Copper	Cu	29	63.546	Niobium, columbium	Nb	41	92.9064	Thulium	Tm	69	168.9342
Curium	Cm	96	(247)	Nitrogen	N	7	14.0067	Tin, stannum	Sn	50	118.69
Dysprosium	Dy	66	162.50	Nobelium	No	102	(254)	Titanium	Ti	22	47.90
Einsteinium	E	99	(254)	Osmium	Os	76	190.2	Tungsten	W	74	183.8
Erbium	Er	68	167.26	Oxygen	O	8	15.9994	Uranium	U	92	238.029
Europium	Eu	63	151.96	Palladium	Pd	46	106.4	Vanadium	V	23	50.9414
Fermium	Fm	100	(257)	Phosphorus	P	15	30.9738	Xenon	Xe	54	131.30
Fluorine	F	9	18.9984	Platinum	Pt	78	195.09	Ytterbium	Yb	70	173.04
Francium	Fr	87	(223)	Plutonium	Pu	94	(244)	Yttrium	Y	39	88.9059
Gadolinium	Gd	64	157.2	Polonium	Po	84	(210)	Zinc	Zn	30	65.38
Gallium	Ga	31	69.72	Potassium, kalium	K	19	39.10	Zirconium	Zr	40	91.22
Germanium	Ge	32	72.59								
Gold, aurum	Au	79	196.9665								

B. Combustion

Glowing Combustion and Flame: Combustion is the process of exothermic, self-catalyzed reactions involving either a condensed-phase fuel, a gas phase, or both. The process is usually (but not necessarily) associated with oxidation of a fuel by atmospheric oxygen. Condensed-phase combustion is usually referred to as glowing combustion, while gas-phase combustion is referred to as a flame. If the process is confined so that an appreciable pressure rise occurs, it is called an explosion. If the combustion wave propagates at supersonic speed, a shock front develops ahead of it. This process is called detonation.

Ignition Temperature (Autoignition Temperature, Autogenous Ignition Temperature): Ignition temperature is the minimum temperature to which the substance in air must be heated in order to initiate, or cause, self-sustained combustion independently of the heating or heated element.

In general, if a fuel molecule and an oxygen molecule are to interact chemically, sufficient energy must be imparted to these molecules to enable a collision between the two in order to result in a chemical transformation and release of heat. The minimum energy which the molecules must possess to permit chemical interaction is referred to as the *threshold energy.* The threshold energy is usually greater than the average energy of the molecules at room temperature.

An increase in temperature increases the number of molecules with energy equal to the threshold energy, and the reaction rate increases. As the temperature is further increased, enough fuel and oxygen molecules eventually react with enough additional thermal energy released to enable the combustion reaction to become self-sustaining until one or the other, or both, of the reactants have been consumed.

The threshold energy for combustion will vary with the type of ignition source, the specific chemical nature and physical character of the combustible, and the composition and pressure of the atmosphere. Regardless of whether the combustible material is a solid, liquid, or gas, initiation of the flame reaction occurs in the gas or vapor phase. In the case of solids or liquids, sufficient thermal energy must first be supplied to convert a part of the fuel to a vapor.

For a fixed oxygen concentration, the threshold ignition energy varies inversely with the square of pressure of the atmosphere. There exists a minimum pressure below which ignition does not occur. As the temperature of a given system increases, less and less energy is required to ignite the mixture until, at a sufficiently high temperature, the mixture will ignite spontaneously. This temperature is referred to as the autoignition (or spontaneous ignition) temperature.

Ignition temperatures observed under one set of conditions may be changed substantially by a change of conditions. In addition to the preceding, variables known to affect ignition temperatures of flammable liquids and gases are shape and size of the space where the ignition occurs, rate and duration of heating, kind and temperature of the ignition source; and catalytic or other effect of materials which may be present also affect ignition temperatures. Just as there are differences in ignition temperature test methods (such as size and shape of containers and method of heating), different ignition temperatures are reported for the same substance by different laboratories.

The effect of percentage composition of the fuel-oxygen mixture is shown by the following ignition temperatures for pentane: 1,018.4°F (548°C) for 1.5 percent pentane in air; 935.6°F (502°C) for 3.75 percent pentane, and 888.8°F (476°C) for 7.65 percent pentane. The following ignition temperatures for carbon disulfide demonstrate the effect of size of space containing the ignitible mixture: in a 200 ml (milliliter) flask the ignition temperature was 248°F (120°C); in a 1,000 ml flask 230°F(110°C), and in a 10,000 ml flask 205°F(92°C).

The ignition temperature of a combustible solid is influenced by rate of air flow, rate of heating, and size and shape of the solid. Small sample tests have shown that as the rate of air flow and the rate of heating are increased, the ignition temperature of a solid drops to a minimum and then increases.

Flammable or Explosive Limits

For ignition to be possible, an adequate fuel concentration must be available in the particular oxidizing atmosphere. Once ignition occurs, the sustainment of combustion requires a continued supply of fuel and oxidant. In the case of combustible gases, vapors, and liquids, two types of mixtures —homogeneous or heterogeneous—can exist within the atmosphere.

A homogeneous mixture is one in which the components are intimately and uniformly mixed so that any small-volume sample is truly representative of the whole mixture. A flammable homogeneous mixture is one whose composition lies between the limits of flammability of the combustible gas or vapor in the particular atmosphere at a specified temperature and pressure.

The Limits of Flammability: The limits of flammability are the extreme concentration limits of a combustible in an oxidant through which a flame, once initiated, will continue to propagate at the specified temperature and pressure. For example, hydrogen-air mixtures will propagate flame between 4.0 and 74 percent by volume of hydrogen at 70°F (21°C) and atmospheric pressure. The smaller value is the lower (lean) limit, and the larger value is the upper (rich) limit of flammability. When the mixture temperature is increased, the flammability range widens (see Figure 2-1A). A decrease in temperature can cause a previously flammable mixture to become nonflammable by placing it either above or below the limits of flammability for the specific environmental conditions.

Note in Figure 2-1A that for liquid fuels in equilibrium with their vapors in air, a minimum temperature exists for

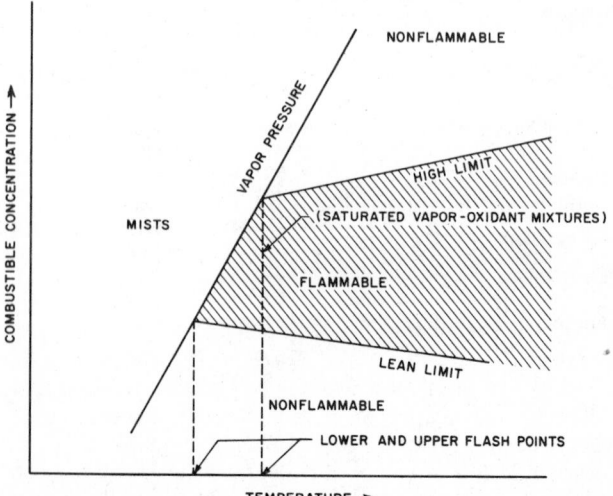

Fig. 2-1A. Effects of temperature on the limits of flammability of a combustible vapor in air.

each fuel above which sufficient vapor is released to form a flammable vapor-air mixture. There is also a maximum temperature above which the vapor concentration is too high to propagate flame. These minimum and maximum temperatures are referred to respectively as the lower and upper flash points in air. The flash point temperatures for a combustible liquid vary directly with environmental pressure.

Fire Point: The lowest temperature of a liquid in an open container at which vapors are evolved fast enough to support continuous combustion is called the fire point. The fire point is usually a few degrees above the flash point.

Catalysts, Inhibitors, and Contaminants

Catalyst: A catalyst is a substance which, when present even in a small quantity, greatly affects the rate of a chemical reaction but is itself not permanently changed by the reaction. For example, a trace of sulfuric acid can cause violent polymerization* of acetaldehyde.

Inhibitors: Also called stabilizers, inhibitors are chemicals which may be added in small quantities to an unstable material to prevent a vigorous reaction. For example, premature polymerization of styrene monomer is inhibited by the addition of at least 10 ppm (parts per million) of tertiary-butyl-catechol (TBC).

Contaminants: Contaminants are foreign materials not normally found in a substance. Some contaminants (such as sand in calcium chloride) may be harmless from a fire hazard standpoint. Dangerous contaminants function by acting as catalysts, or by themselves entering into a potentially dangerous reaction.

Stable and Unstable Materials

Stable Materials: Stable materials are materials which normally have the capacity to resist changes in their chemical composition despite exposure to air, water, heat, shock, or pressure. Stable materials may burn. For example, most solids fall into this category.

Unstable Materials: Unstable materials polymerize, decompose, condense, or become self-reactive when exposed to air, water, heat, shock, or pressure.

C. Principles of Fire

Considerable technical knowledge exists concerning the ignition, flammability, and flame propagation characteristics of various combustible materials (solids, liquids, and gases). However, such knowledge can be inadequate when it becomes necessary to make valid predictions of the probability of fire initiation or of the consequences of such initiation. Most of the exact knowledge relates to premixed gaseous fuel-oxidant combinations because of the obvious advantages of conducting controlled experiments. Unfortunately, most unwanted fires occur under non-premixed conditions. The investigation of the ignition and combustion properties of solid and liquid combustibles is more complex due to the heterogeneity of the reaction mechanisms involved.

Oxidation Reactions

Oxidation reactions involved in fires are exothermic; that is, one of the products of the reaction is heat. They are often complex, and many are not completely understood. However, certain statements can be made that may be helpful.

In order for an oxidation reaction to take place, a com-

bustible material (fuel) and an oxidizing agent must be present. Fuels include innumerable materials not already in their most highly oxidized state. Whether or not a particular material can be further oxidized depends on the chemistry of the material; for practical purposes, it can be claimed that any material consisting primarily of carbon and hydrogen can be oxidized. Most combustible solid organic materials and flammable liquids and gases contain large percentages of carbon and hydrogen.

The most common oxidizing material is the oxygen in the air. Air is composed of approximately one-fifth oxygen and four-fifths nitrogen. Certain chemicals that readily release oxygen under favorable conditions (i.e., sodium nitrate [$NaNO_3$] and potassium chlorate [$KClO_3$] are among the less-common but well-known oxidizing agents met in fires. A few combustible materials such as pyroxylin plastic contain oxygen combined in their molecules in such a way that partial combustion may occur without oxygen from any outside source.

Combustion may also occur in an atmosphere of chlorine, carbon dioxide, nitrogen, and some other gases without oxygen being involved. For example, zirconium dust can be ignited in carbon dioxide. These instances are rare, and the fire protection engineer is primarily concerned with combustion in oxygen.

Ignition and Combustion

Actual burning is a more complicated chemical reaction than is explained by the "fire triangle" which has been generally accepted for simple educational purposes. Actually, as the temperatures rise above the ambient, pyrolysis becomes involved. Pyrolysis is defined as the chemical decomposition of matter through the action of heat. It proceeds through the following stages (these stages use wood as the example):[1]

1. Certain gases, including water vapor, slowly evolve from the decomposition of wood. The combustible component of these gases increase during the early stages of pyrolysis. First, the wood surface is attacked. Then, as charring occurs, the reaction moves deeper into the wood.

2. The gas evolution continues and, if the minimum ignition energy is available, the gases ignite when the lower flammability limit is reached. At the temperature at which ignition occurs, the overall chemical process changes from endothermic to exothermic, and the reactions become self-sustaining.

3. At this ignition temperature, the evolved gases are, at first, too rich in carbon dioxide and water vapor to sustain flame for very long. However, the heat of the flame starts a secondary pyrolysis reaction series and flaming combustion occurs entirely in the gaseous distillate vapor phase. The gas evolution may be rapid enough to blanket the wood's surface and exclude air, thus preventing the char from burning, retarding the penetration of heat, and delaying the attainment of ignition temperatures deeper into the wood. As temperatures continue to increase, the char begins to glow and the incoming air supports combustion.

As pyrolysis begins, it must be considered whether or not a negative heat balance has been created by the action. If the released heat is concentrated and is sufficient enough to keep the oxidation reaction going, and if more heat is being generated than is lost through conduction, convection, or radiation, a positive heat balance exists. If, however, all or most of the heat generated is lost (as with a match flame in a high wind), there is a negative heat balance and the fire goes out. At the same time, a condition known as feedback

---

* Polymerization is a chemical reaction in which molecules link together to form larger aggregates.

can exist. Feedback is the use of some of the generated heat to prepare for burning adjacent portions of the burnable material by causing pyrolysis of the material. If the feedback is inadequate, the fire goes out.

In addition to heat generation during pyrolysis, the concentration of the oxidizing agent is another factor which determines whether or not ignition and combustion can occur. For almost all materials, there appears to be a minimum oxidizing agent concentration below which combustion will not take place. Exceptions to this are those combustible solids (such as cellulose nitrate) that contain available oxygen in their constituent molecules. The oxygen in the molecules can be released by heat even though the supply of air is minimal or nonexistent. It must be kept in mind that it is not necessary to have air present to have a pyrolysis reaction. Examples of this are minimal air supply coking ovens in which wood is reduced to coke and charcoal. Another example is toluene heated in a vented container which is exposed by fire.

In summary, the science of fire protection rests upon the following principles:

1. An oxidizing agent, a combustible material, and an ignition source are essential for combustion.

2. The combustible material must be heated to its ignition temperature before it will burn.

3. Combustion will continue until:
    (a) The combustible material is consumed or removed,
    (b) The oxidizing agent concentration is lowered to below the concentration necessary to support combustion,
    (c) The combustible material is cooled to below its ignition temperature.
    (d) Flames are chemically inhibited.

All of the material presented in this HANDBOOK for the prevention, control, or extinguishment of fire is based on these principles.

D. Heat Measurement

The temperature of a material is the condition which determines whether it will transfer heat to or from other materials. Temperature is measured in degrees.

Temperature Units

Celsius Degree (also called Centigrade): A Celsius (or Centigrade) degree (°C) is 1/100 the difference between the temperature of melting ice and boiling water at 1 atmosphere pressure. On the Celsius scale, zero is the melting point of ice; 100 is the boiling point of water.

Fahrenheit Degree: A Fahrenheit degree (°F) is 1/180 the difference between the temperature of melting ice and boiling water at 1 atmosphere pressure. On the Fahrenheit scale, 32 is the melting point of ice; 212 is the boiling point of water.

Kelvin Degree: A Kelvin degree (°K) is the same size as the Celsius degree. On the Kelvin scale (sometimes called Celsius Absolute), zero is minus 273.15°C.

Rankine Degree: A Rankine degree (°R) is the same size as the Fahrenheit degree. On the Rankine scale (sometimes called Fahrenheit Absolute), zero is minus 459.67°F.

Heat Units

British thermal unit (Btu): The amount of heat required to raise the temperature of one pound of water one degree Fahrenheit (measured at 60°F) is called the British thermal unit.

Calorie: The amount of heat required to raise the temperature of one gram of water one degree Celsius (measured at 15°C) is called calorie. One Btu = 252 calories.

As heat can be measured in any unit, it is sometimes convenient to convert Btu to joules, one Btu equaling 1,055 joules; or to horsepower, one Btu per minute equaling 0.0236 hp.

Heat energy has quantity as well as potential (intensity). For example consider the following analogy:

Two water tanks stand side by side. If the first tank holds twice as many gallons when full as the second, then the first tank holds twice the quantity of water as the second. But if the depths of water in the two tanks are equal, then the pressures or potentials are equal. If the bottoms of the two tanks are connected by a pipe, water will not flow from one to the other because both tanks are at equilibrium pressure. In a similar way, one body may hold twice the quantity of heat energy (measured in Btu or calories) as a second. But if the potentials or intensities of the energies of the bodies are equal (that is, their temperatures are equal), no heat energy will flow from one body to the other when they are brought in contact with each other. The bodies are at equilibrium. If a third body at a lesser temperature were brought into contact with the first body, heat would flow from the first to the third until both body temperatures became equal. The amount or quantity of heat flowing until this equilibrium is reached depends upon the capacities of each body to retain the heat of each of the other bodies involved.

Essentially, ignition is a matter of increasing heat intensity by adding heat, whereas physical fire extinguishment is usually accomplished through reduction of heat intensity by removal of heat. Chemical extinguishment works by another mechanism — by interrupting chemical reactions that are important in the combustion process.[2]

Temperature Measurement

Devices that measure temperature depend either on a physical change (expansion of a solid, liquid, or gas), on a change of state (solid to liquid), or an energy change (changes in intensity of electrical energy, or changes in emission intensities and spectral distribution). The principles of operation of the more common temperature measuring devices are discussed here. For a more detailed discussion, see the latest edition of the *Chemical Engineers' Handbook* published by McGraw-Hill Book Company.

Liquid Expansion Thermometers: These thermometers consist of a tube partially filled with a liquid, which measures expansion and contraction of the liquid with changes in temperature. The tube is calibrated to permit reading of the level of the liquid in degrees of a temperature scale.

Bimetallic Thermometers: Bimetallic thermometers contain two metals with different coefficients of expansion that are laminated and in the form of a strip or coil. As the temperature changes the two parts of the laminate expand or contract to different extents, causing the strip or coil to deflect. The amount of deflection is measured on a scale which is calibrated in degrees of temperature.

Solid Fusion: Solid fusion makes use of the melting or fusion point of a solid (metal, chemical, or chemical mixture) to indicate whether or not a hot object is above or below the melting point of the solid. The eutectic metal in a sprinkler undergoes solid fusion in a fire environment, which activates the sprinkler.

Thermocouples: Thermocouples consist of a pair of wires

of different metals connected to each other at one end; this is the sensing end. The other ends are connected to a potentiometer. When the sensing end is at a different temperature from the potentiometer, a potential difference is set up, the magnitude depending in part on the temperature difference between the two ends. The potentiometer can be calibrated to give readings in degree of temperature.

Pyrometers: Pyrometers measure the intensity of radiation from a hot object. Since intensity of radiation depends on temperature, pyrometers can be calibrated to give readings in degrees of temperature. Optical pyrometers measure the intensity of a particular wavelength of the radiation. Radiation pyrometers measure total radiation, usually by focusing radiation from a hot object on a thermocouple.

Specific Heat

Specific heat, or more properly the heat or thermal capacity of a substance, is the number of Btu required to raise the temperature of a pound of the substance 1°F, or the number of calories to raise one gram 1°C. The specific heats of various substances vary over a considerable range; all common substances, except water, are less than unity. Specific heat figures are significant in fire protection as they indicate the relative quantity of heat needed to raise the temperature to a point of danger, or the quantity of heat that must be removed to cool a hot substance to a safe temperature.

One reason for the effectiveness of water as an extinguishing agent is that its specific heat is higher than that of other substances.

Latent Heat

Heat is absorbed by a substance when the substance is converted from a solid to a liquid, and from a liquid to a gas. Conversely, heat is released during conversion of a gas to a liquid or a liquid to a solid.

Latent heat is the quantity of heat absorbed or given off by a substance in passing between liquid and gaseous phases (latent heat of vaporization), or between solid and liquid phases (latent heat of fusion). Latent heats are measured in Btu or calories per unit weight. The latent heat of fusion of water (normal atmospheric pressure) at the freezing or melting point of ice (32°F) is 143.4 Btu per lb; the latent heat of vaporization of water at the boiling point (212°F) is 970.3 Btu per lb. The high heat of vaporization of water is another reason for the effectiveness of water as an extinguishing agent. 1293.7 Btu are required to convert one pound of ice at 32°F to steam at 212°F. The latent heats of most other common substances are substantially less than that of water. Thus, the heat absorbed by water cannot be used to propagate the flame further by vaporizing more liquid, or by pyrolyzing more solid.

E. Heat Transfer

Transfer of heat is responsible for the start and extinguishment of most fires. Heat is transferred by one or more of three methods: (1) conduction, (2) radiation, or (3) convection.

Conduction: Heat transferred by direct contact from one body to another is transferred by conduction. Thus, a steam pipe in contact with wood transfers its heat to the wood by actual contact: in this example, the pipe is the conductor.

The quantity of heat energy transferred by conduction between two bodies in a given time is a function of the temperature potential and the conductance of the path involved. Conductance depends on thermal conductivities, cross sectional areas normal to the flow path and length of flow path. Rate of heat transfer, then, is simply the quantity of heat per unit time, while heat flux is the quantity of heat per unit cross sectional area per unit time. Thermal conductivity of a material is the heat energy flux due to unit temperature gradient (fall-off of one degree per unit of distance).

The conduction of heat through air or other gases is independent of pressure in the usual range of pressures. It approaches zero only at very low pressures. No heat is conducted in a perfect vacuum. Solids are better heat conductors than gases: the best commercial insulators consist of fine particles or fibers of solid substances, with the spaces between the particles filled with air.

Heat conduction cannot be completely stopped by any "heat-insulating" material. In this respect, the flow of heat is unlike the flow of water which can be stopped by a solid barrier. Heat insulating materials have a low heat conductivity. No matter how thick the insulation, solidly insulating the space between the source of heat and the combustible material may not be sufficient to prevent ignition. If the rate of heat conduction through the insulating material is greater than the rate of dissipation from the combustible material, the temperature of the combustible material may increase to the point of ignition. For this reason there should always be an air space or some way of carrying the heat away by convection, rather than relying solely on the heat insulating material to protect exposed woodwork. By the transmission of heat over a long period, fires have occurred through as much as a 2-ft thickness of solid concrete.

In regard to heat conductions, the most important physical properties of a material are thermal conductivity (K), density (ρ), and specific heat (c). It is unfortunate that the last two quantities are usually listed separately, for only their product (ρc) is of any interest in the field of heat conduction. It is a measure of the amount of heat necessary to raise the unit volume of the material by unit temperature. A typical unit might be kilogram calories per cubic centimeter per degree Celsius ($Kcal/cm^3/°C$), and a possible name for the quantity is thermal capacity per unit volume.

The thermal conductivity of a material is a measure of the rate of flow of heat through unit area of the material with unit temperature gradient. Unit temperature gradient means that in the direction of heat flow, the temperature is falling off one degree per unit distance. A typical unit of thermal conductivity is $Kcal/cm/hr/°C$.

It is rare that the quantities, thermal conductivity and thermal capacity per unit volume, are of much importance individually. In fact, the solution to heat conduction problems is so complex that it cannot be adequately presented herein. However, one or two interesting features can be appropriately mentioned. Probably the most useful feature is concerned with the time constant of a thickness (x) of a material. Thus, if the surface of a material is suddenly exposed to a temperature rise, then the temperature at a depth (x) within the material will begin to change substantially at a time

$$t = \frac{x^2 \rho C}{K}$$

The dimensions of the expression are given as follows:

$$t = \frac{ft^2 \times Btu/ft^3/°F}{Btu/ft/hr/°F} = \frac{cm^2 \times Kcal/cm^3/°C}{Kcal/cm/hr/°C}$$

Centimeters, Kcal, and °C cancel out, leaving the result

that the dimension is hours, i.e., time. This is a time constant; thus, the higher the number, the slower the transfer.

Convection: By convection, heat is transferred by a circulating medium — either a gas or a liquid. Thus, heat generated in a stove is distributed throughout a room by heating the air by conduction; the circulation of heated air through the room to distant objects is heat transfer by convection. Heat is transferred from the air to the objects by conduction. Heated air expands and rises, and for this reason heat transfer by convection occurs in an upward direction, although air currents can be made to carry heat by convection in any direction.

Radiation: Radiation is when energy travels through space or materials as waves. Radiant energy waves travel with the speed of light. On arrival at a body they are absorbed, reflected, or transmitted. Visible light consists of wavelengths 4×10^{-5} to 7×10^{-5} cm (violet to red). Emission from combustion processes stretches from ultraviolet (shorter wavelength than violet) to the infrared region (heat radiation longer than red wavelength).

A common example of radiation is a candle flame. Air heated by the flame rises upward while cooler air moves in toward the candle to supply the flame with more oxygen, thus sustaining the burning process. If a hand is held opposite the flame, the hand is not cooled by this air movement; however, it does experience a sensation of warmth. This can only be from the hand's absorption of energy which is not conducted by the air: this energy is called radiant heat or radiation. While most flames emit visible radiation, flames such as hydrogen-oxygen emit only in the ultraviolet and infrared regions.

Heat is a form of energy and exists in a body by motion of that body's molecules. Heat imparted to a liquid will increase molecular action within the liquid, and may even set up convection currents therein due to any temperature differences in different strata of the liquid. Likewise, heat imparted to gases increases the molecular activity within them, and the phenomenon of pressure is produced by the collisions of the molecules with each other and with the sides of the containing vessel.

Heat from the sun passes through the near vacuum of space until it reaches the earth and is absorbed by something tangible. Radiant heat also passes freely through symmetrical diatomic molecules such as hydrogen (H_2), oxygen (O_2), and nitrogen (N_2). Thus, there is no absorption of heat by air except by tangible air constituents or contaminants such as water vapor, carbon monoxide, carbon dioxide, sulfur dioxide, or hydrocarbons. In general (except in atmosphere furnaces), the concentrations of these absorptive components of air are low enough so that the total radiation absorbed by them is of minor significance. Hence, the quality and quantity of heat radiation depends solely upon the temperature of the radiating body, and the size of the radiating surface. If a portion of such radiation lies within the visible spectrum, light is produced and the process is called incandescence. The spread of forest fires by radiation is very sensitive to relative humidity since the water vapor absorbs infrared radiation.

When two bodies face each other and one body is hotter than the other, radiant energy will flow from the hotter body to the cooler body until they both have the same temperature (i.e., thermal equilibrium). The ability to absorb this radiated heat is a function of the kind of surface of the cooler body and the area of the radiating surface of the hotter body. If the receiving surface is dark in color, it will absorb heat; if it is light in color or is shiny and polished, it will reflect most

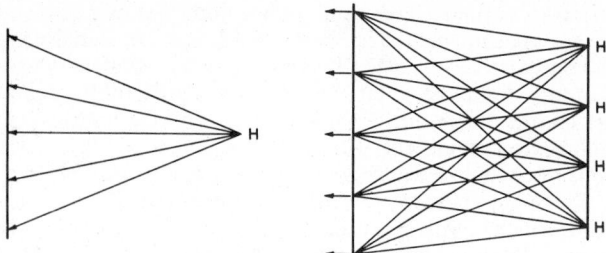

Fig. 2-1B. A comparison of heat absorption by surfaces of similar area from a pinpoint source (left) and a large radiating surface (right).

of the heat away. Some substances are transparent to radiant energy and will allow it to pass through them with minimal absorption.

Radiation energy travels in straight lines. Obviously, heat absorbed from a pinpoint source would be very much less than the same amount of heat absorbed from a large radiating surface, providing the absorbing body also had an appreciable surface area (see Fig. 2-1B).

Heat radiation lies primarily in the red and infrared regions of the spectrum. In absorption and refraction qualities it differs somewhat from sunlight because sunlight is made up of all colors. Radiation may be stopped by any opaque body: thus, in order to furnish temporary protection to combustible surfaces beneath, metal sheets are placed beneath stoves or on heat-exposed walls. Because ordinary glass is transparent, it cannot appreciably stop heat radiation. Practical applications of some of the foregoing theory are contained in the following material.

Radiation from a given source varies as the 4th power of the absolute temperature of the source. To compare changes in temperature, the following proportional equation may be used:

$$Q_1 : Q_2 :: (T_1 + 460)^4 : (T_2 + 460)^4$$

or

$$Q_1 \times (T_2 + 460)^4 = Q_2 \times (T_1 + 460)^4$$

where Q's are quantities of heat radiated at temperatures T.

EXAMPLES: A heater is designed to operate safely with a 500°F outside surface temperature. How much more heat will it radiate when this outside surface temperature is raised to 600°F?

Q_1 is considered and Q_2 is unknown. Thus:

$$
\begin{aligned}
Q_2 : Q_1 &= (600 + 460)^4 : (500 + 460)^4 \\
&= (1060)^4 : (960)^4 \\
&= \frac{(1060)^4}{(960)^4} = (1.104)^4 = 1.5 \text{ approximately}
\end{aligned}
$$

Therefore, increasing the surface temperature by 100°F will increase the radiation about one and a half times.

This characteristic of heat radiation (that it is a function of the 4th power of the absolute temperature) explains the danger of radiation ignition from overheated stoves and space heaters. If heat radiation were merely a function of the 1st power of the absolute temperature, radiation in the preceding example would have been only 1.1 times greater than at the lower temperature.

Where all conditions are known, quantitative calculations may be made of heat transmission by conduction, convection, and radiation.* However, because there are so many unknown factors in fires, any exact calculations are impossible.

The ignition of materials, their continued burning, and the spread of fire along the surface of materials all involve heat balance relationships (i.e., the equating of the rate at which heat is being generated to the rate at which it is distilling off combustible volatiles and being dissipated into the materials by radiation, convection, and conduction). In general, the complexity of this heat balance is such that, for example, the spread of flame along the surface of a material cannot as yet be predicted.

Pure temperature radiation is not completely realized in ordinary light sources, but it characterizes the theoretical "black body" which radiates the maximum possible energy at all wavelengths. Most formulae (including the Stefan-Boltzmann law) for the rate of heat transfer between bodies contain an e factor which is known as the absorption coefficient of the absorbing surface. Some absorption coefficients are:

Black body	1.00	Brass, oxidized	0.60
Lampblack	0.95	Nickel, oxidized	0.42
Paper	0.93	Aluminum, oxidized	0.11
Steel, oxidized	0.79	Nickel, polished	0.03

One exception to the general rule of absorptivity is a white enamelled surface which has almost the same characteristics as oxidized steel or brass.

In the visible spectrum, light can be broken up into colors via prisms, each color having its own specific wavelength. Violet has the shortest visible wavelength, followed by blue, green, yellow, orange, and red. As these wavelengths increase and lengthen, the radiations become invisible in the infrared region. However, as the intensity of radiation in the infrared region increases, the absorbing object may change to visible dull red, to orange, to bright red, and ultimately to incandescence. The Wein law states that the hotter the body is, the shorter will be the wavelength of emitted radiation. Yellow heat is a higher temperature than red heat. The red color of normal wood fires comes from the incandescent soot.

Gases absorb and emit radiation at a limited number of wavelengths which depend on their chemical bonds. Solids absorb and emit a broad continuous spectrum.

The Stefan-Boltzmann law expresses heat radiation as being proportional to the 4th power of the absolute temperature of the radiating source. This can be carried one step further by stating that the quantity of heat from a pinpoint source depends upon the difference between the 4th powers of the absolute temperatures of the heat source and the exposed object. It will also vary inversely as the square of the distance separating them. However, if the pinpoint source is expanded and becomes very large in relation to the distance, small variations in distance will have little or no effect on the severity of the radiated heat transfer. An example would be a large oven within a few inches of a combustible frame wall.

F.   Heat Energy Sources or Sources of Ignition

Since fire prevention and extinguishment are dependent on the control of heat energy, it is important to be familiar with the more common ways in which heat energy can be produced. There are four sources of heat energy: (1) chemical, (2) electrical, (3) mechanical, and (4) nuclear.

Chemical Heat Energy

Oxidation reactions usually produce heat. They are the source of the type of heat which is of primary concern to the fire protection engineer.

Heat of Combustion: The heat of combustion is the amount of heat released during a substance's complete oxidation (combustion) (i.e., conversion to carbon dioxide and water). Heat of combustion, commonly referred to as calorific or fuel value, depends upon the kinds and numbers of atoms in the molecule as well as upon their arrangement. They are commonly expressed in Btu per lb, but are sometimes reported in gram calories per gram (1 gram calorie per gram = 1.8 Btu per lb). In the case of fuel gases, calorific values are usually reported in Btu per cu ft. Calorific values are used in calculating fire loading, but do not necessarily indicate the relative fire intensity of materials since intensity† is dependent on rate of burning as well as on total amount of heat produced.

Also of interest to the fire protection engineer is the fact that heat is produced in incomplete or partial oxidations which occur at some stage in almost all accidental fires and in spontaneous heating by oxidation. For almost all compounds of carbon and hydrogen, or of carbon, hydrogen, and oxygen (which include substances of vegetable or petroleum origin), the heat of oxidation, whether complete or partial, depends on the oxygen consumed. For this class of common substances (i.e., wood, cotton, sugar, vegetable and mineral oils), the heat of oxidation is about 537 Btu per cu ft of oxygen consumed, regardless of the heat of complete combustion of the substance. For this reason, the heat produced either in a fire or in a spontaneous heating oxidation is limited by the air (oxygen) supply in every case.

Spontaneous Heating: The process of increase in temperature of a material without drawing heat from its surroundings is known as spontaneous heating. Spontaneous heating of a material to its ignition temperature results in spontaneous ignition or spontaneous combustion. The fundamental causes of spontaneous heating are few, but the conditions under which these fundamental factors may operate to create a dangerous condition are many and varied. Three conditions which have much to do with whether or not an oxidation reaction will cause dangerous heating are rate of heat generation, air supply, and insulation properties of the immediate surroundings.

If exposed to the atmosphere, practically all organic substances capable of combination with oxygen will oxidize at some critical temperature with evolution of heat. The rate of oxidation at normal temperatures is usually so slow, however, that the released heat is transferred to surroundings as rapidly as formed, with the result that there is no temperature increase in the combustible material being oxidized. This, however, is not true of all combustible materials since certain oxidation reactions at normal temperatures (e.g., oxidation of powdered zirconium in air) generate heat more rapidly than it can be dissipated, with spontaneous ignition being the result.

Enough air must be available to permit oxidation, yet not so much that the heat is carried away by convection as

---

* The Heating, Ventilating, and Air Conditioning Guide gives detailed information on calculations. It is available from the American Society of Heating, Refrigerating, and Air-Conditioning Engineers, Inc., United Engineering Center, 345 E. 47th St., New York, NY 10017.

† Fire intensity may be defined as the rate of heat liberation per unit volume of combustion zone.

rapidly as formed. An oily (vegetable oil) rag which might heat spontaneously in the bottom of a wastebasket would not be expected to do so if hung on a clothesline where air movement would remove heat; nor would it be likely to heat if within a tightly packed bale of rags. On the other hand, because of more air and the insulting effect of the bale, a loosely packed bale might provide ideal conditions for heating. Because of the many possible combinations of the interrelated factors of air supply and insulation, it is impossible to predict with certainty when a material will heat spontaneously.

In the presence of air, substances subject to oxidation will first form products of partial oxidation which may act as catalysts to further oxidation. For example, olive oil which has turned rancid from exposure to the air will oxidize at a higher rate than fresh, pure, previously unexposed oil.

Additional heat can initiate spontaneous heating in some combustible materials not subject to this phenomenon at ordinary temperatures. In these instances the preheating increases the rate of oxidation sufficiently so that heat is produced more rapidly than it can be lost. Many fires have been caused by the spontaneous heating of foam rubber following preheating in a dryer.

A common cause of heating of agricultural crops appears to be oxidation by bacteria, one product of which is heat. Since most bacteria cannot live at temperatures much above the range of 160 to 175°F, continued heating of agricultural products to their ignition temperatures is thought to be due to rapid oxidation initiated after bacteriological preheating.

The moisture content of agricultural products has a definite influence on the spontaneous heating hazard. Wet or improperly cured hay is very likely to heat in barn lofts. Experience has indicated that such heating may result in ignition within a period of from two to six weeks after storage. Alfalfa meal which has been exposed to rain and then stored in bins or piles is very susceptible to spontaneous heating. Soybeans stored in bins have been known to sustain what is called "bin burn" (i.e., the beans next to the bin walls are charred due to the moisture condensation on the inside surfaces of the wall and the self heating of the beans). Other agricultural products susceptible to spontaneous heating are those with a high content of oxidizable oils, such as corn meal feed, linseed, rice bran, and pecan meal.

Heat of Decomposition: The heat of decomposition is the heat released by the decomposition of compounds requiring the addition of heat for their formation. Since most chemical compounds are produced by exothermic reactions, heat of decomposition is not a common phenomenon. Compounds formed from endothermic reaction are often unstable. When decomposition is started by heating to above a critical temperature, decomposition continues with the liberation of heat. Cellulose nitrate is well known for its tendency to decompose with the liberation of dangerous quantities of heat. The chemical action responsible for the effect of many commercial and military explosives is the rapid decomposition of an unstable compound.

Heat of Solution: The heat of solution is the heat released when a substance is dissolved in a liquid. Most materials release heat when dissolved, although the amount is usually not sufficient to have any significant effect on fire protection. In the case of some chemicals (such as concentrated sulfuric acid), the heat evolved may be sufficient to be dangerous. The chemicals that react with water in this way are not themselves combustible, but the liberated heat may be sufficient to ignite nearby combustible material.

In contrast to most materials, ammonium nitrate absorbs heat when dissolved in water. (It is said to have a negative heat of solution.) Some first aid products, for use where cold is recommended, consists of dry ammonium nitrate in water-tight packages. These packages become cold when water is added.

Electrical Heat Energy

Electrical energy produces heat when electric current flows through a conductor, or when a spark jumps an air gap.

In the process of current flow through a conductor, electrons are passed along from atom to atom within the conductor with frequent collisions with atomic particles on the way. The better conductors, such as copper and silver, have the most easily removed outer electrons so that the force or voltage required to establish or maintain any unit electric current (or electron flow) through the conductor is less than for substances composed of more tightly bound atoms. Thus, the electrical resistance of any substance depends on atomic and molecular characteristics; the electrical resistance is proportional to the energy required to move any unit quantity of electrons through the substance against the forces of electron capture and collision. This energy expenditure appears in the form of heat.

Resistance Heating: Resistance heating is when the rate of heat generation is proportional to the resistance and the square of the current. Since the temperature of the conductor resulting from resistance heating depends on dissipation of heat to the surroundings, bare wires can carry more current than insulated wires without heating dangerously, and single wires can carry more current than bunched or closely grouped wires.

The heat generated by incandescent and infrared bulbs is due to the resistance of the filaments in the bulbs. Material of very high melting point is used for the white hot filaments of incandescent lamps, and destruction of the filament by oxidation is prevented by partial evacuation of the bulb and by removal of oxygen. The filaments of infrared lamps operate at a much lower temperature (a "red" heat); the best infrared lamp reflectors are gold because gold is one of the best reflectors for infrared radiation.

Induction Heating: Whenever atoms are subjected to electric potential gradients from external sources, the arrangement of the atom (or of a molecule of several atoms) is distorted, with a tendency for electrons to move in the direction of the positive potential and for protons to move in the opposite direction. This is true whether the externally applied potential is due to a battery or generator, or is the result of a magnetic field. Even though the external potential is insufficient to break away any electrons, the distortion of the normal atomic or molecular arrangement represents an energy expenditure. This is of practically no consequence if the external force is unidirectional, but can be substantial if the potential is pulsating or alternating. For example, the heating of a dielectric (a good insulator) may be considerable if the frequency of alternation of external potential becomes high.

Whenever a conductor is subject to the influence of a fluctuating or alternating magnetic field, or whenever a conductor is in motion across the lines of force of a magnetic field, potential differences appear in the conductor. These potential differences result in the flow of current with attendant resistance heating in the conductor. For rapidly changing or alternating potentials, additional energy is expended and, as the polarity changes, appears as heat energy due to the mechanical and electrical distortion of the molecular structure. This latter type of heating increases with the frequency of alternation. Food in a microwave oven is heated by the molecular friction induced by absorbed microwave energy.

A useful form of induction heating is created by passing a high frequency alternating current through a coil surrounding the material to be heated.

An alternating current passing through a wire can induce a current in another wire parallel to it. If the wire in which a current is induced does not have adequate current-carrying capacity for the size of the induced current, resistance heating will occur in it. In this example the heating is due primarily to resistance to flow, and only in a small degree to molecular friction.

Dielectric Heating: Since all available insulating materials are far from perfect insulators, there is always some current flow when the insulators are subjected to substantial voltages. This flow is commonly referred to as a leakage current and, from the standpoint of heat generation, is usually not important. However, if the insulating material is not suited for the service, or for reasons of economy, space saving, or attempts to attain the maximum capacity in a condenser the material is too thin, leakage currents may exceed safe limits resulting in heating of the insulator with consequent deterioration of the material and ultimate breakdown. Heating from molecular distortion is of no importance with constant unidirectional voltages, but may become a significant factor with alternating voltages (especially those of high frequency).

If a nonconductive material is inserted in the air space between the plates of a condenser, the material may heat due to flow of current through it.

Heat from Arcing: Arcing occurs when an electric circuit which is carrying current is interrupted, either intentionally (as by a knife switch), or accidentally (as when a contact or terminal becomes loosened). Arcing is especially severe when motor or other inductive circuits are involved. The temperatures of arcs are very high, and the heat released may be sufficient to ignite combustible or flammable material in the vicinity. In some instances the arc may melt the conductor, with the result that molten metal is scattered. One requirement of an intrinsically safe electrical circuit is that arcing, due to accidental current interruption, will not release sufficient energy to ignite the hazardous atmosphere in which the circuit is located.

Static Electricity Heating: Static electricity (sometimes called frictional electricity) is an electrical charge that accumulates on the surfaces of two materials that have been brought together and then separated. One surface becomes charged positively, the other negatively. If the substances are not bonded or grounded, they will eventually accumulate sufficient electrical charge so that a spark discharge may occur. Static arcs are ordinarily of very short duration, and do not produce sufficient heat to ignite ordinary combustible materials such as paper. Some, however, are capable of igniting flammable vapors and gases, and clouds of combustible dust. Fuel flowing in a pipe can generate enough static electricity of sufficient energy to ignite a flammable vapor.

Heat Generated by Lightning: Lightning is the discharge of an electrical charge on a cloud to an opposite charge on another cloud or on the ground. Lightning passing between a cloud and the ground can develop very high temperatures in any material of high resistance in its path, such as wood or masonry.

Mechanical Heat Energy

Mechanical heat energy is responsible for a significant number of fires each year. Frictional heat is responsible for most of these fires, although there are a few notable examples of ignition by the mechanical heat energy released by compression.

Frictional Heat: The mechanical energy used in overcoming the resistance to motion when two solids are rubbed together is known as frictional heat. Any friction generates heat. The danger depends upon the amount of mechanical energy transformed to heat, and the rate at which the heat is generated. Some examples of frictional heat are the heat caused by friction of a slipping belt against a pulley, and the hot metal particles (sparks) thrown off when a piece of foreign metal enters a grinding mill.

Friction Sparks: Friction sparks include fires caused by the sparks which result from the impact of two hard surfaces, at least one of which is usually metal. Some examples of friction sparks often reported as responsible for fires are sparks from dropping steel tools on a concrete floor, from falling tools striking machinery (or piping), from tramp metal in grinding mills, and from shoe nails on concrete floors.

Friction sparks are formed in the following manner: heat, generated by impact or friction, initially heats the particle; then, depending on the ease of oxidation and the heat of combustion of the metal particle, the freshly exposed surface of the particle may oxidize at the elevated temperature with the heat of oxidation increasing the temperature of the particle until it is incandescent.

Although the temperatures necessary for incandescence vary with different metals, in most cases they are well above the ignition temperatures of flammable materials (e.g., the temperature of a spark from a steel tool approaches 2,500°F; sparks from copper-nickel alloys with small amounts of iron may be well above 500°F). However, the ignition potential of a spark depends on the total heat content. Thus, the particle size has a pronounced effect on spark ignition. The practical danger from mechanical sparks is limited by the fact that usually they are very small and have a low total heat content, even though they may have a temperature of 2,000°F or higher. They cool quickly and start fires only under favorable conditions, such as when they fall into loose dry cotton, combustible dust, or explosive materials. Larger particles of metal, able to retain their heat longer, are not usually heated to dangerous temperatures. Although the hazard of ignition of flammable vapors or gases by friction sparks is often overemphasized, in areas where any flammable liquids, gases, or vapors are or may be present it is best to avoid the use of grinding wheels and other sources of mechanical sparks. The possibility of ignition due to some unusual condition should not be overlooked.

Nickel, monel metal, and bronze have a very slight spark hazard; stainless steel has much less of a spark hazard than ordinary tool steel, Special tools of copper-beryllium and other alloys are designed to minimize the danger of sparks in hazardous locations. Such tools cannot, however, wholly eliminate the danger of sparks because a spark may be produced under several conditions. NavOrd Report 5205, summarized in the October 1959 NFPA *Quarterly*[3], contains a conclusion by its authors that no benefit is gained by using nonsparking hand tools in place of steel to prevent explosions of hydrocarbons. Leather, plastic, and wooden tools are free from the friction spark hazard.

Overheating of Machinery: The overheating of machinery refers to fires caused by the heat which results from the rolling, sliding, or friction in machinery or between two hard surfaces, at least one of which is usually metal. Ignition sources in this category are heated bearings on rotating machinery and belts which become overheated due to pulley slippage.

Heat of Compression: The heat of compression is the heat released when a gas is compressed. This is also known as the diesel effect. The fact that the temperature of a gas increases when compressed has found practical application in diesel engines in which heat of compression eliminates the need for a spark ignition system. Air is first compressed in the cylinder of a diesel engine, after which an oil spray is injected into the compressed air. The heat released when the air is compressed is sufficient to ignite the oil spray.

The most plausible explanation for disastrous explosions aboard two aircraft carriers is compression ignition of an oil-air mixture in the catapult engines. Tests have shown that when a jet of air (at 15 psia) is directed into a cavity in a block of wood, the wood will ignite. Apparently, compression waves set up in the cavity are converted to heat which raises the wood to its ignition temperature. When pipe fittings are substituted for the wood, an oil film on the inside surface of the fittings can be ignited.

Nuclear Heat Energy

Nuclear heat energy is energy released from the nucleus of an atom. The nucleus is composed of matter held together by tremendous forces which can be released when the nucleus is bombarded by energized particles. Nuclear energy is released in the form of heat, pressure, and nuclear radiation. In nuclear fission, energy is released by splitting the nucleus; in nuclear fusion, energy is released by the joining of two nuclei.

The energy released by bombardment of the nucleus is commonly a million times greater than that released by ordinary chemical reaction. Instantaneous release of large quantities of nuclear heat energy results in an atomic explosion. Controlled release is a source of heat for everyday use (i.e., steam generation for electric generating stations).

A simplified discussion of nuclear reaction is contained in *Radiation Control for Fire and Other Emergency Forces* by A. A. Keil, published by the NFPA. The book contains information for fire department personnel concerned with

setting up radiation control procedures which must be applied by fire departments and other emergency forces.

SI Units

The following conversion factors are given as a convenience in converting to SI units the English units used in this chapter.

1 Btu	=	1.055 kJ
1 calorie	=	4.187 J
1 ft	=	.305 m
1 lb	=	.454 kg
1 psi	=	6.895 kPa
$\frac{5}{9}(°F-32) =$		°C
1°K	=	°C + 273.15
1 in.	=	25.4 mm
1 fluid oz	=	29.574 ml

Bibliography

References Cited

[1] Browne, F. L., "Theories of the Combustion of Wood and Its Control," Report No. 2136, Dec. 1958. U.S. Dept. of Agriculture, Forest Products Laboratory, Madison, Wisc.

[2] Haessler, W. M., "Fire and Its Extinguishment," NFPA *Quarterly*, Vol. 56, No. 1, July 1962, pp. 89–96.

[3] "Friction Spark Ignition of Flammable Vapors," NFPA *Quarterly*, Vol. 53, No. 2, Oct. 1959, pp. 155–157.

Additional Readings

Campbell, J. A., "Friction Spark Ignition in Crash Fires," NFPA *Quarterly*, Vol. 51, No. 2, Oct. 1957, pp. 123–133.

Caydon, A. G., and Woldhard, H. G., *Flames, Their Structure, Radiation, and Temperature*, 3rd ed., Chapman and Hall, London, 1970.

Downing, A. G., "Frictional Sparking of Cast Magnesium, Aluminum and Zinc," NFPA *Quarterly*, Vol. 57, No. 3, Jan. 1964, pp. 235–245.

Fristrom, R. M. and Westenberg, A. A., *Flame Structure*, New York, McGraw-Hill Book Company, 1965.

Johnson, R. H., and Grunwald, E., *Atoms, Molecules and Chemical Change*, 2nd ed., Prentice-Hall, Englewood Cliffs, N.J., 1965.

Selwood, S. W., *General Chemistry*, 4th ed., Holt, Rinehart and Winston, New York, 1965.

Semat, H., *Fundamentals of Physics*, 4th ed., Holt, Rinehart and Winston, New York, 1966.

Van Dolah, R. W., et al. "Flame Propagation, Extinguishment and Environmental Effects on Combustion," *Fire Technology*, Vol. 1, No. 2, May 1965, pp. 138–145.

"Ignition or the Flame-Initiating Process," *Fire Technology*, Vol. 1, No. 1, Feb. 1965, pp. 32–41.

Van Name, F. W., Jr., *Elementary Physics*, 1st ed., Prentice-Hall, Englewood Cliffs, N.J., 1966.

Chapter 2

EXPLOSIONS

The word "explosion" has assumed so many shades of meaning that it cannot be used with any appreciable degree of precision by members of the scientific and engineering communities. By regarding an explosion as an "effect" or "result" of another phenomenon, an understanding of the phenomenon of explosion can be realized. For example, a vessel is filled with a flammable gas-air mixture. The mixture is ignited and the resultant pressure increase ruptures the vessel. This would be termed an explosion. However, if the same vessel were stressed beyond its ultimate stress limits by steam pressure, it could be just as easily ruptured.

Therefore, in the widest sense, an explosion is an effect produced by the sudden violent expansion of gases. This process of rapid physical and/or chemical transformation of a system into mechanical work, accompanied by a change of its potential energy, may also be accompanied by shock waves and/or the disruption of enclosing materials or structures. An explosion may result from: (1) chemical changes such as in the detonation of an explosive or the combustion of a flammable gas-air mixture, (2) physical or mechanical changes such as the bursting of a boiler, or (3) atomic changes.

The mechanical work accomplished during an explosion is due to the rapid expansion of gases, regardless of whether or not they already exist or are formed at the time of explosion.

Associated with the term "explosion" are the terms "deflagration" and "detonation," neither of which, within their intended meanings, may be involved in an explosion. For example, the explosion of a vessel because the design limits are exceeded by excessive steam pressure, or the explosion of a gas cylinder because the walls have been weakened by corrosion, have nothing to do with either deflagration or detonation. It is fairly common, although not correct, for the terms "detonation" and "explosion" to be used interchangeably.

A deflagration is an exothermic reaction which propagates from the burning gases to the unreacted material by conduction, convection, and radiation. In this process the combustion zone progresses through the material at a rate that is less than the velocity of sound in the unreacted materials.

In contrast, a detonation is an exothermic reaction characterized by the presence of a shock wave in the material which establishes and maintains the reaction. A distinctive difference is that the reaction zone propagates at a rate greater than sound velocity in the unreacted material. The principal heating mechanism is one of shock compression; the temperature rise is directly associated with the intensity of shock wave, rather than being determined by thermal conduction. Every material capable of detonating has a characteristic velocity that is constant under fixed conditions of composition, temperature, density, etc. The release of chemical energy in the reaction supplies energy to the shock wave that would otherwise decay in pressure. Thus, a detonation may be thought of as an exothermic, reaction-supported shock wave. In principle, any material which is capable of releasing energy rapidly may support an initiating shock; in practice, the rate of energy must be sufficiently great to overcome energy losses at free boundaries.

In recent years the term "thermal explosion" has come to mean the exothermic decomposition of a confined unstable material throughout its entire mass due to self heating. With increasing temperature, the rate of decomposition of the unstable material increases. The thermal expansion of the material or generation of gases, or both, usually results in failure of the confining vessel.

The circumstances leading to a thermal explosion involve not only the decomposition rate of the unstable material as an exponential function of temperature, but also the geometry of the confining vessel as it affects the heat transfer characteristics. If the rate of heat removal is greater than the rate of heat generation due to chemical decomposition, the reaction will slow down. If the rate of decomposition results in a heat generation greater than the heat removal, the temperature of the mass will increase and result in a constantly accelerating decomposition. Confinement, which can be brought about by the inertia of a large mass of the material, is not always dependent on a containing vessel as such. Normally, the processes involved in setting up a thermal explosion require a long time span in order for temperatures to rise to the point where the reaction accelerates. The ignition processes of a deflagration or detonation are quite short.

A. Explosions from Deflagration or Detonation of Gases

In keeping with the previous definitions, if a vessel contains a flammable vapor-air mixture and is ignited with a resultant pressure buildup which ruptures the vessel, we can state unequivocally that there is an explosion. If the vessel does not rupture, but contains the deflagration or detonation, we have no explosion because the criterion for mechanical work has not been met.

Gas or vapor-air mixture have both flammability (deflagration) and detonability limits; these define the range of fuel-to-oxidant ratio over which the mixtures can be burned or detonated. The limits of detonability are dependent upon the initiating stimulus and the environment; they are usually about the same as flammability limits but in some systems, such as hydrogen-air, they may be quite different.[1] (Note: The terms flammability limits, deflagration limits, and explosion limits, are frequently used interchangeably.) Maximum pressures of approximately 8 times the initial pressure result from deflagrations of stoichiometric gas-air mixtures; the increase may be as much as 20 times in fuel-oxygen systems. The side-on pressures from gas detonations are about twice those from deflagrations, and the reflected pressure is about another factor or two greater. Thus, a detonating fuel-oxygen mixture may give a 40-fold pressure increase. Although the pressures produced in gas detonations are much lower than those encountered with solid or liquid explosives, gas detonations can be very destructive. Since the reaction is supersonic, the pressure cannot be relieved by blowout panels or rupture discs.

Another similarity of detonations and deflagrations is the quenching effect of surfaces. A minimum diameter of tube or opening at flanges is required for propagation. How-

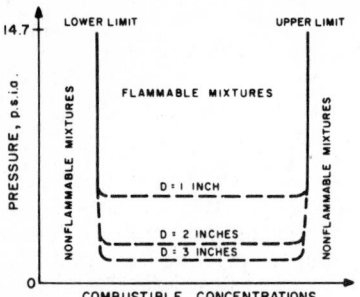

Fig. 2-2A.   Effects of pressure on the limits of flammability of a combustible vapor in air and of pressure and composition on the quenching diameter.

ever, a difference occurs in that a detonation may be re-initiated beyond short tubes of less than minimum diameter, or beyond small flanges by the shock that traverses the barriers[2] (see Fig. 2-2A).

B.   Explosions from Deflagration of Dusts

The burning of combustible dusts in air is similar to flammable gas-air mixtures, with the exception that normally encountered combustible dust-air mixtures have not been known to detonate.[3] In certain cases, such as in coal mines where there is a considerable degree of confinement and lengthy shafts, coaldust clouds have detonated.

C.   Explosions from Deflagrations of Mists

The so-called "mist" explosion is deflagration of a mist or fog consisting of droplets of flammable liquids suspended in air.[4, 5] The mists are usually created by condensation of flammable vapors in the air. Ignition of these mists can result in violent deflagrations (see Fig. 2-2B).

D.   Pressure Release Explosions

During normal use, boilers, gas cylinders and other pressure containers are designed to withstand expected pressures with a reasonable factor for safety to prevent rupture from abnormally high pressures as might occur if a gas cylinder were heated. The bursting pressure of pressure containers is usually four or more times that of normal use pressure. In addition, the containers are usually equipped with one or more emergency pressure release devices such as fusible plugs, rupture discs, or relief valves. Rupture of these containers may occur due to a number of factors, such as: the absence, improper installation, or malfunction of a pressure release device; some defect in the container itself;

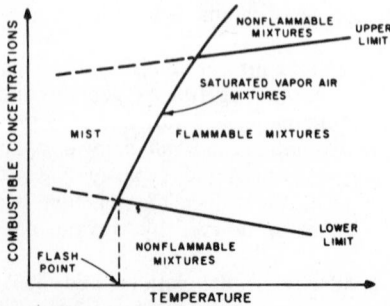

Fig. 2-2B.   Effects of temperature on the limits of flammability of a combustible vapor in air.

localized heating; or the unintentional admixture of materials resulting in a runaway chemical reaction within the container.

Although pressure release explosions do not necessarily involve containers designed to hold certain design pressures, they can be developed by such phenomena as the accidental addition of water to hot molten salt or metal, or the exposure of paint cans to fire.

E.   Decomposition Explosions

Certain endothermic compounds* can be made to decompose almost instantaneously. [6, 7, 8, 9] Explosions of acetylene, hydrogen, and certain metallic azides are the most notable examples of rapid decomposition reactions of this type. Many chemical substances, not classed as explosives, may undergo explosive decomposition under certain conditions. Similarly mixtures that contain both oxidizer and fuel substances can undergo oxidation-reduction reactions that can have an explosive character. Thus the oxygen and fuel need not be in a single compound, as in nitroglycerin, but may be in separate substances, as in black powder, a mixture of carbon, sulfur, and a nitrate.

Explosive decompositions are usually accompanied by the release of large quantities of hot gases. In general, it may be said that the speed with which the hot gases are released, either directly from the reaction or when the container bursts, will determine the violence of the explosion. Black powder and smokeless powder, often called low explosives in the past, normally burn or deflagrate at relatively low pressures. Thus they can be used as propellant explosives in guns, where the gases produced exert a pushing effect. Under higher confinement, or when ignited in very large quantities, propellant explosives can cause severe blast effects; they can even undergo detonation characteristics of ordinary, or high, explosives.

In liquid explosives, as in gases, chemical composition is an important factor. Characteristic of the most powerful, and generally the most readily initiated, liquid materials that can detonate is the existence of two detonation velocity regimes—a high and a low. High-velocity detonations are generally achieved by strong initiation; low-velocity detonations result from weaker ignition sources. In both cases the quantity and geometrical arrangement of the liquid are important factors. For example, nitroglycerin will detonate at a high velocity of about 25,000 fps when initiated directly by another explosive; but if initiation occurs as a result of weak shocks, such as may occur if the container is dropped, a low velocity of about 6,500 fps results. A nitroglycerin film, if thicker than about 50 mils, can be initiated to high-velocity detonation; but if the film thickness is less than this value, only low-velocity detonation will result. Ultimately, at a thickness less than about 10 mils, low-velocity detonation will also fail to propagate. A few liquid systems have been found to undergo a transition from low to high-velocity detonation in thin films. Low-velocity detonation pressures are only about one-tenth (1 to 300,000 psi) that

---

* Most compounds are formed from their elements with a release of heat. These are called exothermic compounds because they contain less energy than the elements from which they are derived. Decomposing them to their elements requires the addition of heat. Endothermic compounds are just the opposite, containing more energy than the elements. Decomposition to the elements releases this energy. Exothermic compounds are listed in most standard references as being negative, while endothermic compounds are positive. Standard heats of formation in references are always expressed with reference to a standard state, usually 25°C and one atmosphere.

of high-velocity detonation pressures which are in the range of millions of pounds per square inch. The blast effects from low-velocity detonations, however, are as destructive as those from high-velocity detonations.

For most solid explosives, the detonation velocity increases with increasing packing density. The sensitivity, that is, ease of initiation of detonation, at less than maximum density is dependent upon the particle size—the smaller the particles, the greater the sensitivity—and on packing density, decreasing as maximum density is approached. Susceptibility to detonation is dependent upon chemical composition, geometric arrangement, and degree of confinement of the system. The dimension of an explosive below which a steady state detonation will fail to propagate is the critical diameter. As the diameter increases above the critical diameter of an unconfined cylindrical column, the detonation velocity will increase until a diameter is reached beyond which no further increase in velocity will be found; this is the limiting diameter. However, if the charge is confined, the maximum velocity can be attained in diameters less than the limiting diameter. The sensitivity of almost all detonable materials increases, and the critical diameters are reduced, with increasing temperatures.

When in sufficiently large quantities or when contaminated, many materials which in themselves are not considered explosives can detonate. A notable example is fertilizer-grade ammonium nitrate which in very large charges can be initiated by very strong shocks such as from explosives. If ammonium nitrate detonates, it will release about one-half the energy of the same weight of TNT. But if an optimum amount of fuel is mixed with the ammonium nitrate, the mixture has approximately the same energy as TNT.

Although detonations are usually initiated by shock waves, they may result from fire. Under certain circumstances, which cannot be precisely defined in all practical cases, the deflagration may accelerate and undergo a transition to detonation. Initiating explosives are characterized by the ability to make this transition almost instantaneously. Commercial and military explosives may burn to detonation, depending upon quantity, confinement, explosive type, and other factors. Insensitive materials exhibit this property only under extreme conditions.

The blast effect from detonations depends primarily upon the quantity of material detonating and its distance from a target. Shock pressures near a solid (or liquid) explosive charge are in the region of thousands of pounds per square inch, but the pressure falls off rapidly with distance due to the expansion of the gas envelope so that the blast pressure from 1,000 lbs of TNT is only 5 psi at 150 ft. Five psi will cause severe damage to most buildings. Severe damage at much greater distances can result from missiles if the detonating charge is confined.

F.   Nuclear Detonations

A nuclear detonation is produced as a result of the formation of different atomic nuclei by the redistribution of the protons and neutrons within the interacting nuclei. This is produced by two processes, fission and fusion. The fission process involves the use of uranium 235 and plutonium 239. In the nuclear fusion process a pair of light nuclei fuse together to form the nucleus of a heavier atom.

This involves the use of a heavy hydrogen isotope known as deuterium.

The type of energy yield of a nuclear detonation depends upon the nature of the nuclear device and the environment of the detonation. As a general rule for an air detonation, blast and shock account for about 50 percent of the energy yield, thermal energy accounts for approximately 35 percent, and nuclear radiation accounts for the remainder. It is beyond the scope of this HANDBOOK to review the many effects associated with nuclear detonations, but it should be noted that the yield of nuclear weapons is expressed as equivalent to kilotons TNT. The first nuclear bombs released energies equivalent to 20 kilotons TNT; presently, megaton weapons are available.[10]

SI Units

The following conversion factors are given as a convenience in converting to SI units the English units used in this chapter.

1 in.	= 25.400 mm
1 ft	= .305 m
1 psi	= 6.895 kPa
$\frac{5}{9}(°F - 32)$	= °C

Bibliography

References Cited

[1] Lewis, B., and Von Elbe, G., *Combustion, Flame, and Explosions of Gases,* 2nd ed., Academic Press, New York, 1961.

[2] Zabetakis, M. G., "Flammability Characteristics of Combustible Gases and Vapors," Bulletin 627, 1965, USDI Bureau of Mines, Pittsburgh.

[3] Palmer, K. N., *Dust Explosions & Fires,* Chapman & Hall, London, 1973. (Distributed by Halsted Press—John Wiley & Sons, Inc., New York.)

[4] Baker, Wilfred E., *Explosions in Air,* University of Texas Press, Austin, Texas, 1973.

[5] Zabetakis, M. G., *Safety with Cryogenic Fluids,* Plenum Press, New York, 1967.

[6] Burgoyne, J. H., "The Flammability of Mists and Sprays," *Second Symposium on Chemical Process Hazards,* Institute of Chemical Engineers, 1963, pp. 1–5.

[7] "Mist and Spray Explosions," *Chemical Engineering Progress,* Vol. 53, 1957, pp. 121–4.

[8] Cook, M. A., *The Science of High Explosives,* Reinhold, New York, 1958.

[9] Urbanski, T., *Chemistry and Technology of Explosives,* Vol. 1, Pergamon Press, New York, 1964; Vol. 2, 1967; Vol. 3, 1967.

[10] Glasstone, S., ed., *The Effects of Nuclear Weapons,* U.S. Atomic Energy Commission, Washington, D.C., April 1962.

Additional Readings

Baum, F. A., *Physics of an Explosion,* Moscow, 1959, p. 4. (Available through Clearinghouse for Federal Scientific and Technical Information.)

Cole, R. H., *Underwater Explosions,* Dover Publications, Inc., New York, 1965, p. 1. (Original Copyright by Princeton University Press, 1948.)

Fordham, S., *High Explosives and Propellants,* Pergamon Press, London, 1966.

Davis, T. L., *The Chemistry of Powder and Explosives,* John Wiley & Sons, New York, 1941-3, p. 1.

Mullins, B. P., and Penner, S. S., *Explosions, Detonation, Flammability and Ignition,* Pergamon Press, New York, 1959, p. 5.

Robinson, C. S., *Explosions, Their Anatomy and Destructiveness,* McGraw-Hill Book Company, New York, 1944.

Kinney, G. F., *Explosive Shocks in Air,* MacMillan, New York, 1962, p. 1.

Van Dolah, R. W., et al., "Review of Fire and Explosion Hazards of Flight Vehicle Combustibles," IC 8137, 1963, USDI Bureau of Mines, Pittsburgh.

Chapter 3

PRODUCTS OF COMBUSTION AND THEIR EFFECTS ON LIFE SAFETY

The products of combustion can be divided into four categories: (1) fire gases, (2) flame, (3) heat, and (4) smoke. These products have a variety of physiological effects on humans, the most important being burns and the toxic effects which result from the inhalation of heated air and gases.

A. Fire Gases

The term "fire gases" refers to the gases which remain when products of combustion are cooled to normal temperatures. Most combustible materials contain carbon which burns to form carbon dioxide when the air supply is ample, but forms dangerous carbon monoxide when the air supply is poor. Unless the fuel and air are premixed, the air supply in the combustion zone is usually poor. When materials burn, some of the other gases which may be formed include hydrogen sulfide, sulfur dioxide, ammonia, hydrogen cyanide, nitrous and nitric oxide, phosgene, and hydrogen chloride. Gases formed by a fire depend on many variables, the principal ones being the chemical composition of the burning material, the amount of oxygen available for combustion, and the temperature.

Toxicity of Fire Gases

Although accurate statistics on actual causes of fire deaths are not available, it is generally recognized that fire fatalities from the inhalation of hot fire gases and hot air are far more common than are fire deaths from all other causes combined. Studies of large-loss-of-life fire disasters reveal that in practically all instances the primary cause of loss of life is inhalation of heated, toxic, and oxygen deficient fire gases.

Several variables determine whether the gaseous products of combustion will have a toxic effect on an individual, including concentration of the gases in air, the time of exposure, and the physical condition of the individual. Almost without exception, analyses of fire gases detect more than one gas, usually several. From a limited number of tests, it might be concluded that the effect will be greater than the sum of the effects of each alone (synergistic effect).[1] On the other hand, in one test the effect appeared to be less. It has been found that the toxic effects on persons inhaling fire gases are greater during a fire because the rate of respiration is increased by exertion, by heat, and by an excess of carbon dioxide. Under such conditions, gas concentrations which are ordinarily considered harmless may become dangerous.

Investigations into the hazardous properties of fire cases have shown the following gases to be the main causes of fire deaths: carbon monoxide, carbon dioxide, hydrogen sulfide, sulfur dioxide, ammonia, hydrogen cyanide, hydrogen chloride, nitrogen dioxide, acrolein, and phosgene.

Carbon Monoxide

Carbon monoxide (the chief danger in most fire gases) is not the most toxic of fire gases, but is always one of the most abundant. Under controlled burning conditions, the carbon of most organic materials can be oxidized completely to carbon dioxide by supplying an excess of oxygen. In the uncontrolled burning of an accidental fire, however, the availability of oxygen is never ideal; some of the carbon is incompletely oxidized to carbon monoxide. Thus, in a confined smoldering fire the ratio of carbon monoxide to carbon dioxide is usually greater than in a well-ventilated, brightly burning fire.

Carbon monoxide poisons by asphyxiation: Carbon monoxide combines with hemoglobin (an oxygen-carrying constituent of blood) to form carboxyhemoglobin 210 times more readily than oxygen does. Thus, carbon monoxide rapidly robs the blood of the oxygen needed by the body. Simultaneously, carbon monoxide prevents the blood from disposing of the waste carbon dioxide it normally brings back to the lungs. This mode of action makes carbon monoxide dangerous at relatively low concentrations, indicated as follows:

Exposure to 0.15 percent for 1 hr or 0.05 percent for 3 hrs is dangerous to life.

Exposure to 0.4 percent or greater is fatal in less than 1 hr.

Exposure to 1.3 percent will cause unconsciousness in two or three breaths, and will cause death in a few minutes.

Many variables (such as exertion, heat, and the presence of carbon dioxide and other toxic gases) affect the amount of carbon monoxide which can be tolerated without causing unconsciousness, permanent damage, or death.

Table 2-3A shows the carbon monoxide-carboxyhemoglobin relationship.[2, 3, 4] A study involving 45 fire fighters at 15 fires showed carboxyhemoglobin levels ranging from 2 to 28 percent.[5] Thirty-three blood samples indicated 5 percent or more; and two, 20 percent or more. In one fire, one man who was not wearing a mask exhibited 12 percent carboxyhemoglobin after 10 minutes. Another exhibited 10 percent carboxyhemoglobin after 10 minutes with an air-supplied mask, followed by two minutes without one; and a third exhibited 28 percent carboxyhemoglobin after 10 minutes without a mask.

A. J. Pryor has reported the results of two full-scale fire tests at Southwest Research Institute in which fires were set in the living room of a three-room assembly, furnished and arranged to represent three contiguous rooms in a one-story dwelling[6] (see Figure 2-3A). The interior was paneled in

Table 2-3A. Carbon Monoxide and Carboxyhemoglobin[2]

Carbon Monoxide Concentration		Maximum Exposure	Approximate Carboxyhemoglobin Levels Reached and Symptoms
PPM	Percent	Hours	Percent
50	0.005	8	10 (no effect)
200	0.02	2	20 (slight effect)
1,000	0.1	1	40 (severe effect)
10,000	1.0	1 minute	20 (fatal)

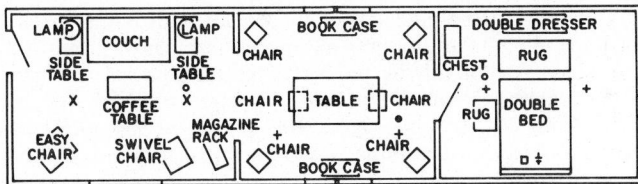

+ THERMOCOUPLES AT 1-, 5- AND 7-FT ELEVATIONS OFF FLOOR
× THERMOCOUPLES AT 1-IN., 1-, 5- AND 7-FT ELEVATIONS OFF FLOOR
⊹ THERMOCOUPLE AT 6-IN. ELEVATION OFF PILLOW ON BED
• GAS PROBES AT 1- AND 5-FT ELEVATIONS OFF FLOOR
○ GAS PROBE AT 5-FT ELEVATION OFF FLOOR
□ GAS PROBE AT 6-IN. ELEVATION OFF PILLOW ON BED

SCALE IN FEET
5 4 3 2 1 0

Fig. 2-3A. Fire tests were conducted by Southwest Research Institute in this three-room building that had been partitioned, finished, and furnished to simulate three rooms of a dwelling. The end points of the tests were attained when the level of heat, carbon monoxide, carbon dioxide, or oxygen in every area of the house reached or exceeded that point where an individual's ability to escape within one or two minutes was severely threatened.[6]

wood. During the test, the door between the living room (where the test fires were set) and the dining room was open; the door between the dining room and the bedroom was closed.

Table 2-3B shows the time when room temperature and concentrations of carbon monoxide, carbon dioxide, and oxygen reached levels generally considered to be fatal to anyone exposed to them for more than a few seconds. Note that temperature was the first of the limiting conditions to be reached in the living room and dining room, and that carbon monoxide was the first to be reached in the bedroom.

Carbon Dioxide

Carbon dioxide is usually evolved in large quantities from fires, and high levels of this gas overstimulate the rate of breathing. This condition, combined with decreased oxygen and the presence of irritating substances in a fire environment, may cause the lungs to swell from an excess of fluid. The speed and depth of breathing are said to be increased 50 percent by two percent carbon dioxide, or 100 percent by three percent carbon dioxide in air. At five percent breathing becomes labored and difficult for some individuals, although concentrations of 5 percent of carbon dioxide in air have been inhaled for up to one hour without serious after effects. Dr. William D. Claudy reported that concentrations near ten percent may cause death if breathed for more than a few minutes.[7] Since high concentrations of carbon dioxide increase the breathing rate, they also increase the rate of intake of other toxic gases that may be present and, therefore, increase the hazard.

Hydrogen Sulfide

The incomplete combustion of organic materials that contain sulfur yields hydrogen sulfide. For example, this gas is formed when wool, rubber, hides, meat, and hair are burned.

Hydrogen sulfide is readily identified by its "rotten egg" smell. However, its smell is unreliable as an exposure warning. At concentrations above 0.02 percent, the average human sense of smell depleted so rapidly that after a few inhalations the presence of the gas is undetectable. Exposure

Table 2-3B. Initial Occurrence of Limiting Conditions[6]

Location	Height (Feet)	Times of Initial Occurrence Test 1 (min.: sec.)	Test 2
T—300° F			
Living room	5	5:50	6:22
	1	14:50	8:58
Dining room	5	6:42	8:01
	1	14:54	17:30
Bedroom	5	26:24	26:06
	3	28:36	27:32
CO—1 percent			
Living room	5	13:20	7:20
	1	14:10	8:20
Dining room	5	14:20	8:30
	1	14:40	9:20
Bedroom	5	24:32	25:30
	3	25:30	26:00
CO₂—12 percent			
Living room	5	14:30	9:30
	1	12:30	10:30
Dining room	5	11:40	11:00
	1	12:40	14:30
Bedroom	5	—*	26:40
	3	—	27:30
O₂—7 percent			
Living room	5	15:00	10:08
	1	19:44	16:40
Dining room	5	15:00	15:45
	1	17:00	22:30
Bedroom	5	26:30	26:40
	3	27:30	27:15
Flashover			
Dining room		24:23	23:30
Bedroom door burned through		26:34	25:30

* Dash indicates that those levels or conditions were not reached.

to 0.04 to 0.07 percent for more than one-half hour is dangerous and can cause such symptoms as dizziness and intestinal disturbances, as well as dryness and pain in the respiratory system. Above 0.07 percent in air, hydrogen sulfide is acutely poisonous and affects the nervous system, almost simultaneously causing an extremely rapid breathing rate followed by respiratory paralysis. These characteristics emphasize the vital importance of taking protective action the moment hydrogen sulfide is detected.

Sulfur Dioxide

Complete oxidation of sulfur-containing organic materials yields sulfur dioxide which gives adequate warning of its presence, as evidenced by an extremely irritating effect on the eyes and the respiratory tract. Concentrations on the order of 0.05 percent are considered to be dangerous for even short exposures. Sulfur dioxide is a combustion product of wool, rubber, and some woods; however, the quantities are said to be too small to be toxic. Large quantities of sulfur dioxide come from burning sulfur.

Ammonia

Ammonia is formed during the burning of combustible material containing nitrogen (i.e., wool, silk, acrylic plastic, and phenolic and melamine resins combined with fillers). As a common refrigerant in commercial and industrial refrigeration systems, ammonia is a potential toxic hazard because of the possibility of accidental release during a fire. Because ammonia is extremely irritating to the eyes, nose, throat, and lungs, people usually won't voluntarily remain in an ammonia-containing atmosphere long enough to suffer serious effects. Exposure to 0.25 to 0.65

percent ammonia in air for one-half hour is sufficient to cause death or serious injury.

Hydrogen Cyanide

Hydrogen cyanide is highly toxic; fortunately in most fires, it is not likely to be produced in dangerous quantities. Relatively large quantities may be produced by incomplete combustion of certain nitrogen-containing materials such as wool, silk, urethane, polyamides, and acrylics. Some nitrogen fixation, combining atmospheric nitrogen with carbon from burning materials, also occurs in wood and paper fires. Hydrogen cyanide is a vermin fumigant, and presents a serious life hazard problem to fire fighters working in buildings being fumigated or in which fumigants may be stored. Exposure to 0.3 percent is fatal. The characteristic bitter almond odor sometimes warns of the presence of hydrogen cyanide; this characteristic does not afford a reliable warning because it may be masked by other odors or the sense of smell may be quickly impaired.

Hydrogen Chloride

Hydrogen chloride is a product of combustion of chlorine-containing plastic materials. Polyvinylchloride is the most notable because of the large quantities used for electrical conductor insulation, conduit, and piping.[8] Although inhalation of concentrations of about 1,500 ppm (parts per million) in air for a few minutes is fatal, hydrogen chloride has a pungent and irritating odor which a person would not be likely to inhale voluntarily. Following the fighting of a fire in an electrical service vault in a Washington, D.C. office building, 31 fire fighters were treated for what appeared to be the effects of inhaling hydrogen chloride.[9] Several instances of metal corrosion by hydrogen chloride released by combustion of polyvinylchloride have been reported.[10, 11, 12]

Nitrogen Dioxide

Nitrogen dioxide (peroxide) is extremely toxic; the concentration in air which may be safe to breathe for a few minutes is only 0.0025 percent. It is formed with other oxides of nitrogen during decomposition and combustion of cellulose nitrate, and in fires involving ammonium nitrate and other inorganic nitrates. It is also formed when nitric acid comes in contact with metals or combustible material. In a fire it can usually be identified by its reddish-brown color.

Nitrogen dioxide tends to anesthetize the throat so that its presence may not be recognized. The toxic effect is delayed unless the exposure is very great. In moderate exposures, effects appear as much as 8 hours later when breathing becomes distressed by the accumulation of fluid in the lungs. Recovery is difficult, and sometimes pneumonia can result. Brief exposures to 200 to 700 parts per million (0.02 to 0.07 percent) may be rapidly fatal.

Acrolein

Acrolein (acrylic aldehyde) is a highly irritating and toxic gas produced during combustion of petroleum products, fats, oils, and many other common materials. Although acrolein is only a minor constituent of fire gases, humans find concentrations of 1 ppm intolerable. Concentrations over 10 ppm are lethal in a short time.

Phosgene

Phosgene is highly toxic, but is not usually present (or is present only in small quantities) in the products of combustion of ordinary combustible materials. When ever a chlorinated compound comes in contact with flame, phosgene is one of the products of combustion. Thus, it may be found in fires involving polyvinylchloride plastic, or when chlorinated solvents are exposed to flame. F. A. Patty, in *Industrial Hygiene and Toxicology*,[13] states that phosgene ordinarily does not produce a serious threat to health except where ventilation is poor or where large quantities of chlorinated vapors are involved. Phosgene has been reported as the cause of death when carbon tetrachloride was used as an extinguishing agent.[14]

B. Flame

The burning of materials in the presence of a normal oxygen-rich atmosphere is generally accompanied by a luminosity called flame. For this reason, flame is considered a distinct product of combustion. Burns can be caused by direct contact with flames, or heat radiated from flames.

The observer can be sure there is fire where flame can be seen. Flame is rarely separated from the burning materials by any appreciable distance. However, in certain types of smoldering fires without evidence of flame, heat, smoke, and gas can develop. Air currents can carry these elements far in advance of the fire.

C. Heat

Heat is the combustion product mostly responsible for the spread of fire in buildings. The physiological dangers of heat range from minor injury to death. Exposure to heated air may directly cause dehydration, heat exhaustion, blockage of the respiratory tract due to fluids, and burns. Heat also causes an increased heart rate. When the intensity of heat exceeds the threshold of human tolerance, it is fatal.

It has been suggested that firemen should not enter atmospheres exceeding 120°F to 130°F without special protective clothing and masks.[7] No one can expect to inhale more than one or two breaths of moisture-saturated air at these temperatures without suffering serious consequences.

In school fire tests conducted at Los Angeles in 1959[15] a temperature of 150°F at the 5-ft level was selected as the temperature beyond which teachers and children could not be expected to enter a corridor from a relatively cool room. This selection assumed exposure to dry air, and only for the brief period of time necessary to reach exits.

In fire tests conducted by the National Research Council of Canada[16], 300°F was taken as the maximum survivable breathing level temperature. A temperature this high can be endured only for a short period and, if moisture is present, not at all. When water is used in fire fighting, steam is produced. Therefore, the atmosphere in a fire area is likely to be moisture-laden.

Burns caused by heat and fire are commonly classified as first, second, or third degree burns. First-degree burns involve only the outer layer of the skin and are characterized by abnormal redness, pain, and sometimes a small accumulation of fluid. Second-degree burns penetrate more deeply into the skin. The burned area is moist and pink, there are blisters, and usually a considerable amount of subcutaneous fluid accumulation. Third-degree burns are the most severe, and penetrate down to the subcutaneous fat. Third-degree burns are usually dry, pearly white or charred, and are not painful because the nerve endings have become inactivated.

Studies reported by Dr. K. Buettner[17] have shown that a skin surface temperature as low as 111°F will result in second degree burns and "unbearable pain" if the skin remains at that temperature long enough (about six hours).

If the skin temperature is increased, the time to produce second degree burns decreases rapidly. For example, burns result in 20 seconds at 131°F, and in one second at 158°F.

However, before the human skin can absorb sufficient heat to raise its surface temperature, other heat absorbing abilities of the body must be considered. These include the heat absorbed in the evaporation of perspiration, and that convected away by the blood circulation. If heat transfer by radiation is a factor, emissivity must be considered. The time for the body temperature to be increased will depend on the exposure temperature which, in most fires, increases rapidly in the first few minutes. Therefore, if initially the skin is exposed to a very high temperature, the skin temperature would immediately be increased faster than the body heat-absorbing properties could function. The minimum temperature at which this would occur has not been established. Dr. Buettner states that calm dry air heated above the range of 280°F to 320°F, or an equivalent of radiant heat, will cause unbearable pain to unprotected skin prior to a breakdown of the whole body.[17]

The cooling effect of evaporation of skin moisture may counteract the skin effect of heat up to 140°F or more in dry air. This limit would be lower in moist air. In designing buildings for safe occupancy and for escape under emergency fire conditions, it would seem that exitways should be protected from ambient temperatures above the range of 120°F to 150°F. This, it should be kept in mind, is the temperature range at approximately shoulder height (not at ceiling levels where temperatures are usually higher).

Death may result from exposure to excessive heat for a sufficient period of time (hyperthermia) without visible signs of burning, as in a flash fire. This condition will occur if the body absorbs heat faster than it can be dissipated by vaporization of surface moisture and outward radiation, thereby elevating the general body temperature sufficiently above normal to cause damage, particularly to the nerve centers of the brain.

Shock is often seen in delayed deaths (survival longer than three hours), and may appear after exposure to heat alone, or irritants, or oxygen deficiency plus high carbon monoxide.

A person exposed to excessive heat may die if the heat is conducted to the lungs rapidly enough to cause a serious decline in blood pressure and failure of circulation due mainly to capillary blood vessel collapse. This condition is also caused by large amounts of irritants such as acid anhydrides, acids (acetic, sulfuric, etc.), and aldehydes such as acrolein.

D. Smoke

Smoke is matter consisting of very fine solid particles and condensed vapor. Fire gases from common combustibles (such as wood) contain water vapor, carbon dioxide, and carbon monoxide. Under the usual conditions of insufficient oxygen for complete combustion, methane, methanol, formaldehyde, and formic and acetic acids are also present. These gases are usually evolved from the combustible with sufficient velocity to carry with them droplets of flammable tars which appear as smoke. Particles of carbon develop from the decomposition of these tars; they are also present in the fire gases from the burning of petroleum products, particularly from the heavier oils and distillates.

It is the small particles of carbon and tarry particles that are visible, and the phenomenon of fire gases rendered visible by the particles is generally defined as "smoke". Certain fire gases (e.g., oxides of nitrogen) and, in some instances, condensed steam and other atomized liquids, contribute to the visibility of fire gases. It is true that there are certain combustion conditions under which materials can burn without producing visible products of combustion: however, smoke generally accompanies fire and, like flame, is visible evidence of fire.

While the heat and toxic qualities of fire gases can be injurious or fatal, the solid and liquid particles in suspension in the gases (defined hereafter as "smoke particles"), also have harmful effects. The particles may be of such color, size, and quantity that they can obscure the passage of light, thus blocking vision to exits and exit signs. The development of quantities of smoke particles sufficient to make exitways unuseable can be very rapid. As evidence in nearly every test in the Los Angeles school fire tests, smoke in the corridors from fires in the basement reached untenable levels before the temperature did.[15] In the tests, smoke (as it pertained to visibility and irritant effects) was the principal life hazard. Smoke frequently provides the early warning of fire, and simultaneously contributes to panic conditions by the very nature of its blinding and irritating effects.

Smoke particles can be irritating when inhaled, and long exposure to smoke particles may cause damage to the respiratory system. Particles lodged in the eyes induce tears which may impair vision; when lodged in the nostrils and throat, they can cause sneezing and coughing at times when the persons so affected need their normal faculties. Smoke particles in air streams may cool to the point where water vapor, acids, and aldehydes will condense on them. If inhaled, such moisture-laden particles might well carry into the respiratory system highly poisonous, or at least irritating, liquids of undetermined composition. They can also cause injury to the eyes.

E. Insufficient Oxygen

When oxygen drops from its usual level of about 21 percent in the air to 15 percent, a person's muscular skill is diminished (anoxia); when it drops lower (into the range of 14 to 10 percent), a person is still conscious but has faulty judgment (which is not self-evident) and becomes quickly fatigued; in the range of 10 to 6 percent, a person collapses but can be revived by fresh air or oxygen. During periods of exertion, increased oxygen demands may result in oxygen deficiency symptoms at much higher percentages.

SI Units

The following conversion factors are given as a convenience in converting to SI units the English units used in this chapter.

$$1 \text{ ft} = 0.305 \text{ m}$$
$$\tfrac{5}{9}(°F - 32) = °C$$

Bibliography

References Cited

[1] Pryor, A. J., Johnson, D. E., and Jackson, M. N., "Hazards of Smoke and Toxic Gases Produced in Urban Fires," OCD Work Unit 2537B, 1969, Southwest Research Institute, San Antonio.

[2] Schultz, J. H., "Effects of Mild Carbon Monoxide Intoxication," *Archives of Environmental Health,* Vol. 7, 1963, p. 524.

[3] Forbes, W. H., Sargent, F., and Roughton, F. J. W., "The Rate of Carbon Monoxide Uptake by Normal Men," *American Journal of Physiology,* Vol. 143, 1945, p. 594.

[4] Henderson, Y. and Haggard, H. W., *Noxious Gases and the Principles of Respiration Influencing Their Action,* Reinhold Publishing Corp., New York, 1943.

[5] "For the Fire Service: The Effects of Carbon Monoxide," *Fire Journal,* Vol. 61, No. 4, July 1967, pp. 46, 47.

[6] Pryor, A. J., "Full-Scale Fire Tests of Interior Wall Finish Assemblies," *Fire Journal*, Vol. 63, No. 2, March 1969, pp. 14–20.

[7] Claudy, W. D., *Respiratory Hazards of the Fire Service*, 1st ed., NFPA, Boston, 1957.

[8] Van der Voort, H. F., "Characteristics of Polyvinyl Chloride Conduit, Insulated Wire, and Piping in Fire Situations," *Fire Journal*, Vol. 66, No. 6, Nov. 1972, pp. 91–94.

[9] "Bimonthly Fire Record: Office Building," *Fire Journal*, Vol. 64, No. 5, Sept. 1970, p. 73.

[10] "Worldwide Trends: Germany," *Fire Journal*, Vol. 62, No. 6, Nov. 1966, p. 64.

[11] "Bimonthly Fire Record: Telephone Exchange," *Fire Journal*, Vol. 63, No. 3, May 1969, p. 53.

[12] "Bimonthly Fire Record: Computer-Manufacturing," *Fire Journal*, Vol. 63, No. 6, Nov. 1969, p. 53.

[13] Patty, F. A., *Industrial Hygiene and Toxicology*, 2nd revised ed., Vol. II, Interscience Publishers, New York, London, 1962.

[14] Fawcett, H. H., "Carbon Tetrachloride Mixtures in Fire Fighting," *Archives of Industrial Hygiene and Occupational Medicine*, Vol. 6, Nov. 1952, pp. 435–440.

[15] *Operation School Burning*, NFPA, Boston, 1959, p. 25.

[16] Shorter, G. W., et al., "The St. Lawrence Burns," NFPA *Quarterly*, Vol. 53, No. 4, April 1960, pp. 300–316.

[17] Buettner, K., "Effects of Extreme Heat on Man," *Journal of the American Medical Association*, Vol. 144, No. 9, Oct. 28, 1950, pp. 732–738.

Additional Readings

Chien, W. P., Seader, J. D., and Birky, M. M., Monitoring Weight Loss in an NBS Smoke Density Chamber," *Fire Technology*, Vol. 9, No. 4, Nov. 1973, pp. 285–298.

Coleman, E. H., "Gaseous Combustion Products from Plastics," *Plastics* (London), Vol. 24, No. 264, Oct. 1959, pp. 461–8.

Comeford, J. J., and Birkey, M., "A Method for the Measurement of Smoke and HCl Evolution from Poly (vinyl chloride)," *Fire Technology*, Vol. 8, No. 2, May 1972, pp. 85–90.

Crowley, D. P., Blash, M. P., Burrell, B. W., and Niehaus, F., "Test Method for the Analysis of Toxic Products from Burning Materials—Phenolic Foam," *Fire Technology*, Vol. 8, No. 3, Aug. 1972, pp. 228–236.

Dufour, R. E., "Survey of Available Information on the Toxicity of the Combustion and Thermal Decomposition Products of Certain Building Materials Under Fire Conditions," *Bulletin of Research*, No. 53, July 1963, Underwriters Laboratories, Inc., Chicago.

Gaskill, J. R., and Veith, C. R., "Smoke Opacity from Certain Woods and Plastics," *Fire Technology*, Vol. 3, No. 3, Aug. 1968, pp. 185–195.

Gaume, J. G., Burtak, P., and Rostami, H. S., "Experimental Results of Time of Useful Function (TUF) After Exposure to Mixtures of Serious Contaminants," *Aerospace Medicine*, Vol. 42, No. 9, 1971, p. 987.

Higgins, E. A., Fiorca, V., Thomas, A. A., and Davis, H. V., "Acute Toxicity of Brief Exposures to HF, HCl, NO_2, and HCN with and without CO," *Fire Technology*, Vol. 8, No. 2, May 1972, pp. 120–130.

Hilado, C. J., "Smoke from Cellular Polymers," *Fire Technology*, Vol. 5, No. 2, May 1969, pp. 130–139.

———, editor, "Smoke and Products of Combustion," Volume 2, Fire and Flammability Series, reprints of articles from *Journal of Fire and Flammability*, Technomic Publishing Company, Inc., Westport, Conn., 1970–1973.

Ives, J. M., Hughes, E. F., and Taylor, J. K., "Toxic Atmospheres Associated with Real Fire Situations," Report 10 807, 1972, National Bureau of Standards, Washington, D.C.

Kishitani, K., "Study on Injurious Properties of Combustion Products of Building Materials at Initial Stages of Fire," *Journal of the Faculty of Engineering*, U. of Tokyo (B), Vol. 31, No. 1, 1971.

Leberman, P. and Bell, D., "Smoke and Fire Propagation in Compartment Spaces," *Fire Technology*, Vol. 9, No. 2, May 1973, pp. 91–100.

Mickelson, R. W. and Traicoff, R. M., "Testing the Smoking Behavior of Fire-Retarded Materials," *Fire Technology*, Vol. 8, No. 4, Nov. 1972, pp. 301–315.

Operation School Burning, No. 2, NFPA, Boston, 1961.

Pace, N., et al., "Formulation of the Principal Factors Affecting the Rate of Uptake of Carbon Monoxide by Man," *American Journal of Physiology*, Vol. 147, No. 2, Oct. 1946, pp. 352–9.

Robertson, A. F., "Effluent Fire Product—A Crude Approach to Fire Gas Hazard Assessment," *Fire Technology*, Vol. 10, No. 2, May 1974, pp. 115–128.

Robison, M. M., Wagner, P. E., Fristrom, R. M., and Schulz, A. G., "The Accumulation of Gases on an Upper Floor During Fire Buildup," *Fire Technology*, Vol. 8, No. 4, Nov. 1972, pp. 278–290.

Tsuchiya, Y., and Sumi, K., "Combined Lethal Effects of Temperature, CO, CO_2, and O_2 of Simulated Fire Gases," *Journal of Fire and Flammability*, Vol. 4, April 1973, pp. 132–140.

Chapter 4

THEORY OF FIRE AND EXPLOSION CONTROL

A composite definition derived from various dictionaries is that "combustion is a reaction which is a continuous combination of a fuel (reducing agent) with certain elements, prominent among which is oxygen in either a free or combined form (oxidizing agent)." This combination also exists with other elements, including fluorine and chlorine. The quality which all these reactions have in common is that they are exothermic (i.e., converting chemical energy trapped in the original molecules into the form of actual thermal energy).

Certain metals such as magnesium, aluminum, and calcium can, under certain conditions, "burn" in a pure atmosphere of nitrogen. Furthermore, there are many materials which, when exposed to sufficiently elevated temperatures, will directly decompose by themselves, emitting light and heat. Examples of these materials are hydrazine (N_2H_4), diborane (B_2H_6), nitromethane (CH_3NO_2), hydrogen peroxide (H_2O_2), and ozone (O_3). For purposes of this chapter, however, fire is referred to in its most usual form of involving rapid oxidation at temperatures above 1,500°F accompanied by the evolution of highly heated gaseous products of combustion and the emission of visible and invisible radiations. The fundamentals of fire control, extinguishment, explosion prevention, and explosion control are presented herein, and detailed explanations of how these fundamentals are applied are contained in Sections 13, 14, and 15 of this HANDBOOK.

The combustion process is observed as occurring in two modes: the flaming type (including explosions), and the flameless surface type (including glow and deep-seated glowing embers). The requirements for sustained burning are illustrated in Figure 2-4A. As shown in Figure 2-4A,

the flaming mode, despite its complexity, is associated with relatively high burning rates, expressed in terms of heat energy released from the originally bound chemical energy per unit time which, together with the weight-time rate and specific heats of effluent gaseous combustion products, determines flame temperature.

An approximate analysis will show that about two-thirds of the heat release passes off to the surrounding environment as sensible heat of the effluent, and one-third as radiative heat flux. For equilibrium conditions, the heat energy generated and the heat energy lost to the environment, both of which are measured on a time basis, must balance. If the former is in excess, the fire will grow; conversely, if the latter is in excess, the fire will diminish. The process is highly heat dependent. One method of fire control does, indeed, upset this heat balance through the instrumentality of water streams, the mainstay of the fire services. There are other means, as well, to control fire. The complexity of the flaming mode provides more options in fire control which can either be used individually or in combination. This is in sharp contrast to the flameless surface glowing mode in which instance only three options for control exist, used either singly or in combination.

While the combustion process is extraordinarily complex and is the subject of much research, sufficient information has been gained to make it possible to visualize it as illustrated in Figure 2-4B. The flaming mode can be conceived of as a tetrahedron in which each of the four sides is contiguous with the other three sides, with each side representing one of the four basic requirements: fuel, temperature, oxygen, and uninhibited combustion chain reactions.[1]

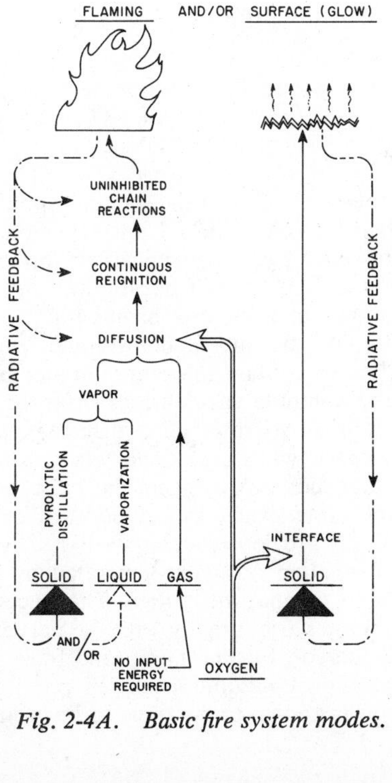

Fig. 2-4A. Basic fire system modes.

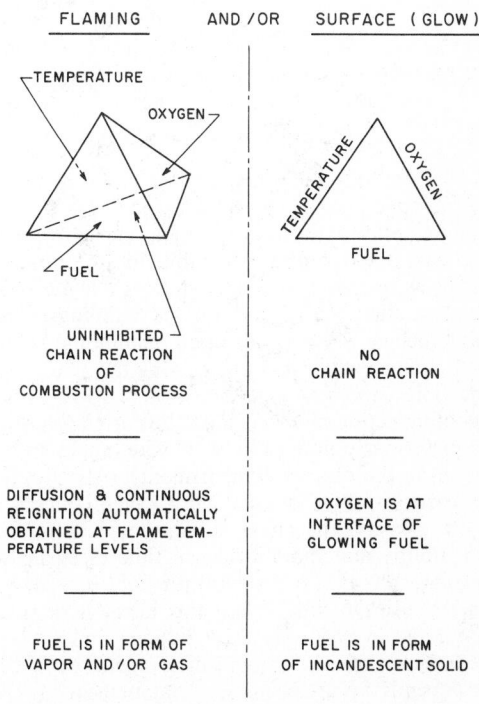

Fig. 2-4B. Basic fire system mode requirements.

As shown on the right side of the illustration, the surface combustion mode can be correctly symbolized in the form of the traditional triangle in which each of the three sides is contiguous with the other two sides, with each side representing one of the three basic requirements: fuel, temperature, oxygen.

These two modes are not mutually exclusive; they may occur either singly or in combination. Flammable liquids and gases burn in the flaming mode only. Most solid plastics can be construed as "frozen flammable liquids," and as such will melt with sufficient thermal feedback prior to burning. The commonality of this variety of fuels is that they must vaporize and be diffused with oxygen immediately before burning.

Examples in which both modes exist are: solid carbonaceous fuels such as coal; solid carbohydrates such as sugars and starches; solid cellulosic/lignins such as wood, straw, brush, and similar vegetable materials; and thermosetting plastics which do not melt. With these latter materials, the early stages of combustion start in the flaming mode with a gradual transition occurring toward the surface combustion mode during which both modes are simultaneously in action. Ultimately, the flaming mode is terminated with the residual surface combustion mode existing alone. Examples in which the surface combustion mode exists alone are pure carbon and other readily oxidizable nonmetals such as sulfur and phosphorus, as well as the readily oxidizable metals such as magnesium, aluminum, zirconium, uranium, sodium, potassium, etc. These latter metals burn with characteristically higher temperatures ranging from 5,000° to 6,000°F, as compared to temperatures ranging from 3,000° to 3,500°F obtained with the atmospheric burning of hydrocarbons. Extinguishing agents which can be used at these extremely high temperatures are described in Section 13, Chapter 6, Combustible Metal Extinguishing Agents.

From the foregoing, it is apparent that with the flaming mode there are four separate and distinct means of fire and explosion control, as compared with the surface combustion (glow) mode in which there are only three separate and distinct means of fire control. (Note that explosion control is not, per se, directly involved unless burnt gases are present; such gases could initiate a flaming mode to start.)

A. Extinguishment by Cooling

Under fire conditions, water, applied either as a straight stream (for range and/or powerful drenching action) or in a wide angle spray pattern, is the most effective means of removing heat from ordinary combustible materials such as wood, straw, paper, cardboard, and other materials used in the construction and furnishing of buildings. The extinguishing mechanism depends upon cooling the solid fuel, thereby reducing and ultimately stopping the rate of release of combustible vapors and gases.

This cooling action also results in the formation of steam which is particularly noticeable with wide angle spray patterns which, in the case of compartment or structural fires, serves to partially dilute the ambient oxygen concentration. Due to low density, the effect is transitory; therefore, the rapid diffusibility and short residence time of steam within the immediate fire area are significant only in a secondary sense. In the case of outside fires this effect is nonexistent, as will be noted in Part B of this Chapter.

The efficiency of an extinguishing agent as a cooling medium depends upon specific and latent heat, as well as upon boiling point. The superior properties of water can be attributed to the relatively high values of specific heat, latent heat, and availability. However, water is heavy and constitutes a burden when it has to be hauled for any distance. Water absorbs the infrared rays radiated from fire, and its cooling action is performed by means of sequentially conducting, evaporating, and convecting heat away from solid surfaces which are either burning, or are hot from exposure. Its capabilities can be summarized as follows:

1. One gpm can be expected to absorb 1,000 Btu/min when applied at 60°F and fully vaporized and superheated to 500°F.

2. Water expands to approximately 2,500:1, greatly reducing the oxygen in closed spaces.

3. Water can unintentionally induct air, depending on the chosen stream. At a 30° spray setting and at 100 psi nozzle pressure, about 30 cfm of air is induced into the water stream. This ventilation can be beneficial or harmful, depending upon its use.

4. Water can be expected to extinguish an interior compartment fire involving "ordinary combustibles" to the extent of 100 cu ft/gpm.

5. Finally, water can be beneficiated by the addition of surfactants to promote soaking and penetration; thickening agents to retard run-off and penetration; ammonium phosphates, alkali carbonates, and alkali borates to leave a residual fire-retardant coating; and foam concentrates to form foam blankets on solids and most liquids.

Since heat is continuously being carried away by radiation, conduction, and convection, it is only necessary to absorb a small proportion of the total heat being evolved by the fire in order to extinguish it by cooling; however, it must always reach the burning fuel directly. Good visibility is needed to do this correctly unless, as with automatic sprinklers, discharge occurs in the early stages of a fire. In high hazard areas, high-piled storage areas, high-rise structures, and other places of difficult accessibility for fire services, automatic fire protection systems become vital. (See Sec. 13, Chap. 1 for further information on water and water additives as extinguishants.)

B. Extinguishment by Oxygen Dilution

As previously stated, oxygen may be present either as free gaseous oxygen in the atmosphere (20.9 percent O_2; 79.1 percent N_2; 1.0 percent argon, CO_2, etc.) or combined, as in the form of hypochlorites, chlorates, perchlorates, nitrates, chromates, oxides, peroxides, etc. The term "dilution" can only be applied to the gaseous state since in the combined state oxygen is locked into the molecule and no dilution is possible. Hence, chemicals in this category will always present a high level of hazard, and oxygen dilution is of no avail in combatting fires having high concentrations of these materials. Because equal volumes of gases (and mixtures of gases) contain the same number of molecules, it is possible to compute gas densities from their molecular weights, as well as to rationalize that the percentage of oxygen in a space will be reduced when "foreign" gases (such as carbon dioxide, nitrogen, etc.) are artificially injected into the same space. This dilution of oxygen is also accomplished (as previously stated in Part A of this chapter) by the formation of steam generated by the application of water in compartment fires. The necessary degree of oxygen dilution varies greatly with the particular fuel, or combinations thereof. Furthermore, solid fuels present their own special array of minimum oxygen requirements. For instance, wood is known to continue to burn in the surface (glow) mode following its earlier flaming combustion mode at oxygen levels as low as 4 to 5 percent. Acetylene requires the oxygen concentration to be below 4 percent. On the other hand, hydrocarbon gases and vapors usually will not burn when the oxygen level is lowered to below 15 percent.

Fires in closed spaces will, of course, consume oxygen; however, this cannot be relied on to achieve self extinguishment since combustion in oxygen-deficient atmospheres results in the copious generation of flammable gases due to incomplete combustion. Inadvertent open entry or improper ventilation involving such spaces becomes an invitation to an explosion or, as the members of the fire services call this dreaded phenomenon, "blow-back."

A typical example of the efficacious use of the oxygen dilution principle is when carbon dioxide is used in total flooding of closed or semiclosed spaces. In the case of local application carbon dioxide systems (and in the case of portable carbon dioxide extinguishers) another flame characteristic is taken advantage of, namely flame velocity which varies with different fuels. A carbon dioxide discharge plume entrains air, the residual velocity of which together with its carbon dioxide content, if properly applied, will dynamically overcome the flame velocity and result in rapid extinguishment.

C. Extinguishment by Fuel Removal

A chemist would define a fuel as a reducing agent. A reducing agent is a substance which can reduce an oxidizing agent, losing one or more electrons. In the process, the oxidizing agent gains the corresponding electrons and the reducing agent becomes oxidized. It is necessary to realize that oxidation and reduction always take place simultaneously, the terms themselves being purely relative. In the presence of sufficiently powerful oxidizing agents, most substances can be viewed as reducing agents (substances which can be oxidized); conversely, in the presence of sufficiently active reducing agents, most substances can be viewed as oxidizing agents (substances which can be reduced). Ordinarily, a substance is not classified as an oxidizing or reducing agent if it manifests its oxidizing or reducing properties only in the presence of extremely active substances of the opposite kind.

Referring to Figure 2-4A, it will be seen that for the flaming mode of combustion it is necessary for solid and liquid fuels to first be vaporized, with the solid fuels being pyrolytically distilled and the liquid fuels being merely evaporated. In some instances (such as in the case of thermoplastic plastics) the solids are melted or fused, following which they vaporize. In the case of fuel gases, no such preparatory steps are required.

Again, referring to Figure 2-4A, the surface or glowing mode of combustion does not call for this gasification since combustion occurs directly at the solid interface with the air; thus, burning rates are small as compared with the flaming mode. Some examples are wood, charcoal, coke, and combustible metals.

From the preceding, it is obvious that many materials can be classed as fuels spreading over wide ranges of ignition temperatures, lower and upper flammable limits in air, flash points (if liquid), compounded in some instances with overtones of chemical activity (decomposition), and solubility in water which influences to a great extent the type of fire combat. In the case of solid fuels, another important influence on fire intensity (Btu per unit of time) is its array (as exemplified in dusts, splinters, shavings, logs, or tim-

bers), and whether that array is horizontal, vertical, cribbed, or piled. In each instance the same fuel will have entirely different burning characteristics.

From a chemical standpoint fuels can be generally categorized as follows:

1. Carbon and other readily oxidizable nonmetals such as sulfur, phosphorus, and arsenic.

2. Compounds rich in carbon and hydrogen (hydrocarbons).

3. Compounds containing carbon, hydrogen, and oxygen —such as alcohols, aldehydes, organic acids, cellulosic, and lignin (wood and vegetable materials).

4. Many metals and their alloys (including sodium, potassium, magnesium, aluminum, zinc, titanium, zirconium, and uranium).

Fuel removal can be accomplished literally by removing the fuel; indirectly by shutting off the fuel vapors to combustion in the flaming mode; or (in the nonflaming mode) by simply covering the glowing fuel. Some prime examples would be:

1. More than a few large tanks of liquid flammables have been extinguished by the expedient of pumping out the burning tank and transferring the liquid to some other empty tank.

2. If (as in Example 1) a condition existed where the liquid flammable has a flash point higher than the ambient storage temperature and it is not possible to transfer the liquid to an empty tank, then proper agitation of the liquid in such a manner as to raise the cooler bottom portion to the top, and to correspondingly displace the hot upper layer to the bottom of the tank, will result in the starving of the flames with respect to the vapors (see Fig. 2-4A).

3. In the case of gas fires resulting from broken lines, cracked flanges, blown packings and gaskets, etc., safe extinguishment can only be obtained by shutting off the gas (usually by closing the valves). See Figure 2-4A which shows that the fuel flow into the combustion zone is not under the control of the radiative feedback, as with flammable solids and liquids; instead, in the case of flammable gases, the fuel flow is controlled by such mechanical entities as the size of rupture, the pressure of the gas, its specific gravity, etc.

4. Standard forest fire fighting procedure includes the tactic of bulldozing a firebreak across the path of an advancing flame front in order to clear the path of all fuel and, by so doing, to halt the fire advance.

5. The only practical method of extinguishing deep-seated fires in silos and piles of solid combustibles is removal of fuel.

6. The coating of woody or vegetable burning material with metaphosphoric acid obtained via the thermal decomposition of mono-ammonium phosphate (multipurpose dry chemical) or diammonium phosphate originally in water solution. The metaphosphoric acid is a glassy infusible substance, is very adhesive, and imparts a fire retarding character to the originally burning fuel.

7. The covering of liquid and solid burning fuels with blankets of fire fighting foams made by the aeration of solutions of water and foam concentrates. This method of fire attack has become standard procedure for aircraft crashes, large tank farms, and oil tankers. Special foam concentrate formulations are required for polar solvents (water soluble).

8. A relatively new version of the method described in Example 7 uses a very thin film (instead of a thick foam) on hydrocarbon fuels. The film, known as aqueous film

forming foam (AFFF), is established by applying a water solution of perfluorocarboxylic acid onto the burning liquid surface and where the surface tension of the fuel is in excess of the aggregate surface tensions of the "film" with respect to the air and the interfacial surface tension of the "film" and the fuel surface.

9. The covering of burning metals by various materials that are inert with respect to the particular metal involved. Examples are dry petroleum coke, various inorganic salts used either singly or in eutectic proportions, sand, coal, foundry fluxes, soda ash, and similar materials.

10. The use of water into which either gelling agents or slurry producing agents (which greatly retard water run-off) have been introduced is a recently developed technique which shows great promise in fighting fires involving solid combustibles such as wood and vegetable materials. Variations of this technique are wide, ranging from thin slimes to thick layers. To date, the principal use has been in forest fire fighting, although other expanded uses can be expected.

11. There are numerous instances where nonwater soluble flammable liquids (such as carbon disulfide) which are heavier than water when burning can be extinguished by applying a light spray of water (so as not to agitate the fuel) which will float on top, thereby effectively covering the fuel. On the other hand, water soluble fuels such as alcohols, ketones, aldehydes, etc., can be sufficiently watered to raise the flash point and lower the vapor pressure of the fuel to a point where fuel vapors rising from the liquid phase are not sufficient to accumulate and form a flammable vapor-air mixture.

12. A technique often used in combatting liquid grease fires from unsaturated animal and vegetable oils and fats is the application of alkaline dry chemicals or alkaline solutions which, upon contact with the burning surface, generate a saponification reaction (as in making soap) and, as a light soap froth containing steam, causes carbon dioxide and glycerine bubbles to float on top of the burning oil. Since the liquid grease cannot burn, the fire is extinguished.

D. Extinguishment by Chemical Flame Inhibition

Extinguishment by cooling, extinguishment by oxygen dilution, and extinguishment by fuel removal are applicable extinguishing methods for all classes of fires of the flaming and glowing modes. (Refer to Figs. 2-4A and 2-4B.) Extinguishment by chemical flame inhibition applies to the flaming mode only. This method is, at best, only partially understood and is the subject of major continuing research. Although there is no doubt that flames can be chemically inhibited, such information is mostly empirical; much more is known at this writing than was known when the previous edition of this HANDBOOK was produced. The outstanding effect of this method is the extreme rapidity and the high relative efficiency with which flames can be extinguished. These virtues can be more fully appreciated when it is realized that this method, when properly executed, is the only means by which an explosion can be prevented in a flammable gas/air (or even a gas/oxygen) mixture after ignition has occurred. Application methods vary from very simple to very sophisticated applications which utilize highly responsive fire detection apparatus (see Sec. 15, Chap. 7).

Before flame inhibition can be discussed, it is necessary to realize that the combustion reactions proceed in a complex series of steps. These steps have a chain reaction characteristic. For example, refer to Figure 2-4C which

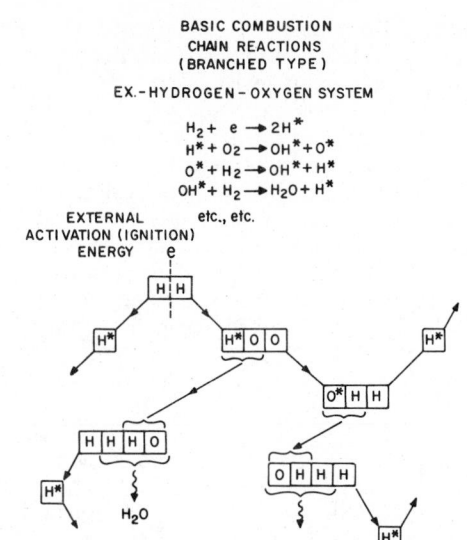

BASIC COMBUSTION
CHAIN REACTIONS
(BRANCHED TYPE)

EX.- HYDROGEN - OXYGEN SYSTEM

$$H_2 + e \rightarrow 2H^*$$
$$H^* + O_2 \rightarrow OH^* + O^*$$
$$O^* + H_2 \rightarrow OH^* + H^*$$
$$OH^* + H_2 \rightarrow H_2O + H^*$$

etc., etc.

EXTERNAL ACTIVATION (IGNITION) ENERGY

Fig. 2-4C. Basic combustion chain reactions (branched type).

illustrates the branched type chain combustion reaction of the hydrogen-oxygen system. This reaction is the simplest (and, incidentally, the most rapid) of all combustion types. Following the initial splitting of the hydrogen molecule, the individual hydrogen atoms (active H* species) interreact with oxygen molecules to produce active OH* and O* species. Note that the active species are formed as products as well as consumed as reactants, and as such have a dual personality; thus, they can be called "chain carriers." Although the example was taken for hydrogen, the same phenomenon generally holds for fuels containing hydrogen in chemical union with carbon and other elements. While it is obvious that the $2H_2 + O_2 \rightarrow 2H_2O$ reaction expresses the weight and volume relationships, it in no way expresses the chemical kinetics involved. As the result of much research, it has been found that the flame velocity is dependent upon the concentration of the active OH* species and upon the pressure at which the reaction proceeds. For example, for the hydrogen-oxygen flame the highest flame velocities (16in./sec at atmospheric pressure) have been determined. For other hydrogen-bearing carbonaceous fuels the hydroxyl concentration decreases with resulting lower flame velocities. For fuels not containing hydrogen, the active species O* becomes the determinant of flame velocity. (An example of the advantage obtained when air velocity exceeds flame velocity is illustrated by the simple act of blowing out the flame of a match or a candle. On a larger scale, a flaming oil gusher can be extinguished with explosives.)

Extinguishment by flame inhibition is possible only when the active species OH*, H*, and O* are not allowed to fulfill their role in sustaining the flame. Extinguishing agents which accomplish this do so without the accompanying action of other methods of flame extinguishment such as cooling, oxygen dilution, or fuel removal or covering. These agents extinguish flames with efficiency and dispatch; however, as previously stated, they do not combat glowing fires except under certain conditions (such as long "soaking" periods following flame extinguishment).

The exact manner in which the active species are interfered with in achieving flame extinguishment is, at present, not certain. However, it is definitely known that substances having this property fall into the following three categories:

1. Gaseous and liquid halogenated hydrocarbons wherein

the effectiveness increases as higher order halogens are used. Some examples presently in use are:

Bromotrifluoro-methane	$CBrF_3$	Halon 1301
Bromochlorodifluoro-methane	$CBrClF_2$	Halon 1211
Dibromotetrafluoroe-thane	$CBrF_2CBrF_2$	Halon 2402

There are many more, but the necessary criteria of stability and acceptable levels of toxicity become limiting factors.

2. Alkali metal salts wherein the cationic portion is sodium or potassium, and the anionic portion is either a bicarbonate, carbamate, or a halide. Some examples presently in use are:

Sodium bicarbonate	So-called "regular dry chemical"
Potassium bicarbonate	Trade name "Purple K"
Potassium carbamate	Trade name "Monnex"
Potassium chloride	Trade name "Super K"

There are many more substances, but the difficulties caused by hydrate formation (extreme hygroscopicity and toxicity) become limiting factors. The most effective salt ever found is potassium oxalate, but the preceding restrictions prohibit its use.

3. Ammonium salts, the most prominent of which is monoammonium phosphate wherein cationic ammonium radical (NH_4^*) and the anionic phosphate radical ($H_2PO_4^*$) are formed with the latter absorbing an H^* active radical becoming orthophosphoric acid which dehydrates to metaphosphoric acid as described in Example 6 of Part C of this Chapter.

Upon injection of these substances into flames, the substances thermally dissociate into their anionic and cationic "free radicals" and catalyze the union of the OH^* and H^* combustion reaction "chain carriers," thereby mitigating their influence upon the continuation of the flame. By this action the flame becomes inhibited, and extinguishment is accomplished when proper amounts of the agent are applied. Agents working in this manner are also referred to as negative catalysts. Unquestionably, with time, more and more of these substances will become available.

E. Environmental Considerations

The preceding parts of this chapter presented the four basic requirements of the flaming mode, and the three basic requirements of the surface, or glowing, mode of burning. Interest was centered on the nature of the fuel, the thermal balance, the degree of ventilation, and the chemical interplay occurring within the flames. The influence of radiative feedback was recognized as a factor of major importance in determining fire intensity (Btu/min). This latter factor is greatly influenced by the environmental effect of whether the fire is internal (compartment, or the so-called structural type) or external (outside open-air type).

The confinement of a fire within a space interferes with the dissipation of heat, gases, and smoke, with the result that the radiative feedback to the seat of the fire is greatly enhanced and initial burning rates build up briskly. As contrasted with outside fires, the environment is underventilated in a general sense; however, the following two situations can exist.

1. Under partially ventilated conditions within a par-

tially enclosed area (such as a room with open doors and windows), carbon dioxide will first be produced until ceiling temperatures of 1,200 to 1,500°F are obtained. Beyond this temperature the carbon dioxide reacts with free carbon to produce carbon monoxide according to the reaction $C + CO_2 \rightarrow 2CO$. Although this reaction is endothermic, it is a prolific source of carbon monoxide and at O_2/CO ratios of between 3 and 1 will form lower flammability mixtures, depending on the prevailing CO_2 concentration.

2. Under sealed, nonventilated conditions, almost the same general chemical conditions exist except that the oxygen concentration is much lower, which together with the prevailing carbon dioxide concentration prevents ignition of the carbon monoxide at the lower flammable limits. Instead, the O_2/CO is much lower, and at levels of 0.06 to 0.07 constitutes the upper flammable limit. Under these conditions, improper ventilation at low levels can cause an explosion known as "blow-back."

In both cases, the wide flammability range of carbon monoxide/air mixtures is responsible for the results. At temperatures in excess of 1,200°F the carbon dioxide reacts with the incandescent free carbon (present as smoke) to produce carbon monoxide at twice the rate that the carbon dioxide is consumed; at 1,500°F this reaction is virtually complete. At temperatures in excess of 1,800°F the water gas reaction prevails and the incandescent carbon reacts with the ever-present water vapor to produce even more carbon monoxide with free hydrogen being given off as well ($C + H_2O \rightarrow CO + H_2$). Again, more gas volumes are being released than are being consumed. This accelerated pace is further heightened by ever-increasing temperatures, and danger is further increased by the extremely wide flammability ranges of carbon monoxide and hydrogen.

The peculiar fire behavior within compartments, whether partially ventilated or completely unventilated, dictates that fire combat should be started before ceiling temperatures reach 1,200° to 1,400°F because at these temperatures the fire gases (together with the incandescent smoke particles) react to form flammable or potentially explosive gas mixtures.

In the following chapters the individual means and systems of fire combat, whether manual or automatic, will be presented in detail. It is necessary to understand that attack can be accomplished by many well-chosen combinations, and that no one answer will suffice since fire presents many "aspects" and "personalities." The fire protection engineer in his planning phase, the safety director and inspector in their installation and maintenance phases, and the combat fire officer and his men in their training, preplanning, and attack phases, have vital roles. The problems all start at the original planning stage and all three groups must do their utmost to prevent the fire in the first place.

SI Units

The following conversion factors are given as a convenience in converting to SI units the English units used in this chapter.

1 sq ft	$= 0.0929$ m^2
1 Btu	$= 1.055$ kj
1 ft	$= 0.305$ m
1 lb (force)	$= 4.448$ N
1 psi	$= 6.895$ kPa
$\frac{5}{9}$(°F $-$ 32)	$=$ °C
1 ft^3	$= 0.283$ m^3
1 gpm	$= 3.785$ litres/min

Bibliography

References Cited

[1] Haessler, W. M., *Extinguishment of Fire*, Rev. ed., NFPA, Boston, 1974, p. 2.

Additional Readings

Adeler, H., "Deductions from Research on Use of Water," NFPA *Quarterly*, Vol. 40, No. 4, Apr. 1947, pp. 283–90.

"Air Agitation for Control of Tank Fires," NFPA *Quarterly*, Vol. 53, No. 2, Oct. 1959, p. 98.

Belles, F. E., "Chemical Action of Halogenated Agents in Fire Extinguishing," National Advisory Committee for Aeronautics Technical Note 3565, Sept. 1955, Washington, D.C.

Belles, F. E., and Berlad, A. L., "Chain Breaking and Branching in the Active Particle Diffusion Concept of Quenching," National Advisory Committee for Aeronautics Technical Note 3409, Feb. 1955, Washington, D.C.

Cray, E. W., "High-Expansion Foam," NFPA *Quarterly*, Vol. 58, No. 1, July 1964, pp. 57–63.

Creitz, E. C., "Inhibition of Diffusion Flames by Methyl Bromide and Trifluoromethyl Bromide Applied to the Fuel and Oxygen Sides of the Reaction Zone," *Journal of Research*, Vol. 65A, No. 4, July—August 1961, National Bureau of Standards, Washington, D.C.

Doyle, W. H., "Explosion Venting of Buildings and Tanks," *Transactions*, National Safety Congress, Vol. 5, 1964, pp. 30–34.

Friedman, R., and Levy, J. B., "Survey of Fundamental Knowledge of Mechanisms of Action of Flame-Extinguishing Agents," Wright Air Development Center Technical Report 56–568, Jan. 1957, Wright-Patterson Air Force Base, Ohio.

Guise, A. B., "Chemical Aspects of Fire Extinguishment," NFPA *Quarterly*, Vol. 53, No. 4, Apr. 1960, pp. 330–336.

Glendinning, W. G., and MacLennan, A. M., "Suppression of Fuel-Air Explosions," NFPA *Quarterly*, Vol. 45, No. 1, July 1951, pp. 61–65.

Grabowski, G. J., "Explosion Protection Operating Experience," NFPA *Quarterly*, Vol. 52, No. 2, Oct. 1958, pp. 109–119.

Johnson, O. W., "Water on Oil Fires," NFPA *Quarterly*, Vol. 55, No. 2, Oct. 1961, pp. 141–146.

Maisey, H. R., "Gaseous and Dust Explosion Venting," *Chemical and Process Engineering*, Part 1, October 1965; Part 2, December 1965.

Pressures Developed by Rapid Combustion, Factory Mutual Engineering Corporation, Norwood, Mass., Sept. 1966.

Skinner, G. B., "Survey of Recent Research on Flame Extinguishment," Air Force Systems Command Technical Documentary Report ASD-TR-61-408, Supp. 1, Dec. 1962, Wright-Patterson Air Force Base, Ohio.

"Survey of Recent Research on Flame Extinguishment," Air Force Systems Command Technical Documentary Report ASD-TR-61-408, Supp. 2, Feb. 1964, Wright-Patterson Air Force Base, Ohio.

Symposium on Fire Control Research, American Chemical Society, Division of Fuel Chemistry, Vol. 1, Sept. 1961, Washington, D.C.

Thompson, N. J., *Fire Behavior and Sprinklers*, 1st ed., NFPA, Boston, 1964.

White, E. J., "The Art of Suppressing an Explosion," *Fire*, Vol. 58, No. 730, Apr. 1966, pp. 571–575.

Chapter 5

SMOKE MOVEMENT IN BUILDINGS

Smoke and the fire gases are important products of combustion which significantly influence the life safety, property protection, and fire suppression practices in buildings. Smoke generation in a building fire can vary widely depending on the amount and type of combustibles and the ventilation of the fire. In some cases the volume of smoke is so great that it may fill an entire building and also obscure visibility at the street level to such an extent that it is difficult to identify the building on fire. In other cases the volume of smoke generation may be considerably less, although the danger to life is not necessarily diminished because of the other airborne products of combustion.

Ventilating a fire, which is the planned, systematic removal of smoke, heat, and fire gases from the building, is an important fire department operation. It involves providing openings through the roofs and walls to permit the escape of the heat and smoke, and is usually effected by cutting openings in the roof and breaking or opening the windows. It may also utilize monitors or smoke vents, and the existing building services, such as air handling equipment or portable blowers and exhausters.

Smoke and fire gases are airborne products of combustion. However, even at levels which reduce visibility to nearly zero, the concentration of these products is not sufficient to materially influence the overall movement of the atmosphere. Consequently, insofar as the physical movement is concerned, a smoky atmosphere usually moves in a manner similar to normal air having the same characteristics of temperature and pressure.

Natural air movement in a building is influenced by a number of factors. The pressures and buoyancy created by the heat of the fire generate movement. This movement is modified by such factors as stack effect, wind pressures, the building geometry and its barriers (such as walls and floors), and ventilation practices. In addition, this natural air movement may be significantly affected by the operation of mechanical air handling equipment in the building. All of these combine to make the prediction of smoke movement in a large building a highly complex problem.

In recent years the problem of smoke movement in buildings has received considerable attention. At the time of publication of this edition of the HANDBOOK, active research and design studies were being conducted by a number of organizations including the National Research Council of Canada and the American Society of Heating, Refrigerating, and Air Conditioning Engineers' Technical Committee 5.6 on Control of Fire and Smoke. This level of activity promises to significantly increase our knowledge of this subject.

A. Expansion of Gases

During a fire in a confined space (such as a room of a building), the atmosphere in the room is a mixture of smoke, fire gases, and air. As noted, a smoky atmosphere and a normal atmosphere usually behave essentially the same with regard to movement. As the fire grows, both the pressure and the temperature increase. During a fully developed room fire, the pressure may rise by as much as 0.1 or 0.2 in. of water. The temperature in a room burning with ordinary combustibles may reach as high as 2,000°F.

The relationship between the volume of a gas, V, and its temperature and pressure is expressed by the universal gas law, $PV = RT$, where R is a constant for each specific gas. The relationship of these variables for two different conditions involving the same gas may be determined by eliminating the constant R to obtain

$$\frac{P_1 V_1}{T_1} = \frac{P_2 V_2}{T_2}$$

The values for temperature and pressure are expressed in absolute units.

The volumetric expansion of gases in a room fire can be determined by letting the subscripts $_1$ represent conditions before a fire occurs and subscripts $_2$ represent conditions when the room is fully involved. It was noted that the pressure rise in a room fire may be in the order of 0.1 to 0.2 in. of water. While this small increase in pressure is enough to cause a substantial flow of smoke and air from the fire, on an absolute scale, $P_1 \approx P_2$ in the above equation.

The absolute temperature in the initial condition is in the order of $T_1 \approx 70° + 460° \approx 530°$. In the fully involved condition, $T_2 \approx 1200° + 460° \approx 1660°$. The change in volume of gas can then be determined as

$$\frac{P_1 V_1}{T_1} = \frac{P_2 V_2}{T_2}$$

$$\frac{V_1}{530} = \frac{V_2}{1660}$$

$$V_2 \approx 3V_1$$

The volume of gases in a room will therefore increase by a factor of three or more. Every cubic foot of fresh air introduced into the burning space is expanded by this factor before it is displaced as a smoky mixture. As the hot gases move away from the fire they cool rapidly, thus contracting to their original volume. However, even though the displaced gases eventually cool to the ambient temperature, the effect of the expansion during fire conditions is a net increase in volume of displaced smoke of approximately twice the volume of the spaces involved. While this quantity of expanded air and smoke is substantial, it is often less significant than the quantity of air that moves through a building during a fire.

Building geometry and space arrangement have a significant influence on the movement of smoke and heat. Consequently, the practice of smoke and heat venting should reflect design objectives and realistic physical behavior. Design features incorporated into one type of structure may be totally inappropriate for another type. To illustrate different conditions which affect smoke and heat movement and venting practices, consider the following four types of buildings:

1. Below ground or windowless areas.
2. Industrial (large open areas).
3. Short buildings (few stories; many rooms; common construction systems).
4. Tall buildings.

Below ground and windowless spaces provide significant ventilation problems. Oxygen reduction causes inefficient combustion resulting in fires which generate dense smoke and carbon monoxide. High temperatures often occur because of the heat buildup which results from inadequate heat venting. Fire department access is limited, and potential locations are also avenues of escape for heat, smoke, and gases, some of which ignite when mixed with greater amounts of oxygen. Proper engineering design of ventilation systems to operate under typical fire conditions is essential for spaces such as these.

The venting of single story industrial buildings having large open areas has been studied.[1, 2, 3] The results of this research forms the basis of NFPA 204, Guide for Smoke and Heat Venting, hereinafter referred to in this Chapter as the NFPA Smoke and Heat Venting guide. Parts B and C of this Chapter describe the NFPA Smoke and Heat Venting guide and industrial practices.

Short buildings which are relatively uncomplicated in function and architectural features are adequately vented by usual fire department practices. The heat and pressures of a compartment fire are sufficient to force the smoke and hot gases outside through window openings or holes in the roof.

High-rise buildings pose new problems with regard to smoke movement. The influence of the building height and temperature differentials causing significant stack pressures has been a subject of considerable study in recent years. A digest of the principles of natural air movement in high-rise buildings is given in Parts D and E of this Chapter.

B. Industrial Building Ventilation

The importance of the properties of heat and smoke was realized at an early date. However, until the advent of effective artificial lighting, buildings were generally small enough so that windows provided adequate smoke venting, other than venting of fire through the roof.

Historical Background

Following the Iroquois Theater fire in 1903, an NFPA standard was adopted which called for automatic smoke vents over theater stages and in the ceilings of theater auditoriums. The height and arrangements of the theater stages were conducive to the effectiveness of vents, but the requirements for auditorium venting received little attention in actual practice.

In 1921 the principle of venting received further impetus when NFPA 87, Standard for the Construction of Piers and Wharves, provided for venting the roof of pier sheds, together with curtain boards or other subdivisions to retard the horizontal spread of smoke. The same principle has been applied to cotton warehouses, and in some cases to aircraft hangars. Smoke and heat venting has also been utilized for many years at the top of enclosures for vertical shafts such as elevator shafts and chutes.

Great impetus to the subject of smoke and heat venting was provided by the General Motors fire at Livonia, Michigan, in 1953 when fire spread horizontally under an un-

vented metal roof, some 34 acres in undivided area. Fire protection engineers were in general agreement that this fire could have been greatly reduced in extent if there had been effective roof venting. The General Motors fire led to a new approach to the subject by the NFPA Committee on Building Construction which prepared the NFPA Smoke and Heat Venting guide, adopted by the NFPA in May, 1961. Essential features specified by the NFPA Smoke and Heat Venting guide include vents of relatively large area, automatically operated, with curtain boards to confine heat and prevent lateral spread of fire. Although this standard was originally intended to apply to one-story buildings, its principles have been applied in a few cases to the venting of two-story structures where vents have been provided through the second floor.

The fact that the NFPA Smoke and Heat Venting guide recommends automatic venting has raised the objection that automatic venting increases the supply of air to a fire, resulting in an increased burning rate. However, in undivided buildings of large floor area, this fact is less relevant to the behavior of fires in their early stages than it is to similar fires in buildings of small area because the fire controls its own supply of air, provided the total flow of entrained air does not require a significant pressure drop across the inlets to the building. This condition, similar to a fire burning in the open, is more likely to be satisfied in large than in small buildings. If a fire in a vented building develops to the point where it burns faster than a fire in a similar unvented building, the latter building would, by that time, probably be charged with smoke.

Roof Venting Methods

Roofs can be vented as follows:

Monitors: Roof monitors with louvers or thin glass windows in the sides may provide the needed venting if properly spaced and subdivided. However, glass may be slow to break.

Continuous Gravity Vents: This type of vent is a continuous narrow slot in the peak of the roof, covered by a weather hood. If provided with shutters, the shutters should be arranged to open automatically in the event of fire.

Unit Type Vents: These vents are relatively small, usually 16 to 100 sq ft in area. Some consist of a metal frame and metal housing with hinged dampers; others are transparent or transluscent plastic domes which open on release of spring loaded lifting levers. In the event of fire, the manual and automatic operation of dampers may be arranged.

Sawtooth Roof Skylights: These skylights may serve as vents only when the glass used is ordinary strength (not wired), or when the skylight is provided with a movable sash which can be operated automatically in the event of fire. The behavior of glass in a fire is unpredictable and cannot be relied upon to provide venting as early as a vent which is operated by a fusible link. Protection against falling glass should be provided for fire fighters.

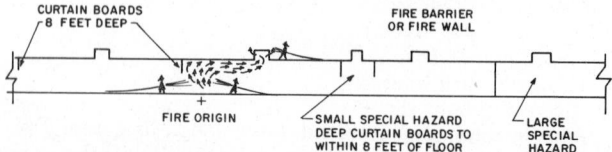

Fig. 2-5B. Behavior of hot gases under monitored and curtained roof. Flat-roofed building same size as that illustrated in Fig. 2-5A, 900 ft high with monitors 8 ft wide having ordinary glass side lights 5 ft high, spaced 100 ft on centers. With these arrangements, note that firemen can reach seat of fire inside of building and also reach it from the roof.

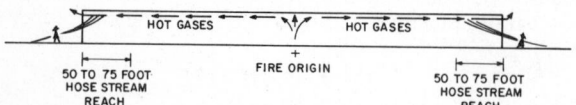

Fig. 2-5A. Behavior of hot gases under a flat-roofed building, 900 ft wide, 20 ft high. This building, unless a warehouse, does not comply with NFPA 101, Life Safety Code.

Exterior Wall Window: Ordinary glass, in windows nearest the eave line, may be expected to fail and provide some venting in the event of fire; glass farther down, especially if below the bottom of curtain boards, is of much less value for venting purposes. Movable sash, which can be operated automatically and promptly may also be used.

Power Ventilators: Power roof ventilators activated by fire conditions eliminate the need for large roof areas to provide the necessary ventilation. These units may also provide normal building ventilation. In fires generating considerable smoke but little heat, gravity vents are not effective because there is little convection flow of air induced. In underground areas where gravity venting is not feasible, power ventilators can provide positive heat and smoke venting.

Automatic Releases: Where automatic operation of venting facilities is provided, the controls should be actuated by fusible links or interlocked with operation of a sprinkler system or other automatic protection equipment covering the same area. Automatic opening of vents is achieved following release by a system of counterweights or other arrangement utilizing the force of gravity, or springloaded levers. Electric power should not be depended upon to open vents because it may be interrupted by fire. Generally, fusible links rated at 212°F or higher, depending on ambient temperature conditions, are used on vents.

Size and Spacing of Vents: There are so many factors affecting the rate of heat release from fires in various occupancies that it is difficult to develop any definite formula for computing the required area of heat venting. Based upon tests and experience, the following occupancy groupings have been suggested by the NFPA Committee on Building Construction:

Low Heat Release Occupancies: This class includes those buildings or portions of buildings containing scattered, small quantities of combustible materials.

Moderate Heat Release Occupancies: This class includes those buildings or portions of buildings containing moderate quantities of combustible materials which are fairly uniformly distributed.

High Heat Release Occupancies: This class includes buildings or portions of buildings containing either hazardous operations or concentrated quantities of combustible materials or both.

The ideal spacing for vents would be to have one over any fire which might be expected. Although this is impractical, the maximum spacing between vents tentatively suggested are:

1. Low Heat Release Content: 150 ft between centers.
2. Moderate Heat Release Content: 120 ft between centers.
3. High Heat Release Content: 75 to 100 ft between centers, depending upon the severity of fire potential.

Venting areas tentatively suggested are based on the following ratios of effective area of vent openings to floor areas for the various occupancy classifications:

1. Low Heat Release Content: 1:150.
2. Moderate Heat Release Content: 1:100.
3. High Heat Release Content: 1:30 to 1:50.

The minimum dimension of an effective vent opening probably should be not less than 4 ft in any direction.

Curtain Boards as Venting Aids

In large area buildings, unless vented areas are subdivided by means of walls or partitions, curtain boards are essential. The function of curtain boards is to delay and limit the horizontal spread of heat by providing the hori-

Fig. 2-5C. Deep curtain board around special hazard. Equipped with proper venting, a noncombustible curtain board extending down from ceiling around special hazards will prevent smoke and heat from mushrooming throughout the plant. Curtain board for a heat treating department is shown here.

zontal confinement needed to obtain the desired "stack" action. The depth of such curtain boards largely determines the height of the "stack" which so vitally affects the capacity of the vent. If an area is protected by automatic sprinklers, curtain boards have added values: confinement of heat tends to speed up operation of sprinklers over the fire, and obstructed lateral spread of heat minimizes the operation of an excessive number of sprinklers resulting in overtaxing the water supplies.

Curtain boards should be made of sheet metal or some other substantial noncombustible material. The depth of curtain boards necessary to assure effective action cannot be established for all conditions; for ceilings of moderate height, a minimum of 6 ft seems to be indicated. Around special hazards the minimum may need to be double that amount, and for higher roofs the curtain should extend to within 8 or 10 ft of the floor (see Fig. 2-5C).

The distance between curtain boards in low or moderate heat occupancies normally does not exceed 250 ft, and the curtained areas are limited to a maximum of 50,000 sq ft. In high heat release occupancies the distance between curtain boards does not exceed 100 ft, and the curtained areas are limited to 10,000 sq ft (see Fig. 2-5D).

If monitors or continuous gravity vents are utilized with prescribed spacing, parallel curtains may not be necessary.

In sawtooth roofs it is good practice to fill in the roof space down to truss level. Because the function of these

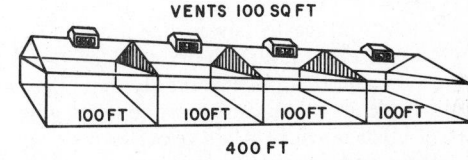

VENTS 100 SQ FT

Fig. 2-5D. Curtain boards and roof vents. The use of curtain boards to produce heat-banking areas under a roof, and vents for the release of smoke and heat through the roof is illustrated by the diagram showing figures from NFPA No. 87, Standard for the Construction of Piers and Wharves. For a pier shed 100 ft wide, the ratio of vent to floor area would be 100—a figure also suggested for storage of moderate heat release content by NFPA No. 204, Guide for Smoke and Heat Venting (1 to 30 to 50 for high heat release, 1 to 150 for low).

partitions is to prevent lateral spread, it is desirable to make a good seal at the top. Small gaps elsewhere will be less critical.

Application of Vents

Vents are most applicable to large area one-story buildings lacking adequate subdivision. They are also useful in windowless and underground buildings. Vents are not a substitute for automatic sprinkler protection.

Where vents are used on windowless buildings it is necessary to ensure that there is an area of openings near the ground, at least equal to the area of the vents, or the vents will not function effectively.

Vents will not function in underground buildings unless provision is made for air to enter the burning compartment near floor level. Fresh air falling through the layer of hot smoky gases will itself become heated and smoky.

Adequate venting is of special importance in industrial and storage occupancies where the presence of flammable liquids, combustible stocks or dusts, or hazardous processes may result in the rapid spread of fire. As previously mentioned, vents are also used over theater stages and auditoriums, and at the top of enclosures for vertical shafts.

Effect of Wind on Roof Vents

Wind may greatly modify the rate of flow of hot gases through a vent, since the pressure due to the layer of hot gases beneath the ceiling (about 0.5 psi for a 10-ft thick layer) may be less than the pressures caused by the wind blowing across the roof which, under unfavorable conditions, may be of the order of several lbs per sq ft. The configuration of the roof is not the only factor which influences the pressure within a building, and a low-level inlet will modify any effect produced by the roof. Wind blowing across a roof will usually result in a suction effect assisting the flow of hot gases through vents. However, with roofs having steep pitches (greater than about 40°), the pressure on the windward slope will tend to oppose the flow of hot gases through the vent, although there will still be a suction effect on the leeward slope. If the opposing pressure due to the wind is greater than the pressure due to the column of hot gases, cold air will flow into the building. Cold air entering in this way could pass through the layer of hot gases in the form of a descending cold plume entraining hot gases as it falls, and the building would soon be charged with smoke at floor level. In large buildings having sawtooth roofs, vents should not be placed in the outward facing steep roof slope because of unfavorable pressure conditions caused by winds. Where this cannot be done, ventilators may be used which are so designed that the wind will always produce a suction effect. Such ventilators should be sufficiently strong to withstand the effects of the fire for as long as the roof withstands fire.

There is an advantage to having openings at floor level (doors, windows, etc.) under the control of the firemen, since they can ensure that in general only those openings on the windward side are open. Care must be taken when opening low level inlets since high air velocities may aggravate mixing of smoke and clear air.

C. Theory of Smoke and Heat Venting for Single Story Buildings

The material in the NFPA Smoke and Heat Venting Standard pertaining to determining the size of vents necessary for a specific fire load situation is the result of research done following the 1953 General Motors fire in Livonia,

Michigan. Since that time, additional research conducted in the United Kingdom has resulted in some formulae which have application to the determination of the size of vents. The following is a summary of findings from that research, based upon experimental and theoretical data, completed to date.[1, 2, 3]

Since the hot combustion products from a fire are less dense than the surrounding air, they rise; in doing so, they entrain cold air which becomes heated and contaminated. Generally, the resulting mass of hot gases is many times the original mass of gases produced by the burning fuel. When the hot gases reach the ceiling they spread out and form a layer which floats above the cold air and mixes only very slowly with it. Once the flames reach the bottom of the layer of hot gas, the mass of gas entering the layer (M_A) in pounds per second can be estimated as

$$M_A = \frac{ph^{\frac{3}{2}}}{40}$$

where p is the perimeter of the fire area in feet, and h is the distance from the floor to the base of the layer in feet.

In the absence of vents, the layer of hot gases becomes progressively deeper until the building is completely full of hot smoky gases; it may take only a few minutes for this to happen. If vents are open, the pressure difference due to the "stack" of hot gases beneath the ceiling will cause the gases to flow out at a rate given by

$$M_v = \frac{0.85A(d\theta)^{\frac{1}{2}}}{\theta + 500}$$

where M_v is mass rate of flow in pounds per second, A is the vent area in square feet, d is the layer depth in feet, and θ is the difference in temperature between the hot gases and the outside air in degrees F.

The variation of M_v with temperature is shown in Figure 2-5E. It will be seen that the efficiency of vents does not vary much with temperature as long as the hot gases are above approximately 250°F, but if they cool to below this temperature the vent efficiency falls off sharply.

The equilibrium depth of the layer for a steadily burning fire may be obtained by equating the flow of hot gases into the layer to the flow through the vents. This gives a useful expression for the vent area

$$A = 0.14ph^{\frac{3}{2}}/d^{\frac{1}{2}}$$

where A is the vent area in square feet, p is the perimeter of the fire area in feet, h is the distance from the floor to the base of the layer in feet, and d is the depth of the layer in feet.

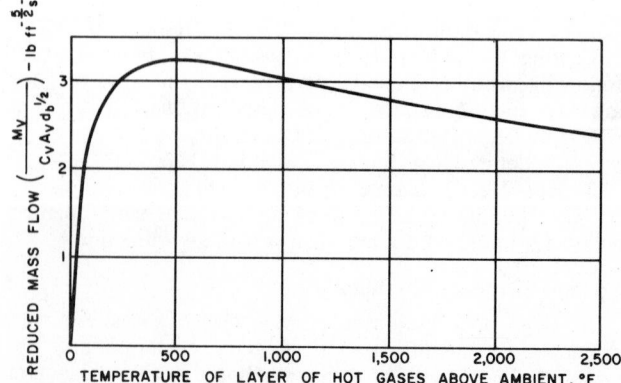

Fig. 2-5E. *Effect of temperature on mass flow through a vent.*

Calculating Vent Areas

Table 2-5A can be used to estimate the performance of any venting system. Alternately, when the initial size of the fire can realistically be identified with the size of the stack in an area where materials are stacked, the size of fire can be used as a basis for design. These data are appropriate to sawtooth roofs and ceilings which are effectively subdivided by draft curtains.

Table 2-5A. Venting Factors for Determining Size of Vents

Height From Floor to Center Line of Vent, Ft	Venting Factors (ft) for Heights of Clear Layer							
	10 ft	15 ft	20 ft	25 ft	30 ft	35 ft	40 ft	45 ft
15	2.0	—	—	—	—	—	—	—
20	1.4	3.6	—	—	—	—	—	—
25	1.2	2.6	5.6	—	—	—	—	—
30	1.0	2.1	4.0	7.9	—	—	—	—
35	0.89	1.8	3.2	5.6	10	—	—	—
40	0.81	1.6	2.8	4.5	7.3	13	—	—
45	0.75	1.5	2.5	3.9	6.0	9.2	16	—
50	0.70	1.4	2.3	3.5	5.1	7.5	11	19

The venting factors, as given in Table 2-5A, are defined as

$$\frac{\text{Area of vent (ft}^2)}{\text{Perimeter of fire (ft)}}$$

(i.e., the vent area required is the product of the fire perimeter (ft) and the venting factor).

It should be noted that:

1. The vent area is approximately proportional to the perimeter of the fire area because the entrained air forms the bulk of the vented gas.

2. The vent area is not very sensitive to the rate of weight loss of the fire which is small compared with the weight of the entrained air.

3. Draft curtains increase vent effectiveness because a deep layer is formed quicker (and automatic vents open earlier). They confine the hot gases so that the gases do not travel long distances to vents far from the fire where the gas temperatures have fallen.

4. Several small vents rather than one vent of equal area are more effective since gas temperatures decrease rapidly as they travel away from the fire under a flat roof. Under a sawtooth roof there is less temperature decrease. The risk to other buildings or other parts of the same building from flying embers and radiation from flames emerging through the roof is less for several small vents, and external winds are less likely to affect the flow from several small vents.

It should be remembered that smoke is not necessarily at very high temperatures: it requires a fairly free-burning fire to produce high smoke temperatures. This fact is important when considering venting for life safety, since smoke temperatures may not be adequate to produce a "stack" effect that would result in useful venting. Smoke will also travel under draft curtains and similar obstructions until adequate draft has been created through a vent to carry the smoke with it.

D.   Smoke Movement in Tall Buildings

Smoke movement can behave very differently in tall buildings than it does in short buildings. In the shorter buildings, the influences of the fire itself (such as heat, convective movement, and fire pressures) are the major factors which cause smoke movement. Smoke removal and venting practices reflect this behavior. In tall buildings, these same factors are modified by the stack effect, which is the vertical natural air movement through the building caused by the differences in temperatures and densities between the inside and outside air. This stack effect can become an important factor in smoke movement and in building design features to combat that movement.

The predominant factors that cause smoke movement in tall buildings are: (1) the expansion of gases due to the temperature (discussed in Section A of this Chapter), (2) the stack effect, (3) the influence of external wind forces, and (4) the forced air movement within the building. The following text describes the theoretical natural air movement which is affected by the first three factors. Forced air movement caused by the building's air handling equipment is presented elsewhere in this HANDBOOK. However, at this point it should be noted that air movement is considerably influenced by the mechanical systems of the building. Many design solutions to the problem of tenability utilize emergency operation of the mechanical systems.

Stack Effect

The stack effect accounts for most of the natural air movement in buildings under normal conditions. During a fire the stack effect is often responsible for the wide distribution of smoke and toxic gases in high-rise buildings. Reports of fire incidents have confirmed that smoke can flow through stairwells and elevator shafts at significant rates, even though the doors of the shafts remain closed.[4]

The stack effect is characterized by a strong draft from the ground floor to the roof of tall buildings. The magnitude of this effect is a function of the building height, the air tightness of exterior walls, air leakage between floors of the building, and the temperature difference between the inside and the outside.

To illustrate the principle of stack effect, consider the schematic of a box having a single opening near the bottom and another near the top, as shown in part a of Figure 2-5F. The theoretical natural draft between the two openings is caused by the difference in weight of the column of air within the box and that of a corresponding column of air of equal dimensions outside the box. The magnitude of the

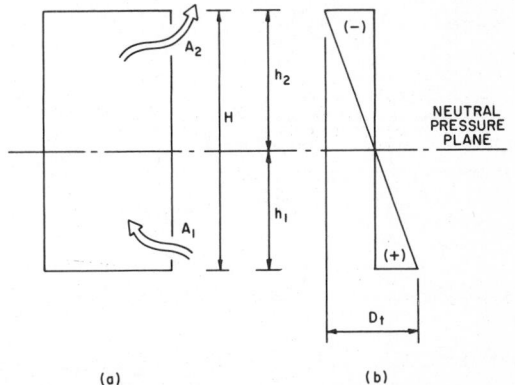

Fig. 2-5F.   (a) Air movements caused by pressure, and (b) location of neutral pressure plane in a structure without horizontal barriers and with the two openings shown.

theoretical natural draft may be computed using the following formula:

$$D_t = 2.96 H B_o \rho \left(\frac{1}{T_o} - \frac{1}{T_i} \right)$$

where

D_t = theoretical draft in inches of water

H = vertical distance between the inlet and the outlet in feet

B_o = barometric pressure in inches of mercury

T_o = temperature of outside air in degrees Fahrenheit absolute

T_i = temperature of inside air in degrees Fahrenheit absolute

ρ = density of air at 0°F and 1 atmosphere pressure in pounds per cubic foot

Assuming values of B_o = 29.9 in. and ρ = 0.0862 pcf, this expression reduces to

$$D_t = 7.63 H \left(\frac{1}{T_o} - \frac{1}{T_i} \right).$$

Vertical air movement in a building is caused by this natural draft, or stack effect, as it is commonly termed. It can be seen that the magnitude of the stack effect is dependent upon both the difference between inside and outside temperatures and the vertical distance between openings. If the inside and outside temperatures are equal, no natural air movement takes place. When $T_o < T_i$ the air moves vertically upward with the lower opening acting as the inlet, and the upper opening becoming the outlet. A reverse stack effect occurs when $T_o > T_i$. Under this condition the upper opening is the inlet, and the lower opening becomes the outlet.

Part B of Figure 2-5F illustrates the pressures that cause these movements. If it is assumed in this Figure that $T_o < T_i$, the exterior pressure will be greater than the interior pressure at the lower opening. This is a positive pressure which forces outside air into the building at that location. The outside pressure at the upper opening is less than the inside pressure. This creates a negative pressure which, at that location, forces the inside air to the outside. The pressure distribution between these two locations is assumed to be linear.

If an opening were present in the exterior wall in a region of positive pressure, air would flow into the building. An opening in a region of negative pressure would cause air to flow out of the building. The neutral pressure plane indicates the location where inside and outside pressures are equal. If there were an opening at this level, air would move neither inward nor outward. The location of the neutral pressure plane in a structure without horizontal barriers and with the two openings shown in Figure 2-5F can be determined from from the following relationship:

$$\frac{h_1}{h_2} = \frac{A_2{}^2 T_o}{A_1{}^2 T_i}$$

where

h_1 and h_2 represent the distances from the neutral pressure plane to the lower and upper openings respectively

A_1 and A_2 represent the cross-sectional areas of the lower and upper openings respectively

T_i and T_o represent the absolute temperatures of the air inside and outside the building respectively

The magnitude of the pressures created by the stack effect described by the $D_t = 7.63 H \left(\frac{1}{T_o} - \frac{1}{T_i} \right)$ equation is shown graphically in Figure 2-5G. These pressures can cause significant air flows, as shown in Figure 2-5H.

An analysis of Figure 2-5G illustrates the significant differences between tall and short buildings with regard to air movement. For example, assume that a fire develops a pressure of 0.1 in. of water in a compartment. Assume further that the outside temperature is 50°F lower than the inside temperature, and that the fire occurs at the same level as the lower opening. The curve $T_i \pm 50°F$ indicates that if the upper outlet were approximately 60 ft above the fire, the inlet stack pressure would balance the pressure caused by the fire. A building taller than 60 ft would create a greater stack pressure, and theoretically the outside air would move into the building. Rather than venting smoke and heat, this would accelerate burning by driving them into the building.

Influence of Floors and Partitions

The theoretical draft described by Figure 2-5F and the $D_t = 7.63 H \left(\frac{1}{T_o} - \frac{1}{T_i} \right)$ equation is modified in real buildings by the presence of floors and partitions. These barriers impede free air movement, although a significant flow can take place through openings in the assemblies.

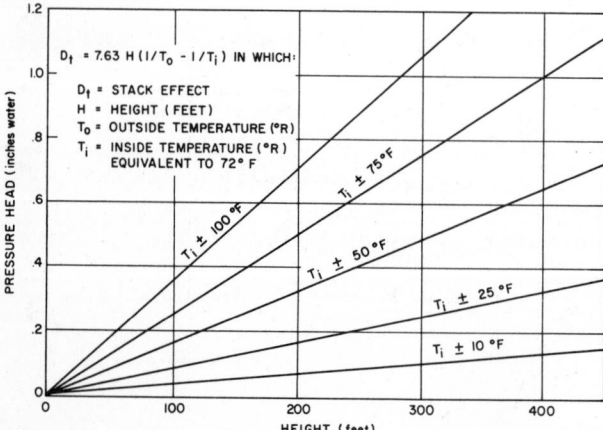

Fig. 2-5G. Stack effect due to height and temperature difference.

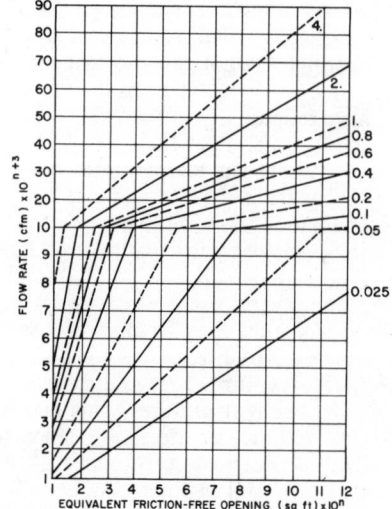

Fig. 2-5H. Air flow required to develop shown pressure in inches of water.

The magnitude and location of the leakage areas in a building naturally varies with its function and type of construction. The National Research Council of Canada conducted studies[5, 6] of air tightness for major separations on four buildings ranging from 9 to 44 stories in height. The measurements were used for computer modeling of the air movement for a 20-story simulated building having a floor plan dimension of 120 by 120 ft, and a floor to floor height of 12 ft.[7] Based on the measurements of the four buildings, the equivalent leakage areas per floor for the computer simulated building were:

Exterior walls	$A_w = 2.5$ sq ft
Floors	$A_f = 3.75$ sq ft
Shafts	$A_s = 5.0$ sq ft
Vertical air ducts	$A_d = 5.0$ sq ft

These leakage areas are sufficient to allow a substantial air movement throughout the building. Most of the air will flow into the vertical shafts, such as stairwells and elevator shafts. Some air will flow vertically from floor to floor through the minor openings in the floor-ceiling assembly. This floor to floor movement is always caused by a pressure differential between the adjacent floors.

Part *a* of Figure 2-5I illustrates the pressure difference characteristics of a building in which stack action causes air movement. The slopes of the pressure lines represent pressure differences between any two regions at the same height. Air flow from one region to another will always be in the direction of the region whose pressure curve is more to the left. This is illustrated by the air flow directions represented by the arrows in Part *b* of Figure 2-5I.

Wind Effects

Wind action is another important feature in the behavior of smoke movement. Again, tall buildings and short buildings behave somewhat differently in this regard. Figure 2-5J illustrates the air pressure distribution along the four sides and the roof of a building. The plan view of the pressures shows that the windward wall is subjected to an inward pressure, while the leeward wall and the two side walls have an outward pressure (suction). The flat roof has an upward pressure, with the maximum amount occurring at the windward edge.

These pressures are caused by the movement of a mass of air around and over the structure. A short, wide building will cause the major volume of air to move over the roof, with correspondingly less air movement around the sides. A narrow, tall building, on the other hand, will cause

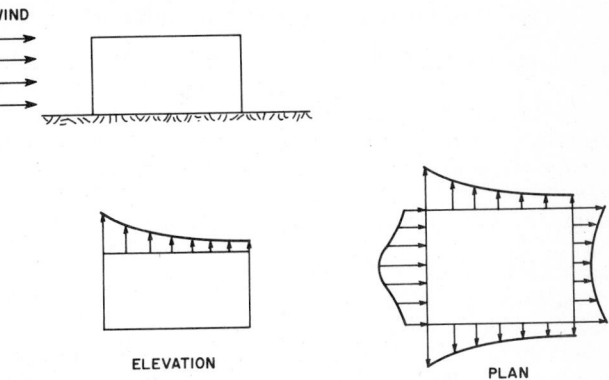

Fig. 2-5J. The air pressure distribution along the four sides and the roof of a building.

the major volume of air to follow its path of least resistance around the building, with less movement over the top. The velocities of these movements are the primary cause of the amount and directions of the pressures on the building.

The effect of wind pressures and suctions modify the natural air movement within a building. For example, the negative pressure on the roof of a tall building has an aspirating effect on a vertical shaft opened at the roof level. This might cause the observed draft to exceed the theoretical draft shown in Figure 2-5G.

Horizontal pressures and suctions cause the neutral pressure planes in exterior walls to move. Positive wind pressure would tend to raise the neutral pressure plane, while negative pressures will lower it. Figure 2-5K illustrates the influence of wind action on air movement in a building.

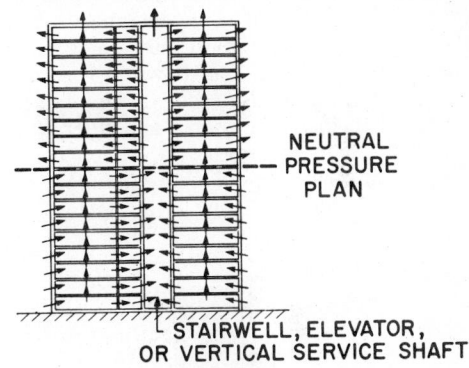

NEGLIGIBLE WIND

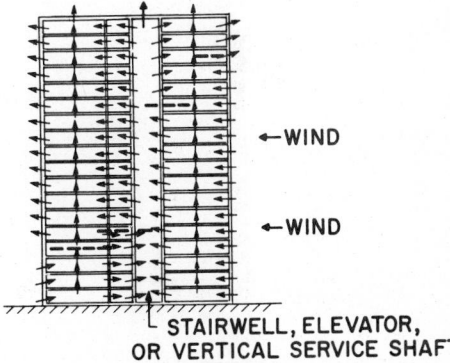

SIGNIFICANT WIND

Fig. 2-5K. Influence of wind action on air movement in a building. Note in the presence of significant wind how the neutral pressure plane changes location throughout the building.

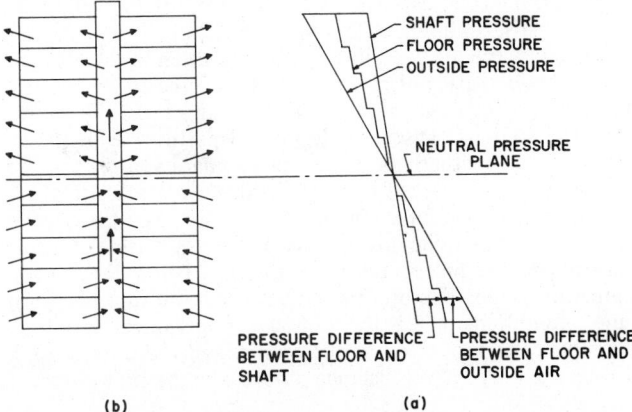

Fig. 2-5I. The pressure difference characteristics of a building in which stack action causes air movement.

E.   Venting Practices in Tall Buildings

Smoke movement in tall buildings and measures to control or remove it are subjects of continuing research. While much new information should be forthcoming, the existing knowledge of theory and behavior of air movement offers a basis for predicting smoke movement during a fire. The venting practices of the fire service, and the design features such as smoke towers and the venting of elevator shafts and stairwells, can be analyzed by this theory to predict their potential success.

As described in Part D of this Chapter, the stack effect has a significant influence in the smoke movement of high-rise buildings. The temperature of the smoke and fire gases decreases rapidly as they move away from the fire. Consequently, the behavior of normal air movements in large buildings is a reasonably good indicator of smoke movements. The influence of the heat and pressures of the fire are significant in the vicinity of the fire itself, and are important because of the expansion of air. However, as the height of the building increases and the difference between the inside temperature and the outside temperature widens, the stack effect plays a more pronounced role in smoke movement.

Influence of Ventilation Openings

The location of neutral pressure plane is of great significance when considering smoke movement and ventilation of high-rise building fires. Air will enter the building from areas below the neutral pressure plane, and will be forced out of the building in areas above the neutral pressure plane. The magnitude of these forces increases in proportion to the distance from the neutral pressure plane.

If it is assumed that a fire occurs on a low floor of a high-rise building and that the outside temperature is lower than the inside temperature, the natural smoke movement would be expected to be similar to that shown in Figure 2-5L. In Figure 2-5L smoke would also occur on floors immediately above the fire due to fire pressures and floor leakage, although this movement is not shown. It can be seen that from smoke movement considerations the most hazardous areas are the top floors. During steady state conditions,

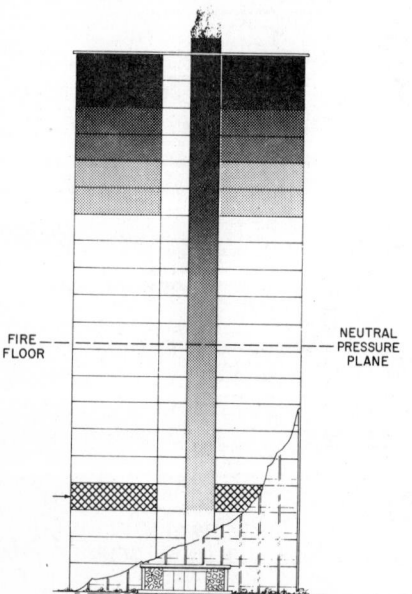

Fig. 2-5L.   Natural smoke movement, assuming that fire occurs on a low floor of a high rise building and that outside temperature is lower than inside temperature.

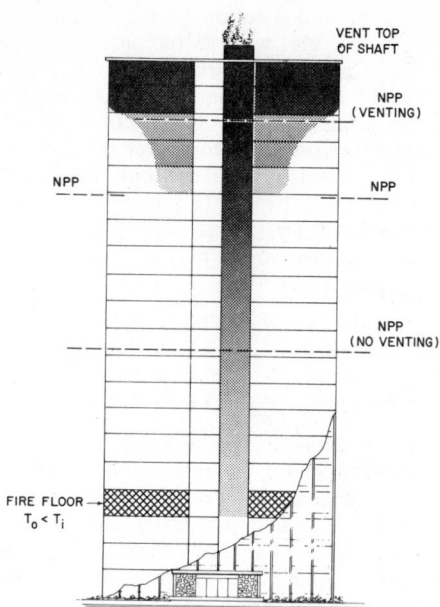

Fig. 2-5M.   Theoretical smoke conditions for situation assumed for Fig. 2-5L, with high level opening established in shaft so that natural pressure plane associated with shaft will be raised. High level venting should improve smoke conditions throughout building.

smoke may become untenable on these floors; yet, the atmosphere may remain tenable on floors near the neutral pressure plane.

If, during the fire conditions described by Figure 2-5L, a high level opening is established in the shaft, the neutral pressure plane associated with the shaft will be raised. The high level venting should improve smoke conditions throughout the building because inlet flows will be increased, and several openings which were outlets become inlets. The theoretical smoke conditions for this situation are illustrated in Figure 2-5M. Again, leakage smoke between floors is not shown.

If, on the other hand, the fire were vented at the fire floor or in the lower portion of the shaft, the neutral pressure plane will be lowered. Smoke conditions would be worsened for a greater number of occupants, as shown in Figure 2-5N. Consequently, the fire service must weigh the potential heat and smoke relief achieved by this practice with the potential additional life safety hazard.

It is difficult to establish the correct ventilation practices for high-rise buildings. Air movement can be significantly affected by the air handling equipment. Even in the absence of this effect, natural air movement is affected by the fire conditions, stack effect, wind action, and internal air movement conditions caused by floors and partitions. However, there are two situations in particular where venting the fire floor must be analyzed carefully with regard to its final results. One occurs during winter conditions when the outside temperature is quite low compared to the inside temperature, and the fire occurs some distance below the neutral pressure plane. The other situation occurs during hot summer conditions when the outside temperatures are high compared to the inside temperatures, and the fire occurs a comparatively great distance above the neutral pressure plane.

In both of these situations the stack effect may cause pressure great enough to overcome the fire pressure. Outside air

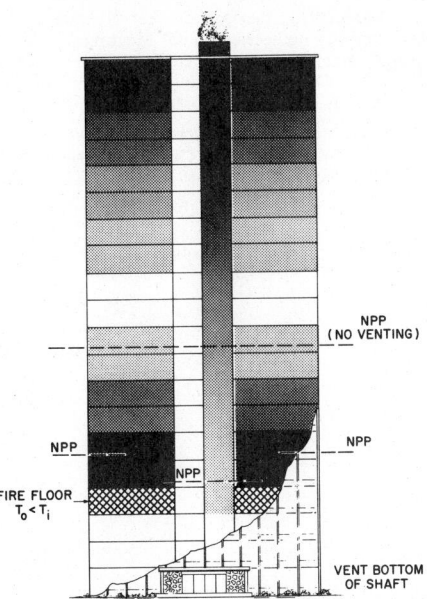

Fig. 2-5N. Theoretical smoke conditions for situation assumed for Fig. 2-5L, with fire vented at fire floor or in lower portion of shaft, thus lowering the neutral pressure plane.

may be forced into the fire zone, rather than allowing the heat and smoke to be released. This accelerates the fire and worsens the smoke conditions. Figure 2-5G gives some guidance as to the pressures to be expected under specific temperature and height conditions.

Smoke Shaft

A smoke shaft is an unobstructed, vertical shaft extending the full height of the building. The shaft has openings to the atmosphere at the top, and openings in the walls at each floor level. The floor level openings are equipped with dampers which open in the event of a fire only on the fire floor.

The smoke shaft is intended to operate as a chimney by collecting smoke from a fire floor and exhausting it to the outside of the building. It operates on the principle of gravity air movement caused by the stack effect. The opening at the top results in the pressure in the shaft being equal to the atmospheric pressure at that point. The neutral pressure plane is therefore at or near the top of the shaft, resulting in air pressures within the building higher than pressures within the shaft at all elevations. This causes air to flow from within the building to the smoke shaft at any level.

The theory of smoke shaft operation suggests that in the event of a fire the damper to the fire floor opens, and air flows from the floor into the shaft. The pressure on the fire floor is therefore reduced. If the pressure on the fire floor were reduced below that of the other vertical shafts at the same level and the floor above, air would flow from these regions to the fire floor. Smoke would therefore not be transferred to other parts of the building.

The sizing of openings has an effect on the pressure developed within the smoke shaft. In order to reduce a build-up of pressure within the shaft, the fire floor vents are calculated to be of different sizes. Tamura, in his computer simulation of smoke shafts, states that stories at or near ground level establish minimum vent size requirements.[8] Neglecting friction pressure loss in the shaft, the minimum vent sizes were found to be independent of building height

and dependent on the leakage areas of the major separations.

Smoke shafts are not always effective in their operation. Since they are dependent on stack action, which is related to the difference between inside and outside temperatures, during those periods when the outside temperature is equal to or greater than the inside temperature, natural upward movement will not occur. In addition, a smoke shaft is not effective when there are large openings on the fire floor to the outside. This may occur when large window areas on the fire floor are broken. The pressure on the fire floor then approaches that of the outside, and the smoke shaft loses its effectiveness.

Tests of smoke shafts in nonfire situations also seem to indicate that they are not universally effective.[9] Variations in expected stack effect drafts were found which tend to negate the desired smoke venting effect of the smoke shaft. Consequently, mechanical exhaust equipment should be considered in conjunction with the natural air movement caused by the draft of the smoke tower.

Existing shafts, such as stairwells and elevator hoistways, are sometimes vented at the top. In some cases these are vented with the intent of maintaining shaft tenability for use by occupants or firefighters. In high-rise buildings this practice is very questionable when the smoke movement principles caused by stack action are considered. Pressurization techniques are far more effective in maintaining smoke-free areas of this type.

Existing stairwells and elevator hoistways are sometimes vented with the objective of incorporating them as smoke shafts under emergency conditions. Additional research into the theory and practice of this multi-use practice is necessary. A careful engineering analysis must be made in these cases in order to account for the large leakage areas of the shaft at each story and the relative restrictions of the vent areas.

SI Units

The following conversion factors are given as a convenience in converting to SI units the English units used in this chapter.

1 sq ft	= 0.0929 m²
1 pcf	= 16.018 kg/m³
1 in.	= 25.4 mm
1 ft	= 0.305 m
1 lb (mass)	= 0.454 kg
1 psi	= 6.895 kPa

$\frac{5}{9}(°F - 32) = °C$

Bibliography

References Cited

[1] Thomas, P. H., et al., "Investigating into the Flow of Hot Gases in Roof Venting," Fire Research Technical Paper No. 7, Ministry of Technology, Industrial and Fire Offices Committee, Joint Fire Research Organization, Her Majesty's Stationery Office, London, 1963.

[2] Thomas, P. H. and Hinkley, P. L., "Design of Roof Venting Systems for Single-Story Buildings," Fire Research Technical Paper No. 10, Ministry of Technology, Industrial and Fire Offices Committee, Joint Fire Research Organization, Her Majesty's Stationery Office, London, 1964.

[3] Langdon-Thomas, G. J. and Hinkley, P. L., "Fire Venting—Small Story Industrial Buildings," Fire Notes No. 5, Ministry of Technology, Industrial and Fire Offices Committee, Joint Fire Research Organization, Her Majesty's Stationery Office, London, 1965.

[4] National Research Council of Canada, Association Committee on the National Building Code, "Explanatory Paper on Control of Smoke Movement in High Buildings," NRC 11413, 1970, Ottawa.

[5] Tamura, G. T. and Wilson, A. G., "Pressure Differences for a Nine Story Building as a Result of Chimney Effect and Ventilation System Operations," American Society of Heating, Refrigeration and Air Conditioning Engineers—Transactions, Vol. 72, Part I, 1966.

[6] Tamura, G. T. and Wilson, A. G., "Pressure Differences Caused by Chimney Effect in Three Story High Buildings," American Society of Heating, Refrigeration and Air Conditioning Engineers—Transactions, Vol. 73, Part II, 1967.

[7] Tamura, G. T., "Computer Analysis of Smoke Movement in Tall Buildings," American Society of Heating, Refrigeration and Air Conditioning Engineers, Annual Meeting, 1969.

[8] Tamura, G. T., "Analysis of Smoke Shaft for Control of Smoke Movement in Buildings," American Society of Heating, Refrigeration and Air Conditioning Engineers, Annual Meeting, 1970.

[9] Fitzgerald, A. F., "City of Chicago Approach to High Rise Fire Protection," Proceedings of the High Rise Fire/Smoke Protection Committee, Canadian Fire Safety Association, Ontario, 1972.

NFPA Codes, Standards, and Recommended Practices (see the latest NFPA Publications and Visual Aids Catalog for availability of current editions of the following documents)

NFPA No. 87, Standard for the Construction of Piers and Wharves.

NFPA No. 204, Guide for Smoke and Heat Venting.

SECTION 3

FIRE HAZARDS OF MATERIALS

Section 3

Chapter 1

WOOD AND WOOD-BASED PRODUCTS

Wood is one of the most commonly used materials in construction. It is used for framing, sheathing, siding, roofing, flooring, and for interior finish. Wood-based products are used for insulation, ceiling tiles, plywood, particle board, chipboard, paper, cardboard, and furniture. Thus it is frequently involved when fire occurs and an understanding of the reaction of this versatile material under fire exposure is important.

This chapter provides general information on the nature of wood and its ignition and burning characteristics. Those interested in a more detailed treatment of the subject should consult the list of references at the end of the chapter. This chapter is a basic introduction to the subject.

Other cellulosic and fibrous materials such as cotton, rayon, silk, and wool are included in this Section in Chapter 2, Fibers and Textiles.

A. The Nature of Wood and Wood-based Products

Wood and wood-based products are combustible—they will char, smolder, ignite, and burn when the thermal environment is conducive to such reactions. Rarely do they self-ignite except in certain forms, and under certain conditions of moisture content and storage. Normally a spark, open flame, contact with hot surfaces, or exposure to thermal radiation is required for ignition. Even then, ignition will be a function of the intensity of the ignition source and the time of exposure as well as of other factors considered in Part C of this chapter.

Fire retardant chemicals can be, and frequently are, added or applied to wood and wood-based products. Properly formulated and used, fire retardants reduce the flammability of wood and wood-based products. Depending on the formulation used, flame and glow also can be reduced once the outside source of heat is removed. A more detailed discussion of the role of fire retardants is found in Section 5, Chapter 10.

Wood and wood-based products also can be used in combination with other materials to provide a greater degree of fire protection. An insulated, plywood-faced, wood stud wall, for instance, will provide a greater degree of fire endurance than one without insulation. The inherent and relatively slow burning or char rate of heavier wood members also provides a degree of protection because of the insulating effect of the char buildup.

B. Chemical Composition of Wood

Wood consists primarily of carbon, hydrogen, and oxygen, with lesser percentages of nitrogen and other elements (see Table 3-1A). For example, while relatively dry wood is a complex of many substances, cellulose $[(C_6H_{10}O_5)_x]$, is its main component by weight. Other chemical components of dry wood are ligno-cellulose; lignin; sometimes sugars, resins, gums, and esters of alcohol; mineral matter (which forms ash when wood is burned); and, most important, from the combustion standpoint, water or moisture (see Part C of this Chapter). The cells

Table 3-1A. Chemical Composition of Dry Woods*

| Species | Constituents, Percent by Weight | | | | |
	Carbon	Hydrogen	Oxygen	Nitrogen	Ash
Oak	50.16	6.02	43.26	.09	0.37
Ash	49.18	6.27	43.19	.07	0.57
Elm	48.99	6.20	44.25	.06	0.50
Beech	49.06	6.11	44.17	.09	0.57
Birch	48.88	6.06	44.67	.10	0.29
Pine	50.31	6.20	43.08	.04	0.37
Poplar	49.37	6.21	41.60	.96	1.86
Calif. redwood	53.50	5.90	40.30	.10	0.20
Western hemlock	50.40	5.80	41.40	.10	2.20
Douglas fir	52.30	6.30	40.50	.10	0.80

* From Kent's Mechanical Engineers' Handbook.[1]

of live wood retain available moisture, but when dead the wood tends to dry out and air replaces much or all of the water in the cellular structure.

Paper and other wood based products and fibrous products such as bagasse, jute, hemp and sisal basically are cellulosic. These may be impregnated, pressure treated or coated with a variety of chemicals to enhance certain qualities such as fire retardance.

C. Variables Influencing Ignition and Burning Characteristics of Wood and Wood Products

Physical Form

The influence of physical form is illustrated simply by the fact that wood kindling will flame and burn from relatively small heat sources while heavier wood logs or timbers show a considerable resistance to ignition. Steel wool and shredded aluminum foil will ignite and burn under some fire exposure conditions although their chemical compositions are the same as in their more massive forms when they have considerably more resistance to ignition. The explanation of this is that as the size of the particle diminishes, the ratio of surface area to volume (mass) increases. Thus, there is both greater exposure of fuel to air and less mass to conduct heat away from the surface of the particle; consequently heat does not readily dissipate within the material. It follows that small, thin forms of combustible solids will continue burning more readily than larger objects of the same material.

Heat Conductivity

The heat conductivity (K factor—the inverse property of insulating value) of a particular material also plays a major role in its behavior under fire conditions. Heat conductivity is a measure of the rate at which absorbed heat will flow through the mass material. For instance, wood is a poor heat conductor, and thus has a high insulating value (steel and aluminum are about 350 and 1,000 times as conductive respectively). This quality of wood finds common illustration in the fact that a wood match burning at one end can be held at the other between the fingers, while a steel needle of similar form, heated at one end, cannot be held at the other with equal comfort.

In fire protection experience, an illustration is that the structural framing of an unsprinklered building of heavy timber construction will withstand for a considerably longer time a fire exposure than will unprotected framing in a light metal-framed building. This can be explained by the insulating effect of the char that develops as wood burns. Investigations in the United States, Great Britain, Japan and elsewhere indicate a char rate of approximately 1.5 inches per hour with an accelerated rate during the first 5-10 minutes of exposure.[2]

Moisture Content

It has been shown in ignition and burning tests in the laboratory that the behavior of combustible solids of the same size, shape, and chemical composition will vary markedly with the moisture content. In some work reported by the British Department of Scientific and Industrial Research (now Ministry of Technology)[3] the influence of the moisture content of oak and western red cedar on the time necessary for these woods to ignite was studied; the results are shown by Figure 3-1A. Radiation intensity in this figure is expressed in terms of the number of calories falling on one square centimeter of the exposed wood in one second, using a test apparatus developed by the DSIR.

Not only susceptibility to ignition, but also rate of burning is influenced by the moisture content of the materials. Nowhere is this better illustrated than in forest fire behavior. Following a prolonged dry spell accompanied by high temperatures, forest vegetation dries and dies, and under such conditions flame spread through a forest can sometimes outrace man's ability to stop it. Under more favorable conditions, the water content of the forest combustibles consumes much of the heat to which the combustibles are exposed as the heat is required to evaporate the water from the fuel. Since water has a high specific heat, the heat consumed to drive off the moisture is quite considerable. In addition, the large quantities of water vapor that are driven off dilute the oxygen in the air in close proximity to the combustibles, and this interferes both with the development of combustible vapors from ordinary carbonaceous materials and with the ignition or continued burning of those combustible vapors.

It is common practice today to take the measurements of the forest fire danger by analysis of the fuel moisture content and allied considerations (atmospheric humidity, wind, condition of vegetation, season of the year). The U.S. Forest Service has developed instruments to aid in the

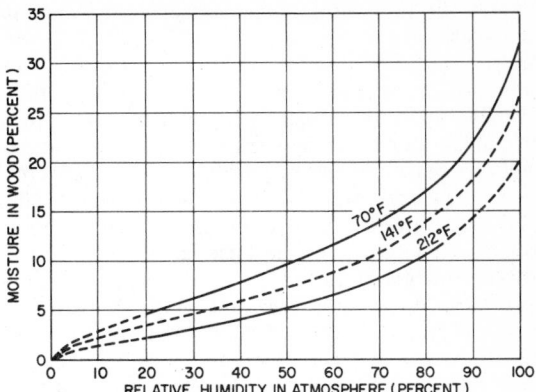

Fig. 3-1B. Equilibrium moisture content of wood.

evaluation of humidity and fuel moisture content of forest duff.

The moisture content of carbonaceous materials is influenced by atmospheric humidity, since most carbonaceous materials absorb moisture. The capacity of these materials to vary in moisture content depends on their character. Some finely divided materials absorb or lose moisture very rapidly and their combustibility can vary accordingly from low to high in a few hours. Examples are shredded newsprint, tissues, and loose forest surface litter. Other dense, compact, ordinary combustibles, e.g., heavy oak timbers and bond paper, change moisture content more slowly.

As a general rule, where the moisture content of wood and similar fuels is above 15 percent ignition is rather difficult even when it is exposed to a relatively high heat source for a prolonged period of time (length depending on the geometry of the fuel and the temperature of the flame applied). Wood held in a room controlled to a temperature of 75°F and a relative humidity of 64 percent will hold about 12 percent moisture content when equilibrium conditions are reached. Figure 3-1B illustrates conditions under which equilibrium will be established at three different temperatures.[4]

In heated buildings in cold climates where indoor relative humidities run below this amount, wood is more susceptible to ignition than in summer under high humidity conditions. Once a fire is well under way, the significance of the moisture factor reduces since the heat radiation and therefore the rate of pyrolysis increases. Under such conditions wood will burn with a moisture content of 50 percent or more.

The effect of humidity on the moisture content of wood and on the way buildings burn can be illustrated by research on the effectiveness of incendiaries during World War II.[5] With considerable care, a group of buildings, representative of German and Japanese dwellings, was erected in Utah by the U.S. National Defense Research Committee. At the same time, the British Building Research Station at Watford, England, also built simulated Japanese dwellings to test the effect of incendiaries. The two programs maintained regular exchange of data but were puzzled by the lack of correlation of the results. After some debate, attention was turned to the weather factors. There was substantial agreement that the tests on the British structures were conducted in humidity conditions higher than actually existed in the enemy countries, but that the humidity conditions in Utah were lower. Thus it was clearly indicated that weather factors (particularly humidity) affected the physical vulnerability of cities to fire destruction and this highlighted the necessity for studying the influence of weather in order to predict

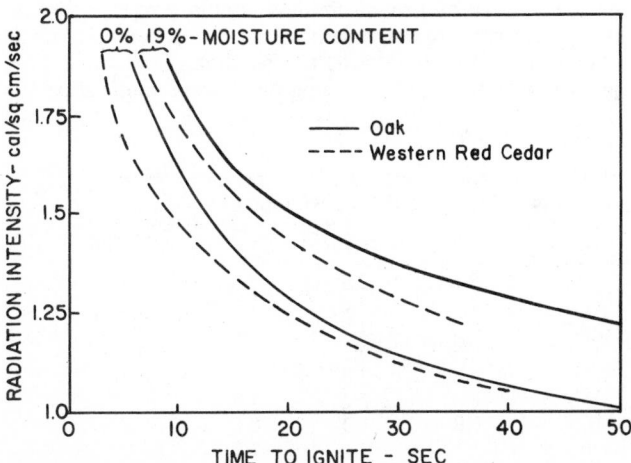

Fig. 3-1A. Effect of moisture content on the ignition of wood.

accurately the results that might be achieved by the use of incendiary bombs.

Another indication of the effect of the moisture content of combustibles as they affect structural fire susceptibility is the conflagration experience in the United States. In many such conflagrations, it has been noted that prolonged dry weather preceded the outbreak of fire and this had a marked effect on the susceptibility of the shingles, as well as all other combustibles present, to ignition from flying brands and thermal radiation. The tragic Peshtigo (Wisconsin) forest fire of 1871 which occurred the same weekend as the great Chicago fire of the same year and which destroyed seventeen towns and claimed 1,152 lives followed a prolonged period of extremely dry weather.

There is a time lag between changes in the fuel moisture content of ordinary combustibles and changes in atmospheric humidity. Most solid combustibles are not immediately absorptive of air-borne water vapor; conversely, the moisture content of most solids will be retained for a longer period of time than air retains its moisture in suspension. Thus the humidity in the ambient air is not always a reliable index of the moisture content of ordinary combustibles.

Ignition of Wood and Wood Products

The thermal degradation of wood is a complex process. Four stages of decomposition of wood on exposure to heat have been described:[6]

Temperature	Reaction
392°F (-200°C)	Production of water vapor, carbon dioxide, formic and acetic acids—all concombustible gases.
392°F-536°F (200°C-280°C)	Less water vapor, some carbon monoxide—still primary endothermic reaction.
536°F-932°F (280°C-500°C)	Exothermic reaction with flammable vapors and particulates. Some secondary reaction from charcoal formed.
over 932°F (500°C)	Residue principally charcoal with notable catalytic action.

Ignition temperatures may vary, depending on the analytical method used. Some exothermic reaction can be observed with some apparatus in the first stage listed above. In the third stage ignitable gases are produced and the "flash point" is reached. When the decomposition has progressed to the point that the evolved gases no longer insulate the charcoal layer from oxygen, spontaneous ignition may result.

Specific ignition temperatures of wood are difficult to determine because of the many variables involved. Leading research groups have attempted to pinpoint the ignition temperature of wood, but the results vary greatly. The Forest Products Laboratory, Madison, Wis., in one series of tests (using untreated, air-dried wood blocks, 1¼ by 1¼ by 4 in. and of nine different species) found that the specimens could be heated to temperatures varying from 315° to 385°F for 40 min in a stream of heated air held at a constant temperature without igniting. In another series of tests by the same laboratory, using the same test procedures but higher temperatures, thirty-four untreated softwood and hardwood species ignited in 4½ to 6 min at temperatures varying from 608° to 660°F for the softwood, and from 595° to 740°F for the hardwood. It was noted that a fairly close relationship existed between the specific gravity of the wood under test and the ignition temperature. In general, low density species ignited at lower temperatures than high density species.[7] The National Bureau of Standards, Washington, D.C., tested three conifers and two hardwoods and reported ignition temperatures from 378°F to 428°F in small samples varying from shavings to match size.

In 1915, R. E. Prince reported at the 19th NFPA Annual Meeting the results of his investigation at the Forest Products Laboratory of the ignition temperatures of wood.[8] Table 3-1B[9] shows the length of time before wood specimens maintained at the specified constant temperatures evolved combustible gases in sufficient quantities to be ignited by a pilot flame located about ½ in. above the specimen. The specimens, 1¼ by 1¼ by 4 in. in size and oven-dry, were heated in a vertical quartz chamber (3 in. in diameter and 10 in. long) maintained at constant temperature by an electric furnace.

C. R. Brown in 1934 reported on ignition temperatures of some materials[10] as shown in Table 3-1C. In his investigations, specimens about 2½ in. long and weighing 3 grams were suspended in a vertical glass container 2½ in. in diameter and 4 1/16 in. high. The container was heated by an electric furnace, the temperature being increased at a predetermined rate. Air, preheated to the temperature of the furnace, was passed through the container at measured rates of flow. The results were found to be affected by the size of the sample, the rate of heating, and the rate of air flow over the specimens.

The National Bureau of Standards in 1947 reported[11] ignition temperatures of wood as shown in Table 3-1D. In these tests the specimens of wood in the form of shavings were heated in a glass test tube in the presence of a measured flow of heated air at optimum velocity. The ignition temperature was taken as the lowest temperature at which the exothermic oxidation reaction culminated in an ignition as indicated by flaming or glowing combustion.

Table 3-1B

Wood	No Ignition in 40 min °F	Exposure Before Ignition, By Pilot Flame, Minutes						
		356°F	392°F	437°F	482°F	572°F	662°F	752°F
Long leaf pine	315	14.3	11.8	8.7	6.0	2.3	1.4	0.5
Red oak	315	20.0	13.3	8.1	4.7	1.6	1.2	0.5
Tamarack	334	29.9	14.5	9.0	6.0	2.3	0.8	0.5
Western larch	315	30.8	25.0	17.0	9.5	3.5	1.5	0.5
Noble fir	369	—	—	15.8	9.3	2.3	1.2	0.3
Eastern hemlock	356	—	13.3	7.2	4.0	2.2	1.2	0.3
Redwood	315	28.5	18.5	10.4	6.0	1.9	0.8	0.3
Sitka spruce	315	40.0	19.6	8.3	5.3	2.1	1.0	0.3
Basswood	334	—	14.5	9.6	6.0	1.6	1.2	0.3

Table 3-1C		Table 3-1D	
Wood	Self-ignition Temperature Degrees F	Wood	Self-ignition Temperature Degrees F
Western red cedar	378	Short leaf pine	442
White pine	406	Long leaf pine	446
Long leaf pine	428	Douglas fir	500
White oak	410	Spruce	502
Paper birch	399	White pine	507

Most commonly, the ignition temperature of wood is quoted to be of the order of 392°F. Wood in contact with steam pipes or a similar constant temperature source over a very long period of time may undergo a chemical change resulting in the formation of charcoal which is capable of heating spontaneously. It has been suggested that 212°F is the highest temperature to which wood can be *continually* exposed without risk of ignition.[12]

It is thus obvious that ignition temperatures of wood vary widely depending on a number of such variables as:

1. The specific gravity of the sample.
2. The physical characteristics of the sample; i.e., its size, its form, and its moisture content.
3. The rate and period of heating.
4. The nature of the heat source.
5. The air (oxygen) supply.

Rate and Period of Heating

The rate and period of heating influence the susceptibility of wood and wood products to ignition. Compared to flammable liquids or gases, combustible solids are usually considered less hazardous because they do not vaporize readily nor do they emit flammable vapors at normal ambient temperatures and atmospheric pressures. Thus, ignition of solid combustibles usually requires contact between the heat source and the material for a long enough period to permit release of ignitable vapors. This contact may only have to be momentary, or it may have to be prolonged with actual ignition depending on the variables discussed earlier in this chapter. An exception is glowing combustion that may occur without vaporization of some materials; e.g., charcoal.

Ignition will occur when a material is heated above its ignition temperature. Thus, moderate heat may cause ignition if applied for a long enough period of time to raise a combustible to its ignition temperature, whereas high heats applied momentarily to a combustible may not cause ignition. For example, over a period of time, a steam pipe in contact with wood may result in ignition, whereas a gas-fired blow-torch held momentarily on a painted wood surface may blister the paint but not ignite the wood, despite the fact that the torch flame temperature is higher than the ignition temperature of the wood. Because the reaction in both cases cannot be determined in advance, it is common practice to avoid direct contact between steam pipes and adjacent combustibles and to condemn as unsafe the practice of burning paint off wood surfaces. The illustrations do, however, vividly show the influence of the rate and period of heating on the ignition of the same type of combustible in roughly the same shape and form.

The shape and form of a sample of combustible material not only influence its susceptibility to ignition as explained earlier in this chapter, but they also affect the reaction of the combustible to any given rate and period of heating, as does the moisture content of the combustible, the air space between the heat source and the material, and other variables.

Fires may be used to illustrate further these factors. It is unfortunately an all too common experience for fire departments to arrive at a fire scene after a delayed alarm and find a structure seriously involved and threatening adjacent combustible structures. If water curtains cannot be established in time, ignition of the adjacent exposed property may occur. There is a direct relationship here between such ignition and the rate and period of heat exposure. In actual fires, accurate measurements of such rates and periods of heating are, of course, not practical. Laboratory fire test work, however, does confirm what takes place (see preceding discussion on ignition temperatures of wood).

Spontaneous Heating and Ignition

Spontaneous heating and ignition of wood and wood-based products usually result only from contamination or induced artificial heating. For instance, cellulosic materials which are clean and dried will not heat spontaneously; on the other hand, those soaked with certain drying oils and stored in unventilated spaces can heat spontaneously. If this process is allowed to continue, ignition results. Similarly, a measure of artificial heating can cause certain combustibles to self-heat to their ignition temperature. Wood fiberboards, for example, not subjected to a direct, artificial heat source either during manufacture or when installed in structures, will not heat spontaneously. On the other hand, tests have shown[13] that heating such fiberboards at relatively moderate temperatures can set up an exothermic reaction leading to their ignition. In one such test, a 22-in. high stack of wood fiberboards ($\frac{1}{8}$ in. thickness) subjected to a heat source of 228°F was ignited in 96 hrs.

An adequate amount of air (oxygen) is essential if combustion is to continue. Combustion engineers have suggested a formula for the minimum volume of air required for complete combustion of solid fuels with air at 62°F:

$$V_m = 147 \left[C + 3 \left(H - \frac{O}{8} \right) \right] \text{ cu ft}$$

where

V_m = minimum volume of air in cu ft, C = part by weight of carbon in 1 lb of fuel, H = parts by weight of hydrogen in 1 lb of fuel, and O = parts by weight of oxygen in 1 lb of fuel. While this formula may have little direct application in fire protection engineering, smoldering fires which are starved of adequate air (oxygen) are frequently encountered by firemen, so that the significance of this factor must not be overlooked.

In some materials, such as compressed alfalfa, hay, and palm kernels, self heating that can lead to possible spontaneous ignition can occur because of microbiological action. In this phenomenon, the exothermic chemical reaction rates can be sufficient to result in ignition under certain conditions. Generally, this type of spontaneous ignition can be avoided by controlling the moisture content of the material prior to stacking or compressing and then by covering the stored material to prevent wetting.

Rate of Combustion

In most fires involving combustible solids, there is a time delay between ignition and rapid combustion. This statement might be questioned because of the exceptional speed of some fires, particularly many of those in dwellings which result in fatalities. In most such cases, however, investigation shows that detection was delayed or that flammable liquids, gases, or similar materials were involved in the origin. The rate of combustion is markedly influenced by the physical form of the combustible, the air supply present, the moisture content, and allied factors, but there is the fundamental need for progressive vaporization of the solid by heat exposure for complete combustion to proceed.

Much attention has been directed in recent years to the phenomenon known as "flashover." A slowly developing fire or source of radiant heat may gradually develop enough energy at wall and ceiling surfaces to start the decomposition process with a release of combustible gases. When the mixture of such gases and ambient air reaches the flammable range any source of pilot ignition may ignite the entire mass almost instantaneously. Any cellulosic material and other forms of combustible materials are susceptible to this reaction and the degree of susceptibility is not necessarily revealed by existing tests for surface burning.

Speed of Flame Propagation

Speed of flame propagation over the surface of a combustible critically affects the severity of a fire in many cases. The 1959 Los Angeles School Fire Tests[14] showed that under controlled test conditions, flames spread over combustible surfaces with such speed that observers had to flee the sudden release of heat and flame. In 1949 the British Department of Scientific and Industrial Research conducted full scale dwelling fire tests on the influence of combustible wallboards vs the use of plaster finish.[15] The record of these tests graphically illustrates the observed Time-Temperature Curves in the living rooms of the two houses. Originating in an easy chair in the living room, the fires in their initial stages were identical in both dwellings. The loading of combustible materials was roughly proportional to the loadings observed in lived-in dwellings in England. It should be noted that in the United States and Canada, earlier ignition and faster flame spread on the combustible surfaces could be expected since winter heating in these countries results in lower relative humidities and thus lower moisture content of the combustibles.

Compared with flammable vapors or gases, the speed of flame propagation across most combustible solids is slow; the presence of readily ignitable vapors with the former materials is the primary reason for this difference. Also, pyrolysis gases from combustible solids must be mixed in proper proportions with air; thus flame spread is frequently influenced by the need of these gases to find an adequate air supply to be progressively consumed.

Amount of Fuel Contributed

The amount of fuel contributed by a substance is normally measured by its heat of combustion. Table 3-1E shows some figures for the heats released by various combustible solids and also gives comparative figures for some other materials. It will be noted that the heat of combustion of most dry ordinary combustible solids is less per pound than that of the other fuels listed. This is of significance to the fire protection engineer for the evaluation of a measured quantity of combustibles to the fire exposure it creates. It is common practice in fire protection engineering to weigh, or estimate the weight of, combustibles in a fire area to determine, for instance, the needed fire resistance of structural elements or the optimum quantity of water required per square foot of floor area for sprinkler discharge. Reasoned judgments are frequently necessary in applying this principle. Libraries, for example, have a phenomenal fire loading. But, while there have been very serious fire losses in these properties, strict application of the calculated fire load to the sprinkler requirements would not be appropriate in most of these cases because of the physical arrangement of

Table 3-1E. Heat of Combustion of Various Wood and Wood-based Products and Comparative Substances

Substance	Heating Value Btu per lb
Wood sawdust (oak)	8,493†
Wood sawdust (pine)	9,676†
Wood shavings	8,248†
Wood bark (fir)	9,496†
Corrugated fiber carton	5,970†
Newspaper	7,883†
Wrapping paper	7,106†
Petroleum coke	15,800
Asphalt	17,158
Oil (cottonseed)	17,100
Oil (paraffin)	17,640

* Extracted from *Kent's Mechanical Engineers' Handbook*.[1]
† Dry

the combustibles. On the opposite side of the picture, a relatively low loading is frequently misused by those seeking to depreciate the need and value of sound fire protection.

The amount of fuel contributed by one combustible vs another, or different forms of the same combustible can also be used to evaluate the desirability of utilizing the material in a given situation. This is particularly true for measuring the fuel contributed by certain forms of building materials.

Products of Combustion

Products of combustion, their importance on the fire scene, their physiological effects on persons trapped in the fire environment, and the degree to which they affect rescue and fire fighting efforts were discussed in Chapter 3 of Section 2. The burning of any combustible material involves a degree of smoke and noxious gases depending on a variety of organic and environmental effects. Wood and wood products are no exception.

The significance of combustion products in terms of life hazard and their means of measurement are not completely understood and many research programs are underway to explore these matters.[16] In the meantime, recognizing the fact that a hazard does exist, and in view of the common use of wood and wood products now and in the past, many building regulations contain a phrase such as interior finish materials shall not produce smoke or toxic gases greater than those produced by untreated wood or paper burned under similar circumstances.[17][18] Some regulations, i.e. New York City, Philadelphia and San Francisco, do incorporate numerical smoke limits as determined by the tunnel test, NFPA 255.[19]

However, the wide variety of end points used reflects the lack of both qualitative and quantitative data by which the hazard of smoke can be defined. Some authorities are proposing to use or are using smoke limits based on the NBS smoke chamber (NFPA 258-T)[20] either by themselves or as an alternate to the NFPA 255 tunnel test.

As with many organic materials, wood and related products can produce copious quantities of smoke in the pre-ignition and early stages of fire. Once the flame is well established the temperature in the immediate fire environment is sufficient to burn most of the unburned carbon particles and aerosols of which smoke is comprised. This of course assumes that other types of combustibles or contaminants are not present. An excellent discussion of smoke and its measurement as related to fires and a detailed description of the smoke chamber was published by the Forest Products Laboratory in 1970.[21]

The gaseous component of smoke is in an even earlier stage of exploration. The hazard of carbon monoxide and other gases that develop in fires was recognized many years ago. An article on the subject appeared in the NFPA Quarterly as early as 1933[22] and a Committee on Fire Gas Research was organized after World War II. A comprehensive report was prepared under the auspices of the latter group and published in 1952.[23] The Committee was disbanded, however, a few years later and little more was done on the subject until the U.S. Public Health Service undertook a study in 1962.[24] This was followed by further studies under the auspices of the U.S. Office of Civil Defense and currently by several programs sponsored by the National Science Foundation under the RANN program.[16]

The combustion process with wood as with any combustible involves the production of water vapor, heat and the combining of oxygen and carbon to form carbon dioxide and carbon monoxide. As indicated in Chapter 3, Section 2 heat, oxygen depletion and carbon monoxide appear to present the primary hazard in fires. In addition, the burning of wood and wood products produces a wide range of aldehydes, acids and other gases that, by themselves or in combination with the water vapor, may be severe irritants at least.

SI Units

The following conversion factors are given as a convenience in converting to SI units the English units used in this chapter:

1 Btu/lb = 2.326 kJ/kg
1 in. = 25.400 mm
1 lb (mass) = 0.454 kg
$\frac{5}{9}$(°F − 32) = °C

Bibliography

References Cited

[1] Salisbury, J. K., ed., *Kent's Mechanical Engineers' Handbook*, 12th ed., Vol. 2, John Wiley & Sons, New York, pp. 2-40.
[2] Imaizumi, Katsuyoshi, "Stability in Fire of Protected and Unprotected Glued Laminated Beams," *Transactions*, No. 263, 1963, Chalmers University of Technology, Gothenburg, Sweden, pp. 46-71.
[3] *Fire Research Report for the Year 1952*, Department of Scientific and Industrial Research and Fire Offices' Committee, Her Majesty's Stationery Office, London.
[4] "Dry Kiln Operators Manual," *Agricultural Handbook* No. 188, 1966, U.S. Government Printing Office, Washington, D.C.
[5] Bond, Horatio, *Fire and the Air War*, National Fire Protection Association, Boston, 1946, pp. 242-243.
[6] Beall, F. C. and Eichner, H. W., "Thermal Degradation of Wood Components: A Review of the Literature," Report No. 130, May 1970, Forest Products Laboratory, Madison, Wis.
[7] Fleischer, H. O., "The Performance of Wood in Fire," Report No. 2202, Nov. 1960, Forest Products Laboratory, Madison, Wis.
[8] "Report of the Committee on the Uses of Wood, Part I," *Proceedings of the 19th Annual Meeting*, National Fire Protection Association, 1915, pp. 109-114.
[9] McNaughton, G. C., "Ignition and Charring Temperatures of Wood," Mimeo No. R1464, Nov. 1944, Forest Products Laboratory, Madison, Wis.

[10] Brown, C. R., "The Ignition Temperatures of Solid Materials," NFPA *Quarterly*, Vol. 28, No. 2, Oct. 1934, pp. 135-145. (Basic text by author entitled, "The Determination of the Ignition Temperatures of Solid Materials," Catholic University Press, Washington, D.C., June 1934.)
[11] Data extracted from Table 1462, *Handbook of Fire Protection*, 11th ed., National Fire Protection Association, Boston, 1954, p. 1462. (Data in Table 1462 based on unpublished material from the National Bureau of Standards.)
[12] McGuire, J. H., "Limited Safe Surface Temperatures for Combustible Materials," *Fire Technology*, Vol. 5, No. 3, Aug. 1969, pp. 237-241.
[13] Mitchell, N. D., "New Light on Self-Ignition," NFPA *Quarterly*, Vol. 45, No. 2, Oct. 1951, pp. 165-172.
[14] Los Angeles Fire Department, *Operation School Burning No. 1*, National Fire Protection Association, Boston, 1959.
[15] *Fire Research Report for the Year 1950*, Department of Scientific and Industrial Research and Fire Offices' Committee, Her Majesty's Stationery Office, London.
[16] "Answers to Burning Questions—Reducing the Hazards of Fire," *Mosaic*, National Science Foundation, Washington, D.C., Spring 1973.
[17] *Uniform Building Code*, Vol. I, Sec. 4202b, International Conference of Building Officials, Whittier, Calif., 1970.
[18] *The BOCA Basic Building Code*, Sec. 922, 5th ed., Building Officials and Code Administrators International, Chicago, 1970.
[19] "Standard Method of Test for Surface Burning Characteristics of Building Materials," NFPA No. 255, 1972, National Fire Protection Association, Boston.
[20] "Tentative Standard Test Method for Smoke Generated by Solid Materials," NFPA No. 258-T, May 1974, National Fire Protection Association, Boston.
[21] Brenden, J. J., "Determining the Utility of a New Optical Test Procedure for Measuring Smoke from Various Wood Products," Research Paper 137, June 1970, Forest Products Laboratory, Madison, Wis.
[22] Ferguson, G. E., "Fire Gases," NFPA *Quarterly*, Vol. 27, No. 2, Oct. 1933.
[23] "Fire Gas Research Report," NFPA *Quarterly*, Vol. 45, No. 3, Jan. 1952.
[24] Bierberdorf, F. W. and Yuill, C. H., "An Investigation of the Hazards of Combustion Products in Building Fires," U.S. Public Health Service Contract No. PH86-62-208, Final Report, Oct. 1963.

Additional Readings

"Flammability of Cellulosic Materials," *Fire and Flammability Series*, Vol. 2, Technomic Publishing Company, Westport, Conn., 1973.
Graf, S. H., "Ignition Temperatures of Various Papers, Woods and Fabrics," Bulletin No. 26, March 1949, Oregon State College, Corvallis, Ore.
Gross, Daniel, and Robertson, A. F., "Self-Ignition Temperatures of Materials from Kinetic-Reaction Data," Research Paper 2909, *Journal of Research* of the National Bureau of Standards, Vol. 61, No. 5, Nov. 1958.
"Ignition, Heat Release and Noncombustibility of Materials," STP 502, 1972, American Society for Testing and Materials, Philadelphia.
"Moisture in Materials in Relation to Fire Tests," STP 385, 1965, American Society for Testing and Materials, Philadelphia.
Parker, W. J., "Thermal Hardening Considerations Pertaining to Residential Areas," USNRDL-TR-984, Feb. 1966, U.S. Naval Radiological Defense Laboratory, San Francisco.
Simms, D. L., "Experiments on the Ignition of Cellulosic Materials by Thermal Radiation," *Combustion and Flame*, Dec. 1961.
Simms, D. L., "On the Pilot Ignition of Wood by Radiation," *Combustion and Flame*, Sept. 1963.
"Smoke and Products of Combustion," *Fire and Flammability Series*, Vol. 2, Technomic Publishing Company, Westport, Conn., 1973.
"Theories of the Combustion of Wood and Its Control," Report No. 2136, Dec. 1958, Forest Products Laboratory, Madison, Wis.
"Wood Fire Behavior and Fire Retardant Treatment," (A Review of the Literature), Canadian Wood Council, Ottawa, Nov. 1966.

Chapter 2

FIBERS AND TEXTILES

Textiles are an intimate part of daily living. The clothing we wear, the chairs we sit on, the carpets we walk on, the beds we lie in are examples of textiles in the human environment. Almost all textile fibers are combustible. This fact, in conjunction with the high degree of involvement of textile products in people's activities, explains the frequency of textile-related fires and the many deaths and injuries that result. The NFPA Fire Analysis Department estimates that approximately 2,600 fatal fires occur in the United States annually in which textile products are the first materials ignited. Of the 2,600 deaths, 1,100 result from clothing ignitions, and 800 from fires originating in bedding.

Many variables affect the way in which a textile burns, the most important being the chemical composition of the textile fiber, the finish on the fabric, the fabric weight, tightness of weave, and flame-retardant treatment.

A. Natural Fiber Textiles

Cotton consists of more than 90 percent cellulose $(C_6H_{10}O_5)_x$. Other plant fibers, such as jute, flax (linen), hemp, and sisal, also are basically cellulose in composition. Cotton and the other plant fibers are combustible (ignition temperature of cotton fiber, 400°C) and when burning produce in addition to heat and smoke, carbon dioxide, carbon monoxide, and water. The plant fibers do not melt. As will be discussed later, the ease of ignition, rate of flame spread, and amount of heat produced by cotton textiles depend on the construction and finish of the textile and on the design of the finished product. The same is true of textile products made from animal or synthetic fibers.

Nonwoven fabrics, commonly referred to as disposables, usually consist primarily of cellulose fibers. Virtually all disposables are flame-retardant treated.

Fibers derived from animals are chemically different from cotton in that they consist of complex protein molecules containing high percentages of nitrogen, as well as carbon, hydrogen, oxygen, and small amounts of sulfur. For example, wool is basically protein. Wool supports combustion with difficulty and other things being equal is more difficult to ignite (ignition temperature of wool fiber, 600°C), burns more slowly, and is easier to extinguish than cotton. One of the products of combustion of wool is hydrogen cyanide.

B. Synthetic Textiles

Rayon, one of the synthetic materials used in wearing apparel and home furnishings, is a "reconstituted" cellulose made from cotton or wood fibers. Cellulose acetate is prepared by reacting cellulose with acetic acid. It was formerly included in the "rayon" category, but the U.S. Federal Trade Commission now lists it in a separate generic category, i.e., "acetate." Rayon and acetate resemble plant fibers chemically, whereas most other synthetic fibers do not.

Under the broad heading of "synthetics" are fabrics woven wholly or predominantly of synthetic fibers. The advent and proliferation of synthetic fibers have created new and difficult problems in evaluating fire hazard properties of textiles due to the tendency of some of them to shrink, melt or drip when heated. At the same time, synthetics offer considerable hope of virtually eliminating all fire problems associated with fabrics.

Table 3-2A lists the various classes of plastic resins that are presently utilized in the production of synthetic fibers. Also shown are some of the more common fiber trade names associated with each class, and the fire hazard properties, including generalized statements about relative flammability.

Table 3-2A. Synthetic Fibers

Plastic Resin Class	Trade Names	Fire Hazard Properties
Acetate	Chromspun, Celaperm, Arnel (Triacetate)	Burns and melts ahead of flame. Ignition temp., 475°C
Viscose	Avisco, Avril, Bemberg (Cuprammonium)	Burns about the same as cotton
Nylon	Antron, Caprolan	Supports combustion with difficulty. Melts and drips—melting point, 160–260°C. Ignition temperature, 425°C and above
Polyester	Dacron, Fortrel, Vycron, Kodel, Terylene	Burns readily. Ignition temp., 450–485°C. Softens, 256–292°C, and drips.
Acrylic	Acrilan, Orlon, Zefchrome, Zefran, Creslan	Burns and melts. Ignition temp., 560°C. Softens 235–330°C
Olefin	Herculon	Burns slowly. Ignition temp., 570°C. Melts and drips.
Modacrylic	Verel, Dynel	Burns very slowly. Melts.
Saran	Rovana, Velon	Does not support combustion. Melts.
Fluorocarbon	Teflon	Does not support combustion. Softens above 327°C. Ignition temperature above 600°C
Spandex	Lycra, Vyrene	Burns and melts. Ignition temp., 415°C. Softens, 230–260°C
Rubber	Lastex	Burns
Phenolic	Kynol	Burns (See also Table 3-2D)

The descriptions of burning are based on small scale tests and for this reason may be misleading. Some of the synthetic fabrics will give the appearance of being flame retardant when tested with a small flame source, such as a match. However, when the same fabrics are subjected to a larger flame or full-scale test, they may burst into flame and consume themselves while generating quantities of black smoke.

C. Noncombustible Textiles

Noncombustible fabrics include those made wholly from inorganic materials. Table 3-2B lists noncombustible fibers.

Table 3-2B. Noncombustible Fibers

Glass	Metal
Beta Fiber	Stainless steel
E-Glass	Super alloy
Quartz	Refractory-Whiskers
Carbonaceous Residue	Alumina
Carbon	Zirconia
Graphite	Boron

Glass fabrics listed by testing laboratories for use as draperies are woven from uncoated glass yarns which do not burn or propagate flame. If a sufficient quantity of combustible coating or decorative materials is applied to glass fabrics or to other noncombustible fabrics, the fabrics will support continued flaming.

The inherent property of brittleness of glass fibers eliminates glass fabrics as practical clothing materials. Nor do any of the other noncombustible fibers appear to have a future in the clothing field, either because of brittleness or weight.

D. Flame-retardant Textiles

Several flame-retardant fibers hold promise for use as clothing and other consumer products. These are shown in Table 3-2C.

Table 3-2C. Flame-retardant Fibers

Plastic Resin Class	Trade Name
Aromatic Polyamides	Nomex, X-100
Polybenzimidazole (PBI)	
Polyoxadiazole	
Polyimide	PRD-14
Poly dihydrodioxo	
Bis Benzimidazo	
Benzo Phenanthroline	
Phenolic	Kynol
Modified Polyamides	Durette; Fypro; Aromatic T
Modified Polybenzimidazole	PBI-S; PBI-T

Ignition temperatures and limited oxygen indexes that have been reported by J. R. Coskrien[1] and E. R. Kaswell[2] for fabrics made from flame-retardant fibers are summarized in Table 3-2D.

Limiting Oxygen Index (LOI) is a new means of measuring the tendency of a fabric, once ignited, to continue to burn after the ignition source is removed. LOI is defined as the minimum volume concentration of oxygen in a mixture of oxygen and nitrogen that will just support sustained combustion of the material when ignited in a vertical position at its uppermost edge.[3] Cotton fabrics, for example, have a LOI of 17 percent which means that if the oxygen is reduced below 17 percent the cotton will not continue to burn after the ignition source is removed. The higher the LOI of a fabric, the greater the probability that it will cease to burn once the ignition source is removed. Fabrics with high ignition temperatures and high LOIs can be expected to be safe for clothing and furnishings since they will not ignite readily and will not continue to burn after an accidental ignition source is removed.

Table 3-2D. Fire- and Heat-retardant Properties of Flame-retardant Fabrics

Flame-retardant Fabric	Weight (oz. per yard)	Ignition Temperature (°C)*	Limiting Oxygen Index (% Oxygen)
Dyed Nomex	5.0	1,500° 5 sec.	25–27
Natural Nomex	6.5	1,600° 1 sec.	27–28
Kynol	7.0	1,500° 3 sec.	29–30
Fypro	4.3	1,600° 1 sec.	29–30
Durette	4.7	1,650° 25 sec.	35–38
PBI	5.4	1,700° 6 sec.	38–43
PBI-S	6.0	1,650° 2 sec.	42–49
Nomex-T	6.5	——	42–52
PBI-T	6.0		65–75

* The number of seconds shown beneath each ignition temperature was the time required to ignite the fabric when in contact with a calrod heated to the temperature indicated.

Many synthetic fabrics shrink when exposed to temperatures approaching their melting or decomposition temperatures. When shrinkage brings the fabric into contact with the skin, the insulating layer of air is eliminated and the amount of heat transferred to the skin is increased significantly. Thermal shrinkage is a particularly important property to consider when selecting fabric for use in protective clothing. Another important property of fabrics in protective clothing is ability of a fabric to maintain its integrity during a fire. Fabrics that split apart and fall away or that burn completely leave the skin directly exposed to the heat.

E. Flame-retardant Treatments

The effects of chemical treatments in reducing the flammability of combustible fabrics are varied and complex, and all phases are not fully understood. There are five different ways in which chemicals or mixtures retard spread of flame and afterglow: (1) chemical or mixture generates noncombustible gases that tend to exclude oxygen from the burning surface, (2) radicals or molecules from degradation of the flame retardant chemical react endothermically and interfere with the chain reactions in the flame, (3) the flame retardant chemical decomposes endothermically, (4) a nonvolatile char or liquid is formed by the chemical which reduces the amount of oxygen and heat that can reach the fabric, and (5) finely divided particles are formed that change the combustion reactions. Usually a flame retardant chemical or mixture affects flammability in more than one of these ways.

Hundreds of different chemicals have been investigated for use on textiles. Some are not suitable because of objectionable characteristics, such as moisture absorption, deterioration under high temperature drying or pressing, corrosiveness, toxicity, or because they adversely affect color, feel, flexibility, tensile strength, and the life of the fabric. Difficult application techniques and the expense involved are other objectionable features of some treatments. Some of the flame retardant treatments currently being used or investigated are shown in Table 3-2E.

At present satisfactory methods have not been found for treating nylon and certain other synthetic fibers so that the finished textile will be free of objectionable characteristics.

Many concerns specialize in the flame retardant treatment of theater scenery, draperies, and other fabrics, using standard chemicals. However, there are some concerns in this field which have not treated fabrics properly or have

Table 3-2E. Flame-retardant Chemicals for Textiles

Fiber	Flame-retardant Chemical
Cotton	Tetrakis (Hydroxymethyl) Phosphonium Chloride (THPC), and related compounds; N-Methylol dialkyl; 2-Carbamyl-ethyl-phosphonate
Rayon (disposable and nondurable finishes)	Diammonium Phosphate; Diammonium Sulfamate
Rayon (modified fiber)	Hexapropoxyphosphotriazene
Acetate	Tris-2,3-Dibromoprobyl Phosphate
Polyethylene Terephalate	Dihydroxyethyl Tetrabromo-Bis-phenol A (with or without antimony oxide); Polyphosphonates based on dihydroxyaromatic compounds; tris-2,3-dibromo-propyl phosphate
Wool	Tetrakis (hydroxymethyl) phosphonium chloride (THPC)
Acrylics	Vinyl chloride; vinylidene chloride
Modacrylics	Vinyl bromide; Bis (2-chloroethyl)-Vinyl phosphonate; tricresylphosphate (with or without antimony oxide)
Polyvinyl Alcohol	Vinyl chloride

used relatively ineffective chemicals. It is therefore advisable to deal only with concerns of known reliability, or, if dealing with an unknown concern, to have treated fabrics tested for adequacy of treatment.

Water-soluble chemicals are used in many of these treatments which are good for "one-use-only" and must be renewed after each washing. Formerly, some of these treatments were able to withstand dry cleaning, but the recent development of water-base soap in dry cleaning chemicals now makes it necessary to know the type of cleaning process being used. If water-base additives are used, then the material probably will have to be treated after cleaning.

Most of the treatments in use today cause very little reduction in the strength of fabrics under normal use. However, when a fabric is subjected to higher than normal temperatures or to sunlight, a decided loss in strength due to a number of factors may result.

It is usually important that color and texture be unchanged by flame retardants, and the majority of treatments will meet this requirement. Except for some of the more complex compounds used in durable treatments, few of the chemicals in common use have any irritating or toxic properties, and there are rarely any problems encountered in the handling of most chemicals or treated fabrics.

The value and effectiveness of flame-retardant treatments for protection against the hazard of cigaraette ignitions is commonly misunderstood. Since no treatments are available today which can make combustible materials immune to fire or heat exposure, sufficient contact with a burning cigarette will char and damage any treated material. Obviously, the treatment of rugs and carpeting to prevent burn damage from cigarettes is useless. Of much greater importance is the matter of protection of overstuffed furniture or mattresses against cigarette ignitions. The flame-retardant treatment of only the outer covering (upholstery or mattress ticking) is of questionable value, and can be effective only if the treatment has good glow resistance, if the charred fabric retains sufficient strength to prevent physical

penetration by the cigarette into the padding below, and if the cover is sufficiently heavy to provide enough heat insulation to prevent the initiation of glowing in the padding. Much more assured protection can be provided if at least the top one-inch layer of padding or batting is likewise effectively flame-retardant treated or is of a material not susceptible to ignition by burning cigarettes.

Methods of Treatment

Water soluble flame-retardant chemicals may be applied by immersion of the fabric in a solution, by spraying, or by brushing. The objective is to deposit the desired chemicals, measured in terms of add-on, on the fibers of the fabric. The particular method of application and the proportion of water used in the solution are unimportant as long as uniform treatment and the desired add-on are obtained. Good results may be obtained by any method by which the fabric may be adequately wetted, as dictated by convenience and by the character of the fabric to be treated. In the case of proprietary flame-retardant chemicals, manufacturers' instructions should be followed.

Effective treatment of cellulosic fabrics (cotton, rayon, linen), wool, and silk may be obtained without professional assistance through the use of nonproprietary solutions of flame-retardant chemicals mixed with water if some experience on their use and if testing of the results can be obtained. However, these solutions are of very limited value, particularly in the case of clothing due to their temporary

Table 3-2F. Typical Flame-retardant Formulas for Fabrics (Not suitable for synthetic fibers)

Formula No. 1

Borax, $Na_2B_4O_7 10H_2O$	6 parts	6 lb
Boric acid, H_3BO_3	5 parts	5 lb
Water	100 parts	12 gal

The fabric is steeped in a cool solution until thoroughly impregnated, then dried. Heavy applications by spray or brush are usually reasonably effective. Such applications may have to be repeated two or three times with drying between applications to obtain the desired degree of flame resistance. The treatment has been used for many kinds of fabrics, including theater scenery. It is recommended for viscose rayon. As in the case of most of the other formulas listed, care must be taken in ironing the fabric to avoid discoloration by heat.

Formula No. 2

Borax, $Na_2B_4O_7 10H_2O$	7 parts	7 lb
Boric acid, H_3BO_3	3 parts	3 lb
Diammonium phosphate, $(NH_4)_2HPO_4$	5 parts	5 lb
Water	110 parts	$13\frac{1}{6}$ gal

This formula gives very satisfactory results both in flame and glow resistance. It will be found effective in weightings of 7 to 15 percent, depending upon the fabric treated. Handwringing the above solution from a fabric leaves a weighting of about 10 to 12 percent.

Formula No. 3

Diammonium phosphate, $(NH_4)_2HPO_4$	7.5 parts	$7\frac{1}{2}$ lb
Ammonium chloride, NH_4Cl	5 parts	5 lb
Ammonium sulfate, $(NH_4)_2SO_4$	5 parts	5 lb
Water	100 parts	12 gal

Either the solution can be applied directly to the cloth, or it can be used in making a starch sizing. The formula has been used for treating curtains and for cotton fabrics in general. The ammonium chloride and, to a lesser extent, the ammonium phosphate are hygroscopic; therefore this formula may not be advisable for treating materials exposed to dampness. The treatment is effective in weightings of 10 to 18 percent, depending upon the type of fabric treated. Handwringing the above solution from a fabric leaves a weighting of about 16 to 18 percent.

nature. Where there is reasonable assurance that articles of clothing will never be laundered or dry cleaned due to their function or manner of use (bridal illusion, Halloween costumes, disposable paper) such treatments can be worthwhile.

The chemicals should be dissolved in clean water. Warm water and stirring will facilitate dissolving; the addition of a small percentage of a wetting agent will help to secure prompt penetration of the fabric. It is necessary to wash new fabrics containing sizing prior to treatment so as to secure proper absorption of chemicals.

When a piece of fabric is immersed, usually at room temperature, in a flame-retardant solution, the container must be large enough so that all the fabric is thoroughly wet, there being no folds which the solution does not penetrate.

Care must be used in wringing the immersed material. If a mechanical wringer in which more of the solution is likely to be extracted is used, a more concentrated solution may be necessary to obtain the desired add-on. Best results will be obtained if the articles can be dried in a horizontal position. Drying in a vertical position permits a certain amount of drainage of the solution depending upon the wetness of the articles. It is advisable to increase the add-on if horizontal drying is not feasible. Also, light-weight fabrics are more difficult to treat and require a higher percentage of add-on.

The three formulas given in Table 3-2F have been found effective within the general limitations previously stated in this chapter.[4]

The flame-retardant treatment of theater scenery, curtains, and draperies in places of public assembly is commonly required by law. Treated fabrics are also used in hotels, hospitals, and other occupancies, in the interest of preservation of lives and property.

F. Relationship of Flammability and End Use of Textiles

So far this discussion of textile flammability has been confined primarily to the textiles themselves. The use to which the textile will be put—clothing, upholstery, bedding, carpets, etc.—is very important when evaluating the flammability of a textile.

Clothing

The true scope and nature of the flammable wearing apparel problem are commonly misunderstood, due in large part to emphasis on highly publicized incidents involving clothing articles of extreme flammability. The most notorious of these were the children's costume articles (cowboy chaps) made of a very long piled rayon fabric, which were the direct cause of several fatalities and many serious burn injuries. These occurred in 1945. In late 1951 and early 1952, the so-called "torch sweaters," also made of brushed rayon, were widely publicized.

Concern over unique wearing apparel fabrics and materials possessing exceptionally flammable properties is certainly proper, and legislation to prohibit such materials is necessary. However, emphasis on these facets of the clothing fire problem has led to a serious lack of understanding of the basic issue, which is simply this: By far the great majority of clothing fire accidents in the United States involves ordinary, everyday fabrics having no unusual flammability characteristics. The fundamental and unfortunate fact is that cotton and rayon are relatively flammable fibers, and comprise a very large part of the total clothing fabric picture.

Another unfortunate fact of increasing importance is that most of the synthetic fibers finding favor for many clothing applications are subject to melting when exposed to sufficient heat. Nylon and acetate, from which practically all women's underclothing is now made, actually melt and liquefy under fire exposure. This cannot help but greatly aggravate the severity of burn injuries under many conditions.

The relative fire hazard potential of an article of clothing is determined by several factors. First, there are the fabric's physical properties, including weight, weave, or construction (whether it is smooth or has a brushed, napped or piled surface). Second, there are the chemical properties of the fiber or fiber mixture in the textile. These determine its basic burning characteristics, since fire is a chemical reaction. And third, there are its thermal properties—an aspect of increasing importance since the advent of synthetic fibers, many of which melt or burn as a liquid under fire exposure. Many textiles are provided with special permanent finishes intended to impart such properties as wrinkle resistance, softness, water repellancy, and washability; these finishes can influence flammability.

Besides the burning properties of fibers and fabrics, there are several other factors to consider when evaluating the fire hazard potential of clothing—the age, physical condition and mentality of the wearer, the type and style of the garment, and the possible sources of ignition.

Although no group is immune, those who are partially or wholly dependent on others for the safety of their environment—the very old, the very young, the infirm and the mentally incompetent—are the most frequent victims. In a study of 3,145 single fatality fires,[5] 545 were clothing fires. Of those, 54 involved children under 5 and 152 people who were 71 years old or older. See Table 3-2G.

The style or type of garment is an important factor when evaluating its fire hazard. For example, a full-length gown containing several yards of flammable fabric could be a death trap whereas a simply styled blouse or shirt made of the same material would present far less danger. Not only would the gown present much more fuel for burning, but its size and shape would make it far more vulnerable to typical sources of ignition. Flared skirts and full-sleeved kimonos are other examples of easily ignited garments. The availability of oxygen for burning on both sides of loosely fitting garments accelerates flame spread.

No matter how flammable the clothing, there can be no fire unless someone through some act of carelessness, negligence or ignorance causes the fabric to be brought into contact with a source of ignition. As will be noted in Table 3-2G, smoking materials (matches, lighters), heaters and cooking equipment are the most frequent clothing ignition sources.

Bedding and Upholstered Furniture

Seventeen percent of the 3,145 fires analyzed in Table 3-2G were caused by smoking in bed or smoking in upholstered furniture. In most of those cases, the fire smoldered during the early stages at least, and the victim was killed by the heated gases or other airborne products of combustion rather than by burns. The victims of smoldering fires in upholstered furniture were frequently asleep in a different room from the room containing the smoldering fire. Although the fire did not spread, the products of combustion did.

In a series of full-scale tests conducted by Southwest Research Institute for the National Bureau of Standards,[6] a single cigarette caused ignition in eight out of twenty-two bedding tests and four of eight chair tests. In four of the

Table 3-2G. The Single-fatality Fire

3,145 Single-fatality Fires

Age of Victim	Clothing Fires	Nonclothing Fires		Attendance		
0–5	54	563		Child unattended	29	221
6–10	20	104		Adult alone	279	1,073
11–15	16	66		Other person nearby	212	1,321
16–20	12	74		Not reported	5	5
21–40	50	407			525	2,620
41–60	114	709				
61–70	103	308		**Cause of Clothing Ignition**		
71 up	152	344		Smoking materials,		
Not reported	4	45		matches, lighters	228	
	525	2,620		Heating stove or furnace	82	
				Cook stove	71	
				Rubbish fire	14	
Sex				Other	96	
Male	257	1,627		Not reported	34	
Female	268	993			525	
	525	2,620				
				Type of Clothing		
				Outer clothing	270	
Cause of Death				Sleepwear	155	
Gas or smoke	88	1,378		Underclothing	23	
Burns	433	1,168		Other	22	
Heart attack	1	14		Not reported	55	
Other	3	60			525	
	525	2,620				

Fabric of Clothing	Clothing Fire	Nonclothing Fire
Cotton	163	
Wool	12	
Other natural fabric	6	
Rayon	7	
Other synthetic	10	
Mixture	29	
Not reported	298	
	525	

Where the Fire Occurred	Clothing Fires		Nonclothing Fires	
Building				
Dwelling	274		1,412	
Apartment	102		669	
Other residential	27		219	
Institution	28		18	
Other building	22		127	
		453		2,445

Transportation				
Automobile	9		105	
Other	7		27	
		16		132

Flammable Liquid Involved		
Type		
Gasoline	43	
Cooking oil	4	
Other or not reported	39	
	86	

Outside Location				
Brush and grass	5		10	
Lawn	31		6	
Other outside location	11		24	
		47		40

Use of Flammable Liquid		
Motor fuel	15	
Cleaning	12	
Cooking fuel	6	
Other or not reported	53	
	86	

	Clothing Fire	Nonclothing Fire
Not reported	9	3
	525	2,620

Causes of Nonclothing Fires	
Smoking in bed	307
Smoking on upholstered furniture	237
Other careless smoking	61
Mishandling flammable liquid	842
Other	971
Undetermined	202
	2,620

Hindrance to Self-help	Clothing Fire	Nonclothing Fire
Condition of victim		
Too young to act	48	509
Bedridden	10	31
Other physical handicap	54	127
Mentally ill, senile	21	29
Intoxicated	29	219
Suicide	11	15
Asleep	61	417
Other	31	115
No handicap reported	260	1,158
	525	2,620

Cause of Failure to Escape	
Fire cut off path to exit	788
Exits inadequate to escape	31
Trapped in burning vehicle	100
Explosion	118
Other	834
Not reported	749
	2,620

tests in which a single cigarette caused ignition, heat and carbon monoxide levels were obtained that would cause death after a 5-min exposure. Levels of temperature and carbon monoxide considered fatal in a 30-min exposure were obtained in all of the tests except one. The exception involved sheets, blankets, and mattresses that were fire-retardant. In those tests in which a cigarette was the ignition source, time before complete obscuration by smoke ranged from 26 min to three hours. In the twelve tests in which ignition was by an open flame, complete obscuration occured in 20 min or less, and in five of the twelve tests within ten minutes.

Carpets

Until 1960 there was very little fire experience to indicate that carpets were a significant factor in fires and consequently floor coverings were customarily exempted from coverage in codes regulating life safety from fire in buildings. Since 1960 the situation has changed and although the number of fires reported in which carpets spread fire has not been great, those that have been reported indicate that carpets can be the prime material involved in the development or spread of a fire.[7, 8, 11, 13, 16] In 1970 a fire in a California dwelling was first seen by an occupant when it was a few feet in diameter on carpeting in front of the fireplace.[17] As the occupant applied water to the burning carpet with a garden hose, the fire spread rapidly on the carpet and had enveloped the entire room including furniture and wood paneling ten minutes after discovery.[17] Because of such experience, carpet flammability is now being regulated at the Federal, state and municipal levels.

Among the many factors in carpet construction, in addition to type of fiber, that may affect ease of ignition and ability to spread fire, important ones are density (loops per square inch), unit weight, pile height, backing material, padding, type of adhesive, single versus double back, and type of dye.

Fabric Flammability Tests

The severity of the hazard of a fabric in a particular type of product, such as a dress, mattress or carpet, depends greatly upon ease of ignition of the product, the speed with which flame spreads on it, the amount of heat generated, susceptability to melting, and the quantity and composition of the smoke and gaseous products of combustion. No individual test method gives a complete evaluation of the hazard and there are no nationally recognized test methods to measure some of the hazards. Carlos J. Hilado has included descriptions of most of the important test methods for textile products in his *Flammability Test Methods Handbook*.[18] Those in common use in the United States are described below.

Clothing (except children's sleepwear)

In 1953 the Federal Flammable Fabrics Act was signed into law by the President of the United States.[19] The Act required that all wearing apparel and fabrics subject to the Act be classified as not so highly flammable as to be dangerous when tested according to Commercial Standard CS 191-53.[20], which is designed to measure ease of ignition and rate of flame spread. It does this by impinging a small gas flame for one second against the lower part of the upper face of a 2-in. by 6-in. sample that is suspended at a 45° angle from the horizontal in a test chamber. If the fabric is ignited by the one-second exposure the time required for the flame to spread a measured distance on the fabric is recorded. This test has kept the dangerously flam-

mable garments, such as the previously mentioned cowboy chaps, out of interstate commerce, but has had no measurable effect on the number of wearing apparel burn injuries since the fabrics involved almost without exception do not classify as dangerously flammable when subjected to test method CS 191-53.

The test method in NFPA No. 702, Standard for the Classification of the Flammability of Wearing Apparel, is the same as that in CS 191-53 with two important exceptions. The Committee that drafted the NFPA Standard had noted that many fabrics, particularly those without raised fiber surfaces, were not ignited when the top surface was touched by a small test flame for 1 sec. Those fabrics could not be evaluated for rate of flame spread. Further, the Committee concluded that the lower edge of a fabric should be easier to ignite than a surface. Consequently the test flame in NFPA No. 702 method is brought in contact with the lower edge of all samples, and in the case of those without raised fiber surface, is held there until ignition occurs.

Children's Sleepwear

Previously cited statistics[5] showed that young children (those under five) are more susceptible to clothing fires than other age groups, and that sleepwear is frequently the first garment ignited. Analysis of 406 wearing apparel burn injuries by the National Bureau of Standards showed that children in the 0 to 5 age group are injured at particularly high frequency by burning of sleepwear; girls being 1.6 times and boys 3.9 times as often as would be expected on the basis of their percentage of total population of the nation.[21] On the basis of these data, a flammability standard was created by the U.S. Department of Commerce with which all sleep-wear up to and including size 6x (sizes normally worn by children five years old and younger) manufactured after July 29, 1973 must comply.[22] Fabrics intended to be used to make small children's sleepwear also had to comply. U.S. Department of Commerce Standard DOC FF-3-71 is much more restrictive than CS 191-53. Samples 3.5 by 10 in. are suspended vertically in a cabinet and subjected to a test flame along the bottom edge. A fabric passes the test if (1) the average char length of five specimens does not exceed 7 in., (2) no specimen has a char length of 10 in., and (3) no specimen has a residual flame for more than 10 sec. The barrel of the test flame burner is ¾ in. below the lower edge of the sample and the test flame is adjusted to extend 1½ in. It exposes the sample for 3 secs. Char length is the distance from the lower edge to the end of the void or tear in the charred, burned or damaged area. The tear is made by lifting the sample by one of the corners near the lower edge after weights had been attached to the other corner near the lower edge. Residual flame time is the time from the removal of the burner until final extinction of flame, smoldering, and afterglow. The small-scale test method in NFPA No. 701, Standard Methods of Fire Tests for Flame-Resistant Textiles and Films, is quite similar to that in DOC FF-3-71.

On May 1, 1974, the U.S. Consumer Product Safety Commission extended the coverage of DOC FF 3-71 to include all children's sleepwear sizes 7 to 14, to take effect May 1, 1975.[23] Sleepwear sizes 7 to 14 must comply with the char length limits, but not those relating to residual flaming.

Protective Clothing

Protective clothing should not burn, melt, or disintegrate on exposure to heat or flame; it should be an effective thermal barrier, should not shrink excessively when heated, and should be durable and comfortable. R. J. Coskren[1] and E. R. Kaswell[2] have described methods used to evaluate these properties. Two tests are used to measure burning properties—an ease of ignition test and a test to measure the tendency of a fabric to burn once the ignition source is removed. Ease of ignition is determined by holding a calrod type heater against the fabric and increasing the temperature of the heater until the fabric ignites. The number of seconds to produce ignition is recorded. Table 3-2D contains time to ignite for several materials, some of which are suitable for protective clothing. Tendency to burn is determined by finding the minimum concentration of oxygen in an oxygen-nitrogen mixture that will just support combustion of a material when ignited in a vertical position at its uppermost edge. The sample is placed vertically in a glass column and ignited at the top so that it burns in a candle-like manner. By varying the oxygen concentration of the mixture flowing up through the column, the minimum concentration that will just support combustion is found. The results are reported as LOI (see Table 3-2D).

Mattresses and Upholstered Furniture

Table 3-2G indicates that smoking in bed and in upholstered furniture accounts for about 23 percent of single fatality fire deaths. During one 12-month period in Los Angeles, 13 percent of 25,000 fires reported originated in mattresses, bedding, and upholstered furniture.[24] In recognition of the life hazard of smoking in bed, the U.S. Consumer Product Safety Commission promulgated regulations applying to the flammability of mattresses and mattress pads. All mattresses and pads manufactured after Dec. 22, 1973 were required to pass the test in DOC FF 4-72, Flammability Standard for Mattresses.[25] In this test, lighted cigarettes are applied to a smooth surface, tape edge, quilted location, and tufted location. Ignition tests are run on the bare mattress and between two sheets on the mattress. The test is passed if the char length on the mattress surface is not more than two inches in any direction from the nearest point of the cigarette. The various types of juvenile product pads such as playpen and carriage pads are subject to the same test requirements.

Carpets and Rugs

Carpets and rugs are currently regulated in the United States by two Federal Test Methods, DOC FF 1-70[26] and DOC FF 2-70.[27] FF 1-70 applies to other than small carpets and rugs and FF 2-70 applies to the small ones, which are defined as having no dimension greater than 6 feet and having an area not greater than 24 square feet. In each of the tests a 9- by 9-in. sample is placed on the floor of a test chamber and a flat steel plate with an 8-in. diameter hole in the center is placed on the sample. A methanamine tablet is placed in the center of the hole and ignited. The sample passes the test if the charred portion does not extend to within one inch of the edge of the hole at any point. Seven of eight specimens of other than small carpets and rugs must pass if carpets made of the tested material are to be permitted to be sold. In the case of small carpets and rugs, those that do not pass the test may be sold if they carry a permanent label stating that they failed to pass FF 2-70.

Hospitals and other institutions receiving financial aid under the provisions of the Hill-Burton Act are required to comply with flammability limits for carpets and other floor coverings used on patient-occupied areas and exit ways. The flame spread of floor coverings must not exceed 75, as determined by ASTM E84[28] (NFPA No. 255, Method of Test of Surface Burning Characteristics of Building Materials). NFPA No. 101, Life Safety Code, suggests in the Appendix that where limitations are to be placed on the flammability of floor coverings, the test method in NFPA No. 255 is to be used. NFPA No. 255, commonly referred to as the tunnel test, is described in Section 6, Chapter 6 in this HANDBOOK. Objections have been raised to its use to evaluate floor coverings because the test specimen is held face downward at the top of the furnace chamber and therefore is being tested in a position that bears no resemblance to its position when in place in a building. The method is also criticized because it may result in delamination, melting, and dripping of test specimens.

To obtain a test method that more nearly represented actual use conditions, Underwriters' Laboratories, Inc., devised a horizontal test chamber in which the specimen is mounted on the chamber floor.[29] The chamber is 10 in. high, 22 in. wide, and 10 ft, 6-in. long and contains air inlets and gas burners at one end and an exhaust outlet at the other. With the test specimen in place and the gas flow to the burners and air flow through the chamber adjusted to 0.5 cfm and 100 ± 5 cfm respectively, the gas diffusion test flame is applied for 12 minutes and then extinguished. On the basis of conditions observed during the 12 minutes with the burners on and during the succeeding 12 minutes, a Flame Propagation Index is calculated using formulas that take into consideration the distances that the flame propagated during the two 12-minute periods.

Textiles in Transport Category Airplanes

The flammability of textiles in the crew and passenger compartments are regulated by the Federal Aviation Administration, U.S. Department of Transportation.[30] A 2- by 12-in. specimen is mounted vertically in a U-shaped metal frame so that the lower 2-in. edge can be exposed by a flame from a Bunsen or Tirrell burner. The top of the burner barrel is to be $\frac{3}{4}$ in. beneath the exposed fabric edge and the burner flame is to have been adjusted to extend upward $1\frac{1}{2}$ in. above the barrel. The burner flame temperature is to be 1,550°F. The flame exposes the specimen for 12 sec. Time of flaming after removal of the burner, burn length, and flaming time of drippings are recorded. The average burn length for three specimens may not exceed 8 in., the average time of burning after removal of the burner may not exceed 15 sec, and the average time that drippings may continue to flame after falling may not exceed 5 sec.

Textiles in Motor Vehicles

Materials used in the occupant compartments of passenger cars, multipurpose passenger vehicles, trucks, and buses in the United States must not burn, or transmit a flame front across the surface, at a rate of more than 4 ipm (inches per minute) when tested according to NFPA No. 302, Fire Protection Standard for Motor Craft.[32] In that standard a specimen is suspended in a horizontal position in a test chamber, and a Bunsen burner flame exposes one end. The specimen is held in a U-shaped clamp and the assembly is suspended so that the top of the barrel of the burner is $\frac{3}{4}$ in. below the exposed edge of the specimen. The burner flame is adjusted to be $1\frac{1}{2}$ in. high and the flame temperature is to be that of a natural gas flame. The specimen is exposed to the test flame for 15 sec. Timing is begun when the flame from the burning specimen reaches a point $1\frac{1}{2}$ in. from the open end of the specimen and timing ends when the flame has progressed to $1\frac{1}{2}$ in. from the closed end.

Tents, Tarpaulins, Air-supported Stuctures

NFPA No. 102, Standard for Tents, Grandstands and Air-Supported Structures Used for Places of Assembly, requires that the following tents, tarpaulins and air-supported structures meet the appropriate flame-resistance requirements in NFPA No. 701, Standard Methods of Tests for Flame Resistance of Textiles and Films: (1) tents and air-supported structures used for assembly, (2) tents and air-supported structures in which animals are stabled, (3) tents and air-supported structures located in a portion of the premises used by the public, (4) tents and air-supported structures in places of assembly in or about which fuel-burning devices are located, and (5) all tarpaulins used in connection with (1) through (4).

The small-scale test in the NFPA Flame Resistant Textiles and Film Standard is similar to the previously described test in U.S. Department of Commerce Standard DOC FF-3-71[22] that is used to evaluate children's sleepwear. The large-scale test in the Standard uses specimens 7 ft long and 5 or 25 in. wide depending upon whether the specimen is to be tested as a single sheet or is to be hung in folds. The single sheet specimen is suspended vertically in an open-ended metal stack and its lower edge is exposed to an 11-in.-high oxidizing flame from a Bunsen burner, the top of whose barrel is 4 in. below the bottom of the specimen. A folded specimen is tested with its folds $\frac{1}{2}$ in. apart in the same metal stack and with the same burner arrangement. For both single sheet and folded specimen, the test flame is applied for 2 mins, then withdrawn, and the duration of flaming combustion recorded. Length of char—the distance from the top of the test flame to the top of the charred area resulting from spread of flame or afterglow—is also recorded. To pass the test, duration of flaming combustion of single sheets shall not exceed 2 sec and the char length shall not exceed 10 in. For specimens in folds, maximum duration permitted of flaming is 2 sec and maximum char length is 35 in., but afterglow may spread in the folds.

G. Textiles in Special Environments

Certain ambient atmospheric conditions have an influence on the behavior of treated textiles in fire situations. They are (1) oxygen-enriched atmospheres, (2) compressed air atmospheres, and (3) exposure to weather.

Action of Treated Textiles in Oxygen-enriched Air

Some industrial processes require men to work in atmospheres enriched above the normal oxygen content. Such atmospheres present a high fire hazard, particularly to the clothing worn by the workers. The effect of flame retardant treatments on the combustibility of the fabrics has been studied in England by the Joint Fire Research Organization of the Department of Scientific and Industrial Research and Fire Offices' Committee.[32]

The study showed that there are levels of oxygen concentration above which no present day flame-retardant treatment is effective. Also, there are levels of add-on beyond which there is no improvement in the retarding effect.

The effectiveness of the treatments depends upon the type, weight, and weave of the fabric, in addition to the percentage increase in the oxygen concentration of the ambient atmosphere where the fabric is used. The most effective treatment of those tested was 70 percent borax and 30 percent boric acid. Even with this treatment on unbleached white cotton drill fabric, 37 percent oxygen in air was the maximum oxygen concentration in which the treat-

ment was effective. Additional add-ons beyond 9 percent were found to provide no added flame-retardant protection to the cloth. With the same fabric, another flame retardant treatment (60 percent boric acid, 40 percent monosodium phosphate) provided protection for an oxygen concentration of only 24 percent oxygen maximum and this with a 19 percent add-on.

Before any fabric is used in an oxygen-enriched atmosphere, it should be tested under conditions of use to determine its flame-resistance rating and the degree of protection it will afford.

The Textile Fibers Department of the du Pont Company has conducted research on their Nomex high-temperature-resistant nylon fiber in both high pressure air environments and oxygen-enriched atmospheres at greater than normal pressures. Nomex fabric was found to retain its flame-retardant qualities under air pressure of four atmospheres (45 psig). At this pressure and higher oxygen concentrations (40 percent and greater), Nomex supported combustion but at a substantially slower rate than did untreated readily combustible fabrics.

An indication of the resistance to burning of flame retardant textiles in oxygen-enriched atmospheres may be inferred from the Limiting Oxygen Indexes in Table 3-2D.

For a more complete discussion of the hazards of oxygen-enriched atmospheres see Chapter 6 of Section 5 of this HANDBOOK and NFPA No. 53M, Oxygen Enriched Atmospheres.

Action of Treated Textiles in Compressed Air

Since compressed air has an increased amount of oxygen per cubic foot of space, it has the effect of an oxygen-enriched atmosphere, but to a lesser extent. With compressed air, the effect of diluent nitrogen is greater, whereas in oxygen-enriched air, the ratio of oxygen to nitrogen is increased. Industrial operations, mining, tunneling, and other processes that use compressed air may necessitate that people work under compressed air conditions.

Taking unbleached white cotton drill again as a sample, the effect of the 70 percent borax, 30 percent boric acid treatment was studied at air pressures up to 75 psig. It was found that a 10 percent add-on produced a treated fabric that would not burn in atmospheres up to 38 psig and would only smolder slowly up to 75 psig, but add-ons up to 5 percent provided little protection up to 40 psig and none above this.

Unique hazards confronting persons working in a compressed air atmosphere are found in hyperbaric chambers, a new medical tool receiving wide-spread attention. Tests in hyperbaric chambers at pressures up to four atmospheres have confirmed that inherently flame resistant or effectively treated fabrics retain their flame-retardant qualities.[33]

Weather-exposed Textiles

Flame-retardant treatments for tents, awnings, tarpaulins and other fabrics exposed to the weather must be of a special character in order to prevent the leaching out of the flame-retardant chemicals in the course of time. If water-soluble chemicals are used, the treatments must be renewed at frequent intervals.

Weather-resistant, flame-retardant fabrics are listed by fire testing laboratories. These are comparatively difficult to ignite and do not propagate flame beyond the area exposed to the source of ignition, even when in drafts. Flameless or smoldering combustion which occurs at ignition may spread in folds, but in the case of single sheets does not extend beyond the area exposed to ignition. The treatments may be expected to remain effective under ordinary conditions of exposure for the useful life of the fabric. However, laundering will reduce the effectiveness of the treatment when so indicated in laboratory listings of individual fabrics.

A wide variety of chemicals may be used for treating fabrics exposed to the weather. Many of the formulas used include chlorinated paraffin, chlorinated synthetic resins, or chlorinated rubber, in combination with various water-insoluble metallic salts, plasticizers, stabilizers, synthetic resins, pigments, binders, mildew inhibitors, etc. Such mixtures are not water soluble and are used with hydrocarbon solvents, or are suspended in water emulsions. The effective application of such treatments calls for techniques and equipment ordinarily available only for factory processing or to concerns specializing in flame-retardant applications. Application of paint to these treated fabrics may lessen their flame resistance.

SI Units

The following conversion factors are given as a convenience in converting to SI units the English units used in this chapter.

1 lb (mass) = 0.454 kg
1 gal   = 3.785 litres

Bibliography

References Cited

[1] Coskren, R. J., "Flame Resistant and Nonflammable Textile Fibers," *SAMPE Quarterly*, Vol. 4, No. 4, July 1973, pp. 13–19.

[2] Kaswell, E. R., "Some Thoughts and Information on Nonflammable Products," *Journal of the American Association of Textile Chemists and Colorists*, Vol. 4, No. 1, January 1972, pp. 33–40.

[3] Osaacs, J. L., "The Oxygen Index Flammability Test," *Journal of Fire and Flammability*," Vol. 1, 1970, pp. 36–47.

[4] Sandholzer, M. W., "Flameproofing of Textiles," C455, National Bureau of Standards, August 1946, Washington, D.C.

[5] NFPA Fire Record Department, "The Single Fatality Fire," *Fire Journal*, Vol. 63, No. 1, Jan. 1969, pp. 34, 35.

[6] Yuill, C. H., "The Life Hazard of Bedding and Upholstery Fires," *Journal of Fire and Flammability*, Vol. 1, 1970, pp. 312–323.

[7] Yuill, C. H., "The Flammability of Floor Coverings," *Journal of Fire and Flammability*, Vol. 1, 1970, pp. 64–70.

[8] Yuill, C. H., "Floor Coverings: What Is the Hazard?," *Fire Journal*, Vol. 61, No. 1, Jan. 1967, pp. 11–19.

[9] "Fire in Acrylic Carpeting," *Fire Journal*, Vol. 62, No. 2, Mar. 1968, pp. 13, 14, 18.

[10] "Fire Spread by Polypropylene Carpeting," *Fire Journal*, Vol. 62, No. 5, Nov. 1968, pp. 24–25.

[11] Peterson, C. E., "Flammable Adhesive Improperly Used," *Fire Journal*, Vol. 63, No. 2, Nov. 1968, pp. 8–11.

[12] Powers, W. R., "Office Building Fire, 919 Third Avenue, New York City," *Fire Journal*, Vol. 65, No. 2, Mar. 1971, pp. 5–7, 13.

[13] Willey, A. E., "Fire, Baptist Towers Housing for the Elderly," *Fire Journal*, Vol. 67, No. 3, May 1973, pp. 15–21, 103.

[14] "Bimonthly Fire Record, Television Set Fire," *Fire Journal*, Vol. 66, No. 4, July 1972, p. 60.

[15] Watrous, L. D., "28 Die in Pioneer Hotel, Tucson, Arizona," *Fire Journal*, Vol. 65, No. 3, May 1971, pp. 22–25, 27.

[16] "Bimonthly Fire Record, Burning Incense Fell on Carpet," *Fire Journal*, Vol. 64, No. 4, July 1970, p. 50.

[17] "Polyester Carpet Fire, Suisun, California," *Fire Journal*, Vol. 64, No. 5, Sept. 1970, pp. 88, 89.

[18] Hilado, C. J., *Flammability Test Methods Handbook*, Technomic Publishing Company, Inc., Westport, Conn., 1973.

[19] "Flammable Fabrics Act," Public Law 88, 67 Stat. III, 15 U.S.C.A. 1191, 1953.

[20] "Flammability of Clothing Textiles," Commercial Standard 191–53, United States Department of Commerce, Washington, D.C.

[21] U.S. Department of Commerce, "Children's Sleepwear—Proposed Flammability Standard," Federal Register, Vol. 35, No. 223, November 17, 1970, pp. 17670–17673.

[22] U.S. Department of Commerce, "Standard for the Flammability of Children's Sleepwear," DOC FF 3–71, *Federal Register*, Vol. 36, No. 146, July 27, 1971, pp. 14062–14073.

[23] U.S. Consumer Product Safety Commission, "Standard for the Flammability of Children's Sleepwear, Sizes 7 through 14," FF 5–74, *Federal Register*, Vol. 39, No. 85, May 1, 1974, pp. 15210–15228.

[24] Statistical Report, Los Angeles Fire Department, Fiscal Year 1966–1967.

[25] U.S. Department of Commerce, "Flammability Standard for Mattresses," DOC FF 4–72, Federal Register, Vol. 37, No. 110, June 7, 1972, pp. 11362–11367.

[26] U.S. Department of Commerce, "Standard for Surface Flammability of Carpets and Rugs," DOC FF 1–70, *Federal Register*, Vol. 35, No. 74, April 16, 1970, pp. 6211–6214.

[27] U.S. Department of Commerce, "Standard for Surface Flammability of Small Carpets and Rugs," DOC FF 2–70, Federal Register, Vol. 35, No. 25, December 29, 1970, pp. 19702–19704.

[28] "Test for Surface Burning Characteristics of Building Materials," ASTM E84-70, American Society for Testing and Materials, Philadelphia.

[29] Engerman, H. S., "Floor Covering Systems—A Test for Flame Propagation Index," *Journal of Fire and Flammability*, Vol. 2, 1971, pp. 11–35.

[30] Title 14, "Aeronautics and Space;" Chapter I, "Federal Aviation Administration, U.S. Department of Transportation;" Part 25, "Airworthiness Standards & Transport Category Airplanes." U.S. Code of Federal Regulations, U.S. Government Printing Office, Washington, D.C., revised annually.

[31] Title 49, Subtitle B, "Other Regulations Relating to Transportation (continued);" Chapter V, "National Highway Traffic Safety Administration, U.S. Department of Transportation;" Part 571, "Federal Motor Vehicle Safety Standards," Paragraph 571. 302, Standard No. 302, "Flammability of Interior Materials." U.S. Code of Federal Regulations, U.S. Government Printing Office, Washington, D.C., revised annually.

[32] Coleman, E. H., and Elkins, G. H. J., "The Burning of Fabrics in Oxygen Enriched Atmospheres," Parts I and II, F. R. Note 360, June 1958. Ministry of Technology and Fire Offices' Committee Joint Fire Research Organization.

[33] Turner, H. L., and Segal, L., "Fire Behavior and Protection in Hyperbaric Chambers," *Fire Technology*, Vol. 1, No. 4, Nov. 1965, pp. 269–277.

NFPA Codes, Standards, and Recommended Practices (see the latest *NFPA Publications and Visual Aids Catalog* for availability of current editions of the following documents)

NFPA No. 53M, Manual on Fire Hazard in Oxygen-enriched Atmospheres.

NFPA No. 101, Code for Safety to Life from Fire in Buildings and Structures.

NFPA No. 102, Standard for Tents, Grandstands and Air-Supported Structures Used for Places of Assembly.

NFPA No. 255, Method of Test of Surface Burning Characteristics of Building Materials.

NFPA No. 701, Standard Methods of Fire Tests for Flame-Resistant Textiles and Films.

NFPA No. 702, Standard for the Classification of the Flammability of Wearing Apparel.

Additional Readings

Bercaw, J. R., "The Melt-Drip Phenomena of Apparel," *Fire Technology*, Vol. 9, No. 1, February 1973, pp. 24–31.

Day, M., and Wiles, D. M., "Carpet Flammability: An Oxygen Index Modification to the Pill Test," *Journal of Fire and Flammability*, Vol. 4, 1973, pp. 165–173.

Drake, G. L., Jr., Perkins, R. M., and Reeves, W. A., "Flame-Resistant Cotton: A Status Report," *Journal of Fire and Flammability*, Vol. 1, 1970, pp. 78–87.

Finley, E. L. and Carter, W. H., "Description of a Fireproof Torso-Form and Ignition System Used as a Testing Technique for Studying Garment Flammability," *Journal of Fire and Flammability*, Vol. 1, 1970, pp. 166–174.

Finley, E. L. and Carter, W. H., "Temperature and Heat Flux Measurements on Life-Size Garments Ignited by Flame Contact," *Journal of Fire and Flammability*, Vol. 2, 1971, pp. 298–320.

Fire and Flammability Series, Volume 1, "Flammability of Cellulosic Materials;" Volume 2, "Smoke and Products of Combustion;" Volume 3, "Flammability of Consumer Products;" Volume 4, "Oxygen Index of Materials;" Volume 5, "Surface Flame Spread;" Volume 6, "Flame Retardants," (Collection of articles originally published in *Journal of Fire and Flammability*, Carlos J. Hilado, ed., Westport, Conn., Technomic Publishing Company, Inc., 1973.)

Freeston, W. D., Jr., "Flammability and Heat Transfer Characteristics of Cotton, Nomex and PBI Fabric," *Journal of Fire and Flammability*, Vol. 2, 1971, pp. 57–76.

Hammack, J. M., "Los Angeles Fire Department Tests—Cigarette Ignition of Bedding," *Fire Journal*, Vol. 59, No. 3, May 1965, pp. 9–11.

Hendrix, J. E., Drake, G. L., Jr., and Reeves, W. A., "Effects of Fabric Weight and Construction on Oxygen Index (OI) Values for Cotton Cellulose," *Journal of Fire and Flammability*, Vol. 3, 1972, pp. 38–45.

"Hospitals and Flammable Fabrics: California Space History," *Fire Journal*, Vol. 66, No. 3, May 1972, pp. 18–24.

Johnston, R. and Radnofsky, "Nonflammable Clothing Development Program," *Fire Technology*, Vol. 4, No. 2, May 1968, pp. 88–102.

Kasem, M. A., and Rouette, H. K., "Flammability and Fire Retardancy of Fabrics," *Journal of Fire and Flammability*, Vol. 3, 1972, pp. 316–329.

Kuchta, J. M., Furno, A. L., and Martindill, G. H., 'Flammability of Fabrics and Other Materials in Oxygen-Enriched Atmospheres: Part I, Ignition Temperatures and Flame Spread Rates," *Fire Technology*, Vol. 5, No. 3, August 1969, pp. 203–216.

Lee, B. T., and Wiltshire, L. W., "Fire-Spread Models of Upholstered Furniture," *Journal of Fire and Flammability*, Vol. 3, 1972, pp. 164–175.

Litchfield, E. L. and Kubala, T. A., "Flammability of Fabrics and Other Materials in Oxygen-Enriched Atmospheres: Part II, Minimum Ignition Energies," *Fire Technology*, Vol. 5, No. 4, November 1969, pp. 341–345.

Quintiere, J., "Radiative Characteristics of Fire Fighters' Coat Fabrics," *Fire Technology*, Vol. 10, No. 2, May 1974, pp. 153–161.

"Report of the National Commission on Fire Prevention and Control: Excerpts," *Fire Journal*, Vol. 67, No. 4, July 1973, pp. 6–23, 114–124.

Schafran, E., "Development of Flammability Specifications for Furnishings," *Fire Journal*, Vol. 68, No. 2, March 1974, pp. 36–39.

Segal, L., "Flameproofing: Facts and Fallacies," *Fire Journal*, Vol. 60, No. 6, November 1966, pp. 41–45.

———, "Letters to the Association: Blankets and Other Nonclothing Fabrics," *Fire Journal*, Vol. 62, No. 3, May 1968, p. 109.

———, "Letters to the Association: Permanent-Press Fabrics," *Fire Journal*, Vol. 64, No. 1, January 1970, p. 93.

"Space-Age Contribution to Residential Fire Safety (Full-Scale Fire Tests of Bedroom Furnishing)," *Fire Journal*, Vol. 68, No. 2, March 1974, pp. 18–25.

Stevens, R. E., "For Architects and Builders: Carpeting as a Fire Hazard," *Fire Journal*, Vol. 64, No. 4, July 1970, p. 65, 66.

"Textile Flammability and Consumer Safety," *Proceedings of an International Conference on Textile Flammability and Consumer Safety*, Gottleib Duttweiter Institute.

Welker, R. R., Wesson, H. R., and Sliepcevich, C. M., "Ignition of Alpha-Cellulose and Cotton Fabric by Flame Radiation," *Fire Technology*, Vol. 5, No. 1, February 1969, pp. 59–66.

Yuill, C. H., "Floor Coverings: What Is the Hazard?" *Fire Journal*, Vol. 61, No. 1, January 1967, pp. 11–19.

Chapter 3

FLAMMABLE AND COMBUSTIBLE LIQUIDS

Liquids are characterized by free movement of molecules among themselves, but the molecules do not have the tendency to separate from one another which is characteristic of gases. Liquids, unlike gases, are only slightly compressible and are incapable of indefinite expansion. They differ from solids in the ease their molecules move one upon another causing them to adapt themselves to the shape of the containing vessel. Some liquids are very viscous, however, and no sharp line can be drawn between liquids and solids. Neither is there a sharp line of demarcation between liquids and gases. Materials can exist in either state depending upon the temperature and pressure conditions. Liquids tend to become gases as their temperature is increased or as their pressure is decreased. On the other hand, gases tend to become liquids as their temperature is decreased or as the pressure is increased with the qualification that a material can only exist as a gas regardless of how high the pressure might be, if its temperature is above the so-called critical temperature. (The Critical Temperature is an intrinsic property of a material and is the temperature above which the material can exist only in the gaseous state.) In all cases, the actual state is determined by the combination of temperature and pressure.

A. Hazards of Flammable and Combustible Liquids

Strictly speaking, flammable and combustible liquids are not a fire cause, though often referred to as such. More correctly, they are contributing factors because a spark or other minor source of ignition which might otherwise be harmless may cause fire or explosion in the presence of flammable vapors.

It is the vapor from the evaporation of a flammable or combustible liquid when exposed to air or under the influence of heat, rather than the liquid itself, which burns or explodes when mixed with air in certain proportions in the presence of a source of ignition. For example, the proportions (flammable range) for carbon disulfide are from about 1 to 44 percent carbon disulfide vapors in air by volume; and for ethyl alcohol, from about 4 to 19 percent by volume. For gasoline, these proportions range from about 1.4 to 7.6 percent by volume. Therefore, storing flammable and combustible liquids in the proper type of closed containers and minimizing the exposure of the liquid to air while in use are of fundamental importance in controlling the fire hazard presented during storage and handling.

Explosions of flammable vapor-air mixtures near the lower or upper limits of the flammable range of a particular vapor-air mixture are less intense than those occurring in the intermediate concentrations of the same mixture. Flammable vapor-air explosions most frequently occur when confined within a space such as a container, tank, room, or building.

The violence of flammable vapor explosions depends upon the concentration and the nature of the vapors as well as on the quantity of vapor-air mixture and type of the enclosure containing the mixture.

Distinct from an explosion of a flammable vapor-air mixture inside a tank or container is the internal buildup of pressure or the overpressuring of a tank which results in a rupture. As with vapor explosions, pressure ruptures vary in their violence. Any closed container of strong construction, whether or not it holds a flammable liquid, may, when exposed to a severe fire, rupture with extreme violence if not insulated or equipped with adequate, properly designed vents and if not adequately cooled with water (see Part C of this chapter).

Flammable and combustible liquid fire and explosion prevention measures embrace one or more of the following techniques or principles: (1) exclusion of sources of ignition, (2) exclusion of air, (3) keeping the liquids in closed containers or systems, (4) ventilation to prevent the accumulation of vapor within the flammable range, and (5) use of an atmosphere of inert gas instead of air. Extinguishing methods for flammable and combustible liquid fires involve shutting off the fuel supply if possible, excluding air by various means, or cooling the liquid to stop evaporation, or a combination of these.

Gasoline is the most widely used flammable liquid. Its generation of flammable vapors at atmospheric temperatures is a matter of common knowledge. There are many other volatile flammable products, some of which have names that give no indication of the character of the liquid. The NFPA publishes a list of proprietary products in NFPA No. 325A, Flash Point Index of Trade Name Liquids. A comprehensive list of the more commonly used flammable or combustible liquids with the characteristics of each, as far as information is available, appears in NFPA No. 325M, Fire Hazard Properties of Flammable Liquids, Gases, and Volatile Solids (see also Table 3-11A in this HANDBOOK).

Flash point, though the commonly accepted and most important criterion of the relative hazard of flammable and combustible liquids, is by no means the only factor in evaluating the hazard. The ignition temperature, flammable range, rate of evaporation, reactivity when contaminated or exposed to heat, density, and rate of diffusion of the vapor also have a bearing. The flash point and other factors which determine the relative susceptibility of a flammable or combustible liquid to ignition have comparatively little influence on its burning characteristics after fire has burned for a short time.

The use of flammable and combustible liquids produced by chemical and petro-chemical companies is increasing rapidly. Although many of these products can be classed as normal or stable liquids, others introduce a new problem of stability or reactivity.

The storage, handling, and use of unstable (reactive) flammable or combustible liquids call for special attention. It may be necessary to increase the distances to property lines and between tanks or to provide extra fire protection. For example, it would be poor practice to locate heat reactive and water reactive flammable or combustible liquid tanks adjacent to each other. It could be anticipated that, in the event of a ground fire, if water were applied to the heat reactive tank for protection, some of it might inadvertently get into the tank of water reactive liquid and cause a violent reaction.

B. Classification of Flammable and Combustible Liquids

For fire protection purposes, an arbitrary division between liquids and gases has been established based upon the definition of a flammable liquid appearing in NFPA No. 321, Basic Classification of Flammable and Combustible Liquids. Liquids are those fluids having a vapor pressure not exceeding 40 psi absolute (2068.6 mm) at 100°F (37.8°C) (approximately 25 psi gage pressure). Additionally, another arbitrary division has been established between liquids and solids for the purposes of this classification system. It is that a liquid is defined as one which has a fluidity greater than that of 300 penetration asphalt.

The concept of the following classification system is to divide liquids that will burn into three categories. It is anticipated that in most areas the indoor temperature could reach 100°F at some time during the year; therefore, all liquids with flash points below 100°F are called Class I liquids. In some areas the ambient temperature could exceed 100°F, or only a moderate degree of heating would be required to heat the liquid to its flash point. Based on this concept, an arbitrary division of 100°F to 140°F was established for liquids in this flash point range to be known as Class II liquids. Since liquids with flash points higher than 140°F would require considerable heating from a source other than ambient temperatures before ignition could occur, they have been identified as Class III liquids.

Flammable Liquids

Flammable liquids shall mean any liquid having a flash point below 100°F and having a vapor pressure not exceeding 40 psia (2068.6 mm) at 100°F (37.8°C.)

Class I liquids shall include those having flash points below 100°F (37.8°C) and may be subdivided as follows:

Class IA shall include those having flash points below 73°F (22.8°C) and having a boiling point below 100°F (37.8°C).

Class IB shall include those having flash points below 73°F (22.8°C) and having a boiling point at or above 100°F (37.8°C).

Class IC shall include those having flash points at or above 73°F (22.8°C) and below 100°F (37.8°C).

Combustible Liquids

Liquids with a flash point at or above 100°F (37.8°C) are referred to as combustible liquids and may be subdivided as follows:

Class II liquids shall include those having flash points at or above 100°F (37.8°C) and below 140°F (60°C).

Class IIIA liquids shall include those having flash points at or above 140°F (60°C) and below 200°F (93.4°C).

Class IIIB liquids shall include those having flash points at or above 200°F (93.4°C).

Underwriters Laboratories, Inc., Classification

Underwriters Laboratories, Inc., has a system for grading the relative flammability hazards of various liquids. This classification is based on the following scale:

Ether class	100
Gasoline class	90-100
Alcohol (ethyl) class	60- 70
Kerosene class*	30- 40
Paraffin oil class	10- 20

* A standard kerosene of 100°F closed cap flash point is rated 40.

Other Classification Systems

There are numerous other classification systems for flammable and combustible liquids. In some cases the break points between classes of liquids are different, or the open cup flash point tester is used for the determination of the flash point. The solubility of the liquid with water is also considered in some classification systems.

Solids with Flash Points

There are many chemicals that are solids at 100°F or above and therefore are classified as solids. However, when heated the solid becomes liquid giving off flammable vapors, and flash points can be determined. When in a liquid state, these solids should be treated as liquids with similar flash points. Other manufactured solids such as paste waxes or polishes may contain varying amounts of flammable liquids. The flash point and amount of liquid in such manufactured solid materials will indicate the degree of hazard.

C. Physical Properties of Liquids

The physical and fire characteristics of liquids as well as of other materials are defined and explained in Section 2, Chapter I. The following is additional information on certain of these characteristics as they relate to flammable and combustible liquids.

Specific Gravity

As the specific gravity of water equals one, a liquid with a specific gravity of less than one, unless it is soluble in water, will float on water; a specific gravity greater than one indicates that water will float on the liquid. This is an important consideration in handling a flammable or combustible liquid fire. The specific gravities of various liquids are given in Table 3-11A.

Vapor Density Ratio

Vapor density is the weight per unit volume of a pure gas or vapor. In fire protection work, vapor density is reported in terms of the ratio of the relative weight of a volume of vapor to the weight of an equal volume of air under the same conditions of temperature and pressure. In this respect, the vapor density ratio is similar to the specific gravity of a liquid except that air is used as the standard in place of water. Air is taken as unity and the vapor density reported as a ratio such that a vapor density of three indicates that the vapor is three times as dense or heavy as air.

$$\text{Vapor density ratio} = \frac{\text{molecular weight (MW) of the material}}{\text{composite molecular weight of air}}$$

$$= \frac{MW}{29}.$$

Vapor density ratios are reported at normal atmospheric temperature and pressure conditions. Conditions deviating widely from normal will appreciably change the density of any compressible fluid.

Generally, pure vapors are seldom found except in cases where the liquid is normally above its boiling point. For those liquids that are stored or handled below their boiling points, the vapor above the liquid will be a mixture of vapor and air.

For liquids having boiling points above the prevailing ambient temperature at atmospheric pressure, the vapor density may be a misleading figure. As an example, the boiling point of ethyl acetate is 171°F. At 70°F its vapor pressure is about 2.35 psi or 0.16 atm (atmospheres). Thus, an equilibrium mixture of ethyl acetate vapor and air at 70°F, as would be encountered in a closed vessel, would have a composition of 16 percent ethyl acetate vapor and 84 percent air. The "theoretical" vapor density of ethyl acetate is 3.0 (see Table 3-11A). The "actual" density of the "vapor-air-mixture" which is given off from ethyl acetate at 70°F and at atmospheric pressure is:

$$.16 \times 3.0 + .84 \times 1 = 1.32.$$

Vapor densities are ordinarily used only as an indication of the settling or rising tendency of a vapor.

Vapor Pressure

Where a liquid is present in a closed container with an atmosphere of vapor-air mixture above the liquid surface, the percentage of vapor in the mixture may be determined from the vapor pressure. The percentage of vapor is in direct proportion to the relationship between the vapor pressure of the liquid and the total pressure of the mixture. For example, acetone at a temperature of 100°F has a vapor pressure of 7.6 psia. Assuming total pressure at 14.7 psia, the proportion of acetone vapor present will be $\frac{7.6}{14.7}$ or 52 percent.

Vapor pressures of petroleum liquids usually are determined by the Reid method as recommended by the American Society for Testing and Materials, ASTM Standard D-323 and gives the psia at 100°F which differs slightly from the true vapor pressure. Vapor pressure figures for many substances will be found in chemical handbooks. If the closed cup flash point of a liquid is known and also the vapor pressure at the flash point temperature, the lower flammable limit for the vapor (at the flash point temperature) in percent by volume at normal atmospheric pressure may be calculated as follows:

$$LFL = \frac{V}{0.147}$$

where *LFL* is percent vapor by volume at lower flammable limit, and *V* is vapor pressure, psia, at flash point temperature. At other pressures,

$$LFL = \frac{100V}{P}$$

where *P* is the ambient pressure in psia.

In a mixture of volatile flammable liquids, the effects of the two vapor pressures, one upon the other, in general, depend upon whether the two liquids are completely miscible, partly miscible, or completely immiscible in each other. If the two liquids are completely miscible, they lower each other's vapor pressures; if they are nearly completely immiscible, the vapor pressure of the mixture is the sum of the partial pressure of each liquid layer (Dalton's Law of Partial Pressure); if both liquids are partially miscible, the relationships are more complex.

Evaporation Rate

Evaporation rate is the rate at which a liquid is converted to the vapor state at any given temperature and pressure. All materials evaporate; it is the differing rates of evaporation of mixtures that is of primary concern to fire protection. In general, as the boiling point decreases, the vapor pressure and the evaporation rate increases.

Viscosity

The viscosity of a liquid is a measure of its resistance to flow resulting from the combined effects of adhesion and cohesion; or, stated differently, it is a measure of internal friction in a fluid. Although there are several recognized devices for determining viscosity, in general the measurement principles are the same. These involve a measure of the time required for a predetermined quantity of liquid to flow into a receiving flask or through an orifice of a prescribed size at a specified temperature.

Latent Heat of Vaporization

Latent heat of vaporization is the heat which is absorbed when one gram of liquid is transformed into vapor at the boiling point under one atmosphere pressure, and is expressed in calories per gram (Cal/gm) or is expressed in Btu per pound.

Solubility in Water and Surface Tension

Solubility in water and surface tension are other characteristics of a liquid which are of interest in the fire protection field. For example, fires in liquids which are soluble in water can be extinguished by dilution of the liquid with water or will require "alcohol type" foams for extinguishment. The use of wetting agents affects the surface tension of a liquid and in some cases aids in fire extinguishment (see Sec. 13, Chap. 1).

D. Fire Characteristics of Liquids

Part D of this chapter supplements the material on the properties of flammable and combustible liquids relating to their fire characteristics as defined and explained in Section 2, Chapter 1.

Flash Point

A vapor mixed with air in proportions below the lower limit of flammability may burn at the source of ignition, that is, in the zone immediately surrounding the source of ignition, without propagating (spreading) flame away from

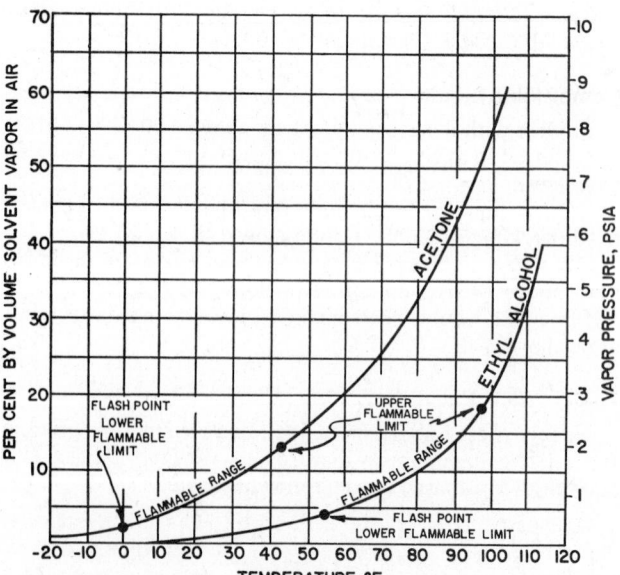

Fig. 3-3A. Relationship between flash point, flammable limits, temperature, and vapor pressure for acetone and ethyl alcohol. Liquid, vapor, and air in equilibrium in a closed container at normal atmospheric pressure.

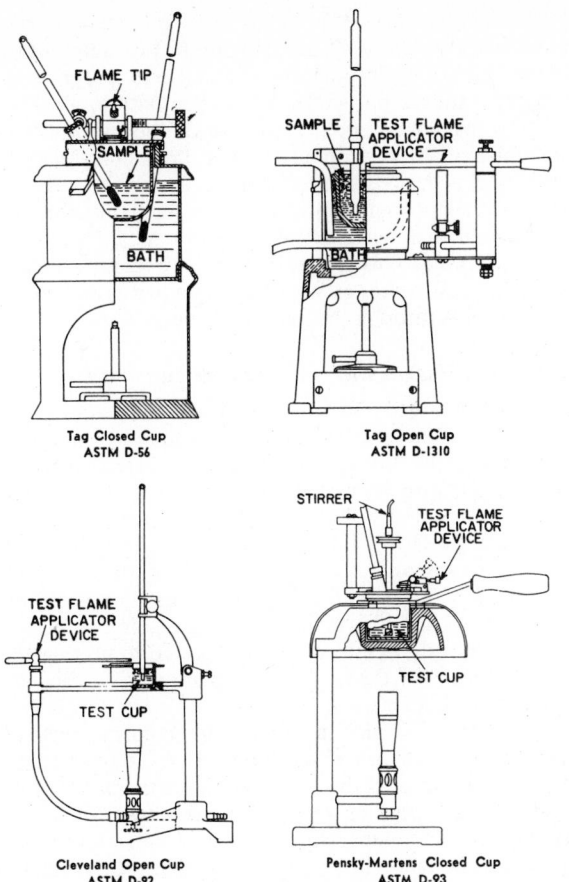

Fig. 3-3B. Four of the commonly used testers for determining flash points of flammable or combustible liquids. The material to be tested is slowly heated, and at periodic intervals a test flame is applied to the vapor space. Flash point is the temperature at which a flash of fire is seen when the test flame is applied. The full details of conducting tests for each type of testing apparatus are given in the applicable standard of the American Society for Testing and Materials or by the manufacturer.

the source of ignition. The flash point of a liquid corresponds roughly to the lowest temperature at which the vapor pressure of the liquid is just sufficient to produce a flammable mixture at the lower limit of flammability.

There are several types of apparatus (see Fig. 3-3B) for determining flash point by test. NFPA No. 321 specifies the Tagliabue (Tag) Closed Tester for testing liquids except for certain viscous or film-forming materials with a flash point at or below 200°F, as described in ASTM D56. The Pensky-Martens Closed Tester, ASTM D93, is specified for testing liquids having flash points above 200°F or for certain viscous or film-forming materials.

As an alternate to the above mentioned closed cup test methods, the Setaflash Closed Cup Tester may be used for testing aviation turbine fuels, ASTM D3243, and for testing paints, enamels, lacquers, varnishes and related products and their components having flash points between 32°F (0°C) and 230°F (110°C), ASTM D3278.

Open cup flash points are sometimes used in grading flammable liquids in transportation and are determined by the Tagliabue (Tag) Open Cup Apparatus, ASTM D1310, or the Cleveland Open Cup Apparatus, ASTM D92. Open cup flash points represent conditions with the liquid in the open and are generally higher than the closed cup flash point figures for the same substances. However, closed cup

flash point figures are generally higher than the actual lower temperature limit of flammability (flash point) when tested in a vertical tube utilizing the principle of upward flame propagation.

It is essential to realize that flash point varies with pressure and with the oxygen content of the atmosphere as well as with the purity of the product being tested, the method of test, and the skill of the operator running the test. It is quite possible to have a flammable mixture far below the stated flash point value if the pressure is considerably less than one atmosphere.

Ignition Temperature (Autoignition Temperature, Autogenous Ignition Temperature)

The autoignition temperature reported for a flammable liquid is generally the temperature to which a closed or nearly closed container must be heated in order that the liquid in question, when introduced into the container, will ignite spontaneously and burn. Time lags of a minute or more are frequently involved. The standard method of test for autoignition temperatures of petroleum products is described in ASTM D2155, Autoignition Temperature of Liquid Petroleum Products.

Ignition Temperatures and Molecular Weights

Within a given hydrocarbon series, such as the straight chain series running from normal methane down through normal decane, ignition temperature decreases as molecular weight or carbon chain length (see Fig. 3-3C) increases, other factors being equal. (See Sec. 2, Chap. I, for molecular weights.) Thus pentane $CH_3(CH_2)_3CH_3$ (Molecular Weight 72.1) has a higher ignition temperature than hexane, $(CH_3CH_2)_4CH_3$ (Molecular Weight 86.2).

Boiling Point

The temperature at which the equilibrium vapor pressure of a liquid equals the total pressure on the surface is known as the boiling point. The boiling point is entirely dependent on the total pressure. (Boiling point increases with an in-

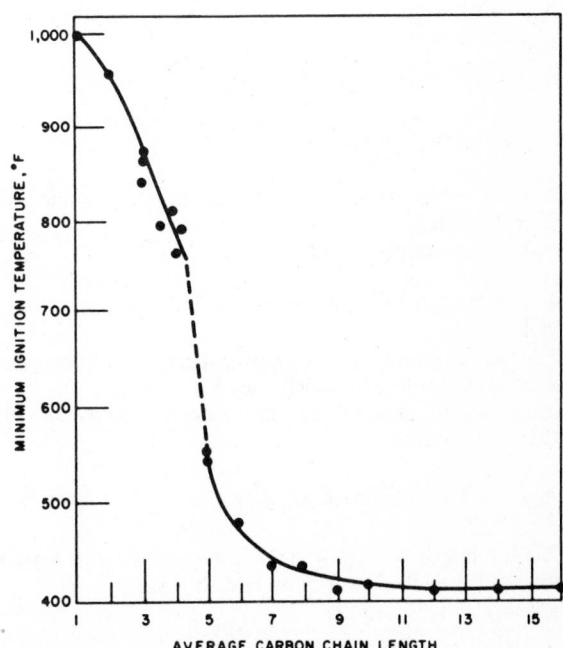

Fig. 3-3C. Minimum ignition temperatures of hydrocarbons of various carbon chain lengths.

crease in pressure.) Theoretically, any liquid may be made to boil at any desired temperature by sufficiently altering the total pressure on its surface. Similarly, unless decomposition takes place, any liquid may be caused to boil at any desired pressure by sufficiently changing its temperature.

The temperature at which a liquid boils when under a total pressure of one atmosphere (14.7 psia) is termed the normal boiling point.

The above definitions apply to pure materials or constant boiling mixtures. The greater quantity of flammable liquids and gases on the market today are mixtures and do not follow the physical laws governing pure materials. The boiling points of mixtures are reported as distillation curves. The 10 percent point of a distillation performed in accordance with ASTM D86, Standard Method of Test for Distillation of Petroleum Products, is used as the boiling point for most NFPA standards.

Flammable (Explosive) Limits

The storage, handling, and use of flammable and combustible liquids within the flammable range, as defined in Section 2, should be avoided wherever possible.

Calculating Vapor Volume and Flammable Mixtures

It is frequently helpful to calculate the volume of air required to provide dilution sufficient to prevent the formation of an ignitible mixture as, for example, in the design of a ventilating system for a drying oven. This can be readily done when the quantity of solvent supplied is known or can be reasonably estimated.

For example, consider a process in which acetone vapor is released. The flammable range for acetone vapor in air is from 2.6 to 12.8 percent by volume. Any mixture containing more air than 100 minus 2.6 or 97.4 percent of air—equivalent to $\frac{97.4}{2.6}$ or approximately 37 volumes of air to one volume of vapor—will be too lean to be ignitible. Hence, if the volume of vapor can be estimated, it is a simple matter to determine the required air volume.

The volume of vapor produced from 1 gal of solvent can be calculated from the specific gravity of the liquid and the vapor density as follows:

Cubic feet of vapor from 1 gal of liquid =

$$\frac{8.33 \times \text{specific gravity of liquid (H}_2\text{O} = 1)}{0.075 \times \text{vapor density of vapor (air} = 1)}$$

where 8.33 is the weight of 1 gal of water in pounds and 0.075 is the weight of 1 cu ft of air in pounds.

Stated more simply:

$$\text{Vapor equivalent of one gal} = 111 \times \frac{Sp.\,G.}{V.D.}.$$

If the vapor density is not known, it can readily be calculated from the molecular weight (see Sec. 2, Chap. 1).

Again taking acetone as an example ($Sp.\,G. = .792$; $V.D. = 2$) we have:

$$\text{Vapor equivalent of one gal is: } 111 \times \frac{.792}{2} = 44 \text{ cu ft.}$$

The volume of air required to dilute vapor from 1 gal of acetone to below the lower flammable limit is:

$$44 \times 37 = 1,628 \text{ cu ft.}$$

If the rate of evaporation of acetone into a given space (oven, etc.) should be 1 gpm, it would require 1,628 cfm

of uncontaminated ventilating air to keep the vapor concentration below the lower flammable limit. For different evaporation rates the air quantity would be in proportion. In practice, a substantial excess of air ventilation, as a factor of safety, would be applied because of the inevitable non-uniformity of the atmosphere within the enclosure.

Where it is desired to keep a space "too rich" to be ignitible, a similar procedure (using the upper flammable limit) may be used to determine the maximum air quantity which can be tolerated. This is not, however, a recommended procedure in most cases, as with this system it is necessary to enter and pass through the flammable range.

Variation in Hazard with Temperature and Pressure

The temperature and pressure to which a liquid is subjected must often be considered in the practical application of the flammable limits of flammable liquids as given in the Table 3-11A, Fire Hazard Properties of Certain Flammable Liquids, Gases, and Volatile Solids in Chapter 11 of this Section. It can be shown that these factors have a pronounced effect on the fire and explosion hazard and are as important considerations in safe handling as are the flammable limits themselves. A liquid which has a flash point above room temperature and, therefore, is not expected to produce flammable vapors will do so if its temperature is raised to its flash point or higher.

The extent to which a liquid will vaporize, when the opposing vapor is that of the liquid itself, is reduced when the pressure opposing this vaporization is increased, and increased as the opposing pressure is decreased. In the same way, at a higher temperature the liquid will have a higher vapor pressure and will tend to vaporize in greater amounts. When, at a given temperature and pressure, the liquid has vaporized to the point where no more vaporization will occur unless conditions are changed, a state of equilibrium is said to be reached. It is evident that equilibrium cannot exist other than in a closed system, as in the open air a vaporizing liquid would continue to vaporize until the supply was exhausted. The pressure-temperature effect, therefore, is applicable only in tanks, pipes, and processing equipment in which the liquid and vapor-air mixture approach equilibrium.

Figures 3-3D and 3-3E show the effect of temperature and pressure on flammable limits as determined by F.C. Mitchell and H. C. Vernon.[1] In using these charts it should be noted that they represent equilibrium conditions, and that prior to the establishment of equilibrium, values may be different. For example, when a liquid is introduced into a pressure container with air at a temperature such that the resultant vapor-air mixture will be above the upper flammable limit according to the chart, some time will elapse before sufficient evaporation has taken place to reach this condition; meanwhile, the mixture may be flammable or explosive.

It should also be noted that the pressures developed, or the violence of an explosion, will vary with the initial pressure of the vapor-air mixture. With high initial pressures, the pressures are greater, as in the familiar example of the gasoline engine. With low initial pressures, the pressures are relatively lower.

The lower limits of flammability of solvent vapors are affected by the temperature. This fact is of concern in such installations as industrial ovens, where pressure is not a factor but where temperature needs to be taken into account in evaluating the hazard. In such industrial ovens, mechanical or forced ventilation is usually employed to dilute

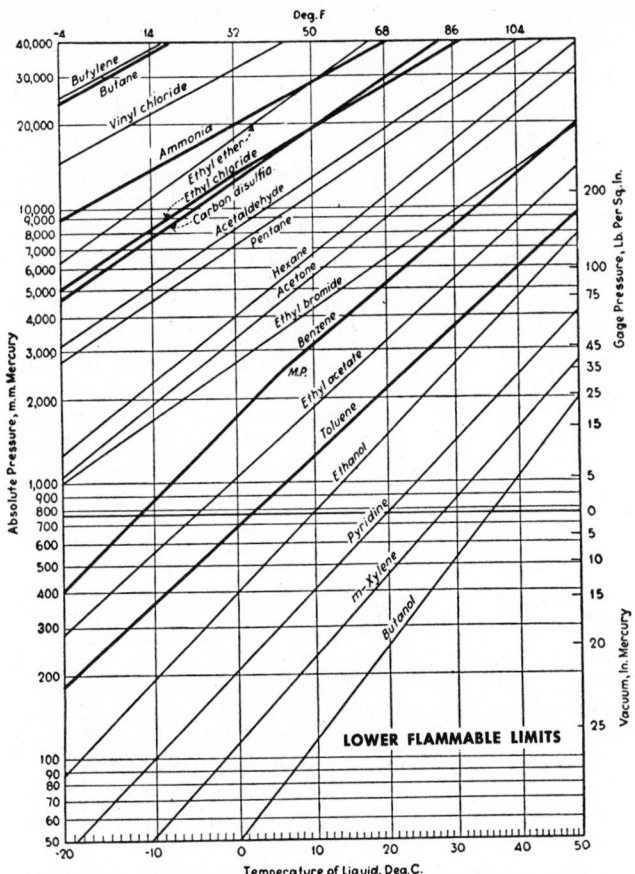

Fig. 3-3D. Variation of lower flammable limits with temperature and pressure. This chart is applicable only to flammable liquids or gases in equilibrium in a closed container. Mixtures of vapor and air will be too lean to burn at temperatures below and at pressures above the values shown by the line on the chart for any substance. Conditions represented by points to the left of and above the respective lines are accordingly nonflammable. Points where the diagonal lines cross the zero gage pressure line (760 mm of mercury absolute pressure) indicate flash point temperatures at normal atmospheric pressure.

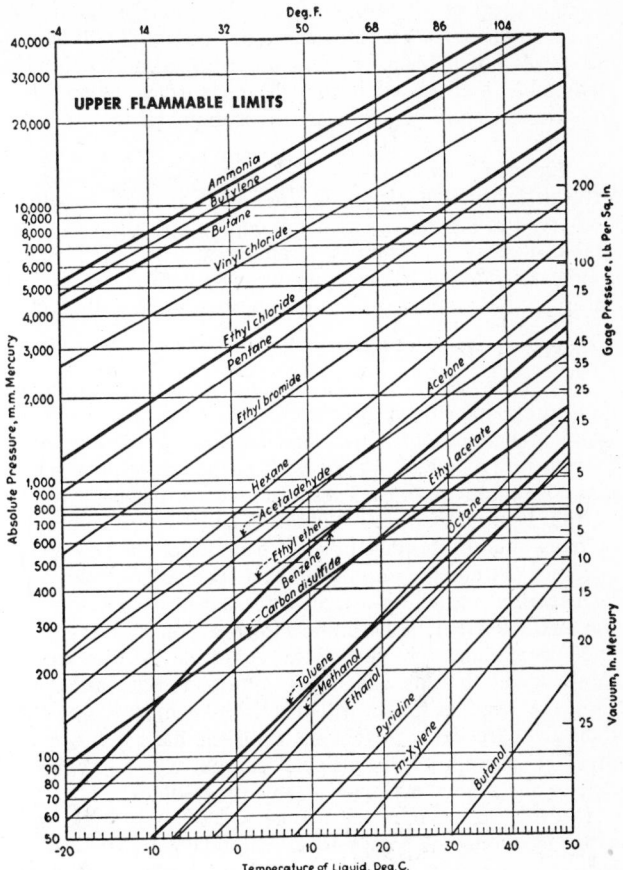

Fig. 3-3E. Variation of upper flammable limits with temperature and pressure. This chart is applicable only to flammable liquids or gases in equilibrium in a closed container. Mixtures of vapor and air will be too "rich" to be flammable at temperatures above and pressures below the values shown by the lines on the chart for any substance. Conditions represented by points to the right of and below the respective lines are accordingly nonflammable.

the concentration of the vapors below their lower flammable limits in air and to remove them from the oven. Information on the lower flammable limits of the vapors at elevated temperatures is needed in order to determine the amount of ventilation required for safe operation of an oven (see Table 3-3A).

Energy Required for Ignition of Vapors

The principal sources of ignition of flammable liquids include flames, hot surfaces, electrical or frictional sparks, and adiabatic compression.

Flames: Except for extremely small ones produced under laboratory conditions, flames are unfailing sources of ignition for mixtures of flammable vapor and air which are within the flammable range. Flames must be capable of heating the vapor to its ignition temperature in the presence of air in order to be a source of ignition. For some liquids and solids it will be necessary for the flame to be of sufficient duration and heat to volatilize the fuel and to ignite the released vapors. Once ignited the radiated heat from the burning vapors perpetuates the burning process.

Electrical, Static, and Friction Sparks: These must have sufficient energy to ignite flammable vapor-air mixtures.

Electrical sparks from most commercial electrical supply installations are above flame temperatures and will usually ignite flammable mixtures. However, friction sparks may fail to ignite a flammable mixture because the spark may be of such short duration as to fail to heat the vapor to its ignition point. Also, not only must an electrical spark have sufficient intensity and length but some variable conditions must be within certain limits before ignition will occur. The nature of the points and surfaces as well as the composition, temperature, and pressure of vapor-air mixtures are the principal variables. Most of these same factors and variables also apply to static electrical sparks and frictional sparks as a source of ignition since in either case the spark must be of sufficient duration or intensity, or both, to create heat enough to cause ignition. For information on the control of static electricity as a source of ignition, see Section 5, Chapter 5.

Hot Surfaces: These are a source of ignition if large enough and hot enough. The smaller the heated surface the hotter it must be to ignite a mixture. The larger the heated surface in relation to the mixture, the more rapidly will ignition take place and the lower the temperature needed for ignition. A flammable liquid, however, must remain in contact with a hot surface a sufficient length of time to form a vapor-air mixture within its flammable range. For example, a single drop of a low viscosity, highly volatile, flammable liquid on the surface of an electric hot plate at 2,000°F may ignite. A hot exhaust pipe in the open seldom ignites a flammable mixture even though the surface temperature may be considerably above the environmental ignition temperature test method.

Adiabatic Compression: This has been the cause of several destructive explosions. When controlled, adiabatic compression is the basis of diesel engine operation. A flammable mixture if compressed rapidly will be ignited when the heat generated by the compressing action is sufficient to raise the flammable vapor to its ignition temperature.

Behavior of Mixed Liquids

The behavior of mixed liquids varies considerably, depending upon the physical characteristics and the environmental conditions. However, the vapor pressure or evaporation rate of mixed liquids is of particular importance in the prevention of fires. These factors are particularly important when a mixture of liquids is listed as nonflammable or has a high flash point but which under conditions of use becomes extremely flammable. As a specific example, sufficient carbon tetrachloride can be added to gasoline so that the mixture has no flash point. However, on standing in an open container, the carbon tetrachloride will evaporate more rapidly than the gasoline. Over a period of time, therefore, the residual liquid will first show a high flash point, then a progressively lower one, until the flash point of the final ten percent of the original sample will approximate that of the higher boiling fractions of gasoline.

In order to evaluate the fire hazard of such liquid mixtures, fractional evaporation tests can be conducted at room temperature in open vessels. After evaporation of appropriate fractions such as 10, 20, 40, 60, and 90 percent of the original sample, flash point tests can be conducted on the residue. The results of such tests indicate the class into which the liquid should be placed if the conditions of use are such as to make it likely that appreciable evaporation will take place.

With other liquid mixtures the flash point may increase as evaporation occurs.

Noncompatible Materials

Noncompatible materials of construction or equipment are those materials with which an unstable flammable liquid or its normal reaction products will combine, or whose products of corrosion are contaminants. For example, if mercury is a harmful contaminant, then mercury thermometers should not be used; if a chlorinated compound slowly releases hydrochloric acid, aluminum should not be used; the aluminum chloride formed by this acid may act as a catalyst. There are many materials which will chemically react with each other, and in case of any question, reference should be made to the NFPA No. 491M Manual of Hazardous Chemical Reactions.

E. Burning Characteristics of Liquids

Since it is the vapors from flammable liquids which burn, the ease of ignition as well as the rate of burning can be related to such properties as the vapor pressure, flash point boiling point, and evaporation rate. Liquids having vapors in the flammable range above the liquid surface at the stored temperature will have a rapid rate of flame propagation. Flammable and combustible liquids having flash points above stored temperature have a slower rate of flame propagation as it is necessary for the heat of the fire to heat sufficiently the liquid surface to form a flammable vapor-air mixture before the flame will spread through the vapor. There are many variables affecting the rate of flame propagation and burning including environmental factors, wind velocity, temperature, heat of combustion, latent heat of vaporization, and barometric pressure.

Table 3-3A. The Effect of Elevated Temperature on the Lower Flammable Limit of Combustible Solvents as Encountered in Industrial Ovens‡

Solvent	Flash Pt Closed Cup	Lower Flammable Limit Percent Vapor by Volume at Initial Temperature, °F						
		Room	212	392	437	482	572	662
Acetone	3	2.67	2.40	2.00*	—	—	—	—
Amyl Acetate, Iso	77	—	1.00	0.82	—	0.76*	—	—
Benzene	—4	1.32	1.10	0.93	—	—	0.80*	—
Butyl Alcohol, Normal	100	—	1.56	1.27	1.22*	—	—	—
Cresol, Meta-Para	202	—	1.06†	0.93	—	0.88*	—	—
Cyclohexane	—4	1.12	1.01	0.83*	—	—	—	—
Cyclohexanone	111	—	1.11	0.96	0.94	0.91*	—	—
Ethyl Alcohol	54	3.48	3.01	2.64	—	2.47	2.29*	—
Ethyl Lactate	131	—	1.55	1.29	—	1.22*	—	—
Gasoline	—45	1.07	0.94	0.77*	—	—	—	—
Hexane, Normal	—15	1.08	0.90	0.72*	—	—	—	—
High-Solvency Petroleum Naphtha	36	1.00	0.89	0.74	0.72	0.69*	—	—
Methyl Alcohol	52	6.70	5.80	4.81	—	4.62	4.44*	—
Methyl Ethyl Ketone	21	1.83	1.70	1.33*	—	—	—	—
Methyl Lactate	121	—	2.21	1.86	1.80	1.75*	—	—
Mineral Spirits, No. 10	104	—	0.77	0.63*	—	—	—	—
Toluene	48	1.17	0.99	0.82	—	—	0.72*	—
Turpentine	95	—	0.69	0.54*	—	—	—	—
V. M. & P. Naptha	28	0.92	0.76	0.67*	—	—	—	—

* Rapid and extensive thermal decomposition and oxidation reactions in vapor-air mixture at this temperature.
† Lower limit determined at 302°F.
‡ From NFPA *Quarterly,* April 1950; UL Bulletin of Research No. 43.

Liquid hydrocarbons normally burn with an orange flame and with the emission of dense clouds of black smoke where alcohols normally burn with a clean blue flame and very little smoke. Certain terpenes and ethers burn with considerable ebullition (boiling) of the liquid surface with resulting difficulty in the extinguishment.

Boilover, Slopover, or Frothover

There are three specific conditions that deserve special mention in regard to fires in open-topped tanks containing various types of oils. They are boilover, slopover, and frothing, and each is described in the following paragraphs.

Boilover: This describes a phenomenon that may occur spontaneously during a fire in an open top tank containing certain types of crude oils, such as is the case when the roof of a tank is blown off by an explosion, usually caused by lightning. After a long period of quiescent burning, there is a sudden overflow or ejection of some of the residual oil in the tank. It is caused by boiling water that forms a quickly-expanding steam-oil froth. The frothing results from the existence of the three following conditions, the absence of any one of which will prevent the occurrence:

1. The tank must contain free water or water-oil emulsion at the tank bottom. This situation will normally prevail in tanks storing crude oil.

2. The oil must contain components having a wide range of boiling points, such that, when the lighter components have been distilled off and burned at the surface, the residue, having a temperature of 300°F (149°C) or over, is more dense than the oil immediately below. This residue sinks below the surface and forms a layer of gradually increasing depth which advances downward at a rate substantially faster than the rate of regression of the burning surface. This sets up the so-called "heat wave" which is the result of localized settling of a part of the hot surface oil until it reaches the colder oil below. It is not heat conduction from the burning surface downwards.

3. Sufficient content of heavy ends in the oil to produce a residue which can form a tough persistent froth of oil and steam.

Slopover: This can result when a water stream is applied to the hot surface of a burning oil, provided the oil is viscous and its temperature exceeds the boiling point of water. Since only the surface oil is involved, a slopover is a relatively mild occurrence.

Frothover: This means the overflowing of a container not on fire when water boils under the surface of a viscous hot oil. A typical example would be when hot asphalt is loaded into a tank car containing some water. The first asphalt is cooled by contact with the cold metal, and at first, nothing may happen. But when the water becomes heated and starts to boil, the asphalt may overflow the tank car.

A similar situation can arise when a tank, containing a water bottom or wet emulsion, is used for storing oil slops or residium at temperatures below 200°F (93°C) and receives a substantial addition of hot residium at a temperature of 300°F (149°C) or higher. After enough time has elapsed for the effect of the hot oil to reach the water in a tank, a prolonged boiling action can take place, which can remove a tank roof and spread froth over a wide area.

Burning Rates of Liquids

The burning rate of flammable liquids will vary somewhat similarly to the rate of flame propagation. Gasoline, being a compound of light and heavy fractions, will burn more rapidly at first while the lighter fractions are burning and the heavier fractions will burn at a rate approaching kerosene. The burning rate for gasoline is 6 to 12 in. of depth per hr and for kerosene the rate is 5 to 8 in. of depth per hr. For example, a pool of gasoline, ½-in. deep, could be expected to burn itself out in 2½ to 5 min.

In a series of tests conducted at the U.S. Bureau of Mines,[2] the burning rates of several liquids and gases were determined and found to approach "a maximum and constant value with increasing pool diameter. This constant burning rate is proportional to the ratio of the net heat of combustion to the sensible heat of vaporization."

Based upon these observed burning rates in petroleum tank fires, an estimate can be made of the extent of area which will be involved in fire from a spill. When a spill is burning, the fire area will first be small and then spread to a point of equilibrium where it will burn as fast as it is released. At a burning rate of 1 fph (foot per hour), a gallon per minute of spillage will reach an equilibrium burning area of about 8 sq ft. Thus, a 10 gpm spill rate will be in equilibrium with 80 sq ft of burning area; 100 gpm, 800 sq ft, etc. For liquids having higher burning rates, the area would be smaller; and, for those liquids having lower burning rates, the area would be larger. Also, the terrain will have an influence on the shape of the burning area.

F. Fire Prevention Methods

Whenever flammable and combustible liquids are stored or handled, the liquid is usually exposed to the air at some stage in the operation, except where the storage is confined to sealed containers which are not filled or opened on the premises or where handling is in closed systems and vapor losses are recovered. Even when the storage or handling is in a closed system, there is always the possibility of breaks or leaks which permit the liquid to escape. Therefore, ventilation is of primary importance to prevent the accumulation of flammable vapors. It is also good practice to eliminate sources of ignition in the vicinity where low flash point flammable liquids are stored, handled, or used, even though no vapor may ordinarily be present.

Whenever possible in manufacturing processes involving flammable or combustible liquids, equipment, such as compressors, stills, towers, pumps, and the like, should be located in the open; this will lessen the fire potential created by the escape and accumulation of flammable vapors. Gasoline and almost all other flammable liquids produce heavier-than-air vapors which tend to settle on the floor or in pits or depressions. Such vapors may flow along the floor or ground for long distances, be ignited at some remote point, and flash back. The removal of such vapors at the floor level including pits is usually the proper method of ventilation. Convection currents of heated air or normal vapor diffusion may carry even heavy vapors upward, and in such instances, ceiling ventilation may also be desirable. Ventilation to eliminate flammable vapors may be either natural or artificial. Although natural ventilation, where it can be used, has the advantage of not being dependent on manual starting or on power supply, it depends upon temperature and wind conditions and is thus not so easily controlled as is mechanical ventilation. Mechanical ventilation should be used wherever indoor operations are extensive.

For further information on blower and exhaust systems, see Section 7, Chapter 5; for calculations of ventilation to avoid flammable mixture, see Part G of this Chapter.

Explosion Venting

In rooms or buildings where possible explosions of flammable vapors may be anticipated, it is recommended that the relief through explosion venting be provided for at least Class 1A liquids and unstable liquids (see Sec. 15, Chap. 7).

Substitution of Nonflammable Liquids

The hazard from the use of flammable liquids may be avoided or reduced by the substitution of relatively safe materials. Such materials should be stable, have a low toxicity, and be either nonflammable or have a high flash point. For example, trichloroethylene, while higher in price, may for some uses be desirably substituted for a more hazardous flammable solvent as it is nonflammable at ordinary temperatures. Tetrachloroethylene (perchloroethylene) is another nonflammable liquid. However, these products are toxic, even though less so than carbon tetrachloride, and should be used only in well-ventilated areas.

There are several commercial-type stable solvents available which have flash points from 140° to 190°F and which have a comparatively low degree of toxicity.

Specially refined petroleum products, first developed as "Stoddard Solvent" but now sold under a variety of trade names by different companies, have solvent properties approximating gasoline, but have fire hazard properties similar to those of kerosene. However, a danger in their use lies in the possibility that persons believing that they are using a safe solvent without fire hazard may neglect ordinary precautions which would be observed with a liquid such as kerosene. When heated to above their flash point (about 100°F) these solvents produce vapors as flammable as those of gasoline at its flash point temperature.

There are several other types of commercial solvents available which are mixtures of liquids with differing rates of evaporation. Some are mixtures of gasoline or one of the various naphthas and a chlorinated solvent having a different and often higher evaporation rate than the flammable solvent which over a period of time would leave the original low flash solvent. These mixtures create a toxicity hazard as well as a fire hazard, and their use in open containers should be discouraged.

Solvents and solvent vapors are toxic in varying degrees, and ventilation is almost always necessary to keep vapor concentration within safe limits. Workmen should keep their arms and hands out of the cleaning solvent because it may be absorbed through the skin, make the skin more susceptible to infection, and cause drying and dermatitis.

G. Tank Storage of Flammable and Combustible Liquids

The first requirement for the storage of flammable and combustible liquids is a properly designed, tight, substantial tank or container. Tanks may be installed aboveground, underground, or inside buildings under certain conditions. Openings and connections to tanks, such as vents and gaging devices and filling and suction lines, are points of hazard unless properly safeguarded.

Assuming well-maintained, modern standard tanks or containers of vapor-tight construction, the greatest hazard is in transferring the liquid to or from storage, rather than in the storage itself. The hazard of storage might seem to depend upon the quantity stored, but as a practical matter the size of the tank or container is less important than other factors, such as characteristics of the liquid stored, design of the tank, foundations and supports, size and location of vents, and related piping and connections.

Flammable liquids expand when heated. Gasolines expand about 0.06 percent in volume for each 10°F increase in temperature within ordinary atmospheric temperature ranges. The effect of temperature increase on the volume of acetone, ethyl ether, and certain other flammable liquids with large coefficients of expansion is greater than in the case of gasoline. To avoid danger of overflow, tanks should not be filled completely full, particularly where cool liquid is placed in a tank in a warm atmosphere, as in the case of filling an automobile tank from an underground gasoline tank on a warm day (see Table on Thermal Expansion of Flammable Liquids in Chapter 11 of this Section).

Several methods are used to prevent loss of gasoline and other volatile liquids by evaporation in storage and by outflow of vapor as the tank is filled. Underground tanks reduce evaporation losses since there is less fluctuation of ground temperature than air temperature. Aboveground tanks often are painted with aluminum or white paint to reflect heat and thus decrease temperature rises of the liquid contents and thereby slow down vaporization. Floating roof tanks without vapor space minimize vapor loss and tend to reduce the hazard. Pressure storage of gasoline in pressure tanks or vessels reduces the loss of vapor through breather vents and in some cases, vapors are conserved by the use of lifter roof or vapor dome tanks, or the vents from several cone-roofed tanks may be connected through manifolds to a vapor dome or pressure-type tank.

The vapor space in tanks storing high vapor pressure flammable liquids (above approximately 4 psia), such as gasoline, is normally too rich to burn, i.e., above the upper flammable limit. However, if the temperature of the liquid gasoline is in the range of −10°F to −50°F, the vapor space will be within the flammable range. Also, when a tank of gasoline, for example, is being pumped out or there is a sudden rainstorm on a hot day there may be a portion of the tank vapor space which will be within the flammable range. Due to possible stratification of the vapors this condition may remain for several hours and even days.

The vapor space in tanks storing low vapor pressure liquids (below approximately 2 psia), such as kerosene, is normally too lean to burn, i.e., below the lower flammable limit. However, in some cases, if the entire body of liquid is heated to its flash point, the vapor space then will be within the flammable range. It is possible for the kerosene to be so heated during refining processes or by exposure fire. It should be noted that it is the temperature of the liquid and not the temperature of the vapor space which determines the presence of a flammable vapor-air mixture. The oil vapors driven off by the heated air in the vapor space are condensed back to liquid by the cooler body of oil. Therefore, the vapors are only flammable for a very short distance above the liquid surface despite the fact that the air within the tank may be considerably above the flash point temperature.

Tank storage of ethyl and methyl alcohol, JP-4 or Jet B turbine fuel, and other liquids of similar vapor pressure (approximately 2 to 4 psia at 100°F) presents an unusual hazard since the vapors are normally in the flammable range. Storage in floating roof or similar tanks or the addition of inert gas in the vapor space is desirable to reduce the possibility of an explosion in the vapor-air mixture in the tank. Floating roof tanks, cone roof tanks with internal floating roofs, lifter roof tanks, and vapordome tanks are also used for vapor conservation purposes for Class I liquids.

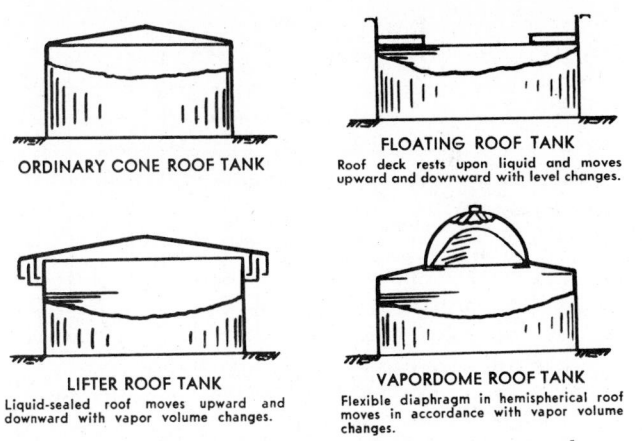

Fig. 3-3F. *Common types of atmospheric storage tanks.*

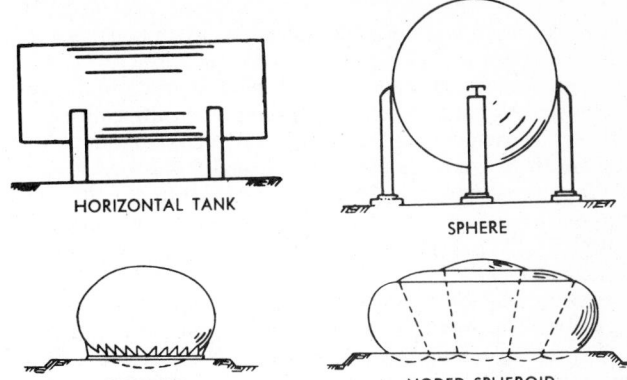

Fig. 3-3G. *Common types of low pressure tanks or pressure vessels.*

Aboveground Storage Tanks

Storage tanks come in a variety of designs; however, they may be divided into three general categories of pressure design: (1) atmospheric tanks, for pressures of 0 to 0.5 pounds per square inch gage, (2) low pressure storage tanks, for pressures from 0.5 to 15 psig, and (3) pressure vessels, for pressures above 15 psig. Some of the more common types of aboveground storage tanks are shown in Figures 3-3F and 3-3G. Pressure type tanks and pressure vessels are normally used for vapor conservation purposes particularly for liquids having high vapor pressures. Floating roof tanks, lifter roof tanks, vapordome roof tanks, and cone roof tanks with internal floating roofs are also used for vapor conservation purposes.

Construction: The thickness of the metal used in tank construction is based not only on strength required to hold the weight of the liquid but also on an added factor for corrosion allowance. When intended for storing corrosive liquids, the specifications for the thickness of the tank shell are then increased to provide additional metal to allow for the expected service life of the tank. In some cases special tank linings are used to reduce corrosion. Periodic inspection should be made to ascertain metal thickness of the tank and to establish safe operating limits and avoid overstressing the tank. The inspection of tanks for corrosion may be performed by visual inspection, drilling, and calipering, use of sonic devices, providing weep holes, or experience gained by the storage of similar materials.

Sonic devices operate on a principle of the length of time it takes for sound waves to reflect. Any difference in metal thickness is quickly disclosed by these instruments and they are particularly effective when large areas with many potential corrosion spots are involved. Weep holes, which are very small holes drilled part way into the tank shell, are used occasionally. The principle of these holes is that the lesser metal thickness at the partially drilled hole will show signs of leakage before the strength of the entire tank would be endangered by corrosion.

All storage tanks should be built of steel or concrete unless the character of the liquid necessitates the use of other materials. Both steel and concrete tanks have resistance to heat conditions which can be expected from exposure fires. Tanks built of materials less resistant to heat, such as low melting point materials, might result in fire spreading from one tank to another which would not have occurred if the tanks had been of steel or concrete construction.

Tanks with the label of Underwriters Laboratories, Inc.,

or the monogram of the American Petroleum Institute are built to exacting specifications. For atmospheric, vertical, cylindrical, and aboveground welded tanks, the following formula from API Standard 650, Welded Oil Storage Tanks, published by the American Petroleum Institute,[3] may be used in calculating the minimum thickness of shell plate:

$$t = 0.0001456 \times D \times (H - 1) \times S,$$

wherein

t = minimum thickness, in inches

D = nominal inside diameter of tank, in feet

H = height, in feet, from the bottom of the course under consideration to the top of the top angle or to the bottom of any overflow which limits the tank filling height

S = specific gravity of liquid to be stored but in no case less than 1.0.

The nominal thickness of shell plates (including shell extensions for floating roofs) is no less than those given in Table 3-3B. The maximum nominal thickness of tank shell plates is $\frac{1}{2}$ in.

Concrete tanks require special engineering and unlined concrete tanks should be used only for the storage of liquids having a specific gravity of 40° API or heavier. Tanks built of material other than steel should be designed to specifications embodying safety factors equivalent to those of steel.

Table 3-3B

Nominal Tank Diameter in Feet	Nominal Thickness in inches
Smaller than 50	$\frac{3}{16}$
50 to, but not including, 120	$\frac{1}{4}$
120 to 200, incl.	$\frac{5}{16}$
Over 200	$\frac{3}{8}$

Installation: Aboveground tanks should be installed in accordance with NFPA No. 30, Flammable and Combustible Liquids Code, referred to hereafter in this chapter as the NFPA Flammable and Combustible Liquids Code, which specifies distances from tanks to property lines that can be built upon and to public ways or to important buildings. These distances will vary depending on whether the pressures, including those attained during fire exposure, in the tanks can be under or over 2.5 psig as well as whether the contents are stable liquids, unstable liquids, or liquids having boil-over characteristics. Other factors affecting distances are the design of the tank, protection for exposures, fire extinguishing or control systems provided, or other protection features. The spacing between tanks is also specified in this code.

Municipal ordinances usually prohibit aboveground storage of flammable and combustible liquids in the congested business districts of cities, and zoning restrictions commonly exclude them from residential areas and from the vicinity of schools and hospitals. Where a tank is located in an area that may be subjected to flooding, applicable provisions in the NFPA Flammable or Combustible Liquids Code, should be followed.

Venting and Flame Arresters: An appropriate vent must be provided for normal operation of any tank to permit the flow of air or vapor to compensate for the maximum flow of liquid as the tank is filled or emptied, and for the maximum expansion or contraction of the tank contents with changes in temperature. API Standard 2000, Venting Atmospheric and Low Pressure Storage Tanks, provides information on sizing vents for product movement and breathing. Clogged vents, or vents too small in comparison with the size of the filling or draw-off connections or too small for the rate of pumping, may result in the rupturing of tanks from internal pressure or their collapse due to internal vacuum. During the filling operation, the vents discharge flammable vapors. If the mixture is sufficiently rich or if the vent location is such that the released vapor is a hazard, the vapors should be piped to a place where they can be dissipated safely. The vapor release should not be located close to doors or windows through which vapors might enter buildings, nor close to possible sources of ignition.

Venting devices, which are normally closed when the tank is not under pressure or vacuum, or approved flame arresters are provided on vent pipes to prevent flash-back into tanks when a flammable mixture is present or for the storage of all Class I liquids. Arresters constructed of banks of parallel metal plates or tubes having a large surface of metal to dissipate heat are more effective for larger openings than screens and are less subject to clogging and corrosion. Heat is absorbed by the metal plates or tubes which lowers the temperature of the vapor below its self-ignition point. If, however, the flame arrester is exposed to long burning

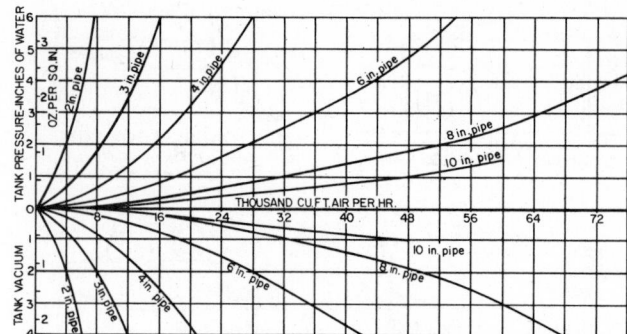

Fig. 3-3I. Average flow capacity of listed flame arresters for oil storage tanks in thousands of cubic feet of air for positive and negative pressures.

periods, the metal plates become sufficiently hot on the bottom side to ignite any flammable vapor-air mixtures in the tank. Figure 3-3H shows average capacities of laboratory tested arresters. Figure 3-3I shows average capacities of flame arrester-vent valve combinations.

Where the liquids stored have flash points in the range of normal summer temperatures, the vapor space above the liquid in the tank will normally contain vapors in the flammable range. On such tanks flame arresters have their most important application. However, condensation and crystallization of certain liquids and freezing of moisture in winter may make conservation vents and particularly flame arresters impractical. Steam tracing (steam heating) is provided in some cases to prevent freezing or crystallization.

Although a wire screen of 40 mesh* ordinarily will prevent the passage of flame through small openings, because of possible physical damage to the wires or clogging of the mesh by dirt or other residues.

Emergency Venting: In addition to the operating vents, emergency relief of internal pressure is required for most aboveground tanks to provide for the condition which may arise if there is fire under or around the tank. In the absence of proper provision for such relief, high pressures may be generated when the tank is exposed to external fire, and rupture the tank in a manner similar to a steam boiler "explosion," or as more correctly stated, a "boiler rupture." Such ruptures are infrequent, but when they do occur the results may be disastrous to life and property. They can be avoided by providing adequate pressure relief, which permits the vapors to escape and burn at the vents instead of rupturing the vessel or tank. Emergency relief venting may be in the form of loose manhole covers which lift under pressure, weak roof-to-shell seams, rupture disks, or the commonly used emergency relief vents designed for the purpose.

Unless they are adequately vented, horizontal cylindrical tanks, under excessive internal pressure, commonly fail at the ends. For vertical cone-roofed tanks, designed with weakened seams at the roof-to-shell joint, the lifting of the roof or top of the roof-to-shell seam affords adequate emergency pressure relief. Vertical cone-roofed tanks are required to have the roof-to-shell seam of weaker construction

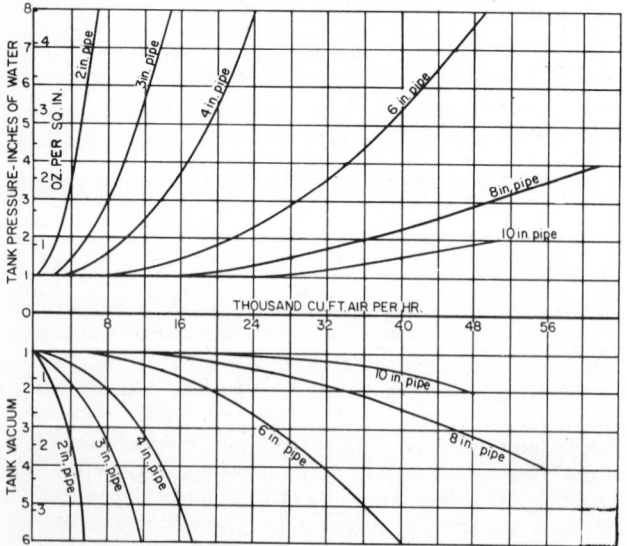

Fig. 3-3H. Average flow capacity of listed flame arrester-vent valve combinations for oil storage tanks in thousands of cubic feet of air for positive and negative pressures.

* A woven wire fabric in which there are 40 wires per in. in each direction, and 1,600 interstices per sq in. The size of the openings depends upon the diameter of the wires as well as upon the mesh of the screens, but the size of wire is approximately uniform for any given mesh, and specifying a screen in terms of its mesh determines the size of the openings with sufficient accuracy for practical purposes. The individual opening in a 40-mesh screen has an area of about 0.00022 sq in.

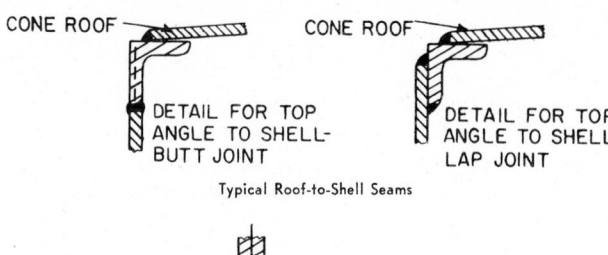

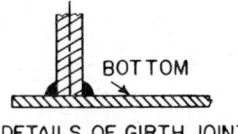

Fig. 3-3J. In cone-roofed tanks the roof-to-shell seams are required to be weaker than the bottom-to-shell seams. Although designed as emergency vents, weakened roof seams, as illustrated, have actually served for explosion relief in some instances as the entire roof has been blown off by an internal explosion.

than the bottom-to-shell seam in order to prevent failure at the bottom of the tank which would release a wave of liquid (See Fig. 3-3J).

The danger of failure of tanks from internal pressure when exposed to fire depends to a considerable extent upon the characteristics of the liquid and the size and type of the tank. The smaller the tank or the lesser the volume of the liquid in the tank, the shorter the time under fire exposure before a pressure buildup occurs.

Table 3-3C is based upon the required discharge from both normal and emergency vents derived from a consideration of the probable maximum rate of heat transfer per unit area; size of tank and the percentage of total area likely to be exposed; time required to bring tank contents to boil; time required to heat unwet portions of the tank shell or roof to a temperature where the metal will lose strength; and effect of drainage, insulation and the application of water in reducing fire exposure and heat transfer. Due to the wide variance in flow characteristics of manufactured vents, each vent design, under 8 in., should be flow tested rather than relying upon vent size. The flow capacity of vents larger than 8 in. may be flow tested or calculated in

accordance with the formula in the NFPA Flammable and Combustible Liquids Code.

The wetted area referred to in Table 3-3C is the internal portion of the tank in contact with the liquid which is anticipated will be exposed to the flame of the external ground fire. It is the heating of the liquid in the tank on which is based the requirements for emergency venting. Therefore, the wetted area exposed to an external ground fire, such as a spill, will vary on different tank designs: 55 percent of the total exposed area of a sphere or spheroid; 75 percent of the total exposed area of a horizontal tank; and, the first 30 ft abovegrade of the exposed shell area of a vertical tank.

For tanks and storage vessels designed for pressures over 1 psig, the total rate of venting is given in Table 3-3D. When the exposed wetted area or the surface is greater than 2,800 sq ft, the total rate of venting is as given or calculated by the following formula:

$$CFH = 1,107A^{0.82}$$

where

CFH = venting requirement, in cubic feet of free air per hour.

A = exposed wetted surface, in square feet.

The foregoing formula is based on $Q = 21,000A^{0.82}$.

The total emergency relief venting capacity for any specific liquid may be determined by the following formula:

$$\text{Cubic ft of free air per hour} = V \frac{1,337}{L \sqrt{M}}$$

where

V = cubic ft of free air per hour from Table 3-3C

L = latent heat of vaporization of specific liquid in Btu per lb

M = molecular weight of specific liquids

The required flow rate may be multiplied by the appropriate factor listed in the following schedule when protection is provided as indicated (only one factor may be used for any one tank):

.5 for approved drainage for tanks over 200 sq ft of wetted area

.3 for approved water spray

.3 for approved insulation

.15 for approved water spray with approved insulation.

When pressure tanks or vessels are exposed to fire, violent overpressure failure may result if the steel in the vapor space is softened by heat. Localized overheating of the tank shell has been caused by vent fires, resulting in pressure ruptures after a pressure buildup within the tank from the exposure fire. The outlets of all vents and vent drains on aboveground tanks designed for 2.5 psi or greater should be arranged to prevent localized overheating of any part of the tank in the event of a vent fire.

Table 3-3C.   Wetted Area Versus Cubic Feet of Free Air per Hour Required for Relief Venting for Aboveground Tanks

(For purposes of calculation the capacity of venting devices, "free air" is defined as air at 14.7 psia and 60°F.)

Sq Ft	CFH*	Sq Ft	CFH*	Sq Ft	CFH*
20	21,100	200	211,000	1,000	524,000
30	31,600	250	239,000	1,200	557,000
40	42,100	300	265,000	1,400	587,000
50	52,700	350	288,000	1,600	614,000
60	63,200	400	312,000	1,800	639,000
70	73,700	500	354,000	2,000	662,000
80	84,200	600	392,000	2,400	704,000
90	94,800	700	428,000	2,800	742,000
100	105,000	800	462,000	and over	
120	126,000	900	493,000		
140	147,000				
160	168,000				
180	190,000				

* Cubic feet per hour.
Note: Interpolate for intermediate values.

Table 3-3D

Sq Ft	CFH	Sq Ft	CFH
2,800	742,000	9,000	1,930,000
3,000	786,000	10,000	2,110,000
3,500	892,000	15,000	2,940,000
4,000	995,000	20,000	3,720,000
4,500	1,100,000	25,000	4,470,000
5,000	1,250,000	30,000	5,190,000
6,000	1,390,000	35,000	5,900,000
7,000	1,570,000	40,000	6,570,000
8,000	1,760,000		

Foundations and Supports: Tanks are set on firm foundations and adequately supported. Vertical tanks are normally set on a slightly elevated pad in order to provide a sound base, and normally above the adjacent ground level in order to protect the bottom of the tank from any water in the area. Any exposed piling or steel supports under any flammable liquid tank are protected by fire resistive materials to provide a fire resistance rating of not less than 2 hrs.

Drainage and Dikes: Where waterways or properties would be endangered by release of liquids stored in tanks, it is necessary to provide a means to control this spillage. The most desirable method is to locate the tanks on sloping ground. Directional dikes or drainage ditches could then divert spillage away from all tanks and into an impounding basin where the liquid could burn safely without exposing other tanks, property, or waterways.

Where impounding basins cannot be used, dikes built around the tanks can prevent the spread of liquid. Dikes may be constructed of earth, concrete, or steel built to withstand the lateral pressure of a full liquid head. When several large tanks are in a single diked enclosure, it may be desirable to place small "spill dikes" between tanks; while only a minimum of 18 in. high, they will prevent any small spills from exposing other tanks in the enclosure. Such spills may result from a leaking valve or connection or from overfilling the tank.

Diked enclosures are designed to contain the greatest amount of liquid that can be released from the largest tank within the enclosure, assuming a full tank. When calculating the volumetric capacity of the diked enclosure, the volume of the tanks within the diked area to the height of the dikes must be considered as unavailable space for the liquid to flow. The fire record of tanks indicates that this capacity is adequate.

Where needed, diked areas are provided with trapped drains to remove rain water or water used for fire fighting. The best practice is to keep drain valves normally closed, opening them at intervals when needed, since permanently opened drains would discharge liquids in case of leakage from the tank. The drain valves should also be accessible under fire conditions which normally means their being located outside the dike. Oil separators are effective in skimming off oil flowing on the surface of water, but types now available will not stop the discharge when the entire flow through the drain is oil.

It is not desirable to use, in lieu of dikes, high walls close to Class I liquid storage tanks because they do not allow space for good ventilation. Flammable mixtures of vapors and air may accumulate in the space between the wall and the tank. When high dikes are installed, special provisions for safe operation are required. Furthermore, high walls make access for fire fighting difficult, and make escape difficult if someone is in the space between the tank and the wall unless safe egress is provided.

Fire Effects on Aboveground Tanks: Actually, the probability of fire in a modern well-constructed and installed tank is much less than in an ordinary building. Where tanks are adjacent to a building, fires in buildings expose the tanks more often than fires in tanks expose the buildings. However, experience proves that if the liquid in a tank not built and installed in strict compliance with NFPA Standards is ignited, the possibility of fire spread is increased materially.

Unfortunately, a not uncommon type of bulk plant installation is to have tanks on unprotected steel supports, with loading of tank trucks by gravity immediately adjacent to the tanks. The typical fire in such installations originates at the tank vehicle and very shortly the unprotected steel supports fail, dropping the tanks to the ground. In falling, the tanks break the piping or rupture on hitting the ground and the entire contents are released. The steel supports, of course, should be protected by 2-hr fire-resistive coverings and the loading rack should be at least 25 ft from the tanks if Class I flammable liquids are handled, and 15 ft for Class II and Class III liquids.

Improper and inadequate emergency venting has been a major factor in tank failures during exposure fire conditions (see discussion of venting in this chapter). Since either inadequate or improperly designed vents have been the cause of severe pressure ruptures of pressure tanks and vessels resulting in deaths and injuries to fire fighters and spectators, it is of vital importance to follow the standards on venting. In fighting tank fires it is essential to cool the shell above the liquid level to keep the steel from overheating which could cause the tank to bulge and rupture, regardless of the adequacy of the venting.

A major factor in fires involving storage tanks has been the failure of the piping and valves to the tanks. These failures have resulted in adding the contents of the tanks to the ground fire. Pipe systems may be located either aboveground

Fig. 3-3K. Fourteen-foot-high dike walls proved to be a severe hazard to fire fighters and a handicap to effective fire fighting at this oil terminal fire on the waterfront at Los Angeles, Calif.

Fig. 3-3L. A portion of a spheroid tank containing the roof plate showing the destructive force of a pressure rupture caused by flame impinging on the tank roof.

or underground. At bulk installations, piping from aboveground tanks normally is placed aboveground to avoid corrosion problems and to aid in detecting leaks. If piping is in open trenches, suitable fire barriers should be placed at periodic intervals to prevent the flow of liquid from one section of the plant to another. Underground piping is not subject to fire exposure, but underground as well as aboveground piping must be protected against physical damage and excessive stresses arising from expansion or contraction, vibration and settlement. Materials, such as cast iron, which are subject to failure due to thermal shock should not be used. Steel or modular iron pipe and valves should be used particularly for external tank connections through which liquid would normally flow unless the chemical characteristics of the liquid stored are incompatible with steel. Welded pipe connections or flanged joints are preferred for aboveground piping particularly for large size pipe. Screwed pipe connections larger than 3 in. in size are subject to disengagement in a long exposure fire unless the connections are back welded. Pipe joints dependent upon the friction characteristics of combustible materials for mechanical continuity of piping are subject to failure under fire exposure conditions.

Most fires involving storage tanks originate with an internal explosion or by a spill fire exposing the tanks. In a typical tank fire, the shell of a large vertical tank above the burning liquid level will fold into the tank without splitting the tank shell.

Internal explosions of storage tanks occur with those liquids which have the vapor space in the flammable range. Liquids with flash points near the stored temperature are most susceptible to ignition. In tanks, liquids with low flash points will have a flammable vapor-air mixture in the vapor space if the temperature is markedly reduced and high flash point liquids will form a flammable vapor-air mixture when heated. During fire exposures internal explosions have occurred in tanks containing liquids with flash points above the stored liquid temperature. Such explosions occur because the liquid is heated by the exposure fire and the vapor passes into the flammable range at the time when a part of the tank shell in the vapor space is hot enough to ignite the vapors.

Floating roof tanks provide maximum fire safety for aboveground installation, and, as a result, they are permitted to be located closer to a property line than are other types of tanks. Explosions may occur, however, when floating roof tanks are virtually empty of liquid or the roof has been allowed to rest on the low level supports, permitting a flammable vapor space to be present. Although fires in floating roof tanks are not common, when they do occur they normally are restricted to the seal space between the roof and the shell and often can be extinguished by portable extinguishers or hand foam lines. There have been a few cases, however, where a floating roof tank has been overfilled or the roof has been sunk.

Fire protection facilities should be installed on tanks where it is judged they are needed. (See NFPA No. 11, Standard for Foam Extinguishing Systems.)

Underground Storage Tanks

Underground tanks are designed to withstand safely the service to which they are subjected, including the pressure of the earth, pavement, or possible vehicle traffic.

Construction: Rigid specifications established by Underwriters Laboratories, Inc., assure reasonable safety for those tanks bearing its label. Underground tanks also may

Table 3-3E. Typical Sizes of Underground Flammable Liquid Tanks

Capacity Gallons	Diameter		Length		Capacity Gallons	Diameter		Length	
	Ft	In.	Ft	In.		Ft	In.	Ft	In.
300	3	0	6	0	3,000	6	0	14	0
560	4	0	6	0	4,000	5	4	24	0
1,000	4	0	11	0	4,000	6	0	19	0
1,000	5	4	6	0	5,000	6	0	24	0
1,000	4	0	11	0	6,000	6	0	29	0
1,000	5	4	6	0	6,000	8	0	16	0
1,500	5	4	9	0	7,500	8	0	20	0
2,000	5	4	12	0	10,000	8	0	27	0
2,500	5	4	15	0	10,000	9	0	21	0
3,000	5	4	18	0	10,000	10	0	17	0
					10,000	10	6	15	7

be of unlined concrete for the storage of liquids having a specific gravity of 40 degrees API or heavier. Lined concrete tanks may be used for liquids having a lighter specific gravity, providing the lining is suitable for the liquid being stored and has satisfactory adherence qualities to the concrete.

Installation: Underground tanks are generally considered the safest form of storage. Such tanks may be buried outside or under buildings. Tanks that are buried underneath buildings should have fill and vent connections outside the building walls. Tanks should be set on firm foundations and surrounded with soft earth or sand well tamped into place.

Underground tanks must be protected against damaging loads imposed by the cover over the tanks and such factors as building foundations and vehicular traffic. Normally, if the tanks are well supported underneath and buried to a sufficient extent, no special protection is needed. However, if tanks are located in areas where higher than normal loads may be imposed, paving or additional earth coverage may be necessary. Piping subject to such possibly damaging loads or vibrations is frequently protected by sleeves, casings, or flexible connectors to ensure the integrity of the line.

The normal expectancy of properly installed underground steel tanks is over 20 years, but if improperly installed and in a corrosive soil they may leak in less than 5 years. The soil in which the tank is buried is of the greatest importance. Some soils may be highly corrosive because of their chemical or moisture content. This is particularly true if construction debris, cinders, shale, or other foreign matter is mixed, even in very small quantities, with otherwise "clean" backfill. The use of homogeneous "clean" backfill and protective coatings prolongs the life of steel tanks and piping. Cathodic protection of buried tanks and piping may be necessary in some cases.

Electrolytic corrosion in an electrically conductive tank and piping system may occur at points where metals having different electromotive qualities, such as steel and brass, are connected. Connections of two dissimilar metals should be avoided to prevent galvanic corrosion.

Stray electrical currents may set up corrosive action, but their presence may be difficult to determine until after the action has progressed to the point where damage has been done to the tank or piping. Cathodic protection or insulation is sometimes used to protect underground tanks from stray currents (see Sec. 11, Chap. 3). Fiber glass reinforced plastic tanks for underground installation eliminate the corrosion problem encountered with steel tanks.

Tanks should be anchored or weighted to prevent floating in locations where ground water level is high or may rise

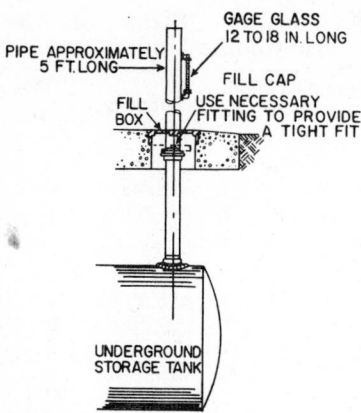

Fig. 3-3M. Simple leak test equipment in a typical underground tank installation.

in case of flood. Details of installation and protection are covered in the NFPA Flammable and Combustible Liquids Code.

The proximity of underground tanks to a building foundation is not a direct measure of the potential danger to the building if a leak should develop in the tanks. Leaking contents from underground tanks have been known to travel several miles underground or penetrate 24 in. of waterproofed concrete before appearing in a building. Tanks suspected of leaking should be tested hydrostatically with the same liquid stored in the tank (see Fig. 3-3M).

Air tests or testing with liquids other than that stored in the tank have been proved to be dangerous and inconclusive for detecting suspected leaks in underground tanks. Additional details of the causes of corrosion, locating leaking tanks, and removal of liquids in the ground are covered in NFPA No. 329M, Leakage from Underground Flammable and Combustible Liquid Tanks.

Tanks Inside Buildings

Design: Tanks designed for installation in fire resistive enclosures within buildings have the same metal thicknesses and design features as required for all tanks. Fuel oil tanks designed for use without being enclosed in a fire resistive, cut-off room inside buildings are normally restricted to less than 660 gal capacity. Although the metal thicknesses for the tanks designed for differing situations are approximately the same, the location of the openings for pipe connections differ. Pipe connections for underground tanks and enclosed fuel oil tanks inside buildings are in the top only, whereas unenclosed tanks are provided with bottom outlets for gravity feed piping to such installations as oil burning equipment. In certain specialized processing operations, large tanks are required and are designed as low pressure storage tanks or pressure vessels as specified for aboveground storage tanks.

Installation: Storage tanks inside buildings will vary depending upon the class of liquid and the occupancy of the building. For specific requirements for the installation of tanks inside buildings, see the NFPA Flammable and Combustible Liquids Code.

Where it is impractical to install a gasoline tank underground outside or under a building, a special liquid vaportight enclosure without backfill may be used. Such an enclosure is constructed of 6 in. of reinforced concrete with access through the top only. Means also are provided for using portable ventilating equipment to discharge flammable vapors to the outside of the building.

Fuel oil tanks over 660 gal capacity may be placed inside

buildings in enclosures with a fire resistance rating of not less than 3 hrs. Such tank enclosures may have an opening protected by a self-closing fire door designed for Class A openings and a raised, noncombustible, liquid-tight sill or ramp. If the sill or ramp is more than 6 in. high, the enclosure walls up to a height corresponding to the calculated liquid level from a possible leaking tank should be built to withstand the lateral pressure caused by the liquid head. Provision also should be made for ventilating the enclosure prior to entering for inspection or repair of the tank. Additional storage may be permitted if the fuel oil tank enclosure is located in a room cut off from the rest of the building by walls, floor, and ceiling of 2-hr fire-resistive materials. The installation of fuel oil tanks connected to oil burners is covered in NFPA No. 31, Standard for the Installation of Oil Burning Equipment.

Where the nature of certain types of processing operations calls for tanks to be located inside buildings, particular attention should be given to the desirability of providing automatic sprinkler systems or water spray systems, thermally actuated valves adjacent to the tanks in pipe lines, and steel valves and pipe.

Vents and fill pipes from tanks inside buildings terminate on the outside of the building.

Gaging of Tanks

Tank openings for gaging or measuring the quantity of liquid may permit the escape of vapors during the gaging operation. Such openings are particularly undesirable in tanks located in buildings or buried under basements and are prohibited by NFPA Standards unless protected by a spring loaded check valve or other approved device. Substitutes for manual gaging include heavy duty flat gage glasses, magnetic, hydraulic or hydrostatic remote reading devices, and sealed float gages. Such devices must, however, be maintained in reliable operative condition. Ordinary gage glasses should not be used since their breakage may permit the escape of liquid.

Cleaning of Tanks

The cleaning or safeguarding of tanks or other containers that have contained liquids, preparatory to making repairs or for other purposes, is extremely hazardous unless precautionary measures are taken to avoid the ignition of flammable vapors which would result in an explosion and to protect personnel against toxic vapors.[4, 5]

Work on empty containers must be done only under the supervision of persons well versed in their fire and explosion potential and in the procedures essential to safeguarding the operations properly. Unless the work can be done with the container and all connected piping and fittings completely filled with water, all vapors should be removed by cleaning with steam or chemical solutions or by displacement with water, air, or inert gas; in some instances the tank vapor space may be filled with inert gas by specially qualified personnel in order to provide a safe atmosphere. The selection of the method to be used to make a tank or container safe to work upon will depend on several factors, such as character of liquid, size of tank or container, flammability and reactivity of residues, and type of work to be performed. With many reactive materials it will be necessary to obtain information from the manufacturer as to the safest method for cleaning.

Removal of Flammable Vapors by Displacement: Sometimes referred to as "purging," this may be accomplished by one of several methods.

1. Displacement with Water: Where the flammable liquid previously contained is known to be readily displaced by or is soluble in water, it can be removed completely by alternately filling the container with water and draining it, repeating the operation several times until the tests with a combustible gas indicator show that the vapors are no longer present. Acetone and ethyl alcohol are examples of water soluble liquids.

2. Displacement with Air: Frequently, flammable vapors may be removed by purging with air by the use of veturi-type air movers or low pressure blowers, and a safe atmosphere sustained by continued ventilation. Air movers should be restricted to those operated by steam or air, or by electric motors approved for use in the atmosphere involved. When steam is used for operation of the air mover, the air mover should be bonded or in electrical contact with the tank. When small container openings cannot accommodate an air mover, the contents can sometimes be purged by compressed air connected to a metallic pipe bonded to the container. Care should be exercised to prevent over-pressuring a small container if compressed air is used. Irregularly shaped containers may not be thoroughly purged by this method if the air stream leaves "pockets" which cannot be effectively reached with the uncontaminated air. In air purging, the concentration of flammable vapors in air in the container may go through the flammable range before safe atmospheres are obtained. Therefore, all precautions must be taken to minimize the hazards of ignition by static electricity. Air movers should be clamped or bolted to and thereby inherently bonded to the vessel being ventilated (see Fig 3-3N).

3. Displacement with Inert Gas: When carbon dioxide in low pressure containers or in solid form (dry ice), or nitrogen in cylinders are available in sufficient quantity, they may be used to purge the flammable vapors from containers under certain conditions without the hazards incident to having the vapor-air mixture in the tank vapor space pass through the flammable range. This procedure should be followed by air ventilation. High pressure carbon dioxide, such as from a fire extinguisher, should not be used because static electricity is generated. Several explosions of fires have occurred from using CO_2 extinguishers for inerting tanks or vessels.

Inerting of the Vapor Space: If properly used, inerting is a means of safeguarding a container so it may be worked on by reducing the oxygen content to the point where combustion cannot take place in the vapor space above the liquid surface in a tank. However, individuals in direct charge of the work must be thoroughly familiar with the limitations and characteristics of the inert gas being used. Attempting such work without proper knowledge or equipment can be hazardous because of the false sense of security engendered. The oxygen content should be maintained at substantially zero during the entire period when work is in progress. Gases used for inerting include carbon dioxide and nitrogen. Both may be obtained in tanks, and carbon dioxide may also be obtained in solid form.

Removal of Residues: Liquid or solid residues might release flammable vapors during "hot work." They must be removed and this can be accomplished by means of steam or chemical cleaning or by other recognized methods. In steam cleaning, the rate of supply of steam should be sufficient to exceed the rate of condensation and the steam nozzle should be bonded to the container shell. This means, of course, that the whole container is heated close to the boiling point of water. Chemical cleaning may be necessary to remove some residues and where used may present personnel health hazards which should be guarded against.

Continuous ventilation of large tanks is done by air movers at the roof manholes. After the atmosphere is sufficiently free for safe entry, more vapor may be released from the residue while it is being removed from the tank. By continuous ventilation during work the vapor concentration can be kept at a safe limit.

Special care must be exercised to eliminate any source of ignition in the vicinity of the container or in the path of vapors being displaced. Bonding, either with special bond wires or by metal-to-metal contact with clamped or bolted connections providing inherent bonding, must be used where static producing devices are used. All electrical equipment, such as inspection lights and motors used in connection with the cleaning operations, is designed to be used in the hazardous vapors present.

Tests for the presence of flammable vapors constitute the most important phase of the cleaning or safeguarding procedure and they must be made before commencing any alterations or repairs, immediately after starting any welding, cutting, or heating operations, and frequently during the course of such work. The tests made with a combustible gas indicator (see Sec. 12, Chap. 4) in good working order will normally produce reliable readings, but considerable care should be exercised to be sure that the indicator is properly calibrated for the vapors involved, is correctly scaled, and is properly used and read and the readings properly interpreted and applied. Where an inert gas is used, normally the oxygen content of the tank is measured to determine whether a hazardous condition exists. This may be determined directly by the use of an oxygen indicator or indirectly by the use of an indicator showing the concentration of the inert gas being used. All testing must be done by persons experienced in the operation and limitations of the indicators used.

When "hot work" is to be done on small tanks or containers that cannot be entered, the combustible gas indicator should show no appreciable indication of the presence of flammable vapors. Extra precautions are necessary if the container, such as an empty drum or barrel, last contained a high flash liquid, as it will show no vapor reading on the indicator. Then if welding or cutting is done, the heat may vaporize some of the liquid, create a flammable vapor-air mixture in the drum, and explode it. Such containers require special precautions.

Under qualified supervision "hot work" may be performed safely in tank cars, tank trucks, and tanks that can

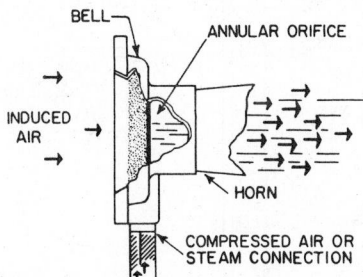

Fig. 3-3N. Schematic drawing of the operation of an air remover. Compressed air or steam is admitted to the bell of the air remover and enters the horn through the annular orifice around the base. As the steam or compressed air passes through the horn its expansion induces a rapid flow of air, equal to approximately ten times the volume of the steam or compressed air.

be entered when the flammable vapors are under 20 percent of the lower flammable limit. Additional precautions, such as protective clothing and self-contained breathing apparatus, are necessary to protect the health of persons entering tanks that have contained leaded gasoline or other highly toxic residues.

Where toxic materials have been stored in a tank, additional tests may be required to determine if the atmosphere is safe from a health standpoint. For example, leaded gasoline tanks need to be lead free before entrance without breathing equipment and specialized protective clothing.

More complete instructions for cleaning tanks or containers are covered in the following publications, which should be referred to and the specific instructions therein carefully followed:

NFPA No. 327, Standard Procedures for Cleaning or Safeguarding Small Tanks and Containers

NFPA No. 306, Control of Gas Hazards on Vessels

NFPA No. 410C, Recommendations on Safeguarding Aircraft Fuel System Maintenance

RP 2013, Cleaning Tank Vehicles Used for Transportation of Flammable Liquids[4]

RP 2015, Cleaning Petroleum Storage Tanks[5]

H.　Other Storage of Flammable Liquids

The principal hazard of closed container storage is the possibility of overpressure failure of the container when exposed to fire. This release of liquid adds to the intensity of a fire and may cause the rupture of other containers, resulting in a rapidly spreading fire. Fire tests prove that ordinary automatic sprinkler systems may be inadequate to control a fire involving drums of flammable liquids or to prevent overpressuring of drums if flammable liquid containers are piled too high. See Table 3-3F for storage limitations in inside storage rooms and Table 3-3G for warehouses.

Container Storage in Buildings

Special storage buildings or rooms, and other rooms or portions of buildings where containers may be stored should be designed to protect the containers from exposure to fires in other portions of the building. The life hazard to the occupants of buildings, exposure to other buildings, building construction, and the degree of fire protection provided are factors to be considered when evaluating the amount of container storage in buildings. Details and limitations on closed container storage are given in the NFPA Flammable and Combustible Liquids Code.

Specially designed metal storage cabinets are available for storing up to a total of 60 gal in small containers (see Fig. 3-3O). Specifications for wooden storage cabinets also are given in the Flammable and Combustible Liquids Code.

Table 3-3F. Storage Limitations for Inside Storage Rooms

Fire Protection* Provided	Fire Resistance	Maximum Size	Allowable Loading Gals/sq ft/floor area
yes	2 hr	500 sq ft	10
no	2 hr	500 sq ft	4
yes	1 hr	150 sq ft	5
no	1 hr	150 sq ft	2

* Fire protection system shall be sprinkler, water spray, carbon dioxide, dry chemical, halon, or other acceptable type of system.

Table 3-3G. Storage Limitations for Warehouses or Storage Buildings

Class Liquid	Storage Level	Protected Storage* Maximum per Pile Gal	Height (See Note 3)	Unprotected Storage Maximum per Pile Gal	Height (See Note 3)
IA	Ground & Upper Floors	2,750 (50)	3 ft (1)	660 (12)	3 ft (1)
	Basement	Not permitted		Not Permitted	
IB	Ground & Upper Floors	5,500 (100)	6 ft (2)	1,375 (25)	3 ft (1)
	Basement	Not Permitted		Not Permitted	
IC	Ground & Upper Floors	16,500 (300)	6 ft (2)	4,125 (75)	3 ft (1)
	Basement	Not Permitted		Not Permitted	
II	Ground & Upper Floors	16,500 (300)	9 ft (3)	4,125 (75)	9 ft (3)
	Basement	5,500 (100)	9 ft (3)	Not Permitted	
Combustible	Ground & Upper Floors	55,000 (1,000)	15 ft (5)	13,750 (250)	12 ft (4)
	Basement	8,250 (150)	9 ft (3)	Not Permitted	

* A sprinkler or equivalent fire protection system installed in accordance with the applicable NFPA Standard. (Numbers in parentheses indicate corresponding number of 55-gal drums.)

Note 1: When two or more classes of materials are stored in a single pile, the maximum gallonage permitted in that pile is the smallest of the two or more separate maximum gallonages.

Note 2: Aisles are provided so that no container is more than 12 ft from an aisle. Main aisles shall be at least 8 ft wide and side aisles at least 4 ft wide.

Note 3: Each pile is separated from each other pile by at least 4 ft. When stored on suitably protected racks or when the storage is suitably protected, containers may be piled up but no closer than 3 ft to the nearest beam, chord, girder or other obstructions. Good practice is to maintain 3 ft clearance below sprinkler deflectors or discharge orifices or other overhead fire protection systems.

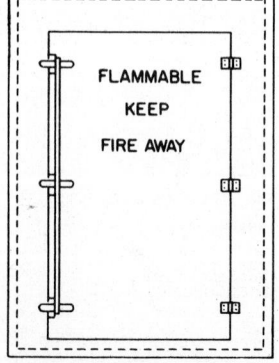
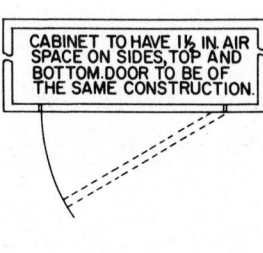

FLAMMABLE KEEP FIRE AWAY

CABINET TO HAVE 1½ IN. AIR SPACE ON SIDES, TOP AND BOTTOM. DOOR TO BE OF THE SAME CONSTRUCTION.

Fig. 3-3O. Typical metal storage cabinet recommended by NFPA Committee on Flammable and Combustible Liquids for quantities less than 60 gal. Material is 18 US gage sheet iron, tight joints. Door has three-point lock with sill raised to at least 2 in. above the bottom of the cabinet.

Table 3-3H. Outdoor Container Storage

Class	Maximum per Pile, Gallons (See Note 1)	Distance between Piles (See Note 2)	Distance to Property Line That Can be Built Upon (See Notes 3 & 4)	Distance to Street, Alley, Public Way (See Note 4)
IA	1,100	5 ft	20 ft	10 ft
IB	2,200	5 ft	20 ft	10 ft
C	4,400	5 ft	20 ft	10 ft
II	8,800	5 ft	10 ft	5 ft
Combustible	22,000	5 ft	10 ft	5 ft

Note 1: When two or more classes of materials are stored in a single pile, the maximum gallonage permitted in that pile is the smallest of the two or more separate maximum gallonages.

Note 2: Within 200 ft of each container, good practice dictates maintaining a 12-ft wide access way to permit approach of fire control apparatus.

Note 3: The distances listed apply to properties that have protection for exposures as defined. If there are exposures, and such protection for exposures does not exist, the distances in Column 4 are doubled.

Note 4: When total quantity stored does not exceed 50 percent of maximum per pile, the distances in columns four and five may be reduced 50 percent, but not less than 3 ft.

Drum Storage Outdoors

Outdoor drum storage should be located in such a manner as to reduce the spread of fire to other materials in storage or to other property. Areas used for drum storage should be kept free of combustibles and open flames, and smoking prohibited (see Table 3-3H).

I. Handling of Flammable and Combustible Liquids

Loading and Unloading

At loading and unloading stations for tank cars and tank vehicles, spills may occur. Tank vehicle and tank car stations for Class I liquids should be located a minimum of 25 ft from storage tanks, other plant buildings, and the nearest line of property that can be built on. Level ground is desirable, and drains, diversionary curbs, or natural ground slope can be utilized to prevent spills from spreading to other parts of the plant or to other property.

Bonding provisions for protection against static sparks must be provided at all loading stations when Class I liquids are loaded, or when Class II or Class III liquids are loaded into tank cars or tank vehicles that have contained Class I liquids on the previous trip. The bonding must be provided between the fill pipe or piping and the tank vehicle. Bonding connections are made before the dome covers are opened. Closed metal piping systems (eliminating exposure to air) for loading and unloading may eliminate the need for special bonding provisions since the piping system is inherently bonded to the vehicle.

Stray electrical current protection is necessary for ship and tank car loading and unloading in those areas where stray currents may be present. See Section 5, Chapter 5 for further information on static and stray current protection.

Tank ships and tank barges are loaded and unloaded at oil piers which may or may not be used exclusively for this purpose. The location of the oil piers is governed by direction and velocity of the waterway, the range of tides, and the direction and frequency of prevailing winds of high velocity. Hazards related to the loading and unloading of vessels are, except for the quantities of liquid involved, comparable to those for tank vehicles and tank cars.

Many liquids, including gasoline, jet fuels, toluene, and light fuel oil, can build up dangerous static electrical charges on the surface of the liquid. If a flammable vapor-air mixture is present at the surface of the liquid at the time high static electrical discharges occur, an explosion or fire can result. Excessive turbulence, pumping two dissimilar materials, the free fall of liquid through the vapor space, and filters capable of removing micron-sized particles are the most common causes of explosions or fires originating from static electricity in aboveground tanks, tank vehicles, tank barges, and tank ships. Where flammable vapors may exist, it is recommended that the delivery rate be 3 fps until the fill pipe is covered in order to reduce static caused ignitions and a minimum of 30 sec relaxation time should be provided downstream of a filter.

Piping and Valves

Substantial piping systems protected against physical damage are preferable to portable containers for conveying quantities of liquids throughout buildings. All piping systems should be so designed that liquid will not continue to flow by gravity or by siphoning in case of breakage of a pipe. Valves should be provided at accessible points to control or stop the flow. Emergency remote controls are frequently provided for valves or pumps particularly at dispensing locations. Other remotely controlled valves installed for normal operating procedure can frequently be used during fire emergency procedures to control or stop the flow of liquids. Valves are available which close automatically if subjected to fire conditions. Dispensing outlets for systems under gas pressure or gravity head should be equipped with self-closing valves.

Pipe materials that are resistant to the corrosive properties of the liquid handled, that have adequate design strength to withstand the maximum service pressure (including shock and surge pressures which may be expected) and temperature, and, when possible, that are resistant to physical damage and thermal shock should be used. Where low melting point materials, such as aluminum and brass, or materials that soften on fire exposure, such as plastics, or nonductile material, such as cast iron, are necessary, special consideration should be given to their behavior on exposure to fire. After installation, piping systems should be tested at 150 percent of the maximum anticipated pressure of the system, or pneumatically tested to 110 percent of the maximum anticipated pressure of the system, but not less than 5 psig at the highest point of the system.

Since some valves are used infrequently, it is necessary to make periodic maintenance inspections to assure they will operate during emergency conditions. All aboveground piping and connections should be inspected periodically to prevent leakage. Internal corrosion in pipes is a particular problem when liquids are corrosive or where piping is used for the continuous flow of liquid under high pressure operations such as at refineries or chemical plants. Maintenance inspections of the thickness of pipe walls can be performed in several ways similar to the inspection of tanks. Underground piping is also subject to external corrosion and should be protected against such corrosion by suitable coatings or cathodic protection. Tests for possible leaks in underground piping can be done hydrostatically using the liquid normally handled in the piping system.

Dispensing and Handling Methods

Large quantities of flammable or combustible liquids are best transferred through piping by means of pumps. Gravity flow is not desirable except as required in process equipment. If positive displacement pumps are used, they should be provided with a pressure relief discharging back to the tank or to the pump section. The transfer of Class I or Class II liquids by means of air pressure is not good practice. Although inert gas may be used for transferring all classes of liquids, and air pressure may be used for transferring Class III liquids, they are acceptable only if the pressure is controlled, including pressure relief devices, to limit the pressure so it cannot exceed the design pressure of the vessel, tank, or container.

The safest method for handling flammable or combustible liquids is to pump from buried storage tanks through an adequately designed piping system protected from physical damage to the dispensing equipment located outdoors or in specially designed inside storage rooms. Such a room should have at least one exterior wall for explosion relief and accessibility for fire fighting, interior walls with 2-hr fire resistance ratings, adequate ventilation and drainage, and be free of sources of ignition.

Where solvents are pumped from storage tanks to the point of use in an industrial building, emergency switches are advisable in the dispensing area at the normal exit door or at other safe locations outside the fire area and at the pumps to shut down all pumps in case of fire and stop the flow of solvent.

Where dispensing by gravity flow, such as filling containers in an industrial operation, a shutoff valve is installed as close as practical to the vessel being unloaded and a control valve near the end of the discharge pipe. Additionally, in some filling operations, a heat-actuated valve is desirable to shut off the flow of liquid in case of a fire.

The preferred method of dispensing flammable and combustible liquids from a drum is by means of a laboratory-tested hand-operated pump drawing through the top. In certain cases a laboratory-tested drum faucet may be used for dispensing from a drum; however, hand-operated pumps are safer than faucets because the hazard of leakage is reduced.

For handling small quantities of flammable and combustible liquids, safety cans of various designs and materials of construction are preferred. Safety cans are substantially constructed to avoid the danger of leakage and designed to minimize the likelihood of spilling or vapor release and of container rupture under fire conditions (see Fig. 3-3P). Dispensing also can be done from the original shipping containers. Open pails or open buckets are never used for storage.

Fig. 3-3P. Typical safety cans having pouring outlets with tight-fitting caps or valves normally closed by springs, except when held open by hand, so that contents will not be spilled if a can is tipped over. The caps also provide an emergency vent when the cans are exposed to fire.

All handling and dispensing of flammable liquids should be done in a well ventilated area free of sources of ignition and bonding should be provided between the dispensing equipment and the container being filled.

J.   Transportation

Tank Vehicles

NFPA No. 385, Recommended Regulatory Standard for Tank Vehicles for Flammable and Combustible Liquids, provides for substantial vehicles and tanks which present relatively little danger of fire when involved in minor traffic accidents. Under these recommendations tanks are constructed to withstand all but violent impact without rupturing and releasing liquid. Vents are provided so that if a tank is subjected to fire, vapor will be released at the vent where it simply burns as a torch, thus avoiding the danger of rupture from excessive internal pressure.

For all but viscous liquids, a shutoff valve located inside the shell of the cargo tank is required and is kept closed except during loading or unloading operations. A shear section is provided in the piping connected to the internal valve. Therefore, in any accident which would damage the piping, the piping breaks at the shear section leaving the internal valve undamaged and closed (see Fig. 3-3Q).

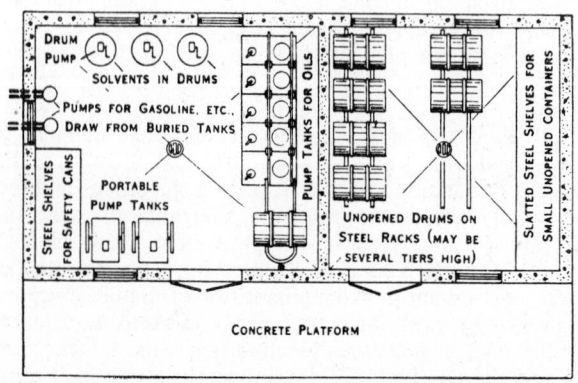

Fig. 3-3Q.   Typical storage and dispensing house.

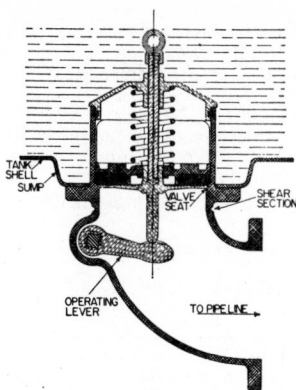

Fig. 3-3R. Shutoff valve located inside tank shell with shear section to leave valve shut if discharge faucet breaks.

The operating mechanism for the valve also is required to have a secondary control remotely located which can be used to shut off the valve in case of fire or severe spillage during unloading. Also a fusible section is required in the control mechanism for the valve which permits the valve to close automatically in case of fire (see Fig. 3-3R). Other important fire protection features are detailed in NFPA No. 385.

In the past many cities have attempted to minimize the fire problem by specifying the maximum sizes of cargo tanks on trucks. The wisdom of this sort of provision is dubious. Assuming, for example, that it is necessary to transport 4,000 gal of gasoline over city streets to make local deliveries, a legal restriction as to maximum size of tank might require the use of four 1,000-gal tank trucks in place of one 4,000-gal tank. This multiplies by four the tank truck traffic, with four times the accident potential. The danger from a gasoline fire is not in direct proportion to the quantity of gasoline. One thousand gallons of gasoline released to burn in the street would be sufficient to kill everyone trapped in the flames. Four thousand gallons, while presumably covering a larger area, would certainly not be expected to cause four times the number of fatalities. Reasoning on this basis, the NFPA Standards have not recommended any limitation on the maximum size of tank trucks.

Tank truck traffic through congested districts of cities should be avoided as far as possible, since any fire is likely to have much more serious consequences in congested districts than in sparsely settled areas. Bypass routes, such as are commonly specified for through truck traffic of all kinds, form the obvious solution to this particular problem.

Parking of loaded tank vehicles is another feature which can be appropriately regulated by municipalities. Such parking can be prohibited on city streets. Similarly, tank vehicles should not be parked in public garages. Permissible parking locations for tank vehicles may be specified, if necessary. Any property zoned for aboveground oil storage, for example the ordinary bulk oil plant, should be a location where tank vehicles can be parked without any undue increase in hazard to the public.

Transportation of flammable liquids in tank vehicles in interstate commerce is governed by regulations of the Department of Transportation (DOT) as contained in the Code of Federal Regulations, Title 49—Transportation.[6] There are comprehensive specifications and labeling requirements for shipping containers for various types of products. Absence of a label does not necessarily mean that the material is nonhazardous. DOT labels are illustrated in Chapter 10 of this section.

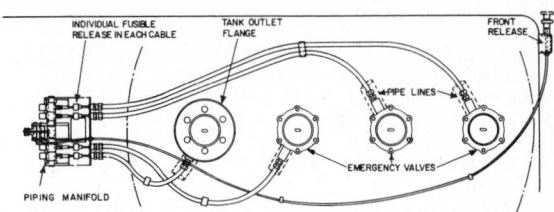

Fig. 3-3S. Bottom view of tank vehicle showing typical installation of emergency valves and controls.

Rail, Ship, and Pipeline

The transportation of flammable liquids by railroad tank cars is under the jurisdiction of DOT (see Title 49 of the Code of Federal Regulations).[6] The design of tank cars is rigidly controlled, and is governed by the nature of the contents being carried in a somewhat similar manner as for tank vehicles including emergency venting requirements. See Section 17, Chapter 3 of this HANDBOOK for general information on the design and use of railroad tank cars.

The transportation of flammable and combustible liquids in bulk on board vessels is under the jurisdiction of the Commandant of the Coast Guard in the United States (see Code of Federal Regulations, Title 46—Shipping).[7] These requirements include the design of the vessel, whether it be a tank ship or tank barge, as well as requirements for extinguishing systems or portable extinguishers. Further requirements include limitations on container storage of drums or portable tanks, restrictions for passenger carrying vessels and many other requirements for the safe transportation of flammable and combustible liquids by water. Details of these requirements can be secured at the nearest U.S. Coast Guard Merchant Marine Inspection Office. See Section 17, Chapter 4 of this HANDBOOK for further information on transportation of hazardous materials aboard vessels.

Standards for liquid pipelines are developed by the American National Standards Institute and are published by the American Society of Mechanical Engineers entitled "Liquid Petroleum Transportation Piping Systems," ANSI B31.4.[8] These standards include piping requirements and installation recommendations.

SI Units

The following conversion factors are given as a convenience in converting to SI units the English units used in this chapter.

$$1 \text{ sq ft} = 0.0929 \text{ m}^2$$
$$1 \text{ in.} = 25.400 \text{ mm}$$
$$1 \text{ ft} = 0.305 \text{ m}$$
$$\tfrac{5}{9}(°F - 32) = °C$$
$$1 \text{ gpm} = 3.785 \text{ litres/min}$$

Bibliography

References Cited

[1] Mitchell, F. C., and Vernon, H. C., "Effect of Pressure on Explosion Hazards," NFPA *Quarterly*, Vol. 31, No. 4, April 1938, pp. 306–313.

[2] Burgess, D. S., Strasser, A., and Grumer, J., "Diffusion Burning of Liquid Fuels in Open Trays," *Fire Research Abstracts and Reviews*, Vol. 3, 1961, pp. 177–192.

[3] Welded Steel Tanks for Oil Storage, Standard 650, 1966, American Petroleum Institute, New York.

[4] "Cleaning Tank Vehicles Used for Transportation of Flammable Liquids," RP 2013, 1967, 4th ed., American Petroleum Institute, New York.

[5] "Cleaning Petroleum Storage Tanks," RP 2015, 1967, American Petroleum Institute, New York.

[6] Title 49, "Transportation," *Code of Federal Regulations,* U.S. Government Printing Office, Washington, D.C.

[7] Title 46, "Shipping," *Code of Federal Regulations,* U.S. Government Printing Office, Washington, D.C.

[8] "Liquid Petroleum Transportation Piping Systems," ANSI B31.4–1974, American National Standards Institute, New York.

NFPA Codes, Standards, and Recommended Practices (see the latest *NFPA Publications and Visual Aids Catalog* for availability of current editions of the following documents)

NFPA No. 30, Flammable and Combustible Liquids Code.

NFPA No. 31, Standard for the Installation of Oil Burning Equipment.

NFPA No. 325A, Flash Point Index of Trade Name Liquids.

NFPA No. 325M, Fire Hazard Properties of Flammable Liquids, Gases and Volatile Solids.

NFPA No. 327, Standard Procedures for Safeguarding Small Tanks and Containers.

NFPA No. 385, Recommended Regulatory Standard for Tank Vehicles for Flammable and Combustible Liquids.

NFPA No. 77, Recommended Practice on Static Electricity.

Additional Readings

Accident Prevention Manual for Industrial Operations, 6th ed., National Safety Council, Chicago, 1969.

Armistead, George, Jr., *Safety in Petroleum Refining and Related Industries,* 1st ed., John G. Simmonds & Co., New York, 1950.

Brookes, Vincent J., and Jacobs, Morris B., *Poisons, Properties, Chemical Identification, Symptoms and Emergency Treatment,* 2nd ed., D. Van Nostrand, Princeton, N.J., 1958.

Carpenter, R. A., Bolze, C. C., and Findley, L. D., "A System for the Correlation and Physical Properties and Structural Characteristics of Chemical Compounds with their Commercial Uses," Midwest Research Institute, Kansas City, Mo. (reprint from American Documentation, Vol. X, No. 2).

Claudy, W. D., *Respiratory Hazards of the Fire Service,* National Fire Protection Association, Boston, 1957, pp. 99–130.

Compilation of Labeling Laws and Regulations for Hazardous Substances, Chemical Specialties Manufacturers Association, N.Y.

Coward, H. F., and Jones, G. W., "Limits of Flammability of Gases and Vapors," Bulletin No. 503, 1952, U.S. Department of the Interior, Bureau of Mines, Washington, D.C.

Factory Mutual Engineering Corporation, *Handbook of Industrial Loss Prevention,* 2nd ed., McGraw-Hill, New York, 1967.

Handbook of Organic Industrial Solvents, 2nd ed., National Association of Mutual Casualty Companies, Chicago, 1961.

Hawley, G. G., ed., *The Condensed Chemical Dictionary,* 8th ed., Van Nostrand Reinhold Co., New York, 1971.

Hygienic Guide Series, American Industrial Hygiene Association, Detroit.

Kirk, R. E., and Othmer, D. F., eds., *Encyclopedia of Chemical Technology,* 2nd ed., 22 vols., Interscience Encyclopedia, Inc., New York, 1963–1969.

Mellan, I., *Industrial Solvents Handbook,* Reinhold, New York, 1970.

Merck Index of Chemicals and Drugs, 8th ed., Merck & Co., Rahway, N.J., 1968.

Perry, J. H., and Chilton, C. H., eds., *Chemical Engineers' Handbook,* 5th ed., McGraw-Hill, New York, 1974.

Safety and Fire Protection Committee, Manufacturing Chemists Association, Inc., *Guide for Safety in the Chemical Laboratory,* 2nd ed., Van Nostrand Reinhold Co., New York, 1972.

Sax, N. I., *Dangerous Properties of Industrial Materials,* 3rd ed., Van Nostrand Reinhold Co., New York, 1968.

Threshold Limit Values, American Conference of Governmental Industrial Hygienists, Cincinatti, Ohio.

Title 46, "Shipping," Parts 146 to 149; Title 49, "Transportation," Parts 171 to 178, *Code of Federal Regulations,* U.S. Government Printing Office, Washington, D.C.

Van Dolah, R. W., et al., "Flame Propagation, Extinguishment and Environmental Effects on Combustion," *Fire Technology,* Vol. 1, No. 2, May 1965, pp. 138–145.

Verralin, C. H., ed., *Fire Protection Manual for Hydrocarbon Processing Plants,* Gulf Publishing Co., Houston, 1973.

Weast, R. C., ed., *Handbook of Chemistry and Physics,* Chemical Rubber Co., Cleveland, 1972–1973.

Welker, J. R., Pipkin, O. A., and Sliepcevich, C. M., "The Effect of Wind on Flames," *Fire Technology,* Vol. 1, No. 2, May 1965, pp. 122–129.

Welker, J. R., and Sliepcevich, C. M., "Bending of Wind-Blown Flames from Liquid Pools," *Fire Technology,* Vol. 2, No. 2, May 1966, pp. 127–135.

Welker, J. R., and Sliepcevich, C. M., "Burning Rates and Heat Transfer from Wind-Blown Flames," *Fire Technology,* Vol. 2, No. 3, August 1966, pp. 211–218.

Zimmerman, O. T., and Lavine, Irvin, *Handbook of Material Trade Names,* Industrial Research Service, Dover, N.H., 1953 (plus supplements).

Chapter 4

GASES

The term "gas" describes the physical state of a substance which has no shape or volume of its own but which, rather, will take the shape and occupy the entire volume of whatever container or other enclosure it occupies. This is in contrast to a liquid which, while having no shape of its own, has volume and to a solid which has both a shape and a volume of its own. The properties and behavior of gases can be understood only with the knowledge that a gas is composed of extremely minute particles in constant motion. The higher the temperature, the more rapid is the motion.

A. Gases Defined

As all substances can exist as gases depending upon the temperature and pressure applied to them, the term "gas" as used in this chapter is applied only to substances which exist in the gaseous state at so-called "normal" temperature and pressure (NTP) conditions (approximately 70°F and 14.7 psia). However, even at normal or near normal temperatures and pressures many substances can exist as *either* liquids or gases. The term "gas" is not rigorously defined in NFPA Standards. Insofar as a flammable liquid is defined in NFPA standards, in part, as a liquid having a vapor pressure not exceeding 40 psia at 100°F, a gas, for comparative purposes, can be considered a substance or mixture of substances which, when in the liquid state, would exert a vapor pressure of 40 psia or greater at 100°F.

B. Classification of Gases

In order to deal effectively with the great number and variety of gases in commerce and our environment (we breathe a gas mixture called "air"), it is advantageous to establish certain classifications of gases. These classifications recognize certain "common denominators" reflecting the chemical and physical properties of gases and their primary uses.

Classification By Chemical Properties

Chemical properties are of primary fire protection concern as they reflect the ability of a gas to chemically react with other materials (or within themselves) with the production of potentially hazardous quantities of heat or reaction products, or to produce physiological effects hazardous to man.

Flammable Gases: In NFPA usage, any gas which will burn in the normal concentrations of oxygen in the air is considered a flammable gas. The burning, or combustion, of flammable gases in air is subject to the same conditions as are flammable liquid vapors, i.e., each gas will burn only within a certain range of gas-air mixture compositions (the flammable or combustible range) and a certain temperature is needed to initiate the reaction (the ignition temperature).

In a few instances, consideration of the width of the flammable range or the magnitude of the lower limit of flammability or both has resulted in classification of an ostensibly flammable gas as nonflammable because the chances of fire are low under certain conditions. Anhydrous ammonia is notable in this respect and is classified by the DOT (U.S. Department of Transportation) as a nonflammable gas for purposes of transportation in interstate commerce (see Anhydrous Ammonia in Part F of this Chapter).

While flammable liquid vapors and flammable gases exhibit similar combustion characteristics, the term "flash point," which is a common and necessary combustion property of flammable liquids, has no practical significance for flammable gases. The "flash point" is basically a measure of the temperature at which a flammable liquid produces sufficient vapors for combustion and this temperature is always below the normal boiling point. A flammable gas is normally at a temperature exceeding its normal boiling point, even when the gas is in the liquid state (as it often is in shipment and storage), and, hence, is at a temperature exceeding its flash point—usually well above it.

Nonflammable Gases: Nonflammable gases are those that will not burn in any concentration of air or oxygen. A number of these gases, however, will support combustion while others act to suppress combustion. Those gases that support combustion are often referred to as "oxidizers" or "oxidizing gases" and are generally either oxygen or mixtures of oxygen with other gases, such as oxygen-helium or oxygen-nitrogen mixtures, which contain considerably more oxygen than is present in the oxygen-nitrogen mixture known as "air," or certain gaseous oxides, such as nitrous oxide.

Gases that will not support combustion are generally known as "inert" gases. Among the most common are nitrogen, argon, helium, and other rare gases in the atmosphere as well as carbon dioxide and sulfur dioxide. There are some metals, however, that can react vigorously in carbon dioxide or nitrogen atmospheres, e.g. magnesium.

Reactive Gases: As most gases can be made to react chemically with some other substance under some conditions, the term "reactive gas" is used to distinguish gases which will either react with other materials or within themselves (with the production of potentially hazardous quantities of heat or reaction products) by a reaction other than burning (combustion) and under reasonably anticipated initiating conditions of heat, shock, etc.

Fluorine is an example of a highly reactive gas as it reacts with practically all organic and inorganic substances at normal temperatures and pressures and often fast enough to result in flaming. Another example is the reaction between chlorine (classed as a nonflammable gas) with hydrogen (a flammable gas), which can occur with production of flames.

Several gases can rearrange themselves chemically when subject to reasonably anticipated conditions of heat and shock, including fire exposure to their containers, with production of potentially hazardous quantities of heat or reaction products. Examples are acetylene, methyl acetylene, propadiene and vinyl chloride. These gases are usually mixed with other substances in containers used in transportation and storage or special containers are used to stabilize them against reasonably anticipated reaction initiators.

Toxic Gases: Certain gases can present a serious life hazard if they are released into the atmosphere. Included are gases that are poisonous or irritating when inhaled or contacted such as chlorine, hydrogen sulfide, sulfur dioxide, ammonia, and carbon monoxide. The presence of these gases may complicate fire control measures involving fire fighter exposure.

Classification by Physical Properties

These properties are of primary fire protection concern as they affect the physical behavior of gases, both when inside containers and after accidental release from their containers.

By their nature, gases must be completely confined in containers in transportation, transfer and storage until used. Regardless of the use, the quantity of gas is important, in terms of its weight, and gases are inherently lighter than liquids or solids. It is a matter of practical economic and ease-of-usage necessity that gases be packaged in containers that contain as much gas as is feasible.

This has resulted in transportation and storage of gases in the liquid state as well as the gaseous state—a situation often confusing to many, but a distinction which must be made for the application of sound fire prevention and protection practices.

Compressed Gases: For purposes of this chapter, a compressed gas is one which at all normal atmospheric temperatures inside its container, exists solely in the gaseous state under pressure. The pressure is basically dependent upon the pressure to which the container was originally charged and upon how much gas remains in the container, although the gas temperature will have some effect (see Part C of this Chapter). There are no universally defined lower or upper limits to the pressure. In America, the lower limit is customarily considered to be 25 psig (pounds per square inch gage) at normal temperatures (70°F to 100°F). The upper limit is limited only by the economics of container construction and is usually in the range of 1,800 to 3,000 psig.

A container of compressed gas still is rather limited in the weight of gas it holds. For example, the largest common portable cylinder of compressed oxygen contains only about 20 lbs of oxygen, or about 245 cu ft of oxygen equivalent at NTP (70°F and 14.7 psia).

Liquefied Gases: For purposes of this chapter, a liquefied gas is one which, at normal atmospheric temperatures inside its container, exists partly in the liquid state and partly in the gaseous state and under pressure as long as any liquid remains in the container. The pressure is basically dependent upon the temperature of the liquid although the quantity of liquid can affect this under some conditions (see Part C of this chapter).

A liquefied gas is a much more "concentrated" quantity of gas than is a compressed gas. For example, the aforementioned size of compressed oxygen cylinder could hold about 116 lbs. of liquefied oxygen, or about 1,400 cu ft of oxygen equivalent at NTP, about six times more. This comparison is valid for illustrative purposes only as compressed oxygen and liquefied oxygen will not be found in the same type of container.

Cryogenic Gases: For purposes of this chapter, a cryogenic gas is a liquefied gas which exists in its container at temperatures far below normal atmospheric temperatures, usually slightly above its boiling point at NTP, and correspondingly low to moderate pressures. A principal reason for this distinction with respect to a liquefied gas is that a cryogenic gas cannot be retained indefinitely in a container by virtue of container design alone as the heat from the atmosphere, which cannot be prevented from entering the container, is continually tending to raise the pressure to a level which, if confined, could greatly exceed any feasible container strength.

Some pertinent physical properties of liquefied gases, including cryogenic gases, are given in Table 3-4A.

It is emphasized that these descriptions of gas classifications by physical properties pertain only to usage in this chapter. Somewhat different descriptions of the terms "compressed gas," "liquefied gas," and "cryogenic gas" may be found in codes and regulations, particularly the DOT Hazardous Materials Regulations applicable to interstate transportation. For example, many liquefied gases are classified as compressed gases by the DOT.

Classification by Usage

Classification of gases by principal uses is of primary concern in fire protection because standards and codes and general industry parlance often use such a classification. It is a far less rigorous classification scheme than the preceding and there is much overlap in uses with the gases. However, those concerned with fire safety should be familiar with this classification.

Table 3-4A. Physical Properties of Cryogenic Gases

(Compiled from data in the *Handbook of Compressed Gases*, (Compressed Gas Association))

Name	Normal Boiling Point				Normal Conditions (70°F, 14.7 psia)			Critical Point	
	Temp °F	Liquid Density lb/cu ft	Gas Density lb/cu ft	Latent Heat Btu/lb	Gas Density lb/cu ft	Cu Ft Gas from 1 cu ft Liquid		Temp °F	Pressure psia
Air	−317.8	54.6	—	88.2	.075	728		−220.3	547
Argon	−302.6	86.98	.356	70.2	.103	842		−188.5	705.4
Carbon monoxide	−312.7	51.12	—	92.8	.073	706		−220	507.5
Ethylene	−154.8	35.4	.130	208.0	.072	487		49.0	745
Fluorine	−306.6	94.1	.363	74.1	.098	961		−200.4	808.5
Helium	−452.1	7.8	.106	10.3	.01	754		−450.3	33.2
Hydrogen	−423	4.43	.084	192.7	.005	850		−400	190.8
Methane	−258.7	26.5	.111	219.2	.042	636		−115.8	673
Nitrogen	−320.4	50.46	.288	85.7	.072	696		−232.9	492.2
Oxygen	−297.4	71.27	.296	91.7	.083	861		−181.1	737

Fuel Gases: Fuel gases are flammable gases customarily used for burning with air to produce heat which in turn is used as a source of heat (comfort and process), power, or light. By far the principal and most widely used fuel gases are natural gas and the liquefied petroleum gases, butane and propane.

Industrial Gases: Industrial gases embrace the entire gamut of gases classified by chemical properties customarily used in industrial processes, for welding and cutting, heat treating, chemical processing, refrigeration, water treatment, etc.

Medical Gases: By far the most specialized usage classification, the medical gases are used for medical purposes such as anesthesia and respiratory therapy. Cyclopropane, oxygen, and nitrous oxide are common medical gases.

C. Basic Hazards of Gases

It is useful for systematic evaluation of gas hazards to make a distinction between the hazards presented by a gas when confined in a container and the hazards presented when a gas escapes from a container—even though these hazards may be simultaneously present in a single incident.

Hazards of Confinement

The hazards of gases confined in their containers basically reflect the fact that (1) they expand when heated and, when confined, heating results in an increase in pressure which can result in gas release and/or cause container failure, and (2) that containers can fail from contact with flames from an exposing fire due to loss in strength of the material from which the container is fabricated.

Compressed gases and liquefied gas are affected somewhat differently when heated. A compressed gas (being solely in the gaseous state) simply attempts to expand and the classic "gas laws" describe the behavior of the gas. No actual gas follows these "laws" exactly, but the laws of Boyle and Charles have been proven sufficiently accurate for most practical purposes to predict the behavior of compressed gases under commonly encountered conditions. In the formulas, T = absolute temperature (degrees F + 459), P = absolute pressure (gage pressure in pounds per square inch + 14.7 psi), and V = volume in cubic feet or any unit of volume.

Boyle's Law

Boyle's Law states that the volume occupied by a given mass of gas varies inversely with the absolute pressure if the temperature is not allowed to change or

$$PV = \text{constant}.$$

Charles's Law

Charles's Law states that the volume of a given mass of gas is directly proportional to the absolute temperature if the pressure is kept constant. Thus

$$\frac{V}{T} = \text{constant}.$$

Therefore, for most gases, within practical working limits, the relation between temperature, pressure, and volume may be closely approximated by the following formula:

$$\frac{T_1}{T_2} = \frac{P_1 \times V_1}{P_2 \times V_2}.$$

T_1, P_1, and V_1 refer to initial conditions; T_2, P_2, and V_2 refer to changed conditions to be determined.

Example: Assume a 10 cu ft cylinder of compressed gas at 70°F has a gage pressure of 1000 psi. Assume that the temperature is increased to 150°F. What will be the pressure?

$$T_1 = 70 + 459 = 529.$$
$$P_1 = 1000 + 14.7 = 1014.7.$$
$$V_1 = 10.$$
$$T_2 = 150 + 459 = 609.$$
$$P_2 = \text{to be determined}.$$
$$V_2 = 10.$$

Substituting in the formula:

$$\frac{529}{609} = \frac{1014.7 \times 10}{P_2 \times 10}$$

$$P_2 = 1014.7 \times \frac{609}{529} = 1170.$$

Therefore, gage pressure will be 1170 − 14.7, or 1155.3 psi.

A liquefied gas, including a cryogenic gas (being partly in the liquid state), exhibits a more complicated behavior as the end result of heating is the net effect of the combination of three effects. First, the gas phase is subject to the same effect as for a compressed gas. Second, the liquid attempts to expand, compressing the vapor. Finally, the vapor pressure of the liquid increases with increasing temperature of the liquid. These combine to result in an increase in pressure when the container is heated.

A most serious pressure rise can occur if the liquid expansion results in the container becoming liquid full (the gas phase condensing). If this happens, a small amount of additional heating results in a large increase in pressure. For this reason, it is vital never to place more liquefied gas in the liquid phase into a container than can be accommodated —leaving a gas space—if the liquid temperature is raised to a level commensurate with the ambient temperatures expected. The proper quantity varies considerably with the liquefied gas and factors affecting expected temperature rises, such as the temperature of the liquid when placed into the container, the size of the container, and whether it is insulated or installed above or below ground. The quantities permitted are commonly expressed as "filling densities" or "loading densities" and are specified for specific gases (in some cases, groupings of similar gases) in codes, standards, and regulations. Filling densities expressed in terms of weight are absolute values, i.e., the weight of gas may always be placed into the container. Filling densities expressed in terms of volume, however, must always be qualified by the liquid temperature.

Table 3-4B is an example of how filling densities are expressed for liquefied gases—in this case liquefied petroleum gases stored at normal temperatures in uninsulated containers. Note that larger quantities of higher specific gravity materials are permitted (reflecting the fact that these liquids tend to expand less), that larger containers can be filled more than smaller ones can (reflecting the fact that it takes longer for them to absorb heat from atmospheric temperatures or sunlight), and that underground containers can be filled even more (reflecting that fact that their ambient temperatures are relatively constant and well below summer atmospheric temperatures).

Overpressure Relief Devices

Usually spring-loaded safety relief valves or bursting discs or both are provided on most compressed and liquefied

Table 3-4B.   Maximum Permitted Filling Density
(LP-G Stored at Normal Temperatures in Uninsulated Containers)

Column 1	Col. 2	Col. 3	Col. 4	Col. 5	Col. 6	Col. 7
	Aboveground Containers				All Underground Containers	
	0 to 1,200 gal.[1]		Over 1,200 gal.[1]			
Specific Gravity at 60°F (15.6°C)	% of WWC[2]	Vol. % at 60°F	% of WWC[2]	Vol. % at 60°F	% of WWC[2]	Vol. % at 60°F
.496—.503	41	82.0	44	88.0	45	90.0
.504—.510	42	82.6	45	88.5	46	90.5
.511—.519	43	83.5	46	89.4	47	91.3
.520—.527	44	84.3	47	90.0	48	91.8
.528—.536	45	84.7	48	90.3	49	92.2
.537—.544	46	85.2	49	90.7	50	92.5
.545—.552	47	85.6	50	91.2	51	93.0
.553—.560	48	86.4	51	91.8	52	93.6
.561—.568	49	87.0	52	92.3	53	94.1
.569—.576	50	87.5	53	92.7	54	94.4
.577—.584	51	87.9	54	93.1	55	94.8
.585—.592	52	88.3	55	93.5	56	95.1
.593—.600	53	88.9	56	94.0	57	95.6

[1] Total Water Capacity, U.S. Gallons (1000 Imperial Gallons, 4550 Litres)
[2] WWC—Water Weight Capacity

gas containers to limit container pressure to a level the container can safely withstand, although fusible plugs are sometimes used on smaller containers. The start-to-discharge pressure settings of these devices are related to the strength of the container. The relieving capacity (in terms of gas flow rate through them) is based upon consideration of heat input rates resulting from fire exposure in most cases, as this is generally the largest anticipated source of heat. In some instances, such as underground or insulated containers, other sources of overpressure may dominate the effect of fire exposure.

As noted, the relieving capacity of these devices is based upon discharge of gas. In the case of liquefied gas containers exposed to fire, it is possible to have conditions such that liquid will be discharged instead of gas, i.e., the container is tipped over. Under such conditions, the relieving capacity will be reduced—in some cases as much as 60 to 70 percent. With the possible exception of the fire exposure condition, this reduction is of little practical significance. Even in the case of fire exposure, this situation is not as critical as it may appear as prevention of container failure under fire exposure conditions requires other safeguards in addition to the overpressure relief device.

Instances of failure of over pressure devices are rather rare even though their inspection, maintenance, and replacement is essentially unregulated and they are subject to many deleterious influences.

Containers of certain poisonous and highly toxic gases are not provided with overpressure relief devices on the basis that the overall hazard of a prematurely operating or leaking relief device outweighs the hazard of container failure from overpressure. It is also the practice in some countries, especially in Western Europe, Asia and the Mediterranean area, not to provide overpressure protection on liquefied gas containers—a practice which reflects the widespread use and installation of such containers inside buildings, including homes, and commercial and institutional buildings. In such cases, the hazard of gas release indoors due to operation of the relief device is felt to outweigh the hazard of container failure due to overpressure.

Container Failures

Containers of compressed or liquefied gases can represent high levels of potential energy release due to the concentration of matter by compression or liquefaction. Container failure releases this energy—often extremely rapidly and violently—with simultaneous release of gas to the surroundings and propulsion of the container or container pieces. Compressed gas container failures are distinguished more by the flying missile hazard than by the results of gas release because they contain lesser quantities of gas. Liquefied gas container failures can release larger quantities of gas.

Because failures of liquefied flammable gas containers from fire exposure occur frequently enough, a special term, the Boiling Liquid—Expanding Vapor Explosion, or BLEVE (pronounced "blevey") has evolved to describe this phenomenon.

The BLEVE

All liquefied gases are stored in containers at temperatures above their boiling points at NTP and remain under pressure only so long as the container remains closed to the atmosphere. This pressure ranges from less than 1 psi for some cryogenic gas containers to several hundred psi for noncryogenic liquefied gas containers at normal storage temperatures. If the pressure is reduced to atmospheric, such as through container failure, the sensible heat which is, in effect, "stored" in the liquid, causes very rapid vaporization of a portion of the liquid to a degree directly proportional to the temperature difference between that of the liquid at the instant of container failure and the normal boiling point of the liquid. For many liquefied flammable gases, this temperature difference at normal atmospheric temperatures can result in vaporization of about one-third of the liquid in the container.

Because overpressure relief devices are set to discharge at pressures corresponding to liquid temperatures above normal atmospheric temperatures (to prevent premature operation), the liquid temperature is higher than this if container failure occurs at the time when a relief device is functioning. Therefore, more liquid is vaporized under these conditions—often over one-half of the liquid in the container. This is the usual situation when a container fails from fire exposure.

The liquid remaining unvaporized is refrigerated by the "self-extraction" of heat when the pressure is reduced to atmospheric and cooled to near its normal boiling point.

Liquid vaporization is accompanied by a large liquid-to-vapor expansion (see Table 3-4A). It is this expansion process which provides the energy for propagation of cracks in the container structure, propulsion of pieces of the container, rapid mixing of the vapor and air resulting in the characteristic fire ball upon ignition by the fire which caused the BLEVE, and atomization of the remaining cold liquid. Many of the atomized droplets burn as they fly through the air. However, it is not uncommon for the cold liquid to be propelled from the fire zone too fast for ignition to occur and fall to earth still in liquid form. In one case, dissolved spots in asphalt paving were noted up to ½ mile from the site of an LP-Gas BLEVE. In other BLEVEs, fire fighters have been cooled by cold liquid passing in their vicinity.

Reduction of internal pressure to atmospheric level in a container results from structural failure of the container. Failure is most often due to weakening of the container metal from flame contact; however, it will happen if the container is punctured or fails for any other reason.

As shown in Figure 3-4A, the strength of carbon steel steadily decreases with temperature rises above about 400°F. Figure 3-4A is based upon a low carbon steel and the curves will vary quantitatively with other steels, but the loss of strength with increasing temperature is valid for all common metals and the critical temperatures are well below those attainable in a fire.

Figure 3-4A also shows why entirely satisfactory performance of a spring loaded relief valve to design parameters cannot prevent a BLEVE. By its nature, such a valve cannot reduce the pressure to atmospheric but only to a point somewhat below its start-to-discharge pressure. Therefore, the liquid will always be at a temperature above its normal boiling point, there will be pressure inside the container, and the container structure will be stressed in tension. This stressed area is shown as a shaded area in Figure 3-4A for a common type of LP-Gas container having a safety relief

valve set for 250 psi. Again, while this area will vary for different steels or pressure vessel-relief valve design characteristics, it is evident that if the metal is heated above this range (quite possible in the event of direct flame contact), the metal will not withstand the stress and the container will fail.

It is extremely difficult to heat the container metal significantly where it is in contact with liquid because the liquid conducts the heat away from the metal and acts as a heat absorber. For example, when the relief valve cited in this example is discharging, the propane liquid cannot be above about 120 to 140°F. As a result, the metal temperature is well within safe limits. This situation does not exist for the metal in the vapor space of the container as vapor is relatively nonheat conductive and the vapor has little heat-absorbing capacity.

In most BLEVEs the failure originates in the metal of the vapor space and is characterized by the metal stretching and thinning out, the appearance of a longitudinal tear which progressively gets larger until a critical length is reached. At this point, the failure becomes brittle in nature and propagates at sonic velocity through the metal in both longitudinal and circumferential directions. As a result the container often comes apart in two or more pieces.

Magnitude of a BLEVE: The size of a BLEVE depends basically upon how much liquid vaporizes when the container fails and the weight of the container pieces. This is analogous in many respects to the performance of rockets as far as propulsion of container parts is concerned. Most BLEVEs occur when containers are from slightly less than half to about three-fourths full of liquid and the liquid-vaporization-expansion-energy to container-piece-weight ratio is such that pieces are propelled for distances up to about ½ mile. Deaths from such missiles have occurred up to 800 ft from larger containers. Fireballs several hundred feet in diameter are not uncommon and deaths from burns have occurred to persons as much as 250 ft from the larger containers. Figure 3-4B illustrates the spectacular dimensions a BLEVE can reach.

Fig. 3-4B. The fireball formed in a BLEVE involving LP-Gas railroad tank cars at Crescent City, Ill., on June 21, 1970. The elevated water tank at lower right is a point of reference in visualizing the tremendous dimensions of the fireball. (Anderson, Watseka, Ill.)

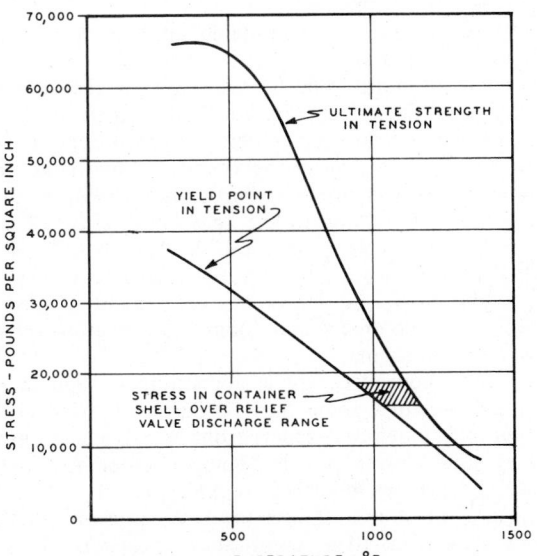

Fig. 3-4A. Behavior of liquefied gas container metal (carbon steel) when exposed to fire.

Time Intervals for BLEVEs: The time between initiation of flame contact and a BLEVE is variable as it depends upon such widely varying factors as the size and nature of the fire as well as the container itself. Uninsulated containers located aboveground can BLEVE in a matter of a very few minutes in the case of small containers to a few hours for very large containers in the absence of water cooling. A study of such LP-Gas storage containers, ranging in size from 1,000 to 30,000 gal, showed a time range from 8 to 30 min with 58 percent occurring in 15 min or less. Data on insulated containers is meager as only cryogenic containers and some reactive gas containers are usually insulated. However, there is no doubt that insulation designed for fire exposure conditions can delay BLEVE times significantly. In one case, involving an insulated LP-Gas railroad tank car, the BLEVE did not occur until 20½ hrs of fire exposure—undoubtedly an extreme example. In comparison fire tests on LP-Gas railroad tank cars, a BLEVE occurred in 93 min in the insulated case as opposed to 25 min for the uninsulated tank.

Protection Against a BLEVE: Protection for an uninsulated liquefied gas container, which can be exposed to fire, is provided by the application of water so that a film of water exists on portions of the container not in internal contact with liquid. The method of applying the water must be decided upon after a sound fire protection analysis of the particular circumstances and can range from the use of hose streams to installation of water spray fixed systems (see Part E of this Chapter).

The term BLEVE is applied only to unreactive liquefied flammable gases. The additional chemical energy in reactive gases introduces chemical factors not present in the purely physical and combustion phenomena involved in a BLEVE even though the outward appearance and general effects are similar. The hazard can be increased by evolution of internal heat of chemical reaction (which adds to the heat from the exposing fire) and the inability of externally applied cooling water to cool the liquid itself.

Combustion within Containers

A less frequent but significant hazard of gas when inside containers is the hazard of container failure from overpressure resulting from combustion of the gas while inside the container. Flammable gas-air or oxygen mixtures are seldom intentionally provided in containers, but can be established accidentally. Most of these explosions have occurred in industrial and medical gas applications where oxygen or compressed air is often used in conjunction with flammable gases. Where such a possibility is inherent in a process, e.g., an oxygen-fuel gas cutting system, provisions are made to prevent the occurrence of such mixtures in containers (see Sec. 4, Chap. 8). More generally, it can be prevented only by education and training in proper container filling procedures. In general, consumers of industrial and medical gases are advised not to attempt to fill containers.

When Released from Containment

The hazards of gases when released from their containers vary with the chemical and physical properties of the gas and the nature of the environment into which they are released.

All gases, with the exception of oxygen and air, present a hazard to life if they displace the breathing air. The inert gases, e.g., nitrogen, helium, argon and other odorless and colorless gases, are particularly hazardous as they give no ready warning. The minimum oxygen concentration in air

for survival is about 6 to 10 percent (compared with the normal 21 percent) by volume, but even at higher concentrations judgment and coordination are affected.

Toxic or Poisonous Gases: These gases present obvious life hazards. Of particular concern is the fact that, when released in the vicinity of a fire, they may impede fire fighting efforts by either preventing access by fire fighters or forcing them to use breathing apparatus.

Oxygen and Other Oxidizing Gases: While nonflammable, these gases can make combustibles ignite at lower temperatures, accelerate combustion, and start fires by causing flames in fuel-burning appliances to extend beyond their combustion chambers. These are covered in more detail in Section 5, Chapter 6.

Liquefied Gases, Including Cryogenic Gases: These gases present a hazard to persons and property when they escape as liquids because of their low temperatures. Contact with cold liquid can cause frostbite, which can be severe if the exposure is prolonged. The properties of many structural materials, particularly carbon steel and plastics, are affected by low temperatures, chiefly by embrittlement which could lead to structural failure.

Flammable Gases: Because of their prevalence, the behavior of flammable gases when released from their containers is of major interest. Released flammable gases present two basic hazards—combustion explosions and fire. Failure to distinguish between the circumstances surrounding these two hazards can result in misapplication of protective measures.

Combustion Explosions

The combustion explosion can be considered as occurring in the following steps:

1. A flammable gas or the liquid phase of a liquefied flammable gas is released from its container, piping, or equipment (including through satisfactory operation of an overpressure relief device). If liquid escapes, it rapidly vaporizes and produces the potentially large quantities of vapor associated with this liquid-to-vapor transition.

2. The gas mixes with the air.

3. With certain proportions of gas and air (the flammable or combustible range), the mixture is ignitable and will burn (see Table 3-4C).

4. When ignited, the flammable mixture burns rapidly and produces heat rapidly.

5. The heat is absorbed by everything in the vicinity of the flame and the very hot gaseous combustion products.

6. When practically all materials absorb heat, they expand. The one material in the vicinity of the flame or hot gaseous combustion products that expands most when it is heated is air. Referring to the "gas laws" cited earlier in this chapter, it will be noted that air expands to double its original volume for every 459°F it is heated.

7. If the heated air is not free to expand because, for example, it is confined in a room, the result is a rise in pressure in the room.

8. If the room structure is not strong enough to withstand the pressure, some part of the room will suddenly and abruptly move and depart from its original position in a hurry, and a bang, woosh, boom, or other noise will be heard. This activity describes an explosion.

Because the source of pressure is combustion, this kind of explosion is called a "combustion explosion." It is also referred to as a "room explosion," "vapor-air explosion," and by other less accurate terms.

A combustion explosion requires an accumulation of a

quantity of flammable gas-air mixture in an enclosure. In addition, the quantity-to-strength-of-enclosure relationship must be such that the strength of some part of the enclosure must be exceeded by the pressure-building potential of the mixture. If the enclosure should be strong enough to withstand the pressure, a combustion explosion would not occur because it is the performance of the enclosure that basically determines whether such an explosion occurs or not. However, few enclosures are this strong.

If an enclosure was full of a flammable gas-air mixture at atmospheric pressure, the enclosure would have to withstand about 60 to 110 psi in order to remain intact to prevent a combustion explosion. If a reactive flammable gas is involved or oxygen-enrichment occurs, even higher pressures are possible. Conventional structures are capable of withstanding pressures only in the order of $\frac{1}{2}$ to 1 psi. This wide pressure disparity shows clearly that conventional structural enclosures are vulnerable even if they are far from full of a flammable gas-air mixture. Experience supports this conclusion, and it has been estimated that most combustion explosions of conventional structures occur with less than 25 percent of the enclosure occupied by the flammable mixture. This should not be overlooked to avoid the pitfall of assuming that enough flammable gas-air mixture had to be present to completely fill a room or building.

The mechanics of gas accumulation in a structure are affected by the rate of gas release, whether it is in the liquid or gas phases, the density of the gas, and the ventilation in the structure. Classic diffusion laws are of little significance under actual conditions as the combination of extremely slow release rates and airtight structures is seldom encountered. For this reason, and the fact that most flammable gas-air mixtures are 90 percent or so air, and, thus, have about the same density as air, the density of the gas itself (that is, whether it is lighter or heavier than air), is seldom a significant factor in gas combustion explosions involving structures.

Reflecting the large and rapid flammable gas-air mixture potentialities of liquefied gases, codes and standards impose severe limitations on the handling of such gases indoors. Considering the "fireball" aspect of the BLEVE, it is evident that an indoor fireball behaves similarly to an ignited gas-air mixture accumulation so that the results of a BLEVE of a container located indoors can be very similar to a combustion explosion.

Combustion Explosion Safeguards

Basic combustion explosion prevention safeguards are designed to limit flammable gas-air mixture accumulation in a structure. A fundamental is that the chances of leakage be minimized by the use of rugged containers and equipment and that the quantity released be minimized by emergency flow control devices and limiting orifices. Burners are often equipped with flame-failure devices which shut off the flow of gas if the flame is extinguished for any reason.

Many gases are colorless and odorless, and it is common to odorize the more widely used fuel gases to increase chances of leak detection. This is particularly true for natural gas and LP-Gas. Codes, standards, and regulations customarily require that these gases be odorized so that they are detectable by a normal person at gas concentrations in air not exceeding one-fifth of the lower limit of flammability. The odorants are usually volatile organic liquids containing chemically combined sulfur which have a characteristic gassy odor.

While an effective safeguard, odorization has limitations.

The functioning detector (the nose-brain combination) is not always present because the premises are vacant or the occupants are asleep. In addition, all odors deaden the sense of smell if smelled long enough as well as the fact that senses of smell vary. Odorants can be scrubbed from the gas by some soils, a factor where leakage is from underground piping.

Mixture accumulations can also be limited by ventilation systems in structures. This is limited essentially to industrial operations, however, and even in such instances only rather nominal release rates can be handled by practical ventilation systems because of the necessity of conditioning the make-up ventilation air for comfort purposes.

Ignition source control is also fundamental to combustion explosion prevention. However, this is also limited mainly to industrial operations and, as many flammable gases are burned in heat producing equipment, an ignition source is often inherent to the structure.

In addition to combustion explosion prevention safeguards, the severity of the explosion can be reduced by special structural design whereby some elements of the structure are designed to dislocate at lower pressures, and other elements are designed to stay in place at the lower pressures which result. This is known as "explosion-venting" (not to be confused with "ventilation") and is covered in some detail in NFPA No. 68, Guide for Explosion Venting (see also Sec. 15, Chap. 7 of this HANDBOOK). Again, however, such building design is not practical for most ordinary buildings and this practice is essentially restricted to certain industrial structures.

Flammable Gas Fires: The flammable gas fire can be considered as an aborted combustion explosion whereby an explosive quantity of flammable gas-air mixture does not accumulate because the mixture is either ignited too quickly or a confining structure is not present. As would be expected, the results of flammable gas escape outdoors are usually fires. However, if a massive release occurs, it is possible for the air or surrounding buildings to comprise enough confinement to lead to a type of combustion explosion known as an "open air explosion" or "space explosion." Liquefied noncryogenic gases are subject to this phenomenon as are hydrogen, ethylene, and some reactive gases because of their extremely rapid rate of flame propagation. An example of the intentional provision of prompt ignition to achieve a fire instead of a combustion explosion is the use of pilots in gas-burning equipment such as range ovens, water heaters, boilers, and furnaces.

Gas fire prevention safeguards include many of the combustion explosion prevention safeguards. However, unlike the combustion explosion, the destructive effects of the gas fire can be minimized by control measures applied after the fact of occurrence (see Part E of this chapter).

D. Gas Containers

Gas containers, whether configured as tank or pipelines, are pressure vessels containing considerable energy per unit of volume and must be carefully designed, fabricated, and maintained. Most countries have promulgated regulations for gas containers which, although basically similar, differ in several respects. This section reflects North American practice.

Tanks

In North America, there are two types of gas "tanks"— cylinders and tanks. Originally, the distinction between cylinders and tanks was based upon size. Cylinders, being the smaller, were considered "portable" and the tanks, being the larger, were essentially used in stationary service. Also, originally, there was a distinction which reflected the pressures in the containers. Cylinders were thought of as being used for high pressure and tanks for low or moderate pressures. Over the years these distinctions have lessened so that today the only real distinction is the regulations or codes under which the "tank" is built.

As practically all gases must be transported (shipped) from the manufacturer to the user, the safety of the container in transportation is of primary concern and criteria for many gas containers reflect transportation safety conditions. Because it could be hazardous as well as uneconomical to require gases to be transferred from a shipping container to a "using" container, every effort has been made to utilize the same container whenever feasible. This is generally the case for the smaller containers.

Gas Cylinders: These are fabricated in accordance with Regulations and Specifications of the DOT (U.S. Department of Transportation) in the United States and the CTC (Canadian Transport Commission) in Canada. The requirements are the same in both countries. Prior to April 1, 1967, the DOT Regulations were promulgated by the ICC (Interstate Commerce Commission) and many cylinders are still in service with ICC markings. Cylinders are generally limited to a maximum water capacity (the capacity when completely filled with water) of 1,000 lbs, or about 120 gal of water.

The regulations cover the service pressure the cylinder must be designed for, the gas or group of gases that it can contain, safety devices, and requirements for in-service (transportation) testing and requalification. The specifications cover such criteria as metal composition and physical testing, wall thickness, joining methods, nature of openings in the container, heat treatments, proof testing, and marking.

Gas Tanks: These tanks are customarily fabricated in accordance with Section VIII (Unfired Pressure Vessels) of the Boiler and Pressure Vessel Code promulgated by the American Society of Mechanical Engineers (ASME) or tank fabrication standards of the American Petroleum Institute (API). ASME tanks are usually applicable to smaller, moderate pressure tanks, and API tanks are usually very large, low pressure tanks.

Cylinders or tanks which are part of transportation units, such as cargo vehicles or railcars, are subject to additional criteria in the Regulations, primarily to reflect the fact that the containers are on wheels. Tanks for cargo vehicles are basically ASME Code tanks. Tanks for railcars are covered by their own specific DOT and CTC Specifications.

A number of such containers are exempted by these Regulations. These include certain very small containers and nonflammable cryogenic gases, including oxygen, where the pressure in the container as shipped is below 40 psia.

There is usually a lag in time between the need to ship a gas which is new to commerce and the promulgation of Specifications for a transportation container. In such cases, DOT or CTC Special Permits are issued which spell out safety criteria agreed upon by the authorities. At the present time, all cryogenic flammable gas cargo vehicles are operated under Special Permits.

The DOT and CTC Regulations, in themselves, apply only to cylinders and tanks in transportation in interstate or interprovincial commerce. However, many concensus codes and standards extend these Regulations to transportation in intrastate commerce and also extend applicable criteria to use and storage at consumer sites.

The aforementioned requirements for "in-service" reinspection and requalification of DOT Specification containers are also extended to use and storage at consumer sites by the consensus standards and codes. However, the ASME Code and API Standards do not contain such provisions. If not covered by consensus standards and codes, in-service inspection and requalification become a matter of owner judgment, such state or local regulations as may apply, or conditions set forth in an insurance contract.

Regardless of degree of structural integrity incorporated into gas containers, their abuse must be avoided. This is especially true of cylinders which, because of their portability, are subject to mishandling. General handling safety precautions for gas cylinders are contained in Compressed Gas Association, Inc., Pamphlet P-1.

Pipelines

Gases used in large volumes are often transported by pipelines. Natural gas is customarily transported by pipeline as is considerable LP-Gas and some industrial gases, such as anhydrous ammonia, oxygen, hydrogen, and ethylene.

Since 1968, most transmission and distribution of flammable gases by pipeline has been regulated in the United States by the DOT (Office of Pipeline Safety) and covered by Federal regulations. These cover such items as pipe materials; design for pressure and other stresses (which, among other criteria, require stronger piping as population density increases); piping components, including valves (emergency flow control valve spacing in the pipeline system being also affected by population density); joining methods; installation of meters, service regulators and services lines; corrosion control; test requirements; certain operating requirements; and maintenance, including leakage surveys.

Normally, the DOT Regulations do not apply to piping on consumer premises. Such piping for the more common gases is covered by consensus codes and standards, notably NFPA No. 54, National Fuel Gas Code (ANSI Z223.1) and the Code for Pressure Piping, ANSI B31.

E. Gas Emergency Control

Controllable gas emergencies resulting from the escape of gas from containers present two basic forms of hazard: (1) toxic, inert, or oxidizing gases can present hazards to persons or property and flammable gases which haven't ignited can become ignited, possibly explosively; ("no fire" emergencies); and (2) gas fires can present thermal hazards to persons or property ("fire" emergencies) and, if such fires expose gas containers, introduce the possibility of container failure and the BLEVE. The hazard of container failure from fire exposure is also present from a fire in any combustible material.

Control of "No Fire" Emergencies

Control generally consists of directing, diluting, and dispersing the gas to prevent contact with persons, to prevent it from infiltrating structures if the leak is outdoors, and to avoid its contact with ignition sources while, if possible, simultaneously stopping the flow of escaping gas. Gas direction, dilution, and dispersion require the use of a carrier fluid, and air, water, and steam have proven to be practical. The use of air, for all practical purposes, is limited to indoor situations and is an extension of the ventilation safeguards against combustion explosion discussed in Part C of this chapter.

Steam has been distributed through systems of fixed nozzles around outdoor ethylene processing equipment and where the large quantities of steam needed are available.

Water in the form of a spray, applied from hoses or monitor nozzles or by fixed water spray systems, is the most common carrier fluid. The use of hose streams is largely a fire department operation because of the manpower requirements. Fixed water spray systems for this purpose are designed differently from the more conventional spray systems used in fire control measure. To date, such systems have been provided at a few outdoor ethylene and LNG facilities.

The physical properties of the escaping gas affect control techniques. With compressed gases, the density of the gas is an important factor. Also, when such gases are colorless and odorless, control tactics may be complicated because instruments may be needed to define the extent of the hazardous area.

Liquefied gases possess an inherent visible indicator of their location because the refrigerating effect of their vaporization condenses water vapor from the air and produces a visible fog. The fog roughly defines the gas area, but invisible ignitible gas-air mixtures often extend for several feet beyond the extremities of the visible fog.

Because noncryogenic liquefied gases contain some sensible heat for vaporization, they will often vaporize so rapidly from contact with the air or ground that they will not exist in the liquid phase once they escape—at least not to the extent that a pool will form. The lower vapor pressure noncryogenic liquefied gases, such as butane and chlorine, and those with high latent heats of vaporization, such as anhydrous ammonia, are exceptions, and even the higher vapor pressure gases, such as propane, will pool if low ambient temperatures exist.

The cryogenic liquefied gases, on the other hand, must obtain nearly all the heat for vaporization from ground or air contact and, therefore, will characteristically form a pool if the leak continues long enough. In such cases, application of a carrier fluid will increase the vaporization rate if applied to the liquid—an often undesirable effect.

The gas produced near the source of vaporization of a liquefied gas is always heavier than air at normal temperatures because of the low temperatures of the gas at that point. This, together with the associated water fog, tends to cause even normally lighter-than-air gases to hug the ground for some distance.

The use of foam, particularly high-expansion foam, to control the flow of gas produced by a vaporizing cryogenic gas which is normally lighter than air has been investigated to some extent. A thick enough blanket can warm the gas to the point where it will rise upon issuing above the blanket instead of flowing horizontally near the ground. However, this is applicable only to established pools of vaporizing liquid and not to the initial escape phase.

Some gases will chemically react with the carrier fluid —particularly steam or water. Chlorine is a notable example—the reaction producing hydrochloric acid. However, the principal problem in this respect is enlargement of the leak as the metal reacts with the acid. A special type of "no fire" control for indoor application to flammable gases is the "explosion suppression system." Actually, such systems do permit ignition to occur, but arrest the combustion of the flammable gas-air mixture before the pressure needed for a combustion explosion is obtained. See Chapter 7 of Section 15 in this HANDBOOK for information on explosion suppression systems.

Control of "Fire" Emergencies

Control in fire emergencies is generally the control of heat from the fire by the application of water while, if possible, stopping the flow of escaping gas. Many gas fires can be extinguished by conventional extinguishing agents, including carbon dioxide, dry chemical, and the halogenated agents. However, the potential conversion of a gas fire into a combustion explosion if gas continues to escape after extinguishment must be recognized. The generally recognized practice is to limit actual extinguishment by agent application to small leaks.

Methods of water application are the same as described for the "no fire" emergencies, i.e., hose streams, monitor nozzle streams, and fixed water spray systems as well as sprinkler systems. The selection of the particular method, or combination of methods, requires a sound fire protection analysis of the conditions existing. This is particularly true where water is to be used to prevent a BLEVE because of the limited time available if uninsulated containers are involved. This, together with the specialized tactics needed for safety of emergency personnel, has been shown to severely tax the capabilities of hose stream application in many instances. Manual actuation of fixed systems (water spray or sprinkler) that have nozzles and dry piping in the fire area is questionable because the immediate intensity of a gas fire can damage the piping quickly before the water is turned on.

Conventional automatic sprinkler protection is limited to indoor or roofed-over areas. However, it has been demonstrated as effective in greatly reducing the number of overpressure relief devices on cylinders which operate during a fire which, in turn, reduces the number of cylinders which may fail from contact with the burning relief device effluents. However, sprinkler spacing and density must be tailored to this hazard.

Foam can control a fire in a pool or tank of cryogenic gas and not extinguish it. The degree of control is dependent upon the extent to which the foam can cover the liquid and the length of time the foam application can be maintained.

F.   Specific Gases

The following contains material on some of the more common gases, arranged to key with the basic information presented in Parts B through E of this Chapter.

Acetylene

Classifications: Reactive, flammable, compressed, industrial.

Chemical Properties: Acetylene is comprised of carbon and hydrogen joined by a triple chemical bond, which is responsible for its reactivity. In the liquid or solid states or in the gaseous state at moderate or high pressures, acetylene can decompose rapidly with the formation of carbon and hydrogen and evolution of heat. Decomposition can be initiated by heat. Decomposition of liquid or solid acetylene also can be initiated by mechanical impact. In a confined space, the heated decomposition gases can cause overpressure and container, piping or equipment failure.

As an indication that a hazardous, heat-producing reaction can occur in the absence of air, an upper flammable limit of 100 percent is often found in the literature rather than the 81 percent given in Table 3-4C. This is a technical misapplication of the flammable range concept which has caused confusion.

Acetylene can react with certain metals to produce metallic acetylides which are extremely shock sensitive, explosive compounds and which, if detonated even in small quantities, can initiate acetylene decomposition. Copper and some copper alloys are notable in this respect and must be avoided in most acetylene piping and equipment. However, these metals can be used in some components of acetylene systems under certain conditions which reflect the reaction kinetics involved. Torch tips, for example, are in this category.

Acetylene is not toxic and has been used as an anesthetic. Pure acetylene is odorless, but the acetylene in general use has a characteristic odor due to minor impurities inherent in its generation from calcium carbide or derivation from other hydrocarbons.

Physical Properties: While considered as a compressed gas, the usual acetylene container used in transportation and storage does not contain solely acetylene in the gaseous phase and is unique in this respect. To assure stability under reasonably anticipated thermal and mechanical impact conditions, acetylene cylinders are filled with a porous-mass packing material containing very small pores or cellular spaces so that any volume of gas therein is also small. This limits the decomposition energy available and restricts communication between spaces. In addition, the mass is saturated with acetone—a flammable liquid in which acetylene is very soluble. In this manner, acetylene gas can be compressed in solution in a manner similar to that of carbon dioxide in water to produce carbonated water. When the pressure is reduced, e.g., by opening a cylinder valve, the gas escapes from solution and thus escapes from the container in the gaseous state. Currently, a charging pressure maximum of 250 psig at 70°F is recognized by DOT and CTC Regulations. There will be a variation of about 2.5 psig rise or fall per °F of temperature change. For each atmosphere (14.7 psi) of pressure, acetone will dissolve about 25 times its own volume of acetylene so that at 250 psig acetone will dissolve about 425 volumes of acetylene.

An acetylene cylinder is illustrated in Figure 3-4C.

Usage: Acetylene is used primarily in chemical processing and as a fuel gas in oxygen-fuel gas cutting and welding operations. Occasionally it is manufactured at the consuming location by reacting calcium carbide (a solid) and water in acetylene generators and piped directly to gas holders or to the point of use.

Hazards Inside Containers: Acetylene is shipped in DOT and CTC cylinders as described previously and stored in

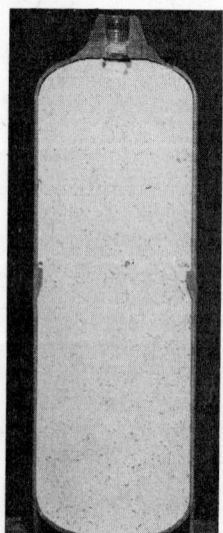

Fig. 3-4C. Cutaway photograph of typical acetylene cylinder showing porous filler material. Cylinder valve and packing for well at top of cylinder not shown.

these or in low pressure gas holders. It is either handled in hoses or piping systems.

Acetylene cylinders are protected against overpressure indirectly by heat actuated devices, usually fusible plugs of eutectic alloys having low melting points similar to those employed in automatic sprinklers. Unlike spring-loaded safety relief valves, operation of fusible plugs results in complete reduction to atmospheric pressure as both the compressed gas and acetone are released. Because of this mode of overpressure protection, acetylene cylinders are not subject to a BLEVE, which, by definition, can not occur if the liquid contents are not above their boiling points at NTP. However, under fire exposure conditions and during charging operations in acetylene cylinder charging plants, internal decomposition has occurred which has resulted in BLEVE effects, such as cylinder rupture and propulsion accompanied by small fireballs.

As susceptibility to decomposition is directly related to pressure, i.e., the higher the pressure the easier it is to initiate decomposition and the more violent the effects, an acceptable degree of stability in most piping systems containing gaseous acetylene is accomplished by limiting the pressure. In general, this pressure does not exceed 15 psi. In applications requiring higher pressures, particularly in acetylene cylinder charging plants, special piping design features can be employed to control this hazard.

The use of acetylene in either the liquid or solid phases is especially hazardous and is prohibited by standards and codes covering conventional applications.

Hazards When Released from Containment: Acetylene presents combustion explosion and fire hazards when released from containment. Because of its reactivity, it is easier to ignite than most flammable gases and burns more rapidly. The latter effect increases the severity of combustion explosions and increases the difficulty of providing explosion venting. Acetylene is only slightly lighter than air (see Table 3-4C).

Because of its reactivity, the design of electrical equipment for use in acetylene atmospheres to control this ignition source is unique to this material and Group A electrical equipment (Article 500, National Electrical Code) is devoted exclusively to acetylene. In practice, electrical equipment is avoided in the more likely areas of acetylene release areas or the release potentials reduced to a level where Group C or D equipment can be used. As a result, available Group A equipment is extremely limited in variety.

Emergency Control: Because of the limited quantities of acetylene in conventional shipping modes and storage practices, "no fire" emergencies seldom occur. The fire situations are similar to those involved with any flammable, nontoxic gas—that is, application of water to containers and stopping the flow of escaping gas, if possible.

Anhydrous Ammonia

Classifications: Flammable, liquefied (including cryogenic), industrial.

Chemical Properties: Anhydrous ammonia is comprised of nitrogen and hydrogen. While often referred to simply as "ammonia," this term is more generally used to describe a solution of anhydrous (which means "without water") ammonia in water. The nitrogen component is inert in the combustion reaction and accounts for the somewhat limited flammability of anhydrous ammonia as manifest by its high lower flammability limit and low heat of combustion (see Table 3-4C).

Moist ammonia will vigorously attack copper and zinc and many of their brass or bronze alloys. This has caused

Table 3-4C.   Combustion Properties of Common Flammable Gases

Gas	Btu per Cu Ft (Gross)	Limits of Flammability Percent by Volume in Air		Specific Gravity (Air = 1.0)	Air Needed to Burn 1 Cu Ft of Gas Cu Ft	Ignition Temp °F
		Lower	Upper			
Natural Gas						
High Inert Type Note 1	958–1051	4.5	14.0	.660– .708	9.2	—
High Methane Type Note 2	1008–1071	4.7	15.0	.590– .614	10.2	900–1170
High Btu Type Note 3	1071–1124	4.7	14.5	.620– .719	9.4	—
Blast Furnace Gas	81– 111	33.2	71.3	1.04 –1.00	0.8	—
Coke Oven Gas	575	4.4	34.0	.38	4.7	—
Propane (commercial)	2516	2.15	9.6	1.52	24.0	920–1120
Butane (commercial)	3300	1.9	8.5	2.0	31.0	900–1000
Sewage Gas	670	6.0	17.0	.79	6.5	—
Acetylene	1499	2.5	81.0	.91	11.9	581
Hydrogen	325	4.0	75.0	.07	2.4	752
Anhydrous Ammonia	386	16.0	25.0	.60	8.3	1204
Carbon Monoxide	314	12.5	74.0	.97	2.4	1128
Ethylene	1600	2.7	36.0	.98	14.3	914
Methyl Acetylene, propadiene, stabilized Note 4	2450	3.4	10.8	1.48	—	850

Note 1: Typical composition CH_4 71.9–83.2%; N_2 6.3–16.20%
Note 2: Typical composition CH_4 87.6–95.7; N_2 0.1–2.39

Note 3: Typical composition CH_4 85.0–90.1; N_2 1.2–7.5
Note 4: MAPP® Gas

some problems in agricultural areas where, because of their similar vapor pressures, anhydrous ammonia and propane are often handled in the same storage tanks, transport containers, and associated equipment at different times of the year. LP-Gas equipment customarily utilizes brass, bronze, copper, and zinc extensively for valves, gages, piping, regulators, etc. This equipment must be changed to steel when converting to anhydrous ammonia service. Subsequently anhydrous ammonia must be carefully purged from a container when re-converting it to LP-Gas service. While a relatively toxic gas, the characteristic pungent odor and irritant properties of anhydrous ammonia serve as warnings. However, the effectiveness of the warning depends upon the rate or release and large clouds have been produced rapidly from large liquid leaks which have trapped and killed people before they could evacuate the area.

Physical Properties: At its normal boiling point of —28°F, anhydrous ammonia has a liquid density of 42.6 pcf, a gas density of 0.055 pcf, and a latent heat of vaporization of 589.3 Btu/lb. At NTP, the gas has a density of about 0.045 pcf and vaporization of a cubic foot of liquid will produce about 885 cu ft of gas.

Usage: Anhydrous ammonia is used primarily as an agricultural fertilizer, as a refrigerant, and as a source of hydrogen for metal heat-treating special atmospheres.

Hazards Inside Containers: Anhydrous ammonia is shipped in DOT and CTC cylinders, DOT Specification cargo trucks and railroad tank cars and barges, and is stored in cylinders, ASME Code tanks, and in cryogenic form in insulated API tanks.

Anhydrous ammonia containers having a capacity of less than 165 lbs are not required to be equipped with overpressure protection devices. This reflects its toxicity and is a safety trade-off between the hazards of container rupture from overpressure and gas release due to operation of an overpressure protective device, especially indoors where the smaller containers are often found.

BLEVEs of uninsulated anhydrous ammonia containers are infrequent—reflecting the limited flammability of the gas which minimizes the probability of it supplying the exposing fire. Where they have occurred, the fire has been in other combustibles.

Hazards When Released from Containment: Anhydrous ammonia presents combustion explosion and fire hazards (as well as a toxicity hazard) when released from containment. However, its high lower limit of flammability and low heat of combustion reduce these hazards substantially.

If released outdoors, it is difficult to reach the lower flammability limit concentration except for small zones in the immediate vicinity of the leak unless large quantities of liquid are released. Even in the latter case, ignitible concentrations tend to be in discontinuous pockets and this, together with the low heat of combustion, reduces the possibilities of sustained burning. Experience indicates that similar circumstances apply when the release occurs indoors in conventional reasonably well-ventilated buildings. In unusually tight buildings, such as refrigerated process or storage areas, however, the release of liquid or large quantities of gas can result in accumulation of hazardous quanties of a flammable mixture and result in a combustion explosion. In such cases, even though the low heat of combustion produces lower pressures than most flammable gases, the pressure is enough to do major structural damage. As a result of these factors anhydrous ammonia fires are infrequent and, where ignition does occur, a combustion explosion is the likely result. In an NFPA fire record analysis of 36 incidents from 1929 through 1969 where released gas or liquid was ignited, 28, or 78 percent, resulted in a combustion explosion. All were indoors.

Emergency Control: At normal temperatures, anhydrous ammonia gas weighs about 0.6 times as much as air.

Because of the pronounced solubility of anhydrous ammonia in water, the spread of escaping gas can be controlled readily by water spray. If done by hose streams, the toxic and initiating properties of anhydrous ammonia require the use of gas masks and, if liquid contact is likely, the use of full protective clothing. If release of liquid in cryogenic form occurs, pooling is possible and application of water to pools should be avoided to prevent increased vaporization rate unless the vapors can be controlled.

Carbon Dioxide

Classifications: Nonflammable (inert), liquefied, industrial.

Chemical Properties: Carbon dioxide is comprised of carbon and oxygen. As the carbon is linked with as much oxygen as it chemically can combine with, further oxidation (combustion) cannot occur which accounts for its nonflammability. While non-toxic, carbon dioxide can cause asphyxiation due to the displacement of air.

Physical Properties: Carbon dioxide exhibits some unique physical properties. At a temperature of −69.9°F and a pressure of 60.4 psig, it can exist in a container simultaneously as a liquid, solid, and gas (the triple point). At temperatures and pressures above these and below 87.8°F, the container contains both liquid and gas. Above 87.8°F, it exists only in the gaseous phase. At normal temperatures, the gas is about 1½ times heavier than air.

Usage: Carbon dioxide is used primarily for carbonating beverages, as an inert atmosphere, and as a fire extinguishing agent. (See Sec. 13, Chap. 2.)

Hazards Inside Containers: Carbon dioxide is shipped in DOT and CTC cylinders and insulated DOT Specification cargo trucks and railroad tank cars and stored in cylinders at a pressure of about 850 psi at 70°F or in insulated ASME Code tanks at pressures of about 200 to 312 psi and temperatures of −20 to +40°F.

Cylinders are provided with overpressure protection in the form of frangible (bursting) discs. Insulated tanks are equipped with safety relief valves.

While technically subject to a BLEVE (minus, of course, a fireball), the NFPA has no reports of such an occurrence.

Hazards When Released from Containment: In addition to the hazard of asphyxiation, contact with cold vaporizing carbon dioxide can cause frostbite. For these reasons, actuation of automatic room flooding extinguishing system applications incorporates a time delay if personnel occupy the protected area.

Emergency Control: Carbon dioxide emergencies are "no fire" emergencies involving potential asphyxiation hazards. Structure ventilation indoors and water spray control outdoors are applicable. Self-contained breathing apparatus should be used.

Chlorine

Classifications: Reactive, nonflammable, liquefied, toxic, industrial.

Chemical Properties: Chlorine is a basic chemical element. While nonflammable, it can react with many organic materials corrosively and, in some instances, explosively, particularly with acetylene, turpentine, ether, gaseous ammonia, hydrocarbons, most fuel gases, and finely divided metals.

The reactivity of chlorine necessitates special attention to container, piping and equipment materials of construction. Below 230°F, steel, copper, iron, and lead are widely used. In contact with water, chlorine forms hypochlorous and hypochloric acids which are corrosive to most metals.

Chlorine is toxic enough to be considered as a poison and has been used in warfare as a poison gas. Liquid chlorine can burn skin. Its sharp odor serves as a warning.

Physical Properties: The normal boiling point of chlorine is about −30°F. At 32°F, the liquid density is 91.7 pcf and the gas density is 0.2 pcf. The latent heat of vaporization at the normal boiling point is 123.7 Btu/lb. At 32°F, the vaporization of 1 cu ft of liquid will produce about 458 cu ft of gas. Chlorine has a greenish-yellow color.

Usage: Chlorine is used primarily in chemical processing, bleaching, purification of drinking water and swimming pools, and sanitation of industrial and sewage wastes.

Hazards Inside Containers: Chlorine is shipped in DOT and CTC cylinders, and DOT Specification portable tanks (so-called "1-ton containers") and in insulated railroad tank cars.

Chlorine cylinders and 1-ton containers are provided with overpressure protection by fusible plugs. Tank cars are protected by safety relief valves. Because the operation of fusible plugs results in complete depressurization, the probability of a BLEVE is low and has not occurred in practice. The NFPA has no record of a BLEVE of a tank car containing chlorine even though theoretically possible.

While steel is suitable for chlorine at normal temperatures, it is rapidly attacked at temperatures above about 230°F and leaks can be so developed by fire exposure. For this reason, as well as for BLEVE protection, water should be applied to fire exposed containers. Insofar as possible, application of water directly upon a leak should be avoided as it may enlarge the leak from acid corrosion.

Hazards When Released from Containment: Chlorine presents primarily a toxicity and corrosion hazard when released from containment. As the chlorine gas is about 2½ times heavier than air, it will hug the ground.

Emergency Control: The gas can be controlled by water spray. If done by hose streams, full protective clothing must be worn. Water applied to liquid chlorine will accelerate vaporization.

The chlorine industry has developed an extensive leak-control program which includes strategic siting of trained emergency personnel and special equipment kits for stopping the more common leaks in cylinders, ton containers, and tank cars. Information on this program is available from the Chlorine Institute, 342 Madison Avenue, New York, N.Y. 10017. A motion picture film on handling chlorine leaks produced by the Institute is available from NFPA.

Ethylene

Classifications: Flammable, compressed, cryogenic, industrial.

Chemical Properties: Ethylene is comprised of carbon and hydrogen and contains a double chemical bond which imparts a degree of reactivity. Except at very high pressures normally encountered only in chemical processing, it is a stable material. It has a wide flammable range (see Table 3-4C) and high burning velocity reflecting its reactivity.

While nontoxic, ethylene is an anesthetic and asphyxiant.

Physical Properties: See Table 3-4A.

Usage: Ethylene is principally used in chemical processing —e.g., manufacture of polyethylene plastic. Lesser amounts are used to ripen fruit.

Hazards Inside Containers: Ethylene is shipped as a compressed gas in DOT and CTC cylinders and as a cryogenic gas in insulated cargo trucks and railroad tank cars by DOT Special Permit. It is stored in cylinders or in ASME Code insulated tanks.

Ethylene cylinders (except for medical cylinders which may have fusible plugs or combination safety devices) are protected against overpressure by frangible (bursting) disks. Insulated truck tanks and tank cars are protected by safety relief valves. Cylinders are subject to failure from fire exposure but not BLEVEs as they do not contain liquid. Insulated containers are theoretically subject to BLEVEs but NFPA has no record of such an occurrence. A few instances of cryogenic truck container overpressure rupture have occurred due to freezing of relief valves closed due to improper installation of the valves.

Hazards When Released from Containment: Ethylene presents combustion explosion and fire hazards when released from containment. The wide flammable range and high burning rate accentuate these hazards. In a number of instances involving rather large outdoor releases, open air or space explosions have occurred.

Emergency Control: Escaping ethylene presents both "no fire" and "fire" emergency situations. At normal atmospheric temperatures, ethylene gas is very slightly lighter than air. Ethylene gas vaporizing from the cryogenic liquid near its normal boiling point is about $1\frac{3}{4}$ times heavier than air is at 70°F and can spread along the ground. Escaping liquid will also pool on the ground. The visible fog created is a rough indication of the extent of the hazardous area.

Escaping gas can be controlled by water spray. Contact between water and pooled ethylene should be avoided to prevent increased vaporization unless the vapors can be controlled.

Water should be applied to fire exposed containers and the flow of escaping gas should be stopped, if possible.

Hydrogen

Classifications: Flammable, compressed, cryogenic, industrial.

Chemical Properties: Hydrogen is a basic chemical element. Hydrogen has an extremely wide flammable range, the highest burning velocity of any gas and, while its ignition temperature is reasonably high, its ignition energy is very low. Because hydrogen contains no carbon, it burns with a very nonluminous flame which is often invisible in daylight. Hydrogen is nontoxic.

Physical Properties: See Table 3-4A.

Usage: Hydrogen is principally used in chemical processing, for hydrogenation of edible oils, in welding and cutting, as a metal heat treating special atmosphere and as a coolant in large electrical generators.

Hazards Inside Containers: Hydrogen is shipped as a compressed gas in uninsulated DOT and CTC cylinders and as a cryogenic gas in insulated DOT and CTC cylinders and in insulated cargo trucks and railroad tank cars by DOT Special Permit. It is stored in cylinders or in ASME Code insulated tanks.

Compressed hydrogen cylinders are protected against overpressure by frangible (bursting) disks or such disks in combination with fusible plug devices. Insulated cylinders, trucks and railcar tanks, and storage tanks are protected by safety relief valves and frangible disks. Compressed gas cylinders are subject to failure, but not BLEVESs as they do not contain liquid. Insulated cryogenic containers are theoretically subject to BLEVEs but NFPA has no record of such an occurrence.

Hazards When Released from Containment: Hydrogen presents both combustion explosion and fire hazards when released from containment. While its wide flammable range and high burning rate accentuate these hazards, its low ignition energy, low heat of combustion on a volume basis, and its nonluminous (low thermal radiation level) flame exert counteracting influences in many instances.

Because of its low ignition energy, when gaseous hydrogen is released at high pressure, nominally rather small heat producing sources, e.g., friction and static generation, often result in prompt ignitions. Accordingly, hydrogen is frequently thought of as "self-igniting" under these circumstances. The record of releases in high pressure applications reveals fires rather than combustion explosions. When released at low pressures, however, "self-ignition" is unlikely and hydrogen combustion explosions are characterised by very rapid pressure rises which are extremely difficult to vent effectively. Open-air or space explosions have occurred from large releases of gaseous hydrogen.

Because of its very low boiling point, contact between liquid hydrogen and air can result in condensation of air and its oxygen and nitrogen components. A mixture of hydrogen and liquid oxygen is potentially explosive even though the quantities involved are likely to be small. Accidents from this source have been generally restricted to small containers of liquid hydrogen which are handled open to the atmosphere and inside liquefaction equipment.

At ordinary temperatures, hydrogen is very light, weighing only about $\frac{1}{15}$ as much as air. The accordingly high diffusion rate makes it difficult for hydrogen to accumulate in conventional structures unless the escape rate is high. This tends to reduce its combustion explosion hazard.

Emergency Control: Escaping gaseous hydrogen seldom presents a "no fire" emergency situation because it either is ignited promptly or rises in the atmosphere rapidly. Hydrogen gas vaporizing from the cryogenic liquid near its normal boiling point is slightly heavier than air is at 70°F and, this, together with the visible fog of condensed water vapor created, causes it to spread along the ground for sizable distances (depending upon leak size and meteorological conditions). Because of the low gas density of vapors produced from vaporizing cryogenic hydrogen liquid, impounding or diked areas are not required.

Ignitable mixtures can extend well beyond the visible cloud. Such escapes can be controlled by water spray. Contact between water and pooled hydrogen should be avoided to prevent increased vaporization unless the vapor can be controlled.

Water should be applied to fire exposed containers and the flow of gas stopped if possible. Because hydrogen burns with a flame which is often invisible in daylight and its flames produce low levels of thermal radiation, such flames have actually been walked into. A broom held in front of a person and throwing of handfuls of dirt ahead, have proven to be useful simple tools when approaching hydrogen fires.

Liquefied Natural Gas (LNG)

Classifications: Flammable, cryogenic, fuel.

Chemical Properties: LNG is a mixture of materials all comprised of carbon and hydrogen. The principal component is methane with lesser amounts of ethane, propane, and butane. The composition will vary, principally depending upon whether the sourse of the natural gas which has been liquefied is a transmisson pipeline or gas wells. In the former instance, more of the propane and butane is removed prior to introduction into the pipeline (see Table 3-4D).

LNG is nontoxic but is an asphyxiant.

Physical Properties: See Table 3-4D.

Usage: LNG is used as a source of natural gas to augment pipeline supplies during periods of extreme demand (peak-shaving), to supply gas distribution systems in areas

Table 3-4D. Approximate Properties of LNG

Composition

Methane	83–99%
Ethane	1–13%
Propane	0.1–3%
Butane	0.2–1.0%

Physical Properties

Normal boiling point	minus 255 to minus 263°F (minus 160 to minus 164°C)
Density liquid at nbp	3½ to 4 pounds per gallon
Density vapor at nbp (compared with air at 70°F)	1.47
Liquid to vapor expansion	600 to 1
Heat of vaporization	220–248 Btu/pound (770–990 Btu/gallon)

Theoretical vaporizing capability of 1 cubic foot of:

Dry earth	6 gallons LNG
Wet earth	20 gallons LNG
Water	24 gallons LNG (1 gallon water = 3.2 gallons LNG)
Air	.0005 gallon LNG

Initial vaporization rate of LNG spill on solid surface—10 cfm vapor per square foot of LNG surface area

Initial vaporization rate of LNG spill on water—700 cfm vapor per square foot of LNG surface area

Steady-state vaporization rate of LNG spill—1 cfm vapor per square foot of liquid surface (1-foot-deep pool evaporates in 10 hours)

Combustion Properties

Flammable range	5–14% (methane at normal temperatures) 6–13% (methane near minus 260°F)
Heat of combustion	22,000 Btu/pound
Burn rate, steady-state pool	0.2–0.6 inch per minute

Pool fire flame height—3 times base dimensions of pool (slight wind)

remote from central distribution systems, and as a basic supply of natural gas. To a small extent, it is used as a vehicle propulsion fuel.

Hazards Inside Containers: LNG is shipped as a cryogenic gas in insulated cargo trucks by DOT Special Permit and in marine vessels under DOT authorization. It is stored in insulated ASME Code or API tanks.

LNG containers are protected against overpressure by safety relief valves. Such containers are theoretically subject to BLEVEs but NFPA has no record of such an occurrence.

Hazards When Released from Containment: LNG presents both combustion explosion and fire hazards when released from containment. At the present time LNG is seldom used indoors and when so used, the structure is designed for a combustion explosion hazard in accordance with national standards and regulations. Available test and experience data indicates that escaping LNG is not subject to open-air or space explosions.

Emergency Control: Escaping LNG presents both "no fire" and "fire" emergency situations. LNG gas vaporizing from the cryogenic liquid near its normal boiling point is about 1½ times heavier than air is at 70°F and will spread along the ground assisted by the visible fog of condensed water vapor created. This distance will depend upon the leak size and meteorological conditions and upon the geometry of the required liquid impounding area provided. Ignitible areas are roughly defined by the visible cloud but can extend beyond the visible area. Such escape can be controlled by water spray. Contact between water and pooled

LNG should be avoided to prevent increased vaporization unless the vapor can be controlled.

Water should be applied to fire exposed containers and the flow of gas stopped if possible.

Liquefied Petroleum Gases (LP-Gas, LPG)

Classifications: Flammable, liquefied (including cryogenic), fuel.

Chemical Properties: LP-Gas is a mixture of materials all comprised of carbon and hydrogen. In commerce, LP-Gas is predominantly either propane or normal butane or mixtures of these with smaller amounts of ethane, ethylene, propylene, iso-butane, and butylene (including isomers). Principal variations in composition occur depending upon whether the source is gas wells or petroleum refineries. See Tables 3-4C and 3-4E.

LP-Gas is nontoxic but is an asphyxiant.

Physical Properties: See Table 3-4E.

Usage: LP-Gas is used principally as a domestic, commercial, agricultural and industrial fuel gas, in chemical processing, and as an engine fuel. In domestic and recreational applications, it is sometimes known as "bottled gas."

Hazards Inside Containers: LP-Gas is shipped as a liquefied gas in uninsulated DOT and CTC cylinders and ASME tanks and in DOT Specification cargo trucks, railroad tank cars and marine vessels. It is also shipped in cryogenic form in insulated marine vessels. It is stored in cylinders, ASME Code tanks and insulated API tanks.

Table 3-4E. Approximate Properties of LP-Gases

	Commercial Propane NLPGA Av.	Commercial Butane NLPGA Av.
Vapor Pressure in psig at:		
70°F	132	17
100°F	205	37
105°F	216	41
130°F	300	69
Specific Gravity of Liquid at 60°F	0.509	0.582
Initial Boiling Point at 14.7 psia, Degrees F	−51	15
Weight per Gallon of Liquid at 60°F, lb.	4.24	4.81
Specific Heat of Liquid, Btu/lb. at 60°F	0.588	0.549
Cu ft of Vapor per Gallon at 60°F	36.39	31.26
Cu ft of Vapor per Pound at 60°F	8.58	6.51
Specific Gravity of Vapor (Air = 1) at 60°F	1.52	2.01
Ignition Temperature in Air, Degrees F	920–1120	900–1000
Maximum Flame Temperature in Air, Degrees F	3,595	3,615
Limits of Flammability in Air, Percent of Vapor in Air-Gas Mixture:		
(a) Lower	2.15	1.55
(b) Upper	9.60	8.60
Latent Heat of Vaporization at Boiling Point:		
(a) Btu per Pound	185	167
(b) Btu per Gallon	785	808
Total Heating Values after Vaporization:		
(a) Btu per Cubic Foot	2,516	3,280
(b) Btu per Pound	21,591	21,221
(c) Btu per Gallon	91,547	102,032

LP-Gas containers are generally protected against overpressure by safety relief valves although some cylinders are protected by fusible plug devices and, occasionally, by a combination of these. Most containers are subject to BLEVEs (see Part C of this chapter for a detailed discussion of BLEVEs).

Hazards When Released from Containment: LP-Gas presents both combustion explosion and fire hazards when released from containment. As most uses of LP-Gas are indoors, the combustion explosion experience dominates. This hazard is accentuated when LP-Gas in the liquid phase is used indoors—reflecting the fact that one gallon of liquid propane or butane will produce about 245 to 275 gal of gas. For this reason, standards and codes severely restrict the uses of liquid-phase LP-Gas indoors.

Large releases of liquid-phase LP-Gas outdoors have led to open-air or space explosions.

Emergency Control: Escaping LP-Gas presents both "no fire" and "fire" emergency situations. LP-Gas vapor is normally $1\frac{1}{2}$ to 2 times heavier than air and LP-Gas vapor vaporizing from the liquid at its normal boiling point is even heavier. Therefore, it will tend to spread along the ground assisted by the visible fog of condensed water vapor created. Ignitable mixtures extend beyond the visible area. Such escape can be controlled by water spray. Noncryogenic propane is unlikely to "pool" except under very low ambient temperature conditions. Noncryogenic butane and cryogenic LP-Gas are likely to pool. Contact between water and pooled LP-Gas should be avoided to prevent increased vaporization unless the vapor can be controlled.

Water should be applied to fire exposed containers and the flow of gas stopped if possible.

Methylacetylene-Propadiene, Stabilized (MPS)

Classifications: Flammable, liquefied, industrial.

Chemical Properties: Methylacetylene-propadiene, stabilized, is a mixture of materials all comprised of carbon and hydrogen. In commerce, and in compliance with standards covering its use as a metal cutting gas, MPS has the following composition:

1. Methylacetylene-propadiene (in combination, with a maximum ratio of 3.0 moles of methylacetylene per mole of propadiene in the initial liquid phase in a storage container) — 68 mole percent *maximum*

2. Propane, butane, isobutane (in combination) — 24 mole percent *minimum*, of which at least $\frac{1}{3}$ (8 mole percent of total mixture) shall be butane and/or isobutane

3. Propylene — 10 mole percent *maximum*

4. Butadiene — 2 mole percent *maximum*

Methylacetylene (also known as "propyne") and propadiene (also known as "allene") contains double and triple chemical bonds and are unstable, reactive materials presenting hazards similar to acetylene. The achievement of an adequate degree of stability for this product depends upon the existence of a sufficient quantity of the propane, butane, and iso-butane components of the mixture. MPS is marketed under various trade names, including "MAPP GAS" (Dow Chemical Company) and "APACHE GAS" (Air Products and Chemicals, Inc.).

MPS has a degree of chemical reactivity with metals similar to acetylene—especially as it pertains to the use of copper and copper alloys (see "Acetylene" in this chapter).

MPS is nontoxic but has some anesthetic and narcotic effects. It has a strong odor detectable at concentrations as low as 100 ppm in air. See Tables 3-4C and 3-4F.

Physical Properties: See Table 3-4F.

Usage: MPS is principally used as a metal cutting fuel gas with oxygen.

Hazards Inside Containers: MPS has physical properties very similar to propane and is shipped as a liquefied gas in uninsulated DOT and CTC cylinders, and DOT Specification cargo trucks and tank cars. It is stored in cylinders and ASME Code tanks. Its hazards inside containers can be considered as analogous to propane. The presence of MPS is piping systems is not restricted.

Hazards When Released from Containment: MPS presents combustion explosion and fire hazards when released from containment. It is easier to ignite (lower ignition energy) than propane and burns more rapidly, being similar to ethylene in these respects.

MPS is classified as a Group C material for purposes of suitability of electrical equipment installed in classified hazardous areas.

Emergency Control: See "Liquified Petroleum Gases" in this chapter.

Oxygen

Classifications: Nonflammable (oxidizing), compressed, cryogenic, industrial, medical.

Chemical Properties: Oxygen is a basic chemical element. It reacts with practically all materials and the general reaction is known as "oxidation." "Combustion" is a particular type of oxidation reaction. In most combustion reactions, the oxygen is accompanied by nitrogen, the mixture of the two being known as "air." Nitrogen, being an inert gas, contributes nothing to the combustion reaction and actually inhibits it. Therefore, concentrations of oxygen in excess or its concentration in air increase most combustion hazards to a degree directly related to the concentration. This affects all basic combustion parameters except for the heat of combustion. For example, ignition temperatures and

Table 3-4F.   Selected Properties of MPS*

Molecular Weight (Average-stabilized mixture)	42.3
Heat of Vaporization	227 Btu/lb
Gross Heat of Combustion	21,700 Btu/lb
Normal Boiling Range, 1 Atm.	−36 to −4°F
Flame Temperature in Oxygen	5301°F
Specific Heat, Liquid C_p — 70°F, 1 Atm.	0.362 Btu/lb°F
Specific Heat, Liquid C_v — 70°F, 1 Atm.	0.277 Btu/lb°F
Critical Temperature	245°F
Critical Pressure	752 psi
Burning Velocity	15.4 ft/sec
Explosive Limits in Oxygen	2.5 to 60%
Vapor Pressure at 70°F	94 psi
Specific Gravity of the Liquid (60/60°F)	0.576
Specific Volume of the Gas at 60°F, 1 Atm.	8.85 cu ft/lb
Heat of Formation	1075 Btu/lb
Minimum Ignition Energy	0.2–0.25 mJ

* MAPP GAS.   Dow Chemical Company

energies are lowered, the flammable range is widened, and the burning rate is increased as the oxygen concentration increases—the ultimate effects occurring at an oxygen concentration of 100 percent. Chapter 6 in Section 5 of this HANDBOOK discusses oxygen enriched atmospheres in more detail.

Reflecting these properties, the design of systems containing 100 percent oxygen requires particular attention to these factors from a compatibility standpoint.

Physical Properties: See Table 3-4A.

Usage: Oxygen is primarily used in the production of steel, in metal welding and cutting, in medical applications, life support systems in aeronautical and aerospace applications, and in chemical processing.

Hazards Inside Containers: Oxygen is shipped as a compressed or cryogenic gas in DOT and CTC cylinders. In cryogenic form in tank cars and trucks, it is shipped at pressures less than 25 psig not subject to Federal Regulations. It is stored in cylinders (insulated or uninsulated) or in ASME Code insulated tanks.

Compressed oxygen cylinders are protected against overpressure by frangible (bursting) disks or a combination of these with fusible plugs. Insulated cryogenic containers are protected with safety relief valves.

Metals for containers and piping must be carefully selected, depending on service conditions. The various steels are acceptable for many applications, but some service conditions may call for other materials (usually copper or its alloys) because of their greater resistance to ignition and lower rate of combustion.

Similarly, materials that can be ignited in air have lower ignition energies in oxygen. Many such materials may be ignited by friction at a valve seat or stem packing or by adiabatic compression produced when oxygen at high pressure is rapidly introduced into a system initially at low pressure.

Oxygen container failures from fire exposure are rare—probably reflecting provisions of standards which require separation of them from flammable gases and other combustibles. Most "failures" of oxygen system components have been due to accumulations of grease, oil, etc., on the surfaces of these components in contact with oxygen reflecting poor "housekeeping" practices. These materials are rather easily ignited in air and even more so in 100 percent oxygen and ignition of these often results in combustion of system components which are noncombustible in air, including metallic components. Such incidents usually involve only small portions of such components, but may occur in rather spectacular fashion and can cause local effects including personnel injury. They are referred to conventionally as "flashes."

Hazards When Released from Containment: Release of compressed or liquefied oxygen is manifested usually by acceleration of the fire in whatever is burning. Release of liquid oxygen in the absence of fire presents an increased possibility that an oxygen-fuel mixture may occur prior to ignition. If ignition delay occurs under these circumstances, an explosion may result. Practically any combination of liquid oxygen and a combustible material is a potentially explosive combination because of the rapid combustion circumstances resulting. Some commercial explosives have been derived in this manner.

Oxygen is slightly heavier than air at the same temperature.

Emergency Control: Escaping oxygen presents basically a "no fire" situation but can create a "fire" situation in the vicinity of fired equipment or arcing electrical equipment by causing these to get out of control. For example, metallic components of internal combustion engines have burned in oxygen-rich atmospheres resulting from oxygen escape. Oxygen gas vaporizing from the cryogenic liquid near its normal boiling point is about four times heavier than air is at 70°F and will spread along the ground assisted by the visible fog of condensed water vapor created. Such escape can be controlled by water spray. Contact between water and pooled liquid oxygen should be avoided to prevent increased vaporization unless the vapor can be controlled.

Water should be applied to fire exposed containers and the flow of gas stopped if possible.

Utility Gases

Classifications: Flammable, fuel.

Chemical Properties: The term "utility gas" is applicable to any flammable gas distributed by gas utilities as a fuel gas. Natural gas dominates this field today. Some LP-Gas is distributed by gas utilities and most utilities use LP-Gas to augment natural gas supplies during short periods of peak demand during unusually cold weather.

Natural gas is the result of decomposition of organic material by heat, pressure, and bacteriological action in the absence of air, usually below ground. As it is evolved underground, it consists of both flammable and nonflammable gases. The flammable gases are comprised of carbon and hydrogen and are principally methane and ethane with some propane, butane and pentane. The nonflammable gases are principally nitrogen and carbon dioxide. In commerce, most of the nonflammable gases are removed prior to distribution so that the natural gas consists of about 70 to 90 percent methane with the remainder mostly ethane (see Table 3-4C).

Natural gas is nontoxic but is an asphyxiant. This is in marked contrast to the manufactured gas formerly widely distributed as utility gas which contained quantities of toxic carbon monoxide.

Utility natural gas has no odor of its own and is generally odorized as distributed.

Physical Properties: With the exception of liquefied natural gas (LNG), utility natural gas is distributed as a compressed gas at pressures ranging from about $\frac{1}{4}$ psi to 1,000 psi. The gas has a density of about $\frac{2}{3}$ that of air.

Usage: Utility natural gas supplies about $\frac{1}{3}$ of the total fuel energy of the United States for domestic, commercial and industrial heating and power.

Hazards Inside Containers: Utility natural gas is distributed practically exclusively by a million mile plus network of underground pipelines in the United States and Canada. It is transported from gas wells in producing areas in large diameter transmission pipelines at pressures up to about 1,000 psi. These pipelines are tapped by utility gas companies and pressures reduced for distribution—generally to around $\frac{1}{4}$ to 60 psi. Regulators and safety relief devices are used to control pressures.

Steel and cast iron pipe is used extensively. In recent years, thermoplastic and thermosetting plastic piping has been used extensively in distribution piping at pressures up to about 100 psi.

As a result of its location underground, fire exposure is not a significant problem. Most failures of utility natural gas piping are the result of mechanical damage due to excavation operations and corrosion.

Hazards When Released from Containment: Natural gas presents both combustion explosion and fire hazards when released from containment. As most uses of natural gas are indoors, the combustion explosion experience dominates. In approximately three-fourths of the combustion explosions, the gas escapes from the underground distribution main in the street or the service connection between the street main and the building piping. In the remainder, the gas escapes from the building piping or gas-burning equipment.

Open-air or space explosions have resulted from failures of large diameter, high pressure transmission pipelines.

Although not "utility gas," combustion explosions of biologically produced natural gas are increasing as a result of the use of the marshy land and former sanitary landfills for buildings.

Emergency Control: Escaping natural gas presents both "no fire" and "fire" emergency situations. While considerably lighter than air, most gas escapes underground and can travel underground—usually following underground water, sewer or water piping or electrical conduits—for hundreds of feet to enter below-grade building spaces or hollow wall spaces. Because of this escape mode, control consists of ventilation rather than through use of hose streams.

Because of its lightness, unignited natural gas escaping outdoors is seldom a problem.

Natural gas fires should not normally be extinguished in any way other than by stopping the flow of gas.

SI Units

The following conversion factors are given as a convenience in converting to SI units the English units used in this chapter.

$$
\begin{aligned}
1 \ \text{Btu/lb} &= 2.326 \ \text{kJ/kg} \\
1 \ \text{pcf} &= 16.018 \ \text{kg/m}^3 \\
1 \ \text{ft} &= 0.305 \ \text{m} \\
1 \ \text{psi} &= 6.895 \ \text{kPa} \\
\tfrac{5}{9}(°F - 32) &= °C \\
1 \ \text{gal} &= 2.785 \ \text{litres} \\
1 \ \text{cu ft} &= 0.0283 \ \text{m}^3
\end{aligned}
$$

Bibliography

NFPA Codes, Standards, and Recommended Practices (see the latest *NFPA Publications and Visual Aids Catalog* for availability of current editions of the following documents)

NFPA No. 12, Carbon Dioxide Extinguishing Systems.
NFPA No. 50, Standard for Bulk Oxygen Systems at Consumer Sites.
NFPA No. 50A, Gaseous Hydrogen Systems.
NFPA No. 50B, Liquefied Hydrogen Systems at Consumer Sites.
NFPA No. 51, Oxygen-Fuel Gas Systems for Welding and Cutting.
NFPA No. 51A, Acetylene Cylinder Charging Plants.
NFPA No. 51B, Cutting and Welding Processes.
NFPA No. 54, National Fuel Gas Code.
NFPA No. 56B, Respiratory Therapy.
NFPA No. 56F, Nonflammable Medical Gas Systems.
NFPA No. 58, Storage and Handling of Liquefied Petroleum Gases.
NFPA No. 59, Liquefied Petroleum Gases at Utility Gas Plants.
NFPA No. 59A, Production, Storage and Handling of Liquefied Natural Gas.
NFPA No. 328, Flammable and Combustion Liquids and Gases in Manholes and Sewers.

Additional Readings

"Acetylene," Pamphlet G-1, Compressed Gas Association, Inc., New York.
ANSI B9.1-1971, Safety Code for Mechanical Refrigeration.
ANSI B31.8-1968, Gas Transmission and Distribution Piping.
ANSI B138.1-1972, Design and Construction of LP-Gas Installations at Marine and Pipeline Terminals, Natural Gas Processing Plants, Refineries, and Tank Farms.
ANSI K61.1-1972, Safety Requirements for the Storage and Handling of Anhydrous Ammonia.
ANSI Z49.1-1973, Safety in Welding and Cutting.
Bahme, C. W., *Fire Officer's Guide to Dangerous Chemicals*, National Fire Protection Association, Boston, 1972.
Chlorine Manual, The Chlorine Institute, New York, "Cleveland Gas Explosion and Fire," Report UNF-7, 1944, National Fire Protection Association, Boston.
Clifford, E. A., "A Practical Guide to LP-Gas Utilization," *LP-Gas Magazine*, 5th ed., Duluth, Minn., 1973.
Compressed Gas Association, *Handbook of Compressed Gases*, Reinhold Publishing Corporation, New York, 1966.
Cryogenic Safety Manual, British Cryogenics Council, London, 1970.
Editors of Chemical Engineering Progress, *Safety in Air and Ammonia Plants*, Vol. 2, 1960; Vol. 3, 1961; Vol. 5, 1963; Vol. 7, 1965; Vol. 8, 1966; Vol. 9, 1967, American Institute of Chemical Engineers, New York.
"Fire and Explosion Hazards Associated with Liquefied Natural Gas," RI 6099, 1962, USDI, Bureau of Mines, Pittsburgh.
First, M. W., Viles, F. J., and Levin, S., "Control of Toxic and Explosive Hazards in Buildings Erected on Landfills," Public Health Reports, Vol. 81, No. 5, May 1966.
"Flammability and Shock Sensitivity Characteristics of Methylacetylene, Propadiene and Propylene Mixtures," Report No. 3849, 1962, USDI, Bureau of Mines, Pittsburgh.
Gayle, John B., "Explosions Involving Liquid Oxygen and Asphalt," *Fire Journal*, Vol. 67, No. 3, May 1973, pp. 12–13.
Graves, W. E., "Safe Handling of Large Quantities of Gaseous Oxygen in Steel Pipelines," *Iron and Steel Engineer*, Jan. 1965.
Handbook of Propane-Butane Gases, 4th ed., Chilton Company, Los Angeles, 1962.
"Hazards Associated with the Spillage of Liquefied Natural Gas on Water," RI 7448, 1970, USDI, Bureau of Mines, Pittsburgh.
"Hydrogen," Pamphlet G-5, Compressed Gas Association, New York.
Kilmartin, John, "Two Liquid Oxygen Explosions," *Fire Journal*, Vol. 65, No. 2, March 1971, pp. 15–22.
Litchfield, E. L., Hay, M. H., and Cohen, D. J., "Initiation of Spherical Detonation in Acetylene-Oxygen Mixtures," RI 7061, Dec. 1967, USDI, Bureau of Mines, Washington, D.C.
"LNG Importation and Terminal Safety," Proceedings of Conference of National Academy of Sciences, Boston, June 13-14, 1972.
LP-Gas Safety Handbook, National LP-Gas Association, Chicago, continuous updating.
Lyons, P. R., "What Can We Do About Methane?" *Fire Command*, Feb. 1973, pp. 24–25.
"Mapp® Industrial Gas," Loss Prevention Data Sheet 7-94, Factory Mutual System, Norwood, Mass., 1969.
Mayes, H. A., and Yallop, H. J., "The Explosive Properties of Liquid Acetylene," *The Chemical Engineer* (London), Jan.-Feb. 1965, pp. 25–28.
National Transportation Safety Board, several reports of investigations of utility natural gas explosions and fires, National Transportation Safety Board, Washington, D.C.
Nieuland and Voght, The Chemistry of Acetylene, American Chemical Society Monograph No. 99, New York.
"Properties and Essential Information for Safe Handling and Use of Anhydrous Ammonia," SD-8, 1960, Manufacturing Chemists' Association, Washington, D.C.
"Properties and Essential Information for Safe Handling and Use of Ethylene," SD-100, 1973, Manufacturing Chemists' Association, Washington, D.C.
Study of LP-Gas Fires and Explosions, National Fire Protection Association, Boston, 1961.
Study of Natural Gas Explosions, National Fire Protection Association, Boston, 1958.
Title 49, "Transportation," Part 192, Code of Federal Regulations, U.S. Government Printing Office, Washington, D.C.
Walls, W. L., "LNG: A Fire Service Appraisal," *Fire Journal*, Vol. 66, No. 1, Jan. 1972 (Part 1); Vol. 66, No. 2, Mar. 1972 (Part 2).
Weintraub, A. A., "Control of Liquid Hydrogen Hazards at Experimental Facilities: A Review," U.S. Atomic Energy Commission, 1965.

Chapter 5

CHEMICALS

Safe storage and handling of chemicals and safe and effective fire control measures when chemicals are involved require a knowledge of the hazardous properties of chemicals. This chapter discusses those chemicals that are hazardous because of properties other than or in addition to combustibility. It also contains fire hazard information on those combustible chemicals that are not discussed elsewhere in this Section of the HANDBOOK. Chapter 9 in Section 4 gives information on chemical processing equipment and describes processing in terms of specific reactions.

For the purposes of this discussion, chemicals are classified according to the following hazardous properties: (1) ability to oxidize other materials, (2) combustibility, (3) instability, (4) reactivity with air or water, (5) corrosiveness, and (6) radioactivity. Although many chemicals possess more than one of these properties, it is customary to classify each by its predominant hazard. The danger of such a procedure, of course, is that an unmentioned hazardous property may be overlooked, and for this reason it is necessary to refer to chemical dictionaries, data sheets, NFPA No. 49, Hazardous Chemicals Data,[1] NFPA No. 491M, the Manual of Hazardous Chemical Reactions,[2] and similar sources of information when evaluating the hazard of a particular chemical. Benzoyl peroxide, for example, is combustible, but it also is an oxidizing agent and, depending on the percentage dilution, may be unstable. Another example is a commercial blasting mixture composed of ammonium nitrate mixed with substances containing carbon. For the purposes of transportation, these mixtures have been classified as oxidizing materials; however, they are also explosives, and NFPA official recommendations for the storage and handling of blasting agents closely parallel those for commercial explosives.

At the end of each hazard classification, the reader will find a discussion of the properties of the most common chemicals in the class and recommendations on storage and fire fighting.

Toxicity of Chemicals

The toxicity of chemicals is of particular importance from the point of view of fire protection, irrespective of the fire hazard of the toxic material. A fire or explosion may subject fire fighters to a severe life hazard if the toxic material is accidentally released while they are present. In other situations where fire officers are aware of a real or potential toxicity hazard, the decision may be made to forego effective manual fire fighting.

Before using a chemical, information on its toxicity should always be obtained and evaluated, and where the toxicity problem appears to be severe, an effort should be made to find a suitable less toxic substitute. Where there is no practical way of eliminating the toxic material, protection should be provided for those subject to daily exposure, and for fire department personnel. Others who may be exposed during a fire or other emergency should be made acquainted with the potential hazard and be advised on proper protective clothing and breathing apparatus. Automatic fire protection should always be provided where a fire hazard may be present in conjunction with a toxicity hazard.

Information on toxicity of chemicals can be obtained from various sources, including the manufacturers of the chemicals; Chemical Safety Data Sheets of the Manufacturing Chemists' Association, Inc.,[1] and NFPA No. 49, Hazardous Chemicals Data.

Protection against the toxic effects of chemicals during handling can be accomplished in two ways. First is by using the most practical of the available methods of controlling and confining the chemical so that the toxic material cannot be contacted, swallowed, or inhaled in dangerous quantities during normal operations. Second is by educating all persons who may be in areas where toxic chemicals are handled as to the hazards, precautionary procedures to be followed, danger signals, and proper steps to take in case of an emergency.

Of the methods available to control and confine toxic chemicals, handling in a closed system has obvious advantages. However, due to the sense of security engendered by closed systems, a leak in the system may subject persons to a severe health hazard without their knowing it unless automatically operated toxic gas indicators and other alarm devices are provided. In some installations it may be possible to maintain a slight negative pressure on the closed system to prevent the escape of toxic materials in case of a minor leak. Some processes can be installed outdoors where natural air movement will dilute and remove toxic gases or vapors.

In those situations where the toxic chemical cannot be handled in a closed system, mechanical exhaust systems can be used to keep toxic concentrations down to safe limits. Continuous supervision of the exhaust system, toxic gas indicators, and emergency alarm systems are necessary.

A.   Oxidizing Chemicals

There are several important groups of chemicals known as oxidizing agents which provide oxygen for combustion. In most instances the oxidizing chemicals themselves are not combustible. They may, however, increase the ease of ignition of combustible materials and invariably increase the intensity of burning. A few oxidizing agents, such as some of the organic peroxides, are themselves combustible as well as being susceptible to spontaneous decomposition (unstable), and thus possess within themselves all the ingredients for a fire or explosion.

Nitrates

The fire hazard properties of the inorganic nitrates are important because of the wide use of these materials in fertilizers, salt baths, and other industrial uses. Under fire conditions, inorganic nitrates may melt and release oxygen, causing the fire to intensify. The molten salt will react with organic materials with considerable violence, and this reaction usually releases toxic oxides of nitrogen. Use of solid streams of water for fire fighting may result in steam explosions when they contact molten material. The common nitrates are discussed below. Other nitrates have somewhat similar properties.

Sodium Nitrate: Although noncombustible, sodium nitrate promotes combustion of other materials. It evolves oxygen when heated a few hundred degrees above its melting point, thereby increasing the intensity of any fire in its vicinity. It is soluble in water and is hygroscopic. This water solubility (common to most nitrates) is indirectly responsible for many serious fires. If paper, burlap, or cloth bags of nitrates become moist during shipment or storage, the bags, on drying, retain an impregnation of nitrate and are highly combustible. For this reason, it is recommended that nitrates be transferred from bags or wooden barrels to noncombustible bins before storage, and the bags or barrels be thoroughly washed. For the same reason, storage of bulk sodium nitrate on wood floors or against wood walls or posts is hazardous. An intimate mixture of sodium nitrate and organic material can be exploded by a flame.

Potassium Nitrate: The properties and hazards of potassium nitrate are similar to those of sodium nitrate. Potassium nitrate is less moisture-absorbent.

Ammonium Nitrate: Like other inorganic nitrates, ammonium nitrate is an oxidizing agent and will increase the intensity of a fire. The oxidizing gas it gives off is nitrous oxide rather than oxygen. Ammonium nitrate must not be confused with certain ammonium nitrate-combustible material mixtures used as explosives. Those explosive mixtures are known as blasting agents or nitro-carbo-nitrates (see Chapter 6 of this Section). All grades of ammonium nitrate can be detonated if they are in the proper crystalline form, if the initiating source is sufficiently large, or if heated under sufficient confinement, with the degree of confinement necessary usually being greatest for the purest material.

As is evident from the shipboard explosions at Texas City, Texas, and Brest, France, both in 1947, and the Red Sea in 1953; the explosion following a freight train wreck at Traskwood, Ark., December 1960, and the explosion in a bulk warehouse near Pryor, Okla., January 1973, certain conditions other than initiation by explosives can cause ammonium nitrate to detonate. An extensive series of tests to determine the explosion hazards of fertilizer-grade ammonium nitrate under fire exposure was conducted by the Bureau of Mines,[2] and from that study it would appear that the following conclusions can be reached:

1. Although the initiation of detonation in ammonium nitrate as a result of fire exposure cannot be ruled out completely, a direct burning-to-detonation transition in commercial fertilizer-grade ammonium nitrate (referred to hereafter as "AN") appears to be possible, if at all, only in a pile of extremely large dimensions with the ignition at the bottom or center of the pile. (The ammonium nitrate involved in the Texas City, Brest, and Red Sea explosions was organic-coated, with substantially different burning characteristics from those of the fertilizer-grade ammonium nitrate manufactured today.)

2. Projectiles derived from nearby explosions can initiate reactions leading to detonations, particularly in hot AN. Ordinary sporting arms bullets are incapable of initiating detonations of AN under normal storage conditions.

3. When AN is intimately mixed with fuel oil, ground polyethylene, or ground paper, transition from burning to detonation is possible, although quite unlikely, in pile sizes that are typical of those to be found in storage and transportation. Such mixtures are properly classified as blasting agents or nitro-carbo-nitrates and should be stored according to the requirements in NFPA No. 495, Code for the Manufacture, Storage, Transportation, and Use of Explosives and Blasting Agents.

4. Gas detonations are incapable of initiating detonation of AN.

5. Hot AN can be detonated by a high-velocity bullet or by projectile impact. (Initiation of detonation of AN in the Traskwood freight train wreck and fire may have been by projectiles derived from a gasoline-nitric acid detonation as tank cars of gasoline and of nitric acid were also in the wreck. Nitric acid may have become mixed with burning gasoline.)

Tests conducted by Underwriters Laboratories, Inc., indicate that mixtures of ammonium nitrate and ammonium sulfate containing not more than 40 percent by weight of ammonium nitrate, and mixtures of ammonium nitrate and calcium carbonate (calcium ammonium nitrate) containing not more than 61 percent ammonium nitrate are not explosive under conditions met in practice. The calcium ammonium nitrate when exposed to fire forms calcium nitrate and ammonium carbonate which absorbs heat while decomposing to ammonia, carbon dioxide, and water. However, the contamination problem has not been thoroughly investigated.

Ammonium nitrate in water solution is not hazardous unless spilled into combustible material and permitted to dry. However, Japanese work has shown that "solutions" containing up to 8 percent water can be detonated.[3]

Cellulose Nitrate: For hazards and properties of cellulose nitrate see Chapter 7 of this Section.

Nitric Acid

See Part E, Corrosive Chemicals, of this chapter.

Nitrites

Nitrites should not be confused with nitrates. They contain one less oxygen atom than the nitrates but are more active oxidizing agents since they melt and release oxygen at lower temperatures. Nitrites in mixtures with combustible substances are hazardous, and such mixtures, should not be subjected to heat or flame. Certain nitrites, notably ammonium nitrite, are by themselves explosive. Nitrite should be treated like nitrates with respect to storage, handling, and fire fighting.

Inorganic Peroxides

Sodium, Potassium, and Strontium Peroxide: These chemicals are themselves noncombustible, but react vigorously with water and release oxygen as well as much heat. In large quantities the sodium and potassium peroxides may react explosively with water. Heat from reaction with just a little water may cause the contents of an entire container to decompose. If organic or other oxidizable material happens to be at hand when this reaction takes place, fire is likely to occur.

Barium Peroxide: Heat releases oxygen from barium peroxide. Intimate mixtures of barium peroxide and combustible or readily oxidizable materials are explosive and are ignited easily by friction or by contact with a small amount of water.

Hydrogen Peroxide: In contrast to the three above-mentioned peroxides, which are white powders, hydrogen peroxide is a syrupy liquid. In pure form, it is relatively stable. When heated to and kept at a temperature of 212°F, 99.2 percent peroxide decomposes at the rate of 4 percent per year, and the 50 to 90 percent material at a rate of something less than 2 percent a day. An increase in temperature increases the decomposition rate of hydrogen peroxide about 1½ times for each 10°F. Near the boiling point the rate of decomposition is very rapid, and if adequate venting is not provided the pressure in the container may be enough to cause it to rupture. In general, the dilute material is less stable than the concentrated.

At concentrations between 86 and 90.7 percent hydrogen peroxide solutions have been demonstrated to be detonable.[4] At a concentration above about 92 percent the liquid can be exploded by shock.

Concentrated hydrogen peroxide vapors can be exploded by a spark. At atmospheric pressure, the boiling material must be 74 percent peroxide, or higher, to produce explosive vapors.

Decomposition of hydrogen peroxide produces water, oxygen, and heat. At concentrations above 35 percent, the heat is sufficient to turn all the water into steam, assuming that the decomposition started at room temperature (72°F). This means that a steam explosion is possible in the event of sudden decomposition of concentrated material. Decomposition may be caused by contamination with iron, copper, chromium, and many other metals (except aluminum) or their salts. Decomposition can also be caused by combustible dust, or by contact with a rough surface, such as ground glass.

Hydrogen peroxide is a strong oxidizing agent and may cause ignition of combustible material with which it remains in contact. This possibility is remote, except in the case of concentrations greater than 35 percent.

Chlorates

An adequate understanding of the fire hazard properties of the chlorates can be gained from the best-known member of the group, potassium chlorate.

Potassium Chlorate: This is a white crystalline substance that is water soluble, noncombustible, a strong oxidizing agent, and which gives up oxygen when heated even more readily than do nitrates. Mixture with combustible material, e.g., floor sweepings, should be prevented for under such conditions it may ignite or explode spontaneously. Drums containing chlorates may explode when heated. Sodium chlorate has properties similar to potassium chlorate.

Chlorites

Sodium Chlorite: This is a powerful oxidizing agent that forms explosive mixtures with combustible materials. In contact with strong acids, it releases explosive chlorine dioxide gas. At 347°F sodium chlorite decomposes with the evolution of heat.

Dichromates

Among the dichromates, all of which are noncombustible, ammonium dichromate is the most hazardous. It starts to decompose at 356°F, and if the temperature is increased to above 437°F the decomposition becomes self-sustaining with swelling, and release of heat and nitrogen gas. Closed containers rupture at the decomposition temperature.

The other dichromates, such as potassium dichromate, react with readily oxidizable materials and in some cases may cause them to ignite. They release oxygen when heated.

Hypochlorites

Calcium hypochlorite may cause ignition of combustible or organic materials on contact. When heated it gives off oxygen. With acids or moisture, it freely evolves chlorine, chlorine monoxide, and some oxygen at ordinary temperatures. It is sold as bleaching powder or, when concentrated, as a swimming pool disinfectant.

Perchlorates

Perchlorates contain one more oxygen atom than chlorates. They have roughly similar properties, but are more stable than the chlorates. They are explosive under some conditions, such as when in contact with concentrated sulfuric acid.

Ammonium Perchlorate: This has great explosive sensitivity when contaminated with such impurities as sulfur, powdered metals, and carbonaceous materials. The pure material can detonate if involved in a fire. A mixture with a chlorate may form spontaneously explosive ammonium chlorate.

Potassium Perchlorate, Sodium Perchlorate, and Magnesium Perchlorate: Each of these chemicals forms explosive mixtures with combustible, organic, or other easily oxidizable materials. Magnesium perchlorate is sometimes used in laboratories instead of calcium chloride as a desiccant. Such use requires vigilance to avoid dangerous contamination.

Perchloric Acid

See Part E, Corrosive Chemicals, of this chapter.

Permanganates

Mixtures of inorganic permanganates and combustible material are subject to ignition by friction or they may ignite spontaneously if an inorganic acid is present. Explosions may occur under such circumstances whether the permanganate is in solution or is dry.

Potassium Permanganate: This chemical reacts violently with finely divided oxidizable substances. On contact with sulfuric acid or hydrogen peroxide it is explosive.

Persulfates

Persulfates, e.g., potassium persulfate, are strong oxidizing agents which may cause explosions during a fire. Oxygen released by the heat of a fire may cause explosive rupture of the container, or the explosion may follow accidental mixture of the persulfate with combustible material.

Storage of Oxidizing Chemicals

In considering storage facilities for oxidizing chemicals, it should be kept in mind that oxidizing agents usually are not themselves combustible but will provide oxygen for accelerated burning of combustible material. Combustible materials, therefore, should not be stored in the same storage areas with oxidizing chemicals, and storage buildings should be of noncombustible or fire resistive construction. Combustible packaging and wood pallets may represent a severe hazard and should be eliminated. As certain oxidizing materials undergo dangerous reactions with specific noncombustible materials, the possibility of dangerous reactions should be considered when deciding on proper storage facilities. Chlorates, for example, should not be stored with acids or with combustible materials. Inorganic peroxides also react with acids to yield hydrogen peroxide. A suitable storage facility for inorganic peroxides would be a dry, fire resistive storage room in which there were no combustible contents or acids.

When classifying chemicals for storage purposes, one should keep in mind that the label on the container required for interstate shipment classifies the chemical by hazard for transportation purposes only; a knowledge of the fire, health and reactivity hazards of the chemical should be the guide when arranging storage.

Because of the probability that spilled material will become mixed with combustible refuse, it is important to clean up all spills immediately and thoroughly. Combustible linings of barrels should be removed from the storage area and burned as soon as the barrels are empty.

Two NFPA standards are directed specifically toward storage of oxidizing chemicals: NFPA No. 43A, Code for the Storage of Liquid and Solid Oxidizing Materials; and NFPA No. 43C, Code for the Storage of Gaseous Oxidizing Materials.

Ammonium Nitrate: Proper storage methods for bagged ammonium nitrate were intensively investigated following the Texas City, Texas, explosion in 1947 involving cargoes of ammonium nitrate aboard vessels.[5] Storage recommendations for bagged and bulk ammonium nitrate published in NFPA No. 490, Code for the Storage of Ammonium Nitrate, cover building construction, pile sizes and spacing, separation of ammonium nitrate from contaminating materials that could increase its sensitivity during a fire, elimination of floor drains into which molten nitrate might flow, cleanliness of the storage area, and precautions against ignition sources.

Fire Protection for Oxidizing Chemicals

With one or two exceptions, water appears to be the only suitable extinguishing agent for fires involving inorganic oxidizing agents. Water in large quantities should be used to control fires involving nitrates, nitrites, and chlorates. Carbon dioxide and other smothering agents are of little or no value as the oxidizing material furnishes the oxygen for combustion. Although inorganic peroxides decompose when moist and liberate oxygen, water should be used on fires in combustible materials in the vicinity of the peroxide.

It may be possible to extinguish a fire involving a peroxide spill with a dry chemical extinguisher or by smothering with dry sand or soda ash. If these methods fail the area should be flooded with water from hose streams.

Self-contained breathing apparatus should be worn by fire fighters in danger of inhaling oxides of nitrogen during a fire involving nitrates. As much ventilation as possible should be provided to permit rapid dissipation of the products of combustion and heat. When water in solid streams strikes molten nitrate, steam explosions may cause a violent eruption of the molten material.

B.   Combustible Chemicals

The materials discussed in other Chapters in this Section are well-known classes of combustible chemicals. There are several other chemicals which are hazardous principally because of their combustibility.

Carbon Black

Carbon black is formed by decomposition of acetylene or by incomplete combustion of natural gas or of a mixture of natural gas and a liquid hydrocarbon, or by cracking hydrocarbon vapor in the absence of air. It is most hazardous immediately following manufacture when bags of finished product may contain red-hot carbon particles. As carbon black adsorbs oxygen, slow smoldering may develop. To prevent this hazard, carbon black is stored in an observation warehouse before shipment or final storage. It is well established that carbon black itself after thorough cooling and airing will not heat spontaneously, although heat may be generated in the presence of oxidizable oils.

Tests show that a dust explosion hazard does not exist. Red-hot metal, electric sparks, and burning magnesium ribbon will not cause explosive ignition of dust clouds, but ignition has been obtained by using 1 oz of gunpowder.

Carbon black comprises 98 percent of the world's production of powdered carbon.

Lamp Black

Lamp black is formed by burning low-grade heavy oils or similar carbonaceous materials with insufficient air. It adsorbs gases to a marked degree, often igniting spontaneously when freshly bagged. It has great affinity for liquids, and heats in contact with drying oils. The possibility of lamp black dust explosions is increased by the presence of unconsumed oil which adheres to the carbon. Bureau of Mines tests indicate that a dust explosion hazard may exist if the oil content exceeds 13 percent. Lamp black should be thoroughly cooled before bagging and stored in a cool, dry area away from oxidizing materials.

Lead Sulfocyanate

Lead sulfocyanate burns slowly. It decomposes when heated, yielding among its decomposition products highly toxic and flammable carbon disulfide and highly toxic but nonflammable sulfur dioxide.

Nitroaniline

The para isomer of this combustible solid melts at 295°F and its flash point is 390°F. In the presence of moisture, it nitrates organic materials and may result in their spontaneous ignition.

Nitrochlorobenzene

Nitrochlorobenzene is a solid material at ordinary temperatures that gives off flammable vapors when heated.

Sulfides

Antimony Pentasulfide: This is readily ignited and is hazardous in contact with oxidizing materials. On contact with strong acids antimony pentasulfide yields hydrogen sulfide.

Phosphorus Pentasulfide: This ignites readily, and in the presence of moisture may heat spontaneously to its ignition temperature (287°F). The products of combustion include highly toxic sulfur dioxide and phosphorus pentoxide. Reaction of phosphorus pentasulfide with water yields hydrogen sulfide.

Phosphorus Sesquisulfide: With an ignition temperature of only 212°F, this chemical is easily ignited and is considered highly flammable. Highly toxic sulfur dioxide is a product of combustion.

Potassium Sulfide and Sodium Sulfide: These are moderately flammable solids that form highly toxic sulfur dioxide when burning and hydrogen sulfide on contact with acids.

Sulfur

Sulfur at ordinary temperatures is a yellow solid or powder consisting of rhombic crystals, which melt in the vicinity of 234°F, depending on their purity. Sulfur boils at about 832°F. Except in small quantities, it is shipped and stored as a liquid at a temperature below 300°F. It is combustible, and its vapor forms explosive mixtures with air. (Its flash point is 405°F.) Finely divided sulfur dust likewise possesses an explosion hazard that requires control during storage and handling. Ignition temperatures of dust clouds vary upward from 374°F (see Chap. 8 of this Section). Sulfur contains varying amounts of hydrocarbons, depending on the source, and these gradually react with the molten material to form combustible and highly toxic hydrogen sulfide. Storage tanks and pits for molten sulfur must be ventilated to prevent accumulation of this gas. Except when in the presence of lamp black, carbon black, charcoal, and a few less common substances, spontaneous ignition of sulfur is practically nonexistent. It melts and flows when burning and evolves large quantities of highly toxic, irritating, and suffocating sulfur dioxide. This gas attacks the eyes and throat, and complicates fire fighting. Sulfur also forms highly explosive and easily detonated mixtures with chlorates and perchlorates, and forms gunpowder when mixed with potassium nitrate and charcoal.

Naphthalene

Naphthalene is combustible both in solid and in liquid form. Naphthalene vapors and dusts form explosive mixtures with air.

Organic Peroxides

All organic peroxides (see Part C, Unstable Chemicals, of this chapter) are combustible and some are explosive when confined. These properties must be taken into consideration when establishing safe handling and storage methods.

Storage and Fire Protection for Combustible Chemicals

Storage and fire fighting procedures for the combustible chemicals discussed here closely follow those for the more common solid combustible materials discussed in other chapters in this section.

Sulfur, which may be considered principally as a combustible chemical, does have some properties that warrant special mention of applicable storage methods and fire fighting tactics. It should be stored away from oxidizing materials, such as chromates, dichromates, nitrates, nitric acid, peroxides, etc. For fighting sulfur fires, water in the form of a spray is recommended principally to avoid stirring up dust clouds, and also because of the cooling effect of water spray and its ability to absorb large amounts of sulfur dioxide. Fires in solid sulfur may be extinguished by smothering with more sulfur.

C. Unstable Chemicals

Certain chemicals spontaneously polymerize, decompose, or otherwise react with themselves in the presence of a catalytic material or even when pure. Such reactions may become violent.

Acetaldehyde

Acetaldehyde contains the carbonyl group (C = O). Like some other carbonyl compounds it undergoes an addition-type reaction, which can become dangerous in the presence of certain catalysts and at elevated temperatures. Acetaldehyde undergoes a dangerous addition reaction in the presence of an acid catalyst. Caustic can cause an "aldol" condensation that may take place with explosive violence.

Ethyl Acrylate, Methyl Acrylate, Methyl Methacrylate, and Vinylidene Chloride: These are flammable liquids that may polymerize at elevated temperatures, as in fire conditions. If the polymerization takes place in a closed container, the container may rupture violently. These liquids usually contain an inhibitor to prevent polymerization.

Ethylene Oxide

Ethylene oxide may polymerize violently when catalyzed by anhydrous chlorides of iron, tin, or aluminum; oxides of iron (i.e., iron rust) and aluminum; and alkali metal hydroxides. Violent polymerization of ethylene oxide may be initiated by heat or shock. Ethylene oxide reacts with alcohols, organic and inorganic acids, ammonia, and many other compounds. The heat liberated by these exothermic reactions may cause polymerization of the unreacted ethylene oxide. Ethylene oxide vapors may detonate if some initiating heat source is present. Ethylene oxide vapors in a tank exposed by fire may be rapidly heated to their ignition temperature unless the tank is kept wet with water spray. The flammable range of ethylene oxide in air is 3 to 80 percent. Although the upper limit is frequently reported to be 100 percent, explosion of mixtures containing greater than 80 percent ethylene oxide are the result of chemical decomposition.

Hydrogen Cyanide

Hydrogen cyanide is flammable and poisonous. In the liquid or vapor state it has a tendency to polymerize. The reaction is catalyzed by alkaline materials, and since one of the products of the polymerization reaction is alkaline (ammonia), an explosive reaction will eventually take place. By addition of sulfuric, phosphoric, or some other acid to neutralize the ammonia, the rate of polymerization in the liquid can be held down to a safe speed. Potassium cyanide and sodium cyanide on contact with acids release poisonous and flammable hydrogen cyanide vapor.

Methyl Acrylate (See Ethyl Acrylate)

Methyl Methacrylate (See Ethyl Acrylate)

Nitromethane

Nitromethane is a combustible liquid. At 599°F and 915 psig it decomposes explosively. Detonations of nitromethane in railroad tank cars occurred at Niagara Falls, N.Y., and at Mt. Pulaski, Ill., in 1958. Although it has been recognized that undiluted nitromethane may detonate under certain conditions of heat, pressure, shock, and contamination, the causes of these two tank car explosions have not been definitely determined. A possible explanation is contamination of the nitromethane by some material previously carried in the tanks. For a discussion of the hazards of nitromethane and other nitroparaffins, see AIA Research Report No. 12.[6]

Organic Peroxides

Organic peroxides are an important group of chemicals widely used in the plastics industry as polymerization reaction initiators, in the milling industry as flour bleaches, and in the chemical and drug industry as catalysts. Many organic peroxides can be decomposed by heat, shock, or friction, the rate of decomposition depending on the particular peroxide and the temperature. Some, like methyl ethyl ketone peroxide, are detonable. Organic peroxides may be liquid (t-butyl perbenzoate) or solid (benzoyl peroxide) and are often dissolved in flammable or combustible solvents. The organic peroxides are themselves combustible and, as in the case of the inorganic peroxides, increase the intensity of a fire. The peroxides are often found wet with water or diluted with stable liquids. With solutions, the possibility exists of forming sensitive crystals in cold weather. Properties of many of the commercially available organic peroxides are contained in AIA Research Report No. 11.[7]

Benzoyl Peroxide: In undiluted form benzoyl peroxide ignites very readily and burns with great rapidity. It is about like burning an equal amount of black powder. Decomposition by heat is rapid, and if the benzoyl peroxide is confined when heated, explosive decomposition will occur. Decomposition can also be initiated by heavy shock or frictional heat. Most benzoyl peroxide is shipped diluted or water-wet to reduce the fire hazard.

Ether Peroxides: During storage practically all ethers form ether peroxides. When the ether-peroxide mixture is heated or concentrated, the peroxide may detonate. With some ethers the quantities of peroxide formed are too small to be of significance. Peroxide formation is a hazardous property of diethyl ether, ethyl tertiary butyl ether, ethyl tertiary amyl ether, and the diisopropyl ethers. Isopropyl ether is said to be considerably more susceptible to peroxide formation than other ethers. Pure dry ether stored under laboratory conditions in a colorless bottle will develop detectable amounts of peroxides in one month. Light seems to be a more important factor than heat, although peroxides have been known to form in amber bottles. Ether sealed in copperplated cans or in otherwise inhibited cans is not likely to form peroxides. Although there is apparently no means yet available to eliminate completely peroxide formation, the use of any one of numerous patented inhibitors, or copper or iron along with storage in metal or opaque amber glass containers, gives sufficient stability for all practical purposes. Ether should not be dry-distilled unless peroxides have been proved absent.

Storage and Fire Protection of Unstable Chemicals

Special precautions must be taken where chemicals are stored that are subject to spontaneous decomposition or other dangerous reactions. The precautions should be planned to minimize the possibility of a dangerous reaction and to prevent injuries and extensive property damage if one should occur. Steps to be taken to protect against the hazard will depend on the conditions that affect the stability of the chemical being stored. Points peculiar to unstable chemicals to be considered are the catalytic effect of containers, materials in the same storage area that could initiate a dangerous reaction, presence of inhibitors, effect of direct sunlight or temperature changes, pressure relief vents for containers, and explosion venting facilities for the storage area. These are in addition to the usual considerations such as storage in a safe outdoor location, automatic sprinkler or water spray protection, and elimination of all combustible material from the storage area.

Fire fighters should be thoroughly briefed on the proper procedures to be followed if called upon to fight a fire involving or exposing a storage area containing unstable chemicals.

Organic Peroxides: This is a widely used group of unstable chemicals deserving special mention, and the following recommendations summarize a detailed treatment of organic peroxide storage and fire fighting found in the AIA's Research Report No. 11.[7]

Organic peroxides should be stored in a separate building constructed and located so that the building and its contents cannot be involved by an exposing fire. The building should be noncombustible and preferably of damage-limiting construction. Ventilation and deluge automatic sprinkler protection are recommended and, except where necessary to prevent freezing of an organic peroxide, the building should not be heated. If a separate building is not practicable, it

may be feasible to store relatively small amounts in weather-tight and heat-insulated cabinets outdoors on the roof.

Containers of organic peroxides should be stored away from all sources of heat, including the direct rays of the sun, and piled so that each container will be wet by sprinkler discharge. Organic peroxides should be the only materials stored in the building and different peroxides should be separated from each other to minimize use of the wrong peroxide. Liquid peroxides should be segregated in a separate storage building or in individual tanks. Storage should be in original shipping containers, kept closed, and with required vents in working order. Containers should not be opened in the storage room.

Water is the recommended extinguishing agent for fires involving organic peroxides (water in spray form if the peroxide is a liquid), and for fires involving those organic peroxides that become unstable and spontaneously explosive at elevated temperatures. Water application should be from as far a distance as possible or from an explosion-protected location.

Nitroparaffin: Although nitromethane is the only nitroparaffin in large quantity use to have been involved in disastrous explosions, all nitroparaffins should be stored and handled with due regard for the possibility of explosive decomposition under certain conditions of heat, shock, and pressure. These conditions, the chemical and physical properties of nitroparaffins, and recommendations for their storage and handling are contained in the AIA's Research Report No. 12.[6] Contamination may increase the sensitivity of nitroparaffins to explosive decomposition. Dilution decreases or eliminates the hazard.

Regarding storage of nitromethane, Research Report No. 12 recommends an outdoor storage facility located, constructed, and protected in such a way that it could not be involved by an exposing fire. If a storage facility is a building, it should be made of fire resistive or noncombustible materials and should be used only for the storage of nitromethane. An automatic deluge type sprinkler system would be desirable. Storage in buildings should be in original drums and the drums should be stacked in several small piles rather than in one large one. Underground tanks and above-ground barricaded tanks are other suitable storage methods mentioned in the AIA report.

NFPA's "Hazardous Chemicals Data" recommends water in large quantities applied by a remotely controlled means if a large fire involves nitromethane. Should containers be exposed by a fire they should be kept cool with water spray. Fires involving small quantities of nitromethane can be fought with water spray from a safe location.

Styrene

Styrene polymerizes slowly at ordinary temperatures, and the rate increases as the temperature increases. Since the polymerization reaction is exothermic, the reaction will eventually become violent as it is accelerated by its own heat. Inhibitors are added to styrene to prevent dangerous polymerization.

Vinyl Chloride

Vinyl chloride is a flammable gas that may polymerize at elevated temperatures, as in fire conditions, and cause violent rupture of the container. Vinyl chloride usually contains an inhibitor to prevent polymerization.

Vinylidene Chloride (See Ethyl Acrylate)

D. Water- and Air-reactive Chemicals

A small group of chemicals important from the point of view of fire protection includes air-reactive and water-reactive chemicals. Significant quantities of heat are liberated during the reactions. If the chemical itself is combustible, it is capable of self-ignition; if noncombustible, the heat of reaction may be sufficient to ignite nearby combustible materials.

Alkalies (Caustics)

Caustic soda (sodium hydroxide or lye) and caustic potash (potassium hydroxide) are the most common alkalies. Caustics are noncombustible, but when mixed with water generate heat. In contact with water, dry solid caustics will react. The heat generated (heat of solution) may be sufficient to ignite combustible material. Caustic solutions may generate hydrogen on contact with zinc, galvanized metals, or aluminum.

Aluminum Trialkyls

Most of these metal-organic compounds are pyrophoric, i.e., they ignite spontaneously on exposure to air, and react violently with water and certain other chemicals. Triethylaluminum, the most common member of this group, ignites spontaneously in air and on contact with water. When it is mixed with strong oxidizing agents or with halogenated hydrocarbons, violent reactions or detonations may occur.

Anhydrides

Acid anhydrides are compounds of acids from which water has been removed. They react with water, usually violently, to regenerate acids. Organic acid anhydrides are combustible and usually are more hazardous than their corresponding acids, since their flash points are lower. Acetic anhydride has a flash point of 129°F; propionic anhydride, 165°F (open cup); butyric anhydride, 190°F (oc), and maleic anhydride, 218°F. Inorganic acid anhydrides, e.g., chromium anhydride and phosphorus anhydride, are not combustible.

Carbides

The carbides of some metals, such as sodium and potassium, may react explosively on contact with water. Many, such as calcium carbide, lithium carbide, potassium carbide, and barium carbide, decompose in water to form acetylene. In addition to the hazard of the formation of flammable gas, another fire hazard of certain carbides is the generation of heat in contact with water. When one-third its weight of water is added to a water-reactive carbide, the temperature may be raised sufficiently to ignite the gas generated. Sodium carbide becomes heated to incandescence when placed in chlorine, carbon dioxide, or sulfur dioxide. The carbides of silicon and tungsten are very stable.

Charcoal

Under certain conditions, charcoal reacts with air at a sufficient rate to cause the charcoal to heat spontaneously and ignite. Charcoal made from hard wood by the retort method appears to be particularly susceptible. Spontaneous heating occurs more readily in fresh charcoal than in old material; the more finely divided it is, the greater the hazard. The principal causes of spontaneous heating of charcoal appear to be: (1) lack of sufficient cooling and airing before shipment; (2) charcoal becoming wet; (3) friction in grinding of finer sizes, particularly of material insufficiently aired

before grinding; (4) carbonizing of wood at too low a temperature, leaving the charcoal in a chemically unstable condition.

Coal

Coal of virtually all grades, except high grade anthracite, under some conditions is subject to spontaneous heating and ignition. Although the basic causes of spontaneous heating of coal are not at all well defined, it is believed that adsorption of oxygen or oxidation of finely divided particles is the main cause. While instances of spontaneous heating of coal are numerous, the number of fires from this cause is insignificant when the large number of coal storage piles is considered.

The principal conditions that are believed to affect the susceptibility of coal to spontaneous heating are: (1) the fineness of the particles, (2) the oxygen-adsorptive abilities of the particles, (3) the trapped and confined moisture content of the coal, (4) air trapped in voids in coal piles, (5) the presence of sulfur in the form of pyrites or marcasites, (6) free gases in the pile, (7) foreign substances in the pile, (8) the method and depth of piling, (9) the temperature of the containing walls and floor or of surrounding or surrounded surfaces, and (10) the type and amount of ventilation.

Hydrides

Most hydrides are compounds of hydrogen and metals. Metal hydrides react with water to form hydrogen gas.

Sodium Hydride: A gray-white crystalline, free-flowing powder, sodium hydride will ignite with explosive violence on contact with water. When exposed to air, absorption of moisture may cause ignition.

Lithium Hydride: This is a combustible solid that reacts vigorously with water with the evolution of hydrogen gas and heat. Lithium hydride dust is likely to explode in humid air. Static electricity may cause the dust to explode in dry air.

Lithium Aluminum Hydride: Like lithium hydride, this chemical is a combustible solid that reacts rapidly with water to form hydrogen gas and heat. The heat will probably cause the hydrogen to ignite. When lithium aluminum hydride is in a solution with ether, a fire involving the solution is essentially an ether fire. Small amounts of water cause the burning to intensify. Combustible materials on which the solution has spilled may ignite spontaneously or be ignited by light friction.

Oxides

Oxides of metals and nonmetals react with water to form alkalies and acids respectively. This reaction takes place violently with the infrequently used sodium oxide. Calcium oxide, more commonly known as quicklime or unslaked lime, also reacts vigorously with water (slaking) with the evolution of enough heat to ignite paper, wood, or other combustible material under some conditions.

Phosphorus

Two forms of phosphorus, white and red, are in common use.

White (or Yellow) Phosphorus: This type is the more dangerous because of its ready oxidation and spontaneous ignition in air. It is common practice to ship and store white phosphorus under water, with the mixture usually in a hermetically sealed metal container. Periodic checks should be made to be sure that containers do not leak. White phosphorus is very toxic and should not be permitted to come in contact with the skin. On ignition, dense white clouds of toxic fumes are evolved which attack the lungs.

Red Phosphorus: This type is less hazardous than white, does not oxidize and burn spontaneously at ordinary temperatures, and can be shipped and stored without the protection of water, although it should be kept in closed containers away from oxidizing agents. It is formed by heating white phosphorus. The solid form is not toxic, but once vaporized it takes on all the fire hazards of white phosphorus to which it reverts on condensation. Care should be taken in opening containers of red phosphorus as spontaneous ignition has been known to take place on exposure to air.

Sodium (See Chap. 9 of this Section.)

Sodium Hydrosulfite

Sodium hydrosulfite burns slowly, sulfur dioxide being one of the combustion products. On contact with moisture and air it heats spontaneously and may ignite nearby combustible materials.

Storage and Fire Protection for Water- and Air-reactive Chemicals

Water-reactive Chemicals: Alkalies, anhydrides, carbides, hydrides, and oxides, etc., should be stored in dry areas in water- and air-tight containers that are kept off the floor by skids. Whether or not the storage area should be protected by automatic sprinklers will depend on the type of chemical reaction that will occur when the chemical comes in contact with water and also upon the combustibility of the storage room and its contents. Fires involving hydrides, for example, can be smothered with a special graphite base powder or with an inert material, such as dry, finely divided calcium magnesium carbonate (dolomite). Hydride fires should not be put out if the continued evolution of hydrogen after extinguishment will create an explosion hazard.

If the water reaction is likely to be violent, the chemical should be stored in a separate fire resistive area where there would be no possibility of a fire requiring water for extinguishment. When the water reaction is not likely to be violent, and when the containers holding the water-reactive chemicals, or other chemicals stored in the same room are combustible, or the storage room itself is combustible, the best fire protection would be an automatic sprinkler system. In the absence of sprinklers, hose streams would be required to control a fire in such a storage area, with due caution being taken by fire fighters to avoid injuries by possible explosions.

Air-reactive Chemicals: These are usually stored under water or other liquid or inert gas. Fires are best controlled with large volumes of water. If the chemical is also water-reactive, metallic sodium under oil, for example, dry chemical is recommended. In the case of fires involving air-reactive white (or yellow) phosphorus, the water will solidify phosphorus melted by the heat of the fire, after which it can be covered with wet sand or dirt. Following a fire involving an air-reactive chemical, all of the chemical released during the fire must be disposed of before it can dry out and reignite.

Charcoal: Prevention of dangerous spontaneous heating hazards with charcoal can largely be controlled by thorough cooling and ventilating before bagging and storage. Precautions to be taken in the storage and handling are to keep the charcoal dry, prevent contamination with foreign combustibles, and avoid contact with a heat source. Small quantities of charcoal are normally shipped and stored in heavy paper bags. The spontaneous heating hazard of individual bags, such as would be kept in a dwelling, is not serious.

When fire occurs in charcoal, water should be used as sparingly as possible. The damaged and wet material should be removed from the building at once because wet charcoal is even more susceptible to self-ignition than when it is dry.

Coal: To avoid the hazard of spontaneous heating in coal, the following precautionary measures for storage are recommended.[8]

1. The ground or the floor of the place where coal is to be stored should be thoroughly cleaned of leaves, grass, weeds, pieces of wood, cotton waste, or other foreign matter, and precautions taken to prevent foreign matter from getting under, into, or on the coal pile.

2. There should be no steam or other pipe, or sewer or other openings under, in, through, or adjacent to coal piles, and the floor and walls of coal storage bins should preferably be noncombustible.

3. Preferably, coal should not be stored where the air temperature or the temperature of the surrounding surfaces (floor, walls, etc.) is in excess of 75° or 80°F.

4. In storing coal, it should not be dropped any considerable distance; otherwise breakage will occur, and it is thought that newly broken fine particles are more than ordinarily susceptible to oxidation.

5. Preferably, storage piles should be limited both in height and in area, as far as surrounding conditions will allow, neither limit being very well defined as to probable safety. If possible, partitions of noncombustible material, such as concrete, should be provided to form "stalls" or bins, each holding 25 to 50 tons. Some authorities advise against storing coal in piles higher than 15 ft.

6. Coal for storage should preferably be deposited in layers rather than in conical piles, as is likely to occur where the coal is all dropped at one point, thus allowing the larger pieces to run to the toe or talus or foot of the pile, making more or less open spaces which allow some ventilation, but often not enough to keep temperature down.

7. Large coal storage piles should be made by depositing the coal in layers of about 3-ft depth and then compacting. After allowing a period of several days for "seasoning," other layers may be added.

8. Alternate wetting and drying should be avoided, and it is also dangerous to have part of a pile wet and another part dry.

9. Where coal is not readily susceptible to disintegration by the weather and where cost is not excessive, it would appear advisable to store only the larger sizes (lump or egg) rather than mine run or mixtures of other sizes and slack. If mine run is stored, precaution should be taken against accumulation of fine coal in a segregated pile or piles.

10. Standing timbers, pipes, etc., in the pile should be avoided as much as possible, as these, surrounded by pieces of coarser coal, may form ducts or flues inducing sluggish air flow, giving sufficient oxygen to cause heating, but not giving sufficient air flow to remove the heat.

11. While not advisable to have standing pipes in storage coal piles, it may be desirable to have $\frac{1}{2}$- to 1-in. pipes at intervals of 15 to 20 ft and extending practically to the bottom of the pile, these pipes to be used for introducing thermometers to ascertain temperatures. The use of automatic heat alarms (thermostats) is a preferable method for ascertaining temperature conditions of storage coal piles.

12. Usually, spontaneous heating in a coal pile takes place within 90 or 120 days after placing coal in storage; its presence may be made known by the gases given off or by

the higher temperature of the coal or the air surrounding the coal pile. If temperatures in excess of 140°F are found, it may be advisable to move the coal or to take other adequate precautions against fire. "Wetting down" the pile upon finding that it is heating is not good policy unless the water can be placed at the seat of the fire or heating.

13. In enclosed spaces, consideration may be given to the use of inert gases, such as carbon dioxide; this method has been tried to extinguish spontaneous coal fires, apparently sometimes with and sometimes without success. Coal sprayed with high flash point mineral oil, a process used to reduce dustiness, decreases the tendency to spontaneous ignition by protection of the surfaces from oxidation.

Spraying coal with a solution of calcium chloride has been reported as decreasing the tendency to spontaneous heating.[9]

Agricultural Products: Spontaneous heating in agricultural products can be prevented by control of moisture, proper curing (as for hay), and adequate aeration to prevent heat buildup. The last-mentioned objective is accomplished by storing in compartments with slatted bottoms and sides or by providing aisles between bales standing on raised slatted bottoms. Where the moisture content cannot be controlled or where any suspicion of spontaneous heating exists, thermometers or thermocouples may be used in stacks or bales. Usually pointed hollow metal rods or pipes with holes drilled in the lower ends are used to permit insertion of such temperature instruments into the subsurface areas of the stored material. In this way, regular checks can be made for the development of any hazardous temperature conditions.

Where evidence of dangerous spontaneous heating is noted, the material should be removed from storage quickly. It is very important, however, to have ample fire fighting facilities available (usually water hose streams) for combating a possible fire which might occur spontaneously upon exposure of the "hot spots" to air or by disturbance of the pile admitting oxygen or air currents into the vulnerable areas. Hay in and around "hot spots" should be thoroughly wetted before complete uncovering or attempted removal. An alternate method sometimes effective on certain agricultural products is the introduction of an inert gas into the heated area by probes to dilute the entrapped air and to reduce temperatures. Carbon dioxide is the usual gas employed when this technique is followed.

Handling Reactive and Unstable Chemicals

Special problems are associated with the handling of reactive or unstable chemicals that can cause fires or explosions. In the handling of air-reactive materials, it may be possible to do all handling in a closed system under vacuum or in an inert gas atmosphere. Blanketing by or dissolving in an organic solvent and maintenance of dry air atmospheres are methods frequently used to keep moisture from water-reactive chemicals during handling. Inhibiting catalysts and refrigeration are useful in keeping unstable chemicals under control. These and other methods used to prevent dangerous reactions of reactive and unstable chemicals should be supplemented by emergency means for relieving dangerous pressures and stopping uncontrolled reactions, such as rupture discs and emergency relief valves on equipment, and emergency dump tanks containing some material that by dilution or reaction can stop the dangerous process. Where reactive or unstable chemicals are handled, fire fighting personnel and others who may be called upon to report in an emergency should be made aware of any unusual health

hazard that may be introduced by the products of reactions of the reactive or unstable chemical.

E. Corrosive Chemicals

The term "corrosive" as used here identifies those chemicals which have a destructive effect on living tissues. They are usually strong oxidizing agents but are separately classified as corrosive chemicals to emphasize their injurious effect on contact or inhalation. It should not be inferred that a chemical is not injurious because it is otherwise classified. For example, caustics, classified as water- and air-reactive chemicals, are also corrosive. Care should be taken to prevent inhalation, ingestion, and contact with all chemicals unless they are known to be harmless.

Inorganic Acids

Concentrated aqueous solutions of the inorganic acids are not in themselves combustible. Their chief hazard lies in the danger of leakage and possible mixture with other chemicals or combustible material stored in the vicinity which would be followed in some cases by fire or explosions.

Hydrochloric Acid: In concentrated solution, hydrochloric acid is hazardous because of its reaction with certain metals, including tin, iron, zinc, aluminum, and magnesium, to form hydrogen gas. Strong oxidizing agents release chlorine gas, and a mixture of nitric and hydrochloric acids generates chlorine and nitrous oxide.

Hydrofluoric Acid: Either anhydrous or aqueous hydrofluoric acid is noncombustible and does not cause ignition of combustible materials in which it comes in contact. However, it attacks metals with the generation of hydrogen, is highly toxic, is irritating to the eyes, and can inflict severe skin burns.

Nitric Acid: Under certain conditions nitric acid nitrates cellulose material. Thus, wood that comes in contact with the acid or its vapor may have its ease of ignition markedly increased. Spontaneous heating follows if strong solutions of the acid mix with organic material. In general, concentrated nitric acid nitrates organic materials; dilute acid oxidizes them and gives off oxides of nitrogen while doing so. These oxide fumes (colorless to brown) are usually present in fires in buildings where nitric acid is being used. A concentration of this gas (in reality a mixture of several gases) so small that it will not seem objectionable at the time of inhalation can result in serious illness or death to the victim, although no effects may be felt for some time. White fuming nitric acid (more than 97.5 percent nitric acid) when spilled into burning gasoline will detonate.[2]

Perchloric Acid: If misused or in concentrations greater than 72 percent, perchloric acid can be extremely dangerous. At the normal commercial strength (72 percent) it is a strong oxidizing and dehydrating agent when heated, but is a strong nonoxidizing acid at room temperature. Because of this and other advantageous properties, it is widely used in analytical laboratories. The rate of burning of organic substances is greatly increased by contact with perchloric acid. Explosions have occurred at wood and plastic laboratory hoods after long exposure of the hoods to perchloric acid vapors. Strong dehydrating agents, such as concentrated sulfuric acid or phosphorus pentoxide, convert perchloric acid solution to anhydrous perchloric acid, which decomposes even at room temperature and explodes with terrific violence. It also explodes on contact with many organic substances. For these reasons, dehydrating agents should never be mixed with perchloric acid.

Sulfuric Acid: This has the added hazardous property of absorbing water from organic material with which it may come in contact. Charring takes place and sufficient heat may be evolved to cause ignition. Particular care must be taken to avoid painful skin burns inflicted by bodily contact. Dilute sulfuric acid will dissolve metals with the evolution of hydrogen.

The Halogens

The members of the halogen (salt-producing) group are all chemically active and have similar chemical properties; the individual elements fluorine, chlorine, bromine, and iodine differ from each other in decrease of activity in the order named, the last two having lesser fire hazards. They are noncombustible, but will support combustion of certain substances. Turpentine, phosphorus, and finely divided metals ignite spontaneously in the presence of the halogens. The fumes are poisonous, and are corrosive and irritating to the eyes and throat.

Bromine: A dark reddish-brown corrosive liquid which may cause fire in contact with combustible materials.

Chlorine: This is a heavy, greenish-yellow poisonous gas given off in some manufacturing processes and by bleaching powder (chloride of lime), especially in the presence of strong acids. It is not flammable itself, but may cause fires or explosions, especially if it comes in contact with acetylene, ammonia, turpentine, or finely powdered metals. Care as to ventilation should be observed in any process where this gas is generated.

Fluorine: A greenish-yellow gas, fluorine is one of the most reactive elements known and combines, in most cases spontaneously, with practically all elements and compounds known under suitable conditions. Flourine reacts violently with hydrogen and many organic materials. It is explosive in contact with metallic powders, attacks glass and most metals, and reacts explosively in contact with water vapor. It may be safely handled in nickel or monel cylinders. Fuorine reacts with these two metals, but forms a protective nickel fluoride layer that prevents further action. However, moisture or other impurities within the cylinder may cause such violent reaction that the metal will melt and ignite in the fluorine. The tank then bursts and scatters molten metal.

Iodine: This chemical is usually in the form of purplish-black, volatile crystals that are corrosive. Reports indicate that iodine is explosive when diffused with ammonia (it forms explosive nitrogen triiodide) and when mixed with turpentine or lead triethyl.

Storage and Fire Protection for Corrosive Chemicals

Storage and fire protection recommendations should be designed to protect against the damaging effect of corrosive chemicals on living tissue as well as against any other fire or explosion hazard associated with the chemical.

Inorganic Acids: These acids, including sulphuric, nitric, and hydrochloric acids, should be stored in cool, well ventilated places away from the sun and not in proximity to other chemicals or waste materials. Storage areas should be protected against temperatures low enough to freeze the acids. Spilled acid should be diluted at once with a large volume of water. Combustible materials contaminated with nitric, sulfuric, or perchloric acid should be thoroughly washed or removed to a safe location before spontaneous ignition can occur.

Water in spray form is recommended for fires in acid storage areas. If a fire involves perchloric acid it should be fought with the understanding that the acid may become mixed with organic material and that an explosion may occur. Ample precautions should be taken to protect fire fighters from possible explosions. Fire fighters should avoid contact with any spilled acids and inhalation of their toxic fumes.

Chlorine and Fluorine Cylinders: If stored inside these cylinders, should be in noncombustible or fire resistive, well ventilated, segregated rooms. As chlorine is a serious inhalation hazard, areas where it is suspected that this gas is leaking should not be entered without self-contained breathing apparatus. Fluorine causes severe flesh burns and is also highly toxic by inhalation, thereby necessitating special protective clothing as well as self-contained breathing apparatus.

F. Radioactive Materials

Radioactive elements and compounds have fire and explosion hazards identical with those of the same material when not radioactive. An additional hazard is introduced by the various types of radiation emitted, all of which are capable of causing damage to living tissue. Thus, under fire conditions, vapors and dusts (smoke) may be formed that could contaminate not only the building of origin but neighboring buildings and outdoor areas. The fire protection engineer's main concern is to prevent the release or loss of control of these materials by fire or during fire extinguishment. For a discussion of hazards of radioactive materials in processes see Sec. 4, Chap. 13.

Storage and Fire Protection for Radioactive Materials

Because of the life hazard introduced by an escape of radioactive dusts and vapors during a fire, it is of vital importance that all practical steps be taken to prevent a fire from involving these materials. Radioactivity is not detectable by any of the human senses; special instruments and measuring techniques are required to identify and evaluate it. The hazard is affected by the form of the material, whether solid, liquid, or gas, and by the container in which it is kept or handled.

Radioactivity can cause injuries, loss of life, damage to and extended loss of use of materials, equipment, and buildings. Manual fire fighting may be limited by the danger to fire fighters from exposure to radioactivity, and there could be delay in salvage work and resumption of normal operations in a property where a fire or explosion causes loss of control over radioactive substances. A complicated problem is the need for decontamination of buildings, equipment, and materials.

The most numerous uses of radioactivity involve relatively small amounts of material and negligible radioactivity as, for example, in the manufacture of luminous watch dials and as tracers for chemical, biological, and other reactions. Significant and often dangerous amounts of radioactivity are involved in nuclear reactors, radiation machines for research such as particle accelerators, and in various medical and industrial equipments. Relatively large amounts of radioactive materials are involved in fuel and waste of nuclear reactors and in nuclear weapons, all of which pose special problems in transportation and storage. Control of most radioactive materials is generally maintained by regulation of national atomic energy authorities, but some materials, such as radium, may not be covered.

Smoke and products of combustion from fires in places where there are radioactive materials must be controlled as must the runoff of water used in fighting fires. Fire fighters require protective clothing and respiratory protection equipment. Fire control must be thoroughly preplanned. With radiation hazards, automatic sprinklers are preferable to measures requiring manual fire fighting as these make it possible to reduce the size of fire. This lessens the amount of radioactive smoke or products of combustion and water runoff to be dealt with.

Handling Radioactive Materials

The possibility of accidental release of radioactive material because of a fire or explosion, with the resultant health hazard to fire fighters and others is a strong argument for careful attention to methods of fire prevention and control in laboratories and other occupancies handling radioactive materials.

Guidance may be obtained from NFPA No. 801, Recommended Safe Practices for Laboratories Handling Radioactive Materials. This publication calls attention to the fact that the basic principles of fire protection for radiological laboratories are the same as for other laboratories. Most radioactive materials, themselves, introduce little or no fire or explosion hazard so the fire hazard of radiological laboratories usually can be determined by a knowledge of the combustibility of the building and its furnishings and the fire and explosion hazards of the nonradioactive chemicals.

The fire and explosion hazard can be substantially reduced by use of a fire resistive building, noncombustible interior finish and furnishings wherever possible, and enforcement of strict controls to minimize the hazards of flammable liquids and other chemicals that may be necessary for laboratory work. One feature of radiological laboratories that can give trouble unless properly designed is the duct system that is usually required for the safe disposal of contaminated vapors, gases, and dusts. Unless this system is properly arranged, it can spread radioactive contaminants to noninvolved parts of a laboratory at time of fire.

Because of the importance of immediate control of any fire that might eventually release radioactive materials, and considering the potential health hazard to those who might be exposed to radiation during manual fire control, there can be no question as to the desirability of automatic sprinkler protection for radiation laboratories and other areas where radioactive materials are handled. Special precautions to be followed by fire fighting personnel may be found in the book, *Radiation Control*.[10] These procedures stress steps that should be taken to protect the fire fighters at all times, including the use of radiation monitoring devices, self-contained breathing apparatus, and regular fire department protective clothing.

G.   Transportation of Chemicals

The safe transportation of chemicals depends on a knowledge of the hazardous properties of the chemicals, the normal and abnormal conditions to which the chemicals may be exposed during shipment, and the conditions of packing and shipping that will minimize the possibility of accidental release or reaction of chemicals.

In the United States shipments of hazardous chemicals in interstate or foreign commerce by land, water or air must comply with DOT regulations. Among items covered by these regulations are construction of containers, method of packing, weight of chemical per package, marking and labeling, loading, placarding, and movement of railroad cars, and regulations for motor vehicle equipment and motor vehicle operation on the highway.

State regulations for intrastate transportation usually agree with those of the DOT for interstate commerce. In Canada, shipments of explosives and other dangerous chemicals are regulated by the Board of Transport Commissioners of Canada. Chemicals shipped in accordance with Canadian regulations may be shipped to a destination in the United States or through the United States.

Principles governing the safe transportation of chemicals include:

1. Make container of material that will not react with or be decomposed by the chemical.

2. Exclude chemicals that can react dangerously with each other from the same outside container.

3. Package toxic and radioactive chemicals so that they will present no health hazard during normal transportation conditions and will not be released in an accident or under other abnormal conditions.

4. Provide sufficient outage for maximum expansion of liquids under conditions to be expected during transportation.

5. Limit the amount of chemical that can be released by container breakage or leakage by limiting maximum size of individual containers.

6. Cushion containers to minimize possibility of breakage.

H.   Waste Chemical Disposal

The safe disposal of flammable, toxic, or radioactive chemicals that are no longer needed introduces many problems. Human and animal life can be endangered and fires and explosions can occur if the operation is not carried out properly. Federal, state, and local health and pollution regulations must be observed and the disposal must be conducted in such a way as to prevent toxic, fire, and explosion hazards.

Safe disposal of chemical waste requires a knowledge of the physical, physiological, and chemical properties of the waste material (flammability, toxicity, and reaction with water and other chemicals), and familiarity with the advantages or limitations of the various methods of disposal (burning, dilution with water, burying, discharge into sewers, and reaction with another chemical to form a product that can be safely disposed). Advice on methods of disposal may be obtained from the supplier of the chemical and from chemical data sheets. Flammable liquid wastes can usually be destroyed by burning in special furnaces.[11]

In the case of radioactive materials with a short half life, it may be practical to hold the material until the radioactivity is reduced to a level safe for disposal. Otherwise, the preferred method may be to mix the radioactive material with cement for burial in the ground.

Considering the hazards involved in the disposal of large quantities of materials with severe hazards, it will be advisable in such cases to use the services of a company specializing in chemical waste disposal.

For disposal of small quantities of chemicals, the Manufacturing Chemists' Association, Inc., has prepared a useful Laboratory Waste Disposal Manual.[12] See Chapter 14 of Section 4 of this HANDBOOK for further information on industrial and emergency waste control.

I.   Mixtures of Chemicals

The preceding paragraphs of this chapter contain several examples of dangerous reaction that can occur when certain chemicals are mixed. Examples are also cited of chemicals that when mixed with a combustible material increase the ease of ignition or the intensity of burning of the latter. In order to recognize the innumerable combinations of so-called incompatible chemicals, it is necessary to have a knowledge of the potentially dangerous reactions of individual chemicals. NFPA No. 491M, Manual of Hazardous Chemical Reactions, which contains more than 3,400 dangerous reactions that have been reported in the chemical literature and elsewhere, is an excellent source for this information.

SI Units

The following conversion factors are given as a convenience in converting to SI units the English units used in this chapter.

1 in.	= 25.400 mm
1 ft	= .305 m
1 lb (mass)	= .454 kg
1 ounce (mass)	= 28.350 g
$\frac{5}{9}(°F - 32)$	= °C

Bibliography

References Cited

[1] Chemical Safety Data Sheets, Manufacturing Chemists' Association, Washington, a series issued and revised at will.

[2] Van Dolah, R. W., et al., "Explosion Hazards of Ammonium Nitrate Under Fire Exposure," RI 6773, 1966, USDI Bureau of Mines, Pittsburgh.

[3] Fukuyama, I., "Sensitive Ammonium Nitrate," *Journal of Industrial Explosives Society*, (Kogyo Kayaku Kyohaishi), Vol. 18, No. 1, 1957, pp. 64–66.

[4] Research and Technologic Work on Explosives, Explosions, and Flames: Fiscal Year 1967," IC 8387, Aug. 1968, USDI Bureau of Mines, Washington, D.C.

[5] "Texas City Disaster," NFPA *Quarterly*, Vol. 41, No. 1, July 1947, pp. 24–57.

[6] "Nitroparaffins and Their Hazards," NBFU Research Report No. 12, 1959, American Insurance Association (formerly National Board of Fire Underwriters), New York.

[7] "Fire and Explosion Hazards of Organic Peroxides," NBFU Research Report No. 11, 1956, American Insurance Association, New York.

[8] "Spontaneous Heating and Ignition of Coal and Other Mining Products," *Proceedings of 39th Annual Meeting*, National Fire Protection Association, 1935, pp. 311–316.

[9] "Calcium Chloride Treatment of Coal," NFPA *Quarterly*, Vol. 39, No. 4, April 1946, pp. 295–298.

[10] Keil, A. A., *Radiation Control for Fire and Other Emergencies*, National Fire Protection Association, Boston, 1960.

[11] Sercu, C. L., "Chemical Plant Waste Incinerator," NFPA *Quarterly*, Vol. 55, No. 1, July 1961, pp. 90–95.

[12] Laboratory Waste Disposal Manual, Manufacturing Chemists' Association, Inc., Washington, revised November 1972.

NFPA Codes, Standards, and Recommended Practices (see the latest *NFPA Publications and Visual Aids Catalog* for availability of current editions of the following documents)

NFPA No. 43A, Code for the Storage of Liquid and Solid Oxidizing Materials.

NFPA No. 43C, Code for the Storage of Gaseous Oxidizing Materials.

NFPA No. 49, Hazardous Chemicals Data.

NFPA No. 490, Code for the Storage of Ammonium Nitrate.

NFPA No. 491M, Manual of Hazardous Chemical Reactions.

NFPA No. 495, Code for the Manufacture, Transportation, Storage and Use of Explosives and Blasting Agents.

NFPA No. 655, Standard for the Prevention of Sulfur Fires and Explosions.

NFPA No. 704M, Recommended System for the Identification of the Fire Hazard of Materials.

NFPA No. 801, Recommended Safe Practices for Laboratories Handling Radioactive Materials.

Additional Readings

"Ammonium Nitrate: Its Properties and Fire and Explosion Hazards, (a review with bibliography)," IC 7463, June 1948, USDI Bureau of Mines, Pittsburgh.

Anderson, W. V., "Hazards of Organic Phosphates," *Fire Journal*, Vol. 60, No. 6, Nov. 1966, pp. 84–85.

Bahme, C. W., *Fire Officer's Guide to Hazardous Chemicals*, National Fire Protection Association, Boston, 1972.

"Bulk Storage of Fertilizer Grade Ammonium Nitrate," Manual Sheet A-10, Supplement No. 1, 1962, Manufacturing Chemists' Association, Inc., Washington.

Burns, J. J., et al., "Investigation on the Explosibility of Ammonium Nitrate," RI 4994, Aug. 1953, USDI Bureau of Mines, Pittsburgh.

Case Histories of Accidents in the Chemical Industry, a series, Manufacturing Chemists' Association, Inc., Washington.

Chemical Hazards Bulletin, a series, American Insurance Association, New York, issued and revised at will.

Coffee, R. D., "Evaluation of Chemical Stability," *Fire Technology*, Vol. 7, No. 1, Feb. 1971, pp. 37–45.

Condensed Chemical Dictionary, 8th ed., Van Nostrand Reinhold Co., New York, 1971.

Doyle, W. H., "Protection in Depth for Increased Chemical Hazards," *Fire Journal*, Vol. 59, No. 5, Sept. 1965, pp. 5–7.

Factory Mutual Engineering Corporation, *Handbook of Industrial Loss Prevention*, 2nd ed., McGraw-Hill, New York, 1967.

Fawcett, H. H., and Wood, W. S., eds., *Safety and Accident Prevention in Chemical Operations*, Interscience Publishers, New York, 1965.

"Fertilizer Grade Ammonium Nitrate," Manual Sheet A-10, July 1960 revision, Manufacturing Chemists' Association, Inc., Washington.

Gibson, J. R., *Handbook of Selected Properties of Air- and Water-Reactive Materials*, Library of Congress, Washington, 1968.

Guide for Safety in the Laboratory, 2nd ed., Van Nostrand Reinhold Co., New York, 1972.

Hygienic Guide Series (reports on individual chemicals, published periodically), American Industrial Hygiene Association, Westmont, N.J.

Kuchta, J. M., Furno, A. L., and Imhof, A. C., "Classification Test Methods for Oxidizing Materials," RI 7594, 1972, USDI Bureau of Mines, Pittsburgh.

Kuchta, J. M., and Smith, A. F., "Classification Test Methods for Flammable Solids," RI 7593, 1972, USDI Bureau of Mines, Pittsburgh.

Lange, N. A., ed., *Handbook of Chemistry*, 10th ed., Handbook Publishers, Inc., Sandusky, Ohio, 1967.

Mandell, N. C., Jr., "A New Calcium Hypochlorite and a Discriminatory Test," *Fire Technology*, Vol. 7, No. 2, May 1971, pp. 157–161.

"Nitromethane Tank Car Explosions," NFPA *Quarterly*, Vol. 52, No. 4, April 1959, p. 324.

Nuckolls, A. H., "Fire and Explosion Hazards of Ammonium Nitrate Fertilizer Bases," Bulletin of Research No. 20, Dec. 1940, Underwriters' Laboratories, Inc., Chicago.

Pingree, D., "Hay Storage," *Fire Journal*, Vol. 61, No. 4, July 1967, pp. 44–45.

"Precautionary Fire and Explosion Safeguards in the Use of Chlorine Dioxide for Industrial Bleaching," NBFU Research Report No. 7, 1949, American Insurance Association, New York.

Radiation and Monitoring Fundamentals for the Fire Service, International Association of Fire Chiefs, New York, 1955.

Standen, A., exec. ed., *Kirk-Othmer Encyclopedia of Chemical Technology*, 2nd ed., Interscience Publishers, New York.

Stecher, P. G., ed., *The Merck Index*, 8th ed., Merck & Co., Inc., Rahway, N.J., 1968.

Steere, N. V., ed., *Handbook of Laboratory Safety*, The Chemical Rubber Co., Cleveland, 1967.

Van Dolah, R. W., Gibson, F. C., and Murphy, J. N., "Further Studies on Sympathetic Detonation," RI 6903, 1966, USDI Bureau of Mines, Pittsburgh.

Van Dolah, R. W., Gibson, F. C., and Murphy, J. N., "Sympathetic Detonation of Ammonium Nitrate and Ammonium Nitrate-Fuel Oil," RI 6746, 1966, USDI Bureau of Mines, Pittsburgh.

Weast, R. C., ed., *Handbook of Chemistry and Physics*, 55th ed., Chemical Rubber Co., Cleveland, 1974.

Section 3

Chapter 6

EXPLOSIVES AND BLASTING AGENTS

This chapter gives a short description of explosives and explosive materials with emphasis on their fire and explosion hazard. The hazardous nature of explosives has been long recognized, and the rapid increase in their production and use makes it necessary to point out those properties that contribute most to the inherent dangers of these very important industrial and military products. In the industrial field alone, almost 2.67 billion pounds of explosives and blasting agents were used in 1972 compared with 0.72 billion pounds in 1950. Of these totals, approximately 82 percent were used in mining and the remainder used principally in construction operations.

Historically[1] black powder was the first explosive known to man, although fireworks and pyrotechnics were known and used many centuries earlier. The preparation and properties of black powder were described by Roger Bacon in the Thirteenth Century and first used for military purposes in the Fourteenth Century. Black powder was first used for mining operations in the latter part of the Seventeenth Century and it remained the dominant commercial explosive until the latter part of the Nineteenth Century. In 1846 the compound nitroglycerin was first prepared and its explosive properties studied. The extremely hazardous nature of this compound prevented its serious consideration until 1867 when Alfred Nobel made the discovery that nitroglycerin absorbed in an inert material, such as diatomaceous earth, produced a mixture which was relatively safe to handle. This explosive mixture, with many modifications and improvement, remained the predominant commercial explosive until the introduction of modern blasting agents in the mid 1950s. In the meantime use of black powder decreased to an insignificant quantity largely because of its great fire hazard. In less than 20 years, blasting agents, based principally on the sensitization of ammonium nitrate, have taken over approximately 88 percent of the market.[2] This change is based largely on economic considerations and the greatly improved safety with non-nitroglycerin explosive materials.

A. Nature of Explosive Materials

An understanding of the nature of explosive materials is essential before one can understand the fire and explosion potential of these admittedly hazardous products. A definition of a few of the terms to be used will provide a background for future discussions.

Terminology

The following terms are used in this chapter to provide the reader with a uniform understanding of the technical material presented.

Explosive: An explosive is a substance or a mixture of substances which when subjected to the proper stimuli undergoes an exceedingly rapid self propagating reaction characterized by the formation of more stable products (usually gases), evolution of heat, and the development of a sudden pressure effect through the action of this heat on produced or adjacent gases. A somewhat simpler, but less accurate, definition would state that an explosive is any chemical compound, mixture, or device the primary or common use of which is to function by explosion. The term includes, but is not limited to, dynamite, black powder, initiating explosives, detonators, safety fuse, squibs, detonating cord, igniter cord, and igniters.

Blasting Agent: Shall mean any material or mixture consisting of a fuel and oxidizer, intended for blasting, not otherwise classified as an explosive and in which none of the ingredients are classified as an explosive. Additionally, the finished product, as mixed and packaged for use or shipment, cannot be detonated by a means of a Number 8 blasting cap when unconfined.

Explosive Material: Shall include explosives, blasting agents, water gels (slurries), and detonators.

Propellant: Shall mean an explosive material which normally functions by deflagration (burning) and is used for propellant purposes.

Detonator: Shall mean any device containing a detonating charge that is used for initiating detonation in an explosive. The term includes, but is not limited to, electric blasting caps of instantaneous and delay types, blasting caps for use with safety fuse, and detonating cord delay connectors.

Explosion: An explosion is an effect produced by the sudden violent production or expansion of gases and may be accompanied by shock waves or the disruption of enclosing materials or structures or both. An explosion may result from (1) chemical changes, such as accompany detonation of an explosive or the combustion of a flammable gas-air mixture, (2) physical or mechanical changes such as the bursting of a steam boiler, or a high pressure reaction vessel, (3) atomic changes such as occur in a nuclear blast.

Fires and Explosions

A distinction must be made between controlled and unwanted fires and explosions. Controlled combustion reactions are basic to the production of power and necessary for an industrial economy. Likewise, detonation reactions are essential for use by the mining and construction industry. On the other hand, the loss of life and natural resources from unwanted fires and explosions is a matter of national concern. Since fire is a major hazard associated with the utilization of explosives and blasting agents, this chapter will point out the basic nature of these materials and methods of reducing the loss from uncontrolled reactions in these materials.

B. Types of Explosive Materials

While this chapter basically deals with commercial explosives, some of the similarities and differences between commercial and military materials should be considered. Most military explosives have high shattering power and relatively high detonation velocities. Military explosives are often kept in storage for relatively long periods of time and therefore must have good stability. It is essential that these explosives detonate reliably even after storage in a wide variety of conditions. While there are no truly military explosives that are equivalent to the blasting agents used in commercial operations, the military uses commercial type explosives and blasting agents for operations such as road building, air strip preparations, and a wide variety of similar operations.

As stated previously, commercial explosives have a wide range of properties. Explosives to be used in underground operations must have relatively good fume characteristics. This requires formulations which are more nearly oxygen balanced and therefore produce a minimal amount of carbon monoxide and oxides of nitrogen. The most widely used military explosives, such as TNT and RDX, are quite oxygen deficient and therefore produce large quantities of toxic gases. Commercial dynamites normally have fairly good storage life, but blasting agents are more often used soon after manufacture and storage then is not an important factor. Prolonged storage of blasting agents may result in serious deterioration, particularly in hot, humid weather.

Commercial Explosive Types

Explosive materials can be divided into a number of specific types depending on their characteristic properties.[3] The following types are generally recognized in industry and are listed in the general order of decreasing hazard, assuming equal safety precautions are employed.

Primary or Initiating High Explosives: These are quite hazardous materials, but they play a very important role in the utilization of explosive materials. Typical explosives of this type are mercury fulminate, lead styphnate, and lead azide. Because of their hazardous nature they are seldom, if ever, used alone and their principal function is to initiate detonation in less sensitive explosives. These primary explosives are readily detonated by the addition of heat or the application of a mild mechanical shock. They are used almost exclusively as the initiating agent in detonators.

Secondary High Explosives: These are materials which are relatively insensitive to mechanical shock and heat and yet are readily detonated by the shock from a primary explosive. They are much more powerful than the primary explosives. They are used for most military purposes and find considerable application in commercial blasting operations. When unconfined, secondary high explosives can generally be burned without detonating, but one should never attempt to fight a fire in stores of high explosives. Secondary high explosives include such products as dynamite, nitroglycerin, TNT, RDX, and PETN. Because of its sensitivity, nitroglycerin is never used alone. Secondary high explosives are generally cap sensitive which distinguishes them from blasting agents.

Low Explosives or Propellants: These are used primarily for propulsion purposes. They normally function by burning rather than detonation, although a few propellants are susceptible to detonation. Black powder, smokeless powder, and solid rocket fuels fall in this category. Fire constitutes the greatest hazard in the handling and use of propellant explosives.

Blasting Agents: As stated previously, almost 90 percent of all blasting operations in the United States are carried out using non-nitroglycerin materials. By definition, blasting agents do not contain ingredients classified as explosive, and the final product as prepared for use will not initiate to detonation by the action of a Number 8 detonator when unconfined. The most commonly used blasting agent is a fuel-oxidizer system which consists primarily of ammonium nitrate and a fuel such as Number 2 diesel fuel. The formulation is termed "ANFO." The addition of approximately 6 percent fuel oil to specially prepared ammonium nitrate prills produces an amazingly successful blasting material. This combination has the advantage of low cost, satisfactory fume characteristics, and greatly increased safety over the nitroglycerin dynamites. While the combination does not burn readily, it still may transit to a serious detonation in a well-established fire. ANFO does have the disadvantage in that it is difficult or impossible to use it under very wet conditions. Many variations of the basic ANFO formulation have been developed and successfully used. More recently, the addition of powdered aluminum is being employed in certain operations to increase the general strength of the material.

Water Gels or Slurries: Operations where a water resistant explosive material is a necessity, and where higher densities than those which can be obtained with ANFO are desirable, have led to the development of a class of blasting agents known as water gels or slurries. Ammonium nitrate is usually the basic oxidizer in this type of explosive, and it may be sensitized by a variety of materials, the most common of which is powdered or flaked aluminum. The addition of special ingredients, such as paint-grade aluminum, to the mixture may cause the combination to become cap sensitive and therefore, would be a high explosive instead of a blasting agent. Water gels are appreciably more expensive than ANFO, but their safety characteristics are generally very good. Approximately 10 percent of the market has been taken over by water gels.

Nuclear Explosives: Nuclear explosives are not classed as commercial but they are mentioned here because of their future potential. The hazardous nature of the nuclear reaction and the cost of the materials make it somewhat questionable as to whether or not this explosive reaction will become commercial in the near future.

C. Classes of Explosives

The Department of Transportation (DOT)[4] divides commercial explosive materials into separate classes for transportation purposes. Industry has generally accepted this classification system since it corresponds roughly to their hazard in handling, storage, and transportation. These explosive materials are discussed in the order of decreasing sensitivity.

Class A Explosives

Explosives of this class possess detonating or otherwise maximum hazard. It includes dynamite, desensitized nitroglycerin, lead azide, mercury fulminate, black powder, blasting caps, detonating primers, and certain smokeless propellants.

Class B Explosives

Explosives of this class have a high flammable hazard and include most propellant materials. Class B explosives are considered less hazardous than Class A explosives.

Class C Explosives

Explosives of this class include manufactured articles which contain limited quantities of Class A or Class B explosives as one of their components. It includes such materials as detonating cord, explosive rivets, etc. Class C explosives will not normally mass detonate under fire conditions.

Blasting Agents

While blasting agents are recognized as an explosive material, they have not been placed in the classification system. They are generally considered safer than Class A, B, or C explosives and yet, when properly initiated they function in the same manner as a Class A explosive. Not being cap sensitive, they require a strong primer consisting of a Class A explosive with a detonator. As a rule, blasting agents will burn without transit to a detonation reaction.

Other Classification Systems

The Bureau of Alcohol, Tobacco, and Firearms (BATF), of the Department of Treasury, has a classification system based on the type of explosive material involved. In their classification system explosive materials are classified as high explosives, low explosives, and blasting agents. Since some low explosives are as hazardous as high explosives, this classification does not indicate relative hazard. While this system is not generally used industrially, it is working satisfactorily for the control of explosive materials from a security standpoint. This classification is employed in the enforcement of Title 11, Regulation of Explosives, of the Organized Crime Control Act of 1970 (18 U.S.C., Chapter 40). At least annually the BATF director publishes a list of explosives determined to be within the coverage of the law.

Permissible Explosives

While the term permissible explosive is not exactly a classification, it does describe a type of explosive which has been tested and approved[5] by the Department of the Interior as meeting the minimum safety requirements for use in underground coal mines. These materials are modified dynamites or water gels which exhibit reduced tendencies to ignite flammable gas-air or gas-air-coal dust mixtures.

Two-component Explosives

Two-component explosives, also referred to as phosophoric substances, consist of two or more unmixed, commercially manufactured, prepackaged chemicals, including oxidizing chemicals, flammable liquids, or solids that independently are not classified as explosives. When combined, however, the mixture is classified as an explosive and is stored, transported, and handled as an explosive.

D. Manufacture of Explosive Materials

With the possible exception of blasting agents, explosive materials are produced in plants under the close supervision of qualified personnel. While the potential for accidents is relatively high, the safety record is very good, largely because the hazards are well recognized. Fire is a principal cause of accidents, but the normal plant layout keeps this hazard within reasonable limits. Smoking is never allowed near the explosive operations, and the use of flame-producing equipment is allowed only in specific locations under strict safety regulations. The greatly reduced fire potential, and the ease of mixing blasting agents, has resulted in many relatively small mixing plants in widely scattered mining areas. While this is not a universal practice, it is an important variation and the safety practices may vary appreciably.

E. Transportation of Explosive Materials

The U.S. Department of Transportation regulates the transportation of all explosive materials in accordance with regulations set forth in a Code of Federal Regulations Title 49, Chapter 1, Parts 170-189. Copies of these regulations can be obtained from the U.S. Government Printing Office, or from the Bureau of Explosives of the Association of American Railroads. The latest edition of the latter publication is R. M. Graziano's Tariff No. 26, entitled "Hazardous Materials Regulations of the Department of Transporta-

tion." It has a list of "forbidden explosives" which covers materials which cannot be transported in Interstate Commerce. Explosive combinations which are forbidden by the Department of Transportation, are the following:

1. Liquid nitroglycerin.
2. Dynamite (except gelatin dynamite) containing over 60 percent of liquid explosive ingredient.
3. Dynamite having an unsatisfactory absorbent or one that permits leakage of a liquid explosive ingredient under any conditions liable to exist during storage.
4. Nitrocellulose in a dry uncompressed condition in quantity greater than ten pounds net weight in one package.
5. Fulminate of mercury in a dry condition and fulminate of all other metals in any condition except as a component of manufactured articles not hereinafter forbidden.
6. Explosive compositions that ignite spontaneously or undergo marked decomposition rendering the products or their use more hazardous, when subjected for forty-eight consecutive hours or less to a temperature of 167°F (75°C).
7. Explosives containing an ammonium salt and a chlorate.
8. New explosives until approved by the DOT, except that a permit may be granted for transportation and possession for laboratory examination of such explosives when under development by responsible research organizations.
9. Explosives not packed or marked in accordance with the requirements of the DOT.
10. Explosives condemned by the DOT.

Most commercial explosives are now transported over public highways by truck. Military explosives are usually transported by rail, although there is considerable long distance transportation by truck. Fire is the most common cause of accidents in transportation. The most probable point of initiation of fire in truck transportation is the tires. Tire fires are quite common and represent a hazard which is difficult to control because the driver of a truck is often unaware of the fire until it has gained considerable headway. Detonators should not be loaded directly into the truck with high explosives or blasting agents, but the Institute of the Makers of Explosives have recently conducted tests which indicate that the transporting of detonators in a separate compartment on the truck cab can be performed with acceptable safety.

Truck transportation over public highways is of particular concern because there is maximum exposure of the public to fire and explosion hazards. Unfortunately, fires and other types of accident situations tend to draw spectators which increases the danger of casualties. While rail transportation generally provides a lesser hazard to the public, there is an increased danger resulting from the mixing of different types of cargo in a given train load.

F. Storage of Explosive Materials

A primary objective for the storage of most nonexplosive industrial materials is to provide protection for such materials from their surroundings. Because of the hazardous nature of explosive materials, additional factors must be considered. Safety to the industrial workers involved and to the general public in the vicinity of such storage are of primary importance. Since most explosive materials are utilized by the mining and construction industries, these industries have primary concern in training their employees to provide maximum attainable safety. Employees of the explosive manufacturing firms are well aware of the hazards of their occupation and safety is an integral part of their work. However, employees of the mining and construction industries are less likely to be aware of the precautions required to obtain a satisfactory degree of safety. Another factor connected with storage is indirectly related to safety and involves the element of security. In recent years it has become increasingly important to protect the public from the illicit use of explosives which are often obtained by individuals through illegitimate means. Most of the explosives used for illegal purposes are obtained from legitimate stores of the materials. To assist in preventing this misuse of explosives, the law now provides that the Bureau of Alcohol, Tobacco, and Firearms of the Department of Treasury (BATF) shall regulate the manufacture, distribution, and storage of explosive materials. Copies of these regulations may be obtained from that agency.

Storage Magazines

To provide proper storage for the wide variety of explosive materials now being produced, five different types of magazines are recognized. The requirement for these five types of magazines are given in the regulations developed by BATF. The specifications for these magazines and the types of materials to be put in them may be obtained from BATF or can be found in NFPA No. 495, Manufacture, Transportation, Storage and Use of Explosive Materials. The following excerpt from this last reference, describes the various types of magazines and the materials which must be stored in each type.

Type 1 Magazine: A permanent magazine for the storage of explosive materials that are sensitive to initiation by a No. 8 test blasting cap and will mass detonate, such as dynamite and nonelectric blasting caps. Type 1 magazines are bullet resistant, fire resistant, theft resistant, and weather resistant.

Type 2 Magazine: A portable or mobile magazine for outdoor or indoor storage of explosive materials that are sensitive to initiation by a No. 8 test blasting cap and will mass detonate, such as dynamite or nonelectric blasting caps. Type 2 magazines are bullet resistant, fire resistant, theft resistant, and weather resistant except that magazines for indoor storage need not be bullet resistant.

Type 3 Magazine: A portable magazine for the temporary storage of explosive materials while attended. An example is a "day box" at the site for blasting operations. Type 3 magazines are bullet resistant, fire resistant, theft resistant, and weather resistant.

Type 4 Magazine: A permanent, portable, or mobile magazine for the storage of explosive materials that do not detonate when initiated by a No. 8 test blasting cap such as blasting agents, certain water gels, smokeless powder, and black powder, or explosive materials that will not mass detonate such as electric blasting caps having leg wires at least 4 ft long. Type 4 magazines are fire resistant, theft resistant, and weather resistant.

Type 5 Magazine: A permanent, portable, or mobile magazine for the storage of explosive materials that do not detonate when initiated by a No. 8 test blasting cap, such as blasting agents and certain water gels. Type 5 magazines include tanks, tank trailers, tank trucks, semitrailers, bulk trailers, bulk trucks, and bins. Type 5 magazines are theft resistant and outdoor Type 5 magazines are also weather resistant.

Magazine storage aside, there is a widespread practice in industry to transport the relatively insensitive blasting agents to the mining or construction site in truck trailers. The manufacturer parks the trailer in a designated area, dis-

connects the cab, and picks up an empty trailer for the return trip. The blasting agents are then transported by small truck to the site of operations. This is considered as providing adequate safety from the fire hazard. When trucks transporting explosive or blasting agents must stop in transit, or the load must be transferred in transit, there are now provided terminals for explosives-carrying motor vehicles in the vicinity of many large cities. These terminals are well guarded and are operated under strict safety regulations. Requirements for these terminals are contained in NFPA No. 498, Standard for Explosives Vehicle Terminals.

While the probability of the accidental initiation of an explosive while in an approved storage magazine is slight, still accidents have occurred. To safeguard the general public the "American Table of Distances" (Table 3-6A) has been prepared to indicate the isolation distances for stores of explosives from points of contact with the public. This table is periodically revised by the Institute of Makers of Explosives. While blasting agents are appreciably less sensitive than Class A explosives, once they are initiated to detonation, the damage produced by such an accident is comparable with that for Class A explosives. Therefore, the American Table of Distances is used to determine the safe distances for stores of blasting agents from inhabited buildings, railroads, etc. However, because of the lower sensitivity of blasting agents, the separation distances between magazines or stores of explosives and blasting agents, need not be as great as that between stores of explosives as shown in Table 3-6A. Table 3-6B shows these recommended separation distances and the thickness of artificial barricades recommended for these less sensitive materials. When no barricades separate stores, the distances shall be increased as shown in Table 3-6B (Note 2).

G. Fire Protection for Explosive Materials

Fire is a principal cause of accidents involving explosive materials. While burning is the common method of destroying unwanted or deteriorated explosives this does not mean that explosive materials are safe in the environment of an uncontrolled fire. Explosives and blasting agents vary in their sensitivity to fire conditions, but all such materials are liable to produce a disastrous explosion when subjected to fire. The only effective method for fire protection with explosive materials is to eliminate the sources of fire. Smoking or the use of any fire producing equipment should not be permitted where explosive materials are produced, handled, stored, or used. Because of the relative insensitivity of blasting agents, there is always danger that workmen will become careless around these materials. A fire and a subsequent explosion in a blasting agent mix house near Norton, Va.,[6] illustrate the potential hazard from the careless use of heat-producing equipment. In this specific case a mechanic started to repair equipment with a torch without adequately cleaning the equipment. Tons of ammonium nitrate and mixed blasting agents were in the same room where these repairs were being made. Subsequently an intense fire broke out, and only the prompt action of the local fire marshal prevented a disaster. This fire also illustrates the fact that blasting agents may detonate under fire conditions.

H. Fighting Fires in Explosives

Many accidents have occurred from attempts to fight a fire in explosives. Fire in the vicinity of quantities of Class A, B, or C explosives may be fought with a relative degree of safety. *However, no attempt should be made to fight a*

Table 3-6A.　American Table of Distances for Storage of Explosives

Distances in feet

As Revised and Approved by The Institute of Makers of Explosives
November 5, 1971.

EXPLOSIVES		Inhabited Buildings		Public Highways Class A to D		Passenger Railways—Public Highways with Traffic Volume of more than 3,000 Vehicles/Day		Separation of Magazines	
Pounds Over	Pounds Not Over	Barri-caded	Unbarri-caded	Barri-caded	Unbarri-caded	Barri-caded	Unbarri-caded	Barri-caded	Unbarri-caded
2	5	70	140	30	60	51	102	6	12
5	10	90	180	35	70	64	128	8	16
10	20	110	220	45	90	81	162	10	20
20	30	125	250	50	100	93	186	11	22
30	40	140	280	55	110	103	206	12	24
40	50	150	300	60	120	110	220	14	28
50	75	170	340	70	140	127	254	15	30
75	100	190	380	75	150	139	278	16	32
100	125	200	400	80	160	150	300	18	36
125	150	215	430	85	170	159	318	19	38
150	200	235	470	95	190	175	350	21	42
200	250	255	510	105	210	189	378	23	46
250	300	270	540	110	220	201	402	24	48
300	400	295	590	120	240	221	442	27	54
400	500	320	640	130	260	238	476	29	58
500	600	340	680	135	270	253	506	31	62
600	700	355	710	145	290	266	532	32	64
700	800	375	750	150	300	278	556	33	66
800	900	390	780	155	310	289	578	35	70
900	1,000	400	800	160	320	300	600	36	72
1,000	1,200	425	850	165	330	318	636	39	78
1,200	1,400	450	900	170	340	336	672	41	82
1,400	1,600	470	940	175	350	351	702	43	86
1,600	1,800	490	980	180	360	366	732	44	88
1,800	2,000	505	1,010	185	370	378	756	45	90
2,000	2,500	545	1,090	190	380	408	816	49	98
2,500	3,000	580	1,160	195	390	432	864	52	104
3,000	4,000	635	1,270	210	420	474	948	58	116
4,000	5,000	685	1,370	225	450	513	1,026	61	122
5,000	6,000	730	1,460	235	470	546	1,092	65	130
6,000	7,000	770	1,540	245	490	573	1,146	68	136
7,000	8,000	800	1,600	250	500	600	1,200	72	144
8,000	9,000	835	1,670	255	510	624	1,248	75	150
9,000	10,000	865	1,730	260	520	645	1,290	78	156
10,000	12,000	875	1,750	270	540	687	1,374	82	164
12,000	14,000	885	1,770	275	550	723	1,446	87	174
14,000	16,000	900	1,800	280	560	756	1,512	90	180
16,000	18,000	940	1,880	285	570	786	1,572	94	188
18,000	20,000	975	1,950	290	580	813	1,626	98	196
20,000	25,000	1,055	2,000	315	630	876	1,752	105	210
25,000	30,000	1,130	2,000	340	680	933	1,866	112	224
30,000	35,000	1,205	2,000	360	720	981	1,962	119	238
35,000	40,000	1,275	2,000	380	760	1,026	2,000	124	248
40,000	45,000	1,340	2,000	400	800	1,068	2,000	129	258
45,000	50,000	1,400	2,000	420	840	1,104	2,000	135	270
50,000	55,000	1,460	2,000	440	880	1,140	2,000	140	280
55,000	60,000	1,515	2,000	455	910	1,173	2,000	145	290
60,000	65,000	1,565	2,000	470	940	1,206	2,000	150	300
65,000	70,000	1,610	2,000	485	970	1,236	2,000	155	310
70,000	75,000	1,655	2,000	500	1,000	1,263	2,000	160	320
75,000	80,000	1,695	2,000	510	1,020	1,293	2,000	165	330
80,000	85,000	1,730	2,000	520	1,040	1,317	2,000	170	340
85,000	90,000	1,760	2,000	530	1,060	1,344	2,000	175	350
90,000	95,000	1,790	2,000	540	1,080	1,368	2,000	180	360
95,000	100,000	1,815	2,000	545	1,090	1,392	2,000	185	370

Table 3-6A. American Table of Distances for Storage of Explosives   (Cont.)

EXPLOSIVES		Inhabited Buildings		Public Highways Class A to D		Passenger Railways— Public Highways with Traffic Volume of more than 3,000 Vehicles/Day		Separation of Magazines	
Pounds Over	Pounds Not Over	Barri-caded	Unbarri-caded	Barri-caded	Unbarri-caded	Barri-caded	Unbarri-caded	Barri-caded	Unbarri-caded
100,000	110,000	1,835	2,000	550	1,100	1,437	2,000	195	390
110,000	120,000	1,855	2,000	555	1,110	1,479	2,000	205	410
120,000	130,000	1,875	2,000	560	1,120	1,521	2,000	215	430
130,000	140,000	1,890	2,000	565	1,130	1,557	2,000	225	450
140,000	150,000	1,900	2,000	570	1,140	1,593	2,000	235	470
150,000	160,000	1,935	2,000	580	1,160	1,629	2,000	245	490
160,000	170,000	1,965	2,000	590	1,180	1,662	2,000	255	510
170,000	180,000	1,990	2,000	600	1,200	1,695	2,000	265	530
180,000	190,000	2,010	2,010	605	1,210	1,725	2,000	275	550
190,000	200,000	2,030	2,030	610	1,220	1,755	2,000	285	570
200,000	210,000	2,055	2,055	620	1,240	1,782	2,000	295	590
210,000	230,000	2,100	2,100	635	1,270	1,836	2,000	315	630
230,000	250,000	2,155	2,155	650	1,300	1,890	2,000	335	670
250,000	275,000	2,215	2,215	670	1,340	1,950	2,000	360	720
275,000	300,000	2,275	2,275	690	1,380	2,000	2,000	385	770

Note 1: "Explosive materials" means explosives, blasting agents, and detonators.

Note 2: "Explosives" means any chemical compound, mixture, or device, the primary or common purpose of which is to function by explosion. A list of explosives determined to be within the coverage of "18 U.S.C. Chapter 40, Importation, Manufacture, Distribution and Storage of Explosive Materials" is issued at least annually by the Director, Bureau of Alcohol, Tobacco, and Firearms, Department of U.S. Treasury.

Note 3: "Blasting Agents" means any material or mixture, consisting of fuel and oxidizer, intended for blasting, not otherwise defined as an explosive: provided that the finished product, as mixed for use or shipment, cannot be detonated by means of a number 8 test blasting cap when unconfined.

Note 4: "Detonator" means any device containing a detonating charge that is used for initiating detonation in an explosive; the term includes, but is not limited to, electric blasting caps of instantaneous and delay types, blasting caps for use with safety fuses and detonating-cord delay connectors.

Note 5: "Magazine" means any building or structure, other than an explosives manufacturing building, used for the permanent storage of explosive materials.

Note 6: "Natural Barricade" means natural features of the ground, such as hills, or timber of sufficient density that the surrounding exposures which require protection cannot be seen from the magazine when the trees are bare of leaves.

Note 7: "Artificial Barricade" means an artificial mound or revetted wall of earth of a minimum thickness of three feet.

Note 8: "Barricaded" means that a building containing explosives is effectually screened from a magazine, building, railway, or highway, either by a natural barricade, or by an artificial barricade of such height that a straight line from the top of any sidewall of the building containing explosives to the eave line of any magazine, or building, or to a point twelve feet above the center of a railway or highway, will pass through such intervening natural or artificial barricade.

Note 9: "Inhabited Building" means a building regularly occupied in whole or in part as a habitation for human beings, or any church, schoolhouse, railroad station, store, or other structure where people are accustomed to assemble, except any building or structure occupied in connection with the manufacture, transportation, storage or use of explosives.

Note 10: "Railway" means any steam, electric, or other railroad or railway which carries passengers for hire.

Note 11: "Highway" means any street or public road. "Public Highways Class A to D" are highways with average traffic volume of 3,000 or less vehicles per day as specified in "American Civil Engineering Practice" (Abbett, Vol. 1, Table 46, Sec. 3-74, 1956 Edition, John Wiley and Sons).

Note 12: When two or more storage magazines are located on the same property, each magazine must comply with the minimum distances specified from inhabited buildings, railways, and highways, and, in addition, they should be separated from each other by not less than the distances shown for "Separation of Magazines," except that the quantity of explosives contained in cap magazines shall govern in regard to the spacing of said cap magazines from magazines containing other explosives. If any two or more magazines are separated from each other by less than the specified "Separation of Magazines" distances, then such two or more magazines, as a group, must be considered as one magazine, and the total quantity of explosives stored in such group must be treated as if stored in a single magazine located on the site of any magazine of the group, and must comply with the minimum of distances specified from other magazines, inhabited buildings, railways, and highways.

Note 13: Storage in excess of 300,000 lbs. of explosives in one magazine is generally not required for commercial enterprises; however, recommendations for storage of quantities greater than 300,000 lbs. in one magazine will be provided upon inquiry.

Note 14: This Table applies only to the manufacture and permanent storage of commercial explosives. It is not applicable to transportation of explosives or any handling or temporary storage necessary or incident thereto. It is not intended to apply to bombs, projectiles, or other heavily encased explosives.

For transportation purposes, the Department of Transportation in Title 49, Transportation CFR, Parts 1–199, subdivides explosives into three classes:

Class A—Maximum Hazard   Class B—Flammable Hazard
Class C—Minimum Hazard

Note 15: All types of blasting caps in strengths through No. 8 cap should be rated at 1½ lbs of explosives per 1,000 caps. For strengths higher than No. 8 cap, consult the manufacturer.

Note 16: For quantity and distance purposes, detonating cord of 50 to 60 grains per foot should be calculated as equivalent to 9 lbs of high explosives per 1,000 feet. Heavier or lighter core loads should be rated proportionately.

Table 3-6B. Table of Recommended Separation Distances of Ammonium Nitrate and Blasting Agents from Explosives or Blasting Agents[1,6]

Donor Weight		Minimum Separation Distance of Receptor when Barricaded[2] (ft)		Minimum Thickness of Artificial Barricades[5] (in.)
Pounds Over	Pounds Not Over	Ammonium Nitrate[3]	Blasting Agent[4]	
	100	3	11	12
100	300	4	14	12
300	600	5	18	12
600	1,000	6	22	12
1,000	1,600	7	25	12
1,600	2,000	8	29	12
2,000	3,000	9	32	15
3,000	4,000	10	36	15
4,000	6,000	11	40	15
6,000	8,000	12	43	20
8,000	10,000	13	47	20
10,000	12,000	14	50	20
12,000	16,000	15	54	25
16,000	20,000	16	58	25
20,000	25,000	18	65	25
25,000	30,000	19	68	30
30,000	35,000	20	72	30
35,000	40,000	21	76	30
40,000	45,000	22	79	35
45,000	50,000	23	83	35
50,000	55,000	24	86	35
55,000	60,000	25	90	35
60,000	70,000	26	94	40
70,000	80,000	28	101	40
80,000	90,000	30	108	40
90,000	100,000	32	115	40
100,000	120,000	34	122	50
120,000	140,000	37	133	50
140,000	160,000	40	144	50
160,000	180,000	44	158	50
180,000	200,000	48	173	50
200,000	220,000	52	187	60
220,000	250,000	56	202	60
250,000	275,000	60	216	60
275,000	300,000	64	230	60

Note 1: Recommended separation distances to prevent explosion of ammonium nitrate and ammonium nitrate-based blasting agents by propagation from nearby stores of high explosives or blasting agents referred to in the Table as the "donor." Ammonium nitrate, by itself, is not considered to be a donor when applying this Table. Ammonium nitrate, ammonium nitrate-fuel oil or combinations thereof are acceptors. If stores of ammonium nitrate are located within the sympathetic detonation distance of explosives or blasting agents, one-half the mass of the ammonium nitrate should be included in the mass of the donor.

These distances apply to the separation of stores only. The American Table of Distances shall be used in determining separation distances from inhabited buildings, passenger railways and public highways.

Note 2: When the ammonium nitrate and/or blasting agent is not barricaded, the distances shown in the Table shall be multiplied by six. These distances allow for the possibility of high velocity metal fragments from mixers, hoppers, truck bodies, sheet metal structures, metal containers, and the like which may enclose the "donor." Where storage is in bullet-resistant magazines* recommended for explosives or where the storage is protected by a bullet-resistant wall, distances and barricade thicknesses in excess of those prescribed in the American Table of Distances are not required.

Note 3: The distances in the Table apply to ammonium nitrate that passes the insensitivity test prescribed in the definition of ammonium nitrate fertilizer promulgated by the National Plant Food Institute;† and ammonium nitrate failing to pass said test shall be stored at separation distances determined by competent persons and approved by the authority having jurisdiction.

Note 4: These distances apply to nitro-carbo-nitrates and blasting agents which pass the insensitivity test prescribed in the U.S. Department of Transportation (DOT) regulations.

Note 5: Earth, or sand dikes, or enclosures filled with the prescribed minimum thickness of earth or sand are acceptable artificial barricades. Natural barricades, such as hills or timber of sufficient density that the surrounding exposures which require protection cannot be seen from the "donor" when the trees are bare of leaves, are also acceptable.

Note 6: When the ammonium nitrate must be counted in determining the distances to be maintained from inhabited buildings, passenger railways and public highways, it may be counted at $\frac{1}{2}$ its actual weight because its blast effect is lower.

* For construction of bullet-resistant magazines see Chapter 3 of NFPA No. 495, Code for the Manufacture, Transportation, Storage, and Use of Explosives and Blasting Agents.

† Definition and Test Procedures for Ammonium Nitrate Fertilizer, National Plant Food Institute, November 1964.

fire once it has actually reached the explosives. The only safe action under these conditions is to evacuate the area surrounding the fire involving explosives. If relatively small quantities of explosives are in the vicinity of an established fire they should be removed a safe distance from the area and protected from initiation sources. Many believe that fires involving Class C explosives may be controlled safely. However, the Luckenback Pier disaster in Brooklyn, New York, in 1959, shows that even Class C explosives represent a potential hazard. Several tons of detonating cord were stored on a pier which became involved in a serious fire. After an appreciable delay, the entire mass detonated with a loss of a number of lives and property damage in the millions of dollars.

I. Fighting Fires in Blasting Agents

When not confined, incipient fires in blasting agents can be fought with copious amounts of water. The water acts only to cool the burning mass to temperatures below the ignition temperature. When fires develop beyond the incipient stage, the only safe method for handling the situation is to abandon direct fire fighting efforts and evacuate the area in anticipation of a possible explosion. The Norton, Va., fire mentioned previously, is a good example of the necessity of retreating from an established fire. Established fires in blasting agents should be fought with water, and only by means of a remotely controlled system. While it is quite improbable that ammonium nitrate will detonate in a fire, it is entirely possible that it will detonate if stores of blasting agents or other high explosives are in close proximity. Water gels or slurries are even less likely to detonate in a fire than are ANFO type blasting agents but it is recommended that any large scale fire involving these blasting agents should be allowed to burn out rather than to try to fight it. Open drains or other types of confinement for the molten materials may readily result in a disastrous explosion.

SI Units

The following conversion factors are given as a convenience in converting to SI units the English units used in this chapter.

$$1 \text{ ft} = 0.305 \text{ m}$$
$$1 \text{ lb (mass)} = 0.454 \text{ kg}$$
$$\tfrac{5}{9}(°F - 32) = °C$$

Bibliography

References Cited

[1] Dixon, W. T., and Fisher, A. W., eds., *Chemical Engineering in Industry*, Chapter 12, American Institute of Chemical Engineers, New York, 1958.

[2] "Apparent Consumption of Industrial Explosives and Blasting Agents in the United States," Mineral Industry Surveys, 1972, USDI Bureau of Mines, Pittsburgh.

[3] Cook, Melvin A., *The Science of High Explosives*, Reinhold Publishing Co., New York, 1958.

[4] Title 49, Chapter 1, "Transportation," Parts 170–189, *U.S. Code of Federal Regulations*, U.S. Government Printing Office, Washington, D.C., 1972.

[5] Title 30, Chapter 1, Subchapter C, Part 15, "Explosives and Related Articles," *U.S. Code of Federal Regulations*, U.S. Government Printing Office, Washington, D.C., 1969.

[6] Van Dolah, R. W., and Malesky, J. S., "Fire and Explosion in a Blasting Agent Mix House Building, Norton, Virginia," RI 6015, 1962, USDI Bureau of Mines, Pittsburgh.

NFPA Codes, Standards, and Recommended Practices (see the latest *NFPA Publications and Visual Aids Catalog* for availability of current editions of the following documents)

NFPA No. 490, Code for the Storage of Ammonium Nitrate.

NFPA No. 492, Recommended Separation Distances of Ammonium Nitrate and Blasting Agents from Explosives and Blasting Agents.

NFPA No. 495, Standard for the Manufacture, Transportation, Storage and Use of Explosive Materials.

NFPA No. 498, Standard for Explosives Motor Vehicle Terminals.

Additional Readings

"Ammonium Nitrate—Fire—Explosion—Health Hazard," American Insurance Association Special Interest Bulletin 311, July 1966, American Insurance Association, New York.

Bahme, C. W., *Fire Officer's Guide to Dangerous Chemicals*, National Fire Protection Association, Boston, 1972.

Blasters Handbook, 15th ed., Explosives Department, E. I. DuPont de Nemours and Co., Wilmington, Del., 1966.

Damon, Glenn H., "Blasting Agents: History, Hazards and Protection," *Fire Journal*, Vol. 59, No. 2, Mar. 1965.

———, "Chemical Engineering in the Explosives Industry," Chapter 12, *Chemical Engineering in Industry*, American Institute of Chemical Engineers, New York, 1958.

Davis, T. L., *The Chemistry of Powder and Explosives*, John Wiley & Sons, New York, 1941–3.

Dick, Richard A., "The Impact of Blasting Agents and Slurries on Explosives Technology," IC 8560, 1972, USDI Bureau of Mines, Pittsburgh.

Ellern, H., *Military and Civilian Pyrotechnics*, Chemical Publishing Co., New York, 1968.

Fordham, S., *High Explosives and Propellants*, Pergammon Press, London, 1966.

Grant, Charles H., "Metallized-Slurry Boosting: What It Is and How It Works," *Coal Age*, Vol. 71, No. 4, pp. 90–91.

Hay, J. E., and Watson, R. W., "Mechanisms Relevant to the Initiation of Low-Velocity Detonations," *Annals of the New York Academy of Sciences*, Vol. 152, Oct. 1968, pp. 621–635.

Kit, B., and Evered, D. S., *Rocket Propellant Handbook*, The Macmillan Co., New York, 1960.

Kinney, Gilbert F., *Explosive Shocks in Air*, The Macmillan Company, New York, 1962.

Langefors, U., and Kihlstrom, B., *The Modern Technique of Rock Blasting*, John Wiley & Sons, Inc., New York, 1963.

Litchfield, E. L., Hay, M. H., and Monroe, J. S., "Electrification of Ammonium Nitrate in Pneumatic Loading," RI 7139, 1968, USDI Bureau of Mines, Pittsburgh.

Mason, C. M., and Aiken, E. G., "Methods for Evaluating Explosives and Hazardous Materials," IC 8541, 1972, USDI Bureau of Mines, Pittsburgh.

McAdam, R., and Westwater, R., *Mining Explosives*, Oliver and Boyd, Edinburgh, 1958.

Meidl, H. H., *Explosive and Toxic Hazardous Materials*, Glencoe Press, Beverly Hills, 1970.

Prugh, Richard W., and Rucker, Klaus G., "Static Electricity Hazard in the Pneumatic Loading of Blasting Agents," *Proceedings of 5th Symposium on Rock Mech.*, University of Minnesota, 1962.

Robinson, R. V., "Water Gel Explosives—Three Generations," Canadian Mining and Metallurgical Bulletin, Vol. 62, No. 692, 1969, pp. 1317–1325.

"Safety Recommendations for Sensitized Ammonium Nitrate Blasting Agents," IC 8179, 1963, USDI Bureau of Mines, Pittsburgh.

Taylor, J., *Detonation in Condensed Explosives*, Clarendon Press, Oxford, 1952.

Teller, Edward, Talley, Wilson K., Higgins, Gary H., and Johnson, Gerald W., *The Constructive Uses of Nuclear Explosives*, McGraw-Hill Book Company, New York, 1968.

Urbanski, Tadensz, *Chemistry and Technology of Explosives*, 3 vols., The Macmillan Company, New York, 1964.

Van Dolah, R. W., et al., "Explosion Hazards of Ammonium Nitrate Under Fire Exposure," RI 6773, 1966, USDI Bureau of Mines, Pittsburgh.

———, "Review of Fire and Explosion Hazards of Flight Vehicle Combustibles," IC 8137, 1963, USDI Bureau of Mines, Pittsburgh.

Van Dolah, R. W., Gibson, F. C., and Murphy, J. N., "Sympathetic Detonation of Ammonium Nitrate and Ammonium Nitrate-Fuel Oil," RI 6746, 1966, USDI Bureau of Mines, Pittsburgh.

———, "Further Studies on Sympathetic Detonation of Ammonium Nitrate and Ammonium Nitrate-Fuel Oil," RI 6903, 1966, USDI Bureau of Mines, Pittsburgh.

Van Dolah, R. W., Mason, C. M. and Forshey, D. R., "Development of Slurry Explosives for Use in Potentially Flammable Gas Atmospheres," RI 7195, 1968, USDI Bureau of Mines, Pittsburgh.

Watson, R. W., Hay, J. E., and Becker, K. R., "Sensitivity of Ammonium Nitrate-Based Explosive Compositions," RI 7840, 1974, USDI Bureau of Mines, Pittsburgh.

Chapter 7

PLASTICS AND OTHER POLYMERICS

Plastics comprise a group of materials consisting primarily of organic substances of high molecular weight (resins). They are solid in a finished state although at some stage of manufacture plastics can be made to flow into a desired shape, usually through the application of heat or pressure or both. Combustibility characteristics of different plastics vary widely.

There are about 30 major classes of plastics or polymer groupings. In addition to the polymers, most finished plastics products contain plasticizers, colorants, fillers, stabilizers, reinforcing agents, lubricants, or other special additives. The variation of individual plastic product formulations runs into the thousands. The ultimate form of each product, whether it appears in solid sections, films and sheets, foams, molded forms, synthetic fibers, pellets, or powders, has a significant effect on the fire properties of individual plastic products. For this reason it is important to test finished products under conditions which simulate the "end-use" environment.

The packaging, storage, and shipping precautions that are customarily observed for ordinary combustible materials apply generally to most plastics. The plastics themselves are in most cases combustible. NFPA No. 231B, Standard for Storage of Cellular Rubber and Plastics Materials, contains recommendations for the Storage of plastic foams when stored up to 20 ft high inside buildings as packaging, fabricated products, or bulk stock. No special shipping requirements for plastics (other than cellulose nitrate) have been adopted by the Department of Transportation.

Manufacture of basic plastics employs most of the standard operations of chemical synthesis. It almost always involves flammable ingredients or solvents. On the other hand, plants which manufacture articles from plastics by molding or machining will have far less fire hazards; indeed, many converting plants have no flammable liquids in their operations.

In recent years, 20 percent of U.S. tonnage has gone into building construction use, aside from furnishings, and the trend is upward. Much of the increase in plastics tonnage is due to ability to tailor compositions with physical and chemical properties for specific uses. It must be recognized that, as with metals, quantitative values assigned to a generic group by a physical or fire test may not apply to all members of that group.

Because of the thousands of variations possible, due to the number of basic polymer types and the modifications which are commercially available, it is virtually impossible to assign a single meaningful fire test value to a plastic group. Flammability characteristics are also influenced by the nature of the plastic additives and the form which the final product takes. Thus flammability tests should be designed to show how each product will perform under "end-use" conditions. The emphasis has been, therefore, to devise performance tests, which examine sizeable components, instead of small-scale comparison tests used as production controls. The small scale tests are, however, useful for research and screening purposes. The large-scale tests, simulating actual fire conditions, are more realistic for product evaluation.

A. Plastics Terminology

Following is a glossary of terms referred to in later sections of this chapter:

Accelerator: A chemical used to speed up a chemical reaction. Most often, as in vulcanizing rubber, the accelerator is an agent used to assure uniform reaction of a primary agent, such as a catalyst, or a crosslinking material. Typical in plastics use are amines, cobalt chloride, or cobalt naphthenate to ensure that peroxygen catalysts act completely and at lower temperatures.

Additive: Any material mixed with a resin to modify its processing or end-use properties. The resulting mix usually is called a "plastic" to distinguish it from the "resin" or principal ingredient. Additives may be dyes, pigments, powdered fillers for stiffening, plasticizers for flexibility, fibers to reinforce, antioxidants, lubricants to aid flow into or release from a mold, or fire retardants.

Binders: The resins in a plastic mixture that hold together all of the other ingredients. They are usually a product of polymerization or a naturally occurring substance of high molecular weight.

Blowing Agent: A material which releases gas upon heating so that the plastic in which it is mixed will expand into foam. The gas may result from boiling of a liquid, or from decomposition of the blowing agent (foaming agent).

Blown Tubing: A thin film made by extruding a tube and simultaneously inflating it with air while hot; distention may be 20 times the diameter of the tube as extruded. The process does not use solvents or a chemical blowing agent, so it is free from fire hazards of those materials. Most thin polyethylene packaging film is made as blown tubing. When a tubing is flattened and wound on rolls it is called "layflat" tube. Edges may be trimmed or slit to give two separate films.

Casting: Flowing material into place with little or no pressure, as contrasted with forcing material into place by molding.

Catalyst: A chemical which initiates or affects the rate of chemical reaction but is itself not permanently changed by the reaction. As used in the plastics industry, "catalyst" usually refers to those chemicals which cause a polymerization reaction to take place but which in the process are themselves permanently changed. In plastics, catalysts are chiefly agents which cause additional polymerization of monomers; they may be peroxygen compounds, which decompose on heating or chemical influence, or metal alkyls, or halides of the aluminum and titanium families.

Copolymers: High molecular weight compounds produced when two or more monomers are involved in a polymerization process.

Crosslinking: The establishing of chemical bonds between adjacent molecules so as to make a network which will reduce solubility or resist flow on heating. The amount of crosslinking may be enough to render the plastic highly resistant to flow at temperatures up to thermal decomposition, in which case the plastic is said to be a thermoset. Also, the number and character of chemical bonds between original molecules may be such as to reduce solubility and flow without much change in softening temperature.

Curing: Crosslinking, or themosetting, to render a plastic relatively insoluble. It is also used to mean removal of solvent or water to make an article harder.

Depolymerization: Reversion to original monomer when a polymer is heated. For polymers, depolymerization usually does not occur appreciably below 500°F, and is accompanied by the formation of other products of thermal decomposition. Above 800°F the rate of depolymerization can be very fast for some plastics, and is the usual mechanism by which plastics provide fuel for their combustion.

Extruder: A machine for softening plastic and pushing it through a die to provide continuous profiles such as sheets, filaments, or pipe. It consists of a cylindrical barrel and internal screw which rotates to compress the material, smear it against the heated barrel, and mix it to obtain uniform pressure and temperature of plastic.

Extrusion: The process of passing softened plastic under pressure, through a die to make an essentially continuous profile; the equipment is called an extruder.

Fabrication: The making of articles by machining, cementing, heat-sealing, or thermoforming of preformed sheets, rods or tubes. The term is used in contrast to "processing."

Fillers: Materials that modify the strength and working properties of a plastic. They may be used to increase heat resistance and alter the dielectric strength. A wide variety of products are used including wood flour, cotton, sisal, glass, and clay.

Film: A general term for plastic not more than 0.01 in. thick, regardless of the process used to make it. "Foil" is used today only to describe metal. Many plastic films for packaging are a composite of two films or one film lacquered or hot-melt coated to improve heat-sealability or barrier properties. Such composites may be called a film or a laminate.

Finishing: This term has three distinct meanings: (1) removal of burrs or flash by filing, sanding, or tumbling, (2) buffing or waxing to polish surfaces, and (3) application of decorative or marking treatment, as by painting or metal plating.

Flash: Unwanted projections from molded articles resulting from flow of plastic into space between matching parts of a mold. The term has no fire connotation.

Foam: Plastic with many small gas bubbles. It is called cellular plastic. Rigid foams have rapidly reached large volume production as thermal insulation boards for construction, cups for hot and cold drinks, trays for prepackaged meats, and shock-resistant packaging, while flexible foams are used for furniture padding, insulation of outer garments, and soft drape upholstery.

Foaming Agent: The same as blowing agent.

Forming: The process in which the shape of plastic pieces, such as sheet, rod or tube, are changed to a desired configuration.

Gate: This term has three definitions: (1) that portion of a mold which admits plastic directly to the cavity which produces desired shape, (2) that portion of a plastic which lies in the gate portion of a mold, or (3) a screen of wire, glass, or plastic which prevents the operator's hands from being caught between the closing parts of a mold.

Inhibitor: A material added to prevent or retard an undesired chemical reaction. The primary definition is a material (usually amine or phenol type) used in a concentration of less than 1 percent in shipping and storing monomer to prevent polymerization by heat or catalyst. The term is occasionally used to mean an antioxidant or material to improve resistance to weathering; for this purpose "stabilizer" or "antioxidant" is preferred over "inhibitor."

Initiators: Substances that speed up or cause polymerization reactions to take place and in the process are themselves permanently changed by the reaction. Organic peroxides, which are capable of being fire and explosion hazards, are widely used for this purpose in the plastics industry. Initiators are frequently erroneously referred to as catalysts in the plastics industry.

Laminate: A composition of several layers of plastic firmly adhered by partly melting one or more of the layers, by an adhesive or by impregnation. Laminates may be flexible films for packaging or rigid sheets of two different colors, which are used for nameplates made by engraving through one color. High pressure laminates are rigid stock made in presses at pressures above 400 psi for counter tops or electrical insulation by impregnating phenolic, melamine, or epoxy resins into paper, fabric, or wood and molding the assembly into a single dense sheet.

Lubricant: Material added to improve feeding of powder or granules into molding or extrusion machines, to improve flow of molten plastic through machines and into molds, or to prevent adhesion of plastic to molds; the last of these uses is called "mold-release." Materials must be nonvolatile to prevent separation from plastic and smearing of surface of moldings. Typical lubricants are zinc stearate, carnauba wax, and silicone oil.

Molding: The process of forcing plastic into a cavity to achieve a desired shape. The term is used in contrast to one form of casting that is taken to mean filling a mold with little or no force.

Monomers: The small starting molecules, usually gaseous or liquid, used to produce the polymer resins (see Part B of this chapter for a further discussion of monomers).

Plasticizers: Organic materials added to plastics to make the finished product more flexible or to facilitate compounding. Some plasticizers increase the combustibility of the plastic while others serve as flame retardants.

Plastics: According to the ASTM definition, these are materials that contain as an essential ingredient an organic substance of large molecular weight, are solid in their finished state, and at some stage in their manufacture of processing into finished articles can be shaped by flow.

Polymers: Large molecules made by combining smaller molecules by chemical reaction.

Polymerization: The process by which molecules of a monomer are made to add to themselves or other monomer in a repetitive way to give a much longer chain-like molecule.

Processing: This term has the meaning in the plastics industry of converting polymers into useful articles by molding or extrusion from granules, depositing film from solvent, or laminating resin and reinforcement. The term is used in contrast to fabricating. Most often the molding operation uses heat but is entirely or largely a physical rather than a chemical process.

Promotor: See "Accelerator."

Reinforced Plastic: A plastic with a filler which significantly increases flexural, impact, or tensile strength. Additives are usually glass, asbestos, cotton, or nylon fibers. Reinforced plastics may be thermoplastic granules for injection molding, or use large areas of reinforcement as in layup molding or pulp molding.

Resin: By the ASTM definition, resin is a solid, semisolid, or pseudosolid organic material which has indefinite and often high molecular weight.

Sheet: A general term for plastics 0.01 in. and thicker, regardless of method of manufacture.

Stabilizer: A material added to prevent or retard an undesired chemical reaction. When used to prevent polymerization, the preferred term is "inhibitor." Stabilizers are usually present in less than one percent. They may be antioxidants, screening agents for ultraviolets, or chemicals to neutralize decomposition products during hot processing.

Thermoforming: The process of stretching or bending a plastic sheet which has been softened by heating.

Thermoplastic: The capability of a material to be repeatedly softened by heating and stiffened by cooling. As with glass, the marked change in fluidity is accompanied by little or no chemical change. Typical applications of thermoplastics are acrylic tail lamp lenses, polyethylene squeeze bottles, and vinyl phonograph records. The term is used in contrast to thermosetting plastics.

Thermosetting Plastics: These are plastics which may be softened by heat but on continued heating undergo chemical reaction which causes hardening, and which—like a hard boiled egg—cannot be resoftened for useful flow at temperatures below that of decomposition. Typical applications of thermosets are phenolic electric plugs and melamine heavy duty dishware. When a plastic is chemically treated, even in absence of heat, so as to crosslink or reduce flow on heating, it is sometimes said to be a thermoset.

B. Plastics Manufacturing

The plastics industry can be regarded as having three broad areas of processing; although distinct in concept, they may be conducted in the same or different plants. First is the manufacturing of the basic plastic, sometimes including compounding with colorants or other additives. These operations may have the hazards of large quantities of flammable liquids or gases. Second is the conversion of the plastics materials into useful articles by molding, extrusion, or casting, all of which usually involve heating the plastic so it will flow into a shape that is retained when the plastic is cooled. Although chemical reactions are not often a significant part of these operations, the plastics industry refers to them as "processing." Third, and finally, there are the largely mechanical operations of bending, machining, cementing, decorating, and polishing, which are termed "fabricating."

These three areas quite well categorize fire and health hazards. It is important to recognize how much more hazardous may be the synthesis of a given plastic as compared to its use in molding or extrusion. Some plants nominally doing only converting or molding may be conducting a chemical operation with flammable or reactive materials.

Flammable Solvents

Flammable organic solvents will be found in nearly every plastics plant. They may be used in very small quantities to apply adhesives, lacquers, or paints to molded or fabricated items; in large amounts to coat plastic on cloth, paper, leather, or metal or on metal belts from which a dried film will be stripped. In these uses, the choice of solvents and hazards in their use is not different from most lacquering operations. There may be some increase in hazard when solvents are applied to plastics, particularly when printing or coating on fast-moving films, as plastics usually have high electrical resistivity; they generate and retain static charges more readily than paper or cotton fabric.

Use of solvents in small plants is increasing for the preparation of rigid or flexible foam plastic. The plastic is moistened with solvent and heated above the boiling point of the solvent in a closed mold or extruder; upon release of pressure the boiling solvent expands the resin and produces a bubbled structure. Another type of foaming process heats a resin containing a chemical additive which evolves gas, usually nitrogen, carbon dioxide, or steam. Either the solvent or the chemical agent is called a blowing agent. The most common rigid foam is made from beads of polystyrene moistened with about 10 percent pentane or similar hydrocarbon. The pentane does not soften the resin at room temperature, but does at the low pressure steam temperature used in molding to shape or extruding as sheet. It is imperative that sources of electric spark or flame be avoided. Resin is usually shipped from the manufacturer with the hydrocarbon blowing agent already mixed with it. Containers will have free vapor of pentane, and should be opened outdoors or with good exhaust ventilation. Expanded articles should be aged under forced hot air to remove nearly all flammable blowing agent before shipping.

Flexible urethane foams for upholstery and garments, or rigid foams for pour-in-place construction or refrigeration insulation, are blown by generation of steam and carbon dioxide which are by-products of formation of the urethane resin from basic ingredients. Urethane foams of lower density may be made with a low-boiling hydrocarbon in the resin mixture to increase the expansion.

For elimination of the fire hazards from solvents in the foaming process, consideration should be given—for both styrene and urethane foams—to replacing hydrocarbon blowing agents with fluorinated hydrocarbons, similar to the nonflammable refrigerants.

Foams of polyvinyl chloride are used in garments and upholstery. These are usually called "expanded vinyl," as the extent of foaming is limited so as to provide an essentially continuous outer surface. These are usually made with the chemical blowing agent azodicarbonamide, also called azobisformamide. Above 300°F it provides nitrogen gas at a controlled rate, is essentially nonhazardous in the proportions used, and does not give off flammable vapors. Drums of the reagent should be cooled with water when exposed to fire, but such reagents do not have nearly the rapid burning or explosive hazards of peroxygen materials.

Improper handling of flammable liquids has caused serious fires in plastics plants. Most frequent causes have been failures to recognize the importance of static spark prevention, explosionproof electrical equipment, and vapor removal systems. (Flammable liquid hazards are discussed in Chapter 3 of this Section.) See Publications of the American Insurance Association,[1] the Manufacturing Chemists Association,[2,3] The Society of the Plastics Industry[4,5,6] and NFPA Standards Nos. 30, 33, 35, 70, 77, 91 and 231 for further information on safeguards to observe in the handling and use of flammable liquids as they apply or may apply to the plastics industry.

Monomers

Monomers are the second kind of flammable liquid used in the plastics industry with special hazards due to their chemical reactivity. Some are gases, and a few are relatively nonvolatile liquids. A monomer molecule may be regarded as a prefabricated group of atoms which is used as a building block from which are made the large molecules called polymers. When the polymer contains only two or three units of nonomer it is called a "dimer" or "trimer." Polymers comprise from several hundred to many thousands of units of monomer, and are spoken of as high molecular weight monomers. When two or more chemically different monomers are combined to give a single large polymer molecule, the product is called a copolymer. The monomer used in lesser proportions is called a comonomer.

A polymer containing many monomer units may be a solid or viscous liquid; in either case it is called a resin. If used directly for molding, the resin may be called a plastic. When fillers, colorants, or other additives are used to make a material for molding, the polymeric ingredient is usually called the resin and the mixed material is called the plastic.

Monomer usage can be illustrated by the three broad areas of processing. First step is synthesis of chemical intermediates, as converting benzene to liquid styrene monomer, which has fluidity like gasoline, a flashpoint of 90°F, and a boiling point of 295°F. Second is manufacturing solid resin, as by polymerization of liquid styrene monomer to solid polystyrene, which softens at about 200°F, flows at 500°F, and does not give off vapors in significant quantities until heated above 650°F. Third is making the plastic composition which will be used for molding; this is called compounding, although rarely does it make any new chemical compound. Compounding may involve mixing with other resins, plasticizers, colorants, or reinforcing materials. In some plastic molding materials there may be no additives; or the additives may be incorporated while the monomer is being polymerized.

The hazards of the synthesis plant are basically those of a chemical plant using processes described in Chapter 9 of Section 4 in this HANDBOOK. In addition, most plants making resins will have three other hazards: (1) monomers which may polymerize with attendant evolution of heat thus accelerating the reaction, even to boiling and rupture of container; (2) monomers which may form unstable peroxides; and (3) organic peroxygen compounds (organic peroxides) which are used as catalysts to polymerize monomer to resin. It should be recognized that many small plants now handle large amounts of monomer with peroxygen catalysts. They may or may not have adequate facilities for fire protection, or personnel trained to insure safe practice. One example of the overlapping nature of molding and resin synthesis operations is a plant which impregnates liquid polyester resin into reinforcing glass fibers for molding of boats or containers. The liquid polyester resin is purchased as a viscous liquid of low volatility and good stability. Such a plant may add styrene monomer to the extent of a third of the weight of polyester to increase fluidity for penetrating fibers, to increase speed of catalyzed polymerization, and to provide harder moldings. In this case, the plastic converter has the hazards of a chemical synthesis plant, rather than the lesser fire and reactivity hazards of a plant which merely shapes an involatile molding powder.

Polymerization of monomers in shipment or storage is prevented by refrigeration or by an inhibitor. This is usually an amine or phenol added in quantities of less than one per cent, which prevents formation of peroxide or other agents which may cause the monomer to polymerize. Prevention of polymerization and its attendant evolution of considerable heat requires that the exposure to heat, radiation, atmospheric oxygen, or peroxides not be such as to overcome the effectiveness of the amount of inhibitor used. Preparation of uninhibited monomer for polymerization is done by distilling it away from the inhibitor, by chemical removal of inhibitor, or by adding more catalyst to overcome the inhibitor.

Plastics are generally without skin or inhalation toxicity, being chemically quite inert and nonvolatile at ordinary temperatures. On heating above 500°F some will slowly revert to monomer or other decomposition products. For many, the rate can be rapid above 800°F, leading to generation of combustible gases. Data obtained by test apparatus (ASTM D 1929)[7] are not precise but are a guide to temperature and rate of decomposition. By this test nearly all plastics have "flash ignition temperatures" from 750° to 950°F. Flash ignition temperature is that at which enough vapors are produced in a vertical electric muffle furnace with a small draft of air to ignite the vapors with a small flame at the top of the test furnace. Wood and paper have such temperatures around 300°F.

Most of the commercially available monomers are listed in Table 3-11A as to flash point, boiling point, flammable limits, extinguishment methods, and health hazards. Heat, ultraviolet, and other radiation may cause polymerization. Unless clearly stated otherwise, all should be regarded as "flammable liquids" (i.e., flash point below 100°F). Most are classified as unstable or reactive liquids in NFPA No. 49, Hazardous Chemicals Data. The only significant exceptions are a few high-boiling esters of polymerizable alcohols, as diallyl phthalate. Chemical reactivity of monomers varies greatly although predictably with composition. With the possible exception of vinyl acetate, all should be considered as having skin and inhalation toxicity. For further information on the various monomers see MCA's Chemical Safety Data Sheets[8] and Chem-Card Manual.[9]

Catalysts (Peroxygen and Others)

In the plastics industry, catalysts are primarily used to cause monomer molecules to link together in addition polymerization or condensation polymerization. For condensation polymerization, catalysts are usually acids, bases, or salts and pose no special hazard. For addition polymerization, catalysts are most often peroxygen compounds, as benzoyl peroxide, butyl hydroperoxide, butyl percarbonate, or peracetic acid; all are customarily called peroxides. Such catalysts are also used to cross-link resins, to make them less soluble.

In the absence of specific information to the contrary, all these organic peroxygen materials should be regarded as highly flammable, even explosive. Many are capable of violent decomposition upon heating or severe impact. Yet some, because they are so stable, or because they are shipped and used in solution in a plasticizer of low volatility, are regarded as of no more hazard than a hydrocarbon of high boiling point. For polymerization, peroxygen catalysts are usually dissolved in monomer to less than one per cent concentrations. Accordingly, the hazards are when the catalyst is alone, or when the conditions of use of the catalyst-monomer mixture are not controlled. U.S. annual production of organic peroxygen compounds now exceeds 16 million pounds. Over 95 percent of this is used for polymerization; the rest for bleaching and chemical synthesis. These peroxides are used today in hundreds of small plants which may not fully appreciate their hazard. Benzoyl peroxide ignites with about one-fifth the flame exposure required to ignite "black powder" explosive, although the explosive force of benzoyl peroxide is only one third that of black powder.

Cushioning materials used around packages of peroxygen compounds should be noncombustible in view of the potent oxidizing nature of these agents. Unless approved by manufacturers, only glass containers should be used for solutions or for liquid peroxygen agents. Even small quantities should not be stored in screw-cap containers because friction of unscrewing the cap can cause explosive breakdown of the liquid or of the solid precipitated in the cap threads.

The more reactive undiluted peroxygen compounds should be stored in isolated buildings, or vaults in hillsides with easily vented roof pointed away from buildings occupied by personnel. Small quantities may be stored in metal sheds on the outside of masonry wall away from traffic areas. Water spray on the roof for cooling should be provided for sheds exposed to hot sun. Only the amount of peroxygen compounds needed for a day should be brought into a laboratory, and it is usually best stored in a refrigerator without an internal ignition source and with a magnetic latch. Larger quantities needed for manufacturing should be handled only by trained employees. For further information on handling and use of peroxygens see NFPA No. 33, Standard for Spray Finishing Using Flammable and Combustible Materials; NFPA No. 49, Hazardous Chemicals Data; AIA Research Reports Nos. 1[1] and 11,[10] and SPI Publication FPC 19,[10, 11] the latter aimed at the nontechnically trained machine operator.

A few chemical types other than peroxygen compounds are used to initiate additional polymerization. Chief of these is azobisisobutyronitrile, which is not shock sensitive and on heating decomposes rapidly but not explosively. It can be used in place of benzoyl peroxide and is also used in some foaming operations because at processing temperatures above 300°F it evolves nitrogen gas.

The advent of low pressure processes for making polyethylene and polypropylene has brought large use to two very flammable classes of catalysts, the metal alkyls and metal halides. Typical are triisopropyl aluminum, tetraethyl titanium, and trifluoride. Many of the metal alkyls will spontaneously ignite in air, and are customarily handled in hydrocarbon solvent. The metal halide catalysts are not combustible but react vigorously with water or moist air, producing large amounts of hydrofluoric or hydrochloric acid. Metal halides are often used as complexes in diethyl ether. The combustible nature of such solutions is heightened by the heat of reaction between metal halide and water, which can rapidly raise the temperature above the boiling point of ether.

Fire fighting techniques for metal halides or alkyls are specialized and therefore the manufacturers of these materials should be consulted. In the absence of such information blanketing with magnesium carbonate or oxide is the general practice; water or carbon dioxide must not be used. Fortunately, it appears that the use if metal halides on alkyls as catalysts will only be for polymerizations carried out by large chemical and petroleum companies, which are prepared to handle metal alkyls and halides.

Dusts

Although when in solid massive form many plastics can be difficult to ignite and will not continue to burn on removal of exterior fuel, nearly all will burn rapidly in the form of dust, and if dispersed in air can be explosively ignited by a spark, flame, or metal surface above 700°F. Dust explosions should be considered possible when operations use pulverized plasic, convey larger grains through pneumatic tubes, or produce dust by machining or sanding in finishing work. Wood flour or finely ground dyestuffs also require safeguarding when being added to plastics.

It is practice to speak of plastic pellets for injection or extrusion molding as molding powder. In reality they are not pulverized material but cubes or cylindrical pellets about $\frac{1}{10}$ in. across. They are usually screened by the maker to remove finer particles to permit more uniform feeding to machines. They are free from hazard of dust explosion; however, dust can be generated by abrasion of these particles when conveyed in a long pneumatic system. Trimmings from injection molding are cut to small size for reuse alone or by blending with fresh (virgin) molding pellets. This cutting is called "regrinding," although it is a shearing and impacting action deliberately intended to avoid making dust and fine particles. Regrinding usually generates some fine powder, and dust hazards should be considered when much regrinding is done.

Compounding of resins refers to mixing with such additives as dyes, pigments, fillers, mold-release or flow-improving lubricants, plasticizers for flexibility, ultraviolet or heat stabilizers, or modifying resins. For rapid mixing, most of these are charged to mixing equipment as fine powders, and dust explosions are possible with any of these ingredients. Some compounding, especially for reclaiming of once-processed materials, is done at molding machines in plastics plants of all types.

Generally, the basic chemical structure of the resin governs the explosibility of its dust. Incorporation of wood flour, cotton flock, or other combustible fillers usually increases the explosibility of dust. Incorporation of low percentages of fire retardants has but little effect on explosibility of dusts.

The hazards of dust, including plastics, are discussed in more detail in Chapter 8 of this Section and explosion prevention, venting and suppression techniques in Section 15, Chapter 7. See also NFPA No. 63, Fundamental Principles for the Prevention of Dust Explosions; NFPA No. 68, Guide for Explosion Venting; NFPA No. 69, Explosion Prevention Systems; NFPA No. 77, Recommended Practice on Static Electricity; and NFPA No. 654, Standard for the Prevention of Dust Explosions in the Plastics Industry, and SPI publication FPC 1[12] for further information on prevention of dust explosions.

Processing—Converting into Useful Articles

Heating processes are used to make plastics, to put them into physical form suitable for further processing, and to convert them to useful shapes and finished articles. Most polymers are first produced as a mass that is pulverized to incorporate additives, or as fine beads or fluff from polymerization in water dispersion. Thorough drying, often to less than 0.1 percent moisture is sometimes essential to produce moldings without steam bubbles or defects due to hydrolysis by chemical interaction at molding temperatures around 500°F. The various types of heat processing are:

Extrusion: The process of passing softened plastic under pressure through a die to make an essentially continuous profile is called extrusion; the equipment is called an extruder. Except for the obsolete method of processing of cellulose nitrate or regenerated cellulose (viscose), solvents are not used in this process and softening is only by heat. The extruder is a machine for softening plastic and pushing it through a die to provide continuous sheets, filaments, or pipe. It consists of cylindrical barrel and internal screw which rotates to compress the material, smear it against the heated barrel, and mix it to obtain uniform pressure and temperature of plastic. The extruder is usually fed with thermoplastic molding powder for production of shapes; a finer powder or precipitated fluff may be used if additives are to be mixed with it. Heating is almost always by electrical resistance heaters wrapped around the outside of the barrel and by the severe shearing action of the screw; electric induction heating is rare. Steam and oil, often used to heat extruders for rubber, are rarely used today for plastics because processing temperatures required are often above 400°F. The extruder is used with various takeoff devices to coat papers, insulate wire, or to provide a melt for blow molding of bottles. As the hot plastic leaves the die, it may be cooled by air as it moves on a conveyor, or by immersion in a trough of water. Principal fire hazards with extruders are dust accumulation during charging of the feed hopper, arcing of leads on strip heaters, overheating of the thermocouple-controlled zone, or failure of a heater to keep the barrel hot enough to maintain fluidity for release of pressure on the melt.

Molding: The process of forcing plastic into a cavity to achieve a desired shape. The term is used in contrast to one form of casting that is taken to mean filling a mold with little or no force. The ten types of molding processes are:

1. Blow Molding is the process of forming hollow articles, such as bottles and toys. It is usually done by first extruding a tube of plastic and then closing a mold around a section of the hot tube, inflating the tube by air or nitrogen to distend the tube into contact with the mold. The mold is then cooled and opened, and the blown object is ejected and the cycle repeated.

2. Cold Molding is shaping of a material in a mold with little or no heat, followed by transfer to a heating medium for curing. Inorganic cold molding is done with mica, clay, or glass powders, or sometimes with a sodium silicate binder. Synthetic resins are rarely used in organic cold molding. Usually the binder is asphaltic with some petroleum oil as a softener, and a large amount of filler, such as clay or asbestos, is included for such end products as heat-resistant electric plugs. The solvent is baked out in subsequent heating.

3. Compression Molding is the process of charging molding powder or preformed briquettes into a mold, closing the mold, applying heat, and then compressing the mold halves or forcing a separate ram into one half of the mold to cause the material to fill the cavity. The process is rarely used for thermoplastics because of the time required to alternately heat and cool the cavity for removal of rigid parts. Compression molding is standard for thermosetting plastics, which can be removed without distortion from a hot mold.

4. Extrusion Molding is the same as "extrusion." Sometimes, it is used to mean use of an extruder to melt and force plastic into a closed mold, as in making large slabs or cylinders.

5. Injection Molding is the principal method for molding thermoplastics and some thermosets. It is similar to die-casting of metals. Plastic is heated in one chamber, the hot material is injected into a cold mold, allowed to solidify, removed from the mold, and the cycle repeated. Plastic is usually charged as a "molding powder." Heating is by electric resistance heaters around the injection cylinder or barrel. Plastic is forced into and through the heating zone, and injected into the mold cavity by a ram or screw. The injection cylinder may contain one to twenty times the amount of material used in each injection shot. All times and temperatures are controlled, usually automatically. It is common practice to make injection molds with from one to several hundred cavities, not all of the same shape or size. Although cavities are cooler than the material injected, they are often heated with oil, steam, water, and glycol, or resistance heaters.

6. Lay-up Molding is the process for molding boats and other large items from resin and reinforcing fibers. A liquid resin (polyester or epoxy) and a reinforcement, which may be fabric or a nonwoven mat of glass or asbestos fibers, or a mixture of resin and chopped glass fiber sprayed from a gun are deposited on the surface of a mold. The resin is often hand rolled to penetrate the reinforcement. Catalyst is mixed with the resin prior to applying it to the fibers. Curing may be in the open air, in an oven, or in matched metal molds. It also may be in a press or in a bag with air pressure to keep the stock under pressure until it is polymerized.

7. Pulp Molding is a process in which a slurry of fibers in water is sprayed onto a screen or porous form, or sucked onto an immersed screen to make a felted preform which approximates the shape of the finished article. The water in the slurry may contain a dispersion or solution of resin. On drying, such preforms may be ready for molding at temperatures which will cause the resin to become a continuous binder or the preforms may be sprayed or immersed to receive plastic for subsequent molding.

8. Rotational Molding is a method for coating the inside of a container, or for coating the inside of a mold which is then opened to remove a hollow article. Finely powdered plastic or molding granules are placed in a heated cavity which is rotated about two axes to distribute the plastic. The material may be thermoplastic or thermosetting, and the rotating mold may be heated from 300° to 700°F before or during the process or continually.

9. Solvent Molding is not a term that is currently favored. It has been used for "cold molding," in which a solvent used to assist flow is subsequently baked out. It also has been used in coating the inside or outside of a container with a solution of plastic, plastisol, or organosol. Heat is applied to remove the solvent or coalesce the resin.

10. Transfer molding is essentially injection molding where the injection chamber contains but one shot or charge of material.

Thermoforming: The process of stretching or bending a plastic sheet which has been softened by heating. The sheet may be sucked into a cavity (vacuum forming), blown into cavity (pressure forming), or pushed into shape by a contoured ram (plug assist or snap-back forming). The operation is usually in a machine with automatic cycling and temperature controls. A sheet is heated by infrared at one station; moves on to a forming station, and sometimes to another station for cooling on jigs. Although the temperature of a sheet rarely exceeds 400°F in thermoforming, some hazard exists through accidental contact with incandescent heaters; or evolution of volatile combustibles on prolonged heating can cause rapid ignition and spread of fire.

Casting: Flowing material into place with little or no pressure, as contrasted with forcing material into place by molding. Several distinct processes are called casting: (1) solvent casting, in which a solution or dispersion of plastic is flowed onto a polished metal belt or drum, heat is applied to evaporate the solvent or coalesce dispersion, and the film is stripped free; (2) sheet casting, in which monomer or partially polymerized viscous syrup is poured into a cavity and polymerized in place to rigid plastic such as sheets of acrylic plastic which are made by pouring syrup into a cell made from two sheets of glass clamped around a peripheral gasket; (3) potting or encapsulating, in which a liquid, usually an epoxy, phenolic, or silicone resin, is poured around electrical components in a split cavity mold; and (4) melt-casting of film, in which an extruder is used to melt plastic and flow it onto a belt or drum to provide a polished or textured surface to one side of film. Processes (1) and (2) may have hazards of flammable solvent or monomer. Process (2) usually employs peroxygen catalysts, although the amount in casting mix is less than 1 percent. Processes (3) and (4) are without solvent or peroxygen types of catalyst, but may have hazards of electrically heated equipment.

Drying: In resin manufacturing drying is usually done in rotary drums with hot air or nitrogen. Direct combustion gases are not used because they would contaminate resin and be a fire hazard. Molding and extrusion plants may dry in trays in gas or electric forced air ovens, or in hopper dryers, which are cannisters which comprise the charging hopper for the machines and through which dry air from 160° to 300°F is forced.

Compounding: Mixing additives into previously formed resin on masticating rolls or calenders, as for rubber, or in kneading mixers or screw extruders of varied design is called compounding. Rolls and kneaders are heated by high pressure steam or heat transfer fluids such as diphenyl ether. Fluid heating is unlikely to permit overheating and may remove some heat produced by the severe physical shearing action in the mixer. Heating fluids may be a hazard if escaping as fine spray from packings. This fog can be ignited by flame or electric arc (see Sec. 4, Chap. 3 for a discussion of heat transfer fluids).

Screw extruders have largely displaced rolls and kneaders for compounding, because they provide better control, continuous output, and less exposure of hot plastic to air. Temperatures range from 300° to 650°F, depending on which plastic is being processed. The upper range is beyond that practical for heating fluid, so electric resistance heating (rarely electric induction) is almost universally employed. Heater bands are required to fuse the resin in the feed section at the upstream end of the extruder barrel. The temperature of the plastic at the downstream end of the barrel may exceed heater band temperature by 100°F due to frictional heat. It is not uncommon for controllers to stick, permitting resistance heaters to run much above the temperature set for the thermocouple controller. In most cases, the character of extrudate will markedly change well before heater bands get hot enough to be a source of ignition. Cleanliness in the compounding areas is vital to reduce the hazard of ignition from overheated bands where dusty material or flammable liquids are used or where flammable vapors may be generated.

Molding end extrusion operations, for shaping articles as well as for compounding, will also have hazards associated with local overheating of electrical components. Some areas within equipment may not be regularly purged by flow of plastic material. Material remaining in such areas can be subject to too high a temperature, or be kept too long at a normally acceptable temperature. Decomposition may then take place, not often forcefully, but with the release of gases that may be combustible. It is good practice to start heating such equipment first at the downstream end to insure fluidity of material and hence relief of pressure.

Electrical wiring in heat processing equipment on plastic machines should be installed in accordance with applicable provisions of NFPA No. 70, National Electrical Code.

Hydraulic Pressure Systems

Hydraulic systems are used to clamp molds and to provide pressure to rams or screws which force molten plastic into molds by compression, transfer, or injection molding. The molten plastic may be at pressures up to 20,000 psi, but the hydraulic systems are normally less than 2,000 psi. Petroleum fluids have been used in plastic operations where heating elements were generally below 600°F; the same fluids have a poor record in die casting because pots for the molten metal are at much higher temperatures.

Fire resistant water-glycol or water-oil emulsions or "synthetic" fluids are available for hydraulic systems. Substituting fire resistant fluids for petroleum fluids should be done only with advice from makers of the hydraulic system components. Precautions and procedures for changing from one type of hydraulic fluid to another are summarized in "Fire Hazards of Hydraulic Fluids in Processing Plastics"[13] and "Recommended Practice for Use of Fire-Resistant Fluids for Fluid Power systems"[14]. See Chapter 4 of Section 4 of this HANDBOOK for further information on fluid power systems.

Static Electricity

Many operations in plastics plants generate static electricity. Because plastics are such good electrical insulators, static electricity on them can rapidly build up to spark discharge, a hazardous condition if dust or flammable vapors are present. Operations which can generate static are stripping of films from production or printing equipment or rapid passage of films across rolls or guides; belts for power transmission also are a significant source of static discharge. Because of their low water-absorption and high resistivity, plastics cannot have their static charge dissipated by high ambient humidity as practiced in cotton, wool, and paper mills. Attention should be given to grounding of equipment and insuring that tinsel conductors firmly contact moving films or filaments. Care should also be given to separating vapor and dust hazards from machines where static electricity ignition sources could develop. See NFPA No. 77, Recommended Practice on Static Electricity, and SPI publications FPC 1[12] and FPC 6[15].

C.   Basic Chemical Types of Plastics

The major groups of plastic materials are described in the following summaries. It must be recognized, however, that there are hundreds of variations for each group which are sold under thousands of individual trade names. Brief descriptions of 25 of the major groups of plastics follow, including identification of the monomers used to produce each, their principal uses, and remarks about major variants. Table 3-7A lists current trade names with each trademark identified by class of plastic and name of manufacturer. This arrangement is designed to facilitate obtaining information on a plastic identified only by its trade name.

Where ASTM has agreed on an abbreviation for a material, that abbreviation is noted in the heading that follows which introduce descriptions of the major plastics groups. Manufacturers have been urged to offer the ASTM abbreviation along with trade mark names to aid in the rapid identification of the material. This is particularly important for plastic products used in building construction, such as ABS (see Styrene Polymers and Copolymers).

Acetal Resins

The acetal resins are made primarily by the polymerization of formaldehyde. Copolymers of acetal are also produced. These materials form one of the strongest and stiffest thermoplastics. The products show good resistance to organic solvents; however, they do react with strong acids or bases. These plastics are widely used for equipment gears, automotive equipment, plumbing parts and appliances.

Table 3-7A. Trade Names of Plastics

(Extracted from Modern Plastics Encyclopedia, copyright 1974 by McGraw-Hill Book Company.)

Trade Name	Class of Plastic	Manufacturer
Ablaphene	Formophenolic resins	Plastimer, S.A.
Absafil	Fiberglass reinforced ABS	Fiberfil Div., Dart Industries, Inc.
Abselex	Extruded ABS sheeting	British Celanese Ltd.
Absinol	ABS	Allied Resinous Products, Inc.
Abson	ABS resins and compounds	Goodrich, B. F., Chemical Co.
Acelon	Cellulose acetate film	May & Baker, Ltd.
Acetophane	Cellulose acetate film	UCB-Sidac
Aclar	CTFE film	Allied Chemical Corp., Plastics Div.
Aclar	CTFE fluorohalocarbon films	Allied Chemical Corp., Fibers Div., Plastic Film Dept.
Acpol	Polyester resin	Freeman Chemical Corp., Div. H. H. Robertson Co.
Acralen	Styrene-butadiene latex	Farbenfabriken Bayer A.G.
Acralen	Ethylene-vinyl acetate polymer	Verona Div., Baychem Corp.
Acronal	Acrylate polymers and copolymers	Badische Anilin- & Soda-Fabrik A.G.
Acronal	Copolymer acrylic ester dispersions	BASF Wyandotte Corp.
Acrylafil	Fiberglass reinforced styrene-acrylonitrile	Fiberfil Div., Dart Industries, Inc.
Acryliglas	Acrylic-coated glass fabric	Natvar Corp.
Acrylite	Acrylic molding compounds; cast acrylic sheet	American Cyanamid Co., Industrial Chemicals & Plastics Div.
Acryloid	Acrylic modifiers for PVC; coating resins	Rohm & Haas Co.
Adrub RTV	Flexible mold-making rubber	Adhesive Products Corp.
Aerazote	Expanded polyethylene sheet	Bakelite Xylonite Ltd.
Aeroflex	Polyethylene extrusion	Anchor Plastics Co.
Aerotuf	Polypropylene extrusions	Anchor Plastics Co.
Ajicoat	Polyamino acid	Ajinomoto Co. of N.Y., Inc.
Akulon	Polyamide 6, 6/6	Akzo Plastics nv
Alathon	Polyethylene resins	Du Pont de Nemours, E. I., & Co.
Alfane	Thermosetting epoxy resin cement	Atlas Minerals & Chemicals Div., ESB, Inc.
Algil	SAN filaments	Bakelite Xylonite Ltd.
Algoflon	Polytetrafluoroethylene resins	Montedison S.p.A.
Alkathene	Low density polyethylene polymers and compounds	Imperial Chemical Industries Ltd., Plastics Div.
Alkor	Furane resin cement	Atlas Minerals & Chemicals Div., ESB, Inc.
Alkydal	Alkyd resins	Farbenfabriken Bayer A.G.
Amberlac	Modified alkyd resins	Rohm & Haas Co.
Amberol	Phenolic resins	Rohm & Haas Co.
Amer-Plate	PVC sheet material	Ameron Corrosion Control Div.
Aminocel	Urea-formaldehyde resins	Montedison S.p.A.
Aminolac	Melamine-formaldehyde-butyl	Plastimer, S.A.
Ampol	Cellulose acetates	American Polymers, Inc.
Ancorene	High impact styrene extrusions	Anchor Plastics Co.
Ancorex	ABS extrusions	Anchor Plastics Co.
Anvyl	Vinyl extrusions	Anchor Plastics Co.
Araldite	Epoxy resins and hardeners	CIBA-GEIGY Corp., Plastics & Additives Div.
Armodur	Rigid PVC sheets	M & B Plastics Ltd.
Armorbond	Vinyl bonded to metal tubing	Lakeland Plastics, Inc.
Arochem	Modified phenolic resins	Ashland Chemical Co., Div. Ashland Oil, Inc.
Arofene	Phenolic resins	Ashland Chemical Co., Div. Ashland Oil, Inc.
Aroflint	Polyester-epoxy resins	Ashland Chemical Co., Div. Ashland Oil, Inc.
Aron Alpha	Cyanoacrylate adhesive	Vigor Co., Div. B. Jadow & Sons
Aroplaz	Alkyd resins	Ashland Chemical Co., Div. Ashland Oil, Inc.
Aropol	Unsaturated polyester resins	Ashland Chemical Co., Div. Ashland Oil, Inc.
Aroset	Acrylic resins	Ashland Chemical Co., Div. Ashland Oil, Inc.
Arothane	Polyester resin	Ashland Chemical Co., Div. Ashland Oil, Inc.
Artfoam	Rigid urethane foam	Strux Corp.
Astradur	High impact vinyl copolymer sheets	Dynamit Nobel of America, Inc.
Astradur	Extruded PVC sheets	Dynamit Nobel, A.G.
Astraglas	Plasticized pressed PVC sheets	Dynamit Nobel of America, Inc.
Astraglas	Plasticized PVC sheets	Dynamit Nobel, A.G.
Astralit	Vinyl copolymer sheets	Dynamit Nobel of America, Inc.
Astralit	Calendered PVC sheets	Dynamit Nobel, A.G.
Astralon	Vinyl and vinyl copolymer sheets	Dynamit Nobel of America, Inc.
Astralon	PVC sheets	Dynamit Nobel, A.G.
Astraprint	PVC copolymer sheets	Dynamit Nobel of America, Inc.
Astratherm	Calendered rigid PVC film	Dynamit Nobel, A.G.
Astratherm	Rigid PVC film	3M Co.
Astrel 360	Polyarylsulfone thermoplastic	ICI America, Inc.
Atlac	Polyester resins	Crespi, Giovanni, S.p.A.
Aurora	PVC sheeting	
Bakelite	Polyethylene, ethylene copolymers, epoxy, phenolic, polystyrene, phenoxy and vinyl resins	Union Carbide Corp., Chemicals & Plastics
Barex	Acrylic barrier resin	Vistron Corp., Sub. The Standard Oil Corp. of Ohio
Baycryl	Acrylic dispersions	Farbenfabriken Bayer A.G.
Baydur	Skinned molded rigid polyurethane foam	Farbenfabriken Bayer A.G.
Baygal	Polyester for casting resins	Farbenfabriken Bayer A.G.
Baylon	Low density polyethylene	Farbenfabriken Bayer A.G.
Baymidur	Isocyanates	Farbenfabriken Bayer A.G.
Baysilone	Silicones	Farbenfabriken Bayer A.G.
Beetle	Urea molding compounds	American Cyanamid Co., Industrial Chemicals & Plastics Div.
Benvic	Polyvinyl chloride compounds	Solvay & Cie S.A.
Betalux	TFE-filled acetal	Westlake Plastics Co.
Bexoid	Cellulose acetate sheet	Bakelite Xylonite Ltd.
Bexphane	Polypropylene film	Bakelite Xylonite Ltd.
Bexthene	Polyethylene film	Bakelite Xylonite Ltd.
Blanex	Cross-linked polyethylene compounds	Reichhold Chemicals, Inc.
Blapol	Polyethylene compounds and color concentrates	Reichhold Chemicals, Inc.
Blavin	Vinyl extrusion compounds and color concentrates	Blane Chemical Div., Reichhold Chemicals, Inc.
Blendex	ABS resins for modifying PVC	Marbon Div., Borg-Warner Corp.
Blu-Sil	Silicone cold molding compound	Perma-Flex Mold Co.
Bolta Flex	Vinyl sheeting and film	General Tire & Rubber Co., Chemical/Plastics Div.

Table 3-7A. Trade Names of Plastics (Contd.)

Trade Name	Class of Plastic	Manufacturer
Boltaron	ABS or PVC rigid plastic sheets	General Tire & Rubber Co., Chemical/Plastics Div.
Bonyl	Biaxially-oriented nylon film	Kohjin Co.
Bronco	Supported vinyl or pyroxylin	General Tire & Rubber Co., Chemical/Plastics Div.
Budene	Polybutadiene	Goodyear Tire & Rubber Co., Chemical Div.
Butaprene	Styrene-butadiene latexes	Firestone Plastics Co., Div. Firestone Tire & Rubber Co.
Butofan	Styrene-butadiene copolymers	Badische Anilin- & Soda-Fabrik A.G.
Cabulite	Cellulose acetate butyrate film and sheets	May & Baker, Ltd.
Calthane	2-component urethanes and epoxies	Cal Polymers, Inc.
Capran	Nylon films and sheet	Allied Chemical Corp., Fibers Div., Plastic Film Dept.
Capran	Nylon 6 film	Allied Chemical Corp., Plastics Div.
Carbamac	Oil-modified urethanes	Commercial Solvents Corp.
Carolux	Filled urethane foam, flexible	North Carolina Foam Industries, Inc.
Cassopal	Urea resins	Cassella Farbwerke Mainkur A.G.
Castethane	Castable molding urethane elastomer system	Upjohn Co., CPR Div.
Castomer	Urethane elastomer systems	Baxenden Chemical Co.
Castomer	Urethane elastomer and coatings	Isocyanate Products Div., Witco Chemical Corp.
Cat-A-Lac	2-component epoxy paint	Bostik-Finch, Inc., Sub. USM Corp.
Cat-A-Last	2-component polyurethane paint	Bostik-Finch, Inc., Sub. USM Corp.
Celanar	Polyester film	Celanese Plastics Co.
Celanex	Thermoplastic polyester	Celanese Plastics Co.
Celastoid	Sliced cellulose acetate sheet	British Celanese Ltd.
Celatron	High-impact polystyrene sheet	British Celanese Ltd.
Celcon	Acetal copolymer resins	Celanese Plastics Co.
Cellastine	Extruded acetate sheeting, tubes, rods	British Celanese Ltd.
Cellidor	Plastified cellulose esters	Farbenfabriken Bayer A.G.
Cellit	Unplastified cellulose esters	Farbenfabriken Bayer A.G.
Cellofoam	Polystyrene foam board	United States Mineral Products Co.
Cellonex	Cellulose acetate sheets	Cynamit Nobel, A.G.
Cellothene	Polyethylene-coated cellulose film	UCB-Sidac
Cellu-Cushion	Low density polyethylene foam	Cellu Products Co.
Celluliner	Resilient expanded polystyrene foam	Gilman Brothers Co.
Cellulite	Expanded polystyrene foam	Gilman Brothers Co.
Celmar	Polypropylene/Glass fiber fabric laminate	British Celanese Ltd.
Celpak	Rigid polyurethane foam	Dacar Chemical Products Co.
Celthane	Rigid polyurethane foam	Dacar Chemical Products Co.
Chem-o-seal	Rubber-based emulsions	Chemical Products Corp.
Chem-o-set	Crosslinked PVC dispersion	Chemical Products Corp.
Chem-o-sol	PVC plastisol	Chemical Products Corp.
Chem-o-thane	Polyurethane elastomer casting compounds	Chemical Products Corp.
Chemfluor	Fluorocarbon plastics	Chemplast, Inc.
Chemglaze	Polyurethane-based coating materials	Hughson Chemicals, Lord Corp.
Chemgrip	Epoxy adhesives for TFE	Chemplast, Inc.
Chempol	Protective coatings and polyurethane foam resins	Freeman Chemical Corp., Div. H. H. Robertson Co.
Cheratolo	Straight phenol resins	Montedison S.p.A.
Cinemoid	Cellulose acetate film	British Celanese Ltd.
Clarifoil	Cast cellulose acetate film	British Celanese Ltd.
Claritex	Wire-reinforced cellulose acetate sheeting	British Celanese Ltd.
Clocel	Rigid urethane foam systems	Baxenden Chemical Co.
Clopane	PVC film and tubing	Clopay Corp., Plastic Film Div.
Cloudfoam	Polyurethane foam	International Foam Div., Holiday Inns of America, Inc.
Co-Mer 7	Polyamide ester	Nypel, Inc.
Co-Rezyn	Polyester resins and gel coats, pigment pastes	Interplastic Corp., Commercial Resins Div.
Cobex	PVC sheet	Bakelite Xylonite Ltd.
Cobocell	Cellulose acetate butyrate tubing	Cobon Plastics Corp.
Coboflow	Teflon tubing	Cobon Plastics Corp.
Cobonol	Polyethylene tubing	Cobon Plastics Corp.
Cobothane	Ethylene-vinyl acetate tubing	Cobon Plastics Corp.
Cobovin	Reinforced PVC tubing	Cobon Plastics Corp.
Collacral	Acrylic polymers and copolymers	Badische Anilin- & Soda-Fabrik A.G.
Conathane	Polyurethane casting, potting, tooling and adhesive compounds	Conap, Inc.
Conolite	Polyester laminate	Woodall Industries, Inc.
Cordo	PVC foam and films	Ferro Corp., Composites Div.
Cordoflex	Polyvinylidene fluoride solutions, etc.	Ferro Corp., Composites Div.
Coro-Foam	Urethane foam systems	Cook Paint & Varnish Co.
Corvic	Vinyl polymers	Imperial Chemical Industries Ltd., Plastics Div.
Courlose	Water-soluble cellulose ethers	British Celanese Ltd.
Coverlight	Coated nylon fabric	Reeves Brothers, Inc.
Covicol	Vinyl compounds	Colcarburo S. A.
Covol	Polyvinyl alcohol	CPC International Inc., Industrial Div.
Crilat	Acrylic polymer solutions and emulsions	Montedison S.p.A.
Crystic	Unsaturated polyester resins	Scott Bader Co.
Curithane (Series)	Polyaniline polyamine	Upjohn Co., Polymer Chemicals Div.
Curon	Polyurethane foam	Reeves Brothers, Inc.
Cyanaprene	Polyurethane	American Cyanamid Co., Organic Chemicals Div.
Cycolac	ABS resins	Marbon Div., Borg-Warner Corp.
Cycoloy	Alloys of synthetic polymers with ABS resins	Marbon Div., Borg-Warner Corp.
Cycopac	ABS resins	Marbon Div., Borg-Warner Corp.
Cycovin	Self-extinguishing ABS graft polymer blends	Marbon Div., Borg-Warner Corp.
Cyglas	Glass-filled polyester molding compound	American Cyanamid Co., Industrial Chemicals & Plastics Div.
Cymel	Melamine molding compounds, crosslinking agents	American Cyanamid Co., Industrial Chemicals & Plastics Div.
Dacovin	PVC compounds	Diamond Shamrock Chemical Co., Plastic Div.
Daiflon	CTFE molding powders, pellets, dispersions	Daikin Kogyo Co.
Daiso Dap	Diallyl phthalate resin	Osaka Soda Co.
Daisolac	Chlorinated polyethylene	Osaka Soda Co.
Daltoflex	Urethanes	ICI America Inc.
Dapon	Diallyl phthalate resins	FMC Corp., Organic Chemicals Div.
Daran	Polyvinylidene chloride emulsion coatings	Grace, W. R., & Co., Organic Chemicals, Dewey & Almy Chemical Div.
Daratak	Polyvinyl acetate homopolymer emulsions	Grace, W. R., & Co., Organic Chemicals, Dewey & Almy Chemical Div.
Darex	Styrene-butadiene latices	Grace, W. R., & Co., Organic Chemicals, Dewey & Almy Chemical Div.

Table 3-7A.   Trade Names of Plastics (Cont.)

Trade Name	Class of Plastic	Manufacturer
Darvic	PVC sheet	Imperial Chemical Industries Ltd., Plastics Div.
Daubond	Epoxy, urethane and elastomer adhesives	Daubert Chemical Co.
Daycollan	Urethane elastomer products	Dayco Corp., Dayflex Plastics Div.
Deconyl	Nylon coating powders	Plastic Coatings Ltd.
Delrin	Acetal resin	Du Pont de Nemours, E. I., & Co.
Demilan	Melamine formaldehyde molding powders	Kreidl, Rutter & Co., Vereinigte Chemische Fabriken
Derakane	Vinyl ester resins	Dow Chemical Co.
Deresit	Phenolic resins; laminating papers	Kreidl, Rutter & Co., Vereinigte Chemische Fabriken
Deroton	Polyester molding compound	Imperial Chemical Industries Ltd., Plastics Div.
Desamin	Melamine formaldehyde resins; laminating papers	Kreidl, Rutter & Co., Vereinigte Chemische Fabriken
Descovil	Supported PVC sheeting	Crespi, Giovanni, S.p.A.
Desmoflex	Polyurethane casting resin	Farbenfabriken Bayer A.G.
Desmopan	Thermoplastic polyurethane elastomer	Farbenfabriken Bayer A.G.
Desmophen	Polyesters and polyethers for polyurethane foam	Farbenfabriken Bayer A.G.
Desurit	Urea formaldehyde molding powders	Kreidl, Rutter & Co., Vereinigte Chemische Fabriken
Dexel	Cellulose acetate molding powders	British Celanese Ltd.
Diakon	Acrylic polymers and compounds	Imperial Chemical Industries Ltd., Plastics Div.
Diarex	Polystyrene	Mitsubishi Monsanto Chemical Co.
Diaron	Melamine resins	Reichhold Chemicals, Inc.
Dielux	Acetal	Westlake Plastics Co.
Dienite	Polybutadiene thermosetting resin	Firestone Synthetic Rubber & Latex Co.
Diofan	Vinylidene chloride copolymers	Badische Anilin- & Soda-Fabrik A.G.
Diolen	Polyester	Akzo Plastics nv
Dion	Polyester resins	Diamond Shamrock Chemical Co., Plastic Div.
Dolphon	Epoxy resin and compounds, polyester resins	Dolph, John C., Co.
Dorvon	Molded polystyrene foam	Dow Chemical Co.
Dri-Lite	Expanded polystyrene	Poly Foam, Inc.
Dural	Acrylic-modified rigid PVC compounds	Alpha Chemical & Plastics Corp.
Duramac	Oil-modified alkyds	Commercial Solvents Corp.
Duranyl	Rigid vinyl compound	Mastic Corp.
Duraplex	Alkyd resins	Rohm & Haas Co.
Durethan	Nylon 6	Farbenfabriken Bayer A.G.
Durethene	Polyethylene film	Sinclair-Koppers Co.
Durocel	Cellular vinyl compound	Mastic Corp.
Dutral-CO	Ethylene-propylene copolymers	Montedison S.p.A.
Dutral-TER	Ethylene-propylene-diene terpolymers	Montedison S.p.A.
Dyal	Alkyd and styrenated alkyd resins	Sherwin Williams Chemicals, Div. Sherwin-Williams Co.
Dyalon	Urethane elastomer material	Thombert, Inc.
Dylan	Low- and medium-density polyethylene	Sinclair-Koppers Co.
Dylark	Styrene copolymer	Sinclair-Koppers Co.
Dylene	Polystyrene resin and oriented sheet	Sinclair-Koppers Co.
Dylex	Latex	Sinclair-Koppers Co.
Dylite	Expandable polystyrene beads, extruded sheet, etc.	Sinclair-Koppers Co.
Dynadur	Unplasticized PVC tubes, sheets, rods	Dynamit Nobel, A.G.
Dynalen	Polyethylene tubes	Dynamit Nobel, A.G.
Dynapol	Polyethylene terephthalate copolymers	Dynamit Nobel, A.G.
Easypoxy	Epoxy adhesive kits	Conap, Inc.
Eccofoam	Plastic, ceramic, silicone foams	Emerson & Cuming, Inc.
Eccosil	Silicone resins	Emerson & Cuming, Inc.
Edilac	Polyvinyl acetate copolymer dispersions	Montedison S.p.A.
Edistir	Polystyrene	Montedison S.p.A.
Edivil	Polyvinyl acetate homopolymer dispersions	Montedison S.p.A.
Edolite	Phenolics	Mitsubishi Gas Chemical Co.
Ekavyl	Polyvinyl chloride	Plastimer, S.A.
El Rexene	Polyethylene, polypropylene, polystyrene and ABS resins	Rexene Polymers Co., Div. Dart Industries, Inc., Chemical Group
Elaprim	Butadiene-acrylonitrile copolymers	Montedison S.p.A.
Elastolur	Urethane elastomer coatings	BASF Wyandotte Corp.
Elastonate	Isocyanate prepolymers	BASF Wyandotte Corp.
Elastonol	Polyester polyols	BASF Wyandotte Corp.
Elastosil	Silicone sealants	Wacker-Chemie GmbH
Electroglas	Cast acrylic sheet, rod, tube	Electro-Seal Glasflex Corp.
Eltex	High density polyethylene	Solvay & Cie S.A.
Elvace	Acetate-ethylene copolymers	Du Pont de Nemours, E. I., & Co.
Elvacet	Polyvinyl acetate emulsions	Du Pont de Nemours, E. I., & Co.
Elvacite	Acrylic resins	Du Pont de Nemours, E. I., & Co.
Elvamide	Nylon resins	Du Pont de Nemours, E. I., & Co.
Elvanol	Polyvinyl alcohols	Du Pont de Nemours, E. I., & Co.
Elvax	Vinyl resins; acid terpolymer resins	Du Pont de Nemours, E. I., & Co.
Embafilm B	Cellulose acetate butyrate film	May & Baker, Ltd.
Enka Perlon	Polyamide 6	Akzo Plastics nv
Enkalon	Polyamide 6	Akzo Plastics nv
Ensocote	PVC lacquer coating	Uniroyal, Inc.
Epi-Rez	Basic epoxy resins	Celanese Resins, Div. Celanese Coatings Co.
Epi-Tex	Epoxy ester resins	Celanese Resins, Div. Celanese Coatings Co.
Epikote	Epoxy resin	Shell Chemical Co.
Epo-Tek	Epoxies	Epoxy Technology, Inc.
Epocap	Two-part epoxy compounds	Hardman, Inc.
Epocast	Epoxies	Furane Plastics, Inc.
Epocrete	Two-part epoxy materials	Hardman, Inc.
Epocryl	Epoxy acrylate resin	Shell Chemical Co.
Epolast	Two-part epoxy compounds	Hardman, Inc.
Epomarine	Two-part epoxy compounds	Hardman, Inc.
Epomin	Epoxy-aminic adducts	Societa Italiana Resine
Epon	Epoxy resin; hardener	Shell Chemical Co.
Eponol	Linear polyether resin	Shell Chemical Co.
Eposet	Two-part epoxy compounds	Hardman, Inc.
Eposir	Epoxy resin	Societa Italiana Resine
Epotuf	Epoxy resins	Reichhold Chemicals, Inc.
Epoweld	Two-part epoxy compounds	Hardman, Inc.
Epoxical	Formulated epoxy resins	United States Gypsum Co.

Table 3-7A.   Trade Names of Plastics (Cont.)

Trade Name	Class of Plastic	Manufacturer
Eraclene	Low-density polyethylene	ANIC, S.p.A.
Ervadiol	Unsaturated polyester resins	Plastimer, S.A.
Ervamine	Melamine molding powder	Plastimer, S.A.
Ervamix	Polyester molding compound	Plastimer, S.A.
Ervaphene	Phenolic resins	Plastimer, S.A.
Ervapon	Polyester resins	Plastimer, S.A.
Ervapreg	Polyester pre-pregs	Plastimer, S.A.
Estane	Polyurethane resins and compounds	Goodrich, B. F., Chemical Co.
Estolan	Polyesters for urethanes	Lankro Chemicals, Ltd.
Estrol	Polyester resin	Indpol
Ethafoam	Polyethylene foam	Dow Chemical Co.
Ethocel	Ethyl cellulose resin	Dow Chemical Co.
Ethofil	Fiberglass reinforced polyethylene	Fiberfil Div., Dart Industries, Inc.
Ethylux	Polyethylene	Westlake Plastics Co.
Evatane	Polyethylene resins	Imperial Chemical Industries Ltd., Plastics Div.
Evenglo	Polystyrene resin	Sinclair-Koppers Co.
Everflex	Polyvinyl acetate copolymer emulsions	Grace, W. R., & Co., Organic Chemicals, Dewey & Almy Chemical Div.
Excelite	Polyethylene tubing	Thermoplastic Processes, Inc.
Excelon	Vinyl tubing	Thermoplastic Processes, Inc.
Extren	Glass fiber-reinforced polyester shapes	Morrison Molded Fiber Glass Co.
Extru-Board	Corrugated polypropylene sheet	Extrudyne, Inc.
Fabrikoid	Pyroxylin-coated fabric	Stauffer Chemical Co., Plastics Div.
Fassgard	Vinyl coating on nylon	Fassler, M. J., & Co.
Fasslon	Vinyl coating	Fassler, M. J., & Co.
Fasslux	Vinyl coating	Fassler, M. J., & Co.
Fassopaque	Acrylic coating	Fassler, M. J., & Co.
Fasstic	Vinyl coating	Fassler, M. J., & Co.
Felor	Nylon filaments	Du Pont de Nemours, E. I., & Co.
Fenlac	Phenolic liquid resin	S.P.R.E.A.
Fertene	Low density polyethylene	Montedison S.p.A.
Flakeline	Flake reinforced polyester coating	Ceilcote Co.
Flamolin	Flame retarded polyolefin	Raychem Corp.
Flexocel	Flexible urethane foam systems	Baxenden Chemical Co.
Flovic	Vinyl copolymer sheet	Imperial Chemical Industries Ltd., Plastics Div.
Fluokem	Teflon spray	Bel-Art Products
Fluon	PTFE powders and dispersions	Imperial Chemical Industries Ltd., Plastics Div.
Fluon	TFE resin	ICI America Inc.
Fluorglas	PTFE-coated and impregnated woven glass fabric, tapes, belting	Dodge Fluorglas, Dodge Industries, Inc., Oak Materials Group, OAK Industries, Inc.
Fluoroblack	Compounds of TFE	Dore, John L., Co.
Fluoroblue	Compounds of TFE	Dore, John L., Co.
Fluorobrown	Compounds of TFE	Dore, John L., Co.
Fluorocomps	Fluorocarbons fortified with glass or other fillers	LNP Corp.
Fluorocord	Fluorocarbon material	Raybestos Manhattan, Inc.
Fluorofilm	Cast Teflon films	Dilectrix Corp.
Fluorogreen	Compounds of TFE and FEP	Dore, John L., Co.
Fluororay	Filled fluorocarbon	Raybestos Manhattan, Inc.
Fluorored	Compounds of TFE	Dore, John L., Co.
Fluorosint	TFE-fluorocarbon base composition	Polymer Corp.
Fluosite	Phenol-formaldehyde molding powders	Montedison S.p.A.
Formadall	Polyester premix compound	Woodall Industries, Inc.
Formaldafil	Fiberglass reinforced acetal	Fiberfil Div., Dart Industries, Inc.
Forticel	Cellulose propionate sheet	Celanese Plastics Co.
Fortiflex	Polyethylene resins	Celanese Plastics Co.
Fosta	Molding and extrusion grade nylon	Foster Grant Co.
Fosta-Net	Polystyrene foam extruded mesh	Foster Grant Co.
Fosta Tuf-Flex	High impact polystyrene	Foster Grant Co.
Fostacryl	Thermoplastic polystyrene resins	Foster Grant Co.
Fostafoam	Expandable polystyrene beads	Foster Grant Co.
Fostalite	Light-stable polystyrene molding powder	Foster Grant Co.
Fostarene	Polystyrene molding powder	Foster Grant Co.
FPC	PVC resins, compound	Firestone Plastics Co., Div. Firestone Tire & Rubber Co.
Fresh-Pak	High density polyethylene film	UCB-Sidac
Fromoplas	High-impact PVC sheet	Bakelite Xylonite Ltd.
Fulton 404	TFE-lubricated acetal	LNP Corp.
Furesir	Furane resin	Societa Italiana Resine
Gabraster	Polyester resins	Montedison S.p.A.
Gabrite	Urea-formaldehyde molding powders	Montedison S.p.A.
Gardenia	PVC sheeting	Crespi, Giovanni, S.p.A.
Genthane	Polyurethane rubber	General Tire & Rubber Co., Chemical/Plastics Div.
Gentro	Styrene butadiene rubber	General Tire & Rubber Co., Chemical/Plastics Div.
Geon	Vinyl resins, compounds, latexes	Goodrich, B. F., Chemical Co.
Gil-Fold	Polyethylene sheet	Gilman Brothers Co.
Gilliner	Fiberglass polyester laminate	Gill, M. C., Corp.
Glaskyd	Alkyd molding compounds	American Cyanamid Co., Industrial Chemicals & Plastics Div.
Glendion	Polyether resins	Montedison S.p.A.
Glitex	Vinyl tubing	Genesee Laboratory, Inc.
Gly-Cel	Diglycidyl ester resin	Celanese Resins, Div. Celanese Coatings Co.
Glyptal	Alkyd solution	General Electric Co., Insulating Materials Dept.
Gold Kast	PVC film	Continental Plastic Co., Div. CPI, Inc.
Gordon Superdense	Polystyrene in pellet form	Hammond Plastics, Inc.
Gordon Superflex	Impact polystyrene in granular or pellet form	Hammond Plastics, Inc.
Gordon Superflow	Polystyrene in granular or pellet form	Hammond Plastics, Inc.
Gore-Tex	Expanded TFE film, tubes, rods	Gore, W. L., Associates, Inc.
Gra-Tufy	Cold molding compound	Perma-Flex Mold Co.
Gracon	PVC compounds	Grace, W. R., & Co., Elm Coated Fabrics Div.
GravoFLEX	ABS sheets	Hermes Plastics, Inc.
GravoPLY	Acrylic sheets	Hermes Plastics, Inc.
GRIL-tex	Copolyamide-based adhesives	Emser Werke A.G.

Table 3-7A. Trade Names of Plastics (Cont.)

Trade Name	Class of Plastic	Manufacturer
Grilamid	Polyamide-12 resin	Emser Werke A.G.
Grilon	Polyamide-6 resin	Emser Werke A.G.
Grilonit	Epoxy resins	Emser Werke A.G.
Halon	TFE molding compounds	Allied Chemical Corp., Plastics Div.
Hartmoltopren	Rigid polyurethane foam	Farbenfabriken Bayer A.G.
Hasfa	Wax-coated cellulose film	UCB-Sidac
Haysite	Polyester laminates	Synthane-Taylor Corp., an Alco Standard Company
Herox	Nylon filaments	Du Pont de Nemours, E. I., & Co.
Hetrofoam	Fire-retardant urethane foam systems	Durez Div., Hooker Chemical Corp.
Hetron	Fire-retardant polyester resins	Durez Div., Hooker Chemical Corp.
Hi-Curl	Expoxy laminated decorative sheet	Hitachi Chemical Co.
Hi-fax	Polyethylene	Hercules Incorporated
Hi-Styrolux	High-impact polystyrene	Westlake Plastics Co.
Hi-zex	High-density polyethylene	Mitsui Petrochemical Industries, Ltd.
Hilex	High-density polyethylene sheet	British Celanese Ltd.
Hiray	Irradiated polyethylene film and tapes	Hitachi Chemical Co.
Hitafran	Furane resin	Hitachi Chemical Co.
Hitalac	Maleic modified resin	Hitachi Chemical Co.
Hitalex	Polyethylene film	Hitachi Chemical Co.
Hitaloid	Acrylic resin	Hitachi Chemical Co.
Hitamide	Polyamide resin	Hitachi Chemical Co.
Hitanol	Phenolic resin	Hitachi Chemical Co.
Hitterlite	Melamine laminated decorative sheet	Dimensional Plastics Corp.
Honey Foam	Urethane-honeycomb fusion	Farbwerke Hoechst A.G.
Hostadur	Polyethylene terephthalate; linear polyester	Farbwerke Hoechst A.G.
Hostaflex	PVC copolymer resin	Farbwerke Hoechst A.G.
Hostaflon	Polytetrafluoroethylene	Farbwerke Hoechst A.G.
Hostaform	Acetal copolymer	Farbwerke Hoechst A.G.
Hostalen (Series)	Polyethylenes; polypropylene	Farbwerke Hoechst A.G.
Hostalit (Series)	PVC plastisols, suspensions, emulsions compounds, etc.	Farbwerke Hoechst A.G.
Hostaset	Melamine, phenolic, polyester, urea molding compounds	American Hoechst Corp., Dyes & Pigments Div.
Hostavinyl	Vinyl dispersions for PVC processing	Farbwerke Hoechst A.G.
Hostyren (Series)	Polystyrene; polystyrene foam	AKU-Goodrich, N.V. Chemische Industrie
Hycar	Rubber and latex	Acme Chemicals Div., Allied Products Corp.
Hydrepoxy	Water-based epoxies	Smithers Co.
Hydro Foam	Expanded phenol-formaldehyde	Dynamit Nobel, A.G.
Hydro-Icdal	Water-soluble alkyds	Dynamit Nobel, A.G.
Icdal	Alkyds	Tokyo Shibaura Electric Co.
Imidalloy	Polyimide products	Rohm & Haas Co.
Implex	Acrylic molding powder	Imperial-Eastman
Impolene	Stabilized polypropylene tubing	Verona Div., Baychem Corp.
Impranil	Urethane prepolymer and adhesives	Indpol
Indpol Monothane	Castable urethane	PLEXCO
Instube	Vinyl tubing	Purethane Div., Easton RS Corp.
Insul F	Thermosetting urethane compounds	Cincinnati Development & Mfg. Co.
Insulstruc	Glass reinforced polyester	Diamond Shamrock Chemical Co., Plastic Div.
Intamix	Rigid PVC compounds	Badische Anilin- & Soda-Fabrik A.G.
Iporka	Foamable urea resin	General Electric Co., Insulating Materials Dept.
Irrathene	Irradiated polyethylene	Great American Chemical Corp.
Irvinil	PVC resins and compounds	Upjohn Co., CPR Div.
Isoderm	Urethane rigid and flexible integral skinning foam	Isocyanate Products Div., Witco Chemical Corp.
Isofoam	Urethane foam systems	UCB-Sidac
Isol	Coated cellulose film	Natvar Corp.
Isolastane	Isocyanate elastomer-coated glass fabric	Upjohn Co., CPR Div.
Isonate	Diisocyanates and urethane systems	Natvar Corp.
Isoplex	3-layer glass/polyester-resin combination	Natvar Corp.
Isoteraglas	Isocyanate elastomer-coated Dacron-glass fabric	Bernel Foam Products Co.
Isothane	Flexible polyurethane foams	Mitsubishi Gas Chemical Co.
Iupilon	Polycarbonate	Solvay & Cie S.A.
Ixan	Vinylidene chloride copolymers	
Jetfoam	Polyurethane foam	International Foam Div., Holiday Inns of America, Inc.
K-Prene	Urethane cast material	Di-Acro, Div. Houdaille Industries, Inc.
Kalex	Two-part polyurethane elastomers	Hardman, Inc.
Kalspray	Rigid urethane foam systems for spray application	Baxenden Chemical Co.
Kauramin	Melamine resin	Badische Anilin- & Soda-Fabrik A.G.
Kauresin	Phenolic resin	Badische Anilin- & Soda-Fabrik A.G.
Kaurit	Urea formaldehyde resin	Badische Anilin- & Soda-Fabrik A.G.
Kemid	Polyimide rod and sheet	Chemplast, Inc.
Kodacel	Cellulosic film and sheeting	Eastman Chemical Products, Inc., Sub. Eastman Kodak Co.
Kohjin-Korap	Biaxially-oriented shrinkable polypropylene film	Kohjin Co.
Koldmount	Acrylic for embedment	Vernon-Benshoff Co.
Komponit	Furan and urea resins	Kreidl, Rutter & Co. Vereinigte Chemische Fabriken
Koracryl H	Acrylic copolymer sheet	Koro Corp.
Korad	Acrylic film	Rohm & Haas Co.
Kostil	Styrene-acrylonitrile copolymers	Montedison S.p.A.
Kralastic	ABS high-impact resin	Uniroyal, Inc.
Kralon	High-impact styrene and ABS resins	Uniroyal, Inc.
Kraton	Styrene-butadiene polymers	Shell Chemical Co.
Krystal	PVC sheet	Allied Chemical Corp., Fibers Div., Plastic Film Dept.
Krystaltite	PVC shrink films	Allied Chemical Corp., Fibers Div., Plastic Film Dept.
Kydex	Acrylic/PVC sheets	Rohm & Haas Co.
Lamelite	Straight melamine resins	Montedison S.p.A.
Lamidall	Laminated plastics	Conolite Div., Woodall Industries, Inc.
Laminac	Polyester resins	American Cyanamid Co., Industrial Chemicals & Plastics Div.
Lamitex	Laminated plastics	Franklin Fibre-Lamitex Corp.
Lankrothane	Urethane coatings and adhesives	Lankro Chemicals, Ltd.

Table 3-7A.   Trade Names of Plastics (Cont.)

Trade Name	Class of Plastic	Manufacturer
Larodur	Acrylate coating resin	Badische Anilin- & Soda-Fabrik A.G.
Leben	Thermosetting PVC-based liquid resin	Dai Nippon Toryo Co.
Leguval	Unsaturated polyester resin	Farbenfabriken Bayer A.G.
Lekutherm	Epoxy resins	Farbenfabriken Bayer A.G.
Levapren	Polyethylene-vinyl acetate copolymers	Farbenfabriken Bayer A.G.
Lexan	Polycarbonate resin; film, sheet	General Electric Co., Plastics Dept.
Lightlon	Polyethylene foam sheet	Sekisui Chemical Co.
Lithene	Liquid polybutadiene	Lithium Corp. of America
Liwapas	Decorative melamine laminates	Dynamit Nobel, A.G.
Lucite	Acrylic resins	Du Pont de Nemours, E. I., & Co.
Lucobit	Polyethylene-bitumen mixture	Badische Anilin- & Soda-Fabrik A.G.
Ludopal	Unsaturated polyester coating resin	Badische Anilin- & Soda-Fabrik A.G.
Lumaline	Metallized cellulose acetate film	M & B Plastics Ltd.
Lumasite	Acrylic sheet	American Acrylic Corp.
Luphen	Phenolic coating resin	Badische Anilin- & Soda-Fabrik A.G.
Lupolen	Ethylene polymers and copolymers	Badische Anilin- & Soda-Fabrik A.G.
Luprenal	Acrylate coating resin	Badische Anilin- & Soda-Fabrik A.G.
Luran	Styrene-acrylonitrile copolymers	Badische Anilin- & Soda-Fabrik A.G.
Luran-S	Terpolymer ASA	BASF Wyandotte Corp.
Lustran	SAN and ABS molding and extrusion resins	Monsanto Co.
Lustrex	Polystyrene molding and extrusion resins	Monsanto Co.
Lutanol	Polyvinyl ether	BASF Wyandotte Corp.
Lutofan	Vinyl chloride copolymers	Badische Anilin- & Soda-Fabrik A.G.
Lutonal	Polyvinyl ethers	Badische Anilin- & Soda-Fabrik A.G.
Lutrigen	Chlorinated polyethylene	Badische Anilin- & Soda-Fabrik A.G.
Luwipal	Melamine-formaldehyde resin	Badische Anilin- & Soda-Fabrik A.G.
Macamoll	Saturated polyester resins	Cassella Farbwerke Mainkur A.G.
Macrynal	Acrylic resins	Cassella Farbwerke Mainkur A.G.
Madurit	Melamine resins	Cassella Farbwerke Mainkur A.G.
Magno-Ceram	3-Component castable epoxy/ceramic	Magnolia Plastics, Inc.
Makrofol	Polycarbonate films	Farbenfabriken Bayer A.G.
Makrolon	Extruded polycarbonate sheet	M & B Plastics Ltd.
Makrolon	Polycarbonate	Farbenfabriken Bayer A.G.
Maprenal	Melamine resins	Cassella Farbwerke Mainkur A.G.
Maranyl	Nylon 6 and 6/6 compounds	Imperial Chemical Industries Ltd., Plastics Div.
Marlex	Polyethylenes, polypropylenes, other polyolefin plastics	Phillips Petroleum Co., Chemical Dept., Plastics Div.
Marvinol	Vinyl resins and compounds	Uniroyal, Inc.
Maurylene	Polypropylene film	Rhodia, Inc.
Melacel	Melamine-impregnated cellulose fiber	Pall Trinity Micro Corp.
Melan	Melamine and urea resins	Hitachi Chemical Co.
Melbrite	Melamine-formaldehyde molding powders	Montedison S.p.A.
Meldin	Polyimide and reinforced polyimide	Dixon Corp.
Melinex	Polyester film	Imperial Chemical Industries Ltd., Plastics Div.
Melinex	Polyester film	ICI America Inc.
Melit	Melamine formaldehyde resin	Societa Italiana Resine
Melsir	Melamine molding compound	Societa Italiana Resine
Melsprea	Melamine formaldehyde molding compound	S.P.R.E.A.
Memoryline	Heat-shrinkable TFE and FEP tubing	Shamban, W. S., & Co.
Merlon	Polycarbonate	Mobay Chemical Co., Div. Baychem Corp.
Meta-Cast	Epoxy casting and potting resins	Metachem Resins Corp., Mereco Products Div.
Metacrylene	Methacrylate-butadiene-styrene-terpolymer	Plastimer, S.A.
Metallex	Cast acrylic sheets	Hermes Plastics, Inc.
Metre-Grip	Epoxy adhesives	Metachem Resins Corp., Mereco Products Div.
Metre-Set	Single-component epoxy systems	Metachem Resins Corp., Mereco Products Div.
Microsol	Vinyl plastisol	Michigan Chrome & Chemical Co.
Micro-Matte	Extruded acrylic sheet with matte finish	Extrudaline, Inc.
Micropel	Nylon powders	Nypel, Inc.
Microthin	Thin-wall Teflon tubing	Shamban, W. S., & Co.
Minit Grip	Epoxy adhesives	Schramm Fiberglass Products Div., High Strength Plastics Corp.
Minit Man	Epoxy adhesive	Kristal Kraft, Inc.
Mipolam	PVC-based sheets and films	Dynamit Nobel, A.G.
Mipoplast	Flexible PVC sheets	Dynamit Nobel of America Inc.
Mipoplast	Plasticized PVC film and sheets	Dynamit Nobel, A.G.
Mirasol	Alkyd resins; epoxy esters	Osborn, C. J., Chemicals, Inc.
Mista Foam	Urethane foam systems	M R Plastics & Coatings, Inc.
Mistapox	Epoxy compounds	M R Plastics & Coatings, Inc.
Moducal	Reinforced polyester embedded decals; FRP tubing	SGL Industries, Inc.
Modulene	Polyethylene	Muehlstein, H., & Co.
Modulite	Glass reinforced polyester embedments	SGL Industries, Inc.
Moldesite	Phenol formaldehyde molding compound	S.P.R.E.A.
Moleculoy	Range of linear polyamides	Belding Chemical Industries
Moltopren	Polyurethane foam	Farbenfabriken Bayer A.G.
Monocast	Direct polymerized nylon	Polymer Corp.
Monopol	Urethane coating	Indpol
Monopoxy	One-component epoxy adhesive	Hardman, Inc.
Monothane	One-component urethane resin	Henley & Co.
Moplefan	Polypropylene film	Montedison S.p.A.
Moplen	Isotactic polypropylene	Montedison S.p.A.
Moplen	Polypropylene	Novamont Corp.
Moplen-RO	High density polyethylene	Montedison S.p.A.
Mowilith	Polyvinyl acetate	Farbwerke Hoechst A.G.
Mowiol	Polyvinyl alcohol	Farbwerke Hoechst A.G.
Mowital	Polyvinyl butyral	Farbwerke Hoechst A.G.
Multranol	Polyether polyols	Mobay Chemical Co., Div. Baychem Corp.
Multron	Polyesters	Mobay Chemical Co., Div. Baychem Corp.
Nabutene	ABS film and sheet	Convert, Ets. G.
Nacrolaque	Cellulose acetate sheet	M & B Plastics Ltd.
Nacrylic	Acrylic latex binders	National Adhesives Div., National Starch & Chemical Corp.
Nafil	Polyisocyanate resin for rigid urethane foam	Chase Chemical Corp.

Table 3-7A. Trade Names of Plastics (Cont.)

Trade Name	Class of Plastic	Manufacturer
Naugahyde	Vinyl coated fabrics	Uniroyal, Inc.
Naugapol	Synthetic rubber	Uniroyal, Inc.
Naxolene	High-impact polystyrene film and sheet	Convert, Ets. G.
Nedox-Nickel	TFE impregnated coating	General Magnaplate Corp.
Neo-zex	Medium-density polyethylene	Mitsui Petrochemical Industries, Ltd.
Neoflon	FEP dispersions	Daikin Kogyo Co.
Neopolen	Polyethylene foam	Badische Anilin- & Soda-Fabrik A.G.
Nepoxide	Epoxy resin coating	Atlas Minerals & Chemicals Div., ESB Inc.
Nevillac	Modified coumarone-indene resin	Neville Chemical Co.
Nimbus	Polyurethane foam	General Tire & Rubber Co., Chemical/Plastics Div.
Nob-Lock	PVC sheet material	Ameron Corrosion Control Div.
Non-Tac	Vinyl sheeting	Strauss, H. B., Corp.
Norchem	Low-density polyethylene resin	Northern Petrochemical Co.
Novodur	ABS resins	Farbenfabriken Bayer A.G.
Novolen	Polypropylene	Badische Anilin- & Soda-Fabrik A.G.
Nupol	Thermosetting acrylic resin	Freeman Chemical Corp., Div. H. H. Robertson Co.
Nybrad	Abrasive-filled nylon filaments	Nypel, Inc.
Nyglathane	Glass-filled polyurethane	Nypel, Inc.
Nylafil	Fiberglass reinforced nylon	Fiberfil Div., Dart Industries, Inc.
Nylasint	Sintered nylon parts	Polymer Corp.
Nylatron	Filled nylons	Polymer Corp.
Nylaweld	Nylon-to-nylon adhesive	Polymer Corp.
Nylo-Seal	Nylon 11 tubing	Imperial-Eastman
Nylode	Talc reinforced nylon	Fiberfil Div., Dart Industries, Inc.
Nypelube	TFE-filled nylons	Nypel, Inc.
Nyprime	Adhesive nylon-metal	Plastic Coatings Ltd.
Nyreg	Glass-reinforced nylon molding compounds	Nypel, Inc.
Oasis	Expanded phenol-formaldehyde	Smithers Co.
Ohmoid	Laminated phenolic	Wilmington Fibre Specialty Co.
Oilon Pv 80	Acetal-based resin; sheets, rods, tubing, profiles	Cadillac Plastic & Chemical Co.
Olefane	Polypropylene film	Amoco Chemicals Corp.
Olefil	Filled polypropylene resin	Amoco Chemicals Corp.
Oleflo	Polypropylene resin	Amoco Chemicals Corp.
Olemer	Copolymer polypropylene	Amoco Chemicals Corp.
Oleplate	Plateable polypropylene resin	Amoco Chemicals Corp.
Oletac	Amorphous polypropylene	Amoco Chemicals Corp.
Olo-Lite	Resilient expanded polystyrene	Swedish Crucible Steel Co., Packaging & Insulation Material Div.
Opalon	Flexible PVC materials	Monsanto Co.
Oppanol	Polyisobutylene	Badische Anilin- & Soda-Fabrik A.G.
Oppanol	Polyisobutylene	BASF Wyandotte Corp.
Packaid	Solvent vinyl strippable coatings	Seal-Peel, Inc.
Pacrosir	Thermosetting acrylic resins	Societa Italiana Resine
Palatal	Unsaturated polyesters	Badische Anilin- & Soda-Fabrik A.G.
Papi	Polymethylene polyphenylisocyanate	Upjohn Co., Polymer Chemicals Div.
Paradene	Dark coumarone-indene resins	Neville Chemical Co.
Paraplex	Polyester resins and plasticizers	Rohm & Haas Co.
Pelaspan-Pac	Expandable polystyrene	Dow Chemical Co.
Pellethane	Thermoplastic urethane	Upjohn Co., CPR Div.
PermaRez	Cast epoxy	Permali, Inc.
Permelite	Melamine molding compounds	Melamine Plastics, Inc., Div. Fiberite Corp.
Perspex	Cast acrylic sheet, block, rod	Imperial Chemical Industries Ltd., Plastics Div.
Petrothene	Low-, medium- and high-density polyethylene	U.S. Industrial Chemicals Co., Div. National Distillers & Chemical Corp.
Petrothene XL	Crosslinkable polyethylene compounds	U.S. Industrial Chemicals Co., Div. National Distillers & Chemical Corp.
Pevalon	Water soluble polyvinyl alcohol films	May & Baker, Ltd.
PeVeClair	Rigid PVC sheeting	Brimar
Pevikon	Polyvinyl chloride	KemaNord AB
Pexco	Extruded tubings	Plastic Extrusion & Engineering Co.
Phenolite	High pressure, laminated, thermosetting plastic	NVF Co.
Phenoweld	Phenolic adhesives for nylon, etc.	Hardman, Inc.
Phenuren	Phenol-formaldehyde resins	Badische Anilin- & Soda-Fabrik A.G.
Philjo	Polyolefin films	Phillips-Joanna Co., Div. Joanna Western Mills Co.
Phtalopal	Phthalate coating resin	Badische Anilin- & Soda-Fabrik A.G.
Phthalkyd	Alkyd resin	Hitachi Chemical Co.
Picco	Resins	Pennsylvania Industrial Chemical Corp.
Piccodiene	Polydicyclopentadiene resins	Pennsylvania Industrial Chemical Corp.
Piccoflex	Acrylonitrile-styrene resins	Pennsylvania Industrial Chemical Corp.
Piccolastic	Polystyrene resins	Pennsylvania Industrial Chemical Corp.
Piccolyte	Pinene polymers	Pennsylvania Industrial Chemical Corp.
Piccopale	Aliphatic type hydrocarbon resins	Pennsylvania Industrial Chemical Corp.
Piccotex	Vinyl toluene copolymer	Pennsylvania Industrial Chemical Corp.
Piccoumaron	Coumarone-indene resins	Pennsylvania Industrial Chemical Corp.
Piccovar	Alkyl-aromatic resins	Pennsylvania Industrial Chemical Corp.
Pinpoly	Reinforced polyurethane foam	International Foam Div., Holiday Inns of America, Inc.
Pioloform	Polyvinyl acetal	Wacker-Chemie GmbH
Plaper	Biaxially-oriented polystyrene film	Mitsubishi Monsanto Chemical Co.
Plaskon	Plastic molding compounds	Allied Chemical Corp., Plastics Div.
Plastazote	Expanded polyethylene	Bakelite Xylonite Ltd.
Plasti-Brass	Metal-like laminated extrusion	Anchor Plastics Co.
Plasti-Copper	Metal-like laminated extrusion	Anchor Plastics Co.
Plasti-Gold	Metal-like laminated extrusion	Anchor Plastics Co.
Plasti-Krome	Metal-like laminated extrusion	Anchor Plastics Co.
Plasticell	Rigid PVC foam	BTR Silvertown Ltd.
Plasticlair	FRP sheeting	Brimar
Plastifilm	PVC film and sheeting	Goss Plastic Film Corp.
Plastiglaze	Polyethylene coating powders	Plastic Coatings Ltd.
Plastopal	Urea formaldehyde coating resin	Badische Anilin- & Soda-Fabrik A.G.
Plenco	Thermoset resins and molding compounds	Plastics Engineering Co.
Pleogen	Polyester resins and gel coats; polyurethane systems	Mol-Rez Div., Whittaker Corp.
Plex	Acrylic sheets and molding powders	Rohm & Haas Co.

Table 3-7A. Trade Names of Plastics (Cont.)

Trade Name	Class of Plastic	Manufacturer
Plexi	Acrylic sheets and molding powders	Rohm & Haas Co.
Plexiglas	Acrylic sheets and molding powders	Rohm & Haas Co.
Plexton	Reinforced fiberglass	Lewis, G. B., Co.
Pliobond	Adhesives	Goodyear Tire & Rubber Co., Chemical Div.
Pliolite	Styrene-butadiene resins	Goodyear Tire & Rubber Co., Chemical Div.
Pliothene	Polyethylene-rubber blends	Ametek/Westchester Plastics
Pliovic	PVC resins	Goodyear Tire & Rubber Co., Chemical Div.
Pluracol	Polyethers	BASF Wyandotte Corp.
Pluragard	Urethane foam systems	BASF Wyandotte Corp.
Pluronic	Polyethers	BASF Wyandotte Corp.
Plymaster	Industrial adhesive film	National Adhesives Div., National Starch & Chemical Corp.
Plyocite	Phenolic impregnated overlays	Reichhold Chemicals, Inc.
Plyophen	Phenolic resins	Reichhold Chemicals, Inc.
Plypac	PVC film	Montedison S.p.A.
Poilopas	Urea-formaldehyde molding powders	Plastimer, S.A.
Polarflex	Hot dip coating	Western Coating Co.
Polidene	PVDC copolymer emulsions	Scott Bader Co.
Poligen	Dispersions	Badische Anilin- & Soda-Fabrik A.G.
Pollopas	Urea formaldehyde compounds	Dynamit Nobel of America Inc.
Pollopas	Urea formaldehyde molding compounds	Dynamit Nobel, A.G.
Polnac	Polyester liquid resin	S.P.R.E.A.
Polvonite	Cellular plastic material in sheet form	Voplex Corp.
Poly bd	Butadiene liquid resins	ARCO Chemical Co.
Poly-Cast	Cast film adhesive	Fortin Laminating Corp.
Poly-Clad	Flexible laminate	Fortin Laminating Corp.
Poly-Core	Flexible laminate	Fortin Laminating Corp.
Poly-Cover	Plastic sheeting	Flex-O-Glass, Inc.
Poly-Dap	Diallyl phthalate electrical molding compounds	U.S. Polymeric, Div. Hitco
Poly-Eth	Low-density polyethylene	Gulf Oil Chemicals Co., U.S. Operations, Plastics Div.
Poly-Eth-Hi-D	High density polyethylene	Gulf Oil Chemicals Co., U.S. Operations, Plastics Div.
Poly-Flo	Polyethylene tubing	Imperial-Eastman
Poly-Preg	Preimpregnated products with fabric base	U.S. Polymeric, Div. Hitco
Poly-Rib	Rib-reinforced polyethylene	Flex-O-Glass, Inc.
Poly-Thane	Integral skin urethane resins	Pelron Corp.
Polyarome	Polyethylene granules with concentrated aroma content	Creative Perfumers & Flavorists, Inc.
Polycarbafil	Fiberglass reinforced polycarbonate	Fiberfil Div., Dart Industries, Inc.
Polyclad	Vinyl protective coating	Carboline Co.
Polycure	Crosslinked polyethylene compounds	Cooke Color & Chemical Div., Reichhold Chemicals, Inc.
Polycure	Crosslinkable polyethylene compounds	Reichhold Chemicals, Inc.
Polydia	Polystyrene sheet	Poly Chemical Co.
Polyfilm	Polyethylene film	Dow Chemical Co.
Polyflon	TFE molding and extrusion powders, dispersions, etc.	Daikin Kogyo Co.
Polyfoam	Polyurethane foam	General Tire & Rubber Co., Chemical/Plastics Div.
Polyguide	Laminates, clad plastics	High Voltage Engineering Corp.
Polyimidal	Thermoplastic polyimide	Raychem Corp.
Polylite	Polyester resins	Reichhold Chemicals, Inc.
Polyloom	Fibrillated polypropylene film	Chevron Chemical Co., Fibers Div.
Polylumy	Biaxially-oriented polypropylene film	Kohjin Co.
Polymet	Plastic-filled sintered metal	Polymer Corp.
Polymul (Series)	Polyethylene emulsions	Nopco Chemical Div., Diamond Shamrock Chemical Co.
Polyox	Water-soluble resins	Union Carbide Corp., Chemicals & Plastics
Polypearl	Expandable polystyrene	Poly Chemical Co.
Polyrex	Polystyrenes	Poly Chemical Co.
Polyset	Unsaturated polyester resin	Hitachi Chemical Co.
Polysystems	Foamed-in-place components	Olin Corp.
Polyteraglas	Polyester-coated Dacron-glass fabric	Natvar Corp.
Polython	Plastic sheeting and tubing	Poly Plastic Products, Inc.
Polyviol	Polyvinyl alcohol	Wacker-Chemie GmbH
Polywrap	Plastic film	Flex-O-Glass, Inc.
Porex	Porous plastics	Glasrock Products, Inc.
Poron	Microporous plastic materials	Rogers Corp.
Portplasto	Rigid PVC extrusions	Brimar
Poxy-Gard	Solventless epoxy compounds	Sterling Div., Reichhold Chemicals, Inc.
Premi-Glas	Polyester molding compounds	Premix, Inc.
Pres-Tock	Moldable wood fibre mats	Weyerhacuser Co., Molded Products Dept.
Pro-fax	Polypropylene	Hercules Incorporated
Profil	Fiberglass reinforced polypropylene	Fiberfil Div., Dart Industries, Inc.
Profilm	Vinyl film	Protective Lining Corp.
Progilite	Phenolic molding powders	Plastimer, S.A.
Prohi	High density polyethylene	Protective Lining Corp.
Propafilm	Polypropylene film	ICI America Inc.
Propafilm	Polypropylene film	Imperial Chemical Industries Ltd., Plastics Div.
Propathene	Polypropylene polymers and compound	Imperial Chemical Industries Ltd., Plastics Div.
Propiofan	Vinyl propionate polymers and copolymers	Badische Anilin- & Soda-Fabrik A.G.
Propiofan	Polyvinyl propionate	BASF Wyandotte Corp.
Propocon	Preblends for urethane foams	Lankro Chemicals, Ltd.
Propylex	Extruded polypropylene sheet	British Celanese Ltd.
Propylux	Polypropylene	Westlake Plastics Co.
Protectolite	Polyethylene film	Protective Lining Corp.
Protron	Ultra-high strength polyethylene	Protective Lining Corp.
Q-Thane	Urethane polymers	Quinn, K. J., & Co.
QuaCorr	Modified furfuryl alcohol polymer	Quaker Oats Co., Chemicals Div.
Quadrol	Polyhydroxy amine	BASF Wyandotte Corp.
Quasilan	Prepolymers for urethane foams	Lankro Chemicals, Ltd.
Quelflam	Isocyanurates, low surface spread flame	Baxenden Chemical Co.
Quirvil	PVC	Rumianca S.p.A.
Rapid-Set	Cyanoacrylate adhesive	Aran Dee Associates Ltd.
Ravemul	Polyvinyl acetate emulsions	ANIC, S.p.A.
Ravikral	ABS resins	ANIC, S.p.A.

Table 3-7A. Trade Names of Plastics (Cont.)

Trade Name	Class of Plastic	Manufacturer
Ravinil	Polyvinyl chloride resins	ANIC, S.p.A.
REN-Shape	Epoxy material	Ren Plastics
REN-Thane	Urethane elastomers	Ren Plastics
REN-Tubing	Plastic fiberglass tubing	Ren Plastics
Renyl	Polyamide resins	Montedison S.p.A.
Resarit	Acrylic molding powders, emulsions and tubes	Resart-IHM A.G.
Resartglas	Cast acrylic sheets, rods, blocks	Resart-IHM A.G.
Resiglas	Polyester resins, etc.	Kristal Kraft, Inc.
Resophene	Phenolic resins	Plastimer, S.A.
Resorsabond	Resorcinol and phenol-resorcinol	Pacific Resins & Chemicals, Inc.
Resticel	Expandable polystyrene	Societa Italiana Resine
Restil	SAN copolymer	Societa Italiana Resine
Restiran	ABS copolymer	Societa Italiana Resine
Restiroid	Modified alkyd resins	Societa Italiana Resine
Restirolo	Polystyrene	Societa Italiana Resine
Reynosol	Urethane, PVC	Reynolds Chemical Products Div., Hoover Ball & Bearing Co.
Rezimac	Resin-modified alkyds	Commercial Solvents Corp.
Rhenoflex	PVC-based plastics	Dynamit Nobel, A.G.
Rhiamer	Polypropylene and polycarbonate block and rod	M & B Plastics Ltd.
Rhodialine	Cast cellulose acetate film	M & B Plastics Ltd.
Rhodialine	Cast cellulose acetate film	Rhodia, Inc.
Rhodialite	Cellulose acetate molding powders	M & B Plastics Ltd.
Rhodiod	Cellulose acetate sheet	M & B Plastics Ltd.
Rhodoglass	Cellulose acetate sheets	M & B Plastics Ltd.
Rhodophane	Cast cellulose acetate film	M & B Plastics Ltd.
Rhodophane	Thin cast cellulose acetate film	Rhodia, Inc.
Rhoplex	Acrylic emulsions	Rohm & Haas Co.
Riblene	Low-density polyethylene	ANIC, S.p.A.
Rocel	Cellulose acetate sliced and extruded sheet	British Celanese Ltd.
Rolox	Two-part epoxy compounds	Hardman, Inc.
Rotothene	Polyethylene resins for rotational molding	Rototron Corp.
Rowlex	Polycarbonate sheet	Rowland Products, Inc.
Roylar	Polyurethane elastoplastic	Uniroyal, Inc.
RT/duroids	Reinforced TFE materials	Rogers Corp.
Rucoam	Vinyl film and sheeting	Ruco Div., Hooker Chemical Corp.
Rucoblend	Vinyl compounds	Ruco Div., Hooker Chemical Corp.
Rucon	Vinyl resins	Ruco Div., Hooker Chemical Corp.
Rucotex	Latexes and concentrates	Ruco Div., Hooker Chemical Corp.
Rucothane	Polyurethanes	Ruco Div., Hooker Chemical Corp.
Rulon	Reinforced Teflon	Dixon Corp.
Rumiten (Series)	Low- and high-density polyethylene	Rumianca S.p.A.
Ryton	Polyphenylene sulfide	Phillips Petroleum Co., Chemical Dept., Plastics Div.
Sadur	Cast acrylonitrile-modified acrylic sheets	Resart-IHM A.G.
Saduren	Melamine-formaldehyde resins	Badische Anilin- & Soda-Fabrik A.G.
Saf-T-Foam	Specially treated and fire retardant polyurethane foam	International Foam Div., Holiday Inns of America, Inc.
Salox	Filled TFE resin	Allegheny Plastics, Inc.
Santoclear	Biaxially oriented polystyrene sheet	Mitsubishi Monsanto Chemical Co.
Santolite	Aryl sulfonamide-formaldehyde resin	Monsanto Co.
Saran	Polyvinylidene chloride resin	Dow Chemical Co.
Scotchpak	Heat-sealable polyester film	3M Co.
Scotchpar	Polyester film	3M Co.
Scottfelt	Permanently compressed polyurethane foam	Scott Paper Co., Foam Div.
Scottfore	Fibre-flocked urethane foam	Scott Paper Co., Foam Div.
Selectrofoam	Urethane foam systems and polyols	PPG Industries, Inc., Resin Products Sales, C&R Div.
Selectron	Polymerizable synthetic resins; polyesters	PPG Industries, Inc., Resin Products Sales, C&R Div.
Setilithe	Cellulose acetate granules	Akzo Plastics nv
Shinko-Lac ABS	Acrylonitrile-butadiene-styrene-copolymers	Mitsubishi Rayon Co.
Shinko Lite	Acrylic sheet; acrylic molding materials	Mitsubishi Rayon Co.
Sho-Allomer	Polypropylene	Showa Yuka K. K.
Sholex	Low- and high-density polyethylene	Showa Yuka K. K.
Shuvin	Vinyl molding compounds	Blane Chemical Div., Reichhold Chemicals, Inc.
Shuvin	Vinyl molding compounds	Reichhold Chemicals, Inc.
Shuvinite	PVC and nitrile rubber mixture	Blane Chemical Div., Reichhold Chemicals, Inc.
Sicron	PVC homopolymers, copolymers and compounds	Montedison S.p.A.
Sidac	Transparent cellulose film	UCB-Sidac
Sidamil	Polyethylene/polyamide or polyester laminate	UCB-Sidac
Sidanyl	Polyamide film or laminate	UCB-Sidac
Sidathene	Polypropylene film	UCB-Sidac
Sidavine	Vinyl films	UCB-Sidac
Silastic	Silicone rubber	Dow Corning Corp.
Silbon	Rayon paper	Kohjin Co.
Silopren	Silicone rubber	Farbenfabriken Bayer A.G.
Siral	Maleic resins	Societa Italiana Resine
Siralkyd	Alkyd resins	Societa Italiana Resine
Siramid	Polyamide resins	Societa Italiana Resine
Siramin	Butylated urea resins	Societa Italiana Resine
Sirester	Polyester resin	Societa Italiana Resine
Sirfen	Phenolic resins	Societa Italiana Resine
Sirfenol	Modified phenolic resins	Societa Italiana Resine
Sirit	Urea formaldehyde resin	Societa Italiana Resine
Siritle	Urea molding compound	Societa Italiana Resine
Sirpol	PVAC emulsions	Societa Italiana Resine
Sirtene	Low density polyethylene	Sekisui Chemical Co.
Softlon	Crosslinked polyethylene foam sheet	Thiokol Chemical Corp., Chemical/Industrial Div.
Solithane	Urethane prepolymers	Solvay & Cie S.A.
Solvic	Polyvinyl chloride and copolymers	Solvay & Cie S.A.
Solvitherm	Chlorinated PVC compounds	Smooth-On, Inc.
Sonite	Epoxy resin compound	Ugine Kuhlman of America, Inc.
Soreflon	Polytetrafluoroethylene	Baxenden Chemical Co.
Spandal	Rigid urethane laminates	

Table 3-7A. Trade Names of Plastics (Cont.)

Trade Name	Class of Plastic	Manufacturer
Spandofoam	Rigid urethane foam board and slab	Baxenden Chemical Co.
Spreacol	Urea formaldehyde glues	S.P.R.E.A.
Stamylan	Polyethylene resins	DSM
Stamylan-P	Polypropylene	DSM
Standlite	Phenolic resins	Hitachi Chemical Co.
Sterpon	Polyester resins	Convert, Ets. G.
Stratoclad	Glass reinforced phenolic	Spaulding Fibre Co.
Stylour	Velour-covered polystyrene sheet	Gilman Brothers Co.
Stypol	Polyesters	Freeman Chemical Corp., Div. H. H. Robertson Co.
Styrafil	Fiberglass reinforced polystyrene	Fiberfil Div., Dart Industries, Inc.
Styretex	Styrenated alkyd resins	Celanese Resins, Div. Celanese Coatings Co.
Styrofan	Styrene polymers	Badische Anilin- & Soda-Fabrik A.G.
Styroflex	Biaxially-oriented polystyrene film	Natvar Corp.
Styrofoam	Polystyrene foam	Dow Chemical Co.
Styrol	Polystyrene	Idemitsu Petrochemical Co.
Styrolux	Polystyrene	Westlake Plastics Co.
Styron	Polystyrene resin	Dow Chemical Co.
Styron Verelite	Light stabilized styrene	Dow Chemical Co.
Styronal	Acrylate-styrene copolymer	Badische Anilin- & Soda-Fabrik A.G.
Styronol	Styrene	Allied Resinous Products, Inc.
Styrophane	ABS film	UCB-Sidac
Styropor	Foamable polystyrene beads	Badische Anilin- & Soda-Fabrik A.G.
Styropor	Polystyrene expandable beads	BASF Wyandotte Corp.
Styvarene	Polystyrene	Plastimer, S.A.
Sulfil	Fiberglass reinforced polysulfone	Fiberfil Div., Dart Industries, Inc.
Super Aeroflex	Linear polyethylene extrusions	Anchor Plastics Co.
Super Dylan	High-density polyethylene	Sinclair-Koppers Co.
Super Modulene	Polyethylene	Muehlstein, H., & Co.
Supresac	Urethanes	ICI America Inc.
Swedcast	Continuous cast acrylic sheet and rolls	Swedlow Inc., Acrylic Sheet Div.
Swedcast 300	Cast acrylic sheets; reinforced and decorative plastics; glass cloth	Swedlow, Inc.
Sylphane	PVC films	UCB-Sidac
Syn-U-Tex	Urea formaldehyde and melamine formaldehyde resins	Celanese Resins, Div. Celanese Coatings Co.
Syntex	Alkyd and polyurethane ester resins	Celanese Resins, Div. Celanese Coatings Co.
T-Lock	PVC sheet material	Ameron Corrosion Control Div.
Tarpo	Textile-reinforced polyethylene film	UCB-Sidac
Technyl	Extruded nylon rods	M & B Plastics Ltd.
Technyl	Polyamide molding compounds	M & B Plastics Ltd.
Technyl	Nylon 6, 6/6, 6/10, etc.	Rhone-Poulenc-Textile
Tecnoflon	Polytetrafluoroethylene rubbers	Montedison S.p.A.
Tecolite	Phenolic molding compounds	Tokyo Shibaura Electric Co.
Teflon	FEP and TFE fluorocarbon resins	Du Pont de Nemours, E. I., & Co.
Tegit	Phenolic-asbestos molding compound	Garfield Mfg. Co.
Tenn foam	Polyurethane foam	Morristown Foam & Fiber Corp.
Tensol	Acrylic cements	Imperial Chemical Industries Ltd., Plastics Div.
Tere-Gard	Solventless polyester compounds	Sterling, Div. Reichhold Chemicals, Inc.
Terlenka	Polyester	Akzo Plastics nv
Terluran	ABS polymers	Badische Anilin- & Soda-Fabrik A.G.
Terphane	Polyester film	Rhodia, Inc.
Tetra-Phen	Phenolic type resins	Georgia-Pacific Corp., Chemical Div.
Tetra-Ria	Amino type resins	Georgia-Pacific Corp., Chemical Div.
Tetronic	Polyethers	BASF Wyandotte Corp.
Texicote	PVA emulsions	Scott Bader Co.
Texicryl	Acrylic polymer emulsions	Scott Bader Co.
Texin	Urethane elastomer molding compound	Mobay Chemical Co., Div. Baychem Corp.
Thanate	Polymeric isocyanates	Jefferson Chemical Co.
Thermalux	Polysulfone	Westlake Plastics Co.
Thurane	Rigid polyurethane foam	Dow Chemical Co.
Tilon	Acrylic molding compound	Ticonium Div., CMP Industries, Inc.
Toshiba Premix	Alkyd molding compounds	Tokyo Shibaura Electric Co.
TPX	Methylpentene polymers	Imperial Chemical Industries Ltd., Plastics Div.
Transtube	Vinyl tubing	PLEXCO
Triafol	Cellulose acetate films	Farbenfabriken Bayer A.G.
Trocal	Rigid PVC profiles	Dynamit Nobel of America Inc.
Trofil	High density polyethylene monofilament	Dynamit Nobel, A.G.
Trofil P	Polypropylene monofilament	Dynamit Nobel, A.G.
Trogamid	Polyamide sheets, etc.	Dynamit Nobel, A.G.
Trogamid T	Polyamide molding compound	Dynamit Nobel of America Inc.
Trolen	Low-density polyethylene film and sheets	Dynamit Nobel, A.G.
Trolen (Series)	Polyethylene and polypropylene sheets	Dynamit Nobel of America Inc.
Trolitan	Phenol-formaldehyde molding compounds	Dynamit Nobel, A.G.
Trolitan (Series)	Phenol formaldehyde compounds; boron molding compounds	Dynamit Nobel of America Inc.
Trosifol	Polyvinyl butyral film	Dynamit Nobel of America Inc.
Trosifol	Polyvinyl butyral sheets	Dynamit Nobel, A.G.
Trosiplast	PVC molding and extrusion compound	Dynamit Nobel of America Inc.
Trosiplast	Polyvinyl chloride compounds	Dynamit Nobel, A.G.
Trovidur	Corrosion-resistant rigid PVC	Dynamit Nobel, A.G.
Trovidur (Series)	Rigid PVC sheets	Dynamit Nobel of America Inc.
Trovipor	Open cell flexible PVC foam	Dynamit Nobel of America Inc.
Trovipor	Flexible PVC foam	Dynamit Nobel, A.G.
Trovitherm	Calendered PVC film	Dynamit Nobel of America Inc.
Tru-Shape	Polyester structural shapes	Fibercast Co., Div. Youngstown Sheet & Tube Co.
Trulon	Polyvinyl chloride resin	Olin Corp.
Trycite	Polystyrene film	Dow Chemical Co.
Tubiceta	Cellulose acetate flakes	Akzo Plastics nv
Tufcote	Thin sheet cast urethane foam	Speciality Converters, Inc.
Tuffak	Adhesive-coated, pressure-sensitive film	Rohm & Haas Co.
Tufram-Aluminum	TFE impregnated coating	General Magnaplate Corp.
Tufrex	Acrylonitrile-butadiene-styrene copolymer	Mitsubishi Monsanto Chemical Co.
Tuftane	Polyurethane film and sheet	Goodrich, B. F., Chemical Co.

Table 3-7A. Trade Names of Plastics (Cont.)

Trade Name	Class of Plastic	Manufacturer
Turbolex	Vinyl tubing	Brand-Rex Co.
Turbotherm	Vinyl tubing	Brand-Rex Co.
Turbozone	Vinyl tubing	Brand-Rex Co.
Twin Weld	Epoxy adhesives	Schramm Fiberglass Products Div., High Strength Plastics Corp.
Tylose	Methyl-carboxymethyl-hydroxyethyl-cellulose	Farbwerke Hoechst A.G.
Tynex	Nylon filaments	Du Pont de Nemours, E. I., & Co.
Tyril	Styrene-acrylonitrile resin	Dow Chemical Co.
U-Thane	Rigid insulation board stock urethane	Upjohn Co., CPR Div.
Uformite	Urea and melamine resins	Rohm & Haas Co.
Ugikral	ABS terpolymer	Plastimer, S.A.
Ultra-Ethylux	Linear polyethylene	Westlake Plastics Co.
Ultra-Glas	Oriented acrylic sheet	Fortin Plastics, Inc.
Ultradur	Polytetramethylene terephthalate	Badische Anilin- & Soda-Fabrik A.G.
Ultraform	Acetal resins	Badische Anilin- & Soda-Fabrik A.G.
Ultramid	Nylon 6, 6/6 and 6/10	BASF Wyandotte Corp.
Ultramid	Polyamide grades	Badische Anilin- & Soda-Fabrik A.G.
Ultrapas	Melamine formaldehyde compounds	Dynamit Nobel of America Inc.
Ultrapas	Decorative melamine laminates	Dynamit Nobel, A.G.
Ultrathene	Ethylene-vinyl acetate resins and copolymers	U.S. Industrial Chemicals Co., Div. National Distillers & Chemical Corp.
Ultrex	Ultra high molecular weight polyethylene extrusions	Spiratex Co.
Ultron	PVC film and sheet	Monsanto Co.
Unichem	Vinyl compounds	Colorite Plastics Co., Div. Dart Industries, Inc.
Unidur	Urethane structural systems	BASF Wyandotte Corp.
Unipoxy	Epoxy resins, adhesives	Kristal Kraft, Inc.
Urabond	Urethane elastomeric coating	Poly Resins
Urafil	Fiberglass reinforced polyurethane	Fiberfil Div., Dart Industries, Inc.
Uralane	Polyurethanes	Furane Plastics, Inc.
Urapol	Urethane elastomeric coating	Poly Resins
Ureflex	Urethane impregnants, solvent free	Purethane Div., Easton RS Corp.
Urefome	Urethane, polyester and polyether foam systems	Purethane Div., Easton RS Corp.
Urepan	Polyurethane elastomer	Farbenfabriken Bayer A.G.
Urepot	Urethane encapsulants and potting compounds	Purethane Div. Easton RS Corp.
Uroflex	Cold-cure urethane foam systems	BASF Wyandotte Corp.
Uropac	Urethane foam systems	BASF Wyandotte Corp.
Uropal	Urea-formaldehyde-butyl resins	Plastimer S.A.
Uroplas	Urea formaldehyde molding compound	S.P.R.E.A.
Urtal	Acrylonitrile-butadiene-styrene terpolymers	Montedison S.p.A.
Urutuf	Polyurethane resins	Reichhold Chemicals. Inc.
USM Suprethane	Jacketed urethane foam	United States Mineral Products Co.
Uvex	Cellulose acetate butyrate sheet	Eastman Chemical Products, Inc., Sub. Eastman Kodak Co.
Valeron	Oriented high-density polyethylene film laminate	Van Leer Plastics (U.S.A.), Inc.
Valox	Engineering thermoplastic polyester	General Electric Co. Plastics Dept.
Varcum	Phenolic resins	Reichhold Chemicals, Inc.
Varex	Polyester resins	McClosky Varnish Co.
Varkyd	Alkyd and modified alkyd resins	McClosky Varnish Co.
Varlan	PVC resins	DSM
Vedril	Polymethyl methacrylate granules and extruded sheet	Montedison S.p.A.
Vedrilcol	Methacrylate-based adhesive	Montedison S.p.A.
Velbex	Flexible PVC sheet	Bakelite Xylonite Ltd.
Velene	Styrene-foam laminate	Scott Paper Co., Foam Div.
Vestamid	Nylon 12 resins and compounds	Chemische Werke Huls, A.G.
Vestolen (Series)	Polyethylene, polypropylene, polybutylene	Chemische Werke Huls, A.G.
Vestolit	PVC resins and compounds	Chemische Werke Huls, A.G.
Vestopal	Polyester resins and compounds	Chemische Werke Huls, A.G.
Vestypor	Expandable polystyrene	Chemische Werke Huls, A.G.
Vestyron	Polystyrene resins and compounds	Chemische Werke Huls, A.G.
Vibrathane	Polyurethane elastomer	Uniroyal, Inc.
Vibrin-Mat	Polyester-glass molding compound	Grace, W. R., & Co., Marco Chemical Div.
Vibro-Flo	Epoxy, polypropylene and polyester coating powders	Armstrong Products Co.
Viclan	Vinylidene chloride copolymers	Imperial Chemical Industries Ltd., Plastics Div.
Vikem	Vinyl spray	Bel-Art Products
Vinavil	Polyvinyl acetate resins	Montedison S.p.A.
Vinavilol	Polyvinyl alcohols,	Montedison S.p.A.
Vinika	Polyvinyl chloride resin	Mitsubishi Monsanto Chemical Co.
Vinnapas	Polyvinyl acetate	Wacker-Chemie GmbH
Vinnol	Polyvinyl chloride/vinyl chloride/acetate copolymers	Wacker-Chemie GmbH
Vinoflex	PVC resins	BASF Wyandotte Corp.
Vinoflex	Vinyl chloride-vinylisobutyl ether copolymer	BASF Wyandotte Corp.
Vinuran	Styrene-modified PVC	Badische Anilin- & Soda-Fabrik A.G.
Vinyclair	Transparent PVC films	M & B Plastics Ltd.
Vinyfix	Self-adhesive vinyl film	UCB-Sidac
Vipac	Opaque PVC films	M & B Plastics Ltd.
Vipla	PVC homopolymers	Montedison S.p.A.
Viplast	Pelletized PVC	Montedison S.p.A.
Viplavil	Vinyl chloride-vinyl acetate copolymer	Montedison S.p.A.
Vista Vinyl	Vinyl film and sheeting	Harte & Co., Sub. Diamond Shamrock Corp.
Vistafix	Self-adhesive polyethylene film	UCB-Sidac
Vistaflam	Self-extinguishing polyethylene film	UCB-Sidac
Vistal	Polyethylene film	UCB-Sidac
Vitel	Polyester resin	Goodyear Tire & Rubber Co., Chemical Div.
Vitredil	Methacrylic sheets	Montedison S.p.A.
Vituf	Polyester resin	Goodyear Tire & Rubber Co., Chemical Div.
Vivicolor	Fluorescent color polyethylene molding compounds	Frilvam, S.p.A.
Vixir	PVC in suspension and emulsion	Societa Italiana Resine
Volara	Closed-cell, low density polyethylene foam	Voltek, Inc.
Volasta	Closed-cell, medium density polyethylene foam	Voltek, Inc.
Voranol	Polyurethane resins	Dow Chemical Co.
Vorite	Urethane prepolymer	Baker Castor Oil Co.
Vorpon	2-part epoxy coatings and adhesives	Vorac Co.

Table 3-7A.   Trade Names of Plastics (Cont.)

Trade Name	Class of Plastic	Manufacturer
Vulco	Extruded PVC sheets and shapes	Vulcan Metal Products Inc.
Vulkollan	Polyurethane elastomer	Farbenfabriken Bayer A.G.
Vybak	Rigid PVC	Bakelite Xylonite Ltd.
Vybond	PVC coating powder	Plastic Coatings Ltd.
Vycoat	Air drying polyvinyl coating	Plastic Coatings Ltd.
Vyflex	PVC coating powders	Plastic Coatings Ltd.
Vygen	PVC resin	General Tire & Rubber Co., Chemical/Plastics Div.
Vylastic	PVC plastisols for coating	Plastic Coatings Ltd.
Vynaclor	Vinyl chloride emulsion coatings and binders	National Adhesives Div., National Starch & Chemical Corp.
Vynaloy	Rigid vinyl film and sheet	Goodrich, B. F., Chemical Co.
Vynan Vinyclair	Unplasticized PVC film	Rhodia, Inc.
Vyprime	Adhesive PVC/metal	Plastic Coatings Ltd.
Vyram	Rigid PVC materials	Monsanto Co.
Watahyde	Vinyl sheeting	Harte & Co., Sub. Diamond Shamrock Corp.
Wataseal	Vinyl film and sheeting	Harte & Co., Sub. Diamond Shamrock Corp.
Wavelock	Reinforced nylon calendered film	Majocchi, T. C., & C., S.p.A.
Weldfast	Epoxy and polyester adhesives	Fibercast Co., Div. Youngstown Sheet & Tube Co.
Well-Blend	Blended nylon 6 and 6/6 resins	Wellman, Inc., Plastics Div.
Well-Fibe	Glass-fiber-reinforced nylon resins	Wellman, Inc., Plastics Div.
Well-Sphere	Glass-sphere-reinforced nylon resins	Wellman, Inc., Plastics Div.
Wellamid (Series)	Nylon 6 and 6/6 molding resins	Wellman, Inc., Plastics Div.
Welvic	Vinyl compounds	Imperial Chemical Industries Ltd., Plastics Div.
Wicaset	Polyvinyl acetate emulsions	Wica Chemicals, Div. Story Chemical Corp.
X-Link	Crosslinking latex coatings and binders	National Adhesives Div., National Starch & Chemical Corp.
Xilocolla	Urea-formaldehyde resins	Montedison S.p.A.
XT Polymer	Acrylic multipolymer	American Cyanamid Co., Industrial Chemicals & Plastics Div.
Zelux	Polycarbonate shapes	Westlake Plastics Co.
Zendel	Polyethylene films	Union Carbide Corp., Chemicals & Plastics
Zitex	Fibrous, porous TFE	Chemplast, Inc.
Zytel	Nylon resins	Du Pont de Nemours, E. I., & Co.

Acrylics

The acrylics are thermoplastics which are basically methyl methacrylate polymers. However, there are several copolymers. The major markets for acrylics include lighting equipment, automotive equipment, architectural panels, decorative surfaces, optical and lens applications, carpeting, packaging and display units, adhesives, lacquers, and paints and carpets. Acrylics have outstanding clarity, weather resistance, shatter resistance, colorability, and electrical resistivity. Heat resistance is not outstanding. Light paths can be precisely controlled.

Alkyd Resins (see Polyesters)

Allyl Resins

Allyl resins and monomers are thermosetting plastics which are commercially available as the diallyl esters of phthalic (DAP) and isophthalic (DAIP) acids. Other monomers in this grouping are diallyl maleate (DAM) and diallyl chlorendate (DAC). The latter is used for flame-resistant formulations because of the high chlorine content of the resins. They can be polymerized by raising their temperature or by the use of peroxide initiators. The molding and electrical properties of these materials are excellent. They are primarily used for electrical components, decorative laminates, sealants, and coatings.

Amino Resins

The amino resins are thermosetting plastics. They are basically the reaction products of organic compounds containing the amino group ($-NH_2$) and an aldehyde. The better known members of this group are urea formaldehyde and melamine formaldehyde. These materials are particularly valuable where hard, rigid plastics are needed that are not rapidly affected by temperature elevations. The primary uses are dinnerware, decorative laminates, textile finishing agents, surface coatings, and paper resins.

Cellulosic Plastics

Cellulosic plastics are produced by the chemical modification of cellulose, a natural polymer that is a major constituent of plant life. The primary sources of cellulose for this purpose are cotton linters and wood pulp. The term "cellulosic plastics" applies only to plastics whose resinous content is an ester or ether of cellulose. Included in this group are cellulose acetate, cellulose acetate butyrate, methyl cellulose, cellulose triacetate, cellulose propionate, ethyl cellulose, cellulose nitrate, cellulose films, and fibers.

Cellulose Acetate: A thermoplastic made by treating cellulose with acetic acid and acetic anhydride with sulfuric acid as a catalyst. It can be formed into molding powder, foamed by rapid evaporation of a solvent, dissolved for lacquers, cast into film and spun from solution into fibers. It has replaced hazardous cellulose nitrate for photographic use under the name "safety" film (see also cellulose triacetate). Cellulose acetate molding compositions are tough, of good color and gloss; hardness is varied by ratio of plasticizer and ranges from rigid to flexible. Primary uses are electronic components, insulation tapes, food packaging, toys, eyeglass frames, and sound recording and computer tapes. Rigid foam is used as the core in sandwich panels and marine floats. Variations in composition include the degree of esterification of cellulose and amount and choice of plasticizer, which is usually a phthalate ester. Molding stocks for general purposes ignite easily, give off burning drips, burn with a dark yellow flame, produce moderate smoke, and have an odor of vinegar, unless masked by the odor of the plasticizer. Flame retarded stocks are widely used for molding.

Cellulose Acetate Butyrate (CAB): A plastic made by treating cellulose with a mixture of acetic and butyric acids and anhydrides in the presence of a catalyst. The ratio of acetic and butyric components can be varied to produce the desirable flexibility. It absorbs less water than cellulose acetate. Compositions with ultraviolet stabilizers are used for small outdoor and indoor signs; major uses are auto steering wheels and tail lights, telephone hand sets, toothbrush handles, business machine keys, appliance housings, piping, and tubing.

Cellulose Propionate (CP): A thermoplastic molding composition made from cellulose and propionic acid. Molding compositions are usually supplied as granules or pellets, and finished articles can be fabricated by injection molding or extrusion. It has similar uses to CA and CAB, but because of better surface hardness than CAB and less moisture sensitivity than CA, it is also used for mechanical pencils, telephones and shoe heels.

Cellulose Triacetate: A thermoplastic film made by reacting cellulose with acetic anhydride and differs from cellulose acetate in chemical structure in that it consists of three acetate groups (instead of two) attached to each glucose unit of the cellulose molecule. Because of its high softening temperature, it is not suitable as molding stock. It has lower water absorption than CA and is now the prevalent base for photographic safety film, drawing and printing film, magnetic tape, and transformer and capacitor dielectrics.

Ethyl Cellulose (EC): A thermoplastic molding compound prepared by reacting sodium cellulose with an ethylating agent, such as ethyl chloride. It has many of the tough, flexible characteristics (particularly at low temperatures) of other cellulose products; however, it is lighter in weight. It is produced in pellet form for molding and extrusion and in sheet form for other uses. With high proportions of a plasticizer, it is extensible and such stocks have been called "ethyl rubber." Hot melts of EC and waxes are used for dip coating a peelable protective cover for metal parts. Some of its uses include electrical appliance parts, tool handles, automotive armrests, football helmets, bowling pins, furniture edging and flashlight cases.

Methyl Cellulose: A plastic produced by treating cellulose with a suitable methylating agent, it is particularly suited to certain uses because of its rapid water solubility. It is not suitable for gas or vacuum packaging because of its gas permeability. It is, however, used for packaging measured quantities of dry milk, medicines, laundry bleaches, detergents and other materials to be dissolved in water. It is also used to increase viscosity of water solutions.

Cellophane: A film made of regenerated pure cellulose. Cotton linters or purified wood fibers are dissolved in a mixture of carbon disulfide and aqueous alkali. The resulting heavy solution is extruded into dilute acid and the cellulose is regenerated or precipitated back into the desirable form. Most packaging films have a thin lacquer coating to provide a moisture barrier or heat sealability.

Cellulose Nitrate

Because of the extreme fire hazards associated with cellulose nitrate in its processing, use and storage, the subject is discussed in detail in a separate part (Part D) of this chapter.

Cold Molded Plastics

Cold molded plastics are produced by mixing binder and solvent with large amounts of filler, molding the putty-like mass and baking to remove solvent. Cold molded plastics are of two types: organic and inorganic. Organic cold molded plastics are produced by mixing a bituminous binder or a phenolic resin binder with a filler (usually asbestos), compressing the mixture in a cold mold, and then curing the molded article in an oven. Inorganic cold molded plastics are produced in the same way, but the binder consists of

an inorganic material (cement, lime or silicon). The filler is asbestos.

These plastics have many applications in electrical equipment because of their resistance to arcs and heat. Examples are battery cases, resistor element supports and plugs on appliance cords. They are also used to make pot handles.

Epoxy Resins

Epoxy resins are primarily produced by the reaction of epichlorhydrin and bisphenol in the presence of a catalyst. By varying the ratio of the ingredients, the resultant product may be a low viscosity fluid or a high melting solid. Two primary classes are available, i.e., the liquid resins which are combined with curing agents for adhesives, potting and tooling compounds and the solid resins which are modified with other resins to make coating materials. The epoxy resins are also used as "body solders" for auto repair, as dies for forming sheetmetal, as piping and tubing, and as foamed blocks for construction insulation.

Fluoroplastics

The fluoroplastics or fluorocarbons are commercially available in eight major groups under the headings poly (ethylene-tetrafluoroethylene) (ETFE); perfluoroalkoxy (PFA); poly (ethylene-chlorotrifluoroethylene) (E-CTFE); polytetrafluoroethylene (TFE); polyfluoroethylenepropylene (FEP); the polychlorotrifluoroethylenes (CTFE); polyvinyl fluoride (PVF); and polyvinylidene fluoride (PVF_2). All eight resins are characterized by resistance to solvents and chemical attack and good to excellent weatherability.

Polytetrafluoroethylene (TFE): A representative of a group of completely fluorinated resins. It is handled as general purpose molding powders, fine granules, and aqueous dispersions. The methods of processing include compression molding, extruding, dip coating, and film casting. TFE has a very extended range of serviceable temperatures, from −450°F to 500°F. It is used as chemical gasketing, high-frequency and high temperature electrical insulation, lubricants, molded bearings, and coated cooking wear.

Polyfluoroethylene-propylene (FEP): A copolymer of tetrafluoroethylene and hexafluoropropylene. FEP can be handled through the melt-flow processes involved in extrusion and injection molding.

It is widely used in industrial applications, particularly as insulation for process industries involving heat and corrosive atmospheres. It is also used as a lining for vessels, pipes, valves and fittings handling corrosive fluids.

Poly (ethylene-tetrafluoroethylene) (ETFE): A copolymer of ethylene and tetrafluoroethylene. It is processed by conventional method of extrusion and injection molding. Its applications include gears, pump components, automotive parts, labware, valve linings, electrical connectors, and wire coatings. ETFE can be reinforced with glass fiber.

Perfluoroalkoxy (PFA): A new melt processible fluoroplastic. Processibility is the result of perfluoroalkoxy side chains connected to the carbon-fluorine backbone. Properties and applications are similar to TFE resins.

Polychlorotrifluoroethylene (CTFE): A thermoplastic resin produced in various formulations of fluoroplastics. It differs from the usual fluoroplastic in that its molecular structure contains chlorine. It flows like FEP for injection molding or extrusion but is less thermally stable. It is chemically resistant to many corrosive liquids. Its serviceable temperatures range from −400°F to 390°F. Its electrical and thermal properties make it valuable for insulation, cable assemblies, printed circuits, and electronic components. It also is used in the chemical process industries in valves, fittings, and gaskets.

Poly (ethylene-chlorotrifluoroethylene) (E-CTFE): A 1:1 copolymer of ethylene and chlorotrifluoroethylene. E-CTFE is processed by extrusion, molding, rotocast, and powder coating techniques. Applications include chemically resistant linings, coating, containers, labware, and moldings, wire coating, fibers and films.

Polyvinyl Fluoride (PVF): A plastic produced through the polymerization of vinyl fluoride. Films are cast from selected hot solvents, and the major use is as a weather-resistant surfacing on building siding of aluminum, wood, composite boards, or polyester glass fiber laminates.

Furane Resins

Furane resins consist primarily of those polymers resulting from polymerization of furfuryl alcohol, of phenol and furfural, and of furfuryl alcohol and phenol. Furfuryl alcohol-modified urea formaldehyde resin is furane resin. The furanes are thermo-setting, and have good bond strength and chemical resistance. Furane resin is used as a bond for sand in foundry molds, as an impregnant for hard board and laboratory bench tops, and as a laminating resin for glass fibers to make tanks and fume ducts.

Ionomer Resins

The term "ionomer" is used to describe the class of thermoplastic polymers in which ionized carboxyl groups create ionic crosslinks in the intermolecular structure. Ionomer resin formulations are available in a wide variety of compositions. They are outstanding plastics with regard to toughness, transparency, and solvent resistance, and have toughness against impact at temperatures as low as −160°F. Articles made from these plastics include housewares, toys, containers, safety shields, tool handles, electrical insulation, and packaging. They are also used in the lamination of various building construction materials.

Methylpentene Polymer

Methylpentene polymer is produced by the polymerization of the monomer at atmospheric pressure. The polymer has many properties that make it desirable for specific uses. It has excellent electrical properties and is highly resistant to many corrosive chemicals. This plastic also has good light transmission characteristics. It is finding use for electrical instrumentation, bottles, chemical process equipment and food handling equipment.

Nylon (Polyamides)

Nylon is a generic name for a thermoplastic group of linear polyamides. They are made basically by condensing a diamine with dibasic acid. Many different types of nylon are possible. However, six major polymers are commercially available. They are: Nylon 6 (polycaprolactam); Nylon 6/6 (hexamethylenediamine and adipic acid); Nylon 6/10 (hexamethylenediamine and sebacic acid); Nylon 6/12 (hexamethylenediamine and dodecanedioic acid); Nylon 11 (11-aminoundecanoic acid); and Nylon 12 (12-amino-dodecanoic acid). Copolymers are made from the six types of nylon. Major applications for nylon include monofilaments, wire and cable jacketing, film and extruded rods, and slabs and tubing. Nylon resins are tough, have high service temperatures, are resistant to abrasion and fatigue, and resist oils and solvents.

Phenolic Resins (PF)

Phenolic resins are the result of a condensation reaction of phenol and an aldehyde (formaldehyde or furfuralde-hyde) in the presence of a catalyst. Variations are made by changing the ratio of phenol to aldehyde. Most products used in molding are thermosetting. Although phenols are the starting materials for such resins as epoxy, phenylene oxides, and sulfone, the term "phenolic resins" is understood as meaning only those made by condensing phenols and aldehydes. There are three main groups of phenolic plastics (1) molding compositions, which include various materials combined with the resin (2) cast phenolics made from a casting resin syrup with or without fillers, and (3) phenolic adhesives and laminating solutions. Mixtures are also made by compounding with butadieneacrylonitrile copolymers.

Condensation is first carried to "A-stage" a viscous or glassy resin. For molding, fillers such as wood flour, asbestos fibers, or cotton fabric are mixed in amounts from 5 to 50 per cent of weight of completed mix. On further heating in the molding process, the thermoplastic A-stage is converted ("cured") to the thermoset "B-stage" which is insoluble and infusible. Products of this process are the standard brown or black electrical plugs, auto distributor housings, ash trays, and heat-resistant handles for utensils.

Paper or fabric, impregnated with A-stage resin in a water or organic solvent, can be wound into tube form or pressed into flat-sheets to make tough thermoset "laminates" with low water absorption and high service temperature. Laminates are used for electrical insulation and bearings for marine propellers and heavy rolling mills. Despite the large content of fibrous materials, these stocks are considered plastics and tested by ASTM plastics test procedures.

A-stage resin can also be mixed with alkyd and drying oil varnishes, and compositions are available to harden on exposure to air or in baking operations. Similar compositions are used as laminating adhesives for exterior grade plywood and as impervious surfacing materials. Paper impregnated with phenolic resin and printed with wood grain is frequently the top surface for wall panels or furniture, with backing of other phenolic laminates or plywood. Phenolics are standard binders for brake shoes, sandpaper, grinding wheels, sand casting foundry molds, and wood chip particle board.

Two types of phenolic foam, reaction foam and syntactic foam, are used in construction or for thermal insulation. Reaction foam is made by curing the phenolic resin so rapidly with agitation that by-product water is vaporized and trapped to make the foam voids. Syntactic foam is made from hollow spheres of phenolic resin with phenolic or other resin binder. Each type is used for cores in sandwich panels, and as bouyancy or stiffening means in marine and aircraft structures.

Cast phenolic resin is largely used for decorative applications.

Because of the large proportion of fillers used in nearly all phenolic resins, fire properties are primarily determined by choice and amount of filler. Thermosetting mixes are virtually dripless. Most are difficult to ignite, although they char readily. Electric arcs establish paths of conducting carbon ("tracks") more readily on phenolics than on most plastics; however, the flammability and service temperature of electrical phenolics is such that they are still preferred for insulation or support of many current-carrying parts.

Polyallomer Copolymers

Polyallomers are made by polymerizing two monomers with catalysts so that blocks of each polymer are formed in the polymer chain. The most common polyallomer contains ethylene and propylene. Applications include films, bottles, appliance parts, automotive parts, toys and closures.

Polycarbonates

Polycarbonates are thermoplastic polyesters of carbonic acid. A commercially available product is produced by linking bis-phenol A and carbonic acid. Other processes of commercial importance involving many different starting materials are available. The resin is available in several different forms including pellets, powder, film, sheet, rod, plate, and tubing. High impact strength, good electrical properties, clarity, and resistance to creep have caused this material to find many applications, such as in appliances, electrical and electronics equipment, food handling products, and sporting goods.

Polyesters

Polyesters or alkyd resins are generally condensation polymers resulting from the reaction of polyhydric alcohols and polybasic acids. The products of these reactions show a wide range of properties and have many different applications.

Unsaturated polyesters comprise an important part of this group. Chemically these materials contain double bonds which make the unsaturated polyester capable of subsequent cross-linking. Reactive monomers such as styrene are blended and reacted with the polyester to copolymerize and form a specific thermoset. Unsaturated polyesters are reinforced with fibrous glass and other strengthening agents to enhance their use. Molding is possible by economical techniques at high and low pressures. A peroxide initiator is frequently used in processing. Unsaturated polyesters show good weathering resistance, light stability, and heat resistance. The primary application is in the production of reinforced plastics. They are used to fabricate structures ranking in size from electrical components to large boat hulls.

Saturated polyesters do not have the double bond that would permit further polymerization by treatment with initiators, such as organic peroxides. Saturated polyesters of high molecular weight, such as ethylene glycol terephthalate, are used principally in fiber and film production. Saturated polyesters are used primarily for magnetic recording tapes, tough or boil-in-bag food packaging, and satellite balloons. They can be back-plated with metals for decorative films and nameplates. The low molecular weight esters are used as plasticizers for vinyl and acrylic resins.

Thermoplastic polyester molding compositions are available. Besides poly (ethylene terephthate)—PET, there are poly (1,4-butylene terephthalate)—PBT, poly (tetramethylene terephthalate)—PTMT, and poly (cyclohexylenedimethylene terephthalate isophthalate)—PCDT. PBT and PTMT are chemically the same.

Thermoplastic polyesters have engineering applications, which include automotive parts, appliance parts, business machine parts, electrical and electronic parts, gears, bearings, pulleys, and pump components.

Polyphenylene Oxide (PPO)

Polyphenylene oxide is a thermoplastic resin formed by the catalyzed oxidation of 2,6-xylenol. It is a specialized, highly engineered plastic with a wide temperature range, good mechanical and electrical properties, and resistance to corrosive materials. It has many electrical and electronic applications, is used for packaging frozen foods and as a replacement for glass and stainless steel in hospital utensils and medical instruments.

Polysulfone

Polysulfone is a thermoplastic resin which contains a diphenylene group. This group imparts certain desirable characteristics to the polymer, including thermal stability, oxidation resistance, and rigidity. Commercial applications include electronic units, electrical circuit breaker parts, automobile engine parts, aircraft interiors, kitchen range hardware, electroplating equipment, and appliance hardware.

Polyethylene (PE)

Polyethylene is a thermoplastic manufactured by polymerizing ethylene. The nature of the polyethylene varies in accordance with the type and the molecular weight. Three major types of polyethylene are marketed, namely the low-density, medium-density and high-density products. In addition, copolymers of ethylene-ethyl acrylate, ethylene-vinyl acetate and ethylene-butylene are produced. There are three density ranges: 0.91 to 0.95 grams per ml, 0.926 to 0.94 grams per ml and 0.941 to 0.965 grams per ml.

Low-density stocks are waxy, relatively limp, and are the toughest of the polyethylenes with an upper service temperature around 160°F. As density increases, so do surface hardness, stiffness, resistance to permeation by oils and water, and softening temperatures. For polyethylenes of the highest density, upper service temperature is 240°F under no-load conditions.

The outstanding properties of polyethylenes are (1) good moldability, (2) good mechanical properties, (3) excellent electrical resistance, (4) low moisture vapor transmission, (5) resistance to solvents and chemicals, and (6) lightness. Polyethylene is widely used as film, sheeting, plastic bottles, piping, tubing, dish pans, garbage containers, laundry baskets, electronic components, insulation, and textiles. Boat and motor vehicle fuel tanks are a recent application for high-density polyethylene.

Polypropylene

Polypropylene possesses the lowest density of the commercially available thermoplastics. In addition, it exhibits good rigidity, high yield strength, good surface hardness, exceptional flexural properties, resistance to chemicals, and excellent dielectric properties.

Primary areas of use include the usual categories of molding as well as in film and piping. It is used for interior trim of automobiles and for many parts of appliances. Because of its superior insulating properties it is used to make electronic components. Carpeting made of polypropylene fibers also is available.

Polyurethane

The polyurethanes consist of a group of polymers which are produced in the following general forms: foams (flexible, semi-flexible, and rigid); elastomers (casting compounds and elastoplastic resins, adhesives, coatings, and spandex fiber). The basic reaction used to produce the urethane polymers involves isocyanates and reactive hydrogen-bearing materials such as polyethers, castor oils, amines, carboxylic acid and water. By varying the number of branchings, it is possible to make polyurethanes that are thermoplastic or thermosetting.

The polyurethane foams are widely used in the production of upholstered furniture, bedding, sponges, toys, wearing apparel, and medical dressings. Rigid urethane foams are used in building construction for insulation. Substantial quantities of the polyurethanes are used to produce coatings and adhesives. Its rubberlike qualities aid in the production of specialty fillers and elastomers. Gears, sprockets, and rolls are produced from urethanes. Very thin films are used to produce containers impermeable to gas and moisture.

Rubbers

Distinctions between rubbers and plastics are steadily becoming more difficult to make, whether by properties of finished articles, processing techniques, or chemical properties. All rubbers burn with considerable smoke.

Chlorinated rubber is made by adding chlorine to some or all of the unsaturated bonds in natural rubber. The most common product is the fully chlorinated thermoplastic used for paints. These coatings are tough, have good resistance to alkali, and are used on concrete flooring.

Rubber hydrochloride is produced by adding hydrogen chloride to unsaturated bonds of natural rubber. It can be made into transparent stretchable films and is used to clarify other rubbers and also as an adhesive.

Acrylic rubbers are copolymers of acrylonitrile and butadiene or other rubber monomers. The principal use is for oil-resistant hose and gaskets. GRN is one designation.

Butadiene rubber refers to those synthetic rubbers that are copolymers with butadiene. GRS is a copolymer of butadiene and styrene.

Neoprene refers to all polymers of chloroprene. These polymers ignite less readily than natural or GRS rubber.

Silicone Resins

The silicone resins comprise a large group of polymers consisting of chains of alternating silicon and oxygen atoms with organic groups, e.g., methyl, attached to the silicon atoms. They are produced by the condensation of organosilicon halide intermediates. The silicons are stable at high and low temperatures, have good dielectric properties, resist weathering, do not react with most chemicals, and repel water.

Silicone emulsions are used as mold release agents, defoamers, and water-proofing material. A compound of liquid silicone and finely divided filler is a grease suitable for high temperature lubrication applications. Silicone paints, varnishes, and enamels have many uses, including cloth and wire coating. With inorganic fillers, such as glass or asbestos, silicones are molded into such products as connector plugs, coil bobbins, insulators on induction furnaces, and heat barriers in jet engine afterburners. Silicone-glass liminate applications include rigid hot air ducts for aircraft, terminal boards, and transformer spools and spacers. Rigid silicone forms can be preformed or foamed in place. High temperature insulation is the principal use of rigid silicone foams. So-called silicone rubber foams are useful where resilience and low density are desired in addition to the other properties of the silicones. They have application where low temperature flexibility is needed, and as cushioning around electrical components and as nursing bottle nipples.

Styrene Polymers and Copolymers

Polystyrene (PS): A thermoplastic polymer produced by the polymerization of styrene, lends itself to many modifications. The primary characteristics of these plastics are hardness, rigidity, clarity, and heat and dimensional stability. By varying the polymerization reaction, polystyrenes have been developed with higher heat distortion temperatures. Styrene polymers are marketed in granular and powder form for extrusion or molding. Beads of polystyrene, containing flammable expanding agent (pentane), are sold for the production of polystyrene foam.

General purposes and impact grades of polystyrene are used for refrigerator liners, appliance housings, automotive applications, films for wrapping, sporting goods, toys and novelties. Heat-resistant polystyrene is used for TV sets, radios and illuminated signs. Glass filled polystyrene is used for business machines, housings, electronic equipment, and military hardware. Polystyrene foam is used to make toys, insulation, displays, shipping containers, and molded furniture. Construction panels consisting of cores of polystyrene foam between sheets of plywood, plastic, or aluminum and foamed-in-place insulation are used in the building industry.

Styrene-acrylonitrile Copolymer (SAN): This plastic group is produced by the copolymerization of styrene and acrylonitrile. Varying the concentration of each material offers materials of different properties. It is superior to the general purpose styrene polymer in hardness, rigidity, and tensile strength.

Acrylonitrile-butadiene-styrene (ABS): Copolymers of this type make up a large family of plastics. They are tougher than polystyrene, less subject to solvent attack, and have better resistance to creep rupture. The uses include pipes and fittings, appliances, business machines, auto dash panels, toys, and refrigerator liners.

PVC (see Vinyl Polymers)

Vinyl Polymers and Copolymers

The vinyl resins are thermoplastics that exist in a wide variety of polymers and copolymers. Commercial production of the vinyl chloride monomer starts with acetylene or ethylene. Most vinyl plants utilize an oxychlorination process with ethylene to produce vinyl chloride. Copolymers of vinyl chloride and vinyl acetate account for a large part of the vinyl production.

The major applications for flexible and rigid vinyls include: automobile seat covers, floor mats, and moldings; shower curtains, window shades, wrappings, bottles, and adhesives; flooring, siding, piping, and wiring; swimming pools; records; and medical appliances.

Polyvinyl Chloride (PVC): This type of plastic is made as a rigid product for a number of building components and as a flexible plasticized stock for upholstery and wearing apparel. It exists in hundreds of individual formulations. It has good abrasion resistance.

The unplasticized PVC softens as it burns, and produces white smoke and acrid fumes which can be corrosive. Most of the chlorine content is released as hydrogen chloride. The fire properties of plasticized PVC are determined to a large extent by the nature of the plasticizer. Building products should be tested individually.

Vinyl Chloride-vinyl Acetate Copolymers (PV-AC): These contain from 5 to 20 percent of vinyl acetate in the polymer. They are used for more flexible stocks than PVC and are more readily softened by plasticizers. The properties are essentially those of PVC.

Polyvinyl Dichloride: Made by chlorinating PVC, this plastic's properties are essentially those of rigid PVC. Its major use has been where greater toughness, stiffness, and heat resistance are needed than offered by PVC.

Vinyl Acetate Polymer: A thermoplastic that is used in coatings, as a wood primer, and as an adhesive in a milky aqueous dispersion. It is not used as a molding or sheet plastic, as the upper service temperature is below 120°F.

Vinyl Alcohol Resins (PVA): Made by hydrolysis of polyvinyl acetate, PVA products swell or dissolve completely in water. They are highly impervious to oils and many lacquer solvents, and are used in hose for spray painting, and as a water-soluble film for dose-packaging detergents, etc.

Polyvinyl Butyral (PVB): Produced by condensing butyraldehyde with polyvinyl alcohol, PVB has remarkable adhesive qualities. It is primarily used as plasticized film for laminating automotive safety glass.

Polyvinyl Formal (PVF): Produced by condensing formaldehyde with polyvinyl alcohol to give a horny resin, PVF is then mixed with small amounts of phenolic resin to improve the bond and reduce creep. It is not to be confused with polyvinyl fluoride (see Fluoroplastics). Its principal use is as standard insulation enamel for magnet wire in small motors and electronic equipment.

Vinylidene Chloride Polymer: A thermoplastic that as a film has low permeability to water vapor. A principal use is as a coating on cellophane. Filaments are used for webbing on garden furniture, and for window screening.

Vinylidene Chloride-vinyl Chloride Copolymer: This plastic is less rigid than PVC and flows more readily in extrusion and molding. Its major use is for coating for metals and molded electrical parts.

D.   Cellulose Nitrate

Cellulose nitrate (also referred to as nitrocellulose and pyroxylin) is made by the action of nitric and sulfuric acids on cellulose materials, such as cotton. Pyroxylin plastic comprises the lower nitrated products, containing from 11 to 12 percent nitrogen.

Cellulose nitrate plastics possess the most unusual and serious burning characteristics of all plastics. Material which has been subjected to heat as that salvaged from a fire, may be so altered in composition as to be subject to spontaneous ignition.

When cellulose nitrate products are heated to temperatures above 300°F, decomposition starts, which generates further heat and soon raises the material to its ignition temperature. Some experimenters have reported decomposition after long continued exposure to temperatures not much above that of boiling water. There are a number of cases on record of ignition from contact with steam pipes and electric light bulbs.

Decomposition of cellulose nitrate materials generates heat and does not depend upon external air supply.

Some of the gases of decomposition are highly toxic. The effect of carbon monoxide is well known. The toxic effect of the oxides of nitrogen is often delayed; persons exposed to these gases may show no immediate ill effects, but fatalities may follow some hours or days after exposure.

Cellulose nitrate when in solution in acetone or any of the various solvents used has no greater hazard than that of the solvent. If the solvent is lost, the hazard reverts to that of cellulose nitrate.

Most articles formerly made of cellulose nitrate are now made from less hazardous plastics. However, some common articles, for example, eyeglass frames, are still being made from cellulose nitrate in certain other countries. Wherever cellulose nitrate plastic is still in use there should be no relaxation of the special fire protection measures which years of experience have made necessary to safeguard life and property from cellulose nitrate fires.

Processing Cellulose Nitrate

Fire safety in plants processing cellulose nitrate plastic consists essentially of four parts: (1) segregation of hazards, (2) elimination of ignition sources, (3) good housekeeping, and (4) strong fire control facilities. In some plants finished cellulose nitrate plastic parts may be assembled with other articles which do not involve any special fire hazard; for example, toilet seats. In such cases, the hazard and necessary protection depend upon the quantity of cellulose nitrate used. If the quantities used are large, the same safeguards should be followed as for plants in which the product is made entirely from cellulose nitrate.

Cellulose Nitrate Storage

Storage of cellulose nitrate plastics require special facilities. Depending on the quantity to be stored, these may be cabinets, vaults, storage rooms, or isolated storage buildings. Storage facilities are described in detail in two NFPA Standards: NFPA No. 43E, Code for the Storage of Pyroxylin Plastic, and NFPA No. 40, Standard for Storage and Handling of Cellulose Nitrate Motion Picture Film.

Cellulose Nitrate Photographic Film

All photographic film made in the United States and Canada since 1952 is of the safety base type, usually cellulose acetate or triacetate or polyester. An engraving process used in some printing plants engraves on cellulose nitrate plates.

There is comparatively little storage of cellulose nitrate X-ray film although some hospitals may still store X-rays made on cellulose nitrate film many years ago. Appreciable quantities of old nitrate motion picture and aero film still exist. Small amounts of portrait, industrial, and amateur nitrate film probably exist, but in the usual storage of this material (in paper envelopes) they offer no serious hazard. Nitrate base film manufactured in Russia or East Germany may occasionally be encountered.

The existence of old nitrate motion picture and aero film does present a hazard, since persons handling this material may not be familiar with its serious hazards and the elaborate precautions necessary to handle it safely. While it is unlikely that nitrate film will be projected in a theater handling present-day motion pictures, it is quite possible that such material may be shown in small "art" or "film society" theaters. Unfortunately, projectionists may not be aware of the fact that a nitrate print is to be shown.

For this reason the theater projection standards should still be kept in effect. However, the open projection of known safety base film does not present hazards from the film itself. Storage of nitrate film should be in accordance with the NFPA Cellulose Nitrate Motion Picture Film Standard.

The amounts of scrap nitrate motion picture film have greatly decreased, and most of the agencies that formerly handled this material are no longer in existence. This has given rise to the possibility the scrap could accumulate in dangerous quantities. Prior to environmental concern with air pollutants from outdoor burning, the best procedure for disposing of scrap nitrate film was to burn it at a remote location in the open, with all personnel at a safe distance upwind insofar as toxic oxides of nitrogen are among the products of combustion. If accumulations of scrap nitrate film are a problem, the best course to follow would be to check with environmental authorities to learn if such open burning is permitted locally.

Transportation of Cellulose Nitrate

The Department of Transportation (DOT) regulates the interstate transportation of cellulose nitrate plastic by rail, highway, or water. These regulations permit dry shipment of cellulose nitrate (pyroxylin) scrap when specially packaged, but if there is evidence of or possibility of decomposition, shipment under water is required. Shipment of cellulose nitrate sheets, rolls, rods, and tubes is not subject to special DOT regulation, except when shipped by rail express or water. Articles manufactured entirely of or containing cellulose nitrate plastic do not require special packaging when shipped by land, rail, or water. Special shipping regulations apply to cellulose nitrate wet with alcohol, solvent, or water.

Shipments of cellulose nitrate motion picture film and X-ray film are permitted when certain packaging requirements are met, including inside containers for individual reels of film made of light metal, cardboard, or fiberboard. The NFPA Cellulose Nitrate Motion Picture Film Standard places restrictions on the transportation of nitrate film on public vehicles to protect the public against the consequences of a possible fire involving the film.

Air transportation of cellulose nitrate plastic scrap is not permitted by regulations of the International Air Transport Association, whereas cellulose nitrate plastic rods, sheets, rolls, tubes, manufactured articles, motion picture, and X-ray films are permitted only when specially packaged.

Extinguishing Cellulose Nitrate Fires

Large volumes of water are required to put out cellulose nitrate fires. Automatic sprinklers constitute the best general protection for areas where cellulose nitrate materials are stored or handled. Water supplies should be particularly strong. Closer sprinkler spacing is required than for ordinary occupancies in order to supply sufficient water to absorb the heat. The water from sprinklers, in addition to its extinguishing and cooling effect, tends to absorb the poisonous oxides of nitrogen fumes but has no effect on carbon monoxide.

If hose streams are required, the objective should be to get large quantities of water on the fire as soon as possible. Fire fighters should be located upwind or protected by self-contained breathing apparatus to prevent inhalation of the products of combustion.

E.   Fire Behavior of Plastics

The fire behavior of plastic materials depends somewhat on the form of the plastic article, on the end use, and on the manner in which it is exposed to ignition, as well as its chemical makeup. All of the major plastic materials are combustible and, in a major fire, all contribute fuel. However, important differences can be seen in the ease of ignition from a small heat source and in the rate of flame propagation during the initial stages of a fire.

Like most organic materials, polymers decompose to combustible gases when heated to high temperatures. These gases provide the fuel to produce more heat and therefore more decomposition. The rate of flame propagation will depend on the rate of gas generation. This in turn depends on the chemical nature of the polymer as well as the heat flux impinging the article or structure and the rate of heat transfer through the article.

Thermoplastic articles tend to melt and flow when heated. This may remove fuel from the ignition source or it may spread a fire by "flaming drips." Thermoset plastic articles tend to hold their shape when heated. Advantages and disadvantages of thermoplastic versus thermoset materials depend on form, configuration, and end use.

Polymers are used in a wide variety of shapes and forms. These physical forms influence the rate of heat transfer and ease of ignition and therefore are important to the flammability question. For this discussion, classifications that are considered are films, forms, filled plastics, and foamed plastics.

Films

Films have very little thickness relative to area. Free films usually exhibit molecular orientation; and when heated, they will shrink and withdraw from the heat source. This makes it difficult to ignite a free film with a match, but large heat sources will provide enough heat to initiate decomposition of the polymer and subsequent flammability. Coatings and adhesives are film forms (frequently containing mineral pigments and other additives) where heat transfer is a function of the adjacent material and composition, as discussed under "Filled Plastics."

Formed Plastic Articles

Formed plastic articles are defined here to include all thick sections such as rods, moldings, and sheets that have significant thickness. Heat transfer and ease of ignition are functions of the polymer.

Filled Plastics

Filled plastics include polymers reinforced with other solid materials. Heat transfer and rate of temperature rise are functions of the base polymer and the filler as well as the relative amounts used in the composite. The ease of ignition is related to the thermal conductivity and specific heat of the composite. The rate of flame propagation is also influenced by the effect of the reinforcement on the flow properties of the molten polymer.

Foamed Plastics

Foamed plastics are produced over a wide range of void to polymer ratios. If the polymer is expanded only slightly, only one to two volumes of blowing agent per volume of plastic, it is essentially like a foamed article and can be considered in that group. Foamed articles with greater volumes of blowing agent per volume of polymer are somewhat different in their fire behavior. There is obviously less fuel per volume of material and the heat transfer will depend on the polymer, the gas filling the voids, and the manner in which the voids are distributed. Low density foams may withdraw from a small ignition source or may burn away without providing enough heat to continue decomposition.

Other Considerations

The end use of plastic articles will influence the form the plastic takes and will determine the probability of exposure to an ignition source and the involvement in the early stages of a fire. Such factors as total mass, surface area, covering if any, location of probable use (proximity of ignition source), and configuration, e.g., vertical versus horizontal, will influence whether ignition is likely and the rate of initial flame spread if ignition occurs. Every end use has certain design requirements—whether mechanical, chemical, or aesthetic. Flammability characteristics must become a part of these design requirements, based on the hazard potential of the particular end use.

Polymer formulations vary in the ease of ignition and in the rate of flame propagation during the early stages of burning. Great care must be used in designing any article or structure due to these variations combined with the many differences (described above) related to form and end use. This entire problem is still in the early stages of technology development. Extensive research and development effort is now being expanded to define the proper end use and form limitations of various plastic materials.

F. Products of Combustion

The hazards from the products of burning plastics are essentially the hazards from the products of combustion in general as described in Section 2, Chapter 3. However, the specially-designed qualities of plastics may be obtained by the introduction of specific chemical or physical characteristics not found in natural products of comparable use. These characteristics, such as halogenated compounds or air spaces in foam, can cause a different type of fire behavior from that associated with natural products used in similar applications.

Smoke

All common fires of mixed origin will produce carbon particles that, when airborne, form the particulate matter of smoke. These particles may carry adsorbed liquid irritants and be mixed with irritant or toxic decomposition gases. Smoke also can "trap" people by obscuring exits and causing panic.

Smoke generation from a given polymer may vary widely depending on the nature of the polymer, the additives present, whether fire exposure was flaming or smoldering, and what ventilation was present. Several comments from Gaskill's comprehensive study on smoke density[16] are especially pertinent:

1. Woods and most polymeric material pyrolytically degrade, yielding smokes that are dense to very dense. Ventilation tends to clear the smoke, but in most cases it does not reduce the intensity to the point of satifactory visibility.

2. Woods and those polymeric materials that burn cleanly will yield smokes, under conditions of heat and flame, of somewhat less density. With fire retardants incorporated into the polymer (at least in the case of solid materials), heat and flame generally produce very dense smokes, and this occurs rapidly.

3. Urethane foams under flaming or nonflaming exposures generally yield dense smokes, and with few exceptions obscuration occurs in a fraction of a minute. Flaming exposure usually causes the smokes to be generated in less than 15 sec and the intensities in this case are usually higher than in the nonflaming case.

Toxicity

In practically all major fire disasters the primary cause of loss of life has been the inhalation of heated and toxic or oxygen-deficient, or both, fire gases. In general, with plastics as with naturally occurring combustibles, carbon monoxide is usually the most lethal fire gas and carbon dioxide may increase the toxic hazard of any other gases present. Similarly, any elements in a polymer other than carbon, hydrogen, and oxygen may also be the source of additional toxic gases depending on the nature of the polymer and fire conditions of temperature and ventilation. (Section 2, Chapter 3 contains a discussion of the fire gases that have received the most attention in recent literature.)

Corrosiveness

Sufficient HCl from thermal decomposition of polyvinyl chloride will attack metal, such as structural and reinforcing steel, and corrode machinery.

G. Fire Tests for Plastics

Because of the thousands of variations possible in basic polymer types, it is virtually impossible to assign a single meaningful fire test value to a plastic group. Combustibility characteristics are influenced by the nature of plastic additives and the form which the final product takes. From the standpoint of the fire protection engineer, tests should be designed to show how each product will perform under "end-use" conditions. The emphasis has been and will continue to be to devise performance tests that examine sizeable components, instead of small scale comparison tests used as production controls. The most desirable tests for evaluating fire characteristics of plastics are the large scale tests that relate to the "end-use" of products; consequently they currently are the same medium- and large-scale tests as used for the more traditional materials (see Table 3-7B). Any one test is generally insufficient to evaluate a "fire condition" completely. Therefore, in certain cases, more than one test should be considered.

Among the many variables that affect the behavior of a plastic when exposed to fire, which are not easily evaluated by small-scale tests, are shape and size of the plastic part, tendency of the plastic to melt and drip, effect of severe heat exposure on large quantities, composition of products of combustion, and methods of installation of plastic materials.

The diversified use of plastics for building construction is increasing rapidly. Plastics are used as structural and finishing materials, such as floor tiles, pipes, insulation, facings, roofing, moisture barriers, and adhesives. Laminates, reinforced plastics, and foamed core sandwich panels are other construction applications.

Plastics that incorporate flame retardants in various proprietary formulations have been used for more than a quarter of a century. When a plastic contains an additive to reduce rate of burning, the plastic is said to be "flame retarded." With the continued supply of heat from an igniting flame, most "flame retarded" stocks will burn or glow. The necessity of complying with building codes has turned more producers to flame-retardant formulations. Polymers to which flame retardants may be added include polyvinyl chloride, polyethylene, polyesters, epoxies, polyurethanes,

Table 3-7B. Medium- and Large-Scale Tests for Combustibility of Plastics

Test for:	Number
Surface Burning of Building Materials	NFPA 255 UL 723[17] ASTM E-84[18]
Fire Tests of Building Construction and Materials	NFPA 251 UL 263[19] ASTM E-119[20]
Fire Tests of Roof Coverings Radiant Panel Test for Flame Spread Factory Mutual Calorimeter Test UL and FM Corner Wall Tests Full Room Burnouts—FM, UL	NFPA 256 ASTM E-162[21]
Flame-Retardant Films	NFPA 701 UL 214[22]

and cellulose acetate. Surface coatings which form intumescent chars are also used on plastic housings for electronic components.

Comparative fire tests of an empirical nature have been used to determine the sprinkler requirements for storage of foamed plastic products (see NFPA Standards No. 231B, Storage of Cellular Rubber and Plastics, and No. 231C, Rack Storage of Materials).

Small Scale Tests for Combustibility of Plastics

The relative combustibility of plastics are measured by small-scale "bench" test methods (ASTM and UL) for the purpose of evaluating materials in product development and production control. These tests were not developed to relate to fire hazards, and fire protection personnel should therefore use these tests only with the utmost in precaution. A brief summary of these tests are listed in Table 3-7C.

H.   Fire Retardant Treatment for Plastics

All organic and some inorganic materials burn under proper conditions, even finely divided steel. Making materials noncombustible under all conditions is impossible. Fire retardants can make a given material more difficult to ignite, and, when ignited, cause it to burn more slowly. Materials that have been "fire retarded" can be made to burn; however, they are more difficult to burn than the corresponding non-fire retardant materials.

Materials are often classed as natural or synthetic. Cotton, wool, and wood are examples of flammable natural materials. Nylon, polystrene, polyurethane, polyvinyl chloride, polyethylene, and acrylics are common types of synthetic materials. Both, natural and synthetic materials are used in construction, furnishings, apparel, etc.

Synthetic materials are fire retarded by making molecular (structural) changes in the reactants used to make synthetic polymers or by blending fire retardant additives into the polymer mix during processing. Fire retardant additives also can be chemically reacted throughout the polymer substrate or on the surface of finished or semi-finished products.

Fire retardancy can be built into synthetic polymers at any step in the process. Natural materials in contrast must generally be fire retarded in the latter stages of product development (see Sec. 5, Chap. 10).

A retardant may function by any of several mechanisms, depending on the particular system to be retarded. Phosphorus additives, for example, appear to improve fire retardancy by promoting (1) formation of char to reduce concentration of carbon-containing gases, (2) by forming a glassy, insulating layer, and (3) either by entering into chemical reactions that remove heat from the combustion system, or by chemically inhibiting the combustion process, or both. Compounds containing halogens, such as chlorine and bromine, tend to inhibit burning in the gas phase by interrupting chain reactions needed for continuous burning.

A complicating aspect of fire retarding plastics and other materials is that a fire retardant chemical that works on one substrate system will not necessarily work in other substrates. Thus, fire retardant chemicals for polystyrene will not necessarily work on polyethylene or nylon or wood or cotton. Fire retardant chemicals often impair some other material properties. For example, fire retardant treatments for cotton fabrics generally reduce fabric strength and wear life. Fire retardants in plastics may reduce allowable processing temperatures and impair physical properties. Costs generally are increased.

Methods Used to Improve Fire Retardancy

The fire retardancy of a plastic can be improved by inhibiting, controlling, or eliminating one or more of the four stages of combustion: heating, decomposition, ignition, and self-propagating combustion.

In the Heating Stage: In the heating stage preceding ignition an external ignition source raises the temperature of the material at a rate dependent on the thermal intensity of the ignition source and thermal properties of the material, such as thermal conductivity, specific heat, latent heats of fusion and vaporization.

There are three ways in which fire retardancy can be improved by reducing rate of heating:

1. Fire retardancy will generally be improved if an additive causes formation of a surface film of low thermal conductivity or high reflectivity that reduces the rate of heating or both.

2. An additive might serve as a heat sink by being preferentially decomposed at a low temperature.

3. A coating that intumesces, i.e., forms a foamed surface layer with low thermal conductivity, will generally provide a barrier to heat transfer to the material.

In the Decomposition Stage: When heated sufficiently, original properties of the material begin to alter and weakest chemical bonds begin breaking. Gaseous combustible products may be formed, with the rate dependent on such

Table 3-7C.   Small-Scale Tests for Combustibility of Plastics

Test Method	Sample Size	Position of Sample	Ignition Source	Time and Limit of Exposure	Value Reported	Usual Material Application
ASTM D635[23]	$\frac{1}{8} \times \frac{1}{2} \times 5$ in.	Horizontal	1-in. Flame	2–30 Sec	Burning rate, ipm*	Rigid Plastic
ASTM D568[24]	$0.05 \times 1 \times 18$ in.	Horizontal	1-in. Flame	15 Sec	Burning rate, ipm	Films
ASTM D229[25]	$\frac{1}{32} \times \frac{1}{2} \times 5$ in.	Horizontal	1-in. Flame	30 Sec	Burning time for 4 samples	Elec. Insulation
ASTM D1692[26]	$\frac{1}{2} \times 2 \times 6$ in.	Horizontal	1-in. Flame	60 Sec	Burning rate, ipm	Foam
UL 94[27]	$\frac{1}{8} \times \frac{1}{2} \times 5$ in. $\frac{1}{8} \times \frac{1}{2} \times 5$ in.	Horizontal Vertical	$\frac{3}{4}$-in. Flame $\frac{3}{4}$-in. Flame	30 Sec 2–10 Sec	Burning rate, ipm Extinguishment Time	Rigid Plastics Rigid Plastics
NFPA 701	$2\frac{3}{4} \times 10$ in.	Vertical	$1\frac{1}{2}$-in. Flame	12 Sec	Length of Char	Films
UL 214[22]	$2\frac{3}{4} \times 10$ in.	Vertical	$1\frac{1}{2}$-in. Flame	12 Sec	Length of Char	Films

* Inches per minute.

factors as intensity of external heat, temperature required for initial decomposition, and rate of decomposition. Decomposition can be retarded as follows:

1. An additive can promote transformation of an organic material to char, thus limiting production of combustible hydrocarbon gases. Reduced fuel provides less heat generation by the flame and may lead to extinguishment. Simultaneously, the char will tend to decrease thermal conductivity of the surface.

2. An additive or structure modification might induce decomposition or melting upon exposure to the external heat source, so the material may shrink or drip away.

3. Where structural modification of a polymer is possible, decomposition can be retarded through selection of chemically stable structural components.

In the Ignition Stage: Flammable gases increase until a concentration is reached that allows sustained oxidation when exposed to an ignition source. Variables include: type of ignition source (flame, spark, or thermal radiation), auto-ignition characteristics of the gas, and availability of oxygen.

At the ignition stage fire retardancy can be improved by an additive or polymer unit that decomposes under external heat to form gases that react chemically in a manner to inhibit combustion in the gas phase.

In the Self-propagating Combustion Stage: After removal of the ignition source, combustion will become self-propagating if sufficient heat is generated and radiated back to the material to continue the decomposition processes. Some variables are: rate of heat release, position of flame with respect to surface, rate of heat transfer to the surface, and rates of decomposition.

In this stage the goal is to decrease the rate of heat evolution or transfer. Any or all of the foregoing mechanisms could function to prevent a fire from being self-sustaining. More than one process may come into play. The selection of a particular approach or combination depends on many factors, including the chemical composition of a product, fabricating conditions, physical and esthetic properties desired, the specific end use of the product, and the magnitude of the ignition source.

A word of caution—the misuse of retardants can increase flammability. For example, a good flame retardant for a cellulosic material may increase the burning rate of a thermoplastic such as nylon—or vice versa. Smoke generation may or may not be significantly reduced by the treatment. For example, many moderately flammable plastics, such as acrylics, acetate, and polyethylene, emit relatively little smoke when burning. However, when treated by chemical change, they become less flammable, but invariably generate more smoke per unit burned. The questions arise: (1) Is it preferable to have more flame spread with less smoke, or less flame spread with more smoke, and (2) which condition is likely to result in the greater total amount of smoke?

For information on the mechanisms of fire retardant and flame resistant treatments of materials other than plastics see Section 5, Chapter 10. Flame retardant treatments for textiles made from both natural and synthetic materials are covered in Chapter 2 of this Section.

I. Fighting Fires in Plastic Plants

Plastics plants have such a wide range of processes and materials that it is not possible to generalize on fire fighting procedures. In view of the speed and frequency with which operations are changed in most plastics plants, it is good practice to invite local fire authorities to tour the plant regularly, and to advise them of changes in operations which have a bearing on fire hazards. Particularly where solvents, monomers, or peroxygen materials are stored or used, plant management must actively work for both fire prevention and protection.

Plastics Products

Plastics other than cellulose nitrate are classified as ordinary combustibles. Consequently, extinguishing methods found suitable for fires involving wood and other ordinary combustibles (Class A fires) should be used to extinguish a burning plastic. Fire protection should consider automatic sprinklers, standpipe and hose systems, and water-type portable extinguishers. These should be supplemented by fire extinguishers or special automatic systems suitable for flammable liquid and electrical fires where these hazards exist.

Physical form of plastics will greatly influence their fire behavior. Molding pellets as shipped in bags, drums, or large cartons, provide but little surface for access to air. These same plastics in such shapes as flashlight cases will have much more access to air and may burn vigorously until heat causes the shapes to melt, thereby reducing the surface area exposed to air. Melting may be a hazard if burning drips carry flame to lower floors or spread fuel for later ignition. For this reason during fire fighting some hose streams should be used to cool exposed plastics to keep them from melting and dripping. This is a major advantage of automatic or manual sprinklers in large storage areas.

Foamed Plastics: These plastics have large surface areas but little heat of combustion per unit volume. Under fire conditions thermoplastic types of foam are readily reduced to small volume. If traces of flammable blowing agent remain in the foamed plastic, a much greater hazard exists. For reasons of fire safety in manufacture and storage, non-flammable fluorinated hydrocarbons should be considered to replace such material as pentane for blowing agent.

Toxicity: Combustion and thermal decomposition products of plastics, possibly because of long chemical names of some plastics, have been cause for concern among fire fighters. For plastics now in commercial use the hazard of carbon monoxide from partial combustion greatly outweighs the toxic effects of other fire gases, both as to nature and amount. Whether this will remain true for future plastics cannot yet be forecast. Presence or absence of chemicals that produce toxic gases should be verified at each regular fire department inspection.

On burning, some plastics, such as polyvinyl chloride or ethylene sulfide rubbery caulking materials, generate hydrogen chloride or sulfur dioxide. These are strongly irritating, and ordinarily force evacuation long before their toxic effects become dangerous. These gases are corrosive to metals and electrical equipment; therefore the equipment should be ventilated, rinsed, or treated with dilute ammonia and rinsed as soon as possible after exposure.

Solvents: The esters, ketones, hydrocarbons, and chlorinated hydrocarbons, common in the paint and lacquer industry, are used in making or converting plastics. Their use with plastics presents no new hazard, but their presence should be expected in many plastic plants.

Monomers: Monomers present two distinct fire fighting hazards: (1) most of them are flammable gases or liquids, and (2) they may be subject to polymerization by heating due to chemical reaction with other materials (sulfuric acid, chlorine, oxidizing agents). General advice is to use dry chemical or carbon dioxide on small fires, water spray on large fires. Most monomers will quickly break down foam-water extinguishants. Fire and health hazards of most commercial monomers are given in Table 3-11A. Advice on fighting fires in many monomers and solvents is also given in Table 3-11A and in NFPA No. 49, Hazardous Chemicals Data.

An external fire may heat a drum of monomer enough to initiate polymerization, and eventually cause violent rupture of the drum with release of vapor. Cooling containers of monomer should be done during and after exposure to heat of a fire.

If the volume of monomer or the exposure to heat is great, or if the fire has already started in a large container, fire fighting should be done from an explosion-resistant location. For materials normally gaseous, as butadiene or vinyl chloride, fires from piping or storage cylinders should not be extinguished unless the flow can be cut off immediately.

Peroxygen Compounds—Catalysts

General advice is to fight fires from an explosion-resistant location. In advanced or massive fires the area should be evacuated. Fires which threaten peroxygen compounds should not be fought with small extinguishers. Cool the threatened material from a safe distance with hose streams, preferably from behind a barricade. Even a 25 percent solution of acetyl peroxide in dimethyl phthalate will decompose violently after a few minutes at 125°F. The most common peroxygen catalyst is benzoyl peroxide, and its properties illustrate why fire fighting in the presence of peroxygen materials should be done only with care and only when lives or large amounts of other combustibles are threatened. Although stable for years at 80°F, benzoyl peroxide stored at 160°F may decompose in several weeks, explosively if confined. At 225°F it will decompose instantaneously and explosively. Often this is without flash or flame, but the gaseous products are unstable and may later ignite in air in absence of other flame.

See NFPA No. 49, Hazardous Chemicals Data, for further information on fighting fires involving peroxygens and cleaning up peroxygen spills, and References Nos. 10 and 11 in the bibliography at the end of this chapter. None of these publications recommend fighting any but very small peroxide fires at close range.

SI Units

The following conversion factors are given as a convenience in converting to SI units the English units used in this chapter.

1 in. $= 25.400$ mm
1 ft $= 0.305$ m
1 psi $= 6.895$ kPa
$\frac{5}{9}$ (°F $- 32$) $= $ °C

Bibliography

References Cited

[1] "Fire Hazards of the Plastics Manufacturing and Fabricating Industries," NBFU Research Report No. 1, 1963, American Insurance Association, New York.

[2] "Flammable Liquids: Storage and Handling of Drum Lots and Smaller Quantities," SG-3, July 1960, Manufacturing Chemists' Association, Washington, D.C.

[3] "Plastics Foams—Storage, Handling and Fabrication," SG-5, Sept. 1960, The Society of the Plastics Industry, New York.

[4] "Flammable Liquid Hazards in the Plastics Industry," SPI-FPC 2, July 1966, The Society of the Plastics Industry, New York.

[5] "Flammable and Combustible Waste Disposal in the Plastics Industry," SPI-FPC 13, Mar. 1964, The Society of the Plastics Industry, New York.

[6] "Fire and Safety Hazards in the Processing of Expandable Polystyrene (Rigid Foam)," SPI-FPC 17, Jan. 1963, The Society of the Plastics Industry, New York.

[7] "Method of Test for Ignition Properties of Plastics," ASTM D 1929, American Society for Testing and Materials, Philadelphia.

[8] Chemical Safety Data Sheets, "Acrylonitrile," SD-31, 1974; "Styrene Monomer," SD-37, 1971; "Butadiene," SD-55, 1954; "Vinyl Chloride," SD-56, 1972; "Vinyl Acetate," SD-75, 1970; "Methyl Acrylate and Ethyl Acrylate," SD-70, Apr. 1960; Manufacturing Chemists' Association, Washington, D.C.

[9] "Chem-Card Manual," Manufacturing Chemists' Association, Washington, D.C., Aug. 1965.

[10] "Fire, Explosion and Health Hazards of Organic Peroxides," AIA Research Report No. 11, 1966, American Insurance Association, New York.

[11] "Explosion and Fire Hazards in the Storage and Handling of Organic Peroxides in Plastic Fabricating Plants," SPI-FPC 19, June 1964, The Society of the Plastics Industry, New York.

[12] "Dust Explosion Hazards in the Plastics Industry," SPI-FPC 1, Mar. 1964, The Society of the Plastics Industry, New York.

[13] "Fire Hazards of Hydraulic Fluids Used in Processing Plastics," SPI-FPC 3, July 1966, The Society of the Plastics Industry, New York.

[14] Recommended Practice for Use of Fire-Resistant Fluids for Fluid Power Systems, 2nd ed., National Fluid Power Association, Thiensville, Wisc., 1964.

[15] "Fire and Explosions Due to Electrostatic Charges in the Plastics Industry," SPI-FPC 6, July 1963, The Society of the Plastics Industry, New York.

[16] Gaskill, J. R., "Smoke Development in Polymers During Pyrolysis or Combustion," Journal of Fire and Flammability, Vol. 1, July 1970, pp. 183–216.

[17] "Test for Surface Burning Characteristics of Building Materials," UL 723, Jan. 1971, Underwriters Laboratories, Inc., Chicago.

[18] "Test for Surface Burning Characteristics of Building Materials," ASTM E 84-70, American Society for Testing and Materials, Philadelphia.

[19] "Test for Fire Resistance of Building Construction and Materials," UL 263, Jan. 1971, Underwriters Laboratories, Inc., Chicago.

[20] "Fire Tests of Building Construction and Materials (Including Tentative Revision)," ASTM E 119-71, American Society for Testing and Materials, Philadelphia.

[21] "Test for Surface Flammability of Materials Using a Radiant Heat Energy Source," ASTM E 162-67 (1973), American Society for Testing and Materials, Philadelphia.

[22] "Flame Tests of Flame-Resistant Fabrics and Films," UL 214, Mar. 1971, Underwriters Laboratories, Inc., Chicago.

[23] "Test for Flammability of Self-Supporting Plastics," ASTM D 635-72, American Society for Testing and Materials, Philadelphia.

[24] "Test for Flammability of Flexible Plastics," ASTM D 568-72, American Society for Testing and Materials, Philadelphia.

[25] "Testing Rigid Sheet and Plate Materials Used for Electrical Insulation," ASTM D 229-72, American Society for Testing and Materials, Philadelphia.

[26] "Test for Flammability of Plastics Sheeting and Cellular Plastics," ASTM D 1692-68, American Society for Testing and Materials, Philadelphia.

[27] "Tests for Flammability of Plastic Materials for Parts in Devices and Appliances," UL 94, June 1973, Underwriters Laboratories, Inc., Chicago.

NFPA Codes, Standards, and Recommended Practices (see the latest NFPA Publications and Visual Aids Catalog for availability of current editions of the following documents)

NFPA No. 30, Flammable and Combustible Liquids Code.

NFPA No. 33, Standard for Spray Finishing Using Flammable and Combustible Materials.

NFPA No. 35, Recommended Practices for the Manufacture of Organic Coatings.

NFPA No. 40, Standard for the Storage and Handling of Cellulose Nitrate Motion Picture Film.

NFPA No. 43E, Code for the Storage of Pyroxylin Plastic.

NFPA No. 49, Hazardous Chemicals Data.

NFPA No. 63, Fundamental Principles for the Prevention of Dust Explosions in Industrial Plants.

NFPA No. 68, Guide for Explosion Venting.

NFPA No. 69, Standard on Explosion Prevention Systems.

NFPA No. 70, National Electrical Code.
NFPA No. 77, Recommended Practice on Static Electricity.
NFPA No. 86A, Standard for Class A Ovens and Furnaces.
NFPA No. 86B, Standard for Industrial Furnaces.
NFPA No. 86C, Standard for Industrial Furnaces Using a Special Processing Atmosphere.
NFPA No. 91, Standard on Blower and Exhaust Systems.
NFPA No. 231, Standard for Indoor General Storage.
NFPA No. 231B, Standard for Storage of Cellular Rubber and Plastics Materials.
NFPA No. 231C, Standard for Rack Storage of Materials.
NFPA No. 251, Standard Methods of Fire Tests of Building Construction and Materials.
NFPA No. 255, Method of Test of Surface Burning Characteristics of Building Materials.
NFPA No. 256, Methods of Fire Tests of Roof Coverings.
NFPA No. 325M, Fire Hazard Properties of Flammable Liquids, Gases and Volatile Solids.
NFPA No. 327, Standard Procedures for Cleaning or Safeguarding Small Tanks and Containers.
NFPA No. 654, Standard for the Prevention of Dust Explosions in the Plastics Industry.
NFPA No. 701, Standard Methods of Fire Tests for Flame-Resistant Textiles and Films.

Additional Readings

Auck, S. E., "High-Piled Foamed Polystyrene Packages," NFPA Quarterly, Vol. 58, No. 1, July 1964, pp. 152–159.
"A Basic Fundamental of Fire Protection for Small Plastics Plants," SPI-FPC 16, 1962, The Society of the Plastics Industry, New York.
Bhatnagar, V. M., Fire Retardant Formulations Handbook, Technomic Publishing Company, Westport, Conn., 1972.
———, "Advances in Fire Retardants, Part 1," Vol. 2, Progress in Fire Retardancy Series, Technomic Publishing Company, Westport, Conn.
Billmeyer, F. W., Textbook of Polymer Chemistry, Interscience, New York, 1957.
Bray, G., and Hoyle, H., "Sprinkler Protection for Foam Rubber and Urethane Foam," NFPA Quarterly, Vol. 57, No. 1, July 1963, pp. 154–164.
"Chem-Card Manual," Manufacturing Chemists' Association, Washington, D.C., Aug. 1965.
Chemical Safety Data Sheets, "Formaldehyde," SD-1, Apr. 1960; "Benzene," SD-2, 1960; "Phenol," SD-4, 1964; "Paraformaldehyde," SD-6, 1974; "Methanol," SD-22, 1948; "Phthalic Anhydride (Commercial)," SD-61, 1956; Toluene Diisocyanate," SD-73, 1971; "Methyl Ethyl Ketone," SD-83, 1961; "Acetone," SD-87, Aug. 1962; "Maleic Anhydride," SD-88, Oct. 1974; "Benzoyl Peroxide," SD-81, 1960, Manufacturing Chemists' Association, Washington, D.C.
Coleman, E. H., "Gaseous Combustion Products from Plastics," Plastics (London), Vol. 24, No. 264, Oct. 1959, pp. 416–418.
"Combustion Toxicology"—Supplement of Journal of Fire and Flammability, Vol. 1, Aug. 1974.
Dufour, R. E., "Toxicity of Combustion and Thermal Decomposition Products of Certain Building Materials," NFPA Quarterly, Vol. 58, No. 1, July 1964, pp. 31–36.
Dyer, A. F., "Polyethylene Fuel Tanks," Fire Journal, Vol. 62, No. 6, Nov. 1968, pp. 11–13, 16–18.
"Fire Hazards of the Plastics Manufacturing and Fabricating Industries," Research Report No. 1, 1963, American Insurance Association, New York.
"Fire Hazards of Welding and Cutting in the Plastics Industry," SPI-FPC 5, 1963, The Society of the Plastics Industry, New York.

"Fire Retardant Chemistry"—Supplement of the Journal of Fire and Flammability, Vol. 1, Aug. 1974.
"Fire Safe Electrical Installations for Hazardous Locations in the Plastics Industry," SPI-FPC 12, 1963, The Society of the Plastics Industry, New York.
"Fire Safety in the Storage of Materials in Plastics Plants," SPI-FPC 21, 1965, The Society of the Plastics Industry, New York.
Gas and Oil Equipment List, Underwriters' Laboratories, Inc., Chicago, published annually with bi-monthly supplements.
Grimaldi, J. V., "The Hazards of Synthetic Plastics," Mechanical Engineering, Vol. 72, No. 12, 1950, pp. 987–989.
Hilado, C. J., ed., "Flame Retardants," Vol. 6; Fire and Flammability Series, Technomic Publishing Company, Westport, Conn., 1973.
———, "The Effect of Chemicals and Physical Factors on Smoke Evolution from Polymers," Journal of Fire and Flammability, Vol. 1, July 1970, pp. 217–237.
Ives, J. M., Hughes, E. E., and Taylor, J. K., "Toxic Atmospheres Associated with Real Fire Situations," National Bureau of Standards Report 10 807, Feb. 16, 1972, Washington, D.C.
The Merck Index of Chemicals and Drugs, 8th ed., Merck and Co., Rahway, N.J., 1968.
"A Method of Measuring Smoke Density," NFPA Quarterly, Vol. 57, No. 1, July 1963, pp. 276–287.
Modern Plastics Encyclopedia. McGraw-Hill, New York, issued annually.
"Nomenclature Relating to Plastics," ASTM D 883-72, American Society for Testing and Materials, Philadelphia.
Nuckolls, A. H., "Cellulose Nitrate and Acetate Film," NFPA Quarterly, Vol. 23, No. 3, Jan. 1930, pp. 236–242.
"Planning Good Fire Protection for Plastics Plants," SPI-FPC 9, 1964, The Society of the Plastics Industry, New York.
"Plastics—General Method of Testing, Nomenclature," Book of ASTM Standards, Part 35, American Society for Testing and Materials, Philadelphia, issued annually.
Reinke, R. E., and Reinhardt, C. F., "Fires, Toxicity, and Plastics," Modern Plastics, Vol. 50, No. 2, pp. 94–95, 97–98.
Rose, A. E., Condensed Chemical Dictionary, 8th ed., Reinhold, New York, 1971.
"Selected Sources of Information on Safety, Fire Protection and Environmental Health for the Plastics Industry," SPI-FPC 22, March 1970, The Society of the Plastics Industry, New York.
Simonds, H. R., and Church, J. M., A Concise Guide to Plastics, Reinhold, New York, 1963.
Steiner, A. J., "Fire Tests and Fire Protection Engineering," NFPA Quarterly, Vol. 52, No. 3, Jan. 1959, pp. 209–220.
"Survey of Available Information on the Toxicity of the Combustion and Thermal Decomposition Products of Certain Building Materials Under Fire Conditions," Bulletin of Research No. 53, July 1963, Underwriters' Laboratories, Inc., Chicago.
"The Control of Smoke in Building Fires—A State-of-the-Art Review," Prepared by Task Group of Subcommittee IV of ASTM Committee E-5 on Fire Tests of Materials and Construction, Materials Research and Standards, Vol. 11, No. 4, 1971, pp. 16–23, 42.
"The Question of Wastebaskets," Fire Journal, Vol. 59, No. 4, July 1965, pp. 90–91.
The Society of the Plastics Industry, Plastics Engineering Handbook, 3rd ed., Van Nostrand Reinhold, New York, 1960.
Troxell, G. E., "Fire Tests of Plastic Vents and Drainpipes," Fire Journal, Vol. 60, No. 4, July 1966, pp. 52–57.
Wilson, J. A., "A Different View on Plastic Fire Hazard Classifications," NFPA Quarterly, Vol. 56, No. 1, Oct. 1962, pp. 162–164.
Winding, C. C., and Hiatt, G. D., Polymeric Materials, McGraw-Hill, New York, 1961.

Chapter 8

DUSTS

Most finely divided combustible materials are hazardous. Deposits of combustible dusts on beams, machinery, and other surfaces are subject to flash fires. When combustible dusts suspended in air are ignited, they can cause severe explosions. If the dusts are oxidizing agents and they accumulate on combustible surfaces, the combustion process would be considerably accelerated in a fire. If an oxidizing agent in the form of a finely divided dust is mixed with other combustible dusts, the violence of the resulting explosion would be expected to be much more severe than an explosion without the oxidizing agent dust. On the other hand, inert materials, such as limestone, are sometimes used to quench or arrest combustible dust fires or deflagrations.[1]

A. Factors Influencing the Explosibility of Dusts

Whether or not a dust cloud will ignite is governed by the size of particles in it, dust concentration, impurities present, oxygen concentration, and the strength of the source of ignition.

Dust explosions usually occur as a series. Frequently, the initial deflagration is rather small in volume, but intense enough to jar dust from beams, ledges, etc., or even to rupture small pieces of equipment within buildings, such as dust collectors or bins, which then creates a much larger dust cloud through which a secondary explosion can propagate. It is not unusual to have a series of explosions propagating from building to building.[1]

Hazards of Dusts

The hazard of any given dust is related to its ease of ignition and the severity of the ensuing explosion. The Bureau of Mines of the U.S. Department of Interior has developed an arbitrary scale, based on small scale tests, which is quite useful for measuring the hazard.[2] The ignition sensitivity is a function of the ignition temperature and the minimum energy of ignition while the explosion severity is a function of maximum explosion pressure and the maximum rate of pressure rise. To facilitate comparisons of explosibility data developed in Bureau of Mines tests, all test results [2,3,4,5] are related to a standard Pittsburgh coal dust taken at a concentration of 0.50 oz per cu ft with the exception of some metal dusts.[4]

The ignition sensitivity and explosion severity of a dust are defined as:

Ignition sensitivity =

$$\frac{\text{(Ign. temp.} \times \text{Min. energy} \times \text{Min. conc.) Pgh. coal dust}}{\text{(Ign. temp.} \times \text{Min. energy} \times \text{Min. conc.) Sample dust}}$$

Explosion severity =

$$\frac{\text{(Max. explo. press.} \times \text{Max. rate of press. rise) Sample dust}}{\text{(Max. explo. press.} \times \text{Max. rate of press. rise) Pgh. coal dust}}$$

The Explosibility Index is the product of ignition sensitivity and explosion severity.

This method allows one to rate the relative hazard of dusts as follows:

Type of Explosion	Ignition Sensitivity	Explosion Severity	Explosibility Index
Weak	< 0.2	< 0.5	< 0.1
Moderate	0.2 – 1.0	0.5 – 1.0	0.1 – 1.0
Strong	1.0 – 5.0	1.0 – 2.0	1.0 – 10
Severe	> 5.0	> 2.0	> 10

Table 3-8A gives the explosibility index, ignition sensitivity, explosion severity, maximum explosion pressure, maximum rate of pressure rise (not necessarily at the concentration of 0.5 oz per cu ft), ignition temperature of both a dust cloud and a layer, the minimum ignition energy of a dust cloud, minimum explosion concentration, and the limiting oxygen concentration in a spark ignition chamber.

Particle Size

The smaller the size of dust particle the easier it is to ignite the dust cloud[6] insofar as the exposed surface area of a unit weight of material increases as the particle size decreases. It is also true that particle size has an effect on the rate of pressure rise. For a given weight concentration of dust, a coarse dust will show a lower rate of pressure rise than a fine dust. The lower explosive limit concentration, ignition temperature, and the energy necessary for ignition will decrease with decrease of dust particle size. Numerous studies by various investigators show this effect for a variety of dusts. [7,8,9,10]

Decrease in particle size also increases the capacitance of dust clouds, i.e., the size of electrical charges that can accumulate on particles in the cloud.[11] As capacitance of solids is a function of surface area, the possibility of developing electrostatic discharges of sufficient intensity to ignite a dust cloud increases with decrease of average particle size. However, to obtain such electrostatic discharges requires, among other things, large quantities of dust in large volumes with relatively high dielectric strengths of the dusts and consequent long relaxation times. Because of the high ignition energies required for ignition of dust clouds in comparison with ignition energies of gases, attributing the cause of dust explosions to static electricity should be held suspect unless definite evidence exists to show that static electricity was a likely cause.[1,6,11,12,13,14]

Concentration

As is true with flammable gases and vapors, there are limiting concentrations of dusts within which an explosion can occur. It is customary to express the concentration figures in terms of weight per unit volume, though without knowledge of the particle size distribution of the sample this expression is meaningless. The results presented in Table 3-8A were obtained with dusts small enough to pass through a 200 mesh screen (74 microns or smaller). Variations in minimum explosive concentrations will occur with change in particle diameter, i.e., the minimum explosive concentration is lowered as the diameter of particles decreases. Sample purity, oxygen concentration, strength of ignition source, turbulence of dust cloud, and uniformity of dispersion also have an effect on the lower explosive limits (LEL) of dust clouds.

Table 3-8A. Explosion Characteristics of Various Dusts

(Compiled from the following reports of the U.S. Department of Interior, Bureau of Mines: RI 5753, The Explosibility of Agricultural Dusts; RI 6516, Explosibility of Metal Powders; RI 5971, Explosibility of Dusts Used in the Plastics Industry; RI 6597, Explosibility of Carbonaceous Dusts; RI 7132, Dust Explosibility of Chemicals, Drugs, Dyes and Pesticides; and RI 7208, Explosibility of Miscellaneous Dusts.)

Type of Dust	Explosi-bility Index	Ignition Sensi-tivity	Explo-sion Severity	Maximum Explosion Pressure psig	Max Rate of Pressure Rise psi/sec	Ignition Temperature Cloud °C	Ignition Temperature Layer °C	Min Cloud Ignition Energy joules	Min Explosion Conc oz/cu ft	Limiting Oxygen Percentage* (Spark Ignition)
Agricultural Dusts										
Alfalfa meal	0.1	0.1	1.2	66	1,100	530	—	0.32	0.105	—
Almond shell	0.3	0.9	0.3	101	1,400	450	210	0.08	0.065	—
Apricot pit	1.9	1.6	1.2	109	4,000	440	230	0.08	0.035	—
Cellulose	2.8	1.0	2.8	130	4,500	480	270	0.080	0.055	C13
Cellulose, alpha	>10	2.7	4.0	117	8,000	410	300	0.040	0.045	—
Cellulose, flock, fine cut	8.7	2.3	3.8	112	7,000	460	260	0.035	0.055	C13
Cereal grass	< 0.1	< 0.1	0.1	65	400	620	230	0.80	0.20	—
Cherry pit	4.4	2.0	2.2	113	4,400	430	220	0.08	0.03	—
Cinnamon	5.8	2.5	2.3	121	3,900	440	230	0.03	0.06	—
Citrus peel	0.6	0.7	0.9	51	1,200	500	330	0.10	0.06	—
Coca bean shell	13.7	3.6	3.8	77	3,300	470	370	0.03	0.04	—
Cocoa, natural 19% fat	0.6	0.5	1.1	68	1,200	510	240	0.10	0.075	—
Coconut shell	4.2	2.0	2.1	115	4,200	470	220	0.06	0.035	—
Coffee, raw bean	< 0.1	0.1	0.1	33	150	650	280	0.32	0.15	C17
Coffee, fully roasted	< 0.1	0.2	0.1	38	150	720	270	0.16	0.085	C17
Coffee, instant spray dried	< 0.1	0.1	0.1	68	500	410	350	†	0.28	—
Corn	6.9	2.3	3.0	113	6,000	400	250	0.04	0.055	—
Corncob grit	5.5	2.5	2.2	127	3,700	450	240	0.045	0.045	—
Corn dextrine, pure	12.1	3.1	3.9	124	5,500	410	390‡	0.04	0.04	—
Cornstarch commercial product	9.5	2.8	3.4	106	7,500	400	—	0.04	0.045	—
Cornstarch (thru No. 325 Sieve)	23.2	4.3	5.4	145	9,500	390	350	0.03	0.04	C11
Cork dust	>10	3.6	3.3	96	7,500	460	210	0.035	0.035	—
Cotton linter, raw	< 0.1	< 0.1	< 0.1	73	400	520	—	1.92	0.50	C21
Cottonseed meal	1.1	0.9	1.2	104	2,200	540	—	0.08	0.055	—
Cube root, South American	6.5	2.7	2.4	69	2,100	470	230	0.04	0.04	—
Egg white	< .1	< 0.1	0.2	58	500	610	—	0.64	0.14	—
Flax shive	0.2	0.7	0.3	108	1,500	430	230	0.08	0.08	—
Garlic, dehydrated	0.2	0.2	1.2	57	1,300	360	—	0.24	0.10	—
Grain dust, winter wheat, corn, oats	9.2	2.8	3.3	131	7,000	430	230	0.03	0.055	—
Grass seed, blue	< 0.1	0.1	0.1	51	400	490	180	0.26	0.29	—
Guar seed	2.4	1.7	1.4	70	1,200	500	—	0.06	0.04	—
Gum, arabic	1.1	0.7	1.6	84	1,500	500	260	0.10	0.06	—
Gum, karaya	0.3	0.2	1.5	83	1,100	520	240	0.18	0.10	—
Gum, Manila (copal)	18.0	6.2	2.9	63	2,800	360	390‡	0.03	0.03	—
Gum, tragacanth	8.1	2.6	3.1	88	2,400	490	260	0.045	0.04	—
Hemp hurd	20.5	3.8	5.4	121	10,000	440	220	0.035	0.04	—
Lycopodium	16.4	4.2	3.9	75	3,100	480	310	0.04	0.025	C13
Malt barley	5.5	2.6	2.1	95	4,400	400	250	0.035	0.055	—
Milk, skimmed	1.4	1.6	0.9	95	2,300	490	200	0.05	0.05	N15
Moss, Irish	< 0.1	< 0.1	< 0.1	35	400	480	230	†	§	—
Onion, dehydrated	< 0.1	< 0.1	< 0.1	35	500	410	—	†	0.13	—
Pea flour	4.0	1.8	2.2	68	1,900	560	260	0.04	0.05	—
Peach pit shell	7.1	3.1	2.3	115	4,700	440	210	0.05	0.03	—
Peanut hull	4.0	2.0	2.0	116	8,000	460	210	0.05	0.045	—
Peat, sphagnum, sun dried	2.0	2.0	1.0	104	2,200	460	240	0.05	0.045	—
Pecan nut shell	7.4	3.1	2.4	112	4,400	440	210	0.05	0.03	—
Pectin (from ground dried apple pulp)	10.3	2.2	4.7	132	8,000	410	200	0.035	0.075	—
Potato starch, dextrinated	20.9	5.1	4.1	120	8,000	440	—	0.025	0.045	—
Pyrethrum, ground flower leaves	0.4	0.6	0.6	95	1,500	460	210	0.08	0.10	—
Rauwolfia vomitoria root	9.2	2.2	4.2	106	7,500	420	230	0.045	0.055	—
Rice	0.3	0.5	0.5	47	700	510	450	0.10	0.085	—
Rice bran	1.4	1.1	1.3	61	1,300	490	—	0.08	0.045	—
Rice hull	2.7	1.6	1.7	109	4,000	450	220	0.05	0.055	—
Safflower meal	5.2	4.0	1.3	90	2,400	460	210	0.025	0.055	—
Soy flour	0.7	0.6	1.1	94	800	550	340	0.10	0.06	C15
Soy protein	4.0	1.2	3.3	98	6,500	540	—	0.06	0.05	C15
Sucrose, chemically pure	3.3	1.1	3.0	76	2,500	420	470‡	0.10	0.045	—
Sucrose	4.8	2.7	1.8	86	5,500	370	400‡	0.03	0.045	—
Sugar, powdered	9.6	4.0	2.4	109	5,000	370	400‡	0.03	0.045	—

* Numbers in this column indicate oxygen percentage while the letter prefix indicates the diluent gas. For example, the entry "C13" means dilution to an oxygen content of 13 percent with carbon dioxide as the diluent gas. The letter prefixes are: C = Carbon Dioxide; N = Nitrogen; A = Argon; and H = Helium.

† No ignition to 8.32 joules, the highest tried.

‡ Ignition denoted by flame, all others not so marked (‡) denoted by a glow.

§ No ignition to 2 oz per cu ft, the highest tried.

Table 3-8A.   Explosion Characteristics of Various Dusts (Cont.)

Type of Dust	Explosi- bility Index	Ignition Sensi- tivity	Explo- sion Severity	Maximum Explosion Pressure psig	Max Rate of Pressure Rise psi/sec	Ignition Temperature		Min Cloud Ignition Energy joules	Min Explosion Conc oz/cu ft	Limiting Oxygen Percentage* (Spark Ignition)
						Cloud °C	Layer °C			
Tea, instant, spray dried	< 0.1	< 0.1	< 0.1	48	400	580	340	†	‡	—
Tobacco stem	< 0.1	< 0.1	< 0.1	53	400	420	230	†	‡	—
Tung kernels, oil free	0.5	0.2	2.3	74	1,900	540	240	0.24	0.07	—
Walnut shell, black	5.1	3.0	1.7	113	4,000	450	220	0.05	0.03	—
Wheat, untreated	2.6	1.0	2.6	72	2,200	500	220	0.06	0.065	—
Wheat flour	4.1	1.5	2.7	97	2,800	440	440	0.06	0.05	—
Wheat gluten, gum	—	1.0	—	—	—	520	—	0.08	0.05	C15
Wheat starch, edible	17.7	5.2	3.4	100	6,500	430	—	0.025	0.045	C12
Wheat starch, allyl chloride treated	35.0	10.6	3.3	117	6,500	380	—	0.025	0.025	—
Wheat straw	5.0	1.6	3.1	117	6,000	470	220	0.050	0.055	—
Wood, birch bark ground	6.7	3.7	1.8	103	7,500	450	250	0.060	0.020	—
Wood flour, white pine	9.9	3.1	3.2	113	5,500	470	260	0.040	0.035	—
Yeast, torula	2.2	1.6	1.4	123	3,500	520	260	0.050	0.050	—
Carbonaceous Dusts										
Charcoal, hardwood mixture	1.3	1.4	0.9	83	1,300	530	180	0.020	0.140	—
Charcoal, activated, from lignite	0.1§	0.1§	—	41	< 100	670	370	‖	2.000	—
Carbon, activated from petroleum acid sludge	0.1§	0.1§	—	—	—	760	490	—	—	—
Gilsonite, Utah	1.1	6.9	1.5	78	4,500	580	500	0.025	0.020	—
Pitch, coal tar	>10	4.0	2.8	88	6,000	710	—	0.020	0.035	—
Asphalt, blown petroleum resin	6.2	2.8	2.2	85	5,000	510	550	0.040	0.035	—
Pitch, petroleum	4.0	2.8	1.4	82	3,800	630	—	0.025	0.045	—
Lampblack	0.1§	0.1§	—	—	—	730	—	—	—	—
Carbon black, acetylene	0.1§	0.1§	—	—	—	¶	900	—	—	—
Carbon, petroleum coke and pitch electrodes	0.1§	0.1§	—	—	—	710	—	—	—	—
Coal, Kentucky (Bituminous)	4.1	2.2	1.8	101	4,000	610	180	0.030	0.050	—
Coal, Pennsylvania, Pittsburg (Experimental Mine Coal)	1.0	1.0	1.0	90	2,300	610	170	0.060	0.055	—
Coal, Pennsylvania (Anthracite)	0.1§	0.1§	—	—	—	730	—	0.100‡	0.065‡	—
Coke, Petroleum	0.1§	0.1§	—	—	200	670	—	‖	1.000	—
Graphite	0.1§	0.1§	—	—	—	¶	580	—	—	—
Lignite, California	>10	5.0	3.8	94	8,000	450	200	0.030	0.030	—
Chemicals										
Acetoacetanilide	>10	6.0	1.8	90	4,800	560	—	0.020	0.030	—
Acetoacet-o-toluidine (2 methylacetoacetanilide)	6	3.2	1.9	90	4,600	590	—	0.035	0.030	—
Acetoacet-p-phenetidide	>10	12	4.9	87	>10,000	560	—	0.010	0.030	—
Adipic acid	1.9	1.7	1.1	84	2,700	550	—	0.060	0.035	—
Anthranilic acid	5.2	3.3	1.6	84	6,500	580	—	0.035	0.030	—
Aryl nitroso methyl amide	>10	5.5	3.3	142	8,500	490	—	0.015	0.050	—
Azelaic acid	6.4	5.3	1.2	76	4,700	610	—	0.025	0.025	C14
a, a′ Azoisobutyronitrile	>10	12.5	4.3	134	8,000	430	350	0.025	0.015	—
Benzoic acid	>10	5.4	2.1	76	5,500	620	Melts	0.020	0.030	—
Benzotriazole	>10	5.1	3.3	103	9,200	440	—	0.030	0.030	—
Bis-phenol A	>10	11.8	2.5	89	8,500	570	—	0.015	0.020	C12
o-Chloroacetoacetanilide	5.4	3.0	1.8	94	3,900	640	—	0.030	0.035	—
p-Chloroacetoacetanilide	>10	4.4	2.4	85	5,500	650	—	0.020	0.035	—
Dehydroacetic acid	>10	10.4	3.4	87	8,000	430	—	0.015	0.030	—
Diallyl phthalate	>10	7.0	2.7	90	8,500	480	—	0.020	0.030	N10
Dicumyl peroxide suspended on CaCO₃ (40–60)	6.8	2.7	2.5	90	6,500	560	180	0.030	0.045	C13
Dicyclopentadiene dioxide	>10	15.9	3.8	89	9,500	420	—	0.030	0.015	—
Dimethyl isophthalate	>10	9.3	2.9	84	8,000	580	—	0.015	0.025	C13
Dimethyl terephthalate	>10	5.9	5.8	105	12,000	570	—	0.020	0.030	C12
3, 5 dinitrobenzoic acid	4	1.9	2.1	138	4,300	460	—	0.045	0.050	—
Dinitrotoluamide (35 dinitro ortho toluamide)	>10	5.4	5.6	153	>10,000	500	—	0.015	0.050	C13
Diphenyl	>10	10.7	1.6	82	3,700	630	—	0.020	0.015	—
Ditertiary butyl para cresol	>10	10.7	3.9	96	19,000	470	—	0.020	0.020	C14

* Numbers in this column indicate oxygen percentage while the letter prefix indicates the diluent gas. For example, the entry "C13" means dilution to an oxygen content of 13 percent with carbon dioxide as the diluent gas. The letter prefixes are: C = Carbon Dioxide; N = Nitrogen; A = Argon; and H = Helium.

† No ignition to 8.32 joules, the highest tried.

‡ Obtained in an oxygen atmosphere.

§ 0.1 designates materials presenting primarily a fire hazard as ignition of the dust cloud is not obtained by the spark or flame source but only by the intense heated surface source.

‖ Guncotton ignition source.

¶ No ignition.

Table 3-8A. Explosion Characteristics of Various Dusts (Cont.)

Type of Dust	Explosi-bility Index	Ignition Sensi-tivity	Explo-sion Severity	Maximum Explosion Pressure psig	Max Rate of Pressure Rise psi/sec	Ignition Temperature Cloud °C	Ignition Temperature Layer °C	Min Cloud Ignition Energy joules	Min Explosion Conc oz/cu ft	Limiting Oxygen Percentage* (Spark Ignition)
Ethyl hydroxyethyl cellulose	6.0	8.6	0.7	94	2,200	390	—	0.030	0.020	C16
Fumaric acid	1.6	1.3	1.2	103	3,000	520	—	0.035	0.085	—
Hexamethylene tetramine	>10	32.7	5.6	98	11,000	410	—	0.010	0.015	C14
Hydroxyethyl cellulose	6.9	4.9	1.4	106	2,600	410	—	0.040	0.025	—
Isatoic anhydride	6.5	3.3	2.0	80	4,900	700	—	0.025	0.035	C13
DL-Methionine	9.3	6.2	1.5	119	5,700	370	360	0.035	0.025	C15
Nitrosoamine	>10	5.0	8.5	175	15,000	270	—	0.060	0.025	—
Para oxy benzaldehyde	>10	17.7	2.4	81	6,500	380	430	0.015	0.020	—
Para phenylene diamine (milled)	9.0	4.3	2.1	94	11,000	620	—	0.030	0.025	—
Para tertiary butyl benzoic acid	>10	7.2	2.8	88	6,500	560	—	0.025	0.020	—
Pentaerythritol	>10	14.6	4.5	90	9,500	450	—	0.010	0.030	C14
Phenyl beta naphthylamine	7.1	4.7	1.5	75	4,300	680	—	0.025	0.025	—
Phthalic anhydride	>10	13.8	1.6	72	4,200	650	—	0.015	0.015	C14
Phthalimide	5.0	2.1	2.3	89	4,800	630	—	0.050	0.030	—
Salicylanilide	5.8	4.1	1.4	61	4,800	610	Melts	0.020	0.040	—
Sorbic acid	>10	14.3	12.0	106	>10,000	470	460	0.015	0.020	—
Stearic acid, aluminum salt (aluminum tristearate)	>10	21.3	1.9	87	6,300	420	440	0.015	0.015	—
Stearic acid, zinc salt (zinc stearate)	>10	19.7	2.3	80	>10,000	510	Melts	0.010	0.020	C13
Sulfur	>10	20.2	1.2	78	4,700	190	220	0.015	0.035	C12
Terephthalic acid	6.9	3.0	2.3	84	8,000	680	—	0.020	0.050	C15
Drugs										
2-Acetylamino-5-nitrothiazole, $\underset{\mid}{NHCOCH_3}$ S—C=N—CH=C—NO$_2$	3.1	0.7	4.4	137	9,000	450	450	0.040	0.160	—
2-Amino-5-nitrotheazole, $\underset{\mid}{NH_2}$ S—C=N—CH=C—NO$_2$	5.4	1.9	2.8	110	5,600	460	460	0.030	0.075	—
Aspirin (Acetylsalicylic Acid) o-CH$_3$COOC$_6$H$_4$COOH	>10	2.4	4.3	88	>10,000	660	Melts	0.025	0.050	—
Gulosonic acid, diacetone C$_{12}$H$_{18}$O$_6$H$_2$O	8.8	4.8	1.8	95	4,500	420	—	0.040	0.025	—
Mannitol (hesahydric alcohol) CH$_2$OH(CHOH)$_4$CH$_2$OH	2.0	1.7	1.2	97	2,800	460	—	0.040	0.065	—
Nitropyridone (C$_{10}$H$_{11}$O$_4$N$_3$)	>10	3.0	5.8	111	>10,000	430	Melts	0.035	0.045	C12
L-Sorbose	1.9	1.0	1.9	76	4,700	370	—	0.080	0.065	—
Vitamin B$_1$, mononitrate, C$_{12}$H$_{17}$ON$_4$SNO$_3$	8.3	2.7	3.1	101	6,000	360	—	0.060	0.035	—
Vitamin C, ascorbic acid, C$_6$H$_8$O$_6$	2.3	1.0	2.2	88	4,800	460	280	0.060	0.070	C15, N12
Dyes, Pigments, and Intermediates										
1, 4-Diamino-2, 3-dihydroanthraquinone (90%) 1 methylamino-anthraquinone (10%) (Violet 200 dye)	1.0	1.1	0.9	64	3,200	880	175	0.060	0.035	—
1, 4-Di-p-toluidineanthra-quinone (70%) β naphthalene-azo-dimethyl-aniline (30%) (green base harmon dye)	1.7	1.7	1.0	73	2,600	770	175	0.050	0.030	—
1-Methylaminoanthraquinone (red dye intermediate)	1.1	0.9	1.2	71	3,300	830	175	0.050	0.055	—
β-naphthalene-azo-dimethylaniline	3.3	3.9	0.8	70	2,300	510	175	0.050	0.020	—
Metals										
Aluminum, atomized collector fines	>10	1.4	7.7	84	20,000+	650	760	0.050	0.045	C2
Aluminum, flake, A 422 extra fine lining, polished	>10	7.3	10.2	127	20,000+	610	326	0.010	0.045	—
Antimony, milled (96% Sb)	< 0.1	< 0.1	< 0.1	28	300	420	330	1.920	0.420	C16
Boron, amorphous, commercial (85% B)	0.8	0.7	1.1	93	3,300	470	400	0.060	<0.100	—

* Numbers in this column indicate oxygen percentage while the letter prefix indicates the diluent gas. For example, the entry "C13" means dilution to an oxygen content of 13 percent with carbon dioxide as the diluent gas. The letter prefixes are: C = Carbon Dioxide; N = Nitrogen; A = Argon; and H = Helium.

Table 3-8A. Explosion Characteristics of Various Dusts (Cont.)

Type of Dust	Explosibility Index	Ignition Sensitivity	Explosion Severity	Maximum Explosion Pressure psig	Max Rate of Pressure Rise psi/sec	Ignition Temperature Cloud °C	Ignition Temperature Layer °C	Min Cloud Ignition Energy joules	Min Explosion Conc oz/cu ft	Limiting Oxygen Percentage* (Spark Ignition)
Cadmium, atomized (98% Cd)	—	—	—	7	100	570	250	4.000	—	—
Chromium, electrolytic, milled (97% Cr)	0.1	0.1	1.2	56	5,000	580	400	0.140	0.230	—
Cobalt, milled (97.8% Co)	—	—	—	—	—	760	370	—	—	—
Copper, electrolytic, Type C (99.5% Cu)	—	—	—	—	—	900	—	—	—	—
Iron, hydrogen reduced (98% Fe)	0.3	0.7	0.4	61	2,200	320	290	0.080	0.120	C11
Iron, carbonyl (99% Fe)	1.6	3.0	0.5	43	2,400	320	310	0.020	0.105	C10
Lead, atomized (99% Pb)	—	—	—	—	—	710	270	—	—	—
Magnesium, milled, Grade B	>10	3.0	7.4	116	15,000	560	430	0.040	0.030	—
Manganese	0.1	0.1	0.7	53	4,900	460	240	0.305	0.125	—
Nickel	—	†	—	—	—	—	—	—	—	—
Selenium, milled	—	†	—	—	—	—	—	—	—	—
Silicon, milled (96% Si)	< 0.1	< 0.1	1.1	87	2,400	780	950	0.960	0.160	C15
Tantalum	0.1	0.1	0.7	55	4,400	630	300	0.120	<0.200	—
Tellurium, electrolytic (98% Te)	—	—	—	—	—	550	340	—	—	—
Thorium (contains 1.2% O2)	>10	>10	0.8	79	5,500	270	280	0.005	0.075	N2, A2, H5‡
Thorium hydride (contains 0.94% H2)	>10	>10	2.0	81	12,000	260	20	0.003	0.080	C6, N5, A4, H5
Tin atomized (96% Sn, 2% Pb)	0.1	0.2	0.3	48	1,700	630	430	0.080	0.190	C16
Titanium (99% Ti)	>10	5.4	2.0	70	6,000	330	510	0.025	0.045	N6, A4, H7‡
Titanium hydride (95% Ti, 3.8% H2)	6.0	1.0	6.0	121	12,000	480	540	0.060	0.070	C13
Tungsten, hydrogen reduced	—	†	—	—	—	—	430	—	—	—
Uranium	>10	>10	0.9	69	5,000	20	100	0.045	0.060	N1, A2, H2‡
Uranium hydride	>10	>10	1.5	74	9,000	20	20	0.005	0.060	N2, A2, H4‡
Vanadium (86.4% V)	< 0.1	0.3	0.2	57	1,000	500	490	0.060	0.220	C13
Zinc, condensed (97% Zn, 2% Pb)	< 0.1	< 0.1	< 0.1	50	1,700	690	540	0.960	0.460	N9
Zirconium, prepared from hydride (contains 0.3% O2)	1.3	1.1	1.2	90	4,900	350	300	0.120	0.045	N4, A3, H5‡
Zirconium hydride (93.6% Zr, 2.1% H)	3.7	1.1	3.3	90	9,500	350	270	0.060	0.085	C8
Alloys and Compounds										
Aluminum-cobalt alloy (60–40)	0.4	0.1	3.5	92	11,000	950	570	0.100	0.180	—
Aluminum-copper alloy (50–50)	0.3	—	0.9	95	4,000	—	830	—	—	—
Aluminum-lithium alloy (15% Li)	0.6	0.3	1.9	96	6,000	470	400	—	—	—
Aluminum-magnesium alloy (Dowmetal)	>10	2.9	4.5	86	10,000	430	480	0.080	0.020	‡
Aluminum-nickel alloy (58–42)	0.6	0.1	4.1	96	10,000	950	540	0.080	0.190	—
Aluminum-silicon alloy (12% Si)	3.6	1.3	2.9	85	7,500	670	—	0.060	0.040	—
Calcium silicide	2.0	0.4	5.0	86	13,000	540	540	0.150	0.060	—
Ferromanganese, medium carbon	0.4	0.4	1.0	62	5,000	450	290	0.080	0.130	—
Ferrosilicon (88% Si, 9% Fe)	< 0.1	< 0.1	0.2	70	1,000	860	—	0.400	0.425	C19
Ferrotitanium (19% Ti, 74.1% Fe, 0.06% C)	1.3	0.5	2.6	55	9,500	370	400	0.080	0.140	C13
Pesticides										
Benzethonium Chloride	6.9	4.4	1.6	91	6,700	380	410	0.060	0.020	—
Bis (2-hydroxy-5-chlorophenyl) methane	1.1	1.5	0.7	70	2,000	570	—	0.060	0.040	C16
Dieldrin (C12H8OCl6) 20% (50% Combustible, 30% Inert)	5.5	2.3	2.4	85	5,500	550	—	0.035	0.045	—
2, 6 Di-tertiary-butyl-para-cresol	>10	10.7	3.9	96	>10,000	470	—	0.20	0.020	C14
Dithane (zinc ethylenedithio-carbamate)	—	—	—	45	300	480	180	—	—	—
Ferric dimethyldithiocarba-mate (Ferbam)	>10	5.2	2.6	86	6,300	280	150	0.025	0.055	—
Manganese vancide [(CH3)2NC(s)s]2Mn	0.6	0.3	1.8	97	4,700	300	120	0.280	0.070	—

* Numbers in this column indicate oxygen percentage while the letter prefix indicates the diluent gas. For example, the entry "C13" means dilution to an oxygen content of 13 percent with carbon dioxide as the diluent gas. The letter prefixes are: C = Carbon Dioxide; N = Nitrogen; A = Argon; and H = Helium.

† No ignition.

‡ Reacts with carbon dioxide.

Table 3-8A. Explosion Characteristics of Various Dusts (Cont.)

Type of Dust	Explosibility Index	Ignition Sensitivity	Explosion Severity	Maximum Explosion Pressure psig	Max Rate of Pressure Rise psi/sec	Ignition Temperature Cloud °C	Ignition Temperature Layer °C	Min Cloud Ignition Energy joules	Min Explosion Conc oz/cu ft	Limiting Oxygen Percentage* (Spark Ignition)
1 Naphthyl-N-methylcarbamate ("Sevin") 15% (85% Inert)	>10	18.0	1.6	90	5,000	560	140	0.010	0.020	—
3, 4, 5, 6-tetrahydro-3, 5,-dimethyl-2H-1, 3, 5 thiadeazine 2 thione, ("Crag" No. 974) 5% (95% Inert)	>10	8.7	2.0	97	6,000	310	330	0.030	0.025	—
a, a′ Trithiobis (N, N-dimethyl-thioformamide)	8.9	3.4	2.6	96	7,000	280	230	0.035	0.060	—
Thermoplastic Resins and Molding Compounds										
Group I. Acetal Resins										
Acetal, linear (Polyformaldehyde)	>10	6.5	1.9	113	4,100	440	—	0.020	0.035	C11
Group II. Acrylic Resins										
Methyl methacrylate polymer	6.3	7.0	0.9	84	2,000	480	—	0.020	0.030	C11
Methyl methacrylate-ethyl acrylate copolymer	>10	14.0	2.7	85	6,000	480	—	0.010	0.030	C11
Methyl methacrylate-ethyl acrylate-styrene copolymer	>10	9.2	1.7	90	4,400	440	—	0.020	0.025	—
Methyl methacrylate-styrene-butadiene-acrylonitrile copolymer	>10	8.4	1.4	87	4,700	480	—	0.020	0.025	C11
Methacrylic acid polymer, modified	0.6	1.0	0.6	97	1,800	450	290	0.100	0.045	—
Acrylamide polymer	2.5	4.1	0.6	85	2,500	410	240	0.030	0.040	—
Acrylonitrile polymer	>10	8.1	2.3	89	11,000	500	460	0.020	0.025	C13
Acrylonitrile-vinyl pyridine copolymer	>10	7.9	2.4	85	6,000	510	240	0.025	0.020	—
Acrylonitrile-vinyl chloride-vinylidene chloride copolymer (70–20–10)	>10	5.9	3.0	87	15,000	650	210	0.015	0.035	—
Group III. Cellulosic Resins										
Cellulose acetate	>10	8.0	1.6	85	3,600	420	—	0.015	0.040	C14
Cellulose triacetate	7.4	3.9	1.9	107	4,300	430	—	0.030	0.040	C12
Cellulose acetate butyrate	5.6	4.7	1.2	85	2,700	410	—	0.030	0.035	C14
Cellulose propionate, 0.3% free hydroxyl	7.5	2.9	2.6	107	4,700	460	—	0.060	0.025	—
Ethyl cellulose 5–10 micron dust	>10	21.8	3.4	120	6,500	370	350§	0.010	0.025	C12
Methyl cellulose	>10	9.3	3.1	133	6,000	360	340	0.020	0.030	C13
Carboxy methyl cellulose, low viscosity, 0.3 to 0.4% substitution, acid product	1.4	0.5	2.7	130	5,000	460	310	0.140	0.060	—
Hydroxyethyl cellulose-mono sodium phosphate sizing compound	1.7	2.1	0.8	110	4,000	390	340	0.035	0.070	—
Group IV. Chlorinated Polyether Resins										
Chlorinated polyether alcohol	0.2	0.6	0.3	88	1,900	460	—	0.160	0.045	—
Group V. Fluorocarbon Resins										
Tetrafluoroethylene polymer (micronized)	0.1‡	0.1‡	—	§	—	670	570†	§	‖	—
Monochlorotrifluoroethylene polymer	0.1‡	0.1‡	—	§	—	600	720†	§	‖	—
Group VI. Nylon (Polyamide) Resins										
Nylon (polyhexamethylene adipamide) polymer	>10	6.7	1.8	95	4,000	500	430	0.020	0.030	C13
Group VII. Polycarbonate Resins										
Polycarbonate	8.6	4.5	1.9	96	4,700	710	—	0.025	0.025	C15

* Numbers in this column indicate oxygen percentage while the letter prefix indicates the diluent gas. For example, the entry "C13" means dilution to an oxygen content of 13 percent with carbon dioxide as the diluent gas. The letter prefixes are: C = Carbon Dioxide; N = Nitrogen; A = Argon; and H = Helium.

† Ignition denoted by flame, all others not so marked (†) denoted by a glow.

‡ 0.1 designates materials presenting primarily a fire hazard as ignition of the dust cloud is not obtained by the spark of flame source but only by the intense heated surface source.

§ No ignition to 8.32 joules, the highest tried.

‖ No ignition to 2 oz per cu ft, the highest tried.

Table 3-8A.   Explosion Characteristics of Various Dusts (Cont.)

Type of Dust	Explosi-bility Index	Ignition Sensi-tivity	Explo-sion Severity	Maximum Explosion Pressure psig	Max Rate of Pressure Rise psi/sec	Ignition Temperature Cloud °C	Ignition Temperature Layer °C	Min Cloud Ignition Energy joules	Min Explosion Conc oz/cu ft	Limiting Oxygen Percentage* (Spark Ignition)
Group VIII. Polyethylene Resins										
Polyethylene, hi-pressure process	>10	7.5	1.4	81	4,000	450	380	0.030	0.020	C13
Polyethylene, low-pressure process	>10	22.4	2.3	80	7,500	450	—	0.010	0.020	—
Polyethylene wax, low molecular weight	5.8	7.2	0.8	74	3,000	400	—	0.035	0.020	C13
Group IX. Polymethylene Resins										
Carboxy polymethylene, regular	< 0.1	< 0.1	2.0	70	5,500	520	—	†	0.325	—
Group X. Polypropylene Resins										
Polypropylene (contains no antioxidant)	>10	8.0	2.0	76	5,500	420	—	0.030	0.020	—
Group XI. Rayon										
Rayon (viscose) flock, 1.5 denier, 0.020 inch maroon	0.2	0.3	0.8	107	1,700	520	250	0.240	0.055	—
Group XII. Styrene Polymer and Copolymer Resins										
Polystyrene molding compound	>10	6.0	2.0	77	5,000	560	—	0.040	0.015	C14
Polystyrene latex, spray-dried, contains surfactants	>10	13.4	3.3	100	7,000	500	500‡	0.015	0.020	—
Styrene-acrylonitrile copolymer (70–30)	1.9	3.8	0.5	71	1,400	500	—	0.030	0.035	—
Styrene-butadiene latex copolymer, over 75% styrene, alum coagulated	>10	7.3	1.7	92	3,900	440	—	0.025	0.025	C13
Group XIII. Vinyl Polymer and Copolymer Resins										
Polyvinyl acetate	0.2	0.6	1.2	69	1,000	550	—	0.160	0.040	C17
Polyvinyl acetate alcohol	1.1	0.9	1.2	89	3,100	520	440	0.120	0.035	—
Polyvinyl butyral	>10	25.8	0.9	84	2,000	390	—	0.010	0.020	C14
Polyvinyl chloride, fine	0.1§	0.1§	< 0.1	28	200‖	660	400	†	‖	—
Vinyl chloride-vinyl acetate copolymer	0.1§	0.1§	—	—	†	690	—	†	‖	—
Vinyl chloride-acrylonitrile copolymer, water emulsion product (60–40)	1.9	3.1	0.6	81	3,200	570	470	0.025	0.045	—
Vinyl chloride-acrylonitrile copolymer, water emulsion product (33–67)	>10	7.2	2.0	95	7,500	530	470	0.015	0.035	C15
Polyvinyl-chloride-dioctyl phthalate mixture (67–33)	2.9	3.6	0.8	72	2,700	320	—	0.050	0.035	—
Vinylidene chloride polymer molding compound	0.1§	0.1§	—	—	†	900	—	†	‡	—
Vinyl toluene-acrylonitrile-butadiene copolymer (58–19–23)	>10	9.5	1.6	85	4,700	530	—	0.020	0.020	—
Thermosetting Resins and Molding Compounds										
Group I. Alkyd Resins										
Alkyd molding compound, mineral filler, not self-extinguishing	< 0.1	0.2	< 0.1	40	300	500	270	0.120	0.155	C15
Group II. Allyl Resins										
Allyl alcohol derivative, CR-39, (from dust collector)	>10	5.6	3.6	91	7,500	510	—	0.020	0.035	C13
Allyl alcohol derivative, CR-149-glass fiber mixture (65–35)	< 0.1	< 0.1	0.2	60	1,000	540	—	1.60	0.345	—

* Numbers in this column indicate oxygen percentage while the letter prefix indicates the diluent gas. For example, the entry "C13" means dilution to an oxygen content of 13 percent with carbon dioxide as the diluent gas. The letter prefixes are: C = Carbon Dioxide; N = Nitrogen; A = Argon; and H = Helium.

† No ignition to 8.32 joules, the highest tried.

‡ Ignition denoted by flame, all others not so marked (‡) denoted by a glow.

§ 0.1 designates materials presenting primarily a fire hazard as ignition of the dust cloud is not obtained by the spark of flame source but only by the intense heated surface source.

‖ No ignition to 2 oz per cu ft, the highest tried.

Table 3-8A. Explosion Characteristics of Various Dusts (Cont.)

Type of Dust	Explosi-bility Index	Ignition Sensi-tivity	Explo-sion Severity	Maximum Explosion Pressure psig	Max Rate of Pressure Rise psi/sec	Ignition Temperature Cloud °C	Ignition Temperature Layer °C	Min Cloud Ignition Energy joules	Min Explosion Conc oz/cu ft	Limiting Oxygen Percentage* (Spark Ignition)
Group III. Amino Resins (Melamine and Urea)										
Melamine formaldehyde, unfilled laminating type, no plasticizer	< 0.1	0.1	0.2	81	800	810	—	0.320	0.085	C17
Urea formaldehyde molding compound, Grade II, fine	1.0	0.6	1.7	89	3,600	460	—	0.080	0.085	C17
Urea formaldehyde-phenol formaldehyde molding compound, wood flour filler	0.2	0.4	0.6	84	1,700	530	240	0.120	0.085	—
Group IV. Epoxy Resins										
Epoxy, no catalyst, modifier or additives	>10	12.4	2.7	94	6,000	540	—	0.015	0.020	C12
Epoxy-bisphenol A mixture	1.9	3.8	0.5	85	2,200	510	—	0.035	0.030	—
Group V. Furane Resins										
Phenol furfural	>10	15.2	3.9	88	8,500	530	—	0.010	0.025	C14
Group VI. Phenolic Resins										
Phenol formaldehyde	>10	9.3	1.4	77	3,500	580	—	0.015	0.025	C17
Phenol formaldehyde, 1-step	>10	7.9	5.3	92	11,000	640	—	0.010	0.040	C14
Phenol formaldehyde, 2-step	>10	13.9	4.0	89	8,500	580	—	0.010	0.025	C14
Phenol formaldehyde, semiresinous	< 0.1	< 0.1	< 0.1	79	800	460	—	†	0.235	—
Phenol formaldehyde molding compound, wood flour filler	>10	8.9	4.7	94	9,500	500	—	0.015	0.030	C14
Phenol formaldehyde, polyalkylene polyamine modified	>10	16.0	2.8	103	6,000	420	290	0.015	0.020	—
Group VII. Polyester Resins										
Polyethylene terephthalate	7.5	2.9	2.6	98	5,500	500	—	0.035	0.040	C13
Styrene modified polyester-glass fiber mixture (65–35)	5.2	2.0	2.6	91	6,000	440	360	0.050	0.045	—
Group VIII. Polyurethane Resins (Isocyanate)										
Polyurethane foam (toluene diisocyanate-polyhydroxy with fluorocarbon blowing agent), not fire retardant	>10	6.6	1.5	87	3,700	510	440	0.020	0.030	—
Polyurethane foam (toluene diisocyanate-polyhydroxy with fluorocarbon blowing agent), fire retardant	>10	9.8	1.7	96	3,700	550	390	0.015	0.025	—
SPECIAL RESINS AND MOLDING COMPOUNDS										
Group I. Cold Molded Resins										
Petroleum resin (blown asphalt), regular	>10	6.3	2.3	94	4,800	510	500‡	0.025	0.025	—
Group II. Coumarone-Indene Resins										
Coumarone-indene, hard	>10	24.4	5.4	93	11,000	550	—	0.010	0.015	C14
Group III. Natural Resins										
Cashew oil phenolic, hard	>10	6.6	1.7	83	4,000	490	200	0.025	0.025	C14
Lignin, hydrolized-wood-type, fines	>10	5.6	2.7	102	5,000	450	—	0.020	0.040	C17
Rosin, DK	>10	34.4	5.5	87	12,000	390	—	0.010	0.015	C14
Shellac	>10	25.2	1.4	73	3,600	400	—	0.010	0.020	C14
Sodium resinate, dry size, grade XXX	2.6	2.4	1.1	84	2,600	350	220	0.060	0.040	C17
Group IV. Rubber										
Rubber, crude, hard	7.4	4.6	1.6	80	3,800	350	—	0.050	0.025	C15
Rubber, synthetic, hard, contains 33% sulfur	>10	7.0	1.5	93	3,100	320	—	0.030	0.030	C15

* Numbers in this column indicate oxygen percentage while the letter prefix indicates the diluent gas. For example, the entry "C13" means dilution to an oxygen content of 13 percent with carbon dioxide as the diluent gas. The letter prefixes are: C = Carbon Dioxide; N = Nitrogen; A = Argon; and H = Helium.

† No ignition to 8.32 joules, the highest tried.

‡ Ignition denoted by flame, all others not so marked (‡) denoted by a glow.

Table 3-8A.   Explosion Characteristics of Various Dusts (Cont.)

Type of Dust	Explosibility Index	Ignition Sensitivity	Explosion Severity	Maximum Explosion Pressure psig	Max Rate of Pressure Rise psi/sec	Ignition Temperature		Min Cloud Ignition Energy joules	Min Explosion Conc oz/cu ft	Limiting Oxygen Percentage* (Spark Ignition)
						Cloud °C	Layer °C			
Rubber, chlorinated	0.1†	0.1†	—	—	‡	940	290	§	‖	—
Group V. Miscellaneous Resins										
Alkyl ketone dimer sizing compound, dimer dispersed on silica (50–50)	>10	5.3	2.4	81	13,000	420	160	0.030	0.030	C15
Chlorinated phenol (bis 2-hydroxy-5-chlorophenyl methane)	1.1	1.5	0.7	70	2,000	570	—	0.060	0.040	C16
Ethylene oxide polymer	5.8	6.4	0.9	106	2,100	350	—	0.030	0.030	C12
Ethylene-maleic anhydride copolymer	0.2	1.0	0.2	75	1,300	540	—	0.040	0.095	C11
Styrene-maleic anhydride copolymer	>10	7.1	4.1	96	9,500	470	490	0.020	0.030	—
Petrin acrylate monomer, crude	>10	10.2	8.7	236	19,000	220	—	0.020	0.045	—

* Numbers in this column indicate oxygen percentage while the letter prefix indicates the diluent gas. For example, the entry "C15" means dilution to an oxygen content of 15 percent with carbon dioxide as the diluent gas. The letter prefixes are: C = Carbon Dioxide; N = Nitrogen; A = Argon; and H = Helium.

† 0.1 designates materials presenting primarily a fire hazard as ignition of the dust cloud is not obtained by the spark foflame source but only by the intense heated surface source.

‡ No ignition.

§ No ignition to 8.32 joules, the highest tried.

‖ Ignition denoted by flame, all others not so marked (‖) denoted by a glow.

Upper explosive limits (UEL) for dust clouds have not been determined mainly because of experimental difficulties. There is also a question of whether a clear-cut upper limit exists at all and from a practical point of view this information is of questionable utility. Curves formed by plotting explosion pressures, rates of pressure rise against concentration, show that explosion pressures and rates of pressure rise are at a minimum at the lower explosive limit and then rise to maximum value at a given optimum concentration and then slowly decrease from this point. It is to be noted that the maximum pressure and the maximum rate of rise do not always occur at precisely the same concentration. The destructive effect is determined primarily by the rate of pressure rise.

It appears then that the most violent explosion occurs at a concentration slightly above that required for reaction with all of the oxygen in the atmosphere. At lower dust concentrations, less heat is generated and smaller peak pressures are developed. With dust concentrations greater than that causing the most violent explosions, absorption of heat by unburned dust is apparently the reason for less than maximum explosive pressures.

Moisture

Moisture in dust particles raises the ignition temperature of the dust because of the heat absorbed during heating and vaporization of the moisture. The moisture in the air surrounding a dust particle has no significant effect on the course of a deflagration once ignition has occurred. There is, however, a direct relationship between moisture content and minimum energy required for ignition, minimum explosive concentration, maximum pressure, and maximum rate of pressure rise. For example, the ignition temperature of cornstarch may increase as much as 122°F with an increase of moisture content from 1.6 percent to 12.5 percent. As a practical matter, however, moisture cannot be considered an effective explosion preventive since most ignition sources provide more than enough heat to vaporize and

heat the moisture and to ignite the dust. In order for moisture to prevent ignition of a dust by common sources, the dust would have to be so damp that a cloud could not be formed. Moisture as a means of preventing accumulation of static electricity in dust clouds is discussed in Section 5, Chapter 5.

Inert Material

The presence of an inert solid powder reduces the combustibility of a dust because it absorbs heat, but the amount of inert powder necessary to prevent an explosion is usually considerably higher than concentrations that would normally be found or could be tolerated as foreign material. The addition of inerts reduces the rate of pressure rise and increases the minimal dust concentration. Rock dusting of coal mines is a practical application of the use of inert dust to prevent explosion of a combustible dust. For general rock dusting of coal mine entries, enough rock dust is usually added to provide an inert dust concentration of at least 65 percent of the total dust.[1,5,15,16]

Oxygen Concentration, Turbulence, and Effect of Flammable Gas

Variations in oxygen concentrations affect the ease of ignition of dust clouds and the explosion pressures. With a decrease in the partial pressure of oxygen, the energy required for ignition increases, ignition temperature increases and maximum explosion pressures decrease. The type of inert gas used as the diluent for reduction of the oxygen concentration also has an effect apparently related to molar heat capacity.

The combustion of dust takes place at the surfaces of the dust particles. The rate of reaction therefore depends on intimate mixing of the dust and oxygen. It is for this reason that turbulent mixing of dust and air results in more violent explosions than those obtained by ignition in relatively quiescent mixtures.[10,12] The data presented in Table 3-8A were gathered by igniting the dust clouds under violently turbulent conditions; thus they cannot be compared to explosion data for flammable vapors which were gathered under comparatively quiescent conditions.

Inert gas is effective in preventing dust explosions because it dilutes the oxygen to a concentration too low to support combustion. For a discussion of the use of inert gas to prevent explosions see Section 15, Chapter 7. In selecting a suitable inert gas, care must be taken to choose one that is not reactive with the dust. Certain metallic dusts, for example, react with carbon dioxide or nitrogen.[4] Helium and argon are suitable diluents in such instances.

Addition of a small amount of flammable gas to a dust cloud and igniting the resultant aerosol greatly increases the violence of the explosion, particularly at lower dust concentrations. The resultant rates of pressure rise are very much higher than usually anticipated. Without the dust the remaining fraction of the total combustible in air, represented by the flammable vapor, would be in itself below the LFL. In certain drying operations involving the evaporation of a flammable vapor from a combustible powder with entrainment of the combustible dust along with the flammable vapor, explosions occurred that were far more violent than anticipated when considering only the fraction represented by the flammable vapor mixture alone.[17] Indeed, explosions occurred in such flammable vapor—combustible dust-air mixtures when the flammable vapor-air portion was below the LFL. These situations when encountered, need special safeguards, such as inert gas dilution, explosion suppression, very large explosion vents, and careful static electricity elimination designs.

B. Dust Cloud Ignition Sources

Dust clouds have been ignited by open flames, lights, smoking materials, electric arcs, hot filaments of light bulbs, friction sparks, high pressure steam pipes and other hot surfaces, static sparks, spontaneous heating, welding and cutting torches and sparks from these operations, and other common sources of heat for ignition. The dust cloud ignition temperatures given in Table 3-8A for the most part fall between 572° and 1,112°F (300° and 600°C) and a large majority of the reported minimum spark ignition energies were between 10 and 40 millijoules. This can be contrasted to flammable vapor ignition energies with a range for the most part between 0.2 and 10 millijoules. As a general rule, combustible dusts require 20 to 50 times the ignition energy of flammable vapors.

As ignition temperatures and ignition energies required for dust explosions are much lower than the temperatures and energies of most common sources of ignition, it is not surprising that dust explosions have been caused by all common sources of ignition. For this reason the elimination of all possible sources of ignition is a basic principle of dust explosion prevention. Ignition sources in dust handling operations are identified and recommendations for their elimination are described in various NFPA standards for the prevention of dust explosions (see Bibliography at the end of this chapter).

C. Factors Influencing the Destructiveness of Dust Explosions

While the destructiveness of a dust explosion depends primarily on the rate of pressure rise, other contributing factors are the maximum pressure developed, the duration of the excess pressure, the degree of confinement of the explosion volume, and the oxygen concentration.

Effect of Rate of Pressure Rise

The rate of pressure rise may be defined as the ratio of the increase in explosion pressure to the time interval of that increase. It is the most important single factor in evaluating the hazard of a dust and principally determines the degree of destructiveness of a deflagration.

The rate of pressure rise is also an important consideration in the design of explosion vents since it largely determines the size of the vent. In many cases an extremely rapid rate of pressure rise indicates that an explosion vent design is impractical. In referring to Table 3-8A the empirical term "Explosion Severity" is of a practical value in evaluating this problem. When explosion severities of between 2 and 4 are encountered very large vent ratios are necessary and close attention to the strength of building and equipment design is necessary. Above an explosion severity of 4 most circumstances would preclude an explosion venting design and demand the use of such protective devices as inert gas or explosion suppression systems.[10,16,17,18,19,20]

Effect of Maximum Explosion Pressure

The maximum explosion pressures reported in Table 3-8A are for the most part in excess of 50 psi and in some cases even exceed 100 psi. These figures are valid only for the conditions of test, and are subject to changes by variation in particle size, concentration, and other variables. The data in Table 3-8A give some indication of the magnitude of the maximum pressures which can be expected. Considering that an ordinary 12-in thick wall can be destroyed by less than 1 psi pressure, it is evident that it is not practical to build a building strong enough to resist the maximum pressures resulting from a dust deflagration.

One reason why the degree of destruction is not greater in many dust explosions is that the dust is not uniformly dispersed throughout the explosion volume. A dust cloud is rarely ignited under optimum concentration conditions with respect to development of maximum explosion pressures.

Effect of Duration of Excess Pressure

Closely associated with maximum pressure and rate of pressure rise as indication of the destructiveness of dust explosions is the length of time the excess pressure is exerted on the surroundings. The area under the time pressure curve determines the total impulse exerted and it is the total impulse rather than the force exerted at any one moment that will determine the amount of destruction.[21,22] This relationship between destructiveness and total impulse explains in part why dust explosions, which generally have slower average rates of pressure rise than gas explosions, may be more destructive than gas explosions.

Effect of Confinement

When a dust explosion occurs, gaseous products are generally formed and heat is released which raises the temperature of the air in the enclosure. Since gases expand when heated, destructive pressures will be exerted on the surrounding enclosure unless enough vent area is provided to release the hot gases before dangerous pressures are reached.

The Bureau of Mines[7,23,24] and others[10,20,25,26,27,28] have examined the effect in some detail. Data from these investigations emphasize the importance of proper vents as a method of reducing damage from explosion pressures. (For a discussion of explosion venting see Section 15, Chapter 7.) In some instances it may be impractical to provide sufficient vent area to reduce pressures to a safe level. In

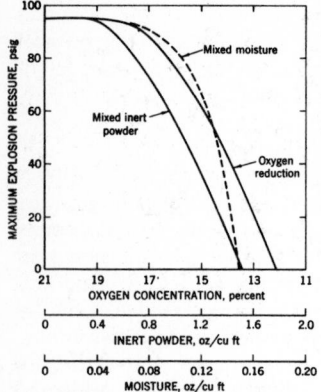

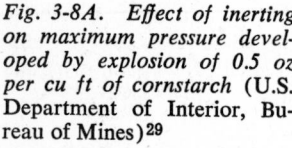

Fig. 3-8A. Effect of inerting on maximum pressure developed by explosion of 0.5 oz per cu ft of cornstarch (U.S. Department of Interior, Bureau of Mines)[29]

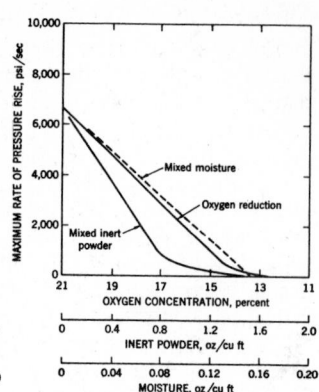

Fig. 3-8B. Effect of inerting on maximum rate of pressure rise developed by explosion of 0.5 oz per cu ft of cornstarch. (U.S. Department of Interior, Bureau of Mines)[29]

these situations the dust producing operation can be conducted in the open, under an inert atmosphere, or protected by an explosion suppression system. The explosion suppression system consists of a flame or pressure detector and a flame quenching agent which is expelled rapidly during the incipient stage of an explosion.

Effect of Inerting on Explosion Pressures and Rates of Pressure Rise

Data published by the Bureau of Mines[29] show that reduction in the oxygen concentration in the atmosphere, and mixture of inert powder (fuller's earth) or moisture with the combustible dust reduces the maximum explosion pressure and rates of pressure rise. These data are shown in Figures 3-8A and 3-8B for explosions of 0.5 oz pcf of cornstarch. A slight reduction in the atmospheric oxygen concentration or slight additions of inert powder or moisture have little effect on the explosion pressure. The effect of the inerting on the dust explosion becomes marked only when limiting values are approached. The maximum rate of pressure rise developed by the explosions appears to decrease almost linearly with use of inerting.

D.   Dust Explosion Test Apparatus and Procedures

There are a number of different types of dust explosion test chambers and even more procedures, for using them each of which can profoundly affect the test results for any given dust sample. For example, the result of the dust explosion test in a closed chamber are affected by the geometry of the chamber, i.e., interior dimensions (cubical, spherical, cylindrical, etc.), and by the method of creating the dust cloud in the chamber (the method affects the turbulence of the cloud and uniformity of particle dispersion). This situation causes considerable difficulty in attempting to compare results obtained by various methods. In fact, unless several test results on the same dust sample are made in different chambers and a consequent correlation developed between the test methods it can be said without reservation that any comparison of data obtained by different tests methods is at the very best, only qualitative.

Lack of uniformity in test procedures also rules out any attempt to compare the pressures and rates of pressure rise resulting from tests on flammable vapors and dusts. By far

the largest amount of dust explosion test data has been obtained from tests conducted by the Bureau of Mines. In the field of vapor-gas explosions there is nothing comparable. The Bureau of Mines test equipment and procedures are described in RI 5624.[30]

Interpretation and Application of Dust Explosion Test Data

Dust explosion test data is gathered in a variety of chambers under conditions ranging from a highly turbulent dust cloud to a practically stagnant cloud. This hinders the use of existing test information in evaluating hazards in relation to building design. However, for a constant velocity of propagation or flame speed in a given dust sample suspended in air (or a flammable vapor-air mixture) the following relationship holds:

$$\frac{R_l}{R_s} = \left(\frac{V_s}{V_l}\right)^{\frac{1}{3}} = \frac{A_l}{A_s}$$

where

R_l = Rate of pressure rise in the large chamber, psi per sec,

R_s = Rate of pressure rise in the small chamber, psi per sec,

V_l = Volume of large chamber, cu ft,

V_s = Volume of small chamber, cu ft,

A_l = Vent ratio of large chamber, sq ft per cu ft of volume, and

A_s = Vent ratio of small chamber, sq ft per cu ft of volume.

The above shows test data gathered in small chambers can be extrapolated to larger chambers with some degree of confidence, though care must be taken to keep the shape of small chambers and large chambers within reasonable limits. If the test is done in small spheres the results cannot be expected to hold up in the design of explosion relief for a long narrow vessel.

It should be pointed out the Bureau of Mines' test data were gathered under highly turbulent conditions in small chambers and as such the same pressures and rates of pressure rise cannot be expected to be obtained in a large building even if the volumes involved are theoretically accounted for in the relationship cited above.

Ignition Temperature

One piece of apparatus developed at the Bureau of Mines consists essentially of an electrically heated vertical cylindrical tube at the top of which is a small container into which a weighed amount of dust is placed. The dust is projected down through the tube as a uniform cloud by a controlled blast of compressed air directed at the sample of dust. The ignition temperature is considered to be the lowest temperature at which flame issues from the open bottom end of the tube. Differences in results are due to differences in the size and shape of test containers.

Ignition in Inert Atmospheres

For the determination of the ignitibility of dust in various inert gas-air mixtures the apparatus consists of a vertical cylindrical tube containing tungsten electrodes to produce a spark for ignition. The tube is designed so that it can be flushed with the inert gas-air mixture prior to test. The dust sample in a container near the top of the tube is projected downward as a cloud by a controlled blast of the inert gas-air mixture. Flame issuing from the open bottom of the tube signifies ignition.

Minimum Energies for Ignition

Apparatus developed at the Bureau of Mines to determine minimum energies to cause ignition of dust clouds consists of a vertical cylindrical lucite tube. In this test the dust is dispersed upward in the tube by controlled discharge of compressed air into the dust sample at the bottom of the tube. A spark discharged by an electrical condenser is used as the ignition source and by using condensers with different capacities, spark energy can be varied. Discharge of the condenser is synchronized with the formation of the dust cloud. Visible flame in the tube signifies ignition.

Explosion Pressures

Apparatus described by the Bureau of Mines for determining maximum explosion pressures and rates of pressure rise consists of a vertical cylindrical steel bomb into which a weighed sample of dust can be dispersed upward by a jet of compressed air. Pressures are measured by a strain gage transducer mounted in the top of the bomb. A pressure time record is obtained on an oscillograph using a light beam galvanometer system.

SI Units

The following conversion factors are given as a convenience in converting to SI units the English units given in this chapter.

1 in. = 25.4 mm
1 ounce (mass) = .454 kg
1 psi = 6.895 kPa
$\frac{5}{9}$(°F − 32) = °C
1 ft³ = .0283 m³

Bibliography

References Cited

[1] Palmer, K. N., *Dust Explosions and Fires,* Chapman & Hall Ltd., London, 1973.
[2] Jacobson, M., et al., "Explosibility of Agricultural Dusts," RI 5753, USDI, Bureau of Mines, Pittsburgh, 1961.
[3] Jacobson, M., Nagy, J., and Cooper, A. R., "Explosibility of Dusts Used in the Plastics Industry," RI 5971, 1962, USDI, Bureau of Mines, Pittsburgh.
[4] Jacobson, M., Cooper, A. R., and Nagy, J., "Explosibility of Metal Powders," RI 6516, 1964, USDI, Bureau of Mines, Pittsburgh.
[5] Nagy, J., Dorsett, H. G., and Cooper, A. R., "Explosibility of Carbonaceous Dusts," RI 6597, 1965, USDI, Bureau of Mines, Pittsburgh.
[6] Boyle, A. R., and Llewellyn, F. J., "The Electrostatic Ignitability of Dust Clouds and Powders," *Journal of Applied Chemistry,* Vol. 69, June 1950, pp. 173–181.
[7] Hartmann, I., Cooper, A. R., and Jacobson, M., "Recent Studies on the Explosibility of Corn Starch," RI 4725, August 1950, USDI, Bureau of Mines, Pittsburgh.
[8] Nagy, J., and Surincik, D. J., "Thermal Phenomena During Ignition of a Heated Dust Dispersion," RI 6811, 1966, USDI, Bureau of Mines, Pittsburgh.
[9] Dawes, J. G., and Maguire, B. A., "Calculation of the Relationship Between Particle Number, Area and Weight Concentration in Coal Mine Dust Clouds," Safety in Mines Research Report No. 150, December 1958, Safety in Mines Research Establishment, Sheffield, England.
[10] "Dust Explosions Analysis and Control," Factory Insurance Association, Hartford, Conn., 1966. (See also Schwab, R. F., and Othmer, D. F., "Dust Explosions," *Chemical and Process Engineering,* April 1964, pp. 165–174.)
[11] Kunkel, W. B., "The State of Electrification of Dust Particles on Dispersion into a Cloud," *Journal of Applied Physics,* Vol. 21, 1950, pp. 820–832.
[12] Geyerstam, O., et al., "Dust Explosions at Kopingebro," *Socker Handingar,* Vol. 18, No. 3, 1963, pp. 29–83.
[13] Kunkel, W. B., "Charge Distribution in Coarse Aerosols as a Function of Time," *Journal of Applied Physics,* Vol. 21, 1950, pp. 833–837.
[14] Magison, E. C., *Electrical Instruments in Hazardous Locations,* 2nd ed., Instrument Society of America, Pittsburgh, 1972, pp. 277–291.
[15] Hartmann, I., Jacobson, M., and Williams, R. P., "Laboratory Explosibility Study of American Coals," RI 5052, April 1954, USDI, Bureau of Mines, Pittsburgh.
[16] Nagy, J., Mitchell, D. W., and Kawenski, E. M., "Float Coal Hazard in Mines: A Progress Report," RI 6581, 1965, USDI, Bureau of Mines, Pittsburgh.
[17] Nagy, J., and Portman, W. M., "Explosibility of Coal Dust in an Atmosphere Containing a Low Percentage of Methane," RI 5815, 1961, USDI, Bureau of Mines, Pittsburgh.
[18] Cotton, P. E., "New Test Apparatus for Dust Explosions," *NFPA Quarterly,* Vol. 45, No. 2, Oct. 1951, pp. 157–164.
[19] "Guide for Explosion Venting," NFPA No. 68, 1974, National Fire Protection Association, Boston.
[20] "Inerting for Fire and Explosion Prevention," NFPA No. 69, 1973, National Fire Protection Association, Boston.
[21] Kinney, G. F., *Explosive Shocks in Air,* Macmillan, New York, 1962.
[22] Baker, W. E., *Explosions in Air,* University of Texas Press, Austin, Texas, 1973.
[23] Hartmann, I., and Nagy, J., "Effect of Relief Vents on Reduction of Pressure Developed by Dust Explosions," RI 3924, May 1946, USDI, Bureau of Mines, Pittsburgh.
[24] Nagy, J., Zerlinger, J. E., and Hartmann, I., "Pressure Relieving Capacities of Diaphragms and Other Devices for Venting Dust Explosions," RI 4636, January 1959, USDI, Bureau of Mines, Pittsburgh.
[25] Maisey, H. R., "Gaseous & Dust Explosion Venting," *Chemical and Process Engineering,* Part I, Oct. 1965, pp. 527–535; Part II, Dec. 1965, pp. 662–672.
[26] Straumann, W., "Size of Pressure Relieving Explosion Vents in Chemical Plant Equipment," *Chemie-Ingenieur-Technik,* Vol. 3, 1965, pp. 306–316.
[27] Donat, C., "Selection and Dimensioning of Pressure Relief Devices for Dust Explosions," *Staub-Reinhaltung der Luft* (English transl.), Vol. 31, No. 4, April 1971, pp. 17–29.
[28] Heinrich, H. J., and Kowall, Reinhard, "Results of Recent Pressure Relief Experiments in Connection with Dust Explosions," *Staub-Reinhaltung der Luft* (English transl.), Vol. 31, No. 4, April 1971, pp. 10–17.
[29] Nagy, J., Cooper, A. R., and Stupar, J. M., "Pressure Development in Laboratory Dust Explosions," RI 6561, 1964, USDI, Bureau of Mines, Pittsburgh.
[30] Dorsett, H. G., et al., "Laboratory Equipment and Test Procedures for Evaluating Explosibility of Dusts," RI 5624, 1960, USDI, Bureau of Mines, Pittsburgh.

NFPA Codes, Standards, and Recommended Practices (see the latest *NFPA Publications and Visual Aids Catalog* for availability of current editions of the following documents)

NFPA No. 48, Standard for the Storage, Handling and Processing of Magnesium.
NFPA No. 49, Hazardous Chemicals Data.
NFPA No. 60, Standard for the Installation and Operation of Pulverized-Fuel Systems.
NFPA No. 61A, Standard for the Prevention of Dust Explosions in Starch Factories.
NFPA No. 61B, Code for the Prevention of Dust Explosions in Terminal Grain Elevators.
NFPA No. 61C, Code for the Prevention of Dust Explosions in Flour and Feed Mills and Allied Grain Storage Elevators.
NFPA No. 62, Standard for the Prevention of Dust Explosions in the Production, Packaging and Handling of Pulverized Sugar and Cocoa.
NFPA No. 63, Fundamental Principles for Prevention of Dust Explosions in Industrial Plants.
NFPA No. 65, Code for the Processing and Finishing of Aluminum.
NFPA No. 66, Standard for Pneumatic Conveying Systems for Handling Feed, Flour, Grain and Other Agricultural Dusts.
NFPA No. 481, Standard for the Production Processing, Handling and Storage of Titanium.
NFPA No. 482M, Guide for Fire and Explosion Prevention in Plants Producing and Handling Zirconium.
NFPA No. 651, Standard for the Manufacture of Aluminum or Magnesium Powder.
NFPA No. 653, Standard for the Prevention of Dust Explosions in Coal Preparation Plants.
NFPA No. 654, Standard for the Prevention of Dust Explosions in the Plastics Industry.
NFPA No. 655, Standard for the Prevention of Sulfur Fires and Explosions.

NFPA No. 656, Code for the Prevention of Dust Ignitions in Spice Grinding Plants.

NFPA No. 657, Code for the Prevention of Dust Explosions in Confectionary Manufacturing Plants.

NFPA No. 664, Code for the Prevention of Dust Explosions in Woodworking and Wood Flour Manufacturing Plants.

Additional Readings

"American Standard Practice for Rock-Dusting Underground Bituminous Coal and Lignite Mines to Prevent Coal Dust Explosions," (ASA Standard M13.1, 1960), IC 8001, 1960, USDI, Bureau of Mines, Pittsburgh.

Baumeister, T., and Mark, L., *Mechanical Engineers Handbook*, 7th ed., McGraw-Hill, New York, 1967, pp. 7-38–7-45.

Brown, H. R., "Dust Explosion Hazards in Plants Producing or Handling Aluminum, Magnesium or Zinc Powder," IC 7148, 1941, USDI, Bureau of Mines, Washington, D.C.

Brown, H. R., et al., "Fire and Explosion Hazards in Thermal Coal Drying Plants," RI 5198, 1956, USDI, Bureau of Mines, Pittsburgh.

Brown, K. C., and Curzon, G. E., "Dust Explosions in Factories: Field Scale Tests on an Explosion Detector and Two Types of Quick Closing Valves," Safety in Mines Research Report No. 194, Dec. 1960, Safety in Mines Research Establishment, Sheffield, England.

Brown, K. C., and James, G. J., "Dust Explosions in Factories: A Review of the Literature," Safety in Mines Research Report No. 201, June 1962, Safety in Mines Research Establishment, Sheffield, England.

Cassel, H. M., "Some Fundamental Aspects of Dust Flames," RI 6551, 1964, USDI, Bureau of Mines, Pittsburgh.

Dufour, R. E., "A New Type of Bomb for Investigation of Pressures Developed by Dust Explosions," Bulletin of Research No. 30, March 1944, Underwriters' Laboratories, Inc., Chicago.

"Dust Explosions in Factories," Ministry of Labour New Series 22, 1963, Her Majesty's Stationery Office, London.

"Dust Hazards in the Starch and Dextrine Industries," (Papers given at a conference held September 19-20, 1961 at the Palace Hotel, Buxton, England), The British Dextrine Manufacturers' Association, London.

Eggleston, L. A., and Pryor, A. J., "The Limits of Dust Explosibility," *Fire Technology*, Vol. 3, No. 2, May 1967, pp. 77–89.

Essenhigh, R. H., "Dust Explosions in Factories: Ignition Testing and Design of a New Inflammator," Safety in Mine Research Report No. 188, May 1960, Safety in Mines Research Establishment, Sheffield, England.

———, "Combustion Phenomena in Coal Dusts," *Colliery Engineering*, Dec. 1966, pp. 534–539; Jan. 1962, pp. 23–28; Feb. 1962, pp. 65–72; Mar. 1962, pp. 103–104.

———, "Dust Explosion Research: An Appraisal Conference on Dust Explosions," Pennsylvania State University, Sept. 1962. (See also *Fire Research Abstracts and Reviews*, Vol. 5, No. 1, 1963, p. 55; and Vol. 6, No. 1, 1964, p. 82.)

Essenhigh, R. H., and Brown, K. C., "Dust Explosions in Factories: A New Vertical-Tube Test Apparatus," Safety in Mines Research Report No. 165, April 1959, Safety in Mines Research Establishment, Sheffield, England.

Essenhigh, R. H., Froberg, R., and Howard, J. B., "Combustion Behavior of Small Particles," *Industrial & Engineering Chemistry*, Vol. 57, No. 9, Sept. 1965, pp. 33–43.

Essenhigh, R. H., and Woodhead, D. W., "Dust Explosions in Factories: Speed of Flame in Slowly Moving Clouds of Cork Dust," Safety in Mines Research Report No. 166, Sept. 1969, Safety in Mines Research Establishment, Sheffield, England.

Factory Mutual Engineering Division, "Dust Explosions," *Handbook of Industrial Loss Prevention*, 2nd ed., McGraw-Hill, New York, 1967, pp. 66-1–66-16.

Grove, G. W., and Freas, G. L., "Small Portable Coal-Dust Explosion Gallery," IC 7520, 1949, USDI, Bureau of Mines, Washington, D.C.

"Guide to the Use of Flame Arrestors and Explosion Reliefs," Ministry of Labour New Series 34, 1965, Her Majesty's Stationery Office, London.

Hartmann, I., and Nagy, J., "Inflammability and Explosibility of Powder Used in the Plastics Industry," RI 3751, May 1944, USDI, Bureau of Mines, Pittsburgh.

———, "Venting Dust Explosions," *Industrial & Engineering Chemistry*, Vol. 49, No. 10, Oct. 1957, p. 1734.

Hartmann, I., Nagy, J., and Jacobson, M., "Explosive Characteristics of Titanium, Zirconium, Thorium, Uranium, and Their Hydrides," RI 4835, Dec. 1951, USDI, Bureau of Mines, Pittsburgh.

Mitchell, D. W., and Nagy, J., "Water as an Inert for Neutralizing the Coal Dust Explosion Hazard," IC 8111, 1962, USDI, Bureau of Mines, Pittsburgh.

Morse, A. R., "A Study of the September 1952 Dust Explosion at Port Arthur Grain Elevator No. 4A," NRC No. 3614, May 1955, National Research Council of Canada, Ottawa.

Nagy, J., Dorsett, H. G., and Jacobson, M., "Preventing Ignition of Dust Dispersions by Inerting," RI 6543, 1964, USDI, Bureau of Mines, Pittsburgh.

Nagy, J., and Mitchell, D. W., "Experimental Coal-Dust and Gas Explosions," RI 6344, 1963, USDI Bureau of Mines, Pittsburgh.

Raftery, M. M., "Explosibility Tests for Industrial Dusts," Fire Research Technical Paper No. 21, 1968, Ministry of Technology and Fire Offices' Committee, Boreham Wood, Herts, Great Britain. (See also Raftery, M. M., *Staub-Reinhaltung der Luft* (English transl.), Vol. 31, No. 4, April 1971, pp. 1–10.)

Rasbash, D. J., and Rogowski, Z. W., "Relief of Explosions in Duct Systems," *Symposium on Chemical Process Hazards with Special Reference to Plant Design*, 1961, Institute of Chemical Engineers, pp. 58–68.

Report of Important Dust Explosions, National Fire Protection Association, Boston, 1957.

Simmonds, W. A., and Cubbage, P. A., "The Design of Explosion Reliefs for Industrial Drying Ovens," *Symposium on Chemical Process Hazards with Special Reference to Plant Design*, Institute of Chemical Engineers, 1961, pp. 69–77.

Singer, J. M., "Ignition of Coal Dust-Methane-Air Mixture by Hot Turbulent Gas Jets," RI 6369, 1964, USDI, Bureau of Mines, Pittsburgh.

Section 3

Chapter 9

Metals

Nearly all metals will burn in air under certain conditions. Some oxidize rapidly in the presence of air or moisture, generating sufficient heat to reach their ignition temperatures. Others oxidize so slowly that heat generated during oxidation is dissipated before they become hot enough to ignite. Certain metals, notably magnesium, titanium, sodium, potassium, calcium, lithium, hafnium, zirconium, zinc, thorium, uranium, and plutonium, are referred to as combustible metals because of the ease of ignition of thin sections, fine particles or molten metal. However, the same metals in massive solid form are comparatively difficult to ignite.

Some metals, such as aluminum and steel, that are not normally thought of as being combustible, may ignite and burn when in finely divided form. Clean, fine steel wool, for example, may be ignited. Particle size, shape, quantity, and alloy are important factors to be considered when evaluating metal combustibility. Dust clouds of most metals in air are explosive (see Chap. 8 of this Section). Alloys, consisting of different metals or metallic compounds combined in varying proportions, may differ widely in combustibility from their constituent elements. Metals tend to be most reactive when in finely divided form, and some may require shipment and storage under inert gas or liquid to reduce fire risks.

Hot, burning metals may react violently when contacted by other materials, such as any of the extinguishants used on fires involving ordinary combustibles or flammable liquids. A few metals, such as uranium, thorium and plutonium, emit ionizing radiations that can complicate fire fighting and introduce a contamination problem. The toxicity of certain metals is also of importance in fire protection.

Temperatures in burning metals are generally much higher than the temperature in burning flammable liquids. Some hot metals can continue burning in nitrogen, carbon dioxide, or steam atmospheres in which ordinary combustibles or flammable liquids would be incapable of burning.

This chapter covers the fire hazard properties of combustible metals, methods of their storage, handling, and transportation to prevent their ignition and to protect against other hazardous properties. Also discussed are the major fire problems that arise while combustible metals are being processed in machine shops and foundries.

Hot burning metal fire properties cover a wide range. Burning titanium produces little smoke, while burning lithium smoke is dense and profuse. Some water-moistened metal powders, such as zirconium, burn with near explosive violence, while the same powder wet with oil burns quiescently. Sodium melts and flows while burning; calcium does not. Some metals, e.g., uranium, acquire an increased tendency to burn after prolonged exposure to moist air while prolonged exposure to dry air may make it more difficult to ignite the metal.

Inasmuch as the extinguishment of fires in combustible metals involves techniques not commonly encountered in conventional fire fighting operations, it is good practice for those responsible for controlling combustible metal fires at a plant to gain experience in this area prior to the actual fire emergency. Fire fighters should practice extinguishing fires in those metals in a detached outdoor location.

Where metals other than those described in this chapter are to be used, it is more important than ever that fire fighters gain some experience in extinguishing test fires involving the specific combustible metals.

Extinguishing agents suitable for use on combustible metal fires are discussed in Section 13, Chapter 6.

A. Magnesium

Properties

The ignition temperature of massive magnesium is very close to its melting point—1,202°F. (See Table 3-9A.) However, ignition of magnesium in certain forms may occur at temperatures well below 1,200°F; magnesium ribbons and shavings can be ignited under certain conditions at about 950°F, and finely divided magnesium powder can ignite below 900°F.

Metal marketed under different trade names and commonly referred to as magnesium may be one of a large number of different alloys containing principally magnesium, but also significant percentages of aluminum, manganese, and zinc. Some of these alloys have ignition temperatures considerably lower than pure magnesium, and certain magnesium alloys will ignite at temperatures as low as 800°F. Since magnesium is principally used in alloy form, it is important to know the combustibility of the particular alloy when considering fire prevention measures.

As is the case with all combustible metals, the ease of ignition of magnesium depends upon its size and shape. Thin, small pieces, such as ribbons, chips, and shavings, may be ignited by a match flame whereas castings and other

Table 3-9A. Melting, Boiling, and Ignition Temperatures of Pure Metals in Solid Form

(Because of the variations in available information, the values given must be considered as being approximate and for guidance only. Generally, if a metal melts and flows before burning, an ignition temperature can be determined. Values were obtained from publications shown in the Bibliography.)

Pure Metal	Temperature °F.		
	Melting Point	Boiling Point	Solid Metal Ignition
Aluminum	1,220	4,445	above 1832*
Barium	1,337	2,084	347*
Calcium	1,548	2,625	1,300
Hafnium	4,032	9,750	—
Iron	2,795	5,432	1,706*
Lithium	367	2,437	356
Magnesium	1,202	2,030	1,153
Plutonium	1,184	6,000	1,112
Potassium	144	1,400	156*S
Sodium	208	1,616	above 239
Strontium	1,425	2,102	1,328*
Thorium	3,353	8,132	932*
Titanium	3,140	5,900	2,900
Uranium	2,070	6,900	below 6900
Zinc	786	1,665	1,652*
Zirconium	3,326	6,470	2,552*

* Ignition in oxygen
S Spontaneous ignition in moist air

large pieces are difficult to ignite with a torch because of the high thermal conductivity of the metal. In order to ignite a large piece of magnesium, it is generally necessary to raise the entire piece to the ignition temperature.

Scrap magnesium chips or other fines may burn as the result of ignition of waste rags or other contaminants. Chips wet with water, water soluble oils, and oils containing more than 0.2 percent fatty acid may slowly generate hydrogen gas. Chips wet with animal or vegetable oils may burn if the oils ignite spontaneously. Fines from grinding operations generate some hydrogen when submerged in water, but they cannot be ignited in this condition. Grinding fines that are slightly wetted with water may generate sufficient heat to ignite spontaneously in air, burning violently as oxygen is extracted from the water with the release of hydrogen.

Burning magnesium reacts violently with carbon tetrachloride; water spray increases the intensity of a magnesium chip fire (see use as an extinguishant in Sect. 13, Chap. 6), and burning magnesium continues to burn in atmospheres of carbon dioxide or nitrogen.

Storage and Handling (Includes Transportation)

The more massive a piece of magnesium, the more difficult it is to ignite, but once ignited, magnesium burns intensely and is difficult to extinguish. The storage recommendations in NFPA No. 48, Storage, Handling and Processing of Magnesium, take these properties into consideration. Recommended maximum quantities of various sizes and forms to be stored in specific locations are covered in this standard. The storage building should preferably be noncombustible, and the magnesium should be segregated from combustible material as fire prevention measures.

With easily ignited lightweight castings, segregation from combustible materials is very important, and in the case of dry fines (fine magnesium scrap) storage in noncombustible, covered containers in separate fire-resistive storage buildings or rooms with explosive venting facilities is preferable. For combustible buildings or buildings containing combustible contents, the NFPA Magnesium Standard recommends automatic sprinkler protection to assure prompt control of a fire before magnesium becomes involved.

Because of the possibility of hydrogen generation and also of spontaneous heating of fines wet with coolants

Fig. 3-9A. Typical magnesium chip fire resulting from improper machining practices.

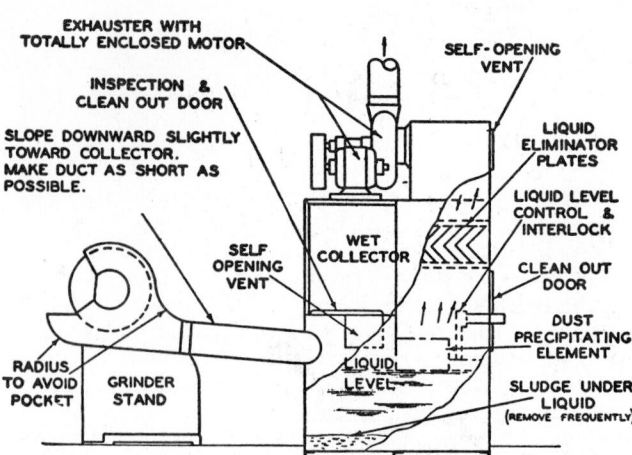

Fig. 3-9B. A schematic diagram of a water precipitation-type collector for use in collecting dry combustible metal dust without creating explosive dust clouds or dangerous deposits in ducts or collection chambers. The diagram is intended only to show some of the features which should be incorporated in the design of a collector. It may be used for all combustible metal dusts.

(other than neutral mineral oil), it is preferable to store wet scrap fines outdoors. Covered noncombustible containers should be vented.

Other than in the form of powder or scrap, no special packaging safeguards are necessary. The U.S. Department of Transportation (DOT) permits the shipment of dry magnesium powder in the same kind of containers as permitted for flammable solids, such as metal barrels or drums.

If dry magnesium scrap in the form of borings, shavings, and turnings is to be shipped in interstate commerce in less than carload lots, the shipper may use closed metal drums. In carload or truckload lots he may also use four-ply paper bags.

Less than carload lots of scrap in the form of clippings or sheets may be shipped in closed metal drums, wooden barrels, or wooden boxes. For bulk shipments, tight box cars, tightly closed steel covered gondola cars, and closed or completely covered truck bodies may be used.

Process Hazards

In machining operations involving magnesium alloys, sufficient frictional heat to ignite the chips or shavings may be created if the tools are dull or deformed (see Fig. 3-9A). If cutting fluids are used (machining of magnesium is normally done dry), they should be of the mineral oil type. Water or water-oil emulsions are hazardous, since wet magnesium shavings and dust liberate hydrogen gas and, if ignited, burn more violently than dry material. Machines and the work area should be frequently cleaned and the waste magnesium kept in covered, clean, dry, steel or other noncombustible drums which should be removed from the building at regular intervals. Magnesium dust clouds are explosive if an ignition source is present. Grinding equipment should be equipped with a water spray-type dust precipitator (Fig. 3-9B). A good grinder installation is designed to operate only if the exhaust blower and water spray are functioning properly. The equipment is restricted to magnesium processing only.

Molten magnesium in the foundry presents a serious fire problem if not properly handled. Sulfur dioxide or melting fluxes are commonly used to prevent oxidation or ignition of magnesium during foundry operations. The action of sulfur dioxide is to exclude air from the surface of the molten magnesium; it is not an extinguishing agent. Fluxes perform both functions.

Pots, crucibles, and ladles that may contact molten magnesium must be kept dry to prevent steam formation or a violent metal-water reaction. Containers should be checked regularly for any possibility of leakage or weak points. Steel-lined runoff pits or pits with tightly fitting steel pans should be provided. The pans must be kept free of iron scale. Leaking metal contacting hot iron scale results in a violent thermite reaction. Use of stainless steel pans or linings will eliminate this possibility.

Heat treating ovens or furnaces where magnesium alloy parts are subjected to high temperatures to modify their properties present another special problem. Temperatures for heat treating needed to secure the desired physical properties are often close to the ignition temperatures of the alloys themselves, and careful control of temperatures in all parts of the oven is essential (see Sec. 4, Chap. 5 for information on oven controls). Hot spots leading to local overheating are a common cause of these fires. Large castings do not ignite readily, but fine fins or projections on the castings, as well as chips or dust, are more readily subject to ignition. For this reason, castings should be thoroughly cleaned before heat treating. Magnesium castings in contact with aluminum in a heat treating oven will ignite at a lower temperature than when they are placed on a steel car or tray.

Magnesium should not be heat treated in nitrate salt baths. Certain commonly used molten mixtures of nitrates and nitrites can react explosively with magnesium alloys, particularly at temperatures over 1,000°F.

Fighting Magnesium Fires

Magnesium and its alloys present special problems in fire protection. Magnesium combines so readily with oxygen that under some conditions water applied to extinguish magnesium fires may be decomposed into its constituent elements, oxygen and hydrogen. The oxygen combines with the magnesium and the hydrogen released adds to the intensity of the fire. None of the commonly available inert gases are suitable for extinguishing magnesium fires. The affinity of magnesium for oxygen is so great that it will burn in an atmosphere of carbon dioxide. Magnesium may also burn in an atmosphere of nitrogen to form magnesium nitride. For these reasons, any of the common extinguishing methods depending upon water, water solutions, or inert gas are not effective on magnesium chip fires. Halogen-containing extinguishing agents (the Halons) react violently with burning magnesium, the chlorine or other halogen combining with the magnesium (see Sec. 13, Chap. 6, for combustible metal extinguishing agents).

The method of extinguishing magnesium fires depends largely upon the form of the material. Burning chips, shavings, and small parts must be smothered and cooled with a suitable dry extinguishing agent. Where magnesium dust is present, care must be taken to prevent a dust cloud from forming in the air during application of the agent as this may result in a dust explosion.

Fires in solid magnesium can be dealt with without difficulty if attacked in their early stages. It often may be possible to remove surrounding material, leaving the small quantity of magnesium to burn itself out harmlessly. Because of the importance of prompt attack on magnesium fires, automatic sprinklers are desirable as they provide automatic notification and control of fire. While the water from the sprinklers may have the immediate effect of intensifying combustion of the magnesium, it will serve to protect the structure and other materials from serious damage. An excess of water applied to fires in solid magnesium (avoiding puddles of molten metal) cools the metal below the ignition temperature after some initial intensification and the fire goes out rapidly. By contrast, the fire may be intensified with a small, finely divided water spray.

Magnesium fires in heat treating ovens can best be controlled with powders and gases developed for use on such fires. By using melting fluxes to exclude air from the burning metal, fires in heat treating furnaces have been successfully put out. Boron trifluoride gas is an effective extinguishing agent for small fires in heat treating furnaces. Cylinders of boron trifluoride can be permanently connected to the oven or mounted on a suitable cart for use as portable equipment. Boron trifluoride is allowed to flow into the oven until the fire is extinguished, or, where large quantities of magnesium are well involved before discovery or where the furnace is not tight, the boron trifluoride will control the fire until extinguishment can be completed by application of flux.

B. Titanium

Properties

Titanium, like magnesium, is classified as a combustible metal, but here again the size and shape of the metal determines to a great extent whether or not it will ignite. Castings and other massive pieces of titanium are not combustible under ordinary conditions. Small chips, fine turnings, and dust ignite readily and once ignited burn with the release of large quantities of heat. Tests have shown that very thin chips and fine turnings could be ignited by a match and heavier chips and turnings by a Bunsen burner. Coarse chips and turnings $\frac{1}{32}$ by $\frac{3}{16}$ in. or larger may be considered as difficult to ignite, but unless it is known that smaller particles are not mixed with the coarser material in significant amounts, the possibility of easy ignition must be considered as present.

Finely divided titanium in the form of dust clouds or layers does not ignite spontaneously (differing in this respect from zirconium, plutonium, and certain other metals). Ignition temperatures of titanium dust clouds in air range from 630° to 1,090°F, and of titanium dust layers from 720° to 950°F. Titanium dust can be ignited in atmospheres of carbon dioxide or nitrogen. Titanium surfaces that have been treated with nitric acid, particularly with red fuming nitric acid containing 10 to 20 percent nitrogen tetroxide, become pyrophoric and may be explosive.

The unusual conditions under which massive titanium shapes will ignite spontaneously include contact with liquid oxygen, in which case it will detonate on impact. It has been found[1] that under static conditions spontaneous ignition will take place in pure oxygen at pressures of at least 350 psi. If the oxygen was diluted, the required pressure increased, but in no instance did spontaneous heating occur in oxygen concentrations less than 35 percent. Another requirement for spontaneous heating was a fresh surface. Under dynamic conditions, such as would be created by a bursting rupture disc, spontaneous ignition occurred at pressures as low as 50 psi provided that the oxygen concentration did not fall below 35 percent. It was noted that once the titanium ignited, combustion could continue at much lower oxygen levels.

A plausible explanation of this spontaneous ignition phenomenon is based on the assumption that a fresh surface of titanium oxidizes rapidly and exothermically in an oxygen atmosphere. If the oxidation rate is fast enough (as affected by oxygen concentration and pressure), the titanium heats until it melts (3,140°F), after which the oxides diffuse rapidly into the metal and fresh molten metal comes to the surface to react. In support of this theory are tests with other metals which showed that only those whose oxides were soluble in the molten metal ignited.

Storage and Handling (Includes Transportation)

Titanium castings and ingots are so difficult to ignite and keep burning that special storage recommendations for large pieces are not included in NFPA No. 481, Standard for the Production, Processing, Handling and Storage of Titanium. Titanium sponge and scrap fines, on the other hand, do require special precautions, such as storage in covered metal containers and segregation of the containers from combustible materials. Because of the possibility of hydrogen generation in moist scrap and spontaneous heating of scrap wet with animal or vegetable oils, a yard storage area remote from buildings is recommended for scrap that is to be salvaged. Alternate recommended storage locations are detached scrap storage buildings and fire resistive storage rooms. Buildings and rooms for storage of scrap fines should have explosion vents.

There are no special shipping requirements for titanium except when in powder form. When possible, titanium powder is shipped wet (not less than 20 percent water) in tightly closed metal shipping containers.

Dry powder can be shipped in metal containers packed in outside wooden boxes. The inside containers are limited to 10 lbs. net weight each, and the gross weight of the outside container cannot exceed 75 lbs. Cushioning of inside containers by noncombustible material, such as rock wool, is required. Single trip metal barrels or drums with cushioned inside metal drums are permitted by the DOT. Inside containers are flushed with inert gas before filling.

Process Hazards

Contact of molten metal with water is the principal hazard during titanium casting. To minimize this hazard, molds are customarily thoroughly predried and provision is made to retain accidental spills under vacuum or inert gas protection.

The heat generated during machining, grinding, sawing, and drilling of titanium may be sufficient to ignite the small pieces formed by these operations or to ignite mineral oil base cutting lubricants. Consequently, waterbased coolants should be used in ample quantity to remove heat and cutting tools should be kept sharp. Fines should be removed regularly from work areas and stored in covered metal containers. To prevent titanium dust explosions, any operation producing dust should be equipped with a dust collecting system discharging into a water-type dust collector (see Fig. 3-9B).

Descaling baths of mineral acids and molten alkali salts may cause violent reactions with titanium at abnormally high temperatures. Titanium sheets have ignited on being removed from descaling baths. This hazard can be controlled by careful regulation of bath temperatures.

Titanium in contact with red fuming nitric acid has been responsible for several laboratory explosions.

There have been quite a few very severe explosions in titanium melting furnaces. These utilize an electric arc to melt a consumable electrode inside of a water-cooled crucible maintained under a high vacuum. Stray arcing between the consumable electrode and crucible resulting in penetration of the crucible, permits water to enter and react explosively with the molten titanium. Indications are that such explosions approach detonation velocities. The design and operation of these furnaces require special attention in order to prevent explosions and to minimize damage when such explosions do occur.

Fighting Titanium Fires

Tests conducted by the Factory Insurance Association on titanium machinings in piles and in open drums showed that water in coarse spray was a safe and effective means of extinguishing fires in relatively small quantities of chips.

Carbon dioxide, foam, dry chemical, and vaporizing liquid type extinguishers are not effective on titanium fires but good results have been obtained with extinguishing agents developed for use on magnesium fires (see Sec. 13, Chap. 6, for combustible metal extinguishing agents).

The safest procedure to follow with a fire involving small quantities of titanium powder is to ring the fire with a special powder suitable for metal fires and to allow the fire to burn itself out. Care should be taken to prevent formation of a titanium dust cloud.

C.   Sodium, Lithium, NaK, and Potassium

Properties

Sodium: At room temperature sodium oxidizes rapidly in moist air, but spontaneous ignitions have not been reported except when the sodium is in a finely divided form. When heated in dry air, sodium ignites in the vicinity of its boiling point (1,616°F). Sodium in normal room air and at a temperature only slightly above its melting point (208°F) has been ignited by placing sodium oxide particles on its surface. This indicates the possibility of ignition at temperatures below the boiling point. Once ignited, hot sodium burns vigorously forming dense clouds of caustic sodium oxide fumes. During combustion sodium generates about the same amount of heat as an equivalent weight of wood.

The principal fire hazard associated with sodium is its rapid reaction with water. The hydrogen liberated by this reaction may be ignited by the heat of the reaction. Sodium (like other burning, reactive metals) reacts violently with halogenated hydrocarbons, such as carbon tetrachloride, with halogens, such as iodine, and with sulfuric acid.

Lithium: Lithium, like sodium and potassium, is one of the so-called alkali metals. Lithium undergoes many of the same reactions as sodium. For example, both sodium and lithium react with water to form hydrogen, but whereas the sodium-water reaction can generate sufficient heat to ignite the hydrogen, the far less violent lithium-water reaction does not. Lithium ignites and burns vigorously at a temperature of 356°F, which is near its melting point. Unlike sodium and potassium, it will burn in nitrogen. The caustic (oxide and nitride) fumes accompanying lithium combustion are more profuse and dense than those of other alkali metals burning under similar conditions. Lithium is the lightest of all metals. During combustion it tends to melt and flow.

NaK (Sodium-Potassium Alloys): NaK is the term used when referring to any of several sodium-potassium alloys. The various NaK alloys differ from each other in melting point, but all are liquids or melt near room temperature. NaK alloys possess the same fire hazard properties as those of the component metals except that the reactions are more vigorous. NaK leaks under pressure have ignited spontaneously.

Potassium: The fire hazard properties of potassium are very similar to those of sodium with the difference that potassium is usually more reactive. For example, the reaction between potassium and the halogens is more violent and in the case of bromine, a detonation can occur. There is an explosive reaction with sulfuric acid. Unlike sodium, potassium forms some peroxides during combustion. These peroxides may react violently with organic contaminants.

Storage and Handling (Includes Transportation)

Because of its reactivity with water, sodium requires special precautions to prevent moisture from coming in contact with it. Drums and cases preferably are stored in a dry, fire resistive room or building used exclusively for sodium storage, and since sprinkler protection would be undesirable, no combustible materials should be stored in the same area. It is good practice to store empty as well as filled sodium containers in the same area and all containers should be on skids. There should be no water or steam pipes, but sufficient heat should be maintained to prevent moisture condensation due to atmospheric changes. Natural ventilation at a high spot in the room is desirable to vent any hydrogen that may be released by accidental contact of sodium with moisture.

Large quantities of sodium are often stored outdoors in above-ground tanks. In such installations weatherproof enclosures should be over tank manholes, and the free space within the tank should contain a nitrogen atmosphere. Argon or helium atmospheres should be substituted for nitrogen in the case of lithium.

Storage recommendations for lithium, NaK, and potassium in general parallel those for sodium.

Dry sodium is customarily shipped in watertight, steel barrels or drums. It is also shipped as a solid in tank car lots. The DOT specifies the type of barrels, drums, and tank cars that are to be used in interstate transportation.

Transfer of sodium to and from tank cars and storage tanks requires heating the sodium to its melting point (207.9°F). This is accomplished by circulating hot oil through pipes within the tank. The sodium is transferred by a vacuum pump, and as sodium is removed from the tank it is replaced by nitrogen. A sodium level indicator should be provided and a low pressure warning device should be part of the nitrogen system.

Sodium covered with an organic solvent may be shipped in 1-qt metal cans, each can placed in another can and cushioned with soda ash. The cans are shipped in wooden boxes of 100 lbs maximum gross weight.

Liquid sodium alloys may be shipped in pressure tested metal cans, cushioned with noncombustible material and packed in wooden boxes. Carload and truckload lots are permitted if special steel barrels and drums are used.

For small scale transfer of solid sodium from a storeroom to the use area, a metal container with a tight cover is recommended. Sodium should be removed from storage in as small quantities as practicable, and when kept on work benches should be in a closed container under kerosine or oil. Sodium—with its great affinity for moisture—may react with any atmospheric moisture at the time it is sealed in a container. Containers should not be opened by hammering on the lid due to the possible presence of hydrogen.

Transportation requirements for lithium, NaK, and potassium resemble those for sodium, but DOT regulations should be referred to in each instance.

Process Hazards

Liquid sodium is valuable as a high temperature heat transfer medium. For example, it is used in hollow exhaust valve stems in some internal combustion engines and in the transfer of heat from one type of nuclear reactor to a steam generator. In the latter process or other large scale use of molten sodium, any equipment leak may result in a fire. Since a leak in a radio-active sodium system would always be in an inert atmosphere, it would not result in a sodium fire. Where molten sodium is used in process equipment, steel pans are located underneath to prevent contact and violent reaction of burning sodium with concrete floors. Tray type covers on the pans catch the sodium and drain it into the pans through drilled holes. Any sodium flowing through the holes (open area about one-third of the total area of the cover) extinguishes itself within the pan.

Processing of sodium is essentially only the remelting to form into sticks or bricks or to add as a liquid to closed transfer systems. During this handling, contact with moist air, water, halogens, halogenated hydrocarbons, and sulfuric acid must be avoided.

Information on sodium may be used as a guide in processing lithium, NaK, and potassium.

Fighting Fires in Sodium, Lithium, NaK, and Potassium

The common extinguishing agents, such as water, foam, and vaporizing liquids, should never be used because of violent reactions with sodium. Special dry powders (essentially graphite) developed for metal fires, dry sand, dry sodium chloride, and dry soda ash are effective. These finely divided materials blanket the fire while the metal cools to below its ignition temperature. Sodium burning in an apparatus can usually be extinguished by closing all openings. Blanketing with nitrogen is also effective. In the case of lithium, argon or helium atmospheres should be used.

Fire fighting recommendations for sodium apply in the case of fires involving lithium, NaK, and potassium (see Sec. 13, Chap. 6 for combustible metal extinguishing agents). Of the cited metals, only potassium creates a superoxide during combustion. Since this product is a strong oxidizing agent, its hazards warrant special recognition during post-fire cleanup.

D.   Zirconium and Hafnium

Properties

Zirconium: The combustibility of zirconium appears to increase with decrease in average particle size (increase in surface to volume ratio), but other variables such as moisture content also affect ease of ignition. In massive form zirconium can withstand extremely high temperatures without igniting whereas clouds of dust in which the average particle size is 3 microns have ignited at room temperature. Dust clouds of larger particle size can be readily ignited if an ignition source is present, and such explosions can occur in atmospheres of carbon dioxide or nitrogen as well as in air. Tests have also indicated that layers of 3-micron dust are susceptible to spontaneous ignition, with the depth of the layer and moisture content being important variables. Spontaneous heating and ignition is also a possibility with scrap chips, borings, and turnings if fine dust is present. Layers of 6 micron diameter dust have ignited on being heated to 374°F. Combustion of zirconium dust in air is stimulated by the presence of limited amounts of water. Very finely divided zirconium powder completely immersed in water is difficult to ignite, but once ignited, burns more violently than in air.

Massive pieces of zirconium do not ignite spontaneously under ordinary conditions, but ignition will occur when an oxide-free surface is exposed to sufficiently high oxygen concentrations and pressure. The explanation for this reaction is the same as that cited for a similar titanium reaction. Zirconium fires (like fires involving titanium and hafnium) attain very high temperatures but generate very little smoke.

Explosions have occurred while zirconium was being dissolved in a mixture of sulfuric acid and potassium acid sulfate. Zirconium has exploded during and following pickling in nitric acid, and also during treatment with carbon tetrachloride. Spontaneous explosions have taken place during handling of moist, very finely divided, contaminated zirconium scrap.

Hafnium: Hafnium is similar to the other combustible metals in that the degree of combustibility is related to its size and shape. Bars, ingots, and other large pieces can be heated to high temperatures without igniting, but turnings and chips ignite easily. Dust clouds will explode if an ignition source is present. Explosions of hafnium dust may take place in nitrogen and carbon dioxide as well as in air. Spontaneous ignition of dust clouds can occur if the particle diameter is below 20 microns.

On ignition hafnium burns with very little flame but with the release of large quantities of heat. Unless inactivated, hafnium in sponge form may ignite spontaneously.

Hafnium is generally considered to be somewhat more reactive than titanium or zirconium of similar form. It reacts with water to form hydrogen gas, but at ordinary temperatures this reaction is not sufficiently vigorous to cause the hydrogen to ignite. Under some conditions, however, ignition of the hydrogen may be expected.

Storage and Handling (Includes Transportation)

Special storage precautions are not required for zirconium castings because of the very high temperatures massive pieces of the metal can withstand without igniting. Zirconium powder, on the other hand, is highly combustible; consequently, it is customarily stored and shipped in 1-gal containers with at least 20 percent water by volume. It is usually advisable to limit the amount on hand to the minimum amount necessary.

Zirconium powder storerooms should be of fire resistive construction equipped with explosion vents. Cans should be separated from each other to minimize the possibility of a fire at one can involving others and to permit checking of the cans periodically for corrosion. One plant handling zirconium has established the procedure of disposing of

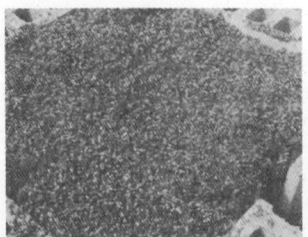

Fig. 3-9C. A 100-lb pile of fine zirconium turnings (left), wet with a water soluble oil coolant and confined in a 3-ft by 3-ft concrete block enclosure produced the fire (right) 33 sec. after ignition.

cans containing powder that have been on the shelf six months.

Storage recommendations for hafnium are generally the same as for zirconium.

Dry zirconium powder or sponge is customarily shipped in inside metal cans in wooden or fiberboard boxes. The DOT does not require compliance with these shipping regulations if the particle size of the powder is greater than 20 mesh.

Wet zirconium powder and zirconium sludge may be shipped in glass or polyethylene containers within metal drums or wooden boxes.

Hafnium transportation regulations are the same as for zirconium.

Process Hazards

Handling of zirconium powder, whenever possible, should be under an inert liquid or in an inert atmosphere. If zirconium or hafnium powder is handled in air, extreme care must be used as the small static charges generated may cause ignition. Hafnium powder is not only highly flammable, but under certain conditions will ignite spontaneously with explosive force.

To prevent dangerous heating during machining operations, a large flow of mineral oil or water base coolant is required. In some machining operations the cutting surface is completely immersed. Turnings should be collected frequently and stored under water in cans. Where zirconium dust is a byproduct, dust collecting equipment discharging into a water precipitation-type collector is a necessity (see Fig. 3-9C).

In general, processing recommendations for zirconium and hafnium can be used interchangeably.

Fighting Fires in Zirconium and Hafnium

Fires exposing massive pieces of zirconium can be fought with water. Limited tests conducted by the Factory Insurance Association have indicated that discharge of water in spray form would have no adverse effect on burning zirconium turnings. When a sprinkler opened directly above an open drum of burning zirconium scrap, there was a brief flare-up after which the fire continued to burn quietly in the drum. When a straight stream of water at a high rate of flow was discharged into the drum, water overflowed and the fire went out.

Where small quantities of zirconium powder or fines are burning, the fire can be ringed with a special extinguishing powder to prevent its spread and the fire allowed to burn out. Special extinguishing powders have been effective in extinguishing zirconium fires. When zirconium dust is present, the extinguishing agent should be applied so that a zirconium dust cloud will not form. If the fire is in an enclosed space, it can be smothered by introducing argon or helium.

Hafnium fires can be fought in the same way as zirconium fires (see Sec. 13, Chap. 6, for combustible metal extinguishing agents).

E. Calcium and Zinc

Properties

Calcium: The flammability of calcium depends considerably on the amount of moisture in the air. If ignited in moist air it burns without flowing at a somewhat lower rate than sodium. It decomposes in water to yield calcium hydroxide and hydrogen, which may burn. Finely divided calcium will ignite spontaneously in air. It should be noted

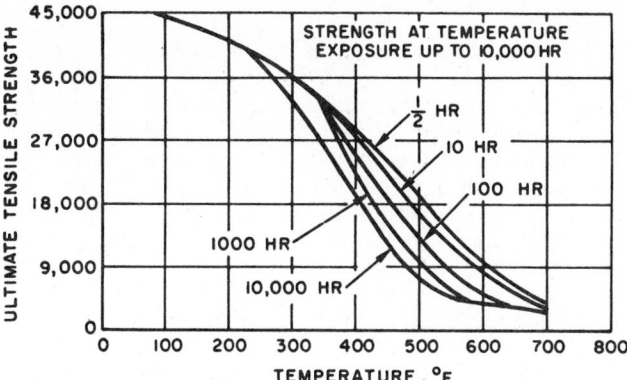

Fig. 3-9D. *Effect of temperature on the strength of 6061-T6 wrought aluminum alloy.*

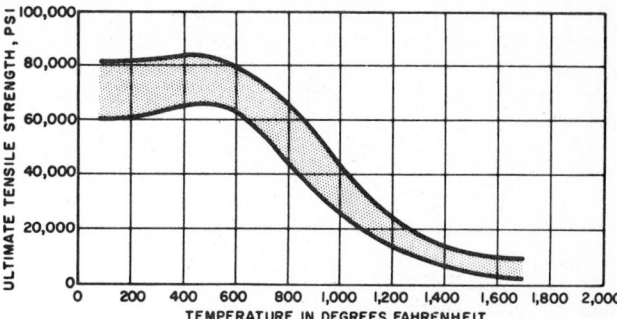

Fig. 3-9E. *Strength of A7 and A36 structural steels at elevated temperature. The band indicates performance of a range of structural steels at elevated temperature. Actual performance will vary with the shape, size and type of assembly exposed to fire conditions. (Data provided by the American Iron and Steel Institute.)*

that barium and strontium are very similar to calcium in their fire properties.

Zinc: Zinc does not introduce a serious fire hazard in sheets, castings, or other massive forms because of the difficulty of ignition, although once ignited, large pieces burn vigorously. Moist zinc dust reacts slowly with the water to form hydrogen, and, if sufficient heat is released, ignition of the dust can occur. Zinc dust clouds in air ignite at 1,110°F. Burning zinc generates appreciable smoke.

Storage, Processing, Fighting Fires in Calcium and Zinc

The storage, handling and processing recommended for magnesium is generally applicable to calcium and zinc.

F. Metals Not Normally Combustible

Aluminum

Aluminum in the forms in which it is generally encountered has a sufficiently high ignition temperature to prevent its burning from being a factor in most fires. However, very fine chips and shavings are occasionally subject to somewhat the same type of combustion as described for magnesium. Powdered or flaked aluminum, however, can be explosive under certain conditions (see Table 3-8A).

Owing to higher ignition temperatures and lesser affinity for oxygen, aluminum does not present the same fire problems as magnesium although it has properties of somewhat similar character. Only in powder or other finely divided form does aluminum present a special fire problem. However, aluminum building siding may melt so rapidly during a fire that it gives the impression of burning.

Where substituted for iron, steel, or copper, the lower melting temperature is an important factor whenever resistance to fire temperatures is essential. Figure 3-9D shows the decrease in strength of an aluminum alloy (6061-T6) at elevated temperatures. Compare this with Figure 3-9E for steel.

The alloy 6061-T6, is typical of those used for architectural applications. Figure 3-9D shows strength at various temperatures for five different heating times (data obtained from MIL-HDBK-5).[2]

Aluminum roofing laid directly on structural supports without a roof deck may be expected to melt through and vent a fire beneath it, thus permitting firemen to enter the building with hose streams or direct water on the fire through the melted roof. There may be a greater hazard to firemen working on such a roof than in the case of steel, due to the strength loss under fire conditions.

Aluminum has been proposed for chimneys and vent connectors for heating appliances on the assumption that with proper combustion controls the temperatures will be maintained below safe limits for aluminum. However, with any failure or derangement of automatic controls, stack temperatures from most heating devices may substantially exceed the melting temperature of aluminum.

Aluminum tubing is used in place of copper in many applications for flammable liquids and gases. While in many respects suitable for such use, it should be employed with proper consideration to its lower melting temperature. A number of aircraft fires have been charged to the failure of thin-walled aluminum alloy tubing used in hydraulic lines containing flammable liquids under pressure when short circuits caused arcs to the tubing, melting the aluminum, and releasing the flammable liquid.

Iron and Steel

Iron and steel are not usually thought of as combustible, and in a massive form, as in structural steel, cast iron parts, etc., they do not burn in ordinary fires. Steel in the form of fine steel wool or dust may be ignited in the presence of excess heat such as from a torch, yielding a form of sparking rather than actual flaming in most instances. Fires have been reported in piles of steel turnings and other fine scrap, presumably containing some oil and perhaps also contaminated by other materials that will facilitate combustion. Pure iron has a specific gravity of 7.86 and a melting point of 2,795°F. Ordinary structural steel has a melting point of 2,606°F. Its strength when subjected to fire temperatures is shown by Fig. 3-9E.

The effect of heat on cast iron varies, depending upon the character of the iron. Some cast iron parts specially designed for use under heat conditions as, for example, grate bars, can withstand substantially higher temperatures without serious distortion or growth.

There are some alloy steels designed for high temperatures which will withstand red heat without material loss in strength. Such alloys, because of expense, are employed only in industrial uses where high strength at high temperature, maintained over long periods, is important as a part of some industrial operation or process.

G. Radioactive Metals

For all practical purposes, radioactivity does not influence nor is it influenced by fire properties of a metal. Radioactive metals include those few that occur naturally, e.g., uranium and thorium, and those produced artificially, e.g. plutonium and cobalt-60. Any metal can be made radioactive. Since radioactivity cannot be altered by fire, radiation will continue wherever the radioactive metal may be spread during a fire. Smoke from fires involving radioactive materials frequently causes more property damage than the fire. The "damage," however, is not physical but rather results from radioactive contamination that must be cleaned up to avoid exposure of humans. To date, no personnel have been seriously injured from radiation received during a fire emergency. However, the potential for injury may exist and readers concerned with such problems are urged to consult standard references—such as the Atomic Energy Commission's publication "Living with Radiation." [3]

Naturally occurring radioactive metals, such as uranium, consist of a mixture of atoms having slightly different sizes. These are called isotopes. Since the radioactivity of each of these uranium isotopes is different, it follows that the radiation hazards from any given piece of uranium will change with its isotopic composition, which can be varied by special processing. Change of isotopic content of a piece of uranium alters the nature and magnitude of radiation hazards but does not alter the chemical or fire properties of the metal. The same is equally true of thorium and plutonium. Prefire planning is particularly important where radioactive materials are involved.

In nuclear reactor service uranium, plutonium, and thorium may build up very considerably higher levels of radioactivity. A few nuclear reactors utilize molten metallic sodium as a coolant and in this service the sodium becomes radioactive. Fortunately, the requirements for fire protection are generally consistent with those independently necessitated for operational reasons.

Uranium

Normal uranium is a radioactive metal that is also combustible. Its radioactivity does not affect its combustibility but can have a bearing on the amount of fire loss. Most metallic uranium is handled in massive forms that do not present a significant fire risk unless exposed to a severe and prolonged external fire. Once ignited, massive metal burns very slowly. A 1-in. diameter rod requires about a day to burn out after ignition. In the absence of strong drafts, uranium oxide smoke tends to deposit in the immediate area of the burning metal. Unless covered with oil, massive uranium burns with virtually no visible flame. Burning uranium reacts violently with carbon tetrachloride and 1,1,1 trichloroethane. For power reactor purposes, uranium fuel elements are always encased in a metal jacket (usually zirconium or stainless steel).

Uranium in finely divided form is readily ignited, and uranium scrap from machining operations is subject to spontaneous ignition. This reaction can usually be avoided by storage under dry oil. Grinding dust has been known to ignite even under water, and fires have occurred spontaneously in drums of coarser scrap after prolonged exposure to moist air. Larger pieces generally have to be heated entirely to their ignition temperature before igniting. Moist dust, turnings, and chips react slowly with water to form hydrogen. Uranium surfaces treated with concentrated nitric acid are subject to explosion or spontaneous ignition in air.

Several combustible metal extinguishing agents that are suitable for use on uranium fires are discussed in Section 13, Chapter 6.

Thorium

Thorium, like uranium, is a naturally occurring element. Both are known as "source materials," being the basic materials from which nuclear reactor fuels are produced. The powdered form of thorium requires special handling techniques because of its low ignition temperature. It is handled dry in a helium or argon atmosphere. The dry metal powder should not be in air as the friction of the particles falling through the air or against the edge of a glass container may produce electrostatic ignition of the powder.

Powdered thorium is usually compacted into solid pellets weighing about one ounce each. In this form it can be safely stored or converted into alloys with other metals. Improperly compacted thorium pellets have been known to slowly generate sufficient heat through absorption of oxygen and nitrogen from the air to raise a steel container to red heat.

Plutonium

Plutonium, like uranium, is radioactive as well as combustible. Plutonium is somewhat more susceptible to ignition than uranium and is normally handled by remote control means and under an inert gas or "bone dry" air atmosphere. In finely divided form, such as dust or chips, it is subject to spontaneous ignition in moist air.

Plutonium metal is never intentionally exposed to water, in part because of fire considerations. The massive metal ignites at about 1,112°F and burns in a manner quite similar to uranium, except that plutonium oxide smoke damage, i.e., airborne radioactive contamination, is more difficult to control and also more hazardous. Because of certain nonfire hazard considerations, it is necessary to limit the quantity of plutonium kept at one location, thus limiting the maximum size of a fire in this metal. Plutonium igniting spontaneously is normally allowed to burn under conditions limiting both fire and radiological contamination spread.

Extinguishing agents that can be used on plutonium fires are discussed in Section 13, Chapter 6.

H. Friction Sparks

Friction sparks result from impact between two hard surfaces, at least one of which is usually metal. The sparks are formed in the following manner. Heat generated by the impact or friction initially heats the particle. Then, depending on the ease of oxidation and the heat of combustion of the metal particle, the freshly exposed surface of the particle may oxidize at the elevated temperature with the heat of oxidation increasing the temperature of the particle until it is incandescent.

Temperatures necessary for incandescence vary with metals, but in most cases are well above the ignition temperatures of flammable materials, e.g., the temperature of a spark from a steel tool approaches 2,500°F, sparks from copper-nickel alloys with small amounts of iron may be well above 500°F. However, the ignition potential of a spark depends on the total heat content, and thus the particle size has a pronounced effect on spark ignition. The practical danger from mechanical sparks is limited by the fact that usually they are very small and have a low total heat content, even though they may have a temperature of 2,000°F or higher. They cool quickly, and start fires only under favorable conditions, such as when they fall into loose dry cotton, combustible dust, or explosive materials. Larger particles of metal, which could retain their heat longer, are not usually heated to dangerous temperatures. Although the hazard of ignition of flammable vapors or gases by friction sparks is often overemphasized, it is best to avoid the use of grinding wheels and other sources of mechanical sparks in areas where any flammable liquids, gases, or vapors are or may be present. The possibility of ignition due to some unusual condition should not be overlooked.

Nickel, monel metal, and bronze have very slight spark hazard; stainless steel much less than ordinary tool steel. Special tools of copper-beryllium and other alloys are designed to minimize the danger of sparks in hazardous locations, but cannot wholly eliminate it because a spark may be produced under several conditions. NavOrd Report 5205, summarized in the October 1959 NFPA *Quarterly*,[4] contains a conclusion by its authors that no benefit is gained by using nonsparking hand tools in place of steel to prevent explosions of hydrocarbons. Leather, plastic, and wooden tools are free from the friction spark hazard.

I. Corrosion of Metals

Corrosion of metals may occur in many ways, principally from the action of oxygen, carbon dioxide, and moisture in the air; from acid fumes; from acid in water (certain soil conditions, such as cinder fill, are particularly conducive to corrosion); from various salts and alkalies dissolved in water, and from electrolysis. Electrolysis may be from galvanic action or from stray electric currents, such as often found near electric railroad tracks.

Galvanic Action

Self-generated electric currents due to galvanic action between different metals in an electrically conducting medium, such as water containing salts, are responsible for corrosion of metal piping, tanks, etc. Wherever dissimilar metals are in contact in the presence of moisture, an effect is produced like that of an electric battery. The direction of the current depends upon the relative position of the metals in the electromotive series.

The metal higher in the series is gradually dissolved where electrolysis occurs (see Table 3-9B). Galvanic action may occur between different compounds as well as between metals, and even between different parts of the same piece of metal or between different forms of the same metal.

Corrosion Prevention

The principal methods of protection against corrosion are the use of impervious coatings of various kinds, and coatings such as galvanizing and certain paint pigments, such as red lead, which tend to protect the base metal by electrolytic action. Cathodic protection, used successfully on large steel tanks and oil and gas pipe lines, involves special electrical equipment to maintain a difference of potential between electrodes and the tank or pipe, so that the direction of current flow will be toward the metal of the tank or pipe. Equipment for this purpose is commercially available. For discussion of cathodic protection to prevent electrolytic corrosion, see Section 11, Chapter 3.

Zinc is a good protector against corrosion of iron because electrolytic action affects the zinc rather than the iron. A zinc coating thus does not necessarily have to be continuous over an iron surface to provide protection against corrosion by electrolysis when the surface is covered with water or other electrolyte.

SI Units

The following conversion factors are given as a convenience in converting to SI units the English units used in this chapter.

1 in.	= 25.400 mm
1 ft	= 0.305 m
1 lb. (mass)	= 0.454 kg
$\frac{5}{9}$ (°F − 32)	= °C
1 qt	= 0.946 litre

Bibliography

References Cited

[1] "Titanium Does a Fast Burn," *Chemical and Engineering News*, Vol. 36, No. 31, Aug. 1958, pp. 36–37.
[2] Metallic Materials and Elements for Aerospace Vehicles, MIL-HDBK-5, U.S. Department of Defense, Washington, D.C.
[3] Brannigan, F. L., "Living with Radiation," Vol. I, "Fundamentals" and Vol. II, "Fire Service Problems," U.S. Atomic Energy Commission, Washington, D.C., 1959, 1960.
[4] "Friction Spark Ignition of Flammable Vapors," NFPA *Quarterly*, Vol. 53, No. 2, Oct. 1959, pp. 155–157.

NFPA Codes, Standards, and Recommended Practices (see the latest *NFPA Publications and Visual Aids Catalog* for availability of current editions of the following documents)

NFPA No. 48, Standard for the Storage, Handling, and Processing of Magnesium.
NFPA No. 481, Standard for the Production, Processing, Handling and Storage of Titanium.
NFPA No. 48M, Guide for Fire and Explosion Prevention in Plants Producing and Handling Zirconium.
NFPA No. 65, Code for the Processing and Finishing of Aluminum.
NFPA No. 651, Standard for the Manufacture of Aluminum or Magnesium Powder.

Additional Readings

Allison, W. W., "Zirconium, Zircaloy, and Hafnium—Safe Practice Guide for Shipping, Storing, Handling, Processing and Scrap Disposal," AEC Research and Development Report WAPD-TM-17, 1960, U.S. Atomic Energy Commission, Washington, D.C.
Ambrose, P. M., et al., "Investigation of Accident Involving Titanium and Red Fuming Nitric Acid," IC 7711, Dec. 1963, USDI, Bureau of Mines, Washington, D.C.
Broadhurst, V. A., "Processing Titanium Safely," *Metal Industry*, Vol. 96, No. 26, June 24, 1960, pp. 515–517.
Cissel, D. W., et al., "Guidelines for Sodium Fire Prevention, Detection, and Control: Report of the Ad Hoc Committee on Sodium Fires," ANL-7691, 1970, Argonne National Laboratory, Argonne, Ill.
Conway, J. B., and Grosse, A. V., "High Temperature Project," Office of Naval Research Contract N9-ONR-87301 Final Report, 1954.
Douglass, D. L., *The Metallurgy of Zirconium*, Unipub, Inc., New York, 1972.
Eisner, H. S., "Aluminum and the Gas Ignition Risk," *The Engineer* (London), Vol. 223, No. 5795, Feb. 17, 1967, pp. 259–260.
"Extinguishment of Alkali Metal Fires," Technical Documents

Table 3-9B. Electromotive Series

Name	Symbol	Volts	Name	Symbol	Volts
Lithium	Li	+2.96	Lead	Pb	+0.12
Potassium	K	+2.92	Hydrogen	H	0.00
Calcium	Ca	+2.87	Antimony	Sb	−0.10
Sodium	Na	+2.71	Bismuth	Bi	−0.23
Magnesium	Mg	+2.40	Arsenic	As	−0.30
Aluminum	Al	+1.70	Copper	Cu	−0.34
Manganese	Mn	+1.10	Oxygen	O_2	−0.40
Zinc	Zn	+0.76	Iodine	I_2	−0.53
Chromium	Cr	+0.56	Silver	Ag	−0.80
Sulfur	S	+0.51	Mercury	Hg	−0.80
Iron	Fe	+0.44	Platinum	Pt	−0.86
Cadmium	Cd	+0.40	Bromine	Br_2	−1.06
Cobalt	Co	+0.28	Chlorine	Cl_2	−1.36
Nickel	Ni	+0.23	Gold	Au	−1.36
Tin	Sn	+0.14			

Report APL TDR 64-114, 1964, MSA Research Corporation, Callery, Penn.

Factory Mutual Engineering Corporation, "Metals and Alloys," *Handbook of Industrial Loss Prevention,* 2nd ed., McGraw-Hill, New York, 1967, pp. 62–1, 62–6.

Fassell, W. M., Jr., et al., "Ignition Temperatures of Magnesium & Magnesium Alloys," *Journal of Metals,* AIME July 1951, pp. 522–528.

"Fire Hazards in Aluminum Processing," *The Institution of Fire Engineers Quarterly,* Vol. 27, No. 65, Mar. 1967, pp. 94–97.

"Fire Precautions in Handling Titanium," *American Machinist,* Vol. 99, No. 7, Mar. 28, 1955, pp. 147-9.

"General Recommendations on Design Features for Titanium and Zirconium Production-Melting Furnaces," DMIC Memorandum 116, July 1961, Defense Metals Information Center, Battelle Memorial Institute, Columbus, Ohio.

Grosse, A. V., and Conway, J. B., "Combustion of Metals in Oxygen," *Industrial Engineering Chemistry,* Vol. 50, 1958, pp. 663–672.

Handbook of Chemistry & Physics, 54th ed., The Chemical Rubber Co., Cleveland, Ohio, 1973-1974.

Handbook on Titanium Metal, Titanium Metals Corp. of America, West Caldwell, N.J.

Harrison, P. L., and Yoffe, A. D., "The Burning of Metals," *Proceedings of the Royal Society,* Vol. 261, 1961, pp. 357–370.

Hill, H. E., "Prevention and Control of Titanium Machining Fires," *Metals Engineering Quarterly,* August 1966, pp. 62, 63.

Jacobson, M., Cooper, A. R., and Nagy, J., "Explosibility of Metal Powders," RI 6516, 1964, USDI, Bureau of Mines, Pittsburgh.

Keil, A. A., *Radiation Control for Fire and Other Emergency Forces,* National Fire Protection Association, Boston, 1960.

Long, G., "Explosions of Molten Aluminum in Water—Cause and Prevention," *Metal Progress,* Vol. 75, No. 5, May 1957, pp. 107–112.

Lustman, B., and Kerze, F., Jr., *The Metallurgy of Zirconium,* McGraw-Hill, New York, 1955.

Lyman, Taylor, ed., Metals Handbook, Vol. 1, The American Society for Metals, Metals Park, Ohio, 1961.

"Metallic Zirconium Explosions During Dissolution with Sulphuric Acid-Potassium Acid Sulphate," Accident and Fire Prevention Issue No. 69, Sept. 1957, U.S. Atomic Energy Commission, Washington, D.C.

Metals Section, NSC, "Magnesium," Data Sheet 426, 1965, National Safety Council, Chicago.

Ibid., "Titanium," Data Sheet 485, 1959, National Safety Council, Chicago.

Markstein, G. H., "Combustion of Metals," *Journal of the American Institute of Aeronautics & Astronautics,* Vol. 1, 1963, pp. 550–562.

Mellor, J. W., *Comprehensive Treatise on Inorganic and Theoretical Chemistry,* Longman, Green & Co., London, 1946-7, and supplements, 1956-1970.

"Methods Used by an AEC Contractor for Handling Sodium, NaK, and Lithium," Accident and Fire Prevention Information, No. 101, Feb. 1960, U.S. Atomic Energy Commission, Washington, D.C.

Milich, W., and King, E. C., "Underwater Disposal of Sodium with EB Nozzle," Technical Report 40, 1955, Mine Safety Appliances Co., Pittsburgh.

Peer, L. H., and Reichling, J. T., "How to Use Pyrophoric Metals Safely," *Mill and Factory,* Vol. 65, No. 2, Aug. 1959, pp. 79–83.

Peloubet, J. A., "Machining Magnesium—A Study of Ignition Factors," *Fire Technology,* Vol. 1, No. 1, Feb. 1965, pp. 5–14.

Peterseim, F. D., "Hazards & Safety Precautions in the Fabrication and Use of Titanium," TML Report No. 63, 1957, Battelle Memorial Institute, Columbus, Ohio.

"Product Information Data Sheet Lithium Metal," Data Sheet Metal 110-1061, Lithium Corporation of America, New York.

"Properties and Essential Information for Safe Handling and Use of Sodium," SD-47, 1952, Manufacturing Chemists' Association, Washington, D.C.

Republic Steel Corp., et al., "Titanium," Data Sheet 485, 1959, National Safety Council, Chicago.

Reynolds, W. C., and Williams, J. J., "An Investigation of the Ignition Temperatures of Solid Metals," NACA Contract NAW-6459, 1957.

Riehl, W. A., et al., "Reactivity of Titanium with Oxygen," R-180, 1963, National Aeronautics and Space Administration, Washington, D.C.

Setting, M., *Sodium—Its Manufacture, Properties and Uses,* Reinhold, New York, 1956.

Smith, R., "Pyrophoric Metals—A Technical Mystery," NFPA *Quarterly,* Vol. 51, No. 2, Oct. 1957.

Smithells, C. J., *Metals Reference Book,* Interscience Publishers, New York, 1962.

Stout, E. L., "Safety Consideration for Handling Plutonium, Uranium, Thorium, the Alkali Metals, Zirconium, Titanium, Magnesium, and Calcium," LA 2147, 1957, Los Alamos Scientific Laboratory, Los Alamos, N.M.

"A Study of the Reactions of Metals and Water," AECD 3664, Apr. 1955, Washington, D.C.

Thomas, D. E., and Hayes, E. T., *The Metallurgy of Hafnium,* U.S. Atomic Energy Commission, Washington, D.C., 1960.

White, E. L., and Ward, J. J., "Ignition of Metals in Oxygen," DMIC Report No. 224, 1966, Battelle Memorial Institute, Columbus, Ohio.

"Zirconium Fire and Explosion Hazard Evaluation," Accident and Fire Prevention Information, Issue 45, Aug. 1956, U.S. Atomic Energy Commission, Washington, D.C.

"Zirconium Powder," Data Sheet 382 (Revised), 1962, National Safety Council, Chicago.

"Zirconium Scrap Burning Tests," NFPA *Quarterly,* Vol. 56, No. 2, Oct. 1960, pp. 110–127.

"159,000 Lbs. of Zirconium Scrap Involved in Fire," Serious Accidents Issue No. 84, 1955, U.S. Atomic Energy Commission, Washington, D.C.

Chapter 10

IDENTIFICATION OF THE HAZARDS OF MATERIALS

The various systems used for identification of the hazards of materials that are available to fire services, emergency services, and others for the prevention, preplanning, controlling, and fighting of fires with minimum hazard are covered in this chapter.

A. Presentation of Information

Methods of Presentation

In the field, hazard information is made available in the following ways:

1. Large placards, signs, or decals on storage tanks, storage areas, and processing equipment. Information is printed in large type for reading at a distance. These placards usually give only a statement of hazard and a simple warning, such as "DO NOT ENTER."

2. Placards posted in local areas. These are usually more detailed, and may contain instructions for procedures and safety equipment.

3. Department of Transportation (DOT) hazardous materials placards. These appear on many, but not all, trucks and railway equipment carrying hazardous materials.

4. Labels on containers and shipping packages.

5. Shipping papers.

Organization of Information

Hazard information is organized into recognizable parts. These are listed below in order of importance:

1. A flag to attract attention: This can be a symbol, a color, a shape, or a word, or a combination of any of these, such as the standardized shapes and colors of roadside traffic signs. On a package label it may be a hazard pictograph or a "signal word" such as DANGER.

2. Statement of hazard, such as FLAMMABLE or CAUSES BURNS: There may also be a symbol such as the skull-and-crossbones on packages of poisons.

3. Precautionary measures telling what to do or what not to do, in order to avoid injury: These also may be presented by a symbol, such as a sign on a laboratory door showing a pair of safety glasses, meaning that safety glasses are required in the area. On a container label, this is part of the text.

4. Treatment in case of exposure: This may be symbolic, such as the symbol for a safety shower or eyebath, or it may be elaborate first aid instructions on a package label.

5. Special instructions for storage or handling.

6. Instructions for handling fires, leaks, or spills.

Hazard Levels

Hazard information systems recognize four classes, or levels, of hazardous materials:

1. Extremely Dangerous Materials: These materials can cause death or disabling injury on brief exposure, or they are extremely volatile flammable liquids or flammable gases, or detonable materials. A further breakdown is:

  (a) Explosives and explosively unstable materials.

  (b) High-level radioactive materials.

  (c) Highly flammable gases and materials which give off extremely flammable vapors.

  (d) Extremely toxic materials which are so poisonous that no bodily exposure should occur, such as parathion and hydrogen cyanide.

  (e) Materials which are extremely corrosive to living tissue, such as bromine, which can injure almost instantaneously, or hydrofluoric acid, which can strike through the skin to the tissues beneath and cause deep, slow-healing burns. Also included are materials that could cause severe eye injury.

  (f) Materials whose combustion products or products of decomposition fit the above descriptions.

2. Dangerous Materials: These are materials that could cause a lost-time injury from exposure to the detrimental effects of highly flammable or highly self-reactive materials such as:

  (a) Flammable liquids and solids.

  (b) Highly toxic materials which are likely to cause some injury or illness but not death from a moderate exposure.

  (c) Materials which could cause destruction of tissue, particularly the eyes, if not removed from the body in a very short time.

  (d) Moderately radioactive materials.

Dangerous materials may, at an extreme, cause some permanent but not disabling injury on exposure.

3. Hazardous Materials: These are materials that could cause temporary disability or injury which presumably would heal without permanent effects. They are moderately combustible or self-reactive, and they include:

  (a) Tear gases.

  (b) Severe irritants.

  (c) Toxic (but not highly or extremely toxic) materials.

  (d) "Combustible" materials which must be heated before they can be ignited.

4. Nuisance Hazards: These could cause temporary irritation or discomfort that would clear up when the exposure is ended or materials which are only slightly combustible such as Class B liquids.

Note that the materials classed as "dangerous" could cause an emergency. The materials classed as "hazardous" would be less likely to cause an emergency, but could add significantly to the seriousness of an emergency. Thus, a "combustible" liquid might not catch fire and cause an emergency. In the presence of a fire arising from some other cause, it could ignite and add to the seriousness of the emergency. In present consumer product labeling practice, materials which could cause an emergency generally use the signal word, DANGER. Materials which could add to the seriousness of an emergency use the signal words WARNING and CAUTION. Note, though, that flammable liquids with flash points between 20 and 80°F bear the signal word WARNING.

A hazard information system is a compromise between two conflicting requirements: immediacy of information and adequacy of information. A hazard symbol, such as the familiar skull-and-crossbones used on poisons, can be read at a glance. It has immediacy. Since it doesn't tell how dangerously poisonous the material is, nor whether it enters the body through the skin, the lungs, or the digestive system, it lacks adequacy. A hazard data sheet can give adequate information, but it takes time and good light to read, and it has to be there to be read. A hazard data sheet offers adequacy but lacks immediacy.

B. Definitions

The following terms are used in this chapter as defined.

Flammability

The NFPA definitions of flammable and combustible liquids, the methods of determining the flash point, and the classes of these liquids are given in Chapter 3 of this Section. However, in some regulations, the classification system is different from the NFPA definitions, not only in the United States but also in other countries. For example, in the United States the labeling for flammability for consumer products is in three classes with the flash point determined by the Tag Open Cup Test Method. Liquids with flash points below 20°F are identified by the signal phrase, DANGER—EXTREMELY FLAMMABLE; liquids with flash points from 20 to 80°F are identified by WARNING —FLAMMABLE; and liquids with flash points from 80 to 150°F are identified by CAUTION—COMBUSTIBLE.

Toxicity

In its broadest sense the term *toxicity* is defined as the ability of a material to cause bodily harm by chemical action. In common usage, the term *toxic substance* describes one which can pass through a body surface, i.e., skin, eyes, lungs, or digestive tract, and enter the blood stream. Toxicity is the measure of the injury produced under test conditions. It can affect organs remote from the point of contact. Where injury occurs at the point of contact, two terms are used: *Irritation* for a minor though possibly troublesome injury which heals without leaving a scar, and *corrosiveness* for an injury caused by destruction of tissue, which leaves a scar when healed.

Several kinds of toxicity are recognized:

Acute Toxicity: This is the effect caused by a single dose or exposure, and may range from simple headache or nausea to disablement or death. Acute toxicity is the kind most important to emergency personnel.

Semi-chronic and Chronic Toxicity: The effect caused by repeated doses of a material.

Sensitization: A person who has been sensitized may suffer an allergic reaction when exposed again to the same material. For example, in *photodynamic sensitization*, a person who is sensitized by a material will suffer an allergic reaction when exposed to strong sunlight or ultraviolet radiation.

Carcinogens, Teratogens, and Mutagens: Carcinogens are materials that can cause cancer, teratogens are materials that can cause pregnant females to bear deformed offspring, and mutagens are materials that can cause exposed persons to bear children with traits differing from those of the parents.

The Occupational Safety and Health Administration now requires labeling on chemicals which are known or suspected of being able to cause cancer. Recognition of the hazards of teratogens and mutagens is so new that they are not yet found in hazard information systems. Because of the type of injury caused, their use will be severely restricted, so the likelihood of encountering them is not great.

Acute toxicity is expressed by the term LD_{50}, which means that a dose of a substance was lethal to 50 percent or more of the animals tested. This term is used for liquids and solids which are swallowed or absorbed through the skin. For inhalation hazards of vapors, mists, fumes, and dusts, the term LC_{50} is used, meaning the concentration in air of a substance which is lethal to half or more than half of the test animals used. The LD_{50} is usually expressed as milligrams of dose per kilogram of body weight of the test animal, and should include the type of test, thus: Oral LD_{50} (rat) = 30 mg/k. Note that the smaller the LD_{50}, the more toxic a material is.

Quantitative LD_{50} limits for the levels of toxicity generally increase by a factor of ten for successive classes of toxicity. Thus, for oral toxicity, *extremely toxic* is applied to materials with an LD_{50} (rat) below 5 mg/kg. For a 70-kg (150-lb) human, this figures out to about seven drops (or less) of a watery liquid. For a solid, it is somewhat less than the weight of a 5-grain aspirin tablet. This means that a very small amount of an extremely toxic material can cause a noticeable illness or injury—the amount, for instance, that might be ingested by swallowing dust trapped in the upper nose if a respirator is not worn. Container labels carry the signal word DANGER and the skull-and-crossbones to indicate the presence of a disabling hazard.

A highly toxic material by oral ingestion is one with oral LD_{50} (rat) of 5 to 50 mg/kg. For a 70-kg human this is $\frac{2}{3}$ of a teaspoonful of a watery liquid, or $\frac{1}{10}$ oz of a solid (the weight of eight or nine 5-grain aspirin tablets). Container labels use the signal word DANGER.

A *toxic* material has an oral LD_{50} (rat) of 50 to 500 mg/kg. It is unlikely that an adult will knowingly swallow enough of a material of this hazard level to cause serious injury. Labels bear the signal word WARNING to indicate a moderate hazard.

Equivalent doses have been worked out for exposure by inhalation (breathing) and absorption through the skin. Rabbits are usually used for skin absorption tests, and rats for inhalation testing.

For materials which cause direct injury at the point of contact, there is an animal test which is used to distinguish between an irritant and a corrosive. So far, there are no quantitative degrees of corrosiveness, but industry practice does make distinction in label statements based on human experience and the toxicologists' interpretations of animal tests. In inspecting a warehouse, the following graded phrases on package labels may be found:

WARNING! MAY CAUSE BURNS
WARNING! CAUSES BURNS
DANGER! CAUSES BURNS
DANGER! CAUSES SEVERE BURNS
DANGER! RAPIDLY CAUSES SEVERE BURNS
DANGER! CAUSES SEVERE BURNS WHICH
HEAL VERY SLOWLY

Wherever possible, levels of hazard should be assigned on the basis of human experience. When human experience is not available, as for a new chemical or because of a good safety program, animal tests are used. Since no animal is exactly equivalent to a human being, most of the value of such animal tests must come from the skilled interpretations of toxicologists.

Instability (self-reactivity) and Chemical Reactivity

Chemical reactions include two types of interest here: Those which absorb energy and those which give off energy. When the energy is in the form of heat, reactions which absorb heat are called *endothermic* and those which give off heat are called *exothermic*. An explanation of these terms is given in Section 2, Chapter 1.

Two kinds of reactivity exist: reactivity and self-reactivity. The term *reactivity* is used when two or more chemicals react with each other, as when sodium and water combine in a violent and dangerous reaction. *Self-reactivity* comes from internal activity of a material, as when a stick of dynamite explodes. Radioactivity is a specialized type of self-reactivity which is always considered separately. Explosives are generally considered a specialized area with separate hazard information systems.

Aside from explosives and radioactive materials, there are no formal hazard levels for reactivity. Hazard information is based on experience. Consumer container labels generally follow the MCA (Manufacturing Chemists' Association) labeling manual, discussed later in this chapter. NFPA 704M, Identification of the Fire Hazards of Materials, is the only hazard information system that attempts to cover the whole span of hazardous self-reactivity. The NFPA 704 System also includes information on hazardous reactivity with water.

The terms *oxidizer* and *oxidizing action* (or *oxidizing reaction*) mean different things in different places. In hazard information systems, the term *oxidizer* or *strong oxidizer* defines a chemical which can give off oxygen to increase the burning rate of other materials. Such chemicals are called *oxygen donors*. Study is being given to use of the term *oxidizer* for chemicals which can ignite other materials on contact, such as bromine or nitric acid. Currently these are recognized in labeling systems by statements of hazard such as "spillage may cause fire." Although *organic peroxides* may be oxygen donors under some conditions, they are classed separately because of the severe fire and self-reactivity hazards which many of them present.

C. The NFPA No. 704 System of Hazard Identification

NFPA 704M, Identification of the Hazards of Materials, is a symbol system intended for use on fixed installations, such as chemical processing equipment, storage and warehousing rooms, and laboratory entrances. It tells a fire fighter what he must do to protect himself from injury while fighting a fire in the area.

The NFPA 704 Diamond

The information system is based on the "704 diamond" (see Fig. 3-10A) which is the vehicle for visually presenting information on flammability, health and self-reactivity hazards as well as special information associated with the hazards.

Numbers from 0 through 4 are placed in the three upper squares of the diamond to show the degree of hazard present for each of the three hazards. The 0 indicates the lowest degree of hazard, the 4, the highest. The fourth square, at the bottom is used for special information. Two symbols for this latter space are suggested. They are:

1. A letter W with a bar through it (W̶) to indicate that a material may have a hazardous reaction with water. This does *not* mean "do not use water," since some forms of water—fog or fine spray—may be used in many cases. What it does say is: "Water may cause a hazard, so use it very cautiously until you have proper information."

2. The "radioactive pinwheel" for radioactive materials.

The NFPA 704 diamond symbol is intended to provide immediacy at some sacrifice of adequacy, and there is a tendency to read more into it than it says. The five degrees of hazard, in the order of their descendency, have these general meanings to fire fighters:

4—Too dangerous to approach with standard fire-fighting equipment and procedures. Withdraw and obtain expert advice on how to handle.

3—Fire can be fought using methods intended for extremely hazardous situations, such as unmanned monitors or personal protective equipment which prevents all bodily contact.

2—Can be fought with standard procedures, but hazards are present which require certain equipment or procedures to handle safely.

1—Nuisance hazards present which require some care, but standard fire-fighting procedures can be used.

0—No special hazards which require special measures.

The NFPA 704 guide describes in detail the hazards and hazard levels which the various numbers indicate for the three hazards. The following, adapted from the appendix of the guide, summarizes the hazard information and recommends actions to protect from the hazards.

Health Hazards

In general, health hazard in fire fighting is that of a single exposure which may vary from a few seconds up to an hour. The physical exertion demanded in fire fighting or other emergency conditions may be expected to intensify the effects of any exposure. In assigning degrees, local conditions must be considered. The following explanation is based upon protective equipment normally used by fire fighters.

4 Materials too dangerous to health to expose fire fighters. A few whiffs of the vapor could cause death, or the vapor or liquid could be fatal on penetrating the fire fighter's normal protective clothing. Protective clothing and breathing apparatus available to the average fire department will not provide adequate protection against inhalation or skin contact with these materials.

3 Materials extremely hazardous to health but areas may be entered with extreme care. Full protective clothing, self-contained breathing apparatus, rubber gloves, boots, and bands around legs, arms and waist should be provided. No skin surface should be exposed.

2 Materials hazardous to health but areas may be entered freely with self-contained breathing apparatus.

1 Materials only slightly hazardous to health.

0 Materials which on exposure under fire conditions would offer no health hazard beyond that of ordinary combustible material.

Flammability Hazards

Susceptibility to burning is the basis for assigning degrees within this category. The method of attacking the fire is influenced by this susceptibility factor.

NFPA 700 DIAMOND

Fig. 3-10A.   The NFPA 704 Identification System Diamond.

4 Very flammable gases or very volatile flammable liquids. If possible, shut off flow and keep cooling water streams on exposed tanks of containers. Withdrawal may be necessary.

3 Materials which can be ignited under almost all normal temperature conditions. Water may be ineffective because of the low flash point of the materials.

2 Materials which must be moderately heated before ignition will occur. Water spray may be used to extinguish the fire because the material can be cooled below its flash point.

1 Materials that must be preheated before ignition can occur. Water may cause frothing if it gets below the surface of the liquid and turns to steam. However, water fog gently applied to the surface will cause a frothing which will extinguish the fire.

0 Materials that will not burn.

Reactivity (Stability) Hazards

The assignment of degrees in the reactivity category is based upon the susceptibility of materials to release energy either by themselves or in combination with other materials. Fire exposure was one of the factors considered along with conditions of shock and pressure.

4 Materials which are so susceptible to detonation that it is too dangerous for fire fighters to approach the fire. Vacate the area.

3 Materials which when heated and under confinement are capable of detonation. These materials are too dangerous to fight with handlines, but may be kept from detonating if unmanned portable monitors or hoseholders can be set up from behind explosion-resistant locations.

2 Materials which will undergo a violent chemical change at elevated temperatures and pressures. Use portable monitors, hoseholders or straight hose streams from a distance to cool the tanks and the material in them. Use caution.

1 Materials which are normally stable but may become unstable in combination with other materials or at elevated temperatures and pressures. Normal precautions in approaching any fire should suffice.

0 Materials which are normally stable and, therefore, do not produce any reactivity hazard to firemen.

SPECIAL INFORMATION

When W appears in 4th space:

4 W is not used with reactivity hazard 4.

3 In addition to the hazards above, these materials can react explosively with water. Explosion protection is essential if water in any form is used.

2 In addition to hazards above, these materials may react violently with water or form potentially explosive mixtures with water.

1 In addition to hazards above, these materials may react vigorously but not violently with water.

0 W is not used with reactivity hazard 0.

Methods of Presentation

Considerable leeway is allowed in the presentation of the numbers. The only basic requirement is that numbers be spaced as though they were in the diamond outline. Several methods which have been used are shown in Figure 3-10B. Appendix A to the guide gives recommended layout and sizes for the symbol. The appendix also gives a distance-legibility table, as well as several examples of the use of the symbol.

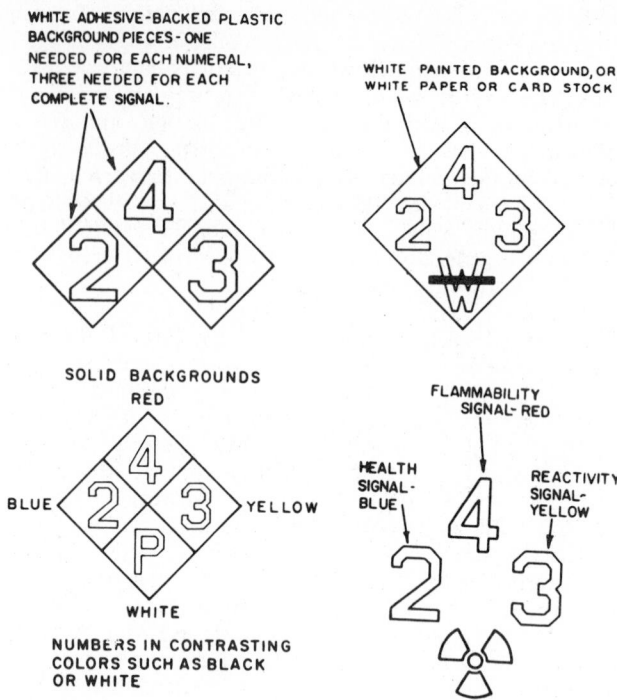

Fig. 3-10B. Methods of presenting NFPA 704 System hazard information.

Assigning Degrees of Hazard

Numbers (degrees of hazard) for use in the diamond are assigned on the basis of the worst hazard expected in the area, whether it be from hazards of the original material or of its combustion or breakdown products. The effects of local conditions must be considered. For instance, a drum of carbon tetrachloride sitting in a well-ventilated storage shed presents a different hazard from a drum sitting in an unventilated basement. See Table 3-11A for suggested assignment of hazard identification numbers for flammable liquids, gases, and volatile solids.

Advantages of the NFPA 704 System

The NFPA 704 System can warn against hazards under fire conditions of materials which other information systems class as nonhazardous. For example, edible tallow produces toxic and irritating combustion products. It would be given a "2" degree of health hazard, indicating the need for air-supplied respiratory equipment.

NFPA 704 also can warn against overall fire hazards in an area. On the door of a laboratory or storage room, it can warn of the worst hazards likely in a fire situation. Such information is useful both in preplanning and in actual fires.

NFPA 704 can be used without a supplementary manual. Because of its simplicity, the general meanings of the numbers can be memorized easily and the whole symbol read and interpreted quickly on the spot and in poor light.

Disadvantages of the NFPA 704 System

The NFPA 704 system makes no provision for oxygen-donor type oxidizers. It gives only minimum information on the hazards themselves. Since the system informs on protective measures, the same number may be used for different types of hazards so that, for instance, a Health Hazard number 3 means "No contact" without saying whether the hazard is corrosiveness to the skin or toxicity by absorption through the skin. Thus, the symbol is useful only to trained or informed persons.

D. Department of Transportation (DOT) Placards

The Hazardous Materials Regulations of the Department of Transportation (DOT) require placarding of trucks, trailers, and railway cars carrying dangerous materials. Hazardous materials must be identified on shipping papers regardless of the quantity shipped. DOT is in the process of changing to more informative placards, but the old placards may be used for some time to come.

Present DOT Requirements

Over-the-road Equipment: Equipment must be marked on front, rear, and both sides with hazard name at least 4 in. tall. Explosives, extremely toxic materials, high-strength radioactives in any amount must be marked, as do highly toxic, flammable, and oxidizing materials, corrosive liquids and both flammable and nonflammable compressed gases, in quantities of 1,000 lbs or over. Ladings presenting mixed hazards totaling over 1,000 lbs carry a DANGEROUS marking, plus marking for explosives, extremely toxic, and high-strength radioactive materials if present. Other than this last, a multiple hazard material is marked only with the name of the most severe hazard present, and a mixed shipment does not identify hazards.

Railway Equipment: Equipment must be placarded on both sides and ends. Placards for explosives and poison gases are rectangular, the smallest being about 10 × 14 in. For other hazards, 10¾-in., diamond-shaped placards are used. Radioactives show the name on the placard, all remaining hazards are identified only by a placard with the word DANGEROUS in large red letters. Ladings which have been fumigated in the car and could bear dangerous residues carry a FUMIGATED placard on or near the door. Placards may be attached directly to the car or placed in special holders. Tank cars which have been emptied but contain residues must carry DANGEROUS—EMPTY placards. These are the same size as originals, but the right-hand half is solid black.

Air Shipments: These are generally small quantities, and many hazardous materials cannot be shipped by air, particularly in passenger aircraft. Placarding of equipment is not required. (See Section 17, Chapter 1, for information on the problems associated with regulation of hazardous materials as air cargoes.)

Transportation Emergencies—Identification Problems

Certain deficiencies in current DOT placarding and labeling practices contribute to difficulties in identifying the hazardous nature of some commodities found in transit. For example, placards are not required on the following:

1. Class C explosives. (These are principally manufactured articles containing explosives, such as fireworks, squibs, and small-arms ammunition.)
2. Moderate and low-level radioactives.
3. Tear gases.
4. Corrosive solids, including those which could dissolve in water to produce corrosive liquids.
5. Over-the-road equipment containing less than 1,000 lbs of highly toxic, flammable, or oxidizing materials, corrosive liquids, or flammable and nonflammable compressed gases, either singly or as a mixed shipment.

Color coding of existing requirements for placards are inconsistent for the various modes of transportation, and with color coding on package labels, so use of colors for quick identification is of doubtful value.

New DOT Requirements

Placarding requirements currently being developed by the DOT are the same for both rail and highway shipments. Placards and package labels use consistent color coding. Multiple labeling and multiple placarding are required for multiple-hazard ladings.

E. Package and Container Labels

A word of warning: *Absence of warning labeling on a package or container does not guarantee that the contents are not hazardous. Also, warnings may be on a label separate from the label bearing the product name or the manufacturer's signature, and may be on a separate face of the package.*

Two separate but related information systems require labels on shipping packages and on product containers.

Department of Transportation (DOT) Labels

Current DOT hazardous materials regulations require diamond-shaped labels on shipping containers holding an amount of hazardous material which could cause a hazardous condition in transportation. These color-coded labels bear a hazard symbol, or pictograph, and the name of the hazard. They carry no warning text. Present regulations generally permit only a single label on a multi-hazard exposure, with the label showing the most dangerous hazard present. Where a material is extremely toxic, explosive, or highly radioactive, the proper label must be used in addition to any other hazard label. In addition the package must be marked with the "name of contents" as it appears on a Commodity List in DOT regulations. This may be a chemical name or a class name such as "Corrosive Liquid N.O.S.," so is of secondary usefulness. On compressed gas cylinders, the label may be on a wire-tied tag.

Proposals now under study would require a DOT label for every regulated hazard present.

Presence of a DOT label on a package or container indicates a dangerous hazard. Because of exemptions, based mostly on the size of inner containers in an outside shipping container, a package without a DOT label may contain significant amounts of fairly dangerous materials, including flammable liquids.

See Figure 10-3C for illustrations of DOT labels.

Warning Labels on Immediate Containers

All warning labeling systems in this country are based on MCA *Guide to Precautionary Labeling of Hazardous Chemicals.*[1] Containers for hazardous materials in interstate commerce usually bear necessary warning labels, but products of small local distributors may not. Warehouses, particularly those of contract packagers, may contain stocks of filled containers intended for labeling to customers' orders. Where the immediate container is also the shipping container, such as a carboy, a drum, or a compressed gas cylinder, both DOT and warning labels may be present, and may be printed on a single label sheet.

Labeling practice is to use the signal word DANGER for corrosive liquids, extremely corrosive solids, poisons, flammable gases, and extremely flammable liquids. The signal word WARNING is used on flammable liquids, less corrosive solids, toxic materials, and similar levels of haz-

Compressed gases: The nonflammable gas label is green with inscription, border, and symbol black. The flammable gas label is red with inscription, border, and symbol black.

Explosives labels: Orange with inscription, border, and symbol black.

Flammable liquid: Red with inscription, border, and symbol black.

Flammable solid: White with vertical red stripes as depicted by the shaded area, with the inscription, border, and symbol black. The phrase "Flammable Solid" must not contact any red stripe.

Oxidizing materials: Yellow with the inscription, border, and symbol black.

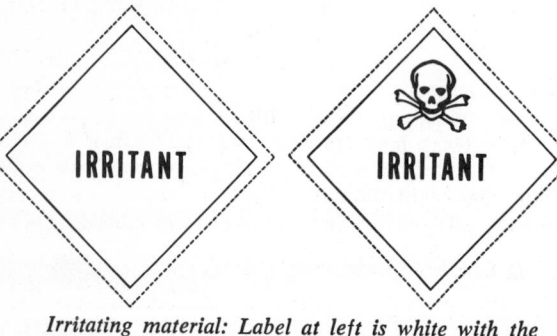

Poisonous materials: White with the inscription, border, and symbol black.

Irritating material: Label at left is white with the inscription in red, the border black (used for domestic (USA) shipments). Label at right is white with the inscription, border, and symbol black (used for USA import or export shipments).

Radioactive materials: Radioactive White-I category: White with the inscription, border, and symbol black, and the vertical bar a red overprint. Radioactive Yellow-II: Upper half yellow and bottom half white; inscription, border, and symbol black; the two vertical bars are a red overprint. Radioactive Yellow-III: Upper half yellow and bottom half white; inscription, border, and symbol black; the three vertical bars are a red overprint.

Fig. 3-10C.   DOT (DEPARTMENT OF TRANSPORTATION) HAZARDOUS MATERIALS LABELS.

Corrosive materials: White with the inscription, border, and symbol black.

Spontaneously combustible materials: Upper half white and lower half red with inscription, border, and symbol black.

Water-reactive material: Blue with the inscription, border, and symbol black.

Etiologic agent: White with the symbol and the phrase "Biomedical Material" in red. Shaded area is red with the inscriptions in white reverse.

CAUTION Unscrew This Bung **SLOWLY** Do not unscrew entirely until all interior pressure has escaped through the loosened threads. REMOVE BUNG IN OPEN AIR. Keep all open flame lights and fires away. Enclosed Electric Lights are safe.

EMPTY

These labels may also be found on shipments. Label at left is for containers with bungs where special instructions may be needed to caution against hazards related to bung removal. The "Empty" label must be at least 6 in. long with each letter at least 1 in. high.

Fig. 3-10C (continued).

ard. The signal word CAUTION is used for the least severe hazards, including combustible liquids and solids, and non-flammable compressed gases. The rest of the warning label is self-explanatory, except to note that warning labels cover only hazards arising from normal use and handling. Hazards under fire conditions are not warned against.

F. Shipping Papers and Chem-Cards

Transport regulations require that a truck driver, a train conductor, or an aircraft pilot have a shipping paper for every shipment of hazardous material in his transport unit. This lists names and quantities of all hazardous materials, including those exempt packages which bear no labels. There may also be a "Chem-Card" [2] giving hazard and emergency handling information.

G. DOT Hazard Information (HI) System

DOT is developing a system for supplying hazard information to emergency personnel in a transportation emergency. Presently proposed is a system which would require placing a two-digit number on all DOT labels, placards, and shipping papers. The number would be keyed to an information manual supplied free by DOT. The first digit of the number would indicate the hazard, i.e. corrosive material, flammable material, toxic material. The second digit would indicate the presence of additional hazards, but not which hazards. The HI system has the advantage of furnishing thumbnail information on hazards, emergency procedures, and cleanup. It has the disadvantages that the numbers are too complex for memorizing, so that access to a manual is required.

H. Hazard Emergency Teams

Emergency assistance in identifying hazards of materials and guidance on handling emergencies involving them is available on quick notice from a variety of sources. The assistance ranges from immediate telephone advice to the dispatching of emergency teams to actually assist in field operation. Among those offering service are:

CHEMTREC.—Phone No. 800-424-9300: CHEMTREC stands for Chemical Transportation Emergency Center, operated by the Manufacturing Chemists' Association, 1825 Connecticut Avenue N.W., Washington D.C. 20009. It handles only transportation emergencies. When called, it

Fig. 3-10D. Non-DOT labels used for air shipment of commodities. Left: Used to indicate that the material labeled is magnetic and must be kept away from the aircraft's compass detector unit. White label with the top half (shaded) blue with white reverse symbols; bottom half white with blue inscription and border. Right: Used to indicate that the material labeled is not to be loaded in passenger planes (cargo aircraft only).

provides immediate advice from its own files, then notifies the shipper. CHEMTREC maintains close liaison with the Department of Transportation.

NACA Pesticide Safety Team Network: A service sponsored by The National Agricultural Chemicals Association, 1155 15th St., N.W. Washington D.C. 20005. It covers only pesticides, and consists of 40 teams of specially trained personnel who go to the scene of emergencies involving pesticides. Phone answering service is supplied by CHEMTREC.

TEAP in Canada: The Canadian Chemical Producers' Association operates a Transportation Emergency Assistance Program through regional teams prepared to give phone and field response.

CHLOREP: The Chlorine Institute, 342 Madison Ave., New York, NY 10017, operates the Chlorine Emergency Plan, in which the nearest chlorine producer responds to a problem.

Coast Guard's "React teams": These operate on both the east and west coast, and give skilled help in spills on water.

The Environmental Protection Agency: The EPA sponsors teams which go to emergencies.

Many manufacturing companies have organized response capabilities for their own products. In many cases an emergency telephone number is placed on the bill-of-lading.

Bibliography

References Cited

[1] "Guide to Precautionary Labeling of Hazardous Chemicals," Manual L-1, 7th ed., Manufacturing Chemists Association, Inc., Washington, D.C., 1970

[2] Chem-Cards (a series of cards giving information on 86 hazardous chemicals), Manufacturing Chemists' Association, Washington, D.C.

NFPA Codes, Standards, and Recommended Practices (see the latest *NFPA Publications and Visual Aids Catalog* for availability of current editions of the following documents)

NFPA No. 325A, Flash Point Index of Trade Name Liquids.
NFPA No. 325M, Fire Hazard Properties of Flammable Liquids, Gases and Volatile Solids.
NFPA No. 43A, Code for the Storage of Liquid and Solid Oxidizing Materials.
NFPA No. 44A, Code for the Manufacture, Transportation and Storage of Fireworks.
NFPA No. 49, Hazardous Chemicals Data.
NFPA No. 490, Code for the Storage of Ammonium Nitrate.
NFPA No. 491M, Manual of Hazardous Chemical Reactions.
NFPA No. 495, Code for the Manufacture, Transportation, Storage and Use of Explosive Materials.
NFPA No. 53M, Manual on Fire Hazards in Oxygen-Enriched Atmospheres.
NFPA No. 57, Standard for Fumigation.
NFPA No. 704M, Recommended System for Identification of the Hazards of Materials.

Additional Readings

Bahme, C. W., *Fire Officer's Guide to Emergency Action*, National Fire Protection Association, Boston, 1974.
Bahme, C. W., *Fire Officer's Guide to Dangerous Chemicals*, National Fire Protection Association, Boston, 1972.
Chemical Safety Data Sheets, Manufacturing Chemists' Association, Washington, D.C., periodically revised.
"Emergency Services Guide for Selected Hazardous Materials," DOT Office of Hazardous Materials, Washington, D.C., 1974.

Section 3

Chapter 11

TABLES AND CHARTS

Table of Contents of Chapter

Table 3-11A.   Fire Hazard Properties of Flammable Liquids, Gases, and Volatile Solids

This tabulation of the available data on the properties of the flammable and combustible liquids and other materials is sponsored by the NFPA Committee on Flammable Liquids and is available in pamphlet form as NFPA No. 325M, Fire Hazard Properties of Flammable Liquids, Gases, and Volatile Solids. Information in this table is based on the 1969 edition of NFPA No. 325M.

The Table summarizes available data on the fire hazard properties of more than 1,000 substances, listed alphabetically by their chemical name. In addition about 500 synonyms are listed alphabetically. The values given have been compiled from the results of tests by the Bureau of Mines, Factory Mutual System, Underwriters Laboratories, Inc., and other recognized sources. The source of each figure used here is on file in the NFPA office and may be ascertained on request.

The values selected are representative figures deemed suitable for general use. In case of a difference between the figures reported by different recognized laboratories, the figure selected is conservative. Slight differences are to be expected even between the most competent agencies owing to differences in the purity of the samples tested, and minor differences in technical manipulation and observations in the use of the test apparatus. In the case of some of the older sources of data, information is lacking as to character of samples and details of testing procedures.

In most cases minor variations in flash point, ignition temperature, and explosive range have little practical significance. In case of difference of opinion as to the actual flash points or other characteristics of any specific material under consideration, tests should be made by some recognized testing laboratory from a sample of the particular liquid or material in question.

Definitions of Fire Hazard Properties

Flash Point: Defined in Section 2, Chapter I, the flash point figures represent closed cup tests except where the open cup flash point is designated by the initials "oc" following the figure. Open cup flash points, determined in a different type of testing apparatus, are usually somewhat higher than the closed cup flash point figures for the same substances. Closed cup flash point figures are commonly used in determining the classification of liquids which flash in the ordinary temperature range, but for certain materials which have relatively high flash points, the open cup flash point testing is sometimes preferred. In the case of some of the older figures quoted in this Table, there are no data to indicate whether the figures are closed or open cup tests. See Chapter 3 of this Section for discussion of flash point testing apparatus.

Ignition Temperature: This term is defined in Section 2, Chapter I.

Flammable or Explosive Limits are defined in Section 2, Chapter I. Figures given in the Table for upper and lower flammable limits have been rounded off to the nearest tenth.

Flammable (Explosive) Range: This is defined in Section 2, Chapter I.

Specific Gravity: Specific gravity is defined in Section 2, Chapter I. The figures given in the Table for specific gravity are rounded off to the nearest tenth. For materials having a specific gravity from 0.95 to 1.0, the information is given as 1.0—. For those materials with a specific gravity of 1.0 to 1.05 the information is given as 1.0+.

In a few cases, where percentage composition of the substance varies, specific gravity information is given as greater than 1 (>1) or less than 1 (<1).

Vapor Density: Vapor density is defined in Section 2, Chapter I. In the Table a figure less than 1 indicates a vapor is lighter than air, and a figure greater than 1 that a vapor is heavier than air. The vapor density figures in the Table have been calculated on the basis of the chemical formula. No vapor density values have been calculated for substances known or believed to dissociate on heating.

Boiling Point: The boiling point of a liquid is the temperature of the liquid at which its vapor pressure equals the atmospheric pressure.

Melting Point: Melting points are reported in the Table for most of those compounds which melt at 70°F or higher. Melting point information is not conveniently available for a few of the less common chemicals.

Water Solubility: Information on the degree to which a flammable liquid is soluble in water is useful in determining effective extinguishing agents and methods. Alcohol-resistant type foam, for example, is usually recommended for water-soluble flammable liquids. Also, water-soluble flammable liquids may be extinguished by dilution although this method is not commonly used because of the amount of water required to make most liquids nonflammable, and there may be danger of frothing if the burning liquid is heated to over 212°F.

There is lack of uniformity in the literature on the method of reporting water solubility. There are also conflicting statements. For those substances in the Table for which reliable solubility information was available, the designation "No" was used to

Table 3-11A. (cont.)

indicate less than 10 grams soluble in 100 ml of water; "Slight" to indicate 10 g to 24 g soluble in 100 ml of water, and "Yes" to indicate 25 g or more soluble in 100 ml of water. "No," "Very slight," "Slight", and "Yes" are sometimes used without definition in the chemical literature to describe water solubility. In those instances where there is doubt as to the effect of water solubility on extinguishment, tests should be run.

Extinguishing Methods

Dry Chemical, Carbon Dioxide, Foam and Vaporizing Liquid: These extinguishing agents have all been found suitable for use on fires involving most flammable liquids. For information on these agents and discussions of portable extinguishers and fixed extinguishing systems, see Sections 13, 15, and 16.

Water Spray (fog): Particularly effective on fires in flammable liquids and volatile solids having flash points between 100°F and 212°F. Water spray protection is discussed in Section 15, Chapter 2.

Automatic Sprinklers: Similar to water spray in extinguishing effectiveness, their principal value, however, being in absorbing heat and keeping surroundings cool until a flammable liquid fire burns out or is extinguished by other means. Overflow drains on open tanks prevent sprinkler discharge from causing burning liquid to overflow and spread the fire. Sprinklers have a good record of fire control in garages, paint and oil rooms, and drum storage areas where flammable liquids are largely in closed containers and water from sprinklers keeps the containers cool. For further information on automatic sprinklers see Section 14.

Hose Streams: Hose streams (solid or straight) are frequently used to keep tanks and other equipment, exposed by flammable liquid fires, cool, or for washing burning spills away from danger points. However, hose streams will cause a spill fire to spread if improperly used and will serve only to spread a fire when directed into open containers of flammable and combustible liquids.

"Wet Water" and High Expansion Foam: These will extinguish flammable liquid and volatile solid fires. Uses and limitations of "wet water" and high expansion foam are set forth in Section 13, Chapter 2 and Section 15, Chapter 3.

Automatic Covers: Automatic covers smother fire when closed automatically by operation of a fusible link. Automatic covers are suitable for any size tank except where objects being dipped or conveyors may prevent tight closing.

Selecting an Extinguishing Method

The selection of the extinguishing method should be made with caution as there are factors to be considered in any individual problem of extinguishment which may affect the choice of extinguishing agent and the method of application. Flowing fires, such as might be caused by a leaking overhead pipe, with the liquid on the ground also burning, are always difficult to extinguish. The amount and rate and method of application of the extinguishing material in relation to the size and type of fire anticipated must be carefully considered and may call for special engineering judgment, particularly in large-scale applications. The use of standard approved equipment is also of major importance.

Extinguishing Method Column

The chemical and physical properties of a flammable substance will also affect the choice of an extinguishing method. Ordinary type foam, for example, would not be suitable on a fire involving a water soluble flammable liquid. These special properties affecting extinguishment were taken into consideration when preparing the statements in the Extinguishing Method column of the Table. The following paragraphs describe the properties of the flammable liquid, volatile solid, or gas, that are responsible for the statements in this column. The statements used in the column appear below in boldface type.

Water may be ineffective: Water may be ineffective in fighting fires with low flash points. In the Table this precautionary wording

is used for materials having a flash point below 100°F. Obviously, the lower the flash point the less effective water will be. However, water can be used on low flash point liquids when applied in the form of a spray to absorb much of the heat and to keep exposed material from being damaged by the fire.

Much of the effectiveness of using water spray, particularly from hose lines, will depend on the method of application. With proper nozzles, even gasoline spill fires of some types have been extinguished when coordinated hose lines were used to sweep the flames off the surface of the liquid.

Water also has been used to extinguish fires in water soluble flammable liquids by cooling, diluting and mixing the flammable liquid with water.

The inclusion of the phrase "water may be ineffective" is to indicate that although water can be used to cool and protect exposed material, water may not extinguish the fire unless used under favorable conditions by experienced fire fighters trained in fighting all types of flammable liquid fires.

Water or foam may cause frothing: This may occur when applied on flammable liquids having a flash point above 212°F or the boiling point of water. This remark is included only as a precaution and does not indicate that water or foam should not or could not be used in fighting fires in such liquids. The frothing may be quite violent and could endanger the life of the fire fighter particularly when solid streams are directed into the hot burning liquid. On the other hand, water spray carefully applied has frequently been used with success in extinguishing such fires by causing the frothing to occur only on the surface and this foaming action blankets and extinguishes the fire. To be considered in this regard are not only those liquids with a flash point above 212°F but also any viscous liquid. For example, certain asphalts have a small amount of low flash point solvent added for fluidity, but because of viscosity, frothing may occur.

Do not use water: This is advised where the chemical properties of the flammable substances are such that a more or less violent reaction would occur if water came in contact with the material.

Decomposes in water: This is mentioned in the column when the chemical literature indicates that a hazardous reaction may occur. The degree of hazard will vary depending upon such environmental conditions as degree of confinement, quantity of water, and violence of reaction. Some decomposition is so slow as to be of no practical significance.

Explodes on heating: A warning that when exposed to fire or other heat sources, the flammable substance may present a severe hazard.

Water may be used to blanket fire: This may be used to accomplish extinguishment when the flammable liquid has a flash point above 100°F, a specific gravity of 1.1 or heavier, and is not water soluble. However, the method of applying water is significant as the water must be applied gently to the surface of the liquid.

Water may be ineffective except as a blanket: This is included in the column as a warning that since the liquid has a flash point below 100°F water may be ineffective except when applied gently to the surface to blanket and extinguish the fire. This statement applies only to those liquids that are not soluble in water and are heavier than water.

"Alcohol" foam: Alcohol foam is recommended for all water soluble flammable liquids except for those that are only "very slightly" soluble. Certain judgment factors are again introduced since for some liquids ordinary foam might be used successfully to extinguish fires for liquids only "slightly" soluble in water particularly if regular foam was applied at increased rates over that normally recommended.

Stop flow of gas: Rather than extinguish the fire, this is usually the best procedure to follow when escaping gas is burning. It may be dangerous to extinguish the flame and allow the gas to

Table 3-11A. (cont.)

continue to flow, as an explosive mixture may be formed with air which, if ignited, may cause far greater damage than if the original fire had been allowed to burn. Extinguishing the flame by carbon dioxide or dry chemical may be desirable where necessary to permit immediate access to valves to shut off supply. In many cases, however, it is preferable to allow the flame to continue, keeping the surroundings cool with water spray to prevent ignition of other combustible materials.

Suggested Hazard Identification

The increasing use of a wide variety of chemicals, many of which introduce problems other than flammability, led to the need for a simple hazard identification system. The purpose of such a system would be to safeguard the lives of those individuals who may be concerned with fires occurring in an industrial plant or storage location.

This recommended system provides simple, readily recognizable and easily understood markings which will give at a glance a general idea of the inherent hazards of any material and the order of severity of these hazards as they relate to fire prevention, exposure, and control. Its objectives are to provide an appropriate alerting signal and on-the-spot information to safeguard the lives of both public and private fire fighting personnel during fire emergencies. It will also assist in planning for effective fire fighting operations and may be used by plant design engineers and plant protection and safety personnel.

This system identifies the hazards of a material in terms of three categories; namely, "Health", "Flammability" and "Reactivity" and indicates the order of severity in each of these categories by five divisions ranging from "four (4)" indicating a severe hazard to "zero (0)" indicating no special hazard.

The columns under "Suggested Hazard Identification" in the listing of materials give the degrees of hazard severity for each category where information was available. Spaces were left blank where adequate information was not available. It should be emphasized that the assignment of degrees is based on judgment and that conditions in plans or processes might change the degrees of hazard. See Chapter 10 of this Section for a further explanation of this system.

Oxygen—Mixtures

The values in this Table, except where otherwise indicated, are based upon experiments in normal air. In oxygen the values may be different and an increase in hazard is probable. Mixtures of two or more flammable materials may have properties different from their components. In the case of mixtures it is common practice to base precautions on the properties of the more hazardous component.

Mists and Froths

In finely divided form, such as a mist or spray, liquids can be ignited at temperatures below their flash points. As in the case of vapors, a minimum concentration of droplets must be present to support combustion. Froths also may be ignited below flash point temperatures.

Abbreviations

The abbreviations used in this Table are in accordance with common practice. Those most frequently used are:

o—ortho	>—greater than	sec—secondary
m—meta	<—less than	sym—symmetrical
n—normal	iso—isometric	ter—tertiary
p—para	prim—primary	

Hazardous Chemicals Data

In various parts of the following tabulation, references will be found to Hazardous Chemicals Data (NFPA No. 49). This compilation of information on hazardous chemicals is available in pamphlet form, as part of the NFPA book, *Fire Protection Guide on Hazardous Materials*, and in *National Fire Codes*. (See the latest NFPA *Publications and Visual Aids Catalog* for availability of current editions of these documents.)

The body of Table 3-11A, Fire Hazard Properties of Flammable Liquids, Gases, and Volatile Solids follows:

	FLASH POINT Deg. F.	IGNI-TION TEMP. Deg. F.	FLAMMABLE LIMITS Per Cent by Vol. Lower	Upper	Sp. Gr. (Water =1)	Vapor Density (Air =1)	Boiling Point Deg. F.	Water Soluble	EXTINGUISHING METHOD See Intro.	SUGGESTED HAZARD IDENTIFICATION Health	Flamma-bility	Reac-tivity
Abalyn	*See Methyl Abietate.*											
Acetal CH₃CH(OC₂H₅)₂ (Acetaldehydediethylacetal)	−5	446	1.6	10.4	0.8	4.1	215	Slight	Water may be ineffective. "Alcohol" foam.	2	3	0
Acetaldehyde CH₃CHO (Acetic Aldehyde) (Ethanal)	−36	347	4.0	60	0.8	1.5	70	Yes	Water may be ineffective. "Alcohol" foam.	2	4	2
	Note: Polymerizes. See Hazardous Chemicals Data.											
Acetaldehydediethyl-acetal	*See Acetal.*											
Acetaldol	*See Aldol.*											
Acetanilide CH₃CONHC₆H₅	345 (oc)	1004			1.21	4.65	582			3	1	
	Note: Melting point 237°F.											
Acetic Acid Glacial CH₃COOH	109	869	5.4	16.0 @ 212°	1.0+	2.1	245	Yes	"Alcohol" foam.	2	2	1 ₩
	Note: See Hazardous Chemicals Data.											
Acetic Acid, Water Solutions (Ethanoic Acid)	*Note: Ordinary acetic acid is the same as glacial acetic acid with water. The properties of ordinary acetic acid depend upon the strength of the solution. In concentrated form its properties approach those of glacial acetic acid. In dilute solution it is non-hazardous.*							Yes				
Acetic Acid, Isopropyl Ester	*See Isopropyl Acetate.*											
Acetic Acid, Methyl Ester	*See Methyl Acetate.*											
Acetic Acid, n—Propyl Ester	*See Propyl Acetate.*											
Acetic Aldehyde	*See Acetaldehyde.*											
Acetic Anhydride (CH₃CO)₂O (Ethanoic Anhydride)	129	734	2.9	10.3	1.1	3.5	284	Yes	"Alcohol" foam.	2	2	1 ₩
	Note: See Hazardous Chemicals Data.											

Table 3-11A (cont.)	FLASH POINT Deg. F.	IGNITION TEMP. Deg. F.	FLAMMABLE LIMITS Per Cent by Vol. Lower	Upper	Sp. Gr. (Water = 1)	Vapor Density (Air = 1)	Boiling Point Deg. F.	Water Soluble	EXTINGUISHING METHOD See Intro.	SUGGESTED HAZARD IDENTIFICATION Health	Flamma-bility	Reac-tivity
Acetic Ester	See Ethyl Acetate.											
Acetic Ether	See Ethyl Acetate.											
Acetoacetanilide $CH_3COCH_2CONHC_6H_5$	365 (oc) *Note: Melting point 185°F.*				1.1 @ melting point			Slight	"Alcohol" foam. Water or foam may cause frothing.	2	1	0
o—Acetoacet Anisidide $CH_3COCH_2CONHC_6$-H_4OCH_3	325 (oc) *Note: Melting point 187.9°F.*				1.1 @ melting point	7.0		No	Water or foam may cause frothing.	2	1	0
Acetoacetic Acid, Ethyl Ester	See Ethyl Acetoacetate.											
m—Acetoacet Xylidide $CH_3COCH_2CONHC_6$-$H_3(CH_3)_2$	340 (oc) *Note: Melting point 197°F.*				1.2			Slight	"Alcohol" foam. Water or foam may cause frothing.	2	1	0
Acetoethylamide	See N—Ethylacetamide.											
Acetone CH_3COCH_3 (Dimethyl Ketone) (2—Propanone)	0	869 (Und. Lab. Class 90)	2.6	12.8 2.40 @ 212°F.	0.8	2.0	134	Yes	Water may be ineffective. "Alcohol" foam.	1	3	0
Acetone Cyanohydrin $(CH_3)_2C(OH)CN$ (2—Hydroxy—2—Methyl Propionitrile)	165 *Note: See Hazardous Chemicals Data.*	1270	2.2	12.0	0.9	2.9	248 Decom-poses	Yes	"Alcohol" foam.	4	1	2
Acetonitrile CH_3CN (Methyl Cyanide)	42 (oc) *Note: See Hazardous Chemicals Data.*	975	4.4	16.0	0.8	1.4	179	Yes	Water may be ineffective. "Alcohol" foam.	2	3	1
Acetonyl Acetone $(CH_2COCH_3)_2$ (2,5—Hexanedione)	174	920			1.0−	3.9	378	Yes	"Alcohol" foam.	1	1	0
Acetophenone $C_6H_5COCH_3$ (Phenyl Methyl Ketone)	180 (oc)	1058			1.0+	4.1	396	No		1	2	0
p—Acetotoluidide $CH_3CONHC_6H_4CH_3$	334				1.2	5.4	583	No		2	1	
Acetyl Acetone	See 2, 4—Pentanedione.											
Acetyl Chloride CH_3COCl (Ethanoyl Chloride)	40 *Note: See Hazardous Chemicals Data.*	734			1.1	2.7	124	Violent decom-position	Do not use water or foam.	3	3	2 W
Acetylene $CH:CH$ (Ethine) (Ethyne)	Gas *Note: Low pressure. Acetylene dissolved in acetone in closed cylinders can carry a 2 reactivity. See Hazardous Chemicals Data.*	581	2.5	100		0.9	−118	No	Stop flow of gas.	1	4	3
Acetylene Dichloride—cis	See Dichloroethylene—cis.											
Acetylene Dichloride—trans	See Dichloroethylene—trans.											
N—Acetyl Ethanolamine $CH_3C:ONHCH_2CH_2OH$ (N—(2—Hydroxyethyl) acetamide)	355 (oc)	860			1.1		304–308 @ 10 mm. Decom-poses	Yes	"Alcohol" foam. Water or foam may cause frothing.	1	1	1
N—Acetyl Morpholine $CH_3CONCH_2CH_2OCH_2CH_2$	235				1.1		Decom-poses	Yes	"Alcohol" foam. Water or foam may cause frothing.	2	1	1
Acetyl Oxide	See Acetic Anhydride.											
Acetyl Peroxide 25% solution in Dimethyl Phthalate $(CH_3CO)_2O_2$	*Note: See Hazardous Chemicals Data.*				1.2	4.1	Explodes on heating	Slight		1	2	4
Acetylphenol	See Phenyl Acetate.											
Acrolein $CH_2:CHCHO$ (Acrylic Aldehyde)	−15 *Note: See Hazardous Chemicals Data.*	455 Unstable	2.8	31	0.8	1.9	125	Yes	Water may be ineffective. "Alcohol" foam.	3	3	2
Acrolein Dimer $(CH_2:CHCHO)_2$	118 (oc) *Note: See Hazardous Chemicals Data.*				1.1		304	Yes	"Alcohol" foam.	3	2	1
Acrylic Acid (Glacial) $CH_2CHCOOH$	130 (oc) *Note: Polymerizes. See Hazardous Chemicals Data.*				1.1	2.5	287	Yes	"Alcohol" foam.	3	2	2
Acrylic Aldehyde	See Acrolein.											
Acrylonitrile $CH_2:CHCN$ (Vinyl Cyanide)	32 (oc) *Note: Polymerizes. See Hazardous Chemicals Data.*	898	3.0	17	0.8	1.8	171	Yes	Water may be ineffective. "Alcohol" foam.	4	3	2

Table 3-11A (cont.)	FLASH POINT Deg. F.	IGNI- TION TEMP. Deg. F.	FLAMMABLE LIMITS Per Cent by Vol.		Sp. Gr (Water = 1)	Vapor Density (Air = 1)	Boiling Point Deg. F.	Water Soluble	EXTINGUISHING METHOD See Intro.	SUGGESTED HAZARD IDENTIFICATION		
			Lower	Upper						Health	Flamma- bility	Reac- tivity
Adipic Acid $HOOC(CH_2)_4COOH$	385	788			1.37	5.04	509 @ 100 mm	No			1	
Adipic Ketone	*See Cyclopentanone.*											
Adipyldinitrile $CN(CH_2)_4CN$ (Adiponitrile) (Tetramethylene Dicyanide)	199 (oc)				0.96	3.73	563	No		4	2	
Alcohol	*See Ethyl Alcohol, Methyl Alcohol, Denatured Alcohol, etc.*											
Aldol $CH_3CH(OH)CH_2CHO$ (3—Hydroxybutanal) (β—Hydroxybuteraldehyde)	150 (oc)	482			1.1	3.0	174- 176 @ 12 mm. Decom- poses @ 176	Yes	"Alcohol" foam.	3	2	2
Allyl Alcohol $CH_2:CHCH_2OH$	70	713	2.5	18.0	0.9	2.0	206	Yes	Water may be ineffective. "Alcohol" foam.	3	3	1
	Note: See Hazardous Chemicals Data.											
Allylamine $CH_2:CHCH_2NH_2$ (2—Propenylamine)	−20	705	2.2	22	0.8	2.0	128	Yes	Water may be ineffective. "Alcohol" foam.	3	3	1
	Note: See Hazardous Chemicals Data.											
Allyl Bromide $CH_2:CHCH_2Br$ (3—Bromopropene)	30	563	4.4	7.3	1.4	4.2	160	No	"Alcohol" foam. Water may be ineffective except as a blanket.	3	3	1
Allyl Chlorcarbonate	*See Allyl Chlorformate.*											
Allyl Chlorformate $CH_2:CHCH_2OCOCl$ (Allyl Chlorcarbonate)	88				1.1	4.2	223- 237	No	"Alcohol" foam. Water may be ineffective except as a blanket.	3	3	1
	Note: See Hazardous Chemicals Data.											
Allyl Chloride $CH_2:CHCH_2Cl$ (3—Chloropropene)	−25	905	2.9	11.1	0.9	2.6	113	No	"Alcohol" foam.	3	3	1
Allyl Diglycol Carbonate	*See Diethylene Glycol Bis (Allylcarbonate).*											
Allylene	*See Propyne.*											
Allyl Ether $(CH_2:CHCH_2)_2O$ (Diallyl Ether)	20 (oc)				0.8	3.4	203	Slight	"Alcohol" foam. Water may be ineffective.	3	3	2
Allylidene Diacetate $CH_2:CHCH(OCOCH_3)_2$	180 (oc)				1.1		225 @ 50 mm.	No	Water may be used to blanket fire.	2	2	1
Allyl Isothiocyanate	*See Mustard Oil.*											
Allylpropenyl	*See 1,4—Hexadiene.*											
Allyl Trichloride	*See 1, 2, 3—Trichloro Propane.*											
Allyl Vinyl Ether	*See Vinyl Allyl Ether.*											
Alpha Methyl Pyridine	*See Picoline—alpha.*											
Aminobenzene	*See Aniline.*											
2—Aminobiphenyl	*See 2—Biphenylamine.*											
1—Aminobutane	*See Butylamine.*											
2—Amino—1—Butanol $CH_3CH_2CHNH_2CH_2OH$	165 (oc)				0.9	3.1	352	Yes	"Alcohol" foam.	2	2	0
Aminocyclohexane	*See Cyclohexylamine.*											
1—Aminodecane	*See Decylamine.*											
Amino Ethane	*See Ethylamine.*											
2—Aminoethanol	*See Ethanolamine.*											
1—Amino—4—Ethoxy-benzene	*See p—Phenetidine.*											
β—Aminoethyl Alcohol	*See Ethanolamine.*											
(2—Aminoethyl) ethan-olamine $NH_2C_2H_4NHC_2H_4OH$	265	695			1.0+		469.4	Yes	"Alcohol" foam. Water or foam may cause frothing.	2	1	0
4—(2—Aminoethyl)-Morpholine $C_2H_4OC_2H_4NC_2H_4NH_2$					1.0	4.5	395.6	Yes	"Alcohol" foam.	2	2	0
1—(2—Aminoethyl)-Piperazine $H_2NC_2H_4NCH_2CH_2-$ $NHCH_2CH_2$	200 (oc)				1.0−	4.4	432	Yes	"Alcohol" foam.	2	2	0
1—Aminoheptane	*See Heptylamine.*											

Table 3-11A (cont.)

	FLASH POINT Deg. F.	IGNITION TEMP. Deg. F.	FLAMMABLE LIMITS Per Cent by Vol. Lower	Upper	Sp. Gr. (Water =1)	Vapor Density (Air =1)	Boiling Point Deg. F.	Water Soluble	EXTINGUISHING METHOD See Intro.	SUGGESTED HAZARD IDENTIFICATION Health	Flamma-bility	Reac-tivity
α—Aminoisopropyl Alcohol	*See 1—Amino—2—Propanol.*											
2—Amino—4—Methyl-pentane	*See 1, 3—Dimethylbutylamine.*											
2—Amino—2—Methyl—1—Propanol (CH₃)₂C(NH₂)CH₂OH	153				0.9	3.0	329	Yes	"Alcohol" foam.	2	2	0
1—Aminooctane	*See Octylamine.*											
2—Aminopentane	*See sec—Amylamine.*											
p—Aminophenetole	*See p—Phenetidine.*											
(m—Aminophenyl) Methyl Carbinol NH₂C₆H₄[CH(OH)CH₃] (m—Amino—α—Methylbenzyl Alcohol)	315 (oc)				1.1		423 @ 100 mm.	Yes	"Alcohol" foam. Water or foam may cause frothing.	2	1	0
1—Amino—2—Propanol NH₂CH₂CHOHCH₃ (α—Aminoisopropyl Alcohol) (Isopropanolamine)	171				1.0—	2.6	320	Yes	"Alcohol" foam.	2	2	0
N—(3—Aminopropyl) Cyclohexylamine C₆H₁₁NHC₃H₆NH₂	175 (oc)				0.9	5.4		Yes	"Alcohol" foam.	2	2	0
N—(3—Aminopropyl) Morpholine C₂H₄OC₂H₄N(CH₂)₃NH₂	220 (oc)				1.0—		438	Yes	"Alcohol" foam. Water or foam may cause frothing.	2	1	0
Ammonia, Anhydrous NH₃	Gas Note: See Hazardous Chemicals Data. *This gas is "1" instead of "4" because it is hard to burn.*	1204	16	25	0.6		−28	Yes	Stop flow of gas.	3	1*	0
Amoxybenzene	*See Amyl Phenyl Ether.*											
Amyl Acetate CH₃COOC₅H₁₁ (1—Pentanol Acetate) Comm.	77 (Und. Lab. Class 55–60) 70	680	1.1	7.5	0.9	4.5	300	Slight	Water may be ineffective. "Alcohol" foam.	1	3	0
sec—Amyl Acetate CH₃COOCH(CH₃)-(CH₂)₂CH₃ (2—Pentanol Acetate)	89				0.9	4.5	249	Slight	Water may be ineffective. "Alcohol" foam.	1	3	0
Amyl Alcohol CH₃(CH₂)₃CH₂OH (1—Pentanol)	91 (Und. Lab. Class 40)	572	1.2	10.0 @ 212°	0.8	3.0	280	Slight	"Alcohol" foam	1	3	0
sec—Amyl Alcohol CH₃CH₂CH₂CH(OH)CH₃ (Diethyl Carbinol)	94 (Und. Lab. Class 40–45)	650	1.2	9.0	0.8	3.0	245	Slight	Water may be ineffective. "Alcohol" foam	1	3	0
tert—n—Amyl Alcohol	*See 3—Pentanol.*											
Amylamine C₅H₁₁NH₂ (Pentylamine)	45 (oc)		2.2	22	0.8	3.0	210	Yes	Water may be ineffective. "Alcohol" foam	3	3	0
sec—Amylamine CH₃(CH₂)₂CH(CH₃)NH₂ (2—Aminopentane) (Methylpropylcarbinylamine)	20				0.7	3.0	198	Yes	'Alcohol" foam. Water may be ineffective.	3	3	0
p—tert—Amylaniline (C₂H₅)(CH₃)₂CC₆H₄NH₂	215				0.9		498–504	No	Water or foam may cause frothing.	3	1	0
Amylbenzene C₆H₅C₅H₁₁ (Phenylpentane)	150 (oc)				0.8–0.9	5.1	365	No		1	2	0
Amyl Bromide CH₃CH₂CH₂CH₂CH₂Br (1—Bromopentane)	90				1.2		128–9 @ 746 mm.	No	Water may be ineffective except as a blanket.	1	3	0
Amyl Carbinol	*See Hexyl Alcohol.*											
Amyl Chloride CH₃(CH₂)₃CH₂Cl (1—Chloropentane)	55 (oc)	500	1.6	8.6	0.9	3.7	223	No	Water may be ineffective.	1	3	0
tert—Amyl Chloride CH₃CH₂CCl(CH₃)CH₃		653	1.5	7.4	1.4	3.7	187	No	Water may be used to blanket fire.	1	3	0
Amyl Chlorides (Mixed) C₅H₁₁Cl	38 (oc)				0.9		185–228	No	Water may be ineffective.	1	3	0
Amylene	*See 1—pentene.*											
β—Amylene—cis C₂H₅CH:CHCH₃ (2—Pentene—cis)	<−4				0.66	2.42	99			0	4	
β—Amylene—trans C₂H₅CH:CHCH₃ (2—Pentene—trans)	<−4				0.67	2.42	97			0	4	

Table 3-11A (cont.)	FLASH POINT Deg. F.	IGNI- TION TEMP. Deg. F.	FLAMMABLE LIMITS Per Cent by Vol.		Sp. Gr. (Water = 1)	Vapor Density (Air = 1)	Boiling Point Deg F.	Water Soluble	EXTINGUISHING METHOD See Intro.	SUGGESTED HAZARD IDENTIFICATION		
			Lower	Upper						Health	Flamma- bility	Reac- tivity
Amylene Chloride	See 1, 5—Dichloropentane.											
Amyl Ether C₅H₁₁OC₅H₁₁ (Diamyl Ether) (Pentyloxypentane)	135 (oc)	338			0.8–0.9	5.5	374	No	"Alcohol" foam.	1	2	0
Amyl Formate HCOOC₅H₁₁	79				0.9	4.0	267	No	Water may be ineffective.	1	3	0
Amyl Lactate C₂H₅OCOOCH₂- CH(CH₃)C₂H₅	175				1.0–	5.5	237–239 @ 36 mm.	Very slight		1	2	0
Amyl Laurate C₁₁H₂₃COOC₅H₁₁	300				0.9		554–626	No	Water or foam may cause frothing.	0	1	0
Amyl Maleate (CHCOOC₅H₁₁)₂	270				1.0–		518–599	No	Water or foam may cause frothing.	0	1	0
Amyl Mercaptan(n) C₅H₁₁SH (1—Pentanethiol)	65 (oc)				0.8	3.59	260			2	3	
Amyl Mercaptans (Mixed) CH₃(CH₂)₄SH	65 (oc)				0.8		176–257	No	Water may be ineffective.	2	3	0
	Note: See Hazardous Chemicals Data.											
Amyl Naphthalene C₁₀H₇C₅H₁₁	255 (oc)				1.0–		550	No	Water or foam may cause frothing.	0	1	0
Amyl Nitrate CH₃(CH₂)₄NO₃	125 (oc)				1.0–		306–315	No		1	2	2
Amyl Nitrite CH₃(CH₂)₄NO₂		410			0.9	4.0	220	Slight	"Alcohol" foam.	1		2
Amyl Oleate C₁₇H₃₃COOC₅H₁₁	366				0.9		392–464 @ 20 mm.	No	Water or foam may cause frothing.	0	1	0
Amyl Oxalate (COOC₅H₁₁)₂	245				1.0–		464–523	No	Water or foam may cause frothing.	0	1	0
p—tert—Amyl Phenol	See Pentaphen.											
p—sec—Amylphenol C₅H₁₁C₆H₄OH	270				1.0–		482–516	No	Water or foam may cause frothing.	1	1	0
2—(p—tert—Amylphen- oxy) ethanol C₅H₁₁C₆H₄OCH₂CH₂OH	280				1.0+		567–590	No	Water or foam may cause frothing.	1	1	0
2—(p—tert—Amylphen- oxy) ethyl Laurate C₁₁H₂₃COO(CH₂)₂O- C₆H₄C₅H₁₁	410				0.9		464–500 @ 6 mm.		Water or foam may cause frothing.	0	1	0
p—tert—Amylphenyl Acetate CH₃COOC₆H₄C₅H₁₁	240				1.0–		507–511		Water or foam may cause frothing.	0	1	0
p—tert—Amylphenyl Butyl Ether C₅H₁₁C₆H₄OC₄H₉	275				0.9		540–550	No	Water or foam may cause frothing.	0	1	0
Amyl Phenyl Ether CH₃(CH₂)₄OC₆H₅ (Amoxybenzene)	185				0.9	5.7	421–444	No		0	2	0
p—tert—Amylphenyl Methyl Ether C₅H₁₁C₆H₄OCH₃	210				0.9		462–469			0	1	0
Amyl Phthalate	See Diamyl Phthalate.											
Amyl Propionate C₂H₅COO(CH₂)₄CH₃ (Pentyl Propionate)	106 (oc)	716			0.9		275–347	No		0	2	0
Amyl Salicylate HOC₆H₄COOC₅H₁₁	270				1.1		512	No	Water or foam may cause frothing.	0	1	0
Amyl Stearate CH₃(CH₂)₁₆COOC₅H₁₁	365 (oc)				0.9		680	No	Water or foam may cause frothing.	0	1	0
Amyl Sulfides, Mixed C₅H₁₁S	185 (oc)				0.9		338–356	No		2	2	0
Amyl Toluene C₅H₁₁C₆H₄CH₃	180 (oc)				0.9		400–415	No		2	2	0
Amyl Xylyl Ether C₅H₁₁OC₆H₃(CH₃)₂	205 (oc)				0.9		480–500	No		2	1	0
Aniline C₆H₅NH₂ (Aminobenzene) (Phenylamine)	158	1139	1.3 (Und. Lab. Class 20–25)		1.0+	3.2	364	Slight	"Alcohol" foam.	3	2	0
	Note: See Hazardous Chemicals Data.											

Table 3-11A (cont.)	FLASH POINT Deg. F.	IGNI-TION TEMP. Deg. F.	FLAMMABLE LIMITS Per Cent by Vol. Lower	Upper	Sp. Gr. (Water = 1)	Vapor Density (Air = 1)	Boiling Point Deg. F.	Water Soluble	EXTINGUISHING METHOD See Intro.	SUGGESTED HAZARD IDENTIFICATION Health	Flamma-bility	Reac-tivity
Aniline Hydrochloride $C_6H_5NH_2HCl$	380 (oc)				1.22	4.46	473			3	1	
Note: Melting point 389°F.												
2—Anilinoethanol $C_6H_5NHCH_2CH_2OH$ (β—Anilinoethanol Ethoxyaniline) (β—Hydroxyethylaniline)	305 (oc)				1.1		547	Very slight	Water or foam may cause frothing.	2	1	0
β—Anilinoethanol Ethoxyaniline	See 2—Anilinoethanol.											
o—Anisaldehyde	See o—Methoxy Benzaldehyde.											
Anisole $C_6H_5OCH_3$ (Methoxybenzene) (Methyl Phenyl Ether)	125 (oc)	887	1.0—	3.7			309	No		1	2	0
Anol	See Cyclohexanol.											
Anthracene $(C_6H_4CH)_2$	250	1004	0.6		1.24	6.15	644			0	1	
Note: Melting point 423°F.												
Anthraquinone $C_6H_4(CO)_2C_6H_4$	365				1.44	7.16	716	No		0	1	
Note: Melting point 354°F.												
Artificial Almond Oil	See Benzaldehyde.											
Asphalt (Cutback)	<50							No	Water or foam may cause frothing.	0	3	0
Asphalt, Liquid-Medium Curing	100 (oc) (min) Grades MC-30 and MC-70 150 (oc) (min) Grades MC-250; MC-800; and MC-3000							No	Water or foam may cause frothing.	0	2	0
Asphalt, Liquid-Rapid Curing	80 (oc) (min) Grades RC-250; RC-800; and RC-3000							No	Water or foam may cause frothing.	0	3	0
Asphalt, Liquid-Slow Curing	150+ (oc) Grade SC-70							No	Water or foam may cause frothing.	0	2	0
	175+ (oc) Grade SC-250									0	2	0
	200+ (oc) Grade SC-800									0	1	0
	225+ (oc) Grade SC-3000									0	1	0
Asphalt (Typical) (Petroleum Pitch)	400+	905			1.0–1.1		>700	No	Water or foam may cause frothing.	0	1	0
Aziridine	See Ethyleneimine.											
Azole	See Pyrrole.											
Banana Oil	See Isoamyl Acetate.											
Benzaldehyde C_6H_5CHO (Artificial Almond Oil) (Benzenecarbonal)	148	377			1.1	3.7	355	No	Water may be used to blanket fire.	2	2	0
Benzedrine $C_6H_5CH_2CH(CH_3)NH_2$ (1—Phenyl Isopropyl Amine)	<212				0.93	4.67	392			0	1	
Benzene	See Benzol.											
Benzenecarbonal	See Benzaldehyde.											
Benzene Carbonyl Chloride	See Benzoyl Chloride.											
Benzine	See Petroleum Ether.											
Benzoic Acid C_6H_5COOH	250	1058			1.27	4.21	482	Slight		2	1	
Note: Melting point 252°F.												
Benzol (Benzene) C_6H_6	12	1040	1.3	7.1	0.9	2.8	176	No	Water may be ineffective.	2	3	0
(Und. Lab. Class 95–100) Note: See Hazardous Chemicals Data.												
Benzol Diluent	− 25	450	1.0	7.0	<1		140–210	No	Water may be ineffective.	2	3	0
Note: Flash point and ignition temperature will vary depending on the manufacturer.												
Benzotrifluoride $C_6H_5CF_3$	54				1.2	5.0	216	No	Water may be ineffective except as a blanket.	4	3	0
Note: See Hazardous Chemicals Data.												
Benzoyl Chloride C_6H_5COCl (Benzene Carbonyl Chloride)	162				1.2	4.9	387	Decom-poses	Decomposes in water.	3	2	1 W
Note: See Hazardous Chemicals Data.												

Table 3-11A (cont.)	FLASH POINT Deg. F.	IGNI- TION TEMP. Deg. F.	FLAMMABLE LIMITS Per Cent by Vol.		Sp. Gr. (Water = 1)	Vapor Density (Air = 1)	Boiling Point Deg. F.	Water Soluble	EXTINGUISHING METHOD See Intro.	SUGGESTED HAZARD IDENTIFICATION		
			Lower	Upper						Health	Flamma- bility	Reac- tivity
Benzyl Acetate $CH_3COOCH_2C_6H_5$	216	862			1.1		417	Slight	"Alcohol" foam. Water or foam may cause frothing.	1	1	0
Benzyl Alcohol $C_6H_5CH_2OH$ (Phenyl Carbinol)	213	817			1.0+		403	Slight	"Alcohol" foam. Water or foam may cause frothing.	2	1	0
Benzyl Benzoate $C_6H_5COOCH_2C_6H_5$	298	896			1.1		614	No	Water or foam may cause frothing.	1	1	0
Benzyl Butyl Phthalate $C_4H_9COOC_6H_4COOCH_2C_6H_5$ (Butyl Benzyl Phthalate)	390				1.1		698	No	Water or foam may cause frothing.	1	1	0
Benzyl Carbinol	See Phenethyl Alcohol.											
Benzyl Chloride $C_6H_5CH_2Cl$ (α—Chlorotoluene)	153	1085	1.1 Note: See Hazardous Chemicals Data.		1.1	4.4	354	No	Water may be used to blanket fire.	2	2	1
N—Benzyldiethylamine $C_6H_5CH_2N(C_2H_5)_2$	170 (oc)				0.9		405–420			2	2	0
Benzyl Ether	See Dibenzyl Ether.											
Benzyl Mercaptan $C_6H_5CH_2SH$ (α—Toluenethiol)	158				1.06	4.28	383			2	2	
Bicyclohexyl $[CH_2(CH_2)_4CH]_2$ (Dicyclohexyl)	165	473	0.7 @ 212°	5.1 @ 302°	0.9	5.7	462	Slight	"Alcohol" foam.	1	2	0
Biphenyl $C_6H_5C_6H_5$ (Diphenyl) (Phenylbenzene)	235	1004	0.6 @ 232° Note: Melting point 158°F.	5.8 @ 311°	1.2		489	No	Water or foam may cause frothing.	2	1	0
2—Biphenylamine $NH_2C_6H_4C_6H_5$ (2—Aminobiphenyl)		842	Note: Melting point 121°F.			5.8	570	No	Water or foam may cause frothing.	2	1	0
Bis(p—tert—Butyl- phenyl) phenyl Phosphate $(C_4H_9C_6H_4O)_2POOC_6H_5$	482				1.1		500–527 @ 5 mm.	No	Water or foam may cause frothing.		1	0
Bis[2—(2—Chloroethoxy) ethyl] Ether $(CH_2ClCH_2OCH_2CH_2)_2O$ (Tetraglycol Dichloride)	>250				1.2		237	Slight	"Alcohol" foam. Water or foam may cause frothing.	2	1	0
Bis(2—Chloroethyl) Ether $(CH_2ClCH_2)_2O$ (Chlorex)	131				1.2	4.9	353	Very slight		2	2	0
Bis(2—Chloroethyl) Formal $CH_2(OCH_2CH_2Cl)_2$ (Di—(2—Chloroethyl) Formal) (2, 2—Dichloroethyl Formal)	230 (oc)				1.2		425	Very slight	"Alcohol" foam. Water or foam may cause frothing.	2	1	0
Bis(β—Chloroisopropyl) Ether	See Dichloroisopropyl Ether.											
Bis(2, 4—Dimethylbutyl) Maleate $[(CH_3)_2CHCH_2CH(CH_3)OCOCH:]_2$ (Di(Methylamyl) Maleate)	290 (oc)				0.9		394 @ 50 mm.	No	Water or foam may cause frothing.	1	1	0
1, 3—Bis(ethylamino) Butane	See N, N—Diethyl—1, 3—Butanediamine.											
Bis(2—Ethylhexyl)amine $[C_4H_9CH(C_2H_5)CH_2]_2NH$ (Diethylhexylamine) (Dioctylamine)	270 (oc)				0.8		537	Slight	"Alcohol" foam. Water or foam may cause frothing.	3	1	0
Bis(2—Ethylhexyl)- ethanolamine $[C_4H_9CH(C_2H_5)CH_2]_2NC_2H_4OH$ (Diethylhexylethanolamine)	280				0.9		421 @ 50 mm.	Slight	"Alcohol" foam. Water or foam may cause frothing.	1	1	0
Bis(2—Ethylhexyl) Maleate $C_8H_{17}OCOCH:CHCOOC_8H_{17}$ (Di(2—Ethylhexyl) Maleate)	365				0.9		408 @ 10 mm.	No	"Alcohol" foam. Water or foam may cause frothing.	0	1	0
Bis(2—Ethylhexyl) Phosphoric Acid $[C_4H_9CH(C_2H_5)CH]_2HPO_4$ (Di(2—Ethylhexyl) Phosphoric Acid)	385 (oc)				1.0−			No	"Alcohol" foam. Water or foam may cause frothing.			

Table 3-11A (cont.)

Material	Flash Point Deg. F.	Ignition Temp. Deg. F.	Flammable Limits Per Cent by Vol. Lower	Upper	Sp. Gr. (Water =1)	Vapor Density (Air =1)	Boiling Point Deg. F.	Water Soluble	Extinguishing Method See Intro.	Health	Flammability	Reactivity
Bis(2—Ethylhexyl) Succinate $(C_{10}H_{19}O_2)_2$ (Di(2—Ethylhexyl) Succinate)	315				0.9		495 @ 50 mm.	Slight	"Alcohol" foam. Water or foam may cause frothing.	0	1	0
N, N—Bis(1—Methylheptyl) Ethylenediamine $HC(CH_3)(C_6H_{13})NHCH_2-CH_2NHCH(CH_3)(C_6H_{13})$	>400				0.8		424 @ 43 mm.	No	Water or foam may cause frothing.	0	1	0
Bis(β—Methylpropyl) Amine	See Diisobutylamine.											
Bis(2, 2, 4—Trimethyl-pentanediolisobutyrate) Diglycolate $C_{28}H_{27}O_9$	383 (oc)				1.1		639		Water or foam may cause frothing.	0	1	0
Blast-furnace Gas	See Gas.											
Borneo Camphor	See Borneol.											
Borneol $C_{10}H_{17}OH$ (Borneo Camphor)	150		1.0+				413 Sublimes	No		2	2	0
Boron Trifluoride Etherate $CH_3CH_2O(BF_3)CH_2CH_3$	147 (oc)		1.1				259	Decomposes—	Decomposes in water.	3	2	1 ₩
Brandy	See Ethyl Alcohol and Water.											
Brazil Wax	See Carnauba Wax.											
Bromobenzene C_6H_5Br (Phenyl Bromide)	124	1049	1.5			5.4	313	No	Water may be used to blanket fire.	2	2	0
1—Bromo Butane	See Butyl Bromide.											
4—Bromodiphenyl $C_6H_5C_6H_4Br$	291						592	No	Water or foam may cause frothing.	2	1	0
Bromoethane	See Ethyl Bromide.											
Bromomethane	See Methyl Bromide.											
1—Bromopentane	See Amyl Bromide.											
3—Bromopropene	See Allyl Bromide.											
o—Bromotoluene $BrC_6H_4CH_3$	174		1.4			5.9	359	No	Water may be used to blanket fire.	2	2	0
p—Bromotoluene $BrC_6H_4CH_3$	185		1.4			5.9	363	No	Water may be used to blanket fire.	2	2	0
Bronzing Liquid	May be below 80							No				
1, 3—Butadiene $CH_2{:}CHCH{:}CH_2$ (Erythrene)	Gas Note: Polymerizes. See Hazardous Chemicals Data.	788	2.0	12.0		1.9	24	No	Stop flow of gas.	2	4	2
Butadiene Monoxide $CH_2{:}CHCHOCH_2$ (Vinylethylene Oxide)	<−58				0.9	2.4	151		Water may be ineffective.	2	3	2
Butanal	See Butyraldehyde.											
Butanal Oxime	See Butyraldoxime.											
Butane $CH_3CH_2CH_2CH_3$	Gas	761	1.9	8.5		2.0	31	No	Stop flow of gas.	1	4	0
1, 3—Butanediamine $NH_2CH_2CH_2CHNH_2CH_3$ (1, 3—Diaminobutane)	125 (oc)				0.9	3.0	289–302	Yes	"Alcohol" foam.	3	2	0
1, 2—Butanediol $CH_3CH_2CHOHCH_2OH$ (1, 2—Dihydroxybutane) (Ethylethylene Glycol)	104				1.0	3.1	381	Slight	"Alcohol" foam.	1	2	0
1, 3—Butanediol	See β—Butylene Glycol.											
1, 4—Butanediol $HOCH_2CH_2CH_2CH_2OH$	250 (oc) Note: Melting point 64–66°F.		1.0+			3.1	442	Yes	Water or foam may cause frothing. "Alcohol" foam.	1	1	0
2, 3—Butanediol $CH_3CHOHCHOHCH_3$		756	1.0+				363	Yes	"Alcohol" foam.	1	1	0
2, 3—Butanedione $CH_3COCOCH_3$ (Diacetyl)	80		1.0−			3.0	190	Yes	"Alcohol" foam.	1	3	0
1—Butanethiol $CH_3CH_2CH_2CH_2SH$ (Butyl Mercaptan)	35				0.8	3.1	208	Slight	"Alcohol" foam. Water may be ineffective.	2	3	0
1—Butanol	See Butyl Alcohol.											
2—Butanol	See sec—Butyl Alcohol.											
2—Butanone	See Methyl Ethyl Ketone.											

Table 3-11A (cont.)

	FLASH POINT Deg. F.	IGNITION TEMP. Deg. F.	FLAMMABLE LIMITS Per Cent by Vol. Lower	Upper	Sp. Gr. (Water =1)	Vapor Density (Air =1)	Boiling Point Deg. F.	Water Soluble	EXTINGUISHING METHOD See Intro.	Health	Flammability	Reactivity
2—Butenal	See Crotonaldehyde.											
1—Butene $CH_3CH_2CH:CH_2$ (α—Butylene)	Gas	725	1.6	10.0		1.9	21	No	Stop flow of gas.	1	4	0
2—Butene—cis $CH_3CH:CHCH_3$	Gas	617	1.7	9.0	0.6	1.9	38.7		Stop flow of gas.	1	4	0
2—Butene—trans $CH_3CH:CHCH_3$ (β—Butylene)	Gas	615	1.8	9.7		1.9	34	No	Stop flow of gas.	1	4	0
Butenediol $HOCH_2CH:CHCH_2OH$ (2—Butene—1, 4—Diol)	263 (oc) Note: Melting point 45°F.				1.1	3.0	286–300 @ 20 mm.	Yes	Water or foam may cause frothing. "Alcohol" foam.	1	1	0
2—Butene—1, 4—Diol	See Butenediol.											
2—Butene Nitrile	See Crotononitrile.											
Butoxybenzene	See Butyl Phenyl Ether.											
1—Butoxybutane	See Dibutyl Ether.											
2, β—Butoxyethoxyethyl Chloride $C_4H_9CH_2CH_2OCH_2CH_2Cl$	190				1.0	6.1	392–437			2	2	0
1—(Butoxyethoxy)—2—Propanol $CH_3CH(OH)CH_2OC_2H_4$- $OC_2H_4C_2H_5$	250 (oc)				0.9		445	Yes	"Alcohol" foam. Water or foam may cause frothing.	2	1	0
Butoxyethyl Diglycol Carbonate	See Diethylene Glycol Bis (2—Butoxyethyl Carbonate).											
β—Butoxyethyl Salicylate $OCH_6H_4COOCH_2CH_2OC_4H_9$	315				1.0+		367–378	No	Water or foam may cause frothing.	0	1	0
Butoxyl	See 3—Methoxybutyl Acetate.											
N—Butyl Acetamide $CH_3CONHC_4H_9$	240				0.9		455–464		Water or foam may cause frothing.	2	1	0
N—Butylacetanilide $CH_3(CH_2)_3N(C_6H_5)COCH_3$	286				1.0−		531–538	No	Water or foam may cause frothing.	2	1	0
Butyl Acetate $CH_3COOC_4H_9$	72 (Und. Lab. Class 50–60)	797	1.7	7.6	0.9	4.0	260	Slight	Water may be ineffective. "Alcohol" foam.	1	3	0
sec—Butyl Acetate $CH_3COOCH(CH_3)C_2H_5$	88 (oc)		1.7		0.9	4.0	221	Slight	Water may be ineffective. "Alcohol" foam.	1	3	0
Butyl Acetoacetate $CH_3COCH_2COO(CH_2)_3$-CH_3	185 (oc)		1.0−	5.5			417	Slight	"Alcohol" foam.	1	2	0
Butyl Acetyl Ricinoleate $C_{17}H_{32}(OCOCH_3)$-$(COOC_4H_9)$	230	725			0.9		428	No	Water or foam may cause frothing.	2	1	0
Butyl Acrylate $CH_2:CHCOOC_4H_9$	120 (oc)				0.9	4.4	293 Polymerizes	No		2	2	2
Butyl Alcohol $CH_3(CH_2)_2CH_2OH$ (1—Butanol) (Propylcarbinol) (Propyl Methanol)	84 (Und. Lab. Class 40)	689	1.4	11.2	0.8	2.6	243	Yes	Water may be ineffective. "Alcohol" foam.	1	3	0
sec—Butyl Alcohol $CH_3CH_2CHOHCH_3$ (2—Butanol) (Methyl Ethyl Carbinol)	75	761	1.7 @ 212°	9.8 @ 212°	0.8	2.6	201	Yes	Water may be ineffective. "Alcohol" foam.	1	3	0
tert—Butyl Alcohol $(CH_3)_2COHCH_3$ (2—Methyl—2—Propanol) (Trimethyl Carbinol)	52	896	2.4	8.0	0.8	2.6	181	Yes	Water may be ineffective. "Alcohol" foam.	1	3	0
Butylamine $C_4H_9NH_2$ (1—Amino Butane)	10	594	1.7	9.8	0.8	2.5	172	Yes	Water may be ineffective. "Alcohol" foam.	2	3	0
sec—Butylamine $CH_3CH_2CH(NH_2)CH_3$	16				0.72	2.52	145			3	3	
tert—Butylamine $(CH_3)_3C:NH_2$		716	1.7 @ 212°	8.9 @ 212°	0.7	2.5	113	Yes	"Alcohol" foam.	2	4	0
Butylamine Oleate $C_{17}H_{33}COONH_3C_4H_9$	150 (oc)				0.9			Yes	"Alcohol" foam.	3	2	0
tert—Butylaminoethyl Methacrylate $(CH_3)_3CNHC_2H_4$-$OOCC(CH_3):CH_2$	205 (oc)				0.9	5.5	200–221	No		2	1	0

Table 3-11A (cont.)

	FLASH POINT Deg. F.	IGNITION TEMP. Deg. F.	FLAMMABLE LIMITS Per Cent by Vol. Lower	Upper	Sp. Gr. (Water = 1)	Vapor Density (Air = 1)	Boiling Point Deg. F.	Water Soluble	EXTINGUISHING METHOD See Intro.	SUGGESTED HAZARD IDENTIFICATION Health	Flammability	Reactivity
N—Butylaniline $C_6H_5NHC_4H_9$	225 (oc)				0.9		465	Slight	"Alcohol" foam. Water or foam may cause frothing.	3	1	0
Butylbenzene $C_6H_5C_4H_9$	160 (oc)	770	0.8	5.8	0.9	4.6	356	No		2	2	0
sec—Butylbenzene $C_6H_5CH(CH_3)C_2H_5$	126	788	0.8	6.9	0.9	4.6	344	No		2	2	0
tert—Butylbenzene $C_6H_5C(CH_3)_3$	140 (oc)	842	0.7 @ 212°	5.7 @ 212°	0.9	4.6	336	No		2	2	0
Butyl Benzoate $C_6H_5COOC_4H_9$	225 (oc)				1.0		482	No	Water or foam may cause frothing.	1	1	0
Butyl Benzyl Phthalate	*See Benzyl Butyl Phthalate.*											
2—Butylbiphenyl $C_6H_5.C_6H_4.C_4H_9$	>212	806				7.26	~554			0	1	
Butyl Bromide $CH_3(CH_2)_2CH_2Br$ (1—Bromo Butane)	65	509	2.6 @ 212°	6.6 @ 212°	1.3	4.7	215	No	Water may be ineffective except as a blanket.	2	3	0
Butyl Butyrate $CH_3(CH_2)_2COOC_4H_9$	128 (oc)				0.9	5.0	305	Slight	"Alcohol" foam.	2	2	0
Butylcarbamic Acid, Ethyl Ester	*See N—Butylurethane.*											
tert—Butyl Carbinol $(CH_3)_3CCH_2OH$ (2, 2—Dimethyl—1—Propanol)	98				0.8	3.0	237	Slight	Water may be ineffective. "Alcohol" foam.	2	3	0
4—tert—Butyl Catechol $(OH)_2C_6H_3C(CH_3)_3$	266				1.0+		545	No	Water or foam may cause frothing.	2	1	0
Butyl Cellosolve $C_4H_9OCH_2CH_2OH$ (2—Butoxyethanol)	160				0.90	4.08	340	Yes		0	2	
Butyl Chloride C_4H_9Cl (1—Chlorobutane)	15	860	1.8	10.1	0.9	3.2	170	No	Water may be ineffective.	2	3	0
sec—Butyl Chloride $CH_3CHClC_2H_5$ (2—Chlorobutane)	<32				0.87	3.20	155			2	3	
tert—Butyl Chloride $(CH_3)_3CCl$ (2—Chloro—2—methylpropane)	<32				0.87	3.20	124			2	3	
4—tert—Butyl—2—Chlorophenol $ClC_6H_3(OH)C(CH_3)_3$	225				1.1		453–484	No	Water or foam may cause frothing.	2	1	0
tert—Butyl—m—Cresol $C_6H_3(C_4H_9)(CH_3)OH$	116				1.0—		451–469	No		2	2	0
p—tert—Butyl—o—Cresol $(OH)C_6H_3CH_3C(CH_3)_3$	244				1.0—		278–280	No	Water or foam may cause frothing.	2	1	0
N—Butylcyclohexylamine $C_6H_{11}NH(C_4H_9)$	200 (oc)				0.8		409	Slight	"Alcohol" foam.	2	1	0
Butyldecalin $C_4H_9C_{10}H_{17}$	500								Water or foam may cause frothing.	1	1	0
tert—Butyldecalin $C_4H_9C_{10}H_{17}$	640								Water or foam may cause frothing.	1	1	0
N—Butyldiethanolamine $C_4H_9N(C_2H_4OH)_2$	245 (oc)				1.0—		504	Yes	"Alcohol" foam. Water or foam may cause frothing.	2	1	0
tert—Butyldiethanolamine $C_8H_{10}NO_2$ [2, 2—(tert—Butylimino) Diethanol]	285 (oc) Note: Melting point 117°F.				1.0—		329–338 @ 33 mm.	Yes	Water or foam may cause frothing. "Alcohol" foam.	2	1	0
Butyl Diglycol Carbonate	*See Diethylene Glycol Bis (Butyl Carbonate).*											
α—Butylene	*See 1—Butene.*											
β—Butylene	*See 2—Butene—trans.*											
γ—Butylene	*See 2—Methylpropene.*											
α Butylene Glycol $C_2H_5CHOHCH_2OH$ (1, 2—Butanediol)	194				1.01	3.10	377			0	2	

Table 3-11A (cont.)	FLASH POINT Deg. F.	IGNI-TION TEMP. Deg. F.	FLAMMABLE LIMITS Per Cent by Vol. Lower	Upper	Sp. Gr. (Water = 1)	Vapor Density (Air = 1)	Boiling Point Deg. F.	Water Soluble	EXTINGUISHING METHOD See Intro.	SUGGESTED HAZARD IDENTIFICATION Health	Flamma-bility	Reac-tivity
β—Butylene Glycol $CH_3CH(OH)CH_2CH_2OH$ (1, 3—Butanediol)	250	743			1.0		399	Yes	"Alcohol" foam. Water or foam may cause frothing.	1	1	0
Butylene Glycol (pseudo) $CH_3(CHOH)_2CH_3$ (2, 3—Butanediol) (Di Hydroxy Butane 2, 3)	185 (oc)				1.01	3.10	356			0	2	
Butylene Oxide $(CH_3)_2COCH_2$	5		1.5	18.3	0.83	2.49	149	Slight		3	3	
Butyl Ethanedioate	*See Butyl Oxalate.*											
N—Butyl Ethanolamine $CH_3(CH_2)_3NHCH_2CH_2$-OH	170 (oc)				0.9	4.0	377	Yes	"Alcohol" foam.	1	2	0
Butyl Ether	*See Dibutyl Ether.*											
Butylethylacetaldehyde	*See 2—Ethylhexanal.*											
Butyl Ethylene	*See 1—Hexene.*											
Butyl Ethyl Ether	*See Ethyl Butyl Ether.*											
Butyl Formate $HCOOC_4H_9$ (Butyl Methanoate) (Formic Acid, Butyl Ester)	64	612	1.7	8.2	0.9	3.5	225	Yes	Water may be ineffective. "Alcohol" foam.	2	3	0
Butyl Glycolate $CH_2OHCOOC_4H_9$	142				1.01	4.45	~356			0	2	
tert—Butyl Hydroperoxide $(CH_3)_3COOH$	<80 or above *Note: May explode. See Hazardous Chemicals Data.*				0.9			Slight	"Alcohol" foam.	1	4	4
2, 2—(Butylimino) Diethanol	*See tert—Butyldiethanolamine.*											
Butyl Isovalerate $C_4H_9OOCCH_2CH(CH_3)_2$	127				0.87	5.45	302			0	2	
Butyl Lactate $CH_3CH(OH)COOC_4H_9$	160 (oc)	720			1.0—	5.0	320	Slight	"Alcohol" foam.	1	2	0
Butyl Mercaptan	*See 1—Butanethiol.*											
tert—Butyl Mercaptan	*See 2—Methyl—2—Propanethiol.*											
Butyl Methacrylate CH_2:$C(CH_3)$ $COO(CH_2)_3CH_3$	126 (oc)				0.9	4.9	325	No		2	2	0
Butyl Methanoate	*See Butyl Formate.*											
N—Butyl Monoethan-olamine $C_4H_9NHC_2H_4OH$	170 (oc)				0.9	4.0	378	Yes	"Alcohol" foam.	1	2	0
Butyl Naphthalene $C_4H_9C_{10}H_7$	680							No	Water or foam may cause frothing.	1	1	0
Butyl Nitrate $CH_3(CH_2)_3ONO_2$	97				1.0+	4.1	277	No	Water may be ineffective.	1	3	3
2—Butyloctanol $C_6H_{13}CH(C_4H_9)CH_2OH$	230				0.8		486	No	Water or foam may cause frothing.	1	1	0
Butyl Oleate $C_{17}H_{33}COOC_4H_9$	356 (oc)				0.9		440.6—442.4 @ 15 mm.	No	Water or foam may cause frothing.	0	1	0
Butyl Oxalate $(COOC_4H_9)_2$ (Butyl Ethanedioate)	265 (oc)				1.0—		472	No	Water or foam may cause frothing.	0	1	0
tert—Butyl Peracetate diluted with 25% of benzene $CH_3CO(O_2)C(CH_3)_3$	<80 *Note: Rapid decomposition at 200°F. See Hazardous Chemicals Data.*						Explodes on heating.	No	Water may be ineffective.	2	3	4
tert—Butyl Perbenzoate $C_6H_5COOC(CH_3)_3$	>190 (oc) *See Hazardous Chemicals Data.*				1.0+		Explodes on heating.	No		1	3	4
tert—Butylperoxide $(CH_3)_3COOC(CH_3)_3$	64 (oc)				0.8		176 @ 284 mm.	Very slight	Water may be ineffective.	1	3	3
tert—Butyl Peroxypiva-late diluted with 25% of mineral spirits $(CH_3)_3COOCOC(CH_3)_3$	>155 (oc) *Note: Rapid decomposition at 90°F. See Hazardous Chemicals Data.*						Explodes on heating.	No		0	3	4
β—(p—tert—Butyl phenoxy)ethanol $(CH_3)_3CC_6H_4OCH_2CH_2OH$	248 (oc)				1.0+		293–313	No	Water or foam may cause frothing.	0	1	0

Table 3-11A (cont.)	FLASH POINT Deg. F.	IGNI- TION TEMP. Deg. F.	FLAMMABLE LIMITS Per Cent by Vol.		Sp. Gr. (Water = 1)	Vapor Density (Air = 1)	Boiling Point Deg. F.	Water Soluble	EXTINGUISHING METHOD See Intro.	SUGGESTED HAZARD IDENTIFICATION		
			Lower	Upper						Health	Flamma- bility	Reac- tivity
β—(p—tert—Butylphen- oxy) ethyl Acetate $(CH_3)_3CC_6H_4OCH_2-CH_2OCOCH_3$	324 (oc)				1.0+		579–585	No	Water or foam may cause frothing.	0	1	0
Butyl Phenyl Ether $CH_3(CH_2)_3OC_6H_5$ (Butoxybenzene)	180 (oc)				0.9	5.2	410	No		1	2	0
4—tert—Butyl—2— Phenylphenol $C_6H_5C_6H_3OHC(CH_3)_3$	320				1.0+		385–388	No	Water or foam may cause frothing.	1	1	0
Butyl Phosphate $PO_4(C_4H_9)_3$ (Tributyl Phosphate)	295 (oc)				0.98	9.12	559			3	1	
Butyl Phthalyl Butyl Glycolate $C_6H_4(COO)_2(C_4H_9)-CH_2COOC_4H_9$	390 (oc)				1.1		653	No	Water or foam may cause frothing.	1	1	0
Butyl Propionate $C_2H_5COOC_4H_9$	90	800			0.9	4.5	295	No	Water may be ineffective.	2	3	0
Butyl Ricinoleate $C_{18}H_{33}O_3C_4H_9$	230				0.9		790	No	Water or foam may cause frothing.	1	1	0
Butyl Sebacate $[(CH_2)_4COOC_4H_9]_2$	353 (oc)				0.9		653	No	Water or foam may cause frothing.	1	1	0
Butyl Stearate $C_{17}H_{35}COOC_4H_9$	320	671			0.9		650	No	Water or foam may cause frothing.	1	1	0
tert—Butyl Tetralin $C_4H_9C_{10}H_{11}$	680								Water or foam may cause frothing.	2	1	0
Butyl Trichlorosilane $CH_3(CH_2)_3SiCl_3$	130 (oc)				1.2	6.5	300	No	Water may be used to blanket fire.	2	2	0
N—Butylurethane $CH_3(CH_2)_3NHCOOC_2H_5$ (Butylcarbamic Acid, Ethyl Ester) (Ethyl Butylcarbamate)	197				0.9	5.0	396–397	No			2	0
Butyl Vinyl Ether	*See Vinyl Butyl Ether.*											
2—Butyne $CH_3C:CCH_3$ (Crotonylene)	<−4		1.4		0.69	1.86	81				4	
Butyraldehyde $CH_3(CH_2)_2CHO$ (Butanal) (Butyric Aldehyde)	20	446	2.5	12.5	0.8	2.5	169	No	Water may be ineffective.	2	3	1
	Note: See Hazardous Chemicals Data.											
Butyraldol $C_8H_{16}O_2$	165 (oc)				0.9		280 @ 50 mm.	Slight	"Alcohol" foam.	2	2	0
Butyraldoxime C_4H_8NOH (Butanal Oxime)	136				0.9	3.0	306	Slight	"Alcohol" foam.	2	2	0
Butyric Acid $CH_3(CH_2)_2COOH$	161	842	2.0	10.0	1.0−	3.0	327	Yes	"Alcohol" foam.	2	2	0
	Note: See Hazardous Chemicals Data.											
Butyric Acid, Ethyl Ester	*See Ethyl Butyrate.*											
Butyric Aldehyde	*See Butyraldehyde.*											
Butyric Anhydride $[CH_3(CH_2)_2CO]_2O$	190 (oc)				1.0−	5.4	388	De- com- poses	"Alcohol" foam.	1	2	1 W
Butyric Ester	*See Ethyl Butyrate.*											
Butyrolactone $CH_2CH_2CH_2COO$	209 (oc)				1 1		399	Yes	"Alcohol" foam.	0	1	0
Butyrone	*See 4—Heptanone.*											
Butyronitrile $CH_3CH_2CH_2CN$	79 (oc)				0.8		243	Slight	"Alcohol" foam.	3	3	0
Camphor Oil (light) (Liquid Camphor)	117				0.9		347–392	No		2	2	0
Caproaldehyde	*See Hexanol.*											
Caproic Acid $(CH_3)(CH_2)_4COOH$ (Hexanoic Acid)	215 (oc)	716			0.9		400	No	Water or foam may cause frothing.	2	1	0
Caprylaldehyde $CH_3(CH_2)_6CHO$ (Caprylic Aldehyde) (Octanal)	125				0.8	4.4	335	Very slight		2	2	0
Caprylic Aldehyde	*See Caprylaldehyde.*											
Caprylyl Chloride $CH_3(CH_2)_6COCl$	180				1.0−	5.6	384	De- com- poses	"Alcohol" foam.	3	2	1

Table 3-11A (cont.)	FLASH POINT Deg. F.	IGNI- TION TEMP. Deg. F.	FLAMMABLE LIMITS Per Cent by Vol. Lower	Upper	Sp. Gr. (Water = 1)	Vapor Density (Air = 1)	Boiling Point Deg. F.	Water Soluble	EXTINGUISHING METHOD See Intro.	SUGGESTED HAZARD IDENTIFICATION Health	Flamma- bility	Reac- tivity
Carbolic Acid	See Phenol.											
Carbon Bisulfide	See Carbon Disulfide.											
Carbon Disulfide CS₂ (Carbon Bisulfide)	−22 (Und. Lab. Class 110+) Note: See Hazardous Chemicals Data.	194	1.3	50.0	1.3	2.6	115	No	Water may be ineffective except as a blanket.	2	3	0
Carbon Monoxide CO	Gas	1128	12.5	74		1.0	−314	Yes	Stop flow of gas.	2	4	0
Carbon Oxysulfide COS (Carbonyl Sulfide)	Gas		12	29		2.1	−58		Stop flow of gas.	3	4	1
Carbonyl Sulfide	See Carbon Oxysulfide.											
Carnauba Wax (Brazil Wax)	540 Note: Melting point 185°F.		1.0—					No	Water or foam may cause frothing.	0	1	0
Castor Oil (Ricinus Oil)	445	840	1.0—				595	No	Water or foam may cause frothing.	0	1	0
Castor Oil (Hydrogenated) (C₁₈H₃₅O₃)₃C₃H₅	401							No	Water or foam may cause frothing.	0	1	0
Cellulose Nitrate Wet with Alcohol (Nitrocellulose)	55 Note: See Hazardous Chemicals Data.							No	Water may be ineffective. "Alcohol" foam.	1	3	3
Cetane	See Hexadecane.											
China Wood Oil	See Tung Oil.											
Chlorex	See Bis (2—chloroethyl) Ether.											
Chlorine Monoxide Cl₂O	Gas		23.5	100			Explodes @ 39°F	Yes	Explodes on heating.	3	4	3
Chloroacetic Acid CH₂ClCOOH	259	8			1.58	3.26	372			3	1	0
Chloroaceto Phenone C₆H₅COCH₂Cl (Phenacyl Chloride)	244				1.32	5.32	477	No		2	1	0
2—Chloro—4, 6—di— tert—Amylphenol (C₅H₁₁)₂C₆H₂ClOH	250				1.0+		320–354 @ 22 mm.		Water or foam may cause frothing.	2	1	0
Chloro—4—tert— Amylphenol C₅H₁₁C₆H₃ClOH	225				1.1		487–509		Water or foam may cause frothing.	2	1	0
2—Chloro—4—tert— Amylphenyl Methyl Ether C₅H₁₁C₆H₃ClOCH₃	230				1.1	7.3	518–529		Water or foam may cause frothing.	1	1	0
Chlorobenzene C₆H₅Cl (Chlorobenzol) (Monochlorobenzene) (Phenyl Chloride)	84 (Und. Lab. Class 40–50) Note: See Hazardous Chemicals Data.	1184	1.3	7.1	1.1	3.9	270	No	Water may be ineffective except as a blanket.	2	3	0
Chlorobenzol	See Chlorobenzene.											
Chlorobenzotrifluoride ClC₆H₄CF₃	117				1.35	6.24	282				2	0
o—Chlorobenzotri- flouride ClC₆H₄CF₃ (o—Chloro—α, α, α— triflurotoluene)	138				1.4	6.2	306			2	2	1
Chlorobutadiene	See 2—Chloro—1, 3—Butadiene.											
2—Chloro—1, 3— Butadiene CH₂:CCl:CH:CH₂ (Chlorobutadiene) (Chloroprene)	−4		4.0	20.0	1.0	3.0	138	Slight	Water may be ineffective. "Alcohol" foam.	2	3	0
1—Chlorobutane	See Butyl Chloride.											
2—Chlorobutene—2 CH₃CCl:CHCH₃	−3		2.3	9.3	0.9	3.1	143–159	Very slight	Water may be ineffective.	2	3	0
Chlorodiethylaluminum	See Diethylaluminum Chloride.											
Chlorodinitrobenzene	See Dinitrochlorobenzene.											
Chloroethane	See Ethyl Chloride.											
2—Chloroethanol CH₂ClCH₂OH (2—Chloroethyl Alcohol) (Ethylene Chlorohydrin)	140 (oc)	797	4.9	15.9	1.2	2.8	264–266	Yes	"Alcohol" foam.	3	2	0
Chloroethyl Acetate C₂H₄ClOOCCH₃	129				1.2	4.2	293	No	Water may be used to blanket fire.	2	2	0

Table 3-11A (cont.)

	FLASH POINT Deg. F.	IGNITION TEMP. Deg. F.	FLAMMABLE LIMITS Per Cent by Vol. Lower	Upper	Sp. Gr. (Water =1)	Vapor Density (Air =1)	Boiling Point Deg. F.	Water Soluble	EXTINGUISHNG METHOD See Intro.	Health	Flamma-bility	Reac-tivity
2—Chloroethyl Acetate $CH_3COOCH_2CH_2Cl$	151				1.2	4.2	291	No	Water may be used to blanket fire.	2	2	0
2—Chloroethyl Alcohol	See 2—Chloroethanol.											
Chloro—4—Ethylbenzene $C_2H_5C_6H_4Cl$	147				1.0+	4.9	364	No		1	2	0
Chloroethylene	See Vinyl Chloride.											
2—Chloroethyl Vinyl Ether	See Vinyl 2—Chloroethyl Ether.											
2—Chloroethyl—2— Xenyl Ether $C_6H_5C_6H_4OCH_2CH_2Cl$	320				1.1		613	Slight	Water or foam may cause frothing. "Alcohol" foam.		1	0
1—Chlorohexane $CH_3(CH_2)_4CH_2Cl$ (Hexyl Chloride)	95				0.9	4.2	270	No	Water may be ineffective.		3	0
Chloroisopropyl Alcohol	See 1—Chloro—2—Propanol.											
Chloromethane	See Methyl Chloride.											
1—Chloro—2—Methyl Propane	See Isobutyl Chloride.											
1—Chloronaphthalene $C_{10}H_7Cl$	270 (oc)	>1036			1.2	5.6	505	No	Water or foam may cause frothing.	1	1	0
2—Chloro—5—Nitro-benzotriflouride $C_6H_3CF_3(2$—Cl, 5—$NO_2)$ (2—Chloro—α, α, α—Trifluro—5—Nitrotoluene)	275				1.6		446		Water or foam may cause frothing.		1	3
1—Chloro—1—Nitro-ethane $C_2H_4NO_2Cl$	133 (oc)				1.3	3.8	344	Slight	"Alcohol" foam.		2	3
1—Chloro—1—Nitro-propane $CHNO_2ClC_2H_5$	144 (oc)				1.2	4.3	285	Slight	"Alcohol" foam.		2	3
2—Chloro—2—Nitro-propane $CH_3CNO_2ClCH_3$	135 (oc)				1.2	4.3	273 Explodes upon rapid heating	Slight	Explodes on heating.		2	3
1—Chloropentane	See Amyl Chloride.											
β—Chlorophenetole $C_6H_5OCH_2CH_2C$ (β—Phenoxyethyl Chloride)	225				1.1		306–311	Slight	"Alcohol" foam. Water or foam may cause frothing.		1	0
o—Chlorophenol ClC_6H_4OH	147				1.3		347	Slight	"Alcohol" foam.	3	2	0
p—Chlorophenol C_6H_4OHCl	250				1.31	4.43	428			3	1	0
2—Chloro—4—Phenyl-phenol $C_6H_5C_6H_3ClOH$	345				<1		613	Slight	Water or foam may cause frothing. "Alcohol" foam.	2	1	0
	Note: Melting point 172–176°F.											
Chloroprene	See 2—Chloro—1, 3—Butadiene.											
1—Chloropropane	See Propyl Chloride.											
2—Chloropropane	See Isopropyl Chloride.											
2—Chloro—1—Propanol $CH_3CHClCH_2OH$ (β—Chloropropyl Alcohol) (Propylene Chlorohydrin)	125				1.1	3.3	271–273	Yes	"Alcohol" foam.	2	2	0
1—Chloro—2—Propanol $CH_2ClCHOHCH_3$ (Chloroisopropyl Alcohol) (sec—Propylene Chlorohydrin)	125 (oc)				1.1	3.3	261	Yes	"Alcohol" foam.	2	2	0
1—Chloro—1—Propene	See 1—Chloropropylene.											
3—Chloropropene	See Allyl Chloride.											
α—Chloropropionic Acid $CH_3CHClCOOH$	225				1.3		352–374	Yes	"Alcohol" foam. Water or foam may cause frothing.		1	0
3—Chloropropionitrile $ClCH_2CH_2CN$	168				1.1	3.0	348.8 Decomposes	Yes	"Alcohol" foam.		2	1
β—Chloropropyl Alcohol	See 2—Chloro—1—Propanol.											

Table 3-11A (cont.)	FLASH POINT Deg. F.	IGNI- TION TEMP. Deg. F.	FLAMMABLE LIMITS Per Cent by Vol.		Sp. Gr. (Water = 1)	Vapor Density (Air = 1)	Boiling Point Deg. F.	Water Soluble	EXTINGUISHING METHOD See Intro.	SUGGESTED HAZARD IDENTIFICATION		
			Lower	Upper						Health	Flamma- bility	Reac- tivity
1—Chloropropylene CH₃CH:CHCl (1—Chloro—1—Propene)	<21		4.5	16	0.9		95–97		Water may be ineffective.	2	4	2
2—Chloro Propylene CH₃CCl:CH₂ (βChloropropylene) (2—Chloropropene)	<—4		4.5	16	0.93	2.63	73			2	4	0
2—Chloropropylene Oxide	See Epichlorohydrin.											
γ—Chloropropylene Oxide	See Epichlorohydrin.											
Chlorotoluene C₆H₄ClCH₃ (Tolyl Chloride)	126 (oc)				1.08	4.37	320			2	2	0
α—Chlorotoluene	See Benzyl Chloride.											
Chlorotrifluoroethylene FCCl:CF₂	Gas		8.4	38.7			—18		Stop flow of gas.	3	4	2
2—Chloro—α, α, α— Trifluoro—5— Nitrotoluene	See 2—Chloro—5—Nitrobenzotrifluoride.											
o—Chloro—α, α, α— Trifluorotoluene	See o—Chlorobenzotrifluoride.											
Cimene	See Dipentene.											
Cinnamene	See Styrene.											
Cleaning Solvent, Kerosene Type	>100	444						No		0	2	0
Cleaning Solvents, 140°F Class	138.2 or higher	453.2 or higher	0.8 @ 302°				Initial 357.8 or higher	No		0	2	0
Coal Gas	See Gas.											
Coal Oil	See Fuel Oil No. 1.											
Coal Tar Light Oil	<80			<1				No		2	3	0
Coal Tar Pitch	405			>1				No	Water or foam may cause frothing.	0	1	0
Cobalt Naphtha (Cobalt Naphthenate)	121	529			0.9			No		1	2	0
Cobalt Naphthenate	See Cobalt Naphtha.											
Cocoanut Oil Refined Crude	420 548 420		Note: Melting point 72°F.		0.9			No	Water or foam may cause frothing.	0	1	0
Cod Liver Oil	412				0.9			No	Water or foam may cause frothing.	0	1	0
Collodion C₁₂H₁₆O₆(NO₃)₄- C₁₃H₁₇O₇(NO₃)₃ Solution of Nitrated Cellulose in Ether- Alcohol	<0								Water may be ineffective. "Alcohol" foam.	1	4	0
Cologne Spirits	See Ethyl Alcohol.											
Columbian Spirits	See Methyl Alcohol.											
Colza Oil	See Rape Seed Oil.											
Corn Oil	490	740			0.9			No	Water or foam may cause frothing.			
Cooking	610 (oc)			<1					Water or foam may cause frothing.	0	1	0
Cottonseed Oil Refined	486	650			0.9			No	Water or foam may cause frothing.			
Cooking	610 (oc)			<1				No	Water or foam may cause frothing.	0	1	0
Cresote Oil	165	637		>1			382–752	No	Water may be used to blanket fire.	2	2	0
o—Cresol CH₃C₆H₄OH (Cresylic Acid) (o—Hydroxytoluene) (o—Methyl Phenol)	178	1110	1.4 @ 300° Note: Melting point 88°F. See Hazardous Chemicals Data.		1.1	3.7	376	No	Water may be used to blanket fire.	2	2	0
m—or—p—Cresol CH₃C₆H₄OH	202	1038	1.1 @ 302° Note: Melting point of meta: 53.6°F; of para: 94.6°F. See Hazardous Chemicals Data.		1.0		395	No		2	1	0

Table 3-11A (cont.)	FLASH POINT Deg. F.	IGNI- TION TEMP. Deg. F.	FLAMMABLE LIMITS Per Cent by Vol. Lower	Upper	Sp. Gr. (Water = 1)	Vapor Density (Air = 1)	Boiling Point Deg. F.	Water Soluble	EXTINGUISHING METHOD See Intro.	SUGGESTED HAZARD IDENTIFICATION Health	Flamma- bility	Reac- tivity
Cresyl Diphenyl Phosphate $(C_6H_5O)_2[(CH_3)_2C_6H_4O]PO_4$	450				1.2		734		Water or foam may cause frothing.	0	1	0
Cresylic Acid	See o—Cresol.											
Crotonaldehyde $CH_3CH:CHCHO$ (2—Butenal) (Crotonic Aldehyde) (Propylene Aldehyde)	55	450	2.1	15.5	0.9	2.4	216	Slight	Water may be ineffective. "Alcohol" foam.	3	3	2
	Note: See Hazardous Chemicals Data.											
Crotonic Acid $CH_3CH:CHCOOH$	190 (oc)		1.0— @ 176°F	3.0			372	Yes	"Alcohol" foam.	3	2	0
	Note: Melting point 162°F.											
Crotonic Aldehyde	See Crotonaldehyde.											
Crotononitrile $CH_3CH:CHCN$ (2—Butenenitrile)	<212				0.8	2.3	230–240.8	No			1	0
Crotonyl Alcohol $CH_3CH:CHCH_2OH$ (2—Buten—1—ol)	91				0.85	2.49	237	To 16%			3	2
1—Crotyl Bromide $CH_3CH:CHCH_2Br$ (1—Bromo—2—butene)			4.6	12.0		4.66				2	3	2
1—Crotyl Chloride $CH_3CH:CHCH_2Cl$ (1—Chloro—2—butene)			4.2	19.0		3.13				2	3	2
Cumene $C_6H_5CH(CH_3)_2$ (Cumol) (2—Phenyl Propane) (Isopropyl Benzene)	111	797	0.9	6.5	0.9	4.1	306	No		0	2	0
Cumene Hydroperoxide $C_6H_5C(CH_3)_2OOH$	175						Explodes on heating.	Slight		1	2	4
	Note: See Hazardous Chemicals Data.											
Cumol	See Cumene.											
Cyanamide NH_2CN	286				1.07	1.45	500 Decomposes			4	1	3
	Note: Melting point 111°F.											
2—Cyanoethyl Acrylate $CH_2CHCOOCH_2CH_2CN$	255 (oc)				1.1	4.3	Poly- merizes	No	Water or foam may cause frothing.	2	1	1
N—(2—Cyanoethyl) Cyclohexylamine $C_6H_{11}NHC_2H_4CN$	255 (oc)				0.9	5.2		No	Water or foam may cause frothing.	2	1	0
Cyanogen $(CN)_2$	Gas		6.6	32	1.8		−6		Stop flow of gas.	4	4	3
	Note: See Hazardous Chemicals Data.											
Cyclobutane C_4H_8 (Tetramethylene)	Gas				1.9		55	No	Stop flow of gas.	1	4	0
Cycloheptane $CH_2(CH_2)_5CH_2$	<70				0.81	3.39	246			0	3	0
Cyclohexane C_6H_{12} (Hexahydrobenzene) (Hexamethylene)	− 4	473	1.3	8	0.8	2.9	179	No	Water may be ineffective.	1	3	0
	(Und. Lab. Class 90–95)											
Cyclohexanol $C_6H_{11}OH$ (Anol) (Hexalin) (Hydralin)	154	572			1.0—	3.5	322	Slight	"Alcohol" foam.	1	2	0
	Note: Melting point 75°F.											
Cyclohexanone $C_6H_{10}O$ (Pimelic Ketone)	111	788	1.1 @ 212°		0.9	3.4	313	Slight	"Alcohol" foam.	1	2	0
	(Und. Lab. Class 35–40)											
Cyclohexene $CH_2CH_2CH_2CH_2CH:CH$	<20	590			0.8	2.8	181	No	Water may be ineffective.	1	3	0
3—Cyclohexene—1— Carboxaldehyde	See 1, 2, 3, 6—Tetrahydrobenzaldehyde.											
Cyclohexenone△ C_6H_8O	93					3.3	313		Water may be ineffective.	1	3	0
Cyclohexyl Acetate $CH_3CO_2C_6H_{11}$ (Hexalin Acetate)	136	635			1.0—	4.9	350	No		1	2	0
Cyclohexylamine $C_6H_{11}NH_2$ (Amino Cyclohexane) (Hexahydroaniline)	90 (oc)	560			0.9	3.4	274	Yes	Water may be ineffective. "Alcohol" foam.	2	3	0
	Note: See Hazardous Chemicals Data.											

Table 3-11A (cont.)

	FLASH POINT Deg. F.	IGNI-TION TEMP. Deg. F.	FLAMMABLE LIMITS Per Cent by Vol. Lower	FLAMMABLE LIMITS Per Cent by Vol. Upper	Sp. Gr. (Water =1)	Vapor Density (Air =1)	Boiling Point Deg. F.	Water Soluble	EXTINGUISHING METHOD See Intro.	SUGGESTED HAZARD IDENTIFICATION Health	Flamma-bility	Reac-tivity
Cyclohexylbenzene $C_6H_5C_6H_{11}$ (Phenylcyclohexane)	210 (oc)				0.9		459	No		2	1	0
Cyclohexyl Chloride $CH_2(CH_2)_4CHCl$ (Chlorocyclohexane)	90				0.99	4.08	288			2	3	0
Cyclohexylcyclohexanol $C_6H_{11}C_6H_{10}OH$	270				1.0 —		304–313	No	Water or foam may cause frothing.	0	1	0
Cyclohexyl Formate $CH_2(CH_2)_4HCOOCH$	124				1.01	4.42	324				2	0
Cyclohexylmethane	See Methylcyclohexane.											
o—Cyclohexylphenol $C_6H_{11}C_6H_4OH$	273 Note: Melting point 116°F.				1.0 +		298 @ 10 mm.	Slight	"Alcohol" foam. Water or foam may cause frothing.	2	1	0
Cyclohexyltrichloro-silane $C_6H_{11}SiCl_3$	196 (oc)				1.2	7.5	406	No	Water may be used to blanket fire.	2	2	1
Cyclopentane C_5H_{10}	<20	716			0.7	2.4	121	No	Water may be ineffective.	1	3	0
Cyclopentanol $CH_2(CH_2)_3CHOH$	124				0.95	2.97	286			0	2	0
Cyclopentanone $OCCH_2CH_2CH_2CH_2$ (Adipic Ketone)	79				0.9	2.3	267	Slight	Water may be ineffective. "Alcohol" foam.	2	3	0
Cyclopropane $(CH_2)_3$ (Trimethylene)	Gas	932	2.4	10.4		1.5	−29	No	Stop flow of gas.	1	4	0
p—Cymene $CH_3C_6H_4CH(CH_3)_2$ Tech. (4—Isopropyl—1—Methyl Benzene)	117 127	817 833	0.7 @ 212°	5.6	0.9	4.6	349 (Und. Lab. Class 30–35)	No		2	2	0
DDS	See Dimethyldichlorosilane.											
Decahydronapthalene $C_{10}H_{18}$ (Decalin)	136	482	0.7 @ 212°	4.9 @ 212°	0.9	4.8	382	No		2	2	0
Decahydronaphthalene—trans $C_{10}H_{18}$	129	491	0.7	5.4	0.87	4.77	369			0	2	0
Decalin	See Decahydronaphthalene.											
Decane $CH_3(CH_2)_8CH_3$	115	410	0.8	5.4	0.7	4.9	345	No		0	2	0
Decanol $CH_3(CH_2)_8CH_2OH$ (Decyl Alcohol)	180 (oc)				0.8	5.5	444.2	No		0	2	0
1—Decene $CH_3(CH_2)_7CH{:}CH_2$	<131	455			0.74	4.84	342			0	2	0
Decyl Acrylate $CH_3(CN_2)_9OCOCH{:}CH_2$	441 (oc)				0.9		316 @ 50 mm.	Very slight	Water or foam may cause frothing.	2	1	0
Decyl Alcohol	See Decanol.											
Decylamine $CH_3(CH_2)_9NH_2$ (1—Aminodecane)	210				0.8		429	Slight	"Alcohol" foam.	2	1	0
Decylbenzene $C_{10}H_{21}C_6H_5$	225				0.9		491–536	No	Water or foam may cause frothing.	2	1	0
tert—Decylmercaptan $C_{10}H_{21}SH$	190				0.9	6.0	410–424			2	2	0
Decylnaphthalene $C_{10}H_{21}C_{10}H_7$	350				0.9		635–680	No	Water or foam may cause frothing.	1	1	0
Decyl Nitrate $CH_3(CH_2)_9ONO_2$	235 (oc)				1.0 —		261 @ 11 mm.	No	Water or foam may cause frothing.		1	0

Table 3-11A (cont.)	FLASH POINT Deg. F.	IGNI- TION TEMP. Deg. F.	FLAMMABLE LIMITS Per Cent by Vol. Lower	FLAMMABLE LIMITS Per Cent by Vol. Upper	Sp. Gr. (Water = 1)	Vapor Density (Air = 1)	Boiling Point Deg. F.	Water Soluble	EXTINGUISHING METHOD See Intro.	SUGGESTED HAZARD IDENTIFICATION Health	Flamma- bility	Reac- tivity
Denatured Alcohol	60	750			0.8	1.6	175	Yes	Water may be ineffective. "Alcohol" foam.	0	3	0
	(Und. Lab. Class 70)											
Government Formula												
CD-5	60–62											
CD-5A	60–61											
CD-10	49–59											
SD-1	57											
SD-2B	56											
SD-3A	59											
SD-13A	<19											
SD-17	60											
SD-23A	35											
SD-30	59											
SD-39B	60											
SD-39C	59											
SD-40M	59											
Deuterium D_2 (Heavy Hydrogen)	Gas		5	75					Stop flow of gas.	0	4	0
Diacetone	See Diacetone Alcohol.											
Diacetone Alcohol $CH_3COCH_2C(CH_3)_2OH$	148	1118	1.8	6.9	0.9	4.0	328	Yes	"Alcohol" foam.	1	2	0
Acetone-free	136	1190										
Commercial (Diacetone) (4—Hydroxy—4— Methyl—2—Pentanone)	148	1118										
Diacetyl	See 2, 3—Butanedione.											
Diallyl Ether	See Allyl Ether.											
Diallyl Phthalate $C_6H_4(CO_2C_3H_5)_2$	330				1.1		554	No	Water or foam may cause frothing.	2	1	0
1, 3—Diaminobutane	See 1, 3—Butanediamine.											
1, 3—Diamino—2— Propanol $NH_2CH_2CHOHCH_2NH_2$	270				1.1		266	Yes	Water or foam may cause frothing. "Alcohol" foam.	2	1	0
1, 3—Diaminopropane	See 1, 3—Propanediamine.											
Diamylamine $(C_5H_{11})_2NH$	124				0.8	5.4	356	Slight	"Alcohol" foam.	3	2	0
	Note: See Hazardous Chemicals Data.											
Diamylbenzene $(C_5H_{11})_2C_6H_4$	225 (oc)				0.9		491–536	No	Water or foam may cause frothing.	0	1	0
Diamylbiphenyl $C_5H_{11}(C_6H_4)_2C_5H_{11}$ (Diaminodiphenyl)	340				1.0—		687–759	No	Water or foam may cause frothing.	0	1	0
Di—tert—Amylcyclo- hexanol $(C_5H_{11})_2C_6H_9OH$	270				0.9		554–572	No	Water or foam may cause frothing.	0	1	0
Diamyldiphenyl	See Diamylbiphenyl.											
Diamylene $C_{10}H_{20}$	118 (oc)				0.8		302			0	2	0
Diamyl Ether	See Amyl Ether.											
Diamyl Maleate $(CHCOOC_5H_{11})_2$	270				1.0—		505–572	No	Water or foam may cause frothing.	0	1	0
Diamyl Napthalene $C_{10}H_6(C_5H_{11})_2$	315 (oc)				0.9		624	No	Water or foam may cause frothing.	0	1	0
Diamyl Oxalate $(COOC_5H_{11})_2$	257				1.0—		500–572	No	Water or foam may cause frothing.	0	1	0
2, 4—Diamylphenol $(C_5H_{11})_2C_6H_3OH$	260 (oc)				0.9		527	No	Water or foam may cause frothing.	2	1	0
Di—tert—amylphenoxy Ethanol $C_6H_3(C_5H_{11})_2OC_2H_4OH$	300 (oc)				1.0—		615	No	Water or foam may cause frothing.	0	1	0
Diamyl Phthalate $C_6H_4(COOC_5H_{11})_2$ (Amyl Phthalate)	245				1.0		475–490 @ 50 mm.	No	Water or foam may cause frothing.	0	1	0
Diamyl Sulfide $(C_5H_{11})_2S$	185 (oc)				0.9		338–356	No		2	2	0
o—Dianisidine $[NH_2(OCH_3)C_6H_3]_2$ (o—Dimethoxybenzidine)	403					8.43					1	0
	Note: Melting point 297°F.											

Table 3-11A (cont.)

	FLASH POINT Deg. F.	IGNI-TION TEMP. Deg. F.	FLAMMABLE LIMITS Per Cent by Vol. Lower	Upper	Sp. Gr. (Water = 1)	Vapor Density (Air = 1)	Boiling Point Deg. F.	Water Soluble	EXTINGUISHING METHOD See Intro.	Health	Flamma-bility	Reac-tivity
Dibenzyl Ether $(C_6H_5CH_2)_2O$ (Benzyl Ether)	275				1.0		568	No	Water or foam may cause frothing.	0	1	0
Diborane B_2H_6	Gas	100–125	0.8	88		1.0–			Stop flow of gas. Reacts violently with halogenated extinguishing agents.	3	4	3 ₩
Note: Ignites spontaneously in moist air. See Hazardous Chemicals Data.												
Dibutoxymethane $CH_2(OC_4H_9)_2$	140				0.8		330–370	No		0	2	0
Note: Melting point 140°F.												
Dibutoxy Tetraglycol $(C_4H_9OC_2H_4OC_2H_4)_2O$ (Tetraethylene Glycol Dibutyl Ether)	305 (oc)				0.9		635	Slight	Water or foam may cause frothing. "Alcohol" foam.	2	1	0
N, N—Dibutylacetamide $CH_3CON(C_4H_9)_2$	225				0.9		469–482		Water or foam may cause frothing.	0	1	0
Dibutylamine $(C_4H_9)_2NH$	125 (oc)				0.8	4.5	322	Slight	"Alcohol" foam.	3	2	0
Di—sec—Butylamine $[C_2H_5(CH_3)CH]_2NH$	75 (oc)				0.8	4.5	270–275	Yes	"Alcohol" foam.	3	3	0
Dibutylamino-ethanol $(C_4H_9)_2NC_2H_4OH$	200 (oc)				0.9		432	No		3	2	0
1—Dibutylamino—2—Propanol	See Dibutylisopropanolamine.											
N, N—Dibutylaniline $C_6H_5N(CH_2CH_2CH_2CH_3)_2$	230				0.9		505–527	No	Water or foam may cause frothing.	3	1	0
Di—tert—Butyl—p—Cresol $C_6H_2(C_4H_9)_2(CH_3)OH$	261						495–511	No	Water or foam may cause frothing.	0	1	0
Note: Melting point 154.4°F.												
Dibutyl Ether $(C_4H_9)_2O$ (1—Butoxybutane) (Butyl Ether)	77	382	1.5	7.6	0.8	4.5	286	No	Water may be ineffective. "Alcohol" foam.	2	3	0
Note: See Hazardous Chemicals Data.												
Dibutyl Isophthalate $C_6H_4(CO_2C_4H_9)_2$	322							No	Water or foam may cause frothing.	0	1	0
Dibutylisopropanol-amine $CH_3CHOHCH_2N(C_4H_9)_2$	205 (oc)				0.8		444	Slight	"Alcohol" foam.	2	1	0
Dibutyl Maleate $(—CHCO_2C_4H_9)_2$	285 (oc)				1.0–		Decom-poses		Water or foam may cause frothing.	1	1	0
Dibutyl Oxalate $C_4H_9OOCCOOC_4H_9$	220				1.0+		472	No	Water or foam may cause frothing.	0	1	0
Di—tert—Butyl Peroxide $(CH_3)_3COOC(CH_3)_3$	65 (oc)				0.8		231	Slight	Water may be ineffective.	2	3	4
Note: See Hazardous Chemicals Data.												
Dibutyl Phosphite $(C_4H_9O)_2P(O)H$	120				1.0–		239			3	2	0
Dibutyl Phthalate $C_6H_4(CO_2C_4H_9)_2$	315	757			1.0+		690	No	Water or foam may cause frothing.	0	1	0
Dibutyl Sebacate $[(CH_2)_4COOC_4H_9]_2$	353 (oc)				1.0–		650	No	Water or foam may cause frothing.	0	1	0
N, N—Dibutyl Steara-mide $C_{17}H_{35}CON(C_4H_9)_2$	420				0.9		343–347 @ 0.4 mm.	No	Water or foam may cause frothing.	0	1	0
N, N—Dibutyltoluene-sulfonamide $CH_3C_6H_4SO_3N(C_4H_9)_2$	330				1.1		392 @ 10 mm.		Water or foam may cause frothing.	0	1	0
Dicaproate	See Triethylene Glycol.											
Dicapryl Phthalate $C_6H_4[COOCH(CH_3)C_6H_{13}]_2$	395				1.0–	9.8	441–453 @ 4.5 mm.	No	Water or foam may cause frothing.	0	1	0
Dichloroacetyl Chloride $CHCl_2COCl$ (Dichloroethanoyl Chloride)	151					5.1	225–226	De-com-poses	"Alcohol" foam.	3	2	1 ₩
3, 4—Dichloroaniline $NH_2C_6H_3Cl_2$	331 (oc)						522	No	Water or foam may cause frothing.	3	1	0
Note: Melting point 161°F. See Hazardous Chemicals Data.												

Table 3-11A
(cont.)

	FLASH POINT Deg. F.	IGNITION TEMP. Deg. F.	FLAMMABLE LIMITS Per Cent by Vol. Lower	Upper	Sp. Gr. (Water =1)	Vapor Density (Air =1)	Boiling Point Deg. F.	Water Soluble	EXTINGUISHING METHOD See Intro.	SUGGESTED HAZARD IDENTIFICATION Health	Flamma-bility	Reac-tivity
o—Dichlorobenzene $C_6H_4Cl_2$ (o—Dichlorobenzol)	151	1198	2.2	9.2	1.3	5.1	356	No	Water may be used to blanket fire.	2	2	0
			Note: See Hazardous Chemicals Data.									
p—Dichlorobenzene $C_6H_4Cl_2$	150				1.5	5.1	345	No	Water may be used to blanket fire.	2	2	0
			Note: Melting point 127°F.									
o—Dichlorobenzol	See o—Dichlorobenzene.											
1, 2—Dichlorobutane $CH_3CH_2CHClCH_2Cl$		527				4.38				2	2	0
1, 4—Dichlorobutane $CH_2ClCH_2CH_2CH_2Cl$	126				1.1	4.4	311	No	Water may be used to blanket fire.	2	2	0
			Note: See Hazardous Chemicals Data.									
2, 3—Dichlorobutane $CH_3CHClCHClCH_3$	194 (oc)				1.1	4.4	241–253			2	2	0
1, 3—Dichlorobutene—2 $CH_2ClCH:CClCH_3$	80					4.3	258		Water may be ineffective.	2	3	0
Dichlorodimethylsilane	See Dimethyldichlorosilane.											
1, 1—Dichloroethane	See Ethylidene Dichloride.											
1, 2—Dichloroethane	See Ethylene Dichloride.											
Dichloroethanoyl Chloride	See Dichloroacetyl Chloride.											
1, 1—Dichloroethylene	See Vinylidene Chloride.											
1, 2—Dichloroethylene $ClCH:CHCl$	43		9.7	12.8	1.3	3.4	141	No	Water may be ineffective except as a blanket.	2	3	2
Dichloroethylene—cis $CHCl:CHCl$ (Acetylene Dichloride—cis)	39		9.7	12.8	1.3	3.3	140	No	Water may be ineffective except as a blanket.	2	3	2
Dichloroethylene—trans $CHCl:CHCl$ (Acetylene Dichloride—trans)	36	860	9.7	12.8	1.3	3.3	119	No	Water may be ineffective except as a blanket.	2	3	2
2, 2—Dichloroethyl Formal	See Bis(2—Chloroethyl) Formal.											
Di—(2—Chloroethyl) Formal	See Bis(2—Chloroethyl) Formal.											
1, 3—Dichloro— 2, 4—Hexadiene $CH_2ClCH:CClCH:CHCH_3$	168										2	0
Dichloroisopropyl Ether $ClCH_2CH(CH_3)OCH-(CH_3)CH_2Cl$ (Bis (β—Chloroisopropyl) Ether)	185 (oc)				1.1	6.0	369	No	Water may be used to blanket fire.	2	2	0
2, 2—Dichloro Isopropyl Ether $[ClCH_2CH(CH_3)]_2O$ (Bis (2—Chloro—1—methylethyl) Ether)	185 (oc)				1.11	5.90	369			2	2	0
Dichloromethane	See Methylene Chloride.											
1, 1—Dichloro—1—Nitro Ethane $CH_3CCl_2NO_2$	168 (oc)				1.4	5.0	255	No	Water may be used to blanket fire.	2	2	3
1, 1—Dichloro—1—Nitro Propane $C_2H_5CCl_2NO_2$	151 (oc)				1.3	5.5	289	Slight	"Alcohol" foam.	2	2	3
Dichloropentanes (Mixed) $C_5H_{10}Cl_2$	106 (oc)				1.0+	4.8	266	No		2	2	0
1, 5—Dichloropentane $CH_2Cl(CH_2)_3CH_2Cl$ (Amylene Chloride) (Pentamethylene Dichloride)	>80 (oc)				1.1	4.9	352–358	No	Water may be ineffective except as a blanket.	2	3	0
2, 4—Dichlorophenol $Cl_2C_6H_3OH$	237				1.4 @ 140°F		410	Slight	"Alcohol" foam. Water or foam may cause frothing.		1	0
			Note: Melting point 113°F.									
1, 2—Dichloropropane	See Propylene Dichloride.											
1, 3—Dichloro—2—Propanol $CH_2ClCHOHCH_2Cl$	165 (oc)				1.4	4.4	346	Slight	"Alcohol" foam.	2	2	0
1, 3—Dichloropropene $CHCl:CHCH_2Cl$	95				1.2	3.8	219	No		2	3	0
α, β—Dichlorostyrene $C_6H_5CCl:CHCl$	225 (oc)							No	Water or foam may cause frothing.	2	1	2
Dicyclohexyl	See Bicyclohexyl.											

Table 3-11A (cont.)	FLASH POINT Deg. F.	IGNI- TION TEMP. Deg. F.	FLAMMABLE LIMITS Per Cent by Vol. Lower	Upper	Sp. Gr. (Water = 1)	Vapor Density (Air = 1)	Boiling Point Deg. F.	Water Soluble	EXTINGUISHING METHOD See Intro.	Health	Flamma- bility	Reac- tivity
Dicyclohexylamine (C$_6$H$_{11}$)$_2$NH	>210 (oc)				0.9		496	Slight	"Alcohol" foam.	3	1	0
Dicyclopentadiene C$_{10}$H$_{12}$	90 (oc)		1.0 — Note: Melting point 91°F.				342	No	Water may be ineffective.	1	3	1
Didecyl Ether (C$_{10}$H$_{21}$)$_2$O (Decyl Ether)		419				10.3				0	1	0
Diesel Fuel Oil No. 1-D	100 Min. or Legal							No		0	2	0
Diesel Fuel Oil No. 2-D	125 Min. or Legal							No		0	2	0
Diesel Fuel Oil No. 4-D	130 Min. or Legal							No		0	2	0
Diethanolamine (HOCH$_2$CH$_2$)$_2$NH	305 (oc) Note: Melting point 82°F.	1224			1.1		514	Yes	"Alcohol" foam. Water or foam may cause frothing.	1	1	0
1, 2—Diethoxyethane	See Diethyl Glycol.											
Diethylacetaldehyde	See 2—Ethylbutyraldehyde.											
Diethylacetic Acid	See 2—Ethylbutyric Acid.											
N, N—Diethylaceto- acetamide CH$_3$COCH$_2$CON(C$_2$H$_5$)$_2$	250 (oc)		1.0 —	5.4			Decom- poses	Yes	Water or foam may cause frothing. "Alcohol" foam.	0	1	0
Diethyl Acetoacetate CH$_3$COC(C$_2$H$_5$)$_2$COOC$_2$H$_5$	170		1.0 —	6.4			412–424 Decom- poses	Very slight		2	2	0
Diethylaluminium Chloride (C$_2$H$_5$)$_2$AlCl (Chlorodiethylaluminum)	Note: Ignites spontaneously in air. See Hazardous Chemicals Data.								Do not use water, foam or halogenated extinguishing agents.	3	3	3 W
Diethylaluminum Hydride (C$_2$H$_5$)$_2$AlH	Note: Ignites spontaneously in air.								Do not use water, foam or halogenated extinguishing agents.		3	3 W
Diethylamine (C$_2$H$_5$)$_2$NH	<0 Note: See Hazardous Chemicals Data.	594	1.8	10.1	0.7	2.5	134	Yes	"Alcohol" foam. Water may be ineffective.	2	3	0
2—Diethyl (amino)- ethanol	See N, N—Diethylethanolamine.											
2—(Diethylamino) ethyl Acrylate CH$_2$:CHCOOCH$_2$CH$_2$- HN(CH$_3$CH$_2$)$_2$	195 (oc)				0.9	5.9	Decom- poses	De- com- poses		2	2	1
3—(Diethylamino)- propylamine (C$_2$H$_5$)$_2$NCH$_2$CH$_2$CH$_2$NH$_2$ (N, N—Diethyl—1, 3— Propanediamine)	138 (oc)				0.8	4.5	337	Yes	"Alcohol" foam.	2	2	0
N, N—Diethylaniline C$_6$H$_5$N(C$_2$H$_5$)$_2$ (Phenyldiethylamine)	185	1166	1.0 —			5.0	421	Slight	"Alcohol" foam.	3	2	0
o—Diethyl Benzene C$_6$H$_4$(C$_2$H$_5$)$_2$	135	743			0.9	4.6	362	No		2	2	0
m—Diethyl Benzene C$_6$H$_4$(C$_2$H$_5$)$_2$	133	842			0.9	4.6	358	No		2	2	0
p—Diethyl Benzene C$_6$H$_4$(C$_2$H$_5$)$_2$	134	806			0.9	4.6	363	No		2	2	0
N, N—Diethyl—1, 3— Butanediamine C$_2$H$_5$NHCH$_2$CH$_2$CH- N(C$_2$H$_5$)CH$_3$ (1, 3—Bis(ethylamino) Butane)	115 (oc)				0.8	5.0	354–365	Yes	"Alcohol" foam.	2	2	0
Diethyl Carbinol	See sec—Amyl Alcohol.											
Diethyl Carbonate (C$_2$H$_5$)$_2$CO$_3$ (Ethyl Carbonate)	77		1.0 —			4.1	259	No	Water may be ineffective.	2	3	1
Diethylcyclohexane C$_{10}$H$_{20}$	120	464	0.8 @ 140°	6.0 @ 230°	0.8		344			2	2	0
1, 3—Diethyl—1, 3— Diphenyl Urea [(C$_2$H$_5$)(C$_6$H$_5$)N]$_2$CO	302 Note: Melting point 160°F.				1.1		620		Water or foam may cause frothing.	1	1	0
Diethylene Dioxide	See p—Dioxane.											
Diethylene Glycol O(CH$_2$CH$_2$OH)$_2$ (2, 2—Dihydroxyethyl Ether)	255	444			1.1		472	Yes	"Alcohol" foam. Water or foam may cause frothing.	1	1	0

Table 3-11A
(cont.)

	FLASH POINT Deg. F.	IGNI-TION TEMP. Deg. F.	FLAMMABLE LIMITS Per Cent by Vol.		Sp. Gr. (Water = 1)	Vapor Density (Air = 1)	Boiling Point Deg. F.	Water Soluble	EXTINGUISHING METHOD See Intro.	SUGGESTED HAZARD IDENTIFICATION		
			Lower	Upper						Health	Flamma-bility	Reac-tivity
Diethylene Glycol Bis (Allylcarbonate) $(CH_2:CHCH_2OCOOCH_2-CH_2)_2O$ (Allyl Diglycol Carbonate)	378 (oc)				1.1		320 @ 2 mm.	No	Water or foam may cause frothing.	1	1	0
Diethylene Glycol Bis (2—Butyoxyethyl Carbonate) $[CH_3(CH_2)_3O(CH_2)_2OO-COCH_2CH_2]_2O$ (Butoxyethyl Diglycol Carbonate)	379				1.1		392–403 @ 2 mm.	Slight	"Alcohol" foam. Water or foam may cause frothing.	1	1	1
Diethylene Glycol Bis (Butyl Carbonate) $[CH_3(CH_2)_3OOCOCH_2-CH_2]_2O$ (Butyl Diglycol Carbonate)	372				1.1		327 @ 2 mm.	Slight	"Alcohol" foam. Water or foam may cause frothing.	1	1	1
Diethylene Glycol Bis (Phenylcarbonate) $(C_6H_5OOCOCH_2CH_2)_2O$ (Phenyl Diglycol Carbonate)	460				1.2		437–444 @ 2 mm.	No	Water or foam may cause frothing.	0	1	1
Diethylene Glycol Butyl Ether Acetate $CH_3COO(C_2H_4O)_2C_4H_9$	241 (oc)	563			0.98	7.05	475				1	0
Diethylene Glycol Diacetate $(CH_3COOC_2H_4)_2O$	275 (oc)				1.1		482	Yes	"Alcohol" foam. Water or foam may cause frothing.	1	1	0
Diethylene Glycol Dibenzoate $(C_6H_5COOCH_2CH_2)_2O$	450		1.2 @ 68°F				457 @ 5 mm.	Yes	"Alcohol" foam. Water or foam may cause frothing.	0	1	0
Diethylene Glycol Dibutyl Ether $C_4H_9O(C_2H_4O)_2C_4H_9$	245 (oc)				0.9		490	Slight	"Alcohol" foam. Water or foam may cause frothing.	1	1	0
Diethylene Glycol Diethyl Ether $CH_3(CH_2OCH_2)_3CH_3$	180 (oc)				0.9	5.6	372	Yes	"Alcohol" foam.	1	2	0
Diethylene Glycol Diethyl Levulinate $(CH_3COC_2H_4COOC_2H_4)_2O$	340				1.14	10.4				0	1	0
Diethylene Glycol Dipropionate $(C_2H_5COOC_2H_4)_2O$	260				1.1		491–529	Slight	"Alcohol" foam. Water or foam may cause frothing.	1	1	0
Diethylene Glycol Ethyl Ether Phthalate $C_6H_4(COO(C_2H_4O)_2C_2H_5)_2$ (Bis[2—(ethoxyethoxy)-ethyl] Phthalate) (Carbitol Phthalate)	406				1.12	13.7	>500			0	1	0
Diethylene Glycol Methyl Ether $CH_3OC_2H_4OC_2H_4OH$ (2—(2—Methoxyethoxy) ethanol)	199 (oc)				1.04	4.14	379			2	2	0
Diethylene Glycol Methyl Ether Acetate $CH_3COOC_2H_4OC_2H_4OCH_3$	180 (oc)				1.04	5.59	410			0	2	0
Diethylene Glycol Monobutyl Ether $C_4H_9OCH_2CH_2OCH_2CH_2OH$	172	442			1.0—	5.6	448	Yes	"Alcohol" foam.	1	2	0
Diethylene Glycol Monoethyl Ether $CH_2OHCH_2OCH_2-CH_2OC_2H_5$	201				1.0—		396	Yes	"Alcohol" foam.	1	1	0
Diethylene Glycol Monoethyl Ether Acetate $C_2H_5O(CH_2)_2O(CH_2)_2-OOCCH_3$	230 (oc)				1.0+		424	Yes	"Alcohol" foam. Water or foam may cause frothing.	1	1	0
Diethylene Glycol Phthalate $C_6H_4[COO(CH_2)_2OC_2H_5]_2$	343				1.1			Yes	"Alcohol" foam. Water or foam may cause frothing.	0	1	0
Diethylene Oxide	See Tetrahydrofuran.											
Diethylene Triamine $NH_2CH_2CH_2-NHCH_2CH_2NH_2$	215 (oc)	750			1.0— Note: See Hazardous Chemicals Data.		404	Yes	"Alcohol" foam. Water or foam may cause frothing.	3	1	0

Table 3-11A (cont.)

	FLASH POINT Deg. F.	IGNITION TEMP. Deg. F.	FLAMMABLE LIMITS Per Cent by Vol. Lower	Upper	Sp. Gr. (Water = 1)	Vapor Density (Air = 1)	Boiling Point Deg. F.	Water Soluble	EXTINGUISHING METHOD See Intro.	SUGGESTED HAZARD IDENTIFICATION Health	Flamma- bility	Reac- tivity
N, N—Diethylethanol- amine $(C_2H_5)_2NC_2H_4OH$ (2—(Diethylamino) ethanol)	140 (oc)				0.9	4.0	324	Yes	"Alcohol" foam.	3	2	0
Diethyl Ether	See Ethyl Ether.											
N, N—Diethylethylene- diamine $(C_2H_5)_2NC_2H_4NH_2$	115 (oc)				0.8	4.0	293	Yes	"Alcohol" foam.	3	2	0
Diethyl Fumarate $C_2H_5OCOCH:-$ $CHCOOC_2H_5$	220				1.0+ @ 68°F		422	Slight	"Alcohol" foam. Water or foam may cause frothing.	1	1	0
Diethyl Glycol $(C_2H_5OCH_2)_2$ (1, 2—Diethoxyethane)	95	401			0.84	4.07	252	Slight			3	0
Diethylhexylamine	See Bis(2—Ethylhexyl)amine.											
Diethylhexylethanol- amine	See Bis(2—Ethylhexyl)ethanolamine.											
Di(2—Ethylhexyl) Maleate	See Bis(2—Ethylhexyl)Maleate.											
Di(2—Ethylhexyl) Phosphoric Acid	See Bis(2—Ethylhexyl)Phosphoric Acid.											
Di(2—Ethylhexyl) Succinate	See Bis(2—Ethylhexyl) Succinate.											
Diethyl Ketone $C_2H_5COC_2H_5$ (3—Pentanone)	55 (oc)	842	1.6		0.8	3.0	217	Slight	Water may be ineffective. "Alcohol" foam.	1	3	0
N, N—Diethyl- lauramide $C_{11}H_{23}CON(C_2H_5)_2$	>150 (oc)				0.9	8.8	331–351 @ 2 mm.	No			2	0
Diethyl Maleate $(—CHCO_2C_2H_5)_2$	250 (oc)				1.1		438	No	Water or foam may cause frothing.	1	1	0
Diethyl Malonate $CH_2(COOC_2H_5)_2$ (Ethyl Malonate)	200 (oc)				1.1		390	No	Water may be used to blanket fire.	0	1	0
Diethyl Oxalate $(COOC_2H_5)_2$	168 (oc)				1.1	5.0	356	Gradual decom- position		1	2	0
Diethyl Oxide	See Ethyl Ether.											
3, 3—Diethylpentane CH_3CH_2C- $(C_2H_5)_2CH_2CH_3$		554	.7	5.7	0.8	4.4	295	No		0	3	0
Diethyl Peroxide $C_2H_5OOC_2H_5$		Ex- plodes on heating.	2.3		0.8	7.7	Explodes on heating.				4	4
Diethyl Phthalate $C_6H_4(COOC_2H_5)_2$	325 (oc)				1.1		565	No	Water or foam may cause frothing.	0	1	0
p—Diethyl Phthalate	See Diethyl Terephthalate.											
N, N—Diethyl—1, 3— Propanediamine	See 3—(Diethylamino)propylamine.											
2, 2—Diethyl—1, 3—Propanediol $HOCH_2C(C_2H_5)_2CH_2OH$	215 (oc) Note: Melting point 142°F.				0.9 @ 142°F		320 @ 50 mm.	Yes	"Alcohol" foam. Water or foam may cause frothing.	2	1	0
Diethyl Selenide $(C_2H_5)_2Se$			2.5		1.2	4.7	226	No		2		0
N, N—Diethylsteara- mide $C_{17}H_{35}CON(C_2H_5)_2$	375				0.9		246–401 @ 1 mm.	No	Water or foam may cause frothing.	0	1	0
Diethyl Succinate $(CH_2COOCH_2CH_3)_2$	230 (oc)				1.0+		421	Slight	"Alcohol" foam. Water or foam may cause frothing.	1	1	0
Diethyl Sulfate $(C_2H_5)_2SO_4$ (Ethyl Sulfate)	220 Note: See Hazardous Chemicals Data.	817			1.2		Decom- poses, giving Ethyl Ether	No, slight de- com- position	"Alcohol" foam. Water or foam may cause frothing.	2	1	1
Diethyl Tartrate $CHOHCOO(C_2H_5)_2$	200				1.2		536	Yes	"Alcohol" foam.	0	1	0
Diethyl Terephthalate $C_6H_4(COOC_2H_5)_2$ (p—Diethyl Phthalate)	243 Note: Melting point 112°F.				1.1		576	No	Water or foam may cause frothing.	0	1	0
3, 9—Diethyl—6— tridecanol	See Heptadecanol.											

Table 3-11A (cont.)

	FLASH POINT Deg. F.	IGNI-TION TEMP. Deg. F.	FLAMMABLE LIMITS Per Cent by Vol. Lower	Upper	Sp. Gr. (Water = 1)	Vapor Density (Air = 1)	Boiling Point Deg. F.	Water Soluble	EXTINGUISHING METHOD See Intro.	SUGGESTED HAZARD IDENTIFICATION Health	Flamma-bility	Reac-tivity
Diethylzinc (C$_2$H$_5$)$_2$Zn (Zinc Diethyl)	Note: Ignites spontaneously in air. See Hazardous Chemicals Data.								Do not use water, foam or halogenated extinguishing agents.	0	3	3 W
Difluoro—1—Chloroethane CF$_2$ClCH$_3$ (R-142B) (1—Chloro—1, 1—difluoroethane)	Gas		6.2	17.9	1.12 @ 1.12 atm	3.47	4				4	0
Diglycol Chlorformate O:(CH$_2$CH$_2$OCOCl)$_2$	295 (oc)						256–261 @ 5 mm.		Water or foam may cause frothing.	0	1	0
Diglycol Chlorohydrin HOCH$_2$CH$_2$OCH$_2$CH$_2$Cl	225 (oc)		1.2				387	Yes	"Alcohol" foam. Water or foam may cause frothing.	0	1	0
Diglycol Diacetate (CH$_3$COOCH$_2$CH$_2$)$_2$:O	255		1.1		6.5		482	Yes	Water or foam may cause frothing. "Alcohol" foam.	0	1	0
Diglycol Dilevulinate [CH$_2$CH$_2$OOC-(CH$_2$)$_2$COCH$_3$]$_2$:O	340		1.1					Yes	Water or foam may cause frothing. "Alcohol" foam.	0	1	
Diglycol Laurate C$_{16}$H$_{32}$O$_4$	290		1.0—				559–617		Water or foam may cause frothing.	0	1	0
Dihexyl	See Dodecane.											
Dihexylamine [CH$_3$(CH$_2$)$_5$]$_2$NH	220 (oc)		0.8				451–469	No	Water or foam may cause frothing.	2	1	0
Dihydropyran CH$_2$CH$_2$CH$_2$:CHCHO	0		0.9		2.9		186	Slight	"Alcohol" foam.	2	3	0
o—Dihydroxybenzene C$_6$H$_4$(OH)$_2$ (Pyrocatechol)	260		1.34		3.79		473	Slight			1	0
p—Dihydroxybenzene C$_6$H$_4$(OH)$_2$ (Hydroquinone)	329	959	1.36		3.81		547				1	0
	Note: Melting point 338°F.											
1, 2—Dihydroxybutane	See 1, 2—Butanediol.											
2, 2—Dihydroxyethyl Ether	See Diethylene Glycol.											
2, 5—Dihydroxyhexane	See 2, 5—Hexanediol.											
Diisobutylaluminum Hydride [(CH$_3$)$_2$CHCH$_2$]$_2$AlH	Note: Ignites spontaneously in air.								Do not use water, foam or halogenated extinguishing agents.		3	3 W
Diisobutylamine [(CH$_3$)$_2$CHCH$_2$]$_2$NH (Bis(β—Methylpropyl) Amine)	85		0.7				273–286	No	"Alcohol" foam. Water may be ineffective.	3	3	0
Diisobutyl Carbinol [(CH$_3$)$_2$CHCH$_2$]$_2$CHOH (Nonyl Alcohol)	165		0.8 @ 212°	6.1 @ 212°	0.8	5.0	353	No	"Alcohol" foam.	1	2	0
Diisobutyl Ketone [(CH$_3$)$_2$CHCH$_2$]$_2$CO (2, 6—Dimethyl—4—Heptanone) (Isovalerone)	140		0.8 @ 212°	6.2 @ 212°	0.8	4.9	335	No		1	2	0
Diisodecyl Adipate C$_{10}$H$_{21}$O$_2$C(CH$_2$)$_4$CO$_2$-C$_{10}$H$_{21}$	225 (oc)		0.9				660		Water or foam may cause frothing.	0	1	0
Diisooctyl Phthalate (C$_8$H$_{17}$COO)$_2$C$_6$H$_4$	450		1.0—				698	No	Water or foam may cause frothing.	0	1	0
Diisopropanolamine [CH$_3$CH(OH)-CH$_2$]$_2$NH	260 (oc)		1.0—				480	Yes	"Alcohol" foam. Water or foam may cause frothing.	2	1	0
Diisopropyl	See 2, 3—Dimethylbutane.											
Diisopropylamine [(CH$_3$)$_2$CH]$_2$NH	30 (oc)		0.7		3.5		183	Yes	Water may be ineffective. "Alcohol" foam.	3	3	0
	Note: See Hazardous Chemicals Data.											
Diisopropyl Benzene [(CH$_3$)$_2$CH]$_2$C$_6$H$_4$	170 (oc)	840	0.9		5.6		401	No		0	2	0

Table 3-11A (cont.)	FLASH POINT Deg. F.	IGNITION TEMP. Deg. F.	FLAMMABLE LIMITS Per Cent by Vol. Lower	Upper	Sp. Gr. (Water =1)	Vapor Density (Air =1)	Boiling Point Deg. F.	Water Soluble	EXTINGUISHING METHOD See Intro.	Health	Flamma-bility	Reac-tivity
N, N—Diisopropyl-ethanolamine [(CH₃)₂CH]₂NC₂H₄OH	175 (oc)				0.9	5.0	376	No		1	2	0
Diisopropyl Maleate (CH₃)₂CHOCOCH:CHCOOCH(CH₃)₂	220 (oc)				1.0+		444	Slight	"Alcohol" foam. Water or foam may cause frothing.	1	1	0
Diisopropylmethanol	See 2, 4—Dimethyl—3—Pentanol.											
Diisopropyl Peroxydi-carbonate (CH₃)₂CHOCOOCO-OCH(CH₃)₂	Note: Rapid decomposition at 53°F. Melting point 46–50°F. See Hazardous Chemicals Data.					Explodes on heating.		No		0	4	4
Diketene CH₂:CCH₂C(O)O (Vinylaceto—β—Lactone)	93	Note: See Hazardous Chemicals Data.	1.1			2.9	261	De-com-poses	"Alcohol" foam.	2	2	2
2, 5—Dimethoxychloro-benzene C₈H₉ClO₂	243					5.9	460–467	Slight	Water or foam may cause frothing. "Alcohol" foam.	2	1	0
1, 2—Dimethoxyethane	See Ethylene Glycol Dimethyl Ether.											
Dimethoxymethane	See Methylal.											
Dimethoxy Tetraglycol CH₃OCH₂(CH₂-OCH₂)₃CH₂OCH₃ (Tetraethylene Glycol Dimethyl Ether)	285 (oc)				1.0+		528	Yes	Water or foam may cause frothing. "Alcohol" foam.	1	1	0
Dimethylamine (CH₃)₂NH	Gas	752	2.8	14.4		1.6	45	Yes	Stop flow of gas.	3	4	0
	Note: See Hazardous Chemicals Data.											
2—(Dimethylamino)-ethanol (CH₃)₂NCH₂CH₂OH (Dimethylethanolamine)	105 (oc)				0.9	3.1	272	Yes	Water may be ineffective. "Alcohol" foam.	2	2	0
2—(Dimethylamino)-ethyl Methacrylate C₈H₁₅NO₂	165 (oc)				0.9	5.4	207 @ 40 mm.	Yes	"Alcohol" foam.	2	2	0
	Note: Polymerizes.											
3—(Dimethylamino)-propionitrile (CH₃)₂NC₂H₄CN	149 (oc)				0.86	3.35	338				2	1
3—(Dimethylamino)-propylamine (CH₃)₂N(CH₂)₃NH₂	100 (oc)				0.8	3.5	278	Yes	"Alcohol" foam.	3	2	0
Di(Methylamyl) Maleate	See Bis(2, 4—Dimethylbutyl)Maleate.											
N, N—Dimethylaniline C₆H₅N(CH₃)₂ C.P.	145 (Und. Lab. Class 20–25) 165	700	1.0−			4.2	379	Slight	"Alcohol" foam.	3	2	0
o—Dimethylaniline	See o—Xylidine.											
1, 2—Dimethylbenzene	See o—Xylene.											
1, 3—Dimethylbenzene	See m—Xylene.											
1, 4—Dimethylbenzene	See p—Xylene.											
2, 2—Dimethylbutane (CH₃)₃CCH₂CH₃ (Neohexane)	−54	797	1.2	7.0	0.6	3.0	122	No	Water may be ineffective.	1	3	0
2, 3—Dimethylbutane (CH₃)₂CHCH(CH₃)₂ (Diisopropyl)	−20	788	1.2	7.0	0.7	3.0	136	No	Water may be ineffective.	1	3	0
1, 3—Dimethylbutanol	See Methyl Isobutyl Carbinol.											
2, 3—Dimethyl—1—Butene CH₃CH(CH₃)C(CH₃):CH₂	<−4	680			0.68	2.91	133			0	3	0
2, 3—Dimethyl—2—Butene CH₃C(CH₃):C(CH₃)₂	<−4	753			0.71	2.91	163			0	3	0
1, 3—Dimethylbutyl Acetate CH₃COOCH(CH₃)CH₂CH(CH₃)₂	113				0.9	5.0	284–297	Slight	"Alcohol" foam.	1	2	0
1, 3—Dimethylbutyl-amine CH₃CHNH₂(CH₂)CH-(CH₃)₂ (2—Amino—4—Methylpentane)	55 (oc)				0.7	3.5	223–228	No	Water may be ineffective.	2	3	0
Dimethyl Carbinol	See Isopropyl Alcohol.											
Dimethyl Carbonate	See Methyl Carbonate.											
Dimethyl Chloracetal ClCH₂CH(OCH₃)₂	111	450			1.0+		259–270			2	2	0

Table 3-11A
(cont.)

	FLASH POINT Deg. F.	IGNI-TION TEMP. Deg. F.	FLAMMABLE LIMITS Per Cent by Vol. Lower	Upper	Sp. Gr. (Water = 1)	Vapor Density (Air = 1)	Boiling Point Deg. F.	Water Soluble	EXTINGUISHING METHOD See Intro.	SUGGESTED HAZARD IDENTIFICATION Health	Flamma-bility	Reac-tivity
Dimethylcyanamide $(CH_3)_2NCN$	160				0.88	255	320			4	2	1
1, 4—Dimethyl-cyclohexane $(CH_3)_2C_6H_{10}$ (Hexahydroxylol)	52				0.8	3.9	248	No	Water may be ineffective.	1	3	0
1, 4—Dimethylcyclo-hexane—cis $C_6H_{10}(CH_3)_2$	61						255			0	3	0
1, 4—Dimethylcyclo-hexane—trans $C_6H_{10}(CH_3)_2$	51						246			0	3	0
Dimethyl Decalin $C_{12}H_{18}$	184	455	0.7 @ 200°	5.3 @ 300°	1.0		455			0	2	0
Dimethyldichlorosilane $(CH_3)_2SiCl_2$ (Dichlorodimethylsilane)	<70		3.4	>9.5	1.1	4.4	158	De-com-poses	Decomposes in water.	3	3	1
1, 3—Dimethyl—1, 3—Diphenyl-cyclobutane $(C_6H_5CCH_3)_2(CH_2)_2$ Note: Melting point 120°F.	289				1.0— @ 122°F		585–588	No	Water or foam may cause frothing.	0	1	0
Dimethyldioxane $CH_3CHCH_2OCH_2-$ $(CH_3)CHO$	75 (oc)				0.9	4.0	243	Slight	"Alcohol" foam. Water may be ineffective.	2	3	0
Dimethylene Oxide	See Ethylene Oxide.											
N, N—Dimethylethanol-amine	See 2—(Dimethylamino)ethanol.											
Dimethyl Ether	See Methyl Ether.											
Dimethyl Ethyl Carbinol	See 2—Methyl—2—Butanol.											
2, 4—Dimethyl—3—Ethylpentane $CH_3CH(CH_3)CH(C_2H_5)CH(CH_3)_2$ (3—Ethyl—2, 4—dimethyl-pentane)		734			0.74	4.43	279			0	3	0
N, N—Dimethyl-formamide $HCON(CH_3)_2$ (Und. Lab. Class 25–30)	136	833	2.2 @ 212°	15.2	0.9	2.5	307	Yes	"Alcohol" foam.	1	2	0
2, 5—Dimethylfuran $OC(CH_3):CHCH:C(CH_3)$	45 (oc)				0.9	3.3 *	200	Slight	Water may be ineffective. "Alcohol" foam.	2	3	0
Dimethyl Glycol Phthalate $C_6H_4[COO(CH_2)_2OCH_3]_2$	369				1.8		446		Water or foam may cause frothing.	0	1	0
3, 3—Dimethylheptane $CH_3(CH_2)_3C(CH_3)_2CH_2CH_3$		617			0.73	4.43	279			0	3	0
2, 6—Dimethyl—4—Heptanone	See Diisobutyl Ketone.											
2, 3—Dimethylhexane $CH_3CH(CH_3)CH(CH_3)-$ $C_2H_5CH_3$	45 (oc)	820			0.7	3.9	237	No	Water may be ineffective.	0	3	0
2, 4—Dimethylhexane $CH_3CH(CH_3)CH(CH_3)-$ $C_2H_5CH_3$	50 (oc)				0.7	3.9	229	No	Water may be ineffective.	0	3	0
Dimethyl Hexynol $C_4H_9CCH_3(OH)C:CH$ (3, 5—Dimethyl—1—hexyn—3—ol)	135 (oc)				0.85	4.35	302			0	2	0
1, 1—Dimethyl-hydrazine $(CH_3)_2NNH_2$ (Dimethylhydrazine, Unsymmetrical)	5	480	2	95	0.8	2.0	145	Yes	"Alcohol" foam. Water may be ineffective.	3	3	1
Dimethylhydrazine-Unsymmetrical	See 1, 1—Dimethylhydrazine.											
N, N—Dimethyliso-propanolamine $(CH_3)_2NCH_2CH(OH)CH_3$	95 (oc)				0.9	3.6	257	Yes	Water may be ineffective. "Alcohol" foam.	2	3	0
Dimethyl Ketone	See Acetone.											
Dimethyl Maleate $(-CHCOOCH_3)_2$	235 (oc)				1.2		393	No	Water or foam may cause frothing.	1	1	0
2, 6—Dimethyl-morpholine $CH(CH_3)CH_2OCH_2CH-$ $(CH_3)NH$	112 (oc)				0.9	4.0	296	Yes	"Alcohol" foam.	2	2	0

Table 3-11A (cont.)	FLASH POINT Deg. F.	IGNI- TION TEMP. Deg. F.	FLAMMABLE LIMITS Per Cent by Vol. Lower	Upper	Sp. Gr. (Water =1)	Vapor Density (Air =1)	Boiling Point Deg. F.	Water Soluble	EXTINGUISHING METHOD See Intro.	SUGGESTED HAZARD IDENTIFICATION Health	Flamma- bility	Reac- tivity
2, 3—Dimethyloctane $CH_3(CH_2)_4CH(CH_3)CH(CH_3)CH_3$	<131	437			0.74	4.91	327			0	2	0
3, 4—Dimethyloctane $C_3H_7CH(CH_3)CH(CH_3)C_3H_7$	<131				0.75	4.91	324			0	2	0
2, 3—Dimethylpental- dehyde $CH_3CH_2CH(CH_3)CH-$ $(CH_3)CHO$	94 (oc)				0.8	3.9	293		Water may be ineffective.	2	3	0
2, 3—Dimethylpentane $CH_3CH(CH_3)CH-$ $(CH_3)CH_2CH_3$	<20	635	1.1	6.7	0.7	3.5	194	No	Water may be ineffective.	0	3	0
2, 4—Dimethylpentane $(CH_3)_2CHCH_2CH(CH_3)_2$	10				0.7	3.5	177	No	Water may be ineffective.	0	3	0
2, 4—Dimethyl—3— Pentanol $(CH_3)_2CHCHOHCH(CH_3)_2$ (Diisopropylmethanol)	120				0.8	4.0	284	Very slight		0	2	0
Dimethyl Phthalate $C_6H_4(COOCH_3)_2$	295	1032			1.2		540	No	Water or foam may cause frothing.	0	1	0
Dimethylpiperazine—cis $C_6H_{14}N_2$	155 (oc)				0.92	3.94	329			2	2	0
2, 2—Dimethylpropane $(CH_3)_4C$ (Neopentane)	Gas	842	1.4	7.5		2.5	49	No	Stop flow of gas.	0	4	0
2, 2—Dimethyl—1— Propanol	See tert — Butyl Carbinol.											
2, 5—Dimethyl- pyrazine $CH_3C:CHN:C(CH_3)CH:N$	147 (oc)				0.99	3.72	311	Yes			2	0
Dimethyl Sulfate $(CH_3)_2SO_4$ (Methyl Sulfate)	182 (oc)	370			1.3	4.4	370	Very slight	Water may be used to blanket fire.	4	2	0
	Note: See Hazardous Chemicals Data.											
Dimethyl Sulfide $(CH_3)_2S$	<0	403	2.2	19.7	0.8	2.1	99	Slight	Water may be ineffective.	4	4	0
	Note: See Hazardous Chemicals Data.											
Dimethyl Sulfoxide $(CH_3)_2SO$	203 (oc)	419	2.6	28.5	1.1		372	Yes	"Alcohol" foam.	1	1	0
	Note: Melting point 65°F.											
2,4—Dinitroaniline $(NO_2)_2C_6H_3NH_2$	435				1.6			No	Water or foam may cause frothing.	3	1	3
	Note: Melting point 370°F.											
1, 2—Dinitro Benzol $C_6H_4(NO_2)_2$ (o—Dinitrobenzene)	302				1.57	5.79	604			3	1	4
	Note: Melting point 244°F.											
Dinitrochlorobenzene $C_6H_3Cl(NO_2)_2$ (Chlorodinitrobenzene)	382		2.0	22	1.7		599	No	Water or foam may cause frothing.	3	1	4
	Note: Melting point 109°F. See Hazardous Chemicals Data.											
2, 4—Dinitrotoluene $(NO_2)_2C_6H_3CH_3$	404				1.52	6.27	572				1	4
	Note: Melting point 158°F.											
Dioctylamine	See Bis(2—Ethylhexyl)Amine.											
Dioctyl Ether $(C_8H_{17})_2O$ (Octyl Ether)	>212	401			0.82	8.36	558			0	1	0
Dioctyl Phthalate $C_6H_4[CO_2CH_2-$ $CH(C_2H_5)C_4H_9]_2$	425 (oc)				1.0—		726	No	Water or foam may cause frothing.	0	1	0
p—Dioxane $OCH_2CH_2OCH_2CH_2$ (Diethylene Dioxide)	54	356	2.0	22	1.0+	3.0	214	Yes	Water may be ineffective. "Alcohol" foam.	2	3	0
	Note: See Hazardous Chemicals Data.											
Dioxolane $OCH_2CH_2OCH_2$	35 (oc)				1.1	2.6	165	Yes	Water may be ineffective. "Alcohol" foam.	2	3	2
Dipentene $C_{10}H_{16}$ (Cimene)	113	458	0.7 @ 302°	6.1 @ 302°	0.9	4.7	178	No		0	2	0
Diphenyl	See Biphenyl.											
Diphenylamine $(C_6H_5)_2NH$ (Phenylaniline)	307	1175			1.2		575	No	Water or foam may cause frothing.	3	1	0
	Note: Melting point 127°F.											
1,1—Diphenylbutane $(C_6H_5)_2CHC_3H_7$	>212	851			0.98	7.26	561			0	1	0
1, 3—Diphenyl—2— buten—1—one	See Dypnone.											

Table 3-11A (cont.)	FLASH POINT Deg. F.	IGNI-TION TEMP. Deg. F.	FLAMMABLE LIMITS Per Cent by Vol. Lower	Upper	Sp. Gr. (Water = 1)	Vapor Density (Air = 1)	Boiling Point Deg. F.	Water Soluble	EXTINGUISHING METHOD See Intro.	SUGGESTED HAZARD IDENTIFICATION Health	Flamma-bility	Reac-tivity
Diphenyldodecyl Phosphite $(C_6H_5O)_2POC_{10}H_{21}$	425 (oc) Note: Melting point 64°F.				1.0+			No	Water or foam may cause frothing.	0	1	0
1,1—Diphenylethane (uns) $(C_6H_5)_2CHCH_3$	>212	824			1.0	6.29	546			0	1	0
1,2—Diphenylethane (sym) $C_6H_5CH_2CH_2C_6H_5$	264	896			1.0	6.29	544			0	1	0
Diphenyl Ether	See Diphenyl Oxide.											
Diphenylmethane $(C_6H_5)_2CH_2$ (Ditane)	266 905 Note: Melting point 79°F.				1.0		508	No	Water or foam may cause frothing.	1	1	0
Diphenyl (o—Xenyl) Phosphate $(C_6H_5O)_2PO(OC_6H_4C_6H_5)$	437				1.2		482–545 @ 5 mm.		Water or foam may cause frothing.	0	1	0
Diphenyl Oxide $(C_6H_5)_2O$ (Diphenyl Ether)	239 1148 0.8 1.5 Note: Melting point 81°F.				1.1		498	No	Water or foam may cause frothing.	1	1	0
1, 1—Diphenylpentane $(C_6H_5)_2CHC_4H_9$	>212	824			0.97	7.74	586			0	1	0
1, 1—Diphenylpropane $CH_3CH_2CH(C_6H_5)_2$	>212	860			0.97	6.77	541			0	1	0
Diphenyl Phthalate $C_6H_4(COOC_6H_5)_2$	435 Note: Melting point 158°F.				1.3		761	No	Water or foam may cause frothing.	0	1	0
Dipropylaluminum Hydride $(C_3H_7)_2AlH$	Note: Ignites spontaneously in air.								Do not use water, foam or halogenated extinguishing agents.		3	3 ₩
Dipropylamine $(C_3H_7)_2NH$	63 (oc)				0.7	3.5	229	No	Water may be ineffective.	3	3	0
Dipropylene Glycol $[CH_3CHOHCH_2]_2O$	280 (oc)				1.0+		449	Yes	Water or foam may cause frothing. "Alcohol" foam.	0	1	0
Dipropylene Glycol Methyl Ether $CH_3OC_3H_6OC_3H_6OH$	185				0.95	5.11	374			0	2	0
Dipropyl Ketone	See 4—Heptanone.											
Ditane	See Diphenylmethane.											
Ditridecyl Phthalate $C_6H_4(COOC_{13}H_{27})_2$	470 (oc)				1.0—		547 @ 5 mm.		Water or foam may cause frothing.	0	1	0
Divinyl Acetylene (:CCH:CH_2)_2 (1, 5—Hexadien—3—yne)	<−4					2.69	183			3	3	
Divinylbenzene $C_6H_4(CH:CH_2)_2$	169 (oc)				0.9		392	No		1	2	2
Divinyl Ether $(CH_2:CH)_2O$ (Ethenyloxyethene) (Vinyl Ether)	<−22 680 1.7 27 Note: See Hazardous Chemicals Data.				0.8	2.4	102	No	Water may be ineffective.	2	3	2
Di (o—Xenyl) Phenyl Phosphate $(C_6H_5C_6H_4)_2PO(OC_6H_5)$	482				1.2		545–626 @ 5 mm.		Water or foam may cause frothing.	0	1	0
Dodecane $CH_3(CH_2)_{10}CH_3$ (Dihexyl)	165	401	0.6	0.8		5.9	421	No		0	2	0
1—Dodeconethiol $CH_3(CH_2)_{11}SH$ (Dodecyl Mercaptan) (Lauryl Mercaptan)	262 (oc)				0.8		289 @ 15 mm.	No	"Alcohol" foam. Water or foam may cause frothing.	2	1	0
1—Dodecanol $CH_3(CH_2)_{11}OH$ (Lauryl Alcohol)	260	527			0.8		491	No	Water or foam may cause frothing.	0	1	0
Dodecyl Bromide	See Lauryl Bromide.											
Dodecylene (α) $C_{16}H_{21}CH:CH_2$ (1—Dodecene)	<212	491			0.76	5.81	406			0	1	0
Dodecyl Mercaptan	See 1—Dodecanethiol.											
tert—Dodecyl Mercaptan $C_{12}H_{25}SH$	205 (oc)				0.9		428–451	No		2	1	0
Dodecyl Phenol $C_{12}H_{25}C_6H_4OH$	325 (oc)				0.9	9.0	597–633	No	Water or foam may cause frothing.	0	1	0

Table 3-11A (cont.)	FLASH POINT Deg. F.	IGNI- TION TEMP. Deg. F.	FLAMMABLE LIMITS Per Cent by Vol. Lower	Upper	Sp. Gr. (Water = 1)	Vapor Density (Air = 1)	Boiling Point Deg. F.	Water Soluble	EXTINGUISHING METHOD See Intro.	Health	Flamma- bility	Reac- tivity
Dypnone $C_6H_5COCH:C(CH_3)C_6H_5$ (1, 3—Diphenyl—2— Buten—1—one)	350 (oc)				1.1		475 @ 50 mm.	Slight	Water or foam may cause frothing. "Alcohol" foam.	1	1	0
Eicosane $C_{20}H_{42}$	>212				0.79	9.75	651				1	0
Epichlorohydrin CH_2CHOCH_2Cl *Note: See Hazardous Chemicals Data.* (2—Chloropropylene Oxide) (γ—Chloropropylene Oxide)	105 (oc)				1.2	3.2	239	Yes	"Alcohol" foam.	3	2	1
1, 2—Epoxyethane *See Ethylene Oxide.*												
Erythrene *See 1, 3—Butadiene.*												
Ethanal *See Acetaldehyde.*												
Ethane CH_3CH_3	Gas	959	3.0	12.5		1.0	−128	No	Stop flow of gas.	1	4	0
1, 2—Ethanediol *See Ethylene Glycol.*												
1, 2—Ethanediol Diformate $HCOOCH_2CH_2OOCH$ (Ethylene Formate) (Ethylene Glycol Diformate) (Glycol Diformate)	200 (oc)				1.2		345	De- com- poses	Decomposes in water.	1	2	0
Ethanethiol *See Ethyl Mercaptan.*												
Ethanoic Acid *See Acetic Acid.*												
Ethanoic Anhydride *See Acetic Anhydride.*												
Ethanol *See Ethyl Alcohol.*												
Ethanolamine $NH_2CH_2CH_2OH$ (2—Amino Ethanol) (β—Aminoethyl Alcohol)	185 200 (oc)				1.0+	2.1	342	Yes	"Alcohol" foam.	2	2	0
Ethanoyl Chloride *See Acetyl Chloride.*												
Ethene *See Ethylene.*												
Ethenyl Ethanoate *See Vinyl Acetate.*												
Ethenyloxyethene *See Divinyl Ether.*												
Ether *See Ethyl Ether.*												
Ethine *See Acetylene.*												
Ethoxyacetylene $C_2H_5OC:CH$	<20				0.8	2.4	124	No	Water may be ineffective.	2	3	1
Ethoxybenzene $C_6H_5OC_2H_5$ (Ethyl Phenyl Ether) (Phenetole)	145				1.0−	4.2	342	No		0	2	0
2—Ethoxy—3, 4—Di- hydro—2—Pyran $C_7H_{12}O_2$	111 (oc)				1.0−		289	Very slight		2	2	1
2—Ethoxy Ethanol *See Ethylene Glycol Monoethyl Ether.*												
2—Ethoxyethyl Acetate $CH_3COOCH_2CH_2OC_2H_5$ (Ethyl Glycol Acetate)	117	716	1.7		1.0−	4.6	313	Yes	"Alcohol" foam.	2	2	0
3—Ethoxypropanal $C_2H_5OC_2H_4CHO$ (3—Ethoxypropionaldehyde)	100				0.98	3.52	275			2	2	0
1—Ethoxypropane *See Ethyl Propyl Ether.*												
3—Ethoxypropional- dehyde $C_2H_5OCH_2CH_2CHO$	100				0.9	3.5	275	Yes	"Alcohol" foam.	2	3	0
3—Ethoxypropionic Acid $C_2H_5OCH_2CH_2COOH$	225				1.0+		426	Yes	"Alcohol" foam. Water or foam may cause frothing.	2	1	0
Ethoxytriglycol $C_2H_5O(C_2H_4O)_3H$ (Triethylene Glycol, Ethyl Ether)	275 (oc)				1.0+		492	Yes	Water or foam may cause frothing. "Alcohol" foam.	0	1	0
Ethyl Abietate $C_{19}H_{29}COOC_2H_5$	352 (oc)				1.0+		662	No	Water or foam may cause frothing.	0	1	0
N—Ethylacetamide $CH_3CONHC_2H_5$ (Acetoethylamide)	230				0.9		401	Yes	"Alcohol" foam. Water or foam may cause frothing.	1	1	0
N—Ethyl Acetanilide $CH_3CON(C_2H_5)(C_6H_5)$	126				0.9	5.6	400	No		0	2	0

Table 3-11A (cont.)

	FLASH POINT Deg. F.	IGNI-TION TEMP. Deg. F.	FLAMMABLE LIMITS Per Cent by Vol. Lower	Upper	Sp. Gr. (Water = 1)	Vapor Density (Air = 1)	Boilng Point Deg. F.	Water Soluble	EXTINGUISHING METHOD See Intro.	Health	Flamma-bility	Reac-tivity
Ethyl Acetate $CH_3COOC_2H_5$ (Acetic Ester) (Acetic Ether) (Ethyl Ethanoate)	24	800	2.2	11.0	0.9	3.0	171	Slight	Water may be ineffective. "Alcohol" foam.	1	3	0
	(Und. Lab. Class 85–90)											
Ethyl Acetoacetate $C_2H_5CO_2CH_2COCH_3$ (Acetoacetic Acid, Ethyl Ester) (Ethyl 3—Oxobutanoate)	184 (oc)	563			1.0+	4.5	356	Slight	"Alcohol" foam.	2	2	0
Ethyl Acetyl Glycolate $CH_3COOCH_2COOC_2H_5$ (Ethyl Glycolate Acetate)	180				1.09	5.04	~365	No		0	2	0
Ethyl Acrylate CH_2:$CHCOOC_2H_5$	60 (oc)		1.8		0.9	3.5	211	Slight	Water may be ineffective. "Alcohol" foam.	2	3	2
	Note: Polymerizes. See Hazardous Chemicals Data.											
Ethyl Alcohol C_2H_5OH (Grain Alcohol, Cologne Spirits, Ethanol)	55	689	3.3	19	0.8	1.6	173	Yes	Water may be ineffective. "Alcohol" foam.	0	3	0
	(Und. Lab. Class 70)											
Ethyl Alcohol and Water 96%	62											
95%	63											
80%	68											
70%	70											
60%	72											
50%	75											
40%	79											
30%	85											
20%	97											
10%	120											
5%	144											
Ethylaluminum Dichloride $C_2H_5AlCl_2$ (Dichloroethylaluminum)									Do not use water, foam or halogenated extinguishing agents.	3	3	3 W
	Note: Fumes vigorously in air. May ignite spontaneously.											
Ethylaluminum Sesquichloride $(C_2H_5)_3Al_2Cl_3$									Do not use water, foam or halogenated extinguishing agents.		3	3 W
	Note: Ignites spontaneously in air.											
Ethylamine $C_2H_5NH_2$ 70% aqueous solution (Aminoethane)	<0	725	3.5	14.0	0.8	1.6	62	Yes	Water may be ineffective. "Alcohol" foam.	3	4	0
	Note: See Hazardous Chemicals Data.											
Ethyl Amino Ethanol $C_2H_5NHC_2H_4OH$ (2—(Ethylamino)ethanol)	160 (oc)				0.92	3.06	322				2	0
Ethylaniline $C_2H_5NH(C_6H_5)$	185 (oc)				1.0-	4.2	401	No		3	2	0
	Note: See Hazardous Chemicals Data.											
Ethylbenzene $C_2H_5C_6H_5$ (Ethylbenzol) (Phenylethane)	59	810	1.0	6.7	0.9	3.7	277	No	Water may be ineffective.	2	3	0
	Note: See Hazardous Chemicals Data.											
Ethyl Benzoate $C_6H_5COOC_2H_5$	>204	914			1.0+		414	No		1	1	0
Ethylbenzol	See Ethylbenzene.											
Ethyl Benzoylacetate $C_6H_5COCH_2COOC_2H_5$	285 (oc)				1.1		291–298	No	Water or foam may cause frothing.	0	1	0
Ethyl Borate $(C_2H_5)_3BO_3$	52				0.9	5.0	233	Decom-poses		2	3	0
Ethyl Bromide C_2H_5Br (Bromoethane)	<−4	952	6.7	11.3	1.4	3.8	100	No	Water may be ineffective.	2	3	0
Ethyl Bromoacetate $BrCH_2COOC_2H_5$	118				1.5		318	No	Water may be used to blanket fire.		2	0
2—Ethylbutanal	See 2—Ethylbutyraldehyde.											
Ethyl Butanoate	See Ethyl Butyrate.											
2—Ethyl—1—Butanol	See 2—Ethylbutyl Alcohol.											
2—Ethyl—1—Butene $(C_2H_5)_2C$:CH_2	<−4	599			0.69	2.90	144			0	3	0
3—(2—Ethylbutoxy) Propionic Acid $CH_3CH_2CH(C_2H_5)CH_2$-OCH_2CH_2COOH	280 (oc)				1.0-		392 @ 100 mm.	No	Water or foam may cause frothing.	2	1	0
2—Ethylbutyl Acetate $CH_3COOCH_2CH(C_2H_5)_2$	130 (oc)				0.9	5.0	324	No		1	2	0

Table 3-11A (cont.)	FLASH POINT Deg. F.	IGNITION TEMP. Deg. F.	FLAMMABLE LIMITS Per Cent by Vol. Lower	Upper	Sp. Gr. (Water =1)	Vapor Density (Air =1)	Boiling Point Deg. F.	Water Soluble	EXTINGUISHING METHOD See Intro.	SUGGESTED HAZARD IDENTIFICATION Health	Flamma-bility	Reac-tivity
2—Ethylbutyl Acrylate CH₂:CHCOOCH₂CH-(C₂H₅)C₂H₅	125 (oc)				0.9		180 @ 10 mm.	No		2	2	0
2—Ethylbutyl Alcohol (C₂H₅)₂CHCH₂OH (2—Ethyl—1—Butanol)	135 (oc)				0.8	3.5	301	No		1	2	0
Ethylbutylamine CH₃CH₂CH₂CH₂-NHCH₃CH₂	64 (oc)				0.7	3.5	232	No	Water may be ineffective.	3	3	0
Ethyl Butylcarbamate	See N—Butylurethane.											
Ethyl Butyl Carbonate (C₂H₅)(C₄H₉)CO₃	122				0.9	5.0	275			2	2	1
Ethyl Butyl Ether C₂H₅OC₄H₉ (Butyl Ethyl Ether)	40				0.8	3.7	198	Slight	Water may be ineffective. "Alcohol" foam.	2	3	0
2—Ethyl Butyl Glycol (C₂H₅)₂CHCH₂OC₂H₄-OH (2—(2—Ethylbutoxy)ethanol)	180 (oc)				0.90	5.05	386			0	2	0
Ethyl Butyl Ketone C₂H₅CO(CH₂)₃CH₃ (3—Heptanone)	115 (oc)				0.8	4.0	299	No		1	2	0
2—Ethyl—2—Butyl—1, 3—Propanediol HOCH₂C(C₂H₅)(C₄H₉)-CH₂OH	280 (oc) Note: Melting point 107°F.				0.9 @ 122°F		352 @ 50 mm.	Yes	Water or foam may cause frothing. "Alcohol" foam.	2	1	0
2—Ethylbutyraldehyde (C₂H₅)₂CHCHO (Diethyl Acetaldehyde) (2—Ethylbutanal)	70 (oc)		1.2	7.7	0.8	3.5	242	No	Water may be ineffective. "Alcohol" foam.	2	3	1
Ethyl Butyrate CH₃CH₂CH₂COOC₂H₅ (Butyric Acid, Ethyl Ester) (Butyric Ester) (Ethyl Butanoate)	78	865			0.9	4.0	248	No	Water may be ineffective. "Alcohol" foam.	0	3	0
2—Ethylbutyric Acid (C₂H₅)₂CHCOOH (Diethyl Acetic Acid)	210 (oc)				0.9		380	Slight	"Alcohol" foam.	2	1	0
2—Ethylcaproaldehyde	See 2—Ethylhexanal.											
Ethyl Carbonate	See Diethyl Carbonate.											
Ethyl Chloride C₂H₅Ci (Chloroethane) (Hydrochloric Ether) (Muriatic Ether)	—58 Note: See Hazardous Chemicals Data.	966	3.8	15.4	0.9	2.2	54	No	Water may be ineffective.	2	4	0
Ethyl Chloroacetate ClCH₂COOC₂H₅	100				1.2		295	No	Water may be used to blanket fire.		3	0
Ethyl Chlorocarbonate	See Ethyl Chloroformate.											
Ethyl Chloroformate ClCOOC₂H₅ (Ethyl Chlorocarbonate) (Ethyl Chloromethanoate)	61	932			1.1	3.7	201	Decom-poses			3	1
Ethyl Chloromethanoate	See Ethyl Chloroformate.											
Ethyl Crotonate CH₃CH:CHCOOC₂H₅	36				0.9	3.9	282	No	Water may be ineffective.	2	3	0
Ethyl Cyanoacetate CH₂CNCOOC₂H₅	230				1.1		401–408		Water or foam may cause frothing.	2	1	0
Ethylcyclobutane C₂H₅C₄H₇	<4	410	1.2	7.7		2.9	160	No		1	3	0
Ethylcyclohexane C₂H₅C₆H₁₁	95	504	.9	6.6	0.8	3.9	269	No		1	3	0
N—Ethylcyclohexyl-amine C₆H₁₁NHC₂H₅	86 (oc)				0.8	4.4		Slight	Water may be ineffective. "Alcohol" foam.	3	3	0
Ethylcyciopentane C₂H₅C₅H₉	<70	500	1.1	6.7	0.8	3.4	218			1	3	0
N—Ethyldiethanol-amine C₂H₅N(C₂H₄OH)₂	280 (oc)				1.0+		487	ᵧes	Water or foam may cause frothing. "Alcohol" foam.	2	1	0
Ethyl Dimethyl Methane	See Isopentane.											
Ethylene H₂C:CH₂ (Ethene)	Gas Note: See Hazardous Chemicals Data.	914	2.7	36.0		1.0	—155	Yes	Stop flow of gas.	1	4	2
Ethylene Acetate	See Glycol Diacetate.											

Table 3-11A (cont.)

	FLASH POINT Deg. F.	IGNI-TION TEMP. Deg. F.	FLAMMABLE LIMITS Per Cent by Vol. Lower	Upper	Sp. Gr. (Water = 1)	Vapor Density (Air = 1)	Boiling Point Deg. F.	Water Soluble	EXTINGUISHING METHOD See Intro.	SUGGESTED HAZARD IDENTIFICATION Health	Flamma-bility	Reac-tivity
Ethylene Carbonate OCH_2CH_2OCO	290 (oc) *Note: Melting point 96°F.*						351 @ 100 mm.	Yes	Water or foam may cause frothing. "Alcohol" foam.	2	1	1
Ethylene Chlorohydrin	*See 2—Chloroethanol.*											
Ethylene Cyanohydrin $CH_2(OH)CH_2CN$ (Hydracrylonitrile)	265 (oc) *Note: See Hazardous Chemicals Data.*				1.1		445 Decomposes	Yes	Water or foam may cause frothing. "Alcohol" foam.	2	1	1
Ethylenediamine $H_2NCH_2CH_2NH_2$										3	2	0
Anhydrous	110 (oc)	725			0.9	2.1	241	Yes	"Alcohol" foam.			
76%	150 (cc)				1.0—		239–252	Yes	"Alcohol" foam.			
Ethylene Dichloride CH_2ClCH_2Cl (1, 2—Dichloroethane) (Glycol Dichloride)	56 (Und. Lab. Class 60–70) *Note: See Hazardous Chemicals Data.*	775	6.2	16	1.3	3.4	183	No	Water may be ineffective except as a blanket.	2	3	0
Ethylene Dicyanide	*See Succinonitrile.*											
2, 2—Ethylenedioxydi-ethanol	*See Triethylene Glycol.*											
Ethylene Formate	*See 1, 2—Ethanediol Diformate.*											
Ethylene Glycol CH_2OHCH_2OH (1, 2—Ethanediol) (Glycol)	232	752	3.2		1.1		387	Yes	"Alcohol" foam. Water or foam may cause frothing.	1	1	0
Ethylene Glycol Diacetate	*See Glycol Diacetate.*											
Ethylene Glycol Diformate	*See 1, 2—Ethanediol Diformate.*											
Ethylene Glycol Dimethyl Ether $CH_3O(CH_2)_2OCH_3$ (1, 2—Dimethoxyethane)	104				0.9		174 @ 630 mm.	Slight	"Alcohol" foam.	2	2	0
Ethylene Glycol Monoacetate $CH_2OHCH_2OOCCH_3$ (Glycol Monoacetate)	215 (oc)				1.1		357	Yes	"Alcohol" foam. Water or foam may cause frothing.	0	1	0
Ethylene Glycol Mono-ethyl Ether $HOCH_2CH_2OC_2H_5$ (2—Ethoxyethanol)	202	455	1.8	14.0	0.9	3.0	275	Yes	"Alcohol" foam.	2	1	0
Ethylene Glycol Mono-methyl Ether $CH_3OCH_2CH_2OH$ (2—Methoxyethanol)	115	545	2.5	14.0	1.0—	2.6	192	Yes	"Alcohol" foam.	2	2	0
Ethylene Glycol, Phenyl Ether $C_6H_5OC_2H_4OH$ (2—Phenoxyethanol)	250				1.1	4.8	473	No	Water or foam may cause frothing.	0	1	0
Ethyleneimine $NHCH_2CH_2$ (Aziridine)	12 *Note: See Hazardous Chemicals Data.*	608	3.6	46	0.8	1.5	132	Yes	"Alcohol" foam.	3	3	3
Ethylene Oxide CH_2OCH_2 (Dimethylene Oxide) (1, 2—Epoxyethane) (Oxirane)	<0 (Und. Lab. Class 100) *Note: See Hazardous Chemicals Data.*	804	3.6	100	0.9	1.5	51	Yes	Vapors explosive. Water may be ineffective. "Alcohol" foam.	2	4	3
Ethyl Ethanoate	*See Ethyl Acetate.*											
N—Ethylethanolamine $C_2H_5NHC_2H_4OH$	160 (oc)				0.9	3.0	322	Yes	"Alcohol" foam.	1	2	0
Ethyl Ether $C_2H_5OC_2H_5$ (Diethyl Ether) (Diethyl Oxide) (Ether) (Ethyl Oxide)	−49 (Und. Lab. Class 100) *Note: See Hazardous Chemicals Data.*	320	1.9	36.0	0.7	2.6	95	Slight	Water may be ineffective. "Alcohol" foam.	2	4	0
Ethylethylene Glycol	*See 1, 2—Butanediol.*											
Ethyl Fluoride C_2H_5F (1—Fluoroethane)					0.72 @ 7.2 atm	1.66	−36				4	0
Ethyl Formate $HCO_2C_2H_5$ (Ethyl Methanoate) (Formic Acid, Ethyl Ester)	−4	851	2.8	16.0	0.9	2.6	130	No	Water may be ineffective. "Alcohol" foam.	2	3	0

Table 3-11A (cont.)	FLASH POINT Deg. F.	IGNI-TION TEMP. Deg. F.	FLAMMABLE LIMITS Per Cent by Vol. Lower	Upper	Sp. Gr. (Water =1)	Vapor Density (Air =1)	Boiling Point Deg. F.	Water Soluble	EXTINGUISHING METHOD See Intro.	SUGGESTED HAZARD IDENTIFICATION Health	Flamma-bility	Reac-tivity
Ethyl Formate (ortho) $(C_2H_5O)_3CH$ (Triethyl Orthoformate)	86				0.90	5.11	291			0	3	0
Ethyl Glycol Acetate	See 2—Ethoxyethyl Acetate.											
2—Ethylhexaldehyde	See 2—Ethylhexanal.											
2—Ethylhexanal $C_4H_9CH(C_2H_5)CHO$ (Butylethylacetaldehyde) (2—Ethylcaproaldehyde) (2—Ethylhexaldehyde)	125 (oc)	387			0.8	4.4	325	Very slight		2	2	1
2—Ethyl—1, 3—Hexanediol $C_3H_7CH(OH)CH-(C_2H_5)CH_2OH$	260 (oc)				0.9		472	Slight	Water or foam may cause frothing. "Alcohol" foam.	1	1	0
2—Ethylhexanoic Acid $C_4H_9CH(C_2H_5)COOH$ (2—Ethyl Hexoic Acid)	260 (oc)				0.9		440	No	Water or foam may cause frothing.	1	1	0
2—Ethylhexanol $C_4H_9CH(C_2H_5)CH_2OH$	185 (oc)				0.8	4.5	359	Slight	"Alcohol" foam.	2	2	0
2—Ethylhexenal	See 2—Ethyl—3—Propylacrolein.											
2—Ethylhexoic Acid	See 2—Ethylhexanoic Acid.											
2—Ethylhexyl Acetate $CH_3COOCH_2CH-(C_2H_5)C_4H_9$ (Octyl Acetate)	190 (oc)				0.9	5.9	390	No		2	2	0
2—Ethylhexyl Acrylate $CH_2:CHCOOCH_2CH-(C_2H_5)C_4H_9$	180 (oc)				0.9		266 @ 50 mm.	No		2	2	1
2—Ethylhexylamine $C_4H_9CH(C_2H_5)CH_2NH_2$	140 (oc)				0.8	4.5	337	Yes	"Alcohol" foam.	2	2	0
N—2—(Ethylhexyl) Aniline $C_6H_5NHCH_2CH(C_2H_5)-C_4H_9$	325 (oc)				0.9		379 @ 50 mm.	No	Water or foam may cause frothing.	3	1	0
2—Ethylhexyl Chloride $C_4H_9CH(C_2H_5)CH_2Cl$	140 (oc)				0.9	5.1	343	No		2	2	0
N—(2—Ethylhexyl)-cyclohexylamine $C_6H_{11}NH[CH_2CH(C_2H_5)C_4H_9]$	265 (oc)				0.8		342 @ 50 mm.	No	Water or foam may cause frothing.	2	1	0
2—Ethylhexyl Ether $[C_4H_9CH(C_2H_5)CH_2]_2O$	235				0.8		517	No	Water or foam may cause frothing.	1	1	0
2—Ethylhexyl Vinyl Ether	See Vinyl—2—Ethylhexyl Ether.											
1, 1—Ethylidene Dichloride CH_3CHCl_2 (1, 1—Dichloroethane)	22		5.6		1.2		135–138	Slight	Water may be ineffective except as a blanket. "Alcohol" foam.	2	3	0
1, 2—Ethylidene Dichloride $ClCH_2CH_2Cl$	55	824	6.2	16	1.25	3.42	183			2	3	0
Ethyl Isobutyrate $(CH_3)_2CHCOOC_2H_5$	<70				0.87	4.0	230			0	3	0
Ethyl Lactate $CH_3CHOHCOOC_2H_5$ Tech.	115 131	752	1.5 @ 212° (Und. Lab. Class 30–35)		1.0+	4.1	309	Yes	"Alcohol" foam.	2	2	0
Ethyl Malonate	See Diethyl Malonate.											
Ethyl Mercaptan C_2H_5SH (Ethanethiol) (Ethyl Sulfhydrate)	<80	572	2.8	18.0	0.8	2.1	95	No	Water may be ineffective.	2	4	0
Ethyl Methacrylate $CH_2:C(CH_3)COOC_2H_5$ (Ethyl Methyl Acrylate)	68 (oc)				0.9	3.9	239–248	No	Water may be ineffective.	2	3	0
Ethyl Methanoate	See Ethyl Formate.											
Ethyl Methyl Acrylate	See Ethyl Methacrylate.											
Ethyl Methyl Ether	See Methyl Ethyl Ether.											
7—Ethyl—2—Methyl—4—Hendecanol $C_4H_9CH(C_2H_5)C_2H_4-CHOHCH_2CH(CH_3)_2$	285 (oc)				0.8		507	Very slight	Water or foam may cause frothing.	0	1	0
Ethyl Methyl Ketone	See Methyl Ethyl Ketone.											

Table 3-11A (cont.)

	FLASH POINT Deg. F.	IGNITION TEMP. Deg. F.	FLAMMABLE LIMITS Per Cent by Vol. Lower	Upper	Sp. Gr. (Water = 1)	Vapor Density (Air = 1)	Boiling Point Deg. F.	Water Soluble	EXTINGUISHING METHOD See Intro.	SUGGESTED HAZARD IDENTIFICATION Health	Flammability	Reactivity
4—Ethylmorpholine $CH_2CH_2OC_2H_4NCH_2CH_3$(oc)	90				0.9	4.0	280	Yes	Water may be ineffective. "Alcohol" foam.	2	3	0
1—Ethylnaphthalene $C_{10}H_7C_2H_5$		896			1.02	5.39	496			0	1	0
Ethyl Nitrate $CH_3CH_2ONO_2$ (Nitric Ether)	50		4.0		1.1	3.1	190	No	Water may be ineffective except as a blanket.	2	3	4
Ethyl Nitrite C_2H_5ONO (Nitrous Ether)	−31	194 Decomposes	3.0	50.	0.9	2.6	63	No		2	4	4
		Note: See Hazardous Chemicals Data.										
3—Ethyloctane $C_5H_{11}CH(C_2H_5)C_2H_5$		446			0.74	4.91	333			0	2	0
4—Ethyloctane $C_4H_9CH(C_2H_5)C_3H_7$		445			0.74	4.91	328			0	2	0
Ethyl Orthosilicate	*See Ethyl Silicate.*											
Ethyl Oxalate $(COOC_2H_5)_2$ (Oxalic Ether)	168				1.1	5.0	367	Slight Grad'l decomposition		0	2	0
Ethyl Oxide	*See Ethyl Ether.*											
Ethyl 3—Oxobutanoate	*See Ethyl Acetoacetate.*											
p—Ethylphenol $HOC_6H_4C_2H_5$	219 *Note: Melting point 115°F.*				1.0— @ 140°F		426	Slight	"Alcohol" foam. Water or foam may cause frothing.	2	1	0
Ethyl Phenyl Ether	*See Ethoxybenzene.*											
Ethyl Phenyl Ketone $C_2H_5COC_6H_5$ (Propiophenone)	210 (oc) *Note: Melting point 70°F.*				1.01	4.63	425				1	0
Ethyl Phosphate	*See Triethyl Phosphate.*											
Ethyl Phthalyl Ethyl Glycolate $C_2H_5OCOC_6H_4OCO$-$CH_2OCOC_2H_5$	365				1.2		608	Yes	Water or foam may cause frothing. "Alcohol" foam.	0	1	0
Ethyl Propenyl Ether $CH_3CH:CHOCH_2CH_3$	>19 (oc)				0.8		158		Water may be ineffective.	2	3	1
Ethyl Propionate $C_2H_5COOC_2H_5$	54	824	1.9	11	0.9	3.5	210	No	Water may be ineffective.		3	0
2—Ethyl—3—Propyl-acrolein $C_3H_7CH:C(C_2H_5)CHO$ (2—Ethylhexenal)	155 (oc)				0.9	4.4	347	No	"Alcohol" foam.	2	2	1
2—Ethyl—3—Propyl-acrylic Acid $C_3H_7CH:C(C_2H_5)COOH$	330 (oc)				0.9		450	Slight	Water or foam may cause frothing. "Alcohol" foam.	2	1	1
Ethyl Propyl Ether $C_2H_5OC_3H_7$ (1—Ethoxypropane)	<−4		1.7	9.0	0.8		147	Yes	"Alcohol" foam.	1	3	0
Ethyl Silicate $(C_2H_5)_4SiO_4$ (Ethyl Orthosilicate) (Tetraethyl Orthosilicate)	125 (oc)				0.9	7.2	334	Decomposes		2	2	0
Ethyl Sulfate	*See Diethyl Sulfate.*											
Ethyl Sulfhydrate	*See Ethyl Mercaptan.*											
m—Ethyltoluene $CH_3C_6H_4C_2H_5$ (1—Methyl—3—ethylbenzene)		896			0.88	4.15	322				2	0
o—Ethyltoluene $CH_3C_6H_4C_2H_5$ (1—Methyl—2—ethylbenzene)		824			0.88	4.15	329				2	0
p—Ethyltoluene $CH_3C_6H_4C_2H_5$ (1—Methyl—4—ethylbenzene)		887			0.88	4.15	324				2	0
Ethyl p—Toluene Sulfonamide $C_7H_7SO_2NHC_2H_5$	260				1.3		208 @ 745 mm.		Water or foam may cause frothing.		1	0
Ethyl p—Toluene Sulfonate $C_7H_7SO_3C_2H_5$	316				1.2		345	No	Water or foam may cause frothing.		1	0
Ethyltrichloro Silane $CH_3CH_2SiCl_3$	72 (oc)				1.2		208 @ 745 mm.		Water may be ineffective.	3	3	0
Ethyl Vinyl Ether	*See Vinyl Ethyl Ether.*											
Ethyne	*See Acetylene.*											

Table 3-11A (cont.)	FLASH POINT Deg. F.	IGNI- TION TEMP. Deg. F.	FLAMMABLE LIMITS Per Cent by Vol.		Sp. Gr. (Water = 1)	Vapor Density (Air = 1)	Boiling Point Deg. F.	Water Soluble	EXTINGUISHING METHOD See Intro.	SUGGESTED HAZARD IDENTIFICATION		
			Lower	Upper						Health	Flamma- bility	Reac- tivity
Fish Oil	420							No	Water or foam may cause frothing.	0	1	0
Fluorobenzene C_6H_5F	5				1.03	3.31	185				3	0
Formal	See Methylal.											
Formalin	See Formaldehyde.											
Formaldehyde HCHO	Gas	806	7.0	73	1.0		−3	Yes	Stop flow of gas.	2	4	0
	Note: See Hazardous Chemicals Data.											
37% Menthanol-free	185						214		"Alcohol" foam.	2	2	0
37%, 15% Methanol (Formalin) (Methylene Oxide)	122									2	2	0
Formic Acid HCOOH	156	1114			1.2	1.6	213	Yes	"Alcohol" foam.	3	2	0
90% Solution	122	813	18	57								
	Note: See Hazardous Chemicals Data.											
Formic Acid, Butyl Ester	See Butyl Formate.											
Formic Acid, Ethyl Ester	See Ethyl Formate.											
Formic Acid, Methyl Ester	See Methyl Formate.											
Fuel Oil No. 1 (Kerosene) (Range Oil) (Coal Oil)	100 Min. or Legal	410	0.7	5	<1		304–574	No		0	2	0
	Note: The legal minimum flash point for kerosene varies in different states. The flash point is usually above 100°F.											
Fuel Oil No. 2	100 Min. or Legal	494			<1			No		0	2	0
Fuel Oil No. 4	130 Min. or Legal	505			<1			No		0	2	0
	Note: Commercial Standard CS 12–48, U. S. Bureau of Stds., gives further details. Fuel Oil No. 3 is no longer a current standard.											
Fuel Oil No. 5	130 Min. or Legal				<1			No		0	2	0
Fuel Oil No. 6	150 Min. or Legal	765			1 ±			No		0	2	0
2—Furaldehyde	See Furfural.											
Furan CH:CHCH:CHO (Furfuran)	<32		2.3	14.3	0.9	2.3	88	No	Water may be ineffective.	1	4	1
Furfural OCH:CHCH:CHCHO (2—Furaldehyde) (Furfuraldehyde) (Furol)	140	600	2.1	19.3	1.2	3.3	322	Slight	"Alcohol" foam.	1	2	1
	(Und. Lab. Class 25–30) Note: See Hazardous Chemicals Data.											
Furfuraldehyde	See Furfural.											
Furfuran	See Furan.											
Furfuryl Acetate OCH:CHCH:CCH2OOCCH3	185				1.1	4.8	356–367	No	Water may be used to blanket fire.	1	2	1
Furfuryl Alcohol OCH:CHCH:CCH2OH	167 (oc)	915	1.8	16.3	1.1	3.4	340	Yes	"Alcohol" foam.	1	2	1
Furfurylamine $C_4H_3OCH_2NH_2$	99 (oc)				1.05	3.35	295				3	0
Furol	See Furfural.											
Fusel Oil	See Isoamyl Alcohol.											
Gas, Blast Furnace			35	74					Stop flow of gas.	2	4	0
Gas, Coal Gas			5.3	32					Stop flow of gas.	2	4	0
Gas, Coke-Oven			4.4	34					Stop flow of gas.	2	4	0
Gas, Natural (Natural Gas)		900– 1170	3.8– 6.5	13– 17					Stop flow of gas.	1	4	0
Gas, Oil Gas			4.8	32.5					Stop flow of gas.	2	4	0
Gas, Producer			20–30	70–80					Stop flow of gas.	2	4	0
Gas, Water			7.0	72					Stop flow of gas.	2	4	0
Gas, Water (Carbureted)			5.6	46.2					Stop flow of gas.	2	4	0
Gas Oil	150+	640	6.0	13.5	<1		599–649	No		0	2	0

Table 3-11A (cont.)	FLASH POINT Deg. F.	IGNI- TION TEMP. Deg. F.	FLAMMABLE LIMITS Per Cent by Vol. Lower	Upper	Sp. Gr. (Water = 1)	Vapor Density (Air = 1)	Boiling Point Deg. F.	Water Soluble	EXTINGUISHING METHOD See Intro.	Health	Flamma- bility	Reac- tivity
Gasoline C_5H_{12} to C_9H_{20}	−45		1.4	7.6	0.8	3–4	100–400	No	Water may be ineffective.	1	3	0
56–60 Octane	−45	536	1.4	7.6								
73 Octane			1.4	7.6		(Und. Lab. Class 95–100)						
92 Octane			1.5	7.6		Note: Values may vary considerably for						
100 Octane	−36	853	1.4	7.4		different grades of gasoline.						
Gasoline 100–130 (Aviation Grade)	−50 (approx.)	824	1.3	7.1						1	3	0
Gasoline 115–145 (Aviation Grade)	−50 (approx.)	880	1.2	7.1						1	3	0
Gasoline (Casinghead)	0 or less							No	Water may be ineffective.	1	4	0
Gin	See Ethyl Alcohol and Water.											
Glucose Pentapropionate $C_6H_7O_6(COC_2H_5)_5$ (Pentapropionyl Glucose) (Tetrapropionyl Glucosyl Propionate)	509				1.2		401 @ 2 mm.	No	Water or foam may cause frothing.	1	1	0
Glycerine $HOCH_2CHOHCH_2OH$ (Glycerol)	320 (Und. Lab. Class 10–20)	698			1.3		554	Yes	Water or foam may cause frothing. "Alcohol" foam.	1	1	0
Glycerin Dichlorohydrin $CH_2ClCHClCH_2OH$	200				1.4		360	Yes	"Alcohol" foam.	2	1	0
Glycerol	See Glycerine.											
Glyceryl Triacetate $(C_3H_5)(OOCCH_3)_3$ (Triacetin)	280	812			1.2		496	Slight	Water or foam may cause frothing. "Alcohol" foam.	1	1	0
Glyceryl Trichlorohydrin	See 1, 2, 3—Trichloropropane.											
Glyceryl Trinitrate	See Nitroglycerine.											
Glycidyl Acrylate $CH_2{:}CHCOOCH_2{-}CHCH_2O$	141 (oc)				1.1	4.4	135 @ 2 mm.	No		0	2	0
Glycol	See Ethylene Glycol.											
Glycol Benzyl Ether $C_6H_5CH_2OCH_2CH_2OH$ (2—Benzyloxyethanol)	264 (oc)	662			1.07	5.20	493	No		0	1	0
Glycol Diacetate $(CH_2OOCCH_3)_2$ (Ethylene Acetate) (Ethylene Glycol Diacetate)	205 (oc)				1.1		375	Slight	"Alcohol" foam.	1	1	0
Glycol Dichloride	See Ethylene Dichloride.											
Glycol Diformate	See 1, 2—Ethanediol Diformate.											
Glycol Monoacetate	See Ethylene Glycol Monoacetate.											
Grain Alcohol	See Ethyl Alcohol.											
Heavy Hydrogen	See Deuterium.											
Hendecane $CH_3(CH_2)_9CH_3$ (Undecane)	149 (oc)				0.7	5.4	384	No	Water may be ineffective.	0	2	0
Heptadecanol $C_4H_9CH(C_2H_5)C_2H_4{-}CH(OH)C_2H_4CH(C_2H_5)_2$ (3, 9—Diethyl—6—Tridecanol)	310 (oc)		Note: Melting point 130°F.		0.8		588	No	Water or foam may cause frothing.	0	1	0
Heptane $CH_3(CH_2)_5CH_3$	25	419	1.05	6.7	0.7	3.5	209	No	Water may be ineffective.	1	3	0
Heptane $(CH_3)_2CH(CH_2)_2CH_3$ (2—Methylhexane)	<32	536			0.68	3.46	194			0	3	0
Heptane $(CH_3)_2CH(CH_2)_3CH_3$ (3—Methylhexane)	<32	536			0.69	3.46	198			0	3	0
2—Heptanol $CH_3(CH_2)_4CH(OH)CH_3$	160				0.8	4.0	320	No		0	2	0
3—Heptanol $CH_3CH_2CH(OH)C_4H_9$	140				0.8	4.0	313	Slight	"Alcohol" foam.	0	2	0
3—Heptanone	See Ethyl Butyl Ketone.											
4—Heptanone $(C_3H_7)_2CO$ (Butyrone) (Dipropyl Ketone)	120				0.8	3.9	290	No		2	2	0
Heptylamine $CH_3(CH_2)_6NH_2$ (1—Aminoheptane)	130 (oc)				0.8	4.0	311	Slight	"Alcohol" foam.	2	2	0

Table 3-11A (cont.)	FLASH POINT Deg. F.	IGNI- TION TEMP. Deg. F.	FLAMMABLE LIMITS Per Cent by Vol. Lower	Upper	Sp. Gr. (Water = 1)	Vapor Density (Air = 1)	Boiling Point Deg. F.	Water Soluble	EXTINGUISHING METHOD See Intro.	SUGGESTED HAZARD IDENTIFICATION Health	Flamma- bility	Reac- tivity
Heptylene $C_5H_{11}CH:CH_2$ (1—Heptene)	<32	500			0.7	3.39	201	No		0	3	0
Heptylene—2—trans $C_4H_9CH:CHCH_3$ (2—Heptene—trans)	<32				0.7	3.34	208			0	3	0
Hexachlorobutadiene $CCl_2:CCICCI:CCI_2$		1130				8.99				2	1	1
Hexachloro Diphenyl Oxide $(C_6H_2Cl_3)_2O$ (Bis(trichlorophenyl) Ether)		1148				13.0				2	1	1
Hexadecane $CH_3(CH_2)_{14}CH_3$ (Cetane)	>212 Note: Melting point 68°F.	401			0.8 @ 68°F	7.8	549	No		0	1	0
tert—Hexadecanethiol $C_{16}H_{33}SH$ (Hexadecyl—tert—Mercaptan)	265 (oc)				0.9		298–307 @ 11 mm.	No	Water or foam may cause frothing.	0	1	0
Hexadecylene—1 $CH_3(CH_2)_{13}CH:CH_2$ (1—Hexadecene)	>212	464			0.78	7.72	525	No		0	1	0
Hexadecyl—tert— Mercaptan	See tert—Hexadecanethiol.											
2, 4—Hexadienal $CH_3CH:CHCH:CHC(O)H$	154 (oc)		1.3	8.1	0.9		339	Very slight		2	2	0
1, 4—Hexadiene $CH_3CH:CHCH_2CH:CH_2$ (Allylpropenyl)	−6		2.0	6.1	0.7	2.8	151	No	Water may be ineffective.	0	3	0
Hexahydroaniline	See Cyclohexylamine.											
Hexahydrobenzene	See Cyclohexane.											
Hexahydropyridine	See Piperidine.											
Hexahydrotoluene	See Methylcyclohexane.											
Hexahydroxylol	See 1, 4—Dimethylcyclohexane.											
Hexaldehyde	See Hexanal.											
Hexalin	See Cyclohexanol.											
Hexalin Acetate	See Cyclohexyl Acetate.											
Hexamethylene	See Cyclohexane.											
Hexanal $CH_3(CH_2)_4CHO$ (Caproaldehyde) (Hexaldehyde)	90 (oc)				0.8	3.6	268	No	Water may be ineffective.	2	3	1
Hexane $CH_3(CH_2)_4CH_3$ (Hexyl Hydride)	−7 (Und. Lab. Class 90–95)	437	1.1	7.5	0.7	3.0	156	No	Water may be ineffective.	1	3	0
1, 2—Hexanediol	See Hexylene Glycol.											
2, 5—Hexanediol $CH_3CH(OH)CH_2-$ $CH_2CH(OH)CH_3$ (2, 5—Dihydroxyhexane)	230				1.0−		429	Yes	"Alcohol" foam. Water or foam may cause frothing.	2	1	0
2, 5—Hexanedione	See Acetonyl Acetone.											
1, 2, 6—Hexanetriol $HOCH_2CH(OH)-$ $(CH_2)_3CH_2OH$	375 (oc)				1.1		352 @ 5 mm.	Yes	Water or foam may cause frothing. "Alcohol" foam.	1	1	0
Hexanoic Acid	See Caproic Acid.											
1—Hexanol	See Hexyl Alcohol.											
2—Hexanone	See Methyl Butyl Ketone.											
3—Hexanone $C_2H_5COC_3H_7$ (Ethyl n—Propyl Ketone)	95 (oc)		~1	~8	0.82	3.46	253			1	3	0
1—Hexene $CH_2:CH(CH_2)_3CH_3$ (Butyl Ethylene)	<20				0.7	3.0	146	No	Water may be ineffective.	1	3	0
2—Hexene (Mixed cis- and trans- isomers) $CH_3CH:CH(CH_2)_2CH_3$	<20				0.7	3.0	155	No	Water may be ineffective.	1	3	0
2—Hexene—cis $C_3H_7CH:CHCH_3$	<−4				0.69	2.90	156			0	3	0
Hexone	See Methyl Isobutyl Ketone.											
Hexyl Acetate $(CH_3)_2CH(CH_2)_2OOCCH_3$ (Methylamyl Acetate)	113				0.9	5.0	285	No	"Alcohol" foam.	1	2	0
Hexyl Alcohol $CH_3(CH_2)_4CH_2OH$ (Amyl Carbinol) (1—Hexanol)	145				0.8	3.5	311	Slight	"Alcohol" foam.	1	2	0

Table 3-11A (cont.)	FLASH POINT Deg. F.	IGNI- TION TEMP. Deg. F.	FLAMMABLE LIMITS Per Cent by Vol.		Sp. Gr. (Water = 1)	Vapor Density (Air = 1)	Boiling Point Deg. F.	Water Soluble	EXTINGUISHING METHOD See Intro.	SUGGESTED HAZARD IDENTIFICATION		
			Lower	Upper						Health	Flamma- bility	Reac- tivity
sec—Hexyl Alcohol C₄H₉CH(OH)CH₃ (2—Hexanol)	136				0.81	3.53	284			0	2	0
Hexylamine CH₃(CH₂)₅NH₂	85 (oc)				0.8	3.5	269	Slight	Water may be ineffective. "Alcohol" foam.	2	3	0
Hexyl Chloride	See 1—Chlorohexane.											
Hexylene Glycol CH₂OHCHOH(CH₂)₃CH₃ (1, 2—Hexanediol)	215 (oc)				0.9		385		Water or foam may cause frothing.	1	1	0
Hexyl Ether C₆H₁₃OC₆H₁₃	170 (oc)	365			0.8	6.4	440	No		2	2	0
Hexyl Hydride	See Hexane.											
Hexyl Methacrylate C₆H₁₃OOCC(CH₃):CH₂	180 (oc)				0.9	5.9	388–464			0	2	0
Hexyl Methyl Ketone	See 2—Octanone.											
Hydracrylonitrile	See Ethylene Cyanohydrin.											
Hydralin	See Cyclohexanol.											
Hydrazine (Anhydrous) H₂NNH₂	100		4.7	100	1.0+	1.1	236	Yes	Vapors explosive.	3	3	2
	Ignition temperatures vary widely in contact with iron rust 74°F; black iron 270°F; stainless steel 313°F; glass 518°F. Note: See Hazardous Chemicals Data.											
Hydrochloric Ether	See Ethyl Chloride.											
Hydrocyanic Acid— 96% HCN (Prussic Acid) (Hydrogen Cyanide)	0	1000	5.6	40.0	0.7	0.9	79	Yes	Vapors extremely toxic.	4	4	2
	Note: See Hazardous Chemicals Data.											
Hydrogen H₂	Gas	752	4.0	75	0.1		−422	Slight	Stop flow of gas.	0	4	0
	Note: See Hazardous Chemicals Data.											
Hydrogen Cyanide	See Hydrocyanic Acid.											
Hydrogen Sulfide H₂S	Gas	500	4.0	44.0	1.2		−76	Yes	Stop flow of gas.	3	4	0
	Note: See Hazardous Chemicals Data.											
o—Hydroxy- benzaldehyde	See Salicylaldehyde.											
3—Hydroxybutanal	See Aldol.											
β—Hydroxybutyral- dehyde	See Aldol.											
N—(2—Hydroxyethyl)- acetamide	See N—Acetyl Ethanolamine.											
β—Hydroxyethylaniline	See 2—Anilinoethanol.											
N—(2—Hydroxyethyl) Cyclohexylamine C₆H₁₁NHC₂H₄OH	249 (oc)							Yes	Water or foam may cause frothing. "Alcohol" foam.	3	1	0
	Note: Melting point 97–102°F.											
(2—Hydroxyethyl)- ethylenediamine CH₂OHCH₂NHCH₂CH₂NH₂	275				1.0+		460–464	Yes	"Alcohol" foam. Water or foam may cause frothing.	1	1	0
4—(2—Hydroxyethyl) Morpholine C₂H₄OC₂H₄NC₂H₄OH	210 (oc)				1.1		437	Yes	"Alcohol" foam.	2	1	0
1—(2—Hydroxyethyl) Piperazine HOCH₂CH₂- NCH₂CH₂NHCH₂CH₂	255 (oc)				1.1	4.5	475	Yes	Water or foam may cause frothing. "Alcohol" foam.	0	1	0
N—(2—Hydroxyethyl) Propylenediamine CH₃CH(NHC₂H₄OH)CH₂NH₂	260 (oc)				1.0−		465	Yes	Water or foam may cause frothing. "Alcohol" foam.	2	1	0
Hydroxylamine NH₂OH (Oxammonium)	Explodes @ 265°				1.2		158	Yes		1	3	3
	Note: Melting point 92°F. See Hazardous Chemicals Data.											
4—Hydroxy—4— Methyl—2— Pentanone	See Diacetone Alcohol.											
2—Hydroxy—2— methylpropio- nitrile	See Acetone Cyanohydrin.											
Hydroxypropyl Acrylate	See Propylene Glycol Monoacrylate.											
o—Hydroxytoluene	See o—Cresol.											

Table 3-11A (cont.)	FLASH POINT Deg. F.	IGNI-TION TEMP. Deg. F.	FLAMMABLE LIMITS Per Cent by Vol. Lower	FLAMMABLE LIMITS Per Cent by Vol. Upper	Sp. Gr. (Water = 1)	Vapor Density (Air = 1)	Boiling Point Deg. F.	Water Soluble	EXTINGUISHING METHOD See Intro.	SUGGESTED HAZARD IDENTIFICATION Health	SUGGESTED HAZARD IDENTIFICATION Flamma-bility	SUGGESTED HAZARD IDENTIFICATION Reac-tivity
Iron Carbonyl $Fe(CO)_5$	5				1.45	6.74	221			2	3	1 ₩
Isano Oil					1.0—				May explode above 502°F.		1	3
		Exothermic reaction above 502° may become explosive.										
Isoamyl Acetate $CH_3COOCH_2CH_2CH(CH_3)_2$ (Banana Oil) (3—Methyl—1—Butanol Acetate) (2—Methyl Butyl Ethanoate)	77	680	1.0 @ 212° (Und. Lab. Class 55–60)	7.5	0.9	4.5	290	Slight	"Alcohol" foam. Water may be ineffective.	1	3	0
Isoamyl Alcohol $(CH_3)_2CHCH_2CH_2OH$ (Isobutyl Carbinol) (Fusel Oil) (3—Methyl—1—Butanol)	109	662	1.2 (Und. Lab. Class 35–40)	9.0 @ 212°	0.8	3.0	270	Slight	"Alcohol" foam.	1	2	0
tert—Isoamyl Alcohol		See 2—Methyl—2—Butanol.										
Isoamyl Butyrate $C_3H_7CO_2(CH_2)_2CH(CH_3)_2$ (Isopentyl Butyrate)	138				0.88	5.45	352				2	
Isoamyl Chloride $(CH_3)_2CHCH_2CH_2Cl$ (1—Chloro—3—methylbutane)	<70		1.5	7.4	0.89	3.67	212				3	
Isobutane $(CH_3)_3CH$ (2—Methylpropane)	Gas	860	1.8	8.4		2.0	11	No	Stop flow of gas.	1	4	0
Isobutyl Acetate $CH_3COOCH_2CH(CH_3)_2$	64	790	2.4	10.5	0.9	4.0	244	No	"Alcohol" foam. Water may be ineffective.	1	3	0
Isobutyl Alcohol $(CH_3)_2CHCH_2OH$ (Isopropyl Carbinol) (2—Methyl—1—propanol)	82	800	1.2 @ 212° (Und. Lab. Class 40–45)	10.9 @ 212°	0.8	2.6	225	Yes	"Alcohol" foam. Water may be ineffective.	1	3	0
Isobutylamine $(CH_3)_2CHCH_2NH_2$	15	712			0.7	2.5	150	Yes	"Alcohol" foam. Water may be ineffective.	2	3	0
Isobutylbenzene $(CH_3)_2CHCH_2C_6H_5$	131	806	0.8	6.0	0.9	4.6	343	No		2	2	0
Isobutyl Butyrate $C_3H_7CO_2CH_2CH(CH_3)_2$	122				0.87	5.0	315			0	2	
Isobutyl Carbinol		See Isoamyl Alcohol.										
Isobutyl Chloride $(CH_3)_2CHCH_2Cl$ (1—Chloro—3—methylpropane)	<70		2.0	8.8	0.9	3.2	156			2	3	0
Isobutylene		See 2—Methylpropene.										
Isobutyl Formate $HCOOCH_2CH(CH_3)_2$	<70	608	~1.7	~8	0.88	3.52	208				3	
Isobutyl Phosphate $PO_4(CH_2CH(CH_3)_2)_3$ (Triisobutyl Phosphate)	275 (oc)				0.98	9.12	302 @ 20 mm.				1	
Isobutyl Vinyl Ether		See Vinyl Isobutyl Ether.										
Isobutyraldehyde $(CH_3)_2CHCHO$ (2—Methylpropanal)	−40	490	1.6	10.6	0.8	2.5	142	Slight	"Alcohol" foam. Water may be ineffective.	2	3	1
Isobutyric Acid $(CH_3)_2CHCOOH$	132	935			1.0—	3.0	306	Yes	"Alcohol" foam.	1	2	0
Isobutyric Anhydride $[(CH_3)_2CHCO]_2O$	139	665			1.0—	5.5	360	De-composes	"Alcohol" foam.	1	2	1 ₩
Isodecaldehyde $C_9H_{19}CO$	185 (oc)				0.8	5.4	387	No		0	2	0
Isodecane $C_7H_{15}CH(CH_3)_2$ (2—Methylnonane)		410			0.73	4.91	333			0	2	0
Isodecanoic Acid $C_9H_{19}COOH$	300 (oc)				0.9	5.9	489	No	Water or foam may cause frothing.	0	1	0
Isodecanol, Mixed Isomers $C_{10}H_{21}OH$	220 (oc)				0.8	5.5	428	No	Water or foam may cause frothing.	0	1	0
Isoheptane, Mixed Isomers	<0		1.0	6.0	0.7		176–195	No	Water may be ineffective.	1	3	0
Isohexane (Mixture of Hexane Isomers)	<−20		1.0	7.0	0.7		134–142	No	Water may be ineffective.	1	3	0
tert—Isohexyl Alcohol $C_2H_5(CH_3)C(OH)C_2H_5$ (3—Methyl—3—pentanol)	115				0.77	3.53	252				2	0
Isooctanoic Acid (Mixed isomers) $C_6H_{15}COOH$	270 (oc)				0.9	5.0	428 Decom-poses	No	Water or foam may cause frothing.	0	1	0

Table 3-11A (cont.)	FLASH POINT Deg. F.	IGNI- TION TEMP. Deg. F.	FLAMMABLE LIMITS Per Cent by Vol.		Sp. Gr. (Water = 1)	Vapor Density (Air = 1)	Boiling Point Deg. F.	Water Soluble	EXTINGUISHING METHOD See Intro.	SUGGESTED HAZARD IDENTIFICATION		
			Lower	Upper						Health	Flamma- bility	Reac- tivity
Isooctyl Nitrate $C_8H_{17}NO_3$	205 (oc)				1.0 —		106–109 @ 1 mm.	No			1	
Isooctyl Vinyl Ether	See Vinyl Isooctyl Ether.											
Isopentane $(CH_3)_2CHCH_2CH_3$ (2—Methylbutane) (Ethyl Dimethyl Methane)	<−60	788	1.4	7.6	0.6		82	No	Water may be ineffective.	1	4	0
Isophorone $\overline{COCHC(CH_3)CH_2C(CH_3)_2CH_2}$	184	860	0.8	3.8	0.9		419	Slight		2	1	0
Isophthaloyl Chloride $C_6H_4(COCl)_2$ (m—Phthalyl Dichloride)	356 (oc)	Note: Melting point 109.9°F.			1.4	6.9	529	No	Water or foam may cause frothing.		1	0
Isoprene $CH_2:C(CH_3)CH:CH_2$ (2—Methyl—1, 3—Butadiene)	−65	428	2	9	0.7	2.4	93	No	Water may be ineffective.	2	4	1
Isopropanol	See Isopropyl Alcohol.											
Isopropanolamine	See 1—Amino—2—Propanol.											
Isopropenyl Acetate $CH_3COOC(CH_3):CH_2$ (1—Methylvinyl Acetate)	60				0.9	3.5	207	Slight	"Alcohol" foam. Water may be ineffective.	2	3	0
Isopropenyl Acetylene $CH_2:C(CH_3)C:CH$	<19 (oc)				0.7	2.3	92	Slight	Water may be ineffective. "Alcohol" foam.	2	4	2
2—Isopropoxypropane	See Isopropyl Ether.											
3—Isopropoxypropio- nitrile $(CH_3)_2CHOCH_2CH_2CN$	155				0.9	3.9	149 @ 10 mm.	Slight	"Alcohol" foam.	1	2	1
Isopropyl Acetate $(CH_3)_2CHOOCCH_3$	40	860	1.8	8	0.9	3.5	194	Slight	"Alcohol" foam. Water may be ineffective.	1	3	0
Isopropyl Alcohol $(CH_3)_2CHOH$ (Isopropanol) (Dimethyl Carbinol) (2—Propanol) 87.9% iso	53 (Und. Lab. Class 70) 57	750	2.0	12	0.8	2.1	181	Yes	"Alcohol" foam. Water may be ineffective.	1	3	0
Isopropylamine $(CH_3)_2CHNH_2$	−35 (oc)	756			0.7	2.0	89	Yes	"Alcohol" foam. Water may be ineffective.	3	4	0
Isopropylbenzene	See Cumene.											
Isopropyl Benzoate $C_6H_5COOCH(CH_3)_2$	210				1.0 +		426	No		1	1	
Isopropyl Bicyclohexyl $C_{15}H_{28}$	255	446	0.5 @ 302°	4.1 @ 400°	0.9		530–541		Water or foam may cause frothing.	0	1	0
2—Isopropylbiphenyl $C_{15}H_{16}$	285	815	0.5 @ 347°	3.2 @ 392°	1.0 —		518		Water or foam may cause frothing.	0	1	0
Isopropyl Carbinol	See Isobutyl Alcohol.											
Isopropyl Chloride $(CH_3)_2CHCl$ (2—Chloropropane)	−26	1100	2.8	10.7	0.9	2.7	95	Very slight	Water may be ineffective.	2	4	0
Isopropylcyclohexyla- mine $C_6H_{11}NHCHC_2H_6$	93 (oc)				0.8	4.9		No	Water may be ineffective.	3	3	0
Isopropyl Ether $(CH_3)_2CHOCH(CH_3)_2$ (2—Isopropoxypropane)	−18	830	1.4	7.9	0.7	3.5	156	Very slight	"Alcohol" foam. Water may be ineffective.	2	3	1
	Note: See Hazardous Chemicals Data.											
Isopropylethylene	See 3—Methyl—1—Butene.											
Isopropyl Formate $HCOOCH(CH_3)_2$ (Isopropyl Methanoate)	22	905			0.9	3.0	153	Slight		2	3	0
4—Isopropylheptane $C_3H_7CH(C_3H_7)C_3H_7$ (m—Dihydroxybenzene)		491			0.87	3.04	155			0	2	0
Isopropyl—2— Hydroxypropanoate	See Isopropyl Lactate.											
Isopropyl Lactate $CH_3CHOHCCOCH(CH_3)_2$ (Isopropyl—2— Hydroxypropionate)	130 (oc)				1.0 —	4.2	331–334	Yes	"Alcohol" foam.	2	2	0
Isopropyl Methanoate	See Isopropyl Formate.											
4—Isopropyl—1— Methyl Benzene	See p—Cymene.											
Isopropyl Vinyl Ether	See Vinyl Isopropyl Ether.											
Isovalerone	See Diisobutyl Ketone.											

Table 3-11A (cont.)	FLASH POINT Deg. F.	IGNI- TION TEMP. Deg. F.	FLAMMABLE LIMITS Per Cent by Vol.		Sp. Gr. (Water = 1)	Vapor Density (Air = 1)	Boiling Point Deg. F.	Water Soluble	EXTINGUISHING METHOD See Intro.	SUGGESTED HAZARD IDENTIFICATION		
			Lower	Upper						Health	Flamma- bility	Reac- tivity
Jet Fuels Jet A and Jet A-1	110–150						400–550			0	2	0
Jet Fuels Jet B	–10– 30									1	3	0
Jet Fuels JP—4	–10–+30	464	1.3	8.0						1	3	0
Jet Fuels JP—5	95– 145	475 (approx.)								0	2	0
Jet Fuels JP—6	100 (oc)	446	0.6	3.7	0.8	<1	250	No				
Katchung Oil	See Peanut Oil (cooking).											
Kerosene	See Fuel Oil No. 1.											
Kerosene, Deodorized	See Ultrasene.											
Lactonitrile CH₃CH(OH)CN	171				0.98	2.45	361	Yes		4	2	1
Lanolin (Wool Grease)	460	833			<1			No	Water or foam may cause frothing.	0	1	0
Lard Oil (Commercial or Animal) No. 1	395 440	833 (Und. Lab. Class 10–20)			<1			No	Water or foam may cause frothing.	0	1	0
Lard Oil (Pure) No. 2 Mineral	500 419 404				0.9			No	Water or foam may cause frothing.	0	1	0
Lauryl Alcohol	See 1—Dodecanol.											
Lauryl Bromide CH₃(CH₂)₁₀CH₂Br (Dodecyl Bromide)	291				1.0+		356 @ 45 mm.	No	Water or foam may cause frothing.	1	1	0
Lauryl Mercaptan	See 1—Dodecanethiol.											
Linseed Oil, Raw Boiled	432 403	650			0.9		600+	No	Water or foam may cause frothing.	0	1	0
Liquid Camphor	See Camphor Oil (light).											
Lubricating Oil, Mineral (Paraffin Oil, includes Motor Oil)	300– 450	500– 700			<1		680	No	Water or foam may cause frothing.	0	1	0
Lubricating Oil, Spindle (Spindle Oil)	169	478			<1			No		0	2	0
Lubricating Oil, Turbine (Turbine Oil)	400 (oc)	700			<1			No	Water or foam may cause frothing.	0	1	0
Maleic Anhydride (COCH)₂O	215 Note: Melting point 127°F. See Hazardous Chemicals Data.	890	1.4	7.1	0.9		396	Slight	"Alcohol" foam. Water or foam may cause frothing.	3	1	1 W
Marsh Gas	See Methane.											
Menhaden Oil (Pogy Oil)	435	828			0.9			No	Water or foam may cause frothing.	0	1	0
2—Mercaptoethanol HSCH₂CH₂OH	165 (oc)				1.1	2.7	315	Yes	"Alcohol" foam.	2	2	
Mesityl Oxide (CH₃)₂CCHCOCH₃	87 Note: See Hazardous Chemicals Data.	652			0.9	3.4	266	Slight	Water may be ineffective. "Alcohol" foam.	3	3	0
Metaldehyde (C₂H₄O)₄	97						subl. 233–240	No	Water may be ineffective.	1	3	1
α—Methacrolein	See 2—Methylpropenal.											
Methacrylic Acid CH₂:C(CH₃)COOH	171 (oc) Note: Polymerizes. See Hazardous Chemicals Data.				1.0+		316	Yes	"Alcohol" foam.	3	2	2
Methallyl Alcohol CH₂C(CH₃)CH₂OH	92				0.9	2.5	237	Slight	Water may be ineffective. "Alcohol" foam.	2	3	0
Methallyl Chloride CH₂C(CH₃)CH₂Cl	11		3.2	8.1	0.9	3.1	162	No	Water may be ineffective. "Alcohol" foam.	2	3	1
Methane CH₄ (Marsh Gas)	Gas	1004	5.0	15.0	0.6		–259	No	Stop flow of gas.	1	4	0
Methanol	See Methyl Alcohol.											
Methanethiol	See Methyl Mercaptan.											
Methox	See Methoxy Ethyl Phthalate.											

Table 3-11A (cont.)	FLASH POINT Deg. F.	IGNI- TION TEMP. Deg. F.	FLAMMABLE LIMITS Per Cent by Vol.		Sp. Gr. (Water = 1)	Vapor Density (Air = 1)	Boiling Point Deg. F.	Water Soluble	EXTINGUISHING METHOD See Intro.	SUGGESTED HAZARD IDENTIFICATION		
			Lower	Upper						Health	Flamma- bility	Reac- tivity
o—Methoxy- benzaldehyde $CH_3OC_6H_4CHO$ (o—Anisaldehyde)	244 (oc)				1.1		469	No	Water or foam may cause frothing.	2	1	0
Methoxybenzene	See Anisole.											
3—Methoxybutanol $CH_3CH(OCH_3)CH_2$- CH_2OH	165 (oc)				0.9	3.6	322	Yes	"Alcohol" foam.	1	2	0
3—Methoxybutyl Acetate $CH_3OCH(CH_3)CH_2CH_2$- $OOCCH_3$ (Butoxyl)	170				1.0—	5.0	275–343	Slight	"Alcohol" foam.	1	2	0
3—Methoxy- butyraldehyde $CH_3CH(OCH_3)CH_2CHO$ (Aldol Ether)	140				0.94	3.52	262			0	2	0
2—Methoxyethanol	See Ethylene Glycol Monomethyl Ether.											
2—Methoxyethyl Acrylate $C_2H_3COOC_2H_4OCH_3$	180 (oc)				1.01	4.49	142 @ 17 mm.			0	2	0
Methoxy Ethyl Phthalate (Methox)	275				1.2		376–412		Water or foam may cause frothing.	0	1	0
3—Methoxy- propionitrile $CH_3OC_2H_4CN$	149 (oc)				0.92	2.94	320			4	2	1
3—Methoxy- propylamine $CH_3OC_3H_6NH_2$	90				0.86	3.07	241			2	3	0
Methoxy Triglycol $CH_3O(C_2H_4O)_3H$ (Triethylene Glycol, Methyl Ether)	245 (oc)				1.0+		480	Yes	"Alcohol" foam. Water or foam may cause frothing.	0	1	0
Methoxytriglycol Acetate $CH_3COO(C_2H_4O)_3CH_3$	260 (oc)				1.1		266	Yes	Water or foam may cause frothing. "Alcohol" foam.	0	1	0
Methyl Abietate $C_{19}H_{29}COOCH_3$ (Abalyn)	356 (oc)				1.0+		680–689 Decom- poses	No	Water or foam may cause frothing.	0	1	0
Methyl Acetate CH_3COOCH_3 (Acetic Acid Methyl Ester) (Methyl Acetic Ester)	14 (Und. Lab. Class 85–90)	935	3.1	16	0.9	2.8	140	Yes	Water may be ineffective. "Alcohol" foam.	1	3	0
Methyl Acetic Ester	See Methyl Acetate.											
Methyl Acetoacetate $CH_3CO_2CH_2COCH_3$	170 Note: Melting point 82°F.	536			1.1	4.0	338	Yes	"Alcohol" foam.	2	2	0
Methylacetylene	See Propyne.											
α—Methylacrolein	See 2—Methylpropenal.											
Methyl Acrylate $CH_2:CHCOOCH_3$	27 (oc) Note: Polymerizes. See Hazardous Chemicals Data.		2.8	25	1.0—	3.0	176	Very slight	Water may be ineffective.	2	3	2
Methylal $CH_3OCH_2OCH_3$ (Dimethoxymethane) (Formal)	0 (oc)	459			0.9	2.6	111	Yes	Water may be ineffective. "Alcohol" foam.	2	3	2
Methyl Alcohol CH_3OH (Methanol) (Wood Alcohol) (Columbian Spirits)	52 (Und. Lab. Class 70)	725	6.7	36	0.8	1.1	147	Yes	Water may be ineffective. "Alcohol" foam.	1	3	0
Methylaluminum Sesquibromide $(CH_3)_3Al_2Br_3$	Note: Ignites spontaneously in air.								Do not use water, foam or halogenated extinguishing agents.		3	3 ₩
Methylaluminum Sesquichloride $(CH_3)_3Al_2Cl_3$	Note: Ignites spontaneously in air.								Do not use water, foam or halogenated extinguishing agents.		3	3 ₩
Methylamine CH_3NH_2	Gas Note: See Hazardous Chemicals Data.	806	4.9	20.7	1.1		21	Yes	Stop flow of gas.	3	4	0
2—(Methylamino)- ethanol	See N—Methylethanolamine.											
Methylamyl Acetate	See Hexyl Acetate.											
Methylamyl Alcohol	See Methyl Isobutyl Carbinol.											

Table 3-11A (cont.)	FLASH POINT Deg. F.	IGNITION TEMP. Deg. F.	FLAMMABLE LIMITS Per Cent by Vol. Lower	Upper	Sp. Gr. (Water =1)	Vapor Density (Air =1)	Boiling Point Deg. F.	Water Soluble	EXTINGUISHING METHOD See Intro.	SUGGESTED HAZARD IDENTIFICATION Health	Flamma-bility	Reac-tivity
Methyl Amyl Ketone $CH_3CO(CH_2)_4CH_3$	120 (oc)	991			0.8	3.9	302	Slight	"Alcohol" foam.	1	2	0
2—Methylaniline	*See o—Toluidine.*											
4—Methylaniline	*See p—Toluidine.*											
Methylbenzene	*See Toluol.*											
Methyl Benzoate $C_6H_5COOCH_3$ (Niobe Oil)	181				1.1	4.7	302	No	Water may be used to blanket fire.	0	2	0
α—Methylbenzyl Alcohol	*See Phenyl Methyl Carbinol.*											
α—Methylbenzylamine $C_6H_5CH(CH_3)NH_2$	175 (oc)				1.0—	4.2	371	Slight	"Alcohol" foam.	2	2	0
α—Methylbenzyl Dimethyl Amine $C_6H_5CH(CH_3)N(CH_3)_2$	175 (oc)				0.9	5.2	384	Slight	"Alcohol" foam.	2	2	0
α—Methylbenzyl Ether $C_6H_5CH(CH_3)OCH-(CH_3)C_6H_5$	275 (oc)				1.0		548	No	Water or foam may cause frothing. "Alcohol" foam.	2	1	0
Methyl Borate $B(OCH_3)_3$ (Trimethyl Borate)	<80				0.9	3.6	156	Decom-poses		2	3	1
Methyl Bromide CH_3Br (Bromomethane)	Practi-cally non-flammable	999	10	15.0	1.7	3.3	40	No		3	0	0
2—Methyl—1, 3—Butadiene	*See Isoprene.*											
2—Methylbutane	*See Isopentane.*											
2—Methyl—1—Butanol $CH_3CH_2CH(CH_3)CH_2OH$	122 (oc)				0.8	3.0	262	Slight	"Alcohol" foam.	2	2	0
2—Methyl—2—Butanol $CH_3CH_2(CH_3)_2COH$ (tert—Isoamyl Alcohol) (Dimethyl Ethyl Carbinol)	67	819	1.2	9.0	0.8	3.0	215	Slight	"Alcohol" foam. Water may be ineffective.	1	3	0
3—Methyl—1—Butanol	*See Isoamyl Alcohol.*											
3—Methyl—1—Butanol Acetate	*See Isoamyl Acetate.*											
2—Methyl—1—Butene (Technical Grade) $CH_2:C(CH_3)CH_2CH_3$	<20				0.7	2.4	₋88	No	Water may be ineffective.	2	4	0
2—Methyl—2—Butene $(CH_3)_2C:CCHCH_3$ (Trimethylethylene)	<20				0.7	2.4	101	Slight	Water may be ineffective. "Alcohol" foam.	2	3	0
3—Methyl—1—Butene $(CH_3)_2CHCH:CH_2$ (Isopropylethylene)	<20	689	1.5	9.1	0.6	2.4	68	No	Water may be ineffective.	2	4	0
N—Methylbutylamine $CH_3CH_2CH_2CH_2NHCH_3$	55 (oc)				0.7	3.0	196	Yes	Water may be ineffective. "Alcohol" foam.	3	3	0
2—Methyl Butyl Ethanoate	*See Isoamyl Acetate.*											
Methyl Butyl Ketone $CH_3CO(CH_2)_3CH_3$ (2—Hexanone)	95 (oc)	991	1.2	8	0.8	3.5	262	Slight	Water may be ineffective. "Alcohol" foam.	2	3	0
3—Methyl Butynol $(CH_3)_2C(OH)C:CH$	77 (oc)				0.9	2.9	218	Yes	Water may be ineffective. "Alcohol" foam.	2	3	0
Methyl Butyrate $CH_3OOCCH_2CH_2CH_3$	57				0.9	3.5	215	Slight	Water may be ineffective. "Alcohol" foam.	2	3	0
Methyl Carbonate $CO(OCH_3)_2$ (Dimethyl Carbonate)	66 (oc)				1.1	3.1	192	Slight	Water may be ineffective. "Alcohol" foam.	2	3	1
Methyl Cellosolve Acetate $CH_3COOC_2H_4OCH_3$ (2—Methoxyethyl Acetate)	~111		1.7	8.2	1.0	4.07	292	Yes		0	2	0
Methyl Chloride CH_3Cl (Chloromethane)	Gas	1170	10.7	17.4		1.8	₋11	Slight	Stop flow of gas.	2	4	0
	Note: See Hazardous Chemicals Data.											
Methyl Chloroacetate $CH_2ClCOOCH_3$ (Methyl Chloroethanoate)	122 (oc)				1.2	3.8	266	Very slight		2	2	1
Methyl Chloroethanoate	*See Methyl Chloroacetate.*											
Methyl Cyanide	*See Acetonitrile.*											

Table 3-11A (cont.)

	Flash Point Deg. F.	Ignition Temp. Deg. F.	Flammable Limits Per Cent by Vol. Lower	Upper	Sp. Gr. (Water =1)	Vapor Density (Air =1)	Boiling Point Deg. F.	Water Soluble	Extinguishing Method See Intro.	Health	Flamma- bility	Reac- tivity
Methylcyclohexane $CH_2(CH_2)_4CHCH_3$ (Cyclohexylmethane) (Hexahydroxytoluene)	25	482	1.2	6.7	0.8	3.4	214	No	Water may be ineffective.	2	3	0
2—Methylcyclohexanol $C_7H_{13}OH$	149	565			0.9	3.9	329	Slight	"Alcohol" foam.		2	0
3—Methylcyclohexanol $CH_3C_6H_{10}OH$	~158	563								0	2	0
4—Methylcyclohexanol $C_7H_{13}OH$	158	563			0.9	3.9	343	Slight	"Alcohol" foam.		2	0
Methylcyclohexanone $C_7H_{12}O$	118				0.9	3.9	325	No			2	0
4—Methylcyclohexene $CH:CHCH_2CH(CH_3)CH_2CH_2$	30 (oc)				0.8	3.3	217	No	Water may be ineffective.	1	3	0
Methylcyclohexyl Acetate $C_9H_{16}O_2$	147				0.9		351–381			1	2	0
Methyl Cyclopentadiene C_6H_8	120	833	1.3 @ 212°	7.6 @ 212°	0.9		163			1	2	1
Methylcyclopentane C_6H_{12}	<20				0.8	2.9	161	No	Water may be ineffective.	2	3	0
2—Methyldecane $CH_3(CH_2)_7CH(CH_3)_2$		437			0.74	5.39	374			0	2	0
N—Methyldiethanol- amine $CH_3N(C_2H_4OH)_2$	260 (oc)				1.0+		464	Yes	Water or foam may cause frothing. "Alcohol" foam.	1	1	0
1—Methyl—3, 5— diethylbenzene $(CH_3)C_6H_3(C_2H_5)_2$ (3, 5—Diethyltoluene)		851			0.86	5.12	394			0	2	0
Methyl Dihydroabietate $C_{19}H_{31}COOCH_3$	361				1.0+		689–698		Water or foam may cause frothing.	1	1	0
Methylene Chloride CH_2Cl_2 (Dichloromethane)	Practi- cally nonflammable	1139	15.5 In pure oxygen.	66	1.3	2.9	104	Slight		2	0	0
Methylene Diisocyanate $CH_2(NCO)_2$	185 (oc)									1	2	1 ₩
Methylene Oxide	See Formaldehyde.											
N—Methylethanolamine $CH_3NHCH_2CH_2OH$ (2—(Methylamino)ethanol)	165 (oc)				0.9	2.6	319	Yes	"Alcohol" foam.	2	2	0
Methyl Ether $(CH_3)_2O$ (Dimethyl Ether) (Methyl Oxide)	Gas	662	3.4	27.0		1.6	−11	Yes	Stop flow of gas.	2	4	0
Methyl Ethyl Carbinol	See sec—Butyl Alcohol.											
2—Methyl—2—Ethyl— 1, 3—Dioxolane $(CH_3)(C_2H_5)COCH_2CH_2O$	74 (oc)				0.9	4.0	244	No	Water may be ineffective.	2	3	0
Methyl Ethylene Glycol	See Propylene Glycol.											
Methyl Ethyl Ether $CH_3OC_2H_5$ (Ethyl Methyl Ether)	−35	374	2.0 Note: See Hazardous Chemicals Data.	10.1	0.7	2.1	51	Yes	Water may be ineffective. "Alcohol" foam.	2	4	0
2—Methyl—4— ethylhexane $(CH_3)_2CHCH_2CH(C_2H_5)_2$ (4—Ethyl—2—methylhexane)	<70	536	~0.7		0.72	4.43	273			0	3	0
3—Methyl—4— ethylhexane $C_2H_5CH(CH_3)CH(C_2H_5)_2$ (3—Ethyl—4—methylhexane)	75				0.72	4.43	284			0	3	0
Methyl Ethyl Ketone $C_2H_5COCH_3$ (2—Butanone) (Ethyl Methyl Ketone)	21	960	1.8 (Und. Lab. Class 85–90)	10	0.8	2.5	176	Yes	Water may be ineffective. "Alcohol" foam.	1	3	0
2—Methyl—3— ethylpentane $(CH_3)_2CHCH(C_2H_5)_2$ (3—Ethyl—2—methylpentane)	<70	860			0.72	3.94	241			0	3	0
2—Methyl—5—Ethyl- piperidine $NHCH(CH_3)CH_2CH_2CH-$ $(C_2H_5)CH_2$	126 (oc)				0.8	4.4	326	Slight	"Alcohol" foam.	2	2	0

Table 3-11A (cont.)	FLASH POINT Deg. F.	IGNI-TION TEMP. Deg. F.	FLAMMABLE LIMITS Per Cent by Vol. Lower	FLAMMABLE LIMITS Per Cent by Vol. Upper	Sp. Gr. (Water = 1)	Vapor Density (Air = 1)	Boiling Point Deg. F.	Water Soluble	EXTINGUISHING METHOD See Intro.	SUGGESTED HAZARD IDENTIFICATION Health	SUGGESTED HAZARD IDENTIFICATION Flamma-bility	SUGGESTED HAZARD IDENTIFICATION Reac-tivity
2—Methyl—5—Ethyl-pyridine N:C(CH₃)CH:CHC(C₂H₅):CH	165 (oc)				0.9	4.2	353	Slight	"Alcohol" foam.	3	2	0
Methyl Formate CH₃OOCH (Formic Acid, Methyl Ester) (Methyl Methanoate)	−2	869	5.0	23	1.0—	2.1	90	Yes	Water may be ineffective. "Alcohol" foam.	2	4	0
	Note: See Hazardous Chemicals Data.											
2—Methylfuran C₄H₃OCH₃ (Sylvan)	−22				0.9		144–147	No	Water may be ineffective.	2	3	1
Methyl Glycol Acetate CH₂OHCHOHCH₂CO₂CH₃ (Propylene Glycol Acetate)	111					4.6				1	2	0
Methyl Heptadecyl Ketone C₁₇H₃₅COCH₃	255						329 @ 3 mm.	No	Water or foam may cause frothing.	0	1	0
	Note: Melting point 127°F.											
Methyl Heptyl Ketone C₇H₁₅COCH₃	160				0.8 @ 86°F	4.9	381	No		0	2	0
Methylhydrazine CH₃NHNH₂	<80		4.0		0.9	1.6	190	Slight	Water may be ineffective. "Alcohol" foam.	3	3	1
Methyl—3—Hydroxy-butyrate CH₃CHOHCH₂COOCH₃	180 (oc)				1.1	4.1	347	Yes	"Alcohol" foam.	1	2	0
Methyl Isoamyl Ketone CH₃COCH₂CH₂CH(CH₃)₂ (oc)	110				0.8	3.9	294	No		1	2	0
Methyl Isobutyl Carbinol CH₃CHOHCH₂CHCH₃CH₃ (1, 3—Dimethylbutanol) (4—Methyl—2—Pentanol) (Methylamyl Alcohol)	106		1.0	5.5	0.8		266–271	Slight	"Alcohol" foam.	2	2	0
Methylisobutylcarbinol Acetate	*See 4—Methyl—2—Pentanol Acetate.*											
Methyl Isobutyl Ketone CH₃COCH₂CH(CH₃)₂ (Hexone) (4—Methyl—2—Pentanone)	73	860	1.4	7.5	0.8	3.5	244	Slight	"Alcohol" foam. Water may be ineffective.	2	3	0
Methyl Isopropenyl Ketone CH₂COC:CH₂(CH₃)			1.8	9.0		2.9	208			2		0
Methyl Lactate CH₃CHOHCOOCH₃	121	725	2.2 @ 212°		1.1	3.6	293	Yes, Decom-poses		1	2	0
			(Und. Lab. Class 30–35)									
Methyl Mercaptan CH₃SH (Methanethiol)			3.9	21.8	0.9	1.7	42.4	Yes	"Alcohol" foam.	2	4	0
β Methyl Mercapto-propionaldehyde CH₃SC₂H₄CHO (3—(Methylthio)propionaldehyde)	142	491			1.03	3.60	~329				2	0
Methyl Methacrylate CH₂:C(CH₃)COOCH₃	50 (oc)		1.7	8.2	0.9	3.6	212	Very slight	Water may be ineffective.	2	3	2
	Note: Polymerizes. See Hazardous Chemicals Data.											
Methyl Methanoate	*See Methyl Formate.*											
4—Methylmorpholine C₂H₄OC₂H₄NCH₃	75				0.9	3.5	239	Yes	Water may be ineffective. "Alcohol" foam.	2	3	0
1—Methylnapthalene C₁₀H₇CH₃		984			1.0+		472	No		2	2	0
Methyl Nonyl Ketone C₉H₁₉COCH₃	192				0.8 @ 86°F	5.9	433	No		0	2	0
Methyl Oxide	*See Methyl Ether.*											
Methyl Pentadecyl Ketone C₁₅H₃₁COCH₃	248						313 @ 3 mm.	No	Water or foam may cause frothing.	0	1	0
2—Methyl—1, 3—Pentadiene CH₂:C(CH₃)CH:CHCH₃	<−4				0.72	2.83	169			0	3	0
4—Methyl—1, 3—Pentadiene CH₂:CHCH₂:C(CH₃)₂	−30				0.7		168	No	Water may be ineffective.	0	3	1

Table 3-11A (cont.)	FLASH POINT Deg. F.	IGNI-TION TEMP. Deg. F.	FLAMMABLE LIMITS Per Cent by Vol.		Sp. Gr. (Water =1)	Vapor Density (Air =1)	Boiling Point Deg. F.	Water Soluble	EXTINGUISHING METHOD See Intro.	SUGGESTED HAZARD IDENTIFICATION		
			Lower	Upper						Health	Flamma-bility	Reac-tivity
Methylpentaldehyde $CH_3CH_2CH_2C(CH_3)HCHO$ (oc) (Methylpentanal)	68				0.8		243	Very slight	Water may be ineffective.	2	3	1
Methyl Pentanal	See Methylpentaldehyde.											
2—Methylpentane $(CH_3)_2CH(CH_2)_2CH_3$	<20	583	1.2	7.0	0.7	3.0	140	No	Water may be ineffective.	1	3	0
3—Methylpentane $CH_3CH_2CH(CH_3)CH_2CH_3$	<20	572	1.2	7.0	0.7	3.0	146	No	Water may be ineffective.	1	3	0
2—Methyl—1, 3—Pentanediol $CH_3CH_2CH(OH)$-$CH(CH_3)CH_2OH$	230				1.0—		419		Water or foam may cause frothing.	2	1	0
2—Methyl—2, 4—Pentanediol $(CH_3)_2C(OH)CH_2CH$-$(OH)CH_3$	205 (oc)				0.92	4.07	385	Yes		0	1	0
2—Methylpentanoic Acid $C_3H_7CH(CH_3)COOH$	225 (oc)				0.9	4.0	381	No	Water or foam may cause frothing.	0	1	0
2—Methyl—1—Pentanol $CH_3(CH_2)_2CH(CH_3)CH_2OH$	135 (oc)				0.8	3.5	298	No		0	2	0
4—Methyl—2—Pentanol	See Methyl Isobutyl Carbinol.											
4—Methyl—2—Pentanol Acetate $CH_3COOCH(CH_3)CH_2$-$CH(CH_3)_2$ (Methylisobutylcarbinol Acetate)	110 (oc)				0.9	5.0	295	Very slight		1	2	0
4—Methyl—2—Pentanone	See Methyl Isobutyl Ketone.											
2—Methyl—1—Pentene $CH_2:C(CH_3)CH_2CH_2CH_3$	<20	572			0.7	2.9	143		Water may be ineffective.	1	3	0
4—Methyl—1—Pentene $CH_2:CHCH_2CH(CH_3)_2$	<20	572			0.7	2.9	129		Water may be ineffective.	1	3	0
2—Methyl—2—Pentene $(CH_3)_2C:CHCH_2CH_3$	<20				0.7	2.9	153		Water may be ineffective.	1	3	0
4—Methyl—2—Pentene $CH_3CH:CHCH(CH_3)_2$	<20				0.7		133–137		Water may be ineffective.	1	3	0
3—Methyl—1—Pentynol $(C_2H_5)(CH_3)C(OH)C:CH$	101 (oc)				0.9	3.4	250	Yes	"Alcohol" foam.	1	2	0
o—Methyl Phenol	See o—Cresol.											
Methyl Phenyl Ether	See Anisole.											
1—Methyl—1—Phenyl-ethylene $C_6H_5C(CH_3)CH_2$ (α—Methyl Styrene)	129	1066	1.9	6.1	0.9		329–331	No		1	2	1
Methyl Phthalyl Ethyl Glycolate $CH_3COOC_6H_4COO$-$CH_2COOC_2H_5$	380 (oc)				1.2		590	No	Water or foam may cause frothing.	2	1	0
1—Methyl Piperazine $CH_3NCH_2CH_2NHCH_2CH_2$ (oc)	108				0.9	3.5	280	Yes	"Alcohol" foam.	2	2	0
2—Methylpropanal	See Isobutyraldehyde.											
2—Methylpropane	See Isobutane.											
2—Methyl—2—Propanethiol $(CH_3)_3CSH$ (tert—Butyl Mercaptan)	<—20				0.8	3.1	149–153	No	Water may be ineffective.	2	3	0
2—Methyl Propanol—1	See Isobutyl Alcohol.											
2—Methyl—2—Propanol	See tert—Butyl Alcohol.											
2—Methylpropenal $CH_2:C(CH_3)CHO$ (Methacrolein) (α—Methyl Acrolein)	35 (oc)				0.8	2.4	154	Yes	Water may be ineffective. "Alcohol" foam.	3	3	2
2—Methylpropene $CH_2:C(CH_3)CH_3$ (γ—Butylene) (Isobutylene)	Gas	869	1.8	9.6		1.9	20	No	Stop flow of gas.	1	4	0
Methyl Propionate $CH_3COOCH_2CH_3$	28	876	2.5	13	0.9	3.0	176	No	Water may be ineffective.	1	3	0
Methyl Propyl Acetylene $CH_3C_2H_4C:CCH_3$ (2—Hexyne)	<14				0.73	2.83	185				3	

Table 3-11A (cont.)	FLASH POINT Deg. F.	IGNITION TEMP. Deg. F.	FLAMMABLE LIMITS Per Cent by Vol. Lower	Upper	Sp. Gr. (Water = 1)	Vapor Density (Air = 1)	Boiling Point Deg. F.	Water Soluble	EXTINGUISHING METHOD See Intro.	SUGGESTED HAZARD IDENTIFICATION Health	Flamma- bility	Reac- tivity
Methyl Propyl Carbinol $CH_3CHOHC_3H_7$ (2—Pentanol)	105				0.8	3.0	247	No		0	2	0
Methylpropylcarbinyl- amine	See sec—Amylamine.											
Methyl n—Propyl Ether $CH_3OC_3H_7$	<—4				0.91	2.56	102			0	3	0
Methyl Propyl Ketone $CH_3COC_3H_7$ (2—Pentanone)	45	941	1.5	8.2	0.8	3.0	216	Slight	Water may be ineffective. "Alcohol" foam.	2	3	0
2—Methylpyrazine $N:C(CH_3)CH:NCH:CH$	122 (oc)				1.02	3.25				2	2	0
2—Methyl Pyridine	See 2—Picoline.											
Methylpyrrole $N(CH_3)CH:CHCH:CH$	61				0.9	2.8	234	No	Water may be ineffective.	2	3	1
Methylpyrrolidine $CH_3NC_4H_8$	7				0.8	2.9	180	Slight	"Alcohol" foam. Water may be ineffective.	2	3	1
1—Methyl—2— Pyrrolidone $CH_3NCOCH_2CH_2CH_2$ (n—Methyl—2—Pyrrolidone)	204 (oc)				1.0+	3.4	396	Yes	"Alcohol" foam.	2	1	0
Methyl Salicylate $HOC_6H_4COOCH_3$ (Oil of Wintergreen)	214	850 (Und. Lab. Class 20–25)			1.2		432	No	Water or foam may cause frothing.	1	1	0
Methyl Stearate $C_{17}H_{35}COOCH_3$	307				0.9		421	No	Water or foam may cause frothing.	0	1	0
α—Methylstyrene	See 1—Methyl—1—Phenylethylene.											
Methylstyrene C_9H_{10}	134 (oc)	923	0.7		0.8	4.1	342	No		2	2	0
Methyl Sulfate	See Dimethyl Sulfate.											
2—Methyltetrahydro- furan $C_4H_7OCH_3$	12				0.9	3.0	176	Slight	Water may be ineffective. "Alcohol" foam.	2	3	0
Methyltrichlorosilane CH_3SiCl_3 (Methyl Silico Chloroform) (Trichloromethylsilane)	<70		7.6		1.29	5.16	151			3	3	0
Methyl Undecyl Ketone $C_{11}H_{23}COCH_3$ (2—Tridecanone)	225				0.8		248	No	Water or foam may cause frothing.	1	1	0
1—Methylvinyl Acetate	See Isopropenyl Acetate.											
Methyl Vinyl Ether	See Vinyl Methyl Ether.											
Methyl Vinyl Ketone $CH_3COCH:CH_2$	20					2.4	177		Water may be ineffective.	2	3	2
Mineral Oil	380 (oc)				0.8–0.9		680	No	Water or foam may cause frothing.	0	1	0
Mineral Seal Oil Typical (Signal Oil)	275 (oc)				0.8		480–680	No		0	2	0
Mineral Spirits Mineral Spirits, 360° End Point	104	473	0.8 @ 212°		0.8	3.9	300	No		0	2	0
Mineral Wax	See Wax, Ozocerite.											
Monochlorobenzene	See Chlorobenzene.											
Morpholine $OC_2H_4NHCH_2CH_2$	100 (oc)	590			1.0	3.0	262	Yes	"Alcohol" foam.	2	3	0
	Note: See Hazardous Chemicals Data.											
Muriatic Ether	See Ethyl Chloride.											
Mustard Oil $C_3H_5N:C:S$ (Allyl Isothiocyanate)	115				1.0+	3.4	304	No		3	2	0
Naphtha 49° Be — Coal Tar Type	107	531						No		2	2	0
Naphtha, Petroleum	See Petroleum Ether.											
Naphtha, Safety Solvent	See Cleaning Solvent.											
Naphtha V.M. & P., 50° Flash	50	450	0.9	6.7	<1	4.1	240–290	No	Water may be ineffective.	1	3	0
	Note: Flash point and ignition temperature will vary depending on the manufacturer.											

Table 3-11A (cont.)	FLASH POINT Deg. F.	IGNI-TION TEMP. Deg. F.	FLAMMABLE LIMITS Per Cent by Vol. Lower	Upper	Sp. Gr. (Water = 1)	Vapor Density (Air = 1)	Boiling Point Deg. F.	Water Soluble	EXTINGUISHING METHOD See Intro.	SUGGESTED HAZARD IDENTIFICATION Health	Flamma-bility	Reac-tivity
Naphtha V.M. & P., High Flash	85	450	1.0	6.0	<1	4.3	280–350	No	Water may be ineffective.	1	3	0
Note: Flash point and ignition temperature will vary depending on the manufacturer.												
Naphtha V.M. & P., Regular	28	450	0.9	6.0	<1		212–320	No	Water may be ineffective.	1	3	0
Note: Flash point and ignition temperature will vary depending on the manufacturer.												
Naphthalene $C_{10}H_8$ (White Tar)	174	979	0.9	5.9	1.1	4.4	424	No		2	2	0
Note: Melting point 176°F. See Hazardous Chemicals Data.												
β Naphthol $C_{10}H_7OH$ (βHydroxy Naphthalene) (2—Naphthol)	307				1.22	4.98	545				1	0
Note: Melting point 253°F.												
1—Naphthylamine $C_{10}H_7NH_2$	315				1.2		572	No	Water or foam may cause frothing.	2	1	0
Note: Melting point 122°F.												
Natural Gas	See Gas.											
Neatsfoot Oil	470	828			0.9			No	Water or foam may cause frothing.	0	1	0
Note: Melting point 84–106°F.												
Neohexane	See 2, 2—Dimethylbutane.											
Neopentane	See 2, 2—Dimethylpropane.											
Nickel Carbonyl $Ni(CO)_4$	<−4		2		1.32	5.89	110				3	1 W
Nicotine $C_{10}H_{14}N_2$		471	0.7	4.0	1.0	5.6	475	Yes	Water or foam may cause frothing. "Alcohol" foam.	4	1	0
Niobe Oil	See Methyl Benzoate.											
Nitric Ether	See Ethyl Nitrate.											
2, 2', 2"—Nitrilotri-ethanol	See Triethanolamine.											
1, 1', 1"—Nitrilotri—2—propanol	See Triisopropanolamine.											
p—Nitroaniline $NO_2C_6H_4NH_2$	390				1.44	4.77	637			3'	1	3
Nitrobenzene $C_6H_5NO_2$ (Nitrobenzol) (Oil of Mirbane)	190	900	1.8 @ 200°		1.2	4.3	412	No	Water may be used to blanket fire.	3	2	0
(Und. Lab. Class 20–30) Note: See Hazardous Chemicals Data.												
1, 3—Nitrobenzotri-fluoride $C_6H_4NO_2CF_3$ (α, α, α—Trifluoronitrotoluene)	217 (oc)				1.44	6.59	397				1	
Nitrobenzol	See Nitrobenzene.											
Nitrobiphenyl $C_6H_5C_6H_4NO_2$	290				1.2		626	No	Water or foam may cause frothing.	2	1	0
Nitrocellulose	See Cellulose Nitrate.											
Nitrochlorobenzene $C_6H_4ClNO_2$	261				1.5		457	No	Water or foam may cause frothing.	3	1	1
Note: See Hazardous Chemicals Data. Melting point 111°F.												
p—Nitrochlorobenzene $C_6H_4ClNO_2$ (1—Chloro—4—nitrobenzene)	261				1.37	5.44	468			2	1	3
Note: Melting point 181°F.												
Nitrocyclohexane $CH_2(CH_2)_4CHNO_2$	190 (oc)				1.07	4.46	403 Decomposes			2	2	3
Nitroethane $C_2H_5NO_2$	82	778	3.4		1.1	2.6	237	Slight	Water may be ineffective except as a blanket. "Alcohol" foam. Explodes on heating.	1	3	3
Note: See Hazardous Chemicals Data.												
Nitroglycerine $C_3H_5(NO_3)_3$ (Glyceryl Trinitrate)	Ex-plodes	518			1.6		502 Explodes	No		2	2	4
Nitromethane CH_3NO_2	95	785	7.3		1.1	2.1	214	Slight	Water may be ineffective. "Alcohol" foam.	1	3	4
Note: May detonate under high temperature and pressure conditions. See Hazardous Chemicals Data.												
1—Nitronaphthalene $C_{10}H_7NO_2$	327				1.3		579	No	Water or foam may cause frothing.	1	1	0
Note: Melting point 140°F.												
1—Nitropropane $CH_3CH_2CH_2NO_2$	120 (oc)	789	2.2		1.0	3.1	268	Slight	"Alcohol" foam. May explode on heating.	1	2	3
Note: See Hazardous Chemicals Data.												

Table 3-11A (cont.)

	FLASH POINT Deg. F.	IGNITION TEMP. Deg. F.	FLAMMABLE LIMITS Per Cent by Vol.		Sp. Gr. (Water = 1)	Vapor Density (Air = 1)	Boiling Point Deg. F.	Water Soluble	EXTINGUISHING METHOD See Intro.	SUGGESTED HAZARD IDENTIFICATION		
			Lower	Upper						Health	Flamma-bility	Reac-tivity
2—Nitropropane $CH_3CH(NO_2)CH_3$ (sec—Nitropropane)	103 (oc) Note: See Hazardous Chemicals Data.	802	2.6		1.0—	3.1	248	Slight	"Alcohol" foam. May explode on heating.	1	2	3
sec—Nitropropane	See 2—Nitropropane.											
Nitrotoluene	See p—Nitrotoluol.											
m—Nitrotoluene $C_6H_4CH_3NO_2$	223 Note: Melting point 61°F.		1.16			4.73	450			2	1	4
o—Nitrotoluene $C_6H_4CH_3NO_2$	223 Note: Melting point 25°F.		1.16			4.73	432			2	1	4
2—Nitro—p—toluidine $CH_3C_6H_3(NH_2)NO_2$	315 Note: Melting point 259°F.		1.31			5.25				2	1	4
p—Nitrotoluol $CH_3C_6H_4NO_2$ (Nitrotoluene)	223 Note: Melting point 126°F.		1.3				460	No	Water or foam may cause frothing.	1	1	3
Nitrous Ether	See Ethyl Nitrite.											
Nonadecane $CH_3(CH_2)_{17}CH_3$	>212 Note: Melting point 90°F.	446			0.79	9.27	628			0	1	0
Nonane C_9H_{20}	88	401	0.8	2.9	0.7	4.4	303	No	Water may be ineffective.	0	3	0
Nonane (iso) $C_6H_{13}CH(CH_3)_2$ (2—Methyloctane)		428			0.71	4.43	290			0	3	0
Nonane (iso) $C_5H_{11}CH(CH_3)C_2H_5$ (3—Methyloctane)		428			0.72	4.43	291			0	3	0
Nonane (iso) $C_4H_9CH(CH_3)C_3H_7$ (4—Methyloctane)		437			0.72	4.43	288			0	3	0
Nonyl Acetate $CH_2 COOC_9H_{19}$	155				0.9	6.4	378	Very slight	"Alcohol" foam.	1	2	0
Nonyl Alcohol	See Diisobutyl Carbinol.											
Nonylbenzene $C_9H_{19}C_6H_5$	210				0.9		468–486	No		0	1	0
Nonylnaphthalene $C_9H_{19}C_{10}H_7$	<200				0.9	8.8	626–653	No		0	2	0
Nonylphenol $C_6H_4(C_9H_{19})OH$	285				1.0—		559–567	Very slight	Water or foam may cause frothing. "Alcohol" foam.	2	1	0
Octadecane $C_{18}H_{38}$	>212 Note: Melting point 82°F.	455			0.78	8.73	603			0	1	0
Octadecylene α $CH_3(CH_2)_{15}CH:CH_2$ (1—Octadecene)	>212 Note: Melting point 64°F.	482			0.79	8.71	599			0	1	0
Octadecyl Vinyl Ether	See Vinyl Octadecyl Ether.											
Octanal	See Caprylaldehyde.											
Octane $CH_3(CH_2)_6CH_3$	56	428	1.0	6.5	0.7	3.9	258	No	Water may be ineffective.	0	3	0
1—Octanol	See Octyl Alcohol.											
2—Octanol $CH_3CHOH(CH_2)_5CH_3$	190				0.8	4.5	363	No		1	2	0
2—Octanone $CH_3CO(CH_2)_5CH_3$ (Hexyl Methyl Ketone)	160				0.8	4.4	336–343	Very slight		1	2	0
1—Octene $CH_2:C_7H_{14}$	70 (oc)				0.7	3.9	250	No	Water may be ineffective.	1	3	0
2—Octene (Mixed cis— and trans—isomers) $CH_3CH:CHC_5H_{11}$	70 (oc)				0.7	3.9	257	No	Water may be ineffective.	1	3	0
Octyl Acetate	See 2—Ethylhexyl Acetate.											
Octyl Alcohol $CH_3(CH_2)_6CH_2OH$ (1—Octanol)	178				0.8	4.5	381	No		1	2	0
Octylamine $CH_3(CH_2)_6CH_2NH_2$ (1—Aminooctane)	140				0.8	4.5	338	Slight	"Alcohol" foam.	2	2	0
tert—Octylamine $(CH_3)_3CCH_2C(CH_3)_2NH_2$ (oc) (1, 1, 3, 3—Tetramethylbutylamine)	91				1.41	4.46	284				3	0
Octyl Chloride $CH_3(CH_2)_7Cl$	158				0.9	5.1	359	No		1	2	0
Octylene Glycol $[CH_3(CH_2)_2CHOH]_2$	230	635			0.9		475	No	Water or foam may cause frothing.	1	1	0

Table 3-11A (cont.)	FLASH POINT Deg. F.	IGNI-TION TEMP. Deg. F.	FLAMMABLE LIMITS Per Cent by Vol.		Sp. Gr. (Water =1)	Vapor Density (Air =1)	Boiling Point Deg. F.	Water Soluble	EXTINGUISHING METHOD See Intro.	SUGGESTED HAZARD IDENTIFICATION		
			Lower	Upper						Health	Flamma-bility	Reac-tivity
tert—Octyl Mercaptan $C_8H_{17}SH$	115 (oc)				0.8	5.0	318–329	No		2	2	0
Oil of Mirbane	See Nitrobenzene.											
Oil of Wintergreen	See Methyl Salicylate.											
Oleic Acid $C_8H_{17}CH:CH(CH_2)_7COOH$ (Red Oil)	372	685			0.9		432	No	Water or foam may cause frothing.	0	1	0
Distilled	364											
Oleo Oil	450				0.9		464	No	Water or foam may cause frothing.	0	1	0
Olive Oil (Sweet Oil)	437	650			0.9			No	Water or foam may cause frothing.	0	1	0
Oxalic Ether	See Ethyl Oxalate.											
Oxammonium	See Hydroxylamine.											
Oxirane	See Ethylene Oxide.											
Palm Butter	See Palm Oil.											
Palm Kernel Oil (Palm Nut Oil)	398				0.9			No	Water or foam may cause frothing.	0	1	0
	Note: Melting point 78–86°F.											
Palm Nut Oil	See Palm Kernel Oil.											
Palm Oil (Palm Butter)	323	600			0.9			No	Water or foam may cause frothing.	0	1	0
	Note: Melting point 80–110°F.											
Paraffin Oil (See also Lubricating Oil)	444								Water or foam may cause frothing.	0	1	0
	(Und. Lab. Class 10–20)											
Paraformaldehyde $HO(CH_2O)_nH$	158	572						Slight	"Alcohol" foam.	2	2	1
Paraldehyde $(CH_3CHO)_3$	96 (oc)	460	1.3		1.0—	4.5	255	Slight	Water may be ineffective. "Alcohol" foam.	2	3	1
	Note: Melting point 54°F. See Hazardous Chemicals Data.											
Peanut Oil Cooking (Katchung Oil)	540	833			0.9			No	Water or foam may cause frothing.	0	1	0
Pentaborane B_5H_9			0.42		0.6	2.2	140		Water may be ineffective. Reacts violently with halogenated extinguishing agents.	3	3	2
	Note: Ignites spontaneously in air. See Hazardous Chemicals Data.											
Pent—Acetate Mixture of Isomeric Amyl Acetates and Amyl Alcohols	98				0.9		260	No	Water may be ineffective.	2	3	0
Pentamethylene Dichloride	See 1, 5—Dichloropentane.											
Pentamethylene Glycol	See 1, 5—Pentanediol.											
Pentamethylene Oxide $O(CH_2)_4CH_2$ (Tetrahydropyran)	−4				0.9	3.0	178	Yes	Water may be ineffective. "Alcohol" foam.	2	3	1
Pentanal	See Valeraldehyde.											
Pentane $CH_3(CH_2)_3CH_3$	<−40	500	1.5	7.8	0.6	2.5	97	No	Water may be ineffective.	1	4	0
1, 5—Pentanediol $HO(CH_2)_5OH$ (Pentamethylene Glycol)	265 (oc)	635			1.0—		468	Yes	Water or foam may cause frothing. "Alcohol" foam.	1	1	0
2, 4—Pentanedione $CH_3COCH_2COCH_3$ (Acetyl Acetone)	105 (oc)	644			1.0—	3.5	284	Yes	"Alcohol" foam.	2	2	0
Pentanoic Acid C_4H_9COOH (Valeric Acid)	205 (oc)				0.9	3.5	366	Very slight		2	1	0
1—Pentanol	See Amyl Alcohol.											
2—Pentanol	See Methyl Propyl Carbinol.											
3—Pentanol $CH_3CH_2CH(OH)CH_2CH_3$ (tert—n—Amyl Alcohol)	105	815	1.2	9.0	0.8	3.0	241	Slight	"Alcohol" foam.	1	2	0
1—Pentanol Acetate	See Amyl Acetate.											
2—Pentanol Acetate	See sec—Amyl Acetate.											

Table 3-11A (cont.)	FLASH POINT Deg. F.	IGNI- TION TEMP. Deg. F.	FLAMMABLE LIMITS Per Cent by Vol. Lower	Upper	Sp. Gr. (Water = 1)	Vapor Density (Air = 1)	Boiling Point Deg. F.	Water Soluble	EXTINGUISHING METHOD See Intro.	SUGGESTED HAZARD IDENTIFICATION Health	Flamma- bility	Reac- tivity
2—Pentanone	See Methyl Propyl Ketone.											
3—Pentanone	See Diethyl Ketone.											
Pentaphen C5H11C6H4OH (p—tert—Amyl Phenol)	232 (oc)	Note: Melting point 195°F.			0.9		482	No	Water or foam may cause frothing.	2	1	0
Pentapropionyl Glucose	See Glucose Pentapropionate.											
1—Pentene CH3(CH2)2CH:CH2 (Amylene)	0 (oc)	527	1.5	8.7	0.7	2.4	86		Water may be ineffective.	1	4	0
1—Pentene—cis	See β—Amylene—cis.											
2—Pentene—trans	See β—Amylene—trans.											
Pentylamine	See Amylamine.											
Pentyloxypentane	See Amyl Ether.											
Pentyl Propionate	See Amyl Propionate.											
1—Pentyne HC:CC3H7 (n—Propyl Acetylene)	<−4				0.69	2.35	104				3	3
Peracetic Acid Diluted with 60% of acetic acid CH3COOOH	105	Note: Decomposes violently at 230°F. See Hazardous Chemicals Data.					221	Yes	Explodes on heating.	3	2	4
Perilla Oil	522				0.9			No	Water or foam may cause frothing.	0	1	0
Petroleum, Crude	20–90				<1			No	Water may be ineffective.	1	3	0
Petroleum Ether (Benzine) (Naphtha, Petroleum)	<0	550	1.1	5.9	0.6	2.5	95–140	No	Water may be ineffective.	1	4	0
	(Und. Lab. Class 95–100)											
Petroleum Pitch	See Asphalt (Typical).											
Petroleum Sulfonate	400 (oc)							No	Water or foam may cause frothing.	0	1	0
β Phellandrene CH2:CCH:CHCH[CH(CH3)2]CH2CH2 (p—Mentha—1(7), 2—diene)	120				~0.9	4.68	340	No		0	2	0
Phenethyl Alcohol C6H5CH2CH2OH (Benzyl Carbinol)	216				1.0+		430	No	Water or foam may cause frothing.	1	1	0
p—Phenetidine C2H5OC6H4NH2 (1—Amino—4—Ethoxybenzene) (p—Aminophenetole)	241				1.1		378–484	Very slight	Water or foam may cause frothing.	2	1	0
Phenetole	See Ethoxybenzene.											
Phenol C6H5OH (Carbolic Acid)	175	1319			1.1	3.2	358	Yes	"Alcohol" foam.	3	2	0
	Note: See Hazardous Chemicals Data. Melting point 108°F.											
2—Phenoxyethanol	See Ethylene Glycol, Phenyl Ether.											
Phenoxy Ethyl Alcohol C6H5O(CH2)2OH (2—Phenoxyethanol) (Phenyl Cellosolve)	250 (oc)	Note: Melting point 58°F.			1.11	4.77	468			0	1	0
N—(2—Phenoxyethyl) Aniline C6H5O(CH2)3NHC6H5	338				1.1		396	No	Water or foam may cause frothing.	1	1	0
β—Phenoxyethyl Chloride	See β—Chlorophenetole.											
Phenyl Acetate CH3COOC6H5 (Acetylphenol)	176				1.1	4.7	384	Slight	"Alcohol" foam.	1	2	0
Phenylamine	See Aniline.											
N—Phenylaniline	See Diphenylamine.											
Phenylbenzene	See Biphenyl.											
Phenyl Bromide	See Bromobenzene.											
1—Phenyl—2—Butene C6H5CH2CH:CHCH3	160 (oc)				0.9	4.6	346				2	0
Phenyl Carbinol	See Benzyl Alcohol.											
Phenyl Chloride	See Chlorobenzene.											
Phenylcyclohexane	See Cyclohexylbenzene.											
Phenyl Didecyl Phosphite (C6H5O)P(OC10H21)2	425 (oc)				0.9				Water or foam may cause frothing.	0	1	0

FIRE HAZARDS OF MATERIALS

Table 3-11A (cont.)	FLASH POINT Deg. F.	IGNI-TION TEMP. Deg. F.	FLAMMABLE LIMITS Per Cent by Vol. Lower	FLAMMABLE LIMITS Per Cent by Vol. Upper	Sp. Gr. (Water = 1)	Vapor Density (Air = 1)	Boiling Point Deg. F.	Water Soluble	EXTINGUISHING METHOD See Intro.	SUGGESTED HAZARD IDENTIFICATION Health	SUGGESTED HAZARD IDENTIFICATION Flamma-bility	SUGGESTED HAZARD IDENTIFICATION Reac-tivity
N—Phenyldiethanol-amine $C_6H_5N(C_2H_4OH)_2$	375 (oc)			1.1 Note: Melting point 136°F.			376	No	Water or foam may cause frothing.	1	1	0
Phenyldiethylamine	See N, N—Diethylaniline.											
Phenyl Diglycol Carbonate	See Diethylene Glycol Bis(Phenylcarbonate).											
Phenyl Di—o—Xenyl Phosphate $(C_{12}H_9O)_2POOC_6H_5$	482			1.2			545–626	No	Water or foam may cause frothing.	0	1	1
o—Phenylenediamine $NH_2C_6H_4NH_2$ (1, 2—Diaminobenzene)	313		1.5 Note: Melting point 284°F.			3.73	513				1	0
Phenylethane	See Ethylbenzene.											
N—Phenylethanolamine $C_6H_5NHC_2H_4OH$	305 (oc)		Note: See Hazardous Chemicals Data.	1.1			545	Slight	Water or foam may cause frothing. "Alcohol" foam.	2	1	0
Phenylethyl Acetate (β) $C_6H_5CH_2CH_2OOCCH_3$	230 (oc)			1.03		5.67	435			0	1	0
Phenylethylene	See Styrene.											
N—Phenyl—N—Ethyl-ethanolamine $C_6H_5N(C_2H_5)C_2H_4OH$	270 (oc)			1.0+			514 @ 740 mm.	Slight	Water or foam may cause frothing. "Alcohol" foam.	2	1	0
Phenylhydrazine $C_6H_5NHNH_2$	192			1.1			Decom-poses	Slight	"Alcohol" foam.	3	2	0
Phenylmethane	See Toluol.											
Phenyl Methyl Carbinol $C_6H_5CH(OH)CH_3$ (α—Methylbenzyl Alcohol)	205 (oc)			1.0+			398	Slight	"Alcohol" foam.	1	1	0
Phenylmethyl Ethanol Amine $C_6H_5N(CH_3)C_2H_4OH$ (2—(N—Methylanilino)ethanol)	280 (oc)			1.07		5.22	378 @ 100 mm.			2	1	0
Phenyl Methyl Ketone	See Acetophenone.											
4—Phenylmorpholine $C_6H_5NC_2H_4OCH_2CH_2$	220 (oc)			1.1			518	Slight	"Alcohol" foam. Water or foam may cause frothing.	2	1	0
Phenylpentane	See Amylbenzene.											
o—Phenylphenol $C_6H_5C_6H_4OH$	255			1.2 Note: Melting point 134°F.			547	Slight	"Alcohol" foam. Water or foam may cause frothing.	1	1	0
Phenylpropane	See Propylbenzene.											
2—Phenylpropane	See Cumene.											
Phenyl Toluene o $C_6H_5C_6H_4CH_3$ (2—Methylbiphenyl)	>212	923		1.01		5.82	500				1	0
Phenyl Trichloro Silane $C_6H_5SiCl_3$ (Trichloro(phenyl)silane)	196 (oc)			1.32		7.36	394			3	2	0
Phorone $(CH_3)_2CCHCOCHC(CH_3)_2$	185 (oc)			0.9 Note: Melting point 82°F.		4.8	388	No		2	2	0
Phosphine PH_3	Gas	212		0.57 @ 20 atm		1.17	−126			4	4	4
Phthalic Acid $C_6H_4(COOH)_2$	334		1.59 Note: Melting point 376°F.			5.73	552		Forms anhydride (Dust explosion hazard)	0	1	1
Phthalic Anhydride $C_6H_4(CO)_2O$	305	1058	1.7 Note: Melting point 262°F.	10.5	1.5		543	No	Water or foam may cause frothing.	2	1	0
m—Phthalyl Dichloride	See Isophthaloyl Chloride.											
2—Picoline $CH_3C_5H_4N$ (2—Methylpyridine)	102 (oc)	1000		1.0−		3.2	262	No		2	2	0
4—Picoline $CH_3C_5H_4N$	134 (oc)			1.0−		3.2	292	Yes	"Alcohol" foam.	2	2	0
Pimelic Ketone	See Cyclohexanone.											
Pinane $C_{10}H_{18}$			0.7 @ 320°	7.2 @ 320°	0.8		336			0		0
α—Pinene $C_{10}H_{16}$	91	491			0.9	4.7	312	No	Water may be ineffective.	1	3	0
Pine Oil Steam Distilled	172 138				0.9		367–439	No		0	2	0

Table 3-11A (cont.)

	FLASH POINT Deg. F.	IGNI-TION TEMP. Deg. F.	FLAMMABLE LIMITS Per Cent by Vol. Lower	Upper	Sp. Gr. (Water = 1)	Vapor Density (Air = 1)	Boiling Point Deg. F.	Water Soluble	EXTINGUISHING METHOD See Intro.	SUGGESTED HAZARD IDENTIFICATION Health	Flamma-bility	Reac-tivity
Pine Pitch	285 Note: Melting point 148°F.				1.1		490	No	Water or foam may cause frothing.	0	1	0
Pine Tar	130	671					208	No		0	2	0
Pine Tar Oil (Wood Tar Oil)	144				0.9			No		0	2	0
Piperazine HNCH$_2$CH$_2$NHCH$_2$CH$_2$	190 (oc)				1.1	3.0	294	Slight	"Alcohol" foam.	2	2	0
Piperidine (CH$_2$)$_5$NH (Hexahydropyridine)	61				0.9	3.0	223	Yes	Water may be ineffective. "Alcohol" foam.	2	3	3
Pogy Oil	See Menhaden Oil.											
Polyamyl Naphthalene Mixture of Polymers	360 (oc)				0.9		667–747	No	Water or foam may cause frothing.	0	1	0
Polyvinyl Alcohol Mixture of Polymers	175 (oc)							Yes	"Alcohol" foam.	0	2	0
Poppy Seed Oil	491				0.9			No	Water or foam may cause frothing.	0	1	0
Potassium Xanthate KS$_2$C-OC$_2$H$_5$	205			9.6	1.56	5.53	392 Decomposes	Yes		2	1	0
Propanal CH$_3$CH$_2$CHO (Propionaldehyde)	15–19 (oc)	405	2.9	17.0	0.8	2.0	120	Slight	Water may be ineffective. "Alcohol" foam.	2	3	1
	Note: See Hazardous Chemicals Data.											
Propane CH$_3$CH$_2$CH$_3$	Gas	842	2.2	9.5		1.6	−44	No	Stop flow of gas.	1	4	0
1, 3—Propanediamine NH$_2$CH$_2$CH$_2$CH$_2$NH$_2$ (1, 3—Diaminopropane) (Trimethylenediamine)	75 (oc)				0.9	2.6	276	Yes	Water may be ineffective. "Alcohol" foam.	2	3	0
1, 2—Propanediol	See Propylene Glycol.											
1, 3—Propanediol	See Trimethylene Glycol.											
1—Propanol	See Propyl Alcohol.											
2—Propanol	See Isopropyl Alcohol.											
2—Propanone	See Acetone.											
Propanoyl Chloride	See Propionyl Chloride.											
Propargyl Alcohol HC:CCH$_2$OH (2—Propyn—1—ol)	97 (oc)				0.97	1.93	239			3	3	3
Propargyl Bromide HC:CCH$_2$Br (3—Bromopropyne)	64 (oc)				1.57	4.10	192			4	3	4
Propene	See Propylene.											
2—Propenylamine	See Allylamine.											
Propenyl Ethyl Ether CH$_3$CH:CHOCH$_2$CH$_3$	<20 (oc)				0.8	1.3	158		Water may be ineffective.	2	3	0
β—Propiolactone C$_3$H$_4$O$_2$	165		2.9		1.1	2.5	311	Yes	"Alcohol" foam.	0	2	0
Propionaldehyde	See Propanal.											
Propionic Acid CH$_3$CH$_2$COOH	130	955			1.0−	2.5	297	Yes	"Alcohol" foam.	2	2	0
	Note: See Hazardous Chemicals Data.											
Propionic Anhydride (CH$_3$CH$_2$CO)$_2$O	165 (oc)				1.0+	4.5	336	De-com-poses	Decomposes in water.	2	2	1
Propionic Nitrile CH$_3$CH$_2$CN (Propionitrile)	36		3.1		0.78	1.90	207	Yes		4	3	1
Propionyl Chloride CH$_3$CH$_2$COCl (Propanoyl Chloride)	54				1.1	3.2	176	De-com-poses	Water may be ineffective. Decomposes in water.	3	3	1
Propyl Acetate C$_3$H$_7$OOCCH$_3$ (Acetic Acid, n—Propyl Ester)	58	842	2.0	8	0.9	3.5	215	Slight	Water may be ineffective. "Alcohol" foam.	1	3	0
Propyl Alcohol CH$_3$CH$_2$CH$_2$OH (1—Propanol)	77 (Und. Lab. Class 55–60)	824	2.1	13.5	0.8	2.1	207	Yes	Water may be ineffective. "Alcohol" foam.	1	3	0
Propylamine CH$_3$(CH$_2$)$_2$NH$_2$	−35	604	2.0	10.4	0.7	2.0	120	Yes	Water may be ineffective. "Alcohol" foam.	3	3	0
	Note: See Hazardous Chemicals Data.											
Propylbenzene C$_3$H$_7$C$_6$H$_5$ (Phenylpropane)	86	842	0.8	6.0	0.9	4.1	319	No	Water may be ineffective.	2	3	0

Table 3-11A (cont.)

	FLASH POINT Deg. F.	IGNI- TION TEMP. Deg. F.	FLAMMABLE LIMITS Per Cent by Vol. Lower	Upper	Sp. Gr. (Water = 1)	Vapor Density (Air = 1)	Boiling Point Deg. F.	Water Soluble	EXTINGUISHING METHOD See Intro.	SUGGESTED HAZARD IDENTIFICATION Health	Flamma- bility	Reac- tivity
2—Propylbiphenyl $C_6H_5C_6H_4C_3H_7$	>212	833				6.77	~536			0	1	0
n Propyl Bromide C_3H_7Br (1—Bromopropane)		914			1.35	4.34	160			2	3	0
n—Propyl Butyrate $C_3H_7COOC_3H_7$	99				0.87	4.49	290			0	3	0
Propyl Carbinol	See Butyl Alcohol.											
Propyl Chloride C_3H_7Cl (1—Chloropropane)	<0	968	2.6	11.1	0.9	2.7	115	Very slight	Water may be ineffective.	2	3	0
Propyl Chlorothiol- formate C_3H_7SCOCl	145				1.1	4.8	311	No		2	2	0
Propylene $CH_2:CHCH_3$ (Propene)	Gas	860	2.0	11.1		1.5	−53	Yes	Stop flow of gas.	1	4	1
	Note: See Hazardous Chemicals Data.											
Propylene Aldehyde	See Crotonaldehyde.											
Propylene Carbonate $OCH_2CH_2CH_2OCO$	275 (oc)				1.2		468	Yes	Water or foam may cause frothing. "Alcohol" foam.	1	1	0
Propylene Chlorohydrin	See 2—Chloro—1—Propanol.											
sec—Propylene Chloro- hydrin	See 1—Chloro—2—Propanol.											
Propylenediamine $CH_3CH(NH_2)CH_2NH_2$	92 (oc)				0.9	2.6	246	Yes	Water may be ineffective. "Alcohol" foam.	2	3	0
Propylene Dichloride $CH_3CHClCH_2Cl$ (1, 2—Dichloropropane)	60	1035	3.4	14.5	1.2	3.9	205	No	Water may be ineffective except as a blanket.	2	3	0
Propylene Glycol $CH_3CHOHCH_2OH$ (Methyl Ethylene Glycol) (1, 2—Propanediol)	210	700	2.6	12.5	1.0+		370	Yes	"Alcohol" foam.	0	1	0
Propylene Glycol Acetate	See Methyl Glycol Acetate.											
Propylene Glycol Methyl Ether $CH_3OCH_2CHOHCH_3$ (1—Methoxy—2—propanol)	100 (oc)				0.92	3.11	248			0	3	0
Propylene Glycol Mono- acrylate $CH_2:CHCOO(C_3H_6)OH$ (Hydroxypropyl Acrylate)	210				1.0+	4.5	171 @ 5 mm.	Yes	"Alcohol" foam.	1	1	0
Propylene Oxide OCH_2CHCH_3	−35		2.8	37.0	0.9	2.0	95	Yes	Water may be ineffective. "Alcohol" foam.	2	4	2
	Note: See Hazardous Chemicals Data.											
n Propyl Ether $(C_3H_7)_2O$ (Dipropyl Ether)	70				0.75	3.53	194				3	0
Propyl Formate $HCOOC_3H_7$	27	851			0.9	3.0	178	Slight	Water may be ineffective. "Alcohol" foam.	2	3	0
Propyl Methanol	See Butyl Alcohol.											
Propyl Nitrate $CH_3CH_2CH_2NO_3$	68	347	2	100	1.1		231	Slight	Water may be ineffective. "Alcohol" foam. May explode on heating.	2	3	3
Propyl Propionate $CH_3CH_2COOCH_2CH_2CH_3$	175 (oc)				0.9	4.0	245	No		1	3	0
Propyne $CH_3C:CH$ (Allylene) (Methylacetylene)	Gas		1.7			1.4	−10		Stop flow of gas.	2	4	2
Prussic Acid	See Hydrocyanic Acid.											
Pyridine $CH<(CHCH)_2>N$	68	900	1.8	12.4	1.0−	2.7	239	Yes	Water may be ineffective. "Alcohol" foam.	2	3	0
	Note: See Hazardous Chemicals Data.											
Pyroxylin Solution	80 May be below							No	Water may be ineffective.	1	3	0
Pyrrole $(CHCH)_2NH$ (Azole)	102				1.0−	2.3	268	No		2	2	0

Table 3-11A (cont.)	FLASH POINT Deg. F.	IGNITION TEMP. Deg. F.	FLAMMABLE LIMITS Per Cent by Vol.		Sp. Gr. (Water = 1)	Vapor Density (Air = 1)	Boiling Point Deg. F.	Water Soluble	EXTINGUISHING METHOD See Intro.	SUGGESTED HAZARD IDENTIFICATION		
			Lower	Upper						Health	Flamma-bility	Reac-tivity
Pyrrolidine NHCH$_2$CH$_2$CH$_2$CH$_2$ (Tetrahydropyrrole)	37				0.9	2.5	186–189	Yes	"Alcohol" foam. Water may be ineffective.	2	3	1
2—Pyrrolidone NHCOCH$_2$CH$_2$CH$_2$ Note: Melting point 77°F.	265 (oc)				1.1	2.9	473	Yes	Water or foam may cause frothing. "Alcohol" foam.	2	1	0
Quenching Oil	365				0.9			No	Water or foam may cause frothing.	0	1	0
Quinoline C$_6$H$_4$N:CHCH:CH		896			1.1	4.5	460	No		2	1	0
Range Oil	See Fuel Oil No. 1.											
Rape Seed Oil (Colza Oil)	325	836			0.9			No	Water or foam may cause frothing.	0	1	0
Red Oil	See Oleic Acid.											
Resorcinol C$_6$H$_4$(OH)$_2$ (Dihydroxybenzol)	261 Note: Melting point 232°F.				1.28	3.80	531				1	0
Ricinus Oil	See Castor Oil.											
Rosin Oil	266	648			1.0—		>680	No	Water or foam may cause frothing.	0	1	0
Rum	See Ethyl Alcohol and Water.											
Salicylaldehyde HOC$_6$H$_4$CHO (o—Hydroxybenzaldehyde)	172				1.2		384	Slight	"Alcohol" foam.	0	2	0
Salicylic Acid HOC$_6$H$_4$COOH Note: Melting point 316–322°F.	315				1.5	4.8	Sublimes @ 169	No	Water or foam may cause frothing.	0	1	0
Sesame Oil	491				0.9			No	Water or foam may cause frothing.	0	1	0
Signal Oil	See Mineral Seal Oil, Typical.											
Soy Bean Oil	540	833			0.9			No	Water or foam may cause frothing.	0	1	0
Sperm Oil No. 1 No. 2	428 460	586			0.9			No	Water or foam may cause frothing.	0	1	0
Spindle Oil	See Lubricating Oil, Spindle.											
Stearic Acid CH$_3$(CH$_2$)$_{16}$COOH Note: Melting point 157°F.	385	743			0.8		726	No	Water or foam may cause frothing.	1	1	0
Straw Oil	315–361							No	Water or foam may cause frothing.	0	1	0
Styrene C$_6$H$_5$CH:CH$_2$ (Und. Lab. Class 40–50) (Cinnamene) (Phenylethylene) (Vinyl Benzene) Note: Polymerizes. See Hazardous Chemicals Data.	90	914	1.1	6.1	0.9	3.6	295	No	Water may be ineffective.	2	3	2
Styrene Oxide C$_6$H$_5$CHOCH$_2$	165 (oc)				1.1					2	2	0
Succinonitrile NCCH$_2$CH$_2$CN (Ethylene Dicyanide) Note: Melting point 130.1°F.	270				1.0—	2.1	509–513	Yes	Water or foam may cause frothing. "Alcohol" foam.		1	0
Sulfur Chloride S$_2$Cl$_2$ Note: See Hazardous Chemicals Data.	245	453			1.7		280	De-composes	Decomposes in water.	2	1	0
Sweet Oil	See Olive Oil.											
Sylvan	See 2—Methylfuran.											
Tallow Note: Melting point 88–100°F.	509				0.9			No	Water or foam may cause frothing.	0	1	0
Tallow Oil Note: Melting point 109°F.	492				0.9			No	Water or foam may cause frothing.	0	1	0
Tartaric Acid (d, l) (CHOHCO$_2$H)$_2$ Note: Melting point 338°F.	410 (oc)	797			1.76	5.18				0	1	0

Table 3-11A (cont.)

Material	Flash Point Deg. F.	Ignition Temp. Deg. F.	Flammable Limits Per Cent by Vol. Lower	Upper	Sp. Gr. (Water =1)	Vapor Density (Air =1)	Boiling Point Deg. F.	Water Soluble	Extinguishing Method See Intro.	Health	Flamma-bility	Reac-tivity
o—Terphenyl $(C_6H_5)_2C_6H_4$	325 (oc)				1.1		630	No	Water or foam may cause frothing.	0	1	0
m—Terphenyl $(C_6H_5)_2C_6H_4$ *Note: Melting point 188°F.*	375 (oc)				1.2		685	No	Water or foam may cause frothing.	0	1	0
Tetraamylbenzene $(C_5H_{11})_4C_6H_2$	295				0.9		608–662	No	Water or foam may cause frothing.	0	1	0
1, 1, 2, 2—Tetrabromo- ethane $CHBr_2CHBr_2$ (Acetylene Tetrabromide)		635			2.97	11.9	275			2	1	0
Tetrachlorbenzene $C_6H_2Cl_4$	311				1.7		475	No	Water or foam may cause frothing.	0	1	0
Tetradecane $CH_3(CH_2)_{12}CH_3$	212	392	0.5		0.8		487	No		0	1	0
Tetradecanol $C_{14}H_{29}OH$	285 (oc)				0.8		507	No	Water or foam may cause frothing.	0	1	0
1—Tetradecene $CH_2:CH(CH_2)_{11}CH_3$	230	455			0.8	6.8	493	No	Water or foam may cause frothing.	0	1	0
Tetraethoxypropane $(C_2H_5O)_4C_3H_4$	190 (oc)				1.12	6.70	621			0	2	0
Tetra (2—Ethylbutyl) Silicate $[C_2H_5CH(C_2H_5)CH_2O]_4Si$	335 (oc)				0.9		460 @ 50 mm.	No	Water or foam may cause frothing.	1	1	0
Tetraethylene Glycol $HOCH_2(CH_2OCH_2)_3-CH_2OH$	360 (oc)				1.1	6.7	Decom-poses	Yes	Water or foam may cause frothing. "Alcohol" foam.	1	1	0
Tetraethylene Glycol, Dibutyl Ether *See Dibutoxy Tetraglycol.*												
Tetraethylene Glycol, Dimethyl Ether *See Dimethoxy Tetraglycol.*												
Tetraethylene Pentamine $H_2N(C_2H_4NH)_3C_2H_4NH_2$	325 (oc)				1.0—		631	Yes	Water or foam may cause frothing. "Alcohol" foam.	2	1	0
Tetra (2—Ethylhexyl) Silicate $[C_4H_9CH(C_2H_5)CH_2O]_4Si$	390 (oc)				0.9			No	Water or foam may cause frothing.	1	1	0
Tetraethyl Lead, Compounds $Pb(C_2H_5)_4$ *Note: See Hazardous Chemicals Data.*	200				1.6	8.6	Decom-poses above 230	No		3	2	3
Tetraethyl Orthosilicate *See Ethyl Silicate.*												
Tetraglycol Dichloride *See Bis[2—(2—Chloroethoxy)Ethyl]Ether.*												
1, 2, 3, 6—Tetrahydro- benzaldehyde $CH_2CH:CHCH_2CH_2CHCHO$ (3—Cyclohexene—1—Carboxaldehyde)	135 (oc)				1.0—	3.8	328	Slight	"Alcohol" foam.	2	2	0
Tetrahydrofuran $OCH_2CH_2CH_2CH_2$ *Note: See Hazardous Chemicals Data.* (Diethylene Oxide) (Tetramethylene Oxide)	6	610	2	11.8	0.9	2.5	151	Yes	Water may be ineffective. "Alcohol" foam.	2	3	0
Tetrahydrofurfuryl Alcohol $C_4H_7OCH_2OH$	167 (oc)	540	1.5	9.7	1.1		352 @ 743 mm.	Yes	"Alcohol" foam.	2	2	0
Tetrahydrofurfuryl Oleate $C_4H_7OCH_2OOCC_{17}H_{33}$	390				0.9		392–545 @ 16 mm.	No	Water or foam may cause frothing.	1	1	0
Tetrahydronaphthalene $C_6H_2(CH_3)_2C_2H_4$ (Tetralin)	160	725	0.8 @ 212°	5.0 @ 302°	1.0—	4.6	405	No		1	2	0
Tetrahydropyran *See Pentamethylene Oxide.*												
Tetrahydropyran—2— Methanol $OCH_2CH_2CH_2CH_2C-HCH_2OH$	200 (oc)				1.0+	4.0	368	Yes	"Alcohol" foam.	1	2	0
Tetrahydropyrrole *See Pyrrolidine.*												
Tetralin *See Tetrahydronaphthalene.*												
Tetramethylene *See Cyclobutane.*												

Table 3-11A (cont.)	FLASH POINT Deg. F.	IGNI-TION TEMP Deg. F.	FLAMMABLE LIMITS Per Cent by Vol. Lower	Upper	Sp. Gr. (Water = 1)	Vapor Density (Air = 1)	Boiling Point Deg. F.	Water Soluble	EXTINGUISHING METHOD See Intro.	SUGGESTED HAZARD IDENTIFICATION Health	Flamma-bility	Reac-tivity
Tetramethyleneglycol $CH_2OH(CH_2)_2CH_2OH$		734			1.0+		230	Yes	"Alcohol" foam.	0	1	0
Tetramethylene Oxide	See Tetrahydrofuran.											
Tetramethyl Lead, Compounds $Pb(CH_3)_4$	100				1.6	6.5	Decom-poses above 212	No		3	3	3
	Note: See Hazardous Chemicals Data.											
2, 2, 3, 3—Tetramethyl Pentane $(CH_3)_3CC(CH_3)_2CH_2CH_3$	<70	806	0.8	4.9	0.7	4.4	273			0	3	0
2, 2, 3, 4—Tetramethyl-pentane $(CH_3)_3CCH(CH_3)CH(CH_3)_2$	<70				0.74	4.43	270			0	3	0
Tetramethyl Tin $Sn(CH_3)_4$	<70		1.9		1.3	6.2	172	No	Water may be used to blanket fire.	2		0
Tetraphenyl Tin $(C_6H_5)_4Sn$	450		1.5			14.7	795	No	Water or foam may cause frothing.	3	1	0
	Note: Melting point 439°F.											
Tetrapropionyl Glucosyl Propionate	See Glucose Pentapropionate.											
Thialdine $SCH(CH_3)SCH(CH_3)-$ $NHCHCH_3$	200 (oc)				1.1		Decom-poses	Slight	"Alcohol" foam.	2	2	1
	Note: Melting point 112°F.											
2, 2—Thiodiethanol $(HOCH_2CH_2)_2S$ (Thiodiethylene Glycol)	320 (oc)				1.2		540	Yes	"Alcohol" foam. Water or foam may cause frothing.	1	1	0
Thiodiethylene Glycol	See 2, 2—Thiodiethanol.											
Thiophene $SCH:CHCH:CH$	30				1.1	2.9	184	No	Water may be ineffective.	2	3	0
1, 4—Thioxane $O(CH_2CH_2)_2S$ (1, 4—Oxathiane)	108				1.12	3.59	300			2	2	0
Toluene	See Toluol.											
Toluene—2, 4—Diiso-cyanate $CH_3C_6H_3(NCO)_2$	270		0.9	9.5	1.2		484		Water or foam may cause frothing.	2	1	1
	Note: See Hazardous Chemicals Data.											
o—Toluidine $CH_3C_6H_4NH_2$ (2—Methylaniline)	185	900			1.0—	3.7	392	No		3	2	0
	(Und. Lab. Class 20–25) Note: See Hazardous Chemicals Data.											
p—Toluidine $CH_3C_6H_4NH_2$ (4—Methylaniline)	188	900			1.0—	3.9	392	No		3	2	0
	Note: Melting point 111°F. See Hazardous Chemicals Data.											
Toluol $C_6H_5CH_3$ (Methylbenzene) (Phenylmethane) (Toluene)	40	896	1.2	7.1	0.9	3.1	231	No	Water may be ineffective.	2	3	0
	(Und. Lab. Class 75–80) Note: See Hazardous Chemicals Data.											
2, 4—Tolylene Diiso-cyanate	See Toluene—2, 4—Diisocyanate.											
o—Tolyl Phosphate	See Tri—o—Cresyl Phosphate.											
o—Tolyl p—Toluene Sulfonate $C_{14}H_{14}O_3S$	363				1.2				Water or foam may cause frothing.	1	1	0
Transformer Oil (Transil Oil)	295 (oc)				0.9			No	Water or foam may cause frothing.	0	1	0
Transil Oil	See Transformer Oil.											
Triacetin	See Glyceryl Triacetate.											
Triamylamine $(C_5H_{11})_3N$	215 (oc)				0.8		453	No	Water or foam may cause frothing.	2	1	0
	Note: See Hazardous Chemicals Data.											
Triamylbenzene $(C_5H_{11})_3C_6H_3$	270 (oc)				0.9		575	No	Water or foam may cause frothing.	0	1	0
Triamyl Borate $B(C_5H_{11}O)_3$	180 (oc)				0.8	9.4	430			1	2	0
Tributylamine $(C_4H_9)_3N$	187 (oc)				0.8	6.4	417	No		2	2	0
	Note: See Hazardous Chemicals Data.											
Tri—n—Butyl Borate $B(OC_4H_9)_3$	200 (oc)				0.85	7.94	446			3	2	1

Table 3-11A (cont.)

	FLASH POINT Deg. F.	IGNI- TION TEMP. Deg. F.	FLAMMABLE LIMITS Per Cent by Vol. Lower	Upper	Sp. Gr. (Water =1)	Vapor Density (Air =1)	Boiling Point Deg. F.	Water Soluble	EXTINGUISHING METHOD See Intro.	Health	Flamma- bility	Reac- tivity
Tributyl Citrate $C_3H_4(OH)(COOC_4H_9)_3$	315	695			1.0+		450	No	Water or foam may cause frothing.	0	1	0
Tributyl Phosphate $(C_4H_9)_3PO_4$	295 (oc)				1.0−		560	No	Water or foam may cause frothing.	2	1	0
Tributylphosphine $(C_4H_9)_3P$		392					473	No		0	1	0
Tributyl Phosphite $(C_4H_9)_3PO_3$	248 (oc)				0.9		244–250 @ 7 mm. Decom- poses	Decom- poses		2	1	1
Trichlorobenzene $C_6H_3Cl_3$	210 (oc)				1.5		415	No	Water may be used to blanket fire.	2	1	0
Trichloroethylene $ClHC:CCl_2$		788	12.5	90	1.5	4.5	188	No		1	1*	0
	Note: *Practically nonflammable.											
1, 2, 3—Trichloro- propane $CH_2ClCHClCH_2Cl$ (Allyl Trichloride) (Glyceryl Trichlorohydrin)	180 (oc)				1.4	5.1	313	No*	Water may be used to blanket fire.	3	2	0
Trichlorosilane $HSiCl_3$	<20 (oc)				1.3	4.7	89	Decom- poses		3	4	1
Tri—o—Cresyl Phosphate $(CH_3C_6H_4)_3PO_4$ (o—Tolyl Phosphate)	437	725			1.2		770 Decom- poses	No	Water or foam may cause frothing.	2	1	0
Tridecanol $CH_3(CH_2)_{12}OH$	250 (oc)				0.8	6.9	525	No	Water or foam may cause frothing.	0	1	0
	Note: Melting point 86°F.											
2—Tridecanone	See Methyl Undecyl Ketone.											
Tridecyl Acrylate $CH_2:CHCOOC_{13}H_{27}$	270 (oc)				0.9		302 @ 10 mm.	No	Water or foam may cause frothing.	1	1	0
Tridecyl Phosphite $(C_{10}H_{21}O)_3P$	455 (oc)				0.9		356 @ 0.1 mm.	No	Water or foam may cause frothing.	0	1	0
Triethanolamine $(CH_2OHCH_2)_3N$ (2, 2', 2″—Nitrilotriethanol)	355				1.1		650	Yes	Water or foam may cause frothing. "Alcohol" foam.	1	1	1
1, 1, 3—Triethoxy- hexane $CH(OC_2H_5)_2CH_2CH-(OC_2H_5)C_3H_7$	210 (oc)				0.9	7.5	271 @ 50 mm. Decom- poses @ 760 mm.	No		1	1	0
Triethylaluminum $(C_2H_5)_3Al$	Note: Ignites spontaneously in air.								Do not use water, foam or halogenated extinguishing agents.		3	3 ₩
Triethylamine $(C_2H_5)_3N$	20 (oc)		1.2	8.0	0.7	3.5	193	No	Water may be ineffective. "Alcohol" foam.	2	3	0
1, 2, 4—Triethylbenzene $(C_2H_5)_3C_6H_3$	181 (oc)				0.9	5.6	423	No			2	0
Triethylborane $(C_2H_5)_3B$	Note: Ignites spontaneously in air.								Do not use halogenated extinguishing agents.	1	3	3 ₩
Triethyl Citrate $HOC(CH_2CO_2C_2H_5)-CO_2C_2H_5$	303				1.1		561	Very slight	Water or foam may cause frothing.	0	1	0
Triethylene Glycol $HOCH_2(CH_2OCH_2)_2CH_2OH$ (Dicaproate) (2, 2—Ethylenedixoydiethanol)	350	700	0.9	9.2	1.1		550	Yes	Water or foam may cause frothing. "Alcohol" foam.	1	1	0
Triethylene Glycol, Dimethyl Ether $CH_3(OCH_2)_3OCH_3$	232 (oc)				1.0−	4.7	421		Water or foam may cause frothing.	1	1	0
Triethylene Glycol, Ethyl Ether	See Ethoxytriglycol.											
Triethylene Glycol, Methyl Ether	See Methoxy Triglycol.											
Triethylenetetramine $H_2NCH_2(CH_2NHCH_2)_2-CH_2NH_2$	275	640			1.0−		532	Yes	Water or foam may cause frothing. "Alcohol" foam.	3	1	0

Table 3-11A (cont.)	FLASH POINT Deg. F.	IGNI- TION TEMP. Deg. F.	FLAMMABLE LIMITS Per Cent by Vol.		Sp. Gr. (Water = 1)	Vapor Density (Air = 1)	Boiling Point Deg. F.	Water Soluble	EXTINGUISHING METHOD See Intro.	SUGGESTED HAZARD IDENTIFICATION		
			Lower	Upper						Health	Flamma- bility	Reac- tivity
Triethyl Phosphate $(C_2H_5)_3PO_4$ (Ethyl Phosphate)	240 (oc)				1.1		408–424	Yes	"Alcohol" foam. Water or foam may cause frothing.	0	1	1
Trifluorochloroethylene $CF_2:CFCl$ (R-1113) (Chlorotrifluoroethylene)	Gas		24.0	40.3	1.31 @ 5.7 atm	4.02	−18				4	0
Triglycol Dichloride $ClCH_2(CH_3OCH_2)_2CH_2Cl$	250 (oc)				1.2		466	No	Water or foam may cause frothing.	2	1	0
Trihexyl Phosphite $(C_6H_{13})_3PO_3$	320 (oc)				0.9		275–286 @ 2 mm. De- com- poses	De- com- poses	Decomposes in water.		1	0
Triisobutylaluminum $[(CH_3)_2CHCH_2]_3Al$	Note: May ignite spontaneously in air.								Do not use water, foam or halogenated extinguishing agents.		3	3 ₩
Triisobutyl Borate $B(OC_4H_9)_3$	185 (oc)				0.84	7.94	413			3	2	1
Triisopropanolamine $[(CH_3)_2COH]_3N$ (1, 1', 1"—Nitrolotri—2—propanol)	320 (oc)				1.0−		584	Yes	Water or foam may cause frothing. "Alcohol" foam.	2	1	0
Triisopropyl Borate $(C_3H_7O)_3B$	82				0.82	6.49	288			3	3	1
Trilauryl Trithiophosphite $[CH_3(CH_2)_{11}S]_3P$	398 (oc)				0.9				Water or foam may cause frothing.	0	1	0
Trimethylaluminum $(CH_3)_3Al$	Note: Ignites spontaneously in air.								Do not use water, foam or halogenated extinguishing agents.		3	3 ₩
Trimethylamine $(CH_3)_3N$	Gas	374 Note: See Hazardous Chemicals Data.	2.0	11.6		2.0	38	Yes	Stop flow of gas.	2	4	0
1, 2, 3—Trimethyl- benzene $C_6H_3(CH_3)_3$ (Hemellitol)		878			0.89	4.15	349			0	2	0
1, 2, 4—Trimethyl- benzene $C_6H_3(CH_3)_3$ (Pseudocumene)	130	959			0.88	4.15	336			0	2	0
1, 3, 5—Trimethyl- benzene $C_6H_3(CH_3)_3$ (Mesitylene)		1022			0.87	4.15	329			0	2	0
Trimethyl Borate	See Methyl Borate.											
2, 2, 3—Trimethyl- butane $(CH_3)_3C(CH_3)CHCH_3$ (Triptane—an isomer of Heptane)	<32	842			0.69	3.46	178			0	3	0
2, 3, 3—Trimethyl—1— butene $(CH_3)_3CC(CH_3):CH_2$ (Heptylene)	<32	707			0.71	3.39	172			0	3	0
Trimethyl Carbinol	See tert—Butyl Alcohol.											
Trimethylcyclohexanol $CH(OH)CH_2C(CH_3)_2-$ $CH_2CH(CH_3)CH_2$	165 (oc)				0.9	4.9	388	No		2	2	0
3, 3, 5—Trimethyl—1— Cyclohexanol $CH_2CH(CH_3)CH_2C(CH_3)_2-$ CH_2CHOH	190 (oc)				0.9	4.9	388	Slight	"Alcohol" foam.	2	2	0
Trimethylene	See Cyclopropane.											
Trimethylenediamine	See 1, 3—Propanediamine.											
Trimethylene Glycol $HO(CH_2)_3OH$ (1, 3—Propanediol)		752			1.1	2.6	417	Yes	"Alcohol" foam.	1		0
Trimethylethylene	See 2—Methyl—2—Butene.											
2, 5, 5—Trimethyl- heptane $C_2H_5C(CH_3)_2(CH_2)_2CH(CH_3)_2$	<131	860			0.73	4.91	304			0	2	0

Table 3-11A (cont.)	FLASH POINT Deg. F.	IGNI- TION TEMP. Deg. F.	FLAMMABLE LIMITS Per Cent by Vol.		Sp. Gr. (Water = 1)	Vapor Density (Air = 1)	Boiling Point Deg. F.	Water Soluble	EXTINGUISHING METHOD See Intro.	SUGGESTED HAZARD IDENTIFICATION		
			Lower	Upper						Health	Flamma- bility	Reac- tivity
2, 2, 5—Trimethyl- hexane $(CH_3)_3C(CH_2)_2CH(CH_3)_2$	55 (oc)				0.7	4.4	255	No	Water may be ineffective.	2	3	0
3, 5, 5—Trimethyl- hexanol $CH_3C(CH_3)_2CH_2CH-(CH_3)CH_2CH_2OH$	200 (oc)				0.8		381	No		2	2	0
2, 4, 8—Trimethyl—6— Nonanol $C_4H_9CH(OH)C_7H_{15}$ (2, 6, 8—Trimethyl—4—nonanol)	199 (oc)				0.82	6.43	491			0	2	0
2, 6, 8—Trimethyl—4— Nonanol $(CH_3)_2CHCH_2CH(OH)CH_2CH-(CH_3)CH_2CH(CH_3)_2$	200 (oc)				0.8		438	No		2	2	0
2, 6, 8—Trimethyl—4— Nonane $(CH_3)_2CHCH_2CH(CH_3)CH_2-COCH_2CH(CH_3)_2$	195 (oc)				0.8	6.3	425	No		2	2	0
2, 2, 3—Trimethyl- pentane $CH_3CH_2CH(CH_3)C(CH_3)_3$	<70	806			0.72	3.94	230			0	3	0
2, 2, 4—Trimethyl- pentane $(CH_3)_3CCH_2CH(CH_3)_2$	10	779	1.1	6.0	0.7	3.9	211	No	Water may be ineffective.		3	0
2, 3, 3—Trimethyl- pentane $CH_3CH_2C(CH_3)_2CH(CH_3)_2$	<70	797			0.73	3.94	239			0	3	0
2, 2, 4—Trimethyl- pentanediol Diiso- butyrate $C_{16}H_{30}O_4$	250 (oc)				0.9	9.9	536		Water or foam may cause frothing.	0	1	0
2, 2, 4—Trimethylpen- tanediol Isobutyrate Benzoate $C_{19}H_{28}O_4$	325 (oc)				1.0		167 @ 10 mm.		Water or foam may cause frothing.	0	1	0
2, 3, 4—Trimethyl—1— pentene $H_2C:C(CH_3)CH(CH_3)CH(CH_3)_2$	<70	779			.72	3.87	214			0	3	0
2, 4, 4—Trimethyl—1— pentene $CH_2:C(CH_3)CH_2C(CH_3)_3$	<20	779			0.7	3.8	214	No	Water may be ineffective.	2	3	0
2, 4, 4—Trimethyl—2— pentene $CH_3CH:C(CH_3)C(CH_3)_3$	35 (oc)	581			0.7	3.8	221	No	Water may be ineffective.	2	3	0
3, 4, 4—Trimethyl—2— pentene $(CH_3)_3CC(CH_3):CHCH_3$	<70	617			0.74	3.87	234			0	3	0
Trimethyl Phosphite $(CH_3O)_3P$	130 (oc)				1.0+	4.3	232–234	No		0	2	0
Trioctyl Phosphite $(C_8H_{17}O)_3P$ [Tris (2—Ethylhexyl) Phosphite]	340 (oc)				0.9		212 @ 0.01 mm.	No	Water or foam may cause frothing.	0	1	0
Trioxane $OCH_2OCH_2OCH_2$	113 (oc) Note: Melting point 147°F.	777	3.6	29			239 Sub- limes	Slight	"Alcohol" foam.	2	2	0
Triphenylmethane $(C_6H_5)_3CH$	>212 Note: Melting point 200°F.				1.01	8.43	678			0	1	0
Triphenyl Phosphate $(C_6H_5)_3PO_4$	428 Note: Melting point 122°F.				1.3		750	No	Water or foam may cause frothing.	2	1	0
Triphenylphosphine $(C_6H_5)_3P$	356 (oc) Note: Melting point 176°F.					9.0	711	No	Water or foam may cause frothing.			0
Triphenyl Phosphite $(C_6H_5O')_3PO_3$	425 (oc)				1.2		311–320 @ 0.1 mm.	No	Water or foam may cause frothing.	0	1	0
Triphenylphosphorus $(C_6H_5)_3P$	356 (oc) Note: Melting point 176°F.				9.0		711	No	Water or foam may cause frothing.	0	1	0
Tripropyl aluminum $(C_3H_7)_3Al$	Note: Ignites spontaneously in air.								Do not use water, foam or halogenated extinguishing agents.		3	3 ₩
Tripropylamine $(CH_3CH_2CH_2)_3N$	105 (oc)				0.8	4.9	313	Very slight		2	2	0

Table 3-11A (cont.)	FLASH POINT Deg. F.	IGNI- TION TEMP. Deg. F.	FLAMMABLE LIMITS Per Cent by Vol.		Sp. Gr. (Water =1)	Vapor Density (Air =1)	Boiling Point Deg. F.	Water Soluble	EXTINGUISHING METHOD See Intro.	SUGGESTED HAZARD IDENTIFICATION		
			Lower	Upper						Health	Flamma- bility	Reac- tivity
Tripropylene Glycol Methyl Ether HO(C₃H₆O)₂C₃H₆OCH₃ $HO(C_3H_6O)_2C_3H_6OCH_3$	250				0.97	7.12	470			0	1	0
Tris(2—Ethylhexyl) Phosphite	See Trioctyl Phosphite.											
Tung Oil (China Wood Oil)	552	855 Note: Melting point 88°F.			0.9			No	Water or foam may cause frothing.	0	1	0
Turbine Oil	See Lubricating Oil, Turbine.											
Turbo Fuels	See Jet Fuels.											
Turkey Red Oil	476	833			1.0—			Yes	Water or foam may cause frothing. "Alcohol" foam.	0	1	0
Turpentine	95	488 (Und. Lab. Class 40–50)	0.8		<1		300	No	Water may be ineffective.	1	3	0
Ultrasene (Kerosene, Deodorized)	175							No		1	2	0
Undecane	See Hendecane.											
2—Undecanol C₄H₉CH(C₂H₅)C₂H₄- CH(OH)CH₃ $C_4H_9CH(C_2H_5)C_2H_4CH(OH)CH_3$	235 (oc)				0.8		437	No	Water or foam may cause frothing.	1	1	0
Unsymmetrical Dimethylhydrazine	See 1, 1—Dimethylhydrazine.											
Valeraldehyde CH₃(CH₂)₃CHO $CH_3(CH_2)_3CHO$ (Pentanal)	54 (oc)				0.8	3.0	217	No	Water may be ineffective.	1	3	0
Valeric Acid	See Pentanoic Acid.											
Vinyl Acetate CH₂:CHOOCCH₃ $CH_2{:}CHOOCCH_3$ (Ethenyl Ethanoate)	18	800 Note: Polymerizes. See Hazardous Chemicals Data.	2.6	13.4	0.9	3.0	161	Slight	Water may be ineffective. "Alcohol" foam.	2	3	2
Vinylaceto—β—Lactone	See Diketene.											
Vinyl Acetylene CH₂:CHC:CH $CH_2{:}CHC{:}CH$ (1—Buten—3—yne)			2	100	0.68 @ 1.7 atm Spont. decomposition	1.80	41				4	3
Vinyl Allyl Ether CH₂:CHOCH₂CH₂O- (CH₂)₃CH₃ $CH_2{:}CHOCH_2CH_2O(CH_2)_3CH_3$ (Allyl Vinyl Ether)	<68 (oc)				0.8		153	Very slight	Water may be ineffective.	2	3	2
Vinylbenzene	See Styrene.											
Vinyl Butyl Ether CH₂:CHOC₄H₉ $CH_2{:}CHOC_4H_9$ (Butyl Vinyl Ether)	15 (oc)				0.8	3.5	202	Slight	Water may be ineffective. "Alcohol" foam.	2	3	2
Vinyl Butyrate CH₂:CHOCOC₃H₇ $CH_2{:}CHOCOC_3H_7$	68 (oc)		1.4	8.8	0.9	4.0	242	Slight	Water may be ineffective. "Alcohol" foam.	2	3	2
Vinyl 2—Chlorethyl Ether CH₂:CHOCH₂CH₂Cl $CH_2{:}CHOCH_2CH_2Cl$ (2—Chloroethyl Vinyl Ether)	80 (oc)				1.0+	3.7	228	Slight	Water may be ineffective. "Alcohol" foam.	2	3	2
Vinyl Chloride CH₂CHCl CH_2CHCl (Chloroethylene)	Gas	882 Note: Polymerizes. See Hazardous Chemicals Data.	3.6	33.0		2.2	7	No	Stop flow of gas.	2	4	1
Vinyl Crotonate CH₂:CHOCOCH:CHCH₃ $CH_2{:}CHOCOCH{:}CHCH_3$	78 (oc)				0.9	4.0	273	Slight	Water may be ineffective. "Alcohol" foam.	2	3	2
Vinyl Cyanide	See Acrylonitrile.											
4—Vinyl Cyclohexene C₈H₁₂ C_8H_{12}	61	517			0.8	3.7	266		Water may be ineffective.	0	3	2
Vinyl Ether	See Divinyl Ether.											
Vinyl Ethyl Alcohol CH₂:CH(CH₂)₂OH $CH_2{:}CH(CH_2)_2OH$ (3—Buten—1—ol)	100		4.7	34	0.84	2.49	233	Yes		0	2	0
Vinylethylene Oxide	See Butadiene Monoxide.											
Vinyl Ethyl Ether CH₂:CHOC₂H₅ $CH_2{:}CHOC_2H_5$ (Ethyl Vinyl Ether)	<—50	395	1.7	28	0.8	2.5	96	No	Water may be ineffective. "Alcohol" foam.	2	4	2
Vinyl 2—Ethylhexoate CH₂:CHOCOCH(C₂H₅)- C₄H₉ $CH_2{:}CHOCOCH(C_2H_5)C_4H_9$	165 (oc)				0.9	6.0	365	No		2	2	2
Vinyl 2—Ethylhexyl Ether C₁₀H₂₀O $C_{10}H_{20}O$ (2—Ethylhexyl Vinyl Ether)	135 (oc)	395			0.8	5.4	352	Slight	"Alcohol" foam.	2	2	2

Table 3-11A (cont.)	FLASH POINT Deg. F.	IGNITION TEMP. Deg. F.	FLAMMABLE LIMITS Per Cent by Vol.		Sp. Gr. (Water = 1)	Vapor Density (Air = 1)	Boiling Point Deg. F.	Water Soluble	EXTINGUISHING METHOD See Intro.	SUGGESTED HAZARD IDENTIFICATION		
			Lower	Upper						Health	Flammability	Reactivity
2—Vinyl—5—Ethyl-pyridine N:C(CH:CH₂)CH:CH- C(C₂H₅):CH	200 (oc)				0.9		248 @ 50 mm.	No		2	2	2
Vinyl Fluoride CH₂:CHF	Gas		2.6	21.7			−97.5	Slight	Stop flow of gas.	1	4	2
Vinylidene Chloride CH₂:CCl₂ (1, 1—Dichloro-ethylene)	0	1058	7.3	16.0	1.3	3.4	99	No	Water may be ineffective except as a blanket.	2	4	2
	Note: Polymerizes. See Hazardous Chemicals Data.											
Vinylidene Fluoride CH₂:CF₂	Gas		5.5	21.3			−122.3	Slight	Stop flow of gas.	1	4	2
Vinyl Isobutyl Ether CH₂:CHOCH₂CH(CH₃)CH₃ (Isobutyl Vinyl Ether)	15				0.8	3.5	182	Slight	Water may be ineffective. "Alcohol" foam.	2	3	2
Vinyl Isooctyl Ether CH₂:CHO(CH₂)₅CH(CH₃)₂ (Isooctyl Vinyl Ether)	140				0.8	5.4	347	No		1	2	0
Vinyl Isopropyl Ether CH₂:CHOCH(CH₃)₂ (Isopropyl Vinyl Ether)	−26	522				3.0	133		Water may be ineffective. "Alcohol" foam.	2	4	2
Vinyl 2—Methoxyethyl Ether CH₂:CHOC₂H₄OCH₃ (1—Methoxy—2—vinyloxyethane)	64 (oc)				0.90	3.52	228			0	3	0
Vinyl Methyl Ether CH₂:CHOCH₃ (Methyl Vinyl Ether)	Gas					2.0	43	Slight	Stop flow of gas.	2	4	2
Vinyl Octadecyl Ether CH₂:CHO(CH₂)₁₇CH₃ (Octadecyl Vinyl Ether)	350				0.8		297–369 @ 5 mm.	No	Water or foam may cause frothing.	0	1	0
	Note: Melting point 82.4°F.											
Vinyl Propionate CH₂:CHOCOC₂H₅	34 (oc)				0.9	3.3	203	Slight	Water may be ineffective. "Alcohol" foam.	2	3	2
1—Vinylpyrrolidone CH₂:CHNCOCH₂CH₂CH₂ (Vinyl—2—Pyrrolidone)	209 (oc)				1.0+	3.8	205 @ 14 mm.	Yes	"Alcohol" foam.	0	1	0
Vinyl—2—Pyrrolidone	See 1—Vinylpyrrolidone.											
Water Gas	See Gas.											
Wax, Microcrystalline	>400				0.9				Water or foam may cause frothing.	0	1	0
Wax, Ozocerite (Mineral Wax)	236				0.9			No	Water or foam may cause frothing.	0	1	0
Wax, Paraffin	390	473			0.9		>700	No	Water or foam may cause frothing.	0	1	0
	Note: Melting point 120–167°F.											
Whale Oil	446	800			0.9			No	Water or foam may cause frothing.	0	1	0
Whiskey	See Ethyl Alcohol and Water.											
White Tar	See Napthalene.											
Wines Sherry and Port High	See Ethyl Alcohol and Water.											
Wood Alcohol	See Methyl Alcohol.											
Wood Tar Oil	See Pine Tar Oil.											
Wool Grease	See Lanolin.											
m—Xylene C₆H₄(CH₃)₂ (1, 3—Dimethylbenzene)	84	986	1.1	7.0	0.9	3.7	282	No	Water may be ineffective.	2	3	0
	Note: See Hazardous Chemicals Data.											
o—Xylene C₆H₄(CH₃)₂ (1, 2—Dimethylbenzene) (o—Xylol)	90	869	1.0	6.0	0.9	3.7	292	No	Water may be ineffective.	2	3	0
	(Und. Lab. Class 40–45) Note: See Hazardous Chemicals Data.											
p—Xylene C₆H₄(CH₃)₂ (1, 4—Dimethylbenzene)	81	986	1.1	7.0	0.9	3.7	281	No	Water may be ineffective.	2	3	0
	Note: See Hazardous Chemicals Data.											
o—Xylidine C₆H₃(CH₃)₂NH₂ (o—Dimethylaniline)	206				1.0−		435	No		3	1	0
o—Xylol	See o—Xylene.											
Zinc Diethyl	See Diethylzinc.											
Zinc Stearate Zn(C₁₇H₃₅COO)₂	530 (oc)	788								0	1	0

Table 3-11B. Thermal Properties*

Material	Heat of Combustion Btu/lb	Latent Heat of Vaporization Btu/lb	Specific Heat Temperature °F	Btu/lb
Acetic Acid	6,277	174	32	.468
Acetone	13,228	242	68	.528
Acetonitrile	13,260	313	70-169	.541
Acetophenone	14,816	139	68-385	.474
Allyl Alcohol	13,711	293	70-205	.665
Amyl Alcohol-iso	16,207	216	68	.535
Aniline	15,690	187	32	.478
Benzaldehyde	14,270	156	72-342	.428
Benzene	18,028	193	68	.406
Benzyl Alcohol	15,609	202	68-212	.511
Butyl Alcohol-n	15,508	454	67	.563
Butyric Acid-n	10,712	205	68-212	.515
Chlorotorm	1,345	116	32	.232
Cresol-m	14,656	181	32-68	.479
Cyclohexanol	16,007	195	59-64	.417
Cymene-p	18,814	122	32	.400
Diethylamine	17,886	164	72	.518
Diethyl Carbonate	9,856	132	68-212	.464
Diethyl Ketone	15,331	163	68-209	.557
Diethyl Oxalate	8,819	121	68	.433
Dimethylaniline	16,973	145	32-68	.418
Dimethyl Carbonate	6,810	159	68-190	.452
Ethyl Acetate	10,970	184	68	.459
Ethyl Alcohol	12,800	368	148	.456
Ethyl Benzene	22,794	171	86	.409
Ethyl Benzoate	13,170	116	68	.389
Ethyl Bromide	5,624	108	41-50	.216
Ethyl Butyrate	13,190	134	68	.459
Ethyl Chloride	8,835	167	32	.368
Ethyl Formate	9,515	175	57-120	.510
Ethyl Propionate	12,176	144	68	.459
Formic Acid	2,463	216	68-212	.526
Furfural	10,482	194	68-212	.418
Heptane-n	20,657	157	68	.490
Hexane-n	20,676	160	68-212	.600
Mesityl Oxide	15,529	154	70-250	.521
Methyl Acetate	9,262	205	59	.468
Methyl Alcohol	9,600	512	68	.600
Methyl Aniline	16,354	172	68-387	.513
Methyl Butyl Ketone	16,088	148	70-261	.553
Methyl n-Butyrate	12,210	144	68	.459
Methyl Ethyl Ketone	14,537	191	68-172	.549
Methyl Formate	6,987	202	55-84	.516
Methyl Propionate	11,284	158	68	.459
Methylene Chloride	2,263	141	59-104	.288
Naphthalene	17,309	136	32	.313
Nitrobenzene	10,808	142	86	.339
Nitromethane	4,995	243	63	.412
Octane-n	20,528	156	68-253	.578
Pentane-iso	20,914	147	46	.527
Piperidine	17,474	161	68-208	.523
Propane	21,486	183	32	.576
Propionic Acid	8,922	178	68-279	.560
Propyl Alcohol	14,193	296	77	.586
Propyl Benzene	18,667	165	32	.400
Pyridine	14,962	193	70-226	.431
Salicylaldehyde	11,733	135	64	.382
Toluene	18,252	177	32	.386
Toluidine-o	16,199	171	72-383	.524
Xylene-o	18,510	176	86	.411
Xylene-m	18,374	173	61-95	.387
Xylene-p	18,466	172	86	.397

* The figures given in this table in Btu's per lb were calculated from published information reported in calorie-gram-centigrade units.

Table 3-11C. Densities of Miscellaneous Materials

Material	Specific Gravity	Density (lbs per cu ft)	Material	Specific Gravity	Density (lbs per cu ft)
Asbestos	2.1–2.8	153	Ice	0.88–0.92	55–57
Ashes	. . . .	43	Masonry	2.24–2.88	150–160
Asphaltum	1.39	87	Paper	0.70–1.15	58
Brick, common	1.79	112	Sand	1.44–1.76	100
Brickwork, mortar	1.6	100	Wood		
Brickwork, cement	1.79	112	Cypress	0.41–0.66	33
Coal, anthracite	1.4–1.8	97	Fir	0.48–0.70	37
Coal, bituminous	1.2–1.5	84	Maple	0.57–0.79	42
Concrete	1.92–2.48	133	Oak, white	0.69–0.86	48
Earth, packed	1.5	93	Pine, white	0.35–0.55	28
Glass, common	2.5–2.75	164	Pine, yellow	0.46–0.76	38
Glass, plate	2.45–2.72	161	Spruce	0.40–0.50	28
Gypsum	2.08–2.4	140			

Table 3-11D. Thermal Expansion of Solids
(Adapted from data published by National Bureau of Standards)

Substance	Coefficient of Linear Expansion per Degree F	Percent Increase in Length for Temp. Rise of 100°F
Aluminum	.000014	0.14
Brass	.000011	0.11
Brick	.000005	0.05
Bronze	.000010	0.10
Concrete	.000006 to .000008	0.06 to 0.08
Copper	.000009	0.09
Glass, Ordinary	.000006	0.06
Pyrex	.000002	0.02
Iron, cast	.000006	0.06
Lead	.000016	0.16
Masonry	.000002 to .000004	0.02 to 0.04
Slate	.000003 to .000006	0.03 to 0.06
Steel	.000006 to .000007	0.06 to 0.07
Wood, Parallel to fiber	.000003 to .000005	0.03 to 0.05
Across the fiber	.000018 to .000034	0.18 to 0.34
Zinc	.000015	0.15

This table gives approximate data for use within ordinary temperature ranges. The actual expansion per degree is not uniform at different temperatures, and at high temperatures, such as are encountered in fires, relative expansion per degree is much greater for many common substances. Thus the expansion of steel, given in the table as .000006 to .000007, becomes about .000015 per degree temperature rise at around 1600°F. Ordinary glass, given in the table as .000006, becomes about .000020 at around 1000°F.

Table 3-11E. Thermal Expansion of Flammable Liquids

Material	Coefficient of Expansion, Volumetric per Degree F	Percent Increase in Volume per 100°F Temp. Rise
Acetone	0.00085	8.5
Amyl acetate	0.00068	6.8
Benzol (benzene)	0.00071	7.1
Butane	0.00107	10.7
Carbon disulfide	0.00070	7.0
Ethyl ether	0.00098	9.8
Ethyl acetate	0.00079	7.9
Ethyl alcohol	0.00062	6.2
Fuel oil	0.0004	4.
Gasoline, ordinary	0.0006	6.
Gasoline natural	0.0008	8.
Methyl alcohol	0.00072	7.2
Propane	0.00168	16.8
Toluol (toluene)	0.00063	6.3

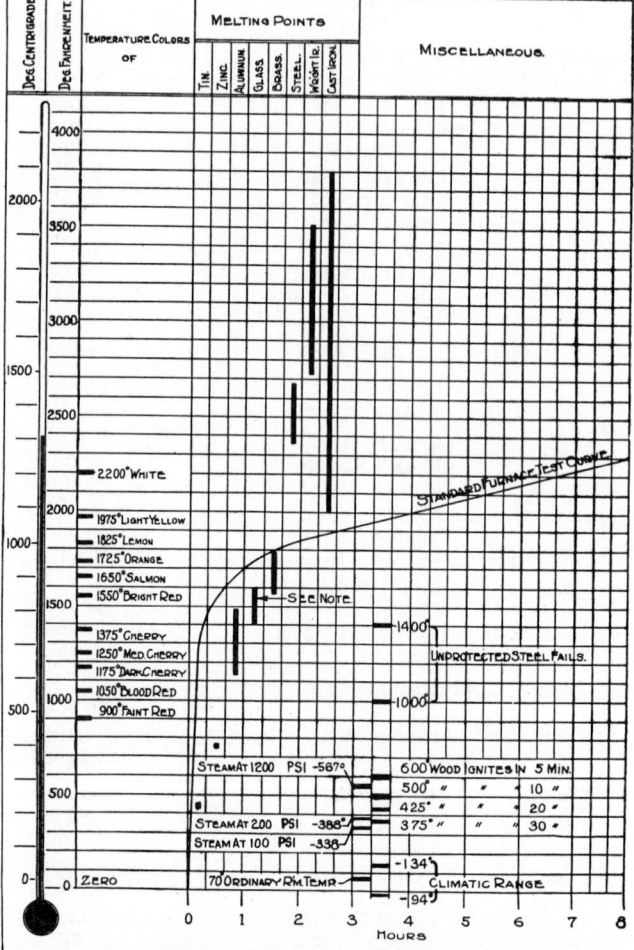

Fig. 3-11A. Temperature colors, melting points of various substances; and data on the behavior of some materials at elevated temperatures and pressures.

Table 3-11F. Specific Gravity Equivalents for Degrees Baumé
(For Liquids Lighter than Water)

Baumé	Specific Gravity	Lbs per Gallon	Baumé	Specific Gravity	Lbs per Gallon	Baumé	Specific Gravity	Lbs per Gallon
10	1.0000	8.33	45	0.8000	6.66	80	0.6667	5.55
11	0.9929	8.27	46	0.7955	6.63	81	0.6635	5.52
12	0.9859	8.21	47	0.7910	6.59	82	0.6604	5.50
13	0.9790	8.16	48	0.7865	6.55	83	0.6573	5.48
14	0.9722	8.10	49	0.7821	6.52	84	0.6542	5.45
15	0.9655	8.04	50	0.7778	6.48	85	0.6512	5.42
16	0.9589	7.99	51	0.7735	6.44	86	0.6481	5.40
17	0.9524	7.93	52	0.7692	6.41	87	0.6452	5.38
18	0.9459	7.88	53	0.7650	6.37	88	0.6422	5.36
19	0.9396	7.83	54	0.7609	6.34	89	0.6393	5.33
20	0.9333	7.78	55	0.7568	6.30	90	0.6364	5.30
21	0.9272	7.72	56	0.7527	6.27	91	0.6335	5.28
22	0.9211	7.67	57	0.7487	6.24	92	0.6306	5.25
23	0.9150	7.62	58	0.7447	6.20	93	0.6278	5.23
24	0.9091	7.57	59	0.7407	6.17	94	0.6250	5.21
25	0.9032	7.53	60	0.7368	6.14	95	0.6222	5.18
26	0.8974	7.48	61	0.7330	6.11	96	0.6195	5.16
27	0.8917	7.43	62	0.7292	6.07	97	0.6167	5.14
28	0.8861	7.38	63	0.7254	6.04	98	0.6140	5.11
29	0.8805	7.34	64	0.7216	6.01	99	0.6114	5.09
30	0.8750	7.29	65	0.7179	5.98	100	0.6087	5.07
31	0.8696	7.24	66	0.7143	5.95	101	0.6061	5.05
32	0.8642	7.20	67	0.7107	5.92	102	0.6034	5.03
33	0.8589	7.15	68	0.7071	5.89	103	0.6009	5.00
34	0.8537	7.11	69	0.7035	5.86	104	0.5983	4.98
35	0.8485	7.07	70	0.7000	5.83	105	0.5957	4.96
36	0.8434	7.03	71	0.6965	5.80	106	0.5932	4.94
37	0.8383	6.98	72	0.6931	5.78	107	0.5907	4.92
38	0.8333	6.94	73	0.6897	5.75	108	0.5882	4.90
39	0.8284	6.90	74	0.6863	5.72	109	0.5858	4.88
40	0.8235	6.86	75	0.6829	5.69	110	0.5833	4.86
41	0.8187	6.82	76	0.6796	5.66			
42	0.8140	6.78	77	0.6763	5.63			
43	0.8092	6.74	78	0.6731	5.60			
44	0.8046	6.70	79	0.6699	5.58			

NOTE: See footnote to Table 3-11I.

Table 3-11G. Physical and Thermal Properties

Material	Density lbs/cu in.	Heat of Combustion Btu/lb	Heat of Combustion Btu/cu in.	Melting Point °F	Boiling Point °F	Mol. Wt
Aluminum	0.098	13,300	1,295	1,220	....	27
Asphalt	0.035	17,150	600	....	....	....
Camphor	0.036	16,720	605	354	408	152
Carbon	0.072	13,480	974	6,330	7,580	12
Carbon disulfide	0.046	5,840	266	....	115	76
Cork dust (compressed)	0.0041	7,200	29	dec.	dec.	....
Cotton seed oil	0.033	17,100	568	50	....	....
Lard oil	0.033	16,750	556	....	....	....
Magnesium	0.063	11,950	752	1,203	2,030	24
Menthol	0.032	17,400	560	100	419	156
Naphthalene	0.041	17,300	712	176	424	128
Oil, lubricating, SAE 40*	0.031	20,400	626	....	....	142*
Palmitic acid	0.031	16,820	516	147	642	256
Paraffin wax	....	20,100	....	165	....	....
Phenol	0.039	14,000	542	108	358	94
Phosphorus	0.054	10,580	568	112	549	31
Pitch	0.040	15,100	605	390SP	....	....
Sodium	0.035	3,870	432	204	1,616	23
Sucrose	0.057	3,960	296	....	....	32
Tallow	0.032	17,100	532	94	....	....
Zinc	0.26	2,300	588	786	1,660	65

* Approximate

Table 3-11H. Calorific Value of Materials*

Substance	Moisture Percent	Calorific Value Btu per lb	Ref.
Coals			
Anthracite (Pennsylvania only)	2.3– 2.2	12,520–13,830	1
Semi-anthracite (Pennsylvania only)	3.4– 3.2	13,120–13,380	1
Semi-bituminous	2.4– 2.0	13,710–14,810	1
Bituminous	14.2– 1.6	10,020–14,700	1
Sub-bituminous	20.5–13.5	8,690–11,140	1
Lignite	43.5–32.6	5,810– 7,360	1
Peat	90.3–54.7	510– 4,100	1
Cannel coal	1.5– 0.4	10,850–15,000	1
Coke	0.2– 0.1	11,690–12,810	1
Charcoal	3.2	12,920	1
Woods			
Ash	Dry	8,480	5
Beech	13	7,510	11
Birch	12	7,580	11
Elm	Dry	8,510	5
Fir	Dry	9,060	5
Hardwood (av. several species)	10.8	8,120	6
Locust	‡	8,640	3
Oak	13	7,180	11
Pine	12.3–10.5	8,080– 8,420	6
Soft wood, resinous	10.4	8,330	6
Straw			
Buckwheat	Dry	5,590	7
Flax	Dry	6,750	7
Wheat	Dry	6,290	7
Tanbark	Dry	9,500	10
Bagasse	53	3,910	7
Petroleum products			
Crude and fuel oil	†	18,610–19,710	6
Gasoline	†	19,800–20,520	6
Kerosine	†	19,710–19,890	6
Coal tar oil	†	17,890–18,400	1
Gas oil	†	19,260–19,580	3
Asphalt, pure	†	17,160	13
Bitumen, pure	†	15,140	5
Ozocerite	†	19,170–19,710	1
Paraffin	†	17,960–20,110	1
Pitch	†	15,120	4
Gas			
Natural (Btu per cu ft)	†	710– 2,250	1
Oil (Btu per cu ft)	†	510– 800	1
Coal (Btu per cu ft)	†	450– 670	1
Producer (Btu per cu ft)	†	100– 180	1
Water (Btu per cu ft)	†	300– 670	1
Cotton, combed	Air dried	7,160	6
Silk, "fibre"	†	9,230	3
Wool, raw	Air dried	9,790	6
Wool, scoured	Air dried	8,890	6
Paper (ash—7.0% to 1.4%)	5.0– 4.8	6,710– 7,830	6
Cellulose	†	7,570	8
Starch	†	7,610	8
Guncotton	‡	1,900	3
Dynamite, 75%	‡	2,320	3
Casein	‡	10,550	12
Fats and waxes			
Animal fats, mean	†	17,100	2
Butter fat	†	16,770–16,850	1
Goose fat	†	17,110	1
Lard	†	17,110–17,380	1
Oleomargarine	†	17,280	1
Tallow	†	17,100	12
Stearic Acid	†	16,870	12
Animal and vegetable oils			
Cod liver	†	16,980	1
Lard	†	17,010	1
Menhaden	†	16,850	1
Shark	†	16,870	1
Sperm	†	17,900	1
Whale	†	17,050	1

Table 3-11H. Calorific Value of Materials (Cont.)

Substance	Moisture Percent	Calorific Value Btu per Lb	Ref.
Arachis	†	16,940	1
Almond	†	17,010	1
Castor	†	15,950	1
Cottonseed	†	16,920	3
Linseed	†	16,860	1
Maize	†	16,950	1
Olive	†	17,020	1
Poppy	†	16,890	1
Rape-seed	†	17,080	1
Sesame	†	16,910	1
Chemicals			
Carbon disulfide	†	6,130	8
Ethyl ether	†	22,000	2
Glycerine	†	7,770	12

* Table prepared by S. H. Ingberg. See list of references below.
† Moisture-free or pure substances assumed.
‡ Moisture content not stated.

REFERENCES

1. International Critical Tables.
2. Smithsonian Tables.
3. Landolt-Börnstein Physikalisch-Chemische Tabellen.
4. Van Nostrand's Chemical Annual.
5. Poole: The Calorific Power of Fuels.
6. Bureau of Standards, by tests.
7. Kent's Mechanical Engineers' Pocket Book.
8. Berthelot.
9. Thomsen.
10. Sherman.
11. Gottlieb.
12. Stohman.
13. Slossen and Colburn.

Table 3-11I. Specific Gravity Equivalents for Degrees Baumé
(For Liquids Heavier than Water)

Baumé	Specific Gravity	Lbs per Gallon	Baumé	Specific Gravity	Lbs per Gallon	Baumé	Specific Gravity	Lbs per Gallon
0	1.0000	8.33	25	1.2083	10.07	50	1.5263	12.72
1	1.0069	8.38	26	1.2185	10.16	51	1.5426	12.85
2	1.0140	8.46	27	1.2288	10.24	52	1.5591	12.99
3	1.0211	8.51	28	1.2393	10.32	53	1.5761	13.13
4	1.0284	8.56	29	1.2500	10.41	54	1.5934	13.27
5	1.0357	8.63	30	1.2609	10.51	55	1.6111	13.42
6	1.0432	8.69	31	1.2719	10.59	56	1.6292	13.57
7	1.0507	8.75	32	1.2832	10.69	57	1.6477	13.72
8	1.0584	8.81	33	1.2946	10.78	58	1.6667	13.87
9	1.0662	8.88	34	1.3063	10.84	59	1.6860	14.04
10	1.0741	8.94	35	1.3182	10.98	60	1.7059	14.21
11	1.0821	9.01	36	1.3303	11.09	61	1.7262	14.38
12	1.0902	9.09	37	1.3426	11.18	62	1.7470	14.55
13	1.0985	9.15	38	1.3551	11.29	63	1.7683	14.72
14	1.1069	9.21	39	1.3679	11.39	64	1.7901	14.91
15	1.1154	9.29	40	1.3810	11.51	65	1.8125	15.10
16	1.1240	9.36	41	1.3942	11.61	66	1.8354	15.29
17	1.1328	9.43	42	1.4078	11.72	67	1.8590	15.48
18	1.1417	9.51	43	1.4216	11.84	68	1.8831	15.68
19	1.1508	9.59	44	1.4356	11.96	69	1.9079	15.89
20	1.1600	9.67	45	1.4500	12.08	70	1.9333	16.10
21	1.1694	9.74	46	1.4646	12.21	71	1.9595	16.32
22	1.1789	9.81	47	1.4796	12.33	72	1.9864	16.55
23	1.1885	9.90	48	1.4948	12.46	73	2.0139	16.78
24	1.1983	9.99	49	1.5104	12.58	74	2.0423	17.01
						75	2.0714	17.25

This table and Table 3-11F have been adopted by the U.S. Bureau of Standards from the formulae:

Liquids heavier than water, degrees Baumé $= 145 - \dfrac{145}{R}$

Liquids lighter than water, degrees Baumé $= \dfrac{140}{R} - 130$

Where R is the ratio of the density of a liquid to that of distilled water, both densities being taken at 60°F.

NOTE: Degrees API, used to measure the density of petroleum oils, differ slightly from the Baumé scale for liquids lighter than water. API specific gravity is determined by a similar formula, using the figures 141.5 and 131.5 instead of 140 and 130.

Table 3-11J. Materials Subject to Spontaneous Heating

(Originally prepared by the NFPA Committee on Spontaneous Heating and Ignition. Omission of any material does not necessarily indicate that it is not subject to spontaneous heating.)

Name	Tendency to Spontaneous Heating	Usual Shipping Container or Storage Method	Precautions Against Spontaneous Heating	Remarks
Alfalfa Meal	High	Bags, Bulk	Avoid moisture extremes. Tight cars for transportation are essential.	Many fires attributed to spontaneous heating probably caused by sparks, burning embers, or particles of hot metal picked up by the meal during processing. Test fires caused in this manner have smoldered for 72 hours before becoming noticeable.
Brewers' Dried Grains. See Distillers' Dried Grains				
Burlap Bags "Used"	Possible	Bales	Keep cool and dry.	Tendency to heat dependent on previous use of bags. If oily would be dangerous.
Castor Oil	Very slight	Metal Barrels, Metal Cans in Wooden Boxes	Avoid contact of leakage from containers with rags, cotton, or other fibrous combustible materials.	Possible heating of saturated fabrics in badly ventilated piles.
Charcoal	High	Bulk, Bags	Keep dry. Supply ventilation.	Hardwood charcoal must be carefully prepared and aged. Avoid wetting and subsequent drying.
Coal, Bituminous	Moderate	Bulk	Store in small piles. Avoid high temperatures.	Tendency to heat depends upon origin and nature of coals. High volatile coals are particularly liable to heat.
Cocoa Bean Shell Tankage	Moderate	Burlap Bags, Bulk	Extreme caution must be observed to maintain safe moisture limits.	This material is very hygroscopic and is liable to heating if moisture content is excessive. Precaution should be observed to maintain dry storage, etc.
Cocoanut Oil	Very slight	Drums, Cans, Glass	Avoid contact of leakage from containers with rags, cotton, or other fibrous combustible materials.	Only dangerous if fabrics, etc., are impregnated.
Cod Liver Oil	High	Drums, Cans, Glass	Avoid contact of leakage from containers with rags, cotton, or other fibrous combustible materials.	Impregnated organic materials are extremely dangerous.
Colors in Oil	High	Drums, Cans, Glass	Avoid contact of leakage from containers with rags, cotton, or other fibrous combustible materials.	May be very dangerous if fabrics, etc., are impregnated.
Copra	Slight	Bulk	Keep cool and dry.	Heating possible if wet and hot.
Corn-Meal Feeds	High	Burlap Bags, Paper Bags, Bulk	Material should be processed carefully to maintain safe moisture content and to cure before storage.	Usually contains an appreciable quantity of oil which has rather severe tendency to heat.
Corn Oil	Moderate	Barrels, Tank Cars	Avoid contact of leakage from containers with rags, cotton, or other fibrous combustible materials.	Dangerous heating of meals, etc., unlikely unless stored in large piles while hot.
Cottonseed	Low	Bags, Bulk	Keep cool and dry.	Heating possible if piled wet and hot.
Cottonseed Oil	Moderate	Barrels, Tank Cars	Avoid contact of leakage from containers with rags, cotton, or other fibrous combustible materials.	May cause heating of saturated material in badly ventilated piles.
Distillers' Dried Grains with oil content (Brewers' grains)	Moderate	Bulk	Maintain moisture 7 percent to 10 percent. Cool below 100°F before storage.	Very dangerous if moisture content is 5 percent or lower.
No oil content	Moderate	Bulk	Maintain moisture 7 percent to 10 percent. Cool below 100°F before storage.	Very dangerous if moisture content is 5 percent or lower.
Feeds, various	Moderate	Bulk, Bags	Avoid extremely low or high moisture content.	Ground feeds must be carefully processed. Avoid loading or storing unless cooled.
Fertilizers Organic, Inorganic, Combination of both	Moderate	Bulk, Bags	Avoid extremely low or high moisture content.	Organic fertilizers containing nitrates must be carefully prepared to avoid combinations that might initiate heating.
Mixed, Synthetic, containing nitrates and organic matter	Moderate	Bulk, Bags	Avoid free acid in preparation.	Insure ventilation in curing process by small piles or artificial drafts. If stored or loaded in bags, provide ventilation space between bags.

Table 3-11J.   Materials Subject to Spontaneous Heating (Cont.)

Name	Tendency to Spontaneous Heating	Usual Shipping Container or Storage Method	Precautions Against Spontaneous Heating	Remarks
Fish meal	High	Bags, Bulk	Keep moisture 6 percent to 12 percent. Avoid exposure to heat.	Dangerous if overdried or packaged over 100°F.
Fish Oil	High	Barrels, Drums, Tank Cars	Avoid contact of leakage from containers with rags, cotton, or other fibrous combustible materials.	Impregnated porous or fibrous materials are extremely dangerous. Tendency of various fish oils to heat varies with origin.
Fish Scrap	High	Bulk, Bags	Avoid moisture extremes.	Scrap loaded or stored before cooling is extremely liable to heat.
Foam Rubber in Consumer Products	Moderate		Where possible remove foam rubber pads, etc., from garments to be dried in dryers or over heaters. If garments containing foam rubber parts have been artificially dried, they should be thoroughly cooled before being piled, bundled, or put away. Keep heating pads, hair dryers, other heat sources from contact with foam rubber pillows, etc.	Foam rubber may continue to heat spontaneously after being subjected to forced drying as in home or commercial dryers and after contact with heating pads and other heat sources. Natural drying does not cause spontaneous heating.
Grain (various kinds)	Very slight	Bulk, Bags	Avoid moisture extremes.	Ground grains may heat if wet and warm.
Hay	Moderate	Bulk, Bales	Keep dry and cool.	Wet or improperly cured hay is almost certain to heat in hot weather. Baled hay seldom heats dangerously.
Hides	Very slight	Bales	Keep dry and cool.	Bacteria in untreated hides may initiate heating.
Iron Pyrites	Moderate	Bulk	Avoid large piles. Keep dry and cool.	Moisture accelerates oxidation of finely divided pyrites.
Istle	Very slight	Bulk, Bales	Keep cool and dry.	Heating possible in wet material. Unlikely under ordinary conditions. Partially burned or charred fiber is dangerous.
Jute	Very slight	Bulk	Keep cool and dry.	Avoid storing or loading in hot wet piles. Partially burned or charred material is dangerous.
Lamp Black	Very slight	Wooden Cases	Keep cool and dry.	Fires most likely to result from sparks or included embers, etc., rather than spontaneous heating.
Lanolin	Negligible	Glass, Cans, Metal Drums, Barrels	Avoid contact of leakage from containers with rags, cotton, or other fibrous combustible materials.	Heating possible on contaminated fibrous matter.
Lard Oil	Slight	Wooden Barrels	Avoid contact of leakage from containers with rags, cotton, or other fibrous combustible materials.	Dangerous on fibrous combustible substances.
Lime, unslaked (Calcium Oxide, Pebble Lime, Quicklime)	Moderate	Paper Bags, Wooden Barrels, Bulk	Keep dry. Avoid hot loading.	Wetted lime may heat sufficiently to ignite wood containers, etc.
Linseed	Very slight	Bulk	Keep cool and dry.	Tendency to heat dependent on moisture and oil content.
Linseed Oil	High	Tank Cars, Drums, Cans, Glass	Avoid contact of leakage from containers with rags, cotton, or other fibrous combustible materials.	Rags or fabrics impregnated with this oil are extremely dangerous. Avoid piles, etc. Store in closed containers, preferably metal.
Manure	Moderate	Bulk	Avoid extremes of low or high moisture contents. Ventilate the piles.	Avoid storing or loading uncooled manures.
Menhaden Oil	Moderate to high	Barrels, Drums, Tank Cars	Avoid contact of leakage from containers with rags, cotton, or other fibrous combustible materials.	Dangerous on fibrous product.
Metal Powders*	Moderate	Drums, etc.	Keep in closed containers.	Moisture accelerates oxidation of most metal powders.
Metal Turnings*	Practically none	Bulk	Not likely to heat spontaneously.	Avoid exposure to sparks.

* Refers to iron, steel, brass, aluminum, and other common metals, for information on magnesium, sodium, zirconium, etc., see Section 5, Chapter 6.

Table 3-11J. Materials Subject to Spontaneous Heating (Cont.)

Name	Tendency to Spontaneous Heating	Usual Shipping Container or Storage Method	Precautions Against Spontaneous Heating	Remarks
Mineral Wool	None	Pasteboard Boxes, Paper Bags	Noncombustible. If loaded hot may ignite containers and other combustible surroundings.	This material is mentioned in this table only because of general impression that it heats spontaneously.
Mustard Oil, Black	Low	Barrels	Avoid contact of leakage with rags, cotton or other fibrous combustible materials.	Avoid contamination of fibrous combustible materials.
Oiled Clothing	High	Fiber Boxes	Dry thoroughly before packaging.	Dangerous if wet material is stored in piles without ventilation.
Oiled Fabrics	High	Rolls	Keep ventilated. Dry thoroughly before packing.	Improperly dried fabrics extremely dangerous. Tight rolls are comparatively safe.
Oiled Rags	High	Bales	Avoid storing in bulk in open.	Dangerous if wet with drying oil.
Oiled Silk	High	Fiber Boxes, Rolls	Supply sufficient ventilation.	Improperly dried material is dangerous in form of piece goods. Rolls relatively safe.
Oleic Acid	Very slight	Glass Bottles, Wooden Barrels	Avoid contact of leakage from containers with rags, cotton, or other fibrous combustible materials.	Impregnated fibrous materials may heat unless ventilated.
Oleo Oil	Very slight	Wooden Barrels	Avoid contact of leakage from containers with rags, cotton, or other fibrous combustible materials.	May heat on impregnated fibrous combustible matter.
Olive Oil	Moderate to Low	Tank Cars, Drums, Cans, Glass	Avoid contact of leakage from containers with rags, cotton, or other fibrous combustible materials.	Impregnated fibrous materials may heat unless ventilated. Tendency varies with origin of oil.
Paint containing drying oil	Moderate	Drums, Cans, Glass	Avoid contact of leakage from containers with rags, cotton, or other fibrous combustible materials.	Fabrics, rags, etc., impregnated with paints that contain drying oils and driers are extremely dangerous. Store in closed containers, preferably metal.
Paint Scrapings	Moderate	Barrels, Drums	Avoid large unventilated piles.	Tendency to heat depends on state of dryness of the scrapings.
Palm Oil	Low	Wooden Barrels	Avoid contact of leakage from containers with rags, cotton, or other fibrous combustible materials.	Impregnated fibrous materials may heat unless ventilated. Tendency varies with origin of oil.
Peanut Oil	Low	Wooden Barrels, Tin Cans	Avoid contact of leakage from containers with rags, cotton, or other fibrous combustible materials.	Impregnated fibrous materials may heat unless ventilated. Tendency varies with origin of oil.
Peanuts, "Red Skin"	High	Paper Bags, Cans, Fiber Board Boxes, Burlap Bags	Avoid badly ventilated storage.	This is the part of peanut between outer shell and peanut itself. Provide well ventilated storage.
Peanuts, shelled	Very slight or Negligible	Paper Bags, Cans, Fiber Board Boxes, Burlap Bags	Keep cool and dry.	Avoid contamination of rags, etc., with oil.
Perilla Oil	Moderate to High	Tin Cans, Barrels	Avoid contact of leakage from containers with rags, cotton, or other fibrous combustible materials.	Impregnated fibrous materials may heat unless ventilated. Tendency varies with origin of oil.
Pine Oil	Moderate	Glass, Drums	Avoid contact of leakage from containers with rags, cotton, or other fibrous combustible materials.	Impregnated fibrous materials may heat unless ventilated. Tendency varies with origin of oil.
Powdered Eggs	Very slight	Wooden Barrels	Avoid conditions that promote bacterial growth. Inhibit against decay. Keep cool.	Possible heating of decaying powder in storage.
Powdered Milk	Very slight	Wooden and Fiber Boxes, Metal Cans	Avoid conditions that promote bacterial growth. Inhibit against decay. Keep cool.	Possible heating by decay or fermentation.
Rags	Variable	Bales	Avoid contamination with drying oils. Avoid charring. Keep cool and dry.	Tendency depends on previous use of rags. Partially burned or charred rags are dangerous.
Red Oil	Moderate	Glass Bottles, Wooden Barrels	Avoid contact of leakage from containers with rags, cotton, or other fibrous combustible materials.	Impregnated porous or fibrous materials are extremely dangerous. Tendency varies with origin of oil.

Table 3-11J.   Materials Subject to Spontaneous Heating (Cont.)

Name	Tendency to Spontaneous Heating	Usual Shipping Container or Storage Method	Precautions Against Spontaneous Heating	Remarks
Roofing Felts and Papers	Moderate	Rolls, Bales, Crates	Avoid over-drying the material. Supply ventilation.	Felts, etc., should have controlled moisture content. Packaging or rolling uncooled felts is dangerous.
Sawdust	Possible	Bulk	Avoid contact with drying oils. Avoid hot, humid storage.	Partially burned or charred sawdust may be dangerous.
Scrap Film (Nitrate)	Very slight	Drums and Lined Boxes	Film must be properly stabilized against decomposition.	Nitrocellulose film ignites at low temperature. External ignition more likely than spontaneous heating. Avoid exposure to sparks, etc.
Scrap Leather	Very slight	Bales, Bulk	Avoid contamination with drying oils.	Oil-treated leather scraps may heat.
Scrap Rubber or Buffings	Moderate	Bulk, Drums	Buffings of high rubber content should be shipped and stored in tight containers.	Sheets, slabs, etc., are comparatively safe unless loaded or stored before cooling thoroughly.
Sisal	Very slight	Bulk, Bales	Keep cool and dry.	Partially burned or charred material is particularly liable to ignite spontaneously.
Soybean Oil	Moderate	Tin Cans, Barrels, Tank Cars	Avoid contact with rags, cotton, or fibrous materials.	Impregnated fibrous materials may heat unless well ventilated.
Sperm Oil—See Whale Oil				
Tankage	Variable	Bulk	Avoid extremes of moisture contents. Avoid loading or storing while hot.	Very dry or moist tankages often heat. Tendency more pronounced if loaded or stored before cooling.
Tung Nut Meals	High	Paper Bags, Bulk	Material must be very carefully processed and cooled thoroughly before storage.	These meals contain residual oil which has high tendency to heat. Material also susceptible to heating if over-dried.
Tung Oil	Moderate	Tin Cans, Barrels, Tank Cars	Avoid contact of leakage from containers with rags, cotton, or other fibrous combustible materials.	Impregnated fibrous materials may heat unless ventilated. Tendency varies with origin of oil.
Turpentine	Low	Tin, Glass, Barrels	Avoid contact of leakage from containers with rags, cotton, or other fibrous combustible materials.	Has some tendency to heat but less so than the drying oils. Chemically active with chlorine compounds and may cause fire.
Varnished Fabrics	High	Boxes	Process carefully. Keep cool and ventilated.	Thoroughly dried varnished fabrics are comparatively safe.
Wallboard	Slight	Wrapped Bundles, Pasteboard Boxes	Maintain safe moisture content. Cool thoroughly before storage.	This material is entirely safe from spontaneous heating if properly processed.
Waste Paper	Moderate	Bales	Keep dry and ventilated.	Wet paper occasionally heats in storage in warm locations.
Whale Oil	Moderate	Barrels and Tank Cars	Avoid contact of leakage from containers with rags, cotton, or other fibrous combustible materials.	Impregnated fibrous materials may heat unless ventilated. Tendency varies with origin of oil.
Wool Wastes	Moderate	Bulk, Bales, etc.	Keep cool and ventilated or store in closed containers. Avoid high moisture.	Most wool wastes contain oil, etc., from the weaving and spinning and are liable to heat in storage. Wet wool wastes are very liable to spontaneous heating and possible ignition.

Table 3-11K. Specific Gravity, Degrees API

The specific gravity of gasoline and other petroleum products is commonly given in Degrees API (American Petroleum Institute). The API degree is based on the following formula:

$$\text{Degrees API} = \frac{141.5}{\text{specific gravity}} - 131.5.$$

The standard method of test for gravity of petroleum and petroleum products by means of a hydrometer specifies 60°F as the test temperature, and the formula is based on the specific gravity of the liquid tested at 60°F as compared with water at 60°F.

Degrees API	Specific Gravity at 60/60°F	Pounds per Gallon at 60°F*	Degrees API	Specific Gravity at 60/60°F	Pounds per Gallon at 60°F*	Degrees API	Specific Gravity at 60/60°F	Pounds per Gallon at 60°F*
0	1.076	8.962	35	0.8498	7.076	70	0.7022	5.845
1	1.068	8.895	36	0.8448	7.034	71	0.6988	5.817
2	1.060	8.828	37	0.8398	6.993	72	0.6953	5.788
3	1.052	8.762	38	0.8348	6.951	73	0.6919	5.759
4	1.044	8.698	39	0.8299	6.910	74	0.6886	5.731
5	1.037	8.634	40	0.8251	6.870	75	0.6852	5.703
6	1.029	8.571	41	0.8203	6.830	76	0.6819	5.676
7	1.022	8.509	42	0.8155	6.790	77	0.6787	5.649
8	1.014	8.448	43	0.8109	6.752	78	0.6754	5.622
9	1.007	8.388	44	0.8063	6.713	79	0.6722	5.595
10	1.0000	8.328	45	0.8017	6.675	80	0.6690	5.568
11	0.9930	8.270	46	0.7972	6.637	81	0.6659	5.542
12	0.9861	8.212	47	0.7927	6.600	82	0.6628	5.516
13	0.9792	8.155	48	0.7883	6.563	83	0.6597	5.491
14	0.9725	8.099	49	0.7839	6.526	84	0.6566	5.465
15	0.9659	8.044	50	0.7796	6.490	85	0.6536	5.440
16	0.9593	7.989	51	0.7753	6.455	86	0.6506	5.415
17	0.9529	7.935	52	0.7711	6.420	87	0.6476	5.390
18	0.9465	7.882	53	0.7669	6.385	88	0.6446	5.365
19	0.9402	7.830	54	0.7628	6.350	89	0.6417	5.341
20	0.9340	7.778	55	0.7587	6.316	90	0.6388	5.316
21	0.9279	7.727	56	0.7547	6.283	91	0.6360	5.293
22	0.9218	7.676	57	0.7507	6.249	92	0.6331	5.269
23	0.9159	7.627	58	0.7467	6.216	93	0.6303	5.246
24	0.9100	7.578	59	0.7428	6.184	94	0.6275	5.222
25	0.9042	7.529	60	0.7389	6.151	95	0.6247	5.199
26	0.8984	7.481	61	0.7351	6.119	96	0.6220	5.176
27	0.8927	7.434	62	0.7313	6.087	97	0.6193	5.154
28	0.8871	7.387	63	0.7275	6.056	98	0.6166	5.131
29	0.8816	7.341	64	0.7238	6.025	99	0.6139	5.109
30	0.8762	7.296	65	0.7201	5.994	100	0.6112	5.086
31	0.8708	7.251	66	0.7165	5.964			
32	0.8654	7.206	67	0.7128	5.934			
33	0.8602	7.163	68	0.7093	5.904			
34	0.8550	7.119	69	0.7057	5.874			

* "Apparent weight," or weight when weighed in air. True weight corrected for weight of air, differs by less than 1/10 of 1 percent.

Table 3-11L.   Total Heat of Combustion at Constant Pressure, Btu per lb
(Data from National Bureau of Standards, 1947)

Methane (gas)	23,861	Benzene (gas)	18,172
Ethane (gas)	22,304	Benzene (liquid)	17,986
Propane (gas)	21,646	Methyl alcohol (gas)	10,250
Propane (liquid)	21,490	Methyl alcohol (liquid)	9,748
n Butane (gas)	21,293	Ethyl alcohol (gas)	13,150
n Butane (liquid)	21,134	Ethyl alcohol (liquid)	12,755
iso Butane (gas)	21,242	Amyl alcohol (gas)	16,463
iso Butane (liquid)	21,096	Amyl alcohol (liquid)	16,209
Butadiene −1,3 (gas)	20,217	Carbon (graphite)	14,087
Butadiene −1,3 (liquid)	21,047	Sulfur (rhombic)	3,980
Acetylene (gas)	21,460	Benzoic acid (crystal)	11,360
Ethylene (gas)	21,625	Naphthalene (crystal)	17,290
Propylene (gas)	21,032	Sucrose	7,090
Hydrogen (gas)	60,958		

SECTION 4

INDUSTRIAL AND PROCESS FIRE HAZARDS

Chapter 1

BOILER-FURNACES

Boiler-furnaces are used to produce steam, which is utilized to supply heat for processes or to generate power. This chapter covers the fuel burning systems and related control equipment for single and multiple burner, industrial and public utility boiler-furnaces.

A. Types of Boilers

Boilers can generally be divided into two types, firetube and watertube. Combustion gases pass through the tubes in firetube boilers and the water circulates around the tubes. Water passes through the tubes in watertube boilers and the combustion gases pass around them. While this chapter is directly concerned with watertube boilers, the general safety principles are equally applicable to firetube boilers.

Fuels

The fuels most commonly used in firing boilers are natural gas, oil, or pulverized coal. When fuels other than these are burned, such as methanol or liquefied petroleum gas, additional firing hazards may be introduced, and special precautions may be required to provide for safe operation of the boiler. In chemical plants and refineries, waste gases or waste flammable liquids may be burned either separately or simultaneously with one of the commonly used fuels mentioned. These fuel mixtures allow inert or excessively rich fuels to enter the fuel system, and boilers burning such mixtures require special consideration to assure safe operation.

Causes of Furnace Explosions

Boiler-furnace explosions are caused by the ignition of an accumulation of a combustible mixture of fuel and air within the confined spaces of the boiler-furnace setting. The setting includes the furnace, the associated boiler passes, and ducts and fans which convey the combustion gases to the stack. The most common situations which produce explosive conditions in connection with the operation of a boiler are: (1) an interruption of the fuel or air supply or ignition energy to the burners, resulting in momentary loss of flame, followed by restoration and delayed reignition of a combustible accumulation; (2) ignition of fuel which has leaked into an idle furnace; (3) ignition of an accumulation of an explosive mixture of fuel and air, resulting from loss of flame at one or more burners, by other burners operating normally or during the lighting of additional burners; and (4) repeated unsuccessful attempts to light off without appropriate purging. Conditions which result in explosions, including "furnace puffs," are the result of improper procedures by operating personnel, improper design of equipment or control systems, or malfunction of equipment or the control system.

Design and Operation

It is important that the manufacturer and purchaser of a boiler cooperate in determining the design of the equipment and the operating criteria. This provides the purchaser the opportunity to assure himself that the unit is not deficient in apparatus which will insure its safe operation insofar as practical, not only with respect to its pressure parts and fuel burning equipment, including air and fuel metering, but also in connection with provisions for safe lighting and maintenance of stable flame.

Since a number of explosions have resulted from interruption of the fuel supply by foreign substances, the design of the fuel supply subsystem should make adequate provisions to prevent such foreign substances from interfering with the fuel supply to the burner.

New boilers should not be started up before completion of the installation of an adequate safeguard and instrumentation system, and not before the safeguards themselves have been tested to operate properly as a system. In some instances, it may be necessary to install temporary interlocks and instrumentation to accomplish this.

Statistics suggest that the cause of the majority of furnace explosions is the result of human error, rather than equipment malfunction or design deficiencies. However, it is important to consider whether the error was the result of: (1) lack of proper understanding of, or failure to use, safe operating procedures; (2) unfavorable operating characteristics of the equipment or its control, or both; or (3) lack of functional coordination of the various components of the steam generating system and its controls.

The operating company has the ultimate responsibility for the proper integration of the various components, consisting of the boiler, burner, fuel and air supply equipment, combustion controls, interlocks and safety devices, operator functions, and operator communication and training. This integration can be accomplished by: (1) providing competent design and operating staffs or, by employing consultants who are capable of achieving these same objectives; and (2) periodic analysis to compare the plant to the evolving technology so that deficiencies can be corrected to make the plants safer and more reliable.

It cannot be assumed that correctly designed equipment and the manufacturer's operating instructions can be relied upon to insure a safe operating system without the benefit of a high level of technical and operating competence in the plant organization. The maintenance of technical competence and operator proficiency is a continuing activity throughout the life of the plant. An operating organization will tend to deteriorate through the years unless supervised and trained on a continuing basis by aggressive and technically competent top level production personnel.

Competent maintenance is necessary to sustain the degree of reliability designed into the equipment, and the quality of maintenance of control equipment must be at least equal to that required to maintain the boiler and its related components in a safe and reliable operating condition. Too frequent maintenance may be required because of poorly designed equipment or by the poor quality of maintenance that is actually done.

B. Special Problems of Boiler-Furnaces

The various types of fuels used in firing boiler-furnaces pose special problems as do environmental requirements for lower levels of emission of oxides of nitrogen in the combustion products. These problems are discussed in the following paragraphs.

Hazards of Gas Firing

Being colorless, leaking natural gas usually cannot be detected visually. Detection by odor cannot be relied upon, and thus provision for leakage detection is desirable.

Potentially hazardous accumulations are most likely to occur within buildings, particularly where gas piping is routed through confined areas without adequate ventilation.

The nature of gas fuel makes possible severe departures from safe air/fuel ratios without any visible evidence at the burners, furnace, or stack, and to cascade into progressively worse conditions. Thus, combustion control systems that respond to reduced boiler steam pressure or steam flow with an impulse for more fuel, unless protected or interlocked to prevent a fuel-rich mixture, are potentially hazardous.

Natural gas may be either "wet" or "dry". A "wet" gas implies the presence of distillate. The carry-over of distillate into the burners can result in momentary flame-out and possible reignition resulting in a furnace explosion. Thus, wet gas supply systems require special attention.

Gas supplied from either single or multiple sources having significant differences in volumetric heating value can introduce unacceptable hazards. With such variable gas supplies, it is necessary to provide suitable instruments responsive to Btu changes (e.g., a specific gravity meter) with appropriate alarms or suitable compensation in the combustion controls, or both.

Discharges from relief valves or any other form of atmospheric vents can present a hazard unless special precautions are taken.

Hazards of Oil Firing

Fuel oil is a complex mixture of hydrocarbons with differing molecular weights and boiling and freezing points. When subjected to sufficiently high temperatures, they will partially decompose or volatize or both, thus creating new liquid, gaseous, and solid fuels with unpredictable properties. While the properties of fuel oils are controlled within limits by refining to meet recognized standards, crude oil properties vary considerably. Crude oils contain volatile light ends, such as propane, butane, and pentane, which are not present in fuel oils, and their flash points can range from below zero to over 150°F.

Fuel oils have high volumetric heats of combustion so that even small leaks can create potential fire hazards. When firing the heavier oils (Grades 4, 5, or 6), it is necessary to hold the viscosity of oil flowing to the burners within acceptable limits to maintain proper atomization.

Water or sludge in storage tanks or improperly located suction take-offs from the tank may result in hazardous interruptions or pulsations of the fuel supply to the burners, causing a flame-out due to plugged strainers or burner tips.

When two shipments of fuel oil having widely different viscosity or specific gravity characteristics are stored in the same tank, this may result in a significant change in the fuel input rate to the burners without a corresponding change in air flow, or without an appropriate change in fuel oil temperature to restore the flowing viscosity to the proper value.

A very small difference in the size of the hole in the tip or sprayer plate of mechanical atomizing burners, either in manufacturing or as a result of wear, may cause a considerable difference in oil flow to individual burners. This may not only be detrimental to boiler efficiency, but on boilers operating with very low excess air, it may also result in the presence of combustibles in the furnace. Also, there is always the hazard of inserting an oil gun in the burner assembly without a tip or sprayer plate, resulting in an unsafe operating condition.

Very rapid transients in oil flow through operating burners can be caused by rapid operation of an oil supply valve, individual burner shutoff valves, or the regulating valve in the return oil line from the burner header. These uncontrolled changes in the fuel input to the furnace can introduce very hazardous conditions.

The oil flow to individual oil guns can be adversely affected by improper burner elevation, distance from the regulating valve, pipe size, etc., all of which can be hazardous on low pressure burners.

Hazards of Coal Firing

As mined, transported, and delivered to the plant, coal can vary in size and in impurities to a degree that exceeds the capability of the plant equipment. Thus, when coals are received from more than one source, care must be exercised to make sure that all coals received are within the specific range of the coal handling and coal burning equipment.

It takes as little as 3 lbs of pulverized coal in 1,000 cu ft (.05 oz pcf) of air to form an explosive mixture, and since a large boiler burns 100 lbs or more of coal per second, adherence to carefully planned operating sequences is necessary to burn pulverized coal safely.

A special hazard is the methane gas that is released from freshly crushed or pulverized coal which may accumulate in enclosed spaces.

Raw coal as delivered to a plant may contain foreign materials, such as scrap iron, wood shoring, rags, excelsior, rock, etc. Much of this foreign material can interrupt coal feed, damage or jam equipment, or become a source of ignition within a pulverizer. Foreign material may interrupt coal flow, causing a total or partial flame-out and possible reignition, resulting in a dangerous furnace puff or explosion. Wide variations in the size of raw coal may cause erratic or uncontrollable coal feeding.

Pulverized coal is conveyed through pipes from the pulverizer to the burner as a mixture of finely divided coal in transport air. Maloperation, such as improper removal of a burner from service, may result in the settling out of pulverized coal in the burner pipes to inoperative burners, which on restarting the burner can cause a furnace puff. To prevent preignition or settling out of pulverized coal in the burner pipes, it is necessary to assure that a minimum transport air velocity is maintained, based upon the lowest velocity for pipe associated with a particular pulverizer.

It is necessary to dry the coal to prevent pulverizer choking or impaired combustion. This is usually accomplished by supplying hot air to the pulverizer. The coal-air temperature leaving the pulverizer must be maintained within limits. Too low an outlet temperature impedes pulverization. Too high an outlet temperature causes coking or burning of burner parts, and increases the possibility of pulverizer fires.

Provisions must be made for cooling down and emptying the pulverizer when shutting down the burners associated with it. This is to prevent spontaneous combustion and a possible explosion in the pulverizer or burner lines.

Combustibles meters are not reliable for use with pulverized coal, since they generally measure only gaseous combustibles. Thus, the lack of meter indication of the presence of combustibles does not prove that unburned coal particles are not present.

Low NOx (oxides of nitrogen) Operation

Federal regulations require that new boiler installations meet NOx emission limits lower than the emissions obtained from many of the presently installed firing systems and furnace designs using past operating procedures. In addition, air quality regulations in some local areas require a reduction in NOx emissions from existing boilers. These regulations apply to all boilers whether fired with gas, oil, or pulverized coal.

To achieve these reductions in NOx emissions, one or more of the following methods are used.

(1) Low excess air firing, i.e., less than the "normal" 10 to 25 percent excess air.

(2) Multistage air admission involving the introduction of combustion air in two or more stages.

(3) Flue gas recirculation into all or a portion of the secondary air.

(4) Reduce secondary air temperature.

(5) On new units, manufacturers may also introduce new burner and furnace designs, such as wider spacing of burners.

The effect of all of these methods is generally to produce lower flame temperatures, and longer, less turbulent flames, which result in lower NOx.

These methods employed for reducing NOx emissions may affect furnace safety, particularly for existing units, and may introduce unacceptable risks if proper precautions are not taken. Low excess air or multistage air admission, or both, tend to reduce the margins formerly available to prevent or minimize accumulations of unburned fuel in the

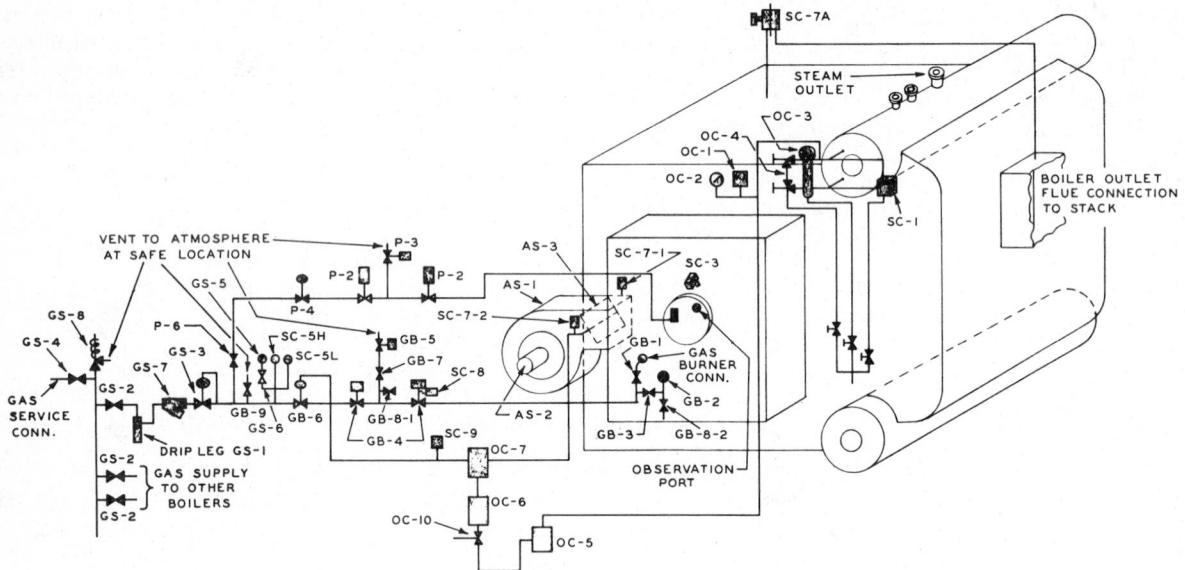

Fig. 4-1A. Typical fuel supply system for a natural gas-fired, single-burner, boiler furnace with automatic (recycling) or automatic (nonrecycling) controls.

LEGEND

Gas Supply System:
GS-1   Drip leg
GS-2-1 Manual plug cock, required only when single pressure reducing valve serves more than one boiler
GS-3   Gas supply pressure reducing valve
GS-4   Manual gas supply shut-off valve
GS-5   Gas supply pressure gage
GS-6   Gas supply pressure gage cock
GS-7   Gas cleaner
GS-8   Relief valve

Air System:
AS-1   Forced draft fan
AS-2   Forced draft fan motor
AS-3   Forced draft fan control damper at inlet or outlet

Igniter (Pilot) System:
P-2   Safety shut-off valves, auto. opening, spring closing (NC)
P-3   Ventvalve, auto. closing, spring opening (NO)
P-4   Gas pressure regulating valve optional depending on igniter pressure requirements

P-5   Gas cleaner
P-6   Manual plug cock

Gas Burner System:
GB-1   Manual plug cock
GB-2   Gas burner pressure gage
GB-3   Gas burner pressure gage cock
GB-4   Safety shut-off valves, auto. opening, spring closing (NC)
GB-5   Vent valve, auto. closing, spring opening (NO)
GB-6   Gas fuel control valve
GB-7   Vent line manual plug cock (locked or sealed in open position)
GB-8-1 Leakage test conn. upstream safety S.O. valve
GB-8-2 Leakage test conn. downstream safety S.O. valve
GB-9   Manual plug cock for venting high pressure from supply when required

Safety Controls: (All switches in "hot" ungrounded lines. See 5652)
SC-1   Low water cut out integral with column or separate from water column

SC-3   Flame scanner
SC-5H   Gas supply high pressure switch
SC-5L   Gas supply low pressure switch
SC-7-1 Windbox pressure switch (note 2)
SC-7-2 Fan damper position switch (note 2)
SC-7A   Purge A.F. switch (note 2)
SC-8   Closed position interlock on GB-4
SC-9   Light-off position interlock

Operating Controls & Instruments:
OC-1   High steam pressure switch (note 1)
OC-2   Steam drum pressure gage
OC-3   Water column with high & low level alarms
OC-4   Water gage and valves
OC-5   Steam pressure controller
OC-6   Manual auto. selector station
OC-7   Combustion control drive unit or units
OC-10   Modulating control low fire start positioner

NOTES: 1. With automatic (nonrecycling) control an overpressure shutdown requires manual restart.
        2. Purge airflow may be proved by providing either SC-7-1 and SC-7-2 (and similar devices for other dampers which are in series) or SC-7A.

furnace during combustion upsets or flame-outs, or both. Any of the methods may narrow the limits of stable flames produced by burner subsystems. When flue gas recirculation is used, special methods and devices are necessary to assure adequate mixing and uniform distribution of recirculated gas and air to the windboxes. Flue gas carbon monoxide analyzers are needed, since all of the methods tend to increase the possibility of unburned combustibles throughout the unit and ducts.

C. The Fuel Burning System

The function of the fuel burning system, whether the fuel is gas, oil, or coal, is to continuously convert any ignitible furnace input into unreactive products of combustion at the same rate that the fuel and air reactants enter the furnace. It is important that the fuel burning system is adequately sized to meet the operating requirements of the unit, is compatible with other boiler component systems, and is capable of being controlled over the full operating range of the unit.

The fuel burning system consists of the following subsystems: air supply, fuel supply, pulverizer (for coal), main burner, atomizing (for oil), ignition, furnace, and combustion products removal. The fuel burning system provides a means for the safe start-up, operation, and shutdown of the combustion process.

Air Supply Subsystem

The air supply equipment provides a continuous steady air flow adequate for all operating conditions on the unit, including the continuation of proper air flow during anticipated furnace pressure pulsations.

Fuel Supply Subsystem

The fuel supply equipment is properly sized and arranged to insure a continuous, steady fuel flow adequate for all operating requirements of the unit. Following are the specific provisions for each type of fuel:

Gas: The incoming gas supply is controlled at the pressure for which the fuel burning system is designed. To prevent excessive fuel gas pressure, either a full relieving capacity vent or a high gas pressure trip may be provided. For systems with more than a single burner, the burner header pressure regulator, burner shutoff valves, and associated piping volume are coordinated to insure against fuel pressure transients which might result in exceeding

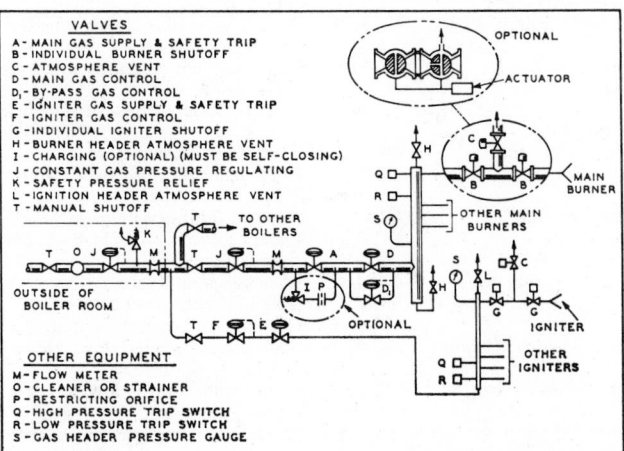

Fig. 4-1B. A typical fuel supply system for natural gas-fired multiple burner boiler-furnace.

burner limits for stable flame as a result of cutting burners in or out of service. Provisions are made to remove any foreign material and prevent contamination of the fuel. To prevent leakage of gas into the furnace, a vent is provided upstream of the last shutoff valve in any line to a burner or igniter. Typical arrangement of a fuel supply subsystem for a single burner boiler is shown in Figure 4-1A, and for a multiple burner boiler in Figure 4-1B.

Oil: The facilities for unloading, storage, pumping, heating, straining, filtering, trapping, and piping are designed and arranged to always provide a suitable, uncontaminated fuel supply. Contaminants in fuel may include salt, sand, sludge, water, and other abrasive or corrosive constituents. Some fuels contain waxy materials which precipitate out, clogging filters and other elements of the fuel system. For systems with more than a single burner, the burner header pressure regulator, burner shutoff valves, and associated piping volume are coordinated to insure against fuel pressure transients which might result in exceeding burner limits for stable flame as a result of cutting burners in or out of service. Routes of piping, valve locations, etc., require special attention to minimize exposure to possible explosion hazards or too high or low temperature sources. Low temperatures may increase viscosity, inhibit flow, or precipitate waxy materials. High temperatures may cause carbonization or excessive pressures and leakage due to fluid expansion in "trapped" sections of the system. Means are needed to prevent or relieve excess pressure from expansion of trapped oil in the fuel system; this is especially important for crude oil.

Burner shutoff valves are located as close to the burner as practical, to minimize the volume of oil which may be left downstream of the valve, which may flow by gravity into the furnace on an emergency trip or burner shutdown. It is important to provide positive means to prevent leakage of oil into an idle furnace. Fuel oil must be delivered to burners at the proper temperature and pressure to insure that the oil is at the viscosity necessary for proper atomization. A typical arrangement of a fuel supply subsystem for a single burner boiler is shown in Figure 4-1C, and for a multiple burner boiler in Figure 4-1D.

Coal: The raw coal unloading, storage, transfer, and preparation facilities are designed and arranged to properly size the coal, to remove foreign material, and to minimize interruption of the coal supply to the coal feeders. This includes the installation of breakers, cleaning screens, and magnetic separators where necessary. Detection and corrective means are needed to insure adequate coal flow to the feeders, since one of the greatest hazards in the operation of pulverized coal-fired boilers is partial or total stoppage of the raw coal supply to the coal feeder. Such interruption causes transients, with significant reduction or cessation of the pulverized coal supply to the burners, and with the accompanying hazard of loss of ignition and reignition of an accumulation. Raw coal feeders and piping are designed with ample capacity range to allow for variations in size, quality, and moisture content of the coal as specified by the purchaser.

Pulverizer Subsystem

Coal pulverizing equipment is designed to provide a range of capacity which will minimize starting and stopping of pulverizers during boiler load changes, and produce satisfactory coal fineness over a specified range of coal analyses and characteristics. Primary air systems provide for transport of the pulverized coal from the pulverizer to the burners, with the air at high enough temperature to properly dry the coal. The fans, ducts and dampers are sized to provide the proper transport velocity throughout the pulverizer operating range, and to maintain a minimum velocity to prevent coal from settling out in the piping to the burners. It is important to isolate the pulverizer system from the burners and the fuel and air supply systems. A typical arrangement of a pulverizing subsystem is shown in Figure 4-1E.

Main Burner Subsystem

The function of the main burner subsystem is to supply fuel to the furnace continuously and within their stable flame limits, independent of the ignition subsystem, over the operating range of the fuel burning equipment. This applies to all three fuels—gas, oil, or coal. Variations in the burning characteristics of the fuel, and the normal variations in fuel handling and fuel burning equipment,

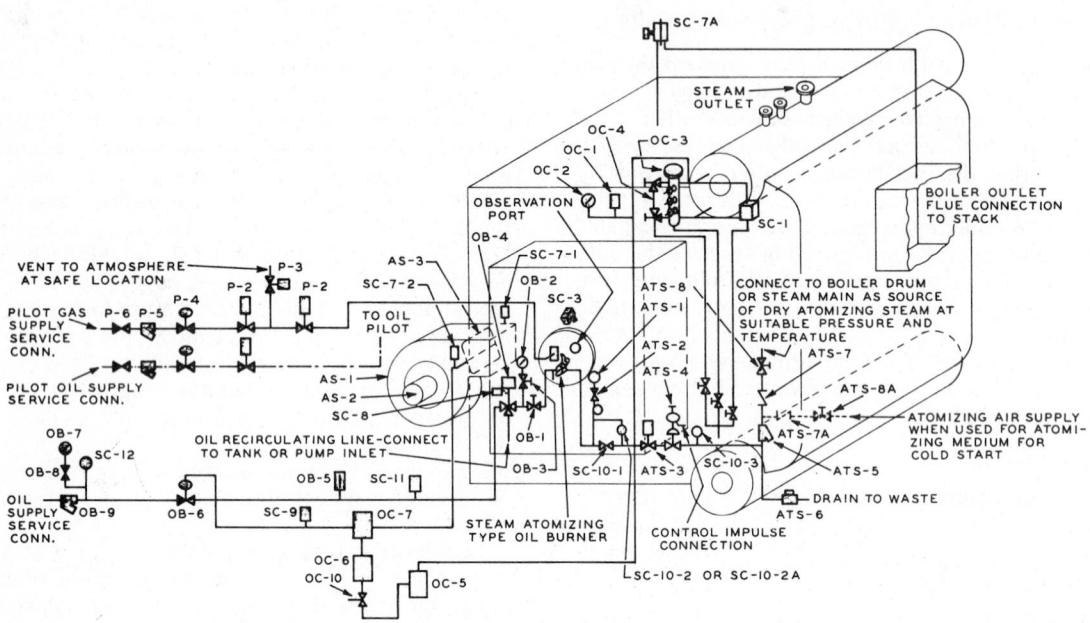

Fig. 4-1C. A typical fuel supply system for a fuel oil-fired single burner boiler-furnace with automatic (recycling) or automatic (nonrecycling) controls.

LEGEND

Atomizing Steam System:

ATS-1	Burner atomizing steam pressure gage
ATS-2	Burner atomizing steam pressure gage cock
ATS-3	Atomizing steam shutoff valve
ATS-4	Atomizing steam differential pressure control valve
ATS-5	Atomizing steam supply strainer
ATS-6	Atomizing steam supply trap
ATS-7	Atomizing steam supply check valve
ATS-7A	Atomizing air supply check valve
ATS-8	Atomizing steam supply shutoff valve
ATS-8A	Atomizing air supply shutoff valve

Air System:

AS-1	Forced draft fan
AS-2	Forced draft fan motor
AS-3	Forced draft fan control damper at inlet or outlet

Igniter (Pilot) System—Gas or Oil:

P-2	Safety shutoff valves—auto. opening, spring closing (NC)
P-3	Vent valve—auto. closing, spring opening (NO)

P-4	Pressure regulating valve—optional depending on igniter pressure requirements
P-5	Strainer
P-6	Manual plug cock

Oil Burner System:

OB-1	Manual oil shutoff valve
OB-2	Oil burner pressure gage
OB-3	Oil burner pressure gage cock
OB-4	Safety shutoff and recirculating valve
OB-5	Oil temperature thermometer or gage (Note 4)
OB-6	Oil control valve
OB-7	Oil supply pressure gage
OB-8	Oil supply pressure gage cock
OB-9	Oil strainer

Safety Controls: (All switches in "hot" ungrounded lines. See 5652.)

SC-1	Low water cut out integral with column or separate from water column
SC-3	Flame scanner
SC-7-1	Windbox pressure switch (Note 2)
SC-7-2	Fan damper position switch (Note 2)

SC-7A	Purge airflow switch (Note 2)
SC-8	Closed position interlock on OB-4
SC-9	Light-off position interlock
SC-10-1	Atomizing steam flow interlock orifice
SC-10-2	Atomizing steam flow interlock differential pressure switch
SC-10-2A	Atomizing steam pressure interlock switch
SC-10-3	Atomizing steam supply pressure interlock switch
SC-11	Low oil temperature interlock (Note 4)
SC-12	Low oil supply pressure interlock

Operating Controls & Instruments:

OC-1	High steam pressure switch (Note 1)
OC-2	Steam drum pressure gage
OC-3	Water column with high & low level alarms
OC-4	Water gage and valves
OC-5	Steam pressure controller
OC-6	Manual auto. selector station
OC-7	Combustion control drive unit or units
OC-10	Modulating control low fire start positioner

NOTES:
1. With automatic (nonrecycling) control, an overpressure shutdown requires manual restart.
2. Purge airflow may be proved by providing either SC-7-1 and SC-7-2 (and similar devices for other dampers which are in series) or SC-7A.
3. Atomizing steam interlock may be accomplished by providing either SC-10-1 and SC-10-2 or SC-10-2A and SC-10-3.
4. Temperature interlock and thermometer omitted for light oils which do not require heating.
5. Arrangement shown is applicable to straight mechanical pressure atomizing oil burners by omitting atomizing steam system.

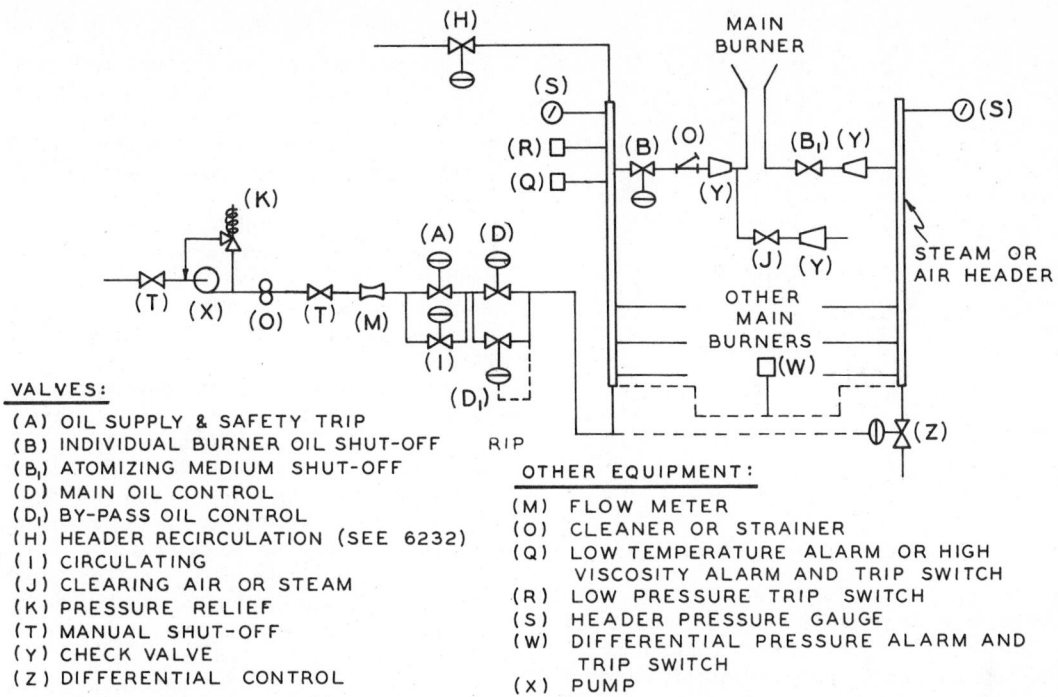

VALVES:
- (A) OIL SUPPLY & SAFETY TRIP
- (B) INDIVIDUAL BURNER OIL SHUT-OFF
- (B_1) ATOMIZING MEDIUM SHUT-OFF
- (D) MAIN OIL CONTROL
- (D_1) BY-PASS OIL CONTROL
- (H) HEADER RECIRCULATION (SEE 6232)
- (I) CIRCULATING
- (J) CLEARING AIR OR STEAM
- (K) PRESSURE RELIEF
- (T) MANUAL SHUT-OFF
- (Y) CHECK VALVE
- (Z) DIFFERENTIAL CONTROL

OTHER EQUIPMENT:
- (M) FLOW METER
- (O) CLEANER OR STRAINER
- (Q) LOW TEMPERATURE ALARM OR HIGH VISCOSITY ALARM AND TRIP SWITCH
- (R) LOW PRESSURE TRIP SWITCH
- (S) HEADER PRESSURE GAUGE
- (W) DIFFERENTIAL PRESSURE ALARM AND TRIP SWITCH
- (X) PUMP

Fig. 4-1D. Typical fuel supply system for oil-fired multiple burner boiler furnace—steam or air atomizing.

introduce an uncertainty to the lower operating limits of the main fuel subsystem in any given furnace design. On multiple burner units, the use of igniters to maintain flame under these circumstances is not permitted unless the igniters have been demonstrated by test to be Class 1 or Class 2 igniters (described in the following material). The limits of stable flame for each burner subsystem producing a separate flame envelope is determined by tests performed without the ignition subsystem in service. These tests are made through the maximum credible deviations from normal, including verification that transients generated in the fuel and air subsystems do not adversely affect the burners in operation, and include the expected range of available fuel. Transients are generated by burner shutoff valves, dampers, etc., that operate at speeds faster than the speed of response of other components of the system.

Atomizing Subsystem

On oil-fired units, fuel oil is introduced into the furnace as an extremely fine mist to intimately mix with the combustion air in order to burn quickly and completely. This is accomplished by breaking up small oil streams either mechanically or by using steam or air. When fuel is atomized by steam or air, the atomizing medium must be free of contaminants that could cause an interruption of service. For steam atomizing, adequate insulation and traps are provided to assure dry atomizing steam to the burners. The atomizing medium must be provided and maintained at the pressure required for proper operation, and arranged so that the fuel cannot enter the atomizing medium line during or after operation.

Ignition Subsystem

The function of the ignition subsystem is to smoothly ignite the main burner input within the limitation of the igniter classification. An igniter is a gas- (Fig. 4-1F) or oil-fired (Fig. 4-1G) device (except as noted under Class 3

Igniters) which provides proven ignition energy to immediately light off the main burner. There are three classes of igniters.

Class 1 (Continuous) Igniters: These igniters are applied to ignite all of the fuel input through the main burner, and to support ignition under any burner light-off or operating conditions. They remain in service at all times that the main burner is in operation.

Class 2 (Intermittent) Igniters: These igniters burn during light-off, and can be placed in or taken out of service while the main burner is firing. They may be used to support ignition under low load or certain adverse operating conditions.

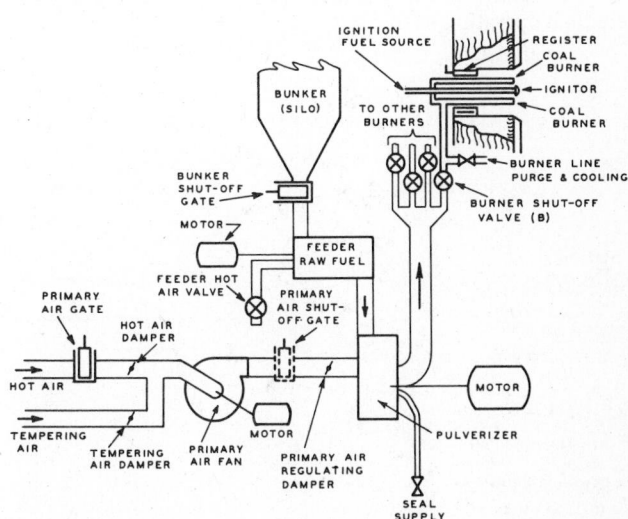

Fig. 4-1E. Typical fuel supply system for pulverized coal-fired multiple burner boiler-furnace—individual external transport type.

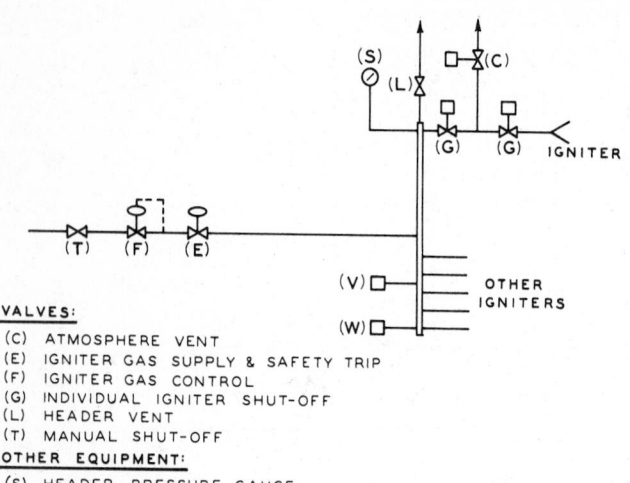

VALVES:
(C) ATMOSPHERE VENT
(E) IGNITER GAS SUPPLY & SAFETY TRIP
(F) IGNITER GAS CONTROL
(G) INDIVIDUAL IGNITER SHUT-OFF
(L) HEADER VENT
(T) MANUAL SHUT-OFF

OTHER EQUIPMENT:
(S) HEADER PRESSURE GAUGE
(V) HIGH PRESSURE TRIP SWITCH
(W) LOW PRESSURE TRIP SWITCH

Fig. 4-1F. Typical gas igniter (schematic).

Class 3 (Interrupted) Igniters: These igniters burn during light-off and are shut off during normal operation of the main burner. These are small igniters applied particularly to gas and oil main burners, and are not intended to support ignition or to extend the burner control range.

Direct Electric Igniter: This is a special Class 3 Igniter, used only for oil-firing, which provides a high energy electrical discharge capable of directly igniting the main oil burner fuel.

Furnace Subsystem

The furnace is sized and arranged with respect to the main burner subsystem so that the main burner product can be fired to maintain stable flame. The furnace and gas passage design are such that they are free from "dead pockets" when prescribed purge procedures are followed.

Combustion Products Removal Subsystem

The flue gas ducts, fans, and stack are sized and arranged to remove the products of combustion at the same rate that they are generated by the fuel burning process during all credible operation of the unit.

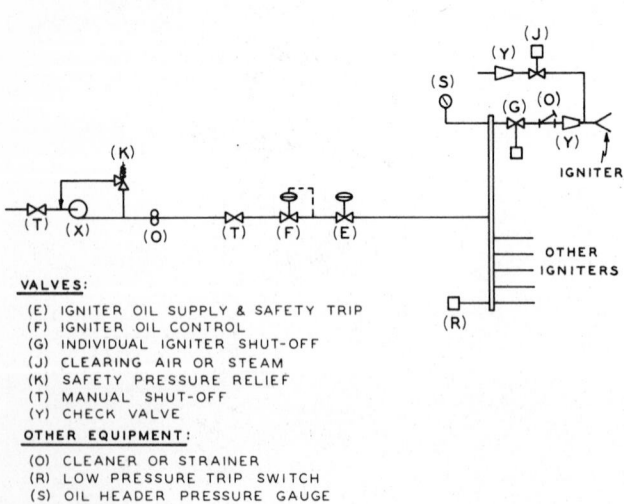

VALVES:
(E) IGNITER OIL SUPPLY & SAFETY TRIP
(F) IGNITER OIL CONTROL
(G) INDIVIDUAL IGNITER SHUT-OFF
(J) CLEARING AIR OR STEAM
(K) SAFETY PRESSURE RELIEF
(T) MANUAL SHUT-OFF
(Y) CHECK VALVE

OTHER EQUIPMENT:
(O) CLEANER OR STRAINER
(R) LOW PRESSURE TRIP SWITCH
(S) OIL HEADER PRESSURE GAUGE
(X) PUMP

Fig. 4-1G. Typical mechanical atomizing light oil igniter (schematic).

D. Combustion Control System

The combustion control system maintains the furnace fuel and air input in accordance with demand. It controls furnace inputs and their relative rates of change to maintain the air/fuel mixture within the limits required for continuous combustion and stable flame throughout the operating range of the unit.

On multiple burner units, a constant volumetric total air flow of not less than 25 percent is maintained for start-up conditions while the fuel is controlled to satisfy start-up rates, within limits compatible with air flow at each burner. The possibility of an unsafe fuel/air ratio condition is also precluded.

The system sets minimum and maximum limits on the fuel and air control subsystems to prevent these systems from providing fuel and air flows beyond the stable flame limits of the fuel burning system. When changing the rate of furnace input, the air flow and fuel flow are changed simultaneously at the proper rates to maintain safe air/fuel ratios during and after the changes.

On coal-fired boilers, the system controls the pulverizer coal-air temperature within the required limits, and assures adequate primary air for transport of the required fuel input.

The provision of oxygen and combustibles (except on coal-fired) meters are helpful as an operating guide on multiple burner boilers.

E. Operating System

The function of the operating system is to sequence the operating events to insure that they occur in the proper order. This sequencing starts with (1) the prefiring requirements, which includes the purge internal and continues through (2) the light-off procedures for either a cold start or for a hot restart, (3) the normal operation, which is accomplished by the combustion control system, and (4) both normal and emergency shutdown. It is essential that the proper sequences are followed, regardless of whether the unit is operated manually, or whether certain functions are accomplished by interlocks or automatic controls.

The operating system only permits fuel to be admitted to

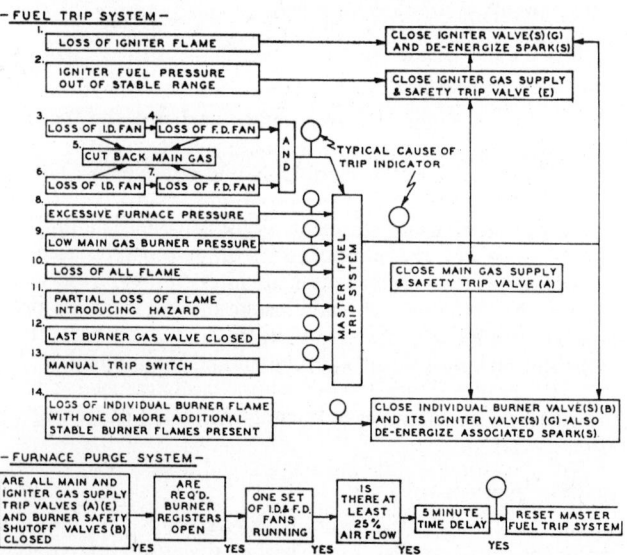

Fig. 4-1H. Interlock system for natural gas-fired multiple burner boiler-furnace.

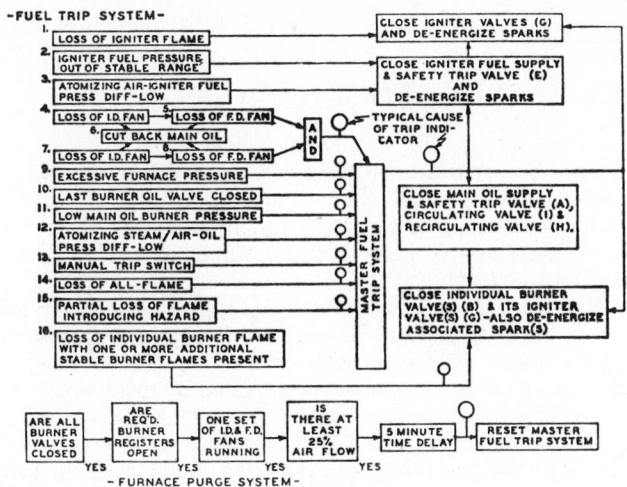

Fig. 4-1I. Interlock system for oil-fired multiple burner boiler-furnace.

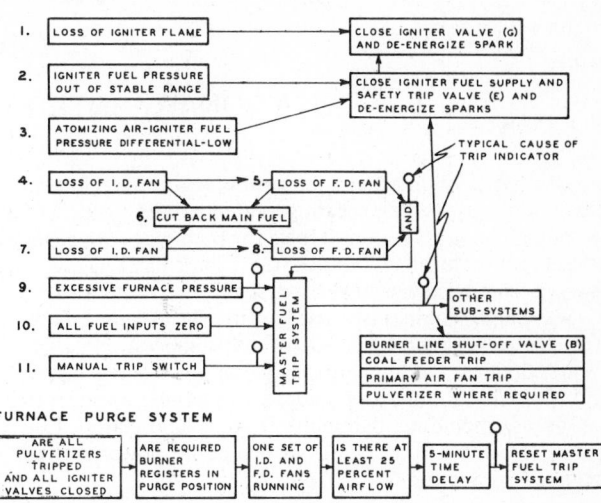

Fig. 4-1J. Interlock system for pulverized coal-fired multiple burner boiler-furnace.

the burners when there is sufficient ignition energy and the correct air flow to ignite the properly prepared fuel as it enters the furnace, and to burn it continuously and as completely as possible within the confines of the furnace.

Soot blowing is necessary to maintain high thermal efficiency in oil-fired or coal-fired boilers. However, if this operation is not performed when heat input to the furnace is at sufficiently high rates to prevent a flame-out, explosions may occur from the formation and ignition of air-soot dust clouds within the boiler.

F. Interlock System

The purpose of an interlock system for a boiler-furnace is to protect personnel from injury and also protect the equipment from damage by excluding improper actions in the operating sequence or by initiating trip devices when approaching an unsafe operating condition. The system supervises the starting procedure and normal operation to insure safe operating practices and sequences. Insofar as practical, it will not require nor permit any manual "defeating" of an interlock in order to start or operate equipment. Where automatic equipment is not available to accomplish the intended function, sufficient instrumentation is needed to enable the operator to complete the safe operating sequence.

Interlock systems for gas-fired, oil-fired, and pulverized coal-fired, multiple burner, boiler-furnaces are shown in block diagrams in Figures 4-1H, 4-1I, and 4-1J, respectively.

G. Alarm System

The purpose of any alarm system is to bring a specific condition to the attention of the operator. Alarms may be used to indicate equipment malfunction, hazardous conditions, and misoperation, primarily to indicate abnormal conditions which might lead to impending or immediate hazards. If both audible and visible alarms are provided to indicate an abnormal condition, the audible alarm may be silenced, but the visual indication remains until the condition has been restored to normal.

Bibliography

NFPA Codes, Standards, and Recommended Practices (see the latest *NFPA Publications and Visual Aids Catalog* for availability of current editions of the following documents)

NFPA No. 30, Flammable and Combustible Liquids Code.

NFPA No. 54, National Fuel Gas Code.

NFPA No. 60, Standard for the Installation and Operation of Pulverized-Fuel Systems.

NFPA No. 70, National Electrical Code.

NFPA No. 85, Standard for Prevention of Furnace Explosions in Fuel Oil- and Natural Gas-Fired Watertube Boiler-Furnaces with One Burner.

NFPA No. 85B, Standard for Prevention of Furnace Explosions in Natural Gas-Fired Multiple Burner Boiler-Furnaces.

NFPA No. 85D, Standard for Prevention of Furnace Explosions in Fuel Oil-Fired Multiple Burner Boiler-Furnaces.

NFPA No. 85E, Standard for Prevention of Furnace Explosions in Pulverized Coal-Fired Multiple Burner Boiler Furnaces.

Additional Readings

Coykendall, L. H., "Preventing Boiler Explosions," *Fire Journal,* Vol. 61, No. 4, July 1967, pp. 10-13, 60.

Factory Mutual Engineering Corporation, "Boiler Furnaces—Fuel Explosions," Chapter 38, *Handbook of Industrial Loss Prevention,* 2nd ed., McGraw-Hill, New York, 1967.

Chapter 2

STATIONARY INTERNAL COMBUSTION ENGINES

Two types of internal combustion engines are in general stationary use—reciprocating engines and gas turbine engines. The most common fuels for both types are gasoline, diesel fuel, natural gas, and LP-Gas. Some large gas turbines have been fueled by pulverized coal.

Stationary engines are used primarily as power sources for electrical generators, pumps, and compressors. In recent years, their use with emergency generator sets has increased substantially. Pumps and compressors handle a wide variety of fluids, including flammable liquids and gases. Use of internal combustion engines as fire pump power sources is covered in Section 11, Chapter 4.

A. Hazards of Stationary Engines

The overall hazard of stationary internal combustion engines reflects the hazards of (1) their fuels, lubricants and, in some cases, the nature of the material being pumped or compressed; (2) the temperature of exposed engine components, particularly exhaust manifolds and lines, which can be high enough to ignite liquid fuels and other flammable or combustible liquids and solid combustible materials; (3) the presence of arcing electrical components, such as starters, generators, distributors and magnetos, which can ignite flammable liquids and gases; and (4) engine disintegration.

B. Installation Safeguards

The hazards of the engine fuels involve the hazards of leakage from supply tanks and piping and malfunction of the engine itself. Many applications, especially for emergency power generation, require on-site fuel supplies and even indoor supply containers for reliability and prompt starting. Indoor containers are restricted as to size and location by codes and standards and, in general, should be limited to the minimum quantity necessary. Supply piping must reflect vibration stresses and special attention must be paid to flexible connectors. Similar factors are involved with lubricating oil supply systems which can comprise large supply tanks and separate pumps in large engine installations.

Provisions for emergency shutdown of the engine and fuel and lubricant supplies are necessary in larger installations.

Escaping fuels and lubricants can present engine room combustion explosion hazards regardless of the degree of flammability of the fuel. Gasoline or other low flash point liquid fuels and gaseous fuels have an obvious potential for producing a hazardous quantity of flammable vapor or gas-air mixtures (See Sec. 3, Chaps. 3 and 4). However, combustible liquid fuels, e.g., diesel fuel, and lubricating oil released under pressure can atomize and burn rapidly enough as mists to lead to room combustion explosions (see Sec. 3, Chap. 3). Such instances are relatively rare and largely associated with large engines. In most installations, the provision of room ventilation, both when the engine is operating and when not operating, is adequate to control this hazard. In some large installations, especially if gasoline or other low flash point fuel or liquid-phase LP-Gas is used, explosion venting construction may be advisable. A similar situation exists if flammable liquids or gases are being pumped or compressed.

Backfires through carburetor and gas-air mixture air intakes occur as a result of engine malfunction. These can ignite grease and oil deposits on and around the engine. Flame arresting equipment is provided at these points if flammable liquids or gases are being pumped or compressed.

A lubricating oil mist is often present in the crankcases of large reciprocating engines which, upon ignition, can result in a combustion explosion in the crankcase. Such engines are often equipped with crankcase explosion vents or the crankcase maintained under a nonflammable atmosphere.

Because of the presence of hot surfaces, engines should be isolated from locations producing combustible dusts or flyings which can be airborne, or liquids and gases having unusually low ignition temperatures. Exhaust manifolds and piping can reach temperatures over 1,000°F but, in order for ignition to occur, conditions must be favorable for reasonably prolonged contact between the combustible and the hot surface. For this reason, these surfaces seldom ignite flammable liquid vapors or flammable gases. Dusts and flyings, however, can deposit on these surfaces. Many fires have been caused by the failure to allow sufficient clearance between exhaust piping and combustible wall, ceiling, or roof construction.

Arcing electrical engine components are safeguarded by flashover shielding, flame arresters, purging, or ventilation if flammable liquids or gases are being pumped or compressed.

Engine disintegration is rare. Gas turbines are somewhat more subject to this phenomenon than reciprocating engines are because of their very high rotational speeds and the design of gas turbines for stationary installations usually incorporates construction features to contain compressor and turbine blades and rotor parts. The hazard is controlled by provision of automatic engine speed governors and, in addition on large engines, an overspeed shutdown device is provided on both types of engines.

A number of other engine protective devices are normally installed to guard against high jacket water temperature and low lubricating oil pressure. Flame-failure protection is provided on gas turbines.

Bibliography

NFPA Codes, Standards, and Recommended Practices (see the latest *NFPA Publications and Visual Aids Catalog* for availability of current editions of the following document)

NFPA No. 37, Standard for the Installation and Use of Stationary Combustion Engines and Gas Turbines.

Additional Readings

Engine Installation Manual, Engine Manufacturers Association, Chicago, 1962.

Chapter 3

HEAT TRANSFER SYSTEMS

The term "heat transfer fluid" refers to the broad spectrum of either liquid or vapor medium used to transfer heat energy from one place to another and control the rate of heat transfer. While practically all industrial processes involve the exchange of heat in one form or another, the use of heat transfer fluids is common in the chemical, paint, textile, plastics, food, petroleum, and paper industries. The fluids are used to heat or cool reaction vessels, to heat stills, to heat rollers for drying paper, for calendering plastics, and for many other forms of processing.

A. Types of Transfer Fluids

Approximately 95 percent of all heat transfer fluids used are either steam or water. If the temperature is above the freezing point of water and below about 350°F (176.8°C), the choice is usually between these two mediums. On the other hand, if the temperature of use is below or above these two points, it is desirable, if not necessary, to consider other fluids. For temperatures below the freezing point of water the most common heat transfer fluids are air, refrigerants such as halogenated hydrocarbons, ammonia, brines, or solutions of ethylene glycol and water.

When temperatures increase above 350°F (176.8°C), the vapor pressure of water increases rapidly, which would require expensive, high pressure processing equipment. Therefore, a more practical and inexpensive means of heating or temperature control at higher temperatures is to use a fluid or vaporizing fluid with a high boiling temperature. Care should be taken to use high flash point, thermally stable, and noncorrosive fluids designed for this purpose. The high boiling point liquids that are commonly used can be gener-

ally categorized as either heat-transfer oils, molten salts, or specially formulated heat-transfer mediums.

Heat-Transfer Oils: These are specially refined petroleum oils for use at temperatures up to approximately 600°F (315.8°C). At temperatures above this, the oils undergo thermal cracking to produce light hydrocarbons and polymers.

Molten Salts: These salts are generally used as heat absorbers or cooling mediums, and thus serve to control exothermic reactions which occur in the manufacture of certain chemicals. The most frequently used of these salts is a mixture of sodium and potassium salts having a relatively low melting point. Since these salts are solid at room temperature, it is obvious that care must be exercised to keep the temperature of the salt above its melting point to prevent solidification in the system. Also care must be taken during start-up to control the heat input so that the mixture will melt slowly.

Organic Fluids: Very widely used as a heat transfer fluid, are a variety of specially formulated organic fluids, many of which are fire resistant because of their chlorinated compounds. For example, the chlorinated biphenyls are fire resistant, although if they are heated to a sufficiently high temperature they do have a flash point and a flammable range. They can create a fire hazard if released into the fire box of a fire heater. Table 4-3A gives the physical properties of some common heat transfer fluids and oils.

When these fluids are used in the liquid state, the unit is referred to as a heater, and when the fluid is vaporized, the unit is called a vaporizer. Two types of equipment are manufactured: (1) fired heaters which are generally designed for heat-duty use in excess of one million Btu per hour, and

Table 4-3A. Physical Properties of Typical Heat Transfer Fluids

Compound	Freezing Point (°F)	Boiling Point (°F)	Flash Point (°F) C.O.C.	Fire Point (°F) C.O.C.
1, 2, 4-trichlorobenzene	63	417	210	*
tetrachlorobenzene (isomer mixture)	170	480	None	*
chlorinated biphenyl	7**	515–680	330	>500
dichlorodiphenyl ether (isomer mixture)	−4	590	335	530
trichlorodiphenyl ether (isomer mixture)	130	650	400	>600
octachlorostyrene	210	——	None	None
diphenyl ether—diphenyl eutectic	54	495	255	275
biphenylyl phenyl ether (isomer mixture)	99	680	370	410
o-biphenylyl phenyl ether	122	670	370	410
di- and triaryl ethers	<0	572	305	315
dimethyl-diphenyl ether (isomer mixture)	−40**	554	——	——
tetramethyl diphenyl ether (isomer mixture)	——	590	——	——
di-sec-butyl diphenyl ether (isomer mixture)	——	705	380	400
dicyclohexyldiphenyl ether (isomer mixture)	——	785	——	——
dodecyldiphenyl ether (isomer mixture)	45**	>800	410	440
ethyldiphenyl (isomer mixture)	< −60**	536	——	——
partially hydrogenated terphenyl	−15**	690	335	375
aliphatic oil	15	720–950	425	475
alkylaromatic oil	20	~650	350	390

*—None to boiling point
**—Pour point

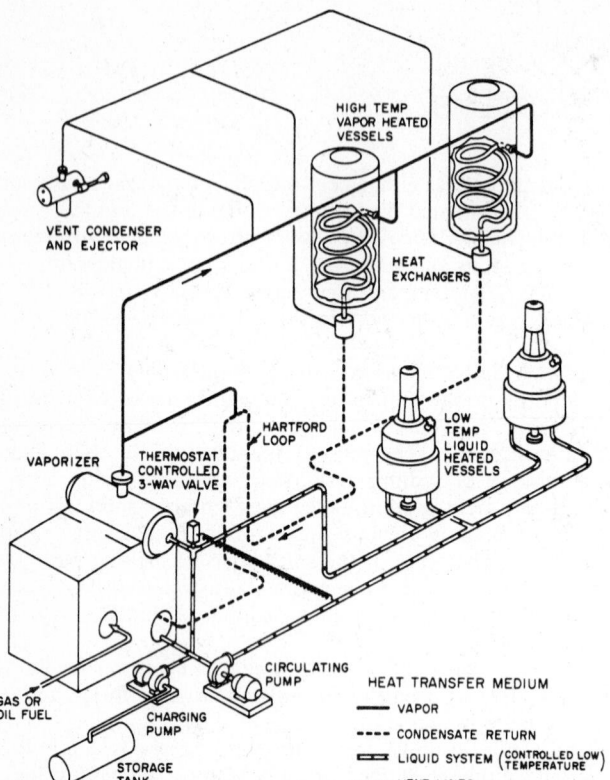

Fig. 4-3A. A combination vapor and liquid heat transfer system showing essential components. Heat from a single vaporizer source may be used for a variety of process equipment with control of individual equipment temperature achieved by throttling the line pressure to the pressure desired. The vaporizer unit preferably should be in a detached area or cut off from the remainder of the building in an area equipped with automatic sprinklers.

(2) electric heaters which are usually designed for heat-duty use of less than one million Btu per hour. Capacities of vaporizers and heaters range from a few thousand to over 175 million Btu per hour.

B. Hazards of Flammable Transfer Fluids

The basic hazards of flammable heat transfer liquids are those associated with the heating and transfer of a high flash point flammable liquid near or above its fire point in a closed system. The location of heaters or vaporizers for the liquids should preferably be an area detached from build-ings. If located inside a building, the heater or vaporizer should be in a suitable fire resistant room, cut off from the rest of the building. Heaters for heat transfer liquids having no fire point, that are located inside a building, can be considered as any other heater or furnace and the same precautions followed. Steam or carbon dioxide smothering lines are usually installed in the furnace portion of vaporizers to extinguish fires resulting from tube failures. Vapor leaks to the atmosphere should be corrected, for while flammability is not a serious hazard, explosive mists are possible. Leaks into the insulating materials are likewise potentially hazardous since "punking" of the insulation binder may occur. Operation of equipment should conform to the manufacturer's recommendations and in no instance should heaters or vaporizers be fired at rates above the rated capacity and temperature. A schematic illustration of a heat transfer system is shown in Figure 4-3A.

Flame impingement caused by improper burners, improper adjustment of a burner, or by poor furnace design, will ultimately result in tube failures. A low circulation rate through the heater can also cause problems and a degradation of the fluid. Contamination of the heat transfer fluid by the process material can cause significant problems depending on the thermal stability and quantity of process fluid added. Excessive fluid degradation also will occur if the equipment is operated above its design pressure, which will cause the fluid to carbonize and form hard carbon scale on the heat transfer surface.

For a discussion of the hazards of heat transfer systems associated with chemical processing equipment see Chapter 9 of this Section.

Bibliography

Additional Readings

Albrecht, A. R. and Seifert, W. F., "Accident Prevention in High Temperature Heat Transfer Systems," paper presented at AIChE Loss Prevention Symposium, 67th Annual Meeting, Atlanta, February 15-18, 1970.

Atomic Energy Commission and Department of the Navy, *Liquid Metals Handbook*, 2nd ed., Government Printing Office, Washington, D.C., June 1952.

Factory Mutual System, "Heat Transfer by Organic Fluids," Chapter 39, *Handbook of Industrial Loss Prevention*, 2nd ed., McGraw-Hill, New York, 1967.

"Heat Transfer Media other than Water," *Kirk-Othmer Encyclopedia of Chemical Technology*, Vol. 10, Interscience Publishers, New York, 1966, pp. 846-862.

"How to Pick Heat for Pilot Reactor," *Chemical Engineering*, Vol. 63, No. 8, Aug. 1956, p. 217.

"Molten Salt for Heat Transfer," *Chemical Engineering*, Vol. 70, May 27, 1963, p. 129.

"Recommended Good Practices for Heat Transfer Mediums in Closed Systems," Factory Insurance Association, Hartford, Conn., 1954.

Chapter 4

FLUID POWER SYSTEMS

Fluid power systems, utilizing a variety of hydraulic fluids, are designed to transmit and control energy by using a pressurized fluid within an enclosed system. They may be either of the hydro-pneumatic or hydraulic type of system. The controls are energized or sequenced by manual, mechanical, pneumatic, hydraulic, or electrical means. Rigid conductors, such as tubing or pipe, or flexible hose with their companion fittings connect the various power components into a working circuit. The use of fluid power systems varies from the steering and power brakes on automotive vehicles to specialized manufacturing operations where pressures exceed 20,000 psi such as in some plastic molds.

A. Petroleum-base Hydraulic Fluids

Petroleum-base hydraulic fluids are the most widely used as hydraulic fluids since their cost is reasonable and lubricity is excellent. However, petroleum-base fluids will burn if released from the system and reach a source of ignition. For example, if a hydraulic system fails and the released hydraulic fluid comes in contact with a hot exhaust pipe on a lift truck or other moveable equipment, a fire may result. If the hydraulic line is under high pressure and a hydraulic line breaks, an oil mist is sprayed over the surrounding area. Oil mists can be easily ignited with a resultant torch-like ball of fire or, if the oil mist is confined, a violent explosion can occur.

When combustible petroleum fluids, which can spray 50 ft or more at high pressure from leaking packings or hose, are used on machines, consideration must be given to: (1) isolating the machines, particularly from metal casting equipment which is in the same plant or from other positive sources of ignition; (2) providing automatic sprinklers, and portable extinguishers for Class B fires; (3) installing automatic or remote manual switches to stop pumps; (4) using armored hose, or enclosing pressure hose in a second tube to contain escaping fluid; and (5) inspecting the entire hydraulic system regularly, particularly at points of flexing or vibration.

B. Fire Resistant Hydraulic Fluid

The hazard of petroleum fluids can be reduced by substituting a fire resistant hydraulic fluid. There are three basic types of fire resistant hydraulic fluids:

1. Straight synthetic liquids, such as phosphate esters, which have the necessary lubrication qualities and resistance to combustion.

2. Water-glycols which are about 50 percent solutions of combustible lubricants in water. The steam from the water serves as a snuffer when the fluid is sprayed out against a hot surface or other potential source of ignition.

3. Water-in-oil emulsion in which water serves as a steam snuffing agent, the same as in the water-glycol type. The amount of water in this type of fluid usually is about 40 percent by volume.

Gaskets, sealing compounds, or paints suitable for use with petroleum hydraulic fluids may be unsuitable for use with some types of fire-resistant hydraulic fluids. However, suitable materials are available. Substituting fire resistant fluids for petroleum fluids should be done only with the advice of makers of all components of the hydraulic system. Damage to pumps, valves, hose, packings, and pistons can be severe unless selection of materials, clearances, and operating temperatures are considered.

C. Operating Characteristics of Systems

Most hydraulic fluid power systems are designed to operate at a maximum of 120°F (49°C) with peaks of 140°F (60°C). Water glycols and water-in-oil emulsions operated at higher temperatures incur the possibility of excessive evaporation, thus reducing their fire resistance. Water-type fluids require periodic inspections to determine and correct water content and possible stratification. Precise water content varies according to the manufacturer's recommendations for the various brands. Synthetic fire resistant fluids or petroleum base fluids can be used at higher temperatures within the recommendations of the respective manufacturers. Shielding of working hydraulic devices is essential when exposed to high temperatures. Water cooled heat exchangers are used to limit fluid temperatures.

Precautions to be used in changing from one type of hydraulic fluid to any other, are given in the publications: *Fire Hazards of Hydraulic Fluids in Processing Plastics;*[1] and *Standard Practice for the Use of Fire Resistant Fluids for Hydraulic Fluid Power Systems.*[2] An information report entitled *Company Trade Names for Hydraulic Fluid Power Fire Resistant Fluids*[3] provides sources, brand names, and generic basis.

SI Units

The following conversion factors are given as a convenience in converting to SI units the English units used in this chapter.

1 in. = 25.400 mm
1 psi = 6.895 kPa

Bibliography

References Cited

[1] "Fire Hazards of Hydraulic Fluids Used in Processing Plastics," Safety and Loss Prevention Bulletin No. 3, rev. ed. 1973, Society of the Plastics Industry, New York.

[2] "Standard Practice for the Use of Fire Resistant Fluids for Hydraulic Fluid Power Systems," National Fluid Power Association, Thiensville, Wisc., 1972.

[3] "Company Trade Names for Hydraulic Fluid Power Resistant Fluids," T3.11.4R1, 1972, National Fluid Power Association, Thiensville, Wisc.

Additional Readings

"Development of Nonflammable Hydraulic Fluids and Lubricants," Olin Corporation, Cryogenics Division (prepared for U.S. Department of Commerce, Office of Technical Services) Stamford, Conn., June 1964.

Foitl, R. J. and Kycera, W. J., "Formation and Evaluation of Fire-Resistant Hydraulic Fluids," *Iron and Steel Engineer,* Vol. 41, No. 7, July 1964, pp. 117-120.

Pingree, Daniel, "Looking at Fire Hazards: Hydraulic Fluids," *Fire Journal,* Vol. 59, No. 6, Nov. 1965, p. 23.

Polack, S. P., "Bureau of Mines Evaluates Fire Resistance of Hydraulic Fluids," *Iron and Steel Engineer,* Vol. 41, No. 8, Aug. 1964, pp. 105-110.

Chapter 5

INDUSTRIAL AND COMMERCIAL HEAT UTILIZATION EQUIPMENT

Explosions in fuel-fired and electric heat utilization equipment constitute a loss potential in life, property, and production. Many guidelines, rules, and methods applicable to safe operation of this type of equipment have been promulgated by the NFPA and others.

Heat utilization equipment is so varied in size, complexity, location, and usage that it is very difficult to draft a single set of rules applicable to every type of furnace or oven, even though the basic principles may be the same for all types.

Safe operation of the fuel-fired equipment is completely dependent upon the controlled release of fuel into a confined space, a strong source of ignition, and the maintenance of a proper fuel-to-air ratio. In the fuel-fired equipment, the fuel-to-air ratio is constantly changing due to the evolution of flammable volatiles from the material being processed and being added to the fuel being burned. Users and designers must utilize engineering skill to bring together that proper combination of controls and training necessary for the safe operation of the equipment.

Causes of practically all failures can be traced back to human failure. The most significant specific failures have been found to be:

1. Inadequate training of operators and maintenance technicians.
2. Faulty design of equipment.
3. Complacency on the part of users.
4. Error in selection of combustion safeguards applicable to the system to be protected.

Any unwanted or uncontrolled transfer of energy, or both, affecting people or property are problems which designers and users must consider. This would include such things as sufficient heat transfer to cause burns, burning or heat stress, falling or swinging objects to cause injury or damage to people and property, rotating parts, electrical shock hazards, the energy of noise, and release of toxic or corrosive vapors into the building or to the environment exterior to the building.

This chapter does not purport to be a guide to solving all of the problems. However, by following the guidelines and principles contained herein, the user would be able to mitigate a number of the problems involved.

A. Industrial Heat Utilization Equipment

Industrial-type heat utilization equipment includes a variety of forges, furnaces, kettles, kilns, ovens, retorts, and others which are heated by gas, oil, solid fuels, or electricity. They may be direct fired, indirect fired, or involve a heat transfer medium heated in an area adjacent to or separated from the process equipment.

Industrial ovens and furnaces, special atmosphere furnaces, vacuum furnaces, after-burners and catalytic combustion systems, dehydrators, dryers, and lumber kilns are discussed in this chapter.

Reference should be made to other sections of this HANDBOOK, particularly Section 3, Chapter 3, "Combustible and Flammable Liquids;" Section 3, Chapter 4, "Gases;" and Section 7, Chapter 3, "Heating Systems and Appliances." The latter chapter gives details concerning fuels and methods of firing.

Grading of Equipment

For fire protection purposes, industrial-type heat utilization equipment may be graded by temperatures developed in the media or material being heated. These grades are also useful in determining adequate clearances from combustibles, the setting of the equipment, and in specifying the type of chimney necessary, if any. Grading of heat-producing appliances is discussed in Section 7, Chapter 3 of this HANDBOOK. (Table 7-3M gives the three grades of low, medium, and high heat appliances; the type of chimney that may be used for each grade; and a selection of appliances that fall in each grade).

Ovens and furnaces are classified by both temperature and pressure in Part B of this chapter.

Fire Problems

Important features in connection with the installation and operation of fixed or stationary equipment are: (1) proximity and combustibility of the contents of the building or room in which they are located; (2) construction of the building; (3) setting; (4) ventilation; (5) location; (6) heat, gas and smoke disposal; (7) maximum temperature required; and (8) handling of heated materials in connection with the equipment.

Furnaces and dryers may be used to treat materials giving off flammable vapors.

Fixed heating equipment, particularly the medium and high heat grades, are best installed in separate buildings or in cut-off sections, preferably those that have fire resistive construction throughout. It is usually necessary to provide natural draft ventilation or mechanical blower ventilation systems to remove excess heat and fumes. Means for replacing the exhausted air is also necessary to prevent negative pressures in the room or building which would adversely affect equipment ventilation and fuel burner operation.

Special precautions are taken with boiling vats, salt baths, and melting furnaces in order than none of the contents will reach combustible material if they should overflow, and such furnaces are equipped with hoods or other means of carrying off hot vapors and heat in addition to providing for proper air circulation.

All rooms or parts of rooms where heated metal is cast, rolled, or power forged should have earth or fire resistive flooring for a distance of 3 ft, and noncombustible walls, partitions, and supports for a distance of 10 ft above and 30 ft at the sides, from any point where hot metal is handled.

B. Ovens and Furnaces

This part covers the location, design, construction, operation, protection, and maintenance of industrial heating enclosures which are known as ovens or furnaces. It does not cover small cabinet or stove-type ovens for domestic use. Heat may be furnished by gas burners, oil burners, electric heaters, infrared lamps, induction heaters, or steam radiation systems. In practically all cases there are fire or explosion hazards from either the fuel in use or flammable volatiles from material in the oven, or from a combination of both.

The dividing line between an oven and a furnace is not clearly defined. A dictionary definition of an oven is "a compartment or receptacle for heating, baking, or drying by means of heat" and a furnace as "an enclosed chamber or structure in which heat is produced for heating a building, reducing ores and metals, baking pottery, etc." It has been a rule of thumb of industry to classify heating devices that do not "indicate color" (operate at temperatures of less than approximately 1,000°F) as ovens. This rule does not always apply as evidenced by the fact that coke ovens operate at temperatures in excess of 2,200°F. Perhaps the only positive statement that can be made is that operations for which material is heated either in ovens or in furnaces extends through a wide range of temperatures.

NFPA Classification of Ovens and Furnaces

The NFPA Standards governing installation of various types of ovens and furnaces classify ovens and furnaces into categories according to the temperatures and pressures at which they operate. (The Standards are NFPA No. 86A, Ovens and Furnaces, NFPA No. 86B, Industrial Furnaces, and NFPA No. 86C, Industrial Furnaces-Special Atmospheres, referred to collectively hereafter in this chapter as the NFPA Ovens and Furnace Standards.) The classifications are:

Class A Ovens or Furnaces: These units are operating at approximately atmospheric pressures and temperatures below 1,400°F (760°C) where there is an explosion hazard from either (or a combination of) the fuel in use or flammable volatiles from material in the oven or catalytic combustion system, i.e., flammable volatiles from paints and other finishing processes, such as dipped or sprayed material, impregnated material, coated fabrics, etc.

Class B Ovens or Furnaces: These are units operating at or above atmospheric pressure and temperatures exceeding approximately 1,400°F (760°C).

Class C Furnaces: These are units in which there is an explosion hazard due to a flammable special atmosphere being used for treatment of material in process. This type of furnace may use any type of heating system and includes the atmosphere generator.

Class D Furnaces: These are vacuum furnaces which operate at temperatures above ambient to over 5,000°F (2,760°C) at pressures below atmosphere down to 1 millimeter of mercury at 1°C (1 torr), using any type of heating system available. These furnaces may include the use of special processing atmospheres.

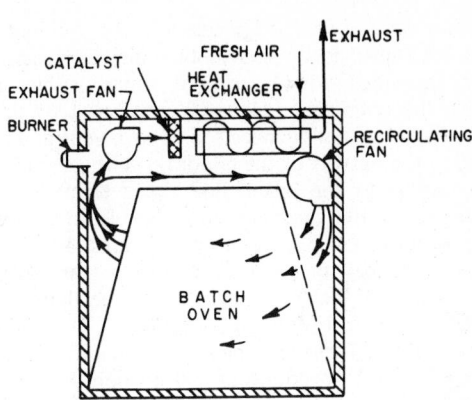

Fig. 4-5B. *Batch oven with a catalytic heater for full air pollution control.*

Classification by Type of Handling System

Ovens and furnaces may be further classified based on the method of handling a material as it passes through the furnace. The two principal types are: (1) the batch oven or furnace, sometimes referred to as "in and out," "intermittent" or "periodic" type, and (2) the continuous oven or furnace.

Batch Type: In the batch oven or furnace the temperature is practically constant throughout the interior. The material to be heated is placed in a predetermined position and remains there until the heating process is complete. It is then removed, generally through the opening by which it entered. Figures 4-5A and 4-5B are examples of this type of furnace and oven.

Continuous Type: In the continuous furnace or oven the material being processed moves through the furnace while being heated. The straight-line furnace is probably the most common. Figure 4-5C, is an example of this type. The hearth of a straight-line oven or furnace usually remains stationery, and the material passes over skids or rolls while being carried down an incline by force of gravity or by mechanical pushers.

A common variation of the continuous-type is one with a moving hearth. The material to be heated is placed on the hearth and is removed after the hearth has completed a revolution. This is known as rotating hearth or rotating-table furnace. Another method is to feed the material being processed through a furnace with a revolving hearth or tube by means of a stationery internal screw thread.

Location and Construction of Ovens and Furnaces

Ovens and furnaces are located where they will present the least possible exposure to life and property, as well as to important features of the building occupancy. Consideration is given to the possibility of fire resulting from overheating or from the escape of fuel and the possibility of building damage and personal injury resulting from an explosion. They may need to be surrounded by walls or partitions and be at or above grade, as basement areas completely below grade do not lend themselves to natural ventilation and offer severe obstacles to providing proper explosion release. The

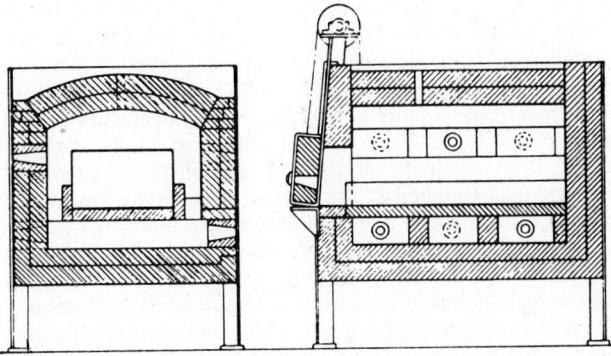

Fig. 4-5A. *A large batch-type, under- and over-fired, semi-muffle, heat treating furnace.*

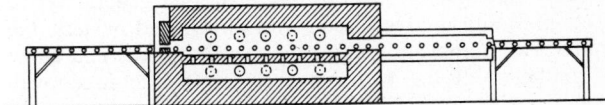

Fig. 4-5C. *A continuous roller hearth furnace.*

construction of the oven or furnace and the building which houses it both need to be noncombustible. Explosion relief venting is provided where required. Combustibles in the vicinity of the oven are adequately separated or properly insulated. Each oven or furnace has its own venting facilities extending to the outside of the building. With gas or oil fuel, separate venting of the heater and the oven or furnace is provided unless the products of combustion discharge directly into the oven. Except in special cases, adequate and separate mechanical means are provided to furnish air for the combustion of the fuel and for the ventilation of the oven; natural draft is usually not adequate.

The need for a furnace exhaust system directly to outdoors for removal of products of combustion, heat, or toxic gases or vapors depends upon the heating process, type of combustion, and the hazard to personnel.

Wherever a furnace is permitted to exhaust directly into a room, the room needs a balanced mechanical ventilation system to bring in fresh air from outside of the building, and exhaust to outdoors. The supply inlets and exhaust outlets are arranged to provide a uniform flow of air throughout the area, without any dead air pockets. The room ventilation system is designed to adequately remove toxic contaminants at their maximum anticipated rate-of-release and keep concentrations below the established MAC (maximum allowable concentration) values.

Certain types of furnaces are constructed of metal with a covering of brick or other masonry; some types are of metal without covering, but well braced with metal supports, while others have an inner lining of metal or fire clay products. In some instances furnaces have air spaces or noncombustible fillers between the outer and inner walls.

Ovens and furnaces are well separated from valuable stock, important power equipment, machinery, and sprinkler risers, thereby securing a minimum interruption to production and protection in case of accidents to the oven or furnace. The installations are positioned so as to be readily accessible with adequate space above to permit installation of automatic sprinklers, the proper use of hose streams, the proper functioning of explosion vents, and performance of inspection and maintenance routines. Roofs and floors of ovens are insulated, and the space above and below ventilated, to keep temperatures at combustible ceilings and floors below 160°F.

Oven and Furnace Heating Systems

There are several methods of transferring heat to material in an oven or furnace: (1) by direct contact with the products of combustion, (2) by convection and direct radiation from the hot gases, and (3) by reradiation from the hot walls of the furnace. In muffle furnaces (see Fig. 4-5A) the products of combustion are separated from the material being heated by a metal or refractory muffle and heat transfer is by radiation. In liquid-bath furnaces, i.e.: salt baths or molten metal, used for tempering, hardening, galvanizing, tinning, etc., a metal pot containing a liquid heating or processing medium is heated and the heat transferred through the medium to the material being processed in the pot. Heat transfer mediums also have other applications in industry, e.g., reactors, stills, kettles, evaporators, and dryers.

Oven Heaters: Oven heaters are of two general types, direct-fired and indirect-fired. With direct-fired heaters, the products of combustion enter the oven chamber and come in contact with the work in process. Indirect-fired oven heaters are so arranged that the products of combustion do not enter the oven chamber; heating is accomplished by

radiation from tubes or by passing air over tubes and then into the oven. The indirect type is somewhat safer because dangerous fuel-air mixtures cannot readily fill the oven space. Nevertheless, the possibility of explosion from vapors given off by the drying process still exists.

There are several arrangements of these two types of oven heaters; namely, direct-fired internal, direct-fired external, indirect-fired internal, and indirect-fired external heaters.

There are three variations of direct-fired external heaters, two of indirect-fired internal heaters, and three of indirect-fired external heaters (see Fig. 4-5D). There are advantages and disadvantages for each type. The direct-fired external type may have a single or relatively small number of burners which simplifies the problem of automatic safety controls. As previously mentioned, the indirect firing arrangement limits the space in which the fuel-air explosion hazard may exist.

Furnace Heaters: The arrangement of furnace heaters is usually the same as those for ovens—direct-fired internal, indirect-fired external, etc. Sometimes the terms used to express these arrangements are different. If products of combustion are under a hearth and then are carried up and into the heating chamber, the furnace is said to be under-fired. When the same thing occurs in a chamber at one side of the furnace and then passes over a bridge wall into the heating chamber, the furnace is referred to as a side-fired furnace. A furnace in which the products of combustion are produced in a space above the heating chamber and then pass through a perforated arch into the heating chamber is called an oven-fired furnace. If the same thing occurs at some distance above the heating chamber and hearth, and the products of combustion are deflected onto the hearth by an arched roof, the furnace is called a "reverberatory" furnace. A radiant tube heated furnace is an arrangement for indirect firing (see Fig. 4-5E).

Sources of Heat: The source of heat for an oven or furnace may be gas burners, oil burners, electric heaters, infrared lamps, electric induction heaters, or steam radiation systems. In each case, the details of the means of supply, burners, lamps, etc., and the auxiliary equipment required, will be found in other parts of this HANDBOOK and in NFPA Standards.

It is important that flames, heated surfaces, or other possible sources of ignition do not constitute a fire hazard by being in proximity to combustibles being processed in an oven, and that they are located where drippings or dust will not fall or otherwise accumulate on them.

(1) **Gas Fired:** Gas fuel may be any type of gas which is in common industrial use. The important thing is that the burner, its adjustment, and the means of combustion are suitable for the gas which is to be burned. The burner may have a single nozzle, with burners located singly or in groups, or the burner may have multiple ports of the perforated pipe, ribbon, or slot type. Burners must light easily, have a stable flame at all ports, and have no tendency to flash back or blow off over the entire range of turndown and under all draft conditions which may exist in the oven. A supply of air adequate for complete combustion is premixed with the gas, supplied at the burner, or otherwise provided in a standard manner under all operating conditions.

(2) **Oil Fired:** Oven heating systems may be fired with fuel oil or with a combination of gas and fuel oil. Provisions for the installation of oil-fired heaters are given in Section 7, Chapter 3, and in NFPA No. 31, Installation of Oil Burning Equipment. For safety, the design and operating characteristics of oil burners are generally the same as for gas.

(3) **Electric Heating Systems:** Electric heating systems

for ovens and furnaces are of five types: resistance, infrared, induction, arc, and dielectric.

(a) Resistance heat is produced by current flow through a resistive conductor. Resistance heaters may be of "open" type with bare heating conductors or "insulated sheath" type with heater conductors covered by a protecting sheath which may be filled with electrical insulating material (see Fig. 4-5F).

(b) Infrared heat is transmitted as electromagnetic waves from incandescent lamps with filaments that operate at temperatures lower than the filament temperature of ordinary incandescent lamps, so that most of the radiation occurs in the infrared part of the spectrum. These waves pass through air and transparent substances but not opaque objects, and therefore release their heat energy to these objects.

(c) Induction heat is developed by currents induced in the charge. Induction heaters have an electric coil surrounding the oven space, and heating is by electric currents induced in the work being processed.

(d) Arc heat is developed by the passage of an electric current between either a pair of electrodes or between electrodes and the work causing an arc which releases energy in the form of heat.

(e) Dielectric heat is developed in dielectric materials when exposed to an alternate electric field. The frequencies used are generally higher (in the order of three megacycles or more) than those in induction heating. This type of heater is useful for heating materials which are commonly thought of as being nonconductive.

Electric systems can be arranged so that the processing operation does not require an oven enclosure.

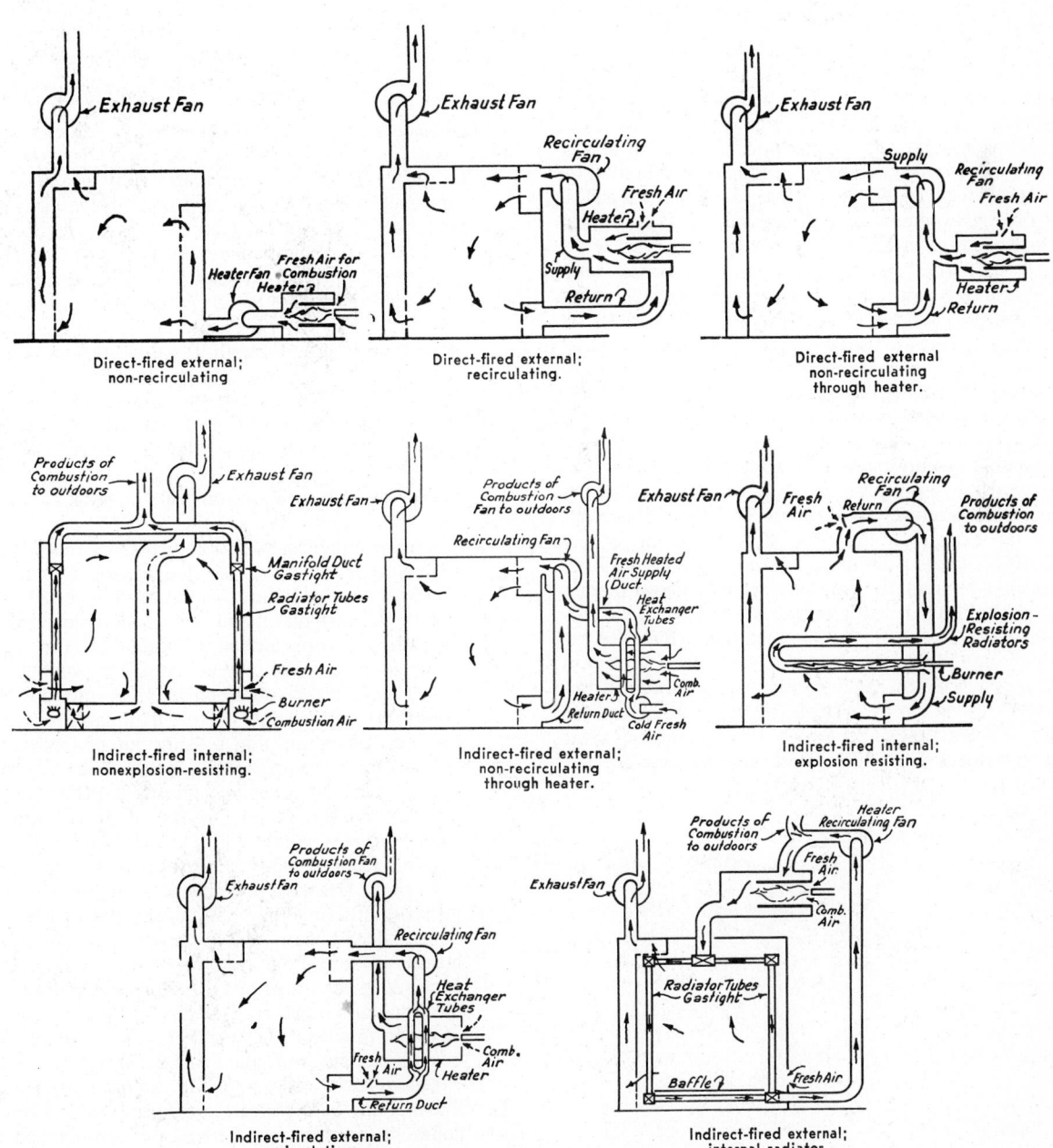

Fig. 4-5D. Types of oven-heating systems.

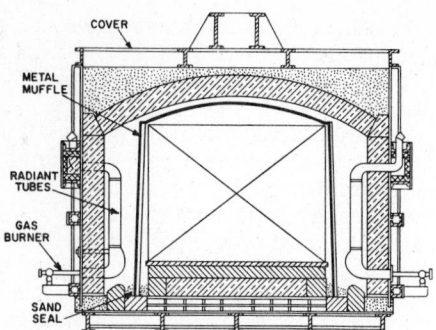

Fig. 4-5E. An annealing muffle furnace.

The use of "oven-less" or unenclosed heating systems can employ lamps, resistance-type electric elements, or infrared heaters in the vaporization of flammable, toxic, or corrosive liquids and their thermal decomposition products. Enclosures around "oven-less" systems are advisable to prevent flammable, toxic, or corrosive vapors from escaping into the general area, and to help provide better ventilation and safeguards for personnel. However, heating systems having an energy input of under 100 kw may be excluded if adequate area ventilation is provided (NFPA No. 70, the National Electrical Code gives guidance for electrical installations in hazardous locations).

All parts of heaters operating at elevated temperatures within an oven or furnace and all other energized parts are protected to prevent contact by persons, as well as to prevent accidental contact with materials being processed, and contact with drippage from the materials.

(4) **Steam Heating Systems:** In steam heating systems, the steam pressure in heat exchanger coils is regulated at the minimum required to provide the proper drying temperatures. This will avoid unnecessarily high temperatures at coil surfaces. The coils are not to be located on the floor of the oven or in any position where paint drippings or other combustibles, such as recirculated lint, may accumulate on them.

Fire and explosion hazards in and around ovens or furnaces may result from combustible materials which are exposed or from flammable vapor-air mixtures. Fires in combustibles can be prevented by adequate separation from the sources of heat or by insulation. Overheating can be prevented by temperature controls. Flammable vapor-air mixtures may result from the materials being processed or

from gas or oil fuel which has not been completely burned. Fires or explosions of vapor-air mixtures are in general prevented by adequate ventilation and controls which keep the flammable vapor content below the lower flammable limit. Some special process ovens and furnaces contain hydrogen or other flammable gases; for safe operation it is necessary to prevent the entrance of air under normal operating conditions. Both normal or unscheduled starts and stops of these ovens require special safety procedures.

Fuel Hazards: With gas and oil fuels there is the hazard of vapors from unburned or incompletely burned fuel which, when mixed with air, may be within the range of ignition and explosion. Such hazards develop during lighting-off, firing, and shutting down the oven or furnace.

In order to cope with the fuel hazard, it is necessary to recognize three different conditions when operating a fuel gas or fuel oil burner:

(1) **Lighting-off:** Before torches, sparks, or other ignition sources are introduced, and until all burners are properly lighted, the operator must exercise every precaution, backed up by such automatic safety controls as are practical, to eliminate or to avoid producing dangerous unburned fuel accumulations.

(2) **Firing:** In the firing phase three conditions are given attention:

(a) Safety requires continuous ignition and complete burning of the fuel before it passes beyond its normal combustion zone at the burner. To maintain this safe condition of a stable flame with complete combustion, the mixer and burner assembly must proportion the particular fuel and air properly throughout the combustion zone, to the correct concentration, and the mixture velocity through the combustion zone must be neither too high, causing extinguishment by blowoff, nor too low, causing flame to flash back or "go out," at any firing rate within the turndown range. It is thus obvious that good burner-mixer design and proper application to the particular heating equipment operating conditions will be one of the main factors in safety during firing.

(b) Air for combustion is obtained from the primary or secondary air supplied at the burner, or from both. Total or partial failure of combustion air supply can result in unstable flame which may lead to flame failure, and introduction of unburned fuel into the combustion chamber. When too little combustion air is supplied, the result is an overrich mixture and incomplete combustion. The flammable incomplete products of combustion passing out of those parts of the system at temperatures high enough for prompt ignition may later become diluted with air down into the flammable range in the oven or recirculating duct work. After a dangerous accumulation has built up ignition from a number of sources may produce an explosion. Overrich combustion may also produce rapid smothering and extinguishment of the burner flame, and the flammable products of incomplete combustion followed by raw fuel may likewise become explosive when diluted by air later or in another part of the system. Therefore, it is essential that precautions be taken to cut off the fuel in event of failure of combustion air, and to require manual reset.

(c) Liquid fuels, such as fuel oil, must be broken up into fine globules by atomization for easy ignition and quick complete combustion. This can be accomplished mechanically by ejecting the liquid fuel at high pressure, or by directing a steam or air jet into the oil stream.

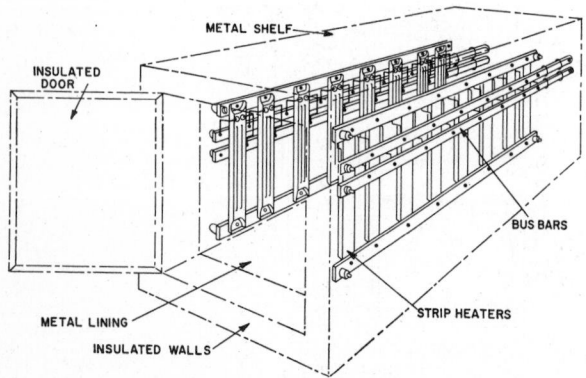

Fig. 4-5F. Strip heaters mounted in a small oven.

Improper oil temperature preventing proper flow, partial obstructions in burner tips, and loss of oil or atomizing medium pressures can cause improper atomization. Failure to atomize properly will usually result in unstable flame which can lead to flame failure. Other factors leading to flame failure are stoppage of fuel supply by an improperly closed fuel valve or other pipe obstruction, and the presence of water in a fuel oil line.

(3) **Shutting Down:** A dangerous accumulation of unburned fuel may occur in an oven and heating system following a shutdown if any manual fuel valves are left open or leaking and/or safety shutoff valves are not tight-closing. Subsequent ignition by hot refractory or an ignition source when starting up may produce an explosion.

Safety Controls for Ovens and Furnaces

It is essential that all ovens and furnaces prossessing flammable materials, or those involving flammable vapors, or heated with combustible fuels, be provided with adequate safety devices. Safety equipment must insure sufficient preventilation and adequate ventilation during operation. This equipment must constantly supervise operating conditions so that safety will be assured and fires or explosions will not be permitted to develop. Safety control means that an adequate number and suitable types of devices, properly arranged, are provided to maintain safe conditions. These devices should "fail safe." While it is true that a competent operator is essential, it is also true that he needs assistance because he cannot continually supervise everything. He is, however, responsible for the proper maintenance and testing of the oven operating and safety equipment.

The type of safety control equipment employed with oven or furnace assemblies depends on the requirements of the particular operation. A list of the principal types of controls employed is given in Table 4-5A. Most of these control

Table 4-5A. Safety Control Equipment for Ovens and Furnaces

Ventilation controls:
 Air flow switches
 Pressure switches
 Fan shaft rotation detectors
 Dampers
 Position limit switches
 Electrical interlocks
 Preventilation time-delay relays

Fuel safety controls:
 Safety shutoff valves
 Supervising cock (FM cock)
 Flame detection units (combustion safeguards)
 Flowmeters
 Firechecks
 Reliable ignition sources
 Pressure switches
 Program relays

Temperature controllers
Temperature limit controls
Continuous vapor concentration indicators and controls
Conveyor interlocks (with steam and electric-resistance heating equipment)
Electrical overload protection (with resistance and induction heating equipment)
Low oil-temperature limit controls (on oil-burner equipment using heavy residual fuel oil, such as No. 5 and No. 6, which require preheating)

units are tested by recognized laboratories and their listings indicate the appropriateness of the devices for varying situations.

Full safety control of a gas- or oil-fired oven, especially of the direct-fired type, may require the following: (1) inspection to determine if all fuel valves are closed and not leaking, (2) establishing and continuing full ventilation, (3) turning on and igniting the gas pilot only at the conclusion of a required preventilation period, and (4) opening fuel valves (including the safety shutoff valve) that supply the burner only after the combustion safeguard shows that the pilot flame has been ignited, and if fuel and air (or other atomizing agent) pressures are right. If the burner flame is not promptly established, the safety valve will close and the entire cycle must be started from the beginning. Operation, once started, continues only as long as the safety controls indicate safe conditions; failure in any one respect shuts down everything and the full cycle must again be started.

The NFPA Ovens and Furnaces Standards (Nos 86A, 86B and 86C) specify in considerable detail the safeguards which are needed for different ovens and furnaces and the types of devices which may be used.

When burner installations are large, the usual safety controls for each pilot and each burner may not be considered practical; in such cases, special devices and arrangements may have to be employed. A special continuous line pilot for multiple burners is illustrated in Figure 4-5G.

Controls for a large number of cup burners with flame propagation between individual burners may be provided as shown in Figure 4-5H.

When burners exist in such numbers that it is not considered practical to provide combustion safeguards at each, a system of supervising cocks and gas safety control may be provided. This makes it possible to determine that all fuel valves are closed and that none is leaking. When interlocking devices indicate that all individual burner valves are closed, the safety shutoff valve may be opened and each burner valve may then be opened manually and the burner lighted. The supervising cock and a typical layout are shown in Figures 4-5I and 4-5J.

During the past few years, multi-burner combustion safeguards have been developed. In many instances, it is now possible to install flame supervision for each burner, where previously the supervisory cock system was the only available application.

When gas-fired burners have a fuel input rating of 400,000 Btu per hr or more, a special arrangement of safety shutoff valves in the fuel line may be required. This consists of two safety shutoff valves with a "reverse acting" (open when safety valves are closed, closed when safety valves are open) solenoid-operated valve in a vent line between the two safety shutoff valves. The vent line discharges outdoors. A manually lubricated plug cock is provided downstream of the safety valves. This arrangement assures positive fuel shutoff with venting of residual gas and of

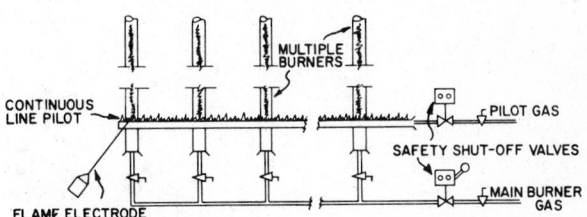

Fig. 4-5G. Arrangement of a continuous line pilot for multiple burners.

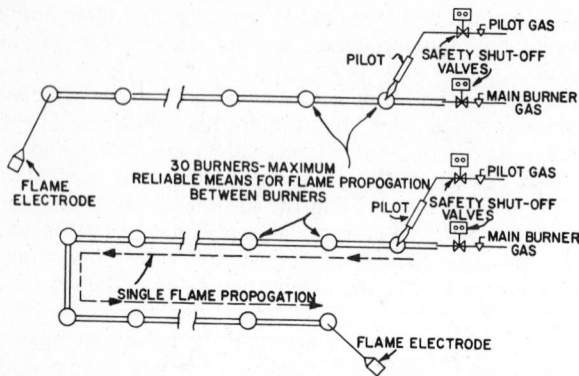

Fig. 4-5H. Typical arrangements for multiple burners of the individual cup type with flame propagation between individual burners.

leakage. The plug cock may be closed and other valves tested for leakage.

It is obvious that safety ventilation is not needed in an oven which never contains flammable or noxious vapors, and that flammable fuel-air mixtures need not be guarded against in an electric or steam heated oven.

Operator Training

The most essential safety consideration is the selection of alert and competent operators. Their knowledge and training are vital to continued safe operation. It is important that new operators be thoroughly instructed and demonstrate an adequate understanding of the equipment and its operations. It is good practice to retrain regular operators at intervals to maintain a high level of proficiency and effectiveness.

Operating instructions are provided by the equipment manufacturer. These instructions include schematic piping and wiring diagrams, as well as:

1. Light-up procedures.
2. Shutdown procedures.
3. Emergency procedures.
4. Maintenance procedures.

Operator training includes:

1. Combustion of air-gas mixtures.
2. Explosion hazards.
3. Sources of ignition and ignition temperature.
4. Atmosphere gas analysis.
5. Handling of flammable atmosphere gases.
6. Handling of toxic atmosphere gases.
7. Functions of control and safety devices.
8. Purpose and basic principles of the gas atmosphere generators.

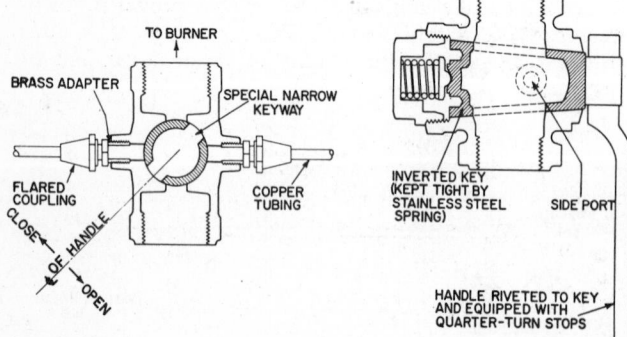

Fig. 4-5I. Details of a supervising cock (FM Cock).

Operators need to have access to operating instructions at all times. An outline of these instructions is posted at the furnace.

Testing and Maintenance for Ovens and Furnaces

It is important that the operating and safety control equipment of each oven is regularly checked and tested, preferably once a week, and at less frequent intervals, probably annually, a more comprehensive test and check are made by an expert. All deficiencies are to be promptly corrected. A regular cleaning program is observed to cover all portions of the oven and its attachments. Suitable access openings are provided for cleaning the oven enclosure and connecting ducts.

A program for inspecting and maintaining oven safety controls is given in the appendices of the NFPA Ovens and Furnaces Standards (Nos. 86A, 86B, and 86C).

C. Class A Ovens and Furnaces

Adequate ventilation and good fire and explosion protection are major considerations for Class A installations.

Ventilation

Ventilation is required for safety while an oven is in operation and flammable vapors are being given off. Control devices assure that the ventilating system is in operation and provide for preventilation of ovens to dissipate accumulated vapors, such as those resulting from fuel leakage or from a work charge left in an unventilated oven. Failure of the ventilating fan causes the shutdown of the heating system and of the conveyor which carries material into a continuous oven. The following discussion of ventilation refers to that required for safety of operation, exclusive of combustion and recirculation requirements. It does not apply to ovens operating in conjunction with solvent recovery systems.

Proper ventilation means a sufficient supply of fresh air and proper exhaust to outdoors with a sufficiently vigorous and properly distributed air circulation to insure that the flammable vapor concentration in all parts of the oven enclosure is safely below the lower flammable limit of the vapor at all times. The basis for determining the quantity of fresh air required for safe ventilation is the amount of vapor produced by the flammable solvent used on the work in process.

In general, mechanical ventilation to outdoors is required for all ovens in which flammable or toxic vapors are liberated, as well as for ovens heated by direct-fired gas or oil heaters. Ovens of 64 cu ft volume or less may not need mechanical ventilation if no flammable or toxic vapors are present in the oven.

Ovens in which no flammable or toxic vapors are released at any time do not require ventilation for safety, if heated by steam or electric energy, or by gas- or oil-fired indirect heating equipment.

On all new ovens, regardless of size, the required ventilation provided by a separate exhauster is advisable whenever appreciable amounts of flammable vapors are given off by the work.

Continuous Conveyor-Type Ovens: The general rule for ventilating continuous conveyor-type ovens is to provide not less than 10,000 cfm of fresh air at 70°F for each gallon of common solvent introduced into the oven. The basis for this general rule is that 1 gal of common solvent produces

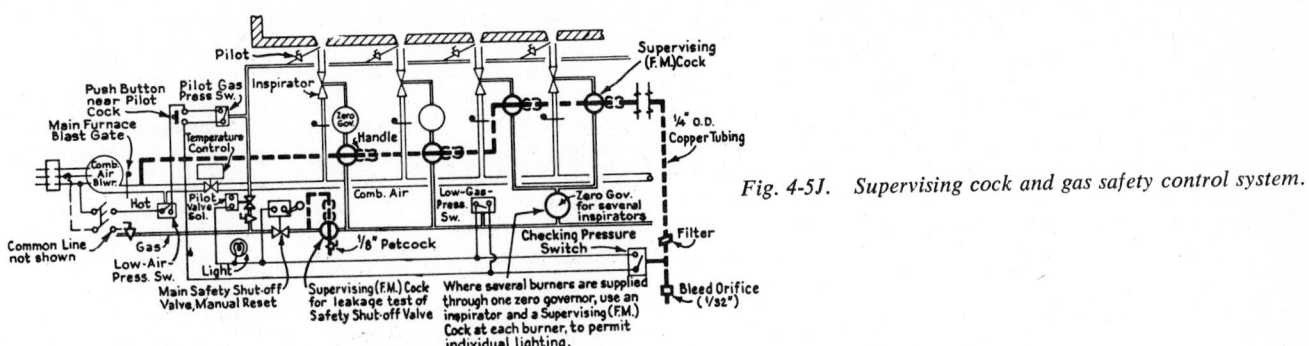

Fig. 4-5J. Supervising cock and gas safety control system.

a quantity of flammable vapor which will diffuse in air to form roughly 2,500 cu ft of the leanest explosive mixture. Since a considerable portion of the ventilating air may pass through the oven without completely traversing the zone in which vapors are given off, and because of a possible lack of uniform distribution of ventilation air, and also to provide a margin of safety, four times this amount of air, or 10,000 cu ft (referred to 70°F), for each gallon of solvent evaporated is allowed. With certain solvents, where the volume of air rendered barely explosive exceeds 2,500 cu ft, the factor of safety decreases proportionately.

When a continuous-type oven is designed to operate with a particular solvent and where ventilating air may be accurately controlled, the required ventilation can be determined by calculation. See NFPA No. 86A for information on how to calculate the volume of vapor produced by 1 gal of solvent and the volume of air required to provide sufficient dilution to prevent an ignitible mixture. As with the general rule for oven ventilation, the calculated rate of air change includes a factor of safety four times the volume of air required to prevent an ignitible mixture.

Batch Process (Box) Ovens: The nature of the work being processed is the main factor in determining the ventilation rate in batch process ovens. Because of the wide variations in the materials, rate of evaporation and coating thickness, it is preferable that tests and calculations be made. However, tests and years of industrial experience have shown that approximately 380 cfm (referred to 70°F) of ventilation for each gallon of flammable volatiles released from a batch of sheet metal or metal parts being baked after dip coating is a reasonably safe rate of air change. Tests of dipped sheet metal in batch process ovens also have shown that in typical 1-hr bakes, practically all the solvent is evaporated in the first 20 min.

For other types of work, the figure of 380 cfm (referred to 70°F) is also used, unless the required ventilation rates can be calculated on the basis of reliable previous experience, or the maximum evaporation rate is determined by tests run under actual oven operating conditions. In the latter case, a margin of safety is introduced by requiring a rate of air change equaling four times the volume of air needed to produce an ignitible mixture. In any event, caution is needed in applying this estimating method to work of low mass which will heat quickly, such as paper, textiles etc., or work coated with materials containing highly volatile solvents. Either condition may give too high a peak of evaporation rate for the estimating method.

Temperature Correction: Temperature corrections must be made in using the above rules, since the volume of a gas varies in direct proportion to its absolute temperature (0°F is equivalent to approximately 460° absolute).

For example, in order to supply 10,000 cu ft of fresh air

referred to 70°F (530° absolute) to an oven operating at 300°F (760° absolute), it is necessary to exhaust $\frac{760}{530} \times 10,000$, or 14,320 cu ft of vapor-laden air.

In some cases, process requirements call for ventilation in excess of that needed to maintain safe conditions in an oven. When this is true, an approximate method of figuring ventilation may be adequate as a means of checking safety requirements. Except in these cases it is important that all factors, including solvent characteristics, type of oven, material being processed, oven temperatures, effect of temperature on LFL, etc., be carefully considered so that an adequate safety factor is assured.

Fire and Explosion Protection

Ovens and furnaces containing or processing sufficient combustible materials to sustain a fire, are equipped with automatic sprinklers or water spray systems as basic fire protection. This includes sprinklers in the exhaust ducts when necessary.

The extent of protection required depends upon the construction and arrangement of the oven as well as the materials handled. Fixed protection extends as far as necessary into the enclosure, if combustible material is processed, or if trucks or racks used are combustible, or subject to loading with excess finishing material; also if an appreciable amount of flammable drippings of finishing materials accumulates within the oven.

If desired, permanently installed, supplementary protection of an approved type such as carbon dioxide, foam, dry chemical, or halon, may be provided. Such protection is not a substitute for automatic sprinklers.

Steam smothering systems are permissible only when oven temperatures exceed 225°F and large supplies of steam are available at all times when the oven may be in operation. Complete standards paralleling those for other extinguishing agents have not been developed for the use of steam as an extinguishing agent, and until this has been done, the use of this form of protection is not as dependable or the results as certain as those qualities of water, carbon dioxide, dry chemical, halon, or foam.

Portable extinguishing equipment is needed near the oven, oven heater, and related equipment, including dip tanks or other finishing processes operated in conjunction with the oven. Small hose with combination nozzles is also provided so that all parts of the oven structure can be reached by small hose streams.

Ovens which may contain flammable gas or vapor mixtures with air are equipped with unobstructed relief vents for freely relieving internal explosion pressures. These vents are provided in the form of gravity retained panels designed to afford adequate insulation and possess the necessary structural strength. These explosion relief panels are proportioned in the ratio of their area in square feet to the explosion-containing volume of the oven, due allowance being made for openings or access doors equipped with approved explosion-relieving hardware. The preferred ratio is 1:15, i.e., 1 sq ft of relief panel area to every 15 cu ft of oven volume. For those fuel-fired ovens in which there is no flammable or explosive solvent hazard, equipped with all recommended fuel safety devices, an explosion venting ratio of 1:30, i.e., 1 sq ft of vent ratio to every 30 cu ft of oven volume is permitted.

D. Class B Industrial Furnaces

This class includes industrial furnaces operating at or above atmospheric pressure and at temperatures above 1,400°F (760°C). It does not include boiler furnaces which are described in Chapter 1 of this Section.

Class B furnaces are basically considered in much the same way as Class A ovens or furnaces. Because of the higher temperatures, there will be little, if anything, which is combustible in the construction or contents of the oven or furnace. In many of these furnaces there will be no flammable vapor hazard, and the only hazard is from the gas or oil fuel. To attain the higher temperatures, the quantity of fuel consumed will be relatively greater and there may be a corresponding increase in the fuel hazard.

In many cases, little or no effective explosion relief venting can be provided so the emphasis must be placed on explosion prevention. This means preventilation before a source of ignition is introduced into the furnace. In some cases, completely automatic purging will be required; in others, it may be partly manual. In either case, safety controls are needed to interlock the ventilation, the fuel supply, combustion air, safety shutoff valve, and flame failure devices.

With multi-burner installations, combustion safeguards with flame supervision are applied where possible and practical. In some installations, furnace design, burner design, and the rigors of the service may preclude the application of flame supervision, and a supervisory cock and gas safety control system may be provided.

The burner ignition is by a fixed gas pilot, burning continuously in furnaces operating below 1,400°F.

Some furnaces have zones operating at different temperatures, which may have to be treated as separate units.

Modification of the usual requirements may be permitted with some of these ovens or furnaces, but if there is a possibility of damaging explosions in them from unburned fuel, the need for adequate safeguards should not be disregarded. An audible alarm may be provided to indicate the development of any unsafe condition.

E. Class C Industrial Furnaces Using a Special Processing Atmosphere

Special atmosphere furnaces are used to improve the quality of metals and metal alloys by heating them in an atmosphere in which air has been replaced by other gases, some of which are combustible. In most cases, the special atmosphere gas is used to prevent oxidation of the metal during heating, but it may also be used to prevent the removal or addition of carbon. Some applications of special atmosphere gases include bright annealing of copper and steel, scale-free hardening and annealing of castings, brazing, and sintering. Examples of protective gases are hydrogen, charcoal gas, dissociated ammonia, and lithium vapor. Also commonly used are various hydrocarbon gases

produced by equipment that processes the gas used for firing, generally in the presence of a catalyst.

Some heat treating furnaces contain an inert atmosphere (carbon dioxide, helium, argon, nitrogen) and so present no special fire hazard; however, these gases could present a health hazard. It is those which have a flammable atmosphere (hydrogen, dissociated ammonia, incompletely burned hydrocarbon gas, carbon monoxide, and methane) which present an explosion hazard and require special safeguards. Atmosphere furnaces are not limited to flammable gases but can also contain acid gases, such as chlorine and anhydrous hydrochloric. When the latter types of gases are used in a special atmosphere, extreme care must be used to keep air from entering the furnace. Regardless of the type of special atmosphere, Class C furnaces have fuel hazards the same as for Class A and B ovens and furnaces explained earlier in this chapter. This present discussion covers in a general way the protection needed for the special atmosphere generator and for the heat treating enclosure.

Hazardous conditions in Class C furnaces exist chiefly before the start of the process when the flammable atmosphere is replacing air in the furnace, when the process is finished and air is being admitted, and when, for some reason, the special atmosphere supply is interrupted and air permitted to enter. If in each of those instances an inert gas could be introduced into the furnace in sufficient quantity to prevent any combustible mixture of special atmosphere and air, there would be no danger of an explosion. Automatic introduction of inert gas upon failure of the special atmosphere supply would be desirable; at the least, an audible alarm would notify the oven operator of the failure.

If the use of inert gas is not considered practical, alternate procedures are to burn out the air at the start of the process and the flammable atmosphere at the finish, or to evacuate the furnace by use of vacuum pumps or exhausters. With furnaces having an operating temperature above 1,400°F, burning may be done at the start by bringing the temperature up to 1,400°F before the special atmosphere is introduced; at this temperature the flammable gas will burn in the oven until the oxygen is used up, then the hazard is removed and operation may be started. At the end of the process, the heating should be continued so the temperature stays above 1,400°F; the flammable gas supply is then shut off and air gradually admitted; when burning stops, the flammable gas has been consumed. When the alarm indicates failure of the flammable gas supply or of the heating system, the oven operator immediately starts the admission of air to burn the flammable gas in the furnace as explained above; this is done before the furnace cools to below 1,400°F.

With furnaces operating at temperatures below 1,400°F, the general procedure is much the same except that a reliable source of ignition must be supplied to produce the burnout. At the start, after the furnace has been brought up to operating temperature, the special atmosphere is turned on and lighted at the point where it is admitted to the oven. If the furnace is almost completely closed, the appearance of flame at the slightly opened door will indicate that the air has been exhausted. When the furnace is to be shut down, the heat is continued, doors opened, flames placed at the openings, flammable gas supply shut off, and burning allowed to continue until all gas is consumed. If there is a failure of the special atmosphere supply, or of the furnace heating, an alarm indicates the failure to the operator who takes immediate action to safely burn out the flammable gas in the furnace.

Detailed instructions are posted in the immediate vicinity

of these furnaces to inform the operator concerning the various tests and checks which must be made before and during normal operations, and also what must be done in event of failure or improper functioning of the equipment.

Special Atmosphere Generators

It is important that the special atmosphere generator be provided with safety controls which will assure the safe and proper functioning of the equipment. These would normally include interlocking of raw gas, air (if needed), burners for heating or processing, feed and discharge pressures, etc. Safety shutoff valves are usually provided in feed and discharge piping, also devices to indicate the pressure or rate of flow of processed gas to the furnace, and also its analysis, if this might vary. The operator would thus be assisted in his efforts to supply the furnace with the desired special atmosphere. (See NFPA No. 86C for further information on protective equipment for gas atmosphere generators.)

The generator manufacturer's instructions are posted at the equipment and are to be followed carefully (see ANS Z83.2-1971, American National Standard for Gas Atmosphere Generators, for details regarding specifications for the operation and maintenance of generators).

The preferable location for the generator and its auxiliary equipment, such as surge tank, compressor, aftercooler, storage tank, etc., is in a separate, detached building of light, noncombustible construction.

F. Class D Vacuum Furnaces

Vacuum furnaces are used for heat treating metals; however, they are not limited to this industry. In a vacuum furnace a vacuum pump is used to displace oxygen, and in most cases, to reduce the water vapor content or dew point as well. A vacuum pump connected to a leakproof furnace can attain low dew points comparing favorably with gaseous systems implemented with efficient atmosphere-dehydration equipment.

Vacuum furnaces are usually batch-type furnaces and are further classified as hot-wall and cold-wall furnaces with the latter in greater use at the present time. In the hot-wall furnace the entire vacuum vessel is heated, usually not above 1,800°F due to the reduction in the strength of materials at elevated temperatures. However, installation of a second vacuum vessel outside of the vacuum retort (within which a roughing vacuum is maintained during the heating cycle), permits construction of larger hot-wall furnaces with higher operating temperatures.

Cold-wall furnaces contain a vacuum vessel that is water cooled, and usually the heating elements are located inside the vacuum vessel. The walls can be maintained at near ambient temperature during high temperature operations. As a result, large units operating at high temperatures (4,000 to 5,000°F) can be constructed. The two most common methods of heating cold-wall furnaces are resistance and induction, with the heating elements located within the vacuum vessel. The heating elements are usually water cooled, but there are cases where air has been used for element cooling. Insulation can be effected by radiation shields constructed of low emissivity, oxidation-resistant metals having proper vapor pressure characteristics. Refractory insulation can be used in some instances; however, this is difficult due to outgasing of entrapped air in the refractory.

Four types of pumping systems in use on both hot-wall and cold-wall furnaces are as follows:

Rotary Pumps: This type pump may be of the oil-sealed rotary cam or rotary piston type, and, when used in conjunction with oil booster or diffusion pumps, can produce vacuum pressures to 10^{-1} torr (1 torr = pressure of one millimeter of mercury at 1°C).

Mechanical Booster Pumps: This type of pump operates down to 10^{-2} torr and may be used with a rotary pump to form a pumping system.

Booster Oil Diffusion Pump: This type of pump operates in the range of 10^{-3} to 10^{-2} torr. This type pump must be "backed" by a supplementary pump.

Fractionating Oil Diffusion Pumps: This type of pump is always backed by a rotary pump, or rotary and mechanical booster combination to produce pressures below 10^{-3} torr. This type system is capable of producing pressures of about 5×10^{-7} torr.

Vacuum furnaces have the same hazards usually associated with Class B furnaces; however, the potential for more serious accidents, when they do occur, is probably greater. Some hazards other than fuel associated with vacuum furnaces are:

1. Explosions can be caused by water leaks in either heating elements or vessel jackets. Entrance of water into the furnace at temperatures at which these furnaces usually operate causes more than just a steam explosion.

2. The furnace wall can collapse due to failure of a relief valve on the water jacket.

3. Improper design of the vessel as related to strength of materials at high temperatures can cause collapse of the vacuum retort in a hot-wall furnace. If this occurs in a gas-fired unit the flame can be pulled into the vacuum pump setting fire to the oil in the pumps.

4. Vacuum pumps can pull fluids (water or oil) from hydraulic seal pots.

5. At the pressures at which this type furnace operates even metals can vaporize, and condensed metallic vapors on electrical insulators can cause short circuiting.

6. Improperly supported heat shields can sag at high temperatures and can cause short circuiting by coming in contact with heating elements.

7. Sagging of heat shields will cause hot spots on furnace walls with the resulting weakening of the furnace wall.

8. Vacumm furnaces offer problems of temperature control and over-temperature protection not found in other type furnaces and ovens. Optical pyrometers must have a line of sight to the work and their accuracy may be seriously impaired by gases, smoke, or discoloration of the sight glass.

9. Thermocouples perform differently in a vacuum from the way they perform in air. Unless the thermocouple is actually attached to the part being measured the heat transfer is based wholly on radiation. In air a thermocouple receives heat by conduction and convection; therefore, with no air (or gas) in the furnace the thermocouple response is slower than in air. A gap of as little as 0.001 in. between the thermocouple and part or surface being measured can significantly change the response time of the thermocouple. A thermocouple on the heating element could mean that the parts would not reach the desired temperatures because the heating elements must of necessity be higher than the temperature of the part (center of furnace) at least until equilibrium conditions have been reached.

10. If the furnace is induction heated, precautions must be taken to keep piping conduits, building columns, beams, etc., out of the induction field. Any one of these items in the proximity of a furnace which has not been properly electrically shielded can be heated from the induction coil inside the furnace. For instance, a steel bar placed so that

it touches the furnace and a metal floor will be heated to visible heat in a matter of minutes. Of course, this also can happen on a Class B induction furnace.

G.   After-Burner and Catalytic Combustion Systems

Fume incinerators are combustion-oxidation chambers designed for thermal destruction of process exhaust vapors or fumes. For many years fume incineration has been used to destroy objectionable exhausts from baking, drying, curing and chemical processes performed in ovens, dryers, kilns, stills and reactors.

Both direct flame and catalytic oxidation are used to reduce fumes, odors, vapors and gases to acceptable exhaust products, such as carbon dioxide and water vapor. Some process exhaust containing other than plain hydrocarbons and oxygenated species may require additional special treatment, scrubbing, and filtration for removal of most particulate materials as well as halogens, hydroxides, sulfur oxides and nitrogen oxides that may be present.

Advantages can include reduced cleaning costs, reduced equipment downtime, reduced fire and explosion hazards, compliance with local and state pollution regulations, and savings in plant heating costs. Process fuel consumption can be reduced by heat recovery from the burned exhaust fumes and the recirculating of the clean hot exhausts.

Fire and explosion experience during the past ten years has shown that installations have been damaged by fire in deposits in ducts between the process units and the incinerator, explosion of accumulated vapors in the ducts prior to or during start-up, improper operation of gas-fired incinerators and excess exhaust fuel resulting in overheating of the catalytic element or the combustion chambers. The causes were inadequate duct cleaning; inadequate duct design; lack of complete prepurge of the ducts, process unit and incinerator; failure of the operator to follow proper operating procedures; and malfunction of burner and temperature controls. Some incidents have involved a single fume incinerator serving several ovens which resulted in loss of all production in the units until repairs were completed. Production may be interrupted for extended periods when an incinerator is damaged.

After-Burner (Direct-flame) Incineration

Direct-flame fume incinerators can be applied to a wide range of organic solvent vapors, organic dusts and combustible gases. For combustion, the fumes must be heated to their autoignition temperatures and have sufficient oxygen with adequate mixing to complete the chemical reaction. Quenching of the burner flame can occur when the capacity of the burner is not sufficient or the flame pattern and mixing are inadequate. The fumes must be retained (dwell time) at the autoignition temperature to permit sufficient

time to complete the chemical reaction (the dwell time is usually 0.4 to 0.8 sec.). The sequence of steps for successful incineration is shown in Figure 4-5K.

Operating temperatures may range from 1,000°F to more than 2,000°F. Ample oxygen, more than 16 percent, is normally available for complete combustion, because the process safety ventilation requirements do not permit exceeding 25 percent of the LEL (lower explosive limit) or 50 percent of the LEL with adequate combustible gas analyzers and interlocks.

Operating temperatures of the combustion chamber are usually 1,200 to 1,500°F. Tests on some units have reported approximately 92 percent conversion efficiency to CO_2 at 1,300°F and 96 percent conversion efficiency at 1,450°F. These conversion percentages of fumes to CO_2 are frequently required by air pollution codes. In any case, for complete combustion the fumes must have sufficient air, proper mixing with the air, adequate dwell time, and adequate combustion chamber temperature.

Direct flame combustion chambers are usually heavy refractory lined with external burners, such as tunnel type burners; or light refractory, with sectional line burners or line burners with mixing plates (see Fig. 4-5L).

When metal construction is used, the design must include consideration for high thermal stresses and possible overheating of the metals. The combustion chambers and burner flames of kilns and boilers are sometimes used as fume incinerators.

Contaminated process waste streams might be inert gases with a low combustible hydrocarbon content. This mixture may be mixed with sufficient air to ensure combustion and then oxidized in a direct flame or catalytic incinerator.

Special precautions must be taken where the concentrated fumes between 25 and 100 percent of the LEL are exhausted from the process. For safety the fumes are usually diluted with air to below 50 percent LEL for transfer to the incinerator.

Concentrated combustible fumes above the lower explosion limit are normally burned in flare stacks or as fuel in various heating equipment. The latter requires special design of the burners and combustion control safeguards.

Catalytic Combustion Systems

The reduction of air pollution from furnaces has been developed in the form of catalytic combustion systems. The heaters for these systems may be direct or indirect. A catalytic heater has been defined as a heater of any construction that employs catalysts to accelerate the oxidation or combustion of fuel-air or fume-air mixtures for eventual release of heat to an oven or other process. Heaters of this type may be employed to burn a fuel gas with substantial portions of the energy being released as radiation to the processing zone. Alternately, catalytic heaters may be installed in the oven exhaust stream to release heat from

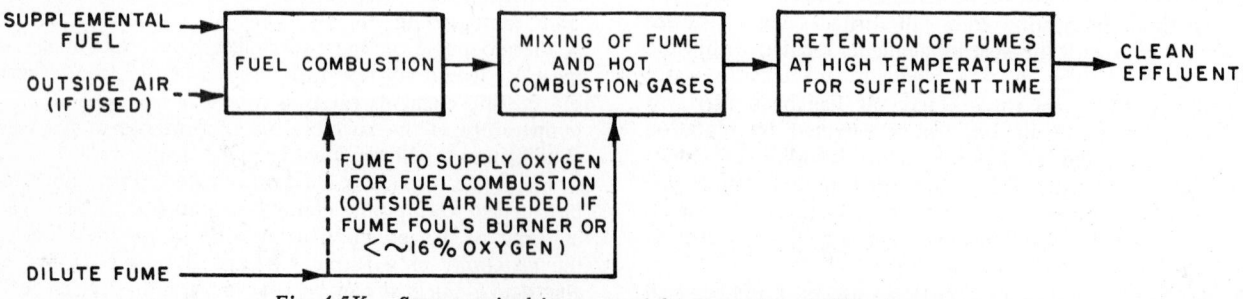

Fig. 4-5K.   Steps required for successful incineration of dilute fumes.

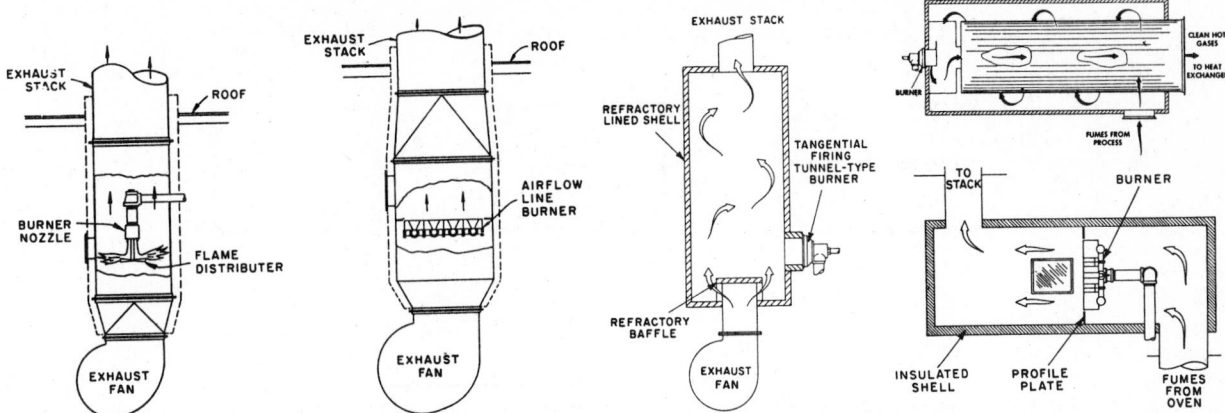

Fig. 4-5L. Typical direct flame fume incinerators. (Maxon Premix Burner Co., Inc.)

evaporated oven byproducts with available energy being returned by a heat exchanger for recirculation through the oven processing zone.

Three basic types of catalytic combustion elements are available. One is a mat of all metal construction available in various dimensions for use as a fuel-fired radiant heater or alternately for oxidation of combustible materials in fume-air mixtures. The second type consists of ceramic or porcelain construction arranged in various configurations for gas fuel or fume oxidation with catalyst media, including a variety of "rare earth" elements, platinum, or metallic salts. Both of these types are classified as "fixed bed" catalysts since they are normally held rigidly in place by clamps, cement, or other means. A third type consists of a bed, or pellets, or granules supported or retained between screens in essentially a fixed position, but with the individual members free to migrate within the bed.

Heating systems employing catalysts are finding wide applications for the conservation of oven fuel and for correction of organic and combustible type air pollution emissions (see Figs. 4-5M and 4-5N). Some limitations must be recognized because of the inability of catalytic heaters to oxidize or consume silicones, chlorine compounds, and metallic vapors as from tin, mercury, and zinc. These elements and various inorganic dusts may retard or paralyze catalysts activity. Consultation with qualified equipment manufacturers is suggested prior to installation of a catalytic system and at periodic intervals during use to assure appropriate maintenance and reliable operation.

Installation

All components of the afterburners and catalytic combustion system, related process equipment and interconnect-

ing ducts are provided with controls and safeguards to maintain safe conditions during start-up, operation and shutdown. In some installations a wide range of fume conditions might develop. The fume collection and delivery to the incinerator is a very important part of the total system. A careful complete investigation of all aspects must be made, including the appropriateness of the design and operating procedures, for the incinerator and the associated equipment (see NFPA No. 86A).

H. Heat Recovery

Heat recovery is frequently provided for economic operation of the process and fume incineration. Both heat exchangers and direct recirculation methods are used. Some plants have calculated that if heat recovery methods are applied on heat generating processes, including fume incineration, the recovered heat would be sufficient to supply a substantial portion of the entire plant demands (see Fig. 4-5O).

Recovered heat may be used for: (1) the process as its only or supplementary source of heat, (2) the process for some zones in a multi-zone unit, (3) other nearby processes, (4) preheating fumes to incinerators, (5) heating plant make-up air, and (6) a waste heat boiler serving multiple plant services.

Dirty streams may leave deposits in the heat exchanger making it inoperable. Heating of combustible deposits and flammable liquids to high temperatures within the heat exchanger could initiate a fire or explosion hazard.

I. Dehydrators and Dryers (Agricultural Products)

Dehydrators and dryers for agricultural products, commonly referred to simply as dryers, utilize heat to reduce the moisture content of the products treated. The hazards of

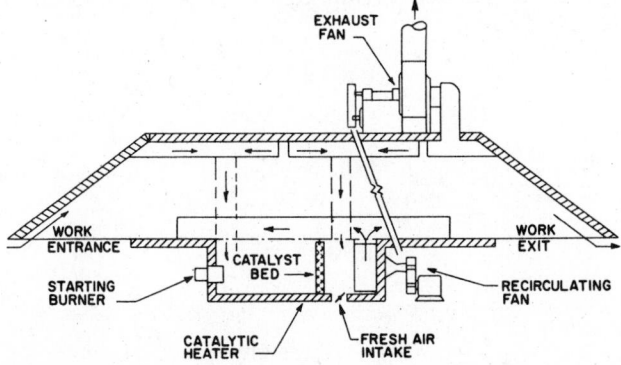

Fig. 4-5M. A direct-type catalytic oven heater for partial air pollution control.

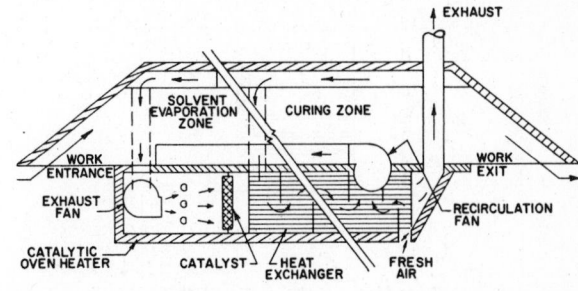

Fig. 4-5N. An indirect-type catalytic oven heater for full air pollution control.

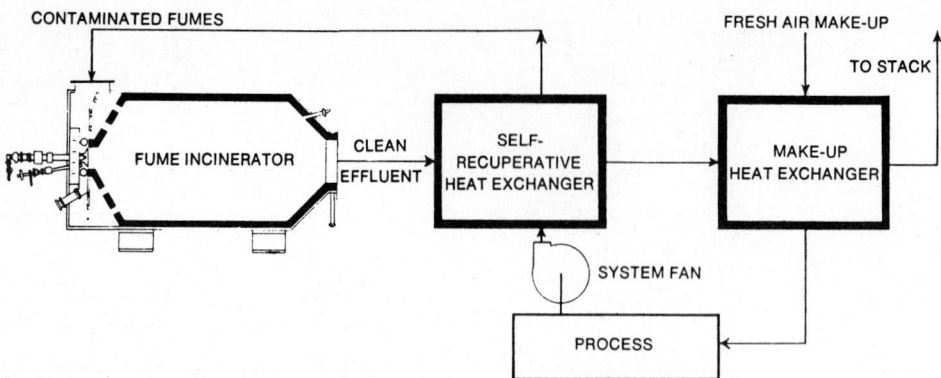

Fig. 4-5O. Typical incineration system incorporating waste heat recovery with fume and process air preheating. (Peabody Eng.)

dryers involve primarily (1) the possibility of igniting combustible materials near them, (2) the utilization of the fuel or electricity as a heat source, and (3) the ignition of stock being dried. The general recommendations for the design, installation, and utilization of these dehydrators and dryers are contained in "Construction, Installation, and Rating of Equipment for Drying Farm Crops," [1] a Standard of the American Society of Agricultural Engineers. NFPA No. 61B, Grain Elevators and Bulk Grain Handling Facilities, dealing with grain contains specific recommendations on dryers. Dryers for other products have generally the same design features of those discussed here or are designed as Class A ovens (see Part B of this Chapter).

Types of Dehydrators and Dryers

Agricultural product dryers are of three general types, depending on the arrangement and operation of the drying chamber. These are continuous, batch, and bulk dryers. Continuous dryers include:

1. Drum dryers for milk, puree, and sludges.
2. Spray dryers for milk, eggs, and soup.
3. Flash dryers for chopped forage crops.
4. Gravity dryers (may also be batch type) for small grains, beans, and seeds (see Fig. 4-5P).

5. Tunnel dryers (may also be batch type, and may be further classified according to flow of air and whether or not intermediate heating is used) for fruits, vegetables, grains, seeds, nuts, fibers, and forage crops.
6. Rotary dryers for milk, puree, and sludges.

Batch dryers (see Fig. 4-5Q) may be either fixed or portable and include pan dryers for sugar, puree, sludges, and other products.

Bulk dryers (see Fig. 4-5R), as the name implies, involve drying the product in a bin, crib, or compartment in which it is to be stored. They are used to dry seeds, grains, nuts, tobacco, hay, and forage.

Methods of Heating

Dryers used for agricultural products may be direct fired (where products of combustion contact the material being dried) or indirect fired. The heaters may be oil-fired, gas-fired, solid-fuel fired electrical, or the dryers may be heated by a heat transfer medium, such as steam. The general requirement for the installation of burners and the storage of fuel is the same as for other heat-producing devices, (see Chap. 3 of Sec. 3). Detailed recommendations are given in NFPA No. 31, Oil Burning Equipment; No. 54, National Fuel Gas Code; No. 58, Liquefied Petroleum Gases; and No. 70, National Electrical Code.

If gas-fired infrared heaters or infrared lamps are used, the focal length should be such that unsafe temperatures are not reached on the surface of the product being dried. Electrical infrared lamps are undesirable for use in dryers where they are so located that combustible dust can collect on the lamps.

Solid-fuel furnaces (other than those burning coke and anthracite coal) are not desirable where the products of combustion can enter the drying chamber. Indirect solid-fuel dryers need temperature-controlled heat-relief openings to the outside air.

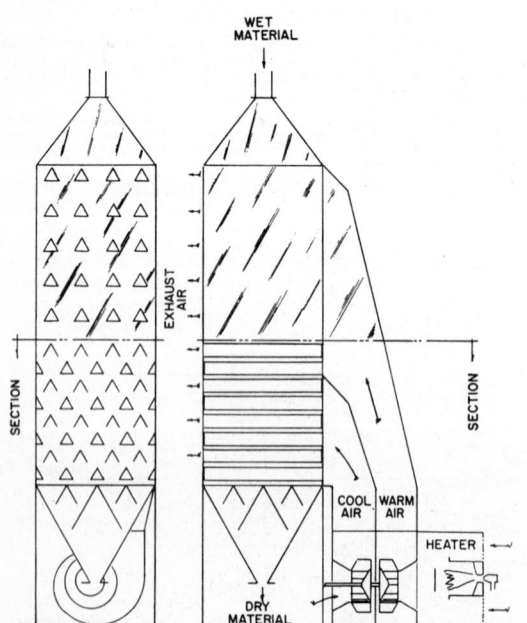

Fig. 4-5P. A continuous flow-type gravity dryer.

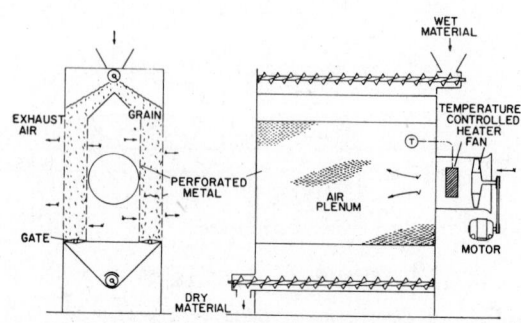

Fig. 4-5Q. A batch-type grain dryer.

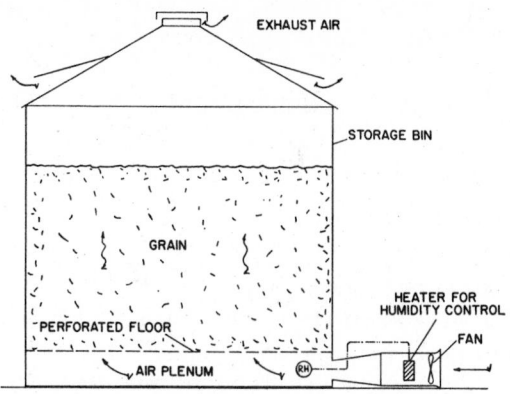

Fig. 4-5R.   A bulk-type grain dryer.

Dryer Controls: Some suggested controls for dryers, excluding those on the heating equipment, include the following:

1. A method for automatically shutting down the dryer in the event of fire or excessive temperature in the dryer.

2. In dryers where the product is fed automatically from the dryer to a storage building, a thermostat in the exhaust air which, in the event of excessive temperature, (a) shuts off heat to the dryer and stops the flow of air (except when the product being dried is in suspension), (b) stops the flow of the product through the dryer, and (c) sounds an audible alarm.

3. A thermostat in combustible dryers, or dryers with combustible trays, which, when the temperature of the combustible reaches 165°F, shuts off heat to the dryer but permits unheated air to pass through the dryer, and sounds an audible alarm.

4. A device to shut off heat to the dryer in the event air movement through the dryer is stopped.

5. A high-limit thermostat located between the heat producing device and the dryer.

Burner Controls: In general, the burner controls for dryers are the same as for other devices that are automatically fired. It is important to install a manual, quick-operating shutoff valve in the supply line of gas- and oil-fired burners, and for the controls to be arranged so that following automatic shutdown due to an unsafe condition, manual restart will be necessary. Other control safeguards include flame-failure protection, automatic shutoff on pilot extinguishment, and preventilation of the combustion chamber before start-up. All safety controls are arranged to "fail safe."

Construction and Installation of Dryers

As dryers operate at elevated temperatures, it is standard practice to construct them of fire resistive or noncombustible construction. If combustible materials must be used, they must not be located where they will be subjected to sustained temperatures in excess of about 165°F. Expansion joints are provided where necessary to prevent damage due to expansion and contraction.

Secondary air openings for direct-fired dryers are screened with ½-in. mesh screen to prevent materials from entering the combustion chamber. Primary air openings require screens not larger than ¼-in. mesh.

An ample supply of easily opened access panels is necessary for inspection, cleaning, and fire fighting.

When stock is moved through the dryers in a manner that results in the generation of static electricity, all conductive parts of the dryers are electrically bonded and grounded.

Like any heat-producing device, a dryer must have adequate clearance from nearby combustibles to prevent overheating (see Sec. 7, Chap. 3).

If there is a combustible dust hazard in the building where the dryer is located, the heating device and blowers are installed in a dust-free room or area separated from the remainder of the building.

Ducts to convey heated air to the dryer and exhaust air from the dryer to the outside are noncombustible.

Extinguishing Equipment

The most satisfactory method of protecting a dryer enclosure is by the installation of water-spray heads or automatic sprinklers within the enclosure wherever it is practicable. An exception to this is the direct-fired rotary dryer, which may be damaged by the internal application of water. A carbon dioxide system is satisfactory for protecting direct-fired rotary dryers.

For manual extinguishment of fires in and around most dryers, a standpipe hose is particularly useful. Water-type portable fire extinguishers may also be used, and for fires in heating equipment, extinguishers rated for Class B (flammable liquid) and Class C (electrical) fires are applicable.

Cooling of Dehydrated Products

Any product being dehydrated or dried requires adequate cooling before being packaged or stored. The degree of cooling required to prevent subsequent ignition will depend upon the properties of each material (whether it will heat spontaneously and subsequently ignite) and the method of packaging or storing.

J.   Lumber Kilns

Enclosures for seasoning or drying lumber by means of artificial heat can present considerable hazard. One method of heating is by steam pipes along the sides of the kiln, or in older kilns, under the kiln tracks. Sometimes steam coils, or hot air furnaces are installed in a separate chamber adjoining the kiln compartments and hot air is blown from this chamber through the lumber piles. Where low pressure steam is used with automatic controls to keep kiln compartment temperatures below 165°F, the dry air process outlined above is generally considered a low hazard occupancy. With higher temperatures, high pressure steam coils or hot

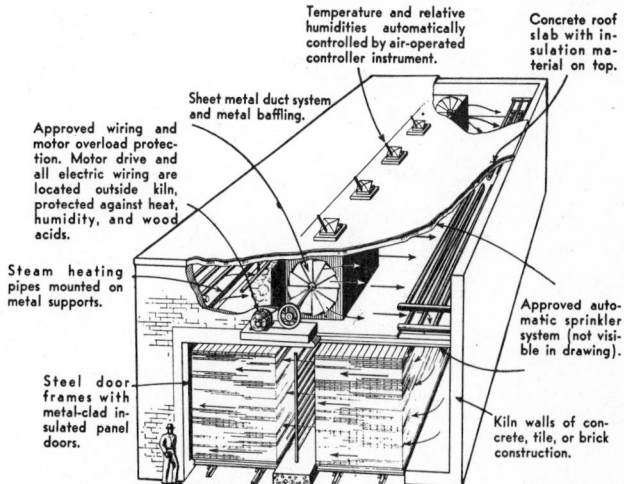

Fig. 4-5S.   A moist-air dry kiln. (Moore Dry Kiln Company)

air furnace heat, the use of dry air lumber drying rooms introduces greater hazards and has resulted in many fires.

The use of direct gas- or oil-fired kilns in which outside air is mixed directly with the hot exhaust gases of the burner and then blown through the lumber, introduces extreme hazards to dry-air lumber drying processes. Installations of this type are essentially Class A oven dryers and require all approved automatic safety devices normally required for gas- or oil-fired Class A drying ovens.

The moist air kiln for drying lumber and cut stock is much superior, both because of the reduced fire hazard and the improved quality of the product. In the moist air kiln, the high humidity and moderate temperature of the circulating air stream is carefully and automatically controlled. It is generally superior in design and construction, provides easy access for cleaning, and is usually sprinklered.

All types of dry kilns, unless of fire resistive, masonry, or heavy timber construction or are well detached from other mill buildings or lumberyards, require a complete installation of automatic sprinklers with adequate water supply. The important features of fire safety are good construction, cleanliness, reliable automatic control of humidity, air circulation, and ventilation. Proper cutoffs between kiln compartments and between kilns and other plant units, and an internal means of fire extinguishment such as automatic sprinklers are necessary. Because of the relative airtight construction and natural humidity of lumber drying, signs stating "Kiln Doors Should Be Kept Closed in the Event of Fire" are provided.

SI Units

The following conversion factors are given as a convenience in converting to SI units the English units used in this chapter.

$$1 \text{ Btu/hr} = 0.293 \text{ W}$$

$$\tfrac{5}{9} \, (°F - 32) = °C$$

$$1 \text{ cu ft} = 0.0283 \text{ m}^3$$

Bibliography

Reference Cited

[1] "Standard for Construction, Installation, and Rating of Equipment for Drying Farm Crops," The American Society of Agricultural Engineers, St. Joseph, Mich., Dec. 1962.

NFPA Codes, Standards, and Recommended Practices (see the latest *NFPA Publications and Visual Aids Catalog* for availability of current editions of the following documents)

NFPA No. 31, Standard for the Installation of Oil Burning Equipment.

NFPA No. 54, National Fuel Gas Code.

NFPA No. 58, Standard for the Storage and Handling of Liquefied Petroleum Gases.

NFPA No. 61B, Standard for the Prevention of Fire and Dust Explosions in Grain Elevators and Bulk Grain Handling Facilities.

NFPA No. 70, National Electrical Code.

NFPA No. 86A, Standard for Ovens and Furnaces: Design, Location and Equipment.

NFPA No. 86B, Standard for Industrial Furnaces: Design, Location, and Equipment.

NFPA No. 86C, Standard for Industrial Furnaces Using a Special Processing Atmosphere.

NFPA No. 325M, Fire Hazard Properties of Flammable Liquids, Gases and Volatile Solids.

Additional Readings

Crouse, Lowell F. and Wald, Donald E., "Incineration of Industrial Fumes by Direct Gas Flame," 1967 Technical Meeting–Central States Section of the Combustion Institute, Lewis Research Center (NASA), Cleveland, Ohio.

Factory Mutual Engineering Corporation, *Handbook of Industrial Loss Prevention*, 2nd ed., Chapter 37, "Process Furnaces," and Chapter 40, "Industrial Ovens and Driers," McGraw-Hill, New York, 1967, pp. 37-1—37-15 and 40-1—40-32.

Goodell, P. H., "Industrial Ovens Designed for Air Pollution Control," *Proceedings of the 52nd Annual Meeting*, Air Pollution Control Association, Pittsburgh, No. 59-37, June 1959, pp. 37-1—37-12.

Segler, C. G., ed., *Gas Engineers' Handbook*, 1st ed., The Industrial Press, New York, 1966.

Chapter 6

OIL QUENCHING AND SALT BATHS

Heat treatment of metals involves a controlled cooling or quenching of heated materials by immersion in a liquid quenching medium to achieve hardening and tempering by imparting metallurgical changes in the surface of the metal. Quenching oils may be mineral, animal, or vegetable, or mixtures of them compounded to close specifications.

Chemical salts, melted to form a liquid bath, are used in industry for immersion heating of steel and other metals to modify their physical properties for specific uses. Other important applications include heating metals for forging, forming, brazing, descaling, cleaning, and coloring. Aqueous alkaline baths, or other baths where the salts are in heated solutions, are not included in this chapter.

A. Oil Quenching

Most quench-oil tanks operate in the temperature range of 100° to 200°F, utilizing a quench-oil having a flash point above 300°F. However, quench-oils having flash points above 500°F are used for hot-oil quench tanks, which operate in the range of 200° to 400°F. Low viscosity is necessary for a uniform rate of heat transfer and for reduced oil consumption. Water and some proprietary nonflammable compounds are used in certain cases, thus reducing the hazard of the combustible quench-oil.

Quenching Methods

Quenching may be accomplished by either batch application or by a continuous conveyor system (see Fig. 4-6A). The quench-oil tank may be part of the heating furnace structure or separated from the furnace and the hot metal conveyed to the quench-oil tank. When the quench-oil tank is a part of the heating furnace, the hot metal may either be discharged from the furnace through a chute directly into the quench tank, or the tank may be totally covered, with a vestibule between the furnace and the quench tank. In the latter case, proper cycling of the doors separating the vestibule from the furnace and the quench-oil tank, respectively, is necessary to prevent ignition of the quench-oil.

In oil quenching operations, it is important that the temperature of the oil is kept well below its ignition temperature. Tanks which have a large volume of oil per unit of load quenched may be cooled adequately by agitation alone, or by recirculation of the oil. Modern installations, however, usually have a small volume of oil per unit of workload which requires cooling of the oil. Cooling may be accomplished by circulating cold water through coils submerged in the quench tank, or by circulating oil through an external heat exchanger. The latter is preferable, since in the event of a leak in the circulating system, oil would leak into the heat exchanger, whereas if a leak occurred in a water cooling coil submerged in the tank, water would enter the quench tank. In large installations having a number of quench tanks, a central cooling system and storage reservoir are provided to supply all quench tanks.

Temperature Controls: Where a heating or cooling system is used to maintain the desired working temperature, automatic temperature controls are provided. Where cooling is provided, interlocks prevent starting the feed conveyor before the cooling system and agitator or recirculating pump are in operation. On heated tanks, interlocks prevent starting the heating system until the agitator or recirculation pump is in operation. A limit switch, independent of the normal temperature controls, is set slightly higher than the normal operating temperature and at least 50°F below the ignition temperature of the oil. It is arranged so that on operation, the switch will actuate an alarm, shut down any

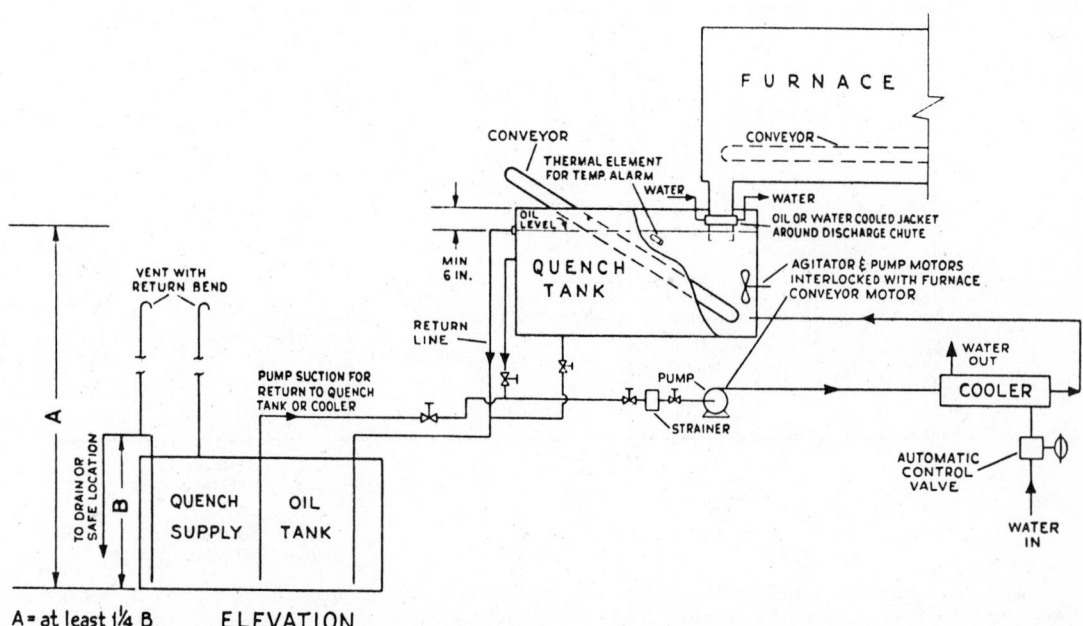

Fig. 4-6A. A schematic of a typical continuous-type oil quench tank. (Factory Mutual System)

quench-oil heating system, and, if not in operation, start up oil recirculation or agitation and the tank cooling system (see Fig. 4-6B).

Hoods and Duct Systems: These are generally installed over oil quenching operations to remove fumes and heat. Where extensive combustible occupancies, or occupancies subject to severe damage by smoke or water, are adjacent to areas containing quench-oil tanks, separation is provided by partitions having at least 1-hr fire resistance. In some cases, draft curtains and ventilation from within the curtained area is adequate.

Good housekeeping, proper maintenance, and well-trained operators are essential for safe quenching operations.

Quenching Hazards

The most common type of fire which occurs in quench-oil tanks is when red-hot work hangs up, and is only partially submerged beneath the surface, and heats the oil locally above its flash point. The fire develops slowly, and if the work can be promptly submerged or removed from the tank, the fire can be readily extinguished with portable extinguishing equipment, or sometimes by simply agitating the oil.

Fires also can occur after the main body of oil in the tank has been heated above its flash point as a result of failure of the controls or inadequate design of the tank's cooling or agitating system, by the introduction of an excessive workload, or by overtaxing the capability of the cooling system. These fires can reach full intensity within a few seconds and are difficult, if not impossible, to extinguish with portable equipment. At flash point temperatures, the oil is heated well above 212°F, so that any water discharged on the tank will turn to steam, and the tank may froth over, spreading the fire over adjacent floor areas.

Other equally serious causes of fires involving quench tanks are: (1) oil comes in contact with the hot furnace as a result of overfilling the tank, (2) splashing by the discharge from recirculation nozzles under conditions of low oil level in the tank, or (3) from steam formation brought on by water accumulating in the tank as a result of leakage from cooling coils and if the oil temperature reaches 212°F, or if the hot work penetrates the water layer. In open tanks, the formation of steam below the surface of the oil causes foaming and frothover. In enclosed tanks, pressure is built up and the oil is ejected through vents or other openings. The many ignition sources present assures ignition of the oil, resulting in intense burning over a wide area.

Fire Protection

Except for small quench-oil tanks, or those containing a nonflammable quenching medium, automatic sprinkler protection is needed over the entire area of quenching operations, including under all hoods. On open tanks, where the quench-oil is of high value, where the operation is essential to continuity of production, or where tanks are supplied from a large capacity centralized supply system, fixed automatic carbon dioxide or dry chemical extinguishing systems are provided in addition to the automatic sprinklers.

Special fixed extinguishing systems are not needed for enclosed quench tanks, since the hazard here is from the oil expelled through small openings in the tank enclosure, and the fire occurs outside of the tank where it is readily controlled by the general area sprinklers.

Portable extinguishing equipment, such as small hose with water spray nozzles, or carbon dioxide or dry chemical extinguishers, is provided to extinguish fires initiated by hot work hung up at the surface or to control fires in the areas surrounding the tank.

B. Molten Salt Bath Furnaces

A molten salt is a melt or fusion composed of one or more relatively stable chemical salts designed to form a liquid-like, inert heating medium into which the work is immersed to provide a specific treatment at the required temperature.

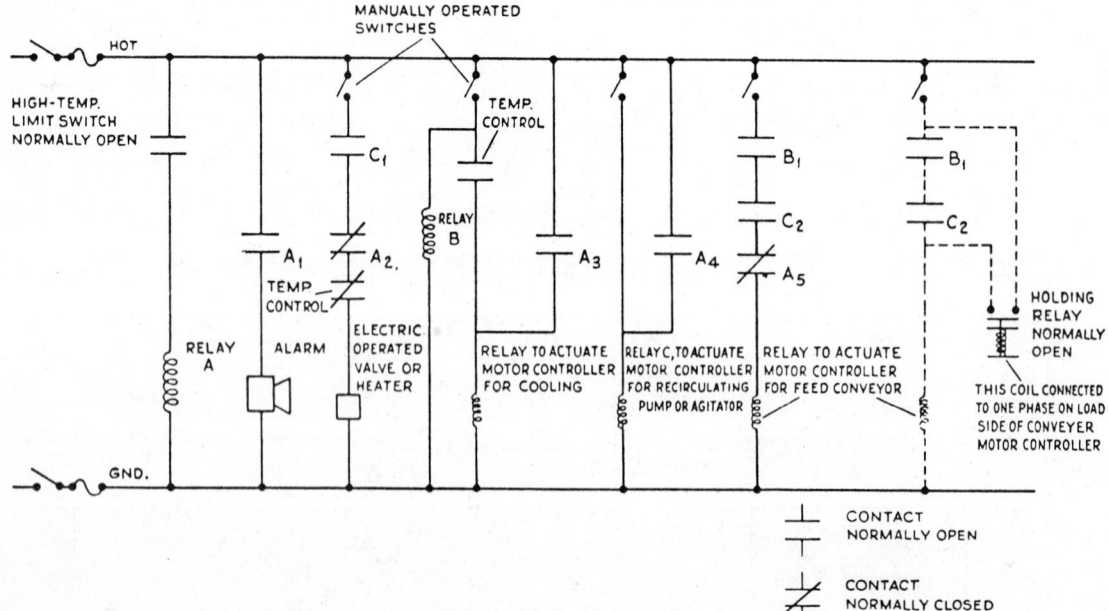

Fig. 4-6B. A schematic wiring diagram of safety controls for an oil quench tank. Contacts A_1 to A_5 and B_1 are actuated by relays A and B respectively. Contacts C_1 and C_2 are auxiliary contacts attached to and actuated by motor controller for recirculating pump or agitator. Broken lines indicate alternate wiring method for feed conveyer where automatic shutdown would damage the conveyer. (Factory Mutual System)

Types of Salt Baths

Low Temperature Salt Baths: These baths operate in the temperature range of 300° to 1,000°F. Salts used in this operation are primarily nitrates and nitrites, usually a 50-50 mixture of sodium nitrite and potassium nitrate. These salts are strong oxidizers and present the principal hazard of the molten salt bath process. Oxygen and nitrogen are evolved when these salts start to decompose at about 700°F, and they will attack the container at approximately 1,100°F. Low temperature salt baths are used for heating aluminum alloys, blueing or tempering steels, quenching of carbon and low alloy strees, cleaning of steel molds used for rubber and plastics, and polymerization of certain plastics.

Medium Temperature Salt Baths: These baths operate in the temperature range of from 1,000° to 1,750°F, and usually consist of chlorides, carbonates, and cyanides. These baths are used for normalizing, annealing and hardening of certain carbon and alloy steels, tempering, annealing of non-ferrous metals, preheating of high speed steels, carburizing, cyaniding, and brazing of metals.

High Temperature Salt Baths: These baths operate at temperatures from 1,750° to 2,400°F, and are more limited in their application. These salts consist of mixtures of barium chloride, borax, sodium fluoride, silicates, and magnesia or lime. Preheating of the work in low and medium salt bath operations is necessary before immersion into the high temperature baths. High temperature baths are used for hardening of high speed steels, heat treatment of certain high alloy steels, and brazing of copper.

Location

The preferable location for molten salt bath furnaces is in a noncombustible building. The bath is installed in a cement-lined pit or curbed area of sufficient capacity to contain the contents of the bath in the event of rupture or leakage during operation. It is important to keep the area around salt baths free of combustible materials, and located so as to prevent any liquids (water, oil, etc.) from any source from entering the tank. Vented hoods over these furnaces are necessary to exhaust excessive heat and corrosive fumes, which must be neutralized before discharging to the atmosphere.

Containers for Salt Baths

In the design and construction of molten salt bath furnaces, selection of the proper container is one of the most important factors in assuring safe operation. The materials used for construction of salt bath containers range from the low carbon steels to the more corrosion resistant, chrome-nickel-alloy steels, and ceramic materials. The required temperature and the nature of the chemical salts to be used will determine the type of material to use for the container. Low temperature nitrate baths subject steel containers to more corrosive fumes and chemicals than do containers exposed to other salts. The reaction between the salt and the container may cause scaling, resulting in uneven and local overheating.

At temperatures of operation above 500°F, salts possess a high heating potential, and also have very low viscosities and little surface tension. These characteristics make it very easy for most molten salts to make their way through any minute cracks or other flaws that may develop from improperly designed or constructed salt bath containers.

Ceramic containers are made of refractory materials consisting of silica and oxides and silicates of magnesium, calcium and aluminum, and are used only in conjunction with electrode furnaces at the higher bath temperatures.

Furnaces

Heat application to the salt bath may be by oil-fired furnaces, gas-fired furnaces (see Fig. 4-6C), electric resistance furnaces, or direct resistance electrode heaters (see Fig. 4-6D). Procedures and precautions for the safe operation of these furnaces are described in NFPA Ovens and Furnaces Standards (Nos. 86A, 86B, and 86C).

The safe design of an oil or gas-fired furnace does not permit a flame to directly impinge or bear directly upon the wall of the container.

In the operation of an electrically heated furnace, leakage of stray currents may lead to the perforation of the bath container wall by electrolytic corrosion.

Temperature Controls

Molten salt baths require accurate and reliable temperature controls to insure proper operation of the process, and to prevent fires and explosions. An adequate number of proper thermocouples must be correctly located in the bath to monitor all possible hot spots. An overtemperature control is provided, arranged to automatically shut off the heat source and actuate visual and audible alarms in the event of malfunction of the normal operating controls and the temperature exceeds the operating range. This may be supplemented by a distinctively different visual and audible alarm device to warn the operator of any excessive temperature rise, thus calling the operator's attention to an abnormal condition before the overtemperature device shuts down the furnace.

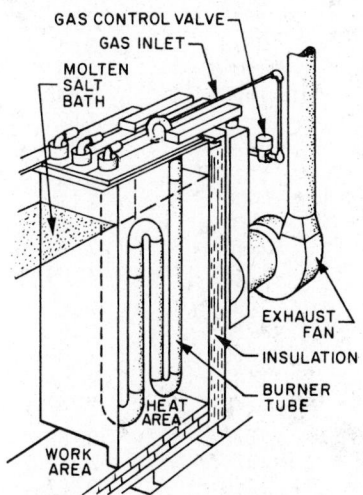

Fig. 4-6C. A typical gas-fired immersion tube heating arrangement.

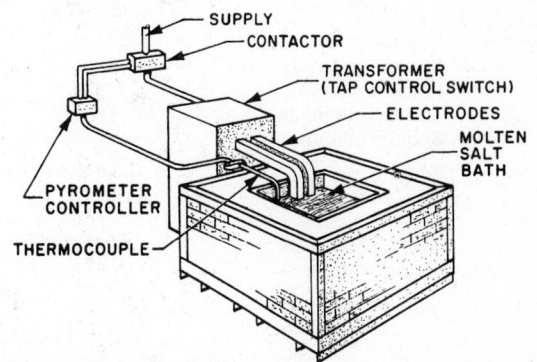

Fig. 4-6D. Typical electrode immersion-type electrical heating arrangement.

Instruments used include thermometers, thermoelectric pyrometers, radiation pyrometers, or safety fuses which melt at specific temperatures. Metal mercury thermometers are used for low temperature nitrate baths, supplemented by additional safety controls. Pyrometers are used for medium and high temperature baths. It is necessary to protect pyrometers and other instruments as much as possible from heat and corrosive fumes.

For electrically heated salt baths, the use of a step-switch power transformer provides for better control during idle periods when the bath is unattended. The heating load may be easily reduced by changing the setting to one of the lower voltage taps, thus circumventing any danger from faulty operation of thermostatic controls or relay circuits.

C.   Fire Hazards of Salt Baths

The possibility of fire is always present at molten salt bath operations. At working temperatures of from 300° to 2,400°F, any contact of the heated salts with combustible materials will result in a fire. The sudden ejection, accidental spilling, leaking from the container, popping, or spattering of the hot salts has caused major fires.

Explosions in molten salt bath furnaces have been caused by both chemical and physical reactions. Molten nitrate salts cannot be safely used at temperatures above 1,000°F, since nitrates will react with mild steel containers and start a brisk combustion process at about 1,100°F. Overheating of nitrates may be caused by poor furnace design and conditions which contribute to local hot spots, by failure of temperature controls, or by the accumulation of sludge or sediment in the bottom of salt bath containers with external heating. Magnesium alloys or aluminum alloys containing more than a small percentage of magnesium will react explosively in nitrate baths. Heated nitrates react strongly with free or chemically combined carbonaceous materials, such as oil, naphthalene, benzene, ortho-xylene, soot, tars, cotton waste, graphite, etc. Injection of water beneath the surface of molten salts will result in the instantaneous generation of steam, resulting in an explosion. Explosions have also been caused by air or moisture trapped in closed tubing or cavities in castings, or when molten nitrates and cyanides have been accidentally mixed. Intensive external reheating and remelting of a solidified salt bath may result in rapid expansion sufficient to bulge or rupture the container, or generate enough pressure to cause the sudden breakage of the salt crust and scattering of the heated salts. Properties of salts and the melting points of commonly used salt mixtures are given in Table 4-6A and 4-B.

Most injuries to personnel are burns from the molten salts. It is essential that operators be protected by heat resistant clothing, safety glasses together with a full safety face shield, heat-resistant gloves, shin guards, and heat-resistant safety shoes. Nitrates and nitrites may break down when undergoing chemical reaction with other materials, or at elevated temperatures, to form injurious gases. Since most chemical salts utilized in molten salt bath furnaces are highly corrosive and hygroscopic, absorbing water from living tissues, personnel must be careful to avoid skin contact with them at all times.

Fire Protection

Fires resulting from spillage or leaks are usually of a fast-spreading nature and difficult to control. Clean dry sand may be used for diking purposes to confine and pre-

Table 4-6A.   Properties of Salts

Salt	Melting Point °F	Melting Point °C	Boiling Point °F	Boiling Point °C	Specific Gravity (Water = 1)
Barium chloride	1764	962	2840	1560	3.856
Barium fluoride	2336	1280	2552	1400	4.828
Boric oxide (anhydride)	1071	577	2732	1500	1.85
Calcium chloride	1422	772	2912	1600	2.152
Calcium fluoride	2480	1360	4532	2500	3.180
Calcium oxide	4662	2572	5162	2815	2.62
Lithium chloride	1135	613	2480	1360	2.068
Lithium fluoride	1548	842	3038	1670	2.295
Lithium nitrate	491	255	———	———	2.38
Magnesium fluoride	2545	1118	4069	2243	3.0
Magnesium oxide	5072	2800	6512	3878	3.65
Potassium carbonate	1636	891	decomp.	decomp.	2.29
Potassium chloride	1429	776	2732	1500	1.988
Potassium cyanide	1174	634	———	———	1.52
Potassium fluoride	1616	880	2732	1500	2.48
Potassium hydroxide	716	380	2700	1316	2.044
Potassium nitrate	631	333	d 752*	d 400*	2.11
Potassium nitrite	567	297	d 662*	d 350*	1.915
Sodium carbonate	1564	851	decomp.	decomp.	2.533
Sodium chloride	1479	804	2570	1410	2.164
Sodium cyanide	1047	564	2714	1490	———
Sodium fluoride	1796	980	3092	1700	2.79
Sodium hydroxide	605	318	2534	1390	2.130
Sodium metaborate	1771	966	2610	1432	2.464
Sodium nitrate	586	308	716*	380*	2.257
Sodium nitrite	520	271	608*	320*	2.168
Sodium tetraborate	1366	741	2865	1574	2.367
Strontium chloride	1603	873	2282	1250	3.052

* Mixtures of these salts give higher boiling and decomposition temperatures than ordinarily encountered with the single salt—probably due to formation of more stable salt complexes.

Table 4-6B. Melting Points of Salt Mixtures

All mixtures are eutectics (Eutectic is that particular mixture of two or more substances which has a lower constant melting point than any other mixture of its constituents) except those marked*. Proportions given are percentage by weight.

Mixture	Melting Point	
	°F	°C
Lithium nitrate-23.3; Potassium nitrate-60.4; Sodium nitrate-16.3	250	121
Potassium nitrate-56; Sodium nitrite-44	295	146
*Potassium nitrate-51.3; Sodium nitrate-48.7	426	219
*Sodium nitrate-50; Sodium nitrite-50	430	221
Lithium chloride-45; Potassium chloride-55	666	352
Barium chloride-31; Calcium chloride-48; Sodium chloride-21	806	430
Calcium chloride-66.5; Potassium chloride-5.2; Sodium chloride-28.3	939	504
Calcium chloride-67; Sodium chloride-33	941	505
Barium chloride-48.1; Potassium chloride-30.7; Sodium chloride-21.2	1026	552
Sodium chloride-27; Strontium chloride-73	1049	565
*Potassium chloride-50; Sodium carbonate-50	1085	558
Barium chloride-35.7; Calcium chloride-50.7; Strontium chloride-13.6	1110	599
Barium chloride-50.3; Calcium chloride-49.7	1112	600
Potassium chloride-61; Potassium fluoride-39	1121	605
Sodium carbonate-56.3; Sodium chloride-43.7	1177	636
Calcium chloride-81; Potassium chloride-19	1184	640
Barium chloride-70.3; Sodium chloride-29.7	1209	654
*Potassium chloride-56; Sodium chloride-44	1220	660
Sodium chloride-72.6; Sodium fluoride-27.4	1247	675
Barium fluoride-70; Calcium fluoride-15; Magnesium fluoride-15	1454	790
Barium chloride-83; Barium fluoride-17	1551	844
Calcium fluoride-48; Magnesium fluoride-52	1738	948

vent the spread of the escaped melt. Carbon dioxide or dry powder-type extinguishers may be used to extinguish burning carbonaceous material around the immediate vicinity of the salt bath. It is important that fire fighters, who would respond in the event of fire, be invited to inspect and become thoroughly acquainted with the location and operation of the molten salt bath furnaces, and be aware of the nature of the hazards involved with the chemical salts being utilized.

Bibliography

NFPA Codes, Standards, and Recommended Practices (see the latest _NFPA Publications and Visual Aids Catalog_ for availability of current editions of the following documents)

NFPA No. 34, Standard for Dip Tanks Containing Flammable or Combustible Liquids.

NFPA No. 86A, Standard for Ovens and Furnaces: Design, Location, and Equipment.

NFPA No. 86B, Standard for Industrial Furnaces: Design, Location, and Equipment.

NFPA No. 86C, Standard for Industrial Furnaces Using a Special Processing Atmosphere.

Additional Readings

American Insurance Association, Engineering and Safety Service, "Industrial Uses of Molten Salts," Special Hazards Bulletin Z-161, Aug. 1970, American Insurance Association, New York.

Factory Mutual System, "Oil Quenching of Metals," Chapter 53, _Handbook of Industrial Loss Prevention_, 2nd ed., McGraw-Hill, New York, 1967.

Chapter 7

FINISHING AND CLEANING PROCESSES

Finishing and cleaning processes are an integral part of industrial and commercial activity. This chapter describes the various processes that are used in cleaning and finishing operations and discusses the fire hazards associated with them. It suggests measures that can be taken to reduce or eliminate the hazards that are encountered.

A. Spray Finishing

Application of paints, varnishes, lacquers, enamels, other flammable finishes, and wood bleaching liquids by the spray process is usually more hazardous than brush application because of the volume of flammable liquids used, the method of application and drying, and formation of flammable residue, which in some cases may be subject to spontaneous heating. Paint spraying even with the so-called "aerosol cans" can present a sizable hazard although the major hazard is generally associated with large-scale quantity production operations. Occasional small-scale operations and house painting by the spray process seldom figure in fire reports. NFPA No. 33, Standard for Spray Application Using Flammable Material, hereinafter referred to in this chapter as the NFPA Spray Finishing Standard covers in detail the hazards and necessary safeguards.

Spray Booths

Spray booths are made of metal or other noncombustible material. Except for certain small operations, a separate exhaust duct leading by the shortest route to outside the building is provided for each booth. Exhaust fans are of the nonsparking type or the housings for them are made of the same material as the fans. Electric fan motors are never located inside the duct or booth, but are on the outside with the fans being driven by a shaft or enclosed belt extending through the wall of the duct. Even motors of the enclosed, explosion-proof type are not suitable for use inside spray booth ducts because accumulations of residue on the outside of the motor will interfere with normal cooling of the motor. Interlocks provide a way of shutting down spraying equipment if the ventilating system stops or fails to deliver the required air flow. Good practice prohibits electric lighting fixtures or other electrical equipment in the booth or close to the face of the booth where overspray deposits may collect. Lighting may be through wired-glass or safety glass panels in the sides or top of the booth, or from lights located at a distance outside the open face of the booth. Open flames or electrical equipment that may produce sparks in the normal course of operation are not located within certain distances of the open face of the spray booth. Where there may be dangerous quantities of flammable vapors, the electrical equipment should be in conformance with NFPA No. 70, National Electrical Code. See Figures 4-7A, 4-7B and 4-7C for electrical classified areas.

Water Wash Booths: In order to minimize overspray deposits in exhaust ducts and reduce air pollution, "water wash" spray booths (see Fig. 4-7D) are frequently used. "Water wash" booths employ water spray nozzles, water curtains, or both, in such a way as to separate the excess oversprayed residue from the air which entrains it. This residue is collected in the water and carried to a tank from

which it is later removed as a sludge. In general, water wash booths require the same protection as other booths, although the hazard in the exhaust ducts is materially reduced. They do, however, require a greater air movement than the normal dry-type spray booth.

Exhaust Air Filters: Filters may be used to collect overspray and reduce air polluting solids in the air stream before it enters discharge ducts, provided certain precautions are observed. Installation and maintenance procedures are established to insure that the average air velocity over the open face of the spray booth will not become less than 100 linear fpm. Visible gages or an audible alarm or pressure-activated devices can indicate or ensure that the required air velocity is maintained.

Because most residues are highly combustible and subject to spontaneous ignition, filter pads or filter rolls when they become excessively dirty are replaced and immediately

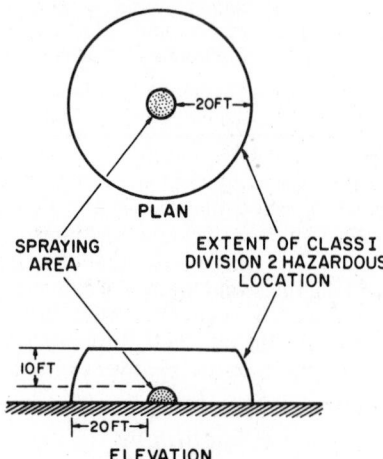

Fig. 4-7A.   Electrical classified area for spray finishing operations when the spraying is not confined to a booth or room.

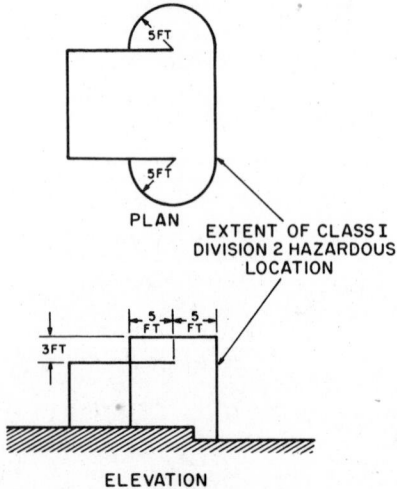

Fig. 4-7B.   Electrical classified area for a spray booth when the ventilation system is interlocked with the spraying equipment.

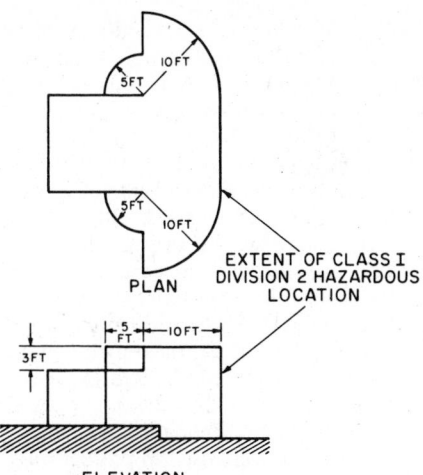

Fig. 4-7C. Electrical classified area for a spray booth when the ventilating system is not interlocked with the spraying equipment.

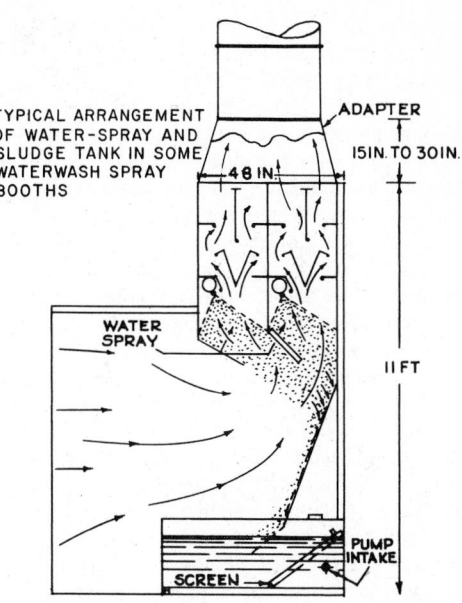

Fig. 4-7D. A water-type spray booth. In this type of booth the exhaust passes through a water spray to collect residues. This simplifies the cleaning problem.

removed to a safe, detached location or placed under water. Clean filters and rolls also help to maintain the required ventilation.

Electrostatic Spraying: This type of spraying involves maintaining a difference of electrical potential between the spray nozzle and the work being sprayed which results in the paint particles becoming electrically charged so they are attracted to the work. This process, utilizing laboratory-tested equipment, can be used both with manual and automatic operation. It introduces additional electrical hazards for which special safeguards are specified in the NFPA Spray Finishing Standard.

Spray Liquid Heaters: These preferably are of the low-pressure steam or hot water type, although they may also be of an electric type. Although less solvent is used in this type of spray paint application, the same precautions are necessary as with the conventional spray painting method. Heaters are not located in the spraying area or where residues can accumulate.

High-pressure Airless Atomization Spray Finishing: This type of spraying has the advantage of decreasing the amount of solvent needed. Since the coating material is placed under quite high pressure with this process, the hose, piping, and equipment must be designed for the pressures used and relief valves are provided to limit applied pressures to a safe value.

Powder Coating: The hazards associated with combustible dusts are present in powder coating processes to a degree depending upon the chemical composition of the material, particle size, shape and distribution. Generally, coating powders are applied by means of a fluidized bed, electrostatic fluidized bed, powder spray guns, or by a fixed or hand-held electrostatic powder spray gun. Powder coating operations are used in properly designed booths or rooms equipped with engineered ventilation systems for the powder used, and connected to a powder recovery system. Other precautionary factors, including protection against electrical hazards, are specified in the NFPA Spray Finishing Standard.

Organic Peroxides and Dual Component Coatings: These are finishing processes widely used in the reinforced plastics manufacturing industry. The plastic is normally applied to the reinforcing material by spraying automatically proportioned mixtures of a resin monomer and an organic peroxide initiator or catalyst. Spraying operations are conducted in

sprinklered spray booths and only spray guns and related handling equipment specifically manufactured for use with organic peroxides should be used. The storage, handling and use of organic peroxides should be carefully controlled and such information is contained in the NFPA Spray Finishing Standard.

Infrared Drying: Flammable coating materials can be dried by infrared heat, and if employed, it is done in such an arrangement that hot particles from a broken lamp cannot fall on overspray deposits or undried coated parts and where there is adequate ventilation to keep the atmosphere free of flammable vapors. Portable infrared apparatus may be used in automobile refinishing booths for periodic, short-duration drying operations provided necessary precautionary provisions are met. Interlocks are to be provided to prevent the spraying apparatus from operating while the drying apparatus is inside the spray enclosure. Also, the ventilation system for the booth is designed to operate to purge the booth before the drying elements are energized and, in the event of failure of the ventilation system, the drying apparatus is shut down automatically.

Bleaching Compounds: Bleaches based on hydrogen peroxide, hypochlorites, perchlorates, or other oxidizing materials require special precautions when they are applied by spraying. Deposits in contact with organic material may result in spontaneous ignition. Booths used in conjunction with the application of bleaches are confined to such work; otherwise they must be thoroughly cleaned if previously used for painting or are to be used for painting afterward.

Automobile Undercoating: Viscous rubber or asphaltic-like compounds are sprayed on to the underside of automobiles to reduce noise and deterioration. If solvents having a flash point below 100°F are used with undercoatings, the process should be safeguarded in a manner similar to that for any spraying operation involving use of flammable solvents.

Fire Hazards of Spray Finishing

Ventilation of Spraying Operations: Adequate ventilation in spraying operations is essential. In general, if sufficient ventilation is provided to prevent the formation of flammable atmospheres outside of the immediate space of spraying, residues from spraying operations will be directed to and confined to the spaces provided for their control. In a conventional cabinet-type spray booth, an air velocity of 100 to 125 fpm into the open frontal area of the booth when operating should normally be sufficient for vapor and overspray removal. Where spraying operations are extensive, additional ventilation may be required. Electrostatic spraying operations may be conducted with an air velocity over the open face of the booth of approximately 60 fpm or more, depending on the volume of the finish being applied and its flammability and explosion characteristics. Ventilation systems should be designed to restrict air turbulence as well as to eliminate "dead air pockets."

Spontaneous Heating: Some of the materials used are subject to spontaneous heating. Wiping rags and impregnated filters, when not properly disposed of, may ignite spontaneously. Certain metallic chromate pigments are especially subject to a spontaneous heating hazard.

Solvents, Vehicles, and Thinners: Paints and other coating materials are made of a great variety of substances. Linseed oil, turpentine, and mineral spirits are used in many paints; some paints use mixtures of xylol, toluol, alcohols and other solvents. Acetone and amyl acetate (banana oil) and occasionally some benzene (petroleum naphtha) are used in lacquers. Flammable paint remover usually contains benzol. The hazards associated with the use of coating material is chiefly related to the flammability of the solvent vehicle and thinner components. NFPA No. 325M, Fire Hazard Properties of Flammable Liquids, Gases and Volatile Solids, reports on the physical properties of these materials (see also Table 3-11A in this HANDBOOK).

In some instances, water emulsion japans and other nonflammable finishes or paint removers are used. These present little or no fire hazard, except some water emulsion finishes, such as pyroxylin, which leave a readily combustible residue.

Residues in Spray Booths: Many spray booth fires start in the residue from spray that is not deposited on the article being painted. Many of these residues are highly combustible, igniting at relatively low temperatures, and some will ignite spontaneously. Water-soluble materials are commonly used to coat the spray booths to facilitate cleanup by permitting the washing of the booths with pressure water streams. Where the use of water is impractical, the booth is coated with a material to prevent adherence of the spray to the walls of the booth. Where necessary, nonsparking scrapers are used to scrape the booths clean. Stacks or ducts are freed of flammable vapor and wet down before they are cleaned. Portable extension lights should not be used in booths or ducts. Good practice dictates that booths and vent pipes are well cleaned and wetted before repairs are made. Scrapings and sweepings are placed in metal receptacles and are promptly removed from the premises.

Booths used for spraying pyroxylin lacquers are not used for other purposes unless thoroughly cleaned before changing operations, as alternating deposits of pyroxylin materials with varnish, oil base stains, air drying enamels, and primers may be subject to spontaneous heating.

Spraying enclosures are not alternately used for spraying and for hot-air drying of the finished product as the latter can cause a material increase in the surface temperature of the spray booth and thus add to the spontaneous heating hazard of the residue (overspray) clinging to the interior surfaces of the booth. However, an open-flame or spark-producing drying or baking unit may be installed adjacent

to a spraying area when an interlocked ventilating system is provided. Portable infrared drying apparatus can be used in automobile refinishing spray booths or enclosures, provided that an interlocked ventilating system is provided.

Sprinkler Protection: One or more automatic sprinklers provide good protection for a spray booth. If sprinkler systems are not available, a dry chemical or carbon dioxide extinguishing system may be used. Ducts also need sprinklers. Sprinklers or other fire extinguishing system outlets in spray booths are subject to loading by paint deposits and require frequent cleaning. Sprinklers or other extinguishing system outlets are located where they are not in the direct path of spray, yet where they will provide complete protection for the interior of the booth. The space within a spray booth, both downstream and upstream of the filters, needs protection by automatic extinguishing equipment. Thin paper or comparable covers used to protect the extinguisher outlets from overspray residue accumulations, are replaced daily.

Spray Painting of Vehicles: Spray painting of automobiles and trucks in repair shops is usually conducted in a paint spray room provided with fire doors at the openings as well as an outward-swinging escape door for the use of personnel. There are also several commercial types of prefabricated metal spray booths available for use in spraying automobiles. Specially designed ventilating systems with multiple exhaust outlets may be necessary. In addition to the ventilation requirements, the usual safeguards for electrical installations, cleaning of spray residue, and sprinkler protection are given consideration in the design, operation, and maintenance of the booths.

B. Dipping Operations

Painting or other finishing which involves dipping articles or materials by passing them through flammable or combustible liquids in tanks or vats usually involves fire or explosion hazards. The severity of the hazard depends on the character and flammability of the liquids and solvents employed, particularly their rate of evaporation, and on the articles or materials processed and on the quantities present. NFPA No. 34, Standard for Dip Tanks Containing Flammable or Combustible Liquids, hereinafter referred to in this chapter as the NFPA Dip Tank Standard, sets forth requirements for safeguarding this process.

Dip Tank Operations

Dipping operations preferably are conducted in a detached sprinklered building or section of a building cut off by fire resistive construction from the remainder of the building. Avoid placing dipping operations in basements where adequate ventilation is difficult to obtain. The hazard is increased where dipping is in the same area with other industrial operations. Dipping operations in connection with baking or drying involve a special hazard (see Chap. 5 of this Section).

Floors of dipping rooms are watertight, sills of doors to other parts of the building are raised, and scuppers or drains are provided to conduct liquid to a safe place outside the building. A carbon dioxide, foam, water spray, dry chemical, or specially designed automatic sprinkler installation can provide good fire protection. Ventilating and conveyor systems are designed to stop operating in case of fire.

Ventilation: A good ventilation system is essential in all extensive dipping operations to keep solvent-air mixtures in the surrounding atmosphere below the flammable range.

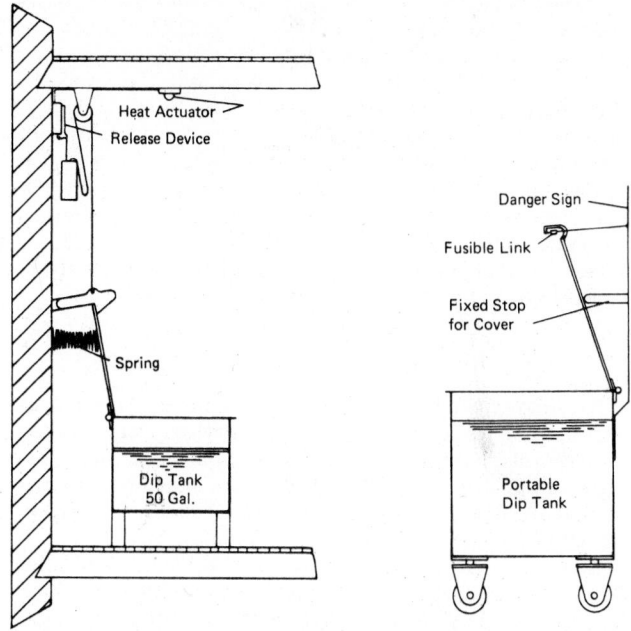

Fig. 4-7E. A typical fixed installation of a small-sized dip tank with an automatic closing cover is shown at left. A portable tank is shown at right.

The system needs interlocks to automatically stop any dipping conveyor system in the event of the failure of the ventilating fan.

Tank Covers: Small dip tanks can be protected by automatic covers. Such covers are held open by a fusible link or other thermosensitive device designed to allow the cover to close in case of fire and thus extinguish fire by cutting off the air supply. Covers are not effective where stock in process may interfere with their closing, as is usually the case where parts to be dipped are handled on a continuous conveyor system. Small dip tank installations are shown in Figure 4-7E.

Overflow Pipes: Pipes are recommended to carry off the liquid and prevent its flowing onto the floor in case water used for fire extinguishment raises the level of the flammable liquid in the tank. Automatic drains arranged to drain the contents of the tank to a safe location are another method of protecting large dip tanks.

Drain Boards: Drain boards on which surplus finish lands, as it drops from articles leaving the dip tank, are a point of hazard and should be included in the fire protection scheme for the tank.

A dip tank of large capacity is shown in Figure 4-7F.

Electrostatic Detearing

Electrostatic detearing removes excess paint from an article which has gone through a dip tank. A difference in electrical potential established between the negatively charged detearing grid and the positively grounded article removes drops of the excess paint from the article. The NFPA Dip Tank Standard sets forth requirements for ventilation and electrical hazards.

Flow, Curtain, and Roll Coat Work

In the flow coating process, enamel or other finish flows from a hose or is sprayed on the parts or material to be painted. Surplus paint is drained to a tank from which it is used again after it is filtered or clarified. A considerable area of flammable liquid surface is exposed to evaporation, thus making the provisions for ventilation of primary importance. Rooms where flow, curtain, or roll coat work is done require a good cut off from other sections of the building.

In the roll coating process, the fabric, paper, or other

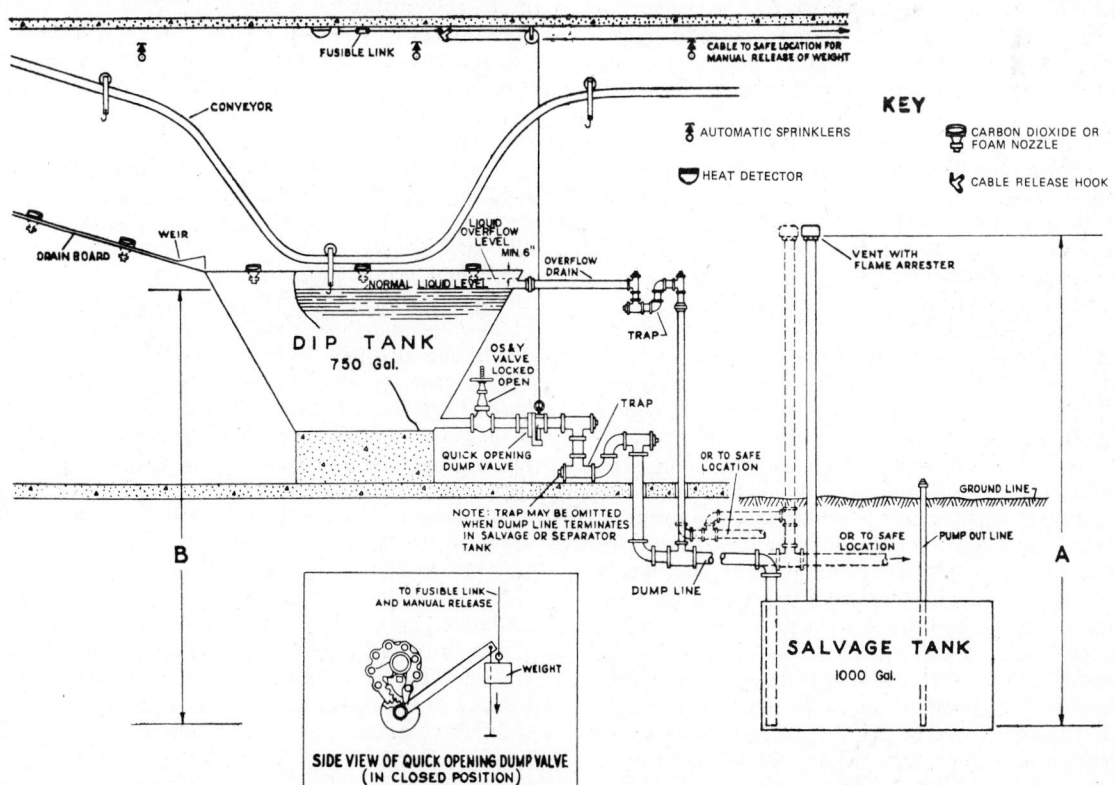

Fig. 4-7F. A typical large dip tank installation.

material is passed directly through a tank or trough containing the coating material, or over the surface of a roller that revolves partially submerged in the material. Protection from static electrical discharges is essential.

Electrical or mechanical interlocks designed to shut off pumps in the event of ventilation failure are provided together with fire protection as required for dip tanks.

C. Special Finishing Processes

Hand Painting

The principal hazards of brush painting by hand are that of spontaneous ignition of wiping rags used with linseed oil paints or other finishes subject to spontaneous heating, and the presence of open containers of readily ignitible liquids. Good housekeeping, with safe disposal of used wiping rags and other waste materials, is essential to fire prevention. The "do-it-yourselfer" usually gets into trouble when using volatile flammable liquids, because of poor ventilation of his work area and the proximity of this area to sources of ignition, such as water heaters, electrical appliances, pilot lights, etc. Except in very confined areas and where the work is concentrated, the accumulation of flammable vapors sufficiently dense to create a hazard is rare. The use of highly volatile materials, such as a flammable paint remover, is a possible exception. Nonflammable paint removers are available and their use is recommended.

Small Spraying Jobs: Small "touch up" spraying (automobile fenders, furniture damages in shipment, etc.) by hand is less hazardous than quantity production spraying. However, this type of work should be conducted only with laboratory-tested equipment in areas where there is ample space, adequate ventilation, no open-flame or spark-producing devices, and suitable fire protection.

Silk Screen Process Printing

In silk screen process printing, inks, paints, or lacquers are squeezed through selected openings in a very fine silk screen to apply a patterned layer of paint on the surface of paper, glass, wood, plastic, metal, textile, leather, etc., underlying the screen. The use of flammable liquids, paints, inks, solvents, and thinners creates a fire and explosion hazard. The principal hazard is in the cleaning of screens. Severity of the hazard depends on the flammability of materials employed.

Generally, processing, printing, and drying equipment are located in a suitable fire resistive room cut off from the rest of the building. The room and equipment must be adequately ventilated and protected by an automatic extinguishing system. If artificial drying is employed, equipment of the electrical or gas-fired type must be of a type suitable for the atmosphere (see Chapter 5 of this Section).

Cleaning of silk screens requires flammable solvents and thinners. Dip tanks or special spray-type cleaning equipment is best located outside of the building or in a special fire resistive room cut off from the rest of the building. The cleaning room must be equipped with an automatic extinguishing system, have adequate ventilation, and properly drained floors. Spray-type cleaning operations should be protected by a special extinguishing system specifically designed for such risks. Underground tanks provide good storage and recovery facilities for flammable liquids used in the silk screen cleaning process.

Bond and ground all equipment against static electricity. Provide metal containers for rags and with appropriate signs restrict smoking and open flame to designated areas. Flammable liquid storage, dispensing, and mixing should be as specified in NFPA No. 30, Flammable and Combustible Liquids Code.

Miscellaneous: There are no requirements covering outdoor spray finishing applications for buildings, tanks, or similar structures nor for small portable spraying apparatus not used repeatedly in the same location. However, the fundamental safeguards pertaining to cleanliness, care of flammable liquids, dangerous vapor-air or powder-air mixtures, and sources of ignition are observed.

The spray application of noncombustible finishing materials presents no hazard unless, as in some materials, the water-type finish may leave combustible residues. In such cases, the hazards of the combustible residues must be considered.

D. Dry Cleaning of Textiles and Furs

The dry cleaning process usually entails a three-cycle operation of washing, extracting, and drying. Depending on the type of equipment and solvents used, these steps may be accomplished separately in different machines or may be contained all within one machine. The single machine reduces time and handling to a minimum.

The wash cycle consists of the introduction of the material to be cleaned into a tumbler containing the dry cleaning solvent. The material is agitated or tumbled in the machine for a fixed period of time at the end of which it is introduced into the extracting cycle. This may be done either by manually removing the material from the tumbler and placing it in an extractor or by a combination type machine which automatically goes into the extraction cycle.

In the extraction cycle, the solvent is spun out of the cleaned material, drained into either a storage tank for subsequent filtration and reclamation or directly into a filtration system and then to a storage tank.

After extracting the solvent, the material is dried either by removing it from the extractor and placing it in a dryer or by the automatic machine going into the drying cycle. If the solvent used is a petroleum base type, the drying is accomplished by steam or other indirectly applied heating method. Processes involving halogenated hydrocarbon base solvents (e.g., perchlorethylene or Fluorocarbon 113 (trichlorotrifluoroethane)) usually use electric heat to dry the material.

Older petroleum base solvent equipment usually requires separate machines and manual handling of the material for each cycle of the process. Newer equipment, however, usually combines the washing and extraction cycles and reduces the handling time and amount of equipment required. Perchlorethylene or trichlorethylene equipment usually consists of a single machine and involves a "dry-to-dry" process combining all three cycles within the machine.

Dry cleaning establishments may use either petroleum base or chlorinated hydrocarbon base equipment exclusively or in combination, depending on the individual operator's needs. The class and type of solvent, as well as the equipment used, is the determing factor in building construction and location. Usually petroleum base solvent operations are subjected to stricter building and zoning requirements. The less restrictive regulations usually are in effect with the chlorinated hydrocarbon equipment when it is used exclusively.

The principal hazards involved in dry cleaning operations consist of the flammability of petroleum base solvents or the toxicity of the chlorinated hydrocarbon solvents.

NFPA No. 32, Standard for Dry Cleaning Plants, hereinafter referred to in this chapter as the NFPA Dry Cleaning Standard, divides dry cleaning plants or systems into categories of hazard, depending on the flammability of the solvent used. It does not deal with the toxicity of the chlorinated hydrocarbon solvents. The six classes are:

Class I Plants: These use a solvent having a flash point below 100°F (37.8°C). They are now prohibited by the NFPA Dry Cleaning Standard.

Class II Plants: These use a solvent having a flash point at or above 100°F (37.8°C) and below 140°F (60°C). They have quite restrictive requirements including being in a separate building with an approved automatic sprinkler system.

Class IIIA Plants: These use what is commonly called "140°F" flash point solvent (minimum flash point 138.2°F) but does permit the use of other solvents with flash points below 200°F (93.4°C). This class of plant can be located in buildings with other occupancies if suitably cut off and equipped with an automatic sprinkler system.

Class IIIB Plants: These use solvents with flash points at or above 200°F (93.4°C) and are used for cleaning and treating materials such as dust mops. They can be located in buildings with other occupancies provided they are suitably cut off from the other occupancies in the same building.

Class IV Plants: These use solvents classed as nonflammable or only moderately flammable at elevated temperatures. Class IV plants are those where the dry cleaning is not conducted by the public nor in coin-operated equipment and can be in buildings with other occupancies.

Class V Plants: These use solvents classed as nonflammable or only moderately flammable at elevated temperatures. They differ from the Class IV plants in that they are coin-operated, self service dry cleaning stores in which the dry cleaning is conducted by the public.

Static electricity, sparking from metal objects, or ignition of matches left in clothing are a hazard in dry cleaning operations using flammable liquids because of movement of the material within the machinery. Spotting operations using small containers of flammable liquids also present a moderate hazard.

The safeguards recommended to overcome these hazards as listed in the NFPA Dry Cleaning Standard are: (1) grounding and bonding equipment to eliminate the static electricity hazard; (2) searching of clothing to remove objects which could cause sparking or a source of ignition; (3) good housekeeping and proper storage of small containers of flammable liquids used for spotting; (4) control of flammable solvents by specifying methods and equipment to be used, and by limiting the amount and method of storage; (5) describing operating requirements for plant personnel; and (6) provision of automatic fire extinguishing systems for washers and dryers in Class II plants and portable fire extinguishers for all dry cleaning plants.

The toxicity hazard of halogenated hydrocarbon solvents is usually limited by requiring fluid-tight systems; mechanical ventilation, and enclosure of rooms where toxic vapors are present and by restricting the amount of exposure to vapors by plant personnel. Fire fighting personnel should use protective clothing and self-contained breathing apparatus during operations in buildings which contain halogenated hydrocarbon solvents.

Fur Cleaning: The cleaning of furs is covered in Part B of NFPA No. 81, Standard for Fur Storage, Fumigation, and Cleaning. Fur cleaning operations utilize "The Furriers Method" which is a process to remove stains from fur garments by using wood sawdust, ground nutshells, ground corn, or similar absorbing mediums with or without the addition of a cleaning liquid, without immersing the garment. The cleaning liquid, where used, may be flammable or nonflammable. The furs to be cleaned are placed in a rotating drum together with the absorbing medium and cleaning solvent, if used.

Plants using cleaning solvents on furs are classified in accordance with the solvent used, the same as in the NFPA Dry Cleaning Standard i.e., Class II, Class III, or Class IV. Additionally, however, there is a potential dust explosion hazard created by the absorbing medium.

E. Parts and Materials Cleaning (Degreasing)

The products of many manufacturing processes require some type of cleaning prior to final finishing or packaging. This cleaning can be done in many different ways using any number of combinations of cleaning agents, or by the use of electrical, chemical, ultrasonic, or mechanical energies.

Design of large-scale cleaning operations having critical criteria for removal of excess parent material and other residue, drying times, and prevention of pitting generally require special engineering assistance, including fire protection engineering. In conjunction with the engineering, the services of an industrial hygienist or other trained specialist may be needed to properly consider the physiological problems. Particular care is given to the moral and legal responsibilities of recommending a physiologically harmful agent in an effort to obtain a fire-safe method. For cleaning of small tanks and containers see Section 3, Chapter 3.

Solvent Cleaning

Solvents may be classed as nonflammable solvents, flammable solvents, and emulsifiable cleaners. Nonflammable solvents are safest from the fire and explosion hazard standpoint. Methylene chloride, chloroform, perchlorethylene, trichloroethane, and trichlorethylene are examples of nonflammable or practically nonflammable solvents. The vapors of all volatile solvents, both flammable and nonflammable, are toxic to some degree and should be used only in well-ventilated areas and under conditions where the operator need not come in contact with the liquid. Volatile flammable liquids such as gasoline, benzol, toluol, etc., create a severe fire and explosion hazard. Solvents with a flash point above 100°F, sold under various trade names, are less hazardous.

An emulsifiable cleaner consists essentially of an emulsifying agent dissolved in a solvent. The hazard of an emulsifiable cleaner is determined by the flammability and toxicity of the solvent.

Precautions must be observed in the evaporation of nonflammable solvents containing a mixture of flammable and nonflammable liquids. The danger period is usually during the last 10 percent of solvent to be evaporated.

The cleaning of parts in dip tanks with flammable or combustible liquids should conform to the NFPA Dip Tank Standard. Equipment used for cleaning small parts is shown in Figure 4-7G.

Fig. 4-7G. Typical small parts cleaning equipment.

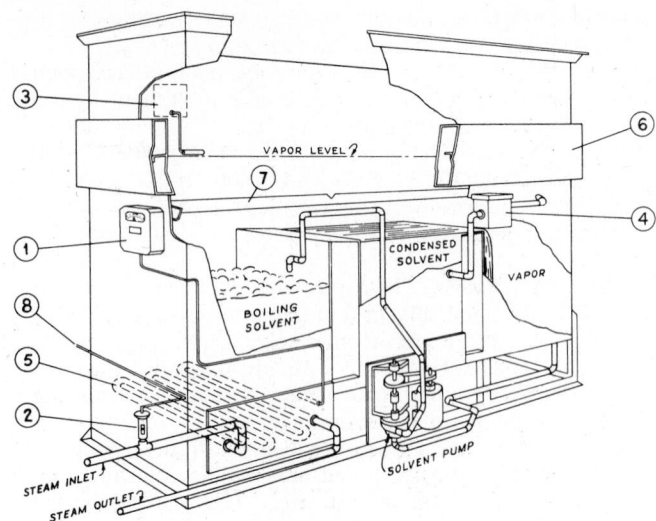

Fig. 4-7H. A vapor degreaser of the three chamber type showing safety controls and essential operating features. Heat to vaporize the liquid solvent is supplied by steam coils (or gas burners or electric immersion heaters). Cooling water is circulated through a jacket or coils. The enclosure is filled with vapor up to the point where it is condensed by the water jacket. Objects to be cleaned are suspended in the vapor space, and the solvent, as it condenses on them, dissolves grease and dirt and carries them with it as it falls to the bottom of the tank. Shown are: (1) temperature limit control for the liquid chamber to shut off heat at 200°F with trichlorethylene or 265°F with perchlorethylene; (2) steam shutoff valve with manual reset; (3) temperature limit control for the space directly above the vapor level to shut off heat at 180°F with trichlorethylene or 240°F with perchlorethylene; (4) water separator; (5) steam coils; (6) water jacket or cooling coils; (7) condensate trough; and (8) control air. (Factory Mutual System)

Vapor Degreasing

Vapor degreasing is widely used for cleaning oil and greasy dirt from metal objects. The solvents used are usually trichloroethane, trichlorethylene and to a lesser extent perchlorethylene. These are good solvents for grease and are practically nonflammable, but they are somewhat toxic. Generally the material is heated. Adequate controls for temperature, ventilation, and vapor recovery are desirable. To accelerate some cleaning processes, mechanical agitation is used by movement of the parts basket or by injection of air or by a solvent pump or occasionally by ultrasonic energy above the audible range of 20,000 cycles per second. A vapor degreaser is shown in Figure 4-7H.

Degreasing of wool, etc., with naphtha should be done only in one-story buildings, observing the usual safeguards for flammable liquid hazards.

Spray Cleaning

Spray cleaning using heated combustible solvents in the flammable range of kerosine should have suitable temperature controls to keep the solvent well below its flash point. One method is an automatic system with a conveyor or belt. This could include a detergent wash or drying process in the enclosed cabinet, thus insuring that the material being cleaned will leave the cabinet vapor free. The cabinet should have a fire extinguishing system as well as a vapor recovery and solvent filtering system (see Fig. 4-7I).

Miscellaneous Cleaning Processes

Chemical Cleaning: In acid cleaning processes, a hot, diluted solution of sulfuric, nitric, or hydrochloric acid is commonly used, followed by successive hot alkaline and water rinses. Phosphoric acid cleaners, which are milder, are sometimes used for the same purpose. Alkaline cleaners in water solution, such as caustic soda, trisodium phosphate, sodium metasilicate, or sodium sesquisilicate, are quite widely used. These are economical and present no fire hazard, although great care must be taken to prevent personal injuries from handling caustic solutions.

Electro Cleaning: A clean surface suitable for electroplating is accomplished by passing a low voltage current (6 to 12 V) through an alkaline solution in which material to be cleaned is immersed. The material serves as one electrode and the tank as the other. However, to minimize the short circuit hazard, separate electrodes are preferable.

Mechanical Cleaning: Widely used mechanical cleaning processes include blast cleaning, tumbling, and wire brushing. In blast cleaning, the material to be cleaned is placed in a metal enclosure lined with rubber or wood and a jet of abrasive grit or shot is impinged on the material.

Heat Cleaning: Heat is used to burn off oil deposits or to loosen rust or scale from metal parts in some operations. The heat may be supplied by a torch or an oven or in some cases the work may be immersed in molten salts (see Chap. 6 of this Section).

SI Units

The following conversion factors are given as a conve-

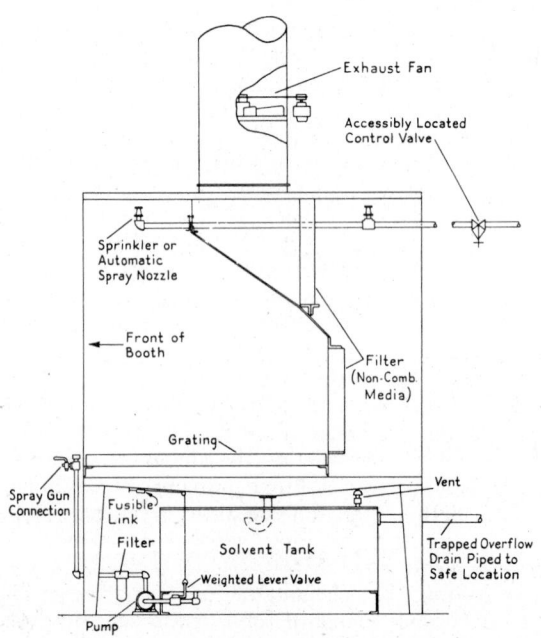

Fig. 4-7I. A well-arranged spray-cleaning booth. Note that the booth itself is sprinklered and that the solvent tank is vented and equipped with an overflow pipe. The vent should be equipped with a flame arrester if the solvent has a flash point below 110°F or if the vent is exposed to combustibles. Preferably the vent should be piped outdoors to a safe location.

nience in converting to SI units the English units used in this chapter.

$$1 \text{ cps} = 1 \text{ Hz}$$
$$1 \text{ ft} = 0.305 \text{ m}$$
$$\tfrac{5}{9}(°\text{F}-32) = °\text{C}$$

Bibliography

NFPA Codes, Standards, and Recommended Practices (see the latest *NFPA Publications and Visual Aids Catalog* for availability of current editions of the following documents)

NFPA No. 30, Flammable and Combustible Liquids Code.
NFPA No. 32, Standard for Dry Cleaning Plants.
NFPA No. 33, Standard for Spray Application Using Flammable and Combustible Materials.

NFPA No. 34, Standard for Dip Tanks Containing Flammable or Combustible Liquids.
NFPA No. 70, National Electrical Code.
NFPA No. 81, Standard for Fur Storage, Fumigation and Cleaning.
NFPA No. 325M, Fire Hazard Properties of Flammable Liquids, Gases and Volatile Solids.
NFPA No. 327, Standard Procedures for Cleaning or Safeguarding Small Tanks and Containers.

Additional Readings

Factory Mutual System, "Dip Tanks," *Handbook of Industrial Loss Prevention*, 2nd ed., McGraw-Hill, New York, 1967, pp. 51-1–51-8.
— "Dry Cleaning with Flammable Solvents," *ibid*, pp. 59-1–59-4.
— "Metal Cleaning," *ibid*, pp. 54-1–54-6.
— "Spray Application of Flammable Materials," *ibid*, pp. 52-1–52-11.
"Printing Plants," Loss Prevention Data Sheet 7-96, 1970, Factory Mutual System, Norwood, Mass.

Chapter 8

WELDING AND CUTTING

Welding and cutting of metals is accomplished by using one of two energy sources—gas or electricity. This chapter describes welding and cutting systems, the hazards associated with them, and the precautions to observe to reduce or eliminate the hazards.

A. Gas Welding and Cutting

Oxygen and acetylene, combined and burned in a suitable torch, produce a flame so intensely hot (about 6,000°F) that it can melt and fuse any of the commercially used metals. With the oxyacetylene flame and a supplementary jet of oxygen, steel sections can be cut or shaped. Hydrogen, natural gas, LP-Gases, and other fuel gases and fuel gas mixtures are used as well as acetylene; the hazards are similar, and the precautions similar irrespective of the kind of fuel gas used (see Sec. 3, Chap. 4).

Gas fusion welding is accomplished by bringing two pieces of metal together and melting the edges in contact. In most cases, additional weld metal is introduced to the joint by means of a welding rod.

In cases when it is not desirable to melt the metal being joined, it is possible to produce sound joints by means of braze welding. This is accomplished by heating the edges of the joint to a dull red heat and applying molten bronze from a welding rod which, at this temperature, will unite with the base metal to form a strong bond. A braze-welded joint is comparable to a fusion weld in many respects. Because braze welding can be done at a lower temperature, it is usually faster and more readily accomplished than fusion welding. Braze welding cannot be used where the weld will be subjected to temperatures above 500°F, nor where the weld must match the color of the parent metal.

Gas Cutting

In gas cutting, the metal is raised to the ignition temperature, and a jet of high-purity oxygen is directed at the heated area. This results in rapid oxidation of the metal in the path of the oxygen stream. Formation of the metal oxide produces heat, which tends to melt the material adjacent to the reaction zone. The combination of oxidation, melting and erosion, together with the movement of heat source and oxygen stream in a predetermined direction, removes the material in the path of the oxygen jet. The development of powder cutting, involving the introduction of a metallic or nonmetallic powder into the cutting oxygen stream, permits the cutting of most nonferrous metals.

A variation of the cutting process is known as gouging. By means of a standard cutting torch equipped with a special nozzle designed to deliver a relatively large jet of oxygen at low velocity, a groove can be gouged out of the surface of the metal.

In addition to hand-cutting operations, various types of machines are used to carry and guide special cutting torches. The most widely used type consists of a small portable carriage, electrically driven, which is provided with the means of controlling the rate, direction, and speed of travel. This type of machine is suitable for straight-line cutting, and by means of a radius rod a wide range of circles can be cut.

Shape-cutting machines are widely used for cutting steel plate or sheet to any desired shape. These machines differ from the straight-line type in that one or more cutting torches can be moved along any predetermined path by means of a motor-driven template tracer.

Oxygen-fuel Gas Apparatus

In its simplest form, an oxygen-fuel gas welding and cutting outfit consists of a cylinder of oxygen, a cylinder of fuel gas, two regulators, two lengths of hose, and a welding torch supplemented either by a cutting attachment or a separate cutting torch.

Cylinders are always supported in such a way that they cannot be accidentally knocked over.

Welding torches have a handle with inlet connections at one end for each gas. Each inlet has a valve that controls the volume or quantity of oxygen or of oxygen-fuel gas passing through. By means of these valves, the desired proportions of oxygen and oxygen-fuel gas are allowed to flow into the torch where they are thoroughly mixed before issuing from the torch at the tip or nozzle. Cutting blowpipes are designed to provide both a stream of pure oxygen that does the actual cutting and smaller oxygen-fuel gas flames. These smaller flames preheat the metal to ignition temperature and also supply the additional heat necessary so that cutting will progress as a continuous operation. In the cutting torch, the oxygen-fuel gas flames are produced at a series of openings at the blowpipe nozzle tip surrounding a larger central orifice through which the cutting oxygen passes.

Regulators, Hose, and Protection Equipment: In using oxygen and fuel gas from cylinders, the cylinders are equipped with regulators to reduce the cylinder pressure to the lower working pressure required at the torch and to maintain the working pressure constant during operation of the equipment. Equipment connections are designed to prevent intermixing of gases, except in the torch. Regulators must be handled with care.

Piping protective equipment prevents (1) backflow of oxygen into the fuel gas supply system, (2) passage of a flash back into the fuel gas supply system, and (3) excessive back pressure of oxygen in the fuel gas supply system. The three functions may be combined in one device or may be provided by separate devices.

With most types of regulators incorrect connection cannot be made because the threads on the oxygen cylinder valve and regulator connection are right-handed, while those on the fuel gas cylinder valve and regulator are left-handed.

Use only standard welding hose for oxygen-fuel gas cutting and welding operations; not ordinary pneumatic hose or hose fittings. Oxygen hose is usually green, fuel gas hose is red, and inert gas or air hose is black. Only standard hose connections of the correct size are used for attaching hose to torches and regulators. It is very important that these connections be tight. No white lead, grease, or pipe-fitting compound of any kind are used in making up connections. Hose is so placed that it will not be trampled on, run over, or exposed to flying sparks, hot slag, and hot objects. Avoid contact with oil or grease. Repair leaks in hose immediately by cutting out the leaking part and inserting a splice. Never attempt repairs with tape. See NFPA

No. 51, Oxygen-Fuel Gas Systems for welding and cutting, for further information on hose and hose connections used in welding.

B.   Electric Arc and Resistance Welding

Arc welding may be classified by the type of electrode, i.e., carbon or metal. Welding with these electrodes, shielded or unshielded, provides further identification of the welding processes. Arc welding processes commonly used are: shielded carbon arc, gas-shielded carbon arc, unshielded carbon arc, twin carbon arc, bare-metal arc, shielded metal arc, gas metal arc, gas tungsten arc, submerged arc, atomic-hydrogen, and stud, both shielded and unshielded. In these processes, an arc is maintained between an electrode and the work, or another electrode. Direct current is required with shielded and unshielded carbon arc welding, inert-gas carbon arc welding, bare-metal arc welding, and stud welding; alternating current is necessary for atomic-hydrogen welding; either direct or alternating current may be used with the other processes.

In resistance welding, coalescence is produced by the heat obtained from the resistance offered by the work to the flow of electric current in the circuit of which the work is a part, and by the application of pressure. Specific processes include spot welding, seam welding, projection welding, upset welding, and flash welding. The resistance of the welding circuit is at the maximum at the interface of the parts to be joined, and the heat generated there must be of value high enough to cause localized fusion. There is an exception to this principle in flash butt welding where a portion of the heat is derived from the flashing and combustion of the metal at the interface. Electrodes are of copper alloyed with such metals as molybdenum and tungsten, which have high electrical conductivity, good thermal conductivity, and sufficient mechanical strength to withstand the high pressures to which they are subjected. The electrodes should be water cooled. The resistance at the surfaces of contact between the work and the electrodes must be kept low. This is normally accomplished by using smooth, clean work surfaces and a high electrode pressure.

NFPA No. 70, National Electrical Code (NEC), covers electric arc welding, resistance welding apparatus, and other similar welding equipment that is connected to an electrical supply system. The NEC provisions cover the ampacity of supply conformer arc welders, and the nameplate marking of transformer arc welders and resistance welders. The NEC requires a switch or circuit-breaker by which each welder and its control equipment can be isolated from the supply circuit and that the current rating of this disconnecting means is not less than the supply conductor rating.

Storage of Oxygen Cylinders

Oxygen cylinders should be stored away from readily combustible material. Inside buildings, oxygen cylinders either should be stored well away from acetylene or other fuel gas cylinders or separated from them by fire resistive

Fig. 4-8A.   How fires start from sparks. Note the burning pile of combustible material at right just at what appears to be the outer limit of the reach of the sparks.

partitions. Storage areas should be well ventilated.

If the temperature gets too high, the safety device on an oxygen cylinder is likely to release the entire contents of the cylinder. Therefore, oxygen cylinders should not be left or stored in any place where they may be overheated. Where cylinders are stored in the open, they should be protected from accumulations of ice and snow and from the direct rays of the sun in localities where extreme temperatures may be encountered.

Metal Spraying

Metal spraying or "metallizing" is a process where various metals are melted by the heat of an oxygen-fuel gas flame and sprayed on a surface to be coated. The precautions previously outlined for oxygen-fuel gas cutting and welding operations generally apply to this process.

C.   Fire Prevention in Welding and Cutting Operations

Fire hazards may occur in the use of all methods of welding, both gas and electric arc, and in flame cutting. Fires rarely occur where equipment is set up for production work, either in welding or cutting, because reasonable safeguards can be built into the setup. The majority of fires occur from the use of portable equipment, many times in the hands of outside contractors doing a specific repair or alteration job, or in the hands of a plant repair crew which does not come under the supervision of the foreman in charge of the part of the plant where the work is to be done. Approximately 6 percent of all industrial fires are ignited in this manner.

Both welding and cutting operations produce dangerous sparks; those from cutting are more hazardous because they are more numerous and are carried greater distances. Most fires start from drops or globules of hot slag or burning metal, which have sufficient mass to retain their heat for an appreciable time. Smoldering fires may be started which are not apparent when the work is completed and later burst into flame when no one is present. Sparks, as well as flames, in the presence of flammable liquids or vapors may start fires or explosions immediately. Figures 4-8A and 4-8B illustrate the dangers that welding sparks can present.

Fig. 4-8B.   Excessive pressure of the cutting oxygen can cause sparks to fly and bounce over wider areas. It also wastes oxygen.

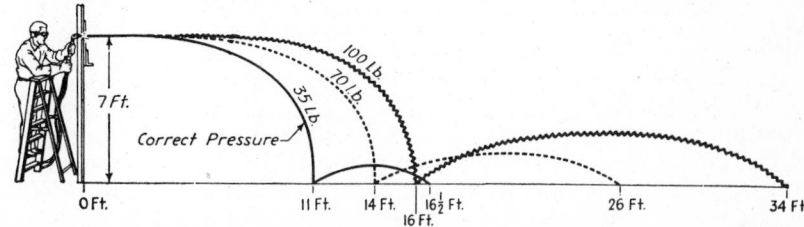

A good procedure for monitoring cutting and welding processes to prevent fires entails the following:

1. Approval is obtained from management or responsible supervisory personnel before starting to cut or weld.

2. The area is inspected by a representative of management to determine that adequate precautions are being followed before granting authorization to proceed. Preferably permission is in the form of a written permit. A suggested form is shown in Figure 4-8C.

3. Assurance is given the person signing the permit or otherwise authorizing the work to be done that the use of the welding or cutting equipment will not jeopardize loss of life or property.

Rules to follow for the prevention of fires in welding and cutting operations are:

1. Do not perform cutting or welding work where an open flame would be dangerous, as in or near rooms containing flammable vapors or liquids, or exposed loose combustible material.

2. Be sure that cutting and welding equipment is not used where there is any possibility of flammable vapors being present, or where sparks or molten metal might pass through broken or open windows, open doorways, cracks, or holes in walls or floors.

3. If the work can be moved, it is preferable to take it to a safe place for cutting and welding rather than to perform the work in a hazardous location.

4. Where welding or cutting must be done in the vicinity of combustible material, make certain that sparks or hot slag do not reach combustible material and thus start a fire. If the work cannot be moved, move the exposed combustible material a safe distance away if possible. Sweep floors clean and, if they are not of fire resistive material, wet them down before starting work. Wooden floors are preferably covered with metal or other suitable noncombustible material where sparks or hot metal are likely to fall. Station a guard near any opening to warn passers-by who might otherwise be burned by sparks or slag. Use sheet metal guards or asbestos curtains where needed. Make sure that the guards and curtains are adequate. Because hot slag may roll along the floor for considerable distances, it is important when using asbestos blankets as a curtain that no opening exists where the curtain meets the floor.

5. When it is necessary to do welding or cutting close to wooden construction or in locations where combustible materials cannot be removed or protected, have small water hose, chemical extinguishers, or pails of water readily available. Station a helper nearby to guard against sparks.

6. Whenever combustible material has been exposed to molten metal or hot slag from cutting operations, keep a watch at the place of the work for at least a half hour after completion to make sure that smoldering fires have not been started.

D.   Safe Welding and Cutting Practices

Work on Containers

Accidents during welding and cutting on containers are not frequent, but when they do occur they are likely to be severe. To guard against injury by explosion or fire, it is essential that any flammable vapors, liquids or solids be removed from a container before welding or cutting operations are commenced, or any type of hot work is started that might create a spark or flame.

While it is theoretically possible to avoid danger of explosion during work on a container that is completely full of a flammable gas or vapor, or in which there is no air or an air-vapor mixture too rich to explode, the only generally accepted safe practice is to make sure that all flammable materials are removed. This may necessitate elaborate time-consuming procedures. The first step is to remove or drain out the container. The residues must then be removed thoroughly. Where the contents are water-soluble, such as acetone, alcohol, or acids (dangerous because of production of hydrogen by reaction of metal), filling with water and thoroughly draining several times may be sufficient. With flammable liquids such as gasoline and

---

(Front)

PERMIT
FOR CUTTING AND WELDING
WITH PORTABLE GAS OR ARC EQUIPMENT

Date ....

Building ....

Dept. .... Floor ....

Work to be done ....

....

Special Precautions ....

Is fire watch required? ....

The location where this work is to be done has been examined, necessary precautions taken, and permission is granted for this work. (See other side)

Permit expires ....

Signed ....
(Individual responsible for authorizing welding and cutting)

Time started .... Completed ....

FINAL CHECK-UP

Work area and all adjacent areas to which sparks and heat might have spread (including floors above and below and on opposite sides of walls) were inspected 30 minutes after the work was completed and were found firesafe.

Signed ....
(Supervisor)

(Rear)

ATTENTION
Before approving any cutting and welding permit, the fire safety supervisor or his appointee shall inspect the work area and confirm that precautions have been taken to prevent fire in accordance with NFPA No. 51B.

PRECAUTIONS
☐ Sprinklers in service
☐ Cutting and welding equipment in good repair

WITHIN 35 FT. OF WORK
☐ Floors swept clean of combustibles
☐ Combustible floors wet down, covered with damp sand, metal or other shields
☐ No combustible material or flammable liquids
☐ Combustibles and flammable liquids protected with covers, guards or metal shields
☐ All wall and floor openings covered
☐ Covers suspended beneath work to collect sparks

WORK ON WALLS OR CEILINGS
☐ Construction noncombustible and without combustible covering
☐ Combustibles moved away from opposite side of wall

WORK ON ENCLOSED EQUIPMENT
(Tanks, containers, ducts, dust collectors, etc.)
☐ Equipment cleaned of all combustibles
☐ Containers purged of flammable vapors

FIRE WATCH
☐ To be provided during and 30 minutes after operation
☐ Supplied with extinguisher and small hose
☐ Trained in use of equipment and in sounding fire alarm

FINAL CHECK-UP
☐ To be made 30 minutes after completion of any operation unless fire watch is provided.

Signed ....
(Supervisor)

Fig. 4-8C.   A suggested form for a written cutting and welding permit. The form may be modified to suit local conditions.

Fig. 4-8D. Method of safe-guarding containers to be welded. Filling with carbon dioxide or nitrogen prevents explosive mixtures of air with vapors from flammable residue in the container.

Fig. 4-8E. Safeguarding by filling with water. Container should be filled to within an inch or two of where work is being done. The vent is left open to the air.

should be provided with adequate protection against the heat of the work and radiation from the flame or arc, and from particles of hot metal that may fly from the operation. Non-combustible (asbestos) clothing (aprons, coats, gloves, leggings, etc.) are available for body protection. Flame-resistant duck and other fabrics are also available as protection (see Sec. 3, Chap. 2). It is advisable that the outer clothing be free from oil or grease and from open pockets, cuffs, and such items into which sparks or hot metal might fly. Cutting operators should wear hats and high safety shoes.

In welding or cutting applications, it is important that the eyes be protected from the heat and glare of the flame and the hot metal, and from particles of hot metal that may fly up from the work. Properly designed and selected colored lenses fitted in goggles will furnish adequate protection to the eyes. The depth of color of the lenses will depend on the nature of the welding or cutting equipment and operation. However, a man wearing goggles may not be able to see a small fire started by sparks; this may call for another man to watch sparks under some conditions.

oil, recommended methods are thoroughly washing with a hot water solution of trisodium phosphate or similar alkali and steaming for a sufficient time to remove all remaining traces of flammable vapors. Before the hot work is commenced, the container should be thoroughly aired and the contents tested with a combustible gas indicator (see Sec. 12, Chap. 4). A further supplementary safety precaution is to fill the container with water or with inert gas (see Fig. 4-8D and 4-8E).

Protection of Personnel

When engaged in welding or cutting work, an operator

Bibliography

NFPA Codes, Standards, and Recommended Practices (see the latest *NFPA Publications and Visual Aids Catalog* for availability of current editions of the following documents)

NFPA No. 51, Standard for the Installation and Operation of Oxygen-Fuel Gas Systems for Welding and Cutting.

NFPA No. 51B, Standard for Fire Prevention in Use of Cutting and Welding Processes.

NFPA No. 70, National Electrical Code.

Additional Readings

"Safety in Welding and Cutting," ANSI Z49.1, 1973, American National Standards Institute, New York.

Chapter 9

PROCESSING EQUIPMENT

This chapter discusses chemical reactions, the means of reaction control and the equipment that are combined to form systems used in the production of chemicals and synthetics, such as some drugs, fibers and plastics, or in chemically changing the properties of materials, as in the chemical pulping of wood or the tanning of leather. However, in approaching fire and explosion prevention and loss control, each system must be considered as a whole when examining appropriate separation distances and other means of minimizing damage.

A. Separation Distances

Common practice has been to put single or allied processes on individual blocks of land with the blocks surrounded by access roads. The theory behind the block approach is that fires or unignited spills can then be approached from the four points of the compass, allowing maximum latitude to take advantage of both wind direction and the shelter afforded by peripheral structures in the block. If the right of way for these roads is 50 ft wide, this insures a minimum distance of 50 ft between structures on adjacent blocks and this distance has, historically, been regarded as adequate to prevent spread of fire through highly protected properties. In this connection, Atallah and Allan, indicate that a flammable liquid fire 75 ft wide could cause ignition of wood 50 ft away.[1] Moreover, fire fighters could not approach such a fire effectively without special heat protective clothing. This means that the 50-ft rule is inadequate if a large liquid spill might become ignited.

However, about two-thirds of the damage and most of the loss of life in chemical plant fires and explosions results from explosions rather than fires. Where an explosion is possible, the 50-ft distance, again, is not enough. One approach has been to place any unit involving an explosion hazard at least 50 ft in from the block perimeter. This gives a minimum distance (in the adjacent blocks) of 100 ft from an explosion hazard to a fire hazard or 150 ft between explosion hazards. In the case of explosion of equipment resulting from an increase in internal pressure, the shock wave would probably be adequately attenuated by that distance. This is so whether the explosion is of the thermal type, represented by an ordinary runaway reaction and failure of the container into two or three pieces, or of the shock type, where the pressure increase is caused by a reaction taking place at supersonic speed. In the latter case, the rapid pressure increase could produce shrapnel so a containment barricade would be needed. If the material that might cause the explosion is a true explosive, whether formed intentionally or accidentally, and whether inside or outside of equipment, the spacing then should be in accordance with Table 3-6A, the American Table of Distances for Storage of Explosives (see also NFPA No. 495, Code for Explosive Materials).

More conservative views on spacing are taken by the American Oil Company. Its booklet No.8[2] says: "Generally, a distance of 250 ft between units or between units and tankage has been used as a desirable spacing." Also, Table 4-9A gives the recommendations of the Oil Insurance Association with respect to Petrochemical Plants.[3]

The greater distances suggested by the American Oil Company and OIA are justified by the large amounts of flammables usually present in equipment and piping in oil refineries and petrochemical plants. They are probably adequate for control of even large flammable liquid fires.

Another type of explosion hazard exists for which no spacing rules have even been suggested. This is the explosion which results when a flammable gas or super heated flammable liquid is released into the atmosphere and mixes with air to form a cloud having much of its volume in the explosive range. Such a cloud can release some two to ten percent of its heat of combustion in the form of explosive energy. If a hydrocarbon releases 20,000 Btu/lb when burned and 5 percent of that or 1,000 Btu were released explosively by ignition of its mixture with air, then 2 lbs of hydrocarbon would release 2,000 Btu explosively, the same as 1 lb of TNT. Where such releases are possible, no one can predict where the cloud may have drifted before it is ignited so spacing is not a reliable defense against damage. However, processes where such leaks might occur should be located to leeward of other areas.

Where a fire or explosion hazard exists it is recommended that pipeways be at grade, rather than elevated. Damage to overhead pipe racks has materially increased exposure to the catastrophic loss, because of subsequent fires in fluids spilled from the damaged pipes. Thus piping for flammables is suggested to be at a level below the surface grade of the operations served by the piping up to the point where the piping enters the individual blocks.[2]

Other Means of Loss Control

As chemical plants process larger quantities of materials, it is apparent that it becomes impractical to provide ever increasing separation of units. Where toxic, flammable, reactive, or otherwise hazardous materials may be spilled, the logical approach is to:

1. Minimize the possibility of uncontrolled spills.
2. But if spills do occur, design features should keep them small.
3. But if spills are large in volume, design features should keep them confined.
4. Control sources of ignition.
5. But if ignition does occur, provide protection for exposed property.

B. Exposure Protection

Automatic fire control and extinguishing systems are the first line of defense against fire and explosion emergencies. However, if an explosion hazard exists, system designs would require barricades for protection of important components such as deluge valves and dry-pipe valves.[4] If they might be exposed to explosion pressure, however improbably, process control houses, including areas where people congregate (change houses), should be of explosion resistant design.[5] Reliably available water at pressure and volume adequate to supply the maximum foreseeable fire fighting and exposure protection demand for a minimum of 4hrs is desirable. Of course, built-in or added fire resistance can give excellent exposure protection.

Table 4-9A. General Recommendations for Spacing in Petrochemical Plants

Minimum Distance in Feet	Process Unit—HH	Process Unit—LH	Tank Farms—HH	Tank Farms—LH	Product Whses—LH	Ship'g. & Rec'g.—HH	Ship'g. & Rec'g.—LH	Service Buildings	Boiler Area	Fire Pumps	Emergency Controls	Water Spray Controls	Turret Nozzles	Emergency Flares	Pilot Plants	Large Cooling Towers	Fire Hydrants	Fired Process Heaters
Process Unit—(High Hazard)B	200A									250	100	50⁵			200	150		50 to 100
Process Unit—(Low Hazard)	100A	50A								150	50				200	100		50
Tank Farms—(High Hazard)C	250¹	250¹	1½ dia. larger							250		100⁵			250	250		200
Tank Farms—(Low Hazard)	200²	100³	1 dia. larger	½ dia. larger						200			50-100 to Center of Target	For 100' Flare that is 25' above Surrounding Equipment, Use 300'	200	200		200
Product Warehouse (Low Hazard)D	150	50⁴	250¹	100³	50⁴					200					200	150	50 to 250	100
Shipping & Receiving (High Hazard)E	200	200	150²	100³	150	50				150	100	50⁵			200	200		200
Shipping & Receiving (Low Hazard)	150	100	100	50	20	50	—			100	50				150	150		100
Service BuildingsF	200	100	200	100	100	150	100	See bldg. chart		100					200	100		100
Boiler Area	200	150	200	150	100	200	100	100	—	—					200	100		100

Recommended Spacing Within Process Units

	React.	Comp.	Tanks	Fract. Equip.	Cont. Rooms
Reactor	25⁶				
Small Compressor House or Pump House	40⁶				
Intermediate Storage Tanks High Hazard Rundown-Feed	100 to 200	100 to 200	1⁷ dia.		
Fractionation Equipment	50	30	100		
Control RoomsG	50⁶ to 100	50 to 100	100	50 to 100	10

Notes:

(A) Distance between process units is measured from battery limits.

(B) A high hazard process unit includes those with high or extreme explosion hazards.

A process with high explosion hazard is one where there is considerable explosion potential or probability with susceptibility to considerable damage or serious delays in restoration. Examples are: acetylene purification; acrylonitrile formation from hydrogen cyanide and ethylene oxide; acrylonitrile formation from hydrogen cyanide and acetylene; alkylation (using acetylene); partial oxidation of low flash point (below 110°F) liquids, such as oxidation of acetaldehyde to acetic acid; vinyl acetate formation from acetylene and acetic acid; vinyl chloride formation from acetylene and hydrogen chloride; and ethylene oxide production, recovery and purification.

A process with an extreme explosion hazard is one employing extreme pressures or is one that is unpredictable and not susceptible to design that will limit the extent of the damage or interruption to minor proportions. These processes, while not susceptible to exact description, can generally be recognized by engineering analysis. A process that uses very high pressures in equipment properly designed for the purpose and in connection with processes of predictable hazard (a synthetic ammonia plant is an example) does not of itself require classification as an extreme explosion hazard. Examples of processes with extreme explosion hazards are: acetylene compression when the partial pressure is 20 psia or higher; storage of organic coated ammonium nitrate or ammonium nitrate with an additive; acrolein drum storage; acrolein recovery and purification and acrolein barreling.

(C) High hazard tanks are those that contain liquids having a flash point below 110°F or are tanks or gas holders containing flammable gases other than anhydrous ammonia (for hazard rating purposes, anhydrous ammonia is classified as a liquid having a flash point above 200°F). Tanks containing unstable liquids or gases, such as acrolein, acrylonitrile, ethylene oxide, hydrogen cyanide, styrene, vinyl acetate and vinylidene chloride require special consideration unless the materials contain stabilizing inhibitors known to be effective.

(D) High hazard product warehouses contain unstable materials, low-flash flammable liquids, or highly combustible solids. These require special consideration.

(E) High hazard shipping and receiving denotes stable materials with flash point below 110°F. High hazard shipping and receiving of unstable materials requires special consideration.

(F) Service buildings include offices, gate houses, change houses, laboratories, shops, garages, maintenance warehouses, cafeterias, hospitals, etc. Experimental laboratories classify as process units.

(G) Control houses serving unusually large or hazardous units and central control houses for multiple units or housing computer equipment, require greater spacing and may require blast-resistant construction.

(1) For specific vertical tank, use 5 diameters.
(2) For specific vertical tank, use 4 diameters.
(3) For specific vertical tank, use 3 diameters.
(4) Standard firewall and sprinklered warehouse acceptable. Limit warehouse to maximum 25,000 sq ft floor area.
(5) Two stations desirable.
(6) Barricades desirable for hazardous reactors.
(7) Over 100,000 gal requires special consideration.

General Notes:

Keep open flames 100 feet from vapor hazard area.

Deviation from the distances in this table requires superior construction or special protective installations such as fixed foam systems, water spray systems, automatic sprinklers, or a water spray from hose lines capable of supplying about 2500 gpm to the points of need and a trained brigade adequately manned to use the water spray.

In borderline cases, high value requires high hazard classification.

Vertical storage tanks should be individually diked. If not, capacity in a single dike should not exceed 25,000 barrels. For horizontal storage tanks, maximum is 400,000 gal per group, with 100 feet between groups, or other suitable arrangement.

Protection for a chemical plant may also require a specialized fire department equipped with full protective clothing, including self-contained breathing apparatus, for each man as well as acid-resistant hose and special extinguishing equipment. NFPA No. 49, Hazardous Chemicals Data, is an excellent source for information on personal protection measures needed in fighting fires involving different chemicals as well as the tactics that should be used in emergencies. Appropriate NFPA 704M, Hazard Identification System, symbols, posted at locations on the property where chemicals are present, can give helpful guidance on inherent hazards of materials present and planning effective fire fighting operations.

C. Ignition Sources

Note G in Table 4-9A recommends that open flames be kept at least 100 ft from any hazardous area. This note contemplates fixed equipment; however, it could also apply to maintenance work. A better approach is to prohibit open flames or other hot work in all but predetermined specified areas unless the area where the hot work is to be done has been examined and found safe and the work is done under a permit that limits scope and duration (see Chap. 8 of this Section). It must be remembered that piping for high pressure steam, heat transfer media, and hot process streams may need insulation to keep it from being a source of ignition.

D. Control of Spills

Large Spill Confinement

Where large flammable liquid spills may occur, means should be taken to impound them. Retaining dikes are often used, but they may keep burning liquid around the spill source and further damage equipment or aggravate the spill unless efficient and prompt, preferably automatic, fire control measures are taken. A better approach is to provide drainage to an impounding basin located where a fire, if not extinguished, can burn out harmlessly or a nonburning toxic material can be appropriately neutralized. Invariably a spill is ignited at some time during the drainage process so means must be taken to avoid damage from that situation. An underground sewerage system could result in explosions in the system, while fire in open drainage ditches could result in damage to anything without adequate protection that is located alongside the ditches or which crosses them, such as utility or piping systems. Problems associated with drainage can be avoided by using the trench system described in NFPA No. 15. (For information on Industrial Waste Disposal, see Chapter 14 of this Section.)

Total confinement of a large flammable gas spill is not possible, because it is three dimensional as opposed to the essentially two dimensional nature of a liquid spill. Hose lines using spray nozzles can be used, because of the air entrained by the spray to dilute the gas cloud and to move it in a desired direction until it dissipates. An unpublished report by W. H. Doyle and L. Eggleston indicates that fixed water spray nozzles may be used to set up curtains to prevent a cloud from drifting to a furnace or other ignition source. Similarly, steam nozzles may be used for this purpose.[6] These techniques are, however, barely past the experimental stage. Further, these techniques can be used only on clouds that hug the ground; they are not effective where the cloud may be deep as when a liquefied gas or a hot liquid may be jetted out under pressure.

Keeping Spills Small

Hazardous spills can be kept small by having only small amounts of hazardous material in the process. This is usually impractical, so the next step is to provide valves to isolate all large quantities. These valves are installed at each outlet of any large container through which material might escape (except at relief devices) and to subdivide long runs of large diameter pipe. The valves preferably are fire safe, i.e., they should not leak appreciably when exposed to fire after being closed, and are arranged to operate both remotely and at the valve. If operated by electric motor, both the power wiring to the motor and the signal wiring to the starting switch are arranged to remain functional during any fire or other emergency requiring valve operation for at least as long as it would take to discover the emergency, transmit the alarm, and operate the valve. A minimum of 15 min fire protection for wiring is suggested. If valves are held open by instrument air pressure and close by spring or gravity when air pressure is lost, plastic tubing is used in the air line, at least near the valve. The plastic melts quickly in a fire, and the valve closes before it is damaged. Since it is important to detect spills before ignition, flammable vapor detectors of the diffusion head type may be used for that purpose (see Sec. 12, Chap. 4).[7]

The dividing line between a small spill and a large one must be fixed individually for each plant. A small spill is one that can be easily handled by the exposure protection and confinement means covered above. All other spills are large. In the case of jets of liquefied flammable gas[8,9] or hot flammable liquid,[10] where spacing is not a reliable defense against explosion damage, quantities (various) have been proposed as limits that must not be exceeded. One organization suggests 10,000 lbs of gas or vapor as a maximum permissible spill. Another suggests a maximum permissible leakage rate as one that would permit formation of no more than 1,000 lbs per minute of flammable gas or vapor.

Preventing Spills

Because many chemicals cause unusual corrosion or abrasion problems, or the processes require unusually high or low temperatures, chemical plants must have knowledgeable selection of construction materials and good maintenance practices. Assuming that there are no problems in these areas, the reaction systems themselves may be the cause of trouble.

In general, reactions are used to produce wanted commodities that differ chemically from the raw materials from which they are made. The differences are produced by controlled chemical changes. Uncontrolled changes tend to produce unwanted materials and more or less violent system failures resulting in spills. The common denominator in these failures is overheating. This may be overheating of a container so that it softens and fails or overheating of the contents so that they create so much pressure that the container bursts. Accidents of these types result from a failure to move heat adequately from a heat source to a heat absorbing system or to a coolant from a heat releasing system. Heat is usually produced when materials dissolve, crystallize, condense, or are adsorbed. Heat is produced mechanically by crushing, grinding, milling, compressing, and pumping. Heat is produced by exothermic chemical reactions. Heat transfer is also required when heat is needed for evaporation, melting, decreasing viscosity, drying, desorbing, distillation, warming expanding gas, initiating exothermic chemical reactions, and driving endothermic reactions. In any case, loss prevention requires an understanding of heat transfer.

E. Hazards of Heat Transfer

When a hot fluid, gas, or liquid transfers heat to a cooler fluid through a barrier, such as the metal wall of a vessel, the resistance to heat flow, as shown by a temperature drop, is mainly in fluid films on the metal surfaces rather than in the metal (see Fig. 4-9A). Flow in the heating and heated fluids is usually turbulent with invisible swirls and eddies but in the films it is laminar with thin layers of molecules sliding slowly over each other. The film layer nearest the metal moves slowest and its temperature is nearest that of the metal. This is important because high temperature causes decomposition of most organic and some inorganic fluids. While a large temperature differential between the fluids moves heat faster than a small one, the hottest part of the heated film must be kept cool enough so that it does not decompose and form a solid film. When a solid film builds up, the temperature of the metal on the heated side may go so high, trying to force the heat through, that the metal is damaged and a "burnout" occurs.

Precautions consist of methods to detect the fluid breakdown such as checking the fluid for tar, solids, or significant change in viscosity or volatility. Where the heater is of a single tube design, an internal buildup will cause a readily observable increased pressure drop as the fluid flows through the tube. For this reason, single tube heaters are to be preferred over those of multiple fluid path design.

When the breakdown of the fluid is intentional, as in the case of cracking a petroleum fraction, the internal deposits are removed on a scheduled basis before they reach dangerous thickness. This usually is done by burning them out with air or a mixture of air and steam.[11] Requirements for safety involve:

1. Purging the unit of flammables, usually with steam, before introducing the oxidizing atmosphere.
2. Purging after burning out the deposits.
3. Safe disposal of the materials purged.
4. A system of valving, usually involving double valves with a purged or vented space between, to insure against mixing air and combustibles.

If the heated fluid is a liquid and starts to boil, heat transfer improves as the film is thinned by the action of bubbles of vapor forming on the metal, growing, and breaking away.

This formation of bubbles on the heated surface is called "nucleate boiling." If the temperature of the heat source is then raised in an attempt to increase the rate of boiling, the temperature may become too high. Vapor bubbles then coalesce into a vapor film, instead of breaking away individually. This is called "film boiling." Vapor films offer more resistance to heat flow, so, again, "burn out" may occur.

Endothermic Reactions

Endothermic reactions are most commonly supplied with heat by combustion processes. This energy may be truly direct, i.e., cracking natural gas to acetylene by burning part of it with oxygen and quenching suddenly, concentrating a liquid by submerged combustion (burning a premixed gaseous fuel beneath the surface of a liquid), or roasting ore or cementitious material in a kiln. It may also be first degree indirect (usually and hereinafter called direct since the container, tube, or kettle is directly exposed to the flames); or second degree indirect (usually and hereinafter called indirect) where the flames heat a heat transfer fluid. In this concept, the use of tempered flue gas constitutes indirect heating.

The same general hazards exist whether the material being heated is a reacting system or one being decomposed or heated. All cases require consideration of metallurgy and construction details of the equipment. These problems are accentuated in the case of direct-fired equipment. The heater must resist corrosion, pitting, and scaling from the materials being heated as well as from combustion on the firebox side, and must often do so at temperatures much higher than is the case with conventional heat transfer media. Construction must be such that heated and cooled portions can expand and contract freely. This is particularly important if the alloys used enter or pass through a brittle phase at any stage of heating or cooling.

Important, but sometimes overlooked, are two other points:

1. The metal of the heater and heat transfer system and the fluids with which they are in contact must be compatible. The common molten salt heat transfer medium, a mixture of sodium nitrate and sodium nitrite, used in indirect-fired heaters will support the combustion of steel if the temperature is high enough and ignition occurs;[12] steel and copper in thin sections, as on the fins of heat transfer tubes, can ignite easily in hit chlorine.

2. The heat transfer medium should not create a hazard if it leaks into the material being heated or vice versa. Where leakage one way but not another can be temporarily tolerated (sulfuric acid into water as opposed to water into sulfuric acid, for example) pressures of the coolant and the cooled material must be suitably different. Alternatively, annular tubes with the annulus separating the two fluids may be used with means to detect leakage into the annulus from either direction. To promote heat transfer, the annulus may be filled with a conducting liquid inert to both fluids or, as in "still" tubes, intermittently bridged with heat conducting metal wires or perforated discs.

The above discussion applies equally well to the cases where the heat transfer is from an exothermic reaction to a fluid used for cooling.

It is impossible to be all-inclusive on the hazards of heat transfer. Two examples, however, may indicate the scope of the problem. In the first case electric induction heat was being used on a cast iron vessel with thermostatic controls. Cast iron growth (caused by precipitation of carbon from the heated cast iron) caused inter-crystalline cracking. The

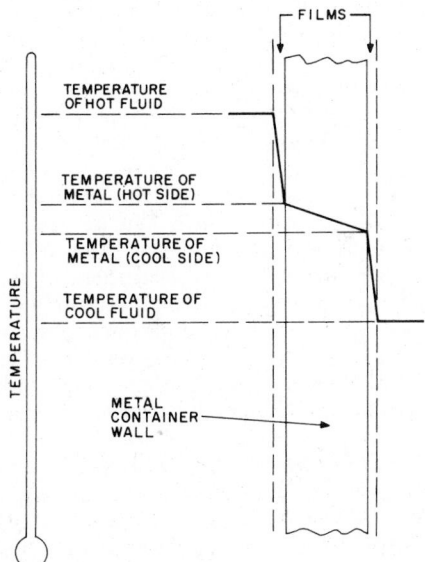

Fig. 4-9A. The effect of fluid films on temperature at the surfaces of the metal wall of a vessel.

cracks interrupted the flow of the induced electric currents throughout the vessel; the thermostats called for more heat and the vessel eventually failed from localized overheating. In another instance sodium silicate was condensed on a stainless steel pipe where it acted as a flux to remove one of the alloying elements so that the pipe lost its corrosion resistance and failed.

See Chapter 3 of this Section for a further discussion on heat transfer systems.

Exothermic Reactions

Proper use of heat transfer principles is essential to the control of exothermic reactions. Such use requires knowledge of the reaction system. First, it is necessary to know the thermal stability and shock sensitivity of the system and each of its components, raw materials, intermediates, products, and by-products. Second, the reaction kinetics must be known; that is, what is the total amount of heat released and how fast is it released. For completely safe process design, it is necessary to have all of these data under the conditions that would exist if the reactants were supplied in grossly wrong proportions, in the wrong order, without mixing (both with and without a subsequent late start of the mixing system), at the wrong temperatures, if power failed, if a coolant line broke, or if any other upset condition that can be visualized should occur.

F.　Stability and Shock Sensitivity

Most chemicals are reasonably stable and insensitive. Where this is not true, data are usually available from the supplier or in the literature. NFPA No. 49 discusses specific chemicals, and NFPA No. 491M, Hazardous Chemical Reactions, covers hazardous systems and both provide lists of references. Where data are not available, thermodynamic calculations and laboratory scale stability testing should be used.[13, 14, 15, 16, 17, 18] Where explosive materials are involved, the hazard may be reduced to an acceptable level by dilution, or barricades may be necessary.

If the instability hazard is less than explosive, there are various ways to reduce it. Chemical reactions go faster as the temperature rises so the methods used involve keeping the material from being heated to an unsafe level. As examples, the boiling point of a liquid is lowered by vacuum. Vacuum or freeze drying can avoid overheating. A high boiling material that becomes unstable at or near its boiling point may have steam bubbled through it at a temperature below the boiling point. Vapor of the material goes along with the steam and separation can be made after condensing the steam-vapor mixture. Viscous materials can be concentrated by running them down the heated interior walls of a wiped film evaporator. Mechanically operated blades keep wiping the interior surface. The film cannot become thick so the film layer nearest the hot wall will not overheat (Fig. 4-9A). Liquid nitrogen or dry ice may be added to material going to a grinder. This not only takes care of the heat produced mechanically but also tends to inert the atmosphere and reduce chances of a dust explosion.

In some cases, pressure may affect stability. Liquids, such as propargyl bromide and nitromethane, will boil away when heated at atmospheric pressure. If heated under pressure, so the boiling point is raised, they sometimes explode. Pure gases such as acetylene, ethylene, and nitrous oxide can be exploded when under sufficient pressure. The testing mentioned above should be thorough enough to detect such a possibility. Also, when considering systems, one should keep in mind that pressure may cause a phase change. For example, chlorine gas liquefies fairly easily and a system easy to control when using the gas may be hard to control if the liquid is accidentally formed.

G.　Reactors

Reaction systems are of two types, continuous and batch. A continuous system may be thought of as a pipe, although it may contain pumps, compressors, bulges that are reactors, etc. with the raw materials and possibly an inert carrier flowing in at one end, or at appropriate intervals along the pipe, with products and by-products coming out the other. In a batch process, the chemicals are added to a single unit, all at once or in appropriate quantities at appropriate time intervals, the reaction takes place, the unit is emptied and the process is repeated. Batch process systems have more flexibility in use than continuous systems.

Continuous Reactors

It is common to have one reactant, pure or diluted, circulating continuously throughout the reactor with another being added, reacted, and the products removed by condensation, washing, filtering, or similar appropriate means. When in normal operation, the major safety control is by the automatic cutting off the appropriate feed stream in event of failure of the heat transfer system. Often, arrangements are made for alternate means of supplying the heat transfer fluids. Reliability of the shut off system may be enhanced by using two valves in series with a vent between. (This is known as the double block and bleed system.) Depending on the complexity of the system, this same shutoff may be actuated by changes in other process conditions. An example might be too low a temperature which would indicate that the reaction was not going properly, and that concentrations of unreacted materials might be building up to the point where they could react all at once with explosive violence, overpowering the means of heat removal or could react in a part of the system designed to recover product rather than control the reaction. Also, when starting up or shutting down, the continuous reactor may go through situations that are more hazardous than when in normal operation.

Batch Reactors

The essential parts of a batch reactor are:

1. The vessel itself, to contain the reaction at the maximum pressure it is supposed to reach.

2. A heat transfer system to control temperature.

3. A stirrer or other mixing system to keep the temperature and composition of the reacting mixtures uniform.

4. A relief system to protect the vessel against over pressure.

The Vessel: This may range from an open wood- or rubber-lined steel tank in which bauxite ore reacts with sulfuric acid to produce a solution of alum to a glass lined or stainless steel pressure vessel. Regardless of size or configuration, the vessel used as a batch reactor will probably have to be entered for cleaning while the continuous reactor can often be cleaned just by following the reactants with a cleaning fluid. Cleaning or entering vessels will require special precautions if flammable cleaning agents are used or if fumes or residues make entry hazardous.

Heat Transfer Methods: Common methods of heat transfer use jackets or coils on the exterior of the vessel or coils on the interior. Others circulate the reacting mixture from the vessel through an external heat exchanger and back to the vessel. Similarly, the reacting mixture is allowed to boil, then the heat of vaporization is removed by condensing the vapor externally, and allowing the condensed liquid to run back and continue the cycle. This latter method does not provide means to heat the material in the vessel and heat may be needed to start the reaction even though cooling is needed as the reaction progresses.

Mixing: This is usually done with an agitator mounted on a shaft driven by an external motor. If an external heat exchanger is used, the mixture leaving it may be jetted back into the vessel to accomplish mixing. Where heat sensitive materials are involved and it is necessary to avoid moving parts because they might rise to a dangerous temperature due to friction, mixing can be done by bubbling in air or inert gas.

Pressure Relief of Batch Reactors

Pressure relief for venting a combustion explosion is discussed in Section 15, Chapter 7, and in NFPA No. 68, Explosion Venting Guide, and is not considered here. Batch reactors in which an explosive atmosphere might sometimes exist are usually designed to contain the pressure that might result from ignition, or they are purged or inerted to eliminate the hazard. If vessels are constructed according to the Pressure Vessel Code of the American Society of Mechanical Engineers, they are required to have a relief device adequate to keep the vessel from being overpressured because of overheating from an external source, including an exposure fire, normal heating, or the introduction of fluids at pressures higher than that for which the vessel is designed. The code gives no guidance for the relief of pressure caused by heat of reaction.

Most chemical reactions double in speed with each rise in temperature of 18°F (10°C). This means that a heat removal system would have to remove twice as much heat at 60°C as at 50°C, four times as much at 70°C, etc. For this reason, it is unsafe to run a batch reaction at a temperature more than 14°C above that of the cooling medium.[19] If the cooling system is overpowered, the reaction keeps increasing in speed, the retained heat builds up pressure, and the pressure must be relieved or the vessel will explode. Austin[20] has given a good explanation of this problem. The Dow Chemical Company's, "Guidelines for Process Scale-up" gives the following comments about runaway reactions:[21]

Can You Prevent Runaway Reactions?	Yes	No
By adequate heat transfer	—	—
By quenching the reaction	—	—
By stopping feed streams	—	—
By dilution of the reactor contents	—	—

Score: Two or more methods—You're in good shape.
Only one method—Better find a second line of defense.
None of the above—You'd better stop right now and reconsider your design for safety.

However, since even multiple safeguards may fail, emergency venting is supplied as last ditch protection for the vessel. For example, loss of mixing could make all the suggested preventive measures inoperative or dangerously inefficient. Materials have leaked into the hollow shaft of an agitator, created pressure, and spewed into the main reaction system materials which speed the main reaction so that it overpowers the cooling system. Other problems were discussed earlier in this chapter under Exothermic Reactions.

A satisfactory empirical solution to the problem of determining an adequate vent size for a stirred batch reactor ordinarily may be reached by using the diagram in Figure 4-9B[22]. Suitable vent sizes are presented as a range of values rather than one specific figure. Values are selected from the upper part of the range if the vent pipe from the vessel to

the outside is long or contains bends, or if the vent device opens at more than about one-third in excess of the absolute pressure at which the reaction normally proceeds. Taking atmospheric pressure as 15 psia, a 5 psia rupture disc (⅓ of 15) is the maximum that should be used with the suggested vent sizes for an atmospheric reaction. A limitation on data in Figure 4-9B is that the diagram was made up with a conventional jacketed batch kettle in mind. Such kettles are usually designed for operation at from full vacuum to 60 to 70 psig internal pressure so the chart may be inadequate and should not be used if the normal reaction pressure exceeds 100 psig.

There is considerable literature on venting batch reactors. Boyle[23] has pointed out that the material vented is not a gas but a multi-phase mixture, requiring experimental data for proper vent system design. Harmon and Martin[24] have reported valuable work along these lines. Huff[25] has developed a computerized approach to the problem of polymerization reactor venting. This finds the chart in Fig. 4-9B reasonably accurate, within its limitations, and expands on the work of Boyle, Harmon, and Martin. Ogiso, Takagi, and Kitagwa[26] point out that the sudden venting of a low viscosity superheated material (they used water) causes an instantaneous pressure reduction to almost atmospheric pressure followed by the onset of nucleate boiling throughout the system. This sudden expansion produces an explosive effect, related to water hammer.

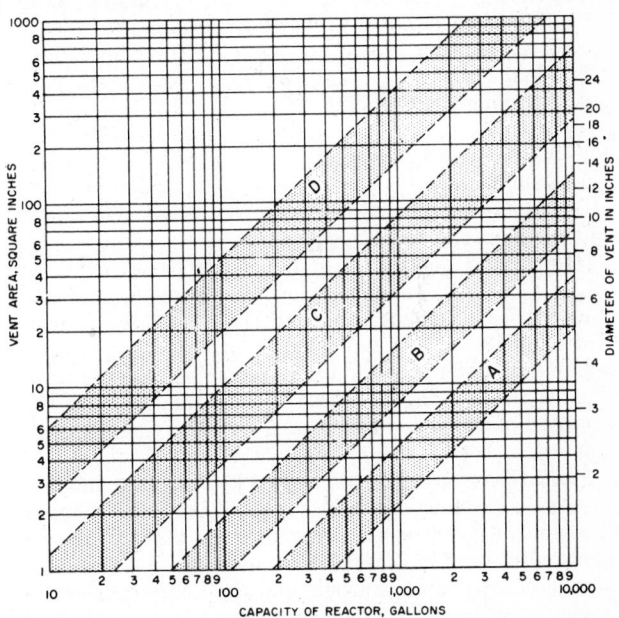

Fig. 4-9B. Vent Sizes for Batch Reaction Vessels
Line A represents endothermic reactions or reactions with a very low exotherm (low heat release).
Line B represents reactions with a low heat release per volume of reaction mass. This would include such reactions as suspension polymerizations of vinyl chloride, styrene, butadienestyrene, etc., where 50 percent or more of the material within the reactor does not take part in the reaction, being present as a diluent only.
Line C represents reactions with moderately high exotherms, such as methyl methacrylate and styrene bulk polymerizations, mono nitration of benzol, toluol, etc., and Freidel-Crafts reactions.
Line D represents reactions with extraordinarily high heat release, such as oxidations using nitric acid, bulk polymerizations of ethyl acrylate, or methyl acrylate, caustic catalyzed phenolformaldehyde condensations, etc. In these cases reactors of over 1,000-gal capacity should be avoided.

Safety Instrumentation

Safety instrumentation will vary from process to process and plant to plant. There are, however, as discussed by Doyle[27], a few general rules:

1. Measure, as directly as possible, the variables of interest. For example, if an agitator is driven by an electric motor, a relay can be used to show that the switch to the motor is closed. An ammeter would be better because that would show current is flowing. A wattmeter would be best because that would show that work is being done and that the impeller has not fallen off the agitator shaft.

2. Reliability and maintenance must be of high quality, e.g., if an external fire could upset the reaction, the instrument that tells of the upset should not be disabled by the fire. Since safety instruments will not have to operate often, frequent checks must be made to make sure they are in operating condition.

3. Provide redundancy or diversity. If temperature is critical, provision of two thermocouples may lead to tossing a coin if they disagree. It is best to provide three and trust the majority. However, since a temperature increase is usually accompanied by a pressure increase, one pressure sensor and one thermocouple may be used, with credence given the more pessimistic report.

H. Chemical Plant Operations and Equipment

The generally accepted unit physical operations require equipment to carry out the following functions:

1. Heat Transfer	7. Evaporation
2. Fluid Flow	8. Crystallization
3. Crushing and Grinding	9. Filtration
4. Mixing	10. Absorption
5. Mechanical Separation	11. Adsorption
6. Distillation	12. Drying

Descriptions of individual pieces of equipment can be found in most engineering handbooks.

Heaters and Coolers (Heat Transfer): These devices are either: (1) direct (flue gas, kilns, spray cooling, vaporization), or (2) indirect (coils and jackets). Heat transfer media usually work by boiling to absorb heat or condensing to give it up but may work just by becoming hotter or cooler without phase change. Hazards of heat transfer have been discussed previously in this chapter (see also Chap. 3 of this Section).

Fluid Flow: This is accomplished by: (1) fans and compressors, (2) pumps, or (3) vacuum jets. Fans, compressors, and pumps heat the materials they move because of mechanical work. Compressors require good aftercoolers. The liquid in pumps can boil, and the pump bearings fail from overheating if a pump operates against a closed discharge valve. If a centrifugal pump suction is inadequate, cavitation may cause the pump to chew itself up. Failure of vacuum devices may let air back into equipment where it should not be as well as cause the temperature in the equipment to rise.

Crushing and Grinding: Equipment for these operations include: (1) mills (impact, ball, hammer, roller, disk), and (2) crushers (cone, gyratory, jaw). All of these devices produce heat and may produce fine material capable of dust explosion. Ball mills may become over-pressured as liquid portions of their contents are heated up. If gaskets blow as a result and the liquids are flammable, a dangerous situation will exist.

Mixers: Devices used in the mixing process include: (1) tumblers; (2) venturi mixers; (3) kneaders, rolls and mullers; and (4) propellers, blades, and turbines. These devices also produce heat in varying degrees. When it is necessary to produce a hazardous mixture, like a blend of starch and an oxidizer for use as a flour ager, the mixer is open to avoid an equipment explosion, and any dust collector should be of the water wash type.

Mechanical Separators: These include: (1) cyclones, (2) bag filters (shake or blow back), (3) ore tabling, (4) screening, (5) electrostatic, (6) flotation, and (7) centrifuges. The first five are usually dry type and the latter two wet, although there are liquid cyclones and wet screening. Devices used in dry service for combustible dusts should have explosion venting or an explosion suppression system. Where collectors have internal combustible bags an internal sprinkler system is desirable. It may not save the bags, but it will save the housing and mechanical devices. When materials wet with flammable liquids are centrifuged, the operation should be under inert gas or with an explosion suppression system.

Stills: The types of stills are: (1) batch, (2) continuous, (3) pressure, (4) vacuum, and (5) steam. All distillations involve heat transfer, and the major hazard is that a flammable vapor may be released to the atmosphere. This and other problems have been discussed by Doyle.[28] The direct use of steam is discussed in Part F, Stability and Shock Sensitivity, of this chapter.

Evaporators: The three types of evaporators are: (1) multiple effect, (2) vacuum, and (3) wiped film. All three use heat transfer. The multiple effect system condenses vapor from the first unit to heat the second, etc. The initial heat transfer medium is used in the first, where the material is most concentrated so it boils at the highest temperature. Vacuums and wiped films have been discussed previously in this chapter.

Crystallizers: The two types of crystallizers are: (1) vacuum, and (2) pan. Both involve cooling to remove the heat of crystallization.

Filters and Agglomeraters: Filtration and agglomeration involve: (1) plate and frame filters, (2) Nutsche filters (vacuum), (3) drum-type, (4) rotary cell-type, (5) agglomerating tables, and (6) pelletizers. No unusual hazards are involved other than possible exposure of flammable liquids to the air.

Adsorbers: The two types of adsorbers are: (1) activated carbon, and (2) zeolites (molecular sieves). Adsorption produces heat just as absorption does. However, when the material being adsorbed is a flammable vapor or gas, the heat is retained in the small pores of the adsorbent and may build up enough to cause fire in the activated carbon or exothermic polymerization of adsorbed reactive materials such as ethylene. This hazard can be eliminated by wetting the adsorbent prior to each use.

Dryers: The six general types of dryers are: (1) spray and fluid bed, (2) vacuum, (3) tray, (4) belt, (5) drum, and (6) azeotropic. All these involve heat transfer. In the case of azeotropic dryers when heat is removed by boiling, condensation, and return of the cool liquid, the unwanted component, usually water, can be discarded if the condensate forms a two-phase system. All other types of dryers may present problems of mixing flammable vapors with air. Spray and fluid bed dryers may expose thermally unstable dry materials to hot heat transfer surfaces.

Conclusion

A summary of what has to be known and done to assure safe chemical processing has been suggested as follows:[29]

1. Know the total reaction energy in your system.
2. Know the rate of energy release.

3. Evaluate thermal and shock sensitivity data.

4. Design your process to control the rate of energy release, and in doing so:

(a) Be alert for trace compounds or catalytic impurities which may accelerate reaction rates.

(b) Prevent build-up or concentration of high energy materials in your system. Calculate a material balance.

(c) Design into your process the ability to safely accommodate inadvertent releases.

SI Units

The following conversion factors are given as a convenience in converting to SI units the English units used in this chapter.

1 Btu	= 1.055 kJ
1 Btu/lb	= 2.326 kJ/kg
1 ft	= 0.305 m
1 lb (mass)	= 0.454 kg
$\frac{5}{9}$(°F − 32)	= °C

Bibliography

References Cited

[1] Atallah, S. and Allan, D. S., "Safe Separation Distances from Liquid Fuel Fires," *Fire Technology*, Vol. 7, No. 1, Feb. 1971, pp. 47-55.

[2] "Engineering for Safe Operations," No. 8, American Oil Company (now AMOCO), Chicago, 1964.

[3] "General Recommendations for Spacing," No. 631, 1972 rev. ed., Oil Insurance Association, Chicago.

[4] Rinder, R. M. and Wachtell, S., "Establishment of Design Criteria for Safe Processing of Hazardous Materials," *Loss Prevention*, Vol. 7, AIChE (American Institute of Chemical Engineers), New York, 1967, pp. 28-30.

[5] Bradford, W. J. and Culbertson, T. L., "Design of Control Houses to Withstand Explosive Forces," *Loss Prevention*, Vol. 1, AIChE, New York, 1967, pp. 28-30.

[6] "The Safe Dispersal of Large Clouds of Flammable Heavy Vapors," Imperial Chemical Industries, Ltd., Heavy Organic Chemicals Division, Billingham, England, May 5, 1971.

[7] Johanson, K. A., "Gas Detectors by the Acre," *Instrumentation Technology*, Vol. 21, No. 8, Aug. 1974, pp. 33-37.

[8] Burgess, D. S. and Zabetakis, M. G., "Detonation of a Flammable Cloud Following a Propane Pipeline Break," RI 7752, 1973, USDI Bureau of Mines, Pittsburgh.

[9] Goforth, C. P., "Functions of a Loss Control Program," *Loss Prevention*, Vol. 4, AIChE, New York, 1970, pp. 1-5.

[10] Kletz, T., "Lessons to be Learned from Flixborough," *Loss Prevention*, Vol. 9, AIChE, New York, 1975, in press.

[11] Armistead, G., Jr., *Safety in Petroleum Refining and Related Industries*, 1st ed., John G. Simmonds & Co., Inc., New York, 1950, pp. 118-119.

[12] "Potential Hazards in Molten Salt Baths for Heat Treatment of Metals," NBFU Research Report RR-2, 1954, American Insurance Association, New York.

[13] Coffee, R. D., "Hazard Evaluation Testing," *Loss Prevention*, Vol. 3, AIChE, New York, 1969, pp. 18-21.

[14] Way, D., "Fire Protection Engineering," *Loss Prevention*, Vol. 3, AIChE, New York, 1969, pp. 23-25.

[15] Coffee, R. D., "Hazard Evaluation: The Basis for Chemical Plant Design," *Loss Prevention*, Vol. 7, AIChE, New York, 1973, pp. 58-60.

[16] Treweek, D. N.; Claydon, C. R.; and Seaton, W. H., "Appraising Energy Hazard Potentials," *Loss Prevention*, Vol. 7, AIChE, New York, 1973, pp. 21–27.

[17] Davis, E. J. and Ake, J. A., "Equilibrium Thermochemistry Computer Programs as Predictors of Energy Hazard Potential," *Loss Prevention*, Vol. 7, AIChE, New York, 1973, pp. 67-73.

[18] Stull, D. R., "Linking Thermodynamics and Kinetics to Predict Real Chemical Hazards," *Loss Prevention*, Vol. 7, AIChE, New York, 1973, pp. 67-73.

[19] Boynton, E. D.; Nichols, W. B.; and Spurlin, H. M., "Control of Exothermic Reactions," *Industrial & Engineering Chemistry*, Vol. 51, No. 4, April 1959, pp. 489-494.

[20] Austin, G. T., "Hazards of Commercial Chemical Reactions," *Safety and Accident Prevention in Chemical Operations*, edited by H. H. Fawcett and W. S. Wood, John Wiley & Sons, New York, 1965.

[21] Kline, P. E., et al., "Guidelines for Process Scale-up," *Chemical Engineering Progress*, Vol. 70, No. 10, Oct. 1974, pp. 67-70.

[22] Sestak, E. J., "Venting of Chemical Plant Equipment," Engineering Bulletin N-53, April 1965, Factory Insurance Association, Hartford, Conn.

[23] Boyle, W. J., Jr., "Sizing Relief Area for Polymerization Reactors," *Loss Prevention*, Vol. 1, AIChE, New York, 1967, pp. 78-84.

[24] Harmon, G. W. and Martin, W. A., "Sizing Rupture Discs for Vessels Containing Monomers," *Loss Prevention*, Vol. 4, AIChE, New York, 1970, pp. 95-102.

[25] Huff, J. E., "Computer Simulation of Polymerizer Pressure Relief," *Loss Prevention*, Vol. 7, AIChE, New York, 1973, pp. 45-57.

[26] Ogiso, C.; Takagi, N.; and Kitagawa, T., "On the Mechanism of Vapor Explosion," *Proceedings of the First Pacific Engineering Congress*, Kyoto, Japan, Oct. 10-14, 1972.

[27] Doyle, W. H., "Instrument Connected Losses in the CPI," *Instrumentation Technology*, Oct. 1972, pp. 38-42.

[28] Doyle, W. H., "Minimizing Serious Fires and Explosions in the Distillation Process," Technology Report 74-2, 1974, Society of Fire Protection Engineers, Boston.

[29] "The ABC's of Reactive Chemical Processing," Dow Chemical Company, Midland, Michigan.

NFPA Codes, Standards, and Recommended Practices (see the latest *NFPA Publications and Visual Aids Catalog* for availability of current editions of the following documents)

NFPA No. 15, Standard for Water Spray Fixed Systems for Fire Protection.

NFPA No. 49, Hazardous Chemicals Data.

NFPA No. 68, Guide for Explosion Venting.

NFPA No. 491M, Manual for Hazardous Chemical Reactions.

NFPA No. 495, Code for the Manufacture, Transportation, Storage, and Use of Explosive Materials.

Section 4

Chapter 10

GRINDING PROCESSES

Many nonmetallic materials, such as wheat flour, sulfur, starch, wood flour, coal, and some plastics, as well as some metals, such as aluminum and magnesium, present potentially severe explosion hazards when they are suspended in air in a finely divided form. Grinding (or pulverizing) is the process by which these materials are broken up into very small particles, and, in so doing, is the source of potentially explosive material. The very nature of the process, by impact or friction actions, may also provide an ignition source to initiate an explosion. This chapter covers only the grinding operations which produce combustible dusts; grinding of inert materials is not covered.

A. Classification of Grinding Equipment

Size-reduction equipment may be classified according to the way forces are applied to the material. It may be (1) between two solid surfaces, (2) at one solid surface by impact, (3) by action of the surrounding medium, or (4) by nonmechanical introduction of energy, such as thermal shock, explosive shattering, or electrohydraulic. For the type of materials being considered in this chapter the first method of applying force, i.e., between two solid surfaces, and the jet-mill method of grinding will be discussed.

Grinding operations may be done either wet or dry. Water is an excellent medium for wet grinding, although other liquids may be used. For example, kerosine is used for the wet milling of magnesium. Since a dust explosion is the principal hazard associated with grinding operations, only dry grinding principally is covered in this chapter.

Grinding processes are either batch or continuous (see Fig. 4-10A). Continuous processes may be either open or closed circuit (see Fig. 4-10A and 4-10B). In air-swept mills, air is blown in at one end, and the ground material is removed at the other end in air suspension. Batch mills are generally used only where small quantities are processed, since batch operation entails high labor costs for charging and discharging the mill. Closed circuit grinding with size classifiers provides greater operating economy to meet a limiting size specification, and with more uniform size distribution.

Particle Size Classifiers

Classifiers separate out the fine product, and return the coarse material (circulating load) to the mill for regrinding with the new material being fed to the mill. With the fines being continuously removed, a mill performs much more efficiently.

Wet classifiers are generally used for large scale wet-milling operations, such as in cement and ore processing plants. The simplest type of wet classifier is a settling basin arranged so that the fines do not have time to settle out and are drawn off, while the coarse material is raked to a central

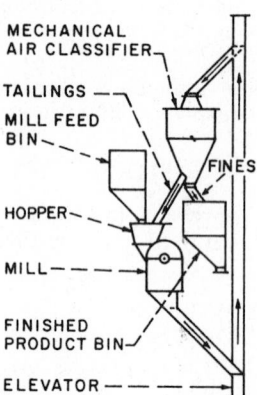

Fig. 4-10B. A hammer mill in a closed circuit with air classifier.

discharge. Wet classifiers of this type do not present an explosion hazard.

Dry classifiers may be installed external to the mill in a closed circuit (see Fig. 4-10B), or they may be internal as an integral part of the mill (see Fig. 4-10C).

Air classifiers are used for most dry milling operations. There are a number of different types, but all are based upon the principles of air drag and particle inertia. One type directs an air stream across a stream of the particles to be classified. One type has adjustable flow baffles, another utilizes the principle of a change in direction of air flow (see Fig. 4-10D). The double-cone classifier utilizes centrifugal action, induced by flow through vanes, which causes

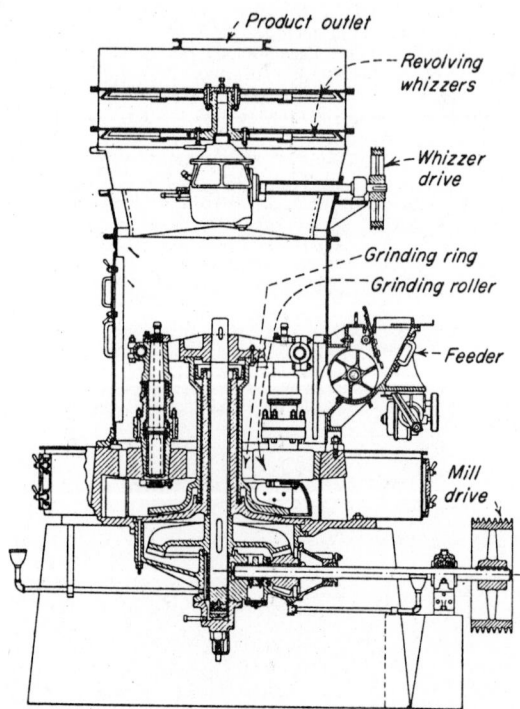

Fig. 4-10C. A Raymond high-side mill with internal whizzer classifier.

Fig. 4-10A. Batch and continuous grinding systems.

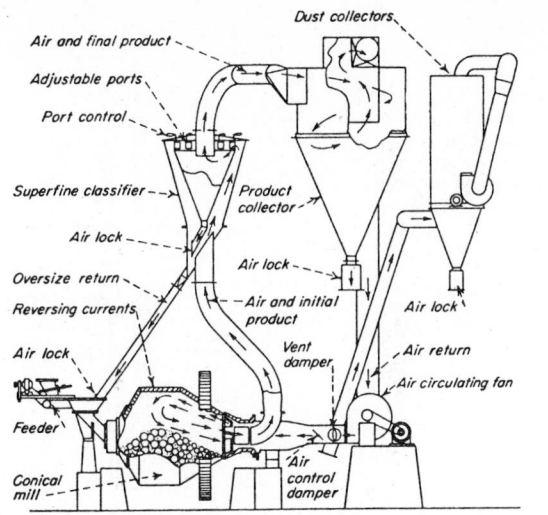

Fig. 4-10D. A Hardinge conical mill with reversed-current air classifier.

coarse particles to move outward and down the wall of the inner cone and thus return to the grinding zone, while the upward moving air stream entrains the fines (see Fig. 4-10E).

Rotating blades constitute the main elements of several types of classifiers. The centrifugal motion established by the rotating blades tends to throw the coarser particles outward and returns them to the grinding zone, while the fines are carried off in the air stream (see Fig. 4-10C).

Each classifier is designed to separate a range of sizes, but these ranges may be extended by design changes, although such changes may result in sacrificing capacity.

Fire and Explosion Safety

All mills producing combustible dusts should be isolated. The preferable location is in a separate, detached, one-story, noncombustible building entirely above grade. Adequate explosion venting is a must (see Sec. 15, Chap. 7). Surfaces of room interiors and equipment are made smooth to minimize dust accumulations and facilitate cleaning. If it is necessary to locate a milling operation within a multiple

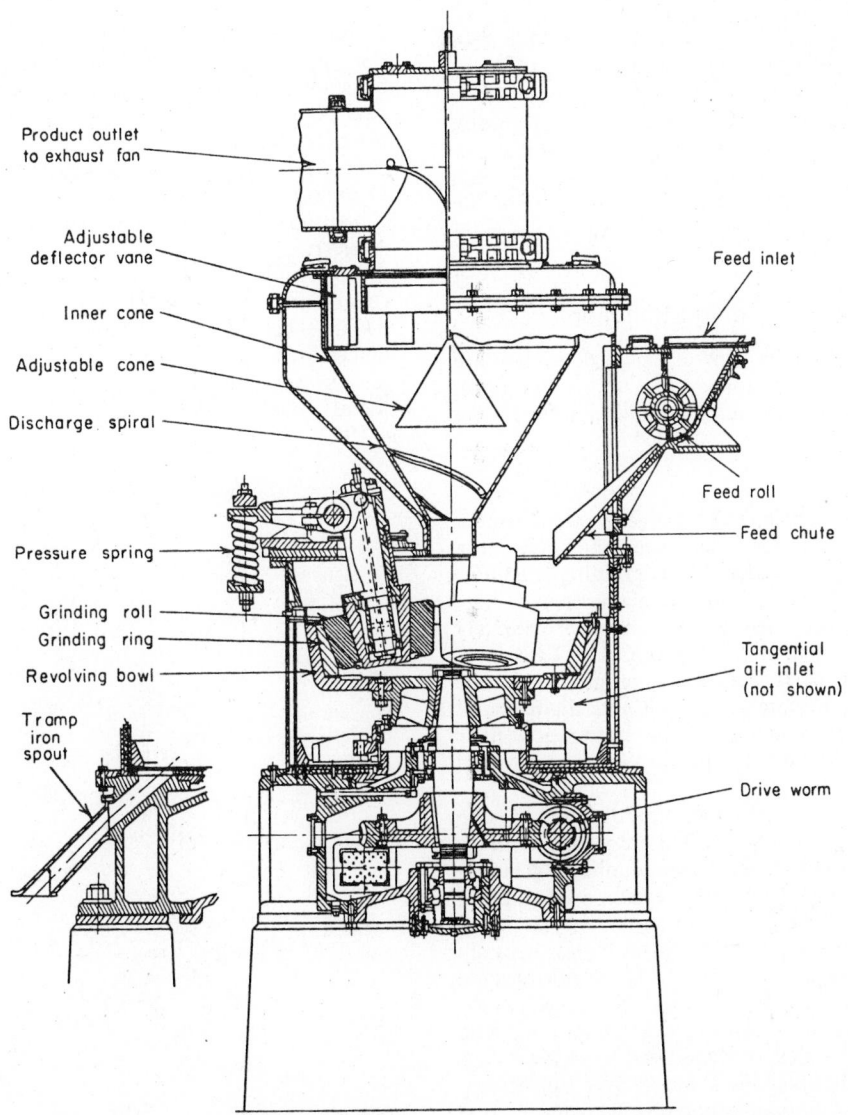

Fig. 4-10E. A bowl mill. (Raymond Div. Combustion Engineering Inc.)

purpose building, the preferable location is in a room with at least one exterior wall that can be arranged to relieve explosion pressures; conversely interior walls around the mill area are of explosion-resistant construction.

While the mill is the source of the combustible dust and may also provide the ignition source, it is seldom directly subjected to explosion pressures. The explosions generally develop somewhere in the system downstream of the mill. Also, mills are generally constructed substantially enough to withstand explosion pressures. Where this is not the case, explosion venting is needed to vent pressure buildup and minimize damage.

Insofar as practical, nonsparking construction materials are used to minimize sparks which might serve as an ignition source. Magnetic separators are installed ahead of mills to remove foreign ferrous metal, and screens are used to remove rock and other nonferrous foreign material. Mills are grounded to minimize the possibility of ignition by static sparks. No open flames or smoking is permitted, and welding and cutting equipment is used only when the mill is shut down and the area has been made entirely dust-free.

Good housekeeping is essential. Well-designed grinding mills minimize dust leakage and reduce necessary cleaning. However, it is not always possible to maintain absolutely tight systems. Vacuum cleaning is preferable for removal of any dust which does escape into the room, since this does not introduce the hazard of putting dust into suspension and forming explosive dust clouds.

Particularly for those grinding operations where ignition sources are difficult to control, the equipment may be protected by introducing a continuous flow of inert gas, such as carbon dioxide, nitrogen, or flue gas, thereby reducing the normal oxygen content within the equipment to a point where an explosion cannot occur.

B. Types of Grinding Equipment

Grinding mills fall into six general categories. They are (1) tumbling mills, (2) ring-roller mills, (3) roller mills, (4) hammer mills, (5) disk attrition mills, and (6) jet mills. Each type is discussed in the following paragraphs.

Tumbling Mills

These include ball, pebble, rod tube, and compartment mills. All have a cylindrical or conical shell and rotate on a horizontal axis. They are charged with grinding mediums consisting of balls of steel, flint, or porcelain, or with steel rods. The ball mill is short in length, generally approximately the same length as its diameter. They use large balls on a coarse feed to produce a relatively coarse product. The tube mill is generally long in comparison with its diameter. It uses smaller balls than a ball mill, and produces a finer product. A ball mill may be either batch type or continuous (see Fig. 4-10F).

The compartment mill is a combination of ball and tube mills. It consists of a cylinder divided into two or more sections by perforated partitions. The preliminary grinding takes place at one end, and the finish grinding takes place at the discharge end.

A pebble mill is a tube mill which utilizes flint or ceramic pebbles as the grinding medium. It may be lined with ceramic or other nonmetallic liners.

Ball and pebble mills are simple to operate and versatile in use. They consist of a steel or stone-lined cylindrical steel shell which is rotated horizontally about its axis. Pulverizing is accomplished by the tumbling action of steel balls or stone pebbles on the material between them.

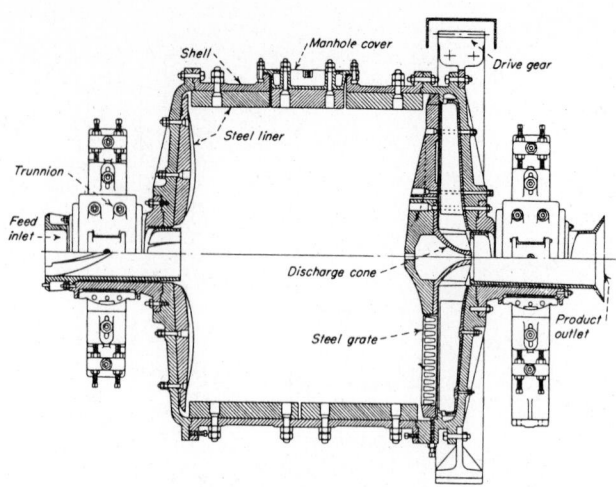

Fig. 4-10F. *A Marcy grate-type continuous ball mill.* (Mine and Smelter Supply Co.)

Ring-Roller Mills

These mills consist of rollers that operate in conjunction with grinding rings (see Fig. 4-10C). They should be distinguished from roller mills. Grinding takes place between the ring and the rollers. Either the ring or the rollers may be stationary, and the grinding ring may be in either a horizontal or vertical position. Ring-roller mills may consist of as many as three rows of balls, one above the other. Pressure is applied either by heavy springs (see Fig. 4-10G) to provide the required load for proper pulverizing, or by centrifugal force of the rollers against the ring (see Fig. 4-10C).

Bowl mills are a type of ring-roller mill where the grinding rollers are stationary and the grinding ring rotates. The distance between the rollers and the ring is set at a predetermined clearance to produce the required fineness. Rollers do not touch the ring, and thus there is no metal-to-metal contact between the grinding surfaces (see Fig. 4-10E).

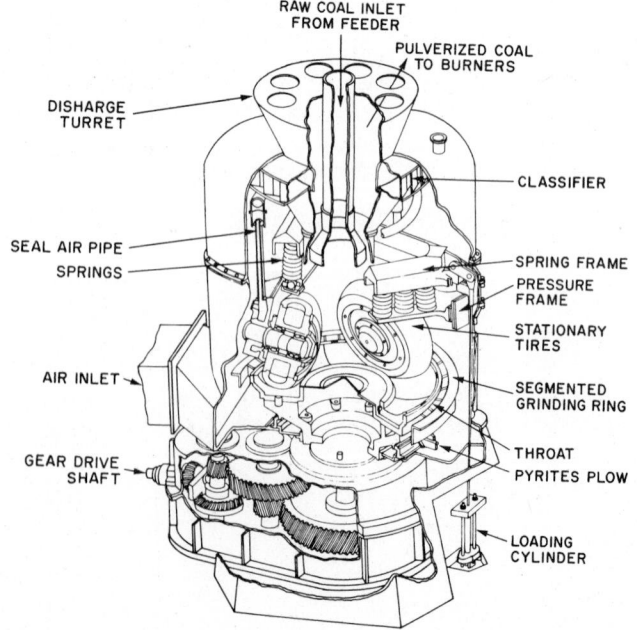

Fig. 4-10G. *A B & W pulverizer, Type M.P.S.* (Babcock & Wilcox)

Roller Mills

In roller mills the material is passed between two or more rolls operating at differential speeds. Smooth rolls are used for pastes, and the material is discharged from the final roll by a scraping blade (see Fig. 4-10H). For milling dry materials, the rolls are made with various types of corrugation. The two types most generally used are the dull and the sharp, which are used in various combinations and various speed ratios.

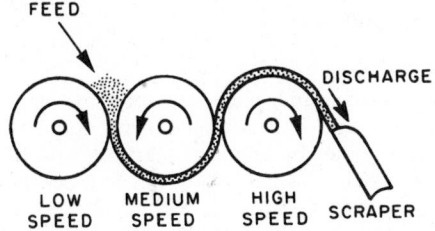

Fig. 4-10H. A roller mill for paint grinding.

Hammer Mills

Hammer mills employ hammers (or beaters) attached to a rotating shaft operating at high speeds to pulverize material. The rotor shaft is generally horizontal, but may operate vertically. The hammers may be T-shaped elements, stirrups, bars, or rings fixed or pivoted to the rotor shaft or to disks fixed to the shaft. The rotor operates the hammers in a housing containing grinding plates or liners. A cylindrical screen or grating usually encloses all or part of the rotor, and serves as an internal classifier. Fineness of the product is determined by rotor speed, feed rate, clearance between hammers and grinding plates, the number and type of hammers, and the size of discharge openings. The grinding action results from impact and attrition between particles being ground, the housing and the grinding elements (see Fig. 4-10I).

In the dual-screen pulverizer, which is used to grind materials to a granular uniform powder of No. 30 or No. 40 sieve fineness, the feed enters opposite ends of the rotor and reduces the size of particles in three stages by hammers of decreasing size.

The disintegrator has a vertical rotating shaft with hammers running at close clearance to the inside of the cylindrical screen which completely encloses the disintegration chamber. Hammers may be either rigidly fixed to the shaft or swinging. The feed enters parallel to the axis of the rotor shaft, and the product is discharged radially out through the perforated sizing screen (see Fig. 4-10J).

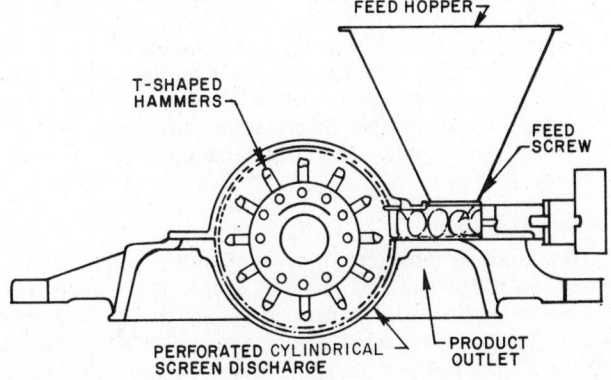

Fig. 4-10I. A Mikro-Pulverizer hammer mill (Pulverizing Machinery Co.)

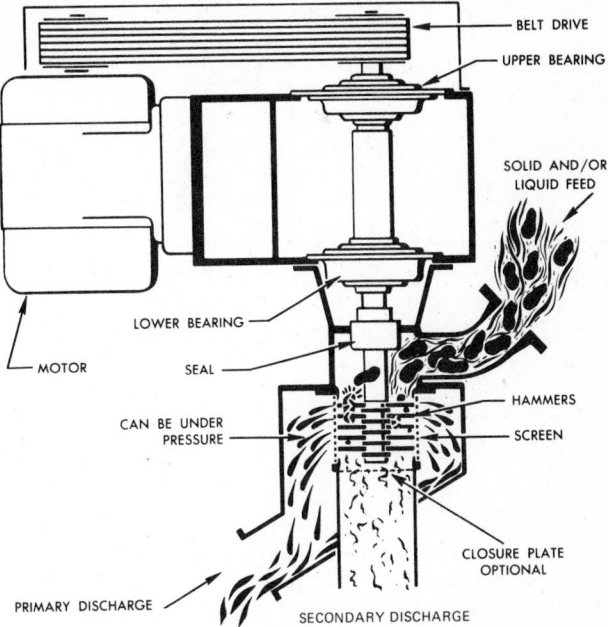

Fig. 4-10J. Reitz disintegrator (Reitz Mfg. Co.)

Pin mills are high-speed mills having pinbreakers in the grinding circuit. Pins may be on a rotor disk with circular rows between stator pins, or pins may be on two rotors operating in opposite directions (see Fig. 4-10K).

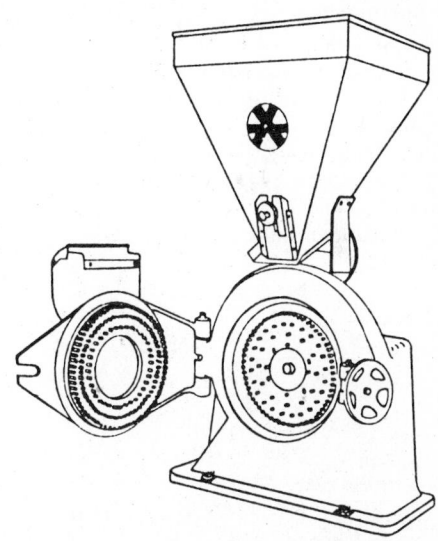

Fig. 4-10K. An Alpine-Kolloplex pin mill (Alpine American Corp.)

Disk Attrition Mills

In attrition mills the grinding takes place between steel disks mounted with interchangeable metal or abrasive grinding plates rotating at high speeds in either a horizontal or vertical plane. One disk may be rotated while the other disk is stationary, or two disks may be rotated in opposite directions. The distance between the disks is adjustable. The material enters near the axis, passes between the grinding plates and is discharged at the periphery of the disks (see Fig. 4-10L).

Buhrstone mills are a type of attrition mill which utilize hard circular stones as the grinding media. Material enters the mill through a center hole in one of the stones, is dis-

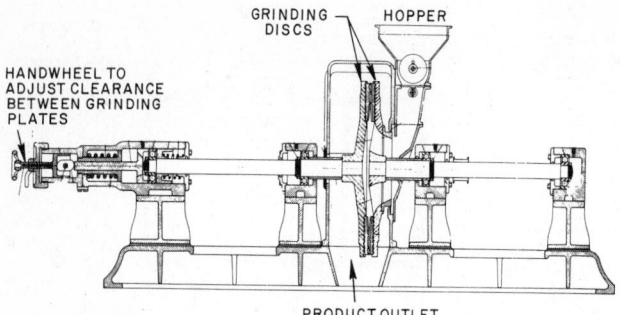

Fig. 4-10L. *A double-runner attrition mill* (Sprout, Waldron & Co.)

tributed between the stone faces and ground while working its way to the periphery.

Jet Mills

In jet mills, gaseous fluid-energy is admitted in high-velocity streams at an angle around the periphery of a grinding and classifying chamber, or the fluid streams may convey the material into a chamber at high velocity where two streams impact upon each other. In either case, as the particles travel around the grinding chamber, there is a high degree of turbulence which causes the particles to grind upon themselves (see Fig. 4-10M).

C.   Application

Agricultural Products

The traditional machine for grinding wheat and rye into high-grade flour is the roller mill. Generally, rolls with dull corrugation are used, but for very tough wheat, a sharp roll is used against a sharp roll, and for other grades, various combinations of dull and sharp rolls at various speeds are used. Rolls with sharp corrugation are used for grinding corn and feed.

High-speed hammer mills or pin mills are used to produce

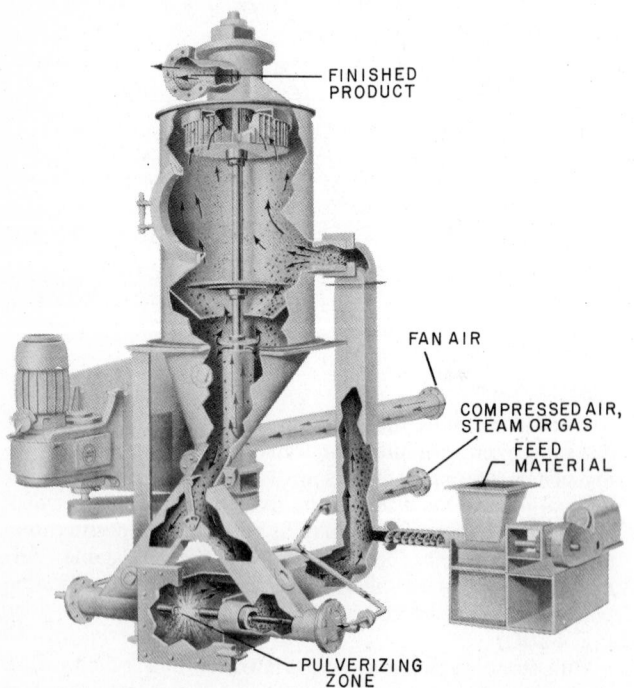

Fig. 4-10M. *A Majac jet pulverizer* (Majac Inc.)

flour with controlled protein content. Disk attrition mills are also used for grinding wheat.

After the oil has been extracted, soybeans or soybean cake is ground in attrition mills or flour rolls, depending upon whether the product is to be a feed meal or flour. In some cases, a hammer mill may be used as a preliminary disintegrator for pressed cakes, including linseed cake and cottonseed cake.

Where only medium fineness is required, a hammer mill is used to produce starch, potato flour, tapioca, and similar flours. For finer flour products, a high-speed impact mill, such as a pin mill, is used.

Carbon Products

Bituminous coal and pitch are used as fuel for firing industrial furnaces, boilers, and rotary kilns. Pulverized coal is burned either by blowing it directly into the furnace as it is pulverized, or by pulverizing it in a central grinding system and storing it in a bin until it is used. Ball, tube, ring-roller, bowl, and ball and ring-type mills are used for direct firing of large installations. Ring-roller mills are also used to pulverize coal for bin systems.

Anthracite coal is harder to reduce than bituminous coal. Ball or hammer mills are used to pulverize anthracite coal for foundry facing mixtures. Calcined anthracite, used in the manufacture of electrodes, is generally pulverized in ball and tube mills, or ring-roller mills.

The grinding characteristics of coke vary from petroleum coke, which is relatively easy to grind, to certain foundry and retort coke, which is difficult to grind. Where uniform size of particles with a minimum of fines is required, rod or ball mills are used in a closed circuit with screens.

Natural graphite is classified in three grades: flake, crystalline, and amorphous. Flake is the most difficult to grind to a fine powder, and the crystalline is the most abrasive. Ball, tube, ring-roller, and jet mills are used for grinding graphite, with or without air classification. For handling large capacities, ball and tube mills are used, especially for the flake and crystalline grades. Graphite for pencils is ground in a jet pulverizer. Ball mills in a closed circuit with air classifiers have been used for grinding artificial graphite.

Charcoal and Gilsonite are ground in hammer mills with air classifiers.

Chemicals

Hammer mills are generally used to pulverize dry colors and dyestuffs, with pebble mills used for small lots. Hammer or jet mills with air classifiers for size limitation are used for dyes that are coarsely crystalline.

For fine grinding of sulfur, a ring-roller mill is used, with inert gas injected into the mill.

Pulverizing of metallic soaps, such as stearates, requires including provisions for keeping the material cool and in rapid motion. Since these materials tend to cake, batch grinding is not practicable. Stearates are pulverized in multi-cage mills, screen mills, and hammer mills with air classification.

Organic Polymers

The grinding characteristics of various resins, gums, waxes, hard rubber, and molding powders are such that when a finely divided product is required, it may be necessary to use a water-jacketed mill or a pulverizer with an air classifier in which cooled air is introduced into the system. Hammer mills are generally used for this purpose. Some resins with low softening temperatures can be ground by mixing dry ice with the material before grinding or by introducing refrigerated air into the mill.

Most gums and resins that are used in the paint, varnish, or plastic industries do not require very fine grinding, and hammer mills or roll crushers will produce a satisfactory product. Some resins used in the phenolic resin industries require very fine pulverization, and a pebble mill, cooled with water or brine in a closed circuit with an air classifier, is used. A ring-roll mill with an internal air classifier is used to pulverize phenolformaldehyde resins.

Hard rubber is ground on heavy steam-heated rollers, with the material passing through a series of rolls in a closed circuit with screens and air classifiers. There is a differential in the roll diameters, and the machines operate at rather low speeds to prevent the generation of an excessive amount of heat.

Molding powders are produced with hammer mills or attrition mills in closed circuits, equipped with either screens or air classifiers.

Cryogenic Grinding

Although cooling is required for some mills because of the material being ground, cryogenic grinding can be applied to any size or type of mill to produce a smaller particle size than could otherwise be obtained. Converting an existing mill can be accomplished by the addition of a liquid nitrogen storage tank, a piping system, and a properly designed hopper. The principle is to provide adequate cooling of the material before grinding.

The material can be pre-cooled in the hopper by creating a nitrogen bath, it can be cooled in the grinding chamber by spraying in liquid nitrogen, or by using both methods simultaneously. Gaseous nitrogen has been used for years to provide an inert atmosphere in mills, particularly in jet mills. Cryogenic grinding can be designed to also provide a protective inert atmosphere within the mill.

In spice grinding, freezing the spice before grinding upgrades the product, giving superior appearance and retaining the aroma and flavor usually lost when the product is not pre-cooled.

Cryogenic grinding has been applied to the production of powdered coatings used for insulation and protective coatings, and for powders used in the manufacture of bearings containing improved wearlife and increased lubrication properties. Other areas where cryogenic grinding may have application are in recycling scrap materials, grinding existing materials for newer applications and processes (rotational molding, spray powder for textile stiffener), and grinding protein concentrations.

Bibliography

NFPA Codes, Standards, and Recommended Practices (see the latest *NFPA Publications and Visual Aids Catalog* for availability of current editions of the following documents)

NFPA No. 61A, Standard for Manufacturing and Handling Starch.

NFPA No. 61C, Standard for the Prevention of Fire and Dust Explosions in Feed Mills.

NFPA No. 62, Standard for the Prevention of Dust Explosions in the Production, Packaging and Handling of Pulverized Sugar and Cocoa.

NFPA No. 63, Fundamental Principles for the Prevention of Dust Explosions in Industrial Plants.

NFPA No. 68, Explosion Venting Guide.

NFPA No. 69, Standard on Explosion Prevention Systems.

NFPA No. 651, Standard for the Manufacture of Aluminum or Magnesium Powder.

NFPA No. 654, Standard for the Prevention of Dust Explosions in the Plastics Industry.

NFPA No. 655, Standard for Prevention of Sulfur Fires and Explosions.

NFPA No. 656, Standard for the Prevention of Dust Ignition in Spice Grinding Plants.

NFPA No. 664, Standard for the Prevention of Dust Explosions in Woodworking and Wood Flour Manufacturing Plants.

Additional Readings

Grobel, Edward, "Cryogenic Grinding Gives Process Flexibility," *Cryogenics and Industrial Gases*, Vol. 9, No. 4, July/Aug. 1974, pp. 27-30.

Perry, Robert H. and Chilton, Cecil H., *Chemical Engineers' Handbook*, 5th ed., McGraw-Hill, New York, 1973.

Section 4

Chapter 11

SOLVENT EXTRACTION AND SOLVENT RECOVERY

Solvent extraction and solvent recovery, two closely related industrial processes, are covered in this chapter.

A. Solvent Extraction

As discussed in this chapter, the term solvent extraction applies only to commercial scale solvent extraction of animal and vegetable oils and fats by the use of flammable solvents such as pentane, hexane, and heptane as covered in NFPA No. 36, Solvent Extraction Plants. Specialized types of solvent extraction processes are utilized in many other industries, such as chemical and mineral, and although this chapter is not applicable to them, many of the fundamentals for solvent handling apply.

Normal hexane and heptane have become the predominant solvents for the extraction of vegetable and animal oils and fats because of their relatively low cost, stability, excellent thermal qualities and selectivity for oils and fats. (The physical properties of these solvents are given in Table 3-11A, Sec. 3, Chap. 11.) However, due to the relatively low flash points of these solvents, they present fire or explosion hazards when used in solvent extraction plants.

The entire process consists essentially of the following operations: (1) storage of raw materials, (2) preparation process, (3) extraction, (4) storage of finished materials, oil and meal, and (5) manufacture of high protein foods.

Probably the simplest of all is the preparation and extraction of fats from animals. The dead animals are ground up and put through a cooker-extractor and cooked until the moisture content is reduced low enough for solvent penetration. After cooling, the vessel is charged with solvent and batch-wise extraction is begun. The end products of this process would be inedible fats and animal feed mixtures. This type of extraction can be more hazardous than continuous extractors, commonly used in vegetable oil extraction, because of the cycling and the greater chance of solvent vapor loss under careless handling.

Although soybeans probably rank as the most widely used bean for oil extraction, other oil-bearing beans or seeds are cottonseed, flax, castor, sunflower, safflower, milo, peanuts, copra nuts, etc. The storage of these raw materials is comparable with those requirements relating to grain storage and NFPA No. 61B, Grain Elevators and Bulk Grain Handling Facilities, provides guidance.

First the beans or seeds are prepared for solvent extraction. In most cases, this is done in a structure located more than 100 ft from the solvent extraction equipment because the preparation process can create a possible source of ignition to solvent vapors that may inadvertently be released during the extraction process. In some cases, the preparation process can be located within 50 ft of the extraction process if an adequate vapor barrier is provided. NFPA No. 61C, Prevention of Fire and Dust Explosions in Feed Mills, provides guidance for the preparation process.

The solvent extraction process, including solvent recovery, is essentially as detailed in Figure 4-11A. The type of extractor may be one of several. They include: (1) the basket type, which can be vertical, horizontal, rectangular, or stationary; (2) rotary; (3) perforated belt; (4) total immersion; (5) filtration; (6) rectangular loop (counter flow);

and (7) batch. Details of most of these are contained in the NFPA Solvent Extraction Plants Standard. Despite the seemingly complicated array of equipment, there are three basic parts of a solvent extraction process, namely extraction, desolventizing, and solvent recovery (distillation) all of which should be segregated from possible ignition sources in the plant. Typical separation distances are recommended in Figure 4-11B.

Bulk solvent unloading and storage locations are covered in NFPA No. 36. Additional guidance is given on repairs that can be made while the plant is operating, as well as for repairs made when plant is closed and purged.

In the extraction stage the oil is removed from the oil-bearing material, but after removal of the oil or fat the material remains saturated with solvent. This is removed by the desolventizer which drives off the solvent by the action of steam heat applied both directly and indirectly.

The miscella, as oil-bearing solvent is termed, goes to the evaporator or distillation system, as it is sometimes called, where the solvent is driven off the oil by the action of heat, direct steam, and vacuum.

The evaporation of solvent from vegetable or animal oil poses little difficulty inasmuch as the solvent has a relatively low boiling range (approximately 146° to 156°F) and most oil can withstand temperatures up to 250°F for short periods without undergoing discoloration or polymerization. Thus, a wide temperature differential plus the use of stripping steam and high vacuum in the final stage facilitates complete desolventizing of the oil.

Solvent recovery from the miscella (oil-solvent-water) is accomplished by condensers usually of the shell and tube type, the tubes containing the cooling water, and the shell the solvent-water vapors. Cold water supplying condensers may be from city water, deep wells, cooling tower ponds, or combination thereof. Many plants incorporate a safety water tank which will automatically supply the condenser needs in

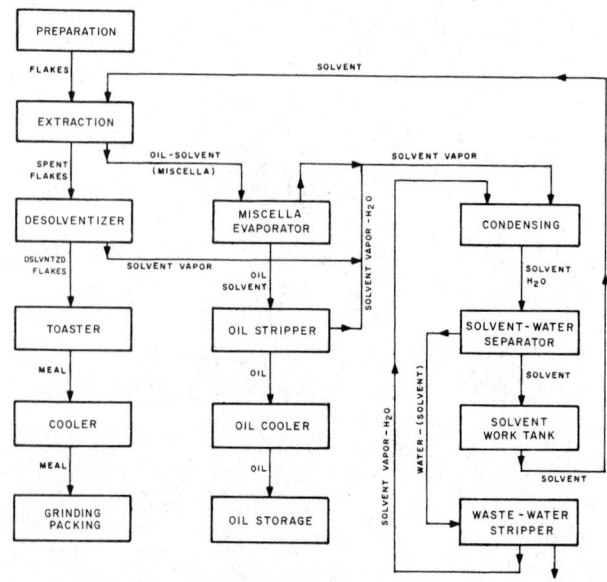

Fig. 4-11A. Generalized flow diagram.

event of normal water source failure until such time as the plant may safely be shut down, thus assuring vapors are not carried through the condensers.

Recovery of solvent from the solids (spent flakes) is accomplished by a desolventizer, usually a multiple kettle steam jacketed unit from which vapors pass via scrubber to remove fines. Solvent-water vapors are recovered by condensers as described above. Condensed solvent-water is collected in a separating tank and water decanted through a waste water evaporator before being discharged to a sump from which it is pumped free of solvent to the sewer.

Following the removal of solvent, the liquid (oil) and solids (meal) are conveyed to storage. To assure complete absence of residual solvent, each is tested and analyzed before reaching the storage facility.

Some meals (spent solvent free flakes) may be further subjected to processes which will enhance their protein content. This process generally employs the use of alcohol and is an entirely separate operation from that of solvent extraction, thus not treated herein. However, such installations should comply with those standards applying to processes employing alcohol or similar solvents.

Protection

Protection of solvent extraction plants is based upon the following tenets:

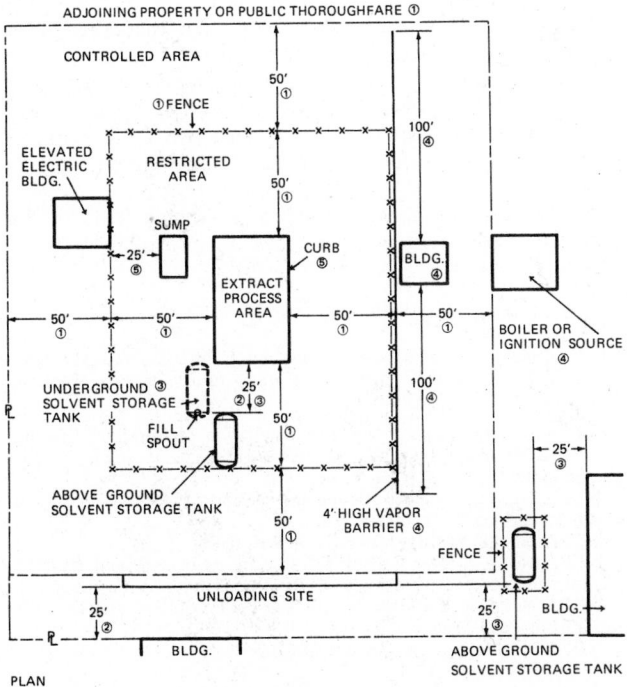

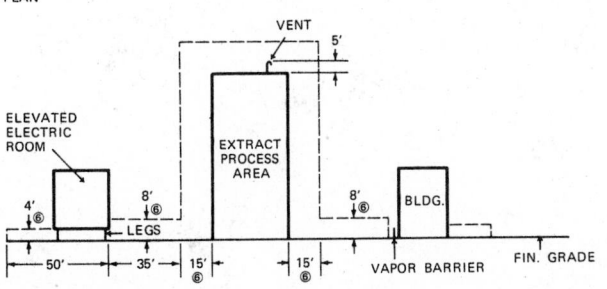

Fig. 4-11B.   A typical distance diagram.

1. Elimination of ignition sources by:
   (a) Static grounding and bonding of all noncurrent carrying parts of electrical machinery, equipment, and buildings (see NFPA No. 77, Recommended Practice on Static Electricity).
   (b) Installing electrical wiring in accord with provisions of NFPA No. 70, National Electrical Code, governing hazardous locations.
   (c) Prohibiting all open flames within restricted areas.
   (d) Using nonferrous rotary parts for fans, blowers, etc.
2. Elimination of fuel sources, combustible mixtures, by:
   (a) Maintaining solvent losses to a minimum.
   (b) Controlling temperatures in desolventizing equipment.
   (c) Using continuous and portable atmosphere analyzers in critical locations.
   (d) Using effective seals in conveying equipment at points in process where vapors may escape.
   (e) Providing adequate continuous mechanical ventilation. A down-draft air flow is suggested because of vapor density of solvents.
3. Institute operating procedures and methods involving:
   (a) An output capacity which does not overtax the plant's design.
   (b) Prestart-up and shutdown methods for vessels that will keep the transition time through explosive range at a minimum.
   (c) Control of solvent losses so such does not exceed .25 percent of the weight of product processed. (New plants are guaranteed to meet a maximum of solvent loss of less than .15 percent.)
   (d) Availability of a reserve safety water system for condensers to function in event of failure of primary supply.
   (e) A monthly plant inspection program with written report to the operations manager.
4. Basic fire protection features:
   (a) A water deluge or similar system to keep all structural members, vessels, and other contents wetted by direct impingement or run-down (see NFPA No. 13, Installation of Sprinkler Systems; NFPA No. 15, Water Spray Fixed Systems; and NFPA No. 16, Foam Water Sprinkler and Spray Systems).
   (b) An outside hydrant loop.
   (c) An adequate number of appropriate portable fire extinguishers that are easily accessible.
   (d) A dependable source of water at adequate volume and pressure for the extinguishing systems and yard hydrants.

B. Solvent Recovery

Solvents or thinners from paint, lacquer, waterproofing compounds, impregnating compounds, and from various extraction processes, such as the degreasing of wool or the manufacture of drug extracts, generally are vaporized by warm air in drying ovens, although vaporization is sometimes produced by direct contact with steamheated surfaces.

The solvent may be recovered from the vapor and this may be accomplished in three general ways:

1. Adsorption by material such as activated carbon or silica gel, revaporization by means of steam, followed by condensation by cooling, with subsequent recovery of the solvent by decanting the separated layers of condensed steam and solvent.

2. Dissolving the vapors in suitable solvents in scrubbing equipment, followed by separation in distillation apparatus.

3. When vapors are in high concentration, they may be recovered by cooling, either with water or special refrigeration equipment, or by first compressing and later cooling; in either case, obtaining the solvent directly without further separation or purification by distillation.

Relatively simple apparatus has been devised in which the vaporization and condensation of the solvent may take place in the presence of air or inert gas in a single piece of equipment which is heated by steam with the vapors condensed by cold water pipes. The circulation of vapor-laden air or other gas from the hot section will take place naturally, carrying the vapors to the cooling pipes. This equipment is usually restricted to small-scale operations. For larger apparatus, forced circulation of gases under exact control is generally necessary.

Recovery Installations

Although differing considerably in detail, solvent recovery equipments for larger operations may be classified into two general groups according to fire hazard:

1. The adsorption and scrubbing type, which involves vapor mixtures of relatively low concentration, generally below the lower flammable limit.

2. The direct condensation type, which usually involves much richer mixtures so that the atmosphere is within or must pass through the flammable range whenever operations are started or stopped.

Low Vapor Concentration Methods: In the first group, particularly the adsorption method, the closer the vapor concentration is to the lower flammable limit, the more efficient is the recovery process. Consequently, the concentration is kept high by reducing ventilation as much as possible while still maintaining conditions below the LFL. This leaves a very small margin of safety, and such operations are provided with every reasonable safeguard against explosion, including ample explosion vents, and continuous supervision and control of vapor conditions by a flammable gas analyzer (see Sec. 12, Chap. 4).

High Vapor Concentration Methods: Solvent recovery from vapor concentrations above the upper flammable limits is done by cooling or by compression. Cooling is especially hazardous because explosive conditions are usually encountered whenever the equipment is started, whenever it is shut down for repairs or for any other reason, and whenever air enters due to some defect or breakdown in equipment. Inert gas is commonly used to keep air out of the equipment.

Distillation

Separation or purification of the recovered vapors by distillation is generally accomplished by means of closed stills heated by steam and operated at low pressures or under a vacuum. The vapor is usually recovered in a water-cooled condenser and conducted directly by gravity to the solvent storage tank.

The danger from distillation equipment, if it contains a vapor-air mixture, is mostly from possible explosions when the equipment is opened for repairs or inspection. Purging the entire system with inert gas negates this hazard. Other dangers are from the bursting of the vaporizer tank due to neglect or failure of auxiliary devices, from liquid escaping from broken gage glasses, and from failure of the water supply to the condenser so that large volumes of vapor are discharged. Suitable relief valves or vapor seals which will operate well within safe working pressure limits and which are vented outdoors are needed on stills. Level indicators are of the nonbreakable type. Where considerable water from vapor is recovered, care should be taken in waste water disposal. Water from separators should be evaporated before entering sewers or bodies of water.

Electrical Safeguards: Follow provisions of the National Electrical Code governing hazardous locations for solvent recovery areas, equipment, and buildings. Provide grounding and bonding of equipment to control static electricity.

Fire Protection Methods: The danger from stills for reclaiming naphtha, alcohol, or other flammable solvents arises primarily when the apparatus is emptied for repairs or inspection and when the receptacle contains a flammable vapor-air mixture. Locations detached from the remainder of the property are best for stills. Fail-safe controls are incorporated in still design.

Solvent recovery processes involving flammable materials in both liquid and vapor states are unusually hazardous and are best conducted in detached locations. If located in a building, good practice requires protection by automatic sprinklers or water spray systems, adequate ventilation and provisions for explosion venting, and floors that are properly drained.

Signs indicating hazards, restrictions, and instructions for operation and emergency procedure are provided.

Bibliography

NFPA Codes, Standards, and Recommended Practices (see the latest *NFPA Publications and Visual Aids Catalog* for availability of current editions of the following documents)

NFPA No. 13, Standard for the Installation of Sprinkler Systems.

NFPA No. 15, Standard for Water Spray Fixed Systems for Fire Protection.

NFPA No. 16, Standard for the Installation of Foam-Water Sprinkler Systems and Foam-Water Systems.

NFPA No. 36. Standard for Solvent Extraction Plants.

NFPA No. 61B, Standard for the Prevention of Fire and Dust Explosions in Grain Elevators and Bulk Grain Handling Facilities.

NFPA No. 61C, Standard for the Prevention of Fire and Dust Explosions in Feed Mills.

NFPA No. 70, National Electrical Code.

Chapter 12

REFRIGERATION SYSTEMS

Refrigeration equipment is of concern because some of the gases used as refrigerants are flammable, while others are toxic and can cause fatalities or personal injuries, or interfere with fire fighting operations in case of escape of gas during a fire.

All refrigeration systems are fundamentally heat pump assemblies used to remove heat from an enclosure, fluid, or other material. The removed heat is pumped away and discharged into some other space or into some heat-absorbing medium such as water or outside air.

Transfer of heat must be accomplished by the use of some transfer material that will readily absorb heat, carry heat, and release heat, all under controlled conditions.

This heat transfer material is called the refrigerant. Effective refrigerants are those that can be changed from a liquid to a gas within the system at the desired temperatures. Heat is absorbed by the refrigerant when it changes from a liquid to a gas. Heat is given off by the refrigerant when it is changed from a gas to a liquid.

A.   Refrigerant Hazard Properties

Refrigerants have been placed into three groups for purposes of categorizing them according to their basic flammability and toxicity hazards. Table 4-12A lists some of the more common refrigerants. In Table 4-12A, the "R" number in parenthesis following the refrigerant name refers to the standard numerical designation in ANSI B79.1, Number Designation of Refrigerants.

B.   Refrigeration Cycles

Two refrigeration cycles are employed—the mechanical compression cycle and the absorption cycle. They have in common the evaporation and condensation of a refrigerant liquid, occurring at two pressure levels within the unit. The two cycles differ in that the absorption cycle uses a heat-operated generator to produce the pressure differential where the mechanical compression cycle uses a compressor. The absorption cycle substitutes physiochemical processes for the purely mechanical processes of the compression cycle. Both cycles require energy for operation: heat in the absorption cycle, and mechanical energy in the compression cycle.

Compressors generally are driven by electric motors although some are driven by steam or internal combustion engines and turbines. Of the many combinations that have been tried for absorption cooling, only the lithium bromide-water, and the ammonia-water cycles remain in common use, the former being used primarily for air-conditioning applications, the latter for large tonnage industrial applications requiring low temperatures for process work and small self-contained units for indirect systems for domestic air conditioning.

Heat energy for operation of absorption systems is supplied by steam, hot water, or gas burners.

In either type of system high pressure warm refrigerant gas passes through a condenser where it gives up heat and condenses to a liquid. It then passes through an expansion nozzle and on to an evaporator where it vaporizes and absorbs heat; the vapor is then compressed or boiled off to complete the cycle. The evaporator is that portion of the system where vaporization occurs to cool the desired location or fluid.

C.   Types of Systems

As the location being refrigerated or cooled may be a tight, insulated space or occupied by people, refrigerant leakage constitutes a principal hazard of refrigeration systems. This hazard is obviously related to the extent to which piping and equipment containing refrigerants occupy such locations. A major distinction is made in this respect depending upon whether a direct system or an indirect system is present.

In the direct system, the evaporator is in direct contact with the material or space refrigerated or is located in air-circulating passages communicating with such spaces. Possibilities of refrigerant leakage into critical hazard areas are greatest with a direct system.

An indirect system is one in which an intermediate heat transfer fluid (called "brine") is first cooled by the refrigerant and then circulated to the material or space refrigerated, or is used to cool the air so circulated. The use of the term "brine" reflects early refrigeration systems that used a sodium or calcium salt and water mixture. Presently organic chemical liquids, such as ethylene glycol, are used as well as brine solutions. Possibilities of refrigerant leakage into critical hazard areas are considerably lessened with an indirect refrigeration system.

D.   Hazards

The hazards of refrigeration systems can be considered in terms of (1) the hazards of equipment failure due to cycle process upsets or mechanical failure, and (2) the hazards resulting from release of refrigerant into structures.

Cycle Process Upsets and Mechanical Failure

As most refrigerants are handled as liquefied gases and processed to produce phase changes from liquids to gases, with corresponding volume changes, possibilities for overpressure exist which could lead to violent rupture of equipment and piping systems. In compression systems, inadvertent introduction of incompressible liquid into the suction of reciprocating compressors has led to mechanical failure of the compressor. Such compressors are also subject to overpressure failures as a result of gas recompression due to faulty valves. Combustion explosions have occurred in compressors handling highly flammable refrigerants (Group 3) as a result of accidental introduction of air.

System fabrication materials must be compatible with the refrigerant handled. Refrigeration systems are occasionally installed in areas conducive to external corrosion.

Release of Refrigerant Into Structures

In addition to the toxicity hazard possessed by many refrigerants, release of Group 2 and 3 refrigerants into structures present fire and combustion explosion hazards.

Table 4-12A.   Basic Hazard Data for Some Common Refrigerants

Classification of refrigerants	Formula	Boiling point, °F	Calculated density gas (air = 1)	Auto-ignition temperature, °F	Flammable limits, percent by volume in air		Toxicity
					Lower	Upper	
Group 1 (Nonflammable, except as noted):							
Carbon dioxide (R-744)	CO_2	−109	1.52				Slightly toxic
Monochlorodifluoromethane (R-22)	$CHClF_2$	−42.0	2.98	1,170	Very weakly flammable		Slightly toxic
Dichlorodifluoromethane (R-12)	CCl_2F_2	−22.0	4.17				Nontoxic for ordinary exposure
Dichlorofluoromethane (R-21)	$CHCl_2F$	48.0	3.55	1,026	Very weakly flammable		Slightly toxic
Dichlorotetrafluoroethane (R-114)	$C_2Cl_2F_4$	38.4	5.89				Nontoxic
Trichlorofluoromethane (R-11)	CCl_3F	74.8	4.79				Slightly toxic
Methylene chloride (R-30)	CH_2Cl_2	105.2	2.93	1,139	Very weakly flammable		Slightly toxic
Trichlorotrifluoroethane (R-113)	$C_2Cl_3F_3$	117.6	6.46	1,256	Very weakly flammable		Slightly toxic
Group 2 (Flammable):							
Ammonia (R-717)	NH_3	−28	0.59	1,204	16	25	Toxic
Dichloroethylene (R-1130)	$C_2H_2Cl_2$	99–141	3.35	856	9.7	12.8	Moderately toxic
Ethyl chloride (R-160)	C_2H_3Cl	54.0	2.22	966	3.8	15.4	Moderately toxic
Methyl formate (R-611)	$C_2H_4O_2$	90.0	2.07	869	5.0	23	Toxic
Group 3 (Highly flammable):							
Butane (R-600)	C_4H_{10}	31.0	2.01	900–1,000	1.55	8.6	Slightly toxic
Ethane (R-170)	C_2H_6	−128.0	1.04	959	3.0	12.5	Slightly toxic
Propane (R-240)	C_3H_8	−44.0	1.52	920–1,120	2.2	9.6	Slightly toxic
Ethylene (R-1150)	C_2H_4	−154.8	0.98	914	2.7	36	Slightly toxic

This is especially true of the Group 3 refrigerants (see Sec. 3, Chap. 4, Part F).

Group 2 refrigerants, while flammable, present lesser hazards—primarily because of their lower heats of combustion and relatively high lower limits of flammability (see "anhydrous ammonia," Part F, Sec. 3, Chap. 4). These refrigerants would normally be considered of little fire hazard but their handling in the unusually air-tight structures represented by refrigerated areas has resulted in fires and combustion explosions.

E.   Safeguards

The basic national consensus standard covering the installation of refrigeration systems is ANSI B9. 1 "Safety Code for Mechanical Refrigeration." This Code covers refrigeration equipment location in respect to flammability and toxicity, type of occupancy of the building, foundations, electrical equipment and wiring, machine rooms, ventilation, pipe and fittings, strength and test pressures, safety devices, gages, discharge means, markings, adding or withdrawing of refrigerants, testing for leaks, gas masks, maintenance, and periodic inspection.

An occupancy distinction is made to determine whether direct or indirect systems may be used. Limitations are placed upon the quantity of refrigerant in a system with relation to the volume of the room the system cools. They are based upon the concentration which would be attained if the entire refrigerant content of the system is discharged into the room knowing the toxicity and flammability characteristics of the refrigerant involved. In the case of the highly flammable Group 3 refrigerants, the quantity limitation is intended to prevent the attainment of a lower flammable limit mixture occupying the entire room. Control over ignition sources is also specified under such circumstances.

Bibliography

Additional Readings

"Number Designation of Refrigerants," ANSI B79.1, 1968, American National Standards Institute, New York.

"Safety Code for Mechanical Refrigeration," ANSI B9.1, 1971, American National Standards Institute, New York.

Chapter 13

NUCLEAR REACTORS, RADIATION MACHINES, AND FACILITIES HANDLING RADIOACTIVE MATERIALS

In general, radioactive substances and operations involving radioactive materials or devices and equipment presenting radiation hazards have fire and explosion features corresponding to those of similar materials and operations not having radiation hazards. However, because of the hazard to personnel and the possibility of long term contamination of property from severe exposure to sudden accidental escape of radioactive substances, the subject of protection from radiation hazards deserves special consideration, particularly the procedures that must be followed in emergencies involving radioactive materials.

A. Nuclear Reactors

Nuclear reactors are now in operation in many countries. They are used for research purposes, irradiation of materials, production of radio isotopes, and for power production. As of 1974, some 100 power reactors alone were in operation worldwide.

A nuclear reactor consists of an assembly of fissionable material in sufficient quantities to form a critical or self-sustaining mass, and is either equipped with controls or designed so that the reaction is limited at some predetermined rate. The fissionable material, in the process of undergoing fission, produces neutrons and other radioisotopes. These processes in turn lead to the production of neutron fields, radiation fields, and heat.

In the case of nuclear research facilities, the neutrons, radioisotopes, and radiation fields are the things which are primarily sought, and the heat dissipation is a nuisance.

Some research reactors are operated at such low power levels that heat removal is not necessary. In power reactors the heat is the desired product, and usually the neutrons and the radioactive materials are the things which necessarily need to be controlled.

Various methods of classifying nuclear reactors are in use, based upon: end use, such as research, power, etc.; the form of fuel, homogeneous or heterogeneous (most reactors are now the heterogeneous type); the speed of neutrons, i.e., fast or thermal: the type of cooling material, water, gas, or liquid metal. No one standard method of terminology is used. In many cases the geographical location is used to designate the reactor (Indian Point), a generic name may be used (Vermont Yankee), or even nicknames. Several of the more common designations in use today include: LMFBR, Liquid Metal Fast Breeder Reactor; BWR, Boiling Water Reactor; and HTGCR (sometimes without the C), High Temperature Gas Cooled Reactor. These are all types of power reactors. Some of the research reactor types are the Swimming Pool and Tank Type. A BWR reactor building complex is shown in Figure 4-13A.

Reactor Control

The term "control" as applied to a nuclear reactor refers to the manner of regulating the nuclear activity and its associated rate of heat generation, which is directly proportional to the nuclear reaction rate.

Independent of controls for regulating power output, a reactor is required to have an automatic safety shutdown system. Instruments which detect unsafe conditions must

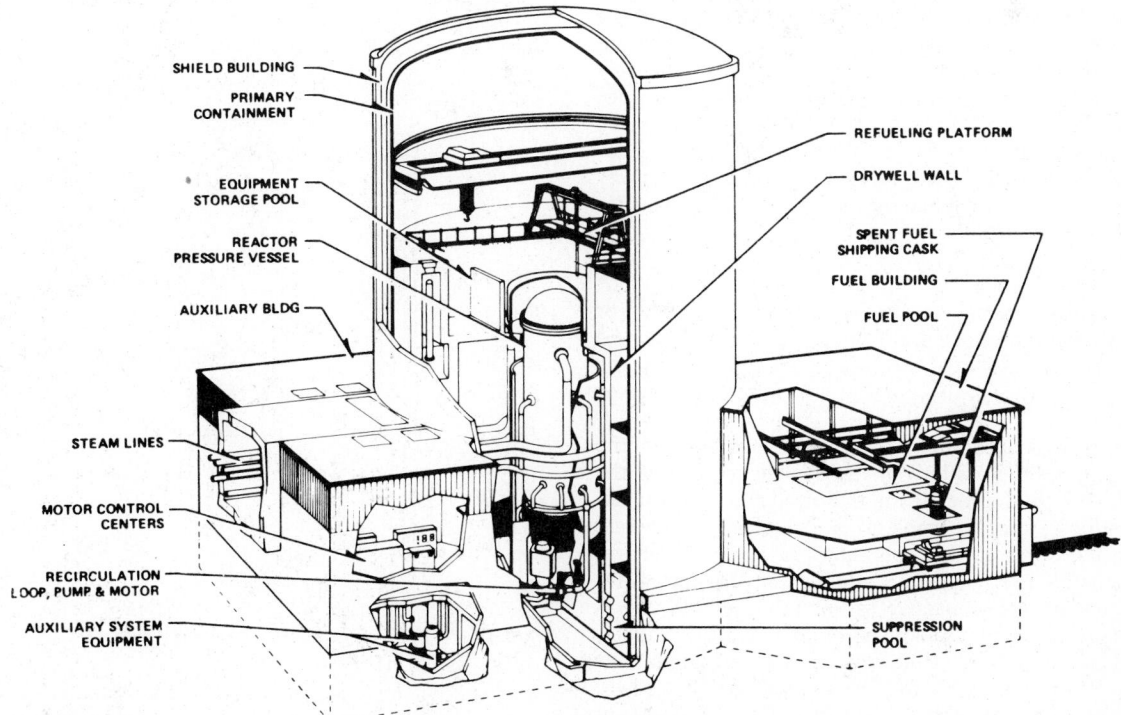

Fig. 4-13A.   A reactor building, fuel building, and auxiliary building which represent the core of a nuclear building complex.

automatically decrease the nuclear reaction. When a reactor is thus shut down automatically by a safety system, it is said to be "tripped" or "scrammed."

The automatic shutdown system may consist of control rods that contain boron, cadmium, or other neutron-absorbing material, pure or as compounds. Safety control devices may be actuated by gravity, hydraulic means, stored inertia devices, heat expansion, springs or other means. Control rods are designed to fail-safe and shut down or "scram" the reactor in case of power or other failures.

Some types of water-moderated reactors have an emergency container of a water-boron, neutron-absorbing solution which can augment the regular control system.

A reactor becomes "critical" when the total rate of production of neutrons, under control conditions, is such that self-sustaining reactions occur. Control methods must be rapid and sensitive, and protected from fire.

The physicist's design of the reactor core is always checked out by approaching the "critical" state in discreet steps. By observing the behavior as the amount of fuel is gradually increased, the point at which the reactor will become critical is determined in advance and proper measures can be taken to prevent either an unanticipated excursion or a runaway chain reaction.

The fissionable reactor fuels uranium-233 and -235, and plutonium-239, must be used, handled, and stored with great care to prevent the accidental formation of a critical mass. Fire fighting should avoid disarray of components. There are no simple methods for evaluating the combined influence of the numerous factors affecting criticality which may exist at the time of a fire or other emergency. Design of facilities for reactor fuel manufacture or fuel storage or handling is such as to avoid criticality, even in event of complete flooding by water from any source, including fire fighting.

If an assembly of fissionable material in a form related to reactor use should become super-critical without suitable control, the excursion can produce considerable pressure. It is not comparable to that produced by explosives, nor approaching the intensity of an atomic bomb because of the very special conditions necessary to produce an efficient bomb. (The energy release generally has been considerably less than that from the explosion of a kitchen gas range oven.) To date, such reactions have resulted in disruption of equipment and a brief, very intense burst of nuclear radiation, both of which have injured persons in the vicinity and which have also resulted in spread of radioactive products over the immediate area.

Heat Removal

All nuclear reactors, even the very low power training or research reactors, produce heat while in operation. This heat must be either dissipated or used, depending upon the amount produced and the purpose for which the reactor was intended.

Poor design, deterioration, or improper operation of the reactor may result in failure of the coolant to remove the heat generated in the fuel at the rate needed to prevent excessive temperature. If cooling is inadequate, the fuel elements and other components may melt, and violent reaction between fuel element cladding and cooling water may occur. Highly radioactive fission products will be released within the reactor and, in extremely remote instances, possibly to the outside. Automatic shutdown should not interfere with necessary continued cooling. After shutdown, the high rate of radioactive decay of some of the fission products continues to liberate heat and requires continuation of considerable cooling capacity.

Radiation Shielding

It is important to shield radiation to reduce radiation hazards outside the reactor. All forms of radiation—alpha, beta, gamma and neutrons—can have harmful biological effects, and the amount escaping must be kept to a minimum. The shield, known as a biological shield, may consist of several feet of special concrete prepared with a large amount of steel punchings and iron filings. Lead makes a good shield against gamma radiation, but not against neutrons.

Containment

To protect the environment from contamination by radioactivity in case of a reactor excursion, or a mechanical breakdown of the reactor or a pressure container containing highly radioactive substances, it is required that power reactors be completely enclosed in a secondary containment structure that would safely resist the pressures developed in the most severe foreseeable accident. The size and type of reactor and the degree of exposure which the installation presents to adjacent property are factors to be considered in containment vessel design. Containment and building shielding is shown in Figure 4-13B.

Construction Problems

Fire records indicate that the most vulnerable period for fire damage in the probable lifetime of a large reactor system—such as found as nuclear power plants—exists during the construction stage (see Fig. 4-13C). Usually the construction of such a plant requires in excess of four years and the construction hazards thus acquire a nearly permanent status and should therefore receive consideration as though the hazards were to be permanent.

Power reactors pose unique fire protection problems during the course of construction since they require a containment vessel as a final protection system. And, since construction techniques require the containment structure to be erected first, the subsequent reactor construction takes place inside a large vessel with limited exits for evacuation and limited access for fire fighting. In addition, the vessel confines smoke and other products of combustion, greatly in-

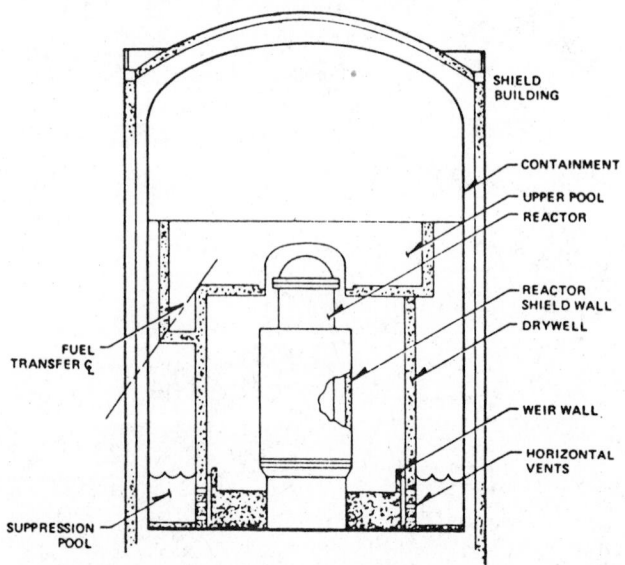

SHIELD BUILDING

CONTAINMENT

UPPER POOL
REACTOR

REACTOR SHIELD WALL
DRYWELL

WEIR WALL

HORIZONTAL VENTS

FUEL TRANSFER C

SUPPRESSION POOL

Fig. 4-13B. The containment and shield building of a BWR reactor. Note that the containment building is encompassed by the shield building in the form of a cylindrical shell with reinforced concrete walls and a domed roof.

Fig. 4-13C. The interior floor of an FFTF facility being prepared for concrete pour. Nuclear facilities are most vulnerable to fire damage during construction, a period of several years, and thus require a good construction fire safety program. (Hanford Engineering Development Laboratory)

creasing the difficulties inherent to evacuation and manual fire fighting. A good construction fire safety program should insure that all penetrations of the containment vessel that may be suitable for evacuation remain open and usable during the period that other construction is taking place within the vessel.

Insofar as access to fire fighters is limited, and the escape of smoke is not facilitated as in normal outdoor construction, it is imperative that all combustible materials incident to construction be severely limited. Metal formwork, scaffolding, platforms, stairways, etc., are preferable to wood. As a minimum, the use of wood in extensive quantities is limited to those appropriately treated to reduce the combustibility and flame spread ratings.

Installation of utilities and equipment in the containment vessel requires special care to maintain a low level of combustibles. Since reactor equipment must meet very high levels of quality assurance, reactor equipment that has been subjected to fire and smoke damage is much more likely to require replacement than similarly exposed equipment in normal industrial installations. Special efforts are warranted to reduce the usual accumulation of packing cases, cartons, insulation, etc., to an acceptable level. This may take the form of conducting all uncrating operations outside the containment vessel and providing special handling devices to transport unpackaged items into the vessel.

B. Radiation Machines

Radiation machines include mechanical and electrical devices that produce or make use of subatomic particles or electromagnetic radiation, or both. X-ray machines are used in radiography, therapeutic treatment, and in studies of the behavior of the radiation and its effects upon materials. Particle accelerators, while a source of radiation, are primarily devices for imparting extremely high energies to subatomic particles to enable them to enter and alter atomic nuclei, and thereby provide means for developing basic information concerning the structure and behavior of matter.

Gamma ray sources in the form of radioactive isotopes are employed in radiography equipment, which may produce intense radiation and have the appearance of, and be called, a machine. The use of isotopes as a source of radiation is not treated here.

X-Ray Machines

Except for the radiation hazard while operating, X-ray machines present mainly the hazards of high potential and high energy electrical equipment. When shut down, there is seldom any appreciable residual radiation to interfere with fire fighting or salvage operations. Ordinarily, no flammable gases and no hazardous amounts of flammable liquids are needed in their operation, but they are frequently encountered in studies of the effects of radiation on a wide variety of substances.

Particle Accelerators

Particle accelerators are used to impart tremendous speeds to atomic particles that are electrically charged. The names of different types of particle accelerators do not follow any consistent practice. Usually they indicate one or more significant characteristics.

Linear Accelerators: Linear acceleration indicates that atomic particles are accelerated in a straight path in a long evacuated tube by passing through a series of open-end sleeves, upon which high frequency alternating voltages from an electronic oscillator are impressed. The timing of the oscillations is such that the particle is given a boost in velocity as it passes from sleeve to sleeve. The desired acceleration can be produced with considerably less voltage than is required in a constant potential nonoscillating accelerator. Fire hazards are of the same general character as described for the Van de Graaff accelerator. Linear accelerators are tremendous. One at Stanford University is two miles long.

Van de Graaff Accelerator: The Van de Graaff apparatus was originally developed as a source of extremely high electrical potentials. For particle acceleration, the Van de Graaff accelerator combines one type of linear accelerator with its high voltage generating unit. In this accelerator, the electrodes, or the source and the target, are at a constant potential difference which can be as great as 12,000,000 volts. The voltage drop along the accelerator tube is in small steps, as developed by a considerable number of sleeves insulated from each other except for a very high resistance voltage divider. Either positive or negative atomic particles can be accelerated by changing the polarity of the source and target. Neutrons are produced by bombarding a suitable target, such as beryllium, with accelerated positive particles. In this mode of operation, such intense X-radiation is given off that heavy shielding is required.

For insulation against the very high voltages, compressed gas—usually noncombustible, such as nitrogen, carbon dioxide, or freon—is used in parts of the generator and accelerator.

Fire hazards of Van de Graaff apparatus are largely those associated with electrical equipment plus the uncertainty of the introduction of ordinary combustibles that are encountered in research and experimental projects, including target and shielding materials. High radiation is present in the path of the accelerated particles during operation. When shut down, the radioactivity is low except in target materials that may have been made radioactive by particle bombardment.

Circular (Orbital) Accelerators: Circular acceleration paths have been devised to avoid extremely long linear accelerators. The operating principle, the kind of particles to be accelerated, and the planned use of the particles give names to these machines, such as Synchro-Cyclotrons, Betatrons, Synchrotrons, and Cosmotrons. Although the accelerating principle is that of the application of exactly timed impulses, the path of the accelerating particle is made circular by the presence of a strong magnetic field. The particle can be made to travel the circular path many times until it is at the desired velocity, which may approach closely the speed of light. It can be made to leave the circular path and strike any desired target.

Due to extremely high particle speeds, stray particles, and secondary radiation, very heavy shielding is required for protection of personnel while the accelerator is operating.

Electric potentials of circular accelerators are high, the electronic devices and controls complicated, and currents for energizing the magnet very heavy. The electrical hazards are consequently unusually severe. Electric cables may be grouped in inaccessible locations, and combustible oils may be used for cooling and insulation. Residual radioactivity at the target after shutdown may make prompt access for manual fire fighting difficult, delayed, or even impossible.

The target for the accelerated particles can be of any substance for which information regarding its behavior under particle bombardment is desired. Not infrequently, the paths and behavior of the particles themselves are studied in a bubble chamber, a thin-walled vessel with mylar windows in which the path of particles can be observed and photographed as a stream of fine bubbles in pressurized and slightly superheated liquid hydrogen. The handling of liquid hydrogen, sometimes produced on the premises, is a special hazard to be recognized and protected against.

C. Facilities Handling Radioactive Materials

The type of equipment used to process radioactive materials depends not only upon the work to be performed but also upon the degree of hazard associated with the material and the process it is to undergo. Materials having low levels of radioactivity and having little or no inherent fire or explosion hazards require less protective equipment than others. For purposes of personnel protection, the amounts and kinds of shielding required will depend upon the types of radiation emitted as well as the activity involved. In addition, the chemical and physical nature of the radioactive materials will dictate the degree of containment necessary, as well as the construction materials used in the containment system. All equipment to be used for handling and processing radioactive materials should be designed to minimize fire and explosion potentials as well as to protect personnel against harmful radiation exposure and damage to property by contamination. There are many types of equipment and systems for handling radioactive materials, but most may be classified as either benches, hoods, glove boxes, or hot cells.

Benches

Benches are generally used for handling relatively small amounts of alpha or beta emitting materials requiring little or no shielding with handling by gloved hands or tongs. No special ventilation for the bench is provided in most instances and its use is thereby restricted to materials which will not easily become airborne.

Benches should be of noncombustible construction with a nonporous continuous working surface which may easily be decontaminated. One or two layers of blotting paper on the bench top to absorb small spills will usually not materially increase the fire hazard.

Hoods

Hoods—sometimes referred to as "fume hoods"—are similar to benches but with the addition of an enclosure and an exhaust system for removing vapors. The nature of the operations conducted within the hood may require a filter system to prevent the spread of radioactive materials. Filters having a low degree of combustibility are desirable.

Glove Boxes

The term "glove box" is used broadly to describe a system designed to contain materials, generally alpha-radiation emitters, which present little or no external radiation hazard but which can present a serious problem if they become airborne. Glove boxes may be large and used to conduct a wide variety of operations involving flammable liquids and gases, combustible solids, and toxic materials. The sides are fitted with long rubberlike gloves which permit manual operations to be conducted without personal contact with the hazardous materials. Special ventilation and fire protection systems are usually considered to be necessary (see Fig. 4-13D).

Hot Cells

A hot cell is a heavily shielded enclosure in which gamma-emitting radioactive materials can be handled by persons using remote manipulators while viewing the operation through shielded windows or periscopes (see Fig. 4-13E).

While possessing all of the fire and explosion hazards of glove boxes, the damage potential is increased by the nature of the high gamma-ray-producing materials used. The safeguards recommended for glove boxes apply equally to hot

Fig. 4-13D. A typical glove box showing gloves extending from the ports in the viewing window at left. Note the portable fire extinguisher adapted for discharging through a fixed piping arrangement into the box. (Savannah River Laboratory)

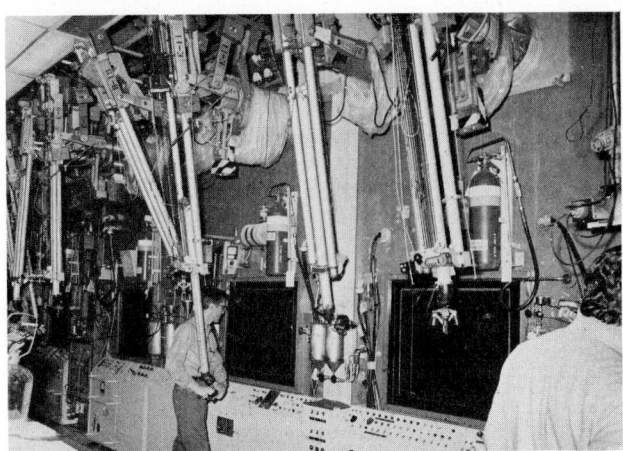

Fig. 4-13E. A typical hot cell installation. Note the manipulators for handling radioactive material within the cells. Portable extinguishers adapted for protection of the interior of the cells can be seen near the tops of the viewing ports. (Savannah River Laboratory)

cells and, in addition, where very high gamma radiation levels are encountered, consideration is given to the possible failure of containers as a result of radiation damage.

Hot cells preferably are constructed of noncombustible materials and contain the minimum amount of combustibles consistent with operational requirements.

D.   Radiation Exposure

Radiation from radiation machines, while of local high intensity, is subject to positive measurement and control and does not present the uncertainties associated with other sources of radiation. The use of nuclear reactors is increasing, and with it the potential for exposure of persons to direct radiation from reactors, to radiation incidental to the handling and processing of reactor fuels, and to the large amounts of radioactivity that would be present in the event of a reactor accident.

Radiation Injury

The harmful effects of radiations are due to their ability to ionize the atoms present in the various compounds of which the body is composed. The detailed mechanism by which the radiations actually damage the living cell is not exactly known.

Unfortunately, the human body has no defense mechanism against radiation. Nuclear radiation cannot be detected by any of the five senses. It is possible to receive a severe exposure to radiation without being aware of the damage being done. Therefore, some form of instrumentation must be employed to detect radioactivity.

The amount of injury to a person by radiation varies with the type of radiation, how much of the body was exposed, and whether it was a one-time exposure or an accumulation of exposures to small amounts of radiation. Injuries from excessive exposures may not become apparent until a delay of days, weeks, months, or years.

Radiation experts report that, similar to many potentially hazardous materials, any exposure to radiation, either external or internal, has some element of risk, which may be too low to be measurable. Certain exposures are believed to be a reasonable risk to be balanced against the benefits from any activity presenting radiation exposure. All medical and dental uses of radiation are a good example of this. How-

ever, since the human race has evolved on a planet which has always been radioactive from the naturally occurring radioisotopes in the air, soil, and water, it is probable that this low "background" radiation is tolerable. The controversy on radiation exposure concerns the additional amounts that may be tolerable. Standards have been set with the objective of lowering risks to the best practicable levels.

Occupational Exposure from Radiation in Air and Water

Radiological authorities have set very low limits of concentrations of radioisotopes in air and water on the basis of quantities which may be inhaled or ingested. Complete treatment of the subject would require consideration of maximum permissible concentrations in both air and water, but the problem of airborne concentrations is of particular concern in fire situations, as fire fighters and other emergency personnel may be confronted with such material in the fumes, dust, smoke, and gases liberated by a fire in which radioactive materials are involved.

A hard and fast rule should be laid down to the effect that self-contained breathing apparatus is to be used whenever exposure to airborne radiation is a possibility, but no such hard and fast rule can be made as to amounts of radiation in atmospheres in which operations may be allowed without masks. Maximum permissible concentrations (MPC) of various radioisotopes in air and water are commonly stated as limits intended to apply to persons who are continuously exposed to the concentrations named. Consequently, they are far below the exposures which could be tolerated for infrequent exposure, as would most often be the case with fire fighters or emergency workers.

Apparatus is available for taking a sample of an atmosphere and the number of radioactive emissions in it can be counted with an appropriate counting instrument. From these counts, the extent to which the particular atmosphere is contaminated can be determined (see Fig. 4-13F).

Air can be continuously monitored for the presence of radiation from fixed sources or from airborne radioactive matter, alarms given, and radiation levels recorded, by available commercial instruments. There should be a program to insure that any space normally occupied by persons not primarily engaged in radiation work is not subjected to unreasonable radiation levels; also that radiation levels are not likely to subject a person outside the installation to excessive exposure through contact with radioactive waste or by other means.

Fire Department Radiation Exposures

Emergency exposures are usually allowed to exceed those tolerable to persons who work continuously with radioactive materials. The New York City Fire Department has adopted a dose limit, for exposure to external radiation, of 25 roentgens per incident (analogous to the quantity of radiation one might receive during a complete X-ray examination by a physician), and a 200 roentgens per lifetime.

External exposure at the time of a single fire emergency can be judged by the use of commercial radiation survey meters measuring radiation in roentgens or by counted disintegration rates, or by the close observation of the indicator of dosimeters carried by individuals. Pocket-size dose rate alarms, which can be carried on the person, are also available. These give an audible signal dependent upon the radiation intensity. Film badges do not provide immediate information.

Evaluation of internal radiation hazard to be combined with the external exposure is usually not attempted. Self-

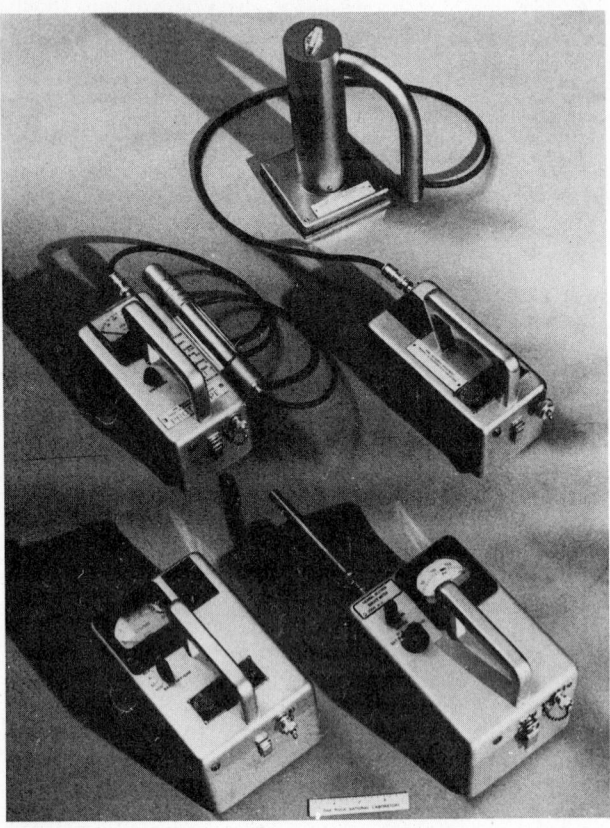

Fig. 4-13F. Portable instruments for measuring radioactivity developed at Oak Ridge National Laboratory. The meters are for fast neutrons (bottom row at left), thermal neutrons (bottom row at right), beta-gamma (top row left), and for alpha particles (top row right) with an alpha scintillation detector at top.

contained breathing apparatus to avoid internal radiation should be used when instruments indicate radiation is present under any condition which would make airborne radiation possible.

E.   Fire Protection

In general, radioactive substances and operations involving such substances, or devices or equipment presenting radiation hazards, have fire and explosion features corresponding to those of similar materials and operations not having radiation hazards. The loss caused by fire, explosion, and other perils and accidents is affected by the presence of radiation or of radioactive substances in the following two major particulars:

1. Possible interference with manual fire fighting due to the presence of harmful radiation or possible criticality.

2. Possible increased delay in salvage and in normal resumption of operations due to the necessity of decontamination of buildings, equipment, or materials.

Contamination of Property

Entire buildings, land, and important equipment can be made unusable for long periods of time as the result of severe radioactive contamination due to sudden accidental escape of radioactive substances.

It is important to note that radiological contamination may not stay on the inside or the outside of buildings and areas. In the form of dust or vapor, it can sift through open-ings or ventilating systems and can spread the radioactive material throughout a structure. Careless movement of persons through a contaminated area could spread contamination to an uncontaminated area.

Once a surface has become contaminated, a decision has to be made as to how the particular contaminating material is to be removed, if this is possible.

Vacuum cleaning can sometimes be used to remove radioactive dust on building surfaces. However, if vacuum cleaning is used, absolute filters must be used on the exhaust. Hosing with water can be used on some surfaces. Cleaning with soap and detergents is often a hand operation which must be carried out with continuous checks on the amount of exposure that may be tolerated by the persons doing the cleaning. Sand blasting or vacuum blasting can be used on some surfaces. Painting may cover alpha contamination.

Plant Fire Protection Organization

In properties where atomic energy is a factor, a fire protection organization is desirable. In nuclear reactors and many other such plants, 24-hr-a-day routines for handling fires and emergencies must be kept in force. For example, it may not be enough to leave a nuclear reactor only in the hands of an untrained custodial force at times when it is not used, such as nights, weekends, or holidays.

Plan for Handling Fires

In plants involving a nuclear reactor, radiation machines, and other facilities handling radioactive materials, the problems affecting decision on how best to deal with a fire or other emergency are not those that can be solved by simply calling the public fire department. As many decisions as possible must be made with respect to the types of fire or emergency to be expected, and these decisions must be made well in advance. The particular fire fighting and personnel safety measures to be taken may involve shutting down or isolating parts of the plant or individual items of equipment. The places where special procedures are necessary must be identified and the procedures for the special areas thoroughly understood.

Arrangements include provisions for prompt calling of the public fire department, usually through a public fire alarm signal box. However, the plant fire protection department must work out in advance with the public fire departments, the nature of the operations of fire fighters coming into the plant so that these will be properly coordinated with steps in the plant's own program for dealing with emergencies.

For fire fighting or other emergency operations in areas where radiation exposure is present, personnel must be fully trained and provided with suitable protective clothing. Respiratory protective equipment is a must, and competent radiological advisors, equipped with instruments for measuring area and local exposure, are necessary to guide emergency personnel. Dosimeters or other instruments for recording each individual's accumulated exposure are helpful.

Emergency planning also covers measures to prevent the spread of contamination and for effective and prompt decontamination in case of accidental release of radioactive substances.

The site of a nuclear reactor needs a generous water supply. It facilitates fire control and can prove helpful in decontamination operations. Facilities for safe disposal or storage of water that may be contaminated must be prearranged.

Noncombustible materials for reactor buildings and equipment avoid complications of fire hazard. For example, all finish materials used for decorative, acoustical, or insulation purposes should be noncombustible and of types that make decontamination easy.

The exposure of a reactor structure to other buildings is taken care of by appropriate distance separation or fire barriers. To prevent exposure to the reactor, it is always proper to separate shops and service spaces from the reactor equipment and structure itself.

Wiring ducts in floors introduce an opportunity for the spread of fire or of contaminated liquid or gas from one space to another. Good seals in ducts separate one space from another.

Subassembly or other operation in the preparation of fuel elements for reactors is carried on in work areas separated from the reactor in such a way that fire cannot communicate to the reactor space.

Equipment for Fighting Fires

Automatic sprinkler systems or specially designed piped water spray systems are the first choice for fire protection in any locations where fires may have to be fought in nuclear reactor plants, properties housing radiation machines, and facilities handling radioactive materials. Sprinklers can operate with full effectiveness under conditions of radiation or contamination that would make approach by fire fighters impossible. It is better to pipe water for fire fighting into spaces where a fire might have to be fought through a system of automatic sprinklers or a system specially designed for the purpose rather than have to fight a fire by directing hose streams into the space and distributing the water in an inefficient manner.

In spaces where water used in fire fighting would be subject to possible contamination, the collection and disposition of water so used must be provided for in the local facilities. This means waterproofed floors and controlled floor drainage. Substantial capacity of such drainage systems would be required if hose streams and manual fire fighting were necessary. By contrast, with sprinklers or a specially designed spray system, it would be necessary to dispose of relatively modest amounts of water.

The difficulties of access and visibility, if a fire occurs in a containment vessel during construction, warrant the provision of temporary fixed automatic extinguishing systems when combustibles cannot be effectively controlled. Temporary interior hose stations and an ample supply of portable extinguishing equipment are desirable within easy reach of all portions of the vessel. Because of the smoke confinement potential, only very fast manual response may be effective and manual fire fighting equipment preferably is provided in quantities considerably in excess of normal construction practice to insure the earliest response.

Incompatible Materials

Careful design analyses are required to reduce the fire protection problems inherent in the use of materials that are incompatible in fire situations. As an example, the use of liquid metal as a reactor coolant/moderator requires special extinguishing systems not compatible with water; in fact, the possibility of a water-liquid metal reaction may justify the exclusion of water systems from the area. If such a decision is made, however, it imposes severe limitations on the presence of flammable oils, plastics, foam insulations, and other materials that generally require copious quantities of water for fire extinguishment. Where such mixed hazards exist, it is imperative that careful consideration be given to the potentials for a failure in one system to cause a failure in the incompatible system. In such cases, either protection systems must be provided that can insure the extinguishment of fire in either system before it can cause a rupture of the other systems, or a single protection system (such as inerting) must be developed that is adequate for either hazard. The difficulties inherent in such problems warrant the most thorough hazards analysis at the earliest design stages.

Bibliography

NFPA Codes, Standards, and Recommended Practices (see the latest *NFPA Publications and Visual Aids Catalog* for availability of current editions of the following documents)

NFPA No. 801, Recommended Fire Protection Practice for Facilities Handling Radioactive Materials.

NFPA No. 802, Recommended Fire Protection Practice for Nuclear Reactors.

Additional Readings

American National Standards Institute, Committee N2, "Glossary of Terms in Nuclear Science and Technology," ANSI N1.1, 1967, American National Standards Institute, New York.

Blatz, Hansen, ed., *Radiation Hygiene Handbook*, McGraw-Hill, New York, 1959.

Brannigan, F. L., *Living with Radiation: Part I, Fundamentals*, U.S. Atomic Energy Commission, Safety and Fire Protection Branch, Washington, 1959.

Brannigan, F. L. and Miles, G. S., *Living with Radiation: Part II, Fire Service Problems*, U.S. Atomic Energy Commission, Safety and Fire Protection Branch, Washington, 1960.

Encyclopedia Britannica, "Radiation, Biological Effects," Vol. 18, Encyclopedia Britannica, Inc., Chicago, 1972, p. 1024.

Factory Mutual Research Corporation, *Glovebox Fire Safety: A Guide for Safe Practices in Design, Protection and Operation*, U.S. Atomic Energy Commission, Washington, 1967.

Glasstone, Samuel, *Source Book on Atomic Energy*, 2nd ed., Van Nostrand Co., Inc., Princeton, N.J., 1950.

Keil, A. A., *Radiation Control for Fire and Other Emergency Forces*, National Fire Protection Association, Boston, 1960.

Kinsman, Simon, *Radiological Health Handbook*, Robert A. Taft Sanitary Engineering Center, Cincinatti.

National Bureau of Standards, "Control and Removal of Radioactive Contamination in Laboratories," Handbook No. 48, 1951, U.S. Government Printing Office, Washington.

National Bureau of Standards, "Maximum Permissible Amounts of Radioisotopes in the Human Body and Maximum Permissible Concentrations in Air and Water," Handbook No. 52, 1953, U.S. Government Printing Office, Washington.

National Bureau of Standards, "Permissible Dose from External Sources of Ionizing Radiation," Handbook No. 59, 1954, U.S. Government Printing Office, Washington.

National Bureau of Standards, "Radiological Monitoring Methods and Instruments," Handbook No. 51, 1952, U.S. Government Printing Office, Washington.

National Bureau of Standards, "Safe Handling of Radioactive Isotopes," Handbook No. 42, 1949, U.S. Government Printing Office, Washington.

National Council on Radiation Protection and Measurements, "Basic Radiation Protection Criteria," NCRP 39, 1971, U.S. Government Printing Office, Washington.

National Council on Radiation Protection and Measurements, "Protection Against Neutron Radiation," NCRP 38, 1971, U.S. Government Printing Office, Washington.

National Council on Radiation Protection and Measurements, "Safe Handling of Radioactive Materials," NCRP 30, 1964, U.S. Government Printing Office, Washington.

U.S. Atomic Energy Commission, *Operational Accidents and Radiation Exposure Experience within the AEC 1943–1970*, U.S. Government Printing Office, Washington, 1971.

U.S. Atomic Energy Commission, *Radiological Emergency Procedures for the Nonspecialist*, U.S. Government Printing Office, Washington, 1969.

U.S. Code of Federal Regulations, Title 10, "Atomic Energy," U.S. Superintendent of Documents, Washington, 1957.

U.S. Federal Civil Defense Administration, "Emergency Exposures to Nuclear Radiation," Technical Bulletin 11-1, 1957, U.S. Superintendent of Documents, Washington.

Chapter 14

INDUSTRIAL AND EMERGENCY WASTE CONTROL

The safe disposal of flammable, toxic, or radioactive chemicals that are no longer needed introduces many problems. Human and animal life can be endangered and fires and explosions can occur if the operation is not carried out properly. Federal, state, and local health and pollution regulations must be observed, and the disposal must be conducted in such a way as to prevent toxic, fire, and explosion hazards.

Safe disposal of chemical waste requires a knowledge of the physical, physiological, and chemical properties of the waste material (flammability, toxicity, and reaction with water and other chemicals), and familiarity with the advantages or limitations of the various methods of disposal (burning, dilution with water, burying, discharge into sewers, and reaction with another chemical to form a product that can be safely disposed). Advice on methods of disposal may be obtained from the supplier of the chemical and from chemical data sheets.

A. Sources of Wastes

The source of any waste material determines, to a great extent, what its composition is, how much there will be, how it will be collected and ultimately what disposal will be practical.

Domestic Waste

Trash collected from homes and many commercial establishments consists largely of paper, glass, metal cans and a wide miscellany of other materials many of which are combustible solids. With good management there is limited hazard but the bulk is great enough to supply fuel for a sizable fire if ignition occurs.

Industrial Plants

The nature of the industry determines the nature of the waste generated. A furniture plant discards wood scrap, sawdust, and shavings as well as oily rags, stain, varnish, lacquer, glue, etc., in addition to paper, metal and other commercial items. Chemical plants may discard substantial amounts of off-grade or reject products, by-products, tars, spent catalyst, precipitates, etc. Obviously the range of hazards is broad.

Processors of materials will occasionally spill some materials in storage and handling. Cleanup operations from filling equipment, fabrication operations, and general plant maintenance will generate some discarded material. Rejected, aged, or damaged packages; off-specification materials; and overruns also will be discarded.

Transportation

The movement of bulk or package goods also generate disposal problems. Broken packages, leaking drums, overheating or freezing of cargo are contributing sources.

Washing of tank cars or tank trucks results in substantial amounts of material which may be emulsified or dissolved in water. Others, such as most petroleum products, can be skimmed off after settling.

Spills resulting from railway, truck, ship, or pipeline accidents constitute serious problems in locations far distant from facilities or experienced personnel needed in controlling loss of cargo or damage to the environment.

Storage

Warehouse inventory control necessitates occasional discard of unmarketable or undesirable materials of all kinds, forms, and hazards.

Tankage must be cleaned as storage needs change, and washing of transfer lines must be handled so as to avoid contamination of products.

Materials handling accidents, such as damage to packages by fork trucks, require cleanup and disposal. Water, fire, or explosion damage can also result in substantial amounts of undesired product.

B. Characterization of Wastes

Safe disposal of hazardous materials is accomplished only if the physical, chemical, and hazardous properties of the materials are known, and the information is properly applied. Not only safe collection and handling, but protection of the future environment may depend upon such knowledge and its application.

(The fire hazard properties of materials are discussed in detail in the various chapters of Section 3, Fire Hazards of Materials, in this HANDBOOK. Particular attention is directed to Table 3-11A in Chapter 3 of that Section. It gives in summary form pertinent information on the fire hazards properties of flammable liquids, gases and volatile solids.)

Physical State

The physical state of materials govern the waste control measures used with them.

Solids: This category includes most domestic, commercial and industrial trash, metal, wood and plastic scrap, solid or dry chemicals. Combustible metals such as magnesium are included. A fringe category is semi-solids such as waxes, soaps, elastomers, etc.

Liquids: Included are aqueous solutions and aqueous slurries. Solvents may be organic and flammable, or they may be synthetic and possibly noncombustible. Viscous liquids, such as pastes, tars, etc., may involve special handling problems. Mixtures of all kinds will be encountered. These could include acid sludges, wax-laden solvent, clay, oil, etc.

Gases: Cylinders of gases are frequently unidentified due to age and weathering, hence constitute unknown problems. Process gas releases may be high volume and their control can be troublesome, particularly if they are highly toxic or corrosive.

Hazards of Materials

Few discarded materials are so compatible with the environment or so inert as to have no short or long term impact. Hazards that appear minor can have unexpected significance during or after disposal. When two or more hazards pertain to a material, the lesser may not receive the necessary consideration. Mixing of two discarded substances can result in chemical or physical interaction that is not expected.

Flammability and Combustibility: Flash point and ignition temperature are the most widely used indicators of the hazard associated with accidental or intentional burning. Flammable limits, ignition energy, and particle size of solids are additional factors.

Flammable Vapors and Heavier Gases: Vapors and gases released during collection or disposal of flammables can travel considerable distances downhill, or downwind on the level, to reach an ignition source, and flash back. In the case of major spills, emergency evacuation may be necessary in order to save lives.

Pyrophoric Materials: Phosphorus, aluminum alkyls and some other materials ignite spontaneously upon exposure to air. Special care and handling procedures are needed to store, collect, and dispose of such materials, usually under a nitrogenous atmosphere.

Reactivity: The reactivity of a material with other materials, including water, must be considered. Sodium, potassium, and aluminum alkyls react violently when combined with water and burn fiercely. Strong oxidizers in contact with organic materials can cause rapid combustion or explosion. Other such combinations are listed in NFPA 491 M, Hazardous Chemical Reactions and efforts to avoid such combinations are essential. Identification of potential reactions and technical competence in evaluating potential reactions are required.

Corrosivity: This is a term that has two commonly used meanings:

1. Ability to severely damage the skin or other living tissue.

2. Ability to cause damage to materials of construction, usually metal.

Toxicity: Some discarded materials may possess toxic problems. The ability to poison animal life, principally by skin contact, inhalation, or contamination of food or water is both a short term and long term problem. Arsenic compounds put on a dump have found their way into drinking water. Acid leached from sludges travels downward and may reach water sources. Animals or even unwary workmen may contact discarded toxic substances directly.

Spills: In-plant and transportation spills have great potential for toxic effects. Emergency response personnel, lacking adequate information about the cargo hazard, may be unduly exposed and the public may also be affected due to wind drift and runoff.

Odors: However foul, odors do not necessarily mean that a toxic hazard exists, but a public response can be expected. Products of combustion from open burning can smell worse than the material before burning. Proper incineration can minimize the odor problem where applicable. Odor can be a warning that containment is inadequate; however, odor should not be relied upon, since some very harmful substances have little odor.

Sensitivity to Heat or Shock: Sensitivity to heat or shock are important factors when explosives, fireworks, organic peroxides, and other such materials are discarded. They constitute deadly hazards if not properly segregated and destroyed very carefully. See NFPA standards and guides for additional information.

Radioactivity: Waste contaminated with radioactivity calls for quite specialized knowledge and skill. Disposal of radioactive wastes is highly regulated and is often done by an outside special contractor. See NFPA 801, Facilities Handling Radioactive Materials.

C. Collection and Handling of Wastes

Ordinary Domestic and Commercial Trash: Collections commonly are by special vehicles adapted to compact the trash into an economic load and haul it to the disposal site. In some commercial and industrial occupancies, trash is placed in large steel boxes which are then dumped into a compactor. Fires frequently occur in the containers (or "buckets") and sometimes in the compactor. See Section 7, Chapter 6 for further information on refuse compactors.

Liquid Waste Solvents: These are collected in cans, drums, or underground tanks and ultimately are picked up by a tank vehicle for transport to the disposal site. The possibility of incompatible mixtures is ever present but problems are rare.

Potentially Unstable or Shock Sensitive Materials: These are usually collected by a special "bomb" squad equipped with shielded containers, personal protection, and special vehicles. Less hazardous materials may be separately collected and given to a contract disposal agent.

Dusts: Manufacturing processes which generate dusts or small particulates collect the fine solids by means of a dust collection and recovery system. Rigid or flexible ducts running from the collection points are manifolded into trunks which conduct the material to a cyclone separator and thence to a blower. The size and characteristics of the blower must be sufficient to move the solids at velocities that will not permit settling in the ducts.

Sometimes a bag house will be needed for complete removal of fines or a scrubber for fumes. Proper engineering design is essential. When flammable dusts are collected or pneumatically conveyed, the fire or dust explosion hazard must be considered. See Section 7, Chapter 5 for further information on air moving equipment.

D. Disposal Methods

The proper choice of a disposal method for a material or for a category of materials is a complex procedure involving many factors.

Incineration

The burning of scrap and refuse under controlled conditions is one of the most satisfactory methods of disposal. Municipal incinerators operated primarily for domestic trash will usually accept industrial refuse as well, so long as its character does not introduce additional hazards or operating problems.

Air pollution control equipment is nearly always needed on industrial incinerators. Depending upon the composition of the stack effluent these control devices would include:

1. Afterburners to ignite combustible particles.

2. Cyclones to remove larger particles.

3. Low energy scrubbers to remove larger particulate.

4. High energy venturi scrubbers to remove fine particulate and/or water soluble acid gases.

5. Electrostatic precipitators to remove fine particulate and mists.

6. Fabric filters (bag houses) to remove fine particulate.

Principal hazards in operation of an incinerator would be:

1. Overtemperature due to feeding a large amount of volatiles.

2. Overtemperature due to increase in calorific value.

3. Structural failure due to overtemperature and/or corrosion.

4. Corrosion of scrubber due to acid.

5. Failure of scrubber system.

See Section 7, Chapter 6 for further information on incinerator installations.

Mulching

One possible reuse of polymers involves chopping the waste into small shreds or granules and selling it as a soil conditioner. The use is very limited and has not yet been widely practiced. The polymer degrades very slowly so its effect on the soil is purely physical.

Pyrolysis

Polymers and organic materials, when heated, have yielded some oils and other recoverable compounds. Pyrolysis has not yet been widely adopted but has promise as a conservation measure. A retort is charged with selected scrap and then heated to cause decomposition and distillation of the volatiles and oils. The process is somewhat similar to a coke oven, and similar operating hazards would be expected.

Open Burning

This antiquated method of disposal is no longer legal in most states and is rapidly being forced out of use. In addition to pollution of the atmosphere, other undesirable effects are possible fire spread, danger to fire fighters from exploding containers, possible injury from radioactive materials, and the use of fire department personnel and equipment for "dump fires" instead of more pressing emergencies.

Landfill

In a landfill operation, discarded material is mixed with earth and then compacted in a wide trench or other depression. Layer upon layer of mixture is added and then 2 ft of earth is spread and compacted on top. See NFPA 82, Incinerators and Rubbish Handling, for additional information on landfills.

Landfill locations should consider the proximity of pipe lines, power lines, oil or gas wells, mines, and other potential hazards.

Successful landfill operation depends heavily upon biological activity within the fill material. There is some tendency for gas to be vented during biological activity. Vents in the soil cover may be needed. Proper drainage to achieve aeration is vital.

Safety and fire protection measures include the following:
1. Fire fighting facilities to deal with an ignition of waste within the landfill.
2. Emergency first-aid facilities.
3. Fencing and posting of the area.
4. Twenty-four-hour surveillance.

Biodegradation

Experiments have shown that many chemical substances when mixed intimately with the top 6 in. of soil will be completely destroyed in six to 24 months. Soil bacteria readily decompose aliphatic hydrocarbons. Unsaturated and branched chains of high molecular weight require more time. Aromatic compounds are most resistant, but once ring cleavage occurs, they are readily degraded and oxidized to carbon dioxide and water.

Burial

Simple burial of an active chemical substance in mass is an invitation to future trouble from discovery or leaching into water resources. Pesticides buried in the 1930s caused arsenic poisoning of eleven persons who drank well water nearly 44 years later.

Disposal Contractors

A convenient means of hazardous materials disposal is to use the services of a contractor. The contractor must be competent, responsible, and dependable and be familiar with the properties and hazards of the materials involved.

E.　Specific Materials

Combustible Refuse

Refuse of a highly combustible nature such as dry waste paper, excelsior, etc. is collected in metal cans or other metal containers and not allowed to accumulate in piles. Quantity storage of these materials is separated from buildings, roadways, and ignition sources of any kind by a distance of 50 ft or more. Transport to an incinerator or landfill on a frequent schedule will minimize fire hazard.

Drying Oils

Rags or paper that have absorbed drying-type oils are subject to spontaneous heating. They are kept in well-covered metal cans and thoroughly dried before collection or transport. Fire in a compactor enroute to the incinerator otherwise could result.

Flammable Liquids and Waste Solvents

Waste solvents have variable flash points, hence varying hazard, depending upon composition. Some may contain solids, tars, waxes and other materials that impede flow. Chlorinated solvents and water may also be present.

Generally, the two most feasible methods of disposal are by incineration or use of a contractor. In either case the solvents are collected in 5-gal cans or 55-gal drums for disposal. If a contractor is used, approximate composition, if known, is given him on a tag.

Installations having substantial amounts of waste solvent will install their own incinerator for the purpose. An auxiliary gas or oil burner is needed to maintain adequate fire box temperature. Usually a scrubber section is used to remove acid gases and other pollutants. See the NFPA Incinerator and Rubbish Handling Standard for further information on industrial incinerator installations.

Liquid and Solid Oxidizing Materials

Used combustible containers such as paper bags, fiber drums, plastic liners, etc. are not allowed to accumulate but are put into closed metal containers and removed to a detached or sprinklered area.

Spilled material and leaking or broken containers are immediately removed to a safe area to await disposal in conformance with applicable regulations and manufacturers' instructions. (See NFPA 43A.)

Most, if not all, oxidizers can be rendered harmless by dilution with water; however, some solutions cause pollution of streams and rivers, and thus require pretreatment.

Combustible and Reactive Metals

Small scraps of sodium from laboratory use can be dissolved in ethyl alcohol (not isopropyl alcohol) and the resulting alkoxide neutralized with acid. Large quantities, several pounds or more, can be offered to the vendor for repurification and recycling. Oil contaminated dispersions or other moderate quantities can be burned in dry pans if provision is made to control the oxide fume, which is highly alkaline. Disposal of sodium by throwing it directly into water is spectacular but extremely hazardous and will contaminate the water with sodium hydroxide. Equipment contaminated with small amounts of sodium may be cleaned by remotely controlled introduction of water or steam.

Potassium, NAK, and lithium are handled in the same manner as sodium. Lithium reacts somewhat less violently with water. See Chemical Safety Data Sheet No. 47, published by the Manufacturing Chemists' Association.

It is usually feasible to reclaim magnesium fines and scrap that is in the form of defective castings, clippings, and coarse chips; if this is to be done either locally or through a smelting firm, the scrap is thoroughly dried before re-melting. No attempt is made usually to reclaim dust and fines.

Scrap in the form of fine chips and dust collector sludge can be disposed of in a specially constructed incinerator or by burning in a safely located outdoor area paved with fire brick or hard burned paving brick. By spreading the scrap or sludge in a layer about 4 in. thick, on which ordinary combustible material is placed and ignited, the combustion of inert magnesium oxide can be conducted safely. Another method of deactivating magnesium sludge is to treat it with a .5 percent solution of ferrous chloride. Since hydrogen is generated by this reaction, this method of disposal is conducted in an open container in an outdoor location where the hydrogen can be safely dissipated (see NFPA 48, Magnesium Storage Handling and Processing).

Spontaneous combustion of titanium has occurred in fines, chips, and swarf that were coated with water-soluble oil. Disposal containers are tightly closed and segregated where spontaneous burning would not involve other exposures. Incineration in the open, as for magnesium scrap, may be feasible (see NFPA 481, Titanium, Production, Handling and Storage).

While small amounts of zirconium fines can be mixed with sand or other inert material and buried, incineration of this combustible metal is generally preferred for larger quantities. Because of the spontaneous ignition potential, personnel carrying scrap wear flame protective clothing and equipment and carry the scrap in buckets on a yoke between them. Ignition of a layer is kindled with excelsior (see NFPA 482M, Zirconium Production Processing and Handling).

Lithium hydride and lithium aluminum hydride can ignite upon contact with water or moist air. Alkaline oxides resulting from incineration are collected and neutralized.

Radioactive Materials

Radioactive materials, which are flammable or combustible, must be handled with due respect to their fire hazard as well as radiation. Large collections of combustible radioactive wastes are not allowed to accumulate. Storage of such wastes near an air intake is particularly undesirable. Should the products of combustion of waste materials containing long-lived radioactive materials be dispersed through air-conditioning or compressed air systems, an extensive decontamination problem could result.

Liquid radioactive wastes can sometimes be concentrated and retained until the radioactivity has decayed to a safe level. Combustible radioactive waste, such as absorbent paper used to wipe contaminated surfaces, is placed in approved containers for disposal. Waste used to apply or absorb nitric acid or other oxidizing chemicals is segregated or stored under water.

For most installations a contractor licensed to dispose of radioactive materials can be engaged (see NFPA 801, Facilities Handling Radioactive Materials).

Bibliography

NFPA Codes, Standards, and Recommended Practices (see the latest *NFPA Publications and Visual Aids Catalog* for availability of current editions of the following documents)

NFPA No. 30, Flammable and Combustible Liquids Code.

NFPA No. 325A, Flash Point Index of Trade Name Liquids.

NFPA No. 325M, Fire Hazard Properties of Flammable Liquids, Gases, and Volatile Solids.

NFPA No. 40, Standard for the Storage and Handling of Cellulose Nitrate Motion Picture Film.

NFPA No. 42, Standard for Storage, Handling and Use of Pyroxylin Plastics in Factories.

NFPA No. 43, Standard for the Storage and Sale of Pyroxylin Plastic in Warehouses and Wholesale, Jobbing and Retail Stores.

NFPA No. 43A, Code for the Storage of Liquid and Solid Oxidizing Materials.

NFPA No. 44A, Code for the Manufacture, Transportation, and Storage of Fireworks.

NFPA No. 48, Standard for the Storage, Handling and Processing of Magnesium.

NFPA No. 49, Hazardous Chemicals Data .

NFPA No. 60, Standard for the Installation and Operation of Pulverized Fuel Systems.

NFPA No. 61A, Standard for Manufacutring and Handling Starch.

NFPA No. 61B, Standard for Prevention of Fire and Dust Explosions in Grain Elevators and Bulk Grain Handling Facilities.

NFPA No. 61C, Standard for the Prevention of Fire and Dust Explosions in Feed Mills.

NFPA No. 61D, Standard for the Prevention of Fire and Dust Explosions in the Milling of Agricultural Commodities for Human Consumption.

NFPA No. 62, Standard for the Prevention of Dust Explosions in the Production, Packaging and Handling of Pulverized Sugar and Cocoa.

NFPA No. 63, Fundamental Principles for the Prevention of Dust Explosions in Industrial Plants.

NFPA No. 82, Standard on Incinerators and Rubbish Handling.

NFPA No. 91, Standard for the Installation of Blower and Exhaust Systems for Dust, Stock and Vapor Removal or Conveying.

NFPA No. 481, Standard for the Production, Processing, Handling and Storage of Titanium.

NFPA No. 482M, Guide for Fire and Explosion Prevention in Plants Producing and Handling Zirconium.

NFPA No. 490, Code for the Storage of Ammonium Nitrate.

NFPA No. 491M, Manual of Hazardous Chemical Reactions.

NFPA No. 492, Recommended Separation Distances of Ammonium Nitrate and Blasting Agents from Explosives or Blasting Agents.

NFPA No. 494L, Model State Fireworks Law.

NFPA No. 495, Code for the Manufacture, Transportation, Storage, and Use of Explosive Materials.

NFPA No. 498, Standard for Explosives Motor Vehicle Terminals.

NFPA No. 651, Standard for the Manufacture of Aluminum or Magnesium Powder.

NFPA No. 653, Standard for the Prevention of Dust Explosions in Coal Preparation Plants.

NFPA No. 654, Standard for the Prevention of Dust Explosions in the Plastics Industry.

NFPA No. 655, Standard for Prevention of Sulfur Fires and Explosions.

NFPA No. 656, Standard for the Prevention of Dust Ignitions in Spice Grinding Plants.

NFPA No. 657, Standard for the Prevention of Dust Explosions in Confectionery Manufacturing Plants.

NFPA No. 664, Standard for the Prevention of Dust Explosions in Woodworking and Wood Flour Manufacturing Plants.

NFPA No. 701, Standard Methods of Fire Tests for Flame Resistant Textiles and Films.

NFPA No. 702, Standard for Classification of the Flammability of Wearing Apparel.

NFPA No. 801, Recommended Fire Protection Practice for Facilities Handling Radioactive Materials.

Additional Readings

"Emergency Services Guide for Selected Hazardous Materials," U.S. Department of Transportation, Washington, D.C.

"A Guide for Incineration of Chemical Plant Wastes," Manufacturing Chemists' Association, Inc., Washington, D.C.

"A Guide for Landfill Disposal of Solid Waste," Manufacturing Chemists' Association, Inc., Washington, D.C.

Laboratory Waste Disposal Manual, 2nd ed., rev., Manufacturing Chemists' Association, Inc., Washington, D.C.

"Properties and Essential Information for Safe Handling and Use of Benzoyl Peroxide," Chem Safety Data Sheet SD-81, 1960, Manufacturing Chemists' Association, Inc., Washington, D.C.

"Properties and Essential Information for Safe Handling and Use of Chlorine," Chem Safety Data Sheet SD-80, 1970 rev., Manufacturing Chemists' Association, Inc., Washington, D.C.

"Properties and Essential Information for Safe Handling and Use of Hydrogen Peroxide," Chem Safety Data Sheet SD-53, 1969 rev., Manufacturing Chemists' Association, Inc., Washington, D.C.

"Properties and Essential Information for Safe Handling and Use of Nitric Acid," Chem Safety Data Sheet SD-5, 1961, Manufacturing Chemists' Association, Inc., Washington, D.C.

"Properties and Essential Information for Safe Handling and Use of Perchloric Acid Solution," Chem Safety Data Sheet SD-11, 1965 rev., Manufacturing Chemists' Association, Inc., Washington, D.C.

"Properties and Essential Information for Safe Handling and Use of Solium (Metallic Sodium)," Chem Safety Data Sheet SD-47, 1969.

"What Can We Do About Methane (CH_4)?" Fire Command!, Vol. 40, No. 2, Feb. 1973, pp. 24-25.

SECTION 5

SPECIAL FIRE PROTECTION AND PREVENTION PROBLEMS

Chapter 1

INDOOR STORAGE PRACTICES

Indoor storage describes the broad range of combustible commodities stored inside of buildings. A commodity is a combination of a product, packing material, and container. Section 3 of this HANDBOOK provides information on the storage of specific materials which may present an explosion hazard in addition to their fire hazard, such as combustible and flammable liquids (Chap. 3), gases (Chap. 4), chemicals (Chap. 5), explosives and blasting agents (Chap. 6), and dusts (Chap. 8), all of which are not covered in this chapter.

A. Fire Protection Principles

Many factors must be considered in providing adequate, yet reasonable, protection for commodities stored in private or public warehouse facilities. Primary considerations are the building construction, physical and chemical properties of the commodity, and the arrangement of the storage. The roof or ceiling height, number of stories, smoke and heat ventilation facilities, the presence or absence of wall openings, size of storage areas, and construction materials used are building features to consider. The ease of ignition, rate of heat release, the quantity, and the configuration of the commodity are important considerations. The arrangement of the storage, including such features as height of storage, aisle widths, size of piles, whether combustible pallets are used, and whether it is in solid piles or in racks are also important consideratons.

Fire Development

Palletized and rack-storage methods provide horizontal and vertical combustible surfaces within as well as at the outside surfaces of the storage. Fire development, both horizontal and vertical, depends principally on these combustible surfaces and the longitudinal and transverse flue spaces between them. The fire duration depends mostly upon the materials within the containers.

Fire develops in a fan-shaped pattern, whether it originates at an exterior surface or within the pile. Fire at the base preheats the material above, which ignites and burns, increasing in size and intensity, as it moves upward.

Sprinkler water easily reaches and subdues an exterior face fire, but cannot reach the horizontal flue spaces, and has difficulty in penetrating the often narrow vertical spaces. Sprinkler water will quickly retard fire travel through the upper part of the pile, but has little immediate effect on fire in the lower spaces. The overall result is a persistant fire requring manual assistance with small hose streams and material-handling equipment to obtain final extinguishment.

Ignition Sources

Minimizing, or if possible eliminating, potential ignition sources is essential. Some of the more common causes of fires in storage facilities are from electrical sources, gasoline or LP-gas material handling equipment, and sparks from cutting and welding operations. The use of welding, cutting, soldering, or brazing torches in storage areas introduces a severe fire hazard. The use of mechanical fastenings and mechanical saws or cutting wheels is preferable wherever possible. The various potential ignition sources must be considered when analyzing an individual situation to provide the maximum possible fire prevention.

B. General Storage Practices

Commodity Classification

Primarily for designing sprinkler systems and water supplies, commodities have been classified in four classes for general storage, in NFPA No. 231, Indoor General Storage. They are:

Class I: These commodities are essentially noncombustible products on combustible pallets, or in ordinary corrugated cartons with or without single thickness dividers, or in ordinary paper wrappings with or without pallets.

Class II: These commodities are defined as Class I products in slatted wooden crates, solid wooden boxes, multiple thickness paper-board cartons, or equivalent combustible packaging material with or without pallets.

Class III: These commodities are defined as wood, paper, natural fiber cloth or products thereof with or without pallets. Products may contain a limited amount of plastics. Metal bicycles with plastic handles, pedals, seats, and tires are an example of a commodity with a limited amount of plastic.

Class IV: These commodities are defined as Class I, II or III products containing an appreciable amount of plastics in ordinary corrugated cartons and Class I, II, and III products in ordinary corrugated cartons with plastic packing with or without pallets. An example of packing material is a metal typewriter in a foamed plastic cocoon in an ordinary corrugated carton.

This classification of commodities applies only to nonencapsulated commodities.

Building Arrangement

One-story buildings without basement are preferable for a warehouse because of greater efficiency for fire fighting, ventilation, and salvage operations. Long narrow buildings provide greater ease in fire fighting than large square buildings. In windowless buildings, adequate emergency access openings are needed to facilitate manual fire fighting. Multistory buildings may be subject to spread of fire from lower to upper floors and water on upper floors may cause damage to commodities on lower floors. Manual fire fighting is difficult in large, undivided 1-story buildings and in multistory buildings due to the inability to reach all areas with hose streams. This is particularly true in areas with limited or no aerial fire apparatus. The disadvantages of multistory buildings can be lessened by fire resistive construction, adequate protection of floor openings, waterproofing or drainage arrangements on the upper stories, narrow building configuration, adequate access, and automatic sprinkler protection throughout.

Fire Areas: Large properties are generally subdivided into fire areas to limit the spread of fire. For subdivision purposes, a fire area is bounded by the exterior walls of the building or by fire walls, and in multistory buildings by fire resistive floors, with all openings protected. Storage areas are isolated from manufacturing areas by fire walls to prevent fires at machinery or processes from spreading to involve concentrations of stored materials, and particularly finished goods. In addition, fire partitions of sufficient fire resistance to protect the warehouse against fire exposure are provided to separate packing and shipping operations, boilers, compressors, garages, and other occupancies from the main storage areas.

The general trend is toward larger fire areas for warehousing operations. In some locations, the maximum permissible size of a fire area is established by municipal ordinances or state laws. The optimum size of a fire area for a warehouse is governed by both economic and fire protection factors. Economic factors include consideration of the efficient flow and storage of commodities, efficient use of space, and construction costs. Fire protection factors include the fire hazard properties of the commodities, storage arrangement, type of building construction, whether the building is sprinklered, and the susceptibility of the commodities to smoke or water damage.

Ventilation: An important consideration when planning a warehouse is the method of ventilation. Smoke removal is essential to manual fire fighting and overhaul. In unsprinklered buildings automatic smoke and heat vents used in conjunction with draft curtains facilitate access for manual fire fighting (see Sec. 6, Chap. 8). In sprinklered warehouses, venting through eaveline windows, doors, roof monitors, or gravity or mechanical exhaust systems is essential for smoke removal. It permits prompt overhaul and mop-up operations after control of the fire by sprinklers is achieved. Charged hose lines must be available before manual venting of the building is started because of a possible increase in fire intensity.

Emergency Access: Entrance to a building for manual fire fighting must be made easy. Often the usual entrances to a building will provide satisfactory access for fire fighters, but in many instances, such is not the case. Satisfactory access through emergency doors or panels close by public or private hydrants and roadways or driveways is important.

Storage Arrangement

The arrangement of the commodity with its packaging or storage aids can have a pronounced effect on the fire growth, intensity, and duration. The same basic commodity, such as paper, can have relatively slow burning characteristics in some forms, and very fast burning characteristics in others. An example of the former is flat paper in sheets on skids; unbanded roll paper stored on end is in the latter category.

General storage includes only those arrangements where commodities are stored in solid piles, with or without pallets, in bin boxes, or on shelves. Bin box storage is storage in five-sided wood, metal, or cardboard boxes, not more than 6 ft by 6 ft by 6 ft in dimensions, with the open face on the aisle. Boxes are self-supporting or supported by a structure so designed that little or no horizontal or vertical space exists around the boxes. Shelf storage is storage on structures less than 30 in. deep, with shelves usually 2 ft apart vertically, and separated by approximately 30 in. aisles.

Piling: Commodities piles continue to go to greater heights with the rate of heat release increasing at an exponential rate as the height of the pile increases. Modern material handling equipment is capable of stacking commodities to heights of up to 30 ft. The stability of the commodity with its handling aid (i.e., pallet) often determines the maximum height of piling.

Piles are arranged to minimize the spread of fire and allow good access for manual fire fighting. Keeping piles as narrow as practical consistent with the configuration of the

Fig. 5-1A. Proper clearance of stock from sprinkler piping is illustrated in this grocery warehouse. Wide aisles give the industrial truck plenty of room to maneuver. The dark pipes at the ceiling are sprinkler lines.

building is also good practice. Adequate main aisles (generally not less than 8 ft) and cross aisles are necessary to provide means of egress as well as access for manual fire fighting (see Fig. 5-1A).

In unsprinklered buildings, good practice is to provide a minimum separation of 8 ft between piles, with pile sizes, excluding surrounding clear spaces, limited as follows:

Noncombustible	No limit
Class I & II	15,000 sq. ft.
Class III	10,000 " "
Class IV	5,000 " "

Floor Loading: When designing for floor loads where water absorbent commodities are to be stored, it is necessary to take into account the added weight of water which can be absorbed during fire fighting operations. Also, these materials that swell appreciably when wet can cause structural damage unless adequate clearance is maintained between the storage and walls or columns. Storage on skids, dunnage, pallets, or elevated platforms will minimize water damage to commodities that are particularly susceptible.

C. Fire Protection for General Storage

The earlier a fire is detected, controlled, and extinguished the less damage will result. As warehouses normally are populated by only a few people during daytime hours, and visited only infrequently by guards or are completely unattended at night, automatic protection and alarm is of utmost importance.

Automatic Sprinklers

Automatic sprinklers are essential for protection of all four classes of commodities. The sprinkler installation is designed to provide an adequate water density to control a fire in the commodity to be protected. Sprinkler design for solid pile storage over 15 ft high, and palletized storage, bin box storage, and shelf storage over 12 ft high is determined from Figures 5-1B and 5-1C. These curves apply to all storage heights up to 30 ft, except for shelf storage which is limited to 15 ft.

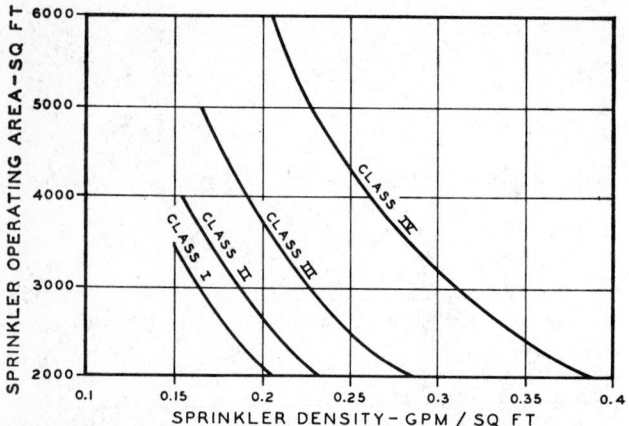

Fig. 5-1B. Sprinkler system design curves for 20-ft-high storage and 165°F sprinklers. For 286°F sprinklers, reduce the sprinkler operating area 40 percent, but to not less than 2,000 sq ft.

As an example of the use of curves, a warehouse containing cereal storage on pallets 20 ft high would be a Class III commodity. Using the Class III curve in Figure 5-1B, any point on the curve can be selected. If 165°F sprinklers are to be used on a wet pipe system, the sprinkler system could be designed to provide a density of .25 gpm over an area of 2,500 sq ft. This requires a water supply of 625 gpm at the proper pressure to supply the area and density selected. At least 500 gpm is added to the sprinkler demand for large and small hose stream demand, thus making the total water supply 1,125 gpm.

Wet systems are preferable for storage warehouses except where it is impractical to provide heat. If a dry system is to be used in the previous example, a density of .25 gpm can still be used but the area of application is increased by 30 percent to 3,250 sq ft. This means the water supply for sprinklers would be 812 gpm.

The suggested duration of the water supply is as follows:

Duration (hours)

Storage Height (ft)	Commodity Class	
	Class I, II, & III	Class IV
Up to 20	1½	2
20 to 30	2	2½

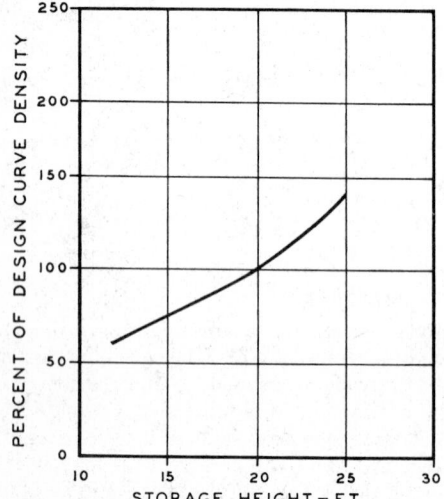

Fig. 5-1C. Adjustment curve for modifying sprinkler discharge densities given in Fig. 4-1B for different storage heights.

High water pressure for the first sprinklers that operate is desirable. A study on the subject was reported in *Fire Technology*.[1]

The use of high temperature (286°F) sprinklers instead of ordinary temperature (165°F) sprinklers can reduce water damage with little or no increase in fire damage, according to tests conducted at Factory Mutual testing facilities.[2] The delay in operation of high temperature sprinklers as compared with the delay for ordinary rated sprinklers was noted to be small, but the number of sprinklers that operated was reduced considerably. By reducing the number of sprinklers that operate, more water at better pressure is available to the sprinklers over the fire itself.

Hose Streams, Hydrants, and Extinguishers

Indiscriminate use of hose streams can reduce the volume and pressure available to sprinklers to the point where the sprinkler discharge in ineffective; thus the water for hose streams must be in addition to requirements for sprinklers. The size warehouse, type of commodity, storage configuration, and related factors may increase the volume requirements above the 500 gpm minimum that is normally required.

Small Hose: The most desirable type of hand extinguishing equipment in warehouses is small hose installations. Sufficient 1½-in. hose stations are located throughout the premises so that all areas can be reached. The hose can be supplied from a wet pipe sprinkler system or a separate piping system.

Hydrants: A system of private hydrants is needed when public hydrants do not provide adequate coverage. Locating hydrants near points of entrances to the building is desirable to minimize the amount of hose needed. When hose is to be provided for use by private fire brigades or emergency organizations, 2½-in. hose together with 1½-in. hose and wye connections are provided since 1½-in. streams are much easier to handle and can be utilized with less personnel. Combination type shutoff nozzles are preferable.

Portable Fire Extinguishers: These are needed to cope with Class B (flammable liquid) and Class C (electrical) fires, and are desirable for Class A (ordinary combustible) hazards even though small hose is available throughout. Class B extinguishers often are mounted on in-plant vehicles. Multipurpose extinguishers are acceptable. However, difficult to reach fires in high piled commodities normally require much more extinguishing medium than is available in portable hand extinguishers. Often a pile has to be manually pulled apart to complete extinguishment, and hand lines are effective for control during mop-up operations.

Planning for Fire Emergencies

A fire organization if trained will prove to be of great assistance at the time of fire and if procedures are planned in advance. It is important that emergency organizations know the peculiarities of the commodities in storage. If water damage is a serious consideration, plans include minimizing the damage by water to stock in the fire area. If the commodity generates heavy black smoke, safety of personnel must be considered. In-plant fire fighting personnel need self-contained breathing apparatus. Proper training of personnel will insure that the alarm is sent promptly. Specific duties are assigned to be sure that sprinkler control valves are promptly checked to be certain that they are open and then supervised continuously, that fire doors are closed, that utilities can be shut off promptly if necessary, that fire pumps are started quickly, that ventilation is provided with the least effort and cost if needed, and many other considerations which may be peculiar to the individual location.

Alarm Service

Good alarm service enables manual fire fighting to start as soon as possible. As most warehouses have only limited personnel in the various parts of the building, particularly at night and on weekends, alarm facilities are even more vital. Local water flow alarms on sprinkler systems may suffice for some conditions. An in-plant proprietary alarm system actuated by the sprinklers is desirable if personnel are continuously nearby in manufacturing areas, or if guard service at a central location is provided. In some instances, a central station supervised system (alarm given at an off-premise location) may be considered necessary.

In addition to alarms actuated by sprinklers, special alarms actuated by heat or smoke, or both, are sometimes considered advisable. Automatic smoke detection systems are used, particularly for high value areas, to speed up the detection and fire fighting, preferably before there is sufficient heat to fuse sprinklers.

Equipment

Most warehousing operations utilize mechanical handling equipment of one type or another. Industrial lift trucks (fork type or squeeze clamp) are the most common. They may be propelled electrically or by gasoline or LP-gas engines. Gasoline and LP-gas introduce a hazard if the trucks are not properly maintained. A fuel leak, especially with propane, is dangerous, as vapors are difficult to disperse and tend to gravitate toward low spots or pits. To minimize exposure to the stored commodities, industrial trucks are refueled only at locations designated for that purpose. Safe outdoor locations for refueling are preferable to those indoors (see Chap. 3 of this Section for further information on industrial trucks).

Building Facilities and Maintenance

Operations incidental to the warehousing operations, such as repairing, refinishing, crating, painting, and general maintenance are separated from the warehouse areas by good walls or partitions, the fire resistive rating of the walls being determined by the exposure presented.

Welding and cutting is preferably done in an enclosed shop area. If not feasible to remove the material from the warehouse to the shop area, adequate precautions must be taken to prevent hot metal from getting into piles with their many cracks and crevices by covering the piles with flame-resistant covers. Combustibles that can be moved, are moved to a safe distance from the work area. A close fire watch is maintained during and after completion of welding and cutting operations. (See Sec. 4, Chap. 8, for further information on welding and cutting safeguards.)

Suitable facilities are provided for waste collection with regular disposal at specific intervals. The use of listed containers is preferable.

Smoking is prohibited except in certain specified safe areas such as offices, lounges, and toilets. Smoking is especially hazardous at shipping docks where it is difficult to control housekeeping in the rail or truck well.

Closures at exterior openings assist in keeping unauthorized persons from gaining entry. Fire doors are protected by guards if subject to mechanical damage. Weekly inspections ascertain that all sprinkler control valves are open, that other fire protection equipment is available and in operating condition, that fire doors will operate satisfactorily, and that conditions related to fire safety are in good order.

CONVENTIONAL PALLET   SLAVE PALLET

Fig. 5-1D. Two typical types of pallets.

D. Rack Storage Practices

Commodity Classification

The classification of commodities stored in racks is essentially the same as the four classes defined for general storage. The differences are:

1. Classifications for rack storage are defined as commodities stored on only wood pallets (see Fig. 5-1D). For general storage, commodities may be stored on wood or plastic pallets or may be stored without pallets.

2. Rack storage includes both encapsulated and nonencapsulated commodities. General storage does not include encapsulated commodities. (Encapsulating is a method of packaging consisting of a plastic sheet completely enclosing the sides and top of a pallet load containing a combustible commodity.)

Building Arrangement

The same basic principles for the arrangement of general storage warehouses, including fire areas, ventilation, and emergency access, also apply to rack storage warehouses. However, rack storage warehouses, while only a single story, may reach heights of 100 ft or more to the roof. In some warehouses, the vertical steel rack members support the building.

Where the storage height exceeds 15 ft and ceiling sprinklers only are installed, steel building columns or rack members supporting the building are protected by 1-hr protective coverings or side wall sprinklers.

Storage Arrangement

Storage racks are either fixed or portable (see Fig. 5-1E). Fixed racks are arranged in single rows, double rows (see Fig. 5-1F), or multiple rows (see Fig. 5-1G). A variation of the double row rack is the cantilever rack (see Fig. 5-1H), and a variation of the multiple row rack is the flow-through rack (see Fig. 5-1I). Aisle widths and depth of racks are determined by the material handling methods.

Equipment

For storage heights up to 30 ft, the same type of materials handling equipment may be utilized as that used for general storage, i.e., industrial lift trucks, with the same attendant

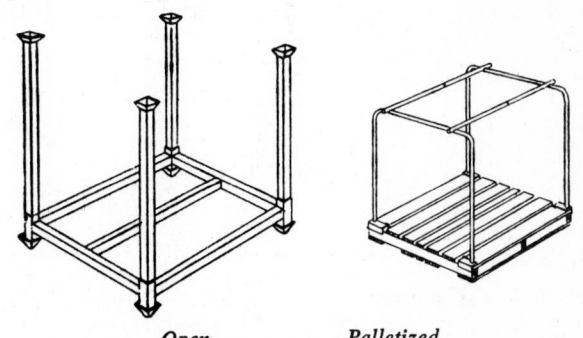

Open   Palletized
Fig. 5-1E. Two types of portable racks.

hazards associated with the fuel used. Particularly for greater heights, stacker cranes and automatic computer-controlled material handling systems are utilized to store and retrieve commodities in the racks.

E. Fire Protection for Rack Storage

The arrangement of commodities stored in racks generally provides greater flue spaces both horizontally and vertically

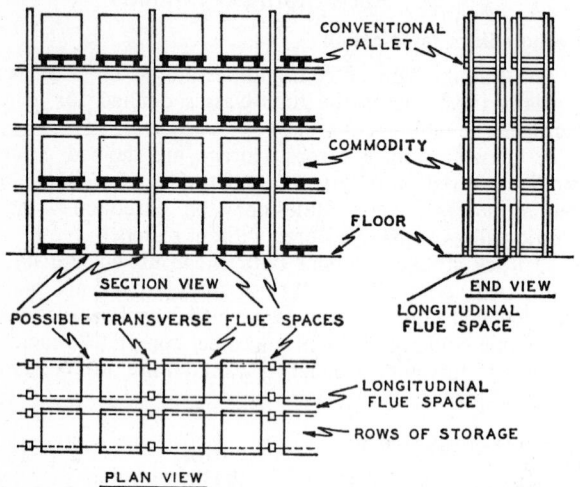

Fig. 5-1F. A typical double row (back-to-back) rack arrangement.

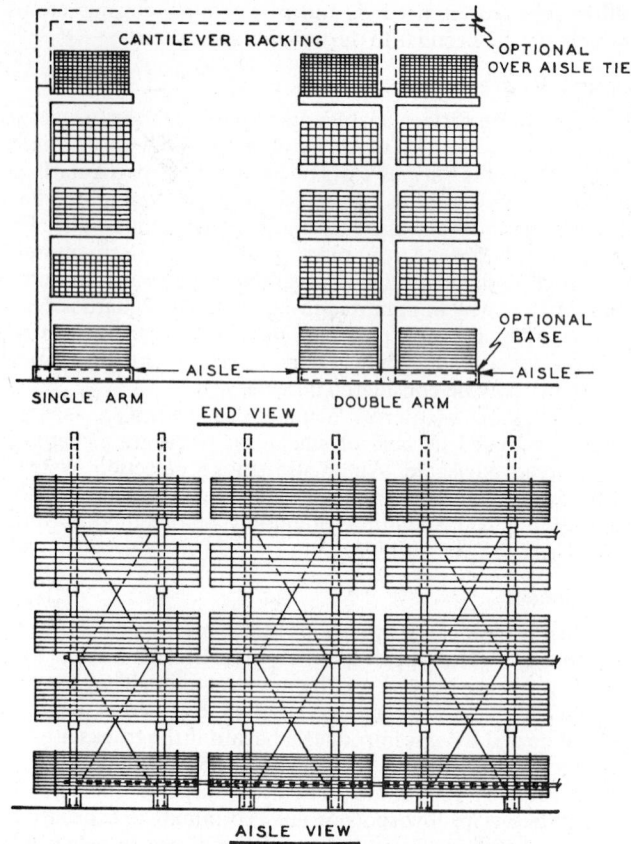

Fig. 5-1H. A cantilever rack.

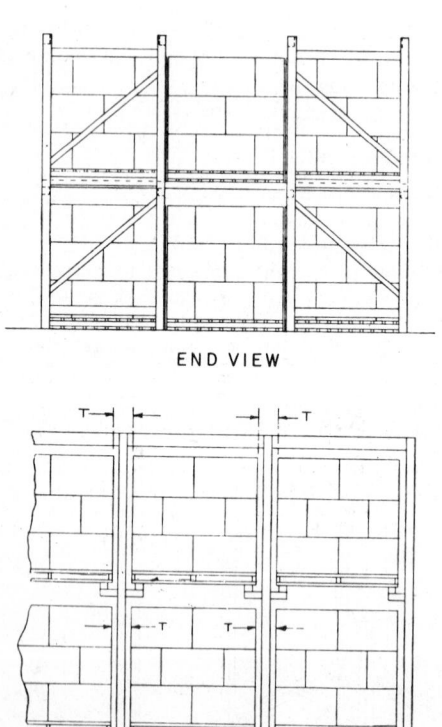

Fig. 5-1G. A multiple row, drive-in rack that is two or more pallets deep. T indicates transverse flue spaces. Fork trucks drive into the rack to deposit and withdraw loads in the depth of the rack.

than palletized general storage. This contributes to the more rapid spread and intensity of a fire. Thus, automatic sprinkler protection is necessary for protection of all four classes of commodities stored in racks.

The design density for ceiling sprinklers is determined by whether or not the commodity is encapsulated, whether in-rack sprinklers are provided, and whether 286° or 165° F sprinklers are installed. Class I and II commodities may be protected by ceiling sprinklers alone, whether in single row, double row, or multiple row racks. Up to heights of 25 ft, the necessity for providing in-rack sprinklers depends upon the commodity class, whether or not the commodity is encapsulated, the depth of racks and the height of storage. For adequate protection, in-rack sprinklers are required for all classes of commodities stored at heights of over 25 ft. Ceiling sprinkler system design curves for all commodity classes in various storage configurations, and in-rack sprinkler arrangements are shown in NFPA No. 231C, Rack Storage of

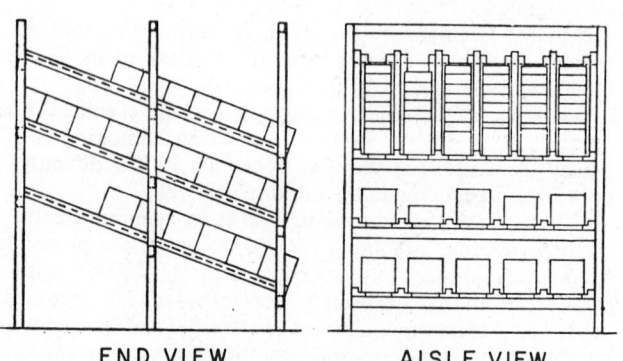

Fig. 5-1I. A flow-through rack.

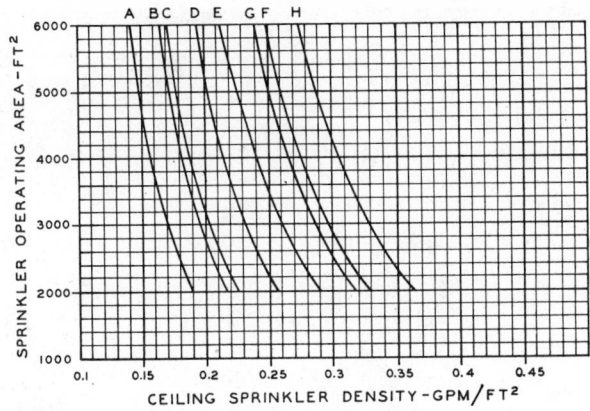

Curve   Legend

*A—8 ft aisles with 286°F ceiling sprinklers and 165°F in-rack
    sprinklers*

*B—8 ft aisles with 165°F ceiling sprinklers and 165°F in-rack
    sprinklers*

*C—4 ft aisles with 286°F ceiling sprinklers and 165°F in-rack
    sprinklers*

*D—4 ft aisles with 165°F ceiling sprinklers and 165°F in-rack
    sprinklers*

E—8 ft aisles with 286°F ceiling sprinklers

F—8 ft aisles with 165°F ceiling sprinklers

G—4 ft aisles with 286°F ceiling sprinklers

H—4 ft aisles with 165°F ceiling sprinklers

*Fig. 5-1J. Sprinkler design curves for Class I nonencapsulated
commodities stored on conventional pallets in 20-ft high, double-
row racks.*

Materials. Typical sprinkler design curves are shown in
Figure 5-1J of this HANDBOOK.

The duration of the water supply for single and double
row racks is a minimum of $1\frac{1}{2}$ hrs for Class I, II, and III
commodities, and 2 hrs for Class IV commodities. For
multiple row racks, the water supply duration is a minimum
of 2 hrs for all classifications of commodities.

When high expansion foam is used in combination with
ceiling sprinklers, the sprinkler design density may be reduced to a minimum of 0.2 gpm per square foot for Class I,
II, or III commodities, and 0.25 gpm per square foot for
Class IV commodities over the most hydraulically remote
2,000 sq ft area. Dry pipe sprinkler systems are acceptable
only where it is impractical to provide heat.

The provision of water for hose streams, small hose,
portable fire extinguishers, hydrants, alarm service, and a
fire organization are the same as for general storage.

F. Storage of Specific Materials

Storage of Empty Pallets

Idle pallet storage introduces a severe fire condition.
Stacking idle pallets in piles is the best arrangement of combustibles to promote rapid spread of fire, heat release, and
complete combustion. After pallets are used for a short time
in warehouses, they dry out and edges become frayed and
splintered. Thus, they are subject to easy ignition from a
small ignition source. Again, high piling increases considerably both the challenge to sprinklers and the probability of
involving a large number of pallets when fire occurs.

A fire in stacks of idle wooden pallets is one of the
greatest challenges to sprinklers. The undersides of the
boards of the pallets create a dry area on which a fire can
grow and expand to other dry or partially wet areas. This
process of jumping to other dry, closely located, parallel
combustible surfaces continues until the fire bursts through

the top of the stack. Once this happens, very little water is
able to reach the base of the fire. The only practical method
of stopping a fire in a large concentration of pallets with ceiling sprinklers is a great amount of prewetting. In high stacks,
this cannot be done without abnormally high water supplies.

The storage of empty wood pallets in an unsprinklered
warehouse containing other storage is a bad practice.

The hazard of storage of empty plastic pallets is so great
that their storage is limited to outdoors.

**Table 5-1A.   Sprinkler Density Requirements for
Pallet Storage**

Height of Wood Pallet Storage	Sprinkler Density Requirements (GPM-Min-Sq Ft)	Area of Sprinkler Operation (sq ft)	
		286°	165°
Up to 6 ft	.20	2,000	3,000
6 to 8 ft	.30	2,500	4,000
8 to 12 ft	.60	3,500	6,000
12 to 20 ft	.60	4,500	—

The suggested protection requirements for the storage of
empty wood pallets are shown in Table 5-1A.

In buildings with exposed steel roof structures where wood
pallets are stored in excess of 8 ft in height, maximum
sprinkler spacing does not exceed 50 sq ft per sprinkler with
$\frac{1}{2}$-in. orifice, and 70 sq ft per sprinkler with $\frac{17}{32}$-in. orifice in
order to provide protection for roof steel.

Paper and Paper Products

Roll Paper: Large rolls of paper are stored on their sides,
either nested between rolls of a lower tier or resting on dunnage placed between tiers, or stacked on end. Rolls may also
be stored in racks. The use of dunnage provides more opportunity for fire to burrow into the pile and makes extinguishment more difficult than where rolls are nested.

The most hazardous storage configuration and the greatest
challenge to sprinkler protection is presented by rolls stored
on end as separate columns. Fire spreading up the side of a
column of roll paper quickly burns through the outer ply,
permitting the paper to unwind and peel away (exfoliate)
from the roll. The peeled material greatly and quickly increases the burning surface, and as the outer layers wet by
the sprinkler discharge are shed, dry paper is exposed. The
vertical shafts or flues formed between the stacks create a
strong updraft during a fire which carries burning pieces of
paper to nearby stacks, thus spreading the fire. The result
is a rapidly developing fire both in size and intensity. Metal
bands or fire retardant treated protective wrappers are
effective in reducing the peeling action during a fire. Where
rolls are all the same size and they are placed in or nearly
in contact, peeling is prevented and the air supply is restricted. If there is less than 4 in. between stacks, fire growth
is slow and the intensity is relatively low. The fire hazard of
rolls stacked vertically on pallets is essentially the same as
without pallets.

Fire extinguishment is best handled by automatic sprinklers. Wet pipe sprinkler systems are most suitable for the
protection of roll paper storage. Dry pipe systems are not
desirable because of the appreciable delay in the application
of water, particularly for on-end storage with 4 in. or more
space between roll columns. In buildings with exposed steel
structural members, sprinklers spaced not more than 50 sq
ft per sprinkler and not more than 10 ft apart are needed for
protection of the primary structural elements and secondary
elements supporting important sprinkler piping.

The rate of water demand for sprinklers is dependent upon

the storage height, storage arrangement, roof support material, and the design of the sprinkler system. Careful management of the use of hose streams is essential so that they do not rob the sprinklers of water, which might cause the loss of fire control. In addition to the high rates of water discharge generally necessary to supply sprinklers, a duration of 6 hrs or more may be needed for protection of large or high storages. For small or low storage a water supply duration of 2 hrs may be adequate.

Baled Wastepaper: Paper stored in bales does not produce the fast heat release fire associated with roll paper but instead has a burrowing characteristic. Fire in baled wastepaper is difficult to extinguish and generates heavy smoke. Broken bales are difficult to handle after wetting. Usually a motorized vehicle with shovel in required to move the debris out of doors to complete extinguishment.

Spontaneous ignition is common in wastepaper due to foreign materials subject to spontaneous heating that become trapped in bales. Fire protection for wastepaper storage follows the same considerations that apply generally to indoor storage practices. In unusually large baled waste storage areas, manual or automatic venting of smoke is very desirable to allow fire fighters to work in the fire area.

Paper in various other forms, such as knocked down corrugated cartons and partitions for boxes, will generate much smoke during a fire, as fire can readily burrow into the pile. Also, the more fibrous the surface of a paper, the greater hazard it presents.

Rubber Tires

Rubber tires are usually rated as a very high fire hazard storage. Tires burn readily with much heat and smoke hampering manual fire fighting.

Tires are stored directly on the floor, either on their sides or in pyramided piles, or in fixed or portable racks. The present trend for storage of tires in large warehouse facilities is to portable racks, either on-tread in open racks (see Fig. 5-1K) or on-side in palletized racks (see Fig. 5-1L). They may also be stored bundled, where a number of tires are strapped together, in palletized portable racks.

When the storage height exceeds 15 ft, the steel building columns are protected either by 2-hr fireproofing, or by a

Fig. 5-1L. On-side storage of rubber tires in palletized racks.

sidewall sprinkler directed at one side of the column. Venting through eave-line windows, doors, monitors, or gravity or mechanical exhaust systems is essential for smoke removal to permit manual fire fighting and overhaul after control of the fire is achieved. Fire tests have indicated that while automatic sprinklers with adequate discharge densities can control a fire in rubber tires, extinguishment by sprinklers alone cannot be expected. It is essential that the behavior of this type of fire is understood if control is not to be lost in the overhaul stage. Suggested sprinkler discharge densities are given in Table 5-1B and Figure 5-1M. Where high expansion foam is provided in conjunction with automatic sprinklers, sprinkler discharge densities may be reduced. Other protection aspects follow those noted for general indoor general storage.

Plastics

The fire hazard of plastic materials in storage is determined by their chemical composition, their physical form,

Fig. 5-1K. On-tread storage of tires in open, portable racks.

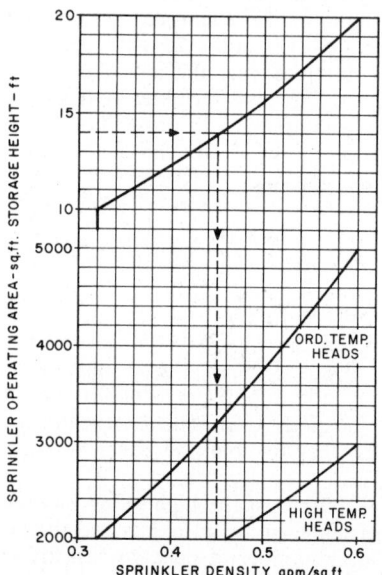

Fig. 5-1M. Sprinkler system design curves for storage of rubber tires; palletized and fixed racks with pallets. To use curves, enter curve at "Storage Height" (example 14 ft); read density (0.45) then down to "Sprinkler operating area" (3,200 sq ft for ordinary sprinklers and 2,000 sq ft for high temperature sprinklers).

Table 5-1B. Sprinkler Discharge Densities for Rubber Tire Storage

Piling Method	Piling Height Feet	Sprinkler Discharge Density—Gallons Per Minute Per Square Foot (See Notes 1 and 2)	Areas of Application Square Feet (See Note 1)	
			Ord. Temp. Spklrs.	High Temp. Spklrs.

1. On Floor
  a. Pyramid piles
  b. Other arrangement such that no horizontal channels are formed
  c. Tires piled on floor on tread (See Note 3)
  d. Off the road tires
	Up to 5
	5 + to 7
	7 + to 8
	8 + to 10
	10 + to 12
		See NFPA No. 13. Standard for Installation of Sprinkler Systems
		0.24
		0.26
		0.28
		0.32
			
			2,000
			2,000
			2,000
			2,000
				
				2,000
				2,000
				2,000
				2,000

2. Palletized On side or tread	9 to 20 20 + to 30	See Fig. 5-1M 0.3 plus Hi-X*	 3,000	 3,000
3. Open Portable Rack Storage On side or tread	12 (approx.) 20 (approx.)	0.6 {0.6 {0.9 or 0.3 plus Hi-X*	5,000 (See Note 4) (See Note 4) 3,000	2,000 5,000 3,000 3,000
4. Double & Multi-row Fixed Rack Storage on Pallets On side or tread	9–20 20	See Fig. 5-1M 0.4 plus 1 line in-rack sprinklers or 0.3 plus Hi-X*	— 3,000 3,000	— 3,000 3,000
5. Double & Multi-row Fixed Rack Storage Without Pallets or Shelves On side or tread	12 20	0.6 {0.6 {0.9 or 0.3 plus Hi-X* or 0.4 plus 1 line in-rack sprinklers	5,000 (See Note 4) (See Note 4) 3,000 3,000	3,000 5,000 3,000 3,000 3,000

*High Expansion Foam

Notes:
1. Sprinkler discharge densities and areas of application are based on a maximum clearance of 10 ft between sprinkler deflectors and the maximum available height of storage.
2. Densities in table are based on standard sprinklers. In buildings where "old style" sprinklers exist, discharge densities are increased by 25 percent.
3. Piles not to exceed 25 ft in direction of wheel holes.
4. Water supply fulfills both requirements.

and the storage arrangement. The physical form may be foam, solid, sheet, or pellets, flakes or random packed small objects, such as toothpaste caps, in bags or cartons. The storage of plastics generally does not exceed a maximum height of approximately 20 ft. The hazard of a particular plastic in any form or storage arrangement is the same whether it is encapsulated or nonencapsulated. Large quantities of smoke are usually generated, making manual fire fighting difficult and venting desirable in building construction considerations.

Plastics such as fluorocarbons, unplastisized polyvinylchloride, and phenolics can be protected the same as any General Storage Class III commodity, regardless of their physical form or storage arrangement. Pellets and small objects can be protected the same as General Storage Class IV commodities.

Thermoplastics, such as polyurethane, polyethylene, plasticized polyvinylchloride, and thermosets, such as polyesters, present a severe fire hazard, exceeded only by thermoplastics such as polystyrene and acrylonitrile-butadiene-styrene (ABS). These plastic materials will melt and break down into their monomers and act and burn like flammable liquids. High sprinkler discharge densities over relatively large areas are necessary to protect these types of plastics, particularly where 165°F sprinklers are used. Large orifice sprinklers ($\frac{17}{32}$-in.) are preferable for the greater storage heights. In the form of a foamed material, these plastics present the most severe fire hazard, requiring the greatest sprinkler density and area of sprinkler operation.

Where automatic high expansion foam systems are provided in conjunction with automatic sprinkler protection, the required sprinkler discharge density generally may be reduced by about one-half. NFPA No. 231B, Cellular Rubber and Plastics Materials, specifies in more detail the protection aspects to consider.

Combustible Fibers

Natural and synthetic fibers have many and varied flammability characteristics (see Sec. 3, Chap. 2). The prime consideration is whether the material is subject to fast-travelling surface fires. Another characteristic is the ability to absorb large quantities of water with swelling and expansion often resulting in building damage, although fire damage has been small.

The method of packaging will usually determine whether there is an unusual hazard or not. A solid wood case of cotton yarn presents no problem other than those associated with ordinary combustibles. However, the combustible burlap wrappings do not fully enclose a bale of cotton thus presenting the possibility of a rapid fire spread. Once the fibrous surface has been consumed, a slow burrowing fire usually follows. Bales usually have to be taken outside and pulled apart to complete extinguishment. Smoke venting facilities are desirable in order to accomplish extinguishment or removal of the bales, or both. Fire areas and height of piles preferably are quite limited. The use of heavy, straight hose streams in a baled cotton warehouse may spread burning fibers. Spray or fog application of water is preferable.

Good aisles, stability of piles, piling limitations, and other factors noted for general storage are important.

Refrigerated Commodities

Temperatures in cold storage warehouses range from 32° to 65°F for products such as fruits, eggs, or nuts that would be damaged by freezing down to 0° to -35°F for initial freezing. Both combustible and noncombustible building construction are common. Insulating materials are generally combustible, such as corkboard or expanded plastics, even though the building itself is noncombustible. Rigid expanded (foam) polystyrene and polyurethane are widely used. These plastics start to melt at about 200°F and burn rapidly at fire temperatures, releasing large quantities of smoke. A coating of portland cement plaster over the exposed plastic surfaces can prevent melting and ignition of the plastic as well as providing protection against normal wear and tear.

Occupancies may vary from combustible to noncombustible. Combustible materials generally found in cold storage warehouses include wood dunnage, wood pallets, wood boxes containing food, fiberboard food containers, wooden baskets, waxed paper, heavy paper wrappings, cloth wrappings, and grease impregnated materials.

All types of material handling systems are used, but fork lift trucks are most common.

Even at the lower temperatures, with sufficient combustibles present and the air that is normally available, a fire severe enough to require sprinkler protection is possible. Refrigerated warehouses need the same protection as comparable combustible arrangements in other warehouse storages. Sprinkler systems may be either preaction or dry type, with the former preferred. The low temperatures add to the problem of maintenance of the sprinkler system, particularly in keeping it free of ice and frost (see Sec. 14, Chap. 6 and NFPA No. 13A).

Bulk Storage

Many combustible materials, such as grains, sugar, starch, flour, and plastic pellets or flakes, are handled and stored in bulk. These may be stored in silos, bins, tanks, or as bulk piles in storage buildings. The construction of storage facilities is generally of concrete or steel. Grain is stored in rein-

Fig. 5-1N. A graphic example of the enormous size that bulk storage of commodities can take is this warehouse of raw sugar in Queensland, Australia, shown after a fire that burned for several days. Although the power shovel appears to be standing on the building floor, it is actually resting on a layer of wet sugar several feet thick. (H. W. Swanton)

forced concrete silos more than 100 ft high and in tanks several hundred feet in diameter and 30 ft or more high.

The bulk handling of combustible materials generates dust which, when present in sufficient quantity, may present an explosion hazard in the storage facility. Thus, where there are a number of adjacent storage silos or bins, it is important that there are no communicating openings between them, and that each is provided with the maximum possible explosion venting area.

A fire in bulk storage may be initiated either on or below the surface. In either case, it results in a burrowing type fire. Automatic sprinkler protection is not effective on such a fire, and extinguishment is only obtained by removing the burning material from the storage facility. Sprinkler protection is only needed where bulk storage is located in a building of combustible construction. If water from hose streams is used on a fire in a bin or silo, it must be applied judiciously, since they generally are not designed to withstand the additional hydrostatic load, and may collapse.

Raw sugar stored in bulk is not easily ignited but has resulted in serious fires. Usually, fire has started in other combustibles, such as a rubber conveyor belt, wood, or a propane-fired vehicle, with the hot fire igniting the sugar. The large areas of sugar warehouses often make access for manual fire fighting difficult. Water from hose streams washes away much of the bulk sugar. Automatic sprinkler protection is needed if ignition sources present in the warehouse are of sufficient magnitude to ignite the bulk sugar or if the building is of combustible construction. (For bulk storage of coal see Section 3, Chapter 5.)

SI Units

The following conversion factors are given as a convenience in converting to SI units the English units used in this chapter.

1 sq ft	= 0.0929 mm²
1 in.	= 25.400 mm
1 ft	= 0.305 m
$\frac{5}{9}(°F - 32)$	= °C
1 gpm	= 3.785 litres/min

Bibliography

References Cited

[1] Suchomel, Miles R., "Factors Influencing the Use of High Temperature Sprinklers," *Fire Technology*, Vol. 1, No. 1, Feb. 1965, pp. 15–22.

[2] Rhodes, J. M., "Temperature Rating and Sprinkler Performance," NFPA *Quarterly*, Vol. 57, No. 1, July 1963, pp. 25–29.

NFPA Codes, Standards, and Recommended Practices (see the latest *NFPA Publications and Visual Aids Catalog* for availability of current editions of the following documents)

NFPA No. 6, Recommendations for Organization of Industrial Fire Loss Prevention.

NFPA No. 7, Recommendations for Management Control of Fire Emergencies.

NFPA No. 13, Standard for the Installation of Sprinkler Systems.

NFPA No. 13A, Recommended Practice for the Care and Maintenance of Sprinkler Systems.

NFPA No. 14, Standard for the Installation of Standpipe and Hose Systems.

NFPA No. 27, Recommendations for Organization, Training and Equipment of Private Fire Brigades.

NFPA No. 51B, Standard for Fire Prevention in Use of Cutting and Welding Processes.

NFPA No. 71, Standard for the Installation, Maintenance and Use of Central Station Signaling Systems.

NFPA No. 72A, Standard for the Installation, Maintenance and Use of Local Protective Signaling Systems for Watchman, Fire Alarm and Supervisory Service.

NFPA No. 72B, Standard for the Installation, Maintenance and Use of Auxiliary Protective Signaling Systems for Fire Alarm Service.

NFPA No. 72C, Standard for the Installation, Maintenance and Use of Remote Station Protective Signaling Systems.

NFPA No. 204, Guide for Smoke and Heat Venting.

NFPA No. 231, Standard for Indoor General Storage.

NFPA No. 231B, Standard for Storage of Cellular Rubber and Plastics Materials.

NFPA No. 231C, Standard for Rack Storage of Materials.

NFPA No. 505, Fire Safety Standard for Powered Industrial Trucks Including Type Designations and Areas of Use.

NFPA No. 601, Recommendations for Guard Service in Fire Loss Prevention.

NFPA No. 601A, Standard for Guard Operations in Fire Loss Prevention.

NFPA No. 604, Recommended Practice on Salvaging Operations.

Additional Readings

Clarke, Graham, "The Idle Pallet Fire Problem," *Fire Journal*, Vol. 66, No. 4, July 1972, pp. 98–101.

Factory Mutual Engineering Corporation, "Combustible Dusts," Chapter 66, *Handbook of Industrial Loss Prevention*, 2nd ed., McGraw-Hill, New York, 1967, pp. 66–12—66–14.

———, "Textiles," Chapter 69, *ibid.*, pp. 69–22—69–25.

———, "Warehouse Storage," Chapter 72, *ibid.*, pp. 72–4—72–8.

Johnson, R. S., "How to Protect Roll-Paper Storage from Costly Fires," *Inland Printer/American Lithographer*, Mar. 1968.

Lownsbury, A. W., "High Stack Fires," *Distribution Age*, Aug. 1965, pp. 44–47.

Russell, Roger, "Space-Age Protection for High-Rise Storage," *Fire Journal*, Vol. 61, No. 6, Nov. 1967, pp. 20–22.

Schirmer, C. W., "Meeting the High-Piled Storage Challenge with Standards," *Fire Journal*, Vol. 65, No. 6, Nov. 1971, pp. 61–66.

Chapter 2

OUTDOOR STORAGE PRACTICES

Various commodities, either due to their bulk or their resistance to damage by weather conditions, are stored in industrial yards, outdoor storage sites, and, in some cases, in open fields. The fire problems associated with outdoor storage are somewhat different from those for materials stored indoors, and, because of the nature of the variables involved, the solutions to the problems are likewise different. In some cases, outdoor storage is preferable to storage in combustible buildings, particularly where such buildings lack adequate interior fire protection. In other cases, the exact opposite is true, e.g., it might be preferable to store materials under efficient sprinkler protection within a structure rather than to risk destruction of such exposed storage outdoors where dependence must necessarily be placed on manual fire control efforts.

It is very difficult to present specific recommendations for fire safety of outdoor storage concentrations. There are so many variables involved as to the site, the utilization of the space available, the types of material being stored, and the fire protection which can be supplied that specific recommendations on piling, height, clearances from combustible structures, and similar recommendations cannot be generally applied. Some materials might ignite from small ignition sources, such as a carelessly discarded cigarette, while others would not be expected to ignite unless subjected to rather intense heat or flame. Some commodities that can be stored outdoors without excessive damage by weather have very quick burning characteristics, and, on exposure to flame, an entire pile of the material may quickly become involved, making fire control most difficult. Other commodities burn slowly, emitting great quantities of smoke as the fire burrows through the pile. Frequently, storage piles must be taken apart to achieve any degree of fire control.

It is possible, in some cases, to calculate rather closely what the heat radiation and convection problems would be under normal prevailing weather conditions for a pile of materials of certain dimensions. When possible, it is feasible to establish specific recommendations for clearances from adjacent piles or structures. In other cases, this cannot be done readily, as variances in humidity, wind, and other weather conditions have a decided effect on the fire hazard and heat transfer characteristics of some commodities.

A big problem with some outdoor storage concentrations is the hazard presented by flying brands. There have been a number of serious fire losses and conflagrations originating in outdoor storage (lumber yards, etc.) where the flying brand hazard was the major factor in fire spread. It was impossible or impractical in a number of these cases to have preplanned for adequate clear spaces around the stored material to prevent the brands from spreading the fire.

For the reasons explained in the previous paragraphs it is not possible to present in the HANDBOOK specific recommendations covering all types of outdoor storage. The best that can be done is to outline the considerations which apply, relying on evaluation of the individual circumstances and the judgment of the persons concerned in the applications of these principles to individual situations.

NFPA No. 231A, Recommended Safe Practices for Outdoor General Storage, is also a good source for general information on outdoor storage practices.

A. Selection of Site

As with indoor storage, there are definite considerations in the selection of outdoor storage sites.

Size

It is extremely important in selecting a site that adequate area is available for the quantity of material to be stored. Consideration is given for future expansion, as the quantities of materials to be stored grows to insure adequate aisle sizes and pile sizes (as discussed below) can be maintained. Where adequate area is not available at a site to be used, additional sites must be considered. Congestion at storage sites is a leading factor in fire development and spread.

Terrain

A first consideration is whether the terrain is suitable for outdoor storage. Level terrain is most desirable for all storage. Sloping terrain can present problems with pile stability and offer a serious hazard to fire fighters during fire suppression activities. Refuse or sawdust filled land, swampy ground or areas where the hazard of underground fire is or could be present are not compatible with good storage practices.

Exposure

Consideration must be given to the exposure fire problem, both from the point of view of the exposure which the storage presents to the neighboring properties and vice versa. NFPA No. 80A, Protection of Buildings from Exterior Fire Exposures, provides guidelines which can be used as a basis when considering distances between piles of materials and adjacent properties or combustible construction.

Zoning regulations often outline distances to a property line which must be maintained. If no such regulations exist, future development on adjacent property not under the control of the same persons who are storing the materials must be considered. Such future development may effectively reduce the size of the storage area if proper separations are to be maintained.

Other factors to be considered in evaluating exposure to and from the yard are the protection from grass, brush, or forest fire exposures; and the chance of ignition from sources such as sparks from railroad rolling equipment, incinerator stacks, electrical transformers on poles, and lighted cigarettes thrown from vehicles on adjacent highways and bridges.

Fire and Police Protection

It is desirable to evaluate municipal services available when selecting a storage site. Both fire and police protection can be provided on a private basis, but this is extremely expensive and generally ineffective for all but incipient incidents. Include in the evaluation the municipal water supply, and its record of reliability, the fire flow available, the type of fire department available and the distance it must respond, and the means available for notifying the fire department. From a security standpoint, the type of police departments and frequency of patrols must be investigated.

The method of handling outdoor storage, including the size of the piles and the clearances required from adjacent piles, building and property boundary lines, is influenced in part by the public protection available.

Floods and Windstorms

The last item of a basic nature is to avoid, where possible, areas subject to flooding or windstorms.

Windstorm is a particular problem in certain coastal areas. In areas having a history of hurricanes, tornadoes, etc., serious consideration must be given to abandoning plans for outdoor storage in favor of indoor storage, if the commodity to be stored is subject to damage or being blown about in high winds.

Aside from storm damage, fires occurring during periods of high winds will present an exposure problem that is almost impossible to protect against. Burning materials and brands will be carried over considerable distances, even though the fire may be confined to a relatively small area.

B. Preparation of the Site

Once a site has been selected, thought must be given to preparing it for outdoor storage, taking into consideration the materials to be handled and requirements for their safety.

Clearing the Site

Vegetation is cleared away regardless of the commodities to be stored so that, in periods of drought or in the winter, dried vegetation does not constitute fuel for ignition or fire spread.

The site is leveled as much as possible and then surfaced, preferably with a hard coating. If the entire yard is not to be hard surfaced, care is taken to insure that fire apparatus can easily maneuver throughout the yard. This requires properly developed roadways capable of supporting heavy trucks throughout the site. Proper drainage of the site is essential.

Layout of the Site

A definite plan for the use of the site is layed out. The plan details where specific materials are to be piled, keeping in mind the proper separation between piles of materials and providing for access to all areas of the site.

While it is difficult to be specific with recommendations for storage of materials outdoors there are some general things which should be kept in mind when laying out the yard or storage site.

The density with which materials are packed will make a tremendous difference in the burning characteristics. Lumber stacked solid in orderly fashion in piles perhaps not over 25 ft high does not present the same problem as the same lumber stored in "sticked" piles. In the latter case, there is an increased chance of rapid fire spread through the air spaces, and thus the piles must be kept in smaller dimensions. As another example, pulpwood may be found stored outdoors in piles perhaps 200 ft in diameter and 100 ft high, containing air spaces and pockets made by the rough and varied shape of the logs.

Some materials possess fast burning characteristics and a high total potential heat output. Baled cotton, hay, lumber, packing materials, pallets, plywood, pulpwood and rubber are examples of such materials. A considerable clearance is required around such piles. (See Part D of this chapter for additional information.)

Access to piles is yet another basic consideration in planning on how materials might be stored safely. Accessibility includes access from the exterior of the yard and from adequate clear aisle spaces within the yard to permit access to individual piles, sheds, or equipment. Storage close to railroad spurs often hinders access due to the presence of boxcars and other railroad equipment left standing on the tracks. Aisle widths equal to the height of the pile are desirable for more hazardous commodities. Aisles of 10 to 15 ft in width are more common for less hazardous materials.

For unusually large storage yards or moderate-sized yards with high value, main aisles or firebreaks may be desirable to subdivide the storage to attempt to accomplish the same purpose as a fire wall for indoor storage. Aisle widths to subdivide areas of the yard will be dependent on the commodity, how it is stored, height of piles, normal and abnormal wind conditions, fire fighting forces, and equipment and other factors.

In some cases, packaging and palletizing influence the storage methods. This is particularly true of materials of irregular shape or small materials that lend themselves to easier storage with pallets. The pallets themselves, if of combustible construction, may present an added fire control problem unless they are firestopped. (See Chap. 1 of this Section for further information on hazards of pallet storage.)

Heavy crating is a technique followed in some packaging practices, and, normally, this does not present an increased hazard except after severe weathering or following careless handling which may result in breakage or splintering. Tarpaulins and other materials used to cover stock should be of fire-retardant treated material. Sheet plastic can be very combustible.

A pile of materials that is stable under normal conditions might constitute a severe hazard under fire conditions. It is wise to anticipate the effects of fire and water on the stability of piles when planning pile sizes and configurations. Collapsing piles have frequently resulted in severe fire spread, particularly where a flying brand hazard may also result.

Areas set aside for special purposes are so designated and properly marked or cordoned off. Included are areas for the servicing and maintenance of materials handling equipment. If a flammable liquid fuel is used, an underground tank is the preferred storage method. If this is not practical, fuel storage tanks are so located that any accidental release of the fuel will not flow under or around the storage, and, conversely, so that a fire in the materials in storage will not constitute an exposure hazard to the flammable liquid tank.

Installation of Fire Protection

During the preparation of the site and before it is used for storage, adequate fire protection must be provided. Depending on the size and location of the site, it may be necessary to locate private water mains and hydrants throughout the yard. These are installed as outlined in Section 11, Chapter 2 of this HANDBOOK. If public hydrants are available, flow tests are conducted to insure there is adequate fire flow for the severity of fire that might be expected. If there is inadequate flow available, it may be necessary to install private water storage facilities, pumping capability, or both. There are a number of ways of providing adequate water supplies and these are discussed in Section 11.

Adequate provisions are made for manual fire suppression equipment. A minimum is appropriately rated portable fire extinguishers located throughout the site, properly marked so their locations can be quickly seen by persons in the storage site. In addition, if the storage site is active and there are people normally working on or near the site, consideration should be given to providing hose houses for use by the employees.

A means for notifying the fire department of a fire is essential. A system that sends a signal directly to the fire department is best, but if this is not feasible, the minimum is a conveniently located telephone.

Many orderly outdoor storage yards that are paved have painted lines to show aisles and roadways, and the location of yard hydrants, extinguishers, water buckets, hose houses, and the like.

Security Measures

Illegal trespassing, vandalism, and theft are definite problems in many outdoor storage yards. Control over children (they like to play in yards and are sometimes responsible for fires) and vagrants seeking shelter frequently make fencing and lighting a requirement. A fence, however, must not be an impediment to accessibility for fire control. Arrangements can be made with the fire department so that any gates which may be locked at night can be opened quickly by fire fighters without the delay that otherwise might result if a watchman or the owner had to open the gate or if the locking mechanism on the gates themselves had to be destroyed to gain the required access.

Consultation with the fire department regarding the incorporation of remote gates into the fencing so additional access can be provided in the event of a serious fire is wise.

Watchman protection is frequently very desirable for outdoor storage yards. NFPA No. 601, Guard Service in Fire Loss Prevention, covers the selection, the duties, and the instruction and training of such personnel.

C. Utilization of the Site

Good operating procedures are necessary for an outdoor storage facility if a good fire safety record is to be maintained. The guide lines are layed down by good management practices.

Management

When a yard is selected and layed out the amount of material it is designed to accommodate is established. It is important that these quantities of material not be exceeded as this will cut down clear space and aisles which are required as part of the fire safety for the yard. Likewise pile heights are kept within design limits.

Tarpaulins or other types of covers and combustible preservative treatments may present problems and increase the fire hazard of the stored materials. In other cases, covering some stocks with noncombustible preservative or flame resistant tarpaulins can tend to reduce the hazard.

Basically the attitude of management toward fire protection in the yard will establish the concern which employees show toward properly maintaining the facilities.

Fire Protection and Prevention

All fire protection equipment on the storage site must be properly maintained and tested in accordance with the schedules recommended for the particular types of equipment. This includes hydrants, fire pumps, fire extinguishers, and any suppression, detection, or alarm systems located on the site.

All materials handling equipment working at the site needs to carry a portable fire extinguisher (Class B or C) suitable for any fire which might occur in the equipment. Also carrying a portable extinguisher capable of extinguishing incipient Class A fires is good practice.

The location of all hydrants, hose houses, portable extinguishers, alarm boxes and other fire protection equipment must be properly marked. Elevated signs are preferable; marking by painting arrows and signs on the pavement is the minimum.

All open flames and other ignition sources must be closely controlled. Cutting and welding should not be allowed in the storage yard, but if the material to be cut or welded cannot be moved to a remote location, the work is done only after adequate precautions are taken. (See Section 4, Chapter 8, of this HANDBOOK, and NFPA No. 51B, Fire Prevention in Use of Cutting and Welding Processes.)

Smoking is prohibited or restricted to given areas only. The option depends on the nature of the material stored and the possibility of it, its covering, or other material becoming ignited. In either case, adequate signs must be displayed and discipline must be exercised over persons with authorized access to the site.

A private fire brigade or emergency organization made up of employees is desirable to provide at least first aid fire fighting. If there are enough employees to organize a fire brigade, the degree of organization, training, and equipment provided will normally be governed by the availability of a public fire department. The larger the storage yard and the higher the values, the greater the need for a fire brigade during the early stages of a fire and as a supplement or aid to the public fire department. NFPA No. 27, Organization, Training and Equipment of Private Fire Brigades, gives helpful information on the organization and training of fire fighting procedures.

Perhaps above all other considerations is the preplanning for the notification of the public fire department when a fire occurs. Brigades and watchmen must be disciplined to call for help while the fire is in its incipient stage even though subsequently the brigade or the watchman may be able to handle the emergency without outside help. In too many cases, delayed alarms have been given to the public fire departments while brigades or watchmen have attempted to control incipient fires unsuccessfully.

Maintenance and Housekeeping

It is important that an active storage area is properly maintained. Repairs to fencing, lighting, and the yard surface itself are performed as required to insure proper access to the yard, and proper security measures are maintained. Materials handling equipment is kept in good condition. Suitable safeguards are provided to minimize the hazard of sparks from such equipment as refuse burners, boiler stacks, vehicle exhausts, and locomotives.

The exercise of good housekeeping obviously includes control over weeds and vegetation in storage sites. Weeds, grass, and other vegetation are sprayed as often as needed with an acceptable herbicide or ground sterilizer or grubbed out. Dead weeds are removed after destruction, but weed burners should not be used.

It is very easy for scrap lumber, broken pallets, and broken containers, bales, or pieces of material stored on the site to be discarded into the clear space around the yard. Check daily for such materials and where found, they should be accumulated for salvage or removal from the yard for proper disposal. Care should be taken to insure that windblown debris and other combustible materials do not accumulate under piles of materials stored in the yard.

If a pile of material should fall into an aisle or clear space, have the stock repiled immediately so the full designed width of the aisle or clear space is maintained.

D. Outdoor Storage of Specific Materials

The outdoor storage of a few of the more commonly found materials is discussed in the following paragraphs. It is recognized that many materials could be subject to storage outside either on a temporary basis or fairly permanent basis. NFPA No. 231A, Recommended Safe Practices for Outdoor General Storage, is a source for good practices to follow in establishing basic guidelines for outdoor storage as are other NFPA publications and industry or insurance company standards applicable to the particular material in storage. Many times, the guidelines applicable to the inside storage of the commodity furnish a good starting point for developing guidelines for outdoor storage.

Wood and Wood Products

The majority of wood and wood products are stored outdoors with few exceptions, and the latter are usually in relatively small quantities.

Logs stored at sawmills, paper mills, and pulp mills can be found in large quantities, insofar as wood is usually moved from the forests only at certain times of the year. The inventory is peaked to carry throughout much of the next 12 months. Piles in large circular form with logs dumped on the top of the pile are called stacked piles. Where logs are stacked in parallel form, like matches in a box, the arrangement is referred to as ranked piles. The former usually are much larger piles with the peak of the pile often approaching 100 ft above grade. The ranked piles are usually not exceptionally high, often in the 10- to 15-ft levels. Aisles can be arranged and separation of piles is easily obtained in ranked piles, thus making fire fighting and control much easier than in stacked piles (see Fig. 5-2A).

Water is needed in large quantities to cope with log yard fires. The total volume required may be as high as 10,000 gpm or above. A looped underground fire main system with hydrants spaced through the yard is in line with good practice. Monitor nozzles on towers have been common in log yards, especially with high stacked piles. In the large stacked piles, a burrowing fire is difficult to extinguish once under control. NFPA No. 46B, Outside Storage of Logs, provides additional guidelines for the storage of logs.

Chip storage is replacing log storage at many pulp and paper mills. There are two completely different types of fires in chip piles, surface fires and internal fires. NFPA No. 46A, Outdoor Storage of Wood Chips, provides guidelines for the structuring of piles and provisions for fire protection of the chips. Experience has shown that large quantities of water are not necessary for wood chip fires and generally 500 gpm is sufficient. Internal fires require uncovering and removing the burning chips, a generally time consuming operation.

Sawdust storage is not too common but once was prevalent at sawmills. Fires in sawdust are not especially serious, but they can smolder and smoke unless the piles are broken open to complete extinguishment.

Lumber storage is quite common in urban areas, often in fairly well built-up neighborhoods. Local ordinances generally prohibit yard storage of any appreciable quantity in zoned areas but many yards were originally located in unzoned areas but expansion has resulted in some heavily built areas close to sizeable lumberyards.

The exposure of the yard storage to adjoining areas is a major consideration. Adequate aisles and good housekeeping along with good procedures for controlling ignition sources, such as salamanders, smoking, etc., will reduce the hazard considerably. Large quantities of water are needed to bring a lumberyard fire under control once fire has gained headway. Flying brands can spread the fire throughout the yard and into adjoining areas readily, particularly if there is much wind. NFPA No. 47, Retail and Wholesale Lumber Storage Yards, provides guidelines for the safe storage of lumber. Where lumber and timber are stored at other than wholesale or retail yards, NFPA No. 46, Outdoor Storage of Forest Products, should be consulted.

Paper and Paper Products

Some paper and paper products are stored outdoors but the majority are stored indoors to protect against rain and wind.

Roll paper is normally banded in large rolls weighing up to 2 tons or more. The paper is tightly wound and most papers are difficult to ignite when in the tightly wound form. See Chapter 1 of this Section for information on storage practices involving rolled paper.

Baled wastepaper does not produce the fast heat release fire associated with roll paper but instead has a burrowing characteristic. Fire in baled wastepaper is difficult to extinguish and generates heavy smoke. Broken bales are difficult to handle after wetting. Usually a motorized vehicle with a shovel is needed to move the debris to complete extinguishment.

Spontaneous ignition is common in wastepaper due to foreign materials subject to spontaneous heating that become trapped in bales. Fire protection for wastepaper storage follows the same recommendations that apply generally to outdoor storage practices.

Rubber

Rubber Tires: These are usually rated as a very high fire hazard storage. Tires burn readily with much heat and smoke hampering manual fire fighting. Narrow piles with good aisles are desirable.

Large quantities of water at high pressures are usually needed as control is difficult due to the shielded nature of fire within a tire casing. Other protection aspects follow those noted for general outdoor storage.

Baled Crude Rubber: Bales are often stored outdoors. The Factory Mutual System recommends individual piles to be limited to 100 tons with a minimum of 30 ft but preferably 50 ft between piles.[1] Piles are grouped to a maximum of 1,000 tons with 100-ft aisles separating them. It is important to insure that burlap used to wrap the bales does not become contaminated with oil and then get tightly packed into a pile as spontaneous heating will result.

Baled Combustible Fibers: It is generally recommended that baled combustible fibers not be stored outdoors but if they are, they should be used first. Factory Mutual recommends that piles should be limited to 500 bales per pile with a preferable clear space of 50 ft between piles or from an

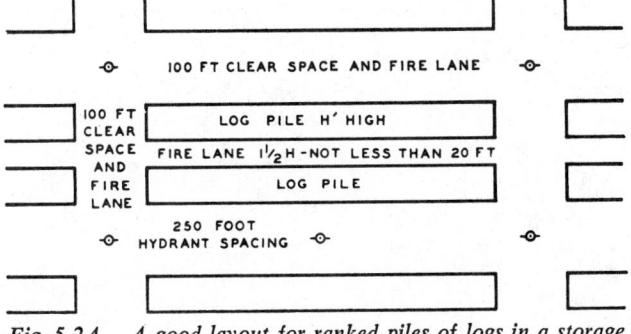

Fig. 5-2A. A good layout for ranked piles of logs in a storage yard.

exterior fence. Piles of uncleaned baled flax straw should be limited to 300 tons and a height of 20 ft. Piles should be 200 ft from important buildings and 100 ft from each other or potential ignition sources. All bales of combustible materials should be skidded off the ground and the tops and sides of all piles covered with a tarpaulin of fire retardant material, securely fastened down.

Coal: The main concern with storage of coal is the spontaneous heating tendency of bituminous coal. Anthracite is not subject to spontaneous heating. Freshly mined coal is more subject to spontaneous heating as it absorbs oxygen more rapidly. Water and coal dust make coal more susceptible to spontaneous ignition. See Section 3, Chapter 5 for further information on storage of coal.

SI Units

The following conversion factors are given as a convenience in converting to SI units the English units used in this chapter.

1 in. = 2.500 mm
1 ft   = 0.305 m
1 gpm = 3.785 litres/min

Bibliography

[1] "Storage of Baled Crude Rubber," *Loss Prevention Data,* DS 8-1, Feb. 1971, Factory Mutual System, Norwood, Mass.

[2] "Baled Fiber Storage," *Loss Prevention Data,* DS 8-7, Mar. 1974, Factory Mutual System, Norwood, Mass.

NFPA Codes, Standards, and Recommended Practices (see the latest *NFPA Publications and Visual Aids Catalog* for availability of current editions of the following documents)

NFPA No. 6, Recommendations for Organization of Industrial Fire Loss Prevention.

NFPA No. 7, Recommendations for Management Control of Fire Emergencies.

NFPA No. 10, Standard for the Installation, Maintenance and Use of Portable Fire Extinguishers.

NFPA No. 24, Standard for Outside Protection.

NFPA No. 27, Recommendations for Organization, Training and Equipment of Private Fire Brigades.

NFPA No. 46, Recommended Safe Practices for Outdoor Storage of Forest Products.

NFPA No. 46A, Recommended Practices for Outdoor Storage of Wood Chips.

NFPA No. 46B, Recommended Safe Practices for Outside Storage of Logs.

NFPA No. 47, Recommended Safe Practices for Retail and Wholesale Lumber Storage Yards.

NFPA No. 51B, Standard for Fire Prevention in Use of Cutting and Welding Processes.

NFPA No. 80A, Recommended Practice for Protection of Buildings from Exterior Fire Exposures.

NFPA No. 231A, Recommended Safe Practices for Outdoor General Storage.

NFPA No. 505, Fire Safety Standard for Powered Industrial Trucks Including Type Designations and Areas of Use.

NFPA No. 601, Recommendations for Guard Service in Fire Loss Prevention.

NFPA No. 601A, Standard for Guard Operations in Fire Loss Prevention.

NFPA No. 604, Recommended Practice on Salvaging Operations.

Additional Readings

Factory Mutual System, *Handbook of Industrial Loss Prevention,* 2nd ed., McGraw-Hill, New York, 1967.

"Outdoor Storage of Wood Chips," *Loss Prevention Data,* DS 8–27, July 1968, Factory Mutual System, Norwood, Mass.

"Sawmills and Lumber Yards," *Loss Prevention Data,* DS 7–25, May 1973, Factory Mutual System, Norwood, Mass.

Chapter 3

MATERIALS HANDLING EQUIPMENT

Materials handling equipment, particularly industrial trucks and mechanical and pneumatic stock conveying systems, are essential services in industrial and commercial activity. This chapter describes the basic types of equipment and systems for materials handling that are encountered, and discusses the fire and explosion hazards inherent with them. Protection methods are also discussed.

A. Industrial Trucks

Industrial lift trucks (fork type or squeeze clamp) are one of the most common types of materials handling equipment. They may be propelled electrically, or by gasoline or LP-Gas engines. Unless these vehicles are of an approved type and properly maintained and used, they may introduce serious fire dangers. Industrial trucks are manufactured in many designs to suit their many uses and types of loads to be handled. All of the vehicles should be selected, outfitted, maintained, and operated in accordance with the hazards of the locations.

Type Designations and Areas of Use

The NFPA Fire Safety Standard for Powered Industrial Trucks lists thirteen different type designations of industrial trucks or tractors, defined in NFPA No. 505, Standard for Powered Industrial Trucks, as follows:

1. Type D units are diesel powered units having minimal acceptable safeguards against inherent fire hazards.

2. Type DS units are diesel powered units that, in addition to all the requirements for the type D units, are provided with additional safeguards to the exhaust, fuel, and electrical systems.

3. Type DY units are diesel powered units that have all the safeguards of the type DS units, and, in addition, do not have any electrical equipment, including ignition. They are equipped with temperature limitation features.

4. Type E units are electrically powered units having minimum acceptable safeguards against inherent fire and electrical shock hazards.

5. Type ES units are electrically powered units that, in addition to all of the requirements for the type E units, are provided with additional safeguards to the electrical system to prevent emission of hazardous sparks and to limit surface temperatures.

6. Type EE units are electrically powered units that have, in addition to all of the requirements for the types E and ES units, the electric motors and all other electrical equipment completely enclosed.

7. Type EX units are electrically powered units that differ from the types E, ES, or EE units in that the electrical fittings and equipment are so designed, constructed, and assembled that the units may be used in atmospheres containing specifically named flammable vapors, dusts, and, under certain conditions, fibers. Type EX units are specifically tested and classified for use in Class I, Group D or for Class II, Group G hazardous locations as defined in the National Electrical Code.

8. Type G units are gasoline powered units having minimum acceptable safeguards against inherent fire hazards.

9. Type GS units are gasoline powered units that, in addition to all the requirements for the type G units, are provided with additional safeguards to the exhaust, fuel, and electrical systems.

10. Type LP units are liquefied petroleum gas powered units having minimum acceptable safeguards against inherent fire hazards.

11. Type LPS units are liquefied petroleum gas powered units that, in addition to the requirements for the type LP units, are provided with additional safeguards to the exhaust, fuel, and electrical systems.

12. Type G/LP units operate on either gasoline or liquefied petroleum gas having minimum acceptable safeguards against inherent fire hazards.

13. Type GS/LPS units operate on either gasoline or liquefied petroleum gas and, in addition to all requirements for the type G/LP units, are provided with additional safeguards to the exhaust, fuel and electrical systems.

Industrial trucks of the various types are limited to the locations specified in Table 5-3A. Many of the fires involving industrial trucks which have spread beyond the truck to involve other property have been the result of operating a less than minimum type truck in a hazardous location.

The greatest potential fire source for gasoline-, diesel- and LP-Gas-powered trucks are fuel leaks which are ignited by the hot engine, hot muffler, ignition system, other electrical equipment, or other sparks. This danger is somewhat less for diesel trucks because of the higher flash point of diesel fuel; however, it is especially present in LP-Gas trucks as the vapors are difficult to disperse and tend to gravitate toward lower spots or pits. Care must be exercised with LP-Gas trucks to avoid the high temperatures near ovens, furnaces, and similar sources of heat. Special safeguards in the designs of some types of gasoline, diesel, and LP-Gas trucks help to reduce these fire hazards, but they cannot be completely avoided and areas of use should be rigidly limited (see Table 5-3A).

To facilitate identification of the trucks and their areas of use, a uniform system of marking has been developed and is described in the NFPA Powered Industrial Trucks Standard. (See Figures 5-3A and 5-3B.)

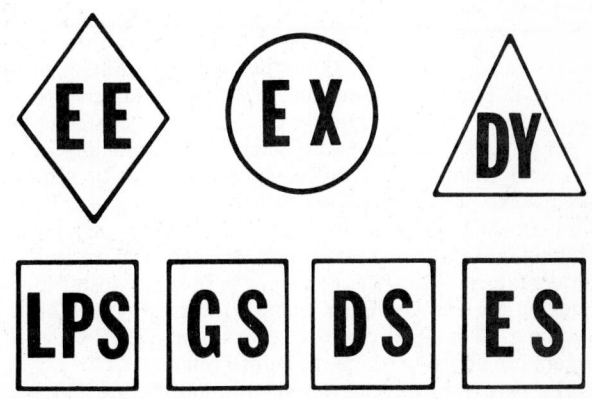

Fig. 5-3A. Markers used to identify the various types of industrial trucks.

Fig. 5-3B. Building signs for posting at entrances to hazardous areas.

Fire Hazards and Prevention

Careless and uninformed operation of industrial trucks has contributed to much property loss. Collision with sprinkler piping, fire doors, and other fire protection equipment; too high tiering of rack storage; and the careless handling of loads, such as containers of flammable liquids, have not only directly contributed to fires but have increased fire fighting difficulties. A complete course of instruction for truck operators can reduce the risk of such accidents. Adequate, clear passageways for truck travel and clear warnings of overhead and exposed piping will also reduce the number of incidents. A good source for safe operating rules is the American National Standard Safety Code for Powered Industrial Trucks, ANSI B56.1-1969.

A high number of fires involving industrial trucks are caused by equipment failure due to a lack of maintenance. A system of regularly scheduled maintenance based on engine-hour or motor-hour experience can greatly reduce the incidence of fires of this nature. Trucks are exposed to severe wear and tear, and maintenance programs must be rigidly adhered to. Requiring special attention is detection of faulty fuel connections on gasoline, diesel, and LP-Gas trucks, and removal of accumulations of grease and dirt. Providing portable extinguishers appropriate to the truck type is good practice.

The number of fires involving battery-powered trucks is comparatively small. Nevertheless, electrical short circuits, hot resistors, arcing and fused contacts, and exploding batteries have contributed to the fire occurrence in industrial trucks.

LP-Gas containers must not be overfilled; use a soap solution to check for leaks, never a match or open flame. Means can be provided in the fuel system to minimize the escape of fuel when removable LP-Gas containers are exchanged (i.e., closing the valve on the LP-Gas container and using an approved automatic quick-closing coupling in the fuel line). Removable LP-Gas containers must be securely mounted to prevent their jarring loose, slipping, or rotating. They are so positioned that the safety pressure relief valve opening is always in contact with the vapor space [top] of the container. When the container is properly installed, an indexing pin and container clamp(s) correctly position the container. It is good practice to examine all LP-Gas containers for defects or damage before refilling.

The two types of batteries in common use are (1) lead, and (2) nickel-iron. They contain corrosive chemical solutions, either acid or alkali, and therefore present a chemical hazard. On charge, they give off hydrogen and oxygen which, in certain concentrations, are explosive. Battery-

charging installations preferably are located in areas specifically set aside for that purpose. The facilities include means for flushing and neutralizing spilled electrolyte; barriers for protecting charging apparatus from damage by trucks; adequate ventilation for dispersal of fumes from gassing batteries; and adequate fire protection. A carboy filter or siphon is used in dispensing acid from carboys. Special care is taken to prevent open flame, sparks, or electric arcs in battery charging areas. When charging batteries, the vent caps are kept in place to avoid electrolyte spray. Care also is taken to assure that vent caps are functioning. The battery (or compartment) cover(s) remain open during charging to dissipate heat.

Recharging and Refueling

Refueling and battery recharging operations are performed by trained and designated personnel, and only in specified, well-ventilated areas (outdoors where practicable), away from manufacturing and service areas. Smoking is always prohibited in these areas.

Trucks using liquid fuels, such as gasoline and diesel fuel, should only be refueled from approved dispensing pumps in safe locations away from sources of heat and ignition. Care must be taken not to spill fuel or overfill the vehicle fuel tank. Approximately 50 percent of the fires involving trucks using liquid fuels are the result of spillage during refueling.

Maintenance and Repair

Repairs are never made to trucks in Class I, II, and III hazardous locations (see Sec. 7, Chap. 3 for definitions of hazardous locations). Repairs to the fuel and ignition systems of industrial trucks that involve fire hazards preferably are conducted in locations designated for such repairs. Repairs to the electrical system of battery-powered industrial trucks are performed only after the battery has been disconnected. All parts of any industrial truck requiring replacement are replaced only with parts providing the same degree of fire safety as those used in the original design. Water mufflers are filled daily or as frequently as is necessary to prevent depletion of the supply of water below 75 percent of the filled capacity. Do not operate vehicles with mufflers having screens or other parts that have become clogged. Remove from service immediately any vehicle that emits hazardous sparks or flames from the exhaust system and do not return it to service until the cause for the emission of such sparks and flames has been eliminated. When the temperature of any part of any truck is found to be in excess of its normal operating temperature and which creates a hazardous condition, the vehicle is removed from service until the cause for such overheating has been eliminated.

It is good practice to keep industrial trucks in a clean condition, reasonably free of lint, excess oil, and grease. Noncombustible agents are preferred for cleaning trucks. Low flash point (below 100°F) solvents are not used. Precautions regarding toxicity, ventilation, and fire hazard should be in keeping with the agent or solvent used. When antifreeze is required in the cooling system, glycol base material is preferred.

B.   Mechanical Conveyors and Elevators

Probably the most commonly used equipment in materials handling are mechanical conveyors and elevators. There are many classes and designs of mechanical conveyors. The primary selection considerations are the distance and inclination over which material is to be conveyed; the types of atmosphere and location through which material is to be conveyed; and the lump-size, density, flowability, abrasive-

Table 5-3A. Recommended Types of Trucks for Various Occupancies
(Source: Factory Mutual System)

Location	Typical occupancies	Types of trucks[b,c] approved and listed
Indoor or outdoor locations containing materials of ordinary fire hazard	Grocery warehouse Cloth storage Paper manufacturing and working Textile processes except opening, blending, bale storage, and other Class III locations Bakery Leather tanning Foundries and forge shops Sheet-metal working Machine-tool occupancies	Electrical—Type E Gasoline—Type G Diesel—Type D LP-Gas—Type LP Dual Fuel—Type G-LP
Class I, Division 1.[a] Locations in which explosive concentrations of flammable gases or vapors may exist under normal operating conditions or where accidental release of hazardous concentrations of such materials may occur simultaneously with failure of electrical equipment	Few areas in this division in which trucks would be used	Electrical—Type EX[f] Gasoline, diesel, and LP-Gas—not recommended for this service
Class I, Division 2.[a] Locations in which flammable liquids or gases are handled in closed systems or containers from which they can escape only by accident or locations in which hazardous concentrations are normally prevented by positive mechanical ventilation	Paint mixing, spraying, or dipping Storage of flammable gases in cylinders Storage of flammable liquids in drums or cans Solvent recovery Chemical processes using flammable liquids Paper and cloth coating using flammable solvents in closed equipment Rubber-cement mixing	Electrical—Types EE, EX Diesel—Type DY Gasoline, diesel Types D & DS, and LP-Gas—not recommended for this service
Class II, Division 1.[a] Locations in which explosive mixtures of combustible dusts may be present in the air under normal operating conditions, or where mechanical failure of equipment might cause such mixtures to be produced simultaneously with arcing or sparking of electrical equipment, or in which electrically conductive dusts may be present	Grain processing Starch processing Starch molding (candy plants) Wood-flour processing	Electrical—Type EX[d] Type EE[d] Diesel—Type DY Gasoline, diesel, and LP-Gas—not recommended for this service
Class II, Division 2.[a] Locations in which explosive mixtures of combustible dusts are not normally present or likely to be thrown into suspension through the normal operation of equipment but where deposits of such dust may interfere with the dissipation of heat from electrical equipment or where such deposits may be ignited by arc or sparks from electrical equipment	Storage and handling of grain, starch, or wood flour in bags or other closed containers Grinding of plastic molding compounds in tight systems Feed mills with tightly enclosed equipment	Electrical—Types EE, EX, ES[e] Type E[e] Gasoline—Type GS[e] Diesel—Type DY, DS[e] LP-Gas—Type LPS[e]
Class III, Division 1.[a] Locations in which easily ignitible fibers or materials producing combustible flyings are handled, manufactured, or used	Opening, blending, or carding of cotton or cotton mixtures Cotton gins Sawing, shaping, or sanding areas in woodworking plants Preliminary processes in cordage plants	Electrical—Types EE, EX Type E[d,e] Diesel—Type DY Gasoline, diesel Types D & DS, and LP-Gas—not recommended for this service
Class III, Division 2.[a] Locations in which easily ignitible fibers are stored or handled (except in process of manufacture)	Storage of textile and cordage fibers Storage of excelsior, Kapok, or Spanish moss	Electrical—Types EE, ES, EX, preferred; E Gasoline—Type GS Diesel—Type DS, DY LP-Gas—Type LPS

NOTES:
  a. Hazardous location as classified in The National Electrical Code.
  b. Type G (gasoline), Type D (diesel), and Type LP (LP-Gas) trucks are considered to have comparable fire hazard.
  c. Type GS (gasoline), Type DS (diesel), and Type LPS (LP-Gas) trucks are considered to have comparable fire hazard.
  d. Acceptable for Group G, and for Groups E and F, but subject to special investigation.
  e. Acceptable but subject to special investigation.
  f. Class I, Division 2, Group D only; no truck should be used in Groups A, B and C.

ness, toxicity, corrosiveness, etc. of the materials themselves which are to be conveyed. Dust materials or dust atmospheres, or both, require equipment which can be adequately enclosed; screw and en masse conveyors are limited in the lump size they can handle; temperatures often rule out belt conveyors; long distances usually require the use of belt conveyors; substantial vertical lifts are best handled by bucket elevators. From the point of view of fire protection, the considerations of temperature and dust are the most important; in addition, the protection of openings and control of static are installation factors that must be given careful attention.

Temperature

Screw conveyors, vibrating types, and certain pan conveyors are normally the best choice for handling very hot materials or for use in high temperature atmospheres. The upper limit for most belt conveyors is 200°F, and normally they are restricted to less than 150°F.[1] Experiments by the Bureau of Mines demonstrate that the highest rate of flame propagation occurs with rubber belts, but that there is little difference in the ignition characteristic among neoprene, rubber, and polyvinyl chloride. Simply, belt conveyors are not suitable for movement of hot or molten materials, and are not used in high temperature atmospheres if at all possible. (See Fig. 5-3C.)

Dust Control

The most frequently occurring factor in the fires involving mechanical conveyors is a dusty material, a dust atmosphere, or the dust inevitably created by the materials handling process, itself. Dust will almost certainly be produced in any materials handling systems, especially at inlet and discharge points and the long chutes for free-falling materials.[2]

Feed dusty material to belt conveyors through a choke feed to prevent dust clouds. Where dusty conditions prevail, provide adequate aspiration to remove dust to collectors in safe locations. If dust clouds cannot be avoided, it is better to use spiral or enclosed-type conveyors where the escape of dust can be more readily prevented. Conveyor piping should be of sufficient strength to withstand the maximum pressure

produced in explosions of the dust involved. Avoid sharp changes in direction wherever possible, and provide vent pipes to outdoors at any necessary changes in direction and at ends of lines. (This should not be construed to prohibit the use of explosion relief vents.) Screw conveyors should be fully enclosed in tight noncombustible housings with free-lifting covers at discharge end and over each shaft coupling. "En Masse" or drag type conveyors should be of substantial metal construction designed to prevent escape of dust, and covers on clean-out, inspection, and other openings should be securely fastened. Conveyors designed and constructed to withstand anticipated explosion pressures, considering the pressure release afforded by explosion relief vents. A choke or seal of proper design, or a suppression system, should be installed in a conveyor (other than pneumatic conveyors) to prevent the propagation of an explosion from one building to another, or from one portion of a building to another separated by a fire wall.

Dust collectors preferably are located outdoors, or in detached rooms with adequate explosion vents for collectors and rooms. Where it is necessary to use bag-type collectors, they preferably are enclosed in a metal housing. Dust collectors should not serve several separate processes. Use individual collectors for progressive stages in any one process. Water spray-type collectors may be located within buildings, but they are not recommended for certain types of dust. (For further information on air moving equipment and dust collecting systems, see Section 7, Chapter 5.)

Static Protection

All parts of the machinery and conveyors are thoroughly bonded and grounded to minimize static discharges. The chances of generating static electricity are increased when heated or dry materials are conveyed, or the conveyor belt is operated in a heated or dry atmosphere.[3] Static electricity can be controlled by the use of belts made of conductive material, by applying a conductive dressing to the belt surface, or by installing a grounded static collector nearly in contact with the belt just beyond the point where the belt leaves the pulley.[4] Pulleys, guards, and other metal bodies are also grounded. (For more details on static control, see Chapter 5 of this Section.)

Protection of Conveyor Openings

Water Spray Method: The protection of openings in walls and floors through which conveyors pass offers difficulties in the installation of ordinary forms of closures owing to the presence of objects carried on the conveyors through the opening. Where fire doors or shutters are impractical for conveyor openings, a method of protection incorporating the pressure effect and cooling action of water spray from directed spray nozzles is available (see Fig. 5-3D). With proper nozzle design and water pressure to provide suitable water velocity and particle size, the pressure effect from the

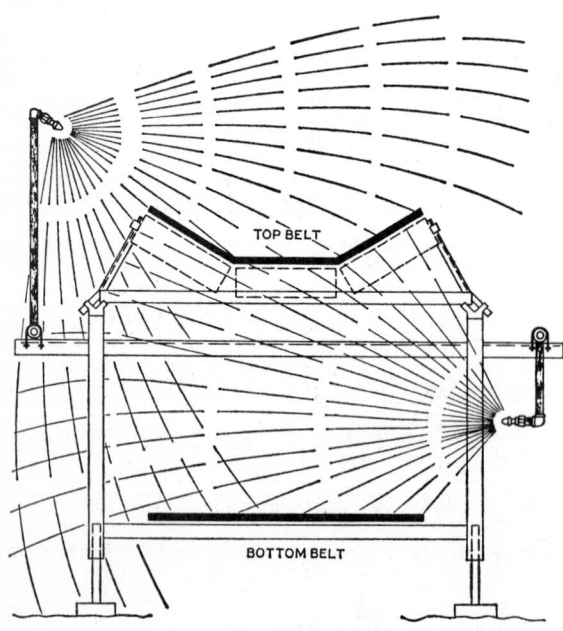

Fig. 5-3C. A cross section of a belt conveyor showing arrangement of water spray nozzles to protect both the top and bottom belts.

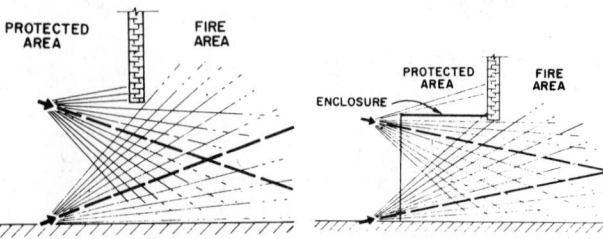

Fig. 5-3D. Spray nozzles protecting a conveyor opening in a fire wall.

Fig. 5-3E. Greater heat absorption is possible by enclosing the opening for the conveyor.

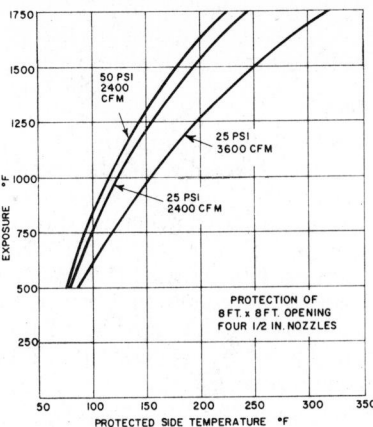

Fig. 5-3F. Exposure temperature vs protected side temperature at various draft velocities and nozzle pressures.

nozzles will overcome draft due to the temperature difference between one side of the wall and the other and the height of the opening above floor level unless adverse air currents are prevalent. Since the cooling effect of the spray is directly proportional to the time of exposure of hot gases in the draft to the spray, the effectiveness of the heat absorption may be increased by adding an enclosure to the opening (see Fig. 513E). Figure 5-3F shows the cooling effect of four ½-in. nozzles on an 8 × 8 ft opening with various draft velocities and nozzle pressures in tests conducted by Factory Mutual Engineering Corporation. The nozzles were discharging water at 28 gpm each, with an effective angle of about 65°.

The Factory Mutual recommendations for installation include the following:

Where fire may be expected to originate on either side of the opening, nozzles are installed on both sides. Nozzles are controlled by an automatic valve actuated by a heat detector. Four nozzles per side are recommended to give complete coverage of the opening. Water discharge rates between 2 and 4 gpm/sq ft or more, depending upon the height of the opening and unfavorable draft effects, are considered desirable. Nozzles are located at an angle not more than 30° between the center line of nozzle discharge and a line perpendicular to the plane of the opening. To prevent the nozzle counterdraft from forcing air from the fire area into other areas, all communicating openings to the fire area are protected in a standard manner.

Conveyor openings through floors may also be protected

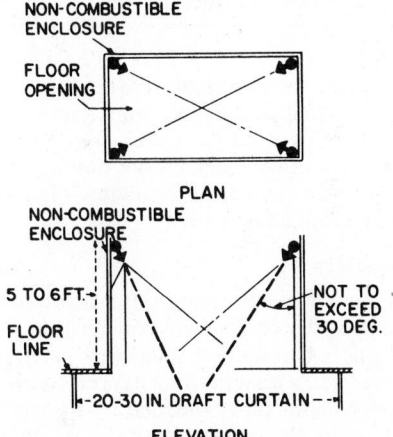

Fig. 5-3G. Spray nozzle protection for floor openings.

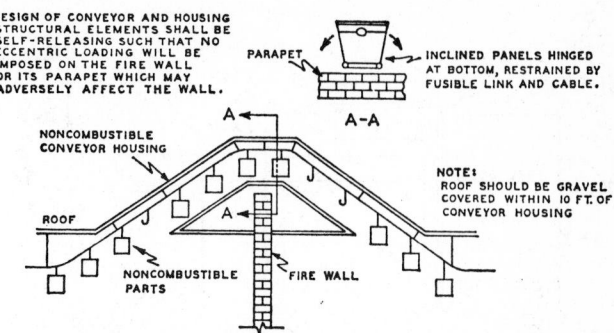

Fig. 5-3H. A conveyor carried over a fire wall.

by this method, provided an enclosure is constructed around the conveyor from the floor up to or slightly beyond the spray nozzles and draft curtains extending 20 to 30 in. below and around the floor opening (see Fig. 5-3G).

The effectiveness of the protection system is, of course, dependent upon rapid detection and appropriate interlocks between the detection system and the machinery. (See Sec. 15, Chap. 2 for further information on water spray systems.)

Fire Doors: It is a misconception that conveyorized openings cannot be protected by fire doors. Where possible, of course, conveyor penetration of a fire wall is avoided by rerouting, or as is sometimes feasible with a one-story building, by running the conveyor through the roof, over the fire wall, and down within an inverted "V" housing arranged to readily vent fire to atmosphere (see Fig. 5-3H). Any cutout of a labeled fire door done in the field to allow for closure about a conveyor track or other components voids its label. This practice should be avoided, if possible. Where notching is distinctly advantageous, a certificate may be furnished by the testing laboratory affixing the label; it is found by inspection that the notched door is in compliance with the laboratory standards in all other aspects.

Figures 5-3I through 5-3K illustrate various conveyor designs and/or programming devices which will minimize or eliminate the threat of obstruction to complete fire door closure by the conveyor or conveyed stock.

The illustrations can only show the basic concepts. Proper performance depends equally on conservative design, good workmanship in installation, operating inspection, and maintenance. Guidelines to observe are:

1. Select a design that is as simple and direct-acting as possible. Emphasis is on "fail-safe" operation.

2. Program the sequence of operating steps and interlocks so that obstruction (conveyor, conveyorized material, etc.) to the door closure is positively and permanently (until manually reset) removed from the door's path before the door is released to close.

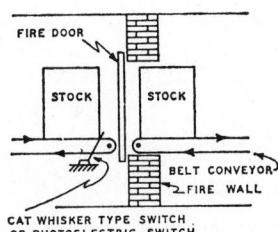

ELECTRO-MAGNETIC FIRE DOOR RELEASE INTERLOCK WITH SWITCH WHICH STOPS CONVEYOR WITH PROPER SPACING OF STOCK TO PREVENT OBSTRUCTION TO DOOR CLOSER.

Fig. 5-3I. Protection of opening when a belt conveyor can be interrupted.

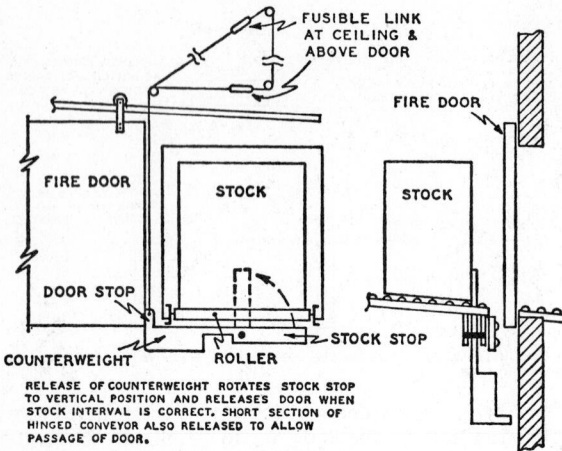

Fig. 5-3J. A method of stopping stock on a gravity roller conveyor.

3. Design structural and mechanical components, linkages, clearances, etc. in a conservative manner. Counterweights, springs, and other operating force (uninterruptable by initial fire stages) must have ample reserve of strength to handle overload introduced by reasonable anticipated minor changes in configuration and weight of conveyorized material, normal wear, friction, etc. Major changes will necessitate complete re-engineering to ascertain adequacy of the design, with reinforcement as necessary.

4. Incorporate self-releasing features in the design of conveyor components (trolley track, chain, supports, etc.) which pass through the opening.

5. Maintain $\frac{3}{8}$-in. clearance between the door and the sill.

6. Provide another fire door on the opposite side of the opening to increase the reliability of the protection of the wall opening in the event of a fire if it is advisable. Similarly, when the property is sprinklered, consideration is given to the advisability of reinforcing the protection of the opening by a water curtain of automatic sprinklers.

7. Conduct a number of operating tests following installation that reflect the range of varied adverse conditions which must be anticipated to ascertain that all components operate smoothly, in proper sequence, within specified time interval, and with adequate clearances and tolerances.

8. Close all fire doors during inoperative periods. Routine closure that stimulates emergency operation can provide a regular inspection of the continued adequacy of the protection of the opening.

Friction, Overheating

Many fires involving materials handling equipment, particularly those used to convey such materials as raw cotton, grains, powders, coal, etc., are caused by the heat of friction which results from the accumulations of grease and dirt and the overheating of defective parts, especially rollers. This frequent fire hazard is easily reduced and controlled by

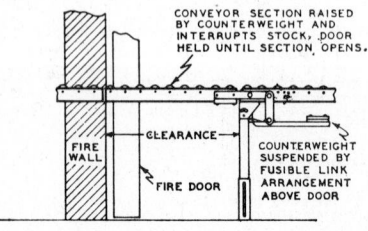

Fig. 5-3K. A counterweight hinged section of a roller conveyor.

patrolling belts, frequent equipment inspection, and the removal of dirt and grease build-ups.[5] Early replacement of old and worn parts is also an important housekeeping item.

Bucket Elevators

These elevators are found in nearly all bulk processing plants to convey loads vertically, and they are susceptible to the same fire hazards as the mechanical conveyors. The same precautions are taken for temperature, dust control, protection of openings, and elimination of friction and overheating. Elevators are best enclosed in substantial dust-tight casings, preferably of noncombustible construction, extending, without reduction in size, through the roof and fitted with light weather-proof covers designed to lift readily and relieve explosion pressure within.

Install elevators close to an outside wall of the building and provide short direct vents through the wall at 20-ft intervals on tall elevator legs. Install doors to provide access to head and boot pulleys. Make all doors in elevator leg casings dust-tight. Provide ample clearance around elevator boots for cleaning and oiling. Safeguard elevators against overheating or choking by automatic releases actuated by overloading or reduction below normal operating speed.

C. Pneumatic Conveyors

Pneumatic conveying is a common method of transferring dusts from place to place in a building or from one building to another. This process presents an explosion hazard because of the possibility of easily and rapidly introducing explosive proportions of dust into the air.[6]

Description of Systems

A pneumatic conveying system consists of an enclosed tubing system in which a material is normally transported by a stream of air having a sufficiently high velocity to keep the conveyed material in motion. Noncombustible gases may be used in place of, or mixed with, air. Such systems are of two principal types, or a combination of the two types.

Pressure-type: Pressure-type systems transport material by utilizing air at greater than atmospheric pressure. They basically consist of a blower, drawing air through a filter; an air-lock feeder for introducing materials into the system; tubing or ducts; and a suitable air-material separator.

Suction-type: Suction-type systems transport material by utilizing air at less than atmospheric pressure. These systems basically consist of a material and air intake; tubing or ducts; a suitable air-material separator; and a suction fan or blower.

See Figure 5-3L for a schematic drawing of a typical combination pressure-type and suction-type system.

Conveyor Ducts

Conveyor ducts are fabricated from nonferrous, minimum-sparking metal, or nonmagnetic, minimum-sparking stainless steel, and are electrically bonded and grounded. Plastic or other nonconductive liners are not desirable. See Section 7, Chapter 5, for further information on ducts for air moving systems and equipment.

Inert Atmospheres

Inert gas is used in conveying systems wherever the concentration of powder or dust will come within the explosive range. The gas is based upon such inert gases as nitrogen, argon, helium, etc.; with a limiting oxygen concentration appropriate to the character of the inerting gas and the particle size of the dust in the system. Basically it contains at least 1 percent oxygen, no carbon monoxide, and has a dew

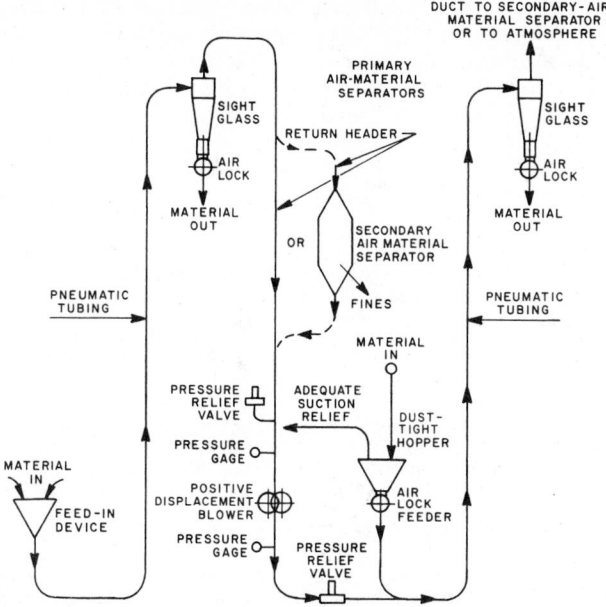

Fig. 5-3L. A typical transfer system of the combination pressure-type and suction-type with a high capacity.

point such that no free moisture can condense or accumulate, or both, at any point in the system. Further limitations are dictated by the type of material being conveyed, and the character of the inert gas. For example, the inert gas for magnesium dust systems should not contain carbon dioxide. Oxygen limits of 3 to 5 percent have been maintained in aluminum powder systems using a controlled type, of flue gas. Other limits are applicable where other inert gases are employed. (See Bureau of Mines Publication RI 3722, "Inflammability and Explosibility of Metal Powder."[7])

A continuous monitor is needed to sound an alarm if the oxygen content of the inert gas is not within the established safe range.

Light Metal Conveying: Light metal and light metal alloy powders are produced by various mechanical means of particle size degradation. These processes, as well as certain finishing and transporting operations, have a tendency to expose a continuously increasing area of new metal surface. Most metals immediately experience a surface reaction with available atmospheric oxygen to form a protective oxide coating which then serves as an impervious layer to inhibit further oxidation. This reaction is exothermic, producing sensible heat. If a fine or thin lightweight particle having a large area of new surface is suddenly exposed to the atmosphere, enough heat will be generated to raise its temperature to the ignition point. Completely inert gas is not used as an envelope to promote operational safety, or for transport of light metal powder in a pneumatic or fluidized transfer device. This would be a very unsafe practice because somewhere in the process of manufacture, packaging, or ultimate use, the powder will eventually be exposed to the atmosphere where the unreacted surfaces will react suddenly with available oxygen to produce enough heat to cause either a fire or an explosion. To provide maximum safety, a means for the controlled oxidation of newly exposed surfaces is provided as soon as they are exposed by regulating the oxygen content of the inert gas. Tests conducted by the U.S. Bureau of Mines and others have disclosed that an inert gas as described herein is effective for this purpose. This mixture serves to control the rate of oxidation, and at the same time provides an environment which materially reduces the fire and explosion hazard.

Air Conveying

If the conveying gas is air, as is often practiced in atomizing, the dust-air ratio throughout the conveying system is held below the minimum explosive concentration of the metal dust as determined by the Bureau of Mines.[8] Although the metal dust-air suspension may be held below the explosive concentration in the conveying system, the suspension will necessarily pass through the explosive range in the collector at the end of the conveying system unless the dust is collected in a liquid such as in a spray tower. Such wet collection is not always possible or desirable. Any liquid used must be nonflammable, nonreactive with metal dust, or reactive at a controlled minimum rate under favorably controlled conditions, and the liquid remaining in or on the product shall be compatible with subsequent processing requirements.

In an air conveying system, any dry collector must be considered as an explosion hazard containing a dust-air mixture in the explosive range. It is, therefore, sited in a safe location and is provided with the requisite barricades or other design means for the protection of personnel. Construction is of nonferrous, nonsparking metal, or nonmagnetic, nonsparking stainless steel. The entire system, particularly the collector, is thoroughly and completely bonded and grounded. The entire ground system when checked with an ohmmeter should show less than 5 ohms resistance to ground.

Where the conveying duct is exposed to weather or moisture, it should be moisture-tight because any moisture entering the system can react with the dust, generating heat and serving as a potential source of ignition.

A minimum conveying velocity is employed throughout the conveying system to prevent the accumulation of dust at any point, and to pick up any powder that might drop out during an unscheduled system stoppage.

If the conveying gas is inducted into the system in a relatively warm environment and the duct work and collectors are relatively cold, gas temperature may drop below the dew point causing condensation of moisture. To avoid this possible condensation, the ducts and collectors are insulated or provided with a heating means.

Relief Vents for Conveyor Ducts

Vents of sufficient area connected to ducts or openings protected with antiflashback swing valves and extending to the outside of the building can provide explosion relief. Care is taken to limit the inertia of swing valves to the minimum required. Rupture diaphragms can be used in place of swing valves. Wherever damage may result from the rupture of a duct, in case the relief vent fails to offer sufficient pressure relief, the duct is designed for an internal working pressure of 100 psi minimum. Where the duct is so located that no damage will result from its bursting, it may be of very light construction to intentionally fail as an auxiliary vent for the system.

Fan Construction and Arrangement

Blades and housing of fans that are used to move air or inert gas in conveying ducts are constructed of conductive, nonsparking metal such as bronze, nonsparking stainless steel, or aluminum. In no case should the design be such that the dust is drawn through the fan before entering the final collector. Personnel should not be permitted within 50 ft of the fan during operation. This means that the fan and associated equipment are shut down for oiling, inspection, or preventive maintenance. If the area must be approached during operation for pressure test or other technical reasons, it must only be done under the direct supervision of competent technical personnel and with the knowledge and approval of operating management. Ultimately, all fans in dust collector systems accumulate sufficient dust to be a potential hazard; for this reason they are preferably located outside of all manufacturing buildings.

It is good practice to equip fan bearings with suitable instruments for indicating the temperature; such instruments are wired with an alarm device to give notice of over-temperature.

Sight Glass

Avoid sight glasses in pneumatic systems whenever possible. If installed, they should be of noncombustible material that is not readily subject to physical damage. The tubing is supported above and below each sight glass so that the sight glass does not carry any of the system weight and is not, in itself, subject to resulting stresses or strains. The electrical bonding of the system must be continuous around all sight glasses. The strength of the sight glass and its mounting mechanism and its inside diameter are equal to the adjoining tube system. In pressure-type systems, connections between sight and tubing are butted squarely and fastened together with rigid, air-tight couplings, connectors, or comparable devices. In suction-type systems, connections between the sight glass and tubing are butted squarely and sealed with approved sleeves extending a minimum of 3 in. above and below the sight glass and tubing connections. The sleeves are of a material that has elastic properties which provide an air-tight seal.

Air-Material Separators

Air-material separators are preferably located outside the building and are provided with lightning protection. Material discharge outlets are provided with a positive choke device, and the separator is electrically conductive and bonded. Exhaust air is always discharged to the outside, except where provision is made to recirculate transport air directly back into the pneumatic conveying system. The air-material separators are preferably constructed of noncombustible materials, and the cloth filters are made of low hazard materials. Where it is necessary to use combustible filter media, flame retardant treatment is desirable. In addition, the cloth filters are housed in metal enclosures, and provision is made for cleaning the filters. The separators are constructed so as to eliminate ledges or other points of dust accumulation. See Section 7, Chapter 5, for further information on separating equipment for air moving systems.

Bibliography

References Cited

[1] Buffington, M. A., "Mechanical Conveyors and Elevators," *Chemical Engineering,* Oct. 13, 1969, pp. 33–49.

[2] *Ibid.,* p. 49.

[3] Factory Mutual Engineering Corporation, *Handbook of Industrial Loss Prevention,* 2nd ed., McGraw-Hill, New York, 1967, pp. 7–11—7–15, 67-1—67-5.

[4] *Ibid.,* p. 30-5.

[5] Mitchell, D. W., et al., "Fire Hazard of Conveyor Belts," RI 7053, Dec. 1967, USDI Bureau of Mines, Washington, D.C.

[6] Factory Mutual Engineering Corporation, *Handbook of Industrial Loss Prevention,* 2nd ed., McGraw-Hill, New York, 1967, p. 66–15.

[7] Hartmann, I., Nagy, J., and Brown, H. R. "Inflammability and Explosibility of Metal Powders," RI 3722, 1943, USDI Bureau of Mines, Pittsburgh.

[8] Jacobson, M., Cooper, A. R., and Nagy, J., "Explosibility of Metal Powders," RI 6516, 1964, USDI Bureau of Mines, Pittsburgh.

NFPA Codes, Standards, and Recommended Practices (see the latest *NFPA Publications and Visual Aids Catalog* for availability of current editions of the following documents)

NFPA No. 15, Standard for Water Spray Fixed Systems.

NFPA No. 63, Fundamental Principles for the Prevention of Dust Explosions in Industrial Plants.

NFPA No. 66, Standard for Pneumatic Conveying Systems for Handling Feed, Flour, Grain, and Other Agricultural Dusts.

NFPA No. 651, Standard for the Manufacture of Aluminum and Magnesium Powder.

NFPA No. 80, Standard for Fire Doors and Windows.

NFPA No. 505, Standard for Type Designations, Areas of Use, Maintenance, and Operation of Powered Industrial Trucks.

Additional Readings

Johanson, J. R., "Feeding," *Chemical Engineering,* Oct. 13, 1969, pp. 75–83.

Jraus, M. N., "Pneumatic Conveyors," *Chemical Engineering,* Oct. 13, 1969, pp. 59–65.

LaPushin, Gideon, "Transportation and Storage," *Chemical Engineering,* Oct. 13, 1969, pp. 19–21.

Patterson, C. B., "Looking at Fire Hazards: Powered Industrial Trucks: Appraising Their In-Plant Fire Safety," *Fire Journal,* Vol. 66, No. 5, Sept. 1972, pp. 103–104.

Chapter 4

PROTECTION OF RECORDS

In recent years the volume of records and types of media used to record information have multiplied to volumes many times greater than that previously visualized. The "information explosion" manifests itself by generating more and more records.

Not many years ago almost all records were kept on paper. Paper records are still important and have multiplied along with other forms of records. On a volume of space basis, paper records still constitute the largest single class of records. Major quantities of information are, however, kept on photographic records, magnetic records, and records composed of digital holes, marks, and impressions on paper or other types of tapes. Almost universally the newer types of record media store more information per square inch or cubic foot than traditional paper records. Even with paper records the methods of depositing the information on the paper have changed. Most records are either the original or copies of typed or printed material. Recent advancements in photographic and electrostatic transfer have produced a new class of paper record.

Each change in records media has resulted in a change in the susceptibility to loss or damage of the information in records by fire, fire produced effects, or fire extinguishment efforts. The general disappearance of water soluble inks has increased the probability of retrieving information from wet paper records. Photographic and magnetic records, on the other hand, are generally much more susceptible to damage from flame, heat, steam, and, in some cases, cold water than paper records. The common practice of housing magnetic tape records in polystyrene or other combustible plastic cases makes these records extremely vulnerable to damage.

The massive increase in the total volume of records also has increased the impact of the problems involved in protecting records from fire. The traditional fire-resistive containers (insulated file cabinets), safes, and vaults have not lost any of their previous capabilities to protect paper records, and recent advances have produced devices that can safeguard magnetic or photographic records. These devices are still important and occupy an essential place in the scheme of protecting records. In many cases, however, the volume of records material has become so great that it is impractical to make the investment in either the devices or the space that would be required to house all the records needing protection. New methods of records storage have been developed that use the maximum cubic capacity of the space allowed for records storage. Some of these storage areas not only place the records in a state of risk, but also contain sufficient fire potential to be a danger to the structure and all of the other operations housed in it.

Records of various types have always been important to every person in the many facets of his life. The official records of births, deaths, land transactions, court decisions, and other official records maintained by local governments have value to every person as well as to every business. Other records are of such extreme importance their loss would be a local or even national calamity. Consider the record of deeds in the typical county courthouse, the accounts receivable in a business, the records of drug examinations, the social security records, or military personnel histories held by the federal government. Some are public treasures such as the records of the Union and Confederate armies (the records of the Continental Army were lost in a fire). Some are not individually important but are critically important when considered in mass, such as records of accounts paid, inventories, and general reference files. Some are important for short periods until newer data are developed (a frequent occurrence when computers are involved), and some remain important permanently, eventually to become of historical value. Some are just convenient and could be done without in an emergency, and some are useless and could well be destroyed.

This chapter considers ways of identifying and classifying valuable records so as to determine the amount of protection against fire and its associated perils which is justified by their value. The relative susceptibility of various records media to flame, heat, smoke, and water exposure is considered. Because water damage is an important by-product of fire containment efforts, information on salvaging water-soaked documents is provided. The different ways in which the risk of extensive loss of valuable records can be mitigated are explored. Protection against perils not associated with fire is not considered.

Detailed discussions of the best methods of providing maximum reasonable protection for records are contained in NFPA No. 232, Standard for the Protection of Records, and NFPA No. 232AM, Manual for Fire Protection for Archives and Records Centers. Further information can be secured from the reference book *Protecting the Library and Its Resources*.[1]

Caution must be exercised that adequate provisions are made for the safety of persons in records storage facilities. This can be a particularly difficult task when the facility is designed to provide maximum security of its contents against illegal entry; however, emergency exits are often a necessity to assure life safety for persons in the records area in case of fire, even if it means some sacrifice in security. General good-practice recommendations for means of egress should be followed (see Sec. 6, Chap. 9).

A. Fire Risk Analysis

Maximum possible protection is neither feasible nor desirable for the bulk of what comprises records storage. Most records can be reconstructed, duplicates are often available in other locations, and their loss may not create any substantial hardship. The value of certain, irreplaceable documents warrants especially sophisticated protective measures, but the great majority of records in a particular collection may dictate consideration of less than total methods of records protection which will still give a high degree of assurance against a significant loss.

Record protection programs should be based on an inventory that determines type, volume, rate of acquisition, rate of disposal, and class of importance of the records. The following classifications are recommended for assessing the value of records:

Class 1. Vital Records: These records underlie the organization of an establishment and give direct evidence of legal status, ownership, accounts receivable, and incurred obligations.

Class 2. Important Records: While not irreplaceable, these records can be reproduced from original sources only at considerable expense.

Class 3. Useful Records: The loss of these records would cause temporary inconvenience but otherwise would entail no serious disadvantages.

Class 4. Nonessential Records: These have no present value and should be destroyed.

Fire Risk Evaluation Factors

In considering the protection of valuable records, four basic items must be evaluated. They are:

1. The severity of exposure to the record collection from the building housing it as well as from neighboring operations, i.e., the possibility of involving the records in a fire originating outside of the records storage activity.*

2. The possibility of fire starting within the records storage activity including the susceptibility to ignition of the records or record's container.

3. The amount of fuel the records represent, particularly as it relates to available or proposed capability for fire extinguishment.

4. The extent and type of damage from fire, fire effects (heat, smoke vapors, etc.), and fire extinguishing efforts (principally water damage from hose streams and other extinguishing devices and physical disruption from manual fire fighting).

When records must be housed in a building that may burn around them, properly rated vaults and containers can give reasonable assurance of records recovery. However, when a separate building or a segregated floor or section of a fire resistive building is used for records storage, the protection methods described in Part C of this chapter will provide protection commensurate with the hazard and the sophistication of the systems. The degree of fire risk and the potential for loss in large collections not suitable for cabinet or vault storage may need to be evaluated by a person knowledgeable in this type of analysis.

Bulk Storage

Bulk storage of records creates a fire hazard in itself. The term bulk storage is used here to describe any sizeable collection of records not contained in vaults, safes, or insulated cabinets. The term includes collections of records ranging from small file rooms to the largest known archives or records centers. Storage methods include, but are not limited to, file cabinets, various types of shelving, palletized cardboard boxes, transport cases, miscellaneous cardboard boxes, and devices for unusually shaped records, such as blueprints, magnetic tapes, photographic film, and other media. Locations may range from an area within a general office complex to specially built records facilities. It is not uncommon to find record collections in basements or attics of public buildings, in office buildings, in converted factory or warehouse buildings of various constructions and levels of quality, in public warehouses, and, recently, in underground or other facilities protected against wartime disasters.

Open Shelf Filing

The trend toward making the maximum use of available space in buildings has sometimes resulted in using open shelf

filing methods, normally with the records either held in file folders or in various styles of cardboard boxes. Typically the racks of records face each other across aisles 25 to 30 in. in width. The exposed faces present a wall of paper made up of the faces of boxes or loose ends of paper sticking out of file folders. They can be almost instantly ignited by any accidental ignition source ranging from a match to a faulty fluorescent ballast, or simply by contact with an exposed incandescent light bulb. (Paper ignites at approximately 450°F.) Cardboard boxes resist ignition slightly longer because of their mass, but there is a good probability that a simple match can initiate combusion, and virtual assurity that ignition of a few pieces of paper, such as might occur on a filing cart, would readily transmit ignition to the faces of the boxes.

Attempts have been made to develop economical methods of increasing the flame resistance of the typical records center cardboard boxes. The most frequently attempted method is coating the box with an intumescent type of fire retardant paint. Tests of records boxes protected by such paint properly applied show that the coating will substantially delay actual ignition of the cardboard box material; however, since intumescent paint does not react to heat effectively under about 400°F, the temperature of any modest exposure fire (such as might occur on a file cart) will weaken the paper in the box to the point where the box will break open under the weight of the paper it contains, exposing the ordinary combustible contents of the box. In a small-scale test, conducted as a joint effort of the NFPA Committee on Records Protection and the U.S. General Services Administration, a fire retardant paint coating on boxes delayed only briefly ignition and the spread of fire up and across the face of the records in storage.

Where records are stored on open shelves, it can be expected that fire will develop in a pattern approximating that demonstrated both in tests of high piled storage conducted by Underwriters Laboratories, Inc.,[2] and tests of 6-ft high archival shelving arrangements conducted by the U.S. General Services Administration. In each test at the end of a relatively short early development stage the fire had preheated a sufficient amount of the exposed boxes so that fire development characteristics changed suddenly, temperatures rose quickly, and the flame enveloped large areas.

Neither of the tests involved exposed loose paper typical of systems involving open shelf filing. In these situations fire development would be almost instantaneous since loose paper ends present a continuous fuel for rapid movement of flame. The close proximity of the opposing sides of the aisle could also result in rapid crossing of the short spaces and increased radiant heat feedback. The higher the stacking and the narrower the aisles the more severe and rapid would be the development of fire.

Plastic Media

The flammability of magnetic media and its containers is of prime importance when they are stored in bulk quantities. Generally, acetate- and polyester-base tapes do not present a hazard more severe than paper. Polystyrene cases and reels, however, present a severe fire hazard condition as they contain a high Btu content and burn fiercely. Tests by Underwriters Laboratories, Inc., have shown that storage systems designed to safeguard materials of cardboard or paper composition would not be adequate to protect materials involving polystyrene. Where the containers are made of another plastic, the condition may vary slightly, though most thermoplastics exhibit similar properties. In any event, it is necessary to limit the height and extent of the storage of reels encased in plastic or to design special protection systems for them.

B. Damageability and Salvage

Records inscribed in stone can be considered to have high resistance to damage from the perils usually associated with fire; but even the ordinary paper record has reasonably good survivability to most of the effects of a fire, except direct exposure to flaming. With rare exceptions, the burned paper record represents a total loss, while a high recovery rate is practical where the records have been exposed only to water, high humidity, smoke, and moderately high temperatures (about 350°F). Nonpaper records media tend to be more damageable than paper.

Photographic Records

Photographic records, be they on the traditional acetate or glass base or on any special base, consist of an image held in place by an emulsion. The image can be distorted or destroyed under any condition which loosens the emulsion. Tests have demonstrated that these emulsions will not withstand high temperature and humidity conditions, and they are particularly susceptible to steam.[3, 4] Since the traditional insulated safe or insulated filing device depends upon the water of crystallization in the insulation material to limit the internal temperature, and since these devices are traditionally vented into the interior of the device, it must be expected that a 212°F or higher steam atmosphere will exist within the records protection equipment during a fire exposure. The tests demonstrated that such exposure would severely damage or destroy the information on photographic media. However, a high degree of safety may be had by placing the photographic media inside a telescoping steel can sealed with a moisture-resistant tape before storing it within a record container.

Where photographic records are stored in bulk facilities, the problem is not extensively different than that encountered with paper records except that in salvage efforts it is important to give first attention to the photographic records. While the cold water used in extinguishing the fire will not immediately attack the photographic emulsion as steam will, it will tend to cause some softening; if salvage efforts are not immediately undertaken, there is a tendency for the emulsion to stick to adjacent material, resulting in damage to the image.

Magnetic Media

The more common magnetic records consist of magnetic impulses retained in an iron oxide or similar deposit held to an acetate, polyester, or similar plastic base material. To a large extent the tapes are wound on polystyrene or similar plastic reels and contained in polystyrene cases. This is particularly true with many tapes used in connection with electronic computer systems. The security of the record is first of all related, as with photographic records, to the stability of the emulsion. Even minor distortion is severe in the case of magnetic records because of the inability for direct reading with the human eye. Machines are not capable of making subjective judgments regarding distortion. Also in the case of magnetic tapes, with any softening of emulsion there is a tendency for the layers of tape to stick to each other on the reel and to be destroyed in efforts to unreel. A tape can be considered safeguarded only up to temperatures in the range of 150°F and a relative humidity not above 85 percent.

Recovering wet records is a problem whether the records are wet or damp as a result of a fire, or from other source, such as flood, hurricane, heavy rainstorm, roof leakage, spillage from operations located above, or a breakdown of any of the numerous water or steam systems in the building. It is generally recognized that virtually any wet paper records can be recovered, provided prompt and proper action is taken.

Good sources for further information on salvaging records are contained in NFPA No. 910, Protection of Library Collections; the Federal Fire Council's Practice No. 2, "Salvaging and Restoring Records Damaged by Fire and Water";[5] and the Library of Congress' "Procedures for Salvage of Water-Damaged Library Materials." [6]

C. Fire Risk Reduction

Since records media are almost always combustible, 100 percent effective protection is not feasible and efforts should be directed to reducing the risk of fire and its associated effects. One of the most effective means of limiting the disastrous effects of a fire in a records storage activity is to prepare duplicates, which are stored away from the originals, where they will not be subject to the same incident. Often the duplicate copy is on microfilm, which is cheap and easily transported and stored at a remote facility. Once such a duplicate has been prepared, the value of the original is reduced considerably unless the original document is required for legal purposes, or is of intrinsic or historic value. If care is taken that the duplication is complete, up-to-date, and orderly, the degree of protection is extremely high, and limited built-in protective measures may be justified for both the original and the duplicate collection.

If the records are on magnetic tape, the latest generation of tapes is used at the computer center and the prior generation is stored at a remote location. While they are not exact duplicates, the earlier tapes still greatly simplify the task of reconstructing the latest records.

Protective Containers

Heavily insulated, massive vaults, safes, and filing cabinets are the traditional method of safeguarding valuable records against the effects of fire. The concept of encapsulating the records so that they are fully protected against the maximum fire exposure which can be anticipated in the building in which they are located is still perfectly valid today; containers are available which will limit the internal temperature and humidity as low as necessary to retain the data on magnetic tape and other temperature-sensitive media.

Vaults are usually used where the volume of valuable records is large; they are often the only practical method of protection in nonfire resistive buildings where the probable fire severity exceeds the rated endurance of 4-hr safes. Safes are used for smaller volumes of records, for convenience in having the records kept close to the point of use, where the cost of vault construction would be prohibitive, or where the building does not lend itself to vault construction.

Record protective containers are rated by tests under standard fire conditions, measured in the time interval before the interior of the container reaches 350°F, which provides a safety factor, since the ignition temperature of most paper is somewhat higher.

Record containers also have been rated for which the interior temperatures do not exceed 150°F and the relative humidity does not exceed 85 percent at temperatures above 120°F. Containers rated with these more stringent requirements are intended to provide protection to many films, magnetic tapes, disc packs, and similar materials. However, the development of new and different record materials requires a careful evaluation of their characteristics in order to assure proper protection. An important limitation on this type of container is that it is not subjected to the traditional drop test with magnetic or similar media records in it since it is accepted that magnetic records would not withstand this test. Even this improved device should not be considered capable of safeguarding magnetic and similar records in any building that could collapse in a fire causing debris to fall on the container or the container itself to fall several floors.

Table 5-4A indicates the approximate fire resistance that can be safely expected from various types of devices. The protection afforded varies considerably, depending on design and materials, and thickness of insulation alone does not give reliable indication of fire resistance, which can be determined accurately only by tests.

Table 5-4A.   Fire Resistance of Record Containers

Insulated record vault doors	2, 4, and 6 hrs
Insulated file room doors	$\frac{1}{2}$ and 1 hr
Steel plate vault doors (with inner doors)	about 15 min
Steel plate door without inner doors	less than 10 min
Modern safes	1, 2, and 4 hrs
"Old Line," "Iron," or "Cast Iron" safes, 2 to 6 in. wall thickness	Uncertain
Insulated record containers (files and cabinets, etc.)	$\frac{1}{2}$, 1, and 2 hrs
Containers with air space or with cellular or solid insulation less than 1 in. in thickness	10 to 20 min
Uninsulated steel files, cabinets— wooden files—wooden or steel desks	about 5 min

An analysis of record container performance based on reports gathered over a 5-year period was prepared by the NFPA.[7] The performance of fifty-three vaults was also analyzed and reported. Table 5-4B summarizes the results of the analysis and shows that the contents of 88 percent of the labeled containers were undamaged whereas only 60 percent of the contents of unlabeled containers came through the fires in good condition. Exposure in excess of the labeled rating was the largest single cause of container failure, and was also the principal reason for damage to contents of labeled containers, confirmation of the importance of considering the probable degree of fire exposure when selecting the proper container. Obsolete design or construction of containers was the most frequent cause of damage to contents in unlabeled containers.

Ninety percent of the vaults equipped with labeled doors protected their contents as compared with 53 percent in the cases of vaults with unlabeled doors. Deficiencies in door construction comprised the principal reason for failures of vaults equipped with unlabeled doors.

The Concept of Early Warning

Records administrators, concerned about water damage, frequently prefer to rely on early warning of the existence of a fire and prompt extinguishment by the staff, rather than taking a chance on accidental water discharge from automatic sprinkler piping. The concept of "early warning" fire detection is valid, and many devices are available that respond to either the visible (smoke) or invisible (molecular size) products of combustion produced from the moment of ignition. In a properly engineered installation, these devices can detect the presence of fire within periods as short as 60 to 90 sec of ignition, giving warning in the very early stages of fire development (see Sec. 12, Chaps. 2 and 3 for further information on warning systems and devices).

If response to the fire is rapid, and effective "hand" fire extinguishment efforts are undertaken within about 1 or 2 min after early warning detector actuation, chances of success are good, but dependence on the combination of early warning detection and hand fire extinguisher attack leaves the facility subject to a major disaster. The facilities seldom are attended by sufficient trained staff personnel 24 hrs a day, and a time lag of at least 5 min must be counted on before the public fire department can respond, enter, and launch an effective attack (even if the fire department is notified automatically by the detection system). There is a high probability that a fire in records storage will develop fully in that time interval, making close approach to the seat of the fire difficult and, often, impossible. As a result, the fire department is immediately forced into using large hose streams for fire control, and a major loss is more the rule than the exception.

Where the value of the collection warrants it, an early warning fire detection system is installed to give the staff and the fire department a chance to extinguish the fire with a minimum of water; but an automatic extinguishing system is provided as backup, starting its control efforts as soon as the fire has progressed into the full development stage.

Human detection capabilities are unreliable. Neither persons in the facility during the day nor watchmen at night or weekends can be relied on to detect a fire in the critical, initial stage. Automatic heat detectors (as opposed to early warning, products of combustion detectors) have an inherent time lag under many fire situations, and they too may not detect a fire until it has already reached the full development stage. Dependable protection cannot be secured for valuable records by these means.

Heat detectors may be used, though, to actuate automatic fire extinguishing systems, and here the delay is an advantage. The faster-acting, early warning detectors usually are not used to actuate extinguishing systems, partly because of the desire to be able to extinguish the fire manually before the system is actuated and partly because of a higher rate of false alarms with these sensitive detectors.

Fire Control Measures

Even if the facility is equipped with an automatic extinguishing system, "manual" fire control devices are provided for use by the staff. Most often encountered are fire extinguishers (see Sec. 16), the preferred types being those containing clear water as the extinguishing agent. Carbon dioxide extinguishers, while leaving no residue and no dampened documents, are not effective on the deep-seated fires likely to occur in records storage. All-purpose dry chemical extinguishers may be provided, but they leave considerable residue and they have only limited effectiveness on deep-seated fires.

Water hose lines (Sec. 15, Chap. 1) may supplement fire extinguishers and sometimes be used in lieu thereof. Linen hose is common, but to reduce the inevitable water damage, rubber-lined hose or all rubber hose is preferable in records storage areas. Its use greatly expands the fire fighting capabilities of the staff. Hose lines, instead of using water, may be connected to carbon dioxide or Halon storage tanks or cylinders, where these may have been installed as part of total-flooding extinguishing systems.

Table 5-4B. NFPA Analysis: Record Container Performance

	Labeled Containers				Unlabeled Totals
	1-hr	2-hr	4-hr	Totals	
Condition of Container					
Normal After Fire	72	40	14	126	74
Abnormal* After Fire	143	54	22	219	220
Totals	215	94	36	345	294
Cause of Abnormal* Container					
Fell	22	11	5	38	29
Struck	14	0	1	15	10
Exploded	0	0	0	0	6
Previous Damage	2	0	0	2	1
Exposure Judged Excessive†	83	29	5	117	105
Other	10	5	7	22	21
Unknown	12	9	4	25	48
Totals	143	54	22	219	220
Condition of Contents					
Preserved	186	84	35	305	178
Heat-Fire Damage	16	6	1	23	70
Smoke Damage	1	1	0	2	5
Water Damage	12	3	0	15	39
Unknown	0	0	0	0	2
Totals	215	94	36	345	294
Cause of Destruction of Contents					
Door Open	7	2	1	10	8
Exposure Judged Excessive†	14	5	0	19	36
Not Insulated	0	0	0	0	4
Obsolete Design or Construction	0	0	0	0	51
Under Water	7	3	0	10	16
Other	1	0	0	1	1
Totals	29	10	1	40	116

* The condition of a container was classified abnormal if, in the judgment of the inspector, the container was so damaged that it could no longer be safely used to protect records.

† For labeled containers, "exposure judged excessive" means exposure in excess of the labeled rating based on the judgment of the reporting agencies. For unlabeled containers, inspection indicated was excessive for the construction.

Fire Prevention and Emergency Planning

While automatic detection and extinguishing systems cannot be ignored, particularly for the bulk storage of valuable records, the first line of defense remains a good fire prevention and risk reduction program. Good housekeeping, orderliness, maintenance of equipment, and absolute prohibition of smoking in records storage and handling areas are fundamental precepts of good records management, and it is not felt necessary to elaborate on them.

An emergency action plan, continually updated and frequently practiced, is essential to limit damage in case a fire occurs. Staff personnel cannot be expected to approach a fire and use extinguishers or hose lines effectively without adequate training. Fire resistive containers and vaults are of little value unless there has been forethought concerning procedures in fire emergency. The following suggestions apply:

1. Restore records to their places of safety accurately, quickly, and without confusion or oversight. In the absence of standard record protection, the best plan is to have the most important records carried out of the building. Record drills to train employees to meet emergencies are not uncommon.

2. Records belonging in vaults or safes should never be left out overnight.

3. Important materials properly belonging under protection should not be allowed to accumulate on desks.

4. Records normally safeguarded are often unprotected while temporarily in other hands. Wherever possible, the originals should be retained and copies given out.

D. Records Storage

Factory-built Devices

Small quantities of valuable records may be stored in factory-built record protection equipment, such as insulated record containers, fire-resistant safes, and insulated filing devices. They are available in varying degrees of resistance to fire, heat, and impact, and the degree of protection to be specified for a particular application will depend on the severity of the exposure and the items to be stored. Underwriters Laboratories Standard UL 72 covers the test procedure applicable to this equipment and the ratings employed,[8] as follows:

Record protection equipment is classified in terms of an interior temperature limit and a time in hours. Two temperature limits are employed. They are either 350°F, which is regarded as a suitable limit for paper records, or 150°F, which is regarded as a limiting temperature for most magnetic tape and photographic records. The time limits employed are 4, 3, 2, 1, or ½ hrs. The complete rating, consisting of two elements, indicates that the specified interior temperature limit is not exceeded when the record container, safe, or filing device is exposed to a standard test fire as described in Standard UL 72, for the length of time specified.

Ratings are assigned to the various categories as follows:

Insulated Record Containers Class 150 — 4 Hours
Class 150 — 3 Hours
Class 150 — 2 Hours
Class 150 — 1 Hour

	Class 350 (A) — 4 Hours
	Class 350 (B) — 2 Hours
	Class 350 (C) — 1 Hour
Fire-Resistant Safes	Class 350 (A) — 4 Hours
	Class 350 (B) — 2 Hours
	Class 350 (C) — 1 Hour
Insulated Filing Devices	Class 350 (D) — 1 Hour
	Class 350 (E) — $\frac{1}{2}$ Hour
Insulated File Drawer	Class 350 — 1 Hour

Insulated record containers and fire resistant safes are required to protect contents from heat, to an extent described in the requirements, before and after an impact due to falling 30 ft. Insulated filing devices are not so tested and are not required to have the strength to endure such an impact.

Insulated record containers, fire resistant safes, insulated filing devices, and insulated file drawers are required to withstand a sudden exposure to high temperatures, to an extent described in the requirements, without the unit exploding as a result of such exposure.

Ordinary, uninsulated steel files and cabinets provide only a small measure of protection since heat sufficient to char contents is quickly transmitted to the interior. However, they are commonly used for records having no significant value and for the organized storage of records in protected facilities, including vaults, file rooms, and document buildings. Files and cabinets made of wood, fiberboard, or other combustible materials add to the fire hazard and preferably are not used where they will expose valuable records storage.

Vaults and File Rooms

Standards for the construction of fire resistive vaults and file rooms are contained in the NFPA Records Protection Standard. The term "vault" refers to a completely fire resistive enclosure up to 5,000 cu ft in volume, used exclusively for storage, with no work to be carried on inside. It is equipped, maintained, and supervised as to minimize the possibility of origin of fire within, and to prevent entrance of severe fire of long duration on the outside, provided the vault door is closed. Fire resistance classifications of 2, 4, and 6 hrs are available, indicating that under standard test conditions, heat will not rise above a specified temperature inside and the construction will withstand both the exposure fire and the application of fire hose streams during that period. Vaults are constructed in the field and do not carry a testing laboratory label. Vault doors, however, are laboratory-tested and carry ratings conforming to the vault construction in which they are to be used.[9] Unlike some other fire doors, vault doors limit the temperature on the interior face to 350°F during fire exposure, so that paper could be stored in contact with it without danger of ignition.

Vault standards prohibit piercing the enclosure for anything except the vault door, which effectively prevents the installation of automatic sprinkler protection or similar fire control systems that require wall openings for pipes, etc. Unless immediately discovered and extinguished with portable fire fighting devices or a "package"-type extinguishing system located completely within the vault, fire within a vault can be disastrous. Fire extinguishers of the water type or fire hose, or both, should be in an accessible location near the door of the vault.

A standard, fire resistive file room is defined as an enclosure not exceeding 50,000 cu ft in volume and a height not exceeding 12 ft, having less resistance to an exterior fire exposure than a vault. The volume and height limitations are for the purpose of restricting the quantity of records exposed to destruction by fire in a single enclosure, and to reduce the possibility of fire originating within the enclosure. File room doors also are labeled as to their fire resistance following a laboratory test under the procedures of UL 155,[9] but the ratings are only for $\frac{1}{2}$ hr or 1 hr, and they anticipate that paper and other combustibles will not be stored nearer than 3 ft from the unexposed face of the door, nor 6 in. to the side from the door jambs.

Lighting, heating, ventilation, etc. are permitted inside file rooms, as are filing cabinets and furniture, provided they are noncombustible. Although it is not to be used as a working space for other than filing purposes, the file room is more susceptible to a fire start than a vault, and the installation of automatic fire detection and fire control systems should be considered in relation to the values involved.

Record Centers and Archives

Bulk storage of records in buildings set aside for that specific purpose or in major portions of other buildings, in rooms exceeding the 50,000 cu ft fire resistive file room limitation, should comply with the recommendations set forth in the NFPA Archives and Records Centers Manual. For facilities of this size, where the most severe hazard may not be from a fire exterior to the facility but from a fire starting and spreading entirely within the records storage area, the level of fire resistive construction and protection must be individually determined. Within such a facility, ancillary operations may have to be segregated from the actual storage by fire resistive construction. A thorough fire risk analysis by qualified personnel is generally indicated, both on account of the high risk of fire due to the concentration of combustibles and on account of the probability of total loss of large volumes of valuable documents.

E. Fire Extinguishing Systems

A variety of automatic fire extinguishing systems are suitable for records storage protection; the choice depends on the economics for a particular situation and the degree of sophistication desired. They are:

Automatic Sprinklers

Automatic sprinkler systems are the most common type of automatic protection, and they have proven themselves effective in records storage fire incidents to limit both fire and water damage. Water is discharged only in the immediate vicinity of the fire, and salvage techniques have been perfected to the point where recovery of wetted items is no longer unusual (see Part B, Damageability and Salvage, preceding, and Sec. 14). Accidental opening of a sprinkler is rare, and the probability of water damage from an accidental discharge can be further reduced using a preaction sprinkler system, where water does not enter the piping until a fire detector operates. A more sophisticated variation is a system where the control valve cycles on and off, depending on the actual presence of fire as sensed by a detector in the fire area. Also available are individual sprinklers which cycle on and off, but in this case the piping remains filled with water.

Foam Systems

Tests[10] have shown high expansion foam to be an effective fire control system for records, though few high expansion foam systems are known to have been installed in record centers to date. Rapid fire control comparable to or possibly even faster than that achieved by automatic sprinkler protection may be expected. Water damage to any single item will be low but will affect all items within the room or fire area involved. (See Sec. 15, Chap. 3).

Carbon Dioxide Systems

Automatic total flooding carbon dioxide systems have a high rate of discharge and can hold a high concentration of gas for an extended period of time. A few such systems have been installed in record storage or library areas, and properly designed systems should promptly control fire with limited damage. The operation of such systems, however, involves a hazard to life and must be delayed until the area to be flooded is cleared of people (see Sec. 15, Chap. 4).

Halon Systems

Automatic total flooding Halon systems utilize flame inhibiting liquefied gas under pressure. Halon 1301 (Bromotrifluoromethane) is being marketed to use in specially engineered systems for the protection of valuable records, although experience to date has been limited. Primary advantages are that the gaseous agent leaves no residue and that it appears not to be toxic in the concentrations in which it is used (see Sec. 15, Chap. 5).

Bibliography

References Cited

[1] Gage-Babcock & Associates, "Protecting the Library and Its Resources," American Library Association, Chicago, 1963.

[2] Jensen, Rolf H., "Report on Fire Tests in High Piled Combustible Stock," Underwriters Laboratories, Inc. (sponsored by FIA and NBFU), Chicago, 1963.

[3] McCrea, J. L., Strand, D. J., and Calhoun, J. M., "Report to the Committee on Protection of Records of the National Fire Protection Association on Fire Tests on Microfilms Stored in Insulated Records Containers," Eastman Kodak Company, Rochester, N.Y. 1956.

[4] McCrea, J. L. and Adelstein, P. Z., "Fire Tests on Microfilm in Insulated Record Containers, Second Report to the Committee on Protection of Records of the National Fire Protection Association," Eastman Kodak Company, Rochester, N.Y., 1958.

[5] "Federal Fire Council Recommended Practice No. 2, Salvaging and Restoring Records Damaged by Fire and Water," 1963. Federal Fire Council, Washington, D.C.

[6] Waters, Peter, "Procedures for Salvage of Water-Damaged Library Materials," Library of Congress, Washington, D.C., 1975.

[7] "Record Container Performance," NFPA *Quarterly,* Vol. 47, No. 2, Oct. 1953, pp. 159–170.

[8] "Tests for Fire Resistance of Record Protection Equipment," UL 72, 1971, Underwriters Laboratories, Inc., Chicago.

[9] "Safe, Office, Fire Resistant, Burglary Protection," AA-S-81b, 1962, General Services Administration, Washington, D.C.

[10] "High Expansion Foam Fire Control for Record Storage Centers," Atomic Energy Commission Report IDO-12050, 1966, Atomic Energy Commission, Idaho Falls, Idaho.

NFPA Codes, Standards, and Recommended Practices (see the latest *NFPA Publications and Visual Aids Catalog* for availability of current editions of the following documents)

NFPA No. 11, Standard for Foam Extinguishing Systems.

NFPA No. 12, Standard on Carbon Dioxide Extinguishing Systems.

NFPA No. 12A, Standard on Halogenated Fire Extinguishing Agent Systems—Halon 1301.

NFPA No. 13, Standard for the Installation of Sprinkler Systems.

NFPA No. 232, Standard for the Protection of Records.

NFPA No. 232AM, Manual for Fire Protection for Archives and Record Centers.

Chapter 5

CONTROL OF ELECTROSTATIC IGNITION SOURCES

The term "static electricity" is used in this chapter to mean the electrification of materials through physical contact and separation, and the effects of the positive and negative charges so formed, particularly where sparks may result which constitute a fire or explosion hazard.

The development of electrical charges may not be in itself a potential fire or explosion hazard. There must be a discharge or sudden recombination of separated positive and negative charges. In order for static to be a source of ignition, four conditions must be fulfilled:

1. There must first of all be an effective means of static generation.

2. There must be a means of accumulating the separate charges and maintaining a suitable difference of electrical potential.

3. There must be a spark discharge of adequate energy.

4. The spark must occur in an ignitible mixture.

Static electricity may appear as the result of motions that involve changes in relative positions of contacting surfaces, usually of dissimilar substances either liquid or solid, one or both of which usually must be a poor conductor of electricity. Examples of such motion, common in industry are:

1. Flow of fluid through pipes, and the subsequent accumulation of a charge on the surface of a nonconducting liquid.

2. Breaking up into drops of a stream of liquid and the subsequent impact of such drops onto a solid or liquid surface.

3. Steam, air, or gas flowing from any opening in a pipe or hose, when the steam is wet or the air or gas stream contains particulate matter.

4. Pulverized materials passing through chutes or pneumatic conveyors.

5. Nonconductive power or conveyor belts in motion.

6. Moving vehicles.

Less than 100 years ago electricity was described as a "subtle agent, without weight or form, that appears to be diffused through all nature, existing in all substances," in the latent state giving no indication of its presence, but, when liberated from its repose, being capable of producing sudden and destructive effects.

With the discovery of the electron, this definition now seems prophetic, and the adjective "static" more meaningful. Electricity can move freely through some substances, such as metals, that are called "conductors," but can flow with difficulty or not at all through or over the surface of a class of substances called "nonconductors" or "insulators." This latter group includes gases, glass, amber, resin, sulfur paraffin, most synthetic plastics, and dry petroleum oils.

When electricity is present on the surface of a nonconductive body, where it is trapped or prevented from escaping, it is termed *static* electricity. Electricity on a conducting body which is in contact only with nonconductors is also prevented from escaping and is therefore nonmobile or "static." In either case, the body on which this electricity is evident is said to be "charged."

The generation of static electricity cannot be prevented, absolutely, because its intrinsic origins are present at every interface. The object of most static-corrective measures is to provide a means whereby charges separated by whatever cause may recombine harmlessly before sparking potentials are attained. If hazardous static conditions cannot be avoided in certain operations, means must be taken to assure that there are no ignitible mixtures at points where sparks may occur.

Certain electrical terms used in this chapter are defined in Part H.

A. Static Generation

When two bodies (usually different) are in close physical contact, there is likely to be a transfer of free electrons between them, one giving up electrons to the other, and an attractive force is established. When the bodies are separated, work must be done in opposition to these attractive forces. The expended energy reappears as an increase in electrical tension or voltage between the two surfaces. If the bodies are insulated from their surroundings, both are now said to be "charged"; the one having the excess of electrons being said to have a negative charge, and the other an equal positive charge. If a conductive path is available between them, the charges thus separated will reunite immediately. If no such path is available, as would be the case with insulators, the potential increase with separation may easily reach values of several thousand volts.

In many cases, one of the objects has a deliberate or inherently conductive path to the earth, and its charge is immediately lost to the earth, which is considered to have as infinite capacity to absorb or give up electrons. The other (insulated) object now retains its "charge" (now often called potential or voltage) with respect to its surroundings. It would hold this charge indefinitely, except for the fact that it must somehow be supported and no supporting insulator (even air) is a perfect nonconductor.

If one of the bodies is itself a nonconductor, flow of electrons across its surface is inhibited, and the charge tends to remain at the points where electron transfer originally occurred. A highly charged insulating surface can be discharged with the appearance of a spark by bringing an "earthed" conductor close to it, but only a limited area will be so discharged, and sparks so produced seldom release enough energy to cause ignition. Thus, nonconductors, the bodies most directly involved in charge separation, are usually not directly responsible for fires and explosions (an exception is flammable liquids discussed later in this chapter). However, such charges can, in some cases, be the agency for building up or accumulating a charge on a conductive body, which can release all of its stored energy in an incendiary spark.

On a conductive body the charge is free to move. Because like charges repel each other, the charge will distribute itself over the surface. If no other body is in close proximity, the concentration will favor the surface having the least radius of curvature; for a point, if the voltage is high enough, the voltage gradient may exceed the break-down potential of air (about 30,000 V per centimeter) and the air can be ionized, and a brush discharge may occur.

Like charges repel each other and unlike charges attract because of forces resident in the electrical fields that surround them. These forces have a strong influence on nearby objects. If the neighboring object is a conductor it will experience a separation of charges by induction. Its repelled charge is free to give or receive electrons as the case may be; if another conductor is brought near, the transfer may occur through the agency of a spark, very often an energetic spark.

When the inducing charge is moved away from the insulated conductor, there follows a reversed sequence of events, and sparks may result. Thus, in many situations, induced charges are far more dangerous than the initially separated ones upon which they are dependent.

If the object close to the highly charged nonconductor is itself a nonconductor, it will be polarized, that is, its constituent molecules will be oriented to some degree in the direction of the lines of force since the electrons have no true migratory freedom. Because of their polarizable nature, insulators and nonconductors are often called dielectrics. Their presence as separating media enhances the accumulation of charge.

Capacitance

Two conductive bodies separated by an insulator constitute a capacitor or condenser, and where a potential difference is applied between these bodies, electricity can be stored. One body receives a positive and the other an equal negative charge. In many instances involving accumulation of static electricity, one of the bodies is the earth, the insulating medium is the air, and the insulated body is some object to or from which a charge (electrons) has been transferred by one of the mechanisms previously described.

When a conducting path is made available, the stored energy is released, or the condenser is "discharged," possibly producing a spark. The energy so stored, and released by the spark, is related to the capacitance of the condenser (C) and the voltage (V) in accordance with the following:

$$\text{Energy} = \frac{C}{2} \times V^2$$

or, in practical units:
Energy (millijoules) $= C/2$ (micromicrofarads) $\times V^2$ (volts $\times 10^{-9}$).

Spark Discharge

The ability of a spark to produce ignition of a flammable mixture is governed largely by the energy transferred to the mixture, which will be some fraction of the total stored energy available because some energy is expended in heating the electrodes. Experiments at atmospheric pressure with plane electrodes have shown that the spark breakdown voltage has a minimum value at a critical short gap distance —about 350 V for the shortest measurable gap (say .01 mm). Increased gaps require proportionately higher voltages. At close spacing the heat loss or flame quenching effect virtually precludes ignition of the electrodes.

At most favorable electrode spacing, tests have shown that optimum mixtures of saturated hydrocarbon vapors and gases in air require about 0.25 millijoules of stored energy to produce ignition. Examples of the capacitance necessary to store the required 0.25 millijoules at various voltages are:

	Potential	Capacitance	Gap Length
	volts	mmf	
A.	350	4,000	Minimum voltage to jump shortest measurable gap. Quenching effect precludes ignition.
B.	1,500	222	Gap about 0.5 mm, just exceeding quenching distance. Incendiary sparks.
C.	5,000	20	1.5 mm
D.	10,000	5	Object the size of a baseball. 3 + mm
E.	20,000	1¼	Object the size of a large marble. 7 mm

For gaps of 1.5 mm or more, substantially longer than the quenching distance, the total energy to produce ignition is increased somewhat in proportion to the excess of spark length over the diameter of the necessary critical flame volume. This, in turn, may require somewhat greater capacitance than indicated above. This explains why corona discharge from a sharp point at very high voltage may not be incendiary.

Ignitible Mixtures

Elimination of ignitible mixtures in the areas where sparks of static electricity can occur is the surest method of preventing static caused fires. This is practical in certain areas, best discussed later in connection with the specific process involved.

Summary

In summarizing, static electricity will be manifest only where highly insulated bodies or surfaces are found. If a body is "charged" with static electricity, there will always be an equal and opposite charge produced. If a hazard is suspected, the situation should be analyzed to determine the location of both charges and to see what conductive paths are available between them. Tests of the high-resistance paths should be made with an applied potential of 500 V or more, in order that a minor interruption (paint or grease film or air gap) will be broken down and a correct reading of the instrument obtained. Resistances as high as 10,000 megohms will provide an adequate leakage path in many cases; when charges are generated rapidly, however, a resistance as low as 1 megohm (10^6 ohms) might be required. Where bonds are applied, they should connect the bodies on which the two opposite charges are expected to be found.

B. Dissipation of Static Electricity

A static charge which already exists can be removed or allowed to dissipate itself. The acts or conditions which can accomplish this are the same as those acts or conditions which permit the separation of charges to occur in the first place. Thus, dissipation of static and prevention of its generation are opposite approaches to the same objective.

Humidification

A static charge cannot persist except on a body insulated from its surroundings. Most commonly encountered materials not normally thought of as conductors, such as fabrics, paper, wood, concrete or masonry foundations, etc., contain a certain amount of moisture in equilibrium with that in the surrounding atmosphere. This moisture content varies, depending on weather, and to a large measure controls the conductivity of the material, and hence its ability to prevent the escape of static electricity. In an analogous manner, under some conditions, water vapor may condense on the surface of some nominally insulating materials, notably glass and porcelain, to render the surface conductive.

The conductivity of the materials under discussion—wood, paper, etc.—is controlled not by the absolute water content of the air but by its relative humidity. This figure, as ordinarily recorded in weather reports and comfort charts, is the ratio of the partial pressure of the moisture in the atmosphere to the partial pressure of water at the prevailing atmospheric temperature. Under conditions of high relative humidity—say 60 to 70 percent or higher—the materials in question will reach equilibrium conditions containing enough moisture to make the conductivity adequate to prevent static accumulations. The generating mechanism may be present, but the generated charge leaks away so fast that no observable accumulation results.

At the opposite extreme, with relative humidities of 30 percent or less, these same materials may dry out and become good insulators, and static manifestations become noticeable. There is no definite boundary line between these two conditions.

It should be emphasized that the conductivity of these materials is a function of relative humidity. At any constant moisture content, the relative humidity of an atmosphere decreases as the temperature is raised. In cold weather, the absolute humidity of the outdoor atmosphere may be low, even though the relative humidity may be high. When this same air is brought indoors and heated, the relative humidity becomes very low. As an example, a saturated atmosphere at an outdoor temperature of 30°F would have a relative humidity of only a little over 20 percent if heated up to a room temperature of 70°F. This phenomenon is responsible for the common belief that static generation is always more intense during winter months. The static problem is usually more severe during this period because static charges on a material have less ability to dissipate when relative humidities are low.

Where static electricity has introduced operational problems, such as the adhesion or repulsion of sheets of paper, layers of cloth, fibers, and the like, humidifying the atmosphere has proved to be a solution. It is usually stated that a relative humidity of about 60 to 70 percent will avoid such difficulties.

Unfortunately, it is not practical to humidify all occupancies in which static might be a hazard. It is necessary to conduct some operations in an atmosphere having a low relative humidity to avoid deleterious effects on the materials handled. High humidity can also cause intolerable comfort conditions in operations where the dry bulb temperature is high. On the other hand, a high humidity may advantageously affect the handling properties of some materials, thus providing an additional advantage.

In some cases localized humidification produced by directing a steam jet onto critical areas may provide satisfactory results without the need for increasing the humidity in the whole room. However, it must be remembered that steam which contains droplets of water may itself generate static. Local static can be reduced by providing a low velocity jet of humidified air.

It does not follow that humidification is a cure for all static problems. In particular, it must be remembered that the conductivity of the air is not appreciably increased by the presence in it of water in the form of a gas. If static electricity accumulates on some surface which is heated above normal atmospheric temperature—cloth passing over heated rollers for example—alterations in the relative humidity in the surrounding air may do no good whatsoever.

Another situation where the control of atmospheric humidity appears to accomplish little is in controlling the charge of static electricity which under some circumstances appears on the surface of oils. Such a surface does not absorb water vapor in the same way as does paper or wood, so it can remain an insulating surface capable of accumulating static charges even though the atmosphere above it may have a relative humidity up to 100 percent.

In summary, humidification of the atmosphere to a relative humidity of about 70 percent may be a cure for static problems where the surfaces on which the static electricity accumulates are those materials which reach equilibrium with the atmosphere, such as paper or wood, and which are not abnormally heated. For heated surfaces and for static on the surface of oils and some other liquid and solid insulating materials, high humidity will not provide a means for draining off static charges, and some other solution must be sought.

Bonding and Grounding

Where natural conditions, including humidity, do not insure a conductive path to prevent static generation (or to drain off charges unavoidably formed), resort may be had to artificial conducting paths.

"Bonding" is the process of connecting two or more conductive objects together by means of a conductor. "Grounding (earthing)" is the process of connecting one or more conductive objects to the ground, and is a specific form of bonding. A conductive object may also be grounded by bonding it to another conductive object that is already connected to the ground. Some objects are inherently bonded or inherently grounded by their contact with the ground. Examples are underground piping or large storage tanks resting on the ground.

Bonding is done to minimize potential differences between conductive objects. Likewise, grounding is done to minimize potential differences between objects and the ground.

Bond wires and ground wires should have adequate capacity to carry the largest currents that may be anticipated for any particular installation. When currents to be handled are small, the minimum size of wire is dictated by mechanical strength rather than current carrying capacity. The currents encountered in the bond connections used in the protection against accumulations of static electricity are in the order of microamperes (one millionth part of an ampere). Because the leakage currents are extremely small, a ground resistance of 1 megohm (one million ohms) is adequate for static grounding. (An exception concerns power circuits discussed later in this chapter.)

A bond or ground is composed of suitable conductive materials having adequate mechanical strength, corrosion resistance, and flexibility for the service intended. Since the bond or ground does not need to have low resistance, nearly any conductor size will be satisfactory from an electrical standpoint. Solid conductors are satisfactory for fixed connections. Flexible conductors are used for bonds that are to be connected and disconnected frequently. Conductors may be insulated or uninsulated. Some prefer uninsulated conductors so that defects can be easily spotted by visual inspections. If insulated for mechanical protection, the concealed conductor is checked for continuity at regular intervals, depending on experience. Permanent connections may be made with pressure-type ground clamps, brazing, welding, or other suitable means. Temporary connections may be made with battery-type clamps, magnetic, or other special clamps which provide metal to metal contact.

A special situation requiring substantial conductors may arise if there is a possibility that a ground wire may be called upon to carry current from power circuits or lightning protection systems. Obviously, any ground that is adequate for power circuits is more than adequate for protection against accumulations of static electricity.

Ionization

Under certain circumstances air may become sufficiently conductive to bleed off static charges.

Static Comb: A static charge on a conducting body is free to flow, and on a spherical body in space it will distribute itself uniformly over the surface. If the body is not spherical the self-repulsion of the charge will make it concentrate on the surfaces having the least radius of curvature.

If the body is surrounded by air (or other gas) and the radius of curvature is reduced to almost zero, as with a sharp needle point, the charge concentration on the point can produce ionization of the air, rendering it conductive. As a result, whereas a surface of large diameter can receive and hold a high voltage, the same surface equipped with a sharp needle point can reach only a small voltage before the leakage rate equals the rate of generation.

A "static comb" is a metal bar equipped with a series of needle points. Another variation is a metal wire surrounded with metallic tinsel.

If a grounded static comb is brought close to an insulated charged body (or a charged insulating surface) ionization of the air at the points will provide enough conductivity to make the charge speedily leak away or be "neutralized." This principle is sometimes employed to remove the charge from fabrics, power belts, and paper.

Electrical Neutralization: The electrical neutralizer is a line-powered high voltage device which is an effective means for removing static charges from materials like cotton, wool, silk, or paper in process, manufacturing, or printing. It produces a conducting ionized atmosphere in the vicinity of the charged surfaces. The charges thereby leak away to some adjacent grounded conducting body.

Electrical neutralizers should not be used where flammable vapors, gases, or dust may be present unless approved specifically for such locations.

Radioactive Material: Another method for dissipating static electricity involves the ionization of the air by radioactive material. Such installations require no redesign of existing equipment. However, engineering problems are involved, such as elimination of health hazards, dust accumulations, determination of radiation required, and proper positioning in relation to the stock, machine parts, and personnel, which are best worked out in consultation with radiation specialists.

Open Flame: Ionization of the air can also be obtained by an open flame. This method is frequently used in the printing industry to remove static from paper sheets as they come off the press, thus avoiding the mechanical problems involving one sheet of paper adhering to another, but obviously not to avoid an ignition source.

C. Control of Ignitible Mixtures

Despite efforts to prevent accumulation of static charges, which should be the primary aim of good design, there are many operations involving the handling of nonconductive materials or nonconductive equipment which do not lend themselves to this built-in solution. It may then be desirable, or essential, depending on the hazardous nature of the materials involved, to provide other measures to supplement or supplant static dissipation facilities.

For example, where a normally ignitible mixture is contained within a small enclosure, such as a processing tank, an inert gas may be used to bring the mixture well below its flammable range (see Chap. 5 of this Section). When operations are normally conducted in an atmosphere above the upper flammable limit it may be practicable to apply the inert gas only during the periods when the mixture passes through its flammable range.

Mechanical ventilation may be applied in many instances to dilute an ignitible mixture to well below its normal flammable range. Also by directing the air movement, it may be practical to prevent the flammable liquids or dusts from approaching an operation where an otherwise uncontrollable static hazard may exist. To be considered reliable, the mechanical ventilation should be interlocked with the equipment to assure its proper operation.

Where a static accumulating piece of equipment is unnecessarily located in a hazardous area, it is preferable to relocate the equipment to a safe location rather than to rely upon prevention of static accumulation.

D. Flammable Liquids

Static is generated when liquids move in contact with other materials. This occurs commonly in such operations as flowing through pipes, and in mixing, pouring, pumping, filtering, or agitating. Under certain conditions, particularly with liquid hydrocarbons, static may accumulate. If the accumulation is sufficient, a static spark may occur. If the spark occurs in the presence of a flammable vapor-air mixture, an ignition may result.

Standard control measures are designed to prevent incendiary sparks, or the formation of ignitible vapor-air mixtures. In many cases, air which may form an ignitible mixture with the vapor can be eliminated or reduced in concentration to render the mixture nonflammable.

Before a container is filled, contact is made between the filling nozzle and the container and the contact should be maintained throughout the filling operation. By this procedure, any difference in potential between the container and

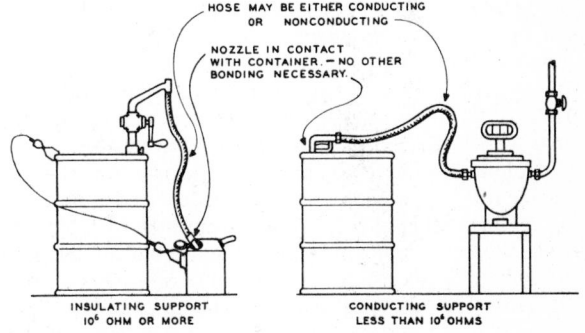

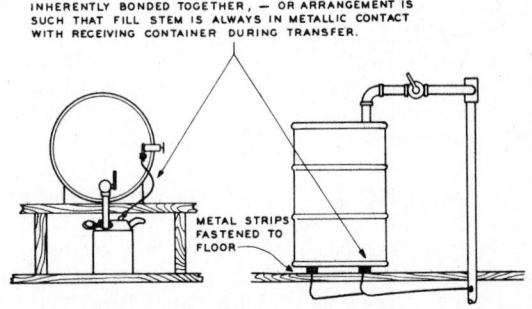

Fig. 5-5A. Recommended methods of bonding flammable liquid containers during container filling.

Table 5-5A.　Approximate Resistivities of Some Pure Liquids Used in Chemical Industries

Liquid	Resistivity Ohm-Cm
Acetaldehyde	5.9×10^5
Acetic Acid	8.9×10^8
Acetic Anhydride	2.1×10^6
Acetone	1.7×10^7
Benzene	1.3×10^7
Ethyl Acetate	1.0×10^9
Ethyl Alcohol	7.4×10^8
Heptane	1.0×10^{13}
Hexane	1.0×10^{18}
Methyl Acetate	2.9×10^5
Methyl Alcohol	2.3×10^6
Methyl Ethyl Ketone	1.0×10^7
n-Butyl Alcohol	1.1×10^8
n-Octadecyl Alcohol	2.8×10^{10}
n-Propyl Alcohol	5.0×10^7
Sulfuric Acid	1.0×10^2
Toluene	1.0×10^{14}
Water	2.5×10^7

Source: British Industrial Solvents Division Distillers Company Ltd. "Interim Report on the Mitigation of Static in Storage Tanks" and "Table of Resistivities of Some Pure Liquids " by N. MacDonald, Shawinigan Resins Corp., September 22, 1955.

nozzle will be dissipated before the filling operation is started, and differences in potential between the nozzle and container are prevented from forming during the filling operation. See Figure 5-5A for methods of bonding containers and nozzles during container filling.

The relative static-generating tendencies of a number of petroleum products have been measured in laboratory tests. In general, aliphatic solvents and lower-boiling hydrocarbons exhibited lower charging tendencies than higher-boiling products. However, the charging tendency of any given product was found to vary widely from one sample to the next. Table 5-5A gives reported approximate resistivities of some chemicals. Variations in this table indicate the difficulties in making these measurements. Reciprocals of the resistivities will provide the values of conductivities.

The production of static electricity by hydrocarbons appears to depend primarily on the presence of trace components which decrease the electrical resistivity. It is not practicable to eliminate completely the production of static by purification of the product. In products of high resistivity, say exceeding about 10^{15} ohm-centimeter, generation is low because of the absence of such ionizable components. In products with increased concentration of ionizable trace components (lower resistivity) higher generation may occur, which is only partially offset by the fact that the leakage rate is higher. In products containing still more of these ionizable components, the resistance becomes so low that the charge leaks away as fast as formed, without producing significant charge. Thus, when the electrical resistivity exceeds about 10^{15} ohm-cm or is less than 10^{10} ohm-cm, net static generation or accumulation is negligible. Between these limits, the net charge generation increases, becoming a maximum when the electrical resistivity is about 10^{13} ohm-cm.

It should be emphasized that there is no predictable relationship between charging tendency and conductivity. Also, the proceeding paragraphs apply only to bulk charging, as distinguished from the charge separation that occurs when a stream of liquid (even a conducting liquid) breaks up into drops as it issues from a nozzle.

The resistivity of a liquid is a measure of its ability to hold a charge. The higher the resistivity, the greater the ability of the liquid to hold a charge. Liquids having resistivities higher than 10^{10} ohm-cm may accumulate a charge. If the resistivity of a liquid is less than 10^{10} ohm-cm, any charges that are generated will leak back together without accumulating to a hazardous potential. Under some conditions water is a good generator of static electricity but usually, due to its low values of resistivity and its wetting properties, the charges leak away as rapidly as produced and electrification is not observed.

Free Charges on Surface of Liquid

If an electrically charged liquid is poured, pumped, or otherwise transferred into a tank or container, the unit charges of similar sign within the liquid will be repelled from each other toward the outer surfaces of the liquid, including not only the surfaces in contact with the container walls but also the top surface adjacent to the air space, if any. It is this latter charge, often called the "surface charge," that is of most concern in many situations.

In most cases the container is of metal, and hence conducting. Two situations can occur, somewhat different with respect to protective measures, depending on whether the container is in contact with the earth or is insulated from it. These two situations are: (1) an ordinary storage tank resting on earth or concrete or other slightly conducting foundation, and (2) a tank truck on dry rubber tires.

In the first situation, the metal container is connected to ground through a resistance invariably found to be less than 1 megohm. The charges that reach the surfaces in contact with the vessel will reunite with charges of opposite sign which have been attracted there. During all of this process the tank and its contents, considered as a unit, are electrically neutral, i.e., the total charge in the liquid and on its surface is exactly equal and opposite to the charge on the tank shell. This charge on the tank shell is "bound" there, but gradually disappears as it reunites with the charge migrating through the liquid. The time required for this to occur is called "relaxation time." The relaxation time depends primarily on the resistivity of the liquid. It may be a fraction of a second or several minutes.

During all of this process, the tank shell is at ground potential. Externally, the container is electrically neutral. But internally, there may be differences of potential between the container wall and the fluid, lasting until charges on the fluid have gradually leaked off and reunited with the unlike charges on the tank walls.

If the potential difference between any part of the liquid surface and the metal tank shell should become high enough to cause ionization of the air, electrical breakdown may occur and a spark may jump to the shell. It is such a spark across the liquid surface which is the ignition hazard where flammable vapor-air mixtures are present. No bonding or grounding of the tank or container can remove this internal surface charge.

In the second situation, when the tank shell is highly insulated from the earth, the charge on the liquid surface attracts an equal and opposite charge to the inside of the container. This leaves a "free" charge on the outside of the tank, of the same sign as that in the liquid, and of the same magnitude. This charge can escape from the tank to the ground in the form of a spark. In filling a tank truck through an open dome, it is this source of sparking which is suspected of having caused some fires; in this case the spark jumps from the edge of the fill opening to the fill pipe which is at ground potential. This hazard can be controlled by bonding the container to the fill pipe before filling starts and until filling is complete. Usually any resistance path of less than 1 megohm will serve.

The foregoing discusses the distribution of charges delivered into a container with a flowing stream. Further generation or separation may occur within the container in several ways to produce a surface charge: (1) flow with splashing or spraying of the incoming stream, (2) disturbance of water bottom by the incoming stream, (3) bubbling of air or gas through a liquid, or (4) jet or propeller blending within the tank.

These charges on the surface of a liquid cannot be prevented by bonding or grounding. If there is likely to be a flammable mixture at the liquid surface, the charge can be rendered harmless by inerting the vapor space, by displacing part of the oxygen with a suitable inert gas, or by increasing the concentration of flammable gas in the vapor space to above the upper flammable limit with a gas, such as natural gas. In some cases, the risk can be controlled by avoiding operations that promote discharge of the surface charge, such as not introducing conductive gaging and sampling devices into the tank until any charge has dissipated.

It must be recognized that mists and foams of flammable and combustible liquids can be ignited by static sparks in much the same way dusts can be ignited. Ignition is possible even though the liquid in the mist is below its flash point.

E. Gases

Gases not contaminated with solid or liquid particles have been found to generate little, if any, electrification in their flow. When the flowing gas is contaminated with metallic oxides or scale particles, etc., or with liquid particles or spray, electrification may result. A stream of such particle-containing gas directed against a conductive body will charge the latter unless it is grounded or bonded to the discharge pipe.

When any gas is in a closed system of piping and equipment, the system need not be electrically conductive or electrically bonded.

Compressed air or steam containing particles of condensed water vapor often manifests strong electrification when escaping.

Carbon dioxide, discharged as a liquid from orifices under high pressure (where it immediately changes to a gas and "snow"), can result in static accumulations on the discharge device and the receiving container. This condition is not unlike the effect from contaminated compressed air or from steam flow where the contact effects at the orifice play a part in the static accumulation.

Hydrogen-air and acetylene-air mixtures may be ignited by a spark energy of as little as 0.017 millijoule. In the pure state, no static charges are generated by the flow of hydrogen. However, as gaseous hydrogen is commercially handled in industry, such as flowing through pipelines, discharging through valves at filling racks into pressure containers, or flowing out of containers through nozzles, the hydrogen may be found to contain particles of oxide carried off from the inside of pipes or containers. In this contaminated state, hydrogen may generate static.

The liquefied petroleum gases (LP-Gases) behave in a manner similar to uncontaminated gases in the gas phase and to contaminated gases in the mixed phase. Bonding is not required when LP-Gas vehicles are loaded or unloaded through closed connections so that there is no release of vapor at a point where a spark should occur, irrespective of whether the hose or pipe used is conducting or nonconducting. (A closed connection is one where contact is made before flow starts and is broken after flow has ended.)

F. Dusts and Fibers

As previously pointed out, the flow of a stream of gas containing small particles can result in a separation of electrons and the accumulation of a static charge on any insulated conductive body with which it comes in contact. Also, dust displaced from a surface on which it rests may develop a considerable charge. The ultimate charge depends on the inherent properties of the substance, size of particle, amount of surface contact, surface conductivity, gaseous breakdown, external field, and leakage resistance in a system. Greater charges develop from smooth than from rough surfaces, probably because of greater initial surface contact. Electrification develops during the first phase of separation. Subsequent impact of airborne particles on obstructions may affect their charge slightly, but if the impact surface becomes coated with the dust, this effect is slight.

Charge generation seldom occurs if both materials are good electrical conductors, but it is likely to occur with a conductor and a nonconductor or two nonconductors. When like materials are separated, as in dispersing quartz dust from a quartz surface, positive and negative charges are developed in the dispersed dust in about equal amounts to give a net zero charge. With materials differing in composition, a charge of one polarity may predominate in the dust. Each of the materials becomes equally charged but with opposite polarity. With a metallic and an insulating material, the former usually assumes positive and the latter a negative polarity.

Electrostatic charge generation in moving dust normally cannot be prevented. High humidity or grounding of the surface from which dust is dispersed will not eliminate the charge generation. The method of dispersion of the dust, the amount of energy expended in dispersal, the degree of turbulence, and the composition of the atmosphere usually do not affect the magnitude or distribution of the charges.

Not only can dust participate in the generation of static; it may also be the material ignited by static sparks. A suspension of finely divided combustible particles in air has much the same properties as a flammable gas-air mixture. It can burn to produce explosive effects. It has a lower flammable limit, although no strictly definable upper limit.

Ignition of Dust by Static Discharge

Dust clouds and layers of many combustible materials (with or without a volatile constituent) have been ignited experimentally by static discharge. In some instances, the charge was generated by movement of dust, in others by a static generator (Winshurst machine), or by electronic equipment. With dust clouds, it has been shown that a minimum dust concentration exists below which ignition cannot take place regardless of the energy of the spark. At the minimum dust concentration a relatively high energy is required for ignition. At higher dust concentrations (5 to 10 times the minimum), the energy required for ignition is at a minimum.

The energy stored in a capacitative circuit has been previously discussed, where it was tacitly assumed that all of this energy was released in the spark (zero circuit resistance). For the ignition of dusts it has been shown that a circuit resistance of 10,000 to 100,000 ohms may be required for optimum igniting power, meaning that some of the energy is dissipated in the circuit instead of being released in the spark, with corresponding increase in the total energy required.

A layer of combustible dust can be ignited by static discharge and will burn with a bright flash, glow, or, for some metallic dusts, with flame. Apparently, there is little correlation in the minimum energy required for ignition of dust layers and clouds. Layers of some metallic dusts such as aluminum, magnesium, titanium, and zirconium require less energy for ignition than carbonaceous materials.

Primary explosives, mercury fulminate, and tetryl, for example, are readily detonated by static spark discharge. Steps necessary to prevent accidents from static electricity in explosive manufacturing operations and storage areas vary considerably with the static sensitiveness of the material being handled.

In all instances in which static electricity was authentically established as the cause of ignition, the spark occurred between an insulated conductor and ground. It has not been verified experimentally that a dust cloud can be ignited by static discharge within itself.

The minimum electrical energies required to ignite some dust clouds and layers are listed in Table 3-8A. Note that many dusts can ignite with less energy than might be expended by a static discharge from machinery or from a human body.

G. Static Detectors

The following devices have an application in the measurement and determination of static electricity within the limitations of each device as described:

Gold Leaf Electroscopes: The gold leaf electroscope is a simple but sensitive device for the detection of electrostatic charges and is commonly used in classroom demonstrations. Comparatively rugged electroscopes are available today that employ foils or vanes less perishable than gold leaf but still sensitive enough to indicate charges of minimum sparking potential (350 V). To avoid damage and false deflections while handling, the instrument should be metal encased with small through-sight windows.

Neon Lamps: A small neon lamp or fluorescent tube will light up feebly when one terminal is grounded (or held in the hand) and the other makes contact with any sizeable conductor that carries a charge potential of 100 V or more. Like the electroscope, it gives but little quantitative information; however, inasmuch as it passes current it may give a rough idea of the rate at which charges are being produced in certain operations. Adjustable series-parallel groupings of such lamps and small capacitors can be arranged to give a semblance of quantitative information.

Electrostatic Voltmeters: These meters operate by electrostatic attraction between movable and stationary metal vanes. No current is passed to maintain deflection because one set of vanes (usually the stationary one) is very highly insulated. Small portable, accurately calibrated instruments are available in several ranges from 100 V to 5,000 V. This type of meter may be used for quantitative electrostatic analysis.

Vacuum Tube Electrometers: Vacuum tube electrometers are frequently used for laboratory and field investigations of static electricity. These instruments employ special tubes designed for high input resistance and low grid current and may be used in several ways. With a small antenna mounted on the grid terminal they are very suitable for detecting transient electrostatic charge effects; in the presence of a constant field the charge induced on the grid will leak off and the meter pointer will return to zero. However, as the rate of leakage is not high, the electrometer finds considerable use for "on the spot" static checks. Often electrometers are equipped with high resistance terminal shunts to convert them to current meters in the micro-micro-ampere range. They can thus be used in many applications to indicate the rate of charge development. A simple adaptation converts the instrument into a megohm meter as explained in the manufacturer's instruction manual.

Modern electrometers built around tubes of the screen-grid type with numbers such as 5803, 5886, 954, 959, 259B, and FP 54 are available commercially.

Field Mills (Generating Voltmeters): A "field mill" is a device that overcomes the serious limitation of the vacuum tube electrometer in that it provides a continuous indication of charge by providing its own transients in the form of continuous grid modulation. It can therefore "look" at a distant charge and determine its potential. The electrical field extending from the charge is chopped by a motor-driven variable condenser or window. The resulting pulsations are transformed, amplified, and rectified to give a dc meter deflection proportional to the strength of the field.

A similar instrument of suitable design can be immersed in a liquid, as in a pipe line, to measure charge density.

Formerly custom made devices, field mills are now commercially available.

Battery or line-power operated instruments must be judiciously handled in hazardous areas. A low resistance probe carelessly introduced into a suspected hazardous location might conceivably cause a spark and trigger an explosion. Test probes placed in ducts or regions containing explosive vapors or dust clouds should be highly insulated where they enter and be made of materials having a resistivity of over 10^4 ohm-cm in order to avoid condensed sparks to or from the probe itself; such resistance will not affect the readings appreciably.

H. Typical Static Electricity Terms

The following terms represent those commonly used when discussing static electricity. They are used throughout the foregoing text and in the text of NFPA No. 77, Recommended Practice on Static Electricity.

Capacitance: Electrons received by an electrically neutral body of material, such as a man, a car, an aircraft, raise the voltage at a rate depending upon the surface area and shape of the body. The voltage is determined by the surface characteristics (capacitance) of the body and the number of electrons on this surface. The larger the body the more electrons are needed to raise the voltage a specific amount; hence the higher the capacitance of this body.

Capacitance is measured in terms of "farads." Actually, the farad is so tremendous a number that it is easier to talk about millionths of a farad or "microfarads," and millionths of 1/1,000,000 of a farad or "micromicrofarads."

Charge: Measured in coulombs or fractions thereof, the static charge on a body is measured by the number of separated electrons *on* the body (negative charge) or the number of separated electrons *not on* the body (positive charge). Electrons cannot be destroyed; so obviously when an electron is removed from one body it must go to another body. Thus there are always equal and opposite charges produced [leaving behind a positive (+) void]. Since it would be awkward to say there are 6,240,000,000,000,000,000 electrons on a body, we say instead that the body has a charge of one "coulomb." A coulomb is simply a name for this specific quantity of electrons. In electrostatics an even more practical unit is a microcoulomb, representing a charge of 6.24×10^{12} electrons.

Current: Just as water flow is measured in terms of the amount of water that passes a certain point in a specific period of time (gallons per minute), so too is the flow of electrons measured by time. The flow is called current. The current is measured in terms of electrons per second, but since this number would be tremendously large, it is more convenient to measure current in terms of "coulombs per second." (See "charge" for a definition of coulomb.) It was difficult to keep saying "coulombs per second" so the word "ampere" was adopted from the French instead. Thus 15 "coulombs per second" became "15 amperes."

Energy Measured in Joules or Fractions Thereof: A spark is energy being expended. Energy is required to do work. The measure of energy takes several forms. Often it is physical energy, which is measured in foot-pounds or gram-centimeters. If it is heat energy, it is measured in British thermal units (Btu); and if it is electrical energy it is measured in watt-seconds or as more easily said, in joules. A joule is quite a bit of energy. It is the energy expended in one second by an electric current of one ampere in a resistance of one ohm, approximately .738 foot-pound. A joule is about equivalent to being hit on the jaw by a $4\frac{1}{2}$-lb sledge hammer that has traveled about a yard in one second of time. Static sparks do not usually have this "wallop" and hence their energy is usually measured in thousandths of a joule (a millijoule). A static spark needs a minimum amount of energy to cause trouble, as discussed in the text.

Exponentials: An exponential number is simply a superscript number such as the 2 in 10^2 and the 3 in 10^{-3}. The superscript indicates the number of times the base number is multiplied by itself.

Potential: Stored energy is able to do work. In hydraulics, pressure is the word used. In electricity, this ability is expressed in terms of the potential of doing work. Potential in electricity is measured in terms of "Volt," "kilovolts," or "millivolts." Potential or voltage is measured from a base point. This point can be any voltage but is usually ground which is theoretically zero voltage. When one point with a potential of "x" Volts to ground is compared with another point with a potential of "y" Volts to ground, then we say that a potential difference of "x−y" volts exists between the two. Then, when a point with a potential of 2,500 (+) V to ground is compared with a point with a potential of 1,500 (−) V to ground the potential difference is 4,000 V.

Resistance: Electrical current encounters difficulty in passing through an electrical circuit or conductor. This difficulty can be measured and is called resistance. In hydraulics, the resistance to water passing through a pipe is called friction loss and is measured in pounds lost in pressure over the length of the pipe. In electricity, resistance can be measured in terms of voltage drop over a part of the circuit but usually is measured in terms of "ohms" or "megohms." The resistance of a circuit in ohms is equal to the ratio of voltage in volts to current in amperes, i.e.,

$$\frac{10 \text{ V}}{1 \text{ amp}} = 10 \text{ ohms}, \quad \frac{1 \text{ V}}{1 \text{ } \mu \text{ amp}} = 1 \text{ megohm}.$$

Bibliography

NFPA Codes, Standards, and Recommended Practices (see the latest *NFPA Publications and Visual Aids Catalog* for availability of current editions of the following documents)

NFPA No. 30, Flammable and Combustible Liquids Code.

NFPA No. 385, Recommended Regulatory Standard for Tank Vehicles for Flammable and Combustible Liquids.

NFPA No. 407, Standard for Aircraft Fuel Servicing Including Aircraft Fueling Hose, Aircraft Fuel Servicing Vehicles and Airport Fixed Fueling Systems.

NFPA No. 77, Recommended Practice on Static Electricity.

Additional Readings

"Electrostatic Properties of Materials," (Std. No. 101B—Method 4046), January 1969, General Services Administration, Washington, D.C.

Beach, R., "Preventing Static-Electricity Fires, Part I," *Chemical Engineering*, Vol. 71, No. 26, Dec. 1964, pp. 73–8.

———, "Preventing Static-Electricity Fires, Part II," *Chemical Engineering*, Vol. 72, No. 1, Jan. 4, 1965, pp. 63–66.

———, "Preventing Static-Electricity Fires, Part III," *Chemical Engineering*, Vol. 72, No. 3, Feb. 1, 1965, pp. 85–88.

Bustin, W. M., Koszman, I., Tobye, I. T., "New Theory for Static Relaxation From High Resistivity Fuel," paper presented to a Special Joint Meeting of the Operating Practices Committee, Division of Refining, and the Central Committee on Safety and Fire Protection, Division of Science and Technology, Esso Research and Engineering Co., Houston, Tex., Oct. 1964.

Eichel, F. G., "Electrostatics," *Chemical Engineering*, March 1967, pp. 153–167.

Guest, P. G., Sikora, V. W., Lewis, B., "Static Electricity in Hospital Operating Suites: Direct and Related Hazards and Pertinent Remedies," Bulletin 520, 1953 (reprinted 1962), USDI Bureau of Mines, Washington, D.C.

Heidelberg, E., "The Ignition of Explosives Mixtures by Static Electricity," *Proceedings of the International Conference on the Safe Use of Electrical Energy in Spaces Where the Danger of an Explosion Exists*, Gottwaldov, West Germany, Paper No. 8, Oct. 1968.

Johnson, O. W., "The Hazard from Static Electricity on Moving Rubber-Tired Vehicles," *Fire Journal*, Vol. 61, No. 1, Jan. 1967, pp. 25–27.

"Let Static Flow," (Part II of article on static sparking), *Record*, Factory Mutual System, May-June 1966.

"Protection Against Ignitions Arising Out of Static, Lightning, and Stray Currents," RP 2003, 1967, American Petroleum Institute, Washington, D.C.

Martel, C. R., "An Evaluation of the Static Charge Reducer for Reducing Electrostatic Hazards in the Handling of Hydrocarbon Fuels," Technical Report AFAPLTR-70-22, July 1970, Air Force Aero Propulsion Laboratory, Wright-Patterson Air Force Base, Ohio.

"The NEC and You," *Fire Journal*, Vol. 66, No. 6, Nov. 1972, pp. 44–46.

"The NEC and You," *Fire Journal*, Vol. 67, No. 4, July 1973, pp. 29–31.

Sommer, E. C., "Preventing Electrostatic Ignitions," paper presented at API Central Committee on Safety and Fire Protection, Tulsa, Oklahoma, Apr. 1967.

Chapter 6

OXYGEN-ENRICHED ATMOSPHERES

Oxygen is a clear, colorless, odorless, and tasteless element found commonly in the gaseous state comprising about 21 percent of the earth's atmosphere. It is by far the most common oxidizing material. An (OEA) oxygen-enriched atmosphere is defined as any atmosphere in which the concentration of oxygen exceeds 21 percent by volume or the partial pressure of oxygen exceeds 160 torr (millimeters of mercury), or both (see Table 5-6A).

This chapter discusses the fire hazards associated with oxygen-enriched atmospheres and the methods that can be used to reduce them and to protect against them.

A. Fire Hazards in Oxygen-enriched Atmospheres

Fire, as a chemical reaction between a fuel and oxygen, is affected by the concentration of the reactants. The commonly encountered fire involves the 21 percent concentration of oxygen available from the atmosphere.

The degree of fire hazard of an oxygen-enriched atmosphere varies with the concentration of oxygen present, the concentration of any nonflammable (diluent) gas present, and the total pressure. An oxygen-enriched atmosphere, as defined, does not, however, necessarily result in an increased fire hazard. Certain oxygen-enriched atmospheres may exhibit combustion-supporting properties similar to ambient air; others are incapable of supporting the combustion of normally flammable materials at all, e.g., a 4 percent oxygen mixture in nitrogen or helium at a total pressure of 12 atm (atmospheres) will not support the combustion of paper even though it is an oxygen-enriched atmosphere because the oxygen partial pressure is 365 torr, while others accelerate the combustion of these materials, facilitate ignition, and, in general, increase the fire hazard.[1] Most commonly encountered oxygen-enriched atmospheres fall into this latter category.

The concentration of oxygen available in the atmosphere is generally sufficient for man's needs. However, oxygen-enriched atmospheres routinely exist, or are utilized intentionally, in medical practice, industry, underwater tunneling and caisson work, space and deep sea exploration, and in commercial and military aviation. They also are inherent to oxygen processing, transport, and storage facilities. In addition, oxygen-enriched atmospheres may develop inadvertently when oxygen or compressed air is transported, stored, or utilized.

Fire and explosions have occurred in many diverse circumstances involving both intentional and unintentional oxygen-enriched atmospheres. Among them are:

1. Oxygen production, transportation, and transfer.
   (a) Liquid oxygen truck delivery.
   (b) High pressure oxygen cylinder recharging.
   (c) Oxygen columns and compressors.
2. Medical.
   (a) Operating rooms.
   (b) Oxygen tents and infant incubators.
   (c) Oxygen respirators such as used by ambulances, rescue squads, fire and police, and near swimming pools.
   (d) Anesthesia machines.
3. Cutting and Welding.
   (a) Welding torch outfits.
   (b) Cutting torch outfits.
4. Industrial Processing (e.g., manufacture of gasoline, ammonia, methanol, acetylene, nitric acid, ethylene, etc.).
5. Hospital and laboratory supply systems.
6. Space and deep sea activities.
   (a) Missile fueling/defueling.
   (b) Rocket engine testing.
   (c) Manned space environment simulation/spacecraft testing.
   (d) Deep sea diving decompression chambers.
7. Aircraft oxygen systems.
   (a) Commercial and military aircraft onboard oxygen breathing systems.
   (b) Aircraft maintenance operations in the presence of oxygen.
8. Inadvertent substitution of oxygen for air or nitrogen.

Table 5-6A.

	Total Absolute Pressure		Altitude Above or Depth Below Sea Level	Partial Pressure of Oxygen if Atmosphere is Air	Concentration of Oxygen if Partial Pressure of Oxygen is 160 mm.Hg. or torr
Atmo-spheres	mm.Hg. or torr	psia	Feet Air or Sea Water	mm.Hg. or torr*	% by Volume
1/5	152	2.9	38,500	32	100.0†
1/3	253	4.9	27,500	53	62.7†
1/2	380	7.3	18,000	80	42.8†
2/3	506	9.8	11,000	106	31.3†
1	760	14.7	Sea Level	160	20.9
2	1,520	29.4	33	320†	10.5
3	2,280	44.1	66	480†	6.9
4	3,040	58.8	99	640†	5.2
5	3,800	73.5	132	800†	4.2

* This column shows the increased available oxygen in compressed air atmospheres.
† Oxygen-enriched atmosphere.

B. Ignition and Combustion of Materials in OEAs

Ignition and Combustion

The minimum energy which molecules (including those of fuels and oxygen) must possess to permit chemical interaction is referred to as the activation energy. If the energy released by this chemical reaction is sufficient to impart activation energy to other molecules on a self-sustaining basis, ignition has occurred. The rate of combustion depends upon the chemical nature and physical characteristics of the fuel and oxidant, their relative concentrations, environmental pressure and temperature, and other physical parameters, such as geometry and ventilation.

The likelihood of ignition and the rate of flame propagation of a combustible are greatly influenced by the oxygen content of the environment. In general (although not in every case), the greater the oxygen concentration, the lower the minimum ignition energy required for ignition, and the faster the flame spread rate. This is shown graphically in Figures 5-6A and 5-6B respectively.

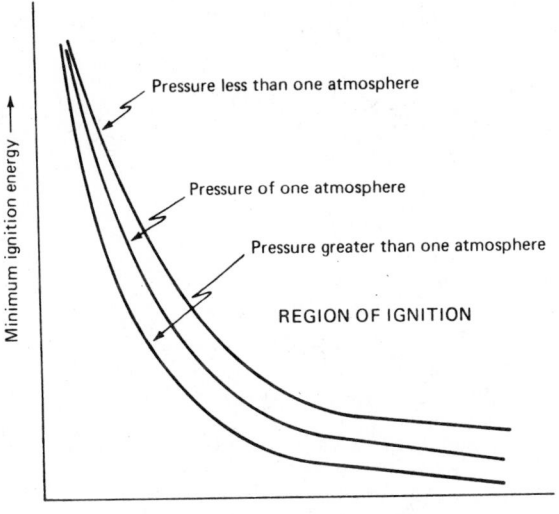

Fig. 5-6A. Minimum ignition energy behavior of combustibles in oxygen-diluent atmospheres at different pressures.[1]

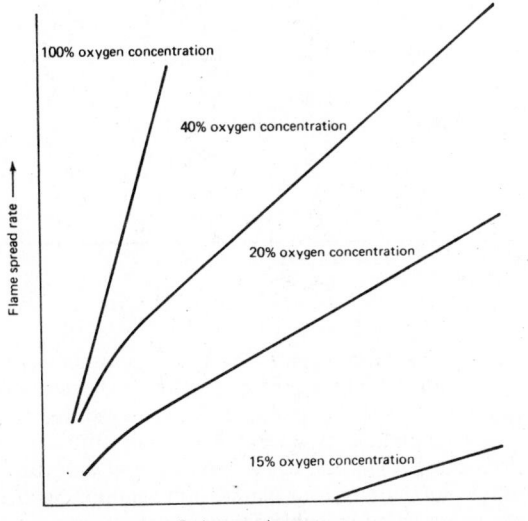

Fig. 5-6B. Effects of atmosphere oxygen content and environmental pressure on flame spread rate.[1]

Thus, in general, the fire hazard in an oxygen-enriched atmosphere is significantly greater than that in an ordinary atmosphere. Almost all materials are flammable in a pure oxygen environment, while increased oxygen concentration may change the classification of a material from the nonflammable to the flammable category.

Figures 5-6C and 5-6D depict three combustion zones for vertical filter paper strips in mixtures of oxygen-nitrogen and oxygen-helium respectively. Those combinations of oxygen concentrations and total pressure lying above the 0.21 atmosphere oxygen partial pressure isobar (lower dashed line) are, by definition, oxygen-enriched atmospheres, but they may be located in any of three zones: noncombustion; incomplete combustion; or complete combustion. Note that

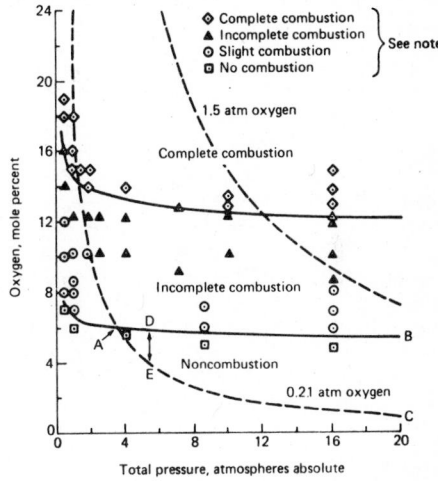

Fig. 5-6C. Illustration of varying degrees of combustion in an oxygen-nitrogen OEA.[2]

NOTE: Complete Combustion: The filter paper strip burns completely. Incomplete Combustion: The filter paper strip burns for a length greater than one centimeter from a resistance wire igniter, but the flame extinguishes itself before the strip is completely consumed. Slight Combustion: The filter paper strip flames or smolders but does not burn more than one centimeter from the resistance wire igniter. No combustion: No ignition.

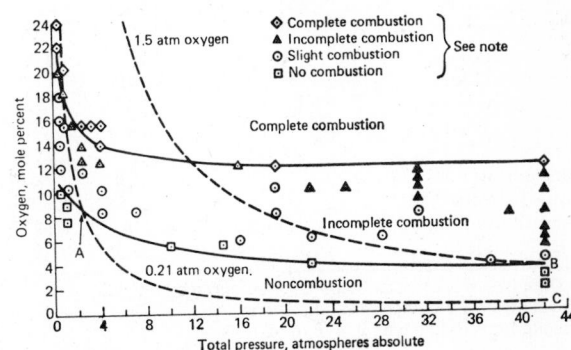

Fig. 5-6D. Illustration of varying degrees of combustion in an oxygen-helium OEA.[2]

NOTE: Complete Combustion: The filter paper strip burns completely. Incomplete Combustion: The filter paper strip burns for a length greater than one centimeter from a resistance wire igniter, but the flame extinguishes itself before the strip is completely consumed. Slight Combustion: The filter paper strip flames or smolders but does not burn more than one centimeter from the resistance wire igniter. No combustion: No ignition.

Table 5-6B. Ignition and Flammability Properties of Combustible Liquids and Gases in Air and Oxygen at Atmospheric Pressure

Combustible	Flash Point* Air °F	Min. Ign. Temperature† Air °F	Min. Ign. Temperature† Oxygen °F	Min. Ign. Energy‡ Air mj	Min. Ign. Energy‡ Oxygen mj	Flammability Limits§ Vol. % Air LFL	Air UFL	Oxygen LFL	Oxygen UFL
Hydrocarbon Fuels									
Methane	Gas	999	—	0.30	0.003	5.0	15	5.1	61
Ethane	Gas	959	943	0.25	0.002	3.0	12.4	3.0	66
n-Butane	−76	550	532	0.25	0.009	1.8	8.4	1.8	49
n-Hexane	25	437	424	0.288	0.006	1.2	7.4	1.2	52*
n-Octane	56	428	406	—	—	0.8	6.5	≤0.8	—
Ethylene	Gas	914	905	0.07	0.001	2.7	36	2.9	80
Propylene	Gas	856	793	0.28	—	2.4	11	2.1	53
Acetylene	Gas	581	565	0.017	0.0002	2.5	100	≤2.5	100
Gasoline (100/130)	−50	824	600	—	—	1.3	7.1	≤1.3	—
Kerosene	100	440	420	—	—	0.7	5	0.7	—
Anesthetic Agents									
Cyclopropane	Gas	932	849	0.18	0.001	2.4	10.4	2.5	60
Ethyl Ether	−20	380	360	0.20	0.0013	1.9	36	2.0	82
Vinyl Ether	<−22	680	331	—	—	1.7	27	1.8	85
Ethylene	Gas	914	905	0.07	0.001	2.7	36	2.9	80
Ethyl Chloride	−58	961	874	—	—	4.0	14.8	4.0	67
Chloroform			—Nonflammable—						
Nitrous Oxide			—Nonflammable—						
Solvents									
Methyl Alcohol	54	725	—	0.14	—	6.7	36	≤6.7	93
Ethyl Alcohol	55	689	—	—	—	3.3	19	≤3.3	—
n-Propyl Alcohol	59	824	622	—	—	2.2	14	≤2.2	—
Glycol	232	752	—	—	—	3.5*	—	≤3.5	—
Glycerol	320	698	608	—	—	—	—	—	—
Ethyl Acetate	24	800	—	0.48	—	2.2	11	≤2.2	—
n-Amyl Acetate	76	680	453	—	—	1.0	7.1	≤1.0	—
Acetone	0	869	—	1.15	0.0024	2.6	13	≤2.6	60#
Benzene	12	1040	—	0.22	—	1.3	7.9	≤1.3	30
Naphtha (Stoddard)	~100	~450	~420	—	—	1.0	6	≤1.0	—
Toluene	40	896	—	2.5	—	1.2	7.1	≤1.2	—
Butyl Chloride	20	464	455	0.332	0.007#	1.8	10	1.7	52#
Methylene Chloride	—	1139	1123	—	0.137	15.9#	19.1#	11.7*	68
Ethylene Chloride	56	889	878	2.37	0.011#	6.2	16	4.0	67.5
Trichloroethane	—	856	784	—	0.092	6.3#	13#	5.5*	57#
Trichloroethylene	90	788	745	—	18*	10.5*	41*	7.5	91#
Carbon Tetrachloride			—Nonflammable—						
Miscellaneous Combustibles									
Acetaldehyde	−17	347	318	0.38	—	4.0	60	4.0	93
Acetic Acid	104	869	—	—	—	5.4#	—	≤5.4	—
Ammonia	Gas	1204	—	>1000	—	15.0	28	15.0	79
Aniline	168	1139	—	—	—	1.2#	8.3	≤1.2	—
Carbon Monoxide	Gas	1128	1090	—	—	12.5	74	≤12.5	94
Carbon Disulfide	−22	248	225	0.015	—	1.3	50	≤1.3	—
Ethylene Oxide	<0	804	—	0.062	—	3.6	100	≤3.6	100
Propylene Oxide	−35	—	—	0.14	—	2.8	37	≤2.8	—
Hydrogen	Gas	1022	1008	0.017	0.0012	4.0	75	4.0	95
Hydrogen Sulfide	Gas	500	428	0.077	—	4.0	44	≤4.0	—
Bromochloromethane	—	842	694	—	—	NF‖	NF	10.0	85
Bromotrifluoromethane	Gas	>1100	1215	—	—	NF	NF	NF	NF
Dibromodifluoromethane	Gas	930	847	—	—	NF	NF	29.0	80

* Data from References 8 and 9; open cup method.
† Data from References 10, 11, 12 and 14.
‡ Data from References 3, 4, 5, 6 and 10.

§ Data from References 7, 10, 11 and 14.
# Data at 200°F.
‖ NF—No flammable mixtures found in Reference 11.

there are certain oxygen-enriched atmospheres which do not produce an increased fire hazard.

Behavior of Materials in OEAs

Since combustible materials ignite more easily and burn more rapidly in an oxygen-enriched atmosphere than in a normal atmosphere, the careful selection of materials for use in association with an oxygen-enriched atmosphere can do much to reduce the fire hazard.

Combustible Liquids and Gases: For combustible liquids and gases, the potential fire or explosion hazard may be defined in part by the temperature required for the formation of flammable mixtures, the temperature and energy requirements for ignition of the mixture, and the critical fuel concentration (limits) for flame propagation. Such information is presented in Table 5-6B for various representative liquid and gas combustibles in oxygen or air atmospheres, or in both.

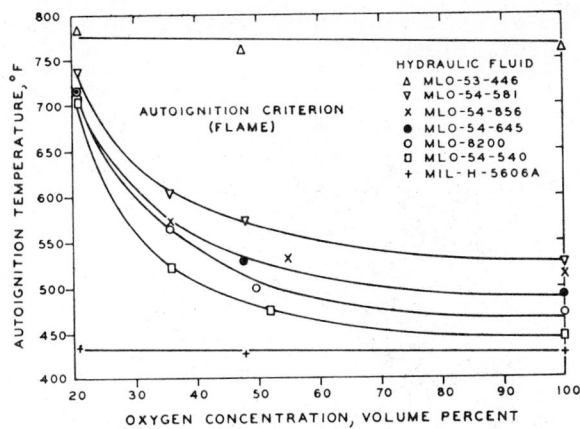

Fig. 5-6E. Minimum autoignition temperatures of seven hydraulic fluids at atmospheric pressure in various oxygen-nitrogen atmospheres (200-cc Pyrex vessel).[13]

The minimum autoignition temperatures (AITs) of most hydrocarbon fuels, solvents, and anesthetic agents fall between 400° and 1,000°F in air at one atmosphere pressure (see Table 5-6B). Although the autoignition temperature tends to be less in oxygen than in air, the differences are not great for many hydrocarbons. In the case of lubricants and hydraulic fluids, however, the effect of oxygen concentration on the AIT tends to be greater than observed for the neat hydrocarbons in Table 5-6B. Figure 5-6E shows that the AITs for five of the hydraulic fluids decrease between 200° and 300°F when the oxygen concentration is increased from 21 to 100 percent.

A correlation of AIT with oxygen partial pressure is shown in Figure 5-6F for several combustible fluids at various pressures and oxygen concentrations.

The limits of flammability are of interest also. Although most lower limits in oxygen do not differ greatly from those in air, the upper limits are usually much higher in oxygen, and tend to be above 50 percent for many materials. Furthermore, some materials, such as the halogenated materials bromochloromethane and dibromodifluoromethane, are

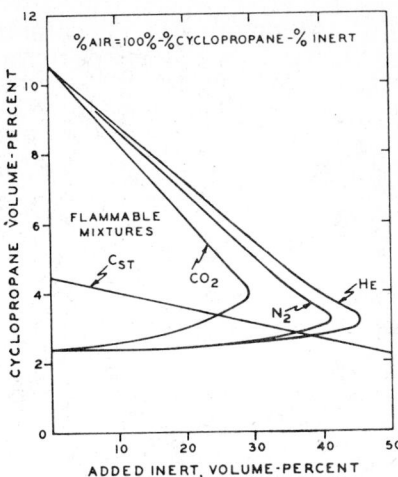

Fig. 5-6G. Limits of flammability of cyclopropane-carbon dioxide-air, cyclopropane-nitrogen-air, and cyclopropane-helium-air mixtures at 25°C and atmospheric pressure.[14] (C_{st} = Stoichiometric composition = line defining amount of combustible vapor required for complete combustion.)

flammable in oxygen over a wide range of mixture compositions, whereas they are not reported as being flammable in air. Of the halogenated solvents, trichloroethylene displays the widest range of flammability in both air and oxygen, although elevated temperatures are necessary.

Nonflammable or inert gases are frequently used for explosion prevention. In general, most flammable liquids and gases can be expected to form flammable mixtures over a wide range of oxygen or oxygen-diluent concentrations. Nitrogen is more effective than helium, but not as effective as carbon dioxide or water vapor. Figures 5-6G and 5-6H show the complete range of flammable mixture compositions that may be expected with a hydrocarbon (cyclopropane) in air or oxygen, and various inert gases at atmospheric pressure.

The minimum oxygen percentage below which most hydrocarbon mixtures are not flammable is about 14 percent with carbon dioxide, and 10 to 12 percent with nitrogen. Corresponding values for hydrogen and carbon monoxide are 6 percent and 5 to 5.5 percent respectively.[1]

Combustible Solids: For combustible solids, ignition and flammability data for any given material are dependent on

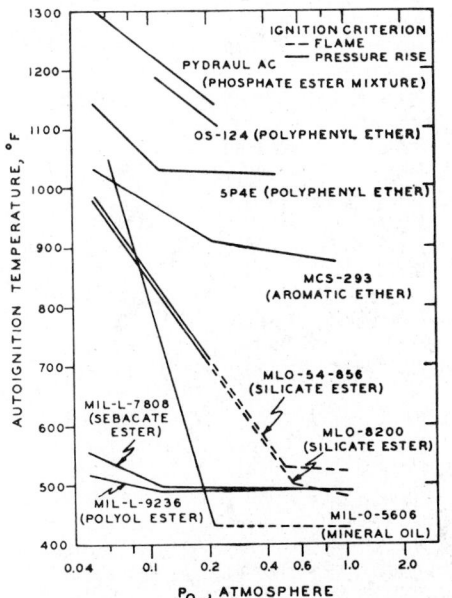

Fig. 5-6F. Variation of minimum autoignition temperature with oxygen partial pressure (PO_2) for various lubricants.[13]

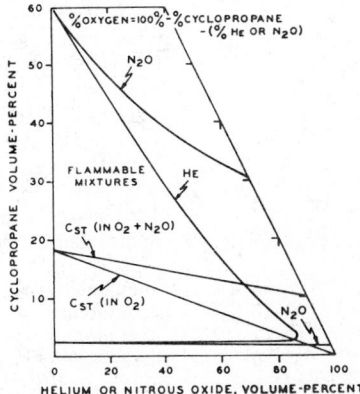

Fig. 5-6H. Limits of flammability of cyclopropane-helium-oxygen and cyclopropane-nitrous oxide-oxygen mixtures at 25°C and atmospheric pressure.[14] (C_{st} = Stoichiometric composition = line defining amount of combustible vapor required for complete combustion.

Table 5-6C. Minimum Hot Plate Ignition Temperatures of Six Combustible Materials in Oxygen-Nitrogen Mixtures at Various Total Pressures*

| Material | Oxidant | Ignition Temperature, °C | | | |
| | | Total Pressure, atmospheres | | | |
		1	2	3	6
Cotton sheeting	Air	465	440(425)‡	385	365
	42% O_2, 58% N_2	390	370	355	340
	100% O_2	360	345	340	325
Cotton sheeting treated†	Air	575	520(510)	485(350)	370(325)
	42% O_2, 58% N_2	390(350)	335	315	295
	100% O_2	310	—	300	285
Conductive rubber sheeting	Air	480	395	370	375
	42% O_2, 58% N_2	430	365	350	350
	100% O_2	360	—	345	345
Paper drapes	Air	470	455	425	405
	42% O_2, 58% N_2	430	—	400	370
	100% O_2	410	—	365	340
Nomex fabric	Air	>600	>600	>600	560
	42% O_2, 58% N_2	550	540	510	495
	100% O_2	520	505	490	470
Polyvinyl chloride sheet	Air	>600	—	495	490
	42% O_2, 58% N_2	575	—	370	350
	100% O_2	390	—	350	325

* See Reference 31.
† Cotton sheeting treated with Du Pont X-12 fire retardant; amount of retardant equal to 12 percent of cotton specimen weight.
‡ Values in parentheses indicate temperature at which material glowed.

Table 5-6D. Flame Resistance of Materials Held Vertically at One Atmosphere Pressure in O_2/N_2 Mixtures*

| NRL Sample Number | Material | Combustion in O_2/N_2 Mixtures | | |
		21% O_2	31% O_2	41% O_2
FM-1	Rosin-impregnated paper	Burned	—	—
FM-3	Cotton terry cloth	Burned	—	—
FM-28	Cotton cloth, white duck	Burned	—	—
FM-4	Cotton terry cloth, Roxel-treated	No	No	Burned
FM-5	Fleece-backed cotton cloth, Roxel-treated	Surface only	Burned	Burned
FM-14	Cotton, O.D. Sateen, Roxel-treated	No	Burned	—
FM-15	Cotton, green whipcord, Roxel-treated	No	Burned	—
FM-16	Cotton white duck, Roxel-treated	No	Burned	—
FM-17	Cotton, King Kord, Roxel-treated	No	Burned	—
FM-29	Cotton white duck, treated with 30% boric acid-70% borax	No	Burned	Burned
FM-30	Cotton terry cloth, treated with 30% boric acid-70% borax	No	Burned	Burned
FM-6	Fire-resistant cotton ticking	No	Burned	—
FM-7	Fire-resistant foam rubber	No	No	Burned
FM-9	Nomex temperature-resistant Nylon	No	Burned	—
FM-10	Teflon fabric	No	No	No
FM-11	Teflon fabric	No	No	No
FM-12	Teflon fabric	No	No	No
FM-13	Teflon fabric	No	No	No
FM-19	Verel fabric	No	Burned	Burned
FM-22	Vinyl-backed fabric	No	Burned	Burned
FM-23	Omnicoated Du Pont high-temperature fabric	No	Burned*	Burned
FM-24	Omnicoated glass fabric	No	No	Burned†
FM-20	Glass fabric, fine weave	No	No	No
FM-21	Glass fabric, knit weave	No	No	No
FM-25	Glass fabric (coarse weave)	No	No	No
FM-26	Glass fabric (coarse weave)	No	No	No
FM-27	Aluminized asbestos fabric	No	No	Burned
FM-32	Rubber from aviator oxygen mask	Burned	Burned	Burned
FM-33	Fluorolube grade 362	No	No	No‡
FM-34	Belco no-flame grease	No	No	No‡

* See Reference 32.　　† Burned only over igniter.　　‡ White smoke only.

many variables: e.g., the specimen's physical characteristics; the ignition source; the orientation of the specimen; the environmental characteristics; ventilation characteristics; inerting diluents; etc. In general, however, ignition temperatures are lower and flame resistance is less in an oxygen-enriched atmosphere than in a normal atmosphere (see Tables 5-6C and 5-6D).

Additionally, the rate of flame spread increases with increase in the oxygen concentration at constant pressure or with increase in the total pressure at a constant percentage of oxygen (increased oxygen partial pressure). Various flame spread rate data are given in Tables 5-6E, 5-6F and 5-6G.

The rate at which flame spreads under a given set of circumstances in an OEA is the most important single property of a solid material from the fire hazard point of view.[1] Several methods for determining flame spread rate characteristics of materials are in use including the following American Society for Testing and Materials methods:

1. ASTM E84-70, Test for Surface Burning Characteristics of Building Materials.

2. ASTM E162-67, Test for Surface Flammability of Materials Using a Radiant Heat Source.

3. ASTM D568-72, Test for Flammability of Flexible Plastic.

4. ASTM D1230-61, Test for Flammability of Clothing Textiles.

5. ASTM D2863-74, Test for Flammability of Plastics Using the Oxygen Index Method.

Selected materials are tested under conditions of intended use prior to utilization in oxygen-enriched atmospheres.

C. Design of Systems for OEAs

Systems Design

Fire hazard considerations in the design of systems associated with oxygen-enriched atmospheres, e.g., heating, ventilating and air conditioning, hydraulic services, gas and compressed air supplies, suction apparatus, both power and electronic electrical systems, etc., include:

1. Materials of construction characteristics (flame spread rate, ignition susceptibility).

2. Risk of fire initiation (expectancy).

3. Presence of potential energy, in the form of compressed gas, etc.

4. Personnel escape paths from occupied areas.

In addition to evaluating the fire-safe characteristics of all materials involved in oxygen-enriched environments under end-use performance conditions, oxygen service durability is evaluated by accelerated time tests for deterioration, and by high energy tests for degradation.

The acceptability of candidate materials for oxygen-enriched atmosphere systems applications are, in part, based on data developed by tests such as: (1) flash and fire points, (2) upward/downward combustion propagation rates; (3) calorific fuel values (heat of combustion); (4) electrical wire insulation, coating, and accessory flammability tests; (5) electrical overload and hot-wire ignition tests; and (6) odor toxicity, off-gassing, etc.

Electrical equipment used in oxygen-enriched atmospheres is limited to that approved at the maximum anticipated oxygen pressure and concentrations. Since most metals burn freely in oxygen-enriched atmospheres, electrical contacts which do not burn in normal atmospheres could burn away and initiate insulation fires in an oxygen-enriched atmosphere.

Some "fire stopping" techniques which may be considered in the design of a system to minimize ignition potential and fire-spread in an oxygen-enriched atmosphere are:

1. Avoidance of mass concentration of combustible materials near potential heat or ignition sources.

2. Spatial separation and configuration to minimize or eliminate flame propagation paths.

3. "Thermal damping" by judicious placement of fire resistant heat sink masses.

4. "Flash-over" barriers.

5. "Sealed packaging," e.g., inerted compartmentation, fire-resistant encapsulation, etc.

6. Automatic fire monitoring, e.g., infrared thermography, etc.

D. Fire Extinguishment in OEAs

Fire extinguishing systems for use in oxygen-enriched atmospheres face new requirements in addition to those imposed on conventional systems because of ignition susceptibility, increased flame spread rate, increased burning intensity, and flammability of normally nonflammable materials. In general, these new requirements cannot be satisfied by the simple extension of classic extinguishment techniques. In addition to special instruction and training of emergency personnel, extinguishing agents and systems must be specially selected.

In view of the increased burning rates of most common materials in oxygen-enriched atmospheres, fire extinguishants should act rapidly to be effective. To protect occupants of affected areas, they should be inherently nontoxic and should not produce significant amounts of toxic extinguishing agent decomposition products.

Water has been shown to be an effective extinguishing agent in oxygen-enriched atmospheres when applied in sufficient quantities.[17, 24, 27] Water at a spray density of 50 mm/min. (1¼ gpm per cu ft) applied for 2 min. will extinguish cloth burning in 100 percent oxygen at a pressure of

Table 5-6E. Effect of Oxygen and Storage in Oxygen on Flame Spread Rates over Various Materials (Edges not Inhibited)*

Material†	In air	Flame spread rate (in./sec.) In 258 mm. Hg. oxygen Before storage	After 30-day storage
Butyl rubber	0.006	0.40 ± 0.04	0.31 ± 0.04
Canvas duck	NP‡	0.25 ± 0.05	—
Cellulose acetate	0.012	0.28 ± 0.12	0.24 ± 0.12
Kel-F	NI	NI	NI
Natural rubber	0.010	0.61 ± 0.05	0.61 ± 0.08
Neoprene rubber	NI	0.32 ± 0.04	0.25 ± 0.05
Nylon 101	NI	0.19 ± 0.05	0.15 ± 0.01
Plexiglas	0.005	0.35 ± 0.01	0.24 ± 0.01
Polyethylene	0.014	0.25 ± 0.05	0.36 ± 0.06
Polypropylene	0.010	0.35 ± 0.01	0.36 ± 0.12
Polystyrene	0.032	0.80 ± 0.20	0.51 ± 0.01
Polyvinyl chloride	NI§	0.10 ± 0.01	0.06 ± 0.01
Silicone rubber	NI	0.14 ± 0.01	0.14 ± 0.01
Teflon	NI	NI	NI
Viton A	NI	0.003 ± 0.002	0.01 ± 0.005

* See Reference 15.
† All samples except canvas duck, 3 by ½ by ⅛ in.: canvas duck, 3 by ½ by 1/20 in.
‡ NP—No sustained propagation of flame.
§ NI—No ignition of material.

1 atm.[17] The method of application of the water to the fire is all-important. Extinguishing systems using water must be carefully designed so that all the protected space is covered by the minimum spray density and distributed to a depth sufficient to extinguish stratified fires in nonhomogeneous materials, e.g., layers of cloth in clothing.

Several halogenated hydrocarbons have been found useful for extinguishing fires in normal atmospheres. Table 5-6H indicates their behavior in pure oxygen as well as their toxicity ratings as given by the Underwriters Laboratories, Inc. (Toxicity ratings for undecomposed vapor range from 1, the most toxic, to 6, the least hazardous).

To date, bromotrifluoromethane (Halon 1301) appears to be potentially useful in oxygen-enriched atmospheres. Limited testing has shown that it will extinguish fires in pure oxygen when used at 50 percent concentration, and in compressed air at 5 percent by volume.[28] Generally, it is effective against few truly deep-seated fires in oxygen-enriched atmospheres. NFPA No. 12A, "Halogenated Fire Extinguishing Agent Systems—Halon 1301" states that concentrations

greater than 10 percent are not used in normally occupied areas, and, even then, are used only where evacuation can be accomplished immediately.[29]

Available data regarding the effectiveness of carbon dioxide is inconclusive.

High expansion foam has been shown to be effective and that respiration in the foam atmosphere is possible.[30] However, the applicability of this agent to each particular candidate system must be evaluated separately with regard to available space and required time.

Little or no data are available on the use of low-expansion foam or dry chemical in oxygen-enriched atmosphere fires. No reliance should be placed on ordinary fire blankets made of wool or asbestos (with an organic binder).[1]

Because of rapid flame spread, fire extinguishing systems in oxygen-enriched atmospheres must be capable of fast automatic actuation by fire detectors, as well as by manual actuation. Fixed systems utilize an extinguishing agent acceptable for use on fires in oxygen-enriched atmospheres and automatic activation occurs in less than one second of

Table 5-6F. Effect of Oxygen and Storage in Oxygen on Flame Spread Rates over Various Space Cabin Materials (Edges not Inhibited)*

Material	In air	Before storage	After 30-day storage
Aluminized Mylar tape	—	1.95	—
Aluminized vinyl tape	NI†	3.1 ± 0.4	3.0 ± 0.4
Asbestos insulating tape	NI	0.08	0.05
Chapstick	NI	1.82	—
Cotton shirt fabric	NP‡	1.50 ± 0.05	2.10 ± 0.3
Electrical insulating resin	NI	0.27	0.20
Electrical terminal board	NI	0.06 ± 0.01	0.06 ± 0.01
Fiberglas insulating tape	NI	4.2 ± 0.6	2.0 ± 0.8
Foam cushion material	0.19	12.4	11.3
Foamed insulation	0.002	2.2 ± 0.2	3.0 ± 0.3
Food packet, aluminized paper	NI	0.28 ± 0.05	0.26 ± 0.05
Food packet, brown aluminum	NI	0.7 ± 0.30	0.8 ± 0.20
Food packet, plastic	0.33	0.55	0.47
Glass wool	NI	NI	NI
Masking tape	0.17	1.82	—
Paint, 3-M velvet	NI	0.15 ± 0.01	0.31 ± 0.02
Paint, Capon ivory	NI	0.38 ± 0.04	0.35 ± 0.02
Paint, Pratt & Lambert, grey	NI	0.60 ± 0.2	0.24
Pump oil	NI	0.89	—
Refrigeration oil	NI	0.82 ± 0.07	—
Rubber tubing	0.03	0.24	0.25 ± 0.05
Silicone grease	NI	0.92	—
Solder, rosin core	NI	0.18	0.25
Sponge, washing	0.07	8.1 ± 0.1	10 ± 2
Teflon pipe sealing tape	NI	NI	NI
Teflon tubing	NI	NI	NI
Tygon tubing	0.18	0.50 ± 0.05	0.52 ± 0.05
Wire, Mil W76B, orange	NI	0.57 ± 0.05	0.54
Wire, Mil W76B, blue	NI	—	0.57
Wire, Mil W76B, yellow	NI	—	0.54
Wire, Mil W16878, green	NI	NI	NI
Wire, Mil W16878, black	NI	NI	NI
Wire, Mil W16878, yellow	NI	NI	NI
Wire, Mil W16878, white	NI	NI	NI
Wire, misc., white, 3/32	NI	0.33	0.25
Wire, misc., black, 3/16	NI	—	0.40
Wire, misc., brown, 7/32	NI	0.51 ± 0.05	—
Wire, misc., yellow, 7/64	NI	0.89	—
Wire, misc., yellow, 5/32	NI	0.41	—

* See Reference 15. † NI—No ignition of material. ‡ NP—No sustained propagation of flame.

Table 5-6G. Typical Measured Burning Rates for Strips of Filter Paper at 45° Angle*

Total pressure, atm. abs.			Burn Rate, cm/sec					
Total pressure, atm. abs.			0.21	0.53	1.00	4.03	7.06	10.09
feet of sea water			—	—	0	100	200	300
Gas Composition (dry basis)								
%O₂	%N₂†	%He						
99.6	0.4	0.0	2.32	3.13	4.19	#	#	#
50.3	49.7	0.0	1.13	1.44	2.36	3.72	5.10	6.34
			1.17			3.77	4.06	
20.95‡	79.05	0.0	§	0.80	1.17	1.82	2.80	3.13
					1.17	1.78	2.28	3.25
					1.10			
49.5	0.0	50.5	1.24	1.87	2.96	4.06	4.90	#
				1.90	2.89		4.82	
					2.89			
20.3	0.0	79.7	§	§	§	2.23	2.61	2.49
47.0	24.6	28.4	#	#	2.74	3.66	4.41	5.53
					2.68		4.64	6.78
20.9	39.6	39.5	#	#	1.38	2.28	2.71	3.72
					1.38	2.28	2.83	3.13
					1.35	1.97	2.74	3.56
					1.27	2.28		3.33
					1.72	1.81		3.00

* See Reference 16.
† Includes any argon that was present.
‡ Compressed air.
§ Sample would not burn, even with brightly glowing igniter grid.
# No run was made under these conditions.

Table 5-6H. Behavior of Halons in Pure Oxygen

Compound	Halon No.	Toxicity*	Behavior in Pure Oxygen†
Carbon tetrachloride, CCl₄	104	3	
Methyl bromide, CH₃Br	1001	2	Flammable
Chlorobromomethane, CH₂BrCl	1011	3	Flammable, decomposes
Dibromodifluoromethane, CBr₂F₂	1202	4	Flammable
Bromochlorodifluoromethane, CBrClF₂	1211	5	Nonflammable over tested concentration (14-95%)
Bromotrifluoromethane, CF₃Br	1301	6	Nonflammable over tested range (12-98%)

* See Reference 25.   † See Reference 26.

the perception of sensible flame development. In addition to the automatic fixed system in occupied areas, a manually operated water hose not less than $\frac{1}{2}$-in. ID, and with an effective nozzle pressure not less than 50 psi above the ambient pressure, is usually provided.[1]

SI Units

The following conversion factors are given as a convenience in converting to SI units the English units used in this chapter.

$$1 \text{ psi} = 6.895 \text{ kPa}$$
$$\tfrac{5}{9}(°F-32) = °C$$

Bibliography

References Cited

[1] "Manual on Fire Hazards in Oxygen-Enriched Atmospheres," NFPA No. 53M, 1974, National Fire Protection Association, Boston.

[2] Dorr, V. A., "Fire Studies in Oxygen-Enriched Atmospheres," *Journal of Fire and Flammability*, Vol. 1, 1970, pp. 91–106.

[3] Lewsi, B. and Von Elbe, G., *Combustion Flames and Explosion of Gases*, Academic Press, New York, 1961, pp. 323–346.

[4] "Basic Considerations in the Combustion of Hydrocarbon Fuels with Air," NACA Report 1300, 1957, National Advisory Committee for Aeronautics, Washington, D.C.

[5] Blanc, M. V., et al., "Ignition of Explosive Gas Mixtures by Electric Sparks. I—Minimum Ignition Energies and Quenching Dis- tances of Methane, Oxygen and Inert Gases," *Journal of Chemical Physics*, Vol. 15, 1947, p. 798.

[6] Calcote, H. F., et al., "Spark Ignition," *Industrial and Engineering Chemistry*, Vol. 44, No. 11, Nov. 1952, p. 2656.

[7] Fenn, J. B., "Lean Flammability Limit and Minimum Spark Ignition Energy," *Industrial and Engineering Chemistry*, Vol. 43, No. 12, Dec. 1951, p. 2865.

[8] "Fire Hazard Properties of Flammable Liquids, Gases, and Volatile Solids," NFPA No. 325M, 1969, National Fire Protection Association, Boston.

[9] Humphrey, H. B. and Morgis, G., "Safety with Solvents, USDI Bureau of Mines Information Circular 7757, Aug. 1957, Washington, D.C.

[10] Litchfield, E. L.; Kuchta, J. M.; and Furno, A. L. "Flammability of Propellant Combinations," USDI Bureau of Mines Explosives Research Report 3997, Oct. 30, 1966, Washington, D.C.; USDI Bureau of Mines Research Report 3958, June 30, 1965, Washington, D.C.

[11] Perlee, H. E.; Martindill, G. H.; and Zabetakis, M. G., "Flammability Characteristics of Selected Halogenated Hydrocarbons," USDI Bureau of Mines RI 6748, 1966, Washington, D.C.

[12] Scott, G. S.; Jones, G. W.; and Scott, F. E., "Determination of Ignition Temperatures of Combustible Liquids and Gases," *Analytical Chemistry*, Vol. 20, Mar. 1948, p. 238.

[13] Kuchta, J. M. and Cato, R. J., "Review of Ignition and Flammability Properties of Lubricants," Air Force Aero Propulsion Laboratory Technical Report AFAPL-TR-67-126, Jan. 1968, Wright Patterson Air Force Base, Ohio.

[14] Zabetakis, M. G., "Flammability Characteristics of Combustible Gases and Vapors," USDI Bureau of Mines Bulletin 627, 1965, Washington, D.C.

[15] Hugget, C., et al., "The Effects of 100% Oxygen at Reduced Pressure on the Ignitibility and Combustibility of Materials," SAM-TR-65-78, Dec. 1965, Brooks Air Force Base, Texas.

[16] Cook, G. A.; Meierer, R. E.; and Shields, B. M., "Screening of Flame Resistant Materials and Comparison of Helium with Nitrogen for Use in Diving Atmospheres," First Summary Report on Combustion Safety in Diving Atmosphere, Mar. 31, 1967, U.S. Department of the Navy, Office of Naval Research and Naval Ship Systems Command, Washington, D.C.

[17] Denison, D. and Cresswell, A. W., "The Fire Risks to Man of Oxygen and Rich Gas Environments," IAM Report No. 320, Apr. 1965 and Report No. 343, Sept. 1965, Civil Aeromedical Institute, Aeronautical Center, Oklahoma City, Okla.

[18] Eggleston, L. A., "Evaluation of Fire Extinguishing Systems for Use in Oxygen Rich Atmospheres," Final Report prepared for Aerospace Medical Division, Brooks Air Force Base, May 18, 1967, Southwest Research Institute, San Antonio, Texas.

[19] Turner, H. L. and Segal, L., "Fire Behavior and Protection in Hyperbaric Chambers," *Fire Technology*, Vol. 1, No. 4, Nov. 1965, pp. 269–277.

[20] Segal, L., et al., "Fire Suppression in Hyperbaric Chambers," *Fire Journal*, Vol. 60, No. 3, May 1966, pp. 17–18.

[21] Ault, W. E. and Carter, D. L., "The Influence of Hyperbaric Chamber Pressure on Water Spray Patterns," *Fire Journal*, Vol. 61, No. 6, Nov. 1967, p. 48.

[22] Harter, J. V., "The Problem of Fire at High Pressure," *Proceedings of the Third Symposium on Underwater Physiology*, ed. by C. J. Lambertsen, The Williams and Wilkins Company, Baltimore, 1967, pp. 76–77.

[23] *Proceedings of Fire Hazards and Extinguishment Conference*, Aerospace Medical Division, Brooks Air Force Base, Texas, May 23, 1967.

[24] Botteri, B. P., "Fire Protection in Oxygen Enriched Atmospheres," *Fire Journal*, Vol. 62, No. 1, Jan. 1967, pp. 48–55.

[25] Tryon, G. H., ed., *Fire Protection Handbook*, 12th ed., National Fire Protection Association, Boston, 1962, p. 34.

[26] Perlee, H. E.; Martindill, G. H.; Zabetakis, M. G., "Flammability Characteristics of Selected Halogenated Hydrocarbons," USDI Bureau of Mines, RI 6748, 1966, Washington, D.C.

[27] "Standard for Hyperbaric Facilities," NFPA No. 56D, 1970, National Fire Protection Association, Boston.

[28] Eggleston, L. A., "Fire Safety in Hyperbaric Chambers," *Fire Technology*, Vol. 6, No. 4, Nov. 1970.

[29] "Standard on Halogenated Fire Extinguishing Agent Systems—Halon 1301," NFPA No. 12A, 1973, National Fire Protection Association.

[30] Charno, R. J., "Evaluation of High Expansion Foam for Spacecraft Fire Extinguishment," N69-20776, Feb. 3, 1969, E. W. Bliss Co., Swarthmore, Penna., prepared for NASA/JSC (Johnson Space Center).

[31] Kuchta, J. M., et al., "Flammability of Materials in Hyperbaric Atmospheres," USDI Bureau of Mines Final Report 4016, Aug. 30, 1967, Explosive Research Center, Pittsburgh.

[32] Johnson, J. E. and Woods, F. J., "Flammability in Unusual Atmospheres, Part I—Preliminary Studies of Materials in Hyperbaric Atmospheres Containing Oxygen, Nitrogen, and/or Helium," NRL Report 6470, Oct. 31, 1966, Naval Research Laboratory, Washington, D.C.

NFPA Codes, Standards, and Recommended Practices (see the latest *NFPA Publications and Visual Aids Catalog* for availability of current editions of the following documents)

NFPA No. 50, Standard for Bulk Oxygen Systems at Consumer Sites.

NFPA No. 51, Standard for the Installation and Operation of Oxygen-Fuel Gas Systems for Welding and Cutting.

NFPA No. 56A, Standard for the Use of Inhalation Anesthetics (Flammable and Nonflammable).

NFPA No. 56B, Standard for Respiratory Therapy.

NFPA No. 56D, Standard for Hyperbaric Facilities.

NFPA No. 56F, Standard for Nonflammable Medical Gas Systems.

NFPA No. 410B, Aircraft Breathing Oxygen System Maintenance Operations.

Chapter 7

MEDICAL GASES

The use of flammable gases in a hospital represents a fire hazard which is different from that of any other type of occupancy. Many patients cannot easily be moved, even under ideal conditions, because of their dependency upon life-support equipment that is not readily portable. This combination of a flammable gas and an immobile patient can be lethal.

The introduction of nonflammable anesthetic agents shortly after World War II has been offset, in part, by the increased use of oxygen, the proliferation of throwaway items made of paper and plastic, and an ever increasing reliance on electrical appliances. Thus, even though great progress has been made, the hospital still represents a fire safety problem that is unique in modern society. This section discusses those parts of the hospital fire safety problem related to the storage and use of medical gases, both flammable and nonflammable.

A. Anesthetic Gases

The introduction of diethyl ether as an anesthetic in 1846 led to dramatic changes in surgical practice. Its benefits were so obvious that general anesthesia rapidly became a technique thoroughly accepted by all segments of the medical world. Yet diethyl ether had many drawbacks (including flammability) and the search for better agents led to the development and introduction of others. Initially, these agents were volatile liquids, i.e., agents which are stored as liquids and converted to a gas in a liquid vaporizer. With the advent of more modern, practical methods for compressing, storing, and delivering gases in regulated amounts, the use of the so-called true gases (e.g., nitrous oxide, cyclopropane) became popular.

The enrichment of the anesthetic atmosphere with oxygen (a step nearly simultaneous with the introduction of nitrous oxide) allowed early anesthetists to give patients high concentrations of anesthetic agents while at the same time maintaining adequate levels of oxygenation. The practice of using oxygen-enriched atmospheres as a component of inhalation anesthesia has persisted to this day.

B. The Flammability of Anesthetics

Initially, most of the anesthetic agents were flammable. The careless use of these agents, through either ignorance or disregard of safety precautions, led to a number of fires, explosions, injuries, and fatalities during the early days of anesthesia. While ether mixed with air will only burn briskly, ether mixed with oxygen generally will explode violently. Cyclopropane-oxygen mixtures create even more violent explosions, since this mixture frequently attains stoichiometric proportions.

Although some anesthesiologists and anesthetists have abandoned the use of flammable agents, they are still used by others. The nonflammable agents currently available do possess certain toxic properties not shared by cylcopropane or ether, and many anesthetists consider them unusable for certain types of patients. Thus flammable agents will be used in many hospitals for a good many years to come.

Flammable agents include cyclopropane and ethylene (true gases) and diethyl ether, divinyl ether, and ethyl chloride (which are volatile liquids). Nonflammable anesthetic agents include nitrous oxide (a true gas) and chloroform, halothane, methoxyflurane, ethrane, forane, and trichloroethylene (all liquids).

One method of reducing the flammability of a hydrocarbon (diethyl ether, divinyl ether, and cyclopropane are hydrocarbons) is to substitute halogen atoms (usually fluorine or chlorine) for some of the hydrogen atoms. For example, chloroform is trichloromethane, a nonflammable but toxic agent, made by substituting chlorine atoms for three of the hydrogen atoms in methane.

The search for a safe, nonflammable agent became intensified after World War II. Ultimately fluroxene was developed, the first of a number of fluorine-containing inhalation anesthetic agents. Fluroxene is minimally flammable because it is partially halogenated and will not burn when used in the usual concentrations of less than four percent. Yet because of its potential hazard it is still considered a flammable agent.

Following its introduction into clinical practice, fluroxene was joined by halothane, methoxyflurane, and then ethrane, all halogenated inhalation agents with minimal (or absent) flammability. If methoxyflurane, halothane, or trichloroethylene are heated, they will burn. Under the usual conditions of use and the absence of any active heating well above room temperature, however, these agents are considered to be nonflammable, and are so utilized in anesthetic situations.

Neither nitrous oxide nor oxygen will burn, although both support combustion readily. The oxygen in the nitrous oxide will be released under flame conditions, contributing to the oxidation-reduction reaction.

C. Safe Practices in Using Anesthetics

A consideration of safe practices in the field of anesthesia and ancillary hospital activities begins with an understanding of the basic chemistry and physics of oxygen and the anesthetic gases, as well as the vapors produced by the volatile liquid agents, such as diethyl ether.

A gas consists of molecules which move individually in a linear fashion at high velocities. The molecular movement increases with a rise in temperature, and decreases as the gas cools. This movement produces a parallel increase or decrease in the pressure exerted by that gas, depending upon its temperature. When a gas is compressed, its individual molecules will be forced closer together, thus increasing molecular movement and the temperature of the gas. Gases possess definite mass, but neither definite shape nor definite volume (i.e., they always assume the shape and volume of their containers, if any).

The relationship between pressure, volume and temperature is given by the various gas laws (see Sec. 3, Chap. 4, Part C for a discussion of these laws).

From all of these gas laws one may establish what is known as the general gas law, i.e., the pressure of any given quantity of gas is proportional to its absolute temperature and inversely proportional to its volume. Algebraically, pressure times volume divided by temperature equals a constant. These gas laws assume the gas is ideal while in actual practice, no gas is ideal.

The gaseous anesthetic agents (cyclopropane, ethylene, nitrous oxide, and oxygen) are stored as compressed gases or as liquids under high pressure. They are dispensed as gases through needle valves and flow meters. In contrast to the true gases, the volatile liquid anesthetic agents (diethyl ether, chloroform, halothane) are stored and dispensed as liquids.

Liquids possess definite volume and mass but no definite shape. At any gas-liquid interface molecules are continually escaping from the liquid state into the gaseous state. The pressure created by the molecules which have escaped into the gaseous state is called vapor pressure. As the temperature of a liquid is continually raised, the vapor pressure also is raised, approaching atmospheric pressure as the temperature of the liquid reaches its boiling point. When the temperature of the liquid reaches its boiling point, molecules will pass freely into the gaseous state and the liquid will boil. See Sec. 3, Chap. 3 for further information on the physical properties and fire characteristics of flammable liquids.

In the operation of a volatile liquid vaporizer during anesthesia the temperature of the liquid never reaches its boiling point. The carrier gases (nitrous oxide and oxygen) which are used to deliver the inhalation anesthetic agents to the patient pass through the vaporizer in a steady flow. These gases carry away to the anesthesia circuit the vaporized molecules of the volatile liquid. In the absence of applied heat, the temperature of the volatile liquid remaining in the reservoir, and that of the reservoir itself, will fall as the volatile liquid vaporizes (the latent heat of vaporization). As the temperature of the remaining liquid falls so does its volatility. Some anesthetic vaporizers are designed to maintain, by one method or another, the temperature of the liquid at or near room temperature, to promote even rates of vaporization.

Safety precautions relating to the use of flammable agents created other hazards. For example, the conductive flooring, necessary to create an equipotential environment and reduce the likelihood of the development of static charges in the members of the operating team and the equipment used in the operating room, led to a definite shock hazard to operating room personnel and patients. This hazard was met by supplying each operating room with isolated electrical power from isolation transformers. Isolated power systems also help prevent sparks (and the corresponding explosion hazard) resulting from certain kinds of electrical appliance failures.

D. Gas Anesthesia Apparatus

Anesthetic agents are administered by a gas anesthesia apparatus. This device consists of a number of components. First, there must be a source of gas, which may either be a cylinder or a connection to a central piping system. Next, a regulator may be utilized to reduce the pressure from a higher tank pressure to a lower working pressure. The gases are then fed to needle valves which precisely control the flow of the gas to be delivered to the anesthesia circuit. To measure the flow of these gases, each gas is passed through a flowmeter.

The flowmeter most commonly encountered in modern gas anesthesia apparatus is the rotameter or Thorpe Tube. This is a tapered glass tube which contains a bobbin or rotor

which floats in the gas stream. The space between the outside of the rotor and the inside of the glass tube consists of an annular orifice which increases as the rotor rises in the tube. When the gas passes across this orifice a fall in pressure occurs. The difference between the upstream and downstream pressures is equal to the weight of the rotor or bobbin when the flowmeter is in equilibrium. Each flowmeter is calibrated by first passing that specific gas through a master flowmeter. Flows are indicated by noting the position of the top of the rotor as related to a card affixed beside the tapered tube.

From the flowmeters the gases enter a common mixing manifold. The mixture of gases then will enter the anesthesia circuit. The anesthetic circuit is the portion of the gas machine from which the patient draws the mixture of anesthetic vapors, gases, and oxygen, and into which the patient exhales.

During exhalation, a small amount of carbon dioxide, a product of the body's metabolism, enters the anesthesia circuit. Some method must be utilized to remove this waste gas from the anesthetic atmosphere. The most common method is chemical absolution, employing an absorber which contains one-half to one liter of granular soda lime (soda lime is a mixture of sodium and calcium hydroxides, water, and a binder).

Valves in the anesthesia circuit allow the patient to breathe in a unidirectional fashion: from his lungs through

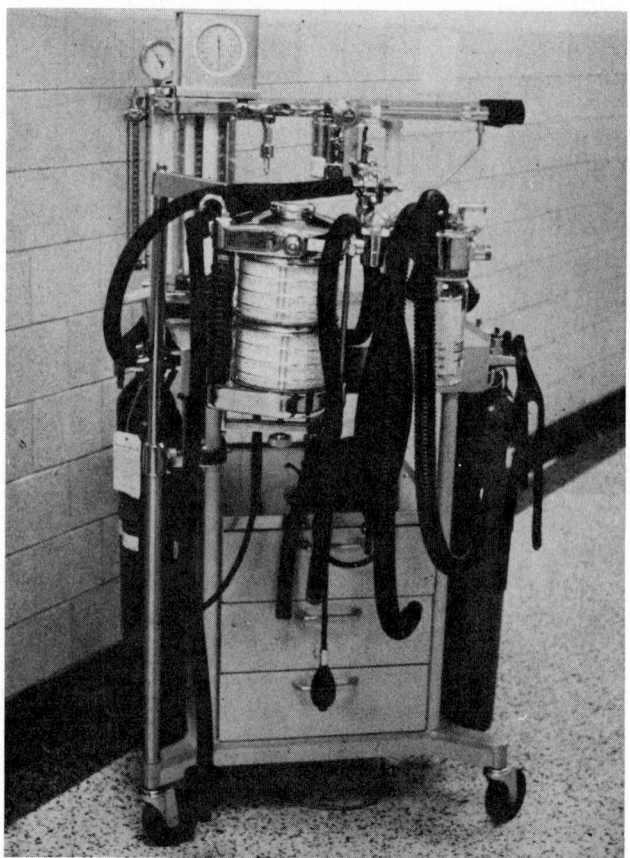

Fig. 5-7A. General view of modern anesthesia apparatus. Nitrous oxide tanks are at left, oxygen tanks at right, with flow-meter and pressure gages at top rear. Carbon dioxide absorber (part of the anesthesia circuit) is glass container at front, draped with hoses. Unit is completely self-contained and requires no electric power. Conductive rubber casters are used to prevent accumulation of static electricity.

Fig. 5-7B. The anesthesia circuit of an anesthesia apparatus as shown in Fig. 5-7A. Glass cannister at left is absorber for carbon dioxide. Smaller glass jar at center is an ether vaporizer. Two corrugated rubber hoses leading to face mask (at right rear) complete the anesthesia circuit via the rebreathing bag (black rubber balloon behind the vaporizer). Mixed anesthetic-oxygen gas is inserted into anesthetic circuit via small diameter hose at left. Waste anesthetic gases are vented to operating room exhaust air plenum via medium diameter hose at upper left.

the absorber to a rebreathing bag, and then back again to his lungs for inhalation. Sometimes the vaporizer is placed in a breathing circuit. At other times it may be located somewhere between the gas delivery of the anesthesia machine and the breathing circuit.

E. Oxygen as a Medical Agent

In the early days of inhalation anesthesia, diethyl ether was administered by the drop technique. Poured or dropped on a gauze covered mask, the ether was volatilized in the air of the operating room atmosphere. No oxygen enrichment was utilized. Today the large majority of inhalation anesthetics are administered with oxygen and in the presence of an oxygen-enriched atmosphere the lower limit of flammability, and the ignition temperature of all flammable agents, are reduced. Additionally, such a mixture may approach stoichiometric concentrations, i.e., the proportions of oxygen and fuel may be close to those which will allow complete combustion of the flammable substance with neither reactant being present in any significant amount after the oxidation-reduction reaction. (See Chap. 5 of this Section for further discussion of hazards of oxygen-enriched atmospheres.)

From a practical standpoint, one cannot eliminate oxygen. Oxygen-enriched atmospheres are commonly utilized in anesthesia apparatus to enhance the administration of the anesthetics and promote a wider margin of safety for the patient. Respiratory therapy also utilizes oxygen-enriched atmospheres to a significant degree. Hyperbaric chambers for various forms of hyperbaric medicine also utilize oxygen-enriched atmospheres either in the form of compressed air or compressed oxygen. Thus, recognizing that oxygen-enriched atmospheres are present to varying degrees, fire or explosion prevention in the hospital must revolve about the control of these fuels and ignition sources.

F. Fire and Explosion Prevention

One method of fire and explosion prevention in medically oriented oxygen-enriched atmospheres would be the use of a nonflammable anesthetic agent. Although a large number of useful nonflammable agents are available, under many medical circumstances one or more flammable agents may be indicated. For example, some of the newer nonflammable agents may cause serious liver, kidney, or cardiovascular problems. For this reason it is very likely that flammable agents will be utilized in some form for many years in clinical anesthesia. Thus, fire prevention must be directed at eliminating all possible sources of ignition.

Sources of ignition in flammable anesthetic atmospheres include adiabatic heating of gases, electric sparks, friction sparks, heated objects (including open flame), and static electricity. In view of the hazards involved, fire prevention methods generally strive for redundancy to establish built-in safeguards of a multifaceted nature so that an explosion or fire will not occur even if one element of the safety recommendations is omitted.

To prevent dangerous adiabatic heating of gases, it is recommended that cylinder valves be opened very slowly to allow gradual introduction of the high pressure gas downstream from the cylinder valve. This will allow a slow buildup of pressure and hence temperature, thus allowing the mass of the metal of the regulator or other gas-containing component to dissipate the heat rapidly enough to prevent the buildup of dangerously high temperatures. Additionally, safety standards forbid the use of any hydrocarbon substance to lubricate any components containing any oxidizing gas at high pressures.

The elimination of electric sparks, other than static sparks, is directed toward the proper design, application, and maintenance of electrical equipment. Specifications for this electric equipment as well as for line cords and power supplies are set forth in NFPA No. 70, National Electrical Code (NEC) and various NFPA publications in the series numbered 56 and 76. Recommendations for the proper use of this equipment by hospital personnel are also spelled out in these publications.

The elimination of static electricity from a hospital operating room is another example of the multifaceted approach to hazard control. First, the humidity in the operating room is controlled so that it never falls below 50 percent. Second, all floors in the hospital operating rooms and immediately adjacent corridors are made conductive (conductive floors are designed to keep all items resting on or moving across the floor at the same potential). Third, personnel entering the operating room are required to wear either conductive shoes or conductive overshoes in proper contact with the skin of their feet or legs, to assure an adequately conductive pathway between the body of the person and the conductive floor. Fourth, equipment for use in flammable anesthetizing locations has certain requirements, including specifications for conductive tops as well as conductive casters or feet. This applies to stools, kick basins, mayo stands, operating tables, and gas anesthesia apparatus. Finally, all outer clothing worn by operating room personnel and all patient gowns, drapes, belting, and other components and accessories are of conductive nature. All of these steps preclude the buildup of static electricity in the hospital operating room. The primary documents controlling the use of anesthetic agents are the NEC and NFPA No. 56A, Inhalation Anesthetics. (See Chap. 6 of this Section for further information on the control of static electricity.)

Because of the danger of electrocution in such a conductive environment, both the shoes and the floor have built-in internal resistances which will prevent a direct, low resistance pathway to ground. Additionally, all electrical appliances in the operating room are fed through an isolated circuit equipped with a line isolation monitor.

Fig. 5-7C. A conductive shoe tester. Located at entrance to sterile corridor of operating room suite, the tester indicates proper function of conductive shoes and "booties." The meter at the top of the frame indicates the resistance between ground and a person standing on the foot plates of the pedestal. Ohio Medical Products (Airco Division).

G. Storage of Flammable Agents

In any operating suite in which flammable agents are utilized, provisions must be made for storage of the reserve supplies of gases and flammable liquids. Specifications for storage include a room with a conductive floor which is ventilated to the outside with a minimum of six to eight air changes per hour.

This room with its conductive floor must not communicate directly with a room utilized for the storage of oxidizing gases such as nitrous oxide, oxygen, or compressed air. In addition, these oxidizing gases may not be stored in the same location as the volatile liquid anesthetizing agents.

Waste ether should be stored in a safety can with a spring closing lid and an internal screen to prevent propagation of flame into the can. Waste ether should be disposed by pouring it into the ground outside the hospital building. There is no other safe way of disposing of diethyl ether within the hospital premises. When not disposed of in this manner, the services of a company equipped for the disposal of hazardous materials must be used.

Open cans of ether must not be stored in a refrigerator unless it is of the laboratory safe variety, with a sealed thermostat to prevent accidental ignition of any vapors within the refrigerator cabinet. Such refrigerators usually carry the label of an independent testing laboratory which specifically indicates that the refrigerator is safe for the storage of flammable liquids.

In some flammable anesthetizing locations ether is used to prep the skin. This is a dangerous practice and is not recommended. There are better nonflammable agents for preparing the skin, such as inhibited 111-trichloroethane or trifluorotrichloroethane. Neither of these solvents will burn, and both are good agents to degrease and prepare the patient's skin for plastic and similar procedures.

H. Oxygen Supplies

The principal method of preparing oxygen for medical use is by the compression and liquefaction of air followed by fractional distillation. Once it has been purified, the oxygen may be transported to, and stored at, the site of consumption as a compressed gas or liquid. Because of the economies in bulk oxygen use, practically all medium size to large hospitals rely on a bulk oxygen storage unit on site. A liquid oxygen bulk storage system is by far the most economical to employ. NFPA No. 50, Bulk Oxygen Systems at Consumer Sites, covers safety standards for the design and operation of such bulk oxygen storage units.

I. Distribution Systems for Medical Gases

Where bulk oxygen is used at a hospital, a piping distribution system is required. A pipeline system also may be employed for nitrous oxide. Oxygen and nitrous oxide pipeline systems, as installed in hospitals, require the use of copper or brass tubing or pipe with screwed, brazed, or high melting point soldered joints. The system must be pressure-tested with oil-free dry air or nitrogen before it is put to use.

The piping system terminates at each bedside or operating room in station outlets. These are equipped with a threaded or quick connect terminal keyed to the specific gas in the pipe. Because it is extremely difficult to extinguish a fire being supplied by a continuous source of oxygen, all piping systems containing an oxidizing gas for use in hospitals (and similar occupancies) require a remote shut-off valve which can shut off the flow of gas to a station outlet involved in a fire.

Whenever a nitrous oxide piping system is to be installed along with an oxygen system, care must be taken to check all station outlets of both systems for delivery of the correct gas before the systems are put in use. Cross connections have been made, with injury or death of patients from anoxia resulting.

All specifications for the design, installation, testing, and operation of oxidizing gas pipeline systems for hospitals are covered in NFPA No. 56F, Nonflammable Medical Gas Systems. Certain Compressed Gas Association publications also cover these requirements (see Bibliography).

Station outlets for medical gas supply and central suction systems must be equipped with noninterchangeable fittings, keyed to the specific supply. Medical gas cylinder outlets are also keyed to the gas supplied. The Diameter Index Safety System is utilized for larger size gas cylinders and mating connectors. For small size cylinders, the Pin Index System is employed. This system uses two holes drilled along a radius beneath the outlet orifice of the valve body, and keyed to that gas. The cylinder yokes are equipped with pins which mate with the holes in the valve body of the cylinder containing the correct gas. The holes and pins are located in such a manner that it is impossible to insert a cylinder in the yoke for a different gas.

Gas cylinders are also color coded. The American standard for color coding includes green for oxygen, blue for nitrous oxide, orange for cyclopropane, brown for helium, red for ethylene, and gray for carbon dioxide. Color combinations are available for gas mixtures of certain percentages.

Cylinder weights, sizes, pressures, and contents are shown in Table 5-7A which is taken from Appendix D of NFPA No. 56A. Data for this Appendix has been supplied by the Compressed Gas Association.

In smaller hospitals and nursing homes oxygen may be supplied to the piping system not by a bulk source but by a manifold to which cylinders are connected. Another common arrangement is individual oxygen cylinders at each site of administration.

Cylinder handling requires certain safety precautions. Cylinders are heavy and mechanical damage to them, as well as injuries to personnel, may result if cylinders are dropped. Transport of cylinders should be only by the use

of an approved cylinder cart. Cylinders in storage must be chained to a wall, affixed to a cylinder stand, or (in the case of smaller cylinders) securely attached to an item of therapy equipment. Cylinders must not be dropped in such a way to damage the valve. When large cylinders are moved the cylinder cap must be tightly affixed. If a valve breaks off the cylinder may be propelled by the reactive release of the high pressure contents. Serious injury or even death of personnel may result.

Oxygen is also utilized in emergency vehicles. Generally small cylinders are employed. Gas anesthesia apparatus also uses cylinders of these sizes. If it is customary practice to use small size cylinders, these must be purchased from a gas supplier. Refilling of gas cylinders by a consumer is prohibited by all standards.

J. Respiratory Therapy

Respiratory therapy began with the use of oxygen-enriched atmospheres employing oxygen tents. Subsequently, various other methods for application of oxygen in medical care were developed. These included oxygen hoods (especially useful for children), incubators for newborn infants,

Table 5-7A. Typical Medical Gas Cylinders—Volume and Weight of Available Contents

Cylinder Style and Dimensions	Nom. Vol. in.³	Name of Gas	Carbon Dioxide	Cyclo-propane	Ethylene	Helium	Nitrous Oxide	Oxygen	Mixtures of Oxygen	
									Helium	CO₂
		Pressure @70°F	838	75	1200 §	1600	745	1900	*	*
A 3″ od × 7″	34	Gallons	50	40	40	15	50	20		
		Liters	189	151	151	57	189	76		
		Cu Ft	6.68	5.35	5.35	2.00	6.68	2.67		
		Lbs-ozs	0–12¼	0–9¼	0–6¼	0–0.3	0–12¼	0–3.6		
B 3½″ od × 13″	87	Gallons	100	100	100	39	100	52		
		Liters	378	378	378	148	378	196		
		Cu Ft	13.37	13.37	13.37	5.21	13.37	6.95		
		Lbs-ozs	1–8½	1–7¼	0–15½	0–0.9	1–8½	0–9.2		
D 4¼″ od × 17″	176	Gallons	250	230	200	79	250	105	79	105
		Liters	946	871	757	299	946	396	299	396
		Cu Ft	33.42	30.75	26.74	10.56	33.42	14.04	10.56	13.98
		Lbs-ozs	3–13¼	3–5½	1–15¼	0–1.8	3–13¼	1–2.5	*	*
E 4¼″ od × 26″	293	Gallons	420	380	330	131	420	174	131	174
		Liters	1,590	1,438	1,249	496	1,590	659	496	659
		Cu Ft	56.15	50.80	44.12	17.51	56.15	23.26	17.51	23.28
		Lbs-ozs	6–7	5–8¼	3–3½	0–2.9	6–7	1–14.8	*	*
M 7″ od × 43″	1337	Gallons	2,000		1,600	598	2,000	795	598	795
		Liters	7,570		6,056	2,263	7,570	3,007	2,263	3,007
		Cu Ft	267.38		213.92	79.95	267.40	106.28	79.95	106.23
		Lbs-ozs	30–10		15–10	0–13.2	30–10¼	8–12.7	*	*
G 8½″ od × 51″	2370	Gallons	3,265		2,800	1,061	3,655	1,408	1,061	1,408
		Liters	12,358		10,598	4,016	13,836	5,331	4,016	5,331
		Cu Ft	436.50		374.36	141.86	488.67	188.24	141.86	188.31
		Lbs-ozs	50–0		27–5¼	1–7.5	55–15¾	15–9.4	*	*
H† 9¼″ od × 51″	2660	Gallons	‡				4,200	1,831		
		Liters					15,899	6,931		
		Cu Ft					561.54	244.79†		
		Lbs-ozs					64–5½	@2,200 psig		

* The pressure and weight of mixed gases will vary according to the composition of the mixture.

† H cylinders of therapy oxygen are also available which have a nominal volume of 2,675 cu in. and contain 250 cu ft of oxygen when filled to a pressure of 2,250 psig @ 70°F.

‡ DOT Regulations prohibit the filling of cylinders, sizes G or H, with carbon dioxide in excess of 50 lbs (3,265 gal). The tabulated weights of the liquefied gases, rounded to the nearest ¼ ounce, do not exceed the maximum permissible filling density established by DOT Regulations.

§ Content based on use of DOT 3A2000 cylinders @ 32.5 percent filling density [DOT Reg. 73.304 (a) (2)].

Fig. 5-7D. A good example of a homemade dolly used for portable oxygen tanks in a hospital. This unit is virtually impossible to tip over and offers good protection against damage to the valve and pressure regulator.

oronasal or nasal masks, and the nasal catheter. The most recent development has been devices to mechanically assist or control the patient's breathing while delivering medical gases. This equipment, which intermittently generates pressure, will deliver mixtures of oxygen and therapeutic agents, or air-oxygen mixtures. These devices may be powered by the pressurized oxygen supply or by an electrically operated motor and pump system.

In any oxygen-enriched atmosphere combustible substances possess a lower ignition temperature and burn much more rapidly than in air. Flame spread is extremely rapid, especially if bedding or clothing are saturated with oxygen. The safe practices for the use of this equipment are detailed in NFPA No. 56B, Respiratory Therapy (see also Chap. 6 of this Section).

Respiratory therapy may also employ helium in its pure form to be mixed with oxygen in the dispensing apparatus, or already premixed with oxygen in the cylinder. Helium neither burns nor supports combustion. It does in fact reduce the flammability of the oxygen mixture because it acts as a heat sink, rendering the mixture more difficult to ignite. The helium also tends to quench any flame which may develop.

K. Hyperbaric Chambers

One use of an oxygen-enriched atmosphere is the hyperbaric chamber. Some chambers may be small and accommodate only a single patient; others may be designed to allow the performance of an operation or other procedure, and are thus large enough to accommodate one or more patients and several attendants. The small hyperbaric chamber is pressurized with pure oxygen, creating a severe fire hazard. The larger hyperbaric chambers are compressed with air which may be delivered by a compressor or from cylinders of compressed air. Safety standards for hyperbaric chambers and facilities are detailed in NFPA No. 56D, Hyperbaric Facilities.

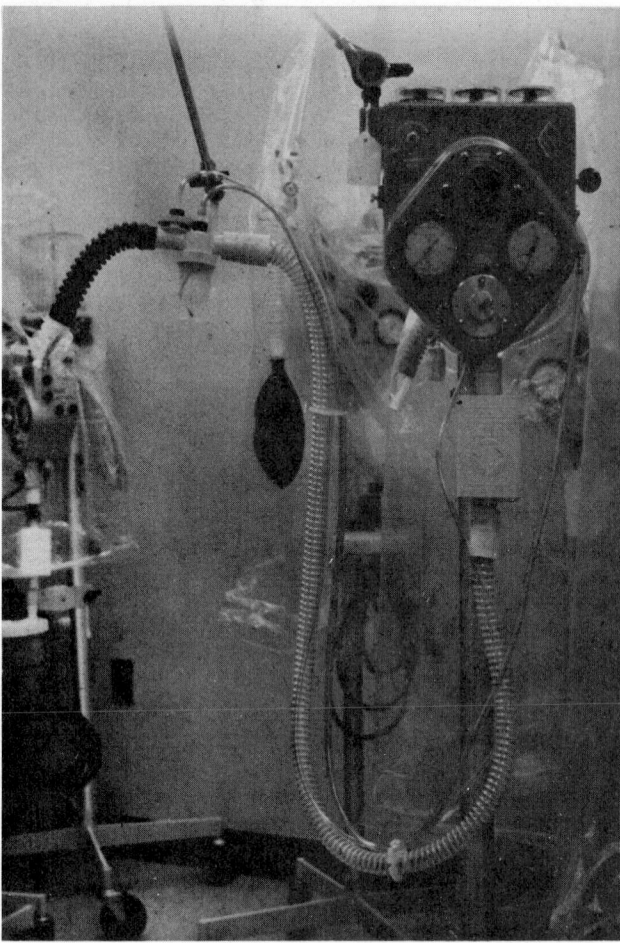

Fig. 5-7E. A respiration unit used for oxygen therapy. The control unit (upper right) is connected to the hospital compressed air and oxygen distribution system via quick-connect couplers on hoses at rear. Desired air-oxygen mixture is fed to patient via bacteria filter (at bottom of control unit) and corrugated hoses at bottom and left. Patient's oxygen mask is attached to black hose at left.

L. Pressurized Air

Air compressed above atmosphere pressure (14.7 psi or 760 Torr) constitutes an oxygen-enriched atmosphere. Although it is not as hazardous as one of pure oxygen, the ease of ignition of combustible substances is nevertheless increased, and flame spreads with much greater rapidity than in atmospheric air at ambient pressures. The fire hazards created by the compressed air atmosphere are significant. It is very difficult to extinguish such a fire unless a water deluge system is employed. Fire blankets and dry chemical agents are ineffective. The burning material must be cooled by water.

If a fire occurs in an electrically powered item of equipment located in an oxygen-enriched atmosphere, it is first necessary to deenergize the equipment. Then, the fire can be fought with water.

Pressurized air has a wide variety of uses in the modern hospital other than the hyperbaric chamber. It may be mixed with oxygen to allow ventilation of the patient's lungs without the necessity for giving the patient pure oxygen to breathe. It can be used in laboratory apparatus. It can also be used in the hospital operating room to drive certain surgical tools. NFPA No. 56F, Nonflammable Medical Gas Systems, includes provisions for the installation of a central piping system for compressed air.

Pressurized Air Supplies

If a hospital elects to utilize a compressor as a source of air, it must be able to produce air of the purity recommended by the Compressed Gas Association (see Bibliography). To meet these specifications, the air supply to the compressor must be pure. It must not come from the basement of the building in which the compressor is located. Additionally, the air must be free of any lubricants or products resulting from the breakdown of lubricants. Under the pressures and temperatures generated in an air compressor, some lubricants may break down and release carbon monoxide which could be distributed in the compressed air system.

In a hospital using a compressor to furnish air for essential hospital services, including the operating room and as an adjunct to respiratory therapy, the compressor must be connected to the emergency standby power source, a recommended safety feature for all hospitals. The specifications for this power source are set forth in NFPA No. 76A, Essential Electrical Systems for Health Care Facilities. If the hospital is not located in an area in which the atmosphere is pure, it may be desirable to utilize compressed air in cylinders rather than compressing it on the site.

Because the supplier of these cylinders may not have a pure source of atmospheric air at his plant, he may utilize an oxygen-nitrogen mixture. This so-called "synthetic air" is much purer than the ambient air because it is made up of pure oxygen and nitrogen in a one to four ratio. It contains no atmospheric pollutants of any kind.

M.   Vacuum Systems

In addition to central pipeline systems for compressed air, oxygen and nitrous oxide, central vacuum systems have become a standard feature in most modern hospitals, even in smaller ones. Station outlets for the vacuum system are commonly installed in emergency rooms, operating rooms, recovery rooms, intensive care facilities, delivery rooms, and even in nurseries. While portable individual compressor pump units have been utilized commonly in the past, the trend is to move away from these except, possibly, for low level suction as might be needed to remove fluids from the patient's gastrointestinal tract.

A central vacuum system requires both collection bottles and trap bottles at the station outlets. The collection bottles collect the fluids. The trap bottles ensure that none of the material will enter the suction line and clog it. A central vacuum system requires adequate piping capacity and pump units of sufficient size to meet peak needs. Generally two pumps are required to meet the peak load to supply the hospital. In most moderate and larger-size installations, the pumps are connected so that they will run alternately, and are used simultaneously only when the load is excessive.

Some central vacuum systems are designed to allow all of the fluids to be drawn into the system for collection in a tank in the basement, which is emptied periodically. Modern practice, however, dictates retaining the suction material at the patient care site. This prevents the possibility of contamination and cross infection within the hospital premises.

A central vacuum system may also be used in the laboratory and other hospital facilities. In the operation of any central vacuum system it is vitally important to avoid drawing any flammable gases or liquids into the system. The discharge of this system is to the outside of the building. Compressors for central suction systems are connected to the standby source of emergency power.

Gas Scavenging

Central vacuum systems of hospitals are being utilized for another purpose: gas scavenging systems. For several years it has been recognized that waste anesthetic gases (notably nitrous oxide and halothane) may create an occupational hazard for operating room personnel. Studies have shown an increased incidence of carcinoma, spontaneous abortion, and minor birth defects in the offspring of such personnel. Anesthesia techniques employed for the use of these agents generally utilize high gas flows. A significant portion of the excess gases are vented to the operating room atmosphere, thus creating the hazard.

If a central vacuum system is to be used to scavenge waste gases, it must have a capacity significantly greater than that commonly installed for conventional operating room vacuum requirements. Thus additional compressors would have to be installed if gas scavenging was implemented in an already existing structure. Additionally, a system of this type cannot be employed when flammable anesthetic agents are used unless special precautions are taken.

A workable alternative scavenging system may be installed if the operating rooms are equipped with an air handling system which affords no recirculation. The scavenging outlets from the anesthesia circuit (and ventilator if one is used) are connected to tubing which extends from the wall adjacent to the gas anesthesia apparatus and terminates in the plenum of the air exhaust duct. A system of this type could be used in the flammable anesthetizing location to scavenge flammable anesthetic agents. In practice the safe use of flammable anesthetic agents requires low flows and a closed anesthetic circuit. Thus, only small amounts of flammable agents would enter such a scavenging system, and then only at the termination of the anesthetic.

Housekeeping Vacuum Systems

In some health care facilities, it may be desirable to have a separate vacuum system for housekeeping purposes. This can be used in conjunction with vacuum equipment for cleaning corridors, drapes, and other related housekeeping chores. This system must, of course, be separate from the central vacuum system used for medical purposes.

N.   Hypobaric Chambers

A new therapeutic technique has recently been introduced into medical care: the hypobaric facility. This is a chamber or room in which the pressure is intentionally lowered for therapeutic (generally respiratory) purposes. Hypobaric facilities require, in addition to the means of sealing the doors, a source of suction to lower the atmospheric pressure. The pumps which are used for this purpose are similar to those employed in the central suction system but of much larger capacity. The safe design and operation of the hypobaric facility is covered in NFPA No. 56E, Hypobaric Facilities.

O.   Hospital Laboratories

Hospital laboratories may utilize a wide variety of gases and gaseous mixtures for chemical analysis, the generation of flames, and other purposes. NFPA No. 56C, Laboratories in Health-Related Institutions, sets forth the design features and practices required for the safe operation of such a laboratory. See Chapter 9 of this Section for further information on fire protection for laboratories.

P. Ambulatory Care Facilities

Many requirements for the safe use of inhalation anesthetics in the dentist's office and other ambulatory care facilities are identical to those for the hospital. Individual vacuum units are commonly utilized in such a facility, rather than a central system, because of the relatively small amount of suction needed in the dentist's office, as compared to the hospital. However, in larger dental offices, or other ambulatory care facilities in which minor operations are performed under general anesthesia, it may be desirable to incorporate a central vacuum system for the operating rooms and the recovery rooms, as well as the central piping of oxygen and nitrous oxide.

Q. Gas Sterilizing

For many years, sterilization by either dry heat or steam heat was standard practice for the eradication of bacteria and other pathogenes from reusable medical equipment. Recent years have seen the introduction of the ethylene oxide sterilizer. This sterilizer employs ethylene oxide, an extremely volatile liquid which vaporizes readily at normal room temperatures, and is an effective bacteriocidal and virocidal agent.

After the sterilizer chamber is evacuated of air, the ethylene oxide gas is admitted. It penetrates the material contained in the chamber and kills all bacteria, viruses, and other pathogenic organisms. Ethylene oxide is flammable and chemically reactive and proper operation of the equipment is required in order to avoid the danger of accidental ignition or explosive chemical reaction.

The liquid is delivered to the hospital in cylinders. These must be stored properly, as is the case with any container of flammable liquid or gas. Ethylene oxide is toxic to man, and proper venting of the ethylene oxide sterilizer to the outside of the building is mandatory.

Other chemical sterilizing and disinfecting agents have been used in the past. These have included chlorine, ozone, sulfur dioxide, and formaldehyde gas. Ozone is generated on site by an ozone generator. The other agents are purchased off site and supplied in cylinders. Chlorine is the most toxic, and leakage from a cylinder will cause a very serious health hazard. Because of the problems in handling these agents, their corrosive nature, and the greater efficacy and safety associated with heat and ethylene oxide sterilization, ozone, formaldehyde, sulfur dioxide, and chlorine are no longer used for medical sterilization purposes.

R. Fire Fighting Problems in Hospitals

Oxygen-enriched atmospheres are encountered during practically every inhalation anesthetic administration and all respiratory therapy. When the patient's bedding and clothing become saturated with oxygen flame spread will be extremely rapid and large quantities of water are required for extinguishment. Dry chemical extinguishers and fire blankets are ineffective. If the fire involves electrical equipment such equipment must first be deenergized. The fire then may be knocked down with water. Safe practices for the prevention of fires during the use of respiratory therapy are covered in NFPA No. 56B, Inhalation Therapy, which

included a recommended response in the event of a fire involving respiratory therapy equipment.

Storage rooms for flammable anesthetic agents exist in many, if not most, hospitals. Flammable solvents are present in all hospitals: in pharmacy storage, the hospital laboratory, and possibly housekeeping and other areas. Special fire problems are created if any of these substances are allowed to enter drains, the central suction system or ventilation ducts. Finally, mechanical hazards are created by the potential energy contained in the compressed gas cylinder.

While high voltage electrical (e.g., radiological) and electronic (e.g., medical monitoring and computer) equipment does not by itself usually create a fire hazard, combustibles stored in the vicinity may be involved in a fire. The free use of water would be inadvisable because of the electric shock hazard to the fire fighter, or damage to the equipment. The presence of radioisotopes may also hamper fire suppression methods. The fire fighter must be made aware of all special problems created by equipment or supplies in any hospital area.

An aid to the identification of hazards associated with medical gases and agents is the NFPA hazards identification symbol system (NFPA No. 704M, Identification of the Hazards of Materials). (See Sec. 3, Chap. 10, for a detailed description of this identification scheme based on the "704M diamond" that can visually present information on flammability, health, self-reactivity as well as special information associated with the hazards of the materials being identified.) NFPA No. 56C, Laboratories in Health Related Institutions, requires application of the NFPA hazards identification symbols to hospital laboratories. It is also a good idea to apply the system throughout a hospital in such areas as general stores, housekeeping, pharmacy, operating rooms, gas and flammable liquid storage rooms, and any other location where volumes of combustible or flammable materials are stored or used, or where certain special fire fighting problems exist.

Adoption by the hospital of the 704M symbol system affords not only enhanced fire protection, but also some measure of prevention and education of employes as well. Fire fighters are instantly apprised of the hazards they face. In addition, hospital employees are educated about the hazardous nature of the materials that they employ daily. Also, it is possible that in deploying the system, personnel may discover hazardous materials no longer in use that may safely be removed from the hospital premises, thus eliminating potential problems.

S. Safety Codes, Standards and Manuals

The basic thrust of NFPA Nos. 56A, 56B, 56C, 56D, 56E, and 56F is toward fire safety precautions; however, a host of other safety precautions are contained in these and other NFPA publications. NFPA No. 76A covers standby power sources for use in emergencies created by an outage of the commercial source of power. NFPA No. 76C covers the safe use of the high frequency electrocautery and other high frequency electrical devices. Many precautions for electrical safety in hospital operating rooms are also covered in NFPA No. 56A.

Other NFPA publications which bear upon fire safety in the hospital are NFPA No. 101, Life Safety Code; NFPA No. 10, Portable Fire Extinguishers; NFPA No. 11, Foam Extinguishing Systems; NFPA No. 12, Carbon Dioxide Extinguishing Systems; NFPA Nos. 13 and 13A, Sprinkler Systems; NFPA No. 15, Water Spray Systems; NFPA No. 17, Dry Chemical Systems; NFPA No. 18, Wetting Agents;

NFPA No. 71, Central Station Signaling Systems; and NFPA No. 701, Flame Resistant Fabrics. These standards together with NFPA Nos. 56A, 56B, 56C, 56F, 76A, and NFPA No. 3M, Hospital Emergency Preparedness, are incorporated by reference in the latest standards for hospital accreditation, published by the Joint Commission on Accreditation of Hospitals, Chicago.

Bibliography

NFPA Codes, Standards, and Recommended Practices (see the latest *NFPA Publications and Visual Aids Catalog* for availability of current editions of the following documents)

NFPA No. 30, Flammable and Combustible Liquids Code.

NFPA No. 43A, Code for the Storage of Liquid and Solid Oxidizing Materials.

NFPA No. 49, Hazardous Chemicals Data.

NFPA No. 50, Standard for Bulk Oxygen Systems at Consumer Sites.

NFPA No. 50A, Standard for Gaseous Hydrogen Systems at Consumer Sites.

NFPA No. 50B, Standard for Liquefied Hydrogen Systems at Consumer Sites.

NFPA No. 53M, Manual on Fire Hazards in Oxygen-Enriched Atmospheres.

NFPA No. 56A, Standard for the Use of Inhalation Anesthetics (Flammable and Nonflammable).

NFPA No. 56B, Standard for Respiratory Therapy.

NFPA No. 56D, Standard for Hyperbaric Facilities.

NFPA No. 56E, Standard for Hypobaric Facilities.

NFPA No. 56F, Standard for Nonflammable Medical Gas Systems.

NFPA No. 56HM, Manual for the Home Use of Respiratory Therapy.

NFPA No. 70, National Electrical Code.

NFPA No. 76A, Standard for Essential Electrical Systems for Health Care Facilities.

NFPA No. 77, Recommended Practice on Static Electricity.

NFPA No. 101, Code for Safety to Life from Fire in Buildings and Structures.

NFPA No. 321, Standard on Basic Classification of Flammable and Combustible Liquids.

NFPA No. 325A, Flash Point Index of Trade Name Liquids.

NFPA No. 325M, Fire Hazard Properties of Flammable Liquids, Gases, and Volatile Solids.

NFPA No. 491M, Manual of Hazardous Chemical Reactions.

NFPA No. 704M, Recommended System for the Identification of the Fire Hazards of Materials.

NFPA No. 801, Recommended Fire Protection Practice for Facilities Handling Radioactive Material.

Health Care Safety—Basic Library (a compilation of NFPA Standards, Codes, and Recommended Practices applicable to health care facilities).

Health Care Safety—Supplemental Library (additional NFPA Standards, Codes, and Recommended Practices applicable to health care facilities).

Additional Readings

The following pamphlets are published by the Compressed Gas Association, New York.

CGA No. C-9, Standard Color-Marking of Compressed Gas Cylinders Intended for Medical Use in the United States.

CGA No. G-4, Oxygen.

CGA No. G-4.2, Standard for Bulk Oxygen Systems at Consumer Sites.

CGA No. G-4.3, Commodity Specification for Oxygen.

CGA No. G-6, Carbon Dioxide.

CGA No. G-6.2, Commodity Specification for Carbon Dioxide.

CGA No. G-7, Compressed Air for Human Respiration.

CGA No. G-7.1, Commodity Specification for Air.

CGA No. G-8.1, Standard for the Installation of Nitrous Oxide Systems at Consumer Sites.

CGA No. G-9.1, Commodity Specification for Helium.

CGA No. G-10.1, Commodity Specification for Nitrogen.

CGA No. P-2, Characteristics and Safe Handling of Medical Gases.

CGA No. P-2.1, Standard for Medical-Surgical Vacuum Systems in Hospitals.

CGA No. V-1, American National-Canadian Standard Compressed Gas Cylinder Valve Outlet and Inlet Connections; ANSI-B57.1; CSA-B96.

CGA No. V-5, Diameter Index Safety System.

Chapter 8

PESTICIDES

Pesticides are extremely diverse in chemical composition and formulation, and reflect the enormous diversity of pests and pest management problems. These tools of pest management are closely regulated under federal law (Federal Environmental Pesticide Control Act of 1972), and are required to be registered with the U.S. Environmental Protection Agency with labeling that must include directions for effective use and prominent warnings of at least the primary dangers to man, his property, and the environment. Fire hazard warnings are included in appropriate cases. The label is also required to include a statement of the name and percentage amounts of the active ingredients.

A. Definition of Pesticides

The definition of a pesticide as provided in the Federal Act is comprehensive and includes any chemical or mixture of chemicals or substances used to repel or combat any animal pest, including insects and other invertebrate organisms, all vertebrate organisms, all vertebrate pests such as rodents, fish, pest birds, snakes and gophers, all plant pests growing where not wanted (such as weeds), and all microorganisms which may or may not produce disease in humans. Plant growth regulators and plant root destroyers are also included.

Pesticides are typed according to their primary specific control purposes, or to reflect the manner in which they are used. Insecticides (insect control), fungicides (fungi and bacteria control), herbicides (unwanted plant control), nematocides (earth and water worm control), and rodenticides (rodent control) are examples of pesticides classified by control purposes. Fumigants are an example of pesticides that are classified by the manner in which they are used, in that a fumigant is a pesticide that acts in the gaseous, or "fume" state.

Well over one billion pounds of pesticides are produced annually in the United States. In addition to manufacturing facilities, pesticides can be found stored in agricultural chemical warehouses, farm supply stores, nurseries, farms, supermarkets, hardware stores, and other retail outlets; on the premises of commercial pest control operators; and in the home. Large quantities are continually being transported in cargo trucks and railcars.

B. Hazards

In addition to the obvious health hazards of pesticides (as what can kill other forms of life can also kill man), most pesticides or other ingredients, or both, used in pesticide formulations are flammable or combustible. The products of combustion from burning pesticides may also be poisonous or toxic. Some formulations, include oxidizing agents, which can accelerate combustion. Run-off water from fire fighting operations is likely to be contaminated. It is not uncommon to find pesticides stored in close proximity to hazardous agricultural chemicals, such as ammonium nitrate fertilizer, because the same customer is often involved.

Pesticides, and their formulations, are encountered in all three states of matter—liquids, solids, and gases. Flammable or combustible liquids are widely used to dissolve solid

pesticides to facilitate application. The hazard of flammable or combustible liquids when released from containers can range from a simple spill fire to a combustion explosion of vapors, fogs, or mists during application. Solids are usually stored and handled as granules, dusts, and powders and, as most are combustible, can present a dust explosion hazard when dispersed into the air.

Liquids and gases are transported and stored in strong containers which can fail from overpressure resulting from fire exposure.

The intrinsic toxicity of pesticides varies considerably although they all must be regarded as dangerous. Variations are taken into consideration in labeling under federal law, and the more toxic materials are required to be labeled with the word "Poison" and a skull and crossbones symbol. Table 5-8A indicates the rather wide range in intrinsic toxicity of several common pesticides.

C. Pesticide Storage Safeguards

Basically, stored pesticides should be segregated in well identified areas of structures designed to minimize fire exposure to them and in a manner reflecting their own intrinsic fire hazards as flammable, combustible, or reactive chemicals.

Where practical, and if large quantities are involved, a detached, noncombustible structure or a first-story, corner room with direct outside access is used. Basements are avoided as much as possible because of difficulties in fire fighting, salvage, and decontamination and in controlling water run-off. Adequate placarding and security is important.

Table 5-8A.   Effect of Pesticides Taken Orally*

Name of Chemical	Approximate Lethal Dose for Humans
TEPP, Thimet	3 drops
Phosdrin	5 drops
Parathion, Systox (Demetron)	9 drops
Methyl parathion, EPN	13 drops
Endrin, Nicotine	15 drops
Guthion	¼ teaspoon
Trithion	⅓ teaspoon
Aldrin	½ teaspoon
Dieldrin, Toxaphene	¾ teaspoon
Heptachlor	1 teaspoon
Thiodan	1¼ teaspoon
Lindane, Rotenone	1½ teaspoon
DDT, Sevin	1 tablespoon
Chlordane, Malathion	1 ounce
Diazionon, Vapam	2 ounces
Sulphenon	3 ounces
Phostex	5 ounces
Perthane	1 pound
Tedion	2 pounds

1 teaspoon = 80 drops — 1 tablespoon = 240 drops — 1 ounce = 240 drops
* Adapted from a chart (No. 4) appearing in the article, "Agricultural Chemicals as a Fire Hazard," by Dr. Robert Jones, in *Fireman*, Vol. 32, No. 4, April 1965, p. 10.

Table 5-8B. Characteristics of Some Common Fumigants

No.	Chemical Name	Chemical Formula	Boiling Point (°F)	Water Soluble[1]	Flammable Limits (% Vol. in Air)	Hazard Signal[2]			Remarks
						H	F	R	
1	Acrylonitrile[3]	CH_2CHCN	171	No	3-17	4	3	2	May polymerize violently on contact with alkali unless inhibited. Decomposes and releases hydrogen cyanide at high temperatures or in contact with acids.
2	Aluminum Phosphide (formulated)	AlP	See Phosphine						Not flammable in dry state but reacts with moisture to produce phosphine gas.
3	Benzene[3]	C_6H_6	176	No	1.3-7.1	2	3	0	Can be absorbed through skin.
4	Calcium Cyanide	$Ca(CN)_2$	See Hydrogen Cyanide						Reacts slowly with moisture to release hydrogen cyanide.
5	Carbon Disulfide[3]	CS_2	115	No	1.3-44	2	3	0	Low ignition temperature—212F.
6	Carbon Tetrachloride[3]	$C Cl_4$	170	No	none	2	0	0	Decomposes at elevated temperatures to form phosgene and hydrogen chloride.
7	Chloroform[3]	$CH Cl_3$	142	No	none	2	0	0	Decomposes at elevated temperatures to form phosgene and hydrogen chloride.
8	Chloropicrin	CCl_3NO_2	233.6	No	none	4	0	1	Causes severe eye irritation (tear gas). May decompose violently when heated above 390F.
9	Ethylene Dibromide	$CH_2Br CH_2Br$	268.7	No	none	3	0	0	
10	Ethylene Dichloride[3]	$CH_2Cl CH_2Cl$	183	No	6.2-16	2	3	0	Decomposes at elevated temperatures to give off phosgene.
11	Ethylene Oxide[3]	CH_2OCH_2	51	Yes	3-100	2	4	3	May polymerize violently in contact with highly reactive catalytic surfaces. Cannot depend upon odor for warning.
12	Hydrogen Cyanide	HCN	79	Yes	6-41	4	4	2	Almondlike odor, but do not depend upon odor for warning. May polymerize violently when unstabilized. Can be absorbed through skin.
13	Methyl Bromide	CH_3Br	40	No	10-16	3	1	0	
14	Methylene Chloride[3]	CH_2Cl_2	104	No	15.5-66 (in oxygen only)	2	0	0	May form explosive mixtures with air at high concentrations.
15	Phosphine	PH_3	−125	No	1.79	3	4	1	Decomposes when heated to give phosphorus oxides. Low ignition temperature 212 to 302F. Explosive under vacuum fumigation conditions.
16	Propylene Oxide[3]	CH_2CHOCH_3	95	Yes	2.1-21.5	2	4	2	Cannot depend upon odor for warning.
17	Sulfur Dioxide[3]	SO_2	14	Slightly	none	3	0	0	Vapors are corrosive to some metals.
18	Sulfuryl fluoride	SO_2F_2	−67	No	none	2	0	0	Cannot depend upon odor for warning.

Notes:
1. From standpoint of use of water for extinguishment by dilution.
2. H = Health, F = Flammability, R = Reactivity. If the fumigant is a mixture of compounds, use numbers corresponding to the properties of the mixture.
3. Seldom used singly as fumigant, but are used as components of mixtures.

Because it minimizes both the risk of exposing fire fighters to toxic hazards and the amount of water needed for fire control, automatic sprinkler protection is provided where an adequate water supply is available. More than usual attention is necessary to disposal of water run-off, regardless of the form of water fire protection provided. Particular attention must be given to providing reasonably water-tight floors and run-off controlling drainage patterns around the storage area.

Safeguards applicable to conventional flammable or combustible liquids or gases are applied to pesticides and their formulations presenting these hazards.

Reactive pesticides and chemicals often associated with them are segregated further. These include ammonium nitrate fertilizer and oxidizing materials for which national standards are followed. Chlorates (oxidizing agents) are often present in herbicides, so herbicides are usually segregated from other pesticides.

D.　Usage Safeguards

Many pesticides do not present significant fire hazards in usage. Fumigants and insecticides applied by fogging techniques, when applied indoors can present significant fire hazards. Fumigation is covered by NFPA No. 57, Standard for Fumigation. An important provision of this Standard is its utilization of the NFPA 704M hazard rating system for both fire prevention safeguards and emergency personnel protection (see Sec. 3, Chap. 10). Table 5-8B includes the common fumigants and the Hazard Signals for them according to the NFPA hazard rating system. A list of commercial fumigants has been published in Underwriters Laboratories, Inc., *Classified Products Index* under various trade names.[1] This list specifies the composition of the material and provides a relative fire hazard classification.

Insecticidal fogging presents combustion explosion or flash fire hazards (see Sec. 3, Chap. 3). Safeguards include the use of solvents having flash points well above normal temperatures and limiting the quantities applied into struc-

tures in relation to their volume. Some fog applicators are examined and listed by nationally recognized testing agencies.

E.　Emergency Handling

Handling of accidental release or fires involving pesticides requires specialized equipment and tactics. These include advance notification of the location of pesticide storage locations and fumigation operations to facilitate planning, use of protective clothing and respiratory protection equipment, utilization of wind direction in approach, restriction of manpower to the minimum needed in the working area, minimal use of straight water streams to avoid container breakage and pesticide dispersal, and specialized medical management backup. The referenced and bibliographical material contains considerable detail on such procedures.

Bibliography

References Cited

[1] *Classified Products Index,* Underwriters Laboratories, Inc., Chicago, issued annually in July.

NFPA Codes, Standards, and Recommended Practices (see the latest *NFPA Publications and Visual Aids Catalog* for availability of current editions of the following documents)

NFPA No. 43D-T, Storage of Pesticides in Portable Containers.
NFPA No. 57, Standard for Fumigation.

Additional Readings

Bahme, C. W., *Fire Officer's Guide to Dangerous Chemicals,* National Fire Protection Association, Boston, 1972.

"Fire Department Operations—Protection of Firemen from Toxic Insecticidal Chemicals During a Fire," Special Interest Bulletin No. 303, 1955, American Insurance Association, New York.

"Fire Protection for Pesticide Storage," *NAC News and Pesticide Review* (National Agricultural Chemicals Association), Vol. 28, No. 2, Dec. 1969.

"Safety Manual for Handling and Warehousing Class B Poison Pesticides," National Agricultural Chemicals Association, Washington, 1969.

Chapter 9

PROTECTION FOR LABORATORIES

This chapter covers the more common hazard problems associated with laboratories that influence the degree of fire protection that may be required. All laboratory facilities present unique fire hazards of a nature not generally encountered elsewhere. The basic requirements of construction and design of laboratories, together with the various means of fire protection systems and procedures for laboratories, are essential items of consideration in both fire protection and prevention. Standard laboratory equipment should be designed primarily with fire prevention and protection and the diminishment of personnel hazards in mind. The use, storage, handling, and disposal of all commonly used laboratory materials, such as flammable and combustible liquids, compressed gases, and biological and radiological materials must be considered in protection and prevention procedures. It is paramount in any laboratory that these concepts be of primary consideration to those responsible for laboratory operations to minimize losses from fire or explosion, or both, and to reduce the possibilities of injury and life-threatening situations that could occur in any incident. This chapter treats the subject of protection for laboratories in a general way with more specific references found elsewhere in this HANDBOOK.

A. Construction and Design

The basic modes of construction and design outlined here are suggested as guides only. Specific details of construction and special facets of consideration change routinely with each type of laboratory. Specialized engineering firms, insurance rating agencies, and the various state and municipal regulatory agencies are good sources to consult to ensure that all requirements are met.

Construction

The construction of laboratories depends on a variety of considerations—the type and quantity of potential hazards involved, the area or location with respect to surrounding activities, and the type of fire protection to be provided. Well-located laboratories are separated from other laboratories and nonlaboratory space by fire resistive construction with a minimum resistance rating of 1 hr. Interior finish used in laboratory construction and the access ways to exits from them are of Class A quality (having a flame spread rating of 0 to 25).

Egress

Means of egress requirements for a laboratory building must agree with the exit requirements specified for the particular occupancy and type of building in question as covered in NFPA No. 101, Life Safety Code. Most laboratory buildings are constructed to comply with the exit requirements for general purpose industrial buildings. Exceptions are laboratory buildings or laboratories located in educational, institutional, or other specialized occupancies. They comply with the exit requirements specified for those particular occupancies.

Generally, two means of access opening to an exit corridor or to the outside of the building, located to provide access to egress from all parts of the area, are provided from a laboratory unit that: (1) is a general laboratory unit with an area in excess of 1,000 sq ft, or (2) is a laboratory unit containing large quantities of flammable liquids and with an area in excess of 500 sq ft. Exit doors from laboratories swing in the direction of egress. Furniture and laboratory equipment in laboratories is arranged so that means of access to an exit may be reached easily from any point in the laboratory unit without undue obstruction.

B. Fire Protection

All laboratories must have fire protection appropriate to the hazards present with a minimum of portable fire extinguishers (appropriate to the hazard), an adequate fire alarm system, and an emergency evacuation plan.

Automatic Fire Extinguishing/Detection Systems

It is good practice to protect laboratories, including associated storage rooms and enclosures, by an automatic sprinkler system designed and installed according to provisions of NFPA No. 13, Standard for the Installation of Sprinkler Systems. Special hazard laboratories in some instances may require nonwater automatic extinguishing/detection systems, such as carbon dioxide, foam, halogenated agents, etc. When such systems are used, they too are installed and maintained in accordance with the appropriate NFPA standards (see Bibliography). Periodic inspection of all automatic extinguishing/detection systems insures that they are cared for properly and maintained in service (see

Fig. 5-9A. A general view of a hospital laboratory. This illustrates the multitude of chemicals and apparatus to be found in a typical clinical laboratory. It is imperative that fire fighters be informed by the laboratory personnel of the types of hazardous materials located here. Note the deluge shower on the ceiling, for use if chemicals are spilled. Also note the large number of metal waste baskets available to prevent accumulation of trash on the floor.

the various chapters of Sections 14 and 15 in this HANDBOOK for information on extinguishing systems.)

The activation of a fire detection system or discharge of a fire extinguishing system activates an alarm system that is arranged to immediately sound an alarm, preferably at a municipal fire department, to insure prompt response. Additionally, the alarm system also is arranged to sound alarms both inside the laboratory area and at a constantly attended location, such as the telephone switchboard, communications center, or security office. Activation of the alarm system in turn should activate automatic electromagnetic door closers that effect the fire protection of the laboratory area. Laboratory building air conditioning also should be automatically shut down or switched to total exhaust.

NFPA No. 72A, Local Protective Signaling Systems; NFPA No. 72B, Auxiliary Protective Systems; NFPA No. 72C, Remote Station Protective Signaling Systems; NFPA No. 72D, Proprietary Protective Signaling Systems; and NFPA No. 72E, Automatic Fire Detectors, give guidance on the various alarm systems and detection equipment that can be used. See also Section 12, Chapters 2 and 3 of this HANDBOOK for further information on detection and alarm systems.

Standpipe and Hose Systems

It is also a good practice in laboratory buildings with two or more stories above or below ground level to provide 1½-in. hose connections with hose and combination straight stream and fog nozzle. NFPA No. 14, Standard for the Installation of Standpipe and Hose Systems, is the guide to follow. (See also Sec. 15, Chap. 1 of this HANDBOOK.)

Portable Fire Extinguishers

Fire extinguishers suitable to the particular hazard of the laboratory are installed and located so that they will be readily available to laboratory personnel. Water-type fire extinguishers suitable for fires in Class A materials are the basic type of unit for laboratories supplemented by sufficient Class B and C extinguishers for fighting flammable liquid and electrical fires. Special Class D fire extinguishers are advisable where the use of metals or metal hydrides indicates a need for them. NFPA No. 10, Standard for Portable Fire Extinguishers, is the guide to follow. See also Section 16 of this HANDBOOK for further information on the installation and use of various types of extinguishers.

Fire Prevention Procedures

It is essential to develop good procedures for handling laboratory emergencies. They include manual alarm activation, evacuation procedures, equipment shutdown procedures, and provisions for fire fighting actions. In addition, the following critical areas require special consideration: handling and storage of flammable liquids, handling and storage of other hazardous materials, smoking area controls, electrical hazards, open flame and spark producing work, and radiological and biological hazards.

Evacuation plans must be thoroughly evaluated and then drawn up to include all contingencies. Testing the evacuation plan periodically insures proper and prompt response by all laboratory personnel who must be trained and evaluated periodically in all aspects of the laboratory fire prevention procedures.

C. Equipment

All equipment in a laboratory, whether fixed or portable laboratory equipment or fixed building service equipment, must meet specific standards and must be evaluated with respect to safety, fire prevention, damage, and loss in any fire threatening situation. Personnel, both laboratory and fire brigade, must be familiar with all aspects of laboratory and building service equipment. Municipal fire department personnel must be made aware of all aspects of laboratory and building service equipment when called to fight fires in laboratories.

Ventilation

Duct systems for laboratory heating and ventilating, including warm air heating systems, general ventilating systems, air cooling systems, and laboratory exhaust and hood systems deserve special attention. NFPA No. 90A, Standard for Air Conditioning and Ventilating Systems, and NFPA No. 91, Standard for Blower and Exhaust Systems are the good practices to follow.

Fresh air intakes for laboratories deserve special attention. They must not draw in flammable or toxic materials or combustion byproducts emitted either from the laboratory building itself or other related structures nearby. Conversely, exhaust systems for laboratories are not located near air intakes for related structures, but are separated and high enough above roof level to afford maximum atmospheric dilution.

Air exhausting from laboratory areas using highly infectious or radioactive materials must pass through high efficiency filters before discharging into the atmosphere. Laboratory units provided with mechanical ventilation throughout or employing fume hoods, or both, as a fixed part of the area exhaust system, are balanced to provide a negative pressure with respect to the corridors and surrounding nonlaboratory spaces. An exception is those laboratories housing such activities as clean rooms that preclude a negative pressure in relation to surrounding space. A slightly positive pressure is required in these areas and precautions must be taken to prevent escape of atmospheric contaminants in the laboratory unit to surrounding spaces.

Electrical

All electrical installations, both fixed and portable, for laboratories conform to the requirements of the NFPA No. 70, National Electrical Code. In addition, all electrical

Fig. 5-9B. *Automated apparatus used for automatically performing medical tests. Apparatus such as shown is especially vulnerable to damage by water and smoke. It is essential that electric power and utilities be shut down, and the equipment covered (if possible), to minimize damage during fire fighting operations.*

appliances and equipment should show listing or approval by a recognized testing laboratory unless the device is one for which test standards have not been established. Electrical equipment for general use in laboratories is of the type that is listed or labeled for general use; equipment intended for use in hazardous atmospheres is listed or labeled for hazardous locations. All electrical appliances and equipment should have an operator's manual together with a circuit diagram available for maintenance personnel. It is also important that all portable electrical equipment intended for laboratory use is properly grounded by recognized methods specified in the National Electrical Code.

Installation of a sufficient number of electrical outlets at convenient locations precludes the use of extension cords. Sufficient circuitry should be installed to prevent overloading fuses or over-current protection devices, and are recommended for all electrical equipment.

It is good practice to provide emergency power for operating exhaust fans, exit lighting, exit signs, evacuation alarms, and other emergency or fire and safety equipment. In addition, several outlets should be provided with emergency power to prevent loss or interruption of electrical power to critical laboratory equipment or experimentation.

Mechanical

Safe operation of laboratory instruments and equipment depends on purchasing or building apparatus with adequate controls and safeguards, installing the apparatus in safe locations, and using the apparatus within the limitations of the original design or appropriate modifications. Safety in design and operation is always considered to avoid unnecessary accidents, damage or destruction of equipment, and potential fire hazards.

Fume Hoods

Laboratory hoods are the most commonly used means of removing gases, dust, mist, vapors, and fumes from laboratory operations, and of preventing toxic exposures and flammable concentrations. To be effective, a laboratory hood and its associated components must confine contaminants within the hood, remove them through the ductwork, and disperse them so that they do not return to the building through air intake systems. Hood face velocities must be sufficient to assure capture velocity for operating conditions. Recommended face velocities are published by the American Conference of Governmental Industrial Hygienists. Laboratory hoods for hazardous operations, such as perchloric acid or radioactive materials, require special design and are constructed of suitable materials that meet rigid criteria. Fume hood controls are so arranged that shutting off the ventilation in one hood will not reduce the exhaust capacity or create an imbalance for any other hood. Face velocity must be adequate to prevent backflow of contaminants, especially in the presence of cross drafts. All shutoff valves for services are located outside the hood enclosure in a readily accessible location. See Section 7, Chapter 5 for further information on air moving systems and fume hoods.

Refrigerators

Refrigerators are a valuable asset in most laboratories, but particular care must be taken to insure their proper use. Ordinary domestic refrigerators are completely unsuitable for the storage of flammable liquids and should be so labelled in red letters on the door. Specific laboratory-safe or explosion-proof refrigerators are available from several

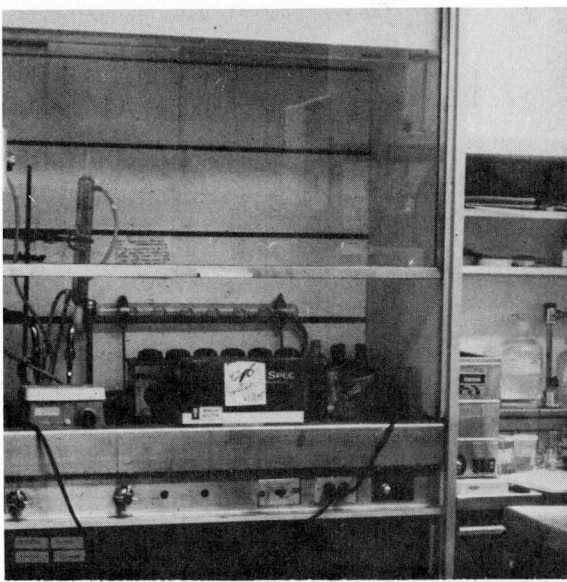

Fig. 5-9C. A laboratory fume hood. The work space is enclosed at the sides, and is covered by a sliding glass panel at the front. Exhaust fans draw in room air from the lower edge of the glass panel and vent it through a plenum to the outside, thus preventing hazardous fumes from entering the room. Special filters are required in the exhaust system if radioactive or hazardous bacteriological materials are used in the hood. Note the sand bucket on the floor for use in case of a hood fire.

manufacturers and should be purchased for storage of flammable liquids. Ordinary domestic refrigeration units can be modified by the removal of all lights, switches, heating units, oven thermostats, and other ignition sources, and by making sure that the unit's entire refrigeration compartment is vapor-tight.

D. Flammable and Combustible Liquids and Hazardous Chemicals

Flammable and combustible liquids present a serious fire and explosion hazard in any laboratory. The hazards from a flammable liquid process or the storage of such materials depend on such conditions as the quantity and flammability of the liquid, whether it is in a closed container or in an open system exposed to the air, the probabilities of leakage or overflow, the location in relation to other buildings, equipment and outside ignition sources, the building construction, and the adequacy of fire protection. See Section 3, Chapter 3 for further information on the fire hazard properties of flammable and combustible liquids.

Storage and Use

Flammable and combustible liquids are used from and stored in approved containers. Established laboratory practices are the limiting factors in determining the working quantity of flammable and combustible liquids that are present. All nonworking quantities are stored in an approved storage cabinet or in approved storage rooms. All laboratory personnel must be thoroughly familiar with the properties and the hazards of flammable and combustible liquids in use.

Handling and Transfer

Only trained personnel are involved in receiving, transporting, unpacking, and dispensing of flammable and combustible liquids. These activities are carried out in locations in a manner that minimizes the hazards. Good practice dictates that transfer from bulk stock containers to smaller containers is done only in storage rooms or within an adequate fume hood.

Disposal

Good safety practices are observed in the disposal of waste flammable and/or combustible liquids. Applicable governmental regulations are also observed. Disposal of these hazardous materials shall be accomplished off the premises by a commercial disposal specialist who is competent and possesses knowledge of the basic character and the hazards of the waste.

Chemicals

Hazardous chemicals are not brought into a laboratory unit unless the design, construction, and fire protection of receiving, using, and storage facilities are commensurate with quantities and hazards of the chemicals involved. All laboratory personnel must be aware of the hazards of all chemicals in use. Special storage facilities are needed for materials having unique physical or hazardous properties, such as temperature-sensitive, water-reactive, or explosive materials. A reference source of information is NFPA No. 49, Hazardous Chemicals Data.

E. Compressed or Liquefied Gases

Compressed or liquefied gases in laboratories present many problems, including their involvement in a wide variety of flammable, toxic, and radioactive materials and experimental mixtures that have properties which are frequently unfamiliar to laboratory personnel.

Storage, Handling, and Use

Containers designed, constructed, and tested in accordance with DOT (U.S. Department of Transportation) specifications and regulations are used for storage of compressed or liquefied gases. Good gas container storage rooms are either a separate room or an enclosure reserved exclusively for that purpose having a fire resistance rating of at least 1 hr and good ventilation. Gas cylinders are stored away from heat or other ignition sources, and in racks secured in position. Flammable gases should be stored separately from other gases and oxidizing gases by construction that has a fire resistance of at least 1 hr. Electrical equipment, if any, in flammable gas storage areas must comply with NEC provisions for Class I Division 2 hazardous locations (see Sec. 7, Chap. 2).

Handling and transporting gas cylinders must be consistent with established safety procedures and with knowledge of the hazardous properties and the hazards of pressurized containers. Gas cylinders in use are secured in place and away from any heat or other ignition source. Pressurized gas cylinders are never used without pressure regulators. See Section 3, Chapter 4, for further information on the fire hazard properties of compressed gases.

Piping Systems

When laboratory equipment is intended to be routinely and frequently operated with flammable gases supplied from compressed gas cylinders, the containers are located outside the building and connected to the laboratory equipment by a permanently installed piping system. Pressure reducing valves are connected to each cylinder and are adjusted to limit pressure in the piping system at the minimum required gas pressure. Pressure regulators must be compatible with the gas for which they are used. Supply and discharge terminals of piping systems are legibly and permanently marked at both ends with the name of the gas to be piped through them. Never use piping systems for gases other that those for which they were designed and identified. Do not attempt to transfer compressed or liquefied gases from one gas container to another.

General Safety Rules

The following general rules are observed for handling compressed or liquefied gas in a laboratory:
1. Know cylinder contents.
2. Know properties of contents.
3. Handle cylinders carefully.
4. Store cylinders in well-ventilated area away from heat.
5. Fasten cylinders in use, transit, or storage.
6. Never tamper with valves, safety plugs, or packing nuts.
7. Do not strike an electric arc on cylinders.
8. Use cylinders only with equipment suitable for the contents.
9. Do not use cylinders without a regulator.
10. Close cylinder valves when not in use.
11. Never attempt to refill a cylinder.

F. Biological Hazards

Laboratory work done with animals, infectious diseases, or toxic materials presents a variety of safety problems both to laboratory workers and to others whose duties may require their presence in such a laboratory unit. In particular, fire, explosions, etc., present two types of problems: (1) the dissemination of biological hazards because of the disaster, and (2) the hazards encountered by fire fighting personnel entering the unit. Laboratory fire brigades and local fire fighting personnel must be educated to the hazards they may encounter in laboratories engaged in biological work. Sufficient masks, air respirators, clothing, gloves, etc., must be readily available for use by fire fighting personnel. Laboratories engaged in this type of work must be clearly labeled, and clear and concise instructions must be posted for all personnel.

G. Radiation Hazards

Laboratories using radioactive materials present hazards to both laboratory workers and other personnel required to enter the facility. While rigid safety and health programs have been established for laboratory workers, it is wise to institute a similar program for other personnel, such as fire fighters. Good rapport between laboratory radiation safety and health officers and public fire fighting personnel can help keep fire fighters informed of all laboratories actively engaged in radioactive work; such rapport can be the basis for helping to establish an education program planned to cope with disasters and emergencies. See Section 4, Chapter 13 for further discussion of the hazards and safeguards associated with nuclear reactors, radiation machines, and radioactive materials.

H. Personnel Protection

Personal protective equipment is essential to a sound safety program in any laboratory unit. It is critical to establish safeguards to prevent potential injuries during a disaster such as a fire or explosion. Personal injuries arising out of a fire or explosion sometimes present serious complications to a fire fighting effort, an effort that is already complicated by the very fact that the disaster involves a laboratory.

Emergency Showers

Safety shower installations are for protection against hazards to personnel from acids, caustics, cryogenic fluids, clothing fires, and other emergencies in which volumes of water are needed for personnel protection by diluting, warming or cooling, flushing off chemicals, or putting out clothing fires. Locate emergency showers in conspicuous spots, preferably in usual traffic patterns but not more than 25 ft from any laboratory entrance. Showers are actuated by pulling on a conspicuously located activating device. Avoid locating showers near electrical apparatus and power outlets. Floor drains are provided and the locations of showers are plainly marked on the floor. The showers are tested and flushed at least every 6 months to ensure they are in operating condition.

Eye Bath

Facilities for quick-drenching or flushing of the eyes are needed within the laboratory work area for immediate emergency use by laboratory workers.

Protective Clothing

Personal protective clothing, including head and foot protection, must be made available for use by all laboratory personnel and other personnel required to enter laboratory areas where specific protective clothing is required by the nature of the operations. Specific education programs are useful in instructing personnel in the needs and requirements of protective clothing. Additionally an eye protection program (safety glasses or goggles) is beneficial in all laboratory areas.

Shields and Barriers

The hazards of explosion, rupture of apparatus and systems from overpressure, implosion due to vacuum, sprays or emission of toxic or corrosive materials, or flash ignition of escaping vapors require substantial physical protection for exposed personnel. Analysis of the potential force and characteristics of the type of hazards involved can aid in the selection of effective and economical solutions to the shield or barrier problem, or both.

Respiratory Protection

Respirators are essential for the protection of laboratory personnel either working directly with, or required to enter areas where, infectious diseases, radioactive materials, harmful dusts, mists, fogs, fumes, sprays, or vapor are present either as a natural result of laboratory work or as the result of an unforeseen disaster. Respirators or masks that are suitable for the specific problem to be dealt with are necessary.

I. Hazard Identification

It is good practice to post signs at entrances to laboratories, storage areas, and associated facilities warning personnel, especially emergency personnel, of unusual or severe hazards therein that may or may not be directly related to an emergency situation. Included are signs relating to particularly unstable chemicals, radioactive chemicals, pathogenic or infectious materials, water-reactive chemicals, and explosives. NFPA No. 704M, Hazard Identification System (see Sec. 3, Chap. 10), is a good system to utilize. Periodic review is necessary to ensure that the particular warning emblem being displayed properly indicates the nature of the material being used within the identified laboratory area. Severe hazards should be discussed with fire fighting personnel to make certain they have sufficient knowledge of what to anticipate, thus ensuring a more prompt response to emergency situations.

All individual containers within a specific laboratory area must also be identified as to their contents. Unlabeled containers present a serious potential hazard to not only laboratory workers but also to other personnel required to enter laboratory areas.

Bibliography

NFPA Codes, Standards, and Recommended Practices (see the latest *NFPA Publications and Visual Aids Catalog* for availability of current editions of the following documents)

NFPA No. 10, Standard for the Installation, Maintenance and Use of Portable Fire Extinguishers.

NFPA No. 11, Standard for Foam Extinguishing Systems.

NFPA No. 11A, Standard for High Expansion Foam Systems (Expansion Ratios from 100:1 to 1000:1).

NFPA No. 12, Standard on Carbon Dioxide Extinguishing Systems.

NFPA No. 12A, Standard on Halogenated Fire Extinguishing Agent Systems—Halon 1301.

NFPA No. 13, Standard for the Installation of Sprinkler Systems.

NFPA No. 14, Standard for the Installation of Standpipe and Hose Systems.

NFPA No. 15, Standard for Water Spray Fixed Systems for Fire Protection.

NFPA No. 30, Flammable and Combustible Liquids Code.

NFPA No. 43A, Code for the Storage of Liquid and Solid Oxidizing Materials.

NFPA No. 49, Hazardous Chemicals Data.

NFPA No. 50, Standard for Bulk Oxygen Systems at Consumer Sites.

NFPA No. 50A, Standard for Gaseous Hydrogen Systems at Consumer Sites.

NFPA No. 50B, Standard for Liquefied Hydrogen Systems at Consumer Sites.

NFPA No. 53M, Manual on Fire Hazards in Oxygen-Enriched Atmospheres.

NFPA No. 56A, Standard for the Use of Inhalation Anesthetics (Flammable and Nonflammable).

NFPA No. 56C, Safety Standard for Laboratories in Health-Related Institutions.

NFPA No. 56F, Standard for Nonflammable Medical Gas Systems.

NFPA No. 68, Standard on Explosion Prevention Systems.

NFPA No. 69, Explosion Prevention Systems.

NFPA No. 70, National Electrical Code.

NFPA No. 72A, Standard for the Installation, Maintenance and Use of Local Protective Signaling Systems for Watchman, Fire Alarm and Supervisory Service.

NFPA No. 72B, Standard for the Installation, Maintenance and Use of Auxiliary Protective Signaling Systems in Fire Alarm Service.

NFPA No. 72C, Standard for the Installation, Maintenance and Use of Remote Station Protective Signaling Systems for Fire Alarm and Supervisory Service.

NFPA No. 72D, Standard for the Installation, Maintenance and Use of Proprietary Protective Signaling Systems for Watchman, Fire Alarm and Supervisory Service.

NFPA No. 72E, Standard for Automatic Fire Detectors.

NFPA No. 76A, Standard for Essential Electrical Systems for Health Care Facilities.

NFPA No. 77, Recommended Practice on Static Electricity.

NFPA No. 86A, Standard for Ovens and Furnaces Design, Location, and Equipment.

NFPA No. 89M, Manual on Clearances for Heat Producing Appliances.

NFPA No. 91, Standard for the Installation of Blower and Exhaust Systems for Dust, Stock and Vapor Removal or Conveying.

NFPA No. 101, Life Safety Code.

NFPA No. 231, Standard for Indoor Storage.

NFPA No. 231B, Standard for Storage of Cellular Rubber and Plastics Materials.

NFPA No. 321, Standard on Basic Classification of Flammable and Combustible Liquids.

NFPA No. 325A, Flash Point Index of Trade Name Liquids.

NFPA No. 325M, Fire Hazard Properties of Flammable Liquids, Gases and Volatile Solids.

NFPA No. 491M, Manual of Hazardous Chemical Reactions.

NFPA No. 801, Recommended Fire Protection Practice for Facilities Handling Radioactive Material.

NFPA No. 704M, Recommended System for the Identification of the Fire Hazards of Materials.

Health Care Safety—Basic Library (a compilation of NFPA Codes, Standards, and Recommended Practices applicable to health care facilities.

Health Care Safety—Supplemental Library (additional NFPA Codes, Standards, and Recommended Practices applicable to health care facilities).

Additional Readings

Bond, R. G., Michaelson, G. S., and DeRoos, R. L., *Environmental Health and Safety in Health-Care Facilities,* MacMillan, New York, 1973.

Chemical Fire and Chemicals at Fires, The Institution of Fire Engineers, London, 1959.

Christensen, H. E., ed., *The Toxic Substances List,* 1973 ed., National Institute for Occupational Safety and Health, Rockville, Md., June 1973.

Ibid., 1974 ed., June 1974.

Christian, F. T., "A Guide to Safety in the Science Laboratory,"

Bulletin 74, 1968, Department of Education, State of Florida, Tallahassee, Fla.

Fawcett, H. H. and Wood, W. S., *Safety and Accident Prevention in Chemical Operation,* Interscience Publishers, New York, 1965.

Laboratory Waste Disposal Manual, Manufacturing Chemists' Association, Washington, D.C., 1969.

Lange, N. A., ed., *Handbook of Chemistry,* rev. 10th ed., McGraw-Hill, New York, 1969.

Manufacturing Chemists' Association, *Guide for Safety in the Chemical Laboratory,* Van Nostrand, New York, 1972.

Meidl, J. H., *Flammable Hazardous Materials,* Glencove Press, Beverly Hills, Calif., 1970.

———, *Hazardous Materials Handbook,* Glencove Press, Beverly Hills, Calif., 1972.

Muir, G. D., *Hazards in the Chemical Laboratory,* Royal Institute of Chemistry, London, 1971.

Pieters, H. A. and Creighton, J. W., *Safety in the Chemical Laboratory,* Butterworths Scientific Publications, London, 1957.

President's Science Advisory Committee, Panel on Chemicals and Health, *Chemicals and Health,* U.S. Government Printing Office, Washington, D.C., 1973.

Quam, G. N., *Safety Practice for Chemical Laboratories,* Villanova Press, Villanova, Penna., 1963.

Steere, N. V., *Handbook of Laboratory Safety,* The Chemical Rubber Company, Cleveland, Ohio, 1967.

———, *Safety in the Chemical Laboratory,* Vol. 1, American Chemical Society, Easton, Penna., 1967.

Ibid., Vol. 2, 1971.

Ibid., Vol. 3, 1974.

"Threshold Limit Values for Chemical Substances and Physical Agents in the Workroom Environment with Intended Changes for 1973," American Conference of Governmental Hygienists, Cincinnati, Ohio, 1973.

Section 5

Chapter 10
FIRE RETARDANT AND FLAME RESISTANT TREATMENTS

This chapter discusses the basic principles of fire retardant and flame resistant treatments, their uses and limitations, and methods of treatment for wood, fiberboard, paper, and miscellaneous decorative materials. Flame retardant plastics are discussed in Section 3, Chapter 1. Information on flame retardant fabrics will be found in Section 3, Chapter 2.

There are many situations when, in the absence of more suitable noncombustible counterparts, it may be necessary to use combustible materials. It is in such situations that treatments for combustible materials have their proper field of application.

Popular usage has created a variety of terminology associated with this subject, resulting in an undesirable degree of ambiguity and frequent misconceptions, misunderstandings and misuses. Terms such as "fire resistant," "fire retardant," "flame resistant," "flame retardant," and "flameproof" are used indiscriminately and often incorrectly.

Of these terms, the term "fire resistant" should never be used in this context. Fire resistant is used properly only to signify the ability of a structure, material, or assembly to resist the effects of a large scale severe fire exposure, and is associated with a specific hourly time period as determined by fire tests incorporating the standard time-temperature curve. "Flameproof" and its derivatives are also misleading and subject to abuse and misunderstanding; their use should be discouraged.

"Fire retardant" signifies a lesser degree of protection than fire resistant. It should be used in reference to chemicals, paints, or coatings used or intended for the treatment of combustible building materials, and to such treated materials. "Flame retardant" and "flame resistant" may be used more or less interchangeably and denote decorative materials which, due to chemical treatment or inherent properties, do not ignite readily or propagate flaming under small to moderate fire exposure. "Flame retardant" also is preferable to denote chemicals, processes, paints, or coatings used for the treatment of these materials, which include fabrics, foliage, Christmas trees, and similar materials in the class of decorations or furnishings.

Fire retardant or flame retardant treatments have been frequently misused. They have a widespread appeal due in part, perhaps, to a general lack of understanding of the limitations of the treatments, and a failure to differentiate between those which are effective and those which are not. One popular misconception is that fire retardant treatments give a fire resistance rating. This is not true since the treated material does not resist destruction and is still subject to complete consumption by exposing fire. The treatment does, however, retard both the rate of burning and the rate at which fuel is contributed by the treated material. This action can reduce the fire intensity of some materials which otherwise might be very fast burning.

A. Basic Principles

Treatments to reduce the combustibility of wood, fabrics, and other combustible materials have had a long history known to have reached back at least to the time of Moses. The early use and development of chemical retardants was limited to materials that were accidently found to be effec-

tive. Research in basic combustion processes and action of retardants was greatly expanded during World War II due to increased military needs for flame resistant fabrics and fire retardant wood; this expansion has continued in recent years. Because cotton textiles and wood have by far the longest history of use and the greatest economic importance, research has been directed primarily toward these cellulosic materials.

Burning of Cellulose

The chemical reactions and the mechanisms involved in the combustion of untreated cellulose are, by themselves, highly complex and not yet fully understood. The addition of fire retardant chemicals greatly complicates an already difficult problem.

Wood (cellulose) normally does not burn directly (see Sec. 3, Chap. 1). The initial reaction to high heat exposure is pyrolysis, in which some of the products given off are combustible gases, vapors, or mists which can form flammable mixtures with air. On ignition, the combustion of these products is evidenced by visible flames. The solid residues include charcoal, which can undergo a different form of combustion by combining directly with oxygen, as evidenced by glowing. This is an important distinction, since many chemicals which are effective flame inhibitors have little or no effect in retarding flameless combustion, or afterglow. For most applications, flame retardance is more important, but there are some instances where glow resistance is equally necessary.

Theories of Chemical Mechanisms

Four general theories have evolved to explain the mechanisms by which chemicals retard flaming or glowing of cellulosic materials. It is agreed that no single theory is adequate to explain these mechanisms, and that in most cases more than one mechanism is involved.

The four theories which offer the most satisfactory explanations for the function of flame retardant and fire retardant chemicals are as follows:

Thermal: Certain retardants may act to dissipate heat of combustion by increasing the thermal conductivity of the treated material. Some chemicals may also undergo a change of state or decomposition which acts to absorb heat. These possible effects are generally considered to be of minor significance in comparison with other mechanisms.

Coating: Some retardants melt or fuse at relatively low temperatures, and it is believed that they may form an insulating coating over the fibers of the treated material, acting to exclude oxygen and inhibit the escape of combustible gases. Other retardants exhibit a bubbling or foaming action, creating an insulating barrier. Intumescent paints and coatings are good examples of this mechanism.

Gas: Some chemicals probably function by releasing nonflammable gases under heat exposure. Others act to increase the amount of water vapor and carbon dioxide formed during combustion, at the same time reducing the production of carbon monoxide. The net result is less flammable gases and more nonflammable gases.

Chemical: Simplified representations of the chemical mechanism are shown in Figures 5-10A and 5-10B which illustrate the different effects of fire on untreated and

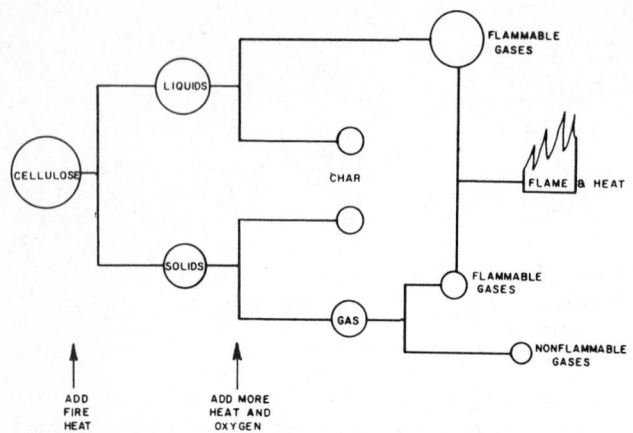

Fig. 5-10A. Schematic diagram of the burning sequence of untreated cellulose. The size of the circle is representative of the volume of product. Note predominance of liquid and flammable gas products.

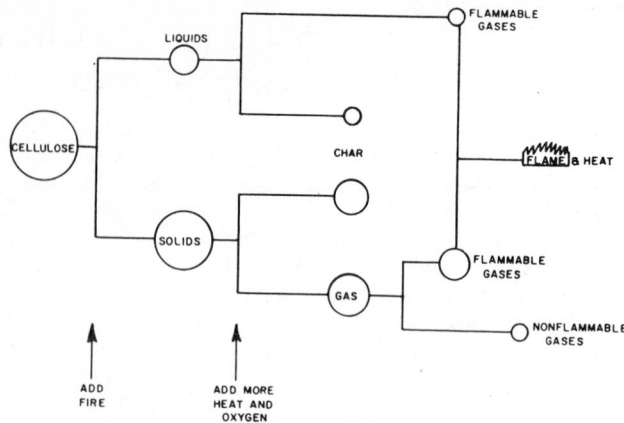

Fig. 5-10B. Schematic diagram of the burning sequence of treated cellulose. The size of the circle is representative of the volume of product. Note the predominance of solids and the severe reduction in liquids and flammable gases emanating from the liquids as compared with the same burning sequence for untreated cellulose as illustrated in Fig. 5-10A.

treated cellulose that are diagramatically explained in *Flameproofing Textile Fabrics*.[1] Untreated cellulose breaks down into liquids and a smaller amount of solids. The liquids in turn break down into flammable gases and a little char, and the solids decompose into char and gases, some of which are flammable, some not. The flammable gases volatilized from the liquids combine with those from the solids to cause flaming and the emission of additional heat which continues the reaction.

With treated cellulose, less liquids and more solids are formed, and more of the solids become char. The reduced amount of liquids creates some char and some flammable gases. As the amount of flammable gases from both the liquid and solid phases is now significantly less, the flaming is less as is the amount of heat released, resulting in complete flame resistance or at least a reduced burning rate. Another postulate, an expansion of the chemical theory known as the catalytic dehydration theory, has been advanced by Schuyten, Weaver, and Reid.[2]

Studies at the U.S. Forest Products Laboratory[3] have shown that pyrolysis reactions (without the presence of oxygen) for the lignin component of wood start at approximately 220°C (428°F), while that for the cellulose fraction starts near 270°C (518°F). However, once pyrolysis for the cellulose fraction is started, its decomposition is primarily an endothermic reaction and is nearly completed when 400°C (752°F) is reached. The lignin decomposes more slowly, almost in an entirely exothermic reaction, and loses less than half its weight in pyrolysis to 600°C (1,112°F).

Fire retardant salts greatly influence the pyrolysis reaction of the cellulose fraction, frequently reducing from 270°C to 230°C (518°F to 446°F), the temperature at which decomposition starts. But as a result, the decomposition of the cellulose is promoted directly to form char and water, instead of forming intermediate flammable gases and tar products; and the char yield from the cellulose at 360°C (680°F) is increased from 15 percent up to 30 to 35 percent. The chemical treatment also increases the char yield from the lignin component from 49 percent up to 57 percent, but here the significance is less.

It was further shown that the combustion reactions for wood can be primarily divided into two exothermic stages, one near 330°C (626°F) associated with flaming as the cellulose fraction of the wood undergoes decomposition

into flammable gases and tars and becomes ignited, and a second reaction near 430°C (806°F) associated with glowing as the lignin fraction of the wood, which has been changed to charcoal, undergoes oxidation. Fire retardant salts greatly reduce the intensity of the first peak, and some salts also reduce the intensity of the second peak, thus reducing the heat released by the treated wood over a wide temperature range. Other salts reduce the first peak and intensify the second, thus requiring a second salt to result in maximum retardant performance. Heat release during the pyrolysis reactions for wood was found to be less than 5 percent of that released during the combustion reactions.

All of these data tended to prove that one of the principal reactions of fire retardant salts impregnated into wood is to accelerate chemical reactions at certain temperature ranges, thus eliminating the release of certain intermediate products such as levoglucosan tars and flammable gases, which may contribute to the flaming of wood, and also results in the formation of greater percentages of charcoal and water. Some salts are then further effective in reducing the oxidation rate for the charcoal residue. An excellent discussion of these basic principles is contained in the Forest Products Laboratory report, "Theories of the Combustion of Wood and its Control."[4]

B. Fire Retardant Treating Methods

There are four basic methods of treatment to produce fire retardance in materials: (1) chemical change (substitutions, admixtures), (2) impregnation (saturation, absorption), (3) pressure impregnation, and (4) coating. Chemical change and pressure impregnation are limited to manufacturing processes and procedures, and are not adaptable for field use. Impregnation and coating methods may be used in the field. Generally, though, methods employed in manufacturing processes are to be preferred as they provide greater uniformity, permanence, and dependability. Applications in the field, or subsequent to manufacture of the basic material, are more subject to variation in skill and integrity of the processor or applicator. Treatments of the coating and pressure impregnation type are covered in NFPA No. 703, Fire Retardant Treatments of Building Materials.

Chemical Change

Fire retardant chemical changes are primarily effective with plastics and with synthetic fibers. When one compound or element in the chemical composition of a fiber or plastic is replaced by another compound or element, resulting in a reduced burning rate from that of the original material, the material may be said to have been fire retardant treated by chemical change. The following are common examples: Polyesters that are relatively combustible have been given some fire retardance by chemical substitution, in quantities up to 30 percent, of chlorine for hydrogen through the use of a chlorinated dibasic acid; vinyl plastic films plasticized with dioctyl phthalate (DOP) are relatively flammable, while those plasticized with tricresyl phosphate (TCP) can be quite flame resistant.

Another type of substitution or replacement can be construed as a chemical change. In textile fabrics, inherently flame resistant fibers can be used in lieu of combustible fibers, resulting in decorative materials which meet the requirements of standards such as NFPA No. 701, Standard Methods of Test for Flame Resistant Textiles and Films. In a similar sense, relatively flammable building materials, such as fiberboard made entirely from combustible cellulose fibers, can have their rate of burning reduced by replacement of some of the organic fiber with mineral fibers, such as glass or asbestos.

Impregnation

Impregnation refers to a technique for treating absorbent materials. The flame retardant chemicals are either dissolved or dispersed in a solvent, usually water, and the material to be treated is thoroughly wetted or saturated with the solution. The solution may be applied by spraying or by immersion of the material. The latter process is used for treatment of large volumes of fabric yardage, excess solution being extracted by passing the saturated material through squeeze rollers before drying.

In the simple water-soluble salt impregnation processes, the result is merely to deposit minute crystals of the salts within or on the surface of the fibers. The process is purely physical, no chemical reaction being involved. With durable treatments, insoluble deposits are formed by chemical reactions or other means.

Certain cellulose-based products, such as paper, acoustical tile, and fiberboard, incorporate a wet pulp stage during the manufacturing process. It is feasible to add fire retardant chemicals at the wet pulp stage, resulting in even distribution of the chemicals through the entire mass of the finished product. This practice is prevalent in manufacturing treated papers of many types, and is currently in use by several producers of building materials. Wood fiber acoustical tile and building boards processed by this method have a flame spread rating of 20–25.

Pressure Impregnation

Fire retardant pressure impregnation is used for treating relatively dense nonabsorbent materials, such as wood. This process replaces the air in the wood cells with a fire retardant salt. The treating solution is usually forced into the wood by the standard vacuum-pressure methods used in the wood-preserving industry.

Since the fire retarding effect of the treatment is directly related to the amount of the chemical deposited within the wood, it is interesting to compare the effect of an ordinary brush treatment with a pressure-impregnation treatment. A 10-ft high fence 50 ft long of nominal 1-in. pine boards would absorb about 4 gals of treating solution if applied by brush. The effect on flame spread would be minor. When the same boards are pressure impregnated to refusal, they absorb about 225 gals of chemical and the flame spread is cut to one-fourth of the original.

Coating

Fire retardant coatings are of several types and are useful in treating many materials. Coatings may be applied at any stage from manufacture to use. They may either actively inhibit flame spread to some degree or present a noncombustible surface over which flame cannot spread. They are used predominately on nonabsorbent building materials which cannot be treated by any other method, on Christmas trees and similar decorative materials, and to a limited extent on paper and fabrics which for various reasons cannot be treated effectively by impregnation.

The effectiveness of a coating depends on the chemical and physical properties of the material to which the coating is applied, the effectiveness of the coating on this material, the ability of the applier, and the thoroughness of the treatment. Since types of coatings and their effects vary from material to material treated, the subject is covered under material subsections of this chapter.

C. Practical Limitations of Treatments

Ideally, a fire retardant treatment would eliminate all flame spread, fuel contribution, and smoke generation characteristics from a material throughout its useful life. The color, feel, strength, weight, and other key characteristics of the basic material would not suffer from the treatment. The method would be inexpensive, easy, and safe. There are no present day treatments meeting all of these qualifications.

There are practical limits to fire retardant treatments. They are often not permanent; they do affect some properties of the treated material, and they add expense. They do, however, provide protection on a competing basis with nonfire retardant treatments and coatings. Fire retardant paints have been improved to the point where many provide a colorful, protective coating with the wear resistance and strength of normal oil paint.

D. Misuse of Fire Retardants

Fire retardant treatments are used for reduction of flame spread on structural wood members, and combustible interior finish, such as wood paneling, acoustical tile, and fiberboard. Flame retardant treatments are used for reducing the flammability of contents, furnishings, and decorative materials, such as curtains, draperies, upholstery, crepe and corrugated papers, Christmas trees, and miscellaneous dry plants and foliage. In all these applications, there are opportunities for misuse or misrepresentation, some of the more prevalent being the following:

1. Promoting indiscriminately pressure impregnated wood for uses where noncombustible materials are conventionally required. Such substitutions are appropriate in certain limited applications, but even the most effective treatments cannot entirely eliminate some contribution of fuel and smoke.

2. Advocating the use of pressure impregnated or coated materials in locations which are exposed to the weather or unusually high humidity conditions (see discussion in Part E of this chapter).

3. Attempting to treat the newer synthetic fiber fabrics with common water-soluble-salt flame retardant solutions. Such solutions (for examples see Sec. 3, Chap. 2) are effective only on cellulose fibers, such as cotton and rayon, and the common animal fibers wool and silk. They are not effective for the treatment of nylon, acetate, Orlon, Dacron, Acrilan, or any of the similar synthetics presently in wide common use.

4. Marketing flame retardant solutions in small aerosol spray containers for home use. This practice is subject to many abuses. Product labels often fail to indicate the limitations of the contents, and instructions for proper application are not adequate. Advertising frequently contains wildly exaggerated claims for the product's utility, giving the impression that the contents of one can will "flameproof" virtually everything in the home. The greatest deficiency is in the very limited quantity obtained for a comparatively high cost. The product itself may be excellent and the convenience of application cannot be denied, but there is a great risk that the average user of the product will not achieve an effective degree of flame resistance. With few exceptions, flame retardant treatments can be entrusted safely only to skilled persons.

5. Advocating the use of ordinary water-soluble-salt solutions, for the treatment of nonabsorbent materials. Effective treatment of nonabsorbent materials can be achieved only by means of a substantial surface coating, requiring that the treating solution be of a syrupy or paint-like consistency (see discussion on Christmas trees in Part E of this chapter).

The art of flame retardant treatment is highly useful, and can do much to increase fire safety. It is also a field which is especially vulnerable to entry by unskilled entrepreneurs and charlatans. Let the buyer beware!

E. Wood

Wood may be fire retardant treated by either pressure impregnation or coatings. While both of these treatments will reduce the flame spread of wood, neither is significantly effective in increasing the resistance of wood to degradation under sustained fire exposure, or in preventing reduction of its load-bearing capacity.

The maximum benefit that could be expected from any fire retardant treatment of wood known to date is that combustibility of the wood would be reduced to such an extent that it would not contribute fuel to a fire already in progress. This degree of treatment is not available; however, the spread of flame from the immediate area of an incipient fire can be retarded and, in some cases, prevented by present day treatments with a corresponding substantial reduction in fuel and smoke contribution.

Fire Retardant Pressure Impregnation

Pressure impregnation treatments deposit chemicals within the fibrous passages of wood. Many chemicals exhibit fire retardant properties, but because of cost limitations or various other objectionable characteristics, comparatively few are considered practical. Chemicals commonly used include monobasic and dibasic ammonium phosphates, ammonium sulfate, borax, boric acid, zinc chloride, and sodium dichromate, usually in various combinations.

The impregnation operation can be controlled to secure a predetermined absorption of solution. The important considerations are the depth of penetration and the amount of chemical deposited per unit volume of the wood.

A load or "charge" of wood is locked in a large cylinder, which can be up to 8 ft in diameter and over 140 ft long. The air is then withdrawn and the resulting vacuum draws much of the entrapped air from the wood cells. After a delay to allow the vacuum to stabilize, the retardant chemical solution is bled into the cylinder. After the cylinder has been filled with the treating solution, additional chemicals are forced into it under pressure. As the pressure is raised (up to 200 psi), the chemicals are forced into the empty wood cells.

The process can be run to "refusal," the point where no more salts are absorbed by the wood. The unabsorbed salt solution is drained from the cylinder and a slight vacuum may then be drawn to remove surface chemicals that would cause dripping and slow drying. The charge is removed and dried, ready for shipment and use.

Advantages: Pressure impregnation permits a large amount of fire retardant chemical to be deposited in the wood under close control and with uniform and predictable results. Samples for test are readily available. Of primary importance, the treatment can be considered permanently effective under normal and proper conditions of use. Since most of the chemicals used are water soluble, they tend to leach out if exposed to weather, and may be adversely affected by exposure to unusually high humidity; however, the application of a primer coat and two coats of typical oil-based paint to exposed surfaces can offer considerable protection against weathering.

Disadvantages: A limit on pressure impregnation is that the wood must be treated before use and after dimensioning. Also, the strength of pressure treated wood may be reduced slightly—although there have been no reports of any structural failures attributable to this cause—while the weight may be increased as much as 4 lbs per cu ft. Finally, a principal complaint is that workability of pressure treated wood after treatment is more difficult, particularly with high absorptions.

Other aspects to be considered are possible corrosion by some treating chemicals of bolts, nails, straps, and other metal fastenings; possible adverse effects of chemicals on paints, stains or other surface finishes; moisture absorption by hygroscopic chemicals making the treated wood objectionably damp in high relative humidities.

Fire Hazard Characteristics: The pressure impregnation process can substantially reduce the fire hazard characteristics of wood, as measured by the Tunnel Test (see Sec. 6, Chap. 6). The effect can be illustrated by a study of a typical wood, Douglas Fir, as shown in Table 5-10A.

Table 5-10A. Maximum Effect of Pressure Impregnation on Douglas Fir

	Untreated	Pressure-Impregnated
Flame spread	100	As low as 15
Fuel contribution	100	As low as 10
Smoke generation	100	As low as 0

Testing: The effectiveness of fire retardant pressure impregnation treatments is tested by several methods. The Tunnel Test has been used to determine the fire hazard characteristics of many pressure impregnation treatments. The City of New York originally established three tests—crib (ASTM E160),[5] shavings, and timber—for evaluating fire-retardant treated wood. The fire tube test (ASTM E69),[6] developed at the Forest Products Laboratory, has been extensively used both in the United States and in several other countries to measure the effectiveness of fire retardant treatments. Other tests, such as fire penetration and ignition tests, have been used by different organizations and individuals.

Recent advances in product standards and quality control have encouraged the use of treated lumber, particularly in some roof deck assemblies and partitions within noncombustible and fire resistive buildings. Lumber for construction can be treated by pressure impregnation to achieve a flame spread rating as low as 15.

Plywood: Fully treated plywood is satisfactory only when surface appearance is unimportant. For decorative purposes where the face veneer must have the beauty of natural wood, untreated face veneers of various species are laminated to treated cores. The flame spread classification of these treated plywood products varies in approximately inverse proportion with the density of the face veneer, and ranges generally from 25 to 75, satisfying all but the most restrictive requirements.

Fire Retardant Coatings

In existing structures of untreated wood, or in cases where fire retardant pressure impregnations are impracticable, fire retardant coatings can be used.

Coatings can be applied to any exposed surface of structural members, interior finish, or contents. They may be applied by means of brush, roller, sprayer, or trowel. As in the case of pressure impregnations, the degree of the flame-spread reduction secured by a coating is dependent upon the original combustibility of the surface to be protected, the effectiveness of the coating material used, the amount of coating used, the thoroughness of the application, and the size and severity of the exposing fire.

With normal paints, the usual aim is to get maximum coverage with minimum material. The approach is different in the application of fire retardant coatings. Here the objective is to provide the needed amount of coating per unit area required to insure a definite degree of protection.

Among the many proprietary fire retardant coatings, several have been listed by recognized testing laboratories. Beware of any so-called fire retardant or "fireproof" paint that has not been certified as to its flame-spread characteristics by a nationally recognized testing laboratory.

There are three types of fire retardant coatings for wood. In order of their effectiveness they are:

Paints, Intumescent: These coatings, upon the action of heat, expand from a thin, paint-like coating to a thick, puffy, burnt-marshmallow type coating. The puffy coating results in one or all of the following effects: insulation of fuel from heat, exclusion of oxygen from fuel, production of diluent gases, and reduction of flammable gases. It will retain its effectiveness until broken up either by high heat or by sustained heat.

Mastics: These materials are applied by trowel or by heavy duty spray equipment and form a thick coating on the surface of the combustible material. They vary from hard, ceramiclike materials to soft, tarlike coatings. All withstand significant amounts of heat and inhibit flame spread by the impervious noncombustible membrane they form.

Paints, Gas Forming: These coatings when heated release quantities of noncombustible gas which dilutes the oxygen at the protected surface so there is not sufficient oxygen to support combustion.

The customary finishing materials for wood, such as ordinary stains, oil paints, enamels, varnishes, shellac, lacquer, and waxes, are of no appreciable value in protecting wood against fire and in some cases increase combustibility. Paint, however, may be of value in preventing absorption of oil and in promoting cleanliness. It should also be noted that dry, decayed wood is more susceptible to ignition by small sparks from cigarettes than is sound wood, and that paint coatings tend to prevent surface decay.

Advantages: Fire retardant coatings have the following advantages: (1) they can be used on combustible materials already in place, (2) they are relatively inexpensive, and (3) they may be easily applied.

Disadvantages: Fire retardant coatings have the following disadvantages: (1) ease of application can lead to thin and ineffective treatments, (2) unexposed surfaces cannot be treated, (3) limited life and durability, (4) susceptibility to damage, and (5) the treatments must be maintained.

Fire Hazard Characteristics: Fire hazard of wood can be reduced through the use of fire retardant coatings. The amount of reduction is determined by the effectiveness of the treatment. Underwriters Laboratories, Inc., has established as a minimum standard of effectiveness for listing coatings a flame spread rating of 50 or less in the Tunnel Test, or a 50 percent reduction in flame spread as compared to the untreated surface, whichever is the lower.

Listed coatings, when properly applied, are effective in reducing fire hazard characteristics, some to a point well below the limits noted above. The variation in the effect of listed fire retardant coatings on Douglas fir is shown as an example in Table 5-10B.

Permanence: Some fire retardant paints and coatings have good permanence when used in interior locations of relatively normal humidity and temperatures. Water resistant, oil-based, intumescing fire retardant coatings have been developed.[7] But the use of fire retardant coatings in exterior locations, in areas of relatively high humidity, and in areas of high temperature has not been thoroughly tested. One difficulty in testing these exterior paints is the problem of weathering samples. Samples for small-scale tests can be placed in a weather accelerator or weatherometer and the

Table 5-10B. Variations in Effect of Different Fire Retardant Coatings on Unprimed Douglas Fir

	Untreated	Painted with Coating X†	Painted with Coating Y†	Painted with Coating Z†
Total coverage (sq ft per gal)	—	100	100	200
Flame spread*	100	60	10	25
Fuel contributed*	100	35	15	10
Smoke developed*	100	40	5	10
Rate per coat (sq ft per gal)	—	300	200	200
Number of coats	—	3	2	1

* Where a range of values was obtained, the figure given here is the highest obtained.
† Each coating is listed by Underwriters Laboratories, Inc., as meeting the minimum requirements for a fire retardant coating.

results measured. These small-scale tests, however, do not give significant flame spread results. There is also doubt as to the comparability of weatherometer exposures and actual long-term weathering. The samples required for the currently acceptable large-scale tests are too large for accelerated weathering and thus must be exposed to actual weathering which requires long periods of time. Until this testing problem can be solved, the use of fire retardant coatings in exterior locations must be subject to doubt.

Strength and Deterioration: Strength and deterioration of both the materials coated and their fastenings is not a problem with most fire retardant coatings.

Moisture: Moisture is absorbed and reduces effectiveness of only those coatings which use water-soluble fire retardant chemicals.

Toxicity: Toxicity of the total products of combustion should be considered when examining fire retardant coatings.

F.   Preservative Treatments

Where subject to decay or insect attack, or to attacks by marine borers, timber is commonly pressure-treated with coal-tar creosote or other standard wood preservatives. Such treatments are used in piers, bridges, trestles, and similar structures, and to a limited extent in buildings.

Creosote and other preservative treatments are commonly applied by the standard vacuum-pressure impregnation method. Application of preservative materials to a completed structure by brush or spray is of limited value because of the lack of sufficient penetration by the preservative into the wood.

There is evidence that creosote treatments cause an increase in fire hazard as compared with untreated wood. Fire is reported to spread more rapidly and generate higher surface temperatures in structures containing newly creosoted wood than in structures of untreated wood, particularly where general fire temperatures are sufficiently high to vaporize the creosote oils. The adverse fire experience in fires in creosoted pier substructures, however, is due primarily to the excessive areas of wooden construction without firebreaks, which are inaccessible for manual fire fighting and lack automatic sprinkler protection.

Fire retardance can be provided for wood treated with oil-type preservatives, such as creosote. Tests have shown that a proper ratio of a phosphorus-halogen mixture added to an oil-type preservative will reduce the combustibility of the wood treated with the preservative to that of untreated

wood; however, there is an initial flash of "light-ends" not found in tests of untreated wood.[8] The phosphorus-halogen mixture used consisted of a triaryl phosphate and 2, 4, 6-tribromoaniline. The latter was found to be a good halogen carrier when used with a phosphate.

Figure 5-10C shows the increased efficiency of the combined phosphate and bromine mixture over the use of either compound alone.

Figure 5-10D shows the variation of the combustibility with a fixed phosphate percentage in the creosote solution. This graph indicates the need for increased percentages of fire retardant chemicals for higher absorptions.

Zinc chloride and other standard water-borne salt preservatives, when used in the normal concentrations for preservative treatments of wood, do provide some fire retardant effect, but normal concentrations are not recognized as effective fire retardant treatments. For instance, a chemical compound which provides both preservation and fire retardance requires an absorption of approximately 1 pcf to provide adequate wood preservation. But to provide a fire retardant classification, an absorption of at least 3 pcf is required. Certain proprietary treatments and the standards for fire retarding formulations combine fire retardance and resistance to decay and attack by insects.

Christmas Trees

Christmas trees become extremely flammable when cut long in advance of use and when brought indoors where heat and low humidity accelerate drying. To reduce the hazard, the tree should be kept indoors only as long as absolutely necessary, and the trunk should be sawed off at an angle at least 1-in. above the original cut end and kept standing in water during the period the tree is in the house. Water should be added at intervals to the pail or tub in which the tree stands to keep the water level always above the cut.

To achieve a satisfactory degree of flame resistance in any combustible material, it is essential to get a certain minimum quantity of effective flame retardant chemical either into or on the surface of the material to be treated. Since Christmas trees by their nature are not absorbent, the only effective method of treatment is by application of a surface coating. Efforts to treat Christmas trees with simple solutions of water-dissolved chemicals, such as borax-and-boric-acid, diammonium phosphate, or ammonium sulfate are completely and emphatically useless. Solutions such as these can be effective flame retardant agents for cotton or rayon fabrics, paper, dry grass, and similar cellulose-based

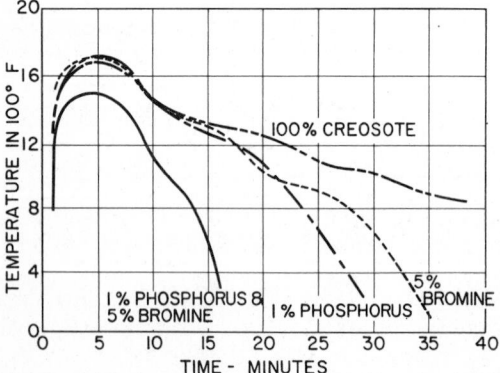

Fig. 5-10C. Effect of phosphorus (as triaryl phosphate) and bromine (as 2, 4, 6-tribromoaniline) in creosote on the time-temperature relationship during burning of Douglas fir cribs. Treament was constant at 19 pcf total solution.

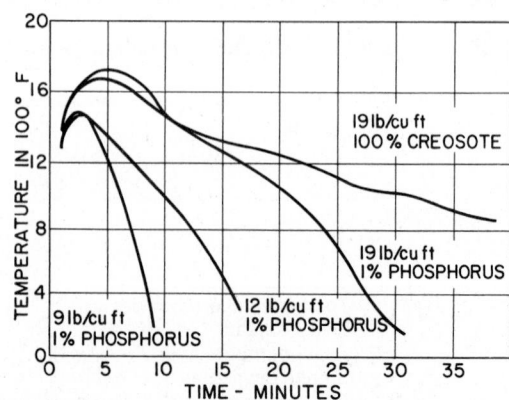

Fig 5-10D. Effect of retention of treating solution with a constant 1 percent phosphorus (as triaryl phosphate) in creosote on the time-temperature relationship during burning of Douglas fir cribs.

materials which will absorb water containing the dissolved chemical. However, Christmas trees will not absorb such solutions, therefore, the only chemical which can be retained by the tree is that which dries on the surface. This positively cannot be enough to have any significant flame retardant value unless the solution is thick or syrupy enough to form a fairly heavy coating. The chemicals noted above cannot be made to form such a thick solution except by means of special ingredients and manufacturing methods not available to the amateur. Publications which recommend the use of the above chemicals mixed with water for the flameproofing of Christmas trees are in error, regardless of the source.

Much misunderstanding in this area results from tests of fresh trees treated with simple water-thin solutions of the type described above. Such tests lead to the erroneous conclusion that the treatment is effective, when, as a matter of simple fact, the tree was naturally flame resistant due to its water content. Tests of the same treated tree after thorough drying would quickly reveal the total ineffectiveness of the so-called treatment. From the inspection standpoint, tests on a treated fresh tree are meaningless. Proper evaluation requires that a sample be taken and dried adequately before test, even though this may seem to be a cumbersome procedure.

In California, the State Fire Marshal's Office promulgates annually an Approved List of Flame Retardant Chemicals which includes several products intended for treating Christmas trees. These are all of the coating type.

Pressurized aerosol containers of flame retardant Christmas tree coatings have undeniable convenience but are of dubious value because of the very limited quantity of the contents. Many cans would be necessary for the adequate treatment of all parts of larger trees, and because of prohibitive cost, there is a strong temptation to apply only a token (and useless) coating.

The subject of Christmas tree protection is covered further in *Fire Journal*.[9, 10]

Forest and Brush Treating

The use of fire retardant chemical additives with water in fighting and controlling forest and brush fires is discussed in Chapter 12 of this Section.

G. Fiberboard

Fiberboard and fiberbased acoustical tiles can be fire retardant treated by chemical change (admixtures), impregnations, and coatings. These treatments vary in their effect. They can produce a noncombustible product, or they can affect flame spread only slightly.

Fiberboard is a mixture of fibrous material and binder formed under pressure into board-like shapes or into acoustical tiles. Boards made of wood and vegetable fiber are highly combustible under fire exposure. Since fiberboard has been a commonly used interior finish, and since the untreated or improperly treated combustible varieties present a serious life-safety hazard, it warrants separate treatment in this chapter.

Admixtures

Mineral fibers, such as glass or asbestos, added to a mixture of organic fibers, will reduce the combustibility of the mixture depending upon the amount of mineral fiber used. If mineral fibers completely replace the organic fibers, then the product becomes noncombustible provided the binder used to join the fibers is noncombustible or has a sufficiently high ignition temperature.

Impregnations

Attempts have been made to reduce the combustibility of organic fiberboard by pressure impregnation of the finished product and by treatment of the raw fiber product itself. Treatments have included soluble salts, insoluble complexes, and chemical reactions with the organic materials themselves.

The effect of these treatments on combustible fiberboard varied with respect to the type of treatment and type and quantity of chemicals used. Treatment by pressure impregnation has not proved to be commercially feasible and is not currently practiced. At least one manufacturer has developed a successful wood pulp treatment process for both fiberboard and acoustical tile, and similarly treated wood fiber acoustical tile is produced by other manufacturers.

Coatings

The treatments previously mentioned are made during the manufacture of the material. Coatings can be applied during manufacture or to material already in use. Factory-applied coatings consist of fire retardant paints and many are of questionable effectiveness when exposed to severe fire conditions. Their main effect is to remove the fuzzy surface of the untreated fiberboard.

The application of fire retardant paints of the intumescent variety to existing fiberboard will provide good protection for the exposed side of the fiberboard, provided the coatings are maintained. Combustible fiberboard exhibits considerable dimensional instability and will expand when damp and contract when dry. This movement may expose cracks and gaps in the material which will open untreated areas to the action of heat and rapid flame spread.

As no coating can protect combustible fiberboard that does not stay in place, heat resistive adhesives or mechanical fasteners must be provided to insure that the material stays firmly anchored.

For additional information on fire retardant paints, see Part E of this chapter.

Fire Hazard Tests of Fiberboard

The effectiveness of the treatments of fiberboard can be shown with test apparatus. Several methods that can be used to test the flame spread of treated fiberboard are described in Section 6, Chapter 6.

H. Paper

Paper may be flame retardant treated by impregnation. Ideally, such treatment would protect paper from deterioration due to heat, yet not affect its other qualities. This degree of treatment is not available.

Paper can be treated, however, to make it flame- and glow-retardant after the ignition source has been removed. In addition to the use on various forms of paper, i.e., building paper, wrapping, packing, and decorative paper, these same treatments can be used on preserved foliage, leaves, grass skirts, broom straw, excelsior, and similar materials if they are sufficiently absorbent. Adequate wetting may be achieved by dipping or spraying with some materials, while others may require soaking for several hours or even days.

The development of flame retardant products has been given impetus by the requirements for nonflammable display and decorative material in hotels, theaters, schools, hospitals, nursing homes, and other high life-hazard buildings. Decorative crepe paper, corrugated display cardboard, textiles, and window shade materials may be made flame resistant during manufacture, which is the most reliable method.

The California State Fire Marshal's Office lists several products of this type in their "Approved List of Flame Retardant Chemicals, Fabrics, Materials, and Application Concerns,"[12] while Underwriters Laboratories, Inc., also lists some treated decorative crepe papers.[13]

Field treating paper is difficult due to the questions of various paper finishes, sizing, and color fastness. It is preferable to purchase factory treated materials.

I.   Plastics and Fabrics

Plastics

Plastics can be flame retardant treated by chemical change and to a limited extent by coatings. While both these treatments will reduce the flame spread over the surface, neither will add significantly to the fire resistance of the material.

Ideally, treated plastics would retain their color, strength, and form under the influence of moderate fire exposure. Such a treatment is not available to date. For further information on flame retardant plastics see Section 3, Chapter 7.

Fabrics

Fabrics may be flame retardant treated by chemical change, impregnation, or coating. While these treatments will reduce the flammability of fabrics, none is effective in preventing damage due to sustained heat.

The ideal flame retardant would not affect any of the fabric's normal qualities, but would provide permanent protection against charring and decomposition when the fabric is exposed to flame at high temperature. This degree of performance is not available.

Present day treatments of combustible fabrics can reduce considerably their flammability and tendency toward smoldering or flameless combustion. These fire hazards are best avoided, however, by the use of noncombustible fabrics, and such fabrics are preferable when they are practical for the intended use. Chapter 2 of Section 3 contains a detailed discussion of flame retardant fabrics and chemicals for treatment of fabrics.

SI Units

The following conversion factors are given as a convenience in converting to SI units the English units used in this chapter.

1 ft	$= 0.305$ m
1 psi	$= 6.895$ kPa
$\frac{5}{9}(°F - 32)$	$= °C$
1 gal	$= 3.785$ litres

Bibliography

References Cited

[1] Little, R. W., Church, J. M., and Coppick, S., *Flameproofing Textile Fabrics*, ACS Monography 104, Reinhold, New York, 1947.

[2] Schuyten, H. A., Weaver, J. W., and Reid, J. D., "Some Theoretical Aspects of the Flameproofing of Cellulose," Advances in Chemistry Series No. 9, 1954, American Chemical Society, Washington, D.C.

[3] Eickner, H. W., "Basic Research on the Pyrolysis and Combustion of Wood," *Forest Products Journal*, Apr. 1962; Browne, F. L. and Tang, W. K., "Thermogravimetric and Differential Thermal Analysis of Wood and of Wood Treated with Inorganic Salts During Pyrolysis," *Fire Research Abstracts and Reviews*, Vol. 4, Nos. 1 and 2, 1962, pp. 76–91; Tang, W. K. and Neill, W. K., "Effect of Flame Retardants on Pyrolysis and Combustion of Alpha-Cellulose," *Journal of Polymer Sciences*, Part C6, pp. 65–81, 1964; Brenden, J., "The Influence of Inorganic Salts on the Products of Pyrolysis of Ponderosa Pine," M.S. Thesis, University of Wisconsin, 1963; Tang, W. K., "Effect of Inorganic Salts on the Pyrolysis, Ignition and Combustion of Wood, Cellulose, and Lignin," Ph.D. Thesis, University of Wisconsin, 1964; Browne, F. L. and Tang, W. K., "Effect of Various Chemicals on the Thermogravimetric Analysis of Ponderosa Pine," U.S. Forest Service Research Paper RPL-6, May 1963, Forest Products Laboratory, Madison, Wis.

[4] Browne, F. L., "Theories of the Combustion of Wood and Its Control," Report No. 2136, Dec. 1958, Forest Products Laboratory, Madison, Wis.

[5] "Standard Method of Test for Combustible Properties of Treated Wood by the Crib Test," ASTM E 160-50, 1969, American Society for Testing and Materials, Philadelphia.

[6] "Standard Method of Test for Combustible Properties of Treated Wood by the Fire-Tube Apparatus," ASTM E 69-50, 1969, American Society for Testing and Materials, Philadelphia.

[7] Verburg, G. B., et al., "Water-Resistant, Oil-Based, Intumescing Fire Retardant Coatings, I, Developmental Formulations," *Journal of The American Oil Chemists' Society*, Vol. 41, Oct. 1964.

[8] Gooch, R. M., Kenaga, D. L., and Tobey, H. M., "The Development of Fire Retardants for Wood Treated with Oil-Type Preservatives," *Forest Products Journal*, Vol. 9, No. 10, Oct. 1959.

[9] Tryon, G. H., "Looking at Fire Hazards—Christmas Trees," *Fire Journal*, Vol. 60, No. 6, Nov. 1966, p. 29.

[10] Segal, L., "Flameproofing: Facts and Fallacies," *Fire Journal*, Vol. 60, No. 6, Nov. 1966, pp. 41–45.

[11] Davis, J. B., et al., "Gelgard—A New Fire Retardant for Air and Ground Attack," *Fire Technology*, Vol. 1, No. 3, Aug. 1965, pp. 216–224.

[12] "Approved List of Flame Retardant Chemicals, Fabrics, Materials, and Application Concerns," California State Fire Marshal's Office, Sacramento, Calif., published annually in September.

[13] "Building Materials List, Part I," Underwriters Laboratories, Inc., Chicago, published annually with bi-monthly supplements.

NFPA Codes, Standards, and Recommended Practices (see the latest *NFPA Publications and Visual Aids Catalog* for availability of current editions of the following documents)

NFPA No. 101, Life Safety Code.
NFPA No. 220, Standard Types of Building Construction.
NFPA No. 702, Standard for Classification of the Flammability of Wearing Apparel.
NFPA No. 703, Standard for Fire-Retardant Treatments of Building Materials.

Additional Readings

Arledter, H. F., Knowles, S. E., and Druck, J. U., "Flame-Retardant Papers and Laminates," TAPPI (Technical Association of the Pulps and Paper Industry), Vol. 47, No. 8, Aug. 1964.

Bescher, R. H., "Fire Retardant Treated Wood," *The Construction Specifier*, Vol. 23, No. 3, Mar. 1970, pp. 59–62.

Eichner, H. W. and Schaffer, E. L., "Fire-Retardant Effects of Individual Chemicals on Douglas Fir Plywood," *Fire Technology* Vol. 3, No. 2, May 1967, pp. 90–104.

George, C. W. and Aylmer, D. B., "Energy Release Rates in Fire Retardant Evaluation," *Fire Technology*, Vol. 6, No. 3, Aug. 1970, pp. 203–210.

Lyons, J. W., *The Chemistry and Uses of Fire Retardants*, Wiley Interscience, New York, 1970.

Rayne, E. T., et al., "Water-Resistant, Oil-Based, Intumescing Fire-Retardant Coatings," *Journal of the American Oil Chemists' Society*, Vol. 41, Oct. 1964, pp. 670–674.

"Wood Fire Behavior and Fire Retardant Treatment: A Review of the Literature, November 1966," Canadian Wood Council, Ottawa, 1966.

Chapter 11

HOUSEKEEPING PRACTICES

Housekeeping, or the maintenance of orderly cleanliness and neatness, is basic to good fire safety. Good housekeeping practices, both indoors and outdoors, reduce the danger of fire simply because they are time-proven methods of controlling the presence of unwanted fuels, obstructions, and sources of ignition. Otherwise, through indifference and neglect, they can lead to extremely hazardous exposures both to life and property.

The importance of housekeeping in relation to fire safety extends to every occupancy from the simplest dwelling to the most sophisticated industrial complex. Certain aspects of housekeeping are a common denominator to practically all properties whatever their use; others are peculiar to a particular occupancy and must be dealt with by means of special procedures. It is neither practical nor possible to include here a recital of all features of housekeeping for all conceivable occupancies and situations. In dealing with the subject, one must exercise imagination in visualizing possible hazardous situations, and, in anticipating the fire dangers and danger to life, take appropriate steps to minimize them. The axiom, "a place for everything and everything in its place," while lacking in imagination, summarizes succinctly the proper attitude to take in approaching the task of assuring good order and tidiness on the premises.

While this chapter discusses in broad terms the elements of good housekeeping, other chapters in this HANDBOOK address themselves to specific practices and equipments that are associated with housekeeping practices for specific situations. Those chapters are referenced at appropriate locations throughout this chapter.

A. Principles of Good Housekeeping

As discussed here, housekeeping comprises the simpler aspects of building care and maintenance, operational tidiness and order, proper control of waste, and regulation of personal practices (i.e., smoking) that without sensible controls can lead to hazardous conditions. The effort must be organized and ongoing to be effective.

Responsibility for Housekeeping

No matter what the occupancy there must be recognition that waste materials and obstructions to orderly movement throughout the premises will accumulate and that it is imperative that they are removed systematically. Simply being aware that they accumulate and obstruct and then removing them when the bulk of the material becomes unwieldy and its presence a nuisance is not enough. Discipline is required to assure that prescribed housekeeping practices are followed in a systematic manner, that debris and trash are removed, and that materials and equipment are stored in an orderly manner. The same is true for routine building maintenance chores; neglect them and the property suffers, reflecting too that perhaps the routines of maintaining fire defenses are also neglected.

In a large industrial or commercial organization housekeeping is usually an assignment of maintenance staff who are charged with the routines involved in housekeeping and maintenance. But direction for the overall effort rests with management who must give the effort the positive sense of

urgency that good housekeeping routines require to be effective. Without direct and vigorous support from the top, housekeeping goals and objectives can fall to a low priority.

In smaller properties without maintenance staff, good housekeeping is more an individual effort. Yet the principles are the same; vigorous and systematic attention to the tenets of orderliness and cleanliness led by a concerned management are required.

The Tenets of Good Housekeeping

Basically there are not many requirements for good housekeeping aside from the somewhat specialized activities of basic building maintenance. Essentially they are:

1. Proper layout and equipment.
2. Correct materials handling and storage.
3. Cleanliness and orderliness.

When proper attention is given to establishing the routines for the preceding three factors, good housekeeping is certain to result.

Layout and Equipment: Ample working space, adequate and proper storage facilities, and the right facilities for moving material are the components of an adequately designed work area. Otherwise good housekeeping is frustrated as work area becomes clogged, materials back up waiting for processing, and overall cleanliness falls below par by the very nature of the messy surroundings. A careful review of space requirements for the actual operations being carried on may suggest potentials for rearrangement that can improve the levels of housekeeping considerably.

Materials Handling and Storage: Materials stored in a haphazard manner through lack of adequate facilities to move them about properly and to arrange them in neat convenient storage areas compound the housekeeping problem. Exitways can become blocked too easily; access to fire extinguishers, small hose stations, and automatic extinguishing system control valves can become obstructed; and other fire protection equipment, such as fire doors, are made inoperative. Disordered storage lends itself to collection of debris and trash in neglected corners and cul de sacs. Good storage practices are discussed in Section 5, Chapter 1, and materials handling equipment in Chapter 2 of that Section.

Cleanliness and Orderliness: No matter what the occupancy, the level of fire safety is immeasurably improved where attention is paid to the very basic need to keep all areas as clean and neat as possible. Each individual's personal sense of responsibility and desire to keep his surroundings neat and clean, backed up by efficient and timely waste removal programs are the principal defenses against unsightly and dangerous accumulations of unwanted materials and trash.

B. Building Care and Maintenance

Several common procedures necessary to proper care and maintenance of buildings are noteworthy, either because they involve inherent fire hazards or are calculated to reduce the fire danger to the building.

Cleaning and Treatment of Floors

The cleaning and refinishing of floors may present a fire

hazard if flammable solvents or finishes are used or if combustible residues are produced in quantity. For example, many fires have resulted from use of gasoline to clean garage floors. In general, cleaning or finishing compounds containing solvents with flash points below room temperature are too dangerous for ordinary use except in very small quantities. The hazard depends upon conditions of use and the precautions taken. Many cleaning compounds presenting little or no hazard are listed by fire testing laboratories.

Sweeping Compounds: These compounds consisting of sawdust or other combustible material treated with oil are hazardous, the degree of danger depending upon the character of the oil. The use of sawdust or similar materials to absorb oil spillage increases the fire hazard unnecessarily since noncombustible oil-absorptive materials are available for this purpose.

Floor Oils: Compounds containing oils and low-flash-point solvents are a hazard particularly when freshly applied. The possibility that component oils may be subject to spontaneous heating must be recognized and suitable attention given to the safe storage of oily mops and wiping rags in metal or other noncombustible containers. Any combustible oil used to excess increases the combustibility of the floor. Oil soaked floors, the product of years of use, also show increased combustibility.

Waxes: Low-flash-point solvents are hazardous, especially when used with electric polishers. Water emulsion waxes are preferable.

Furniture Polishes: Polishes containing oils subject to spontaneous heating become hazardous when rags saturated with the material are not disposed of properly.

Flammable Cleaning Solvents: These are normally not required since a number of nonhazardous cleaning agents are available, and there are a number of relatively safe materials which have high flash point, stability, and low toxicity. There are several commercial-type stable solvents available which have flash points from 140° to 190°F and have a comparatively low degree of toxicity. Safe materials are available for most of the preceding purposes (see Sec. 3, Chap. 3).

Dust and Lint Removal

In many occupancies, the removal of combustible dust and lint accumulations from walls, ceilings, and exposed structural members is a necessary procedure. Unless performed in a safe manner, as by vacuum cleaning, it may present a fire or explosion hazard. In some cases, vacuum cleaning equipment must be equipped with dust-ignition-proof motors to assure safe operation in dust-laden atmospheres. At any rate, care should be exercised not to dislodge into the atmosphere any appreciable quantities of combustible dust or lint which might become ignited or form an explosive mixture with air. Much labor can be eliminated by applying suction at locations where dust may escape from processing machinery and conveying the aspirated dust to safely located collectors (see Sec. 7, Chap. 5). Blowing down dust with compressed air may create dangerous dust clouds, and such cleaning should be done only when other methods cannot be used and after all possible sources of ignition have been eliminated. In most localities, it is possible to obtain the services of reliable professional industrial cleaning specialists to remove dust accumulations in a safe manner.

Chimney Cleaning

Chimneys need periodic cleaning, and the frequency will depend on the fuel and how carefully boilers and furnaces are operated. Soft coal and wood fuels may make cleaning necessary at least once yearly. Mechanical cleaning is best, but experienced chimney sweeps are seldom available. In their absence, a brick wrapped in an old piece of carpet material may be let down the flue on the end of a rope. A piece of chain, bunched, may be used similarly.

Various proprietary products are sold for the purpose of soot removal. Some of them operate to promote combustion of the soot and dispose of it by specially controlled burning. However, some soot removing compounds containing oxidizing agents have been known to cause explosions when thrown into stoves or furnaces. At best the use of any chemical means for eliminating soot is of uncertain value according to tests by the National Bureau of Standards.

Kitchen Exhaust Ducts and Equipment

Exhaust ducts from hoods over restaurant ranges present troublesome problems due to condensation of grease in the interior of the ducts and on exhaust equipment. Grease accumulations may be ignited by sparks from the range or, more often, by a small fire in cooking oil or fat due to overheating of frying pans and deep fat fryers.

There is no practical method for the complete prevention of fire in kitchen ducts, but the danger can be minimized through a combination of precautions as outlined in NFPA No. 96, Vapor Removal from Cooking Equipment.

It is good practice to clean hoods, grease removal devices, fans, ducts and associated equipment at frequent intervals. Depending on how much use the exhaust system gets it should be inspected daily or weekly to determine if grease or other residues have been accumulating.

In cleaning the system avoid using flammable solvents or other flammable cleaning aids. Do not start the cleaning process until all electrical switches, detection devices and extinguishing system supply cylinders are turned off or locked in a shut position to prevent accidental starting of the exhaust fan or actuation of the fire extinguishing system if the exhaust duct is equipped with one. Once the cleaning process is completed, the switches and other controls are turned to normal operating position.

Cleaning ducts is likely to be neglected because it is a difficult and unpleasant job. One source of help is the commercial firm that undertakes this sort of work. Never, though, try burning the grease out; it is a dangerous practice even though duct systems installed according to NFPA standards are designed to withstand burnout.

Satisfactory cleaning results have been obtained with a powder compound consisting of one part calcium hydroxide and two parts calcium carbonate. This compound saponifies the grease or oily sludge, thus making it easier to remove and clean. The process requires proper ventilation.

Another method is to loosen the grease with steam and then scrape such residue out of the duct. This has proven to be quite effective.

C.   Occupancy and Process Housekeeping

Rubbish Disposal

Rubbish handling is an integral part of the housekeeping process, and its success depends primarily upon having and observing a satisfactory routine. The proper and regular disposal of combustible waste materials is of the utmost importance. In industrial and commercial properties, the removal of combustible waste products at the end of each day's work or at the end of each work shift is common practice, although, in some circumstances, even more frequent waste disposal is necessary. In other properties, collection of waste, its safe storage pending disposal, and the routine for disposal vary with the nature of the property use, but having an adequate program to deal with this problem is a fire safety essential. Keeping a place tidy also depends on providing enough wastebaskets, bins, cans, and other proper containers so that building users will find tidiness convenient.

Receptacles: Disposal of waste and rubbish should be in noncombustible containers. This is true even of such small receptacles as ash trays and wastebaskets and applies, of course, to the larger units found in commercial and industrial properties. Industrial waste barrels should be of metal and be equipped with a fitted cover. Care should be taken to avoid the mixing of waste materials where such mixing introduces hazards of its own.

Plastic wastebaskets of varying sizes are available on the market, and enjoy popularity because of their many desirable features, such as quietness, attractiveness, and scratch and dent resistance. Not all plastic baskets have the same burning characteristics; some readily melt and burn creating a comparatively serious fire exposure problem by collapsing and spilling out a mass of burning contents as well as adding fuel to the fire. Other baskets may contribute relatively little fuel to the fire while maintaining their shape fairly well. If a plastic basket is to be used, it should be kept in mind that some plastic baskets are superior to others. Several manufacturers of plastic wastebaskets have been sufficiently concerned to make marked improvements in the fire behavior of their products, and the prospective buyer should look for information concerning such superiority in the manufacturer's literature (see Fig. 5-11A).

Control of Smoking: The control of smoking habits is sometimes a difficult problem to solve. The desire on the part of some people to smoke sometimes is in direct conflict with the concern the effect of smoking in certain areas will have on the level of fire safety and other activities for which a smoke-filled atmosphere is detrimental. In some instances complete prohibition is unrealistic; often careful regulation of smoking can achieve the same results.

If smoking regulations are necessary, they should be specific as to location and preferably as to time. The area where smoking is prohibited as well as those areas where it is limited or prohibited must be clearly marked by appropriate signs so there is no question.

The consequences of fire in areas containing flammable liquids and dusty and linty atmospheres are fairly obvious;

Fig. 5-11B. Two styles of well-designed ash trays.

interest in self-preservation makes smoking control relatively easy. It is in the less obvious areas, such as shipping and receiving areas with their large quantities of loose packing materials and storage spaces, which may have high-piled concentrations of combustible materials, where control of smoking is required.

Smoking control, in addition to sensible regulations, also requires adequate receptacles for spent smoking materials. Not only are properly designed ash trays essential to safe smoking, but the disposal of the contents of ash trays must be done with due realization of the possibility that a live "butt" may be present in apparently innocuous ashes. Covered metal containers, reserved for discarded smoking materials only, are desirable for this purpose.

Ash trays of improper design may constitute a hazard, particularly types which allow a partially consumed cigarette to fall or roll off the tray, since the lighted "butt" may readily come in contact with combustible materials and start a fire under certain conditions. Ash trays preferably are of noncombustible materials, and have grooves or snuffers to hold cigarettes safely, with sides steep enough so that users are forced to place cigarettes entirely within the tray (see Fig. 5-11B). In business and industrial buildings, large containers of sand are a convenient and safe means for the extinguishment and disposal of smoking wastes.

Housekeeping Hazards

In many occupancies there are special housekeeping problems presented by the nature of operations conducted; for these, specific planning and arrangements are necessary.

Drip Pans: These are essential at many locations, notably under some motors, machines using cutting oils, bearings, and in connection with borings and turnings that may contain oil. Pans preferably are of noncombustible material. Oil-absorbing compounds, consisting largely of diatomaceous earth are commercially available and are used in preference to sawdust or sand. Regular removal of oil-soaked material is recommended.

Flammable Liquid Spills: These may be anticipated wherever such products are handled or used, and it is essential that the means necessary to cope with the situation be at hand. Where practical to limit spillage, a supply of suitable absorptive material together with tools for spreading it should be readily available. Appropriate steps to cut off sources of ignition, ventilate the area, and safely dissipate any flammable vapors should be understood and promptly taken.

Flammable Liquids Waste Disposal: These often present a troublesome problem. Waste liquids, such as automobile crankcase drainings, are never drained into sewers but are placed in metal drums until safely disposed of. In some cities, there are concerns that make a specialty of collecting waste petroleum products and refining them for further use.

Fig. 5-11A. Waste containers designed to snuff out accidental fire in contents and to limit external container surface temperatures to no more than 175°F above room temperature. (Justrite Mfg. Co.)

Waste products are not burned in oil burners except where the burner is designed or has been adapted to consume waste flammable liquids. Many fire departments like to receive waste oils for training firemen in handling flammable liquid fires.

Coatings and Lubricants: Paints, grease, and similar combustibles are widely used, and good housekeeping will necessitate the collection and safe disposal of combustible residues. For the cleaning of spray booths and associated exhaust fan blades and ducts, the use of nonsparking tools is recommended to avoid possible ignition of combustible residues. Particular care must be taken to maintain sprinklers free from deposits. A thin coating of grease placed on sprinklers and cleaned frequently is one satisfactory method. Another is to enclose each sprinkler in a light paper bag which is changed daily. The discharge of vapors from spray booths is so arranged that the vapors are conducted directly to the outside and the residues are not accumulated in an unsafe manner or location.

Clean Waste and Rags: Clean cotton waste or wiping rags are generally considered to be mildly hazardous, chiefly because they are readily flammable when not baled, and there is always the likelihood that dirty waste may become mixed with them. The presence of dirty waste, or small amounts of certain oils, may lead to spontaneous heating. Reclaimed waste is considered somewhat more hazardous than new waste. It is common practice to handle clean waste in the same manner as dirty waste, although the fire hazard is relatively small.

Large supplies of clean waste are best kept in bins, either made entirely of metal or of wood lined with metal, and provided with covers which are normally kept closed. Several bins may be provided where the supplies are large, or where different kinds of waste are kept. The covers on such bins preferably are counterweighed so that they may be readily raised and lowered, and counterweight ropes can have fusible links to insure automatic closing of covers in event of fire. Local supplies of clean waste are usually kept in small waste cans, properly marked.

By providing local supply points for clean waste, it will be possible to get away from the practice of keeping waste in clothes lockers, drawers, benches, and similar points. There is the danger that, if clean waste is allowed in such places, some which is more or less oily will also be placed there with possible resulting fire.

Oily Waste: Oily wiping rags, sawdust, lint, clothing, etc., particularly if containing oils subject to spontaneous heating, are highly dangerous. For all such materials in ordinary quantities, a standard waste can is best; satisfactory cans

Fig. 5-11C. A portable metal waste can equipped with a self-closing cover for storage of oily waste materials, particularly if it is subject to spontaneous heating. (The Protectoseal Co.)

have been tested and approved or listed by recognized testing laboratories (see Fig. 5-11C). For large amounts, heavy metal barrels with covers are ideal. Good practice calls for cans containing oily waste to be emptied daily and wiping rags kept in covered metal containers until laundered.

Packing Materials: These are practically all combustible and, consequently, hazardous. Excelsior, straw, sawdust, burlap, and the like should be treated as clean waste except that where large quantities are used, special vaults or storerooms are frequently needed. Automatic sprinklers are desirable where any considerable quantity of packing materials is stored or handled even if the balance of the building is not so protected.

The prompt removal and disposal of used or waste packing materials and crating from receiving and shipping rooms is essential to minimize the danger of fire. Ideally the packing and unpacking processes are conducted in an orderly manner so that excessive quantities of packing materials do not become strewn about the premises.

Refuse Chutes

All manner of dry waste may not safely be dumped into chutes. For example, combustible dusts and metal powders should not be dumped into chutes because of the danger of explosion. Waste stock from process operations may often be best handled by an exhaust system installed in compliance with NFPA No. 91, Blower and Exhaust Systems. Where such facilities are provided, a systematic cleaning schedule should be established to assure proper operation and efficiency as well as safe disposal of the waste. Pressurized containers such as the ubiquitous aerosol can should not be incinerated or mixed with rubbish which may subsequently be burned. Similar precautions should be taken with mercury batteries, commonly used in portable radios and photoflash equipment. If subjected to fire, such batteries can explode. See Section 7, Chapter 6 for further information on refuse handling systems and equipment, including the installation of various types of refuse chutes, trash compactors, and incinerators.

Combustible Metal Waste

In plants where combustible metals such as magnesium and titanium are processed, special housekeeping procedures are necessary. Such metals and their behavior are discussed in Section 3, Chapter 9. Frequent collection of chips, turnings, and other fines is essential in order to help to avoid any large accumulations.

Certain combustible metals such as titanium and zirconium in finely divided form are subject to spontaneous heating and ignition in the presence of oil and certain common contaminants and thus present an additional fire hazard.

Whatever material is to be salvaged should be placed in covered, plainly labeled, clean, dry, steel containers and stored in an outside yard area safely distant from any buildings or removed to a detached scrap storage building or special scrap storage room. Combustible metal fines which are not to be salvaged should be disposed of by burning in thin layers at a safe location.

Sludge from dust collectors and liquid precipitation type separators should be removed at least daily, oftener if conditions warrant, and placed in covered, noncombustible containers, preferably of not over 50 lbs capacity for transportation to the place of disposal. Safe disposal of combustible metal sludge varies with the particular material involved. See Section 4, Chapter 14 for guidelines for correct disposal of combustible metals. NFPA Standards on Aluminum (No. 65), Magnesium (No. 48), Titanium (No.

481), and Zirconium (No. 482M) provide further guidance on these matters.

Radioactive Wastes

In plants or laboratories handling radioactive materials, not only are the highest standards of general housekeeping necessary, but special procedures for waste disposal must be observed. Liquid wastes from so-called "hot" areas must be handled by a separate sewer and drain system discharging to retention tanks where radioactive substances having a short half-life can become less active. When the level of radioactivity is beyond safe limits, the liquid waste must be processed and disposed of properly. See Section 4, Chapter 14, for further information on disposal of radioactive wastes.

Lockers and Cupboards

The lack of cleanliness in lockers and their general use as storerooms for waste material are fire hazards. This is particularly true when such locker stores of waste include oily rags and cloths or clothes smeared with paint. Pipes and cigars which are not extinguished before being placed in lockers are, naturally, extremely dangerous, as is the careless disposition of matches in lockers. The danger of fire spreading from lockers is minimized when the lockers are constructed of metal. When wooden lockers are used, regular inspections should be conducted.

Since fire can often be confined to a locker which is of the solid type of construction, lockers should have solid backs and solid dividing partitions rather than those made of expanded metal or wire screen. Lockers which are arranged in two tiers, one upon the other, are generally unsatisfactory. They will not hold clothes without mussing them, and it becomes the habit of persons using such lockers to keep their clothes outside of the locker or to fold or throw them haphazardly into the locker, thus increasing the danger of spontaneous heating if such clothing is spotted with oil or paint.

Where lockers are provided with mechanical exhaust ventilation, NFPA No. 91, Blower and Exhaust Systems, should be followed, to avoid danger of spread of fire originating in a locker.

In a few industrial plants where protective clothing is furnished and washed by the company, a system of wire baskets, suspended from the ceiling by a small chain running over a pulley, with each employee having his own basket, has proved successful in maintaining cleanliness and thereby reducing the fire hazard.

Where automatic sprinklers are installed, expanded metal or screen tops are necessary on lockers to enable water from sprinklers to reach contents. Paper can be pasted on top to keep dust out. Sloping tops are advisable both from the fire and the accident prevention standpoints. Material cannot be placed on top of a locker so designed.

Wooden supply cupboards constitute a fire hazard in such places as machine and paint shops, where woodwork becomes oil or paint soaked, and where there is a possibility that clothes or oily waste will be left in the cupboards. At all such points, regular inspection is necessary to make certain that proper conditions of cleanliness are being maintained. The ideal cupboards for tools and similar materials are ones made entirely of steel.

D. Outdoor Housekeeping

Good housekeeping is as essential out-of-doors as it is within homes and plant properties. Failure to perform this function well may threaten the fire security of exposed structures and goods stored out-of-doors. The accumulation of rubbish and waste and the growth of tall grass and weeds adjacent to buildings or stored goods are probably the most common hazards. A regular program for the policing of grounds is essential.

Weed and Grass Control

Dry weeds and grass around buildings and along highways and railroad properties present a definite fire hazard, and it has always been the aim of those responsible for the maintenance of these properties to destroy such vegetation. A method often used is the application of some chemical solution which acts as a poison on the weeds. Among the chemicals used have been chlorate compounds, particularly sodium chlorate. Those who have used chlorate compounds, however, have not always realized that they are oxidizing agents; that although they do not burn themselves, they furnish optimum conditions for fire or explosion when in contact with combustible materials. During hot periods in the summer, large numbers of fires have resulted from the use of sodium chlorate solutions on dry grass and weeds. Also fires have been reported in buildings and other properties where such solutions may have been spilled. A personal hazard has arisen when people's clothing has become saturated while servicing a process that has involved the use of such solutions.

Calcium chloride and agricultural borax, applied dry or in solution, are effective nonhazardous weed killers. Various proprietary weed-killing solutions do not involve a fire hazard or serious toxic hazard. Sodium arsenite and other compounds containing arsenic are efficient herbicides but are poisonous and are not generally recommended. Ammonium sulfamate and various other commercial chemical weed killers are available having little or no fire hazard and only a slight toxic hazard. The amounts of various chemicals needed for effective weed killing, and the duration of their effect, vary depending upon the weed-killing agent used, the character of the vegetation, and climatic and soil conditions. Manufacturers' directions indicate the amounts that should be used under various conditions.

Removal of dry grass and weeds by burning is a frequent cause of ignition of buildings when grass fires spread beyond control. Controlled burning at the proper time of the year under direct fire department supervision largely avoids this hazard. A desirable method is to cut grass and remove it or, where outdoor burning is permitted by environmental regulations, burn it in piles, with adequate fire-extinguishing equipment available. Flame-throwing torches, sometimes used for this purpose, have the advantage that they may be used at times when the vegetation is not sufficiently dry to propagate fire readily beyond the area reached by the flame thrower, but themselves introduce a hazard if not carefully operated.

Fire permits issued by fire departments aid in controlling grass and brush fires. These permits provide an opportunity for the fire department to educate the public in safe burning. Also, they provide an opportunity to prohibit burning during hazardous periods, and provide control of burning during other periods.

Refuse and Rubbish Disposal

Where goods are stored outdoors, proper housekeeping will require that passageways between storage piles be kept clear of combustibles of all kind and unobstructed. This latter requirement is necessary to permit efficient fire fighting operations should the need arise. Assuming that the storage itself is properly located with respect to distance from buildings of combustible construction or from other combustible storage which might constitute an exposure hazard, it becomes a housekeeping function to assure that these separations are maintained and not diminished by the introduction, even temporarily, of such things as contractors' shacks, discarded crates, or other combustibles. Proper housekeeping will also require that smoking in areas of outdoor storage be controlled through suitable posting and provision of large, noncombustible receptacles for the disposal of smoking materials before entering a "no smoking" area.

Where combustible waste materials from industrial operations are stored out-doors to await subsequent disposal, it is important that the accumulation be not less than 20 ft and preferably 50 ft distant from buildings, that it be enclosed in a secure noncombustible fence of adequate height, and that it be a safe distance (at least 50 ft) from public highways and sources of ignition, such as incinerators.

For most locations the most satisfactory solution to the rubbish disposal problem is the regular public collection of rubbish. The burning of rubbish is generally unsafe and not permitted in built-up city areas.

Wherever rubbish is dumped, there is a fire danger, even where rubbish is used for land fill. From a dump fire or a bonfire, sparks and flying brands may carry fire long distances. This is true also of burning rubbish in an incinerator which lacks an adequate spark arrester.

In most parts of the United States and Canada, there are certain days when things are so dry that any burning is dangerous. Usually it is safer to burn in the early morning and at night than in the daytime, because of the effect of night moisture in reducing the chance of ignition from sparks. This consideration is the basis for certain regulations of fire departments and forest wardens as to the days or time of day during which burning rubbish outdoors is permitted, if it is permitted at all.

Bibliography

NFPA Codes, Standards, and Recommended Practices (see the latest *NFPA Publications and Visual Aids Catalog* for availability of current editions of the following documents)

NFPA No. 48, Standard for the Storage, Handling and Processing of Magnesium.

NFPA No. 65, Standard for the Processing and Finishing of Aluminum.

NFPA No. 82, Standard on Incinerators and Rubbish Handling.

NFPA No. 91, Standard for the Installation of Blower and Exhaust Systems for Dust, Stock and Vapor Removal or Conveying.

NFPA No. 96, Standard for the Installation of Equipment for the Removal of Smoke and Grease-Laden Vapors from Commercial Cooking Equipment.

NFPA No. 481, Standard for the Production, Processing, Handling and Storage of Titanium.

NFPA No. 482M, Guide for Fire and Explosion Prevention in Plants Producing and Handling Zirconium.

Additional Readings

"How to Apply Good Housekeeping as Protection," Chapter 23, *The Handbook of Property Conservation*, Factory Mutual System, Norwood, Mass., 1973, pp. 189–193.

Morrow, L. C., ed., "Sanitation and Housekeeping," Section 14, *Maintenance Engineering Handbook*, 2nd ed., McGraw-Hill, New York, 1957, pp. 14-1—14-71.

Chapter 12

FOREST, BRUSH, AND GRASS FIRES

Each year, in the United States and Canada, hundreds of thousands of fires occur, involving forest, grass and brush areas and requiring the response of manpower, apparatus and equipment from fire departments, forestry agencies, or both. These fires may range in size and duration from the "nuisance" incident handled by a couple of men and one brush truck from a local fire department, or the "campaign" fire which may continue for days and weeks and necessitate work by hundreds or thousands of fire fighters. The types of fires and tactics, and the apparatus and equipment used for controlling them, vary considerably. Alaska has fires in heavy timber and the long-burning, smoky fires in frozen tundra. British Columbia, Washington, and Oregon have extensive commercial timber problems covering thousands of square miles and fires in these properties may involve timber and debris on the ground, or develop into the fast-moving crown fire that usually requires aerial attack. In the State of California, forest, brush and grass fires are a constant menace, especially from May through December. In the southern portions of that state highly flammable chaparral brush covers thousands of square miles and dangerous, extensive fires occur every year to threaten human life and property.

In the flat, midwestern portions of Canada and the United States grain field fires and grass fires are a constant problem, particularly along railroad rights-of-way when fields are ignited by hot carbon particles emanating from railroad engine exhaust systems or from brake shoes on railroad cars. Most of these fires are handled by small rural and volunteer fire departments, sometimes in cooperation with state and provincial forestry agencies. Usually four-wheel drive vehicles capable of pumping water while in motion are utilized for fire attack in these properties.

In the Eastern Canadian provinces and the northeastern states there are large commercial properties of timber grown primarily for pulp and paper manufacturers. Most of these areas are under close supervision and control of forestry agencies and industrial firms but fires, when they occur in prolonged dry weather, can be extremely bothersome and difficult to control. In New Jersey, Pennsylvania, and other eastern states there are extensive areas of timber land and commercial stock, such as Christmas tree plantations. In the southeastern and south central states there are increasing developments of pine and pulp wood plantations, supplementing the natural growth of scrub pine, oak, and swampland vegetation. The state of Florida has rather unique fire problems. Palm trees, gallberry trees, and commercially grown timber are in the northern portion of the state; the famous Everglades swamps with their quickburning saw grass cover the central portion of the state; and in the south there are large plantations of cypress trees which can be extremely difficult problems when fire develops.

A.   Causes of Fires

By far, the leading cause of forest, brush, and grass fires is human carelessness or accidental action. A second cause of ignition is lightning, but its frequency varies considerably in different geographic areas. The third cause of fire is spontaneous ignition, generally a result of bacteriological action in the vegetative matter. Forestry agencies, fire departments, and all organizations concerned with these fire problems maintain continual public education programs in an attempt to diminish the frequency of those fires attributed to human carelessness.

The frequency of fires started by lightning differs in the several states and provinces. In Florida about 5 percent of all recorded outdoor fires are caused by lightning. In Canada, the Department of Lands and Forests in Ontario attributed 13 percent of outdoor fires to lightning. In Montana, Idaho, Washington, Oregon, and British Columbia lightning strokes can be much more frequent and severe, sometimes starting thirty or forty simultaneous fires. When these fires occur in mountain areas or inaccessible wilderness, they may burn for days and weeks before control is established.

The size and frequency of outdoor fires is greatly affected by seasonal and climatic conditions. Generally, the fire season begins in early spring when surface vegetation and ground litter is dried by strong winds. The fire frequency may subside in some areas as new vegetative growth develops in early summer but then, if long, hot, dry weather occurs this vegetation may contribute to the fire load. The fire potential increases during summer and fall and begins to subside when winter arrives. However, in the southern states, particularly in lower California and Florida, the last two months of the year can bring high fire incidence because of large amounts of dead and desiccated vegetation and extremely high winds. The "Santa Ana" wind condition which sweeps northward from southern California has been a major influence in the disastrous fires and conflagrations that have occurred in that region.[1] In 1970 a long period of dry weather and heavy wind conditions led to multiple fires throughout the state which eventually caused losses estimated at $175,000,000 and damage or destruction of more than 600 homes.

B.   Fire Control Operations

Response to fires in grass, brush, and forested areas involves two types of operations. The first is in areas under organized fire department protection in which outside fires are generally handled by the same personnel charged with structural fire fighting. Where outside fires are common (and they are in most municipalities) it is not unusual for the fire department to maintain special auxiliary apparatus to cope with them. The apparatus may include patrol cars with small water tanks and pumps, tankers, bulldozers, reserve apparatus carrying water tanks, and small hose. Special aircraft, including helicopters, operated on a contract basis or owned and operated by local, state, provincial, or federal authorities, are used increasingly for this type of fire control work.

In the majority of communities, men are detailed to the special apparatus as needed because, in general, outdoor fires are seasonal and depend largely upon weather conditions. The outdoor fire problem presents one of the chief conflagration hazards in hundreds of communities including many major cities. Thousands of dwellings, many with combustible roofs, have been located in areas having extremely combustible ground cover. In addition to specialized apparatus, regular engine companies are frequently used to combat outdoor fires. The high number of such calls during dry, windy weather may seriously reduce the number of companies and manpower available for structural fire fighting, thus requiring use of mutual aid, off-duty personnel, and reserve apparatus.

The other type of operation involves fires on properties which are the responsibility of federal, state, and private forest fire protection agencies. Some districts protected by forestry organizations adjoin municipal fire department areas, and mutual assistance pacts are in effect between the various agencies. In several states the state forest fire fighting equipment is on call from fire officials of the various municipalities. In a number of fire districts, forestry agencies also provide structural fire fighting service, sometimes under contract with small municipalities.

In the United States, protection of national forests and Federal land is divided between the Forest Service, U.S. Department of Agriculture, and the Bureau of Land Management, U.S. Department of Interior. The BLM protects eleven states plus the state of Alaska, a total land area of 400,000,000 acres. The Forest Service protects the national parks and remaining Federal properties throughout the states. A third measure of fire protection is provided by the individual state forestry agencies which altogether protect 500,000,000 acres of woodland under their jurisdiction. Then there are the thousands of paid, call and volunteer fire departments which work closely with the various forestry agencies when the situations demand. In most states, the local fire chiefs are also designated as forest fire wardens.

The agencies concerned chiefly with wildland protection basically have a somewhat different form of organization and different types of equipment from the municipal fire department companies. (NFPA No. 295, Wildfire Control by Volunteer Fire Departments, gives details on the organization and management of this type of fire suppression agency.) Forestry agencies commonly employ labor crews who depend upon lightweight small capacity hose and portable pumps, hand tools for cutting and trenching fire lines, and the use of backfires or control fires. Increasing attention is being given to use of fire retardant chemical solutions for maintaining fire lines and retarding spread of flames at key points. For preventing spread across fire lines, it has been found desirable to trench down to mineral soil so that fire will not eat through dried ground duff and roots and thus pass the intended barrier. It is also necessary that all burning snags be felled and removed or extinguished so that a breeze will not spread sparks across the defense line. In many cases, wetting agents have been successfully employed to make water penetrate burning materials.

Wildland fires frequently do not spread along a uniform front or at a constant speed. Shifting winds are a common problem. At times winds may be traveling in different directions and altitudes, making it difficult to predict the course of a fire.

Fingers of fire may reach the defense line at various times, and when an area is burned over it helps to reduce the fuel available for the main fire. Under skilled leadership, backfires may be employed ahead of the main fire to widen the defense area, to protect isolated properties in the path of the flames, or to eliminate the hazard of a "finger" of unburned terrain in a fire area. In large forest fires part of the threatened area may be sacrificed to reduce the perimeter which must be manned and defended. Frequently, when insufficient forces are available at the early stages of a fire, the decision must be made to abandon certain areas in order

to prepare a more effective stand further back. Such operations require a thorough knowledge of the terrain and fire fighting facilities available and how quickly these can be mobilized. Modern wildland fire fighting operations involve: (1) carefully organized chain of command and command posts, (2) preplanned services of supply, (3) aerial reconnaissance, (4) frequent issuance of fire line maps, and (5) coordinated communications with sufficient radio or communication channels to handle all tactical and supply functions.

A number of the states and provinces have become involved in fire protection compact commissions through which legal requirements for mutual aid operation have been established between states and between the United States and Canada. The Northeastern Fire Protection Compact Commission, for example, involves the six New England states plus New York State and the provinces of Quebec and New Brunswick, covering a total of fifty-five million acres. Aircraft, personnel, and ground apparatus and equipment can be moved quickly to any locations within the compact area. There is a similar arrangement between the state of Alaska and the Yukon Territory of Canada with each country protecting 10 miles each side of the border. Agreements exist between other states and provinces with mutual borders between the two countries.

C. Aircraft Operation

In most wildland areas under organized fire protection, patrols and aircraft are used during fire seasons to spot incipient fires. Air drops of fire fighters and equipment are made where fires are in remote locations. Fire trails are maintained along ridges, in valleys, and other places where access is needed at ground level. These trails may also serve as limited firebreaks. They should be located, constructed, and maintained under the direction of professional foresters if they are to be of appreciable value in fire control. As fires commonly spread with extreme rapidity up slopes, fire trails usually follow the terrain to prevent flames from spreading over a ridge and down the opposite side or to prevent spreading from one slope or flat area to an opposing hillside. Extreme caution must be exercised in fighting a fire that is spreading uphill. Many persons have been killed when caught in such situations. Flanking tactics are used to narrow and channel the fire while men and equipment are deployed for a stand along a line favorable to defense. Air drops are useful in pinching off the head or point of the fire.

The use of fixed wing and rotating wing aircraft for fire control operations has increased significantly during the past decade. At present, something in excess of 150 aircraft are available on contract for reconnaissance and actual fire fighting operations, primarily for the application of water and fire retardance on fires that are beyond the control of ground fire forces. The type and quantity of these aircraft vary between the states and provinces. For example, the Province of Quebec has twelve to fourteen planes available, and these are used for direct application of extinguishing agents on fires or for moving "shock troops" of personnel for strategic operations in fire combat. In Ontario, forty aircraft operate from twenty-six bases primarily for fire detection and attack. Ontario has about 250,000 lakes and ponds, so amphibious aircraft with especially designed scoops use these water sources for quick loading. In the United States, the State of California has about twelve operational aircraft and is planning to increase this to seventeen. Washington, Oregon, and most of the other western states have used aircraft increasingly for forest fire recon-

Fig. 5-12A.   A Lockheed C-130 (MAFFS) airtanker dropping fire retardant.

naissance and fire attack. In most of the other states, fixed fire watch towers are being dismantled because observation and reconnaissance of fire can be done much more effectively by aircraft (see Figs. 5-12A and 5-12B).

The first recorded use of aircraft for fire detection was in the State of Wisconsin in August, 1915. In 1924 the Province of Ontario was using airplanes for this purpose. By 1938 a method was developed for dropping supplies to remote fire camps and in 1939 smoke-jumping started. In 1956 water and chemicals were dropped directly on fires as part of a well-developed operation.

The State of Pennsylvania, for example, includes seventeen million acres of forest land. To protect this territory, the State Division of Forestry has nine helitankers and fixed wing aircraft operating under contract arrangement with thirty-five other aircraft available for fire detection. In 1973 the state had eighty fire towers still in operation but these were gradually being eliminated because of the effectiveness of the air reconnaissance.

At this writing, an interesting trend is the adaptation of military and commercial aircraft for forest fire fighting. Modular units have been developed for helicopters and cargo aircraft to permit accurate dropping of large quantities of fire retardant chemicals. For example, a C-130 aircraft can place three thousand gallons of retardant in an unbroken swath 200 ft wide and 2,000 ft long. Similarly, converted military helicopters can move and hover over specific fire areas to place retardants in the most effective applications.

D. Chemical Fire Retardants

A variety of chemical additives has been developed for use with water in fighting forest, grass, and brush fires. Some of these mixtures are intended as short-term fire retardants; others for long term. All are more effective than plain water at time of application and shortly thereafter, because more water remains on the fuel surfaces. Mixtures that leave a coating on the fuel after the water evaporates provide longer protection against reignitions and burning.

Because of the need for environmental and ecological protection chemicals used as fire retardants must not be toxic or otherwise harmful to fish, animal and human life

Fig. 5-12B.   A Bell helicopter with a 450-gal firebucket.

and to vegetation. In addition, they must be noncorrosive, inexpensive, easy to handle, and stable, that is, capable of retaining their characteristics in water suspension over a period of time. Chemical fire retardants can be applied directly on burning brush or timber or on areas that will soon be exposed to fire. These slurries can also serve to widen fire breaks, control backfires and extinguish spotfires.

Application of chemicals can be made by surface vehicles or by helicopters and fixed-wing tankers. While the use of aircraft for forest fire "bombing" was first tried in 1921, it was not until 1954 that the container or "bomb" method was replaced by the quick-opening tank method. Since then, the tactical use of aerial tankers has increased tremendously.

Those additives which serve only to thicken water are more properly designated as short-term retardants, or fire suppressants, being primarily effective at the time of application. Chemicals used in past years for this purpose included algin (sodium alginate), CMC (carboxymethyl-cellulose), bentonite and other clays, and a proprietary synthetic polymer. Normally thickened solutions are referred to as "viscous water," while "gels" are very thick solutions made by using larger quantities of chemical, or supplementary additives such as calcium alginate.

Mixtures containing thickeners plus flame-inhibiting chemicals are properly referred to as long-term retardants, since they can remain effective long after the water has evaporated by forming actual fire retardant coatings on the

Fig. 5-12C. All-terrain truck developed for BLM, Department of Interior, includes pump, tanks for 1,000 gal of water and 200 gal of fire retardant, two 200-ft hose reels, two 50-degree boom nozzles, a turret nozzle and two outlets for 1,000 ft of hose. Vehicle has 8-wheel drive, a 225 hp engine, and can travel at 50 mph.

fuel. These have included sodium calcium borate with bentonite clay, diammonium phosphate (DAP) or monoammonium phosphate (MAP), with algin or CMC, and ammonium sulfate with attapulgite clay. The phosphates and sulfates offer the added advantage of having fertilizing values, and in fact the chemicals commonly used are commercial grade fertilizers.

In the past few years a lot of research has been in process to evaluate and develop appropriate chemical additives for water application and the most efficient equipment. The U.S. Forest Service laboratories at Missoula, Montana, and San Dimas, California, have been engaged in this research and a number of contracts for such work have been arranged with private firms.

Much of the research effort has been directed to evaluation of aerial application, drop characteristics, tank and gate design on aerial tankers, and techniques of dropping from aircraft. Other research has been concerned with corrosion problems, corrosion inhibitors, chemicals in slurries, and rheological problems of retardants.

An excellent source of information on this subject is the NFPA book, *Chemicals for Forest Fire Fighting,*[2] which discusses the various chemicals, their application, mixing equipment and storage.

E. Research

The U.S. Forest Service, Department of Agriculture and the Bureau of Land Management, Department of Interior maintain continual research programs to develop effective means of fire protection and control. The Forest Service has laboratories at Macon, Georgia, Missoula, Montana, and San Dimas, California. At the time of this writing, projects underway include evaluation of free-burning wildfires in which 60,000 acres of wilderness land have been designated in Montana and Idaho for research in determining what will happen if wildfires are allowed to burn freely. When a lightning fire, or other fire that is accidentally started, occurs, it is permitted to burn, while a second fire nearby is started

and evaluated under precise conditions of temperature, humidity, fuel, terrain and other factors. Then the second fire is attacked and controlled and all results are tabulated and analyzed. Similar experiments are conducted in Louisiana and New Mexico.

Additional research projects include: evaluation of fuel residue, fuel management, the use of helicopters in night operations, and the use of special night vision goggles which utilize starlight. Prescribed burning, the establishment of automatic weather and rainfall reporting stations and computer control of operations are other projects underway.

The BLM has been applying its research with computers for fire problem identification; balloons attached to cables for radio relay and illumination of night operations; and apparatus development, including conversion of surplus military vehicles for forestry pumping units and development of large capacity tank trucks (1,500 to 2,000 gallons) for retardant application.

The forest services in the U.S. and Canada are developing fire danger rating systems for national application. In Ottawa, the Fire Research Institute and the Canadian Forest Service has extended research into fire weather forecasting, lightning detection, fire retardant application, and the tactical use of igniting backfires from aircraft. Both countries have also made extensive use of infrared cameras for fire detection in aerial observation, tied in with a ground computer network.

Bibliography

References Cited

[1] Wilson, Rexford, "The Devil Wind and Wood Shingles," *NFPA Quarterly,* Vol. 55, No. 3, Jan. 1962, pp. 242–287.
[2] *Chemicals for Forest Fire Fighting: A Report of the NFPA Forest Committee,* 2nd ed., National Fire Protection Association, Boston, 1967.

NFPA Codes, Standards, and Recommended Practices (see the latest NFPA Publications and Visual Aids Catalog for availability of current editions of the following documents)

NFPA No. 224, Standard for Homes and Camps in Forest Areas.
NFPA No. 295, Wildfire Control by Volunteer Fire Departments.

Additional Readings

Air Operations for Forest, Grass and Brush Fires, 2nd ed., National Fire Protection Association, Boston, 1975.
"Heliborne Fire Suppression System," *Fire Command!,* Vol. 40, No. 11, Nov. 1973, p. 17.
Lowden, M. S., "Down to the Earth with Fire Fighting Chemicals," *Fire Command,* Vol. 42, No. 7, July 1975, pp. 18–20.
———, "Looking Ahead with the U.S. Forest Service," *Firemen,* Vol. 37, No. 1, Jan. 1970, pp. 17–19.
Lyons, P. R., "Dangers of Outdoor Fires," *Fire Command!,* Vol. 40, No. 3, Mar. 1973, pp. 12–14.
McGuire, B., "Safety First—A Management Challenge," *Fire Command!,* Vol. 41, No. 4, Apr. 1974, pp. 52–54.
Pearson, T. F., "Emulsion Fire Retardant Experiment," *Fire Command!,* Vol. 40, No. 11, Nov. 1973, p. 16.
"Research—U.S. Forest Service," *Fire Command!,* Vol. 39, No. 3, Mar. 1972, pp. 24–25.
"Telecommunications Systems: Principles and Practices for Rural and Forestry Fire Services," National Fire Protection Association, Boston, 1975.
"Training Aids for Forest Fire Control Instructors: A Report of the NFPA Forest Committee," 1st ed., National Fire Protection Association, 1973.

Chapter 13

ELECTRICAL POWER SOURCES

The generation, transmission, and distribution of electrical energy by private electric-power companies and by publicly owned and operated commissions or administrations present many fire prevention and fire protection problems. The power is produced at the generating station, transformed to a higher voltage, sent out over transmission lines to substations, transformed to lower voltage, connected to distribution systems, transformed to still lower voltages, and then supplied through service conductors to the consumer. (Sometimes additional transformations are needed.) There are also many self-contained generating systems, including emergency and stand-by systems.

A. Power Plants

Large generators in power plants produce almost all the electric power used today. Typical power plant generators may have a capacity of 100,000 kW (kilowatts). Turbines drive almost all electric generators in power plants. The two main kinds of turbines are steam and water turbines. Some power plants use gas turbines.

Generating Stations

Power plants using steam turbines produce about four-fifths of the electric power in the United States, and more than two-thirds of the world's electric power. Steam turbine power plants in the United States have a capacity of more than 176 million kilowatts of electricity.

Water turbine plants produce slightly more than one-sixth of the electric power produced in the United States and just less than one-third of the electric power produced in the world.

Some power plants install gas-turbine generators to supply added electric power during periods when the demand for power rises, such as on a dark, cloudy day when more than the normal number of lights may be turned on. Gas turbines can be started more easily and quickly than steam turbines; however, they are not used to produce the normal output of a power plant, because they cost more to operate than steam turbines.

Atomic power plants generate electricity in exactly the same manner as steam-turbine electric power plants. The only difference is an atomic power plant uses a nuclear reactor as a furnace to heat water into steam (see Sec. 4, Chap. 13), instead of using coal or oil burning boilers and furnaces (see Sec. 4, Chap. 1).

Generators driven by diesel engines are widely used as a primary source of electricity in the United States (a total capacity of more than three million kilowatts). Small diesel-, gas-, and gasoline-engines are used to drive small generators, which are used to supply emergency or stand-by power for lighting and equipment in the event of failure of normal power supply in health care facilities, factories, etc. (see Part E of this Chapter).

Fire Causes in Power Plants

Disastrous fires have occurred in power plants caused by ignition of oil used in large steam-turbine-driven generators.

Modern generators of this type (ranging from 15,000 to 1,000,000 kVA) are generally hydrogen cooled, and completely enclosed and pressurized. The hydrogen, kept automatically at 95 percent purity, presents no fire or explosion hazard in the generator itself, as long as the percent purity is maintained, even if insulation failure develops.

Oil lubricates the generator and turbine bearings, provides pressure to operate the turbine governor, and furnishes a seal to prevent the escape of hydrogen from around the bearings. If a leak should develop and spray oil onto any of the hot turbine parts or steam piping operating at temperatures in excess of 500°F, ignition would be immediate. The fire will generally grow beyond control by portable extinguishers while the turbine coasts to a full stop, sometimes a matter of as long as 20 min, at which time the oil stops flowing.

The retaining rings on the rotors of large generators sometimes fail mechanically, and large pieces of the retaining rings, sometimes weighing hundreds of pounds, can be thrown through the generator casing, breaking the oil lines and causing the oil to ignite. Under these conditions, on a few occasions, the escaping hydrogen has mixed with air and exploded.

Fire Protection for Power Plants

A suitable supply of portable and wheeled type portable extinguishers, and ample small hose equipped with water spray nozzles is the first line of defense. Fixed fire protection systems with the capability of protecting bearings, high pressure oil lines, oil filters, coolers, reservoirs, etc., and oil storage rooms and the supporting members of the turbo-generator, should receive serious consideration.

A suggested safeguard against the oil fire hazard is locating the pressurized oil supply lines to generating units inside return piping or drain lines and separating the whole assembly as much as possible from steam lines or hot turbine parts. Exposed hot parts are insulated and the insulation covered with metal or some other covering impervious to oil. Parts, such as stop valves, that cannot be well insulated are shielded for protection against water discharged from sprinkler or spray systems. The basement area under the turbine, where the oil equipment is located, is protected with automatic sprinklers (see Sec. 14). Any oil piping at locations such as the governor, pressure regulators, gages, etc., is protected with directional spray nozzles (see Sec. 15, Chap. 2).

The trend towards remote or automatic control of generating stations, with the attendant reduction in operating personnel, emphasizes the need for this type of automatic fire protection.

Generators smaller than 15,000 kVA are usually not hydrogen cooled. Fires in these smaller units (up to about 3,000 kVA, of the open-frame or the air-cooled type) usually can be controlled with hand extinguishers. Units from 3,000 to 15,000 kVA of the totally enclosed recirculating air-cooled types are usually protected with automatic carbon dioxide systems (see Sec. 15, Chap. 4). These machines may have additional protection against damage from internal faults through installation of differential relays that trigger the carbon dioxide system if an electrical fault occurs in the windings.

Construction of Power Plants

Most large steam-electric power plants consist essentially of three main areas: the boiler section, the turbo-generator section, and the switch section. In older installations, these three sections were located side by side with fire walls separating them. The practice now is to have one large open building housing the turbo generator and its condensing apparatus at one side, and the boiler house with its many balconies, steel platforms, and floors at the other side. The electrical switching apparatus is contained in large steel cabinets, usually located on one of the balconies. Some power plants have been built without enclosing walls for the boiler house, and in warm climates even the turbine is exposed to the weather.

There is a tendency in colder climates to construct modern buildings without windows or adequate venting means to relieve the pressure of an internal explosion and permit the escape of the heated products of combustion. It is important that in windowless turbine rooms, the rooms be equipped with large skylight areas or large automatic vents. (See Fig. 5-13A.)

Power Plant Switchgear

It is a generally accepted practice that high-voltage switchgear associated with the power plant be located out-of-doors. Failure of every piece of switchgear should be considered a possibility, and provisions should be taken to limit the magnitude and area of such failure. Safety of operating personnel, major apparatus, and equipment from contact with high-voltage circuits, fire, and water, at the time of serious trouble, must be assured as it is on these precautions power plant service can be restored with the least delay. Power plant design is based on the causes of failure and the means of minimizing their effects. The switchgear, which is required for the operation of the power plant, is designed from the standpoint of simplicity and reliability of operation (see Part C of this chapter).

Power Plant Grounding

Grounding at power plants ensures that noncurrent-carrying parts, such as equipment frames, are at ground

Fig. 5-13A. The extent of damage at the Picway Generating Station in Columbus, Ohio, from a fire caused by ignition of lubricating oil escaping under 15 psi from the lubricating system of a 30,000 kW turbo-generator. The fire burned with such intensity that steel roof trusses 50 ft overhead collapsed.

potential even though insulation fails. In addition, good grounding practices require a ground connection for grounded neutral systems; a means of positively discharging and deenergizing feeders or equipment before proceeding with maintenance on them; and a discharge path for lightning arresters, gaps, and similar devices. On occasion power plants have experienced extensive damage and hazardous conditions where grounding was inadequate. An adequate ground that will not burn off or permit dangerous rise in voltage under abnormal conditions is essential. Metallic water pipes of adequate size are used for ground connections; where metallic water pipes are not available, other available electrodes are used (see Part D, Sec. 7, Chap. 2).

B. Transmission Lines

Generating electricity is only part of the process of supplying electrical energy. The electricity must be transmitted from the power plant to the area where it is to be used—then, from that area to the individual user.

Electric power companies generally operate a number of generating plants at various locations. The transmission lines of one station are usually connected in a network with the transmission lines of the utilities of other power plants. If one power plant receives a demand for additional power, it has the assistance of the other power plants to meet the demand. The transmission systems of several utility companies can be linked together. This interconnecting network of transmission lines is called a "grid." A grid provides reserves of electrical energy. Each utility usually has spare generators that can supply power as needed. If any one utility has a power failure the individual users in that area should not be without power.

At the generating station, the voltage is frequently stepped up from about 13.8 kV to as high as 66 kV for general transmission to substations. Where the transmission line is of great length and carrying a heavy power load, the voltage may be stepped up to well over 100 kV. Then at a bulk power station it may be stepped down again to 27 kV or 13 kV. At the substations, the voltage is further reduced for the overhead and underground distribution systems. At or near the consumers' premises, it is again reduced to suitable voltages for motors, lighting, and other industrial requirements. Fig. 5-13B is a graphic illustration of a typical layout and the voltages for transmission and distribution lines, although these voltages vary widely in different sections of the country.

Overhead Lines

Overhead lines are commonly used for power transmission lines in rural and residential areas. The so-called "high line" (meaning high voltage line) is normally suspended by long insulators from galvanized steel towers. To protect the current-carrying phase wires from a direct hit by lightning, one or two grounded wires are usually stretched from tower to tower above the phase wires to furnish a better path to ground for the lightning.

In some parts of the country, high voltage transmission lines are carried on "A" frames or "H" frames built up from wood poles (see Fig. 5-13C).

There is no combustible material of any kind in a high-line steel tower, but the very slender, highly stressed tower structural members may weaken and possibly buckle if a serious grass or brush fire should occur at the base of the tower. Hence, all brush should be controlled by cutting or

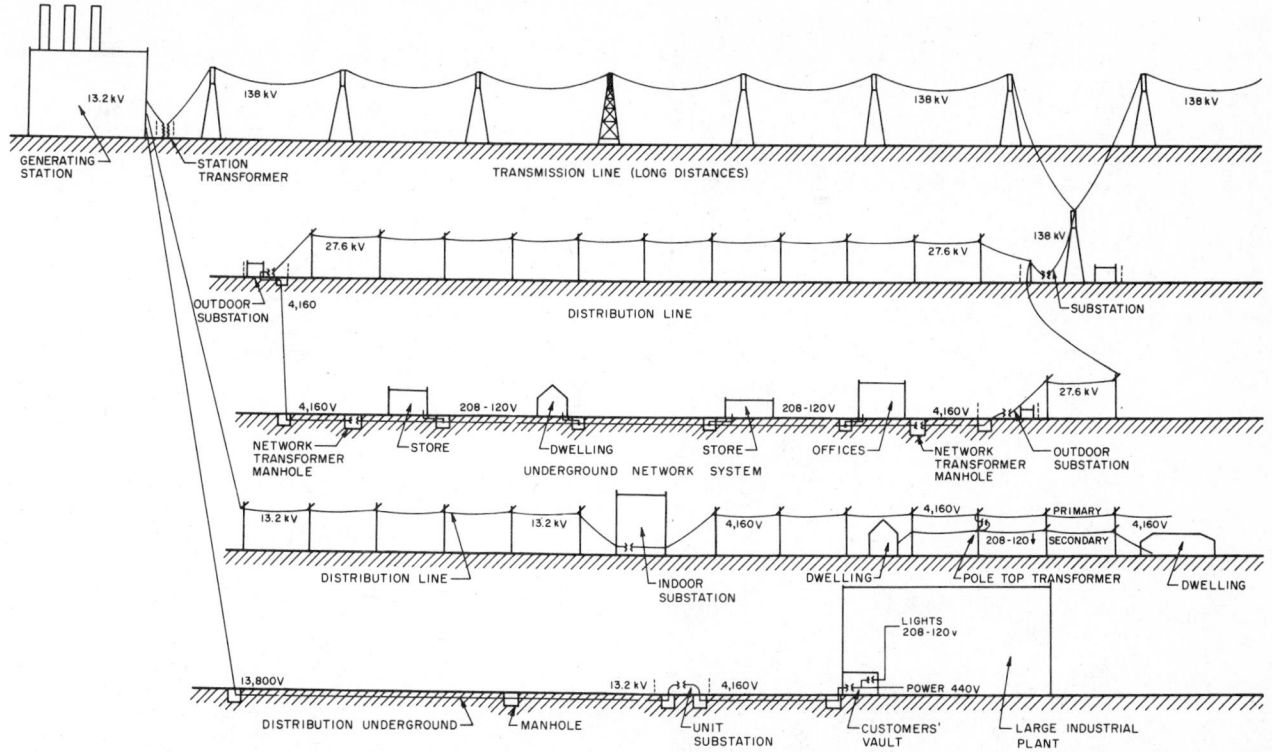

Fig. 5-13B. Overhead and underground electric transmission and distribution systems are schematically shown in this diagram. The voltages shown are typical but vary in different sections of the country. The high tension lines are normally suspended from steel towers, and to protect these lines against direct lightning strokes, two grounded wires are usually stretched from tower to tower above the phase wires to minimize insulation flashover by furnishing a good path to ground. These grounded wires are not shown on the diagram.

chemicals within about 25 ft of the tower legs and from wood-pole structures (see Fig. 5-13D).

As shown in Fig. 5-13E, the ordinary transmission or express primary wires are carried on large insulators mounted

Fig. 5-13C. A wood "H" frame high voltage transmission line tower. Undergrowth at the base of towers poses a potential fire hazard. Brush can be controlled by cutting or by use of herbicides within 25 ft of the poles.

on the top crossarms of wood poles. The distribution primary wires are carried on the next lower crossarm, and the secondary wires serving the customer are usually on a still lower crossarm or on a bracket mounted vertically on the side of the pole.

Of interest particularly to fire fighters are the approximate voltages of the wires on the various crossarms. The position of the wire on the insulator, the size and shape of the insulator, and its position on the pole assist in identifying the wires. Transmission lines on single wood poles sometimes have the three-phase wires arranged in a triangle, one wire being at the top of the pole and one at each end of the top crossarm. Fire fighters should also have respect for any wire stretched from pole to pole, since a high voltage line might possibly be mistaken for a telephone cable. Fire fighters should be wary of any wire or cable on a utility pole.

In other than rural areas, a static wire, as such, is seldom provided on wood poles for protection against lightning, although on one of the crossarms of the pole there are usually three-phase wires and a grounded neutral wire. This neutral wire under certain conditions will carry current and also, when properly located above the phase wires, will shield them against lightning strokes. At some poles lightning arresters are installed at the phase wires to protect nearby transformers. Particularly in residential and business areas, small size transformers and regulators are suspended from the crossarms of wood poles at crossarm levels (see Part D of this chapter).

Wood poles are usually impregnated with oil-type preservatives such as creosote or penta-chlorophenol-petroleum for protection against insects and decay. Occasionally, due to a flashover or other abnormal condition, the wood at the top of a pole may become ignited. This condition frequently results in a slow, smoky fire which can usually be easily

Fig. 5-13D. High voltage transmission lines supported on large steel towers. Fire at the base of the towers could seriously weaken or possibly collapse them.

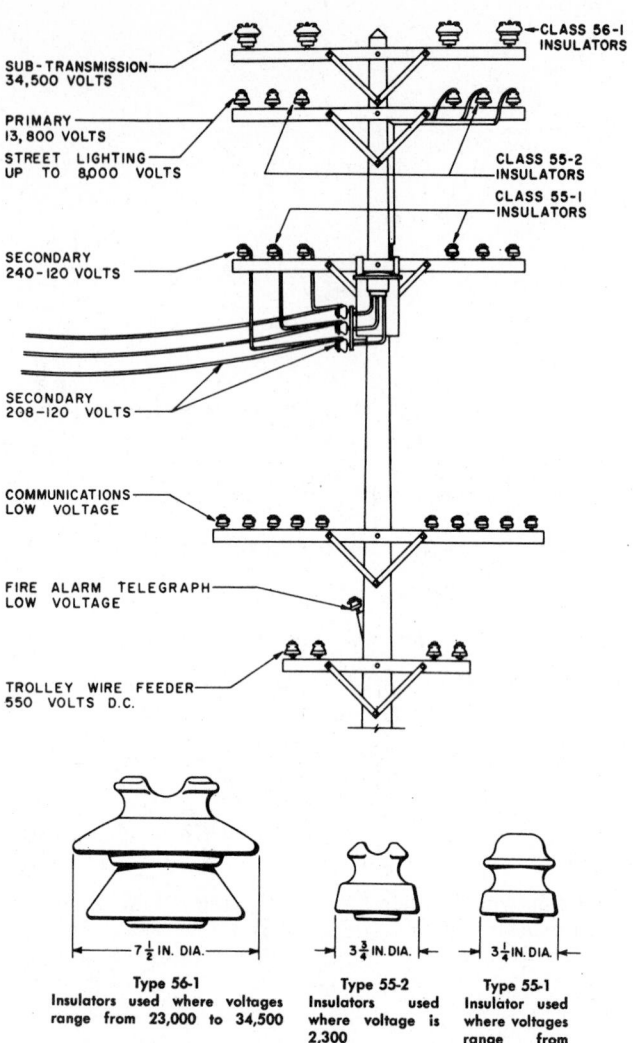

Fig. 5-13E. Types of insulators and the range of voltages carried on each. (The pole illustrates many types of circuits but is not a typical installation.)

extinguished by using an appropriate portable extinguisher after the power circuit has been deenergized. All combustible vegetation near poles should be kept down and combustible trash kept away.

Underground Lines

Underground lines are used in the congested sections of large cities for the primary and secondary power lines. Concrete vaults or "manholes" are located several hundred feet apart along the line to act as junctions for branch lines and for services into customers' premises. The NEC (National Electrical Code) requires that the open ends of the ducts or conduits carrying the service cables into buildings be sealed within the building by a suitable sealing compound to prevent the passage of gases and vapors from underground network systems into buildings. This rule also applies to spare raceways from such systems. High voltage cables are sometimes covered with asbestos tape or asbestos and cement to prevent damage by arcing or fire in case of insulation failure in manholes, and stress cones are provided at terminals.

Some large manholes contain network transformers and network protectors for serving the network or grid of cables supplying the area. The secondary (frequently 120/208 volts) cables are often fed by several network transformers so that in event of failure of a single power cable or transformer, the others will keep the system in service.

It is dangerous for anyone but an authorized electric company employee to enter a manhole in event of a fire. Fire fighters arriving in response to a manhole fire alarm must keep in mind that, in most electrical fires, the damage has

been done at the instant of the short circuit, and that the affected transformer or other apparatus will have to be replaced. Therefore, there is usually nothing to be gained by rushing in to extinguish the resulting smoky insulation fire. Carbon dioxide or dry chemical hose line applications or extinguishers may be used without entering the manhole; otherwise, fire fighters should await the arrival of the electric company's emergency crew, and then cooperate with them.

For many residential developments, direct burial underground services have come into wide use to eliminate poles and overhead wires. This type underground service usually has no manholes, but may have handholes. In most cases, the supply is derived from aboveground, pad-mounted transformers and terminates in aboveground junction boxes mounted outside or just inside the walls of the residences, usually a basement wall for residences with basements. Such underground services are encased in short lengths of raceway where they emerge from the ground; but the raceway in this type of underground installation is not required to be sealed where it enters a building because the supply end is not terminated in a network tunnel, as it is in underground services that are derived from a network system in which gases may be present.

C. Substations

In power plants of all types, whether they are steam, hydro, or gas turbine, the larger units transmit the power from the generator through isolated phase buses to the main power transformer for each unit and then to a substation, a location remote from the power plant where the main breakers are located.

Modern designs for substations have revolutionized the building of power plants. The acceptance of electronic relaying, millisecond switching operations, vacuum and gas-breaker technology, and the use of compressed gas insulation has aided the advancement and growth.

Substations are of several types, such as the bulk power switching station; the older style indoor substation; the more modern outdoor substation; the small isolated unit substation consisting of three single-phase transformers or one three-phase transformer, and some control cabinets surrounded by a chain-link fence; the transformer vault in the premises of a large industrial plant or under the sidewalk; and the transformer manhole located under a city street.

When selecting the site for a proposed substation, consideration should be given to the fire exposure presented by neighboring buildings of nonfire resistive construction to the high value electrical apparatus. Likewise, a transformer fire should not endanger neighboring buildings.

Substation Transformers

Transformers installed in the various types of substations are quite similar, varying mostly in size and in fire hazard. Most transformers are liquid cooled using a nonconductive liquid, usually askarel (a synthetic nonflammable liquid) or

Fig. 5-13F. A large substation transformer. Note the fans, much like large domestic fans, that cool the unit.

a flammable, inhibited mineral insulating oil. The liquid is circulated around the hot core of the transformer and carries the heat to the radiator fins outside of the transformer casing where the liquid is air cooled. (This is quite similar in operation to the cooling system on an automobile engine.) In many installations large electric fans (see Fig. 5-13F), similar in appearance to a domestic fan, bring more air into contact with the cooling coils or fins and assist in keeping the transformer cool. Some large transformers have the oil cooled by pumping it through heat exchangers. Other types of transformers are oil and water cooled, air cooled, or gas cooled. Sulfur hexa-fluoride (SF_6) is now being used in specially designed transformers. It is noncombustible. (See Part D of this chapter.)

Substation Switchgear

There are three insulating mediums used for substation switchgear (high-voltage): oil, air, and sulfur hexafluoride (SF_6).

Oil-filled Circuit Breakers: These may be found in units up to 345 kV in size. Although this type of circuit breaker is the easiest to assemble and install, there are limitations on application because of voltage stress and the lack of control of the magnitude of switching surges. If switching surge voltage exceeds 2.5 times its rating, an oil breaker should not be used.

Air-blast Breakers: These use dry air at high pressures, ranging from 350 to 800 psi for insulation between live parts and across the contacts and the pressure enclosure tank. During interruption of the circuit, high pressure air is used for extinguishing the arc. The air is compressed to approximately 2,000 psi. The need for high pressure containments and the requirement for dry air are drawbacks in the air-blast breakers. Any rupture in the pneumatic system can drop the pressure to the point where electrical clearance to the tank or between contacts would be inadequate and a flashover could result. Any rupture or interruption in the pneumatic system can cause the pneumatic trip mechanism not to function; the breaker then would not be able to open and interrupt the fault. Loss-of-pressure relays installed to trip the breaker at prescribed settings, and motor-operated breaker disconnects that will open and isolate the breaker prior to flashover are recommended. Disconnects would open under load if sudden loss of pressure occurred. To prevent damage under this condition, the opening of remote breakers must be relayed properly. Eighty percent of the breakers installed at substations are air-blast breakers. It is important that relaying is correct.

Gas-filled Breakers: These are becoming more common because of the insulation values that have been inherent with their use. Air for a number of reasons does not provide a better breaker than electronegative gas; gas has a super insulating characteristic in comparison to air. This permits operation at lower pressures while still sustaining the same voltage levels and operational characteristics as compressed air breakers. SF_6 breakers operate at approximately 45 psi, and the gas is stored at approximately 270 psi. SF_6 will provide protection against contact-to-contact or contact-to-enclosure tank flashover even if used at atmospheric pressure at normal system voltage. The gas-filled breaker permits interruption of higher currents than compressed air without use of any other means. Complete interruption of the fault has been reduced to two cycles from the time the relay energizes the trip coil until the circuit is cleared.

Vacuum Breakers: These are used up to and including 230 kV. They are economical and operate in 2 cycles or less. Their major application, as an alternative to other breakers, has been in transformers with limited ratings of 600 amp continuous and 4,000 amp interrupting. Violent reaction usually does not occur if the load imposed exceeds the breaker's rating, but could result in excessive contact erosion. The low mechanical shock experienced when clearing a fault and the low noise and lack of flammable oil content has made the use of vacuum breakers attractive for low voltage protection.

Substation Grounding

A low resistance grounding system cannot be over-emphasized at a substation. Ground current surges must be dissipated effectively to limit the potential rise across the insulation, thus eliminating line-to-line and line-to-ground fault. The grounding grid at the substation must have the capabilities to handle fault currents and discharge surges. Relaying depends on consistant grounding resistance, and personal safety is only possible through adequate grounding. Good practice calls for testing the ground system at the substation annually to assure its integrity within acceptable limits of resistance.

Lightning Protection for Power Sources and Distribution Lines

Lightning protection is provided for generating stations and substations in locations where thunderstorms are frequent and where circuits entering or leaving the station are overhead. (See Sec. 15, Chap. 8 for a full discussion on lightning protection.) Lightning arresters are designed to protect electrical equipment by providing a safe path to ground for high potentials caused by lightning discharges and thus prevent the breakdown of insulation and danger of ensuing fire in the electrical equipment so protected.

A lightning arrester preferably should be connected to each ungrounded overhead conductor entering or leaving the station, but where several overhead circuits are connected to a station bus, a single set of arresters may be connected to the bus where means are provided to protect circuits that may remain disconnected from the bus. (For lightning protection of overhead transmission and distribution feeders, see Fig. 5-13F.)

A lightning arrester usually consists of a series gap and so-called "valve" material which becomes conducting only when exposed to high potentials.

Alternating current generators and other ac rotating machines which are connected to exposed overhead lines are especially susceptible to damage by lightning surges coming in over supply lines and need special protection. This consists of two types of lightning arresters and a set of protective capacitors. One set of standard line type arresters should be installed on each exposed line connected to the machine located approximately 1,500 ft from the machine, and a set of low impulse spark-over station type arresters in parallel with protective capacitors should be installed at the machine terminals. To obtain protection against direct lightning strokes to the exposed line or lines connected to the machine, the overhead lines should be shielded by overhead ground wires for a distance of at least 1,500 ft from the machine. They should be installed in such a manner that the protected wires are within an angle of 20 degrees of a vertical line through the ground wire. This overhead ground wire should also be connected to the ground wire at the line arresters and to the common ground connection for the machine arresters and capacitors and the machine frame.

D. Transformers

Although transformer failures appear to be common, percentage-wise they are few, considering the hundreds of thousands in service. A study of all transformer failures over a 5-year period, excluding instrument and furnace transformers, showed fire developing in 64 of 430 losses caused by lightning, electrical breakdown, and fire.

There are three major types of transformers in use: the dry-type, the askarel-insulated type, which contains a nonflammable insulating liquid, and the oil insulated.

Dry-type transformers are safer than the oil-insulated type. The dry-type transformer has only one-half the impulse resistance of the liquid-insulated type making them more susceptible to lightning damage. They are impregnated with varnish and will burn if subjected to a sustained short circuit. Dry-type transformers are available as sealed tank transformers. The sealed tank type are constructed with the windings installed in a tightly sealed tank and the interior filled with sulfur hexaflouride gas (SF_6). With the SF_6 type, no special safeguards are required as there is no fire or explosion hazard.

Askarel-insulated type transformers are most desired because the askarel liquid is noncombustible; however, the cost of askarel-insulated transformers is higher than the oil-insulated type.

Oil-insulated type transformers are the most popular. Internal failure in this type transformer can result in the expulsion of burning oil through a tank vent or rupture, extensively damaging the transformer and the surrounding area, making the oil-insulated transformer the least desirable from a fire-hazard standpoint. For outdoor installations the oil-insulated type transformer is widely used.

The NEC provides detailed requirements for installing transformers at both indoor and outdoor locations. These requirements give consideration to voltage, size, drains, combustibles in close proximity, fire resistant construction, vaults, raised curbs, separation, and overcurrent protection (see Sec. 7, Chap. 2).

Protection Against Transformer Fires

Electrical failures and fires in transformers, feeders, etc., may be caused by events occurring at a distance from the substation, such as by a lightning discharge or other heavy surges of current, a squirrel climbing on a transformer insulator bushing, or a laborer digging in a city street and driving the point of a pneumatic drill into a conduit and thence into a high voltage power cable. From any of these causes, a disturbance or interruption in the substation or generating station·is certain to follow.

Transformers containing appreciable quantities of flammable, inhibited mineral insulating oils with flash points ranging from 130°C (260°F) to 135°C (280°F) are placed at least 25 ft away from windows or other openings in the walls of the substation control building and from other important structures or placed in a vault of the type specified in the NEC. Askarel-insulated transformers are vented to the outside if placed indoors and if rated in excess of 25 kVA. If rated at more than 35,000 V, askarel types are placed in vaults (as defined in the NEC) if indoors.

Oil-insulated transformers may be placed on or near the outside walls of buildings or structures provided that they are separated from combustible materials, windows, or other openings, fire escapes, etc., by fire resistant barriers, and that they are provided with enclosures for oil from ruptured transformers. Automatic fire protection equipment is commonly utilized to protect such installations. If the substation is to be located on sloping ground, the oil drainage conditions must be considered.

Transformer vent discharge pipes are generally arranged so as not to throw burning oil onto other transformers, buildings, public streets, etc. To prevent such a hazard in a congested area, it is common to find walls constructed between the adjacent transformers and along the property line. In fact, such barriers are often placed on three sides of each large transformer (see Fig. 5-13D).

A concrete basin is frequently built under the transformer to confine the transformer oil should it leak from the casing. Usually this basin is filled with 1½-in. crushed stone to a depth of from 6 in. to several feet (see Fig. 15-2B). If the leakage of burning oil from the ruptured casing is not excessive, the voids around the stones may contain most of the oil, thus permitting only the thin coating remaining on the top stones to burn off and the fire to go out. A drain pipe is often installed to carry away the oil to a pit or to a low area a safe distance away, but the pipe should contain a liquid-seal trap to extinguish any flame entering the pipe.

Modern transformers, because of their cost, sometimes in excess of a half million dollars, warrant special fire protection such as water spray or carbon dioxide systems (see Sec. 14, this HANDBOOK). There is sufficient value in the thousands of gallons of oil and external attachments (fans, controls, tap changing equipment, instruments, bushings, lightning arrestors) to justify some type of fixed fire extinguishing equipment. Barriers of noncombustible material are recommended between adjacent oil-insulated transformers.

E. Other Power Sources

Generally, there are two possible sources of electrical energy. The one most commonly used is the electric utility that serves the area; the other is the private generating plant. Storage batteries are used as a source of electrical energy when other sources fail or are not available.

Self-contained Electric Systems

In remote areas not served by an electric utility, usually because the cost is prohibitive to extend power lines from the nearest source, self-contained electric systems are used. These systems vary in size and type according to need and availability of fuel to supply the prime mover (see Sec. 4, Chap. 2). Self-contained automatic gas-, gasoline-, or diesel-engine generators are widely used for an emergency source in the event of power failure. The voltage and frequency of these sources are the same as the normal supply. The emergency or stand-by source is connected to the system or a portion of the system by means of an automatic or manual transfer switch.

Emergency systems are generally installed in places of assembly, hotels, theatres, sports arenas, hospitals and similar institutions and high rise buildings. Emergency systems may provide power for such functions as essential refrigeration, operation of mechanical breathing apparatus, ventilation when essential to maintain life, illumination and power for hospital operating rooms, fire alarm systems, fire pumps, industrial processes where current interruption would produce serious hazards, public address systems and similar functions (see Sec. 7, Chap. 2).

Standby electric systems are generally installed to provide an alternate source of electric energy to serve loads, such as heating and refrigeration systems, communications systems, and industrial processes that, when stopped during any power outage or failure, could cause discomfort, serious

interruption of the process, or damage to the product or process, or the like.

Generators

Electric generators, dynamos, rotary converters, and motor-generator sets present the usual hazard of rotating electrical equipment. They should be in clean, dry locations, preferably in a separate room or section of a building with adequate supervision. They may be placed outdoors if of a type approved for the purpose. The locations are such that necessary maintenance can be readily accomplished. Any combustible material adjacent to them is suitably protected. Constant potential generators are protected from excessive current by circuit breakers or fuses. Alternating-current generators can be so designed that on excessive overload the voltage falls off sufficiently to limit the current and power output to values that will not injure the generator during a short period of time. Whether or not automatic overcurrent protection of a generator should be omitted is a question that can best be answered in each individual case. It is omitted sometimes where there is an operator in constant attendance who will shut the machine down only if the overload is excessive. This is to avoid unnecessary power interruptions because of harmless momentary overloads.

Storage Batteries

The term "battery" is commonly used today in the context of describing the electrical storage battery, or a series of two or more cells connected together to furnish electrical current. Knowing the hazards that can be encountered with batteries is particularly important insofar as batteries are being used more and more as a power source for many different mobile devices and emergency power units.

Storage batteries are of several types. One is the so-called lead-acid type, in which the positive plates consist of lead grids having openings filled with a semi-solid compound, commonly lead peroxide, and the negative plates are covered with sponge lead, the plates being immersed in dilute sulfuric acid. A second type is the alkali type, in which the active materials are nickel peroxide for the positive plate and iron oxide for the negative plate, and the electrolyte is chiefly potassium hydroxide. A third type is the nickel cadmium battery. In this type, the positive material is nickelic hydroxide $Ni(OH)_3$ mixed with about 25 percent graphite and the negative material is cadmium containing about 25 percent iron oxide. The electrolyte is potassium hydroxide (KOH) in distilled water.

Storage batteries in unsealed jars or tanks, where the aggregate capacity at the 8-hr discharge rate exceeds 5 kwh, should be kept in separate battery rooms.

Hydrogen evolved when electric batteries are recharged can give rise to an explosion risk if it is allowed to accumulate sufficiently—but the danger is small in the case of the modern enclosed type of lead-acid battery. Dispersing the hydrogen by providing effective ventilation throughout the charging room is the most essential precaution. Hydrogen is lighter than air and will tend to concentrate at ceiling level, so ventilation must be provided in the ceiling or roof or, failing this, high up on outside walls; avoid unventilated structural pockets in the ceiling. A ban on smoking and naked lights in the vicinity of charging batteries must be strictly enforced.

When open batteries are recharged there is an additional risk because of the trace amounts of acid vapor that may be liberated into the atmosphere above. Though the vapors will not be present in toxic quantities, the acid may corrode nearby metalwork, thus producing more hydrogen. In rooms for charging this type of battery, or in charging rooms located in the middle of a building, it may be necessary to install forced ventilation in the ceiling or roof. But the fan motor should not be placed within the duct or gas stream since hydrogen may accumulate when the motor is shut down, and may be ignited when it restarts; the fan should be driven by a suitably sealed drive through the wall of the duct.

Experience of incidents in charging areas has shown that there is also a risk of explosions occurring in the battery casings themselves, because of the presence of dissociated hydrogen and oxygen within the casing. The most likely source of ignition is arcing when terminal leads are connected or disconnected in a careless way, and the main danger if an explosion occurs is that the casing will shatter and splash the operator with acid.

Battery output is greatly reduced at low temperatures. The liquid in a battery, when fully charged, has a specific gravity of 1.275 at a temperature of 80°F. As temperature drops, the ampere-hour capacity decreases to 75 percent of the ampere hour capacity at 40°F, and to 50 percent at 10°F. Reduction in temperature causes a further loss of energy in the cells due to a drop in voltage. A partly discharged cold battery may not have sufficient power, although the same battery may be adequate at 80°F. On the other hand, the time that a battery will hold its charge decreases as temperatures increase. At 80°F a battery will completely discharge in 120 days, but at 100°F it will completely discharge in only 50 days, and at 120°F, in 20 days.

SI Units

The following conversion factors are given as a convenience in converting to SI units the English units used in this chapter.

1 in.	= 25.400 mm
1 ft	= 0.305 m
1 psi	= 6.895 kPa
$\frac{5}{9}(°F - 32)$	= °C

Bibliography

NFPA Codes, Standards, and Recommended Practices (see the latest *NFPA Publications and Visual Aids Catalog* for availability of current editions of the following documents)

NFPA No. 12, Standard on Carbon Dioxide Extinguishing Systems.
NFPA No. 13, Standard for the Installation of Sprinkler Systems.
NFPA No. 68, Guide for Explosion Venting.
NFPA No. 70, National Electrical Code.
NFPA No. 70B, Electrical Equipment Maintenance.
NFPA No. 78, Lightning Protection Code.
NFPA No. 801, Recommended Fire Protection Practice for Facilities Handling Radioactive Materials.
NFPA No. 802, Recommended Fire Protection Practice for Nuclear Reactors.

SECTION 6

FIRESAFETY IN BUILDING DESIGN AND CONSTRUCTION

Chapter 1

FUNDAMENTALS OF FIRESAFE BUILDING DESIGN

Building design and construction practices have changed significantly during the past century. One hundred years ago structural steel was unknown, and reinforced concrete was a material that had not yet been used for structural framing applications. The first "high rise building" had yet to be built in the United States of America.

The design professions have also advanced significantly during the past century. The practice of architecture has changed markedly, and techniques of analysis and design are available to engineers today that were unknown a century, or even a generation ago. Building design has become a very complex process, integrating many skills, products, and technologies into its system.

Fire protection engineering has made strides in its professional development similar to that of the other parts of the building industry. At the turn of the century conflagrations were a common occurrence in cities. Increased knowledge of fire behavior and building design enabled buildings to be constructed where a hostile fire could be confined to the building of origin, rather than the block of origin or larger areas. Progress continued to be made in the field of fire protection engineering so that a generation ago a hostile fire could be confined to the floor of origin. At the present time knowledge is available that enables a hostile fire to be confined to the room of origin or even to smaller spatial subdivisions.

In recent years tremendous progress has been made in the technology of fire protection and fire design. This Section of the HANDBOOK will identify the system of building design for firesafety. It will attempt to identify the state of the art in a field that is changing dynamically in its analysis and design capabilities.

A. Design and Firesafety

The conscious, integrated design for building firesafety must be done as a part of the architectural design process if it is to be effective and economical. All members of the traditional building design team should include emergency fire conditions as an integral part of their design activities. The earlier firesafety objectives are identified and engineering design decisions are made, the more effective and economical the final results will be.

America Burning: The Report of the National Commission on Fire Prevention and Control,[1] identifies several areas in which building designers create unnecessary hazards, often unwittingly, for the building occupants. In some cases this is the result of oversight or insufficient understanding of the interpretations of test results. In other cases it is due to a deficiency in the knowledge on which firesafety standards are based.

The Commission's report cites that conscious incorporation of firesafety into buildings is too frequently given minimal attention by the designer, and further that building designers are content, as are their clients, to meet the minimum safety standards of the local building code. Often both assume incorrectly that the codes provide completely adequate measures, rather than minimal ones. In other instances, building owners and occupants see fire as something that will never happen to them, as a risk that they will tolerate because firesafety measures can be costly, or as a risk adequately balanced by the provisions of a fire insurance policy.

Unfortunately, conditions arising from these attitudes need not exist, much less continue. There is information available for the design professional to incorporate a greater measure of fire protection into his designs. Its use requires that the various members of the building design team recognize that fire conditions are a legitimate element of their design responsibilities. In addition, it will require a greater understanding on the part of the building designer of the special loadings that fire causes on building elements, and of the countermeasures that can be incorporated into their designs.

Objectives of Firesafety Design

Before the building designer can make effective decisions relating to firesafety, he must clearly identify the specific needs of the client with regard to the function of the building. The designer must consciously ask appropriate questions and ascertain the general and the unique conditions that are incorporated into his building. These questions center around decisions relating to the following three areas:

1. Life safety.
2. Property protection.
3. Continuity of operations.

The art of probing to identify firesafety objectives is an important design function. The degree of risk that will be tolerated by the owner and the occupants is a difficult design decision. Consequently, it is often not identified in a clear, concise manner that will enable the designer to provide properly for the realization of the design objectives. And, unfortunately, it is impossible in a handbook to provide more than guidelines for the identification of the objectives.

Life Safety: When considering life safety, for example, it is not sufficient to say: "Save everyone!" Rather, one must ask: "Who will be using the building, and what will they be doing most of the time?" After identifying the specific functional patterns, constraints, and handicaps, specific design features that recognize the occupant conditions can be incorporated into the design. This is merely an extension of the analysis of traffic circulation patterns in a building. Protective devices can then be installed in locations that reflect the identified life safety needs.

Property Protection: These requirements are often somewhat easier to identify and control. For instance, is there any specific high-valued property that needs special design protection? Card catalogs for libraries, for example, often the most valuable contents of a library, are particularly sensitive to fire and water damage. Do these vital records, or other specific items, need special design considerations?

Continuity of Operations: The aspect of continuity of operations is the third general category of consideration. In this area, the owner must identify the degree of "downtime" that can be tolerated. Often, specific functions are more essential to continuity of operations than others. (The card catalog cited in the example of the library relates very directly to continuity of operations.) Where operations can be transferred to other locations, the degree of protection need not be as complete as those operations which are vital to continued functioning.

Handbook Intent and Scope

At the time of publication of this HANDBOOK much activity was taking place with regard to building design for fire safety. The general thrust of some developments appeared to be directed toward identifying a rational, objective or goal-oriented design methodology, rather than the traditional go or no-go specifications type of approach. The knowledge in the field of fire protection has and is undergoing a systemization and an organization that may enable the building design team to achieve fire safety objectives in a more rational, efficient manner. In addition to these advances, more products both in the areas of building construction and building protection, are being developed that will aid in realizing the design objectives.

This edition of the HANDBOOK continues to provide the basic information given in previous editions that is necessary to improve building construction. In addition, it introduces some new concepts that are being developed in the field of fire protection as they relate to building construction. In that way it is hoped the HANDBOOK can be more useful to the building designer.

B. Fire Hazards in Buildings

The products of combustion that must be considered by the building designer may be categorized as flames, heat, smoke, and gases, as shown schematically in Figure 6-1A. The exposed people and property can be protected through effective building design from the dangers posed by these products. The challenge to the designer is to recognize the type of danger posed by each component and to incorporate effective countermeasures into the structure.

Smoke and Gases

Experience has shown that the most common hazard to humans in a building fire is from smoke and toxic gases. Nearly three-fourths of all building-related fire deaths is directly related to these nonthermal products of combustion. Death often results from oxygen deprivation in the blood-stream caused by the replacement of oxygen in the blood hemoglobin by carbon monoxide. In addition to the danger of carbon monoxide, many other toxic gases that are present in building fires cause a wide range of symptoms such as headaches, nausea, fatigue, difficult respiration, confusion, and impaired mental functioning.

Smoke, in addition to accompanying toxic and irritant gases, contributes indirectly to a number of deaths. Dense smoke obscures visibility and irritates the eyes. Consequently, the occupant may not be able to identify escape routes and utilize them. To these may be added the problems of fear, panic, and emotional shock.

Heat and Flames

Heat and flames which result in burns are often incorrectly assumed to be the primary cause of fire death and injury. Although heat injuries do not compare in quantity to those caused by inhalation of smoke and toxic gases, they are painful, serious, and cause shock. Statistically, these thermal products of combustion account for nearly 25 percent of fire deaths. In addition to these deaths, the pain and disfigurement caused by burns result in serious, long-term complications.

Building Elements and Contents

Property is also affected by both the thermal and the nonthermal products of combustion. Often smoke damage occurs to goods long distances from the effects of the heat and flames.

The collapse of structural building elements can be a serious hazard. Although statistically it has not resulted in many deaths or injuries to building occupants, it is a particular hazard to fire fighters. A number of deaths and serious injuries to fire fighters occur each year because of structural failure. While some of these failures result from inherent weaknesses, many are the result of renovations to existing buildings that materially, though not obviously, affect the structural integrity of the support elements. A building should not contain surprises of this type for fire fighters.

The major concerns to occupants are due to smoke and toxic gas contamination and to fast flame spread over finish materials or building contents. In addition, vertical propagation of fire is a serious concern. The ability of the fire service in containing or extinguishing a fire is significantly diminished if the fire spreads vertically to two or more floors. With a given potential for fire growth, the prevention of this vertical fire spread is influenced principally by architectural and structural decisions involving details of compartmentation.

C. Elements of Building Firesafety

Building firesafety may be achieved either by fire (ignition) prevention or, if a fire does occur, by managing its impact through building design. Fire prevention is accomplished by separating ignitors from ignitable materials. While this is certainly an important aspect of the total firesafety picture, experience shows that firesafety cannot rely totally on fire prevention.

The persons responsible for fire prevention are not the same ones who are responsible for the building design. Table 6-1A describes the elements that comprise fire safety from a prevention consideration. The decisions concerning these elements are predominantly under the control of the building owner or occupant, or both. Included in this table

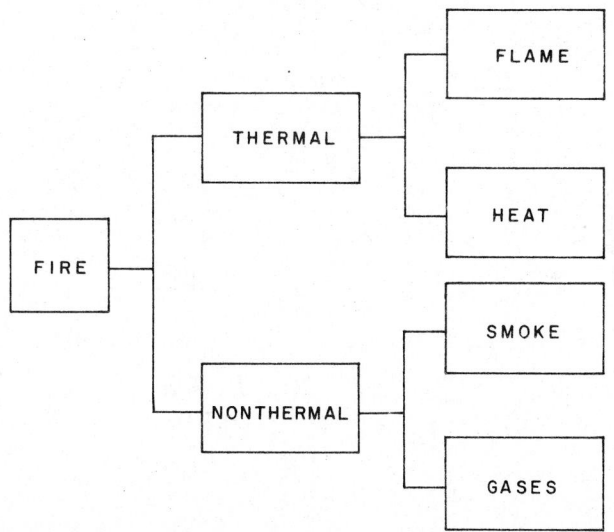

Fig. 6-1A. Schematic representation of products of combustion influencing building design.

Table 6-1A. Fire Prevention and Emergency Preparedness

1. **Ignitors**
   a. Equipment and devices
   b. Human accident
   c. Vandalism and arson
2. **Ignitable Materials**
   a. Fuel load
   b. Fuel distribution
   c. Housekeeping
3. **Emergency Preparedness**
   a. Awareness and understanding
   b. Plans for action
      —Evacuation or temporary refuge
      —Self help extinguishment
   c. Equipment
   d. Maintenance—operating manuals available

are the elements of emergency preparedness in case of fire as they are also the responsibility of the owner/occupant.

Table 6-1B describes the building design and construction features that influence safety. These elements are within the decision-making authority of various members of the design team, based on the assumption their fire safety objectives are clearly defined by management, the owners, or other responsible parties, both public and private. The design and construction elements are organized in a manner that can give a quick overview of the major aspects that must be considered. They show features which include both active and passive design considerations.

Table 6-1B. Elements of Building Firesafety

Building Design and Construction Features Influencing Firesafety

1. **Fire Propagation**
   a. Fuel load and distribution
   b. Finish materials and their location
   c. Construction details influencing fire and products of combustion movement
   d. Architectural design features
2. **Smoke and Fire Gas Movement**
   a. Generation
   b. Movement
      —Natural air movement
      —Mechanical air movement
   c. Control
      —Ventilation
      —HVAC
      —Barriers
      —Pressurization
   d. Occupant Protection
      —Egress
      —Temporary refuge spaces
      —Life support systems
3. **Detection, Alarm, and Communication**
   a. Activation
   b. Signal
   c. Communication systems
      —To and from occupants
      —To and from fire department
      —Type (automatic or manual)
      —Signal (audio or visual)

Table 6-1B. (Cont.)

4. **People Movement**
   a. Occupant
      —Horizontal
      —Vertical
      —Control
      —Life support
   b. Fire Fighters
      —Horizontal
      —Vertical
      —Control
5. **Suppression Systems**
   a. Automatic
   b. Manual (self-help; standpipes)
   c. Special
6. **Fire Fighting Operations**
   a. Access
   b. Rescue operations
   c. Venting
   d. Extinguishment
      —Equipment
      —Spatial design features
   e. Protection from structural collapse
7. **Structural Integrity**
   a. Building structural system (fire endurance)
   b. Compartmentation
   c. Stability
8. **Site Design**
   a. Exposure protection
   b. Fire fighting operations
   c. Personnel safety
   d. Miscellaneous (water supply, traffic, access, etc.)

Fire Emergency Considerations

1. **Life Safety**
   a. Toxic gases
   b. Smoke
   c. Surface flame spread
2. **Structural**
   a. Fire propagation
   b. Structural stability
3. **Continuity of Operations**
   a. Structural integrity

D. Design Standards

With the exception of emergency preparedness provisions, the elements described in Table 6-1A are normally found in fire prevention codes. In addition to the community and state fire prevention legislation, the NFPA and model code organizations have developed fire prevention codes.

The following chapters in this Section of the HANDBOOK are directed toward building design and construction relative to fire safety. A listing of the NFPA codes and standards pertaining to that phase of building design and construction covered by a particular chapter will be found in the bibliography at the end of that chapter.

Bibliography

Reference Cited

[1] *America Burning: The Report of the National Commission on Fire Prevention and Control,* Superintendent of Documents, U.S. Government Printing Office, Washington, D.C., 1973.

Section 6

Chapter 2

SYSTEMS CONCEPTS OF FIRESAFE BUILDING DESIGN

Firesafety can be incorporated into building design by three different methods. The first is to require design and construction to conform to requirements stated in building codes and standards. The requirements are based on fire analyses and experiences, and traditionally are stated in a manner that allows little deviation or flexibility. Alternatives are detailed, and design innovations are difficult to achieve. Objectives of a code are aimed at public safety, but specific objectives are not articulated in a manner which can be defined quantitatively.

To overcome the inflexibility of specification codes, interest has centered in recent years on performance codes. With regard to the firesafety aspects, performance codes have been slow to develop. A major drawback to this approach is that building components are considered on an ad-hoc basis. The definition of firesafety performance of the separate components, and the measurement of that performance are difficult to obtain. In addition, when considering the entire building as a system, the satisfactory physical performance of individual components does not assure the desired level of safety for the building as a whole.

A third avenue of achieving firesafe design of buildings is being developed. This approach recognized firesafety as an integrated subsystem of the building in a manner similar to the aesthetic subsystem, the functional subsystem, the structural subsystem, the electrical subsystem, or the mechanical subsystem. Buildings can be designed for firesafety utilizing an engineering methodology, rather than for strict compliance with codes. This approach to achieving firesafety requires a professional technology in its application, just as do the architectural and engineering disciplines. Moreover, it shows promise of achieving a greater level of cost effectiveness in its utilization.

This chapter will attempt to describe the organization of systems concepts to firesafe building design. The formal methodology is quite new, and requires considerable additional development. However, it has already demonstrated its effectiveness, and shows promise of providing an effective alternative to building code requirements.

A. Background

During the 1960s there was a growing awareness that modern high rise buildings designed in accordance with building codes and standards contained potential weaknesses with regard to firesafety. Various researchers and organizations, led by the National Research Council of Canada, identified aspects of weakness. For example, studies identifying the time of evacuation of high rise buildings were published, and the problems relating to air movement in tall buildings were identified. Careful analysis of two fires in New York City, the One New York Plaza Fire[1] and the 919 Third Avenue Fire,[2] focused attention even more clearly on the problem areas.

In response to these problems an International Conference on Firesafety was convened at the Airlie House in Warrenton, Virginia in April, 1971. The proceedings of this conference[3] were published in May, 1971. In October of the same year the Conference was reconvened, and additional proceedings consisting of various task group reports

were published[4]. In these proceedings, a decision tree was published that formally identified the elements in the firesafety system and their interrelationships.

About this time the National Fire Protection Association considered establishment of a committee on high rise structures. After initial meetings, this committee determined that its contribution should not be toward developing standards for high rise construction, but rather toward identifying the system of firesafety for all buildings. The decision tree shown in Figure 6-2A was developed by the NFPA Committee on Systems Concepts for Fire Protection in Structures as the committee was eventually named.

B. Decision Tree Organization

The decision tree shown in Figure 6-2A describes the elements that must be considered in building firesafety and the interrelationship of those elements. It enables a building to be analyzed or designed by progressively moving through the various levels of events in a logical manner. Its success depends on the completeness by which each level of events is satisfied. Lower levels on the decision tree, however, do not represent a lower level of importance or performance. They represent a means for achieving the next higher level.

Firesafety Objectives

The use of the decision tree requires that the firesafety objectives (goals) be clearly identified. These objectives describe the degree to which the building should protect its occupants, property contents, and neighbors. They should be quantified wherever possible, rather than stated in broad, general terms.

The life safety objective, for example, might state that all occupants be safeguarded against the intolerable or untenable effects of the fire. It may be further stated that emergency personnel, such as fire fighters, who may be expected to stay in areas considered too dangerous for the occupants, should be protected against unexpected collapse or entrapment. A range of specific life safety objectives may be appropriate for varying types of occupancies. Nursing home requirements, for example, are vastly different from those of offices. Both are different from industrial occupancies or storage facilities.

To identify the property protection objectives, the building designer must ask a number of questions. For example, is there any property that has significantly higher value? What property cannot be replaced, or would significantly affect continued operations if it were destroyed? Are there specific functions at the site that are vital to continuity of operations? Further, are there other functions that may be performed at other sites on an emergency basis? Proper identification of factors such as these can enable the designer to tailor his design to reflect the proper sensitivity to the client's needs.

Prevent Fire Ignition or Manage Fire Impact

After the firesafety objectives have been identified they can be achieved either by preventing fire ignition, or, if a fire does occur, by managing the fire impact in a manner

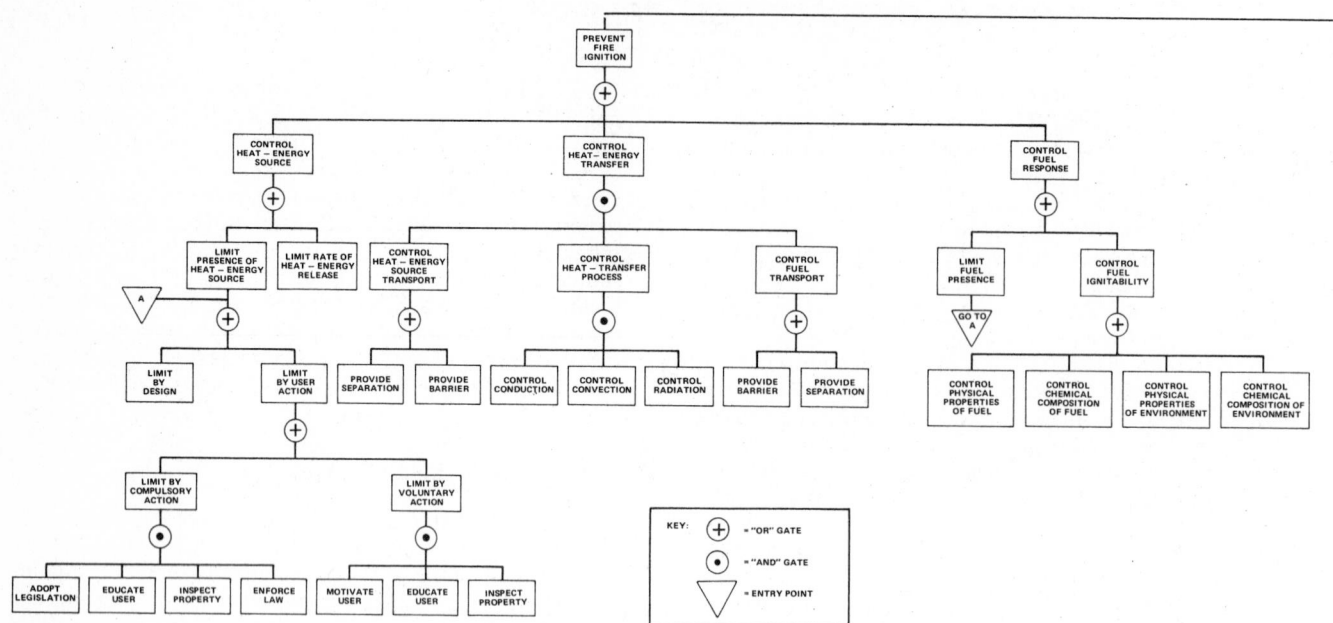

Fig. 6-2A.   The decision tree as developed by the NFPA

that will satisfy the objectives. To express this concept on the decision tree in Figure 6-2A, an "or" gate, symbolized by the symbol ⊕ is used. This type of gate indicates a logical "and-or" relationship but makes little or no allowance for contingent relationships. This means that inclusion of all the events below the gate is acceptable, but not necessary, to achieve the goal of the event shown above. In this case it is acceptable both to prevent the fire, and also to provide means of managing it if a fire should happen to start. However, it is also acceptable (within the framework of the logic system, but not necessarily within the framework of the local laws and codes) either to prevent fires or to permit them to be ignited and then manage the impact in a manner that will accomplish the stated objectives.

The "Prevent Fire Ignition" branch of Figure 6-2A (and the performance standards associated with it) essentially form a fire prevention code. Most of the events described in this branch require continuous monitoring for success. Consequently, the responsibility for satisfactorily achieving the goal of fire prevention is essentially an owner/occupant responsibility. The designer, however, may be able to incorporate certain features into the building that may assist the owner/occupant in preventing fires.

It is impossible to prevent completely the ignition of fires in a building. Therefore, in order to reach the overall objective, from a building design viewpoint, a high degree of success in the "Manage Fire Impact" branch assumes a significant role. Essentially this branch (and the firesafety standards associated with it) may be considered as a building code by the design team. After an ignition occurs, all considerations shift to the "Manage Fire Impact" branch to achieve the firesafety objectives.

The impact of the fire can be managed either through the "Manage Fire" or "Manage Exposed" avenues (see Fig. 6-2A). The "or" gate indicates that the objectives may be reached through either avenue of design, and it is not necessary to do both as long as the avenue selected is completely

satisfied. Naturally, it is acceptable to do both, which will increase the probability of success.

Manage Fire Avenue

The firesafety objectives can be achieved by managing the fire itself. Figure 6-2B shows that this can be accomplished by (1) controlling the combustion process, (2) by suppressing the fire, or (3) by controlling the fire by construction. Here, again, any one of these avenues will satisfy the "Manage Fire" event.

The combustion process can be controlled either by controlling the fuel or by controlling the environment. The events that affect each of these are shown in Figure 6-2C. The triangle containing the command "Go to A" indicates that all elements below "A" on the "Prevent Fire Ignition" branch should be incorporated at this step in the analysis.

The events that control the "Suppress Fire" event are shown in Figure 6-2D. In this figure a new symbol is introduced. The symbol ⊙ (a bold dot in the center of a circle) represents a logical "and" gate, and signifies that all of the elements in the level immediately below the gate are necessary to achieve the event above the gate. To accomplish the automatic suppression event, for example, all three events of detecting the fire, initiating action, and controlling the fire are necessary. Similarly, to suppress the fire manually, all six events must take place. The omission of any one event is sufficient to break the chain and cause the failure of this event.

In considering the "Control Fire by Construction" event, structural integrity must be provided, and also the movement of the fire itself must be controlled. As shown in Figure 6-2E, this can be accomplished either by venting the fire or by confining and containing it.

Manage Exposed Avenue

As shown by Figure 6-2A the fire impact can be managed either by managing the fire or by managing the exposed.

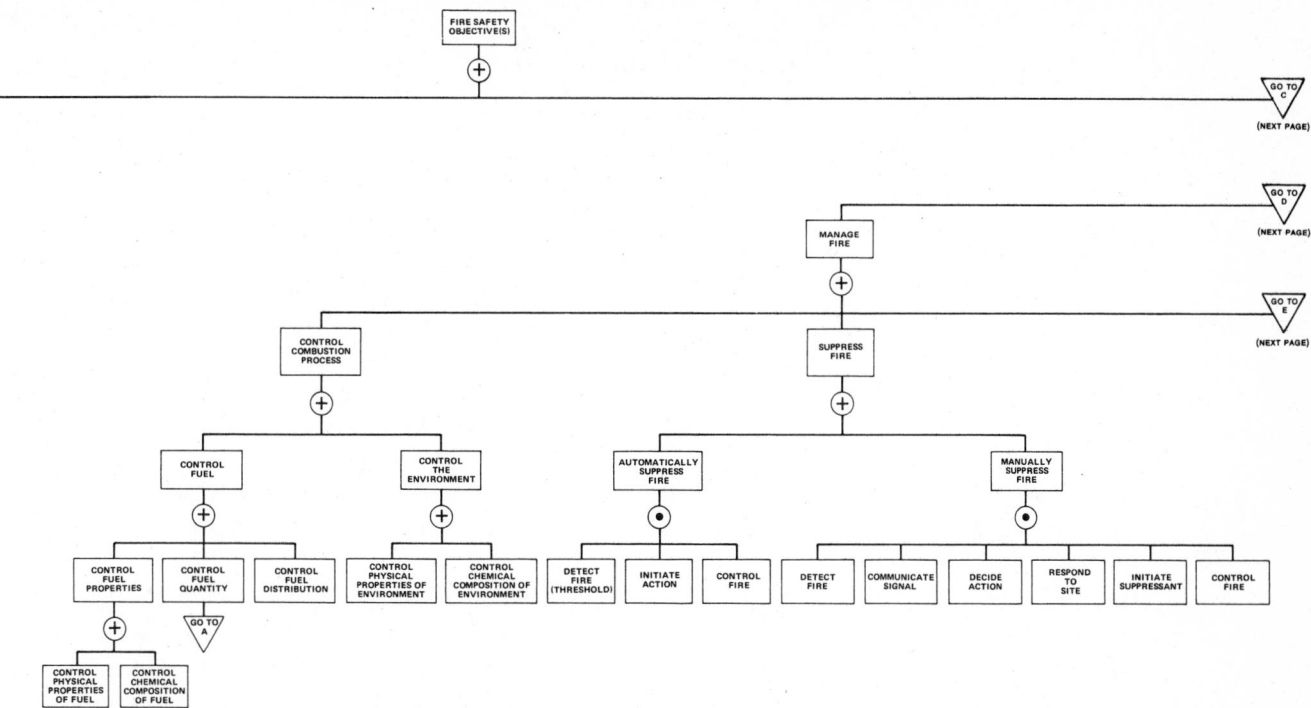

Committee on Systems Concepts for Fire Protection in Structures.

The "exposed" may be people, property, or functions depending on the design aspects being considered. In considering the "Manage Exposed" branch, it can be successful either by limiting the amount exposed or by safeguarding the exposed. For example, the number of people as well as the amount or type of property in a space may be restricted. Often this is impractical. If this is the case, the objectives may still be met by incorporating design features to safeguard the exposed.

The exposed people or property may be safeguarded either by moving them to a safe area of refuge or by defending them in place. For example, people in institutionalized occupancies such as hospitals, nursing homes, or prisons must generally be defended in place. To do this, the "Defend in Place" branch shown in Figure 6-2F would be considered. On the other hand, alert, mobile individuals, such as may be expected in offices or schools could be moved to safeguard them from fire exposure on either a short term or long range basis dependent on other key design elements. Figure 6-2G describes the events that must be satisfied if the designer is to be successful in safeguarding the exposed by moving them.

C. Use of the Decision Tree

Fire Prevention/Building Codes

The decision tree can be adapted for a number of different functions. A particularly useful aspect of the decision tree is the descriptive feature of important code requirements. The "Prevent Fire Ignition" branch is essentially a fire prevention code. It describes and shows the interrelationship between the essential features of such a code.

The "Manage Fire Impact" branch (see Fig. 6-2A) is essentially a building code. It enables the code writer to organize the important elements of the building code and to identify their interrelationships. An important feature

for building codes, for example, is the subject of alternatives, or "tradeoffs." The only legitimate areas in which alternatives can be established is among those factors below an "or" gate in the decision tree. The "and" gate, on the other hand, describes a situation where all events below the gate are necessary for success of the event above the gate. Alternatives involving elements found beneath "and" gates would not contribute to firesafety objectives.

Building Analysis

The decision tree provides a framework to support firesafety analyses. It is a fundamental necessity that objectives be established and concurred with before they can be acted upon. Once the fundamental firesafety objectives for a particular building are identified, the designer-architect can analyze the building's design by progressing successively through the various levels of events. Redundancies and deficiencies can be specifically identified and evaluated. Often the weaknesses become so apparent that specific and effective solutions can be economically devised.

The building analysis, supported by the framework of the decision tree, has among its advantages the capacity of considering separately fire prevention considerations and the requirements involved in managing the fire impact in the event an ignition occurs. This definite separation of events can enable the owner/occupant to take immediate corrective action with regard to fire prevention, and then take thoughtful, effective action to correct the building deficiencies.

Building Design

The use of the decision tree can be effectively employed in building design. If the architect incorporates its process during the preliminary planning phase of design, many important decisions and alternatives can be established more effectively. For example, decisions regarding evacuation vs. temporary refuge, and their implications on the functions

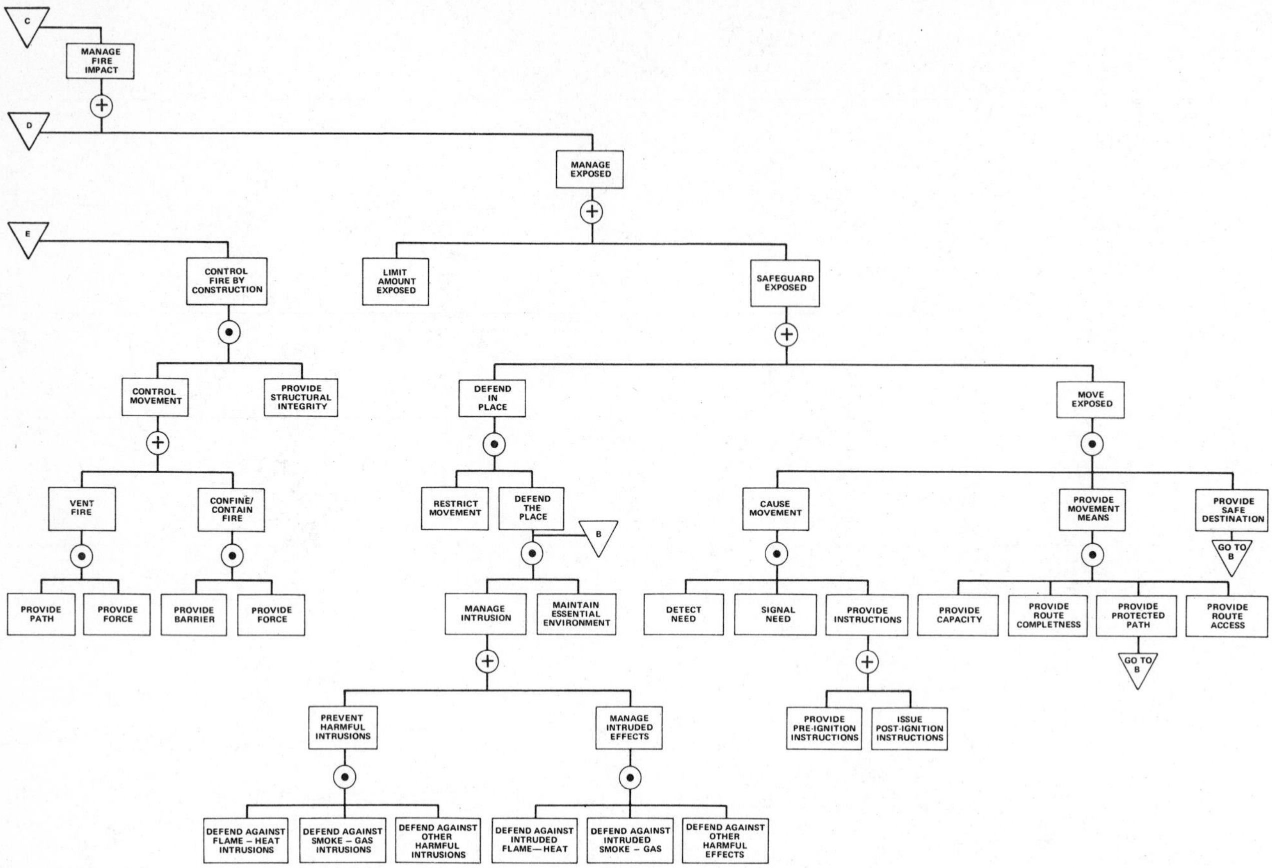

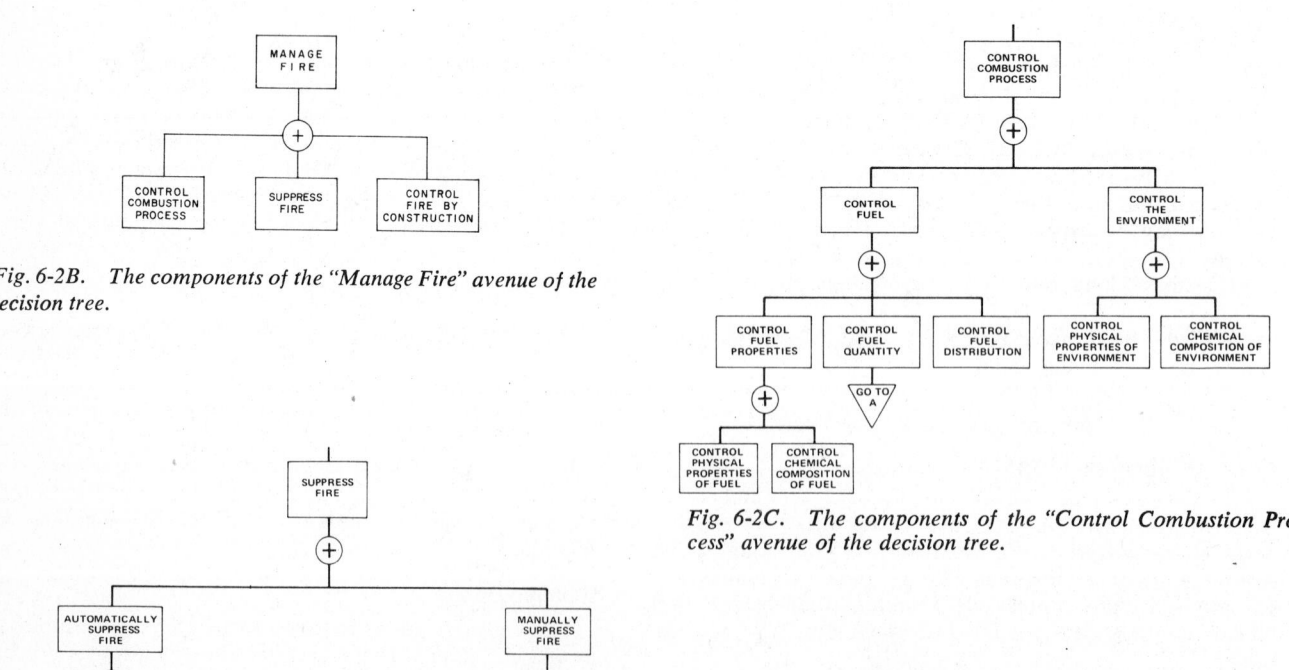

Fig. 6-2A (continued from page 6-7)

Fig. 6-2B.   The components of the "Manage Fire" avenue of the decision tree.

Fig. 6-2C.   The components of the "Control Combustion Process" avenue of the decision tree.

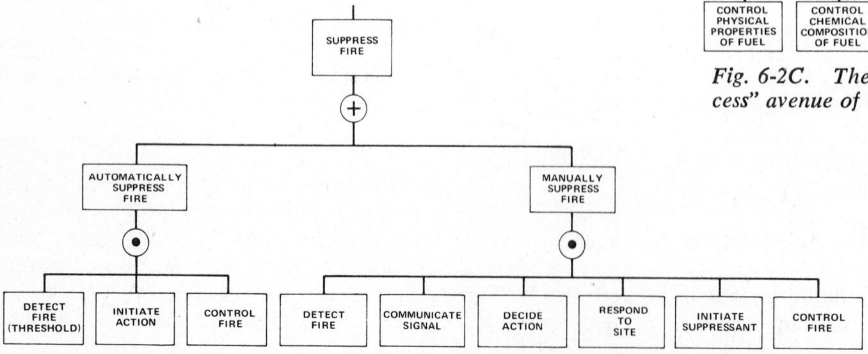

Fig. 6-2D.   The components of the "Suppress Fire" avenue of the decision tree.

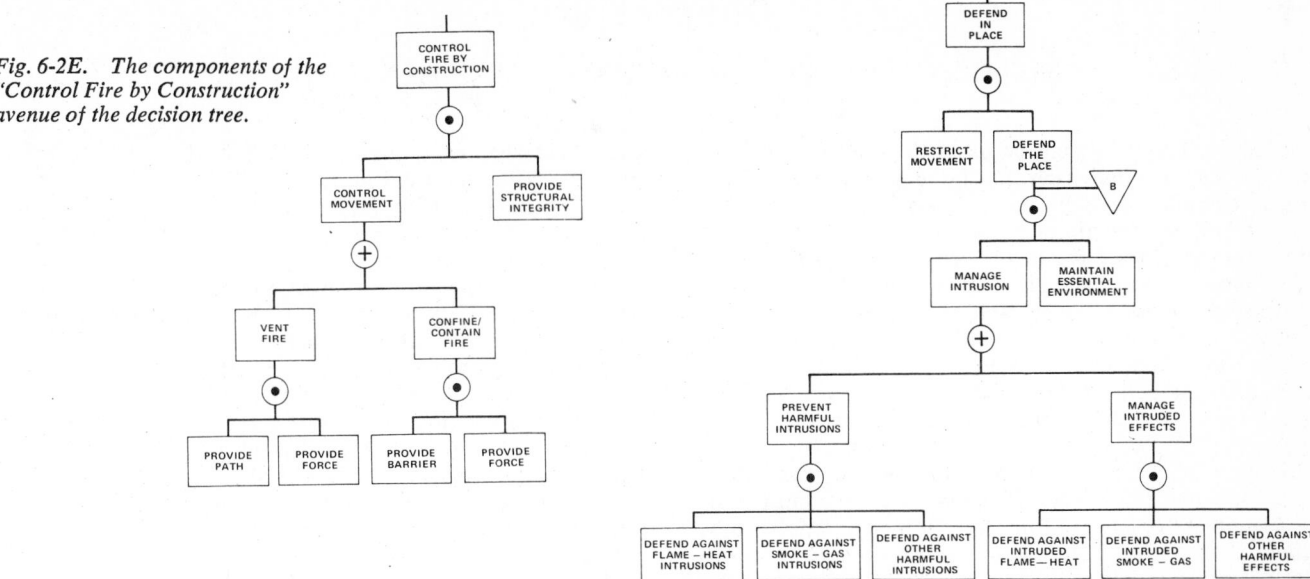

Fig. 6-2E. The components of the "Control Fire by Construction" avenue of the decision tree.

Fig. 6-2F. The components of the "Defend in Place" avenue of the decision tree.

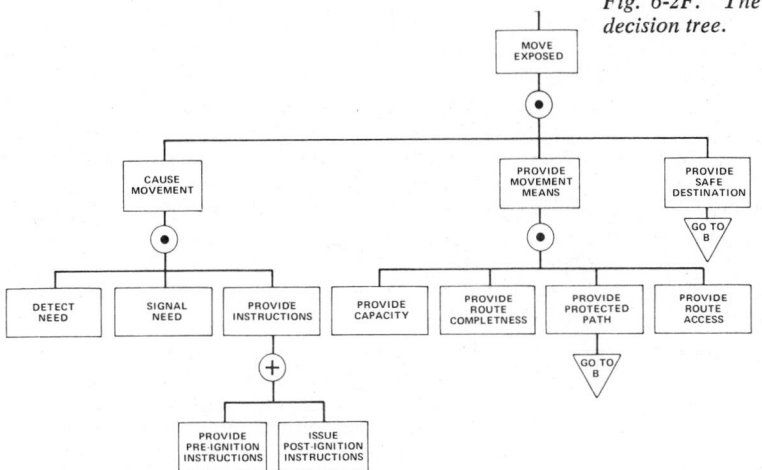

Fig. 6-2G. The components of the "Move Exposed" avenue of the decision tree.

of the building can be made. Specific needs with regard to the decision are then recognized.

The decision tree also enables the functions of fire prevention and building design to be separated. In this way the responsibilities of the owner/occupant can be differentiated from those of the building design team. Those events that are eventually incorporated into the design can be identified with a specific member of the building design team.

Local building code requirements and NFPA standards are still important factors in building design. The decision tree should not supersede those documents. Rather, it enables those documents to be interrelated and consequently used more effectively. The use of the decision tree in design facilitates decision making with regard to firesafety. Specific design guidelines and standards are still the appropriate domain of the local codes and the standards writers.

D. Future Developments of Systems Concepts

The NFPA Systems Concepts Committee was established in 1971. It is responsible for developing system concepts and criteria for fire protection in structures. The criteria are reported to the Standards Council of the NFPA, which may assign the criteria to the appropriate technical committee for preparation of, or amendments to, standards.

The systems concepts work is relatively new in the field of fire protection. Because its scope is broad it has the capability of uniting the various subsystems of fire protection into a rational, integrated discipline. As the work is developed, it is possible that the approach to fire protection engineering may change. Future editions of the HANDBOOK will be better able to document the progress and attention to interim developments is recommended.

A major contribution of the systems work has been to develop the decision tree. Beyond this, the activities of various standards and code groups can be coordinated and integrated in a manner that will enable designers to make better decisions regarding firesafety. Also, if the events can be quantified, and, if rational theoretical guidelines established, fire protection can progress to a theoretical design discipline.

Bibliography

References Cited

[1] Powers, W. Robert, "New York Office Building Fire," *Fire Journal*, Vol. 65, No. 1, Jan. 1971, pp. 18–23, 87.
[2] ———, "Office Building Fire, 919 Third Avenue, New York City," *Fire Journal*, Vol. 65, No. 2, Mar. 1971, pp. 5–7, 13.
[3] *Public Buildings Service International Conference on Firesafety in High-Rise Building,* April 12–16, 1971, Warrenton, Va., General Services Administration, Washington, D.C.
[4] *Proceedings: Reconvened International Conference on Fire Safety in High-Rise Buildings,* Oct. 5, 1971, General Services Administration, Washington, D.C.

Additional Readings

Designing Buildings for Fire Safety, National Fire Protection Association, Boston, 1974, 125 pp.
Fires in High-Rise Buildings, National Fire Protection Association, Boston, 1974, 120 pp.
High Rise Building Fires and Fire Safety, National Fire Protection Association, 1974, 164 pp.

Chapter 3

BUILDING AND SITE PLANNING FOR FIRESAFETY

Effective, firesafe design begins with conscious analysis and decision making early in the design process. This broad, overall approach includes consideration of both interior building functions and layout, as well as exterior site planning. One of the newer concepts of building fire-safety involves the philosophy that the building itself must be designed to assist the manual suppression of fire. The fire service cannot be expected to provide complete protection for building occupants and property. They must be assisted by the building fire defenses, both active and passive, in order to provide reasonable safety from the effects of fire.

In order to incorporate the building's fire defenses effectively into the design, the firesafety objectives must first be identified. (Chapter 2 of this Section discusses this briefly.) After this, decisions must then be made regarding the means to achieve the objectives. The decision tree of Chapter 2 can be used to give an overall perspective of the firesafety system. This chapter will present some broad guidelines to be considered by the building designer. Detailed information of the various aspects can be found elsewhere in this HANDBOOK.

A. Building Interior Design Considerations

The architectural design of a building has a significant influence on its firesafety capabilities. Interior layout, circulation patterns, finish material, and building services are all important factors in fire safety. Manual suppression of fires, particularly by fire department operations, is another important consideration. The building design influences significantly the efficiency of fire department operations. Consequently, manual suppression activities should be considered during all architectural design phases.

Interior Layout

During a fire the occupant is exposed to two types of danger. One is exposure to flame and hot products of combustion. This is a problem in the vicinity of burning, but the danger decreases rapidly as the distance from the fire increases. Smoke and toxic gases, on the other hand, present a different type of hazard. The greatest number of fire deaths result from these latter products of combustion, and the danger is present at considerable distances from the location of the fire.

Most fires, even relatively minor ones, produce tremendous quantities of smoke and gases. These products obscure vision and irritate the eyes to the extent that visibility is reduced to practically zero. Occupants familiar with their surroundings often experience great difficulty in locating means of egress. The problem is compounded for transients and occasional visitors to the building.

Architectural layout and normal circulation patterns are important elements in emergency evacuation. For example, many large office buildings are a maze of offices, storage areas, and meeting rooms. Even under normal conditions, a visitor can become confused and have difficulty in exiting the building. Clearly marked emergency travel routes would enhance life safety features in buildings of this type.

Means of egress are discussed in Chapter 9 of this Sec-

tion. That chapter, based on NFPA No. 101, Life Safety Code, describes the elements that must be considered when designing for life safety from fire. The reader is referred to Chapter 9 for more complete design guidance for various types of occupancies.

The building height also bears a relationship to the interior layout and firesafety. Modern city fire department aerial equipment normally reaches to about the seventh floor. Buildings taller than about 90 ft pose special fire-safety problems. Occupants above the seventh floor cannot evacuate the building by exterior aerial equipment, and a high level fire must be attacked from inside the building. Consequently, interior layout and its relationship to occupant evacuation and protection and fire department operations becomes more significant.

Figure 6-3A shows a common floor plan arrangement of a high rise office building. The floor plan shows a central core surrounded by rentable office space. The office space can be divided into smaller rooms by movable partitions. The central core contains elevator banks, stairwells, air shafts, electrical closets, and other building services.

In this arrangement, elevators cannot be considered means of egress. Occupants evacuating the building by stairs are travelling in a direction opposite to the fire fighters attacking the fire. Stairwell doors may be left open long enough to smoke log the space. In addition, the time of total evacuation for the occupants may be excessive.

Galbreath computed the time of evacuation of high-rise buildings.[1] The results of his calculations are shown in Table 6-3A. These times are based on the assumptions that evacuation is through a single, two-unit stairwell and movement is the maximum possible volume per unit time. Experimental verification of these theoretical values is difficult, but there is indication that actual evacuation may be considerably longer than the times shown in Table 6-3A. Consequently, temporary refuge areas are now considered an important element of interior layout. Dual refuge areas are important considerations in interior layout design. Chapter 9 of this Section describes some alternative methods of providing temporary refuge in case of emergency.

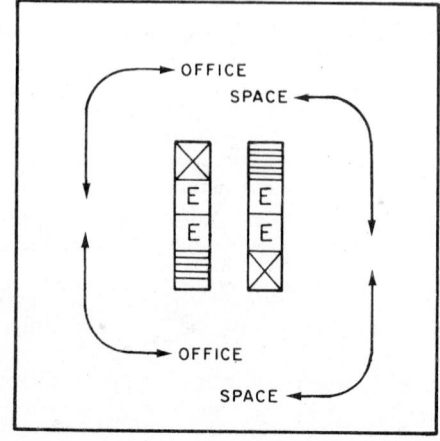

Fig. 6-3A.   Floor plan of a typical high rise office building.

Table 6-3A. Time for Evacuation by One Stair

Height of Building, Stories	Time Required for Evacuation of:				
	240 Persons per Floor		120 Persons per Floor		60 Persons per Floor
	Hrs	Min	Hrs	Min	Min
50	2	11	1	6	33
40	1	45		52	26
30	1	18		39	20
20		51		25	13
15		38		19	9

Area of stair tower: 99 sq ft.
Stair width: 44 in. (2 units of exit width).

In addition to influencing emergency evacuation of occupants, the interior layout plays an important role in fire department operations. Search and rescue operations, for example, are greatly influenced by the arrangement of spaces; so, too, are the base of the fire attack, ease of water application, ventilation practices, salvage, and overhaul.

B. Building Design and Fire Department Operations

The building designer must become aware of the basic operations of the fire service during fire emergencies. In this way he can incorporate features into his building that will aid, rather than hinder, fire fighting operations. A brief description of these operations is given here; a more complete treatment may be found in some of the excellent reference books[2,3,4,5,6,7,8] on this subject, and in Section 9 of this HANDBOOK.

Briefly, the operations may be broadly grouped as occupant protection and rescue, fire suppression operations, and salvage and overhaul activities. (Occupant protection and rescue and their relationship to the architectural layout was discussed earlier.) In the event people become trapped in a building, an important function of the fire service is to rescue them. This search and rescue operation takes manpower away from fire suppression activities and can be a very time consuming, difficult operation.

Accessibility for Fire Fighting

Building design features are important factors in the spread of fire and the ease of suppression. One of the more important involves access to the fire area. This includes access to the building itself as well as access to the interior by fire fighters and their equipment.

Access to the interior of a building can be greatly hampered where large areas exist, and where buildings have blank walls, false façades, solar screens, or signs covering a high percentage of exterior walls. Inadequate means of ventilation to remove dense smoke obscures the vision of fire fighters to the extent that the location of interior fires is extremely difficult. Lack of adequate interior access can also delay or prevent fire department rescue of trapped occupants.

A particular problem exists in windowless buildings and in basement areas. A fire in these spaces often becomes an excessively smoky fire. In addition, heat buildup is usually more intense because heat venting in inadequate. Fire fighters are therefore often placed in the position of attacking fires in these spaces in the face of the heat and smoke.

Spaces in which adequate fire fighting access and operations are restricted because of architectural, engineering, or functional requirements should be provided with effective protection. A complete automatic sprinkler system with a fire department connection is probably the best solution to this problem. Other methods which may be used in appropriate design situations include access panels in interior walls and floors, fixed nozzles in floors with fire department connections, and roof vents and access openings.

Ventilation

Ventilation is an important fire fighting operation. It involves the removal of smoke, gases, and heat from building spaces. Ventilation of building spaces performs the following important functions:

1. Protection of life by removing or diverting toxic gases and smoke from locations where building occupants must find temporary refuge.

2. Improvement of the environment in the vicinity of the fire by removal of smoke and heat. This enables fire fighters to advance close to the fire to extinguish it with a minimum of time, water, and damage.

3. Control of the spread or direction of fire by setting up air currents that cause the fire to move in a desired direction. In this way occupants or valuable property can be more readily protected.

4. Provision of a release for unburned, combustible gases before they acquire a flammable mixture, thus avoiding a backdraft or smoke explosion.

The building designer should be conscious of these important functions of fire ventilation and provide effective means of facilitating venting practices whenever possible. This may involve access panels, movable windows, skylights, or other means of readily opened spaces in case of a fire emergency. Emergency controls on the mechanical equipment may also be effective means of accomplishing the functions of fire ventilation. Each building has unique features, and consequently a unique solution should be incorporated into the design.

Water Supply and Use

Water is the principal agent used to extinguish building fires. Although other agents may occasionally be employed (e.g., carbon dioxide, foams and surfactants, and halons), water remains the primary extinguishing agent of the fire service. Consequently, the building designer should anticipate the hydraulic needs of the fire service and automatic extinguishing systems, and provide an adequate supply of water and water pressure.

Water must be transported to the location of the fire. This is first through the city water distribution system to the building area and then to the fire from area hydrants or standpipes and sprinkler systems in the building. Few cities can supply sufficient water at required pressures to every part of the city. Consequently, water supplied to hydrants, standpipes, or sprinklers must be boosted by pumps located on fire department apparatus or in the buildings themselves.

Careful attention must be given to water supply, distribution, and pressure for emergency fire conditions. High-rise buildings are particularly sensitive because of the volumes needed, and the pressures involved with the building height. Large area buildings must also be given more careful attention to their needs. Section 11; Section 9, Chapter 5; Section 13, Chapter 1; Section 14, Chapters 1 and 4; and Section 15, Chapter 1 of this HANDBOOK provide useful information on aspects relating to water supply and its use in fire fighting.

Fire conditions that require operation of a large number

Fig. 6-3B. The Burlington Building (right), Chicago, March 15, 1922. Fire in a group of brick, wood-joisted buildings (left) spread across the 80-ft street to ignite the upper seven floors of the 15-story office building, which was of fireresistive construction but lacked exposure protection for street front windows. Wind carried hot gases against the Burlington Building. Updraft due to convection made exposure most severe above the level of exposing buildings.

of sprinklers or use of a large number of hose streams can reduce pressure in standpipe and sprinkler systems to the point where discharge and distribution is adversely affected. Fire department (siamese) connections for sprinklers and for standpipes are therefore important components of the building fire defenses. They are so important the building designer must carefully consider details of location and installation to make sure they will be easily located, readily accessible, and properly marked. See Section 14, Chapter 2 and Section 15, Chapter 1 for further information on fire department connections for sprinkler systems and standpipe systems.

Water Removal: Watertight floors are important in this respect. Salvage efforts can be greatly affected by the integrity of the floors. Of greater importance is the number and location of floor drains. If interior drains and scuppers are available, salvage teams can remove water effectively with a minimum of damage. Chapter 4 of this Section describes watertight floors and installation of scuppers and floor drains.

C. Building Design and Fire Suppression

The building designer has a significant influence on the relative ease and effectiveness of fire suppression operations. Not only is it important to incorporate the needs of the fire service into the functional layout of the building and its services, but also to properly plan for automatic fire detection and extinguishing capabilities. Some buildings create an impossible situation for manual and automatic fire suppression. Others effectively incorporate advance planning to facilitate emergency fire activities.

The various chapters of this and other Sections of this HANDBOOK provide some basis for effective building design practices. Effective building firesafety features and the ease of fire fighting activities are, of course, closely interrelated. An outline of the more important aspects along with cross references to appropriate chapters in this HANDBOOK are provided below.

Compartmentation

Fire department efficiency decreases rapidly as the fire propagates vertically. Fires on two or more floors are extremely difficult to control. Modern construction methods utilizing such techniques as open stairwells, curtain wall construction, poke-through assemblies, and air handling ductwork provide avenues of vertical spread. It is more difficult to compartmentate a space effectively in modern construction than it was in pre-World War II construction. Yet, it can be done if attention is paid to the details of design and construction. Chapter 8 of this Section describes some of the principles of compartmentation.

Detection, Alarm, and Communication

Time is one of the most significant parameters of fire control. A matter of minutes, if it is during the early development stages of a fire, is a significant factor both in life safety and in fire extinguishment capabilities. Consequently, effective fire detection becomes a vital element in fire safety. After a fire detector is activated, appropriate action must be initiated. This may involve alarm, communication, initiating suppression action, or a combination of these. Alarm may alert building occupants to the existence of a fire, but what action should then be taken? Evacuation is the normal procedure in smaller buildings. High-rise buildings, on the other hand, cannot be evacuated within a reasonable period of time. Consequently, instructions must be given concerning the appropriate course of action.

Communication is a vital link in fire control. Communication is also vitally necessary to warn occupants and, hopefully, to provide sufficient instructions for action. It is also necessary to alert the fire department early about the existence and location of a fire. Too often, fire department notification has been delayed because occupants were under the mistaken impression that a local alarm notified the fire department.

Section 12 of this HANDBOOK describes the elements of detection, alarm, and communication systems.

Automatic Fire Suppression

Sprinklers have been the most important single system for automatic control of hostile fires in buildings for nearly a century. Many desirable aesthetic and functional features of buildings which might offer some concern for firesafety can be protected by the installation of a properly designed sprinkler system.

Among the advantages of automatic sprinklers is the fact that they operate directly over a fire. Smoke, toxic gases, and reduced visibility do not affect their operation. In addition, much less water is used because only those sprinklers fused by the heat of the fire operate. Section 14 of this HANDBOOK describes sprinkler systems, their design, features, and maintenance.

Other automatic extinguishing systems (carbon dioxide, halon agents, high expansion foam) also find use in providing protection for certain portions of buildings or type of occupancies for which they are particularly suited. Further information on the design and use of these systems will be found in appropriate chapters of Section 15.

D. Site Planning

The architect must utilize a given site in designing his building. He must adapt the functional and engineering considerations to the particular site conditions that are present. In a similar manner, he should give consideration of the site features to his decisions on fire protection. A particular set of site characteristics may significantly influence the type and kind of building fire defenses incorporated by the design team. Among the more significant features are traffic and transportation conditions, fire department access, and water supply. The water supply was briefly discussed in Section C of this chapter. A few additional considerations are given here.

Traffic and Transportation

Time is a vital factor in fire control, particularly when a major component of the fire defenses is the response of the fire department. Fire apparatus must respond to a location along streets. At certain times of the day, this can cause significant delay in response to some locations.

Limited access highways may or may not be helpful in considering fire department response. Highways may attract motorists, thus improving traffic conditions on other city streets. On the other hand, the limited access highway may divide a community into sections. Means of travel to locations intermediate to the access points can be delayed. This can have a significant effect on response distances from fire stations, and must be considered by the design team in selecting the appropriate fire defenses for the building.

Fire Department Access

Ideal exterior accessibility occurs where a building can be approached from all sides by fire department apparatus. This, unfortunately, is not often possible. In congested areas only the sides of buildings facing streets may be accessible. In other areas, topography or man-made obstacles can prevent effective use of apparatus in combatting the fire.

Some shopping centers and buildings located some distance from the street make the approach of apparatus difficult. If obstructions or topography prevent apparatus from being located near enough to the building for effective use, such equipment as aerial ladders, elevating platforms, and water tower apparatus are rendered useless. Valuable manpower must be expended to carry ground ladders or hand carry hose lines long distances.

The matter of access to buildings has become far more complicated in recent years. The building designer must consider this important aspect in his planning. Inadequate attention to site details can place the building in an unnecessarily vulnerable position. If its fire defenses are compromised by preventing adequate fire department access, the building itself must make up the difference in more complete internal protection.

Water Supply

An adequate water supply delivered with the necessary pressure is important to control a fire. In many new developments, such as shopping centers, apartments, and housing projects, inadequate attention is given to the number and location of hydrants. There are examples of areas that present extremely difficult fire fighting problems where mains are so small and hydrants are so poorly spaced that adequate water is not available. The building designer must consider these conditions when planning for the fire defenses of his project.

E. Exposure Protection

A fire in one building creates an external fire hazard to neighboring structures by exposing them to heat by radiation, and possibly by convective currents, as well as to the danger of flying brands of the fire. Any or all of these sources of heat transfer may be sufficient to cause an ignition in the exposed structure or its contents. This part of the chapter describes a method for evaluating exposure severity and suggests methods for the protection of buildings from exterior fire exposures. They are aimed at protecting combustibles within and on the exterior of an exposed building. Considering these recommendations, it is assumed that effective fire fighting activities are at the scene. NFPA No. 80A, Protection of Buildings from Exterior Exposure Fires, is a source for further information on exposure protection.

Factors Influencing Severity of Exposure

When considering protection from exposure fires, there are two basic types of conditions to be considered. They are: (1) exposure to horizontal radiation, and (2) exposure to flames issuing from the roof or top of a burning building in cases where the exposed building is higher than the burning building. Radiation exposure can result from an interior fire where the radiation passes through windows and other openings of the exterior wall. It can also result from the flames issuing from the windows of the burning building or from flames of the burning facade itself.

There are a number of factors that significantly influence the danger and intensity of exposing fires to neighboring exposed structures. Among the more important parameters is the severity of the exposing fire itself. Fire severity is a description of the total energy of a fire. It involves both the temperatures developed within the exposing fire and the duration of burning. NFPA 80A describes three levels of exposure severity as light, moderate, or severe. The classifications are based upon: (1) the average combustible load per unit of floor area, and (2) the characteristics of an average flame spread rating of the interior wall and ceiling finishes. Tables 6-3B and 6-3C serve as a guide in assessing severity on the basis of these properties. In using these Tables, the more severe of the two classifications should govern.

The duration of the exposing fire and the total heat produced by the fire are related to the guide expressed by Table 6-3B. The speed of fire buildup is influenced by both the nature of the combustibles and by the combustibility

Fig. 6-3C. Typical ignition of wood frame dwelling by heat radiated from an exposure fire. Distances of 10 to 20 ft between frame buildings, as commonly specified by building codes, do not eliminate the exposure hazard, but usually provide space for fire department operations.

Table 6-3B.　Classification of Exposure Severity Based on Fire Loading

Classification of Severity	Fire Loading in Pounds per Square Foot of Floor Area
Light	0–7*
Moderate	7–15
Severe	15-up

* Excluding any appreciable quantities of rapidly burning materials such as certain foamed plastics, excelsior, or flammable liquids. Where these materials are found in substantial quantities, the severity should be classed as moderate or severe.

Table 6-3C.　Classification of Exposure Severity Based on Flame Spread of Interior Finish

Classification of Severity	Average Flame Spread Rating of Interior Wall and Ceiling Finish
Light	0–25
Moderate	26–75
Severe	75-up

NOTE: Where only a portion of the exposing building has combustible interior finish (i.e., some rooms only, ceiling only, some walls only, etc.), this factor is considered in judging severity classification in as much as it reduces the average flame spread rating.

of the interior wall and ceiling finish. Table 6-3C relates the flame spread classification with severity (See Chap. 6, of this Section).

Besides the temperature and duration of the exposing fire, other variables influence the severity of exposure on buildings. Some of these variables include the following:

1. **Exposing fire**
    (a) Type of construction of exterior walls and roofs.
    (b) Width of exposing fire.
    (c) Height of exposing fire.
    (d) Percent of openings in exposing wall area. Ex-

terior walls that are combustible or which do not have sufficient resistance to contain the fire should be treated as having 100 percent openings.
    (e) Ventilation characteristics of the burning room.
    (f) The fuel dispersion, or surface to volume ratio of the fuel.
    (g) The size, geometry, and surface-to-volume ratio of the room involved.
    (h) The thermal properties, conductivity, specific heat, and density of the interior finish.

2. **Exposed building**
    (a) Type of construction of exterior walls and roofs.
    (b) Orientation and surface area of exposed exterior walls.
    (c) Percent of openings in exterior wall area.
    (d) Protection of openings.

Fig. 6-3D.　Fire starting in Wellesley, Mass. (left), ignited a building in Newton (right) by radiated heat across the Charles River, 100 ft distant, against the wind. The river prevented access for fire department operations to protect the exposure.

Fig. 6-3E.　Above are two types of free standing fire walls. At left is a brick fire wall reinforced with concrete abutments to make it free standing. At right is a reinforced concrete fire wall which protected the dwelling from a fire in an adjacent lumberyard.

Fig. 6-3F.　This wired-glass window in a metal frame, though cracked by intense heat of an exposure fire, held in place and combined with an open sprinkler to prevent fire from entering the building. Note the open sprinkler at top outside the window.

Fig. 6-3G. Outside sprinklers, combined with wired glass in steel sash and automatic shutters, provide good protection against exposures at windows and other openings.

    (e) Exposure of interior finish and combustibles to the radiation, convection, and flying brands of the exposing fire.

    (f) Thermal properties, conductivity, specific heat, density, and fuel dispersion of the interior finish materials and the building contents.

3. Site and protection features

    (a) Separation distance between exposing and exposed building.

    (b) Shielding effect of intervening noncombustible construction.

    (c) Wind direction and velocity.

    (d) Air temperature and humidity.

    (e) Accessibility for fire fighting operation.

    (f) Extent and character of fire department operations.

Design Guidelines for Exposure Protection

When analyzing or designing a building for exposure protection, two situations are considered. The first occurs where the exposing building is of equal or greater height than the exposed building. In this case, only the thermal radiation from walls or wall openings is considered. The second case arises when the exposing building is of lesser height than the exposed building.

The criteria for protection is based on the separation distance between the exposing and the exposed buildings for the two cases described above. Tables 6-3D and 6-3E provide guidelines for determining separation distances that should protect exposed structures from fire spread. They are based on the condition that separation distances are great enough so that ignition of the exposed building or its contents is unlikely, assuming that no means of protection are installed in connection with either building.

In Table 6-3D, the parameters include severity classification (described in Tables 6-3B and 6-3C), width and height of exposing fire, and percent of openings in exposing wall area. The definitions of the terms are as follows:

Width of Exposing Fire (w): The length in feet of the exposing wall between interior fire separations or between exterior end walls where no fire separations exist. Fire separations (such as fire partitions or fire walls) should have sufficient resistance to contain the expected fire.

Height of Exposing Fire (h): The height in feet of the number of stories involved in the exposing fire, considering such factors as building construction, closure of vertical openings, and fire resistance of floors. The relevant fire separations must have sufficient fire resistance to contain the expected fire.

Percent of Openings in Exposing Wall Area: This is the percentage of the exposing wall made up of doors, windows, or other openings within the assumed height and width of the exposing fire. Walls without the ability to withstand fire penetration for the expected duration of the fire should be treated as having 100 percent openings.

In using Table 6-3D, for example, assume that a building has a moderate severity (7-15 psf of fire load). Assume further that the width and height of exposing fire is 100 ft and 50 ft respectively, and that 60 percent of the exposed wall area is open. Using a width-to-height ratio of 100/50 = 2.0, a moderate severity, and 60 percent openings, a guide number of 2.15 is obtained from Table 6-3D. This indicates that the minimum separation an unprotected building should have from an exposing fire in the building described should be 2.15 times the smaller dimension plus 5 ft.* In this case the separation should be 2.15 × 50 + 5 or 112.5 ft.

---

* The 5 ft is added to the computed values of separation distances partly to account for the horizontal projection of flames from windows and partly to guard against the risk of ignition by direct flame impingement where small separations are involved.

Table 6-3D.   Guide Numbers for Minimum Separation Distances

Severity			Width/Height or Height/Width Ratio																
Light	Moderate	Severe	1.0	1.3	1.6	2.0	2.5	3.2	4.	5.	6.	8.	10.	13.	16.	20.	25.	32.	40.
	Percent Openings		Guide Number (Multiply by Lesser Dimension, Add 5 Feet, to Get Building-To-Building Separation)																
20	10	5	0.36	0.40	0.44	0.46	0.48	0.49	0.50	0.51	0.51	0.51	0.51	0.51	0.51	0.51	0.51	0.51	0.51
30	15	7.5	0.60	0.66	0.73	0.79	0.84	0.88	0.90	0.92	0.93	0.94	0.94	0.95	0.95	0.95	0.95	0.95	0.95
40	20	10	0.76	0.85	0.94	1.02	1.10	1.17	1.23	1.27	1.30	1.32	1.33	1.33	1.34	1.34	1.34	1.34	1.34
50	25	12.5	0.90	1.00	1.11	1.22	1.33	1.42	1.51	1.58	1.63	1.66	1.69	1.70	1.71	1.71	1.71	1.71	1.71
60	30	15	1.02	1.14	1.26	1.39	1.52	1.64	1.76	1.85	1.93	1.99	2.03	2.05	2.07	2.08	2.08	2.08	2.08
80	40	20	1.22	1.37	1.52	1.68	1.85	2.02	2.18	2.34	2.48	2.59	2.67	2.73	2.77	2.79	2.80	2.81	2.81
100	50	25	1.39	1.56	1.74	1.93	2.13	2.34	2.55	2.76	2.95	3.12	3.26	3.36	3.43	3.48	3.51	3.52	3.53
***	60	30	1.55	1.73	1.94	2.15	2.38	2.63	2.88	3.13	3.37	3.60	3.79	3.95	4.07	4.15	4.20	4.22	4.24
***	80	40	1.82	2.04	2.28	2.54	2.82	3.12	3.44	3.77	4.11	4.43	4.74	5.01	5.24	5.41	5.52	5.60	5.64
***	100	50	2.05	2.30	2.57	2.87	3.20	3.55	3.93	4.33	4.74	5.16	5.56	5.95	6.29	6.56	6.77	6.92	7.01
***	***	60	2.26	2.54	2.84	3.17	3.54	3.93	4.36	4.82	5.30	5.80	6.30	6.78	7.23	7.63	7.94	8.18	8.34
***	***	80	2.63	2.95	3.31	3.70	4.13	4.61	5.12	5.68	6.28	6.91	7.57	8.24	8.89	9.51	10.05	10.50	10.84
***	***	100	2.96	3.32	3.72	4.16	4.65	5.19	5.78	6.43	7.13	7.88	8.67	9.50	10.33	11.15	11.91	12.59	13.15

Table 6-3E. Separation Distance Based on Building Height

Number of Stories Likely to Contribute to Flaming Through the Roof	Horizontal Separation Distance or Height of Protection Above Exposing Fire.—(Feet)
1	25
2	32
3	40
4	47

Naturally, site conditions and economic constraints preclude the opportunity of providing most buildings with the calculated separation distance. When this occurs, the separation may be reduced by protecting the structure. Some of the means of protecting buildings from exposure fires, and thus reducing the desirable separation distance, are as follows:

1. Clear space between buildings.
2. Total automatic sprinkler protection.
3. Blank walls of noncombustible materials.
4. Barrier walls (self-supporting) between building and exposure.
5. Extension of exterior masonry walls to form parapets or wings.
6. Automatic outside water curtains for combustible walls.
7. Elimination of opening by filling it with equivalent construction.
8. Glass block panels in openings.
9. Wired glass in steel sash (fixed or automatic closing) in openings.
10. Automatic or deluge sprinklers outside over openings.
11. Automatic (rolling steel) fire shutters on openings.
12. Automatic fire doors on door openings.
13. Automatic fire dampers on wall openings.

The application of the means of protection described above will enable the separation distance to be reduced. Guidelines for the distance reduction are given in Table 6-3F:

Table 6-3F. Adjustments for Reducing Separation Distances

Means of Protection	Separation Distance Adjustment
Frame or Combustible Exterior Wall:	
1. Replace with blank fire-resistive wall (3 hrs minimum)	Reduce to 0 ft
2. Install automatic deluge water curtain over entire wall with no windows or with wired-glass windows closed by ¾-hr protection	Reduce to 5 ft
3. Install automatic deluge water curtain over entire wall with ordinary glass windows	Reduce by 50 percent
Noncombustible Exposed Exterior Wall (Fire Resistance Less Than 3 Hrs):	
1. Replace wall with blank fire-resistive wall (3-hr minimum)	Reduce to 0 ft
2. Close all wall openings with material equivalent to wall, or with ¾-hr protection and eliminate combustible projections	Reduce by 50 percent

Table 6-3F. (Cont.)

3. Install automatic deluge water curtain over entire wall with no windows or with glass windows or with windows closed by ¾-hr protection	Reduce to 5 ft
4. Install automatic deluge water curtain on all wall openings equipped with ordinary glass and on combustible projections	Reduce by 50 percent
Veneered Exposed Exterior Wall (Combustible Construction Covered by a Minimum of 4 in. of Masonry):	
1. Replace wall with blank fire-resistive wall (3-hr minimum)	Reduce to 0 ft
2. Close all wall openings with ¾-hr protection and eliminate combustible projections	Reduce by 50 percent
3. Close all wall openings with material equivalent to wall construction and eliminate combustible projections	Reduce to 5 ft
4. Install automatic deluge water curtain over windows equipped with wired glass or over ¾-hr closed openings and on combustible projections	Reduce to 5 ft
5. Install automatic deluge water curtain over windows equipped with ordinary glass and on combustible projections	Reduce by 50 percent
Fire Resistive Exposed Exterior Wall (Minimum 3-Hr Rating):	
1. Close all openings with material equivalent to wall or protect all wall openings with 3-hr protection	Reduce to 0 ft
2. Protect all openings with 1½-hr protection	Reduce by 75 percent (maximum required = 10 ft)
3. Protect all wall openings with ¾-hr protection	Reduce by 50 percent (maximum required = 20 ft)
4. Install automatic deluge water curtain on all wall openings with wired glass or with ¾- or 1½-hr protection	Reduce to 5 ft
5. Install automatic deluge water curtain on all wall openings equipped with ordinary glass	Reduce by 50 percent

Bibliography

References Cited

[1] Galbreath, M., "Fire Research Note No. 8, Time of Evacuation by Stairs in High Buildings," Fire Marshal's Quarterly News, Vol. 5, No. 2, First Quarter, 1969, pp. 1–5.
[2] Brannigan, Francis, L., *Building Construction for the Fire Service*, National Fire Protection Association, Boston, 1971.
[3] Kimball, Warren, Y., *Fire Attack 1*, National Fire Protection Association, Boston, 1966.
[4] ———, *Fire Attack 2*, National Fire Protection Association, Boston, 1968.
[5] Layman, L., Attacking and Extinguishing Interior Fires, National Fire Protection Association, Boston, 1960.
[6] ———, Fire Fighting Tactics, National Fire Protection Association, Boston, 1953.
[7] Fried, E., Fireground Tactics, H. M. Ginn Corporation, Chicago, 1972.
[8] Clark, W. E., Fire Fighting Principles and Practices, Donnelly Publishing Corporation, New York, 1974.

NFPA Codes, Standards, and Recommended Practices (see the latest *NFPA Publications and Visual Aids Catalog* for availability of current editions of the following documents)

NFPA No. 80A, Recommended Practice for Protection of Buildings from Exterior Fire Exposures.

Additional Readings

Law, M., "Heat Radiation from Fires and Building Separation," Technical Paper No. 5, Joint Fire Research Organization, Boreham Wood, England, 1963.

McGuire, J. H., "Spatial Separation of Buildings," *Fire Technology,* Vol. 1, No. 4, Nov. 1965, pp. 278–287.

Shorter, G. W., et al., "The St. Lawrence Burns," *Quarterly,* Vol. 53, No. 4, Apr. 1960, National Fire Protection Association, pp. 300–316.

Thomas, P. H., "The Size of Flames from Natural Fires," *Ninth Symposium on Combustion,* Academic Press, 1963, pp. 844–859.

Williams-Leir, G., "Approximations of Spatial Separation," *Fire Technology,* Vol. 2, No. 2, May 1966, pp. 136–145.

Yokai, S., "Study on the Prevention of Fire Spread Caused by Hot Upward Current," Report No. 34, Nov. 1960, Building Research Institute, Japan.

Chapter 4

BUILDING CONSTRUCTION

Each new building is unique. In creating it, the designer integrates the function and structure into a definable form. Form, function, and building technology are all integrated to build the unique structure.

The variety and complexity of buildings is very great, and, consequently, the components that are combined in their construction are numerous and varied. In order to establish a base for fire protection design by construction, the components of a building and their interrelationships must be identified. This chapter will define the major elements of building construction that are of interest with respect to fire protection. In this chapter, however, the fire safety aspects will not be included. They are covered in later chapters of Section 6.

A. Structural Frame

The structural frame is the skeleton of the building which supports not only the dead load of the building itself, but also all superimposed live loads, such as people, building contents, wind, snow, and ice. In modern construction, building practices have resulted in several reasonably well-defined framing systems that utilize the common materials of structural steel, reinforced concrete, prestressed concrete, and wood.

Buildings are merely a grouping of horizontal and vertical surfaces attached in some manner to provide a combination of volumes of space. Some of these elements are critical to the stability of the structure. Other elements are either of limited importance or are not essential for structural stability. Foundations, while important, are not of great significance in structural design for fire conditions. Thus, only elements of the superstructure are considered here.

For the purpose of classification, the horizontal and vertical elements of a building are grouped as given in Table 6-4A.

The elements of the building described in Table 6-4A are independent of the materials of construction. In some structural systems, the distinctions described above blend together. However, this organization does offer a convenient identification of elements that progressively increase in significance for structural safety.

Nonload bearing ceilings and partitions support only their own weight. Consequently, their removal or collapse,

Table 6-4A.   The Horizontal and Vertical Elements of a Building

1. Nonload bearing surfaces
   a. Ceilings
   b. Partitions

2. Deck
   a. Roof
   b. Floor

3. Horizontal supports
   a. Intermediate flexural framing
   b. Primary flexural framing

4. Vertical supports
   a. Columns
   b. Load bearing walls

from a structural point of view, is not significant. From a functional, environmental, and fire safety point of view these elements are important and, in order to integrate them into the classification, they are included here. Their construction is described more fully in Sections B, C, and D of this chapter.

Figure 6-4A is the floor plan of a structural steel framework supporting a reinforced concrete floor. For the purpose of describing different types of floor systems, it may be considered the "base system". The reinforced concrete floor slab is the floor deck (Item 2b of Table 6-4A). In the reinforced concrete slab, the reinforcing steel bars carry the tensile forces of flexure and are placed in the regions of tension in the continuous slab. These would be near the top of the slab over the supporting beams and at the bottom of the slab between beams.

The steel beams of Figure 6-4A support the reinforced concrete slab. The beams are considered the intermediate flexural framing (Item 3a of Table 6-4A). The steel beams are, in turn, supported by girders. The steel girders are the primary flexural framing (Item 3b of Table 6-4A). Interior girders support beams from both sides. Since interior partitions are often located over and under these girders, they are often hidden within the partitions. In this figure, the girders are supported by structural steel columns. The columns are the vertical supports (Item 4a of Table 6-4A).

The seriousness of failure increases with each succeeding element of the hierarchy described by Table 6-4A. Localized failure of a floor beam is somewhat more serious, but still comparitively localized. Failure of a girder becomes far more critical. Not only does it affect a significant area, but it also can trigger progressive collapse of the framing system. In addition, the failure of one or two girders can cause instability of a column, potentially, leading to a progressive collapse. A column failure is the most serious type of structural instability. The collapse of a single column can, depending on the column's location, potentially trigger extensive collapse damage to the structure.

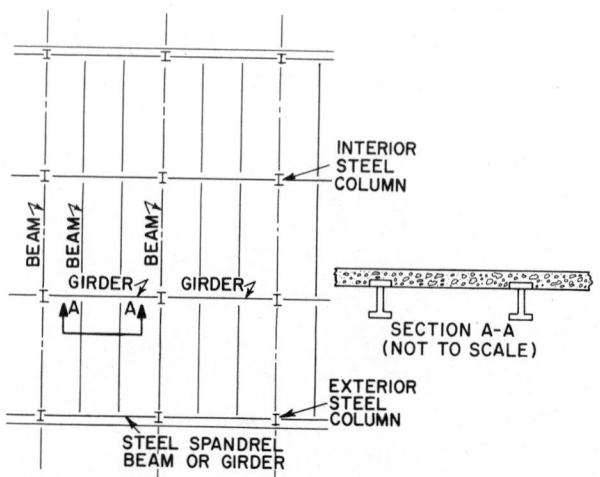

Fig. 6-4A.   Portion of floor plan of steel frame structure.

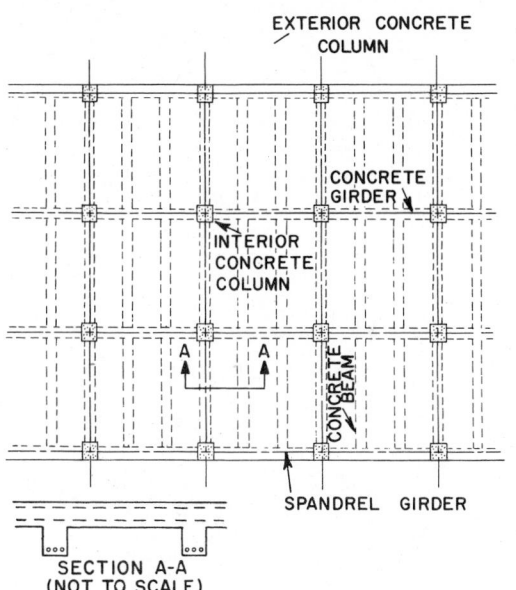

Fig. 6-4B. Portion of floor plan of concrete beam and girder construction.

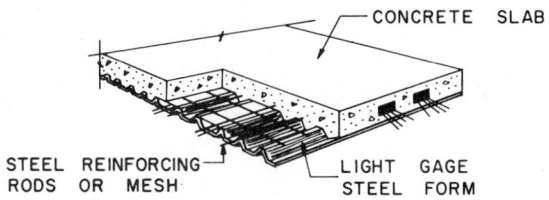

Fig. 6-4C. Example of concrete floor construction showing composite floor assembly.

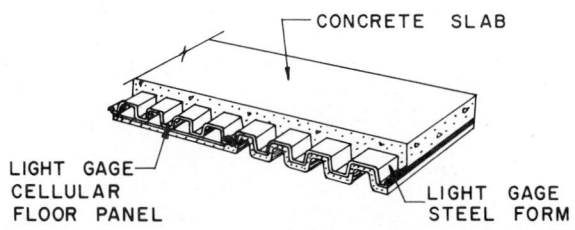

Fig. 6-4D. Example of concrete floor construction showing light gage cellular floor panels alternated with light gage steel forms.

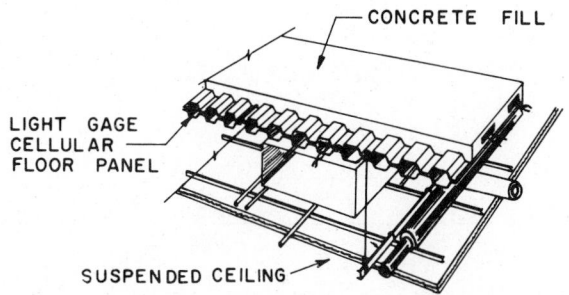

Fig. 6-4E. Example of a concrete floor poured over light gage cellular floor panels.

Floor Framing Systems

The outline of the building elements described in Table 6-4A can be used as a framework to identify quickly and easily other forms of building construction. Figure 6-4B, for example, illustrates a slab, beam, girder, column system cast monolithically of reinforced concrete. The functions of the various elements are the same as those described above.

The floor slab supported by the steel beams of Figure 6-4A need not be of reinforced concrete. Alternate types of deck are the composite decks shown in Figure 6-4C, 6-4D, and 6-4E. This type of floor system offers many construction advantages. The metal deck acts as a form for the concrete that remains in place after curing. In addition, the cellular panels can be used for electrical raceways where desired. A feature of this floor system is that the steel deck also acts as the tensile reinforcement of the concrete floor slab. From a fire safety viewpoint this is significant since protection of the steel reinforcing is not assured, as it is with reinforced concrete.

Another modification of the floor deck is to replace the reinforced concrete floor slab with a precast concrete system. Figure 6-4F illustrates three common precast concrete floor slabs. The precast concrete planks generally have voids through their length. These voids both reduce the weight of the planks and also act as electrical raceways. The planks may be supported either by steel beams or by reinforced concrete beams, although steel supports appear to be more common.

When the steel beams of Figure 6-4A are spaced closely together, the beams can be of much more lightweight construction. Open web joists replace steel beams as the intermediate flexural framing when the spacing becomes approximately two feet. Figure 6-4G illustrates this form of construction. The open web joists are lightweight prefabricated trusses. They are a very common type of construction both for floors and roofs. The spacing of roof joists is generally about 4 ft.

Because the spacing of the joists is so close, the floor slab can be much more lightweight. Often the deck is of corrugated steel forms with $2\frac{1}{2}$ in. of concrete as a wearing surface. Because the span is so small, the corrugated deck is usually strong enough to act as a form for the concrete and also to support the live loads. Thus, lightweight concrete is often used in place of normal weight concrete.

In a similar manner, the reinforced concrete beams of Figure 6-4B can be spaced more closely together. This permits both a thinner slab and smaller beams. This type of construction is generally called a ribbed reinforced concrete system or a concrete joist system. The ribbed system can be either cast in place or precast. Figure 6-4H illustrates the concrete joist floor, while Figure 6-4EE illustrates two of the more common forms of ribbed precast systems. In each of these illustrations, the ribs are the intermediate flexural framing (Item 3a of Table 6-4).

There are other modifications of floor framing that are in common use. An increasingly popular floor system is the two-way flat slab. Two-way reinforced concrete slabs have been built since the turn of the century. The main reinforcement is placed in two directions, and the slab performs the functions of deck, intermediate flexural framing, and primary flexural framing. The underside of the slab may be either flat or ribbed in two directions. Figures 6-4I and 6-4J illustrate two different forms of this construction.

Wooden floor systems can be designed to perform the same functions as the basic model of Figure 6-4A. If the reinforced concrete deck were replaced by heavy wood

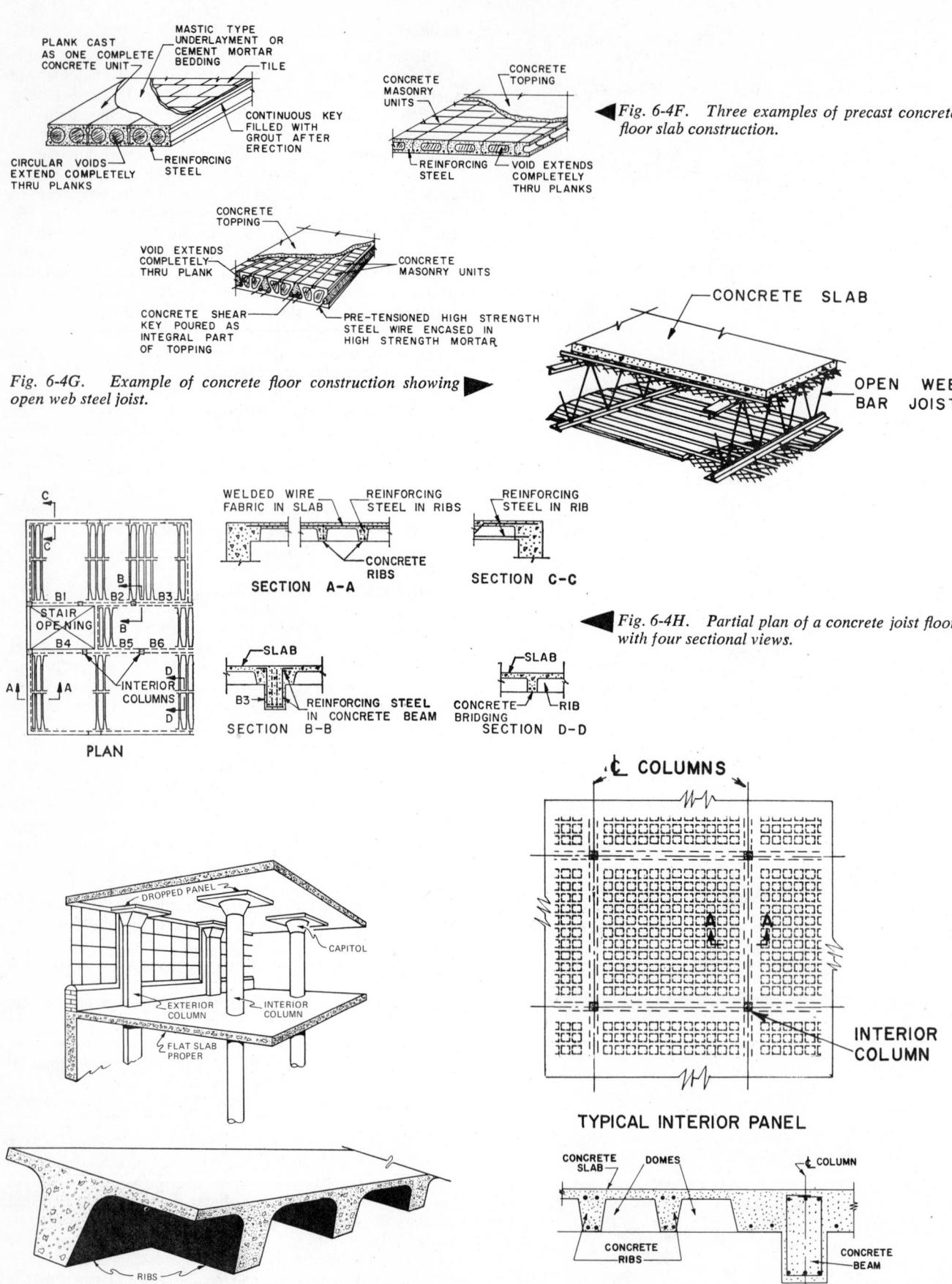

Fig. 6-4F. *Three examples of precast concrete floor slab construction.*

Fig. 6-4G. *Example of concrete floor construction showing open web steel joist.*

Fig. 6-4H. *Partial plan of a concrete joist floor with four sectional views.*

Fig. 6-4I. *Two types of two-way flat slabs: flat underside and two-way ribbed underside.*

Fig. 6-4J. *Partial typical interior two-way ribbed floor slab with section view A-A.*

planking, 2 in. or more in thickness, and the steel beams, girders, and columns with large wooden members having a minimum dimension of 6 in., the basic form would be that of mill construction. This construction, shown in Figure 6-4K, was quite common for industrial buildings and warehouses during the last century. While the structure itself contains a significant amount of fuel, the thickness and the burning characteristics of the members provide a greater length of time before structural collapse in a fire. This greater time before collapse can provide a better opportunity to employ fire suppression agents to the building.

Lightweight, wood frame construction is utilized in smaller buildings. The floor joists are normally spaced 16 in. center-to-center and the vertical supports are often 2- by 4-in. wall bearing studs, again spaced 16 in. center-to-center. The stud walls may extend only from floor to floor, or they may be extended continuously for two or three floors (balloon construction). The former condition is used in platform framing and is shown in Figure 6-4L.

Wood frame construction is not very resistant to fire, particularly when flames and hot gases penetrate into the

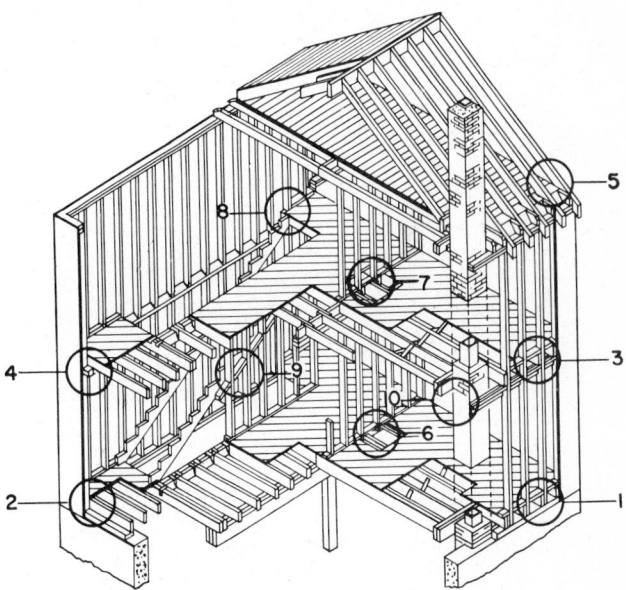

Fig. 6-4K. Components of a heavy timber building showing floor framing and identifying components of a type known as semimill.

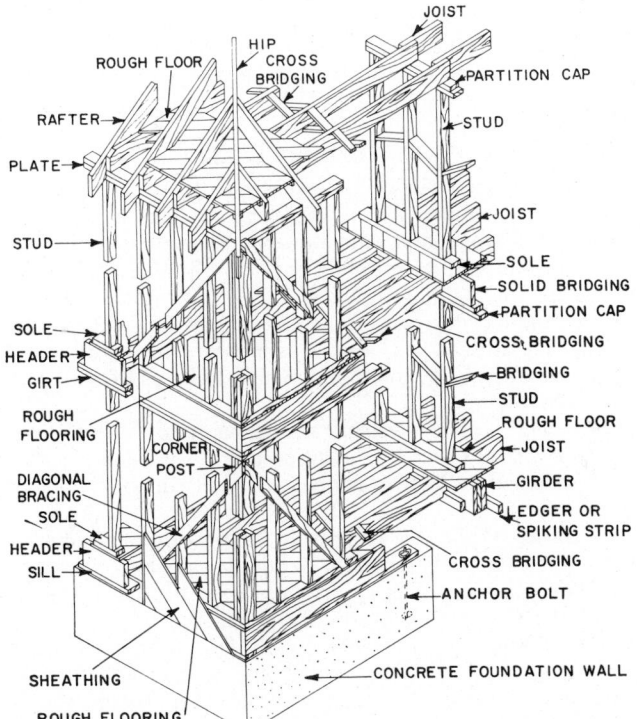

Fig. 6-4L. Example of wood frame platform construction common to dwellings. Structural members are identified.

Fig. 6-4M. Example of wood balloon frame construction showing points to be firestopped. Expanded views of points are shown in Figure 6-4O.

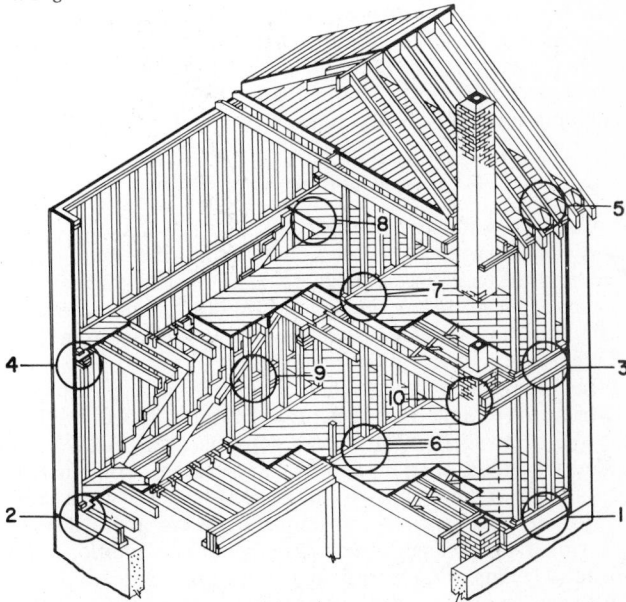

Fig. 6-4N. Example of wood platform frame construction showing points to be firestopped. Expanded views of points are shown in Figure 6-4O.

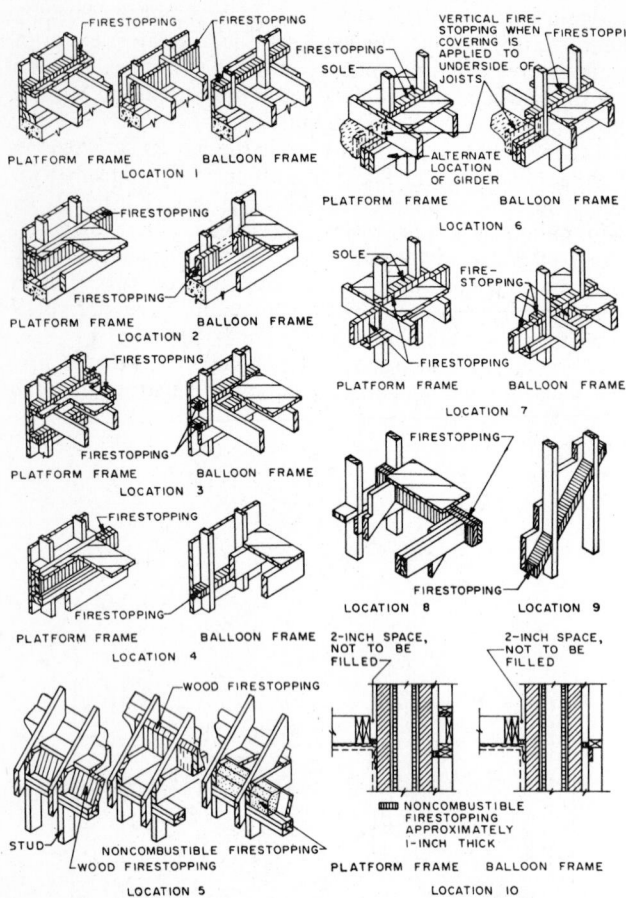

Fig. 6-4O. Details of the application of firestopping to platform and balloon framing. Location numbers coincide with locations circled in Figs. 6-4M and 6-4N.

spaces between the joists or the studs. In order to prevent the rapid vertical and horizontal spread of fire, firestopping is installed at strategic locations throughout the building. The firestops are normally made of wooden blocks or noncombustible material. Figures 6-4M and 6-4N illustrate critical locations for firestopping in balloon frame and in platform frame construction. Figure 6-4O shows the firestopping for these constructions in greater detail.

B. Floor/Ceiling Assemblies

Ceiling assemblies are nonload bearing in that they support only their own weight. Consequently, if a ceiling collapses it does not directly trigger a more extensive structural collapse. Nevertheless, ceiling assemblies, or more specifically the floor/ceiling assemblies, have an important influence on the firesafety of buildings.

In the event of fire within a room, the ceiling acts as a barrier to protect the structural framing above it. The degree of protection, of course, depends upon the type of material, its installation, and its completeness. Combustible ceilings or ceilings that do not remain in place when subjected to the pressures and temperatures of a fire do not provide a significant degree of protection. In addition, suspended ceilings that permit hot gases and flame to travel in the space between the ceiling and the floor or roof framing above are not effective.

Ceilings may be applied directly to the underside of the floor framing, or they may be suspended. Figure 6-4EE

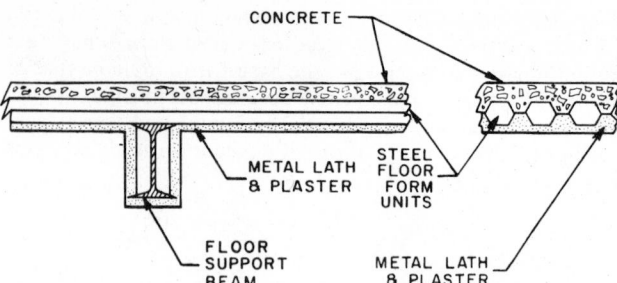

Fig. 6-4P. Plaster applied directly to underside of floor slab construction.

illustrates a ceiling connected directly to the floor framing system, while Figure 6-4E shows a ceiling suspended from the floor slab. It is also common to apply plaster or gypsum board directly to the bottom surface of the floor slab. Figure 6-4P illustrates a floor slab having plaster applied directly to the steel floor deck.

Suspended membrane ceilings are a popular method of increasing fire resistance of floor/ceiling assemblies. There are two types of suspended membrane ceilings in common use. One type consists of a lay-in system in which the panels are supported by a grid. Hold-down clips are necessary to prevent the panels from lifting out of place when pressures develop within a room. The other common type of membrane is installed by fitting slits in the panels into tee sections of the suspension system.

The material used for membrane ceiling is important. Gypsum plaster and lath was a common construction of early membranes. Special mineral tile formulations are used for the acoustical panel systems. Because it is important that the tiles not shrink and fall out during a fire, the material is specially "batched" to prevent this excess shrinkage.

Lighting fixtures and duct openings are important features of membrane ceilings if they are to be used in fire rated assemblies. Fire test performance (described in Section 6, Chapter 7) is based on specific lighting fixtures and areas. Indiscriminate substitution of lighting fixtures can cause premature failure. If duct openings are installed in membrane ceilings, they should be dampered.

C. Exterior Walls

The primary function of exterior walls is to protect the inside of the building from the elements, such as heat and cold, water, wind, and wind blown particles. In addition, the exterior walls of many buildings serve as the support for floor and roof framing systems.

In building construction there are many different types of walls. The definition of the walls provides an indication of their function. The more common definitions of walls are given as follows:

Bearing Wall: A bearing wall supports a vertical load, such as a floor or roof, in addition to its own weight.

Nonbearing Wall: A nonbearing wall supports only its own weight.

Exterior Wall: An exterior wall separates the interior from the exterior of a building, and is usually exposed to the weather, although this is not always so. It does, however, form the extent or boundary of the building.

Party Wall: A party wall usually lies on an interior lot line dividing two buildings, which may or may not belong to the same ownership. A party wall, however, is common to both buildings and can be either bearing or nonbearing.

Fire Wall: A fire wall may be broadly defined as a wall erected to prevent the spread of fire. To be effective, fire walls must have sufficient fire resistance to withstand the effects of the severest fire that may be expected to occur in the building and must provide a complete barrier to the spread of fire. Any openings in a fire wall must be suitably protected.

Partition: A partition is an interior wall, one story or less in height, that separates two areas. Such a wall may be either bearing or nonbearing.

Fire Partition: A partition which serves to restrict the spread of fire, but does not qualify as a fire wall.

Curtain Wall: A curtain wall is an exterior wall, usually supported by the structural frame.

Enclosure Wall: An enclosure wall is an interior wall enclosing a stair well, elevator shaft, duct space, or any other vertical opening through a floor. It may be either bearing or nonbearing.

Cavity Wall: A cavity wall is built of masonry units, so arranged that an air space is provided between the inner and outer wythes (vertical sections of walls, one masonry unit in thickness) of the wall, which, in turn, are held together by metal ties.

Faced Wall: A faced wall is composed of two different masonry materials. One material forms the facing wyth; the other forms the back-up wythe. The wythes are bonded together so that they act as a unit under load.

Hollow Wall: A hollow wall is the same as a cavity wall, but with no provisions for metal ties to hold the inner and outer wythes together.

Veneered Wall: A veneered wall is a wall with a masonry facing attached to a backing, but is not so bonded together that the veneer and backing act as a unit under load.

Parapet Wall: A parapet wall is that portion of a wall that extends above the roof.

Types of Wall Construction

Load bearing exterior walls are generally constructed of masonry, such as stone, brick, concrete block, or a combination of these materials. Brick veneer is sometimes used as a facing in wood frame construction. In this case, the wood studs support the applied loads, while the veneer provides an attractive, useful exterior surface. Veneers are also used as the exterior face of cavity walls. Figures 6-4Q, 6-4R, 6-4S, 6-4T, and 6-4U illustrate some common forms of exterior wall construction.

Exterior walls can also be constructed of reinforced concrete. The reinforced concrete can be either poured in place or precast. Masonry veneers are often used as the exposed surface of reinforced concrete walls. The brick veneer is tied to the concrete by means of metal ties fastened to the concrete and set into the bed mortar joints of the masonry. If the walls are load bearing, the reinforced concrete is designed to support all of the applied loads.

In many buildings, exterior masonry walls are nonload bearing i.e., they support only their own weight. The floor and roof framing is supported by columns that transfer the loads to the foundation. Usually, each story of the exterior wall is supported on spandrel beams which frame into the columns. It is, of course, important from a firesafety viewpoint to ascertain whether the exterior walls are bearing or

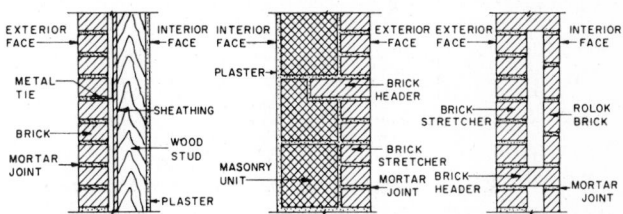

Fig. 6-4R. Typical types of wall assemblies showing (left to right) an exterior brick veneer on wood frame wall, a 12-in. exterior faced or veneered wall, and an 8-in. exterior hollow Rolok Bak brick wall.

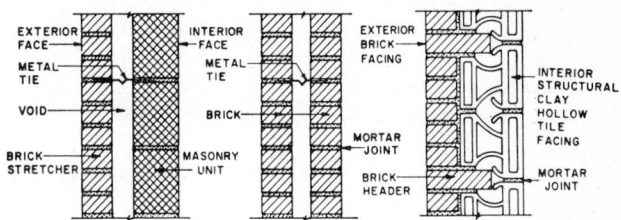

Fig. 6-4S. Typical types of wall assemblies showing (left to right) two examples of exterior nonbearing cavity walls and a 12-in. exterior bearing wall.

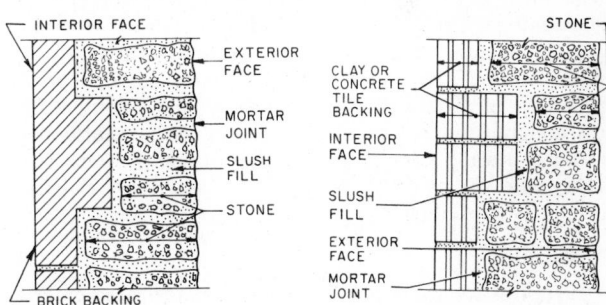

Fig. 6-4T. Stone-faced wall assemblies, one with brick backing, the other with tile.

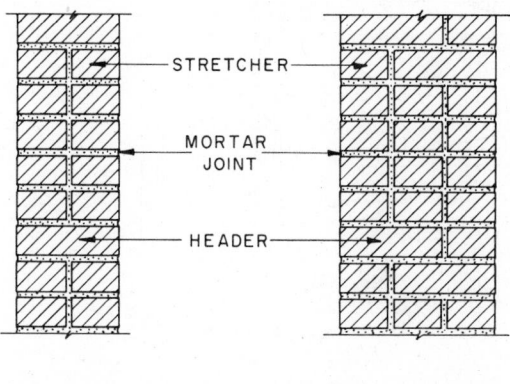

8" BEARING
BRICK WALL

12" BEARING
BRICK WALL

Fig. 6-4Q. Typical types of wall and partition assemblies showing an 8-in. brick bearing wall and a 12-in. brick bearing wall.

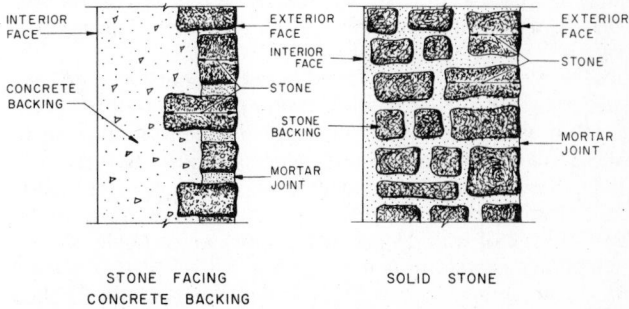

STONE FACING
CONCRETE BACKING

SOLID STONE

Fig. 6-4U. At left a wall of concrete backing and stone face; at right a solid stone wall.

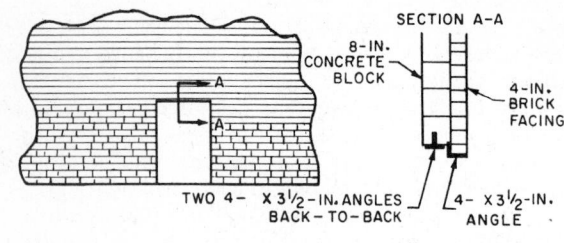

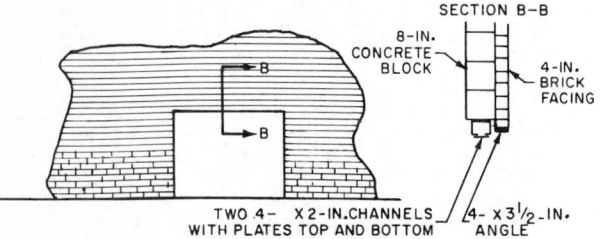

Fig. 6-4V. Lintels formed from steel angles and channels in brick-faced, concrete block walls.

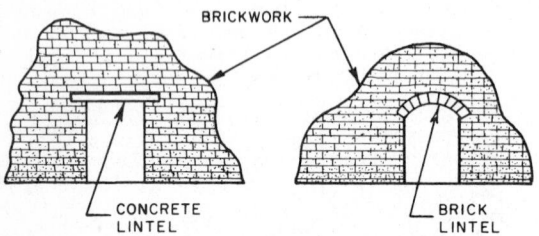

Fig. 6-4W.   Use of concrete and brick lintels in masonry walls.

nonbearing. This can be done by plans examination or field examination.

The openings in masonry walls, such as doors and windows, must have supports to carry the masonry units above the openings. These supports, called lintels, are short beams over the openings to support the masonry against collapse. Lintels can be constructed of several materials. Steel angles and beams in various combinations are commonly used. Precast concrete lintels, or brick arch lintels have also been common means of preventing the masonry units from falling into the opening. Figures 6-4V and 6-4W illustrate several types of lintels.

Curtain Walls

Curtain walls are nonload bearing, prefabricated exterior wall panels that are supported by the structural frame of the building. Generally, whenever a skeleton frame is designed, whether it be structural steel or reinforced concrete, curtain walls are used as the exterior walls. The type of curtain wall that is of principal interest from the firesafety viewpoint is the light weight, prefabricated type.

There are a wide variety of materials and types of construction for curtain walls. Aluminum and stainless steel curtain walls are, by far, the most popular. In addition to these materials, copper and copper alloys, carbon steel, galvanized metals, procelain enamel finish, concrete glass, and plastics are used. Broad areas of windows are common in this type of wall. Figure 6-4X shows an example of contemporary curtain wall construction.

A complete curtain wall consists of a panel with finished outside and inside surfaces, insulation, and means of attachment to the building frame. However, so complete an as-

semblage is not used as frequently as is a metal or glass skin which is backed up by conventional construction.

From a firesafety viewpoint, the method of attachment and the details of construction between the panel and the floor slab are important. Curtain walls are generally bolted to clips attached to the columns, the spandrel, or the floor slab. There is usually a space between the end of the floor slab and the inside of the curtain wall. Unless adequately firestopped, this space acts as an avenue of vertical fire propagation.

D.   Interior Walls and Partitions

Spaces are created within a building by constructing interior partitions. These interior partitions may be either bearing or nonbearing. Bearing partitions are common in the older, wall-bearing construction systems and are also employed with industrialized building systems, particularly those of precast concrete.

The open space flexibility of modern construction has enabled interior partitions to be installed at any location convenient to the occupant. These partitions, called movable partitions, are often made of steel studs and gypsum board. They may be installed, then dismantled and reinstalled at another location, when occupancy needs change. Normally, movable partitions extend only from the floor to the underside of the ceiling.

Interior partitions, particularly nonload bearing partitions, can be installed with a number of other different materials. Wood stud and gypsum board or plaster is a very common type of partition. In addition, partitions constructed of masonry units, such as concrete block, structural clay tile, terra cotta, and gypsum block are common in a wide variety of buildings. Figure 6-4Y shows typical partition constructions.

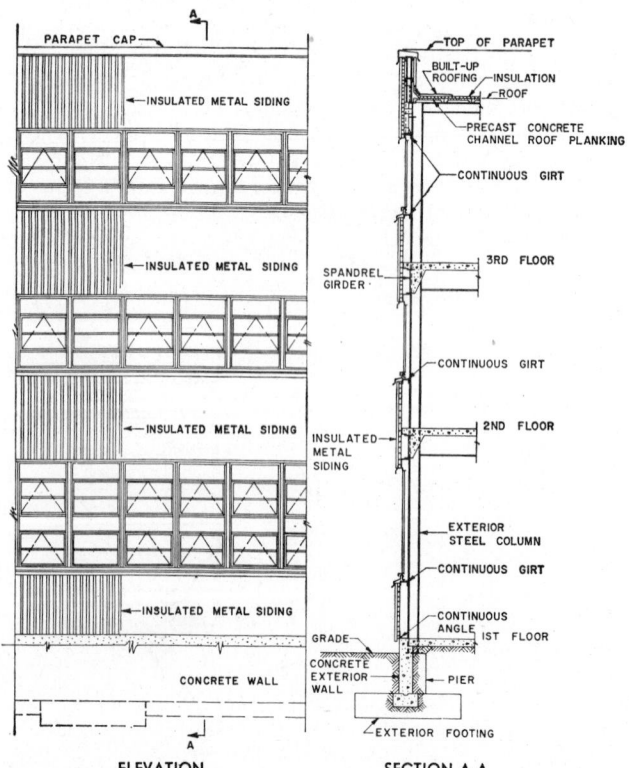

Fig. 6-4X.   Elevation of typical bay of steel frame-curtain wall construction.

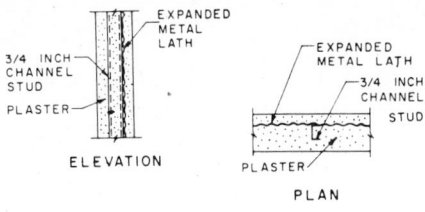

SOLID PLASTER PARTITION

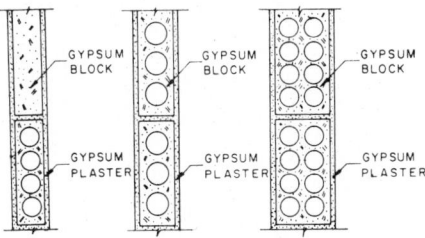

GYPSUM PARTITIONS

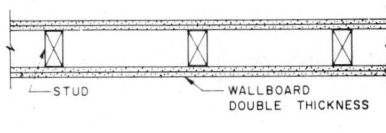

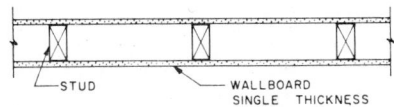

WOOD STUD CONSTRUCTION WITH WALLBOARD FACING

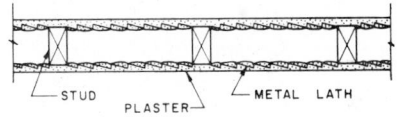

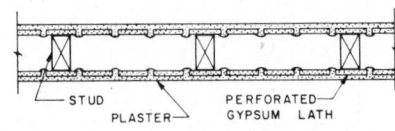

WOOD STUD CONSTRUCTION WITH PLASTER FACING

Fig. 6-4Y. Typical interior wall and partition constructions.

Fire Walls

In building construction, the interior partitions act as barriers to the spread of fire. The evaluation of these barriers is discussed in Chapter 7 of this Section. However, in order to protect certain areas more completely than would be possible with ordinary partitions, fire walls and fire partitions are constructed. Proper construction techniques of these barriers provide effective protection against the spread of fire.

Fire walls are customarily self-supporting and should be designed so as to maintain structural integrity even in cases of complete collapse of the structure on either side of the fire wall. To withstand heat expansion effects, they are commonly made thicker than would be required by normal fire resistance ratings. Also, if of considerable

height or length, they may be buttressed by cross walls or pilasters. In fire resistive buildings, structure-supported fire division walls may be used.

Fire walls must extend through and above combustible roofs to prevent the spread of fire in these roofs when they extend over the tops of the building walls. Fire walls need not be extended through fire resistive roof decks.

When a fire involves a combustible building, the danger of ignition of the roof of an adjoining combustible building of equal height will depend on the effectiveness of the fire wall and the height of its parapet. Where walls extend only a few inches above the roof, ignition of an adjoining roof may readily occur, the probability depending on wind direction and velocity and the character of the roof covering. The Factory Mutual System, for example, specifies a parapet height of 30 in. Greater heights may be necessary for safety in some cases, as in walls over 50 or 60 ft. in length. Many building codes permit lesser heights and, in large sections of the country, 18-in. parapets are considered standard. The higher the parapet, the greater the degree of safety, but considerations of expense and appearance dictate practical compromises with resultant general use of parapets of intermediate height, which perform satisfactorily under ordinary conditions in small buildings.

Fire may also extend around the ends of fire walls where the exterior walls of the building on both sides of the fire wall are combustible. There are two methods of minimizing this danger—one to extend the fire wall several feet out beyond the wall of the building, the other to provide a T section at the end of the wall. Where combustible roofs or cornices project beyond the walls of the building, fire walls should be extended so as to form a break in such combustible construction, as shown in Figure 6-4Z. Many otherwise effective fire walls have failed to perform their designed function by reason of wood platforms or projecting canopies along the sides of buildings which have served to spread fire from one fire area to another.

Fire Partitions

A fire partition normally possesses somewhat less fire resistance than a fire wall and does not extend from the basement through the roof, as does a fire wall. Usually, a fire partition is used to subdivide a floor or an area and is

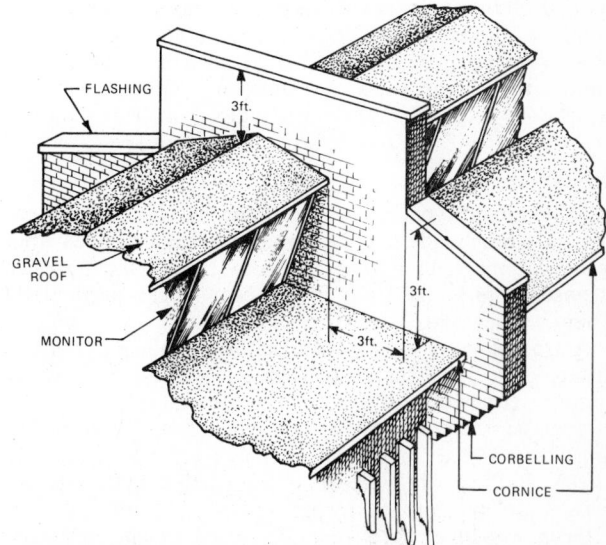

Fig. 6-4Z. Fire wall installation on building with combustible roof and monitor.

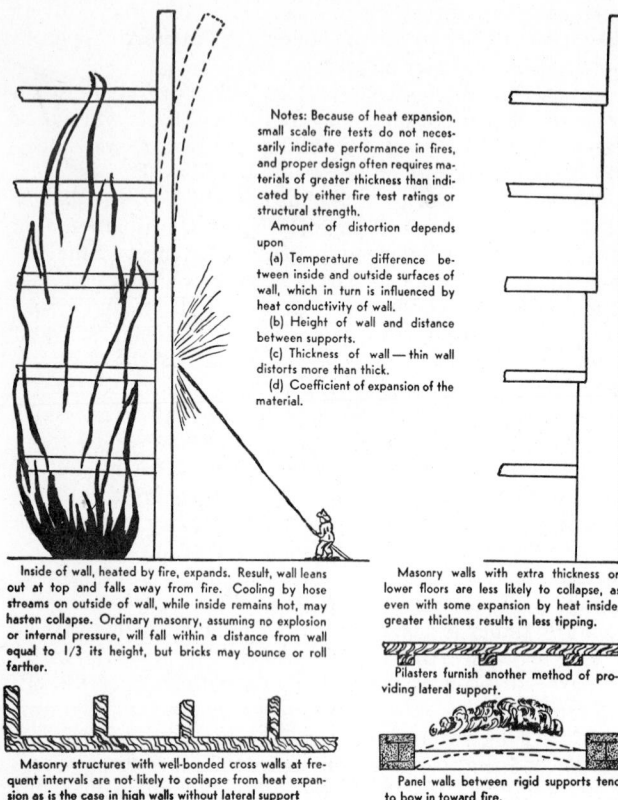

Notes: Because of heat expansion, small scale fire tests do not necessarily indicate performance in fires, and proper design often requires materials of greater thickness than indicated by either fire test ratings or structural strength.

Amount of distortion depends upon

(a) Temperature difference between inside and outside surfaces of wall, which in turn is influenced by heat conductivity of wall.

(b) Height of wall and distance between supports.

(c) Thickness of wall — thin wall distorts more than thick.

(d) Coefficient of expansion of the material.

Inside of wall, heated by fire, expands. Result, wall leans out at top and falls away from fire. Cooling by hose streams on outside of wall, while inside remains hot, may hasten collapse. Ordinary masonry, assuming no explosion or internal pressure, will fall within a distance from wall equal to 1/3 its height, but bricks may bounce or roll farther.

Masonry walls with extra thickness on lower floors are less likely to collapse, as even with some expansion by heat inside, greater thickness results in less tipping.

Pilasters furnish another method of providing lateral support.

Masonry structures with well-bonded cross walls at frequent intervals are not likely to collapse from heat expansion as is the case in high walls without lateral support

Panel walls between rigid supports tend to bow in toward fire.

Fig. 6-4AA.   Heat expansion effects on ordinary masonry walls.

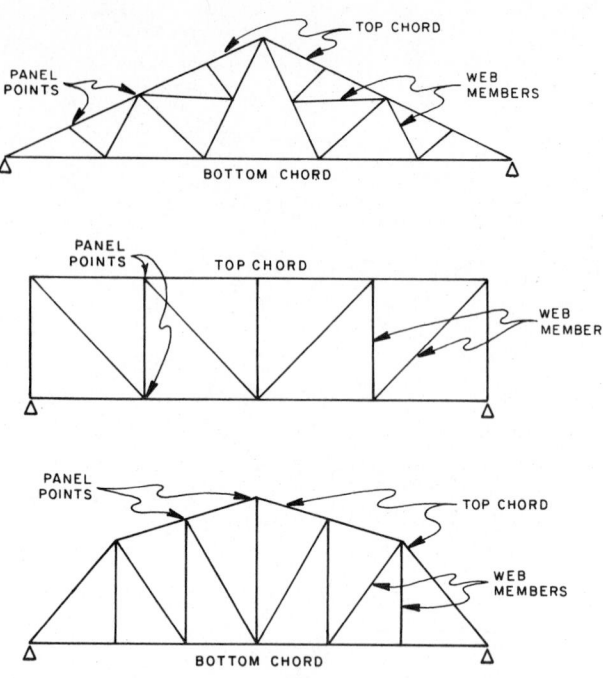

Fig. 6-4BB.   Some common types of roof trusses.

erected to extend from floor to the underside of the floor above. Fire partitions are constructed of noncombustible, limited combustible, or protected combustible materials and are attached to and supported by structural members having fire resistance at least equal to that of the partition. The fire resistance ratings for such partitions range from 2 to 4 hrs.

E.   Roof Systems

The design and construction of roof systems follow the general pattern of floor framing systems described in Section A of this chapter. There are frequently some modifications, however, to reflect the different requirements roof framing must fulfill. Roof loads are usually much lighter than floor loads. In addition, architectural considerations often demand longer spans than floor framing, and the shape of the roof is often other than level.

Steel Roof Systems

A common type of roof framing is the truss. Roof trusses can be made to conform to any roof shape, whether it be flat, pitched, or curved. Roof trusses have proven themselves to be light weight and economical, particularly when long spans are required.

A truss is a frame that consists of a group of triangles arranged in a single plane. Figure 6-4BB shows several common forms of roof trusses. The top and bottom chords of roof trusses are normally constructed of double angles or structural tees. The web members are usually double angles. Purlins, which are roof beams that span between trusses, are connected at the panel points.

Open web steel joists are often used in flat roof construction. An open web joist is merely a lightweight, parallel chord truss. Open web joists are spaced closely together, usually about 4 ft center to center. This close

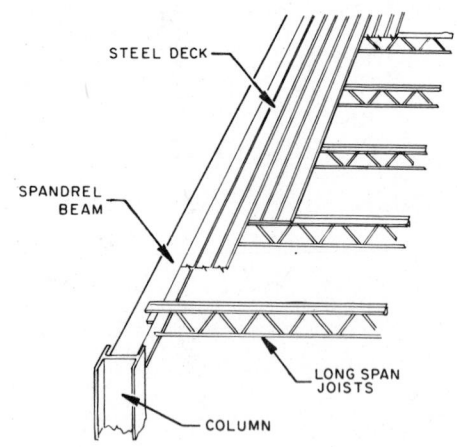

Fig. 6-4CC.   Long span joist framing.

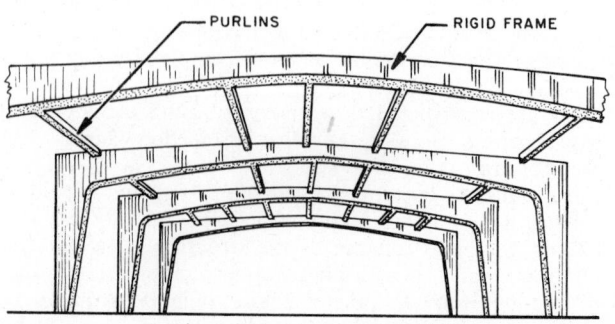

Fig. 6-4DD.   A rigid frame.

spacing avoids the necessity of purlins, as the roof deck can easily span between the joists. Figure 6-4CC illustrates this type of roof framing.

In single story buildings which require a large open space, rigid frames are sometimes used rather than roof trusses. A rigid frame is a continuous framework of a steel wide flange section. The beam spanning the roof is rigidly connected to the column to form a single member. Figure 6-4DD shows a rigid frame structure.

Reinforced Concrete

Flat slab and ribbed slab systems similar to those described in Section A of this chapter are commonly used for roof construction in those buildings in which that is the predominant type of framing. Other systems utilizing long span prestressed concrete double-tee or channel sections are also common (see Fig. 6-4EE).

Roof decks are often made with precast reinforced concrete planks. These planks are manufactured in three general types: square-edge, channel slab, and tongue and groove. They are fabricated with aerated concrete using lightweight aggregates. Planks are fastened to the structural steel supports by galvanized metal clips, as shown in Figure 6-4FF.

F. Floor Construction Features

Floor construction for fire conditions is more than a matter of structural integrity and stability at elevated temperatures. Also, the floor construction should retard damage on lower floors due to water used to extinguish a fire. Consequently, watertight construction and proper floor drainage are important features.

In certain occupancies where easily ignitable materials are present, the installation of nonsparking floors is advised. Where such floors are provided, they should also be electrically conductive. Such floors are commonly found in areas of hospitals where flammable anesthetics are used.

Watertight Floors

Fire loss records have shown that lack of waterproofing and inadequate drainage have been responsible for heavy water damage in fire situations, sometimes exceeding that attributable to the fire.

Complete watertightness at walls, columns, pipe, and other floor penetrations is as important as the watertightness of the floor itself. Ordinarily the waterproofing should be carried up 4 to 6 in. at walls and columns. All pipes and legs of heavy machinery secured directly to the floor proper should be provided with watertight collars.

Wood Floors: Basically, all wood floors are difficult to waterproof. Generally speaking, waterproofing membranes, such as common roofing felt or plastic sheeting are placed between the subfloor and the finished floor. Maintenance is a critical factor in keeping the floor watertight. When

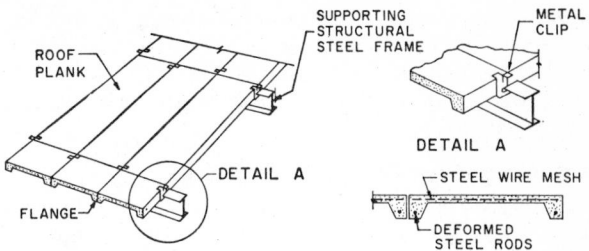

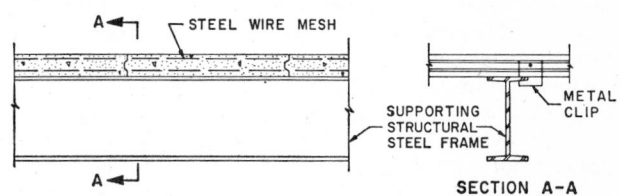

LIGHTWEIGHT TONGUE AND GROOVE CONCRETE ROOF PLANK

Fig. 6-4FF. Lightweight precast concrete planks.

wood floors are used in areas where they will absorb oils, greases, solvents, or paints, applications of mastic coatings or membranes not only serve as waterproofing, but also minimize absorption of the combustible substances.

Concrete Floors: Concrete floors topped with a good grade of well-trowelled concrete are generally watertight. Additives may be included in the concrete mix to enhance the inherent watertight characteristics, as well as to resist cracking and retard shrinkage. Although these integrally mixed compounds are valuable, they cannot compensate for poor workmanship nor can they be expected to fill in cracks or joints. A number of good surfacing compounds are on the market, including mastics, asphalts, epoxies, oxychloride plasters, and other tested and acceptable proprietary materials.

Concrete floors should be inspected frequently and any cracks filled in with a good quality repair compound. Fine hairline cracks can easily be repaired with floor paint.

Hot Asphalt Mastic Surfacing

This floor surfacing is composed of sand, peastone, and asphalt. It is laid hot and about 1 in. or more in thickness. Because of its dark appearance and the thickness required, it is not adaptable to some situations. However, it is well suited for such locations as warehouses. If properly applied, it should yield a 20- to 30-yr service life.

Hot asphalt mastic is suitable for rough usage and for nonrigid floors. It should not be used in areas where light oils are handled; such materials will soften the surface of the mastic. A proper mix is necessary to prevent a too-soft

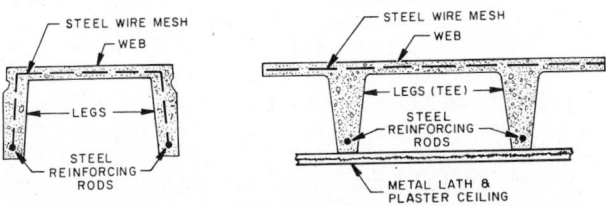

Fig. 6-4EE. Sections through channel and double tee-concrete slabs. The slab at right shows a metal lath and plaster ceiling attached directly to the ribs of the slab.

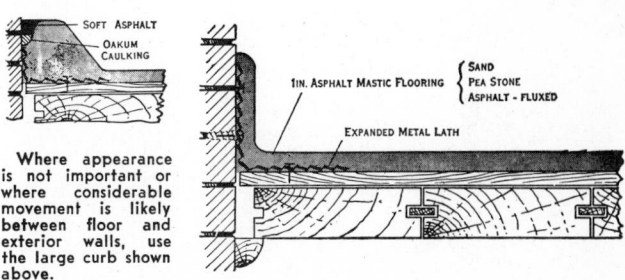

Where appearance is not important or where considerable movement is likely between floor and exterior walls, use the large curb shown above.

Fig. 6-4GG. Hot asphalt mastic flooring.

surface, which results in increased trucking effort and imprints under standing loads. Conversely, when too hard, the surface is liable to crack and its efficiency will be impaired. Bearing pressure from static or dynamic loading should not exceed 30 psi.

Oxychloride (Magnesite) Cement Surfacing

This type of floor surfacing, over a comparatively rigid base, is suited for light traffic where an attractive appearance is desired. It may also be used where light oils are used, since it will not soften as will the asphalt base floorings. The flooring is composed of marble chips, magnesium oxide, and magnesium chloride laid over a base of expanded metal lath. It is ½ to ¾ in. thick when finished.

Good results can be obtained if laid over a suitable base by an experienced applicator. It cannot be applied successfully over a flexible base, nor can it be subjected to heavy loading or rough usage. Aggregates having an all-mineral base are preferred, as aggregates having a wood-fiber base are subject to cracking. If properly installed, this floor should give a service life of 5 to 15 years.

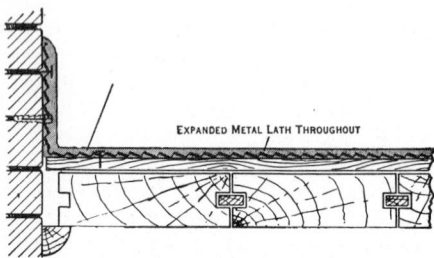

Fig. 6-4HH. Oxychloride cement flooring.

Asphalt Emulsion Surfacing

This type of floor surfacing is laid cold, ½ in. thick. It consists of a mixture of sand, cement, peastone, and emulsified asphalt. It is laid on top of an asphalt-saturated waterproofing fabric which is, itself, set in a heavy priming coat of asphalt. A second priming coat of asphalt is applied after the fabric is laid. With this surfacing, the mastic flooring provides some waterproofing; however, the real dependence is placed on the heavily coated waterproofing fabric.

Asphalt emulsion flooring can be used over wood or concrete base, but must not be used under heavy traffic when installed over a yielding base or when subjected to light oils which will soften the surface. It provides a somewhat harder surface than the hot mastic flooring.

Pitch Mastic Surfacing

This surfacing is similar to hot asphalt mastic flooring, except that tar pitch is used instead of asphalt. It is un-

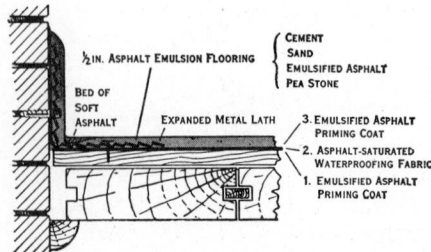

Fig. 6-4II. Asphalt emulsion surfacing.

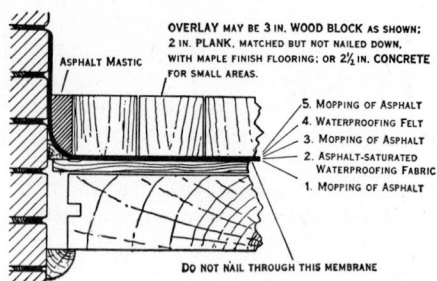

Fig. 6-4JJ. Protected membrane flooring.

affected by light oils, most acids and alkalies, and is able to withstand a greater static load.

Protected Membrane Surfacing

This method of flooring employs a two-ply, three-mop waterproofing membrane which must be free of holes and over which a wearing surface is placed, such as 3 in. wood blocks or 2 in. matched planks with maple overlay. The first, third, and fifth coats of the membrane are of mopped asphalt, the second is asphalt-saturated waterproofing fabric, and the fourth is waterproofing felt. A 3 in. space should be left at the walls and at columns to allow for swelling. This space should be filled in with asphalt mastic.

The success of this type of waterproofing depends on the quality of workmanship and the care taken in protecting the membrane against carelessly piercing it. A 15- to 20-yr service life can be expected.

Lightweight Special Surfacing

For light service, linoleum, rubber tile, asphalt tile, or vinyl tile laid over a waterproofing fabric, such as that used as a base for the asphalt emulsion flooring, has given satisfactory service. The life of the waterproofing effect depends on the durability of the surfacing that protects the fabric.

Protection for Special Hazards

Rooms containing spray booths and other processes which may require large quantities of water for fire suppression should not be located on floors above those having high value contents which are subject to water damage, unless the floor is reasonably watertight and is provided with means for drainage.

Any of the noncombustible watertight floor coverings described above will give satisfactory service for the protection of wooden floors in welding and other spark-producing areas and can also be used to advantage for the covering of oil-soaked wood floors to eliminate the fire hazard from ignition of such floors.

Floor Drainage

Without drainage, water will soon overtax the waterproofing or rise above the flashing at walls; it will also add considerable weight. The common and usually the most satisfactory type of drainage is to provide scuppers in the walls. Floor drains connected to ample size leaders or a combination of scuppers and floor drains may be used.

Scuppers and Floor Drains: The number of scuppers or drains is dependent upon the hazard and the amount of water likely to be used for fire suppression. For average conditions, the following is considered good practice and is based upon the use of wall scuppers with 4- by 4-in. outlets, or interior drains 4 in. in diameter, which have a discharge capacity substantially equivalent to a 4-in. square scupper.

Floor Areas	No. of 4-in. scuppers or drains
For floor areas 500 sq ft or less	2
For floor areas 750 sq ft	3
For floor areas 1,000 sq ft	4
Additional scuppers for areas over 1,000 sq ft	

For extra hazard occupancies (quantity and combustibility of contents is very high) or floors of questionable watertightness, or contents especially subject to water damage —one scupper for each additional 500 sq ft.

For moderate hazard occupancies (quantity and combustibility of contents is moderate) with watertight floors —one scupper for each additional 1,000 sq ft or fraction thereof.

For ordinary hazard occupancies (quantity and combustibility of contents is low) with strictly watertight floors—one scupper for each additional 2,000 sq ft or fraction thereof.

Table 6-4B provides the basis for a ready determination of the number and types of drains needed to remove runoff water where the probable water discharge has been reliably estimated. The present trend toward protecting severe hazards with hydraulically designed automatic sprinkler systems gives opportunity to estimate the amount of runoff that could be expected from sprinklers. Some sprinkler systems employ open sprinklers in which the area of sprinkler discharge is more definitely established.

Table 6-4B. Scupper and Drain Discharge*

Depth of Water In.	Discharge gpm
1	33
2	71
3	132
4	188
5	218
6	245

* Based on tests of 4- by 4-in. wall scuppers and typical floor drains having 4-in. diameter outlets.

Preferably, drainage facilities should be provided for the total runoff anticipated from sprinklers and hose streams plus an additional reserve drainage capacity. It may not be practical in all cases to provide this amount of drainage capacity; if not, provision should be made for immediate drainage of sprinkler discharge since the sprinkler system may operate when no one is present. Allowance for hose stream runoff could be through opening of access doors. Where there are no access doors, "knock out" panels in exterior walls could be provided for opening by the fire department.

While wall scuppers are preferable, floor drains may be substituted where scuppers are not practicable. However, interior floor drains are more likely to become clogged than wall scuppers. In order to prevent stoppages in floor drains, cover grills or beehive type floor plates should be provided for the outlets.

Scuppers in exterior walls are so placed that drainage will not flow into windows or other openings directly below. The outer ends of scuppers should be so designed that materials falling from above will not clog or injure the outlets. Scuppers should protrude a sufficient distance out from the wall so that they are not easily sealed by ice formed from water flowing down the side of the building.

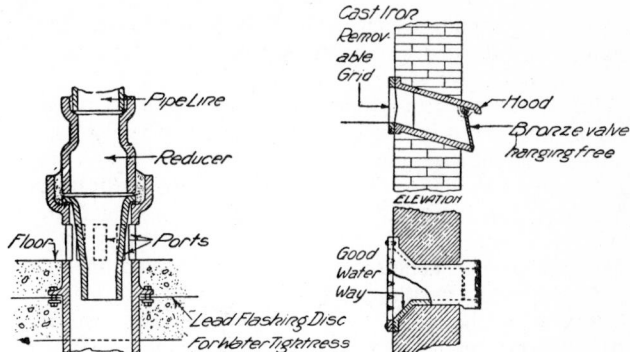

Fig. 6-4KK. Typical scupper installations. At left is an interior scupper; at right an exterior scupper.

Scuppers are constructed of cast iron with bronze clappers pivoted on bronze pins to prevent entrance of wind, birds, etc. Scuppers of good design are listed or approved by recognized testing laboratories. See Figure 6-4KK for typical scupper installations.

Mechanical Water Removal: Although gravity flow drainage is the most reliable means of removing water, mechanical means may have to be used in some cases, such as in areas below grade. A waste removal pump is best, and it should take suction from a screened sump. Electric power should be taken off ahead of the service disconnecting means so that power can be interrupted for fire fighting without interfering with the pump operation.

In evaluating the degree of reliability required of waste pump power supply and controls, it is important to recognize that fire in below-grade areas is extremely difficult to fight and may be of such duration that complete flooding may be a threat. Similarly, complete flooding may become a necessary fire department strategy to prevent structural collapse of a multiple-floored building; therefore, placarded remote control for the sump pump should be available at an accessible location.

Floor Slope: In some occupancies, ordinary drainage facilities are inadequate since a slight depth of water can be destructive to contents. Large rolls of newsprint paper stored on end, for example, could be badly damaged by a small amount of water due to the absorbency of the paper. A good slope would be a desirable storage feature to limit water spread. Slope discharge may be picked up by drainage trenches, wall scuppers, or drainage pipes.

Where large amounts of flammable and combustible liquids are handled, provision should be made for rapid removal into trapped drains in preference to scuppers. Since most combustible liquids are lighter than water and can readily flow to adjacent areas, isolation tactics should be employed.

In large areas protected by deluge sprinkler systems, drains and scuppers could be overtaxed. Sloping floors ending at a trench would be desirable.

Protection of Doorways and Other Openings: Doorways providing access to and from enclosures or areas with waterproof floors on which water or flammable liquids may be discharged should be protected to prevent flow through the doorways. This may be done by providing raised sills, 3 in. or more above the floor levels, with ramps as necessary to permit trucking through the opening or to prevent stumbling. An alternate arrangement is to provide a trough, protected by a grating and connected to a 4 in. or larger drainpipe, in the floor in front of the door opening.

All other openings, such as those for conveyors and belts, should be provided with curbs or otherwise arranged to prevent the flow of water.

Exposure Fire: Provision should be made to prevent runoff water used in fire fighting from entering neighboring building yard areas.

Supplemental Fire Department Activities: Municipal fire departments providing salvage operations contribute a valuable service in reducing water damage either by supplementing existing facilities or providing drainage in buildings not equipped with proper drainage.

Reference should be made to the American Insurance Association publication "Fire Department Salvage Operations," [1] and to NFPA 604, Recommended Practice on Salvaging Operations.

Nonsparking and Electrically Conductive Floors

In addition to the hazard of static electricity, there may also be the hazard of sparks due to friction or impact, such as those produced by contact of ferrous metals with a concrete floor or machinery. In certain occupancies where easily ignitable materials are present, such as explosives, sulfur, or carbon disulfide, and where the possibility of ignition from frictional (mechanical) sparks of relatively low energy and short duration exists, the provision of nonsparking floors is advisable. Where nonsparking floors are provided, they should also be electrically conductive, since greater ignition energies can be produced by static than frictional sparks of the type indicated above.

Where combustible gas-air or vapor-air mixtures, which require relatively greater energy for ignition, may be present, such as in areas where flammable anesthetics are administered, the provision of electrically conductive floors is essential, but they need not necessarily be of the nonsparking requirement.

Nonsparking Floors: The probability of producing sparks by striking tools or other hard objects on a floor depends upon the composition of the floor surface. Generally, soft floor surfaces will minimize the spark hazard. A nonsparking floor should be made of a material that contains the appropriate ingredients to minimize the danger of production of mechanical sparks. In addition it should be able to withstand wear and have reasonable durability.

There are no NFPA or other national standards for determining the relative spark hazard of floorings; any test would have to take into consideration the variable factors of humidity and the character and amount of the flammable materials or vapors in the particular occupancy as well as the capability of the floor surface material to resist spark production.

Ordinary wooden floors and floor coverings of linoleum, asphalt, vinyl, or rubber tile are considered nonsparking. Certain types and formulations of oxychloride flooring, and some cement floors with metallic aggregate surfaces also have satisfactory nonsparking qualities.

Electrically Conductive Floors: Electrically conductive floor surfacings provide an electric path to the ground which will drain off static electricity from any person or object in contact with the floor before sufficient potential has developed to produce a spark of sufficient intensity to ignite flammable vapors or other materials in the area. Floors providing an electrical path to ground with a resistance of less than 1,000,000 ohms, measured between two electrodes placed 3 ft. apart anywhere on the floor, are considered satisfactory since high electrical conductivity is not necessary to achieve the desired result. Ordinary dry concrete floors have a resistance of about 100 megohms

(100,000,000 ohms) or more, too high to provide protection against static sparks. Concrete which is in contact with moist earth, as in basement floors, may have a relatively high conductivity. Any concrete floor can be made temporarily conductive by wetting. Calcium chloride solutions, sometimes used for this purpose, may be retained in the pores of concrete for an appreciable time, but are not considered a satisfactory substitute for a permanent conductive flooring installation.

In many locations where there may be a shock hazard from live electrical equipment, it may be desirable to use a flooring material with resistance sufficiently high to minimize the danger of electrical shocks. NFPA 56A, Inhalation Anesthetics, recommends a floor resistance of more than 25,000 ohms and less than 1,000,000, ohms, as measured between a ground connection and an electrode placed at any point on the floor and also as measured between two electrodes placed 3 ft. apart at any point on the floor. This is considered adequate protection from both static sparks and electrical shock. A conductive floor also produces a definite shock hazard in the absence of an ungrounded electrical system.

Materials for many types and formulations of proprietary floor finishes meet requirements for conductive floors, some being applied integrally in the original floor construction, others over concrete or combustible floor assemblies. In addition to the selection of materials and grounding to avoid the accumulation of static charges, consideration must also be given to other characteristics of the flooring, such as resistance to traffic, resistance to damageability from repeated washings with hot water, and resistance to damage by solvents, oils, greases, etc. In general, conductive floors are usually specified to be free from cracks, reasonably smooth, and not subject to buckling, wrinkling, or sloughing off under conditions of use. Various types of materials meet one or more of the requirements of use, such as lead, conductive rubber, mastic floors, conductive linoleum, vinyl, or asphalt tile coverings, ceramic tile, proprietary formulations which include some types of oxychloride cement, concrete floor finishes which include metallic dusts in the mix, viscous mixtures of plastics, solvents and conductive materials, etc. The necessary degree of conductivity in rubber, asphalt, linoleum, and similar materials which are normally nonconductive is secured by a mixture of acetylene black or other conductive material.

Humidity is automatically controlled by air conditioning equipment in many locations, but most conductive floors are exposed to wide variations in relative humidity. The oxychlorides were the only materials, of a number of various types of flooring tested, whose electrical resistance was materially affected by changes in humidity. As shown in Figure 6-4LL it is evident that the electrical resistance of oxychloride type flooring is dependent upon its moisture content; therefore it is not considered a good material for a conductive floor.

Age of some flooring materials has an effect on resistance —the resistance increases with age. Floors of such materials should have an initial resistance low enough to permit increases in resistance with age without exceeding the 1,000,000-ohm resistance previously mentioned.

Grounding by special floor-to-ground connections is not necessary. Contact between the conductive flooring and water or heating pipes, armor on electrical wiring, or metallic structural members normally provides sufficient grounding qualities. The accumulation of electrical charges in the flooring is also prevented by the movement of

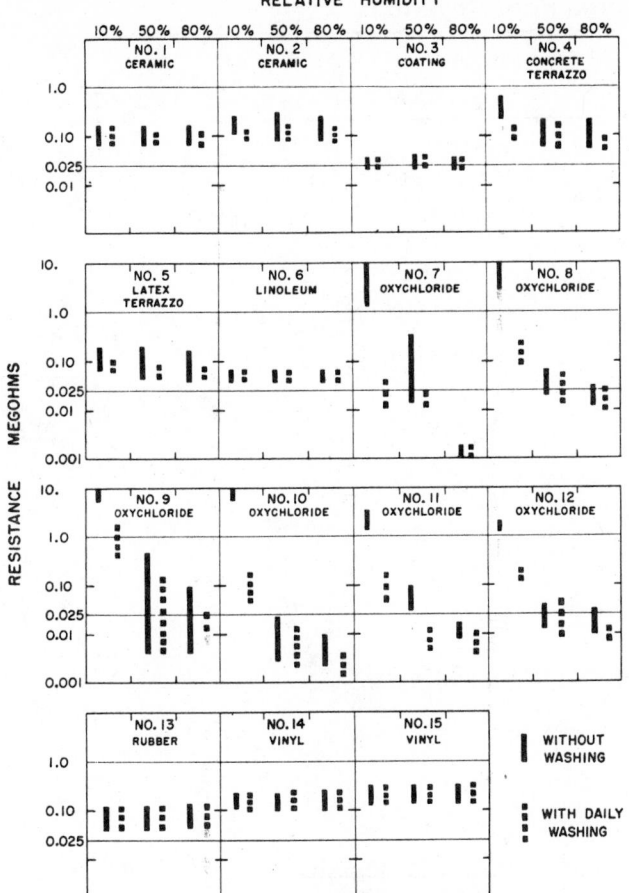

Fig. 6-4LL. Effect of ambient relative humidity and daily washing on electrical resistance of conductive flooring materials. Reproduced from National Bureau of Standards Monograph No. 11, "Conductive Flooring for Hospital Operating Rooms." [2]

persons or objects over the floor, provided there is proper conductivity between them and the floor.

Maintenance practices provide that the resistance of conductive floors should be tested and recorded prior to use and at least monthly thereafter, when the room or area is free from explosive mixtures. The test procedure for determining performance of conductive flooring is contained in the NFPA Inhalation Anesthetics Standard. To be effective, conductive flooring must not be insulated by a film of oil or wax. Any waxes, polishes, or dressings used on conductive floors should be of the electroconductive type.

G.   Roof Coverings

Roof coverings range from highly combustible wood shingles without a fire retardant treatment to built-up or prepared coverings that are effective against severe external fire exposure. The limitations of the different types of coverings must be recognized, as the coverings play an important part in the protection of buildings from exposure fires. In some cases, they are also factors in the spread of fire from one building to another.

Since the General Motors fire at Livonia, Mich. in 1953, major attention has been paid to the combustibility of insulated metal roof decks. In that fire, the asphalt mopping in the felt vapor barrier beneath the insulation on the 1,502,500-sq-ft, flat, steel deck roof melted and vaporized.

Asphalt vapor under pressure entered the building through the joints in the steel deck and burned inside. As a result of this and similar fires, research was conducted to find a solution to the problem. The significant findings are summarized in the subject of Roof Deck Insulation and Vapor Barriers later in this chapter.

A recurring problem has been the use of wood shingles on dwellings and similar properties. See the subject "Wood Shingles" in this chapter.

Classification of Fire Retardant Roof Coverings

Fire retardant classifications for various roof coverings were originally prepared by an NFPA committee in 1911. At that time, six classes, A to F, were established, ranging from the highest to the lowest fire retardancy. The definitions of the three lower classes, D, E, and F, all indicated such low fire retardance that they were soon dropped from consideration, and only the three upper classes, A, B, and C, were retained. The definitions of these three classes, modified through experience, are now given by Underwriters Laboratories Inc., as follows:

Class A Coverings: Class A includes roof coverings which are effective against severe fire exposures. Under such exposures, roof coverings of this class are not readily flammable and do not carry or communicate fire, afford a fairly high degree of fire protection to the roof deck, do not slip from position, possess no flying-brand hazard, and do not require frequent repairs in order to maintain their fire retardant properties.

Class B Coverings: Class B includes roof coverings which are effective against moderate fire exposures. Under such exposures, roof coverings of this class are not readily flammable and do not readily carry or communicate fire, afford a moderate degree of fire protection to the roof deck, do not slip from position, possess no flying-brand hazard, but may require infrequent repairs in order to maintain their fire retardant properties.

Class C Coverings: Class C includes roof coverings which are effective against light fire exposure. Under such exposures, roof coverings of this class are not readily flammable and do not readily carry or communicate fire, afford at least a slight degree of fire protection to the roof decks, do not slip from position, possess no flying-brand hazard, and may require occasional repairs or renewals in order to maintain their fire retardant properties.

Building codes commonly require Class A or B coverings within the fire limits of cities or wherever fire resistive construction is required. Class C roofing is appropriate for other buildings. Many cities specify Class C as the minimum standard for roofing anywhere in the city. The National Building Code[3] of the American Insurance Association, for example, calls for Class A or B roofing, except that Class C roof coverings are acceptable on dwellings, wood-frame buildings, and buildings located outside the fire limits which, on the basis of height and area, could be of wood-frame construction.

Fire Testing Laboratories classify metal deck roof assemblies by type of construction.[4] These classifications are discussed later in this chapter.

Prepared and Built-up Coverings

Fire retardant roof coverings fall within either of two groups in describing their form and method of application to roof decks. One is the built-up covering which, as the name implies, consists of several layers of materials applied or "built-up" on the roof decks according to specifications which give in detail the exact procedures that must be followed in applying the materials. What is known as a "tar

Table 6-4C. Typical Prepared Roof Coverings*

Description	Minimum Incline In. to Ft	CLASS A	CLASS B	CLASS C
Brick Concrete Tile Slate		Brick, $2\frac{1}{4}$ in. thick. Reinforced portland cement, 1 in. thick. Concrete or clay floor or deck tile, 1 in. thick. Flat or French-type clay or concrete tile, $\frac{3}{8}$ in. thick with $1\frac{1}{2}$ in. or more end lap and head lock, spacing body of tile $\frac{1}{2}$ in. or more above roof sheathing, with underlay of one layer of Type 15 asphalt-saturated asbestos felt or one layer of Type 30 or two layers of Type 15 asphalt-saturated organic felt. Clay or concrete roof tile, Spanish or Mission pattern, $\frac{7}{16}$ in. thick, 3-in. end lap, same underlay as above. Slate, $\frac{3}{16}$ in. thick, laid American method.		
Metal Roofing	12	Sheet roofing of 16-oz copper or of 30-gage steel or iron protected against corrosion. Limited to noncombustible roof decks or non-combustible roof supports when no separate roof deck is provided.	Sheet roofing of 16-oz copper or of 30-gage steel or iron protected against corrosion or shingle-pattern roofings with under-lay of one layer of Type 15 saturated asbestos-felt, or one layer of Type 30 or two layers of Type 15 asphalt-saturated organic felt.	Sheet roofing of 16-oz copper or of 30-gage steel or iron, protected against corrosion, or shingle-pattern roofings, either without underlay or with underlay of rosin-sized paper.
				Zinc sheets or shingle roofings with an underlay of one layer of Type 30 or two layers of Type 15 asphalt-saturated organic-felt or one layer of 14 lbs un-saturated or one layer of Type 15 asphalt-saturated asbestos felt.
Cement-Asbestos Shingles	Exceeding 4	Laid to provide two or more thicknesses over one layer of Type 15 asphalt-saturated asbestos felt.	Laid to provide one or more thicknesses over one layer of Type 15 asphalt-saturated asbestos felt.	

Table 6-4C.   Typical Prepared Roof Coverings (Cont.)*

Description	Minimum Incline In. to Ft	CLASS A	CLASS B	CLASS C
Asphalt-Asbestos Felt Sheet Coverings	Not Exceeding 12	Factory-assembled sheets of 4-ply asphalt and asbestos material.	Factory-assembled sheets of 3-ply asphalt and asbestos material or sheet coverings of single thickness with a grit surface.	Single thickness smooth surfaced.
Asphalt-Asbestos Felt Shingle Coverings	Exceeding 4		Asphalt-asbestos felt grit surfaced.	
Organic-Felt (previously referred to as rag felt) Sheet Coverings	Exceeding 4			Sheet coverings of asphalt organic felt either grit surfaced or aluminum surfaced.
Organic-Felt (previously referred to as rag felt) Shingle Covering, with special coating	Sufficient to permit drainage	Grit surfaced, two or more thicknesses.	Grit surfaced, two or more thicknesses.	
Organic-Felt (previously referred to as rag felt) Shingle Coverings	Sufficient to permit drainage	Grit surfaced, two or more thicknesses.	Grit surfaced, two or more thicknesses.	Grit surfaced shingles, one or more thicknesses.
Asphalt Glass Fiber Mat Shingle Coverings	Sufficient to permit drainage	Grit surfaced, two or more thicknesses.	Grit surfaced, one or more thicknesses.	Grit surfaced shingles, one or more thicknesses.
Asphalt Glass Mat Sheet Covering	Sufficient to permit drainage			Grit surfaced.
Fire-retardant treated red cedar wood shingles and shakes	Sufficient to permit drainage			Treated shingles or shakes, one or more thicknesses; shakes require at least one layer of Type 15 felt underlayment.

* Prepared roof coverings are classified as applied over square-edge wood sheathing of 1-in. nominal thickness, or the equivalent, unless otherwise specified. See footnote (Built-Up Roof Coverings) to Table 6-4D. Laid in accordance with instruction sheets accompanying package. Limited to decks capable of receiving and retaining nails.

Where organic-felt is indicated, asbestos felt of equivalent weight can be substituted.

By end lap is meant the overlapping length of the two units, one placed over the other. Head lap in shingle-type roofs is the distance a shingle in any course overlaps a shingle in the second course below it. However, with shingles laid by the Dutch-lap method, where no shingle overlaps a shingle in the second course below, the head lap is taken as the distance a shingle overlaps one in the next course below.

Prepared roofings are labeled by Underwriters' Laboratories which indicate the classification when applied in accordance with direction for application included in packages.

and gravel" roof is actually a built-up roof covering consisting of several layers of roofing felts and insulating panels or sheets bonded together by hot or cold cements and topped with roofing gravel (see Fig. 6-4MM).

Prepared roof coverings include fire retardant shingles and sheet coverings which can be applied only to roof decks capable of receiving and retaining nails and which are inclined sufficiently to permit drainage. In some instances, however, the incline must not exceed a specified maximum to meet specifications for either a Class A, B, or C fire retardant rating. Asphalt organic-felt shingles are a common example of prepared roof coverings. They are frequently found on dwellings and are known as "composition" roofs (see Fig 6-4NN).

Prepared roof coverings also include such noncombustible coverings as brick, concrete, tile, and slate. Test methods have been developed by Underwriters Laboratories for measuring the fire retardant characteristics of roof coverings against fire originating outside the building on which they have been installed. These test methods have been adopted as NFPA 256, Methods of Fire Tests of Roof Coverings, Tables 6-4C and 6-4D list various types of prepared and built-up roof coverings and their fire retardant classifications. Any roof covering can be used for a less severe exposure than the one for which it is listed.

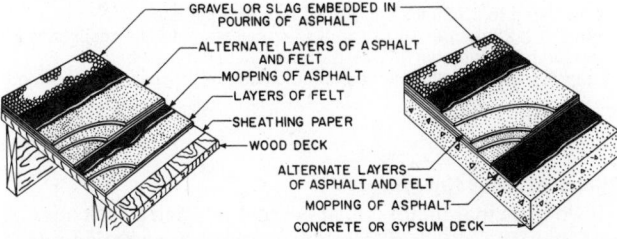

(a) 5-PLY BUILTUP ROOF OVER WOOD   (b) 4-PLY BUILTUP ROOF OVER CONCRETE

Fig. 6-4MM. Typical built-up roof coverings with hot asphalt mopping or coal tar pitch between each two layers.

Table 6-4D.   Built-up Roof Coverings*

Description	Minimum Incline In. to Ft	CLASS A	CLASS B	CLASS C

Asphalt organic-felt, bonded with asphalt and surfaced with 400 lbs of roofing gravel or crushed stone, or 300 lbs of crushed slag per 100 sq ft of roof surface, on coating of hot mopping asphalt.	3	4 (plain) or 5 (perforated) layers of Type 15 felt.
		  1 layer of Type 30 felt and 2 layers of Type 15 felt.
		  1 layer of Type 15 felt and 2 layers of Type 15 or 30 cap or base sheets.
		  3 layers of Type 15 or 30 cap or base sheets.
		  3 layers of Type 15 felt. Limited to non-combustible decks.
			4 layers of perforated Type 15 felt.
			  3 layers of Type 15 felt.
			  2 layers of Type 15 or 30 cap or base sheets.	

Tar-asbestos-felt or organic-felt bonded with tar and surfaced with 400 lbs of roofing gravel or crushed stone, or 300 lbs of crushed slag per 100 sq ft of roof surface on a coating of hot mopping tar.	3	4 layers of 14-lb asbestos-felt or Type 15 organic-felt. 3 layers of 14-lb asbestos-felt or Type 15 organic-felt.	3 layers of Type 14-lb asbestos-felt or Type 15 organic-felt.	
Steep tar organic-felt	5	4 layers of Type 15 tar-saturated organic-felt, bonded with steep coal-tar pitch, surfaced with 275 lbs of $\frac{5}{8}$-in. crushed slag per 100 sq ft of roof surface on steep coal-tar pitch.		

Asphalt organic-felt, plain or perforated, bonded and surfaced with a cold application coating.	12			3 layers of Type 15 felt.
				  1 layer of Type 30 felt and 1 layer of Type 15 felt.
				  2 layers of Type 15 or 30 cap or base sheets.
				  2 layers of Type 15 felt and 1 layer of Type 15 or 30 cap or base sheets.

   * Built-up roof coverings are classified as applied over square-edge wood sheathing of 1-in. nominal thickness, or the equivalent, unless otherwise specified.
   From the standpoint of relative effectiveness of the different types of wood roof sheathing, the tongue-and-groove boards and $\frac{3}{4}$-in. moisture-resistant plywood give better results in the brand and flame tests than square-edge sheathing with boards spaced about $\frac{1}{4}$-in. apart. For classifications based on square-edge sheathing, tongue-and-groove or plywood sheathing can be substituted. Square-edge sheathing boards should be butted together as closely as possible. Reference to $\frac{1}{4}$-in. spacing is to indicate fire test procedure intended to simulate actual conditions after shrinkage of boards due to age or other reasons.
   The minimum weight of cementing material between separate layers of felt is considered to be 25 lbs per 100 sq ft of roof surface.
   Types 15 and 30 felts are defined as saturated felts weighing a minimum of 14 lbs and 28 lbs per 100 sq ft of the finished materials, respectively. Where saturated felts are referred to by weight, the weight is minimum and is expressed in pounds per 100 sq ft of the finished material.
   Materials intended for built-up roof coverings are labeled by Underwriters' Laboratories. The classifications indicated are of generally accepted combinations.

In addition to the built-up roof coverings described in Table 6-4D there are several other types consisting of asbestos, combinations of asbestos and rag felt, fiberglass, aluminum, and tile applied in a special manner with special listed proprietary cements that are listed by testing laboratories.

Choice of Roof Coverings
Two principal factors must be kept in mind in selecting a roof covering that provides adequate fire protection for a building. They are (1) the construction of the building as a whole with particular emphasis placed on the construction and fire resistance of the roof assembly, and (2) the severity

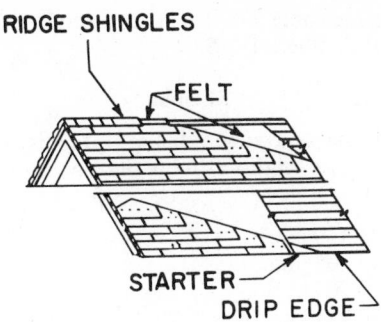

Fig. 6-4NN. Installation of a typical prepared roof covering.

of the threat from exposure fires. The aim is to select a covering that fulfills its intended purpose of offering protection and insulation from the weather and is properly designed and installed to resist damage from windstorm. At the same time, it does not detract from the other fire protection features of the building.

An example of an obviously poor choice is placing asphalt organic-felt shingles on an improperly drained combustible roof deck of a brick building located in a congested area where the exposure hazard is severe. First, asphalt organic-felt shingles carry only a Class C fire-retardant rating (effective only against light exposures and offering only slight protection to the roof deck). Second a shingled covering on a poorly drained deck only invites the problems of a leaky roof. The best selection would be a Class A built-up covering (effective against severe fire exposures and offering a fairly high degree of protection to the roof deck) which has good weatherproofing properties for roofs of small incline. A fire resistive roof deck is not affected by heat from an exposure fire transmitted to it through the covering. All that is required of coverings on fire resistive decks is that they shall not spread fire, produce burning brands, or slip from position. These conditions are met by all three classifications of fire-retardant coverings. A good quality of built-up roofing is used almost universally on concrete, hollow tile, or gypsum decks which require a covering. For steeper roofs, slate, tile, metal, or prepared coverings are advisable.

Metal deck roofs with combustible vapor barriers or with large amounts of combustible adhesive between the deck and the insulation above may pose a protection problem from fire originating under the roof deck (see following discussion on Roof Deck Insulation and Vapor Barriers). Roof deck constructions that eliminate the asphalt or severely restrict its use below the insulation are preferred, particularly where large areas are involved and the building is not sprinklered.

Wood Shingles

Untreated wood shingles may be readily ignited by small sparks from chimneys or exposure fires, by radiated heat, or by burning brands. Burning shingles themselves also produce brands which may be carried by the wind to start other fires. Age and low humidity increase the susceptibility of wood-shingled roofs to ignition.

Treatment of wood shingles with fire-retardant coatings has been proposed at various times but has not, to date, proved practical as ordinary flame resistant treatments lose their effectiveness with continued exposure to the weather. Wood shingles impregnated with a fire retardant solution are available. These shingles have been tested and carry a Class C rating.

Untreated wood shingle roofs are prohibited by law in the congested sections of practically all large cities and a very large number of cities and towns prohibit their use within the municipal limits.

In certain areas particularly subject to windstorm damage, wood shingles have enjoyed popularity over asphalt shingles because of somewhat greater susceptibility of non-sealing asphalt shingles to windstorm damage. However, since the development of a self-sealing type of asphalt shingle with good fire retardance, windstorm damage has been materially reduced.

Roof Deck Insulations and Vapor Barriers

The combustibility of a roof is usually determined by the physical characteristics of the roof deck and its supporting structure, with no consideration given to the combustibility of the roof insulation and covering. Thus, combustible fiberboard insulation and asphalt-impregnated felt roof covering normally will not affect the classification of a noncombustible roof deck on noncombustible supports. However, large scale fire tests, confirmed by actual fire experience, have shown that some metal deck assemblies, under certain conditions, can contribute to an interior fire.

A series of full-scale tests were conducted at Factory Mutual testing facilities to compare the performance of various metal roof deck constructions with respect to the spread of flame along the underside of the deck. The tests were run in cooperation with the Metal Roof Deck Technical Institute (now Steel Deck Institute) and the Insulation Board Institute, and the results were published in the pamphlet, "Insulated Metal Roof Deck Fire Tests." [4] The traditional construction, with the insulation fastened to the metal deck with complete moppings of asphalt or with vapor barriers using complete asphalt moppings above and below one or more plies of felt, was shown to contribute significant amounts of fuel when exposed to the heat of an intensive interior fire below the deck. The asphalt, vaporized by the heat of the fire below, and unable to escape upwards through the roof covering, was being forced down through the joints in the deck, to be ignited, helping to spread the fire under the roof deck. A typical built-up roof covering is shown in Figure 6-4OO.

Recognized fire testing laboratories now list metal roof deck construction and components which will not contribute significantly to an interior fire and which meet certain performance standards.

Metal roof deck constructions use both combustible and noncombustible insulations over the deck, fastened with noncombustible adhesives or mechanical fasteners. Asphalt can also be used as the adhesive if applied in strips (strip-mopping), and the total amount used between the deck and

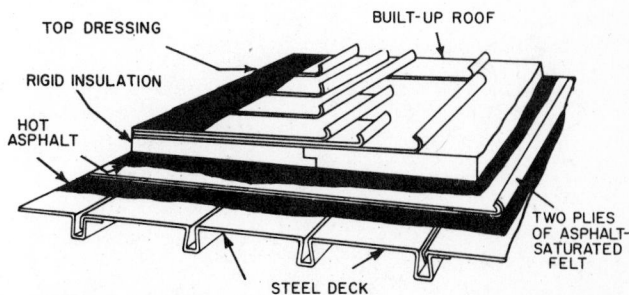

Fig. 6-4OO. Typical built-up roof covering with a combustible vapor barrier adhered to the roof deck and to roof insulation by a combustible adhesive.

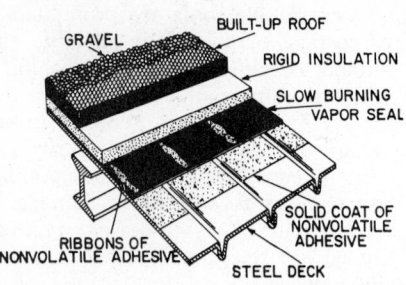

Fig. 6-4PP. Typical built-up roof covering with a slow burning vapor seal adhered to the roof deck and to the insulation by a nonvolatile adhesive.

the insulation does not exceed 12 to 15 lbs per 100 sq ft of roof area. There are no restrictions on the use of asphalt in conventional built-up roofing used above the insulation. When a vapor seal is used between the deck and the insulation, a listed, noncombustible or slow-burning material is recommended, fastened to the deck and insulation with a noncombustible adhesive or strip-mopping. Testing laboratories list various manufacturers of acceptable vapor seals and adhesives. A roof cover with a slow-burning vapor seal is shown in Figure 6-4PP.

The Factory Mutual System classifies metal deck roof assemblies into two classes. Class II construction is any insulated-metal-roof-deck construction using asphalt in sufficient quantity to provide adequate adhesion for wind resistance, with or without felts between the insulation and the deck and regardless of the type of insulation used. This class of construction does not meet FM standards and can provide fuel that will contribute significantly to an interior fire. Class I construction is any insulated-metal-roof-deck construction having a special vapor barrier (if any is used) and an adhesive which will not contribute significantly to an interior fire and which will meet FM performance standards or their equal. Under test conditions, a Class I construction will limit the increase in flame spread over the length of the igniting fire to not more than 10 ft during a 10 min exposure, and not more than 14 ft during a 30-min exposure; those constructions which

are found acceptable are listed in Factory Mutual Loss Prevention Data Sheet 1-28S.[5]

SI Units

The following conversion factors are given as a convenience in converting to SI units the English units used in this chapter.

$$1 \text{ in.}^2 = 645.160 \text{ mm}^2$$
$$1 \text{ in.} = 25.400 \text{ mm}$$
$$1 \text{ ft} = 0.305 \text{ m}$$
$$1 \text{ lb} = 0.454 \text{ kg}$$

Bibliography

References Cited

[1] "Fire Department Salvage Operations," Special Interest Bulletin 48, Mar. 1955, American Insurance Association, New York.

[2] Boone, T. H., et al., "Conductive Flooring for Hospital Operating Rooms," *Journal of Research of the National Bureau of Standards, Engineering and Instrumentation*, Vol. 63C, No. 2, Oct.-Dec. 1959 pp. 125–140.

[3] *National Building Code,* American Insurance Association, New York, 1967, p. 100.

[4] "Insulated Metal Roof Deck Fire Test," Factory Mutual System, Norwood, Mass, May 1955.

[5] "Insulated Steel Deck, Acceptable Class I Construction," Loss Prevention Data Sheet 1-28, 1972, Factory Mutual System, Norwood, Mass.

NFPA Codes, Standards, and Recommended Practices (see the latest *NFPA Publications and Visual Aids Catalog* for availability of current editions of the following documents)

NFPA No. 56A, Standard for the Use of Inhalation Anesthetics.

NFPA No. 92M, Waterproofing of Floors, Drainage and Installation of Scuppers.

NFPA No. 256, Standard Methods of Fire Tests of Roof Coverings.

NFPA No. 604, Recommended Practice on Salvage Operations.

Additional Readings

Bescher, R. H., "A New Class C Treatment for Wooden Shingles and Shakes," *Fire Journal*, Vol. 61, No. 5, Sept. 1967, pp. 52–56.

Platzker, J., "Regulations on Wood-Shingle Roofing: A Survey," *Fire Journal*, Vol. 60, No. 4, July 1966, pp. 36–39.

Wilson, R., "Wood Shingles, 1959," NFPA *Quarterly*, Vol. 53, No. 2, Oct. 1959, pp. 99–110.

Yuill, C. H., "Floor Coverings: What is the Hazard?" *Fire Journal*, Vol. 61, No. 1, Jan. 1967, pp. 11–19.

Chapter 5

CLASSIFICATION OF BUILDING CONSTRUCTION

The determination of the relative risk of a building with respect to fire resistance has been the desired goal of building and code officials, as well as insurance underwriters, for some time. For this reason, the use of construction classifications has proliferated, both as a means of organizing building code requirements and as a tool in establishing insurance rates. Conversely, the code requirements and underwriting practices control the construction type and the size of buildings based on anticipated fire hazard. The National Fire Protection Association and every major building code identify various construction types. Although the classification pattern is essentially the same for all, each agency may classify the various types of construction differently.

At one time, there were only two classifications: "fireproof" and "nonfireproof". The term "fireproof" was misleading, however, as it conveyed a false sense of security. Consequently, the term "fire resistive" was coined to provide a more realistic assessment of the resistance of certain buildings to the effects of fire. This term also provided for the identification of relative fire resistance. The development of newer construction methods has led to the designation of five basic types of construction: fire resistive, noncombustible,* heavy timber, ordinary, and wood frame.

In the fire resistive and noncombustible categories, the requirements identify a minimum fire resistance of assemblies and structural elements. The fire resistance of an assembly or an element is the time, in minutes or hours, that materials or assemblies have withstood a fire exposure as established by test. The test procedure (NFPA No. 251, Methods of Fire Tests of Building Construction and Materials) and failure criteria are described in Chapter 7 of this Section.

The use of the construction types often relates to the fire loading normally expected in the various occupancies, as well as to the fire severity expected. A description of fire loading and its relationship to fire resistance is found in Chapter 8 of this Section.

This chapter will describe each of the five basic types of construction, as defined in NFPA 220, Types of Building Construction. The basic systems are consistant with most codes. The major differences are found in the number of subcategories within each of the five basic types.

A. Fire Resistive Construction

Fire resistive construction is defined in NFPA 220 as: ". . . that type of construction in which the structural members including walls, partitions, columns, floors, and roofs are of noncombustible or limited-combustible materials and have fire resistance ratings not less than those specified in Table 6-5A."

A building classified as being of fire resistive construction has more ability to resist structural damage from fire than any of the other building construction types. A review of Table 6-5A shows that critical structural members are required to be more resistant to damage than "secondary"

structural members (those supporting a floor or roof) which, in the event of failure, would not affect the overall structural stability of the building. These too, however, have considerable fire resistance; thus, a building classified as fire resistive can withstand considerable exposure to fire without major damage.

Buildings of fire resistive construction (4- and 3-hr) are commonly referred to in building codes as Type I and Type II or Type A and Type B. Under the height and area restrictions of building codes, such buildings are allowed more undivided floor area and permitted to be built higher than any other type of construction. Their susceptibility to fire damage is generally considered to be minor.

Table 6-5A. Fire Resistance Requirements for 4-Hr and 3-Hr Fire Resistive Construction

Building Element	Fire Resistance Rating of Structural Members in Hours	
	Classification	
	(4-hour)	(3-hour)
Bearing walls or bearing portions of walls, exterior or interior Bearing walls and bearing partitions must have adequate stability under fire conditions in addition to the specified fire resistance rating.	4	3
Nonbearing walls or portions of walls, exterior or interior NC—Noncombustible LC—Limited-Combustible Fire resistance may be required for such walls by conditions such as fire exposure, location with respect to lot lines, occupancy, or other pertinent conditions.	NC or LC	NC or LC
Principal supporting members including columns, trusses, girders and beams for one floor or roof only	3	2
Principal supporting members including columns, trusses, girders and beams for more than one floor or roof	4	3
Secondary floor supporting members, such as the beams, slabs, and joists, not affecting the stability of the building	3	2
Secondary roof supporting members, such as beams, purlins, and slabs, not affecting the stability of the building	2	1½
Interior partitions enclosing stairways and other openings through floors One-hour partitions of noncombustible or limited-combustible materials may be permitted under certain conditions.	2	2

---

* The NFPA uses the term "noncombustible/limited-combustible".

Noncombustibility

In fire resistive construction, only noncombustible (and, in some cases, limited combustible) structural materials are permitted. Over the years, the definition of noncombustible has caused great confusion. Materials such as steel, iron, brick, tile, concrete, slate, asbestos, glass, and plaster are examples of traditionally noncombustible materials on the basis that no part of these materials will ignite or burn when subjected to a fire.

In 1956, the term "noncombustible" assumed a somewhat expanded definition. Many building materials were being developed which were not completely noncombustible, yet provided significant protection from fire. Gypsum board, for example, is composed of a noncombustible gypsum core in an envelope of paper. Although the paper burns, the gypsum itself is an effective barrier to fire. Consequently, it was felt that materials of this nature, which still offered realistic protection, should be permitted under the definition of noncombustible. Thus, the definition was expanded to include:

(a) Materials no part of which will ignite and burn when subjected to a fire.

(b) Materials having a structural base of noncombustible material, as defined in (a), with a surfacing not over $\frac{1}{8}''$ thick which has a flame spread rating not higher than 50.

(c) Materials, other than as described in (a) or (b), having a surface flame spread rating not higher than 25 without evidence of continued progressive combustion and of such composition that surfaces that would be exposed by cutting through the material in any way would not have a flame spread rating higher than 25 without evidence of continued progressive combustion.[1]

The flame spread ratings referred to in (b) and (c) are obtained according to NFPA No. 255, Method of Test of Surface Burning Characteristics of Building Materials. This test method is more popularly used for determining the flame spread characteristics of interior surface finish and is described in detail in Chapter 6 of this Section.

With the wide variety of building materials available, this expanded definition has also led to problems in usage and in interpretation. The purpose of the test is to provide a relative classification of materials, based on surface flame spread. It is possible, however, to develop a product that can be accepted in accordance with this test procedure, yet still be combustible by the very nature of the materials of which it is composed. Consequently, a more accurate definition of noncombustible was felt to be necessary.

In May 1974, the NFPA Committee on Building Construction obtained tentative adoption of a revised edition of NFPA 220. The major change from the previous 1961 edition was the introduction of the term "limited-combustible" and amendment of the term "noncombustible." [2] The definition of the latter was changed to: ". . . means a material which, in the form in which it is used and under the conditions anticipated, will not ignite, burn, support combustion, or release flammable vapors when subjected to fire or heat." Thus, the definition of noncombustible was greatly narrowed.

The new term "limited-combustible" was defined as:

"Limited-combustible, as applied to a building construction material, means a material, not complying with the definition of noncombustible material, which, in the form in which it is used, has a potential heat value not exceeding 3,500 Btu per pound,[3] and complies with one of the following paragraphs (a) or (b). Materials subject to increase in combustibility or flame spread rating beyond the limits herein established through the effects of age, moisture, or other atmospheric condition shall be considered combustible.

(a) Materials having a structural base of noncombustible material, with a surfacing not exceeding a thickness of $\frac{1}{8}$ of an inch which has a flame spread rating not greater than 50.

(b) Materials, in the form and thickness used, other than as described in (a), having neither a flame spread rating greater than 25 nor evidence of continued progressive combustion and of such composition that surfaces that would be exposed by cutting through the material on any plane would have neither a flame spread rating greater than 25 nor evidence of continued progressive combustion."

The revised edition of NFPA 220, Standard Types of Building Construction, along with the new definition of limited-combustible and the narrower definition of noncombustible, was adopted officially by the NFPA on May 15, 1975. The use of these two terms will require building code officials and building designers to fully understand the nature of the test methods applicable and the meaning of the results.

Life Safety and Property Damage Consideration

It must be recognized that fire resistive building construction does not necessarily assure safety to life and property in case of fire. A fire resistive building will not contribute fuel to a fire; also, the probability of collapse due to fire damage is small. Nevertheless, attention must be paid to the details that are important to protection of life and property. This is the responsibility of the designer.

Numerous case histories of fires in fire resistive buildings describe high life loss and severe property damage, while the building required only redecoration to restore it to full use. Fire resistive construction is an important factor in fire safe design. The many other details that are essential to fire safety must also be incorporated.

B.　Noncombustible/Limited-Combustible Construction

Noncombustible limited combustible construction does not qualify as fire resistive construction, as defined in Table 6-5A, yet the walls, partitions and structural members are of noncombustible or limited-combustible materials. In this type of construction, the materials may not contribute fuel to the fire; however, the unprotected structural members may be damaged by heat.

The main feature of noncombustible/limited-combustible construction is its inability to spread fire. This, of course, assumes that the noncombustible or limited-combustible structural components are not nullified by use of combustible materials for other purposes. For example, materials such as asphalt and felt vapor barriers on metal roof decks, insulation in paper batts on the underside of a roof or corrugated metal wall panels protected with asphalt base coatings can spread fire rapidly in an otherwise noncombustible building.

Typical of unprotected, noncombustible/limited-combustible construction are metal framed, metal clad buildings. These buildings are economical, easily field erected, and lend themselves to many different applications. In situations where the contents are of low fire hazard, or when automatic sprinklers are provided, this type of building offers an economical solution to many user needs.

Besides pre-engineered metal buildings, there are many

Fig. 6-5A. A noncombustible/limited combustible building with a low hazard metalworking occupancy.

Fig. 6-5B. Failure of unprotected steel in "noncombustible construction" in the General Motors fire, Livonia, Mich., Aug. 12, 1953.

other forms of construction which can be categorized as noncombustible/limited-combustible. For example, a concrete block building having a metal deck roof supported by an unprotected open web joist system would qualify. In addition, unprotected structural steel framing and a wide variety of assemblies can be constructed for use under this category. Figure 6-5A illustrates this type of construction.

The principal danger from noncombustible/limited-combustible construction is its potential for collapse. Figure 6-5B depicts the results of fire severity exceeding the resistance of the structural elements. Consequently, noncombustible/limited-combustible construction is used most frequently where expected fire severity is low or within the capabilities of available fire suppression methods.

Protected Noncombustible/Limited-Combustible Construction

Noncombustible/limited-combustible construction may be designated as "protected" when bearing walls or bearing portions of walls, exterior or interior, are of noncombustible or limited-combustible material and have minimum hourly fire resistance ratings and are stable under fire conditions. In addition, roof and floor construction and their supports must have the same minimum hourly rating.

To provide rated bearing walls or bearing portions of walls which are suitable as exterior walls usually requires the use of masonry units, brick, tile, or reinforced concrete. If the exterior wall is nonbearing, it need not have a fire resistance rating, although the construction material must still be noncombustible or limited-combustible. Structural framing in such walls must still have the minimum hourly fire resistance rating.

C. Heavy Timber Construction

In heavy timber construction bearing walls and bearing portions of walls are noncombustible and have a minimum fire resistance rating of 2 hours, as well as stability under fire conditions. Nonbearing exterior walls must also be noncombustible. Columns, beams, and girders are commonly heavy timber with wood floor and roof construction built without concealed spaces. Where concealed spaces are allowed, they must be tightly closed by wood cover plates, in accordance with detailed construction limitations.

The minimum 2-hr resistance of bearing walls may be increased where required in individual properties, depend-

ing on the occupancy and fire exposure hazards; nonbearing exterior walls may be required to have a given degree of fire resistance, depending on similar factors. Note that combustible bearing walls or bearing portions of walls and combustible nonbearing exterior walls are not permitted in buildings of this type, despite the use of the word "timber" in the name.

For a building with wood columns to qualify as heavy timber construction, the columns cannot be less than 8 in. in any dimension. Wood beams and girders cannot be less than 6 in. in least dimension, nor less than 10 in. in depth. (All dimensions stated in this discussion of heavy timber construction are nominal.) Materials other than wood may be used for interior structural members (columns, beams, girders, trusses, etc.) if they are of the same dimensions as the wood members they replace and if they have a fire resistance of not less than 1 hr.

One type of floor used in heavy timber construction is constructed of splined or tongue-and-groove planks, not less than 3 in. thick, covered with 1 in. flooring laid crosswise or diagonally. An alternative method uses laminated planks of 4 in. minimum width. These are set on edge and spiked together at 18 in. intervals. They are then overlaid with 1 in. flooring.

Timber arches or trusses may be used to support roof loads if of certain minimum dimensions. The framing members cannot be less than 4 in. by 6 in., except that spaced members may be composed of two or more pieces not less than 3 in. in thickness when blocked solidly throughout their intervening spaces or when such spaces are tightly closed by a continuous wood cover plate of not less than 2 in. thickness secured to the underside of the members. Splice scabs are not to be less than 3 in. thick.

Roof decks on heavy timber structures are of matched or splined plank not less than 2 in. in thickness or of laminated planks not less than 3 in. in width, set on edge and laid as required for floors. Beams and girders supporting roof loads only are not less than 6 in. in least dimension.

Interior partitions enclosing stairways and other openings through floors in heavy timber buildings are so designed as to have not less than 1-hr fire resistance.

Explanation of Heavy Timber Construction

In the United States, buildings of this type had their origin in New England to provide satisfactory structures for the textile industry. They were identified as "mill," "plank-on-timber," or "slow-burning" construction. A compromise of the true heavy timber building was subsequently devised and was identified as "semi-mill." This type of structure had greater column spacing, made possible by the introduction of beams that rested on girders. Both the beams and the girders supported the floor planks.

Heavy timber construction, however, for a time was threatened with obsolescence because of the availability of other structural materials which are more economical and the gradual disappearance of satisfactory sizes of sawn lumber meeting the dimensional requirements for this type. However, new techniques for forming large-dimension timbers have revitalized this basic construction classification. Glued laminated lumber structural elements, comprise of relatively small pieces of lumber bonded into large single units, have been developed which possess, when properly engineered, approximately the same degree of fire resistance as did the old solid timber members. New methods of fastening have aided in the reestablishment of this basic building type. Some of the modern-day structures employing glued laminated timbers meet or exceed the minimum timber size requirements of the definition; others employ certain components (such as trusses) which comply with the definition but other details do not meet the specifications for the construction type and must properly be placed in the ordinary (brick, wood-joisted) classification or in the wood frame class.

Heavy timber construction, by virtue of the size and mass of planks and timbers, provides a slow-burning building. Since the ratio of the exposed surfaces to the total volume of these combustible members is small, and since heat conduction through them is relatively slow, failure under heat and flame attack is retarded. When the exposed wood surfaces char in a fire, the insulation effect of the charred wood further retards heat penetration.

While no specific fire resistance ratings based on fire tests are given for individual components in this type of building except for walls, it is generally accepted that true heavy timber construction performs in a superior way to unprotected noncombustible structures under fire conditions. This evaluation is further brought out by the fact that, where the use of other than wood of the specified sizes is authorized, such as metal structural components, a 1-hr. fire resistance rating for the assembly is required. Height and area limits for buildings of heavy timber construction are generally more liberal than those applied to unprotected noncombustible structures.

Potentially, the weakest points in the fire resistance of heavy timber construction are the edges, joints, and connections of timber members. Considerable attention is thus given to these details. For instance, corners of columns are rounded or chamfered; stone, cast iron or steel bases are used under columns; and cover plates are applied under spaced chord and web members or solid blocking is fitted to members at truss joints.

The requirement for masonry, reinforced concrete, or other noncombustible materials in exterior and bearing walls in buildings of heavy timber construction is primarily to prevent spread of fire to or from adjoining or exposed structures.

As in any type construction, the provision of automatic sprinklers is an excellent means of controlling the life hazard and property damage potentials in heavy timber buildings. The record of such protection in these structures has been excellent.

Buildings have been erected which fall into this basic building type but in which the timbers used had been given a fire retardant impregnation treatment. Approximately seven million square feet of fire retardant treated timber was used in three large airship hangars erected in Florida during World War II. When a hurricane destroyed these buildings, a fire developed in the wreckage after the fuel tanks of aircraft, blimps, and automobiles stored therein were damaged. Timbers outside the range of the hottest gasoline-fed fires remained sound and uncharred despite considerable splintering occasioned by the structural collapse.

Elements of Construction

Figures 6-5C, 6-5D, 6-5E, and 6-5F illustrate various details of heavy timber construction, as published by the National Forest Products Association. These sketches are only representative of some of the methods used in erecting heavy timber structures. The size of framing members, the timber connectors, the number of lag screws, bolts, etc., have been limited in the sketches to show clearly the essential features of the methods.

Glued laminated structural members are wood planks or boards bonded together in such a way that the grain of all laminations is approximately parallel. The Forest Products Laboratory has issued a technical bulletin on the fabrication and design of glued laminated wood structural members[4] and the National Forest Products Association has issued a design specification for stress-grade lumber and its fastenings,[5] which contains a special part on glued

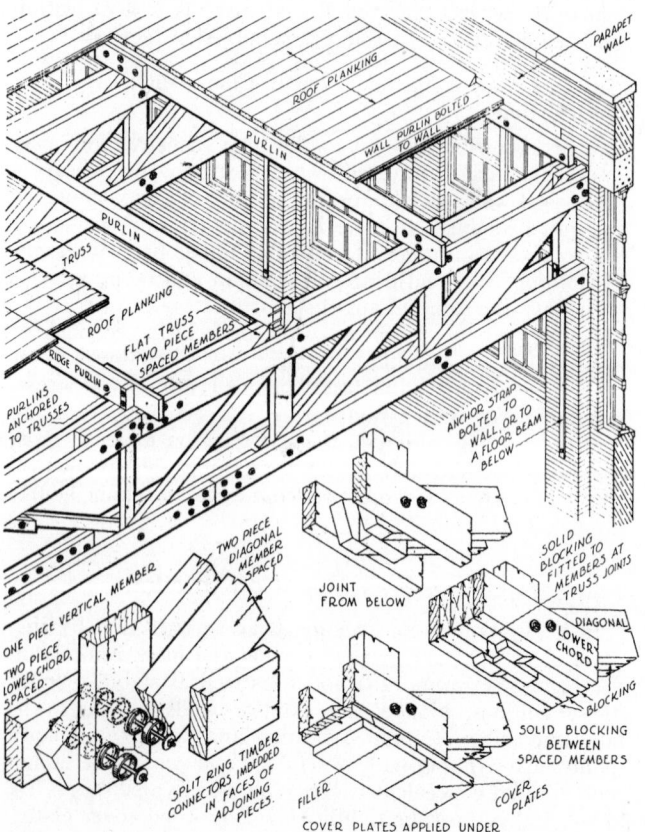

Fig. 6-5C. Heavy timber construction showing truss and purlin roof framing. (National Forest Products Association)

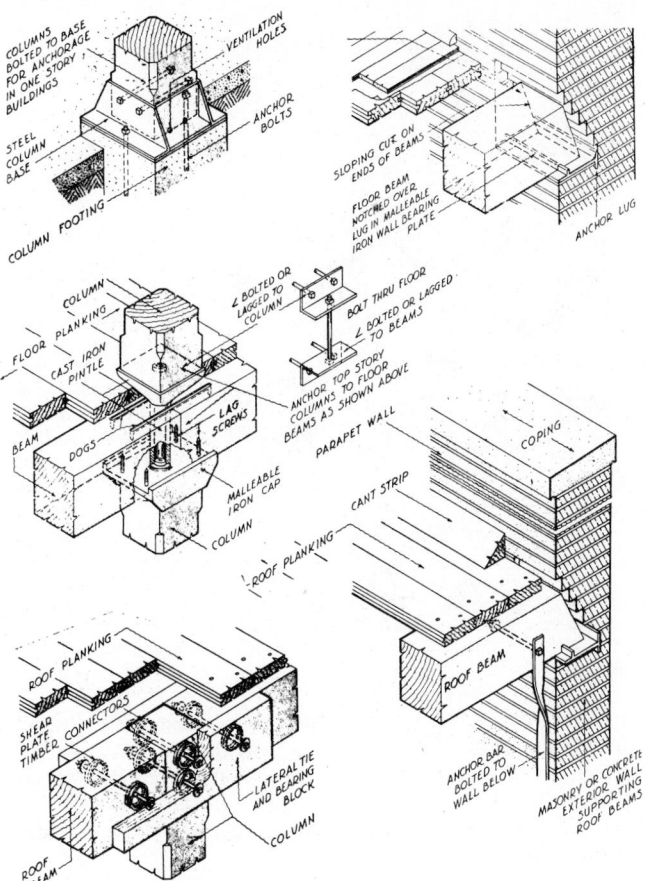

Fig. 6-5D. *Details of column and beam connections in heavy timber construction.* (National Forest Products Association)

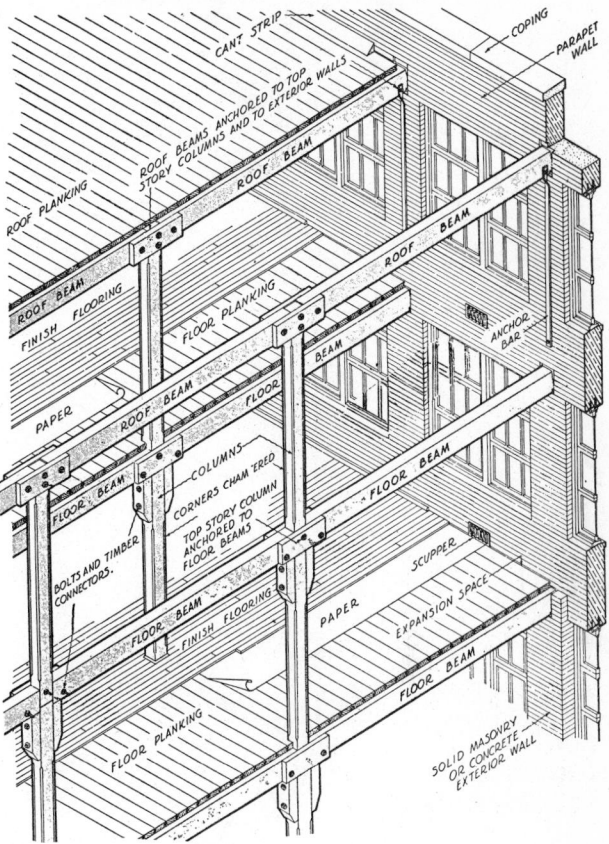

Fig. 6-5E. *Heavy timber construction of the plank floor and beam type.* (National Forest Products Association)

laminated lumber giving information on allowable loads, unit stresses and standard sizes. In actual fires, glued laminated timbers conforming to these specifications have performed similarly to solid sawn beams of similar size. Figure 6-5G shows a glued laminated beam (9 in. by 27¼ in.) which had been subjected to a test fire for 1 hr.

When the test was started, the temperature was 1,300°F. After 35 min it reached 1,850°F, and at the end of 1 hr. it had dropped to 1,500°F. The test was conducted outdoors, and the fuel consisted of 6,000 lbs. of dry Douglas fir. A total of 63 in. of the laminated beam was exposed to the test fire. After the test about 51 percent of the original section of the beam was uncharred. No load was applied to the beam during the test.

It will be noted that the burning on the surfaces is quite uniform and the glue lines have little, if any, effect on the fire resistance of the timber. Obviously the glues used must be regulated carefully to prevent delamination under any conditions of use and under flame and heat attack.

The effects of humidity on wood structural members, which lead to rotting and the vulnerability of wood to attack by termites, are problems with heavy timber structures as with other structures employing wood. Preservative treatments are available.

D. Ordinary Construction

NFPA 220 defines ordinary construction as: ". . . that type of construction in which exterior bearing walls or bearing portions of exterior walls are of noncombustible or limited-combustible materials and have minimum hourly fire resistance ratings and stability under fire conditions; nonbearing exterior walls are of noncombustible or limited-combustible materials, and roofs, floors, and interior framing are wholly or partly of wood of smaller dimensions than required for Heavy Timber Construction." [6]

Ordinary construction is widely used and is also referred to as "brick, wood-joisted" or "brick-joist" construction, though wall construction of noncombustible or limited-combustible materials (other than brick) can also qualify for inclusion under Ordinary Construction in most building codes. The term "open-joist" is also used and denotes ordinary construction in which interior combustible structural members are exposed. The essential differences between open-joist and heavy timber construction are the dimensions of the wood structural members and the pockets between joists (joist channels), as compared with the relatively flat ceilings in heavy timber buildings.

Ordinary construction has all the inherent hazards attributed to construction where wood or other combustible material is used. Therefore, the ability of ordinary construction to withstand an interior fire or to confine the spread of fire to one area is no better than the degree of protection given to its combustible structural components.

Interior sheathing for wood floor and interior wall framing offers varying degrees of protection for wood or other combustible structural members. For example, some types of gypsum wallboard, when used over wood joist framing will yield an assembly having a fire resistance rating of up to 2 hrs.

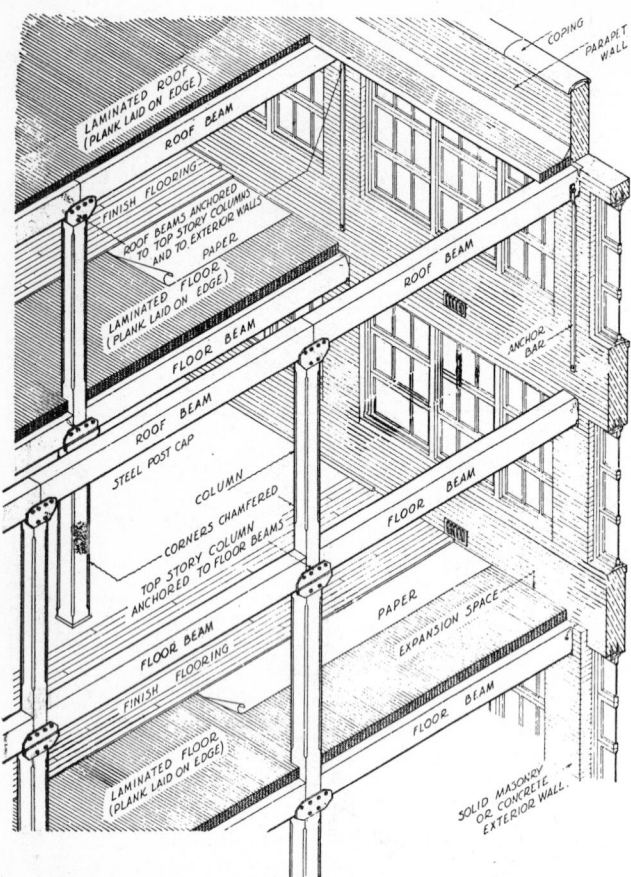

Fig. 6-5F. Heavy timber construction of the laminated floor and beam type. (National Forest Products Association)

Fig. 6-5G. Cross section of glued laminated beam after being subjected to a fire test of 1-hr duration. This test was not the test described in NFPA No. 251, Standard Methods of Fire Tests of Building Construction and Materials. No load was applied to the beam during the test.

Ordinary construction at one time was the most common type for commercial (mercantile and office buildings), multiple-occupancy habitational buildings (hotels, apartment houses), schools, churches, and other institutional occupancies. Buildings of this type dominate in congested areas of many large U.S. cities and most are deficient in providing protection for life safety including proper exits, limitation of highly combustible interior finish, and similar safeguards.

Ordinary construction, unlike fire resistive and noncombustible/limited-combustible buildings, when sheathed, has concealed wall and ceiling spaces which contain combustible materials. Fire may originate in such concealed spaces. Likewise, fire originating in other parts of the structure may enter into such spaces and spread throughout the structure undetected unless the spaces are safeguarded by fire stopping or other means.

Open-joist construction, often used in industrial and other buildings where appearance is not a factor, increases the area of exposed wood. On the other hand, the absence of concealed spaces between joists makes it easier to attack fire that has spread into joist channels providing the involved channels are located in an area accessible for fire fighting. Many otherwise well-built brick, wood-joisted buildings have been left vulnerable to damage from fire originating in their basements (difficult areas for fire fighting) because of failure to protect wood joists supporting the first or ground floor.

Building codes place limitations on heights and areas of buildings of combustible construction. Hospitals and other institutional buildings of combustible construction where occupants must be assisted in leaving the building are specific occupancies with height and fire area limitations. These limitations apply not only to brick, wood-joisted buildings but to all buildings where combustible structural materials are used.

Elements of Ordinary Construction

Walls: Typical examples of materials used in exterior bearing walls are brick, reinforced concrete, and concrete or other masonry units. Wall assemblies of these materials must not only meet the fire resistance requirements in the definition of ordinary construction, but must also be properly proportioned for strength and stability. Substantial exterior masonry walls, both bearing and nonbearing, are advantageous as protection against exposure fires and for limiting the spread of fire to adjacent properties provided the walls are properly parapeted where necessary and openings safeguarded.

Framing: Wood columns, beams, girders, and joists, while of lesser dimensions than timbers used in heavy timber construction, must be of sufficient size to insure structural stability. Wood columns in buildings of several stories must be directly over one another with loads transmitted to columns directly below and with proper connections between the columns. If steel columns, beams, and girders have been added for structural strength, a protective covering for the steel is desirable but necessary only if the combustible assemblies are covered. In all probability the comparatively light combustible assemblies in a building where interior structural members are without protective coverings would be destroyed in a severe fire before failure of the steel assemblies could become a critical factor.

Floors: Wood floors consisting of a subflooring overlaid with finish flooring for a total nominal thickness of 2 in. (double board floor) are common in ordinary construction. Subflooring topped with laminated wood sheets and covered with asphalt, rubber, or plastic tile, or other decorative coverings also is much in use today.

In buildings without basements, it is good practice not

to use combustible materials in grade floors to avoid creating combustible concealed spaces between the ground and the floors. These areas are very difficult to reach for fire fighting.

Roofs: The type of covering which should be used on a combustible roof deck is principally dictated by the severity of the threat from exposure fires and limitations of local building codes. The choice generally rests between a Class A or Class B covering, although in some locations Class C coverings are permitted.

The NFPA Life Safety Code and most building codes require that large concealed spaces, such as attics under combustible roof decks, be either subdivided by partitions dividing the spaces into small areas or protected by sprinklers.

Partitions around stairways and other floor openings in protected ordinary construction have a minimum fire resistance rating of 1 hr., and doors at partition openings are of the same resistance rating. The design of the partition assemblies is dependent on whether or not they are load bearing.

Protected Ordinary Construction: Ordinary construction may be designated, "Protected Ordinary Construction" when roofs and floors and their supports have minimum hourly fire resistance ratings.

E. Wood Frame Construction

Wood frame construction is defined by NFPA 220 as "that type of construction in which exterior walls, bearing walls and partitions, and floors and roofs and their supports are wholly or partly of wood or other combustible material, when the construction does not qualify as Heavy Timber Construction or Ordinary Construction." [7] Wood frame construction may be designated "protected" if roofs and floors and their supports have minimum hourly fire resistance rating.

Wood frame construction, commonly called "frame" construction, differs from ordinary construction only with respect to exterior wall construction. However, when fire walls and party walls are required for the purpose of reducing areas subject to total burnout and as protection against exposure fires, fire resistance requirements for these walls are the same as requirements for similar walls in brick, wood-joisted construction.

Most building codes do not differentiate between protected and unprotected (structurally) wood buildings, although the codes, without exception, require firestopping and other important safeguards similar to those required for brick, wood-joisted construction. This lack of differentiation between protected and unprotected assemblies is based largely on the assumption that conventional dwellings and other wood structures normally have interior finish materials that provide protection in some degree for structural members, however brief such protection may be during a fire.

Large multistory frame buildings are often popularly evaluated by their exterior walls and characterized as "firetraps." But blanket condemnation of wood frame as a basic building type because of the inherent hazards of combustible construction is not warranted. Frame construction, although inferior to fire resistive construction from a fire safety point of view, can be made reasonably safe if proper attention is given to protection against the horizontal and vertical spread of fire, to protection against exposure fires, and to providing fire protection facilities within frame structures sufficient to meet fire conditions which may be anticipated on the basis of expected fire loads.

While the minimum hourly fire resistance requirement for protection of combustible assemblies and floor openings in protected wood frame construction is the same as required for protection in brick, wood-joisted buildings, the provision of adequate firestopping in concealed spaces between outside walls and interior finish, between floors, and within partitions is of utmost importance. When wood is used for firestops, 2-in. nominal thickness is required at specified locations in the structure. Several layers of bricks can also be used to advantage in firestopping the spaces between studs in partitions. Filling the voids and concealed spaces with noncombustible insulating materials is also an acceptable practice. The best protection for frame buildings against exposure fires is adequate clear spaces. Other methods of protection against exposure hazards, which can be applied to buildings of wood frame construction, are discussed in Chapter 3 of this Section.

Elements of Construction

The basic form of exterior wood wall construction is vertical wood studs, commonly 2 × 4 in. with 1-in. boards nailed to the studs and with an exterior covering of wood siding. There are many variations of exterior wall construction, all coming within the classification of wood construction, and similarly treated in building codes. Various composition boards may be used in place of wood, and many exterior wall covering materials are used. The following are some common types:

Wood Shingles, Clapboards (wood, plastic, or metal), Matched Boards, etc., nailed to exterior sheathing with building paper between.

Brick Veneer: Consists of a single thickness of brick around a wood-framed structure, depending upon bonding to the wood structure for stability. This type gives a building the appearance of standard brick construction, but is not in any way equivalent. It does provide some degree of protection against external exposure, such as from grass fires.

Brick-nogged Walls: Found in some old buildings, these walls have brick laid solid in the spaces between wood studs. Such walls, if there are no cracks or openings, have some degree of fire resistance.

Metal-clad Construction: A sheet metal covering is nailed over wood siding. While the metal covering may prevent ignition of the wood by small flames, it has relatively slight value in protection against exposure.

Metal Clapboards and Shingles: These coverings may be applied directly over wood sheathing or over an existing wall covering. Protection against exposure afforded by these coverings is of slight value.

Skeleton Metal-clad Construction: Corrugated iron or other metal is attached directly to the wood frame without intervening boards. This type has little fire resistance, but contributes less fuel to a fire than walls of all-wood construction.

Cement-asbestos Corrugated Sheets: Coverings used in a manner similar to that described under skeleton metal construction, and metal-clad construction. Asbestos-cement shingles are also used as a covering over wood walls. Such asbestos-cement wall coverings may provide limited protection against exposure fires.

Asphalt-composition Siding: A finish simulating brick or stone that is similar to the material used for roofing. Tests and experience have shown that such material has satisfactory fire retardant properties for use as a roof covering, but test data are lacking as to its fire retardant properties when used on exterior walls where due to its position it is more susceptible to ignition and sustained combustion.

Stucco: Cement plaster on lath over wood frame construction. It has a degree of fire resistance depending upon the type of lath used and the thickness of the plaster.

Prefabricated Plywood Walls: These walls are substantially the equivalent of the basic type of wood studs, boards, and wood siding.

Structural requirements for framing, floors, and roofs in wooden buildings are generally the same as for brick, wood-joisted buildings with the principal difference being the method of supporting joists in frame walls as opposed to the method used in masonry walls.

Bibliography

References Cited

[1] Standard Types of Building Construction, NFPA No. 220, 1961, pp. 220–3.

[2] Ibid., NFPA No. 220-T-1974, p. 220–6.

[3] Gross, D. and Natella, M. G., "Tentative Method of Test for Potential Heat of Materials in Building Fires," *Fire Test Performance*, ASTM STP 464, 1970, pp. 147–152.

[4] Freas, A. D., and Selbo, M. L., "Fabrication and Design of Glue Laminated Wood Structural Members," U.S. Department of Agriculture Technical Bulletin 1069, 1954, Forest Products Laboratory, Madison, Wis.

[5] "National Design Specification for Stress Grade Lumber and Its Fastenings," 1962, National Forest Products Association, Washington, D.C.

[6] NFPA No. 220, Standard Types of Building Construction, 1961, p. 220–4.

[7] NFPA No. 220, Standard Types of Building Construction, 1961, p. 220–6.

Chapter 6

INTERIOR FINISH

Three principal elements which determine the fire hazard of a building are the fire resistance of the structure, the contents or process enclosed by the structure, and the characteristics of the interior finish of the structure. These three elements, whose importance are frequently misunderstood or underestimated, should be considered separately and as fully as possible for proper understanding of their impact.

This chapter will discuss interior finish materials such as wood, plaster, wallboards, acoustical tile, insulating materials, and decorative materials—in general, the materials commonly used for wall, ceiling, and floor finishes inside buildings. Fire resistance and fire resistance ratings, which have no essential relationship to the fire properties of interior finish materials, are fully discussed in Chapter 7. (An example of this "non-relationship": heavy timber construction may have a fire resistance rating of one hour or more, but still presents a combustible interior surface; conversely, bare sheet metal construction has a low fire resistance rating, since heat penetrates it quickly, but presents no surface combustibility.)

A. Definition of Interior Finish

Interior finish is generally considered to consist of those materials or combinations of materials that form the exposed interior surface of wall, ceiling, and floor constructions. Variations of this basic definition are found in some building regulations where counter tops, built-in cabinets, and even doors are included in the definition of interior finish. Many codes, such as NFPA No. 101, Life Safety Code, exclude trim and incidental finish from the requirements for wall and ceiling finish. This is done by setting less rigid requirements for trim comprising less than 10 percent of the aggregate wall and ceiling area.

Free-hanging draperies that cover most or all of a wall surface have, on occasion, been subjected to the requirements for interior finish, as have been framed, flexible (folding) door assemblies. Normal tests for interior finish combustibility do not accurately predict fire behavior in these cases. Such materials are more properly tested according to NFPA 701, Standard Methods of Fire Tests for Flame Resistant Textiles and Films. However, when applied to a solid backing, drapery material can be considered interior finish and tested accordingly.

Some building codes, including the NFPA Life Safety Code, do not consider floor coverings to be interior finish. Thus, they are excluded from interior finish requirements, unless the authority having jurisdiction determines that the material used poses an unusual hazard. Only recently has the potential hazard of floor coverings been considered, due to the absence of any clear indication from fire experience that a problem existed. The last decade, however, has seen the expansion of many local building regulations to include floor coverings under the definition of interior finish. Further, the Department of Commerce, under the Flammable Fabrics Act, now regulates rugs and carpets in interstate commerce. Determination of hazard under the Flammable Fabric Act is based on the Methanamine "Pill" Test.

B. Types of Interior Finish

The types of interior finish materials are numerous and include such commonly used materials as plaster, gypsum wallboard, wood and plywood, plywood paneling, fibrous ceiling tiles, plastics, and a variety of wall coverings. Surface coatings, such as paint, varnish, etc., may also be included, along with the substrate to which they are applied. Collectively, these finishes serve several functions—aesthetic, acoustical, insulation, as well as protection against wear and abrasion.

Interior finishes are not necessarily limited to the walls, ceilings, and floors of rooms, corridors, stairwells, and similar buildings' spaces. Some authorities include the linings or coverings of ducts, utility chases and shafts, or plenum spaces as interior finish as well as batt and blanket insulation, if the back faces a stud space through which fire might spread.

The development of certain types of cellular plastics in board, poured-in-place, and spray-on form has provided lightweight materials having exceptional thermal insulation characteristics. The incorporation of fire retardants into these cellular plastics made it possible for them to meet building code requirements for interior finishes. As a result, cellular plastics, particularly the sprayed-on type, have been widely used as exposed insulation. Rapid fire spread in several widely publicized fires involving exposed cellular polyurethane and polystyrene materials has led to federal action and industry recommendations for protection of such surfaces against ignition and fire spread.[1, 2]

C. The Role of Interior Finish in Fires

Most building fires begin with the ignition of decorative materials or furnishings, by failures in electrical systems or mechanical equipment, or in accumulations of waste. Interior finishes are not usually the first items ignited, except when ignition occurs by overheated electrical circuits, careless use of plumbers' torches, or direct impingement of flame from some other source, e.g., a candle or a match. After the fire has started and gained some ground, however, the interior finish can become involved and can contribute extensively to the spread of fire.

Recent full-scale room and building fire tests have shed new light on the phenomenon called "flashover." Previously, it was believed that combustible gases, released during the early stages of a fire, collected at the ceiling level, gradually mixing with air until within the flammable range. At this point, ignition would occur, suddenly and rapidly; hence, the descriptive term flashover. It is currently held that, while this ignition of combustible gases may occur, it precedes the flashover. Flashover is now believed to be caused by thermal radiation feedback from the ceiling and upper walls, which have been heated by the fire. This radiation feedback gradually heats the contents of the fire area. When all the combustibles in the space have become heated to their ignition temperatures, simultaneous ignition occurs.

Interior finish plays an important role in the occurrence of flashover. An interior finish that absorbs heat readily and holds it, as an insulator would, might reduce the time to flashover. If the finish material is combustible, it will also be a source of fuel for the fire. Considering the nature of thermal radiation, the size and shape of the space in which the fire occurs becomes a critical factor.[3] More recently, the term "flameover" was coined to denote the rapid spread of flame over one or more surfaces. This reaction was observed in corridor tests conducted by the National Bureau of Standards.[4]

Once a room fire reaches the stage of full involvement or flashover and openings to adjoining spaces allow escape of heat, smoke, and combustion gases, combustible interior finish of any kind or quantity becomes a significant factor in the spread of fire to other areas. Several full scale fire tests have demonstrated that heat, smoke, and noxious combustion gases from burning furnishings pose a greater threat to the life safety of persons unable to evacuate the room of fire origin than do those from interior finishes.[5, 6] From the points of view of both the life safety of others in the building and property damage, however, the nature of the interior finish in and beyond the room of origin continues to be a grave concern.

The characteristics of interior finishes which are most relevant to the fire problems include their ability to (1) spread fire, (2) contribute fuel to the fire, and (3) develop smoke and noxious gases when burning. Thus, materials which exhibit high rates of flame spread contribute substantial quantities of fuel to the fire, or produce hazardous concentrations of smoke or noxious gases, are undesirable, particularly in occupancies accommodating many people. It should be noted that there is no consistent relationship between these factors or between the numbers assigned as ratings to these factors.[7]

The first concerted effort to develop controls on the use of interior finish gained impetus in 1946. In that year, three hotel fires—the Winecoff in Atlanta, Ga.; the LaSalle in Chicago, Ill.; and the Canfield in Dubuque, Iowa—took the lives of 199 persons. Common to all three fires were delayed discovery of the fires, open stairways, and combustible interior finish.

The seriousness of the life safety hazard frequently associated with interior finish materials is further illustrated by many recent fires such as the following:

Marietta, Ohio	Jan. 9, 1970	Nursing Home	32 dead
Minneapolis, Minn.	Aug. 5, 1970	Apartment House	12 dead
Tucson, Ariz.	Dec. 20, 1970	Hotel	28 dead
Buechel, Ariz.	Jan. 14, 1971	Nursing Home	9 dead
Boston, Mass.	Mar. 31, 1971	Apartment House	8 dead
Denver, Colo.	Sept. 15, 1971	Nursing Home	6 dead
Meade Co., Ky.	Sept. 19, 1971	Mobile Home	6 dead
Texas Twns., Pa.	Oct. 19, 1971	Nursing Home	15 dead
Rosecrans, Wis.	Apr. 4, 1972	Home for Aged	10 dead
Springfield, Ill.	May 5, 1972	Nursing Home	10 dead
Kearny, Neb.	Nov. 27, 1972	Nursing Home	4 dead
Pleasantville, N.Y.	Jan. 29, 1973	Retirement Home	10 dead
New Orleans, La.	June 24, 1973	Cocktail Lounge	32 dead
Jerry City, Ohio	Oct. 9, 1973	Mobile Home	8 dead
Wayne, Pa.	Dec. 4, 1973	Nursing Home	15 dead
Brookhaven, Miss.	Aug. 16, 1974	Nursing Home	15 dead

A much greater loss of life was recorded during the same period in five fires in other countries. These are cited below. Again, interior finish was one of several deficiencies reported.

St. Laurent, France	Nov. 1, 1970	Dance Hall	144 dead
Seoul, Korea	Dec. 25, 1971	Hotel	163 dead
São Paulo, Brazil	Feb. 24, 1972	Dept. St./Office	16 dead
Isle of Man, England	Aug. 2, 1973	Recrea. Center	50 dead
São Paulo, Brazil	Feb. 1, 1974	Office	179 dead

In most, if not all, of the fires listed above, interior finish was only one of the factors contributing to the losses sustained. Design deficiencies, construction deficiencies, delayed discovery, poor housekeeping, and lack of training of responsible personnel were also evident.

D. Methods of Application

The application of an interior finish can have a serious effect on its behavior when exposed to fire. For this reason, the manufacturer's specifications for application should be strictly adhered to. Items that require special attention include size and spacing of nails or similar fasteners, type and application of adhesives, and the number of coats and the application rate of fire retardant coatings. Application details are equally important in repair or replacement of interior finishes. Any new material should have surface burning characteristics at least equal to those of the material being replaced. It should be stressed at this point that substandard application or substitution of "equivalent" materials without supporting test data has delayed the occupancy of many new buildings.

Surface finishes should be considered with recognition of the substrate material to which they are attached. A thin combustible finish applied to a noncombustible substrate may present little hazard. The same finish material, however, on a combustible backing presents considerably greater hazards. In the former situation, the substrate will not ignite and will absorb heat during the early stages of fire development. In the latter case, both the surface finish and the backing material become involved.

The adhesive used is also a factor in the fire behavior of interior finishes. Adhesives that soften at moderate temperatures will allow wall or ceiling finishes to drop or peel from place during the growing stage of a fire. This not only increases the susceptibility of the surface material to ignition, but also exposes the substrate material which, if combustible, adds fuel to the fire.

Some building codes specify that wall and ceiling finishes should not become detached under exposure to elevated temperature (200-300°F) for a specified time interval (usually 30 min). Unfortunately, no standard test method has yet been developed for this purpose.

Most building regulations provide that a combustible material, in the form of thin sheets less than $\frac{1}{28}$ (0.036) in. thick, shall not be subject to the requirements for interior finishes. This exception has been shown by test to be valid for the paper surface on gypsum wallboard and for successive coats of ordinary paint. This, of course, assumes proper application procedures.

Some building regulations further require that combustible interior finish materials of other than the most restrictive class, less than $\frac{1}{4}$ in. thick and intended to be applied directly to studs or joists, shall be applied over a substrate of a noncombustible material. This requirement was the result of several rapidly burning residential fires where thin combustible paneling, applied directly to the framing, was held to be the basic fault.

Recently, the use of sprayed-on materials for interior finishes has been proliferating. Some of these materials are coatings that are inherently resistant to attack by fire. However, other materials, especially the sprayed-on cellular (foamed) plastics, are used for insulation or decorative effects, and are not resistant to attack by fire. This is particularly true of cellular plastics, especially when exposed. Based on recent fire experience, it would appear that cellular plastics should not be installed exposed. NFPA

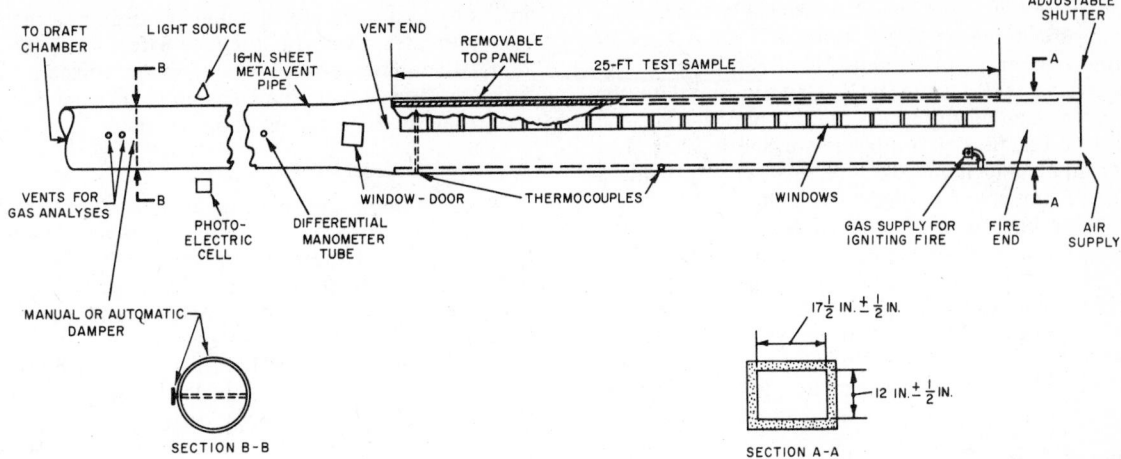

Fig. 6-6A. A schematic diagram of the Steiner Tunnel Test apparatus used for the fire hazard classification of building materials.

205M-T, "Guide for Plastics in Building Construction," expands on this point and recommends the use of a thermal barrier applied over the plastic.*

E. Fire Tests for Interior Finishes

The nature of materials and the fire environment vary so widely that the development of a fire test becomes a highly complex matter. Three factors must be taken into account in this development process:

1. The start and growth of fire in a building is affected by the ignition source, by space geometry, by ventilation, and by nature, amount, and location of other processes and materials.

2. The changing conditions during a fire, such as oxygen concentration, rate of heat release, protection systems, etc.

3. Variations in form, composition, density, and application of materials present.

With these variables in mind, the difficulty in designing a test that will provide a basis for predicting performance under fire exposure becomes obvious. Equally obvious is the impracticality of designing tests to represent all fire conditions. On the other hand, a test designed to represent a "typical" fire situation or to expose materials to one set of "standard test" conditions may not provide a reliable basis for predicting "real-life" performance of all materials tested. Thus, there is a constant search for improved test methods having a numerical range of results, and for an adequate array of tests to suitably describe the behavior of the various materials available.

The Steiner Tunnel Test

The 25-ft Steiner Tunnel Test, also known as ASTM E84, NFPA 255, and UL 723, was developed by A. J. Steiner at Underwriters Laboratories, Inc. after World War I and was used as an in-house test method for more than 20 years.[8] After the fatal hotel fires of 1946, mentioned earlier in this chapter, the need for some method for control of interior finishes was recognized and the tunnel test proposed. The method was adopted by ASTM as a tentative standard in 1950 and as an official standard in 1958. The National Fire Protection Association adopted the test method tentatively in 1953 and officially in 1958, as NFPA

No. 255, Test of Surface Burning Characteristics of Building Materials.

Figures 6-6A and 6-6B show the general appearance and basic dimensions of the furnace. A detailed description may be found in NFPA 255. Briefly, a 20-in. × 25-ft specimen is placed on a ledge in the top of the furnace in a face-down position and the removable lid is set in place and sealed. This leaves an exposed area of $17\frac{1}{2}$ in. × 25 ft. A double-jet gas burner, located 1 ft in from the air intake end of the tunnel, is adjusted to provide approximately 5,000 Btu per minute during the 10-min test period. An induced air flow of 240 ft per min is drawn through a 3-in. × $17\frac{1}{2}$-ft intake aperture. This pulls the gas flame downstream for approximately $4\frac{1}{2}$ ft at the beginning of the test, leaving a distance of $19\frac{1}{2}$ ft of specimen for the flame to advance. Flame travel is observed through sealed windows on one side of the furnace, forming the basis of the rating for flame spread.

Furnace temperature and smoke obscuration are also recorded, providing a basis for calculating fuel contributed by the specimen and smoke density. All three measurements are relative to cement-asbestos board, arbitrarily assigned a 0 rating, and to red oak flooring, arbitrarily assigned a rating of 100. Provision may be made for the measurement and analysis of combustion gases.

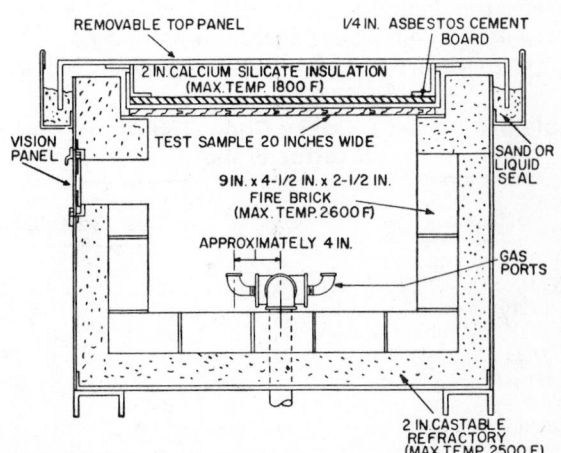

Fig. 6-6B. A cross-sectional view of the Steiner Tunnel Test apparatus.

---

* At the time of this writing, there were no known commercially available cellular (foamed) plastics that were recommended for use as interior finish.

The tunnel test was designed to provide a moderately severe exposure (approximately 1,400°F in the area of flame impingement) under controlled conditions. The specimen size is scaled sufficiently large to simulate the effect of joints, lack of uniformity within the material, and the synergistic reaction of composite surface finishes. The draft, fuel input, and flame size are such as to provide a wide range of numerical results. Where the igniting flame does not spread beyond the "zero" point, the flame spread rating would be zero. If the flame spread covered the entire 19½-ft length, i.e., to the end of the specimen, in 30 sec, the flame spread rating would be 1,100.

At least fifteen tunnel furnaces are known to be in use in the United States and Canada. While several are reserved for product development purposes by individual companies, the majority are available for product acceptance testing.

Application of Tunnel Test Results

There is a considerable degree of uniformity in the application of tunnel test results with regard to flame spread ratings. Smoke density ratings are used more extensively today, with less uniformity. Fuel contributed factors have been applied only in a few scattered instances. Likewise, most building regulations base requirements for interior wall and ceiling finish on tunnel test results and an increasing number are extending the requirements to floor coverings.

Recognizing that variations do exist, the treatment of interior finish in NFPA 101, Life Safety Code, is typical. The classification of materials is based on the following:

Classification	Flame Spread Range
A	0–25
B	26–75
C	76–200
D	201–500
E	over 500

In many building regulations, vertical exits are most severely restricted with a requirement for flame spread not exceeding 25 (or Class A), with up to 75 flame spread rating (Class B) in horizontal exitways. Typical of the limits set forth in the 1973 edition of the Life Safety Code are those given in Table 6-6A.

The performance of materials in the tunnel test depends on the quality and composition of the material tested, as well as its application or use. Generally, the higher the numerical rating, the greater the flammability hazard. Recognizing an alternative method of providing automatic fire suppression, the NFPA Life Safety Code will allow

Table 6-6A. Life Safety Code Requirements for Interior Finish

Occupancy	Exits	Access to Exits	Other Spaces
Health Care Facilities			
New	A	A	A
Existing	B	B	B*
Places of Assembly	A	A	B†
Hotels	B	B‡	C
Apartments			
New	B	B	C
Existing	B	C	C

* Class C permitted with automatic extinguishing system.
† Class C permitted if occupancy limited to 300.
‡ Class C permitted if not part of exitway.

interior finish materials of a higher class when the structure is so protected. Likewise, the Life Safety Code recommends that, when floor coverings are to be considered interior finish, materials with flame spread ratings one grade higher than that specified for walls and ceilings may be used.

Eight-foot Tunnel Furnace

Many attempts have been made to develop a smaller scale test that can be used by manufacturers and testing laboratories in place of the 25-ft tunnel furnace. The advantages of such a facility are obvious—less space required for the equipment, smaller specimens needed, and lower costs.

Such an effort was undertaken at the Forest Products Laboratory in 1951. Initially a furnace was built following the plan of the 25-ft furnace, but reduced in scale.[9] The reduction in scale, however, lengthened the tongues of flame from burning specimens making visual measurement of the flame front difficult. A new approach was devised and a test apparatus developed that was quite different from the 25-ft tunnel furnace. The test method for using this apparatus was tentatively adopted by ASTM in 1965. It was officially adopted in 1968.[10]

In this test, a 13¾-in. by 8-ft specimen is supported at 30° from the horizontal by a perforated panel of 12-gage stainless steel. This panel separates the upper part of the furnace from the combustion chamber. A burner at one end of the combustion chamber provides the proper ratio of gas-to-air to produce a blue flame at about 3,400 Btu per min. Open view ports on one side of the furnace also allow air to be drawn across the specimen and into a full-length stack via self-induced draft. As in the 25-ft furnace, cement-asbestos board and red oak flooring are used as comparison standards and assigned flame-spread ratings of 0 and 100, respectively.

Several manufacturers have built this furnace for product development purposes and some authorities will accept results in lieu of other test data. For many materials, good correlations with the large tunnel furnace have been obtained. Also, some manufacturers have constructed scale models of the 25-ft furnace with good results reported for specific products.

The Radiant Panel Furnace

While the Forest Products Laboratory was developing the 8-ft tunnel furnace, the National Bureau of Standards developed the Radiant Panel Test apparatus. This utilized a much smaller test specimen, 6 × 18 in., and measured hazard in terms of both flame spread and rate of heat release after ignition. The test method was adopted as a tentative research and development standard by ASTM in 1960 and as a full standard in 1967.[11]

In this test, the specimen is positioned at an angle of 30° to the horizontal in front of a gas-fired, porous refractory vertical panel. The specimen slants toward the radiant panel at the top and a small pilot flame at that location provides ignition of flammable gases developing from the surface of the specimen. Air is drawn over the surface of the specimen at a controlled rate by a fan in the hood under which the equipment is located. The rate of flame travel from top to bottom of the specimen is noted, as well as temperatures that develop in the stack. Smoke generated can be measured by weighing deposits on a filter located in the stack. The test is continued for 15 min or until the surface flaming reaches the lower edge of the specimen.

This test apparatus is available commercially and is in use in many research, commercial, and industrial laboratories. The numerical results are on a numerical scale similar to that of the 25-ft and 8-ft furnaces. In several jurisdictions, radiant panel test results are acceptable in lieu of 25-ft tunnel test results.

In this test, as with the 8-ft tunnel furnace, the air flow is against the direction of flame travel or across it. This provides a clear definition of the interfacial burning. With the 25-ft furnace, the flame travel and air flow coincide and with some materials the flame front may be several feet in front of the interfacial burning.

The Corner Test

Seeking a more realistic assessment of the hazard of interior finishes, several laboratories conducted simulated room corner tests some 20 years ago. These usually comprised an 8-ft high corner construction with 2- to 4-ft wing walls. A simulated ceiling of the same material was provided. A wood crib, placed in the corner at floor level was used for ignition. The degree of flame spread and the rate and amount of smoke developed were the primary observations.

Current interest in the rapidity of flame spread across the surface of allegedly low flame spread cellular plastics in actual fires has revived use of the corner test. Corner tests of much larger scales have been conducted by Factory Mutual Research Corporation and Underwriters Laboratories, Inc. Corners up to 25 ft high with wing walls of up to 50 ft long have been used to determine the burning characteristics of these cellular plastics and the effectiveness of protective measures, such as automatic sprinkler protection or use of a thermal barrier.[12] Results have lent weight to the premise that fire hazard cannot be fully judged on the basis of any single fire test method.[13]

Work is also in progress on the development of a small-scale test that will correlate with the large-scale corner test. One such effort consists of a 24-ft inverted tunnel furnace. Known as the Factory Mutual Wall-Ceiling Channel Test, it is still in the development stage. It is anticipated that this test method will eventually replace the more expensive full-scale corner test.[14]

Small-scale Tests

Many small-scale tests are used in industry for research and development and quality control purposes. Use of such tests for promotional purposes has been curtailed following action by the Federal Trade Commission in 1973. The FTC findings, in fact, included some of the larger tests as well, further emphasizing the probability that no one test will predict the reaction of materials when exposed to fire under the wide range of use experienced.

Many of the smaller tests relate to specific types of materials: wood, plastics, and others. The SS-A-118b Federal Specification Test for flammability of ceiling tiles and the ASTM C209 inclined panel test for cellulosic fiber insulation board generally have been replaced by the 25-ft tunnel furnace. Both tests are still used in the respective industries to some extent.

The following is a list of small-scale fire tests relating to the flammability of building materials that are primarily useful for product development and experimental laboratory work:

Combustible Properties of Treated Wood by the Crib Test, ASTM E 160-50.

Combustible Properties of Treated Wood by the Fire Tube Apparatus, ASTM E 69-50.

Fire Retardancy of Paints (Cabinet Method) ASTM D 1360-58.

Fire Retardancy of Paints (Stick and Wick Method) ASTM D 1361-58.

Flammability of Plastics 0.050 in. and Under in Thickness, ASTM D 568-61.

Flammability of Rigid Plastics Over 0.050 in. Thickness, ASTM D 635-63.

Flammability of Flexible Thin Plastic Sheeting, ASTM D 1433-58.

Incandescence Resistance of Rigid Plastics, ASTM D 757-74.

Flammability of Treated Paper and Paperboard, ASTM D 777-46.

Flammability of Plastics, Foams and Sheeting, ASTM D 1692-59T.

Flammability of Rigid Cellular Plastics, ASTM D 3014-73.

Flammability of Plastics using the Oxygen Index Method, ASTM D 2863-70.

Flammability of Finished Textile Floor Covering Materials, ASTM D 2859-70T.

In addition to the above, there are two tests for surface flammability that have become of interest. Both make use of a small sample of material to be tested, approximately 4 in. by 24 in., placed face down in an inclined position and a small heat source applied at the lower end. These test methods have been described in an article by H. L. Vandersall,[15] and a technical paper by M. M. Levy.[16]

Special Tests for Floor Coverings

Fire tests for interior finishes were developed primarily with wall and ceiling finishes in mind well before carpeting became popular as a floor finish in institutional, commercial, and other occupancies subject to high human occupancy loads. Official attention was directed toward a possible hazard with soft floor coverings in 1960 and 1961 as a result of a series of small fires in the Washington, D.C. area.[17] A well publicized dwelling fire on the West Coast in 1967, followed by the Harmer House nursing home fire (Ohio, 1970), focused attention on the subject, although carpets were a contributing rather than a causative factor.[18, 19]

In 1965, the Public Health Service of the U.S. Department of Health, Education and Welfare issued a directive calling for flame spread limits on floor coverings in federally-aided hospitals, citing the 25-ft tunnel test as the control mechanism. Since the test specimen in this test is held face down, a problem developed for carpets having synthetic fibers of the type that melt, drip or delaminate when exposed to elevated temperatures. Also, the mounting of carpets with separate underlays or pads posed a difficult problem. Thus, there has been a need for a test specifically designed for floor coverings.

The Methanamine Pill Test was developed by the National Bureau of Standards as a means of preventing the distribution of highly flammable soft floor coverings. Based on an earlier government purchasing specification, this method was adopted in 1970 as DOC FF-1-70,[20] for carpets, and DOC FF-2-70,[21] for rugs.

In this test, eight 9-in. square sections of a carpet are oven-heated to drive off excess moisture, brought to room temperature in a desiccator, and tested. Each specimen in turn is placed on the bottom of a 1-ft enclosed cube, which is open at the top, and held in place by a 9-in. square metal plate having an 8-in. circular cutout. The methanamine tablet is placed at the center of the 8-in. circle and lighted. The specimen fails if the flame advances at any point to within 1 in. of the metal ring or hold down plate. At least seven of the eight specimens must pass the test to meet the established criteria.

In 1969, Underwriters Laboratories, Inc., started work on a new test for floor coverings with the test specimens mounted in a floor position.[22] The program was sponsored by the U.S. Public Health Service and resulted in what is known as the UL Floor Covering Chamber Test. In essence it is an 8-ft version of the 25-ft tunnel furnace with appropriate modifications in heat input, burner design, air flow, and other test specifications.

Another test for floor coverings was developed in the laboratories of the Armstrong Cork Company. This is a modification of the radiant panel test for interior finishes with an 8-in. by 30-in. specimen in a horizontal position.[23] Thermal energy is supplied by the radiating gas panel, a pilot light at one end provides an ignition source, and flame travel is observed through a window in one side of the test chamber.

The National Bureau of Standards has been conducting further development work on the Armstrong Floor Covering Test and on both a large-scale corridor test facility and a small-scale model corridor. This last would be the choice for a standard test procedure.[24]

It is anticipated that an acceptable standard test method for floor coverings will evolve within a few years. In the meantime, the 25-ft tunnel test, the UL Chamber, the Radiant Panel, and the Methanamine Pill Test are in use in the United States for tests of floor coverings.

Full-scale Tests

Many fire tests have been conducted on a large scale using existing buildings slated for demolition or available for other reasons. Carefully planned, such tests can and have added significantly to the body of knowledge concerning the growth and spread of fire in buildings.

One of the first of this type of fire test was conducted in Great Britain under the auspices of the Fire Research Station.[25] Two 2-story dwellings were used in these 1949 tests, one with cellulose fiber insulation board lining and the other with plaster board over fiberboard. One test in each house, both with real or simulated furnishings, was with bedroom doors open and the other with the doors closed. With both types of lining, temperatures in the living room where the fire was started became intolerable in a few minutes. Also, as in many other tests and actual fires, the value of the closed door in minimizing the life hazard in bedrooms was clearly demonstrated.

In 1958, the Division of Building Research of the National Research Council of Canada conducted a series of full-scale tests, known as the "St. Lawrence Burns," in six dwellings and two larger buildings.[26] Here, too, one objective was to study fire spread as it would affect life safety of second floor bedroom occupants behind open and closed doors. All dwellings became "smoke-logged" within 6 min of the ignition of the wood cribs, regardless of the type of interior finish. Temperatures and gaseous combustion products developed much faster in the dwellings with combustible finishes and in those tests where the bedroom doors were open.

Many large buildings scheduled for demolition were partially burned under the auspices of the IIT Research Institute. In these and in extensive room/corridor tests much information was developed relative to fire spread, flashover phenomena, and factors affecting life safety in fires.

The Office of the State Fire Marshal in California sponsored a series of tests in unused buildings at Camp Parks. The objective was the development of criteria for egress facilities, particularly corridors. The final report discusses, among other things, the reaction and interaction of wall, ceiling, and floor finishes.[27] Precedent for the full-scale corridor burns had been established earlier in 1959 and 1960 by the Fire Department of the City of Los Angeles. Final reports on these tests were published in two volumes by NFPA.[28, 29]

Furnished room burnout and corridor tests conducted at the Forest Products Laboratories of the U.S. Department of Agriculture compared the relative importance of room furnishings vs. room finishes. The conclusion that lethal levels of combustion products developed from burning furnishings before the wall finishes were seriously involved was supported by later work at Southwest Research Institute.[30, 31] These and other studies recognize that, once a fire is well established, the probability is great that all combustibles present will become involved. It is also recognized that early detection, containment, and extinguishment in the room of fire origin is important not only for early evacuation from the fire area, but also for the safety of persons elsewhere in the building and for the protection of the building.

The National Bureau of Standards in 1974 completed construction of a Fire Research Building incorporating a 40-ft test corridor and burn rooms in addition to standard fire test facilities.[32] This expands the capability of Bureau personnel to continue studies of floor coverings and other interior finishes under well controlled conditions. The work done in this new facility will undoubtedly result in great progress towards the development of meaningful fire test methods and data.

SI Units

The following conversion factors are given as a convenience in converting to SI units the English units used in this chapter.

$$1 \text{ in.} = 25.400 \text{ mm}$$
$$1 \text{ ft} = 0.305 \text{ m}$$
$$\tfrac{5}{9}(°F - 32) = °C$$

Bibliography

References Cited

[1] "Disclosure Requirements and Prohibitions Concerning the Flammability of Plastics," Federal Trade Commission, Washington, D.C., Aug. 6, 1974.

[2] "Fire Safety Guidelines for Use of Rigid Urethane Foam Insulation in Building Construction," Urethane Safety Group Bulletin, The Society of the Plastics Industry, Inc., New York, May 1974.

[3] Waterman, T. E., "Room Flashover—Model Studies," *Fire Technology*, Vol. 8, No. 4, Nov. 1972, pp. 316–325.

[4] National Bureau of Standards, "NBS Corridor Fire Tests: Energy and Radiation Models," NBS Technical Note 794, Oct. 1973, Superintendent of Documents, U.S. Government Printing Office, Washington, D.C.

[5] Bruce, H. D., "Experimental Dwelling Room Fires," FPL Report No. 1941, Apr. 1959, Forest Products Laboratory, Madison, Wisc.

[6] Pryor, A. J., "Full Scale Fire Tests of Interior Wall Finishes," *Fire Journal*, Vol. 63, No. 2, Mar. 1969, pp. 14–20.

[7] Yuill, C. H., "Flame Spread Tests in a Large Tunnel Furnace," ASTM STP No. 344, 1962, American Society for Testing and Materials, Philadelphia, pp. 3–17.

[8] Wilson, J. A., "Surface Flammability of Materials: A Survey of Test Methods and Comparison of Results," ASTM STP No. 301, 1961, American Society for Testing and Materials, Philadelphia, pp. 60–82.

[9] Peters, C. C. and Eichner, H. W., "Surface Flammability as Determined by the FPL 8-Foot Tunnel Method," FPL Report No. 2257, Nov. 1962, Forest Products Laboratory, Madison, Wisc.

[10] "Standard Method of Test for Surface Flammability Using an 8-ft (244 M) Tunnel Furnace," ASTM E 286–69, American Society for Testing and Materials, Philadelphia.

[11] "Standard Method of Test for Surface Flammability of Materials Using a Radiant Heat Energy Source," ASTM E-162-67, American Society for Testing and Materials, Philadelphia.

[12] Christian, W. J. and Waterman, J. E., "Fire Behavior of Interior Finish Materials," *Fire Technology,* Vol. 6, No. 3, Aug. 1970, pp. 165–178.

[13] Maroni, W. F., "Large Scale Fire Tests of Rigid Cellular Plastic Wall and Roof Insulations," *Fire Journal,* Vol. 67, No. 6, Nov. 1973, pp. 24–30.

[14] ———, "SLRP Analysis of Recommended Protection for Foamed-Plastic Wall-Ceiling Building Insulations," *Fire Journal,* Vol. 68, No. 5, Sept. 1974, pp. 51–55.

[15] Vandersall, H. L., "The Use of a Small Flame Tunnel for Evaluating Fire Hazard," *Journal of Paint Technology,* Vol. 39, No. 511, 1967, pp. 494–500.

[16] Levy, M. M., "A Simplified Method for Determining Flame Spread," *Fire Technology,* Vol. 3, No. 1, Feb. 1967, pp. 38–46.

[17] Yuill, C. H., "Floor Coverings: What is the Hazard?" *Fire Journal,* Vol. 61, No. 1, Jan. 1967, pp. 11–19.

[18] "Fire in Acrylic Carpeting," *Fire Journal,* Vol. 62, No. 2, Mar. 1968, pp. 13–14.

[19] Sears, A. B., Jr., "Nursing Home Fire, Marietta, Ohio," *Fire Journal,* Vol. 64, No. 3, May 1970, pp. 5–9.

[20] "Carpets and Rugs—Notice of Standard," *Federal Register,* Vol. 35, No. 74, Apr. 16, 1970.

[21] "Small Carpets and Rugs—Notice of Standard," *Federal Register,* Vol. 35, No. 251, Dec. 29, 1970.

[22] "Standard Method of Test for Flame Propagation Classification of Flooring and Floor Covering Material," Subject 992, Feb. 1971, Underwriters Laboratories, Inc., Northbrook, Ill.

[23] Hartzell, L. G., "Development of a Radiant Panel Test for Flooring Materials," *Journal of Fire and Flammability/Consumer Product Flammability Supplement,* Vol. 1, Dec. 1974, pp. 305–353.

[24] Denyes, W. and Quintiere, J., "Experimental and Analytical Studies of Floor Covering Flammability with a Model Corridor," *Journal of Fire and Flammability/Consumer Products Flammability Supplement,* Vol. 1, Mar. 1974, pp. 32–109.

[25] "British Fire Tests of Fiberboard," *NFPA Quarterly,* Vol. 45, No. 3, Jan. 1952, pp. 218–224.

[26] Shorter, G. W. et al., "The St. Lawrence Burns," *NFPA Quarterly,* Vol. 53, No. 4, Apr. 1960, pp. 300–316.

[27] *Project Corridor: Fire and Life Safety Research,* Western Fire Journal, North Highlands, Calif., 1974.

[28] *Operation School Burning: Official Report on a Series of School Fire Tests conducted April 16, 1959, to June 30, 1959, by the Los Angeles Fire Department,* National Fire Protection Association, Boston, 1959.

[29] *Operation School Burning, No. 2: Official Report on a Series of Fire Tests in an Open Stairway, Multistory School conducted June 30, 1960 to July 30, 1960, and February 6, 1961 to February 14, 1961 by the Los Angeles Fire Department,* National Fire Protection Association, Boston, 1961.

[30] Bruce, H. D., "Experimental Dwelling Room Fires," Report No. 1941, April 1959, U.S. Department of Agriculture, Forest Products Laboratory, Madison, Wisc.

[31] Pryor, A. J., "Full Scale Fire Tests of Interior Wall Finish Assemblies," *Fire Journal,* Vol. 63, No. 2, Mar. 1969, pp. 14–20.

[32] "New Fire Research Building," *Dimensions,* Vol. 58, No. 6, June 1974, pp. 123–124.

Additional Readings

America Burning: The Report of the National Commission on Fire Prevention and Control, Superintendent of Documents, U.S. Government Printing Office, Washington, D.C., 1973.

Christian, W. J., "The Effect of Structural Characteristics on Dwelling Fire Fatalities," *Fire Journal,* Vol. 68, No. 1, Jan. 1974, pp. 22–28.

Fung, F. C. W., Suchomel, M. R., and Ogelsby, P. L., "The NBS Program on Corridor Fires," *Fire Journal,* Vol. 67, No. 3, May 1973, pp. 41–48.

Groah, W. J., "The ASTM 'Tunnel' Test: What It Is and How It Works," *The Building Official and Code Administrator,* Vol. 8, No. 6, June 1974, pp. 4–6.

Harmathy, T. Z., "A New Look at Compartment Fires, Part I," *Fire Technology,* Vol. 8, No. 3, Aug. 1972, pp. 196–217; ibid., "Part II," Vol. 8, No. 4, Nov. 1972, pp. 326–351.

Klitgaard, P. S. and Williamson, R. B., "The Impact of Contents on Building Fires," *Journal of Fire and Flammability/Consumer Product Flammability Supplement,* Vol. 2, Mar. 1975, pp. 84–113.

Lieberman, P. and Bell, D., "Smoke and Fire Propagation in Compartment Spaces," *Fire Technology,* Vol. 9, No. 2, May 1973, pp. 91–100.

Magnusson, S. E. and Thelandersson, S., "A Discussion of Compartment Fires," *Fire Technology,* Vol. 10, No. 3, Aug. 1974, pp. 228–246.

Schaffer, E. L. and Eickner, H. W., "Corridor Wall Linings—Effect on Fire Performance," *Fire Technology,* Vol. 1, No. 4, Nov. 1965, pp. 243–255.

"Space Age Contribution to Residential Fire Safety," *Fire Journal,* Vol. 68, No. 2, Mar. 1974, pp. 18–25,

Thomas, P. H., "Old and New Look at Compartment Fires," *Fire Technology,* Vol. 11, No. 1, Feb. 1975, pp. 42–47.

Thomm, E. C., "Effect of Carpet Variables on the Methanamine Pill Test," *Journal of Fire and Flammability,* Vol. 4, July 1973, pp. 207–209.

Waksman, D. and Ferguson, J. B., "Fire Tests of Building Interior Covering Systems," *Fire Technology,* Vol. 10, No. 3, Aug. 1974, pp. 211–220.

Waterman, T. E., "Room Flashover—Model Studies," *Fire Technology,* Vol. 8, No. 4, Nov. 1972, pp. 316–325.

Williamson, R. B. and Baron, F. M., "A Corner Fire Test to Simulate Residential Fires," *Journal of Fire and Flammability,* Vol. 4, Apr. 1973, pp. 99–105.

Chapter 7

STRUCTURAL INTEGRITY DURING FIRE

The stability of the structural frame of a building, and the integrity of the compartment barriers, such as floors, walls, and partitions, are important design considerations in a fire situation. The collapse of a major structural element, such as a column, girder, floor beam, or roof framing, may remain localized or it may trigger a more extensive failure. In any event, a failure of structural stability of any of these elements is of serious concern. Of additional concern is the breach of the compartment barriers by a fire due to the lack of structural integrity of the assembly.

In order to minimize the probability of structural collapse of the framing elements and of failure of the barriers to contain the fire, the designer must incorporate adequate resistance of these elements to the fire loading. This involves a recognition of the behavior of common structural materials at elevated temperatures so that the inherent material weaknesses can be adequately protected. In addition, it requires an understanding of fire testing of structural assemblies so that proper interpretation of the results can be reflected in appropriate selection and construction practices.

Section A of this chapter describes the behavior of common structural materials at elevated temperatures. It considers both the parameters that are important to the designer and some aspects of protection of the structural elements. The structural integrity of assemblies and their endurance to fire loadings is presented in Section B. Finally, Section C describes the advantages and limitations from a fire consideration of some of the more common forms of building construction.

A. Structural Materials at Elevated Temperatures

All structural materials used in building construction are adversely affected by the elevated temperatures caused by fire. The degree and significance of this adverse behavior depends primarily on the function of the elements and on the degree of protection afforded. The mechanical properties of strength and stiffness decrease as the temperature rises. Other adverse behavior, such as excessive expansion and accelerated creep, also develops with increasing temperatures. In general, however, the design parameters that concern the engineer at normal temperatures are the same parameters that are of concern at elevated temperatures.

Structural Steel

Steel is the backbone of modern building design. Whether it acts as the reinforcement for concrete or the skeleton framework for buildings, it constitutes the major load-carrying material in modern building construction. From the designer's viewpoint steel possesses many qualities, such as high strength and good ductility, that make it an ideal structural material. However, steel, like all other materials, is adversely affected by fire.

Steel is noncombustible and does not contribute fuel to a fire. These properties have often provided a false sense of security with regard to its durability in a fire because they overshadow the fact that steel loses strength when subjected to temperatures easily attained in a fire. The relative seriousness of the problem depends on several factors, such as the function of the steel element, its level of stress, its surface area and thickness, and the temperature within the steel itself. This temperature can be quite different from the ambient temperature in the compartment.

From a structural viewpoint, the yield stress of steel is the significant parameter in establishing load carrying capacity. The tensile stress-strain diagram for A-36 steel at various temperatures is shown in Figure 6-7A[1]. The compressive stress-strain diagram for this same steel at various temperatures is shown in Figure 6-7B[2]. It can be seen that both the yield stress and the modulus of elasticity decreases with increasing temperatures. Figure 6-7C[2] shows the tensile and the compressive yield stress values for A36 steel at various temperatures.

The intensity of stress in a steel member influences the load carrying capacity. The higher the load stress, the more quickly a member will fail at elevated temperatures. A temperature of 1,100°F is normally considered to be the

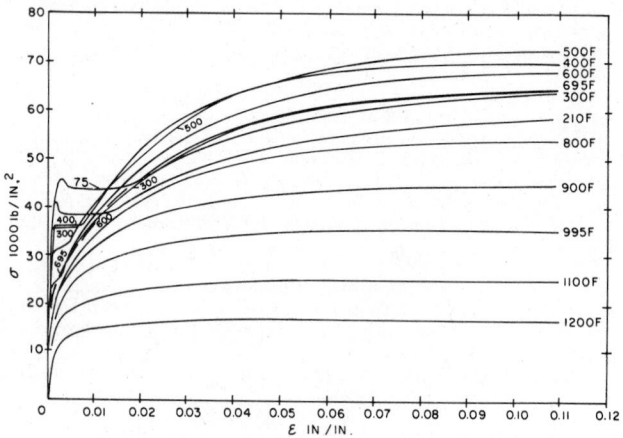

Fig. 6-7A.   Stress-strain curves for an ASTM A36 steel.

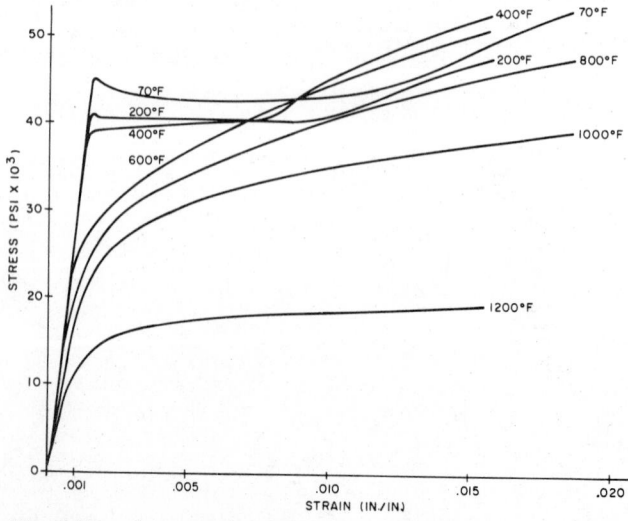

Fig. 6-7B.   Stress-strain curves for A36 steel at various temperatures.

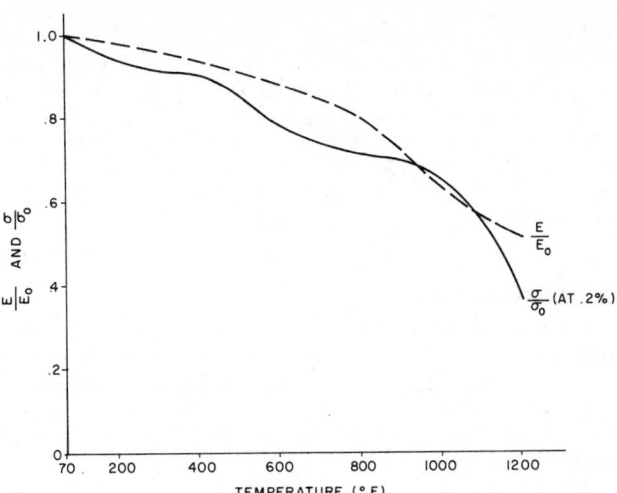

Fig. 6-7C. Ratio of modulus and yield strength with temperature—A36 steel.

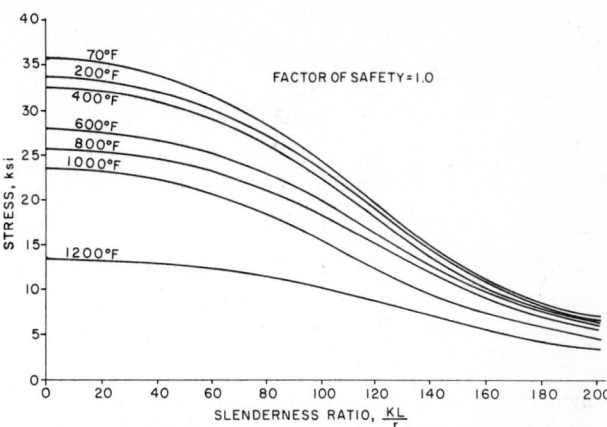

Fig. 6-7D. Critical stress as a function of the slenderness ratio for various temperatures—A36 steel.

critical temperature. At this temperature the yield stress in the steel has decreased to about 60 percent of the value at room temperature. This is approximately the level normally used as the design working stress.

This reduction in stress, combined with the reduction in the modulus of elasticity, causes compression members to be more sensitive to higher temperatures than tensile or flexural members. Figure 6-7D[3] shows the influence of temperature on the critical stress of compression members of A36 steel.

It should be recognized that the temperature considered for stress limitations is the temperature within the steel, and not the ambient temperature. Because steel has a high thermal conductivity it can transfer heat away from a localized heat source rather quickly. This property, in conjunction with its thermal capacity, enables steel to act as a heat sink. When the steel has an opportunity to transfer heat to cooler regions, it can take a relatively long time for a member to reach its critical value. On the other hand, an extensive fire that distributes heat over a greater area reduces this time considerably.

Related to this thermal activity is the effect of mass and surface area of structural steel members. Heavy, thick sections have a far greater resistance to the effects of building fires than do lighter ones. Unprotected light weight sections, such as those found in trusses and open web joists, can often collapse after 5 or 10 min of exposure.

Another property of steel that has an effect upon its performance at elevated temperatures it its coefficient of expansion. The linear coefficient of expansion of steel at temperatures up to 1,100°F is given as:

$$\alpha = 0.0000061 + 0.0000000022\ \Delta t\ \text{in which}$$
α is the coefficient of expansion
Δt temperature in degrees Fahrenheit.

This high coefficient affects the structure in two ways. If the ends of a structural member are axially restrained, the attempted expansion due to the heat causes thermal stresses to be induced in the member. These stresses combine with those of the normal loading causing more rapid collapse. If the structural member is not axially restrained, the increased stresses described above do not occur; instead, movement takes place. This movement causes the ends of steel columns to be moved laterally, producing an eccentrically loaded column. In other cases, walls can be moved

to the point of collapse by expansion of beams. This creates an extremely hazardous condition both for the building itself and for the men fighting the fire.

To illustrate the magnitude of movement, consider a 50 foot long steel beam that is heated uniformly over its length from 72°F to 972°F. The average value for α is 0.0000073, and the increase in length, δ, becomes approximately,

$$\delta = \alpha \angle \Delta t = (7.3 \times 10^{-6})\ (50 \times 12)\ (900)$$
$$\delta = 3.9\ \text{inches}$$

Fire Protection of Structural Steel

Because unprotected structural steel loses its strength at high temperatures, it must be protected from exposure to the heat produced by building fires. This protection, often referred to as "fireproofing", insulates the steel from the heat. The more common methods of insulating steel are encasement of the member, application of a surface treatment, or installation of a suspended ceiling as part of a floor-ceiling assembly capable of providing fire resistance. In recent years, additional methods, such as sheet steel membrane shields around members and box columns filled with liquid have been introduced.

Over the years, encasement of the structural steel member has been a very common and a very satisfactory method of insulating steel to increase its fire resistance. In floor systems of reinforced concrete slabs supported by structural steel beams, the encasement can be placed monolithically with the floor. Figure 6-7E illustrates this method. The major disadvantage is the cost, which is related both to the added formwork and concrete and to the increased

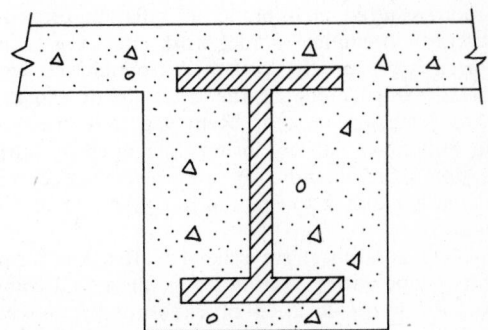

Fig. 6-7E. Encasement of a steel beam by monolithic casting of concrete around the beam.

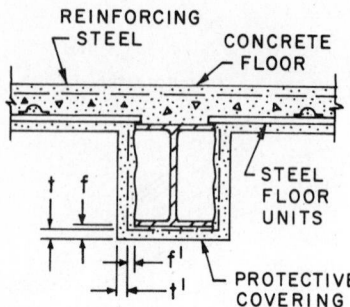

Fig. 6-7F. Furred steel beams with noncombustible protective coverings.

weight of the supporting members due to the added dead load. To reduce the cost of encasement, systems utilizing lath and plaster of gypsum boards have been developed, as shown in Figure 6-7F.

Because of labor costs and the weight increases of the encasement method, surface treatments applied directly to the member are quite popular. Sprayed-on mineral fiber coatings are widely used for protecting structural steel. While the protection is excellent if applied correctly, it can easily be scraped off the member during construction or renovations. Consequently, sprayed-on mineral fiber coatings are suspect in their effectiveness over long term use. Cementitious materials, such as Gunite, have been used as sprayed-on coverings. During a fire, however, they can spall. Adhesion problems have also been experienced with this type of sprayed-on coating. Thus effective application, complete coverage, and long term maintenance are attributes that must be evaluated in considering sprayed-on applications.

In recent years, intumescent paints and coatings have been utilized to increase the fire endurance of structural steel. These coatings intumesce, or swell, when heated, thus forming an insulation around the steel. They are primarily used for nonexposed steel subjected to elevated temperatures as prolonged exposure to flame can't destroy the char coating.

Suspended ceilings consisting of lath and plaster, gypsum panels, or acoustical tile supported on a grid system as part of a floor-ceiling assembly are a popular method of fireproofing. The grid system can be suspended from wire hangers or it can be attached directly to the bottom chord of joists or to the bottom flange of beams. To provide protection so that the pressures that occur in building fires will not lift them out of place, the ceiling tiles are either mechanically fastened or fitted into splines.

The overall effectiveness of this type of barrier protection, often called membrane protection, is questionable. This is due to experiences where a lack of control during construction resulted in improper installation procedures. In addition, maintenance to duct work and fixtures in the plenum area is frequently done by personnel who are not aware of the importance of the integrity of the ceiling to the fire protection system. Removed tiles are not replaced in a manner that will insure their integrity during a building fire. Consequently, the unprotected steel in the plenum area is exposed to fire and hot gases which reduce its strength.

Water-filled columns have received attention for their fire resistive capabilities. During a fire, the liquid transfers heat away from the location of exposure by convection currents set up in the liquid. Consequently, the heat is transferred before it has an opportunity to raise the temperature of the unprotected steel to its critical value.

Although the principle of operation is valid and a few tests have been performed, this type of construction has never been exposed to an actual building fire.

Structural steel members can also be protected by sheet steel membrane shields. The sheet steel holds in place inexpensive insulation materials, thus providing a greater fire endurance. In addition, polished sheet steel has been used in recent tests to protect spandrel girders. The shield reflects radiated heat and protects the load carrying spandrel.

Reinforced Concrete

Concrete is often used as a means of encasing other materials. Consequently, reinforced concrete buildings give a sense of fire security. However, concrete as a material is also affected by the heat of a fire. Although collapse of reinforced concrete structures are rare, loss in strength, spalling, and other deleterious effects do occur.

When the temperature of a reinforced concrete member is raised, the member loses strength. The amount of strength reduction is influenced by a number of factors. Among the more significant from a structural viewpoint are the type of aggregate, moisture content, type of loading, and level of stress during the fire exposure.

One of the more significant factors in determining the change in strength and the thermal characteristics of concrete is the type of aggregate. Aggregate types can vary widely in different sections of the country. Consequently, numerical values of strength properties are related to a percentage of the original strength, rather than a specific stress value. The qualitative behavior of concrete is generally accurate, however.

Lightweight concrete performs better at elevated temperatures than does normal weight concrete. Not only does it retain more of its strength during heat buildup, it also has a lower coefficient of thermal conductivity. Concrete using aggregates of vermiculite or perlite are particularly good at protecting structural steel from a heated environment.

Figures 6-7G and 6-7H illustrate the effect of aggregates on the fire resistance of reinforced concrete slabs.[4] The light weight aggregates, such as expanded shale and expanded slag, have considerably more fire endurance than do normal weight concretes made from carbonate and silicious aggregates.

The moisture content of concrete has a significant influence on its thermal performance. A considerable quantity of the heat energy of a fire is expended in vaporizing the absorbed and capillary moisture in concrete. In the case of horizontal members, the water vapor is driven upward and maintains a temperature at the top of the member of 212°F until the water has been driven off. This increases the fire

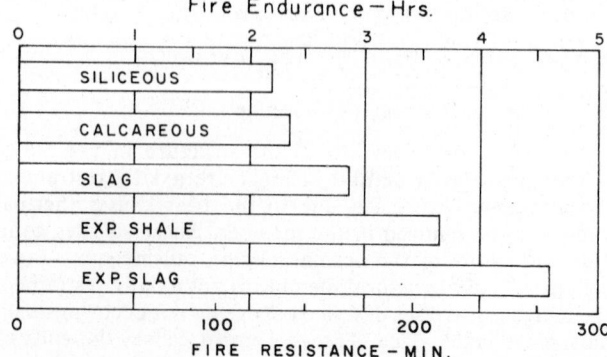

Fig. 6-7G. Effect of various types of aggregate on the fire endurance of 4¾-in. slabs.

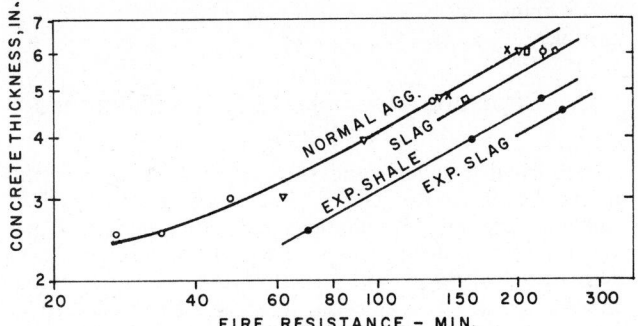

Fig. 6-7H.   Relationship of slab thickness and type of aggregate to fire endurance.

endurance, as it keeps the temperature on the unexposed side below that defined as the failure temperature. The voids caused by the evaporation of water contribute to shrinkage and a decrease in concrete strength.

The mechanical properties of concrete are significantly reduced at elevated temperatures. Figure 6-7I shows the effect on the compressive strength and modulus of elasticity by increasing the temperature.[5] There is some question about whether concrete completely regains its strength after exposure to high temperatures.

Prestressed Concrete

The factors that are significant in the behavior of prestressed concrete are similar to those that affect reinforced concrete. In addition to the influences of moisture content and aggregate, the higher strength concrete and the function and type of steel used for prestressing are important considerations.

The concrete used for prestressed concrete is of a higher strength than that used in ordinary reinforced concrete construction. The overall fire resistance of this concrete is somewhat better than the lower strength concrete. The heat transmission is about the same for the two systems. However, there is a somewhat greater tendency for prestressed concrete to spall, thus exposing the prestressing steel.

The greatest problem of prestressed concrete subjected to elevated temperatures involve the prestressing steel. The fact that the steel is put under a high initial stress, coupled with the fact that the reinforcing wires are high carbon, cold-drawn, rather than low carbon, hot-rolled steel, is the root of the problem.

Normal prestressing losses due to deformation and creep are considered in prestressed concrete design. At elevated

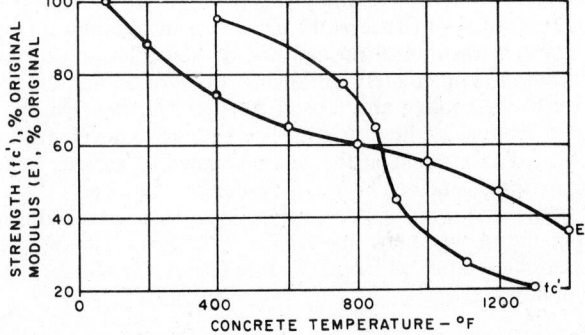

Fig. 6-7I.   Effect of temperature on modulus of elasticity and compressive strength (curves are taken from two different specimens).

temperatures these losses are accelerated. Creep in the steel increases, and the modulus of elasticity of the prestressing wires is reduced by 20 percent when the temperature reaches 600°F. These losses reduce the carrying capacity of the member.

The type of steel used for prestressing is more sensitive to elevated temperatures than the steel used in reinforced concrete construction. Not only is its strength reduced at temperatures somewhat less than those for hot-rolled steel, but also that strength is not regained after cooling. Prestressing wires are permanently weakened when they reach a temperature of about 800°F.

Wood

Depending on its form, wood may or may not provide reasonable structural integrity in a fire. The important factors seem to be the physical size and the moisture content of the members.

Fire retardant treatments delay ignition and retard combustion, thus providing time for extinguishing procedures. However, all wood will burn. The burning of wood produces a charcoal on the surface at the rate of about $\frac{1}{40}$ in. per min. This charcoal provides a protective coating that insulates the unburned wood and isolates it from the flame. Therefore, thicker members provide much more structural integrity over the period of fire exposure than do thin ones.

Heavy timber construction (see Chapter 5 of this Section) has proven to be an excellent form of construction. It maintains its integrity during a fire for a relatively long time, providing an opportunity for extinguishment. Much of the original strength of the members is retained and reconstruction is possible.

In recent years, glued laminated frames, arches, and beams have become increasingly popular. These members also provide a reserve strength during a fire, although this is lost if the wood delaminates. Unfortunately, the aesthetic appeal of these members is destroyed when they are charred.

Wood frame construction utilizes structural members considerably smaller than mill construction. The exposed area is greater, and the fire resistance considerably reduced. This type of construction offers relatively little structural integrity in a fire.

Fire Behavior of Other Building Materials

Many materials other than steel, concrete, and wood are commonly used in modern building construction. They frequently make up a large volume and/or surface area of the structure. Nonbearing partitions, insulation, building services, and finish materials are all important parts of building construction. Some of the nonstructural, thermally inert materials are used as fireproofing. Others contribute significantly to a potential fire.

Glass

Glass is utilized in three common ways in building construction. The most obvious is glazing for windows and doors. In this capacity the glass has little resistance to fire. It quickly cracks because of the temperature difference between the surfaces. Double glazing does not provide much improvement. Wire reinforced glass in an improvement as it provides somewhat greater integrity in a fire if it is properly installed. However, no glazing should be relied upon to remain intact in a fire.

A second common use of glass in buildings is in fiberglass insulation. The fiberglass does not burn and is an excellent insulator. The fiberglass is often coated with a resin binder, however, which is combustible and which can spread flames.

A third form in which glass is found in buildings is as reinforcement for fiberglass reinforced plastic building products. The products, such as translucent window panels and siding and prefabricated bathroom units are becoming much more common. They have distinct advantages of economy and aesthetic appeal. The fiberglass acts as reinforcement for a thermosetting resin, usually a polyester. The resin, combustible even with fire retardants incorporated in the composition, frequently comprises 50 percent or more of the material. While the fiberglass itself is noncombustible, the products are quite combustible.

Gypsum

Gypsum products, such as plaster and plaster board, are excellent fire protection materials. The gypsum has a high proportion of chemically combined water. Evaporation of this water requires a great deal of heat energy, making gypsum an excellent, inexpensive, fire retardant building material.

Lightweight Concrete

Lightweight concrete, made with noncombustible aggregates resists high temperatures without degradation extremely well. Vermiculite and perlite are the most common types of light concrete used for this purpose. Vermiculite is an inert aggregate made from weathered mica. The mica is crushed and roasted, which causes it to expand to form pellet-like aggregates. Perlite is a volcanic rock which is crushed and heat treated. The heat treatment causes the rock to expand in volume. During the process, water vapor is absorbed by the rock particles, and the perlite takes the form of glasslike, cellular structured particles.

Asbestos

Asbestos is a mineral fiber which is used in several forms in building construction. When it is used with a cementicious binder and sprayed onto structural members, it forms an excellent fireproofing agent. However, the asbestos fibers are a health hazard, and they can be easily scraped off the members, so its use has been significantly curtailed in recent years.

Asbestos is combined with portland cement to make asbestos cement products. Although these products are noncombustible, they often shatter during the temperature buildup of a fire, thus reducing their effectiveness. However, asbestos is also combined with materials other than portland cement to form products, such as asbestos insulation board and asbestos wood. These products behave quite well in fires, providing a great deal of fire resistance and protection.

Masonry

Brick, tile, and concrete masonry products behave well when subjected to the elevated temperatures of a fire. Hollow concrete blocks may crack from the heat, but they generally retain their integrity. Brick can withstand high temperatures without severe damage.

Plastics

There is a wide range of plastic products used by the building industry. They provide numerous aesthetic, physical, and economic advantages in building applications. Their major disadvantage is that all plastics are combustible. Although there are certain treatments which increase ignition temperatures or inhibit flame spread, there is no known treatment which will make them noncombustible.

B. Structural Assemblies and Fire Endurance Testing

Performance under standard fire test procedures is the accepted criterion for judging the fire resistance of various building materials, combinations of building materials, and structural assemblies. The severity of the fire produced by the occupancy and the structural characteristics of the building are the two essential factors to be considered in defining the fire resistance needed in a given situation. Other factors, such as life safety, exposure from or to other buildings, possible disruption of community life or business, and efficacy of fire services, should be taken into consideration when designing adequate construction.

Anticipating Fire Severity

By close examination of a building and its contents, the fire severity caused by their burning can be estimated. The character of the combustible materials and the manner in which they are distributed through the building have a marked effect on the rate of combustion, duration of fire, and resultant damage to the building. These two characteristics also determine, to a great extent, the difficulty of fire suppression. Combustible contents and combustible materials in the building construction itself make up the fire load (see Chapter 8 of this Section).

Fire Test Methods

Both time and temperature are measured for the effects of fire on building components and materials. (See Part A of Chapter 7 of this Section for a discussion of the Standard Time-Temperature curve.) High temperature fires of short duration may have little effect on concrete construction; conversely, a lower temperature over an extended period of time may result in complete disintegration. Heat expansion effects, particularly from temperature gradients, may warp or even disrupt building components. Masonry walls distorted by heat can become unstable and are subject to collapse.

Test methods such as NFPA 251, Fire Test of Building Construction and Materials, have been developed with the view to making determinations, insofar as practical, of the various effects of fire of controlled intensity on such building components as columns, floors, walls, partitions, and ceiling or roof assemblies. The results of such tests are recorded as the duration of fire resistance, in hours or minutes. The tests signify that the component tested resists, to the required degree, the effects of the controlled fire under specific conditions of restraint or load or both for that duration. In certain instances, in order to qualify for a fire resistance rating, the construction must have withstood, immediately following the prescribed fire exposure, the cooling and erosive effects of a standard jet of water from a fire hose nozzle. The ratings so developed are accepted as a guide to the fire resistance of various building materials and construction assemblies.

Doors and windows are subjected to fire tests differing from the above. They are NFPA 252, Fire Tests of Door Assemblies, and NFPA 257, Fire Tests of Window Assemblies.

History of Fire Resistance Tests

One review of fire test methods for building constructions refers to tests on metal and masonry columns conducted in

Germany as early as 1884–1886.[6] The first large scale fire tests in this country are reported to have been conducted on masonry arches in Denver, Colorado in 1890. These were followed by tests in New York City in 1896.

Efforts to establish an acceptable test procedure were initiated by Professor Ira H. Woolson of Columbia University and Rudolph P. Miller, Chief Engineer, Building Bureau, New York City. Preliminary tests by the Bureau, "necessitated by the rapid development of the sky scraper" led to the development of a test furnace (using railroad ties as fuel). This provided a means of establishing hourly ratings for floor constructions.

In 1905, after the Baltimore conflagration, the American Society for Testing Materials established a committee to standardize the test method with Prof. Woolson as Chairman and Mr. Miller as Secretary. A test method for floor constructions was proposed in 1906 and adopted by ASTM in 1907. A procedure for testing wall and partition constructions was proposed in 1908 and adopted in 1909.[7]

These Standards were presented to the NFPA Committee on Fire Resistive Construction for consideration in 1914. In 1916, a joint committee composed of representatives from eleven engineering societies, including NFPA, was organized to revise and update the standard. This was done and the revised standard was adopted subsequently by NFPA, ASTM, and the American Engineering Committee (now the American National Standards Institute). The standard was adopted in NFPA as a tentative standard in 1917 and advanced to official standard status in 1918.

The British standard time-temperature curve closely parallels that of the American curve and test results should not be significantly different. However, the British test uses bare, rather than shielded, thermocouples. Thus, the test is slightly less severe during the early part of the test, when temperatures are rising rapidly.[8] Time-temperature curves developed in other countries follow the same general pattern, with minor differences.

Fire Test Procedure

Fire test procedures usually require that columns, floors, partitions, walls, and other structural elements be loaded in a manner calculated to develop, as nearly as practical, the theoretical working stresses contemplated by the design. Separate test procedures are provided for load bearing and nonload bearing constructions, and for constructions involving restrained and unrestrained beams and girders. Special tests are provided also for ceilings that are not an integral part of the floor construction, for protection of combustible framing, and for combustible facings on the unexposed side of walls, partitions, and floors.

The Appendix to NFPA 251 contains detailed specifications for asbestos pads, a guide to the determination of restraint required, if any, and a suggested report form. The standard specifies in detail the preparation and conditioning of the test specimens. Further information on restraint, conditioning (including measurement of moisture in thick specimens) will be found in the references and additional readings listed at the end of this chapter.

Acceptance criteria are specific for the construction or element tested and on predetermined conditions of test (load or no load—restrained or unrestrained). The criteria may include:

1. Failure to support load.
2. Temperature increase on the unexposed surface 250°F over ambient.
3. Passage of heat or flame sufficient to ignite cotton waste.
4. Excess temperature (as specified) on steel members.
5. Failure under hose stream (walls and partitions).

Fire Resistance Ratings

The standard fire test takes into consideration the capacity of the test structure to perform its intended functions during fire exposure, as well as its subsequent load capacity. It does not consider its suitability for further use. Many effects from fire tests are observed indirectly, if at all. For example, the temperature gradient through a wall or floor slab results in internal strains and deflections. The strains may cause spalling or other disruptions and distortions may be severe enough to crack floor slabs and walls, sometimes leading to collapse. The greater the area exposed, the more serious are the results of unequal expansion. General deterioration of the test specimen is not considered, except when it has been involved in failure of the test specimen.

While the test standard specifies the preparation and conditioning of specimens, there are many opportunities for differences between a test specimen and an actual structural element in a building. The test specimen may be superior in both materials and workmanship to those found in a building. It is usually smaller than the construction it represents. Restraints to thermal expansion may be of different magnitudes. Therefore, discretion in the application of fire test results is in order.

The principal agencies in the United States which test assemblies of building construction materials for fire resistance are Underwriters Laboratories, Inc., and the National Bureau of Standards. There are a number of other agencies which have furnaces or equipment for fire tests of various special assemblies. These include the Factory Mutual System laboratories in Norwood, Mass.; the Forest Products Laboratory at Madison, Wisconsin; the Engineering Experiment Station at Ohio State University, Columbus; University of California at Berkeley; the Portland Cement Association, Skokie, Illinois; Armstrong Cork Co., Lancaster, Pa.; the Corbetta Construction Company at College Point, Borough of Queens, New York; and the National Gypsum Co., Buffalo, N.Y.

In England, there are the facilities at the Testing Station of the Joint Fire Research Organization of the Fire Offices' Committee and the Department of the Environment at Boreham Wood, Hertfordshire. In Canada, there are facilities at the Underwriters Laboratories of Canada, at Toronto, and the Building Research Division of the National Research Council of Canada, at Ottawa. Throughout the world, many well-equipped fire testing laboratories are making significant contributions to the literature and to the development of international fire test standards.

Underwriters Laboratories, Inc., publishes annually in its *Building Materials List* (with bi-monthly supplements) the fire retardant classifications of building construction and materials tested, including a variety of plaster bases and composite materials. Because of the variation in the character and quality of materials, the user should note carefully the recommendations of the UL Lists; in the case of materials such as concrete block, which vary widely in properties, there is a special UL service certifying the quality. Underwriters Laboratories, of Canada publishes annually a list of building construction and materials tested by that organization.

The results of many fire tests by the various North American testing agencies are given in *Fire-Resistance Ratings* published periodically by the American Insurance Association.

The results of fire tests by governmental agencies have been published in various reports and technical papers. Those issued by the National Bureau of Standards may be consulted in many depository libraries, and lists of those available for purchase may be obtained on request from the NBS. The bulletins and reports of the British Ministry of Technology on the subject are obtainable by purchase from H.M. Stationery Office, or the British Information Services, New York, N.Y.

The Factory Mutual System publishes annually in its *Approval Guide* illustrations of building assemblies that have met the test requirements for various fire resistance hourly ratings.

Various building codes which specify fire resistance in terms of fire test results also include tabulations of construction forms which will be accepted as meeting code requirements for specific fire resistance ratings. Such tables are usually based upon fire test data, but some include ratings determined on a judgment basis or estimated from limited test data.

Not listed are the many useful data sheets and summary tables published by trade associations of the building materials manufacturers. These sources are not cited because they are so numerous and because the information published either pertains to the products of a specific manufacturer or consists of tabulated ratings for a single type of construction material.

Variation in Test Results

Differences in the results of fire tests on apparently equal test specimens of building constructions arise from many factors, such as undetermined differences in the quality of materials, workmanship, moisture content, and test procedures. The standard method of test requires the materials in the specimen and the workmanship involved, as well as the load applied and the conditions of edge restraint to be representative of those in actual buildings. Due to uncertainties of the actual restraint in buildings, considerable variation in restraint can occur.

The standard method also requires that the dampest part of a specimen must be reduced to a relative humidity of 70 percent; but formerly the moisture condition was left to the judgment of the testing agency.

The test method permits the intensity of the fire exposure to deviate as much as 10 percent (formerly 15 percent) from that prescribed as standard, and requires adjustment in the reported results to correct for such deviations only for tests of $\frac{1}{2}$ hr or greater duration. The effects of several of the variables encountered in fire testing procedures are found in the technical reports listed in the bibliography at the end of the chapter.

The character and proportions of aggregates and binders have an important influence on results of fire resistance tests. For example, lightweight aggregates, such as perlite and vermiculite, have been introduced for use in plaster and concrete. Gypsum plaster with lightweight aggregates, mixed with from 2 to 3 cu ft to each 100 lbs of gypsum, has been shown by test to provide fire resistance from 10 to 70 percent greater than equal thicknesses of sanded gypsum plaster. The use of such aggregate in specific constructions should be adopted only after consulting the lists of ratings based on tests in which these aggregates have been used.

Vermiculite aggregate plaster, if applied too wet, may be subject to shrinkage cracks. Such cracks, if they develop, are likely to occur within a short time. Some expanded perlite aggregates tend to absorb atmospheric moisture and may show destructive expansion after a few years. There

may be considerable variation in this effect as perlite is a natural volcanic glass or rock from many sources and varies in composition.

Finishing lime produced from dolomite contains magnesium oxide. That which is designated as "normal" finishing hydrate may not be sufficiently hydrated, and sometimes subsequent gradual hydration results in destructive expansion. Plasters containing such lime are subject to rapid destruction in the event of fire. This difficulty is avoided with lime hydrated under high temperature and pressure and now known as "special" or "autoclaved" lime.

So-called stabilized gypsum plaster containing a small percentage of the normal hydrated lime may similarly be subject to deterioration with age and in tests did not provide the fire resistance to be expected from such constructions.

The effects mentioned are not such as to preclude the use of these materials where long life is not a factor or where adequate guarantees are provided against such deterioration.

Although standard fire tests are made on fairly large specimens representative of building constructions or assemblies, they do not necessarily produce heat-expansion effects such as result from fires in buildings having larger wall or floor areas. It may be necessary to specify thickness of construction or lateral support in addition to rated fire resistance in order to guard against the adverse effects of heat expansion or temperature gradients.

Estimates of Fire Resistance by Interpolations

A number of useful empirical formulas for estimating the fire resistance of columns, floors, partitions, and walls have been developed. These have been formulated from the results of fire tests.

Carl Menzel's formula, $P = CW^n$, was based on fire tests of walls of concrete masonry units, in which P was the fire resistance of the wall in minutes, W the weight of the wall in lbs per sq ft, C a constant, and n an exponent derived from analyses of the results of tests he conducted in 1934. The values of C and n vary with the kind of aggregates in the concrete units and are given in Table 6-7A.

The values of fire resistance computed from the formula were for well dried walls and will be found to be about 90 percent of values found by Underwriters Laboratories, Inc., in fire tests of walls made from like units and aggregates.

Neisel's formula,

$$F = 10^{0.692-0.0093\rho}\left(\frac{d}{k} + \frac{\rho d}{12}\right)^{1.54}$$

$$\log F = 0.692 - 0.0093\rho_b + 1.54 \log\left(\frac{d}{k} + \frac{\rho d}{12}\right),$$

was developed for materials of lower ranges of density. It can be adapted to constructions having laminations of different densities by setting the term in parentheses to show the conductivity and density of each lamination thus:

Table 6-7A.

	Haydite	Cinders	Slag	Limestone	Calcareous Gravel	Siliceous Gravel
C	.130	.180	.168	.146	.180	.154
n	2.03	1.82	1.77	1.75	1.66	1.67

$$\frac{d_1}{k_1} + \frac{d_2}{k_2} + \cdots + \frac{\rho_1 d_1}{12} + \frac{\rho_2 d_2}{12} + \cdots$$

with k taken for appropriate mean temperature for the particular lamination represented. In this formula F is the rating period in minutes, d is the thickness of the construction in inches, k the thermal conductivity at the mean temperature through the thickness in Btu per (hour) (square foot) (Fahrenheit degree per inch of thickness) at 500°F, ρ the density of the construction in lb per cu ft, and ρ_b the bulk density in lb per cu ft.

The National Bureau of Standards formula for Walls is $R = (CV)^n$ in which R is the fire resistance period, C a coefficient depending on materials and design of wall and units of measurement of R and V, V the volume of material per unit area, and n an exponent depending on the rate of increase of temperature on the face of the wall. If the wall is made up of differing laminae,

$$R = (C_1 V_1 + C_2 V_2 + C_3 V_3 + \cdots)^n$$

or

$$R = (R_1^{1/n} + R_2^{1/n} + R_3^{1/n} + \cdots)^n.$$

The value of $n = 1.7$ is approximate only for several materials, such as clay bricks, hollow tiles, and plaster.

The formula for computing the fire resistance of steel columns encased with monolithic concrete takes the form

$$R = C \left(D - a \frac{d^2}{D} \right)^n.$$

In this formula C is a coefficient related to the character of the concrete aggregates. It was developed by analysis of the fire tests of concrete encased steel columns made at Underwriters Laboratories, Inc., in 1917 and 1918. (See Figure 6-7J, for approximate values of C for various concrete mixes and identification of other terms used in the formula).

Among steel columns encased with lath, and plaster which were tested by UL and NBS, the fire resistance for a given construction varied linearly with the sum of the thicknesses of lath, sand plaster, and plaster key. To estimate the fire resistance of such columns in minutes, multiply the sum of the thicknesses in inches less 0.35, by 105 for plaster of 1:2 mix for scratch coat and 1:3 for brown coat; and for both coats of $1:2\frac{1}{2}$ mix multiply by 120. A factor of about 135 is applicable for sprayed mineral fibers or the direct application of lightweight gypsum plasters up to a thickness of $2\frac{3}{4}$ in.

The fire resistance of columns encased with 1:2, 1:3 gypsum-lightweight aggregate plasters on gypsum lath is increased by 10 to 20 percent by the use of lightweight wire fabric reinforcement in the plaster. The size or weight of the steel column shaft in the range of 6 to 10 in. for H columns makes a slight, but probably insignificant, difference in fire resistance; the smaller, or lighter, the section the less its fire resistance.

Example: It is required to design a column having 4-hr (240 min) fire resistance; the encasement to be mill-mix $1:2\frac{1}{2}$ gypsum-lightweight aggregate plaster on metal lath. The solution is: $\frac{240}{135} + 0.35 = 1.78 + 0.35 = 2.13$ or $2\frac{1}{8}$ in. including equivalent of solid plaster or plaster keys.

If it is desired to use gypsum lath and 1:2 and 1:3 mixes of lightweight-plaster on gypsum lath, the solution is: $\frac{240}{105} + 0.35 = 2.29 + 0.35 = 2.64$ in. total thickness of gypsum lath, plus plaster required. If the plaster is to be reinforced with metal fabric, such as stucco mesh or chicken wire, divide 2.64 by 1.15 to derive a total thickness of 2.28 in.

Graphical and Logarithmic Solutions

All the empirical formulas given are adapted to logarithmic or graphical solutions. Menzel's formula is solved for the value of P thus: $\log P = \log C + n \log W$. Or if two or more test results are plotted for different weights on log-log graph paper using the fire resistance as ordinates and the weights of the walls per sq ft as abscissae, a straight line drawn through the plotted points defines the relation of weight to fire resistance for all points between and can be depended upon for reasonable extrapolations above or below the range of weights covered. For example, if tests show that the average weight of three 4-in. walls of calcareous gravel three-core concrete units is 30.5 lb per sq ft and the fire resistance averages 50 min; and that for sixteen 8-in. walls of the same type of units weighting 58 lb per sq ft is 152.2 min, then by plotting these two values on log-log graph paper and joining them by a straight line, we find we can say that if walls of three-core units are required to provide 1-hr fire resistance they should weigh 34 lb per sq ft; for $1\frac{1}{2}$-hr fire resistance, 43 lb per sq ft; for 2 hrs, 51 lb per sq ft; for 3 hrs, 64 lb per sq ft; and for 4 hrs, 75 lb per sq ft. This method is used by Underwriters Laboratories for interpolations for fire resistance ratings on the basis of equivalent thickness of net volume of concrete units.

Figure 6-7J provides for ready solution of the problem of encasing steel columns and other free standing steel members such as truss chords or web members. Example: An 8-in. H column is required to have encasement of solid monolithic trap rock concrete to provide 6 hrs fire resistance. Referring to Figure 6-7J entering on the left at

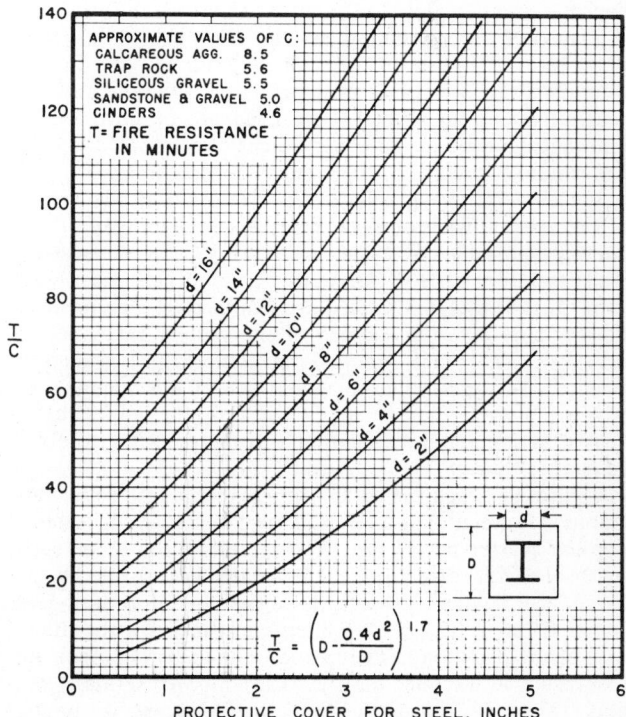

Fig. 6-7J. Encasing requirements of steel columns and other free standing steel members.

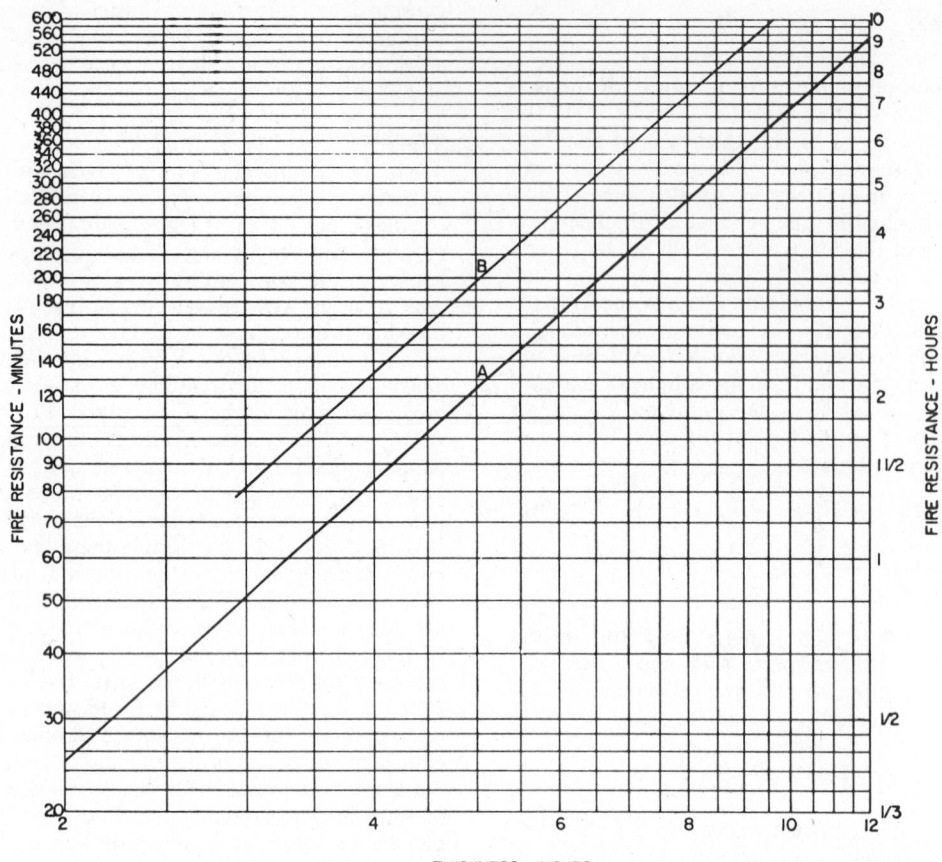

Fig. 6-7K.   Fire resistance of burned clay brick walls: **A,** *unplastered;* **B,** *plastered both sides.*

$\dfrac{T}{C} = \dfrac{360}{5.6}$ min $= 64.3$ and proceeding to the right to intercept the curve for the 8-in. column we arrive at $2\frac{3}{4}$ in., the thickness of cover required. A 6-in. H column is found to need $3\frac{3}{8}$-in. thickness of the same concrete to meet the requirement for 6-hr fire resistance. This solution requires that all re-entrant spaces between flanges be filled solidly and that the concrete covering flanges be reinforced to hold the concrete in place in the event of its cracking.

Figure 6-7K is a graphical representation of the results of fire tests on walls of burned clay bricks. The lines drawn show graphically the values of $R = 8t^{1.75}$ for unplastered walls and $R = 11.7t^{1.75}$ for walls plastered both sides with $\frac{1}{2}$-in. thickness of 1:3 sanded gypsum plaster. The formula does not refer to the stability of the wall or resistance to cracking. These are functions of temperature gradients, strength, and expansion characteristics of the materials of which the wall is constructed. Ordinarily the values represented by the graph will be found to represent the true fire resistance ratings.

Figure 6-7L represents the fire resistance of solid partitions of metal lath and neat wood fibered or sanded gypsum plaster partitions. The fire resistance, R, of such partitions with respect to heat transmission is solved by the formula $R = 40t^{1.7}\ g^{0.8}$ or the logarithmic formula, Log $R = 1.60206 + 1.7 \log t + 0.8 \log g$ in which t is the thickness of the partition in inches and g the decimal proportion of gypsum in the mix; for 1:2 (0.33) mix for scratch coat and 1:3 mix (0.25); and for 1:2 scratch coat and 1:3 brown coat the value of g would be 0.29, assuming equal volumes of each mix. A similar diagram (Fig. 6-7M) for hollow

sanded gypsum plaster partitions with wood or metal studs leads to the formula, $R = 40t^{1.7}g^{1/3}$ in which t is the sum of the net thickness of the plaster on the two faces of the partition. The formula applies equally well to partitions faced with Type X gypsum wallboards in single or double thickness on each face. The logarithmic formula becomes Log $R = 1.60206 + 1.7 \log t + \frac{1}{3} \log g$.

If the two facings of the hollow partition are of neat wood fibered gypsum plaster or gypsum boards the last term of the logarithmic formula becomes zero.

Combustible vs. Noncombustible Construction

Distinction should be made between materials of a combustible character and those which are noncombustible, even though the same fire resistance ratings may be given. Fire resistance ratings under standard tests are based upon performance with the sample subjected to specified controlled fire temperatures. No distinction is made in the test rating between those cases where part of the heat in the test furnaces is supplied by burning of the exposed sample itself and those where all of the heat comes from the furnace fuel. Fire resistance ratings, in terms of hours or minutes, should also include the designation "combustible," to define the character of the construction. Tables listing fire resistance ratings of various types of assemblies appearing later in this chapter carry the notation "combustible" under the title of the assembly if that particular assembly is made up in whole or in part of combustible materials.

Fire Resistive Constructions

The two modern types of fire resistive construction are

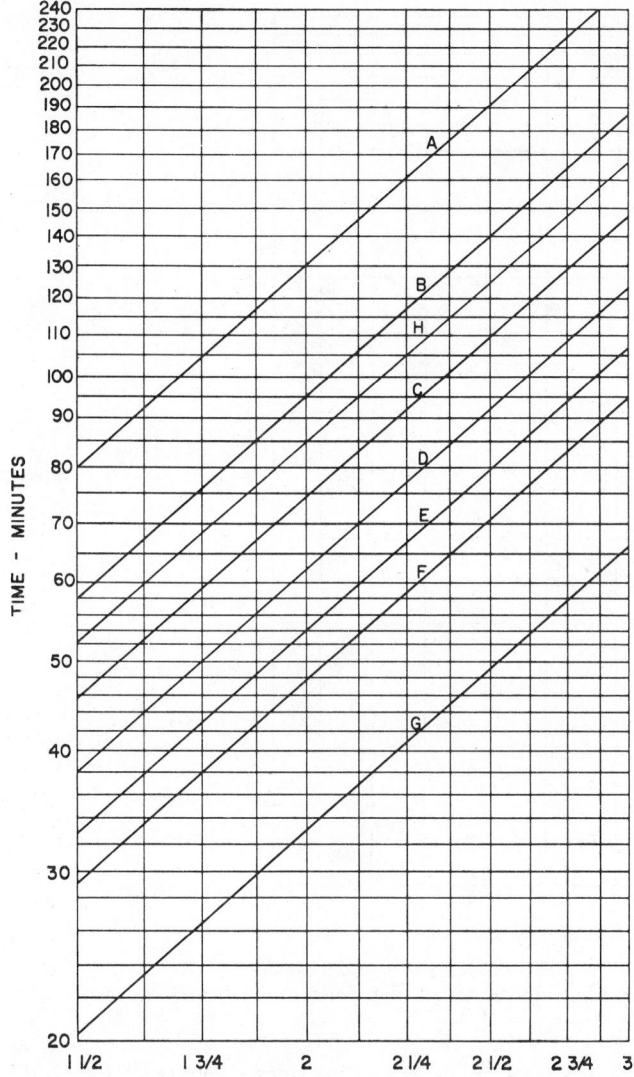

*Fig. 6-7L. Fire resistance of solid partitions of metal lath and plaster: **A**, wood fiber gypsum; **B**, 1:½ gypsum-sand; **C**, 1:1 gypsum-sand; **D**, 1:1½ gypsum-sand; **E**, 1:2 gypsum-sand; **F**, 1:2 and 1:3 gypsum-sand; **G**, 1:2 and 1:3 portland cement + 0.2 lime to cement.*

structural steel and reinforced concrete. Each has certain advantages and disadvantages in resisting fire. A brief discussion of the characteristics of each is pertinent.

Concrete Constructions

Among the appealing characteristics of concrete constructions are its permanence and fire resistance. Both of these are affected by the concrete mix proportions, the kind of aggregates used, and the workmanship. The amount of water and cement in a given volume and thoroughness of mix, as well as choice of aggregates for a given service, need intelligent and honest consideration if good results are to be assured.

The details of construction and kind of aggregates affect the fire resistance of concrete structures. Very thin sections surrounded by heavier framing are prone to break or shatter as the result of restraint against expansion. The expansion of the concrete is affected to a degree by the expansion and heat conductivity of the aggregates as they affect the temperature gradients of concrete exposed to fire. The spalling of concrete exposed to fire usually stems from stresses set up by steep temperature gradients or from entrapped moisture, or both. Hence, dense rigid high-strength concretes made of a given aggregate, while still damp, are more likely to spall on exposure to fire than are the dry more porous yielding types. Steep temperature gradients also have an effect toward such results.

Although concretes made with lightweight aggregates have relatively steep temperature gradients when exposed to fire, spalling rarely occurs because ordinarily they yield readily to the stress gradient. High-strength concretes, even the lightweight varieties, sometime spall or explode if the structure is such that steam generated within has no way to escape.

The Building Officials Conference of America divides concretes into two grades on the basis of the fire resistance as affected by aggregates. The two grades are defined as follows:

Grade 1 concrete shall mean concrete made with aggregates such as blast-furnace slag, burned clays, and calcareous igneous, and most silicate crushed stones and gravels and shales, as well as any other aggregates performing as required by the Basic Code for the appropriate construction when tested in accordance with standard methods of fire tests of building construction and materials listed in Appendix G. (The reference is to NFPA 251.)

Grade 2 concrete shall mean concrete made with aggregates such as cinders and crushed stones and gravels composed of essentially quartz and quartzite cherts, as well as any other aggregates performing as required by the Basic Code for the appropriate construction when tested in accordance with standard methods of fire tests of building construction and materials listed in Appendix G.

The fire resistances of reinforced concrete floors of varying thicknesses and weight are given in Figure 6-7N, and for reinforced concrete walls in Figure 6-7O.

The fire resistance ratings for reinforced concrete beams are given in Table 6-7B and for prestressed concrete girders, beams, and slabs in Table 6-7C. As the cold-drawn, high-strength steel tendons used in prestressed concrete are more adversely affected by high temperatures than is normal reinforcement steel, these tendons require a thicker protective cover than is required in conventional reinforced concrete. As shown in Table 6-7C, the cover for the pre-

Table 6-7B. Reinforced Concrete Beams and Girders of Medium Size

Concrete Grade*	Protective Cover of Reinforcement, Inches	Fire Resistance Rating† Hours,
1	¾	1
	1	2
	1¼	3
	1½	4
2	¾	½–1‡
	1	1–2‡
	1½	2–3‡
	2	2–4‡

* For lightweight concrete having an oven-dried density of 110 pcf or less, the cover shown for Concrete Grade 1 may be reduced 25 percent.

† May be increased if some bars are better protected by being away from corners or in an upper layer, or if beam is large. Should be decreased if beam is small.

‡ Variable depending on spalling characteristics of aggregate. The use of mesh to hold cover in place will give ratings about as high as for concrete of Grade 1.

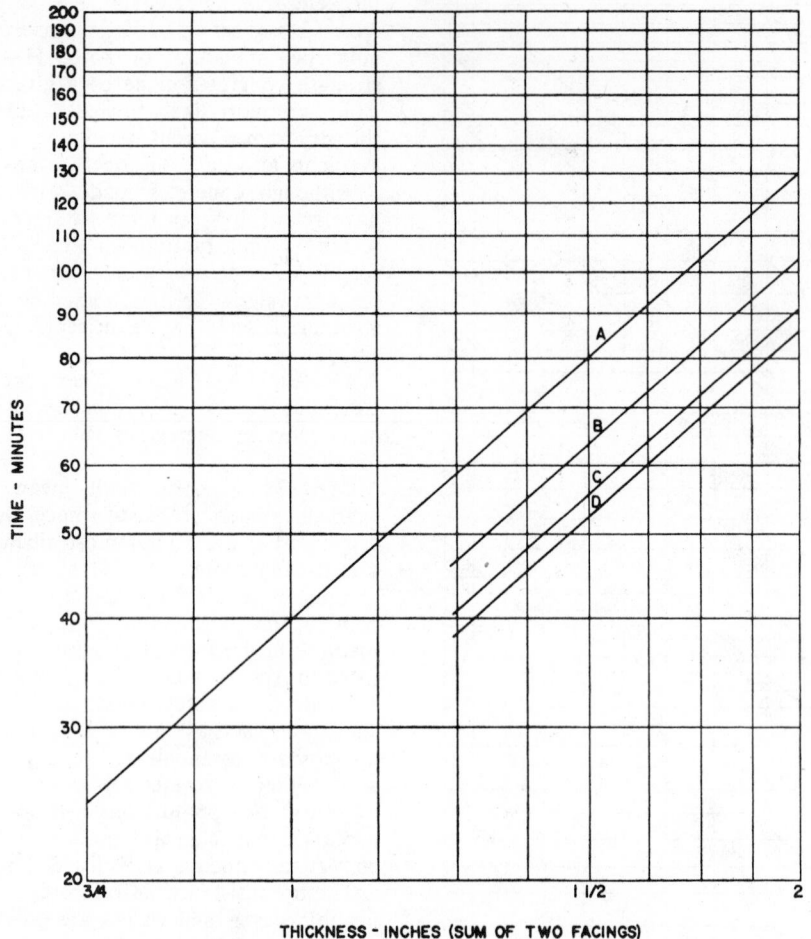

Fig. 6-7M. Fire resistance of wood or metal stud partitions faced with gypsum wallboards or gypsum plaster on metal lath: **A,**
Type X gypsum wallboards or wood fiber gypsum plaster; **B,** *1:1 gypsum-sand plaster;* **C,** *1:2 gypsum-sand plaster;* **D,** *1:2 and*
1:3 gypsum-sand plaster.

stressing tendons is less when the element is restrained, as
then the restraint maintains the prestress in the concrete
even after the prestressing tendons have expanded and lost
part or even all of their prestressing effect.

Steel Construction

The popularity of steel frame construction for fire resistive buildings derives from its high strength, ease of
fabrication, and assured uniformity of quality. The steel
frame, however, is vulnerable to fire damage. In order to
have fire resistance, it must be protected from high temperatures encountered in fires. The use of masonry
materials at first, and then concrete, to provide protection
was the natural outgrowth of building experience. With
suitable sheer connectors and bonding, concrete used as
protection for steel may be considered to assist in supporting
loads to which the structure may be subjected.

A number of new developments have appeared to give
competition to masonry and concrete as protection for steel
framework. Among such protections are gypsum or portland cement plasters using either natural or lightweight
sands, and sprayed mineral fibers. Fire retardant paints with
mineral fibers incorporated are being developed. The weight
reductions afforded by these new developments in fire protective insulating systems are attractive from the standpoint
of weight economy. Thus, for 4-hr protection to a 10-in. H
column, lightweight gypsum plaster would weigh only

40 percent as much as crushed stone concrete, and sprayed
fiber insulation would weigh approximately half as much
as the lightweight gypsum plaster, or one-fifth as much as
the concrete. The vulnerability of the lightweight materials
to impact damage, however, must be considered a liability.
For lesser degrees of fire resistance, mineral fibers bonded
with an intumescent material developed as a fire-retardant

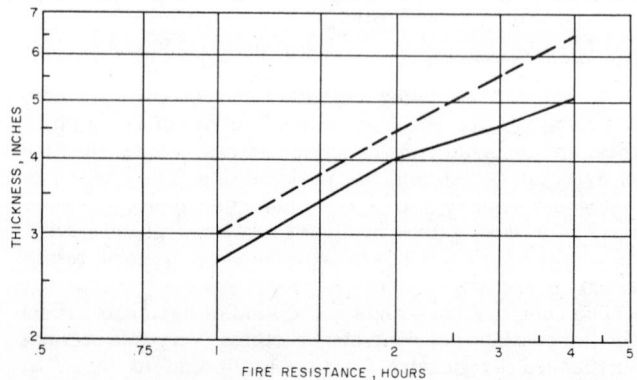

*Fig. 6-7N. Fire resistance ratings of reinforced concrete floors
of varying thicknesses. The dotted line represents concrete floors
made with regular aggregates and the solid line represents lightweight concretes.*

Table 6-7C. Prestressed Concrete Girders, Beams, Joists and Slabs
(Grade I Concrete)

Type of Unit	Condition of Restraint	Cross-Sectional Area, sq in.†	Cover in Inches for Fire Rating Shown*			
			1 Hr	2 Hr	3 Hr	4 Hr
Girders, beams and joists	Unrestrained	40 to 150	2	2.5	—	—
		150 to 300	1.5	2.5	3.5‡	—
		Over 300	1.5	2.25	3‡	4‡
	Axially restrained	40 to 150	1.5	2	—	—
		150 to 300	1	1.5	2	—
		Over 300	1	1.5	1.5	2
Slabs, solid or covered, with flat undersurface	Unrestrained		1	1.5	2	2.5
	Biaxial restraint		0.75	1.25	1.5	2

* Cover for an individual steel tendon is measured to the nearest exposed surface. For several tendons in the same member having different concrete covers, the minimum cover may be reduced slightly. The covers shown may be reduced 25 percent for lightweight concrete having an oven-dried density of 110 pcf or less. For Grade 2 concrete the cover may need to be increased.

† In computing the cross-sectional area of joists, the area of the flange shall be added to the area of the stem, but the total width of the flange so used shall not exceed three times the width of the stem.

‡ Provide against spalling of the cover by means of a light, 2-in., U-shaped mesh, covered about 1 in.

Note: Data in this table are based on 67 Standard ASTM fire tests.

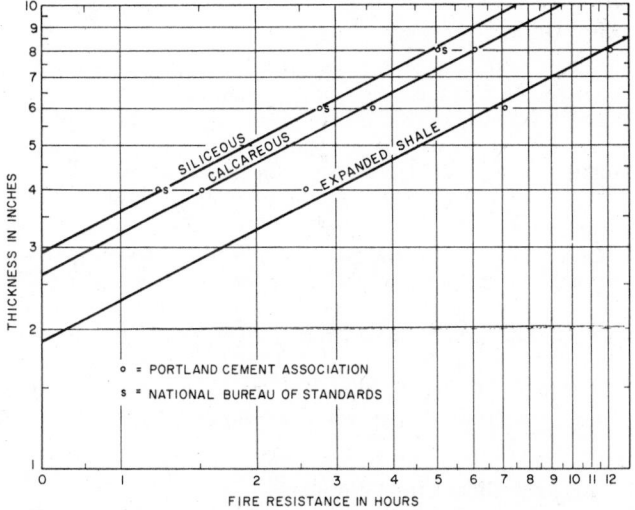

Fig. 6-70. Fire resistance ratings for solid concrete walls of varying thickness and made with various aggregates.

paint offer the possibility of an attractive insulation against fire of one or two hours duration.

Tables 6-7D and 6-7E show the thicknesses of the two grades of concrete for the protection of structural steel building components.

Walls and Partitions

Tables 6-7F to 6-7L show the comparative fire resistance of the more commonly used types of walls and partitions erected under conditions of good average workmanship. All individual ratings are necessarily approximate, because of variations in material and workmanship and details of design which cannot be covered within the space limitations of these tabulations. For further information, reference should be made to Underwriters Laboratories listings, publications of the National Bureau of Standards, and other indicated sources.

Fire resistance periods and fire resistance ratings are based on the results of tests made in accordance with the NFPA No. 251.

The assigned fire resistance rating, however, does not

Table 6-7D. Concrete Protection for Steel Trusses or Girders
(All reentrant portions filled)

Fire Resistance Rating		Thickness of Concrete Protection, Inches							
		Grade 1 Size of Member (flange width)				Grade 2 Size of Member (flange width)			
Hr	Min	2 to 3¾ in.	4 to 5¾ in.	6 to 7¾ in.	8 in. and over	2 to 3¾ in.	4 to 5¾ in.	6 to 7¾ in.	8 in. and over
4	—	4	3¼	2½	2	4¾	3¾	3	2½
3	—	3½	2½	2	1½	4	3	2½	2
2	—	2½	2	1½	1	3	2½	1¾	1¼
1	30	2	1½	1	1	2½	1¾	1¼	1
1	—	1½	1	1	1	1¾	1¼	1	1

Note: Protective concrete having thickness one-fourth of flange width or less shall have steel wire reinforcement spaced not more than four times the thickness of the concrete covering the flange.

Table 6-7E. Monolithic Concrete Protection for Structural Steel Columns
(All reentrant portions filled)

Fire Resistance Rating		Concrete Protection, Inches			
		Grade 1 Size of Column		Grade 2 Size of Column	
Hr	Min	8 in. or Larger	6-in.	8 in. or Larger	6-in.
4	—	2	2½	2½	3
3	—	1½	2	2	2½
2	—	1	1	1¾	2¼
1	30	1*	1	1	1¼
1	—	1	1	1	1

Note: Protective concrete having thickness one-fourth of flange width or less shall have steel wire reinforcement spaced not more than four times the thickness of the concrete covering the flange.

* Application of thicknesses less than 1 in. with reinforcement not feasible.

necessarily reflect the full fire resistance of a given construction. Such ratings are set at such periods as 30 min, 45 min, 1 hr, 1½ hrs, 2 hrs, and at hourly periods thereafter. If in the test an end point is attained at 2 hrs 55 min, the rating is 2 hrs or 70 percent of its proven value. Conversely, a construction attaining a 1 hr 55 min. rating could not be rated at 2 hrs.

Many fire tests are stopped arbitrarily before an end point criterion has been attained. In some cases the indications are that had the test been continued, the construction would have qualified for a higher fire resistance rating than that assigned to it.

Plaster thicknesses are usually measured from the face of the plaster base. Plaster on metal lath has keys which add to its effective thickness. The mix proportions for sanded plasters have, for several years, been specified on a weight basis, and those for other plasters are on the basis of weight (one 100-lb bag) of plaster to specific volumes (cu ft) of aggregate. Mixtures of gypsum plaster and expanded perlite or vermiculite are usually proportioned on the basis of one bag (1½ cu ft) of plaster to 2, 2½, or 3 cu ft of aggregate. Where two mix proportions are given, the first is for the

scratch coat, the second for the brown. Where only one ratio is given, both coats are of the same proportions, or the plaster may have been applied by the double-up method.

Floors

Tables 6-7M to 6-7Q show the comparative fire resistance of commonly used types of floors installed under conditions of good average workmanship.

The various types of floors can be expected to prevent the spread of fire between areas separated by them for the period of time given. Variations in combustibility of the floors are not fully reflected in the ratings. Where ratings are comparable for different construction, the less combustible types are usually preferred.

The safe fire resistance ratings given in the Tables are the results of tests made in accordance with NFPA No. 251. The data were compiled from reports in publications of the National Bureau of Standards and Underwriters Laboratories, Inc. In all tests, the fire exposure was on the underside of the floor construction.

Plaster thickness and proportions previously described under Walls and Partitions also apply to floor constructions.

For new construction with ratings less than ¾ hr, rosin-sized building paper is the recommended membrane. For ratings of ¾ hr or more, the recommended membrane is asbestos felt, at least 12 lbs per 100 sq ft.

Roof Decks

The fire resistance ratings for the various types of floor constructions in the tables in this chapter are applicable to similar constructions for roof decks with ceilings of the types shown. Tests by the National Bureau of Standards for the steel roof deck industry on formed sheet steel roof decks with insulation boards under built-up asphalt membrane roofing indicated that if 1-hr fire resistance was desired, protection, such as that afforded by a suspended ceiling or a sprayed-on application, was needed. Table 6-7R gives fire resistance ratings for three common types of formed steel roof decks supported on steel framing and with fiber-board insulation and built-up asphalt roofing above and protected below by suspended ceilings of expanded metal or wire lath and gypsum-sand plaster.

Table 6-7F. Load-Bearing Brick and Clay Tile Walls

Material	Wall Thickness Inches	Solid Content of Walls Percent	Hollow Units Number of Cells in Wall Thickness	Thickness of Shells of Unit Inches	Combustible Members Framed 4 in. into Wall No Plaster	Combustible Members Framed 4 in. into Wall Plaster on Two Sides	No Combustible Members Framed into Wall No Plaster	No Combustible Members Framed into Wall Plaster on Two Sides
Brick, clay or shale	12	90 to 100	—	—	8	9	10	12
	10*	72	2-in. cavity	—	2	2½	5	7
	8	90 to 100	—	—	2	2½	5	7
	4†	90 to 100	—	—	—	—	1	1½
Load-Bearing Hollow Tile (not partition tile)	12	45	3	0.7	2½	3½	3	6
	12‡	48	4	⅝	2½	4	5	7½
	10*	36	2+2-in. cavity	—	—	1¼	—	4
	8	48	3 or 4	—	1	1¾	2½	3½
	8	40	2	—	¾	1½	2	3
	6†	40	2	⅝	—	—	¾	1½

* Cavity wall with metal ties across cavity.
† Nonload-bearing wall restrained on all edges.
‡ Two units, 8 by 12 by 12-in. 6-cell and 3¾ by 12 by 12-in. 3-cell tiles, in wall thickness.

Table 6-7G. Concrete Masonry Estimated Fire Resistive Ratings

Aggregate Type	Minimum Equivalent Thickness,* Inches, for Rating of:			
	1 Hr	2 Hrs	3 Hrs	4 Hrs
Pumice	1.8	3.0	4.0	4.7
Expanded slag	2.2	3.3	4.2	5.0
Expanded shale or clay	2.5	3.7	4.7	5.5
Limestone, scoria, cinders, or unexpanded slag	2.7	4.0	5.0	5.9
Calcareous gravel	2.8	4.2	5.3	6.2
Siliceous gravel	3.0	4.5	5.7	6.7

* Equivalent thickness of a concrete masonry unit is the thickness of a theoretical 100 percent solid unit containing the same volume of concrete as the unit with core holes, but recast into a unit of the same length and height without core holes. For example, an 8-in. hollow block may be between 52 and 62 percent solid; and this value is shown in the ordinary laboratory compressive strength reports. Multiplying the percentage solid by the actual unit thickness (usually $\frac{3}{8}$ in. less than the nominal size) gives the equivalent thickness. Thus, for a nominal 8-in. hollow unit (actual thickness 7.625 in.), that is reported to be 54 percent solid, the equivalent thickness is 7.625×0.54 or 4.1 in. where walls are plastered, stuccoed, or faced with bricks, the thickness of plaster, stucco, or brick may be included in determining the equivalent thickness.

Table 6-7H. Wood Stud Walls and Partitions (Combustible)

(Bearing and nonbearing: 2- by 4-in. studs spaced 16 in. on centers, fire stopped)

Material	Fire Resistance Rating			
	Partition Hollow		Partition Filled with Mineral Wool†	
	Hr	Min	Hr	Min

Plasterless Types of Construction

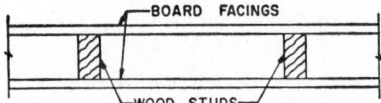

The following are applied to both sides of studs:

Material	Hr	Min	Hr	Min
Sheathing boards (tongue-and-groove) $\frac{3}{4}$ in. thick	—	20	—	35
Gypsum wallboard, $\frac{3}{8}$ in. thick	—	25	—	—
Gypsum wallboard, $\frac{1}{2}$ in. thick (nonload-bearing only for mineral wool filled)	—	40	1	—
Gypsum wallboard, $\frac{3}{8}$ in. thick, in two layers each face	1	—	—	—
Gypsum wallboard, $\frac{1}{2}$ in. thick, in two layers each face	1	30	—	—
Gypsum wallboard, $\frac{1}{2}$ in. thick, Type X*, one layer each face	—	45	—	—
Gypsum wallboard, $\frac{5}{8}$ in. thick, Type X*, one layer each face	1	—	—	—
Gypsum wallboard, $\frac{5}{8}$ in. thick, Type X*, on fire-retardant wood fiberboard, $\frac{1}{2}$ in. thick	1	—	—	—
Fir plywood, $\frac{1}{4}$ in. thick	—	10	—	—
Fir plywood, $\frac{3}{8}$ in. thick	—	15	—	—

Table 6-7H. (Cont.)

Material	Fire Resistance Rating			
	Partition Hollow		Partition Filled with Mineral Wool†	
	Hr	Min	Hr	Min

Plasterless Types of Construction

Material	Hr	Min	Hr	Min
Fir plywood, $\frac{1}{2}$ in. thick	—	20	—	—
Fir plywood, $\frac{5}{8}$ in. thick	—	25	—	—
Cement-asbestos board, $\frac{3}{16}$ in. thick	—	10	—	40
Cement-asbestos board, $\frac{3}{16}$ in. thick, on gypsum wallboard, $\frac{3}{8}$ in. thick	1	—	—	—
Cement-asbestos board, $\frac{3}{16}$ in. thick, on gypsum wallboard, $\frac{1}{2}$ in. thick	1	25	—	—

Plaster and Lath Construction

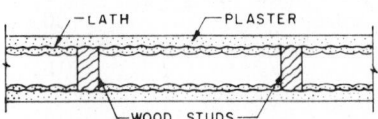

The following are applied to both sides of studs:‡

Material	Hr	Min	Hr	Min
Gypsum-sand plaster, 1:2, 1:3, $\frac{1}{2}$ in. thick on wood lath	—	30	1	—
Lime-sand plaster, 1:5, 1:7.5, $\frac{1}{2}$ in. thick on wood lath	—	30	—	45
Gypsum-sand plaster, 1:2, 1:2, $\frac{1}{2}$ in. thick on $\frac{3}{8}$ in. perforated gypsum lath	1	—	—	—
Gypsum-sand plaster, 1:2, 1:2, $\frac{3}{4}$ in. thick on metal lath	1	—	1	30
Gypsum lath, $\frac{1}{2}$ in. thick, Type X*, and $\frac{1}{2}$ in. gypsum-sand plaster, each face	1	—	—	—
Gypsum wallboard, $\frac{1}{2}$ in. thick, Type X*, and $\frac{1}{16}$ in. gypsum plaster, each face	1	—	—	—
Portland cement-lime-sand plaster, 1:1/30:2, 1:1/30:3 and asbestos-fiber plaster, $\frac{7}{8}$ in. thick on metal lath	1	—	—	—
Gypsum-vermiculite, or perlite plaster, 100 lb gypsum to $2\frac{1}{2}$ cu ft aggregate, $\frac{1}{2}$ in. thick on $\frac{3}{8}$ in. perforated gypsum lath	1	—	—	—
Gypsum perlite plaster, 1:2, $\frac{3}{4}$ in. thick on metal lath	1	—	—	—

Exterior Bearing Wall

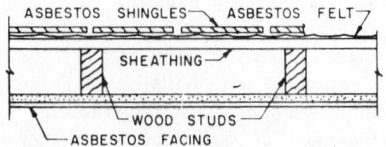

Material	Hr	Min	Hr	Min
Outside: Cement-asbestos shingles, $\frac{5}{32}$ in. thick, on layer of asbestos felt on wood sheathing, $\frac{3}{4}$ in. thick, on wood studs. Inside: Cement-asbestos facing, $\frac{1}{8}$ in. thick on fiberboard, $\frac{7}{16}$ in. thick	—	30	—	—
Outside: Gypsum sheathing, $\frac{1}{2}$ in. thick. Inside: 1:2 gypsum-sand plaster, $\frac{1}{2}$ in. thick on $\frac{3}{8}$ in. perforated gypsum lath	1	30	—	—

Note: For other similar constructions, see UL *Building Materials List*.
* See footnote ‡ to Table 6-7K.
† Mineral wool fill requires some degree of anchorage so as to be held in place after partition facing has been burned away.
‡ See Table 6-7I for one side ratings.

Table 6-7I. Various Finishes Over Wood Framing, One Side (Combustible) with Exposure on Finish Side

(See Table 6-7H for 2-side ratings)

Material	Fire Resistance Rating* Min
Fiberboard, $\frac{1}{2}$ in. thick	5
Fiberboard, flameproofed, $\frac{1}{2}$ in. thick	10
Fiberboard, $\frac{1}{2}$ in. thick, with $\frac{1}{2}$ in. 1:2, 1:2 gypsum-sand plaster	15
Gypsum wallboard, $\frac{3}{8}$ in. thick	10
Gypsum wallboard, $\frac{1}{2}$ in. thick	15
Gypsum wallboard, $\frac{5}{8}$ in. thick	20
Gypsum wallboards, laminated, two $\frac{3}{8}$ in.	28
Gypsum wallboards, laminated, one $\frac{3}{8}$ in. plus one $\frac{1}{2}$ in. thick	37
Gypsum wallboards, laminated, two $\frac{1}{2}$ in. thick	47
Gypsum wallboards, laminated, two $\frac{5}{8}$ in. thick	60
Gypsum lath, plain or indented, $\frac{3}{8}$ in. thick, with $\frac{1}{2}$ in. 1:2, 1:2 gypsum-sand plaster	20
Gypsum lath, perforated, $\frac{3}{8}$ in. thick, with $\frac{1}{2}$ in. 1:2, 1:2 gypsum-sand plaster	30
Gypsum-sand plaster, 1:2, 1:3, $\frac{1}{2}$ in. thick, on wood lath	15
Lime-sand plaster, 1:5, 1:7.5, $\frac{1}{2}$ in. thick, on wood lath	15
Gypsum-sand plaster, 1:2, 1:2, $\frac{3}{4}$ in. thick, on metal lath (no paper backing)	15
Neat gypsum plaster, $\frac{3}{4}$ in. thick on metal lath (no paper backing)†	30
Neat gypsum plaster, 1 in. thick, on metal lath (no paper backing)†	35
Lime-sand plaster, 1:5, 1:7.5, $\frac{3}{4}$ in. thick, on metal lath (no paper backing)	10
Portland cement plaster, $\frac{3}{4}$ in. thick, on metal lath (no paper backing)	10
Gypsum-sand plaster, 1:2, 1:3, $\frac{3}{4}$ in. thick, on paper-backed metal lath	20

* From National Bureau of Standards BMS-92.
† Unsanded wood-fiber plaster.

Ceilings

The method of attaching ceilings is a major factor in determining the fire resistance of floors. The nailing of plaster bases of gypsum lath, metal lath, or gypsum wallboards to the soffits of wood joists is often critical. The longer thinner nails, particularly those with cement coatings, conduct less heat to char the wood surrounding them than do the common types of wire nails. Nails in gypsum lath or gypsum wall board should not have the heads sunk below the surface in a manner to crush the friable gypsum core. The minimum sizes of nails for the attachment of metal lath may be 6d common wire nails or 6d cement-coated nails, driven slightly inclined not less than $1\frac{1}{4}$ in. into the joist and bent over, or $1\frac{1}{2}$-in. $11\frac{1}{2}$-gage barbed roofing nails driven full depth. The spacing of such nails should not exceed 6 in. along each support. Thin nails such as box nails or the cement-coated types of greater length which provide greater depth of penetration than previously mentioned nails, give increased fire resistance.

Self-tapping screws, made particularly for the attachment of gypsum boards, offer greater holding power and less damage to the core materials than do nails. Such screws can be used to attach wall boards to either wood or cold-rolled channels without previous drilling.

Consideration must also be given to the character of the plaster base with respect to loosening of plaster mixes from

Table 6-7J. Load-Bearing Steel-Framed Brick-Veneered Walls

Materials	Fire Resistance Rating			
	Plaster Side Exposed		Brick-Faced Side Exposed	
	Hr	Min	Hr	Min
On outside, 1-in. magnesium oxysulfate wood-fiberboard sheathing attached to studs, 1-in. air space, and $3\frac{3}{4}$-in. brick secured with metal ties to steel frame every fifth course. Inside facing of $\frac{7}{8}$ in. of 1:2 sanded gypsum plaster on metal lath secured directly to studs	1	45	4	—
Same as above except with $\frac{7}{8}$-in. gypsum vermiculite or perlite plaster for inside facing	2	—	4	—
On outside, $\frac{1}{2}$-in. wood-fiberboard sheathing next to studs, $\frac{3}{4}$-in. air space formed with $\frac{3}{4}$-in. by $1\frac{5}{8}$-in. wood strips placed over the fiberboard and secured to the studs; paper-backed wire lath nailed to these strips, $3\frac{3}{4}$-in. brick veneer held in place by filling a $\frac{3}{4}$-in. space between the brick and the paper-backed lath with mortar. Inside facing of $\frac{3}{4}$-in. neat† gypsum plaster on metal lath attached to $\frac{5}{16}$-in. plywood strips secured to the edges of the studs. Rated "combustible" because of the sheathing	1	30	4	—
On outside, paper-backed wire lath attached to studs and $3\frac{3}{4}$-in. brick veneer held in place by filling a 1-in. space between the brick and lath with mortar. Inside facing of 1-in. paper-enclosed mineral wool blanket weighing 0.6 lb per sq ft attached to studs, metal lath or paper-backed lath laid over the blanket and attached to the studs, and $\frac{3}{4}$-in. gypsum plaster, 1:2, 1:3	4	—	5	—

† Unsanded wood-fiber plaster.

the base on application of heat sufficient to char combustible surfaces. The use of wire, or better yet, wire fabric, to reinforce the plaster mixes applied to such plaster bases assures increased fire resistance. Clearances for longitudinal expansion of metal furring members are required to prevent damage from buckling. The tendency of certain plaster bases and plaster mixes to expand or contract with changes in atmospheric humidity should also be given consideration where resultant cracking might affect the fire resistance of structures incorporating such plaster.

Suspended ceilings with openings for air diffusers and light troffers should be designed so that such openings are not points of vulnerability to fire. Continuous construction above recesses for lighting fixtures and properly designed self-closing dampers for air ducts provide protection.

Beams, Girders, and Trusses

Protections for steel beams, girders, and trusses, such as encasements of concrete, clay, tile, or gypsum blocks, are now often superseded by plastered or sprayed-on applications applied either to a furred plaster base, such as expanded metal lath, or to the surface of the member to be

Table 6-7K. Solid Partitions: Nonbearing

Materials	Fire Resistance Rating	
	Hr	Min
Sheathing planks (tongue-and-groove), in 2 layers, each ¾ in. thick (1 in. nominal) and with joints staggered	—	15*
Same, with layer of 30-lb asbestos felt between planks	—	25*
Planking, pine (tongue-and-groove), 2 in. thick (nominal), set vertically	—	12*
Wallboard, ⅜-in. gypsum, full height facings on two thicknesses ½-in. coreboard, full height, cemented with staggered vertical joints to form 1¾-in. thick partition, external joints finish taped	1	—
Wallboard, ⅝-in. gypsum, Type X‡, full height facings, cemented and nailed or screwed to ribs made of two thicknesses of ½-in. gypsum board 3½ or 6½ in. wide and to 1- by 1⅝-in. wood runners top and bottom, external joints finished taped	1	—
Wallboard, ½-in. gypsum, full height, nailed and cemented to 1-in.-thick coreboard factory laminated from two ½-in.-thick by 24-in.-wide coreboards with staggered edges, external joints staggered, butted and finish taped with joint finisher	2	—
Gypsum tile, 3 in. thick, cored	1	—
Gypsum tile, 4 in. thick, cored	1	—
Gypsum tile, 3 in. solid, no cores	3	—
Gypsum tile, 3 in. cored, ½ in. of 1:3 gypsum-sand plaster on each side	3	—
Gypsum tile, 4 in. cored, ½ in. of 1:3 gypsum-sand plaster on each side	4	—
Gypsum-vermiculite or perlite plaster, 1½:2, 1½:3 by vol., ¾ in. thick on each side of ½-in. gypsum lath, vertical full height, tied to floor and ceiling runners, no studs	1	30
Gypsum-sand plaster, 1:2, 1:3 by wt, ¾ in. thick on each side of ½-in. gypsum lath vertical full height, tied to floor and ceiling runners, no studs	1	—
Partition tile, burned clay, 4 in. thick, 1 cell in thickness	—	10†
Cinder block, 4 in. thick, solid	1†	—
Cinder block, 6 in. thick, 1 cell in thickness	1	15†
Calcareous gravel concrete tile, 4 in. thick, 65 percent solid	—	45†
Calcareous gravel concrete tile, 8 in. thick, 55 percent solid	2	30

  * Combustible.
  † When plastered on both sides with ½-in. 1:3 gypsum-sand plaster, the tile partition described has 45-min fire resistance and the cinder block and 4-in. concrete tile assemblies described have 2-hr fire resistance.
  ‡ Type X gypsum wallboard designates gypsum wallboard with a specially formulated core which provides greater fire resistance than regular gypsum wallboard of the same thickness.

protected. The applications may be conventional plasters of portland or gypsum cements combined with appropriate aggregates, or one of the many combinations of mineral fibers with binders such as asbestos or mixtures of asbestos and artificial fibers of mineral wool or fiberglass. While affording equal protection from fire and weighing anywhere from 20 to 60 percent of the first mentioned encasements, the latter do not have equal resistance to damage from impacts. Fire tests have shown that sprayed-on protection made with portland cement and sand, such as Gunite, spalls badly when exposed to fire. The addition of an aggregate to afford yielding to thermal strains appears to

Table 6-7L. Steel-Framed Partitions: Bearing and Nonbearing

Material	Fire Resistance Rating	
	Hr	Min
Hollow Steel-Framed Partitions: Bearing		

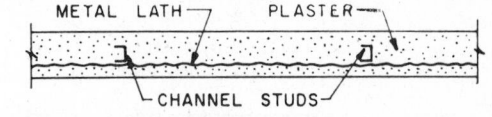

Stiffened expanded metal lath, attached to 1-section studs, spaced 24 in. on centers, 1-in. neat gypsum plaster	2	30
Same as above, except ¾-in. unsanded wood-fiber gypsum plaster	1	30
Same as above, except ¾-in. gypsum-sand plaster, 1:2, 1:2 mix	1	—

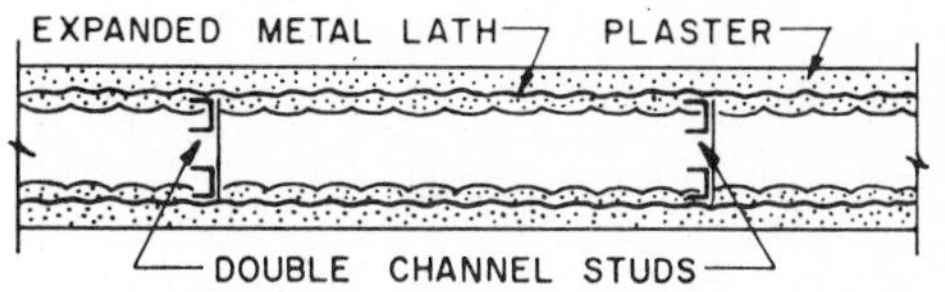

Hollow Partitions, Plaster and Metal or Gypsum Lath on Metal Studs: Nonbearing (Not less than 2-in. air space)

Gypsum-sand plaster, 1:2, 1:2, both sides, ¾ in. thick, on metal lath	1	—
Gypsum-sand plaster, 1:2, 1:2, both sides, ½ in. thick, on ⅜-in. gypsum lath	1	—
Gypsum-sand plaster, 1:2, 1:3, both sides, ⅞ in. thick, on metal lath	1	—
Gypsum-perlite plaster, 1:2.5, both sides, on metal lath 1 in. thick	2	—
Unsanded wood-fiber gypsum plaster, both sides, ¾ in. thick, on metal lath	1	30
Portland cement-sand plaster, 1:2, 1:3, plus 3 lb asbestos fiber per bag of cement, both sides, ⅞ in. thick, on metal lath	1	—

Hollow Partitions, Metal Studs: Nonbearing

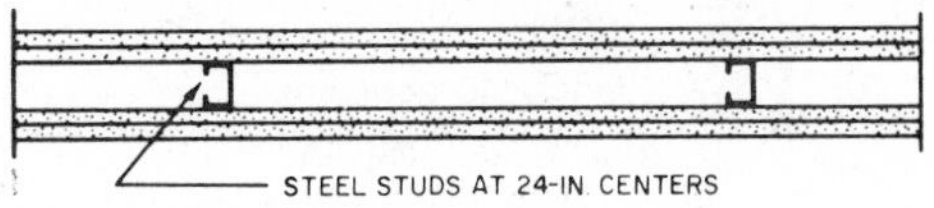

Mineral board, ½ in. thick, and ⅝-in. Type X* gypsum wallboard on each face of 2½-in. studs	2	—
Gypsum wallboard, ½-in. Type X*, and 1/16-in. 1:2 gypsum-sand plaster on each face of 2½-in. studs	1	—
Gypsum lath, ⅜-in. Type X*, and ½-in. 1:2, 1:3 gypsum-sand plaster on each face of 2½-in. studs	1	—
Gypsum wallboard, ⅝ in., and ⅝-in. Type X* gypsum wallboard on each face of 1⅝-in. studs	2	—
Gypsum wallboard, ½-in. Type X*, two layers on each face of 1⅝-in. studs	2	—
Fiberglass board, ½ in., and ½-in. Type X* gypsum wallboard on each face of 1⅝-in. studs	1	—
Fiberglass board, ½ in., and ⅝-in. Type X* gypsum wallboard on each face of 1⅝-in. studs	1	30

Solid Partitions, Steel-Framed, Metal Lath: Nonbearing

Portland cement-sand plaster, 1:2, 1:3, 2 in. thick	—	30
Gypsum-sand plaster, 1:2, 2¼ in. thick	1	—
Unsanded wood-fiber gypsum plaster, 2 in. thick	1	45
Unsanded wood-fiber gypsum plaster, 2¼ in. thick	2	30
Unsanded wood-fiber gypsum plaster, 2½ in. thick	3	—

  * Type X gypsum wallboard designates gypsum wallboard with a specially formulated core which provides greater fire resistance than regular gypsum wallboard of the same thickness.

Table 6-7M. Steel Joist Floor or Roof Constructions

Joists			Thickness			Thickness	Fire Resistance Rating	
Type	Depth In.	Floor Slab	In.	Furring	Ceiling Kind	In.	Hr	Min
I or S*	8	T & G wood flooring on 2- by 2-in. wood strips	$\frac{25}{32}$	3.4-lb metal lath	Gypsum—sand plaster	$\frac{3}{4}$	—	45†
I or S*	8	T & G wood flooring on 2- by 2-in. wood strips	$1\frac{5}{8}$	3.4-lb metal lath	Gypsum—sand plaster	$\frac{3}{4}$	1†	—
I or S*	8	Reinforced concrete, precast concrete, or gypsum planks	2	3.4-lb metal lath	Gypsum—sand or portland cement-sand plaster	$\frac{3}{4}$	1	—
S	8	Reinforced concrete or precast gypsum tile	$2\frac{1}{4}$	3.4-lb metal lath	Gypsum—sand plaster, 1:2; 1:3 mix	$\frac{3}{4}$	2	—
S	10	Reinforced concrete or reinforced gypsum tile or planks	2	3.4-lb metal lath	Neat†† gypsum, or gypsum-vermiculite plaster, 1:2; 1:3	$1\frac{3}{4}$	2	30
S	10	Reinforced concrete	$2\frac{1}{2}$	3.4-lb metal lath	Gypsum—sand plaster	$\frac{7}{8}$	2	30
S	8	Reinforced concrete	$2\frac{1}{2}$	3.4-lb metal lath	Gypsum-perlite or gypsum-vermiculite plaster, $1\frac{1}{2}$:2; $1\frac{1}{2}$:3	$\frac{3}{4}$	3	—
S	8	Reinforced concrete perlite, or vermiculite aggregate	$2\frac{1}{2}$	3.4-lb metal lath	Gypsum-perlite or gypsum-vermiculite plaster, $1\frac{1}{2}$:2; $1\frac{1}{2}$:3	$\frac{3}{4}$	3	—
S	10	Reinforced concrete, 1:2:4 gravel aggregate	$2\frac{1}{2}$	3-lb metal lath	Gypsum-vermiculite or gypsum-perlite plaster, $1\frac{1}{2}$:2; $1\frac{1}{2}$:3	1	4	—
S	10	Reinforced concrete, 1:2:4 gravel aggregate	2	Gypsum lath‡	Gypsum-perlite or gypsum-vermiculite plaster, $1\frac{1}{2}$:$2\frac{1}{2}$	$\frac{5}{8}$	1	—
S	10	Reinforced concrete, 1:2:4 gravel aggregate	2	Gypsum & wires§	Gypsum-perlite or gypsum-vermiculite plaster, $1\frac{1}{2}$:$2\frac{1}{2}$	$\frac{1}{2}$	2	—
S	10	Reinforced concrete, 1:2:4 gravel aggregate	2	Gypsum‖	Gypsum-vermiculite or perlite plaster, $1\frac{1}{2}$:2; $1\frac{1}{2}$:3	1	4	—
S	10	Reinforced concrete, 1:2:3.4 gravel	$2\frac{1}{2}$	Gypsum & wires§	Sprayed-on mineral fiber	$\frac{3}{4}$	3	—
S	10	Reinforced concrete, 1:2.5:3.5 gravel	2	Special Z section#	Special acoustical tiles (see UL list)	$\frac{5}{8}$	2	—
S	12	Reinforced concrete, gravel aggregate	2	Nailing channels 16 in. o.c.	Type X** wallboard	$\frac{5}{8}$	1	30
S	12	Reinforced concrete, 1:3:$3\frac{3}{8}$ gravel aggregate	2	$2\frac{3}{4}$ × $\frac{7}{8}$ in. 26-gage channels 14 in. o.c.	Type X** wallboard applied with No. 6 by 1-in. wallboard screws	$\frac{5}{8}$	1	30
S	10	Reinforced concrete, 1:2:4 gravel aggregate	2	25-gage nailing channels 16 in. o.c.	Gypsum wallboard applied with $1\frac{1}{4}$-in. long barbed nails $\frac{3}{8}$-in. diam. head	$\frac{5}{8}$	1	—

* I-beam or open web type joists.
† Combustible construction.
‡ All gypsum lath $\frac{3}{8}$-in. perforated type.
§ Gypsum lath and No. 20 gage wires attached to nailing channels. Wires attached diagonally to reinforce and support lath and plaster.
‖ One-in. hexagonal mesh wire fabric to reinforce plaster and hold up lath and plaster.
\# Special No. 25 gage galvanized steel Z runners 12 in. o. c.
** Type X gypsum wallboard designates gypsum wallboard with a specially formulated core which provides greater fire resistance than regular gypsum wallboard of the same thickness.
†† Unsanded wood-fiber plaster.

Table 6-7N. Wood Joist Floors with Wallboard Ceilings (Combustible)

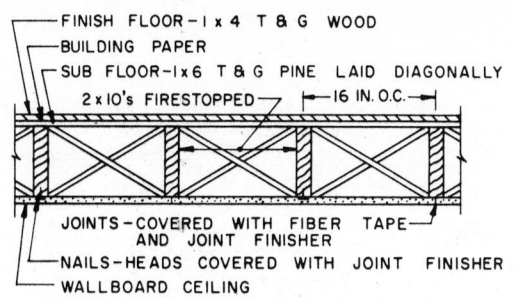

Type	Wallboard Thickness Inches	Core Materials	Nails Type	Size	Gage	Length Inches	Spacing Inches	Fire Resistance Rating Hr	Min
Gypsum	$\frac{5}{8}$	Type "X"* special fire-retardant gypsum	Cement-coated wire	6d	13	$1\frac{7}{8}$	6	1	—
Gypsum	$\frac{1}{2}$	Type "X"* special fire-retardant gypsum	Cement-coated wire	5d	$13\frac{1}{2}$	$1\frac{5}{8}$	6	—	45
Gypsum	$\frac{3}{8}$	Type "X"* special fire-retardant gypsum	Cement-coated wire	4d	14	$1\frac{3}{8}$	6	—	30
Two thicknesses of gypsum	$\frac{1}{2} + \frac{1}{2}$	Gypsum	Box wire	5d(1) 6d(2)	14 $10\frac{1}{4}$	$1\frac{3}{4}$ $2\frac{1}{4}$	18 6	1†	—
Two thicknesses of gypsum	$\frac{3}{8} + \frac{1}{2}$	Gypsum	Plasterboard cement-coated	$1\frac{1}{2}$ in. 6d	13 13	$1\frac{1}{2}$ $1\frac{7}{8}$	7 6	—	40
Two thicknesses of gypsum	$\frac{1}{2} + \frac{3}{8}$	Gypsum	Plasterboard cement-coated	$1\frac{1}{2}$ in. 6d	13 13	$1\frac{1}{2}$ $1\frac{7}{8}$	7 6	—	35
Two thicknesses of gypsum‡	$\frac{3}{8} + \frac{3}{8}$	Gypsum	Box	$4\frac{1}{2}$d(1) $4\frac{1}{2}$d(2)	— —	$1\frac{1}{2}$ $1\frac{1}{2}$	6 6	—	35
Gypsum	$\frac{1}{2}$	Gypsum	Box	$4\frac{1}{2}$d	15	$1\frac{1}{2}$	6	—	25
Gypsum§	$\frac{3}{8}$	Gypsum	Box	$4\frac{1}{2}$d	15	$1\frac{1}{2}$	6	—	25
None‖	—	—	—	—	—	—	—	—	14
Acoustical Tile	$\frac{5}{8}$	12- by 12-in. mineral fiber tiles mounted on special channels						1	—

* Type X gypsum wallboard designates gypsum wallboard with a specially formulated core which provides greater fire resistance than regular gypsum wallboard of the same thickness.
† 1-in. hexagonal mesh 20-gage wire fabric between wallboards nailed with 8d nails 8 in. o. c.
‡ NBS test on floor $4\frac{1}{2}$ by 9 ft; joints of wallboard staggered, but no tape and joint finisher.
§ NBS test: bottom of ceiling covered with 14 lb asbestos paper applied with paperhanger's paste and casein paint.
‖ NBS test on 2 specimens of open-joist floors, each $4\frac{1}{2}$ by 9 ft; fire endurance 15 min and 12 min.
Note: For other similar constructions, see UL *Building Materials List*.

be necessary. The National Bureau of Standards tests (Building Materials and Structure Report 131) gave up to 100 percent increase in fire resistance of Gunite when wood sawdust was used as replacement of as much as 50 percent by volume of the usual 1:4 proportion of sand aggregates.[9] Likewise, tests have also shown that the protection afforded steel columns by gypsum concrete is increased by the use of wood shavings as aggregates. The upper limit of such increase was about 37 percent when the shaving content of the mix was about 1/7 of that of gypsum stucco by weight.

Table 6-7D gives the permissible minimum thicknesses of portland cement concrete encasement prescribed for the protection of steel members of trusses and girders. These are also applicable to beams serving as elements of floors.

Protective coverings of plaster or sprayed-on application to furred metal lath beam encasements are given in Table 6-7S.

Beam encasements of sprayed fiber or cementitious mixtures with gypsum cement bases are given in Table 6-7T.

Columns

Numerous fire tests have demonstrated that structural steel columns must be insulated from attainment of temperatures in the ranges above 1,000°F if they are to support loads imposing stresses represented by the commonly used formulas for column design. Structural steel columns loaded to stresses represented by the formula $(17,620 - 72\frac{1}{r})$psi were found in fire tests at Underwriters Laboratories to fail at temperatures represented by formula $(1040 + 1.8\frac{1}{r} \pm 50)$°F for slenderness ratios ranging from 40 to 112. Design stresses for structural steel columns are currently somewhat higher and failure can be expected to occur at temperatures approximately 60°F lower than given by the formula.

Among the ninety-one columns subjected to fire tests at UL in the 1917-1918 series were seventy-one steel columns of nine section types, eight hollow, round cast iron columns,

Table 6-70.   Wood Joist Floors with Plaster Ceilings (Combustible)

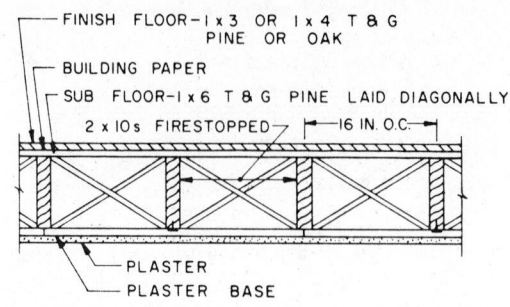

Plaster Base						Plaster					Fire Resistance Rating	
	Thickness in inches or wt. per sq yd	Nails							Thickness	Ceiling Thickness		
		Size or Length		Head Diam	Spacing							
Type		Inches	Gage	Inches	Inches	Type	Aggregate	Mix	Inches	Inches	Hr	Min
Wood lath	$\frac{3}{8}$	3d	15	$\frac{11}{64}$	$1\frac{7}{8}$	Lime	Sand	1:4½	$\frac{5}{8}$	1	—	30
Wood lath	$\frac{3}{8}$	3d	15	$\frac{11}{64}$	$1\frac{7}{8}$	Gypsum	Sand	{1:2, 1:3}	$\frac{1}{2}$	$\frac{7}{8}$	—	35
Gypsum, perforated	$\frac{3}{8}$	$1\frac{1}{8}$	13	$\frac{5}{16}$	$3\frac{1}{2}$	Gypsum	Sand	1:2	$\frac{1}{2}$	$\frac{7}{8}$	—	30
Gypsum, perforated	$\frac{3}{8}$	$1\frac{1}{8}$	13	$\frac{3}{8}$	$3\frac{1}{2}$	Gypsum	Sand	1:2	$\frac{1}{2}$	$\frac{7}{8}$	—	45
Gypsum, perforated	$\frac{3}{8}$*	$1\frac{3}{4}$	12	$\frac{1}{2}$	$3\frac{1}{2}$	Gypsum	Sand	1:2	$\frac{1}{2}$	$\frac{7}{8}$	1	—
Gypsum, plain	$\frac{3}{8}$†	{5d, 8d}	{13, 12½}	{$\frac{5}{16}$, $\frac{5}{16}$}	{$3\frac{1}{2}$, 8}	Gypsum	Vermiculite or perlite	1½:2½	$\frac{1}{2}$	$\frac{7}{8}$	1	40
Gypsum, perforated	$\frac{3}{8}$	4d	—		$3\frac{1}{2}$	Gypsum	Vermiculite or perlite	1½:2½	$\frac{1}{2}$	$\frac{7}{8}$	1	—
Metal lath	3.4 lb	{6d, $1\frac{1}{4}$}	{11½, 11}	{$\frac{1}{4}$, $\frac{3}{8}$}	{6, 6}	Gypsum	Sand	{1:2, 1:3}	$\frac{3}{4}$	$\frac{3}{4}$	—	45
Metal lath	3.4 lb	$1\frac{1}{2}$	11	$\frac{7}{16}$	6	Gypsum	Sand	{1:2, 1:3}	$\frac{3}{4}$	$\frac{3}{4}$	1	—
Metal lath	3.0 lb	8d	11½	$\frac{1}{4}$	6‡	Gypsum	Sand	{1:2, 1:3}	$\frac{3}{4}$	$\frac{3}{4}$	1	15
Metal lath	3.4 lb	$1\frac{1}{2}$	11½	$\frac{7}{16}$	5	Portland cement§	Sand	{1:2, 1:3}	$\frac{3}{4}$	$\frac{3}{4}$	1	—
Metal lath	3.4 lb	$1\frac{1}{2}$	11	$\frac{7}{16}$	$5\frac{1}{2}$	Gypsum	Vermiculite or perlite	{1½:2, 1⅓:3}	$\frac{3}{4}$	$\frac{3}{4}$	1	30

* Three-in.-wide strips of metal lath with two $1\frac{3}{4}$-in. 12-gage $\frac{1}{2}$-in. head barbed roofing nails in each joist covering joints of lath to reinforce plaster.
† Plaster reinforced with 1-in. hexagonal mesh wire fabric (1 lb/sq yd) nailed to joists with 8d $2\frac{3}{4}$-in.-long cement-coated nails spaced 8 in. on centers at each joist.
‡ Additional support for metal lath by ties of 18-gage wire spaced 27 by 32 in. and nailed 2 in. up on sides of joists.
§ Three-lb asbestos fiber and 15-lb hydrated lime per bag of cement added.

one of which was filled with concrete; six concrete columns, four of round section and two square, including three with limestone and three with trap rock aggregates; six timber columns, four of them of long leaf yellow pine and two of Douglas fir. Two columns were of unprotected steel pipe filled with concrete, one having starred angles in the core. One column or more of each type was subjected to fire test without benefit of protective insulation, nine steel columns, representative of six section types, had no protection other than that afforded by concrete filling internal or reentrant spaces. The protection afforded 8-in., $34\frac{1}{2}$-lb rolled H columns by concrete is illustrated by these examples: unprotected, the column failed at $11\frac{1}{4}$ min; when protected by reentrant fill of granite concrete, failure occurred at $48\frac{1}{4}$ min; when encased with 2-in. thickness of trap rock concrete, failure occurred at $278\frac{1}{2}$ min; and when encased with a 4-in. thickness, failure occurred at 478 min. Similarly, a 6-in. plate and angle column, without protection, failed at $19\frac{1}{4}$ min; with reentrant spaces filled with trap

rock concrete, failure occurred at $44\frac{1}{2}$ min; with 2-in. concrete encasement, failure was reached at $233\frac{1}{4}$ min; and with 4-in. thick round encasement, failure occurred at $454\frac{1}{2}$ min. Encasements of limestone concrete proved more effective; for example, two 8-in. $34\frac{1}{2}$-lb H columns encased with 2-in. thickness of limestone concrete failed in the tests at $393\frac{3}{4}$ and $429\frac{1}{4}$ min. Gypsum concrete having $12\frac{1}{2}$ percent by weight wood shavings provides protection comparable to that of limestone concrete. (NBS Research Paper 563, Fire Tests of Columns Protected with Gypsum, 1933.)[10]

Encasements of brick, hollow clay tiles, and gypsum blocks were less effective than concrete. In a number of instances encasements of such units fell away to expose the column shaft to fire much before the effective insulating value of the material had been used. Even wire ties or metal bonding of units were not uniformly effective in holding such covering materials in place.

Portland cement-sand plaster on metal lath provided protection for steel columns averaging in point of time

Table 6-7P. Concrete Floor Constructions

Material	Fire Resistance Rating	
	Hr	Min

Reinforced Concrete
(Free or partly restrained, 1500–2500 psi)

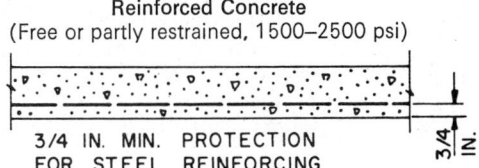

3/4 IN. MIN. PROTECTION FOR STEEL REINFORCING

3 in. thick	—	45
4 in. thick	1	15
6 in. thick; 1-in. minimum protection for steel	2	—

Reinforced Concrete on Precast Joists

I IN. MIN. PROTECTION FOR STEEL REINFORCING

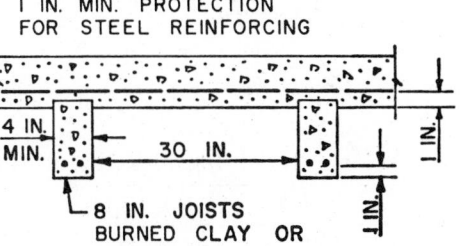

4 IN. MIN. 30 IN. 8 IN. JOISTS BURNED CLAY OR EXPANDED SLAG AGGREGATE

Reinforced concrete, 1:3½:4, 3 in. thick, no ceiling	—	45
Reinforced concrete, 1:3½:4, 3 in. thick, ceiling of gypsum wallboard ½ in. thick, nailed to wood, strips wired to joists	1	—

Combination of Tile and Concrete Floors

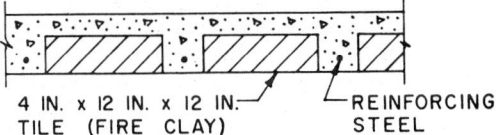

4 IN. x 12 IN. x 12 IN. TILE (FIRE CLAY) — REINFORCING STEEL

Concrete 2 in. or 1½ in. thick, and fire clay tile 6 in. or 4 in. thick, no ceiling finish	1	—
Concrete 1½ in. thick, and tile 4 in. thick with gypsum-sand plaster ceiling finish, 1:3 mix, ⅝ in. thick	1	30
Concrete 2 in. thick, and fire clay tile 6 in. thick with gypsum plaster ceiling finish, 1:3 mix, ⅝ in. thick	2	—
Concrete 2½ in. thick, limestone aggregate 4 in. thick, expanded slag concrete tile	3	—

Reinforced Concrete Ribbed Slab

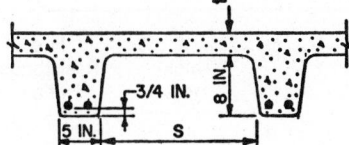

3/4 IN. 8 IN. 5 IN. S

Concrete, ribbed slab, limestone aggregate, t = 1½ in., S = 20 in.	—	20
Concrete, ribbed slab, limestone aggregate, t = 2½ in., S = 20 in.	—	45
Same with metal lath and ⅞-in. gypsum-sand plaster ceiling, 1:2, 1:3 mix	2	30
Concrete, ribbed slab, limestone aggregate, t = 3 in., S = 30 in.	1	—

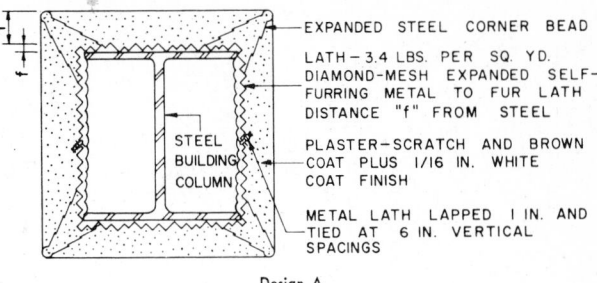

EXPANDED STEEL CORNER BEAD

LATH – 3.4 LBS. PER SQ. YD. DIAMOND-MESH EXPANDED SELF-FURRING METAL TO FUR LATH DISTANCE "f" FROM STEEL

PLASTER–SCRATCH AND BROWN COAT PLUS 1/16 IN. WHITE COAT FINISH

METAL LATH LAPPED I IN. AND TIED AT 6 IN. VERTICAL SPACINGS

STEEL BUILDING COLUMN

Design A

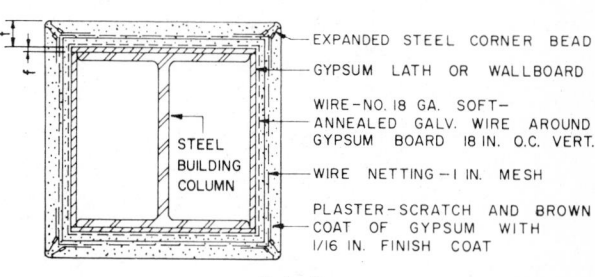

EXPANDED STEEL CORNER BEAD

GYPSUM LATH OR WALLBOARD

WIRE–NO. 18 GA. SOFT-ANNEALED GALV. WIRE AROUND GYPSUM BOARD 18 IN. O.C. VERT.

WIRE NETTING – I IN. MESH

PLASTER–SCRATCH AND BROWN COAT OF GYPSUM WITH 1/16 IN. FINISH COAT

STEEL BUILDING COLUMN

Design B

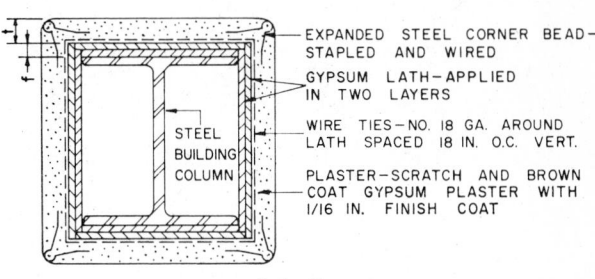

EXPANDED STEEL CORNER BEAD-STAPLED AND WIRED

GYPSUM LATH–APPLIED IN TWO LAYERS

WIRE TIES–NO. 18 GA. AROUND LATH SPACED 18 IN. O.C. VERT.

PLASTER–SCRATCH AND BROWN COAT GYPSUM PLASTER WITH 1/16 IN. FINISH COAT

STEEL BUILDING COLUMN

Design C

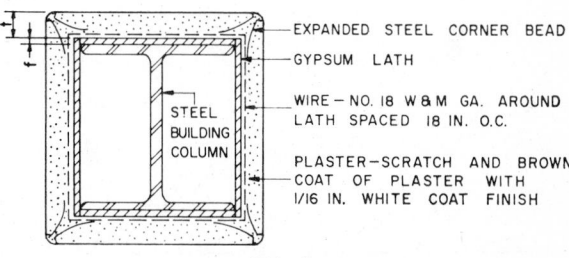

EXPANDED STEEL CORNER BEAD

GYPSUM LATH

WIRE–NO. 18 W & M GA. AROUND LATH SPACED 18 IN. O.C.

PLASTER–SCRATCH AND BROWN COAT OF PLASTER WITH 1/16 IN. WHITE COAT FINISH

STEEL BUILDING COLUMN

Design D

Fig. 6-7P. Steel column protection of lath and plaster, designs A, B, C, and D. For fire resistance ratings, see Table 6-7U. Note: Values given in tables of fire resistance of columns conform closely to the present standard method of reporting results of fire tests, rather than using two-thirds of the fire test endurance limits as has been done in some previously published values.

85 percent or more of that obtained with equal thicknesses of gypsum-sand plaster and about 70 percent or more of that obtained in tests of columns encased with metal lath and gypsum plaster with either vermiculite or perlite aggregate.

The results of sixteen fire tests on steel H columns encased in gypsum lath and gypsum plaster have demonstrated the effectiveness of that combination in protecting the column shaft from fire (NBS Building Materials and Structures Report 135).[11] Consistently better performance was indicated when both scratch and brown coat plaster mixes were one part gypsum plaster to 2½ parts aggregate

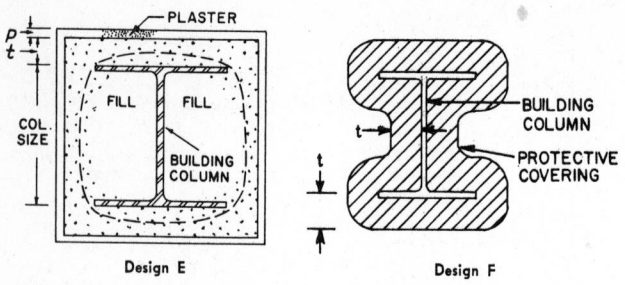

Fig. 6-7Q. Steel column protections of concrete, masonry or sprayed fibers, designs E and F. For fire resistance ratings, see Table 6-7V.

than when the scratch coat was 1:2 and the brown coat 1:3. Wire fabric, either applied on the lath or between the scratch and brown coats of the thicker applications, improved the performance in point of time to failure by about 20 percent in tests of over 3 hours duration.

Gypsum plasters applied on metal lath in thicknesses, including plaster key, comparable with the total thickness of both gypsum lath and plaster applied thereon, gave in fire tests comparable results, except that gypsum laths at the end of the tests, in several instances, fell away leaving the column shaft bare or partly bare.

The size of the steel column shaft would be expected to make a difference of some significance in results of fire

Table 6-7Q.   Floors of Concrete on Steel Floor and Form Units
(Plaster or Sprayed on Fire Protective Covering)

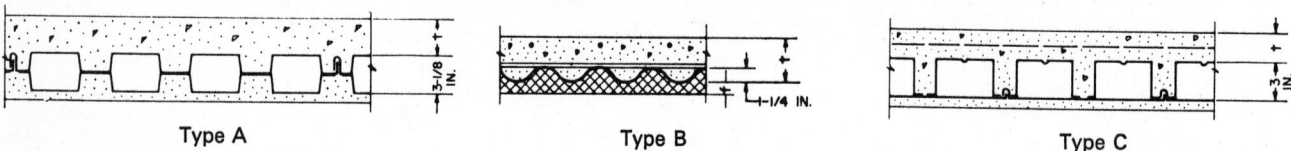

Type of Floor Unit	Thickness of Floor In.	Furring	Protective Covering Material	Application	Thickness In.	Fire Resistance Rating Hr	Fire Resistance Rating Min
A	$5\frac{5}{8}$	None	Mineral fibers applied to floor units	Sprayed	$\frac{1}{2}$ to 2	5	—
C	$5\frac{1}{2}$	None	Same	Sprayed	$1\frac{1}{2}$	5	—
A	$5\frac{5}{8}$	None	Vermiculite or perlite acoustical plastic	Sprayed	$1\frac{1}{16}$ to $1\frac{9}{16}$	4	—
B	$4\frac{1}{2}$	None	Same	Sprayed	$\frac{1}{2}$ to $1\frac{1}{4}$	4	—
B	$4\frac{1}{2}$	See Footnote*	Gypsum-vermiculite or perlite plaster	Troweled or Sprayed	$\frac{3}{8}$ to $1\frac{5}{8}$	4	—
C	4	None	Mineral fiber applied to floor units	Sprayed	$\frac{3}{4}$	3	—
A	$5\frac{5}{8}$	None	Vermiculite acoustical plastic, cellular floor units	Sprayed	$\frac{1}{2}$ to 2	2	—
B	$5\frac{1}{4}$	None	None†	—	—	2	—
B	$4\frac{1}{4}$	None	None‡	—	—	1	—
A	8	See Footnote§	Gypsum-vermiculite or perlite plaster. 100 lb gypsum to 2 cu ft for scratch coat and 3 cu ft for browncoat plaster, white finish $\frac{1}{16}$ in.	Troweled	$\frac{3}{8}$	4	—
A	8	See Footnote§	Same	Troweled	1	5	—
A	$6\frac{5}{8}$	See Footnote‖	Acoustical tiles, T & G edges with saw kerfs	Sheet metal clips	$\frac{3}{4}$	4	—

* Expanded metal lath tack welded or tied to bottom of corrugated steel floor units.
† Floor slab, limestone concrete, $5\frac{1}{4}$ in. thick.
‡ Floor slab, limestone concrete, $4\frac{1}{4}$ in. thick.
§ 24-gage, 3.4-lb, $\frac{3}{8}$-in. mesh expanded metal lath suspended $2\frac{1}{2}$ to $7\frac{1}{2}$ in. below floor units.
‖ Special furring system to which acoustical tiles are clipped $10\frac{3}{4}$ in. below floor units.

Table 6-7R.   Protected Steel Roof Deck Construction (Combustible)*

Above Deck Insulation†	Thickness In.	Plaster‡ Kind	Plaster‡ Mix Scratch	Plaster‡ Mix Brown	Thickness In.	Fire Resistance Rating Hr	Fire Resistance Rating Min
Cement bonded wood-fiberboard	$1\frac{1}{2}$	Gypsum-sand	1:2	1:2	$\frac{7}{8}$	2	—
Wood fiberboard, one thickness or two	1	Gypsum-sand	1:2	1:3	$\frac{3}{4}$	1	30
Wood fiberboard, T & G wood sheathing or plywood	$\frac{3}{4}$	Gypsum-sand	1:2	1:3	$\frac{3}{4}$	1	—

* The constructions shown are combustible by reason of either combustible insulation between the formed steel deck and asphalt roofing, or mop coating of asphalt on steel deck.

† Concrete made with lightweight aggregates and one and one-half times as thick will qualify construction as noncombustible except for asphalt.

‡ Plaster shown is for suspended ceilings. Sprayed on fiber or plaster preparations giving equal protections can be substituted.

tests in which the protective cover is of lath and plaster as large columns require more heat transmission through the protective cover to raise their temperature.

Tables 6-7U and 6-7V give respectively the fire resistance of steel columns with lath and plaster coverings and those encased with concrete, masonry, or sprayed-on applications.

Tables 6-7W and 6-7X give respectively the fire resistance of concrete and miscellaneous column constructions.

C. Structural Systems

The stability of a structure is important because the premature failure of a structural element may trigger a more extensive building collapse or broaching of fire barriers.

Reinforced Concrete Systems

Reinforced concrete construction has had a good experience record with regard to structural collapse. Because concrete has a low thermal conductivity and a low thermal capacity, it provides an effective cover for reinforcing steel. Figure 6-7R[9, 12] shows the temperature gradient in a 6-in. slab after a 2-hr fire exposure. Although undoubtedly the moisture in the concrete greatly influences the values, the significant feature is the fact that the temperatures vary considerably throughout the thickness, even after a considerable time exposure.

This feature provides some insight into the reason that reinforced concrete systems usually perform comparatively well during fire exposure. Consider, for example, a con-

Table 6-7S. Furred Steel Beams with Noncombustible Protective Coverings

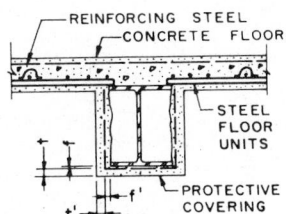

Und. Lab. Listing		Beam Depth In.	Furring			Protective Covering		Thickness		Fire Resistance Rating	
				Spacing							
Class	Design No.		Material	f In.	f′ In.	Material		t In.	t′ In.	Hr	Min
B-4	18	12	Rib lath, 3.4-lb $\frac{3}{8}$-in. diamond mesh	$\frac{3}{8}$	$2\frac{3}{8}$	Sprayed on fiber		2	2	5	—
B-4	19	10	Lath, 24-gage 3.4-lb $\frac{3}{8}$-in. mesh expanded metal	$\frac{3}{8}$	$\frac{3}{8}$	Gypsum-vermiculite or gypsum-perlite plaster, 1:2, 1:3		$1\frac{1}{2}$	$1\frac{1}{2}$	5	—
B-4	20	8	Rib lath, 24-gage 3.4-lb $\frac{3}{8}$-in.	$\frac{1}{2}$	$\frac{1}{2}$	Sprayed on fiber		$1\frac{1}{2}$	$1\frac{1}{4}$	4	—
B-4	8	12	Self furring lath, 3.4-lb $\frac{3}{8}$-in. diamond mesh	$\frac{3}{8}$	$\frac{3}{8}$	Gypsum-perlite plaster, 1:2		$1\frac{1}{2}$	$1\frac{1}{2}$	4	—
B-4	10	12 WF	Lath, 24-gage 3.4-lb diamond mesh expanded metal	$\frac{3}{8}$	$\frac{3}{8}$	Vermiculite acoustical plastic or plaster		2	2	4	—
B-4	16	12	Lath, 3.4-lb $\frac{3}{8}$-in. diamond mesh expanded metal	1	$\frac{7}{8}$	Sprayed on fiber		$1\frac{1}{8}$	$1\frac{1}{8}$	4	—
B-4	15	12	Rib lath, 24-gage 3.4-lb, $\frac{3}{8}$-in. mesh expanded metal	$\frac{5}{8}$	$\frac{5}{8}$	Gypsum-perlite plaster, 1:2$\frac{1}{2}$		$1\frac{1}{2}$	$1\frac{1}{2}$	4	—
B-4	24	8	Lath, 3.4-lb self furring $\frac{3}{8}$-in. mesh expanded metal	$\frac{3}{8}$	$\frac{3}{8}$	Cementitious mixture		2	2	4	—
B-4	29	8	Lath, 3.4-lb self furring $\frac{3}{8}$-in. mesh	$\frac{3}{8}$	$\frac{3}{8}$	Mill mixed gypsum plaster		$1\frac{1}{2}$	$1\frac{1}{2}$	4	—
C-3	12	12	Lath, 24-gage 3.4-lb $\frac{3}{8}$-in. mesh expanded metal	$\frac{1}{8}$	$\frac{1}{8}$	Gypsum-vermiculite plaster 1:2$\frac{1}{2}$		$1\frac{5}{8}$	$1\frac{5}{8}$	6	—
C-3	15	8	Lath, 3.4-lb, $\frac{3}{8}$-in. rib lath on No. 6 wire	$\frac{1}{2}$	$\frac{1}{2}$	Sprayed fibers		$1\frac{1}{2}$	$1\frac{1}{2}$	4	—
C-3	19	8 WF	Lath, 24-gage 3.4-lb $\frac{3}{8}$-in. mesh expanded metal	$\frac{3}{8}$	$\frac{3}{8}$	Mill mixed gypsum plaster		$1\frac{1}{4}$	$1\frac{1}{4}$	3	—
D-2	6	8 WF	Lath, 24-gage 3.4-lb. $\frac{3}{8}$-in. mesh expanded metal	$1\frac{3}{8}$	$\frac{3}{8}$	Mill mixed gypsum plaster		$1\frac{1}{8}$	$1\frac{1}{8}$	2	—
D-2	3	12	Lath, 24-gage 3.4-lb, $\frac{3}{8}$-in. mesh expanded metal	$\frac{1}{8}$	$\frac{1}{8}$	Gypsum-vermiculite plaster 1:2, 1:3		1	1	2	—
D-2	7	10	Lath, 24-gage 3.4-lb, $\frac{3}{8}$-in. mesh expanded metal	$\frac{3}{8}$	$\frac{3}{8}$	Gypsum-perlite acoustical plaster		$1\frac{3}{4}$	$1\frac{3}{4}$	2	—
E-1	3	12	Lath, 24-gage 3.4-lb, $\frac{3}{8}$-in. mesh expanded metal	$\frac{3}{8}$	$\frac{3}{8}$	Gypsum-perlite plaster 1:2, 1:3		1	1	1	—
E-1	6	12	Lath, 24-gage 3.4-lb, $\frac{3}{8}$-in. mesh expanded metal	$\frac{3}{8}$	$\frac{3}{8}$	Gypsum-perlite plaster 1:2, 1:3		$\frac{7}{8}$	$\frac{7}{8}$	1	—

Table 6-7T.   Steel Beams with Sprayed-on Cover Applied to Surfaces

(Adhesive, if required, applied before application of encasement)

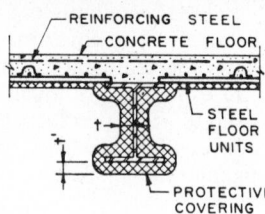

UL Listing		Depth of Beam, In.		Thickness, In.		Fire Resistance Rating	
Class	Design No.		Covering Material	t	t'	Hr	Min
B-4	25	8	Sprayed fiber	1⅞	1⅞	5	—
B-4	26	10	Sprayed fiber	3⅛	3⅛	4	—
B-4	28	8	Sprayed fiber	1¾	1¾	4	—
B-4	9	10	Sprayed fiber	2½	2½	3	—
C-3	9	12	Sprayed fiber	2½	2½	3	—
B-4	23	12	Cementitious mixture	2½	2½	4	—
D-2	—	12	Cementitious mixture	2⅛	2⅛	4	—
C-3	16	8	Spray plaster-cementitious mixture	2	2	3	—
D-1	—	12	Troweled mill mixed plaster	1	1	2	—

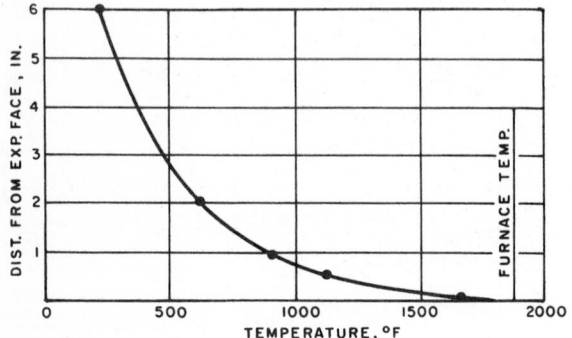

Fig. 6-7R.   *Thermal gradient in a 6-in. slab after 2-hr fire exposure (see Reference 12).*

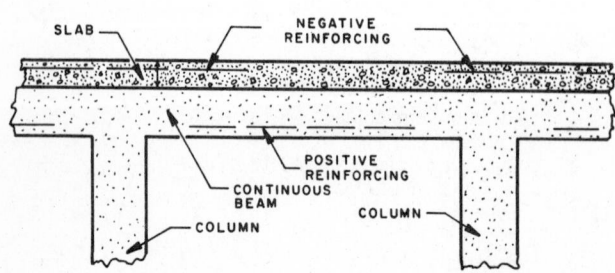

Fig. 6-7S.   *Monolithic reinforced concrete beam and slab.*

tinuous, monolithic reinforced concrete beam or slab, as shown in Figure 6-7S. Considering the temperature gradient of Figure 6-7S it will take some time before the tension steel at midspan is affected. Even after it reaches its yield value, the negative steel over the supports has not been seriously affected because of the insulating effect of the concrete and the moisture.

Continuous construction of this type has inherent strength capabilities far greater than statically determinate construction. Considerable stress redistribution can take place before collapse will occur. It takes time before excessive rotation will develop at all three necessary locations causing structural collapse of the member. Although the member is weakened by the fire, structural stability against collapse will remain for a considerable period of time.

A factor which can significantly reduce the capacity of a reinforced concrete member is its tendency to spall, thus exposing the reinforcing steel to a rapid temperature increase. Lightweight aggregates seem to be particularly resistant to spalling. In normal weight concrete, siliceous aggregates tend to spall much more readily than do calcareous aggregates. Sharp edges on structural members tend to spall more readily than do beveled or rounded edges.

Two types of spalling have been observed. During times of rapid temperature increase in concrete having a relatively high moisture content, an explosive spalling can occur. Apparently, when the moisture cannot move away from the heat rapidly enough a pressure develops, causing the concrete cover to spall explosively. The other type of spalling is merely a dropping away of the concrete without any explosive action.

The level of stress in a reinforced concrete member exposed to the elevated temperatures of a fire has a significant influence on its endurance. Table 6-7Y illustrates the effects of stress level on the fire endurance of reinforced concrete columns. The columns used for these tests[10] were 15×15 in. containing four No. 9 reinforcing bars. It can be seen that the magnitude of stress during a fire causes significant reductions in capacity. This is attributed primarily to the reduction in the mechanical properties of steel and concrete at elevated temperatures.

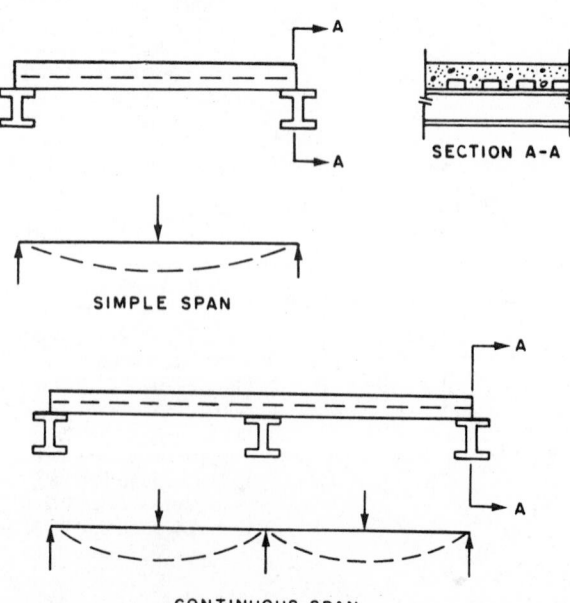

Fig. 6-7T.   *Influence of structural continuity on collapse mechanisms.*

Table 6-7U. Fire Resistance of Steel Columns with Lath and Plaster Protective Coverings

Type of Section	Size In.	Wt per Lin Ft Lb	Area of Metal Sq In.	Design	Plaster Type	Aggregate	Mix, Volumes	Thickness t† In.	Furring t† In.	Bond of Covering	Total Area of Materials Sq In.	Hr	Min	Notes
H	6	44	13	—	Portland cement & lime	Sand	1:1/10:2½	$\frac{7}{8}$	1	Metal lath	40	—	45	Metal lath furred out
H	6	31	9	—	Two thicknesses of above	Sand	1:1/10:2½	$\frac{7}{8}$ + $\frac{7}{8}$	1 & 1	Metal lath	80	1	30	Metal lath furred out
H	10	49	14.5	A	Gypsum-cement mixture	Light-weight*	Mill mix	1¾	$\frac{3}{8}$	Wire fabric	125	3	25	
H	10	49	14.5	A	Gypsum-cement mixture	Light-weight*	Mill mix	1⅞	$\frac{5}{8}$	Metal lath	125	4	—	½-in. channel behind lath
H	10	49	14.5	A	Gypsum	Light-weight*	1½:2 1½:3	1¾	$\frac{3}{8}$	Metal lath	125	4	—	Self furring lath
H	10	49	14.5	A	Gypsum	Light-weight*	1½:2 1½:3	1⅜	$\frac{3}{8}$	Metal lath	102	3	—	Self furring lath
H	10	49	14.5	A	Gypsum	Light-weight*	1½:2 1½:3	1	$\frac{3}{8}$	Metal lath	78	2	—	Self furring lath
H	10	49	14.5	B	Gypsum	Light-weight*	½:3½ ½:4	2⅛	½	18-gage wire & wire fabric	145	4	—	Gypsum lath
H	10	49	14.5	C	Gypsum	Light-weight*	1½:2 1½:3	1½	1	18-gage wire & wire fabric	140	4 to 4	15 to 40	Gypsum lath
H	10	49	14.5	B	Gypsum	Light-weight*	1½:2½	1½	½	18-gage wire & wire fabric	110	3	40	Gypsum lath
H	10	49	14.5	D	Gypsum	Light-weight*	1:2½	½	$\frac{3}{8}$	18-gage wire ties	53	1	20	Perforated gypsum lath
H	10	49	14.5	D	Gypsum	Light-weight*	1:2½	$\frac{5}{8}$	$\frac{3}{8}$	18-gage wire ties	60	1	30	Perforated gypsum lath
H	10	49	14.5	D	Gypsum	Light-weight*	1½:2 1½:3	1	$\frac{3}{8}$	18-gage wire ties	80	2	15	Perforated gypsum lath
H	10	49	14.5	D	Gypsum	Light-weight*	1½:2 1½:3	1½	$\frac{3}{8}$	18-gage wire ties	104	2	30	Perforated gypsum lath
O	7	51	15.5	—	Portland cement & lime	Sand	1:1/10:2½	1¼	$\frac{7}{8}$	$\frac{7}{8}$-in. rib lath	70	2	45	Metal lath on cast iron column

* Lightweight aggregate can be either perlite or vermiculite.
† Dimensions as shown in Figure 6-7P.

Structural Steel Systems

The structural integrity of structural steel framing subjected to elevated temperatures depends on such factors as degree of protection, continuity of construction, stress levels, and the size and shape of the section. Thermal expansion is also a factor that can cause failure of structural framing due to outward thermal forces or resulting eccentricity of compression members or both.

Figure 6-7T illustrates the effect of continuity on structural stability. The composite floor deck that is simply supported can readily collapse when the deflection at the center becomes excessive. The continuous floor deck, on the other hand, can support more load over a greater temperature increase because the continuity prevents immediate collapse. There is a general characteristic for statically indeterminate structures to exhibit better stability because the collapse mechanism requires more than one yield location before failure.

Unprotected structural steel trusses and open web joists are particularly vulnerable to elevated temperatures of a fire. An exposed joist system, for example, may collapse after only 5 or 10 min of exposure. To prevent this, membrane ceilings are installed to act as a barrier for the heat below the joists. As long as the ceiling remains unviolated, the floor system is protected. However, experience has shown that, either because of inadequate installation pro-

Table 6-7V.　Fire Resistance of Steel Columns Encased with Concrete, Masonry, or Sprayed Fibers

Steel Column				Protective Covering						Fire Resistance Rating		
Type of Section	Size In.	Wt per Lin Ft Lb	De-sign	Type of Covering	Thickness Outside Steel t‖ In.	Re-entrant Portion Filled	Plaster Thickness P‖ In.	Section Area of Solid Material Sq In.	Bond of Covering	Hr	Min	Notes
H	8	34		None	0	No	0	8	—	—	10	Bare column
H	6	20	E	Siliceous gravel concrete, 1:2½:3½ mix	2	Yes	0	100	8-gage wire spiral 8-in. pitch	3	30	NBS test
Plate & angle	6	34	E	Traprock or cinder concrete, 1:6 mix*	2	Yes	0	130	6-gage wire spiral	3	45	UL test
H	8	34	E	Limestone concrete, 1:6 mix*	2	Yes	0	144	6-gage wire spiral	6	30	UL test
H	8	34	E	Limestone concrete, 1:6 mix*	4	Yes	0	256	6-gage wire spiral	7	30	UL test
H	8	34	E	Traprock, granite, cinders, 1:6 mix*	4	Yes	0	256	6-gage wire spiral	7	—	UL test
Plate & angle	6	34	E	Gypsum concrete†	2	Yes	½	114	4-in. mesh fabric	6	30	NBS test gypsum plaster
Plate & angle	6	34	E	Gypsum block	2	No	½	107	1 by ⅛-in. ∩ clamps	4	—	NBS test gypsum plaster
Plate & angle	6	34	E	Cinder block	3¾	Yes	¾	240	Block bond	7	—	NBS test gypsum plaster
H	8	34	E	Common brick	4¼	Yes	0	270	Brick bond	7	—	UL test
H	8	34	E	Semi-fireclay hollow tile	2	No	0	96	Wire ties	1	30	UL test
H	8	34	E	Semi-fireclay hollow tile	4	No	0	158	Wire ties	1	30	UL test
H	10	49	F	Sprayed mineral fiber‡	2¼	Yes	—	164	No special adhesive	5	—	
H	10	49	F	Sprayed mineral fiber‡	3⅜	Yes	—	238	Special adhesive	5	—	
H	8	28	F	Sprayed mineral fiber‡	2	Yes	—	44	Special adhesive	5	—	
I	8	28	F	Sprayed asbestos fiber‡	2	Yes	—	38	No special adhesive	3	—	
	8	35	E	Sprayed asbestos fiber‡	1	Yes	—	90	No special adhesive	2	—	
	8	35	E	Sprayed asbestos fiber‡	1¾	Yes	—	98	No special adhesive	4	—	
	8	35	E	Sprayed asbestos fiber‡	1⅞	Yes	—	120	No special adhesive	4	—	
I	8	28	F	Sprayed asbestos fiber‡	1½	Yes	—	28	No special adhesive	2	—	UL test
O	7.6	24		None (Bare steel pipes filled with concrete)§	0	Yes	0	46	—	—	35	UL test

* Concrete mix—1 part cement to 6 parts total aggregate including sand and coarse aggregate.
† Gypsum concrete—7 parts gypsum stucco to 1 part wood shavings, by weight.
‡ Mineral fibers, with bonding agent as required, sprayed on to all surfaces of column shaft to thicknesses indicated. (Thickness differed on account of characteristics of fiber and binder.)
§ Concrete-filled columns require vent holes to prevent explosion in the event of fire.
‖ Dimensions as shown in Fig. 6-7Q.

Table 6-7W. Fire Resistance of Reinforced Concrete Columns*

No.	Section In.	Section Area Sq In.	Load in 1000 Lbs	Aggregates Fine	Aggregates Coarse	Mix Cement Fine Coarse	Vertical Number	Vertical Bar Size No.	Vertical Sq In.	Lateral Diam In.	Lateral Spacing In.	Concrete Cover Thickness In.	Fire Resistance Hr	Fire Resistance Min
70	16 × 16	256	101	Fox River Sand	Chicago limestone	1:2:4	4	9	4.00	¼	12	2¼	8 (13+	40 —)
71	16 × 16	256	101	Long Island Sand	New York trap rock	1:2:4	4	9	4.00	¼	12	2¼	7	22
72	17 dia	227	107.5	Fox River Sand	Chicago limestone	1:2:4	6	9	6.00	¼	12	2½	8 (12+	04 —)
73	17 dia	227	107.5	Long Island Sand	New York trap rock	1:2:4	6	9	6.00	¼	12	2½	7	57
74	17 dia	227	129	Fox River Sand	Chicago limestone	1:2:4	6	6	2.64	¼	1½	2¼	8 (13+	06 —)
75	17 dia	227	129	Long Island Sand	New York trap rock	1:2:4	6	6	2.64	¼	1½	2¼	8	02
25	16 × 16	256	92	Pittsburgh Sand	Pittsburgh gravel	1:2:4	4	8	3.16	¼	12	1½	4 (6	— 30)
44	16 × 16	256	92	Long Island Sand	Pure quartz gravel	1:2:4	4	8	3.16	¼	12	1½	4 (6	— —)
51	16 × 16	256	92	Pittsburgh Sand	Blast furnace slag	1:2:4	4	8	3.16	¼	12	1½	4 (8	— —)
56	16 × 16	256	92	Pittsburgh Sand	New Jersey trap rock	1:2:4	4	8	3.16	½	12	1½	4 (7	— —)
7	18 dia	254	99.75	Pittsburgh Sand	Pittsburgh gravel	1:2:4	8	6	3.52	¼	12	1½	5 (6	— —)
2	18 dia	254	141	Pittsburgh Sand	Pittsburgh gravel	1:2:4	8	6	3.52	3⁄16	2	1½	4	—
48	18 dia	254	141	Pittsburgh Sand	Blast furnace slag	1:2:4	8	6	3.52	3⁄16	2	1½	4 (10+	— —)
85	18 dia	254	141	Elgin, Ill. Sand	Elgin, Ill. gravel	1:2:4	8	6	3.52	3⁄16	2	1½	4 (12+	— —)
12	18 dia	254	81	Pittsburgh Sand	Pittsburgh gravel	1:2:4	None	—	—	—	—	—	4	
33	12 dia	113	51	Pittsburgh Sand	Pittsburgh gravel	1:2:4	4	5	1.24	¼	2⅛	1½	Avg. of 2 3	—

* Columns Nos. 70 to 75 tested at UL. Test No. 70 of the group was stopped at 8 hr 40 min, others at failure or at 8 hr, and all loaded to failure at end of fire exposure (NBS Tech. Paper 184). All other columns tested at NBS Laboratory at Pittsburgh, Pa. The fire endurance test of Col. No. 7 stopped at 5 hr, all others of series stopped at 4 hr. Figures in parentheses are estimates of fire resistance if tests had continued to failure (NBS Tech. Paper 272).

Table 6-7X.   Miscellaneous Column Constructions

Type and Thickness of Protection	Type of Column Section and Details of Protection	Minimum Area of Solid Material Sq In.	Useful Fire Resistance Period Hr	Useful Fire Resistance Period Min
Round Cast-Iron Columns*				
Unprotected. Unfilled	Minimum wall thickness 0.60 in.	12	—	20
Unprotected. Interior filled with concrete	Same	35	—	30
High-ribbed metal lath and plaster. One covering (1½ in. thick)	Mixture 1:1/10:2½ portland cement, hydrated lime and sand, ½-in. air space	60	2	30
2-in. concrete Traprock, granite or hard-coal cinder aggregate	Mixture 1:6 or 1:7. Concrete tied with not less than equivalent of No. 5 (Brown & Sharpe) gage wire on 8-in. pitch	70	3	—
2-in. hollow tile Porous semi-fire clay	Outside wire ties. Mortar joint between tile and column	70	2	—
Reinforced Concrete Columns				
2-in. integral concrete protection	Round or square vertically reinforced or hooped reinforced. Grade 1 concrete, 1:6 mixture of cement to aggregate	220	5	—
2-in. integral concrete protection	Round or square vertically reinforced or hooped reinforced. Limestone concrete, 1:6 mixture of cement to aggregate	220	8	—
Timber Columns				
Unprotected.	Unprotected steel plate cap bearing	120	—	25
Unprotected.	Unprotected cast-iron cap and pintle bearing	120	—	25
⅜-in. gypsum wallboard	Cast-iron or steel plate cap bearing, protected	140	—	45
Metal lath and plaster One covering (1 in. thick)	Cast-iron or steel plate cap bearing, protected. Mixture 1:1/10:2½ portland cement, hydrated lime and sand, ¾-in. air space	160	1	30

	Prefabricated Building Columns		
Type of Section and Typical Sizes	Type of Protection	Minimum Area of Solid Material (Nominal)	Useful Fire Resistance (Hr)
Square, shell sizes 6 × 6 in. to 14 × 14 in.	Various steel sections enclosing a proprietary insulating concrete	36 sq in. to 208 sq in.	1 hr, 2 hr, 3 hr, 4 hr. (depending on size and weight)
Rectangular, shell sizes 7 × 5 in. to 15 × 11 in.	Various steel sections enclosing a proprietary insulating concrete	35 sq in. to 165 sq in.	1 hr, 2 hr, 3 hr, 4 hr. (depending on size and weight)
Round, shell sizes 6⅝ in. to 18 in.	Various steel sections enclosing a proprietary insulating concrete	35 sq in. to 286 sq in.	1 hr, 2 hr, 3 hr, 4 hr. (depending on size and weight)

* These columns require a vent hole to relieve steam or air pressure that may build up in the column under fire temperatures.

Table 6-7Y.   The Influence of Stress on the Fire Resistance of Concrete Columns[13]

Applied Load, % Design Load	Fire Resistance, Minutes
150	68
100	124
75	198
50	248
30	358

cedures or because of required maintenance after a ceiling has been installed, membrane ceilings will not resist the effects of a fire well.

Structural Integrity

Structural integrity of the walls and floors is an important feature of fire design. Violations of the barrier, either because of failure or because of penetrations for the building services are important for the prevention of fire propagation. Often the protection of a fire-rated wall or floor is negated because the penetrations for needed building services are inadequately protected or installed.

Section B of the chapter described fire testing of assemblies and the interpretation of these tests. It is important to recognize that selection and installation of assemblies requires judgment and understanding. Too often in building construction well-intentioned, expensive assemblies are rendered ineffective because of lack of construction supervision or inattention to significant details.

The protection of openings in floors, walls, and partitions becomes an important factor in maintaining the structural integrity of these barriers. It is difficult to protect the openings properly. Nevertheless, this bears a significant relationship to the relative protection afforded by the barriers.

Chapter 8 discusses design and construction practices to achieve more complete structural integrity.

Table 6-7Z identifies the design and construction deficiencies primarily responsible for the spread of flame, heat, smoke, and gases. These deficiencies consider the spread of the products of combustion both throughout a building and also from one building to another.

Table 6-7Z. Design Deficiencies Responsible for Spread of Fire, Heat, and Smoke

1. Throughout a Building Due to:
   Lack of or inadequate vertical and/or horizontal fire separations.
   Unprotected or inadequately protected floor and wall openings for stairs, doors, elevators, escalators, dumbwaiters, ducts, conveyors, chutes, pipe holes, and windows.
   Concealed spaces in walls and above ceilings without adequate fire-stopping or fire divisions.
   Combustible interior finish including combustible protective coatings and insulation.
   Combustible structural members (beams, girders, and joints) framed into fire walls.
   Improper anchorage of structural members in masonry bearing walls.
   Explosion or pressure damage to the building due to lack of or inadequate explosion venting where required.
   Damage to unprotected framing resulting in weakening or destruction of floors and walls used as fire barriers.
   Lack of means to ventilate fire gases.

2. From One Building to Another Due to:
   Lack of or inadequate fire division walls between adjoining buildings.
   Unprotected or inadequately protected openings in fire division walls between adjoining buildings or in fire walls between detached buildings.
   Exterior walls having inadequate fire resistance.
   Inadequate separation distance.
   Combustible roofs, roof coverings, roof structures, overhanging eaves, trim, etc.
   Lack of protection at openings to passageways, pipe tunnels, conveyors, ducts, etc., between detached buildings.
   Explosion or pressure damage to adjoining or detached buildings.
   Collapse of exterior walls.

Bibliography

References Cited

[1] Harmathy, T. Z. and Stanzak, T. T., "Elevated-Temperature Tensile and Creep Properties of Some Structural and Prestressing Steels," ASTM Special Technical Publication 464, American Society for Testing and Materials, Philadelphia, 1969, pp. 186–208.
[2] DeFalco, F. D., "An Investigation of Modern Structural Steels at Fire Temperatures," Ph. D. Thesis, University of Connecticut, 1974.
[3] Ibid.
[4] Benjamin, I. A., "Fire Resistance of Reinforced Concrete," Symposium on Fire Resistance of Concrete, American Concrete Institute, Detroit, Mich., 1961.
[5] Ibid, p. 31.
[6] Clay, W., "Standard Fire Tests," Proceedings of the 13th Annual Meeting of the Building Officials' Conference of America, Chicago, 1927, pp. 74–88.
[7] Shaub, H., "Early History of Fire Endurance Testing in the United States," ASTM Special Technical Publication 301, American Society for Testing and Materials, Philadelphia, 1961, pp. 1–9.
[8] Menzel, C., "Tests of the Fire Resistance and Thermal Properties of Solid Concrete Slabs and Their Significance," Proceedings of the 1943 Annual Meeting of the American Society for Testing and Materials, Philadelphia, 1943, pp. 1019–1153.
[9] Mitchell, N. D., "Fire Tests of Gunite Slabs and Partitions," Building Materials and Structures Report 131, May 12, 1952, National Bureau of Standards, Washington, D.C.
[10] "Fire Tests of Columns Protected with Gypsum," NBS Research Paper No. 563, 1933, National Bureau of Standards, Washington, D.C.
[11] Mitchell, N. D. and Ryan, J. V., "Fire Tests of Steel Columns Encased with Gypsum Lath and Plaster," Building Materials and Structures Report 135, Apr. 3, 1953, National Bureau of Standards, Washington, D.C.
[12] Benjamin, I. A., op cit., p. 31.
[13] Ibid., p. 29.

NFPA Codes, Standards, and Recommended Practices (see the latest NFPA Publications and Visual Aids Catalog for availability of current editions of the following documents)

NFPA No. 251, Standard Methods of Fire Tests of Building Construction and Materials.
NFPA No. 252, Standard Methods of Fire Tests of Door Assemblies.
NFPA No. 257, Standard for Fire Tests of Window Assemblies.

Additional Readings

Brannigan, F. L., Building Construction for the Fire Service, National Fire Protection Association, Boston, 1971.
"Fire Resistance Classifications of Building Constructions," Building Materials and Structures Report 92, 1942, National Bureau of Standards, Washington, D.C.

Chapter 8

CONFINEMENT OF FIRE AND SMOKE IN BUILDINGS

This chapter is concerned with the confinement of fire and of the products of combustion in buildings. The latter includes thermal components (flame and heat) and non-thermal components (smoke and combustion gases). A building is able to protect people and property by either confining the fire and products of combustion to the area of origin, or providing areas of refuge in the building. In either case, barriers must be provided to prevent fire and its products of combustion from penetrating to certain other areas.

The barriers provided must be able to withstand the impingement of any forces that result from a fire. These include thermal forces from flame and heat, and pressure forces from expansion of combustion gases. An evaluation of the fire load in a structure is a good basis on which to calculate the strength of fire barriers that may be required. Fire load is directly related to the duration of a fire and, thus, to the required fire resistance of structural assemblies. Studies have been made of the fire loadings that could be expected in various occupancies,[1] and the concept is explained in detail in Section A of this chapter.

Section B discusses the confinement of fire by compartmentation and protection of service penetrations. Section C discusses various methods for the confinement or control of smoke and gaseous products of combustion.

A. Fire Loading

The fire load is the expected maximum of combustible material in a given fire area. In a normal building, this consists of the combustible structural elements and the combustible contents contained within a single fire area. Fire load is usually expressed as weight of combustible material per square foot of fire area. Heat liberation can be calculated based on the calorific value of the materials.

Fire severity is determined by the material burned and its rate of burning. Also, arrangement of the material has a pronounced effect on the rapidity of combustion and, therefore, cannot be neglected if reasonably sound conclusions are to be drawn.

With respect to fire duration, the principal factor is the quantity of material available to burn. However, judgment must be exercised because the same quantity of a fast burning material will not necessarily create a fire duration comparable to slow burning material.

The Standard Time-Temperature Curve

The standard time-temperature curve in NFPA 251, Standard Methods of Fire Tests of Building Construction and Materials (see Fig. 6-8A), is somewhat near the maximum representative of the severity of a fire completely burning out a brick, wood-joisted building and its contents. Following adoption of the time-temperature curve, the National Bureau of Standards conducted a fire test with two such buildings.[1] These were allowed to burn to destruction to determine the actual fire behavior of the buildings, compared with the conditions represented on the curve. The buildings were loaded with waste lumber and similar materials to represent a combustible occupancy (see Fig. 6-8B). The test showed that, while the tem-

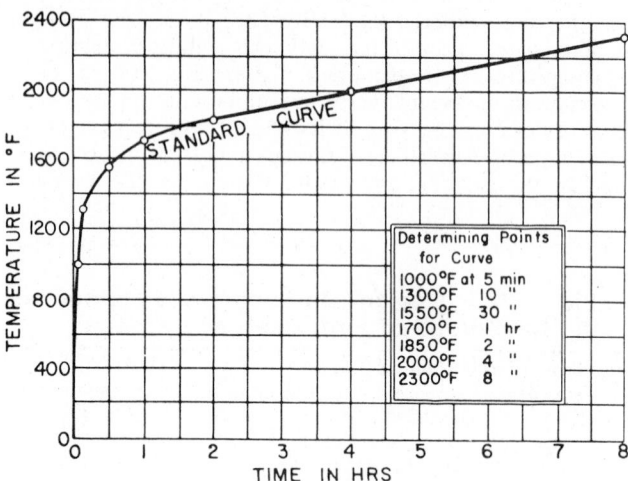

Fig. 6-8A. The standard time-temperature curve.

Fig. 6-8B. Full-scale fire test of five- and two-story brick, wood-joisted buildings with unprotected vertical openings at Washington, D.C., June 17, 1928, conducted by the National Bureau of Standards, in cooperation with the NFPA Committee on Protection of Records. The buildings were loaded with waste lumber to represent the combustible contents of an office or mercantile occupancy, with 7½, 15, and 30 lbs per sq ft per floor in the front center, and rear sections respectively. The picture shows the conditions from 10 to 20 min after the start of the fire. Temperatures reached 2,000°F at several points within 20 min; maximum temperatures between 2,200° and 2,400°F were reached at a few points within 40 min. Floor construction began to collapse after 15 min and walls began to collapse at 28 min. Owing to the early collapse of the building, the fire exposure effects above the debris did not exceed the severity represented by 1½ to 2 hrs on the standard time-temperature curve, but temperatures in debris blanketed by fallen brick walls remained in the vicinity of 1,000°F for two to three days.

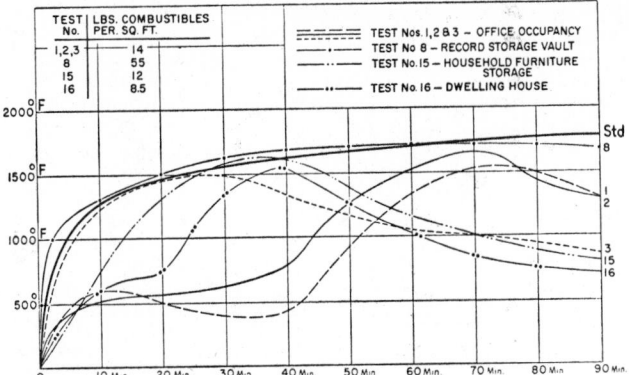

Fig. 6-8C. Actual time-temperature curves recorded in tests as compared with the standard time-temperature curve. This indicates the relative fire severity depending upon different fire loading. The standard time-temperature curve, while used as a convenient measure for general fire testing, actually represents a condition of high fire severity met in the early stages of actual fires only where combustible materials are of such a character as to favor rapid development of high temperatures.

perature rise during the initial stages of the test was more rapid than that represented by the standard time-temperature curve, over-all results indicated that the curve approximated the maximum fire severity of the actual test.

The National Bureau of Standards produced additional data on fire severity by burning various amounts of materials, representative of office, record room, and household occupancies, in two fire-resistiive buildinigs. The results of the tests provided data useful in the design of buildings and component elements. The curves in Figure 6-8C show the rate-of-rise of temperature within an area when different types of occupancies were involved. Note that, in some cases, rapid temperature rise occurred immediately, while, in others, it was delayed. Also, in most cases, the temperatures at the start or soon thereafter reached the intensity represented by the standard time-temperature curve.

By analysis of these data, a relationship of the fuel loading (wood, paper, and similar materials having calorific values of 7,000 to 8,000 Btu per lb) that will produce an exposure equivalent to the standard time-temperature curve for a specific duration has been approximated. (See Table 6-8A.)

The area under any fire test curve and above a base line taken as the maximum temperature to which the materials under consideration may be exposed without damage, expressed in "degree-hours," is an approximation of the severity and duration of a fire involving ordinary combustibles. Thus, any fire test data can be compared to the standard time-temperature curve by relating the area under the test curve to that under the standard curve. For an example, see Figure 6-8D.

Fire Loads by Occupancy

By utilizing these principles, the severity and duration of fire, in terms of material available to burn, can be evaluated. Before this can be made practicable for use, however, information indicating the fire load in various occupancies must be available. The National Bureau of Standards has made surveys of ten types of occupancies to determine weights of combustibles per square foot of floor area (see Table 6-8B).

Considerable variations in fire loads in buildings of the same type of occupancy were found. For example, in one

Table 6-8A. Estimated Fire Severity for Offices and Light Commercial Occupancies
Data applying to fire-resistive buildings with combustible furniture and shelving

Combustible Content Total, including finish, floor, and trim psf	Heat Potential Assumed* Btu per sq ft	Equivalent Fire Severity Approximately equivalent to that of test under standard curve for the following periods:
5	40,000	30 min
10	80,000	1 hr
15	120,000	1½ hrs
20	160,000	2 hrs
30	240,000	3 hrs
40	320,000	4½ hrs
50	380,000	7 hrs
60	432,000	8 hrs
70	500,000	9 hrs

* Heat of combustion of contents taken at 8,000 Btu per lb up to 40 psf; 7,600 Btu per lb for 50 lbs, and 7,200 Btu for 60 lbs and more to allow for relatively greater proportion of paper. The weights contemplated by the tables are those of ordinary combustible materials, such as wood, paper, or textiles. The relative Btu value of various materials is shown in the table on Calorific Value of Materials in Section 3, Chapter 11, from which estimates may be made of probable fire severity where materials have different Btu values.

of two furniture factories surveyed, fire loads up to 10 psf of floor area were found in only 1.5 percent of the total floor area while in the other factory the same range of loading was found in 54.7 percent of the area. This indicates that discretion must be exercised in the design of buildings in reference to fire loads. Possible changes of occupancy, arrangement, and of burning characteristics of the contents also must be considered.

Classifying Building Contents

In order to use to advantage the fire loading principle in the design of a building, its anticipated contents should be classified for fire severity and duration. The classifications shown in Table 6-8C were based upon available fire test data, fire experience, and the known burning characteristics of materials.[2]

Once the equivalent fire severity under the standard time-temperature curve has been established, the designer may relate this fire severity time to his selection of structural assemblies based upon their fire resistance ratings, such as those given in Chapter 7 of this Section.

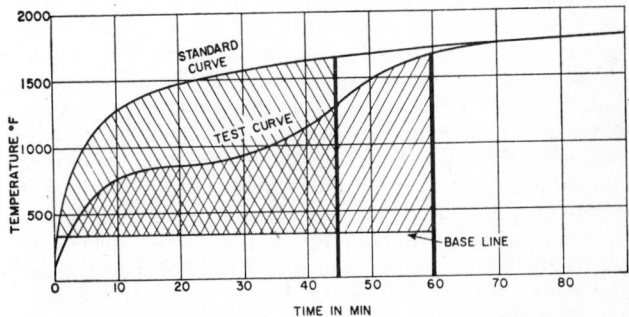

Fig. 6-8D. If, for example, the area, expressed in degree-hours, under the test curve and above a base line for 60 min is determined to be the same as the area under the standard time-temperature curve for a 45-min period, the severity of the fire under both curves is approximately the same.

Table 6-8B. Average Amounts of Combustibles Per Sq Ft of Floor Area
(Contents, finished flooring, interior finish, and trim)*

Occupancy	Percent of Total Floor Area	Range of Combustible Contents, lbs per sq ft	Occupancy	Percent of Total Floor Area	Range of Combustible Contents, lbs per sq ft
Printing plant	36.7	0.0– 14.9	Furniture factory B	54.7	0.0– 9.9
	27.8	15.0– 49.9		37.3	10.0– 29.9
	35.5	50.0–100 +		8.0	30.0– 65 +
Newspaper plant	67.6	0.0– 14.9	Warehouse A	86.3	0.0– 29.9
	30.2	15.0– 49.9		13.7	30.0– 75
	2.2	50.0–100			
Department store A	12.6	0.0– 4.9	Warehouse B	18.1	0.0– 29.9
	76.6	5.0– 14.9		50.9	30.0– 74.9
	10.8	15.0– 40 +		31.0	75.0–257
Department store B	7.8	0.0– 4.9	Elementary school A (public)	99.2	0.0– 14.9
	78.4	5.0– 14.9		0.8	15.0– 75
	13.8	15.0– 40 +			
Clothing factory A	35.3	0.0– 9.9	Elementary school B (public)	100.0	0.0– 15
	53.6	10.0– 14.9			
	11.1	15.0– 30	High school A (public)	66.4	0.0– 4.9
Clothing factory B	85.7	0.0– 9.9		25.4	5.0– 9.9
	5.7	10.0– 14.9		8.2	10.0–288†
	8.6	15.0– 40	High school B (public)	32.6	0.0– 4.9
Mattress factory A	10.8	0.0– 4.9		64.1	5.0– 9.9
	67.1	5.0– 14.9		3.3	10.0–256‡
	22.1	15.0– 50	Offices	59.2	0.0– 14.9
Mattress factory B	7.9	0.0– 4.9		19.2	15.0– 29.9
	46.3	5.0– 14.9		21.6	30.0– 86
	45.8	15.0–100 +	Hospital (medical and surgical building)	82.1	0.0– 4.9
Furniture factory A	1.5	0.0– 9.9		17.0	5.0– 14.9
	81.4	10.0– 29.9		.9	15.0– 20 +
	17.1	30.0– 65 +	Apartments (average of 13 units)	100.0	10.0

* Data from National Bureau of Standards, BMS 92 (1942) and BMS 149 (1957).

† Includes fire loading for storage areas: 25 percent of floor area ranging from 25 to 100 lbs per sq ft (general storage) and 0.2 percent at 288 lbs per sq ft (textbook storage).

‡ Includes 0.3 percent of floor area at 256 lbs per sq ft (textbook storage).

British Fire Loading Studies

The British have attained a similar objective by grading building occupancies according to hazard. Three classifications, low, moderate, and high fire loads, are defined in terms of Btu per sq ft as follows:

Occupancies of Low Fire Load: The fire load of an occupancy is described as low if it does not exceed an average of 100,000 Btu per sq ft of net floor area of any compartment, nor an average of 200,000 Btu per sq ft in limited isolated areas, provided that storage of combustible material necessary to the occupancy may be allowed to a limited extent if separated from the remainder and enclosed by fire resisting construction of an appropriate grade. Examples of occupancies of normal low fire load are offices, restaurants, hotels, hospitals, schools, museums, public libraries, and institutional and administrative buildings.

Occupancies of Moderate Fire Load: The fire load of an occupancy is described as moderate if it exceeds an average of 100,000 Btu per sq ft of net floor area of any compartment but does not exceed an average of 200,000 Btu per sq ft, nor an average of 400,000 Btu per sq ft on limited isolated areas, provided that storage of combustible material necessary to the occupancy may be allowed to a limited extent if separated from the remainder and enclosed by fire

resisting construction of an appropriate grade. Examples of occupancies of normal moderate fire load are retail shops, factories, and workshops.

Occupancies of High Fire Load: The fire load of an occupancy is described as high if it exceeds an average of 200,000 Btu per sq ft of net floor area but does not exceed an average of 400,000 Btu per sq ft of net floor area, nor an average of 800,000 Btu per sq ft on limited isolated areas. Examples of occupancies of normal high fire load are warehouses and other buildings used for the storage in bulk of commodities of a recognized nonhazardous nature.

The low fire load grading of occupancies used by the British is about equivalent to the classification of occupancy represented by the Temperature Curve A; moderate fire load grading by Temperature Curves B, C, and D, and the high fire load grading by Temperature Curve E in Figure 6-8E.

B. Confinement of Fire

Confinement or, as it is sometimes termed, compartmentation must involve the entire building. It has been known for many years that efforts to estimate where fire may start do not provide a rational approach to fire pro-

Table 6-8C. Fire Severity Expected by Occupancy
(See Fig. 8-1E.)

Temperature Curve A (Slight)
Well-arranged office, metal furniture, noncombustible building.
Welding areas containing slight combustibles.
Noncombustible power house.
Noncombustible buildings, slight amount of combustible occupancy.

Temperature Curve B (Moderate)
Cotton and waste paper storage (baled) and well-arranged, noncombustible building.
Paper-making processes, noncombustible building.
Noncombustible institutional buildings with combustible occupancy.

Temperature Curve C (Moderately Severe)
Well-arranged combustible storage, e.g., wooden patterns, noncombustible buildings.
Machine shop having noncombustible floors.

Temperature Curve D (Severe)
Manufacturing areas, combustible products, noncombustible building.
Congested combustible storage areas, noncombustible building.

Temperature Curve E (Standard Fire Exposure—Severe)
Flammable liquids.
Woodworking areas.
Office, combustible furniture and buildings.
Paper working, printing, etc.
Furniture manufacturing and finishing.
Machine shop having combustible floors.

tection. With widespread vandalism and arson and the changing nature of fire loads, there is an even greater incentive today to plan fire safety for the whole building.

Changing concepts in design—open planning with extensive, undivided areas, increasing heights with demonstrated inability to evacuate an entire building, and new materials and combinations of materials—all indicate a need for review of innovations with proper consideration given to their affect on safety.

In recent years, serious fires have disclosed conditions

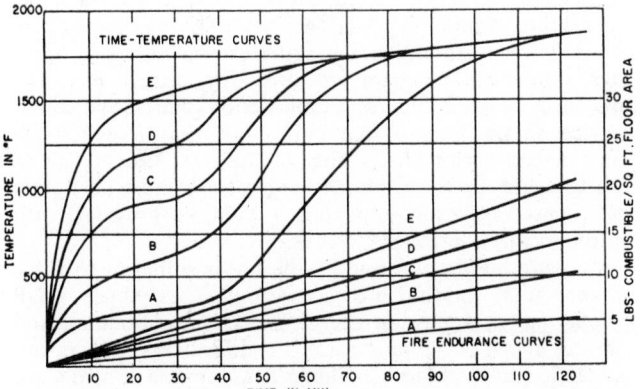

Fig. 6-8E. Possible classification of building contents for fire severity and duration. The straight lines indicate the length of fire endurance based upon amounts of combustibles involved. The curved lines indicate the severity expected for the various occupancies (see Table 6-8D). There is no direct relationship between the straight and curved lines, but, for example, 10 lbs of combustibles per sq ft will produce a 90-min fire in a "C" occupancy, and a fire severity following the time-temperature curve "C" might be expected.

and areas representing previously unrecognized gaps in our knowledge of how fires spread. Climatic conditions that cause downward flow of air within high buildings (the so-called "stack effect"); the spread of fire from floor to floor by way of windows in exterior walls and through insulating spaces in spandrel walls; the speed with which smoke and deadly gases can travel through buildings—these are some of the problems adding to the need for the "built-in" fire protection provided by designed compartmentation. Extensive research programs and investigations have been launched to determine effective and viable countermeasures. Not all of the answers are known, but certainly the ability exists to avoid the more common and long standing deficiencies in building design of unlimited areas, open doors, open stairways, "poke-through" construction, and inadequate fire-stopping. That such things do occur indicates a compromise between cost and safety.

Division of Areas—The Room of Fire Origin

Containment begins with the walls, ceiling, and floor surrounding the space in which the fire starts and any openings therein. Building codes set forth the degree of fire protection to be afforded by these building elements in accordance with the degree of hazard represented by the occupancy, the type of building construction, and the function served (e.g., bearing or nonbearing wall). A lesser degree of protection usually is required for floor openings, since furnishings would not normally be placed in their immediate vicinity.

Window openings in exterior walls require special protection when in close proximity to an adjoining building. This is to prevent spread of fire to the adjoining building. In the light of several fires involving window-to-window fire spread in the same building, however, attention is being given to feasible counter measures. Extension of the floor slab or an increase in the spandrel area between windows are the primary means taken to prevent such fire spread.

Protection of Openings in Fire Barriers

Fire doors are the most widely used and accepted means for the protection of both vertical and horizontal openings. Suitability of fire doors is determined by test by nationally recognized testing laboratories, and doors not tested cannot be relied upon for effective protection. The doors are tested as they are installed in the field; that is, with the frame, hardware, wired-glass panels, and other accessories necessary to complete the installation.

NFPA 80, Standard for the Installation of Fire Doors and Windows, hereinafter in this chapter referred to as the NFPA Fire Doors and Windows Standard, classifies openings from "A" to "E" for the purpose of identifying the various types of openings commonly encountered. This classification does not apply to the fire door as it frequently is erroneously assumed.

Openings are classed as A, B, C, D, and E in accordance with the character and location of the wall in which they are situated. In each of the following classes, the minimum fire protection ratings are shown; doors, shutters, or windows having higher ratings are acceptable.

Class A Openings: These are in walls separating buildings or dividing a single building into fire areas. Doors for the protection of these openings have a fire protection rating of 3 hrs.

Class B Openings: These are in enclosures of vertical communication through buildings (stairs, elevators, etc.). Doors for the protection of these openings have a fire protection rating of 1 or $1\frac{1}{2}$ hrs.

Class C Openings: These are in corridor and room partitions. Doors for the protection of these openings have a fire protection rating of ¾ hr.

Class D Openings: These are in exterior walls which are subject to severe fire exposure from outside of the building. Doors and shutters for the protection of these openings have a fire protection rating of 1½ hrs.

Class E Openings: These are in exterior walls which are subject to moderate or light fire exposure from outside of the building. Doors, shutters, or windows for the protection of these openings have a fire protection rating of ¾ hr.

Types of Doors

There are several types of construction for fire doors; these are as follows:

Composite Doors: These are of the flush design and consist of a manufactured core material with chemically impregnated wood edge banding and untreated wood face veneers, or laminated plastic faces, or surrounded by and encased in steel.

Hollow-metal Doors: These are of formed steel of the flush and paneled designs of No. 20 gage or heavier steel.

Metal-clad (Kalamein) Doors: These are of flush and paneled design consisting of metal covered wood cores or stiles and rails and insulated panels covered with steel of 24 gage or lighter.

Sheet-metal Doors: These are of formed No. 22 gage or lighter steel and of the corrugated, flush, and paneled designs.

Rolling Steel Doors: These are of the interlocking steel slat design or plate-steel construction.

Tin-clad Doors: These are of two- or three-ply wood core construction, covered with No. 30 gage galvanized steel or terneplate (maximum size 14 by 20 in.); or No. 24 gage galvanized steel sheets not more than 48 in. wide.

Curtain Type Doors: These consist of interlocking steel blades or a continuous formed spring steel curtain in a steel frame.

The suitability of a fire door should be judged on the class of opening in which it is to be installed, not on the fire resistance rating of the wall in which it is to be installed. Once the class of opening has been determined, there is no choice of door hourly ratings, except in the case of the Class B openings.*

If the opening is in a wall dividing a building into separate fire areas, the door should be suitable for installation in a Class A opening (3-hr fire protection rating). The same door can be used whatever the fire resistance rating of the wall. If a wall encloses a vertical communication, the door should be suitable for a Class B opening.

The NFPA Fire Doors and Windows Standard gives recommendations on the installation of suitable approved doors, windows, and shutters, and it also specifies how the opening shall be constructed and how the door or window shall be mounted, equipped, and operated.

Use of Double and Single Doors

A fire wall is designed to remain standing and effectively stop the passage of heat and flame even when fire has progressed on one side of the wall to the point where the building on that side has suffered great damage or even collapsed. It should be obvious that doors at openings in a fire wall must retain practically the same degree of effec-

tiveness as the wall. To accomplish this, some authorities consider it necessary to provide a 3-hr door for a Class A opening on each side of the wall opening. The reasoning behind this requirement is threefold: one of the doors may be blocked by stock or otherwise unable to close; the portion of the building on the fire side of the wall may collapse and the fire door, if surface-mounted, may be torn from the wall by the falling building; and, finally, two doors give lower temperature on the unexposed side.

For Class B openings, which are in vertical enclosures for stairs, elevators, chutes, etc., the effectiveness of the enclosure in preventing fire spread to another story is retained if fire is prevented from passing through one door into the enclosure and thence through another door into another part of the building. Each door may, therefore, have a lesser degree of fire resistance than for a fire wall opening. These doors may have a 1½-hr or a 1-hr fire protection rating, depending on the severity of the conditions.

Corridor and room partitions are normally employed under conditions which do not contemplate resistance to progress of fire and smoke of great intensity for long periods of time. Doors for openings in these partitions are usually single (on one side of a wall) and have a ¾-hr fire protection rating.

Recognizing the hazard of smoke and other combustion products (heat and gases), more consideration is being given today to tight fitting doors. This provides protection for persons using a corridor for escape when the fire is in a room and for people in the room if fire is in the corridor. With the increasing use of carpeting in buildings, there is an advantage in undercutting doors to provide easier operation. The gain, however, involves considerable risk as was demonstrated in the Baptist Towers Fire.[3]

Another failure in observing the principle of containment is the practice of permitting a door to remain open between a fire-involved room and a corridor. It would appear that, in a significant nursing home fire, had the door to a fire-involved room been closed after a patient had been safely removed, none of thirty-two fatalities would have occurred.[4] Today, an increasing number of building codes require self-closing doors between apartments and corridors and between hotel guest rooms and corridors.

Other openings in the walls, ceiling, and floor of the room of fire origin can include those made to allow passage of heating, ventilating, and air conditioning ducts; penetrations made for plumbing and electrical services; openings into plenum chambers used for return air; and openings to pipe chases, dumb-waiter shafts and other service shafts. One source points out that a pencil-size opening can permit the passage of sufficient heat to spread fire to other areas.[5] All such penetrations must be tightly firestopped. Necessary openings should be provided with automatically controlled closures.

Pressure build-up caused by the fire is sufficient to force smoke, heat, and noxious gases through extremely small cracks and openings. In the case of air conditioning and heating ducts, large quantities of combustion products can be carried throughout a building if automatic controls are not activated. Where return air ducts are to be used for smoke removal, provision must be made for proper controls.

The open-plan design for buildings is popular today, particularly in schools and some office buildings. Here, an entire floor may be subdivided only by 6-ft high partitions and, in effect, the entire floor becomes one room. After several high-rise building fires, regulations have been adopted that, in one code at least, require complete

---

* In the transition from designating doors by intended location to designation by intended location plus fire exposure, Class B doors were given a 1-hr and 1½-hr fire exposure.

sprinkler protection for residential and office occupancies over twelve stories in height and sprinkler protection *or* refuge areas on floors over 30,000 sq ft in area in buildings of six to twelve stories in height. In the latter case, floors exceeding 30,000 sq ft are divided into two areas approximately equal in size and separated by a 2-hr rated horizontal wall with no duct penetrations and sealed penetrations for piping and conduit.[6] Access doors to the refuge area are fitted and gasketed to prevent the passage of smoke and gases.

The Hazard of Concealed Spaces

Most buildings contain a wide variety of concealed spaces behind walls, over suspended ceilings, in pipe chases and attics, and elsewhere. These may vary from 1¾-in. stud spaces to 8-ft interstitial truss spaces. Usually, such spaces contain combustible materials in the form of thermal insulation, insulation for power supplies, and ducting. The larger spaces may contain walkways and be lighted for convenience in servicing and repairs. The space over suspended ceilings frequently is used as a plenum chamber for air conditioning and heating systems. All provide a ready made flue for fire and combustion products unless adequate precautions are taken during construction.

This potential hazard can be minimized or eliminated in one of three ways:

1. By eliminating all combustible materials—often an impractical solution.

2. By providing automatic fire detection and suppression within the space.

3. By the use of firestopping.

In combustible frame construction, spaces between joists should be fire-stopped at walls and partitions (see Chapter 4 of this Section). Spaces over suspended ceilings are usually fire-stopped every 1,000 sq ft. Attic spaces, such as those found over one-story rows of stores or apartment houses, are required to be fire-stopped, under most codes, every 2,000 sq ft. Even so, many fires starting in one apartment burn through to the attic space, spread horizontally, and burn down into adjoining apartments.

To be effective, horizontal fire-stopping must be continuous to wall, ceiling, or roof surfaces with tight joints where the surfaces meet. All open spaces around penetrations must be protected if the firestopping is to effectively serve its purpose.

A common fault even in the most fire resistive types of construction is the gap frequently left between the floor slab and exterior walls. In a Bogota, Colombia, high-rise building fire it was found that such a gap was closed with a plywood-on-stud enclosure and was a factor in the spread of the fire.[7] In the New York Plaza high-rise fire, a gap was found between the curtain wall and the metal skin—again providing a path for fire to spread to the floor above.[8] A fire in the World Trade Center, New York City, also is reported to have spread horizontally and vertically through hidden spaces—ducts and shafts—that had not been fire-stopped.[9]

In a less direct sense, elevator shafts, laundry chutes, and other vertical enclosures which, because of their function, cannot be cut off at floor levels, can also be considered hidden spaces. Protection is available, however, in the form of fire-rated enclosures and protection at openings into the enclosures.

Corridors and Stairs

Perhaps most important, since they provide the primary avenue of escape and rescue for persons caught in a building in which there is a fire, are the corridors and stairs. These provide the main source of escape to adjoining floors or to the street. NFPA 101, Life Safety Code, provides a comprehensive treatment of exits in general and for various types of occupancies involving both new and existing buildings. Detailed requirements are given for enclosing walls, doors, stairs, ramps, escalators, and other components of an exit system.

The concept of containment is maintained in the Life Safety Code through requirements for subdivision of building spaces, horizontal exits, and doors. Smoke partitions are required in new hospitals and nursing homes, for instance, to divide into at least two compartments each story used by inpatients for sleeping or treatment and any story having an occupant load of fifty or more persons. The compartments are required to enclose areas of 22,500 sq ft or less, with the length or width 150 ft or less. Doors in the partitions must have a minimum fire resistance rating of 20 min and be self-closing, but they may be provided with approved hold-open devices.

The effectiveness of self-closing doors to rooms and stairs frequently is canceled out when wooden or other types of wedges are used to hold these doors open. A similar practice is sometimes used in connection with swinging smoke-stop doors in corridors. Hold-open devices having automatic releases that are actuated by smoke or particle of combustion detectors are the acceptable means for holding doors in the open position.

A less obvious breach of good design in corridors occurs when the smoke partition or doors across corridors stop at a suspended ceiling that forms part of the rated floor/ceiling construction. Under these circumstances, fire and products of combustion in the space above the ceiling can be carried over the smoke-stop partition or doors and enter the "safe" side of the protective construction. The Jan. 14, 1971 fire at the Presbyterian Home for Senior Citizens in Beuchel, Ky. provides a classic example of how corridor compartmentation can fail.[10]

Another serious problem to be considered is that persons using stairs to escape a smoke-filled corridor must open the stair door letting smoke and heated gases into the stairway, rendering them unusable in the worst cases. Smokeproof towers or adequately vented stairs provide a satisfactory answer, but the added space required mitigates against their common use. Design trends today point towards pressurization of stairways as an effective countermeasure. See Section C of this chapter for a more detailed discussion of smoke control.

Special Problems to Consider

Thievery and other forms of criminal action frequently make it necessary to render stairway doors inoperable from the stair side. This poses a problem where fire on any one floor makes it necessary for the occupants of that floor to seek refuge on floors above or below. The solution, where a central control is maintained, as in the case of many high-rise buildings, is to provide for the unlocking of all stairway doors from the control room in an emergency. Where central control does not exist, a compromise measure is to have the door on every third floor operable from the stair side.

Much consideration and research has been directed toward wall and floor penetrations by plastic pipe. Large scale tests indicate that, by surrounding the plastic pipe with a noncombustible material at the point of penetration, completely closing the opening around the pipes, any hazard present will be minimized.[11]

Escalators

Escalators also pose a problem in maintaining compartmentation. Several solutions are available:

The Sprinkler Vent Method: This is of a combination of an automatic fire or smoke detection system, automatic exhaust system, and an automatic water curtain.

The automatic exhaust system must have sufficient capacity to create a down draft through the opening of not less than 300 fpm. The system is actuated by some approved means, i.e., a thermal device, a sprinkler system, or a smoke detection system.

The water curtain consists of open sprinklers or spray nozzles which surround the floor opening and which discharge not less than 3 gpm per lineal foot of opening. Operation is by the same detection device that starts the exhaust system.

The Spray Nozzle Method: This involves a water spray installation much like those discussed in Section 5, Chapter 3 for the protection of horizontal or vertical conveyor openings. Briefly, the spray nozzle method consists of a combination of an automatic fire or smoke detection system and a system of high velocity water spray nozzles. The nozzles are of the open type and water is discharged into the system by a valve actuated by releases connected to the automatic fire or smoke detection system. The number of nozzles and the water discharge pattern from the nozzles is such that the floor opening is completely filled with dense water spray when operating. The water discharge from the nozzles is also arranged to take full advantage of the cooling and counter-draft effect. A noncombustible draft curtain at least 20 in. deep should extend completely around the floor opening. Manual control valves are provided to prevent excess water damage.

The Rolling Shutter Method: This consists of a self-closing rolling shutter that completely encloses the top of the moving stairway. The shutter is actuated by an automatic heat or smoke detection system. The speed at which the shutter is closed is limited to 30 fpm, and the leading edge of the shutter is made sensitive to a force applied against it causing the shutter to stop its closing progress, reverse and back off about 6 in. and then close again. This safety feature is provided to avoid injury to a person who may be in the opening when the shutter starts to close. The shutter may also be closed manually and is designed to withstand a predetermined vertical load.

Rolling steel shutters are not recommended, however, at the tops of moving stairways between basements and street floors even though the stairways are not required exits under provisions of the NFPA Life Safety Code. Persons seeking egress in an emergency from basements served by moving stairs could be trapped by fully closed rolling shutters at the street floor level even though other means of egress were available to them. It has also been observed that there is a quite different psychological reaction by those confronted with a closed shutter above their heads as they figuratively try to climb to safety from a basement than by those faced with a closed shutter at an exit way on the same level as the floor from which they are attempting egress. In the latter case operation of the shutter would be clearly visible and other means of egress could be readily found and used if requirements of the Life Safety Code had been followed in the building.

The Partial Enclosure Method: This method of protecting moving stairways involves a partial enclosure of so-called "kiosk" construction with a fire resistance equivalent to that specified for other stairway enclosures in the same building and with openings protected by self-closing doors.

C. Confinement or Control of Smoke

Control and confinement of smoke is a very serious problem in building fires, particularly those fires involving high-rise buildings. Smoke, gaseous products of combustion, and air-borne particulate matter are the leading causes of death in fires. Dense smoke also severely hampers fire fighters in their efforts to find and extinguish the fire. The awareness, on the part of the building designer, of smoke and its properties, as well as the role of smoke as an engineering design function, is relatively new, and effective solutions to the problem are still being developed.

Chapter 5 of Section 2 described smoke generation and smoke movement in four types of buildings. These types included below-ground or windowless spaces, single story, large area buildings, multi-story conventional buildings, and the modern high-rise structures. Each type of building involves different conditions and, with the current state of the art, utilizes different solutions to the smoke problem. It is recommended that the principles of that chapter be reviewed as background for this following discussion.

Single story, large, open area buildings employ roof vents and smoke curtains to counteract the problem of smoke from fire. Multi-story buildings, if not of too great floor area, generally rely on emergency venting by breaking or opening exterior windows, as well as by opening the roof. However, windowless and below-ground structures and high-rise buildings remain problem areas in the realm of smoke control.

There are several approaches to smoke control in these types of buildings. One is to attempt to control the building contents to limit the potential generation of smoke. Another approach relies on rapid fire suppression, directed at extinguishing a fire before it can build up to significant intensity. Still other approaches involve the use of smoke shafts, smoke barriers, ventilation, pressurization, or a combination of these.

Limitation of Combustibility

A convenient solution to the problem of smoke generation is the control of the materials used in the building, both construction and contents. Unfortunately, lack of legislation and enforcement controls, combined with the difficulties of product formulation and manufacture to accomplish this end, does not make control of materials a feasible approach at this time. Nevertheless, smoke generation is one of the measured parameters of the "tunnel test" (NFPA 255, Method of Test of Surface Burning Characteristics of Building Materials) allowing some control over the smoke generation of finish materials.

On the other hand, if the fire is extinguished at its incipient stage, it does not have the opportunity to generate the large volumes of smoke that are present in more fully developed fires. Therefore, automatic fire suppression remains one of the most reliable means of controlling the products of combustion.

Principles of Smoke Control

Section 2, Chapter 5 of this HANDBOOK described many of the forces causing smoke movement within a building. These included expansion of gases due to increases in temperature in the fire area, stack effect, influence of wind on the exterior of the building, and internal air movement resulting from building ventilation fans and ductwork. Particularly in high-rise buildings, the general pattern of smoke movement can be crudely identified.

Smoke movement or smoke-logging of spaces, or both,

can be controlled in buildings. The methods of control generally involve dilution, exhaust, or confinement. Usually, a combination of these is utilized. These principles, combined with the functional spaces and engineering systems within the building can offer temporary refuge and reasonable protection to the occupants.

Dilution is a popular concept of smoke control. In theory, if a building is large enough and smoke is exhausted by normal venting methods, the effects of the smoke and products of combustion will be diluted to the point where the problem no longer exists. A human can tolerate about 1 percent smoke contamination in a space for an extended period of time.[12] Further, a human can tolerate 2 to 3 percent contamination for short periods of time, such as would occur during evacuation to places of refuge. Unfortunately, the combination of gas expansion and the stack effect can readily cause an overconcentration of smoke in certain areas of a building.

Dilution can be successful only by infusion of massive quantities of uncontaminated air or after the passage of a considerable period of time during which constant exhaust of contaminated air takes place. This duration would be beyond the point of human tolerance for occupants in critical locations. Consequently, occupant protection by dilution alone is not considered a satisfactory solution. Its application is limited to small fires which are easily extinguished. This would generally be the case where automatic fire suppression systems were available.

A second method of smoke control involves exhaust. Exhausting the smoke, particularly in high-rise buildings or below-ground spaces, offers many advantages. In order to exhaust effectively, the smoke needs both a path to travel and a force to move it along the path. The force is provided by a pressure gradient.

Smoke shafts are one path by which exhausted air can be directed to the exterior of the building. A smoke shaft is a vertical shaft through the building, from bottom to top, terminating above the roof. It has dampers at each floor, so arranged that each damper remains closed until a fire occurs on its level. The force needed to exhaust the smoke is provided by the stack effect or by an auxiliary fan. In theory, smoke shafts should be an effective means of exhaust. As detailed in Section 2, Chapter 5, they do not always perform as expected.

The building HVAC (heating, ventilating, and air conditioning) system can also be utilized in emergency situations for the purpose of exhausting smoke and other products of combustion. The objective of the exhaust mode is to dilute the concentration of contaminants down to the level of human tolerance. Unfortunately, most building fan systems do not have the capacity to exhaust sufficient quantities of fire-generated smoke to make the environment tolerable. However, exhausting is a practice which can be readily combined with other modes of smoke control to develop an effective system.

A third method of smoke control involves confinement. The objective in this case is to provide a barrier to the passage of smoke into specific areas. This is accomplished in one of two ways. One way involves a physical barrier, such as a door, wall, or damper which blocks smoke movement. These physical barriers are important in that they reduce the size of the opening, thus reducing smoke penetration. However, no workable systems have been devised as yet that are able to confine smoke by means of physical barriers alone.

An alternative to physical barrier confinement is the use of a pressure differential between the smoky atmosphere and the protected area. This pressurization, with or without simultaneous exhausting, does create an effective barrier. The combination of pressurization with physical barriers seems to be the most practical method of protecting an area from the intrusion of any products of combustion.

Temporary refuge areas, stairwells, and elevator shafts are often the principal areas where pressurization and barriers may be utilized effectively. The Federal Building in Seattle, Wash., for example, utilizes exhaust of the fire floor combined with physical barriers and pressurization of spaces above and below the fire to confine the smoke to the fire area and to protect the occupants in refuge areas within the building.

Temporary Refuge Areas

A great amount of experimental and theoretical work has been conducted in recent years in the field of smoke movement. The National Research Council of Canada has been a leader in this respect. Many of the references at the end of the chapter are reports of its work. In addition, experimental studies, such as the Henry Grady Fire Tests[13] and others, are valuable references for quantitative verification.[14]

The experimental studies cited above demonstrate the feasibility of pressurizing stairways to ensure smoke-free conditions. From a theoretical viewpoint, the magnitude of pressures need be only slightly greater than the pressure of the smoky atmosphere. From a practical viewpoint, a positive pressure of 0.05 to 0.10 in. of water will enable

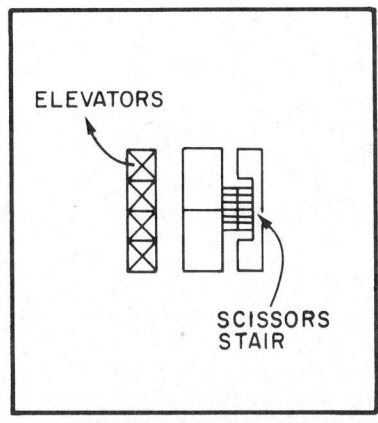

BEFORE MODIFICATION

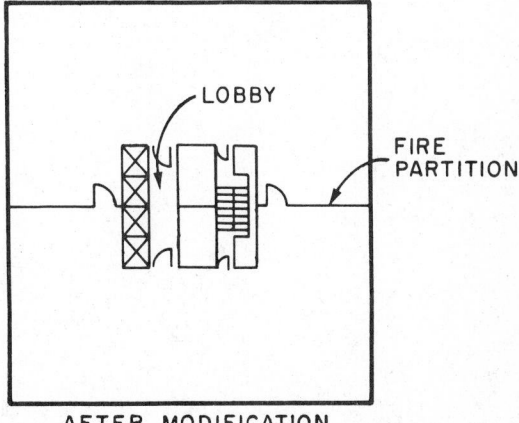

AFTER MODIFICATION

Fig. 6-8F. Modification of an open floor area of a typical office building by addition of a fire partition and lobby access doors.

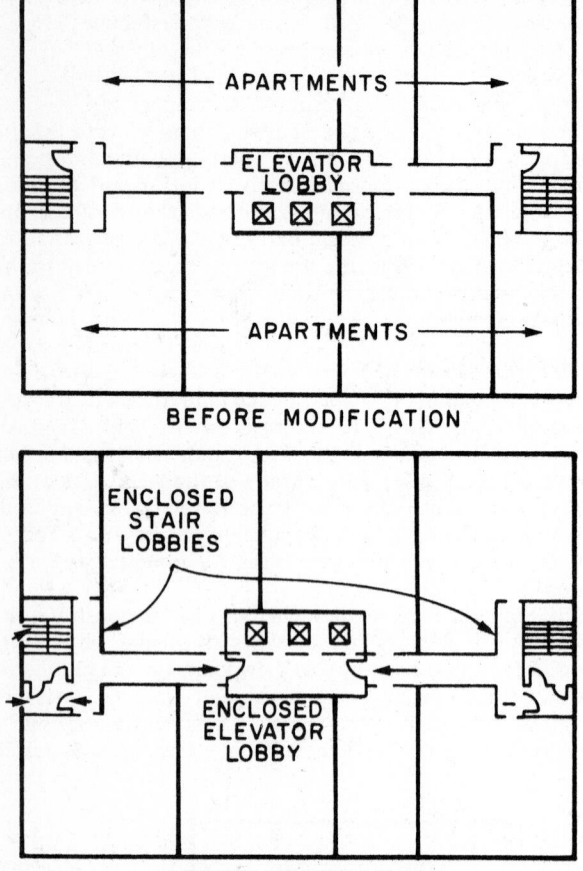

BEFORE MODIFICATION

AFTER MODIFICATION

Fig. 6-8G.   Modification of a floor of a typical apartment build-ing by providing a ventilated lobby to access stairs and elevators. The floor is now divided into two areas.

pressures to be maintained, even with as many as three stairwell doors open.

In tall buildings, the stairwell pressure required might be large enough to prevent doors from being opened. To alleviate this problem, separate compartments within the stairwell, approximately five floors in height, have been proposed. Each compartment would have its own pres-surization fan. In this configuration, fan capacity can be reduced considerably. In addition, pressures can be reduced

significantly and a fan failure in one segment would not seriously impair the effectiveness of the entire system.

The National Building Code of Canada identifies a num-ber of alternative methods for providing smoke control in high-rise buildings. These methods involve the principles of dilution, exhaust, and pressurization. It recognizes that each building represents a unique situation and provides for alternative method of controlling smoke. In this way, the building designer can adapt the system most compatible with his requirements to his particular situation. Figures 6-8F and 6-8G illustrate some of the concepts of smoke control.[15]

Bibliography

References Cited

[1] Ingberg, S. H., "Tests of the Severity of Building Fires," NFPA *Quarterly*, Vol. 22, No. 1, July 1928, pp. 43–61.

[2] Corson, R. L., "The Significance of Fire Loading," NFPA *Quarterly*, Vol. 47, No. 1, July 1953, pp. 65–72.

[3] "A Study of the Baptist Towers Housing for the Elderly Fire," National Fire Protection Association, Boston, 1973.

[4] Sears, A. B., Jr., "Nursing Home Fire—Marietta, Ohio," *Fire Journal*, Vol. 64, No. 3, May 1970, pp. 5–9.

[5] *Fire Protection Through Modern Building Codes*, American Iron and Steel Institute, Washington, D.C., 1971.

[6] *Standard Building Code*, Southern Building Code Congress, Bir-mingham, Ala., 1973, pp. 00–00.

[7] Sharry, J. A., "South America Burning," *Fire Journal*, Vol. 68, No. 4, July 1974, pp. 23–33.

[8] Powers, R. W., "One New York Plaza Fire," New York Board of Fire Underwriters, New York, 1970.

[9] "Fire Safety Lapse Noted in Safe Tower," *Engineering News Record*, Vol. 194, No. 20, May 15, 1975.

[10] Sears, A. B., Jr., "Another Home for the Aged Fire: Ten Killed," *Fire Journal*, Vol. 65, No. 3, May 1972, pp. 5–8, 17.

[11] "Fire Testing of Plastics—DWV Systems," Plastic Pipe Institute, Society of the Plastics Industry, New York, 1974.

[12] "Building Firesafety Criteria—Appendix D, Change 2," General Services Administration, Washington, D.C., 1972.

[13] Koplon, N. A., "Report of the Henry Grady Fire Tests," City of Atlanta Building Department, Atlanta, Ga., Jan. 1973.

[14] DeCicco, P. R., et al, *Report of Fire Tests, Analyses, and Evaluation of Stair Pressurization and Exhaust in High-Rise Office Buildings*, Baywood Publishing Company, New York, 1972.

[15] Galbreath, M., "Fire in High Buildings," Fire Study No. 21, National Research Council of Canada, Division of Building Re-search, Ottawa, Apr. 1968.

NFPA Codes, Standards, and Recommended Practices (see the latest *NFPA Publications and Visual Aids Catalog* for availability of current editions of the following documents)

NFPA No. 80, Standard for Fire Doors and Windows.

NFPA No. 101, Code for Safety to Life from Fire in Buildings and Structures.

Chapter 9

CONCEPTS OF EGRESS DESIGN

A. Fundamentals of Design

Exit design decisions should be based upon an evaluation of a building's total fire defense system coupled with an analysis of population characteristics and hazard of occupancy. The design of the means of egress should be treated as an integral part of the "whole" system which provides reasonable safety to life from fire. In the case of buildings used as schools or theaters housing highly "mobile" occupants, studies have shown certain reproducible "flow" characteristics on the part of persons exiting from the building. The flow characteristics follow certain basic factors which are worthy of study to further the understanding of movement of people within portions of the means of egress. It should be recognized that psychological factors affecting the use of exits during emergencies are difficult to measure. Further, no amount of practical exit facilities can prevent injury or loss of life to persons if a blockage of flow results in a panic.

Human Factors

The design and capacity of passageways, stairways, and other components within the total means of egress is related to physical dimensions of the body. The tendency of people to avoid bodily contact with others should be recognized as a major factor in determining the number of persons projected as occupying a given space at any given time. Given a choice, people usually automatically establish "territories" to avoid bodily contact with others.

Studies have shown that the majority of adult men measure less than 20.7 in. at the shoulder with no allowance for additional thicknesses of clothing.[1] A concept of "body ellipse" is used to develop the design of pedestrian systems. The major axis of the body ellipse measures 24 in., whereas the minor axis is considered 18 in. This ellipse equals 2.3 sq ft, which is assumed to provide a factor determining the maximum practical standing capacity of a space.

Movement of persons results in a swaying action which varies from male to female and also depending upon the type motion involved, e.g., stairs, free movement, or dense crowds. Sway has been observed at $1\frac{1}{2}$ in. left and right during normal free movement. Where movement is reduced to shuffling in dense crowds and movement on stairs a range of sway of almost 4 in. has been observed. In theory, this indicates a width of 30 in. would be required to accommodate a single file of pedestrians travelling up or down stairs.

Crowding of people into spaces where 3 sq ft or less per person is available under nonemergency conditions has resulted in panic situations and injuries. When the average area occupied per person is reduced to $2\frac{3}{4}$ sq ft per person or less, unavoidable contact will be experienced. Needless to say, under the stresses imposed during a fire emergency, such crowding and contact could contribute to crowd pressures resulting in injuries. Experience indicates that so long as movement continues in a direction toward supposed safety, the danger of panic is reduced. When a queue occurs, either because of some artificial, temporary situation or because of some permanent design feature, crowd control will become difficult and the well-being of individuals is threatened.

Factors Affecting Movement of People

An understanding of factors affecting the relative rate at which people may be expected to flow through various components of the total means of egress may be of assistance in resolving design items.

Studies have shown in level walkways, an average walking speed of 250 fpm (feet per minute) is attained under free flow conditions with 25 sq ft available per person. Speeds below 145 fpm are indicative of shuffling restricted motion. Figure 6-9A adapted from Research Report No. 95 of the London Transport Board[2] shows the rate of reduction in speed for concentrations less than 7 to 8 sq ft per person. Speeds of less than 145 fpm are considered to constitute "shuffling" and finally a jam point concentration is indicated at a concentration of one person every 2 sq ft. A significant panic exposure exists (whether or not a real fire emergency exists) any time movement is restricted and the problem becomes urgent under fire conditions when concentrations approach one person every 3 sq ft.

Calculations of flow rates using speed (feet per minute) and density (people per square foot) will reveal flow (people per minute per foot of width) increases as pedestrian area decreases until a point is reached when forward movement becomes restricted to a point that flow begins to drop. Interestingly, observations of flow rates in one study noted the same flow rate sometimes occurred even though walking speeds were significantly different. Investigation reveals the rate of decrease of speed with increase in density provides for uniform flow rates over a wide range of conditions.

A study of footways indicates for passageways over 4 ft wide, flow rates are directly proportional to width. The London Transport Board, Research Report No. 95,[2] determined the flow rate in level passages to be 27 persons per min per ft width; travel down stairways was determined to be 21 people per min per ft width whereas travel in the upward direction was reduced to 19 persons per min ft width. Where the width of a footway is less than 4 ft in

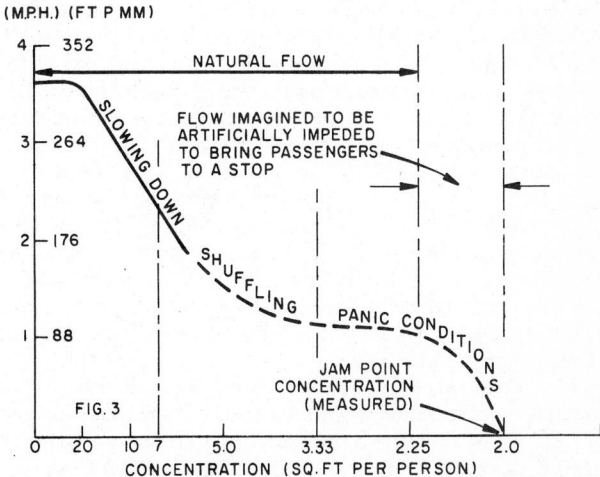

Fig. 6-9A. Speed in Level Passageways. (Adapted from Research Report No. 95, London Transport Board, "Second Report of the Operational Research Team on the Capacity of Footways."[2]

width, the flow rate depends upon the number of traffic lanes which are possible. Absolute maximum flow rates occur when approximately 3 sq ft is occupied per person, which is applicable both to level walkways and stairs. An interesting observation confirmed by two separate studies indicates where flow in opposite directions takes place within a passageway (up to the point where two flows were of equal magnitude in opposite directions) no significant reduction in total flow below that which would be predicted on the basis of a unidirectional flow in the same passage.

Further, observations made of flow rates at short passages (less than 10 ft long) indicate flow can be 50 percent greater than through a long passage of the equivalent width. Further, minor obstructions within a passageway do not appear to have a significant effect on flow. Observations made within a 6-ft wide passage indicated no effect on flow rates when a 1-ft projection was introduced. A 2-ft projection (33 percent reduction in width) reduced the flow rate approximately 10 percent. It should be noted a major obstruction, such as that which occurs at a ticket booth, turnstile and the like, may be expected to interrupt the movement of people and thereby reduce flow rates.

Corners, bends and slight grades (up to 6 percent) are apparently not factors in determining flow rates. A slight reduction in speed does occur; however, the flow rate is maintained by an increased concentration of persons.

A center hand rail or mullion, which has the effect of dividing a passageway into narrower sections, can reduce the capacity of the passageway. In one study, the observed capacity of a 6-ft wide stairway after installation of a center hand rail revealed a reduction from 130 to 105 persons per min after installation of the hand rail.

Except for the very young and very old, age does not appear to be a significant factor in determining travel speed. Studies have shown a significant reduction in walking speeds for persons over 65 years of age. Studies have further revealed a 40 percent increase in the normal walking speed is possible which tends to discount this factor as a major influence on flow rates.[1]

Methods of Calculating Exit Width

Two major principles have been utilized to determine the necessary exit width based upon anticipated population characteristics identified with a specific occupancy.

The Capacity Method: This is based upon the theory that adequate stairways should be provided in a building to adequately house all occupants of the building within the stairway without requiring any movement (flow) out of the stairway. In theory, assuming the stairwell provides a safe and protected area of refuge for all occupants within the protective barrier created by the stairway enclosure, evacuation of the building may then be undertaken on a more leisurely basis thereby permitting people to travel at a rate within their physical ability. The capacity method recognizes that evacuation in the case of high rise buildings is physically very demanding. Further, evacuation of a health care facility is likely to be slow with delays and therefore design criteria is established to permit holding of occupants within exits.

The Flow Method: This method uses the theory of evacuation of a building within a specified maximum length of time. Flow rates have traditionally been set at 45 persons per 22-in. width per min through level passageways and doorways. The flow method appears to have obvious application in assembly occupancy (theaters, for example) and educational occupancies where people are alert, awake, and assumed to be in good physical condition.

Application

The "capacity and flow methods" both have application to efficient design of the means of egress depending upon the specific circumstances. In the situation where people may be assumed to be asleep, sick, aged, or incapacitated from any physical or mental standpoint, evacuation and use of the flow method would seem to be unwise. Therefore, the capacity method that provides a place for everyone within the stairwell enclosure seems to be appropriate.

There is little time between alerting and when exits come into full use in assembly occupancies, and maximum flow rates with reductions in area per person may result in reduced traffic flows which are conducive to panic. On the other hand, the control of children in an educational setting, coupled with the childrens' familiarity with surroundings and their presumed high physical capabilities as well as with a program of drills, should allow rapid evacuation times with minimal probabilities for panic. The flow method appears to have its primary application in those occupancies where people are considered to be alert, awake, and of normal physical ability.

Design of Means of Egress

The design of a means of egress involves more than numbers, flow rates, and densities. Safe exit from a building requires provision of a safe path of escape from fire, arranged for ready use in case of emergency, and sufficient to permit all occupants to reach a place of safety before they are endangered by fire, smoke, or panic. Good exits permit everyone to leave the fire area in the shortest possible time by efficient use of exits. Prompt discovery of fire and alerting of occupants are essential considerations facilitating evacuation early in the fire sequence.

Evacuation times are related to the fire hazard of the occupancy: the higher the hazard, the shorter the exit time.

Depending upon detection and alerting facilities, fire or smoke may prevent the use of one means of egress; therefore, at least one alternate facility, remote from the first, is desirable. Provision of two separate means of egress having no common elements is a fundamental safeguard except where a building or room is so small and so arranged that a second exit would not provide an appreciable increase in safety. The principle of "separate" facilities can be violated by travel through a common space or use of common structural features wherein failure results in simultaneous loss of the two separate exits.

One example of a "common" structure is indicated in the design of multistory buildings, when scissors stairs (two stairs enclosed within a common shaft, separated by a partition common to both stairs) are used. Scissors stairs are sometimes used to increase exit capacity while minimizing loss of valuable floor space. However, where a set of scissors stairs are provided as the only means of egress, where "two remote exits are required," a fundamental principle of exit design is violated. The common partition between stairs could result in the loss of both exits simultaneously during fire leaving no alternate path available.

In some portions of the United States, it is considered acceptable practice to discharge 100 percent of exits through a lobby space at the street floor level. This practice results in travel through a common space. This philosophy further presumes the lobby may be considered a "safe" area for all future uses during the life of the building. Where two remote means of egress are required, this practice becomes questionable.

NFPA No. 101, Life Safety Code, referred to hereinafter

in this chapter as the Life Safety Code, limits openings in exit enclosures to those necessary for access to the enclosure from normally occupied spaces and for egress from the enclosure. Penetration of enclosures by ducts or other utilities constitute a point of weakness and may result in contamination of the enclosure during fire. Furthermore, it is good practice not to use exit enclosures for any purpose which could interfere with its value as an exit. For example, piping for flammable liquids or gases should not be routed through such spaces.

It has been estimated 12 million people within the United States have limited mobility due to physical disabilities. In excess of 250,000 are confined to wheelchairs. Each year, an estimated 100,000 children are added to the total as a result of birth defects. In the design of an emergency means of egress from a building, the removal of handicapped persons is an important consideration. A 30-in. doorway is considered the minimum width to accommodate a person within a wheelchair. In those facilities (government buildings, clinics, etc.) where a concentration of handicapped are present, special life safety considerations are indicated.

B. The Life Safety Code

The Life Safety Code (formerly the Building Exits Code), dating from 1927 and revised and reissued in successive editions, is developed by the NFPA Committee on Safety to Life, a representative international group dedicated to life safety from fire. The Life Safety Code is concerned primarily with life safety. This is the difference between the Life Safety Code and fire protection provisions in building codes which concern themselves with the preservation of property in addition to life.

Exits alone are no guarantee of life safety from fire. They provide no protection to the individual against his own carelessness in such acts, for example, as setting his own clothes on fire. Neither do exits alone provide protection in such places as hospitals, nursing homes, prisons, and mental institutions where occupants are confined, or are physically or mentally unable to escape without assistance. The Life Safety Code does recognize such situations and provides measures, such as fire resistive construction and automatic sprinkler protection, designed to restrain the spread of fire and "defend" occupants in place until help can be secured to assist occupants in the use of exits, or until the fire is extinguished.

In general, life safety from fire requires the following, all of which are specified in the Life Safety Code:

1. A sufficient number of unobstructed exits of adequate capacity and properly designed, with convenient access thereto.

2. Protection of exits against fire and smoke during the length of time they are designed to be in use.

3. Alternate exit and means of travel thereto for use in case one exit is blocked by fire.

4. Subdivision of areas and fire resistive construction to provide areas of refuge in those occupancies where evacuation is the last resort.

5. Protection of vertical openings to limit fire effects to a single floor.

6. Alarm systems to alert occupants and notify the fire department in case of fire.

7. Adequate lighting of exits and paths of travel to reach them.

8. Signs indicating ways to reach exits where needed.

9. Safeguarding of equipment and of areas of unusual

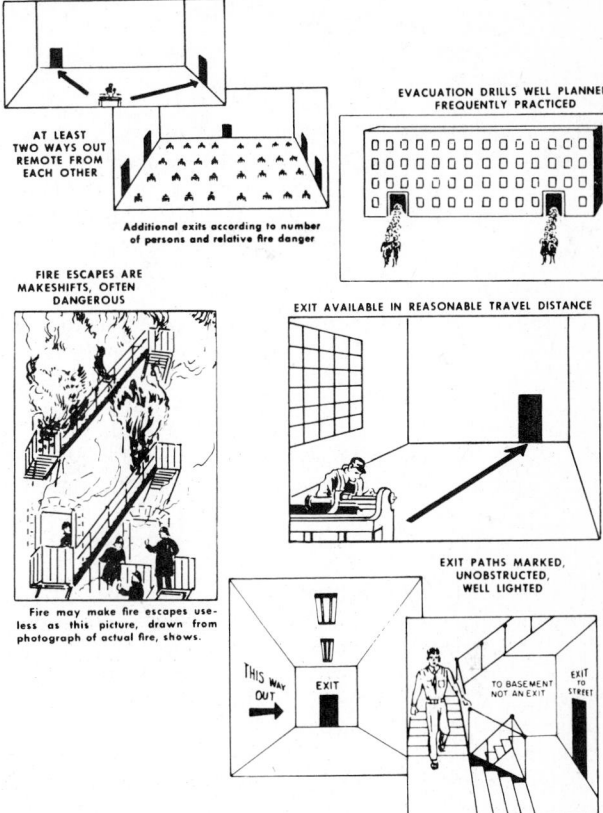

Fig. 6-9B.   Principles of exit safety.

hazard which could produce a fire capable of endangering the safety of persons on the way out.

10. Exit drill procedures to assure orderly exit.

11. Control of psychological factors conducive to panic.

12. Control of interior finish and contents to prevent a fast spreading fire that could trap occupants.

Figure 6-9B illustrates some of the principles of exit safety.

The Life Safety Code recognizes full reliance cannot be placed on any single safeguard. Any item may not function due to mechanical or human failures, and for this reason two or more safeguards, any one of which will result in reasonable life safety, should be provided. The Code also calls for the safeguarding of fire hazards and specifies various details of automatic sprinkler installation and other protective features.

The Life Safety Code is widely used as a guide to good practice and as a basis for laws or regulations. It differs from building codes in that it makes little distinction between different classes of building construction; however, where rapid evacuation of a building is not possible, due either to occupant characteristics or because of the size of the building, construction type becomes an important factor and is treated.

The Code also recognizes that all buildings contain sufficient quantities of combustible contents to produce lethal quantities of smoke and heat; thus, smoke is considered to be the first hazard to life.

The Life Safety Code covers both new construction and existing buildings, and is intended to provide safety to life from fire in both. The enforcing authority is given considerable latitude in dealing with existing buildings. Each existing building represents a special problem requiring individual attention for the most effective and economical method of treatment.

The time-honored argument that a building complied with all legal requirements when erected many years ago, and that the owner should not now be penalized, is not accepted as an excuse for subjecting the occupants to unnecessary peril from fire. Neither is the argument that the cost of improvements would be prohibitive, so they should not be required. If the cost of reasonable safety is too great the use of the structure should be changed or prohibited as there is no justification for subjecting building occupants to the menace of fire.

There is a large area of possible disagreement as to what constitutes reasonable safety in any given case. It is not possible to provide 100 percent safety from fire, but below a certain point the building becomes a "firetrap." Where should the line be drawn? The Life Safety Code provides guidance in such decisions—guidance not only established on a judgment basis by a large group of experts, but with the help of studies of the major loss of life fires and tests that have contributed substantially to the knowledge of this subject.

The Life Safety Code treats various occupancy groups according to their hazard, including psychological factors as well as strictly physical factors. These groups are: (1) assembly, (2) educational, (3) health care and penal, (4) residential, (5) mercantile, (6) office, (7) industrial, (8) storage, and (9) miscellaneous.

Separate and different exit requirements are made for each group, with various sub-groups included. These classifications, based on hazard to life, often differ from building code occupancy classifications. For example, mercantile and office occupancies are often grouped together in building codes. There is an increased hazard to life in mercantile properties, owing to the displays of combustible merchandise, the greater density of population, and the transient character of most occupants. These factors are not found in office buildings which have a relatively low contents combustibility, lower population density, and occupants who remain day after day and presumably have opportunity to familiarize themselves with the exits.

C. Hazards of Contents

Hazard of contents is meant to convey the relative danger of the start and spread of fire in a building, the probable smoke or gases generated by the fire, and the possibility of an explosion or other occurrence endangering the lives and safety of the occupants. The degree of hazard is usually determined by the character of the contents and the processes or operations conducted in the building. Most of the Life Safety Code requirements are based upon the exposure created by ordinary hazard contents. Special requirements for buildings with high hazard contents also are provided.

Influence of Occupancy

To assist in evaluating hazards, the Life Safety Code establishes three classifications of contents: ordinary, high, and low.

Low Hazard: These are contents of such low combustibility that no self-propagating fire can occur in them; consequently, the only probable danger requiring the use of emergency exits will be from panic, fumes or smoke, or fire from some external source.

Ordinary Hazard: These are contents that are liable to burn with moderate rapidity and to give off a considerable volume of smoke, but from which neither poisonous fumes nor explosions are to be feared in case of fire. This class includes most buildings and represents the basis for the general requirements of the Code.

High Hazard: These are contents that are liable to burn with extreme rapidity or from which poisonous fumes or explosions are to be feared in the event of fire. Examples are occupancies where flammable liquids or gases are handled, used, or stored; where combustible dust explosion hazards exist; where hazardous chemicals or explosives are stored; where combustible fibers are processed or handled in a manner to produce combustible flyings; and similar situations.

Influence of Building Construction and Design

A building of fire resistive construction is designed to permit a burn-out of contents without structural collapse. Fire resistive design does not assure safety of occupants of such buildings. However, the ability of a structural frame to maintain building rigidity under fire exposure is important to the maintenance of exit enclosures. Where a 2-hr fire-rated exit enclosure is required, a fire resistant structural frame to maintain building rigidity under fire exposure is important to the maintenance of exit enclosures. Where a 2-hr fire-rated exit enclosure is required, a fire resistant structural frame capable of withstanding stresses imposed by fire for a similar time period is also necessary. Restated, it is inconsistent to provide a 2-hr exit enclosure in a building having a structural frame rated at a lesser level (1 hr, for example) unless special precautions are taken to prevent structural failure from affecting exit enclosures.

One of the most significant factors in the design of multistory buildings from the standpoint of life safety and exit design is the protection of vertical openings. Because of the natural tendency of fire to spread upward within a building, careful attention to details of design and construction are required to minimize this effect. The greatest hazard to life results from fires which start below occupants, as in basements. Similarly, fires in multistory buildings may result in smoke spread into enclosed exits prior to evacuation. Conversely, escape is relatively simple from fires which occur overhead, providing warning is given and adequate exits are available.

The influence on life safety of materials used in building construction depends largely upon whether or not the materials will burn, support combustion or create unusual amounts of smoke when exposed by fire initially involving contents. The use of certain plastics for insulation, for example, could contribute to rapid flame/smoke spread. Brick walls enclosing a wood "fire trap" interior are a little better than wood outside walls around the same interior structure; in fact, brick walls may actually increase the danger by engendering a false sense of security whereas if the exterior walls were all wood, the hazard to life would be popularly recognized and greater precautions would be taken.

Exit requirements are based upon buildings of conventional design; unusual buildings call for special treatment. Buildings without windows are an example. Windows provide a number of advantages. Persons at windows have access to fresh air, can see fire department rescue operations in progress, and are less subject to panic. Windows provide an emergency means of escape and for rescue. They also serve the extremely important function of accessibility to the building by the fire department for rescue and fire fighting. Automatic sprinklers are considered a requirement for life safety in windowless buildings and in underground structures.

Table 6-9A.   Summary of Life Safety Code Requirements for Interior Finish

Occupancy	Class of Interior Finish*		
	Exits	Access to Exits	Other Spaces
Places of assembly—Class A†	A	A	A or B
Places of assembly—Class B‡	A	A	A or B
Places of assembly—Class C§	A	A	A, B, or C
Educational	A	A	A, B, or C
Educational—unsprinklered open plan buildings‖	A	A or B ⎫	A or B
Flexible plan buildings#	A	A ⎭	C or low height partitions
Institutional, existing—hospitals, nursing homes, residential-custodial care	A or B	A or B	A or B
Institutional, new—hospitals, nursing homes, residential-custodial care	A	A	A B in individual room with capacity not more than 4 persons
Residential, new—apartment houses	A or B	A or B	A, B, or C
Residential, existing—apartment houses	A or B	A, B, or C	A, B, or C
Residential—dormitories	A or B	A, B, or C	A, B, or C
Residential, new—1- and 2-family, lodging or rooming houses			A, B, or C
Residential, existing—1- and 2-family, lodging or rooming houses			A, B, C, or D
Residential, new—hotels	A or B	A or B	A, B, or C
Residential, existing—hotels	A or B	(1) A or B if required path of exit travel; (2) A, B, or C if not used as required path of exit travel	A, B, or C
Mercantile—Class A**	A or B		ceilings—A or B walls—A, B, or C
Mercantile—Class B††	A or B		ceilings—A or B walls—A, B, or C
Mercantile—Class C‡‡	A or B		A, B, or C
Office	A or B	A or B	A, B, or C
Industrial	A, B, or C	A, B, or C	A, B, or C
Towers	A or B		A or B

* There are five classes of interior finish: Class A, flame spread 0-25; Class B, flame spread 25-75; Class C, flame spread 75-200; Class D, flame spread 200-500; and Class E, over 500. Where a standard system of automatic sprinklers is installed, an interior finish with a flame spread rating not over Class C may be used in any location where Class B is normally specified, and with a rating of Class B in any location where Class A is normally specified, unless specifically prohibited elsewhere in the Life Safety Code.
† Class A Places of Assembly—1,000 persons or more.
‡ Class B Places of Assembly—300 to 1,000 persons
§ Class C Places of Assembly—100 to 300 persons
‖ Open plan buildings—includes all buildings where no permanent partitions are provided between rooms or between rooms and corridors.
Flexible plan buildings have movable corridor walls and movable partitions of full height construction with doors leading from rooms to corridors.
** Class A Mercantile Occupancies—stores having aggregate gross area of 30,000 sq ft or more, or utilizing more than 3 floor levels for sales purposes.
†† Class B Mercantile Occupancies—stores of less than 30,000 sq ft aggregate gross area, but over 3,000 sq ft, or utilizing any floors above or below street floor level for sales purposes, except that if more than 3 floors are utilized, store shall be Class A.
‡‡ Class C Mercantile Occupancies—stores of 3,000 sq ft or less gross area, used for sales purposes on street level only. (A single balcony or mezzanine floor with less than half the area of the street level floor and which is used for sales purposes is not counted as another floor.)

Influence of Interior Finish, Furnishings, and Decorations

Unreasonably rapid spread of flame over the surface of walls and ceilings may prevent orderly exit. The Life Safety Code in general limits flame spread characteristics of interior finish to a maximum of 200 based upon results of tests conducted in accordance with NFPA No. 255, Method of Test of Surface Burning Characteristics of Building Materials (Tunnel Test—see Chap. 6 of this Section), with lower ratings for interior finish used in exits and access to exits. Select-grade red-oak produces a flame spread rating of 100. Lower rated finishes are also required in certain areas in individual occupancies. A fire retardant coating may be used on existing finishes to reduce rate of flame spread. Automatic sprinklers sometimes permit the use of materials with higher flame spread ratings. Table 6-9A is a summary of interior finish requirements contained in the Life Safety

Code for various types of occupancies. (See Chapter 6 of this Section for further discussion of interior finish.)

Furnishings and decorations—particularly furnishings—are playing an increasingly important role in loss of life by fire. Decorations can be flame retardant treated (see Sec. 3, Chap. 2 and Sec. 5, Chap. 10). Furnishings, on the other hand, are only occasionally considered in assessing the fire hazard; yet furnishings can represent practically the only combustibles present in some occupancies.

The use of plastics in furnishings results in "fuels" easily ignited (by a match, for example), capable of rapid fire growth with accompanying large amounts of smoke. A recent fire principally involving plastic seating in the BOAC Passenger Terminal at Kennedy Airport, New York, in August, 1970,[3] is an illustration. A fire on December, 1974, at the Sac-Osage Hospital, Osceola, Mo. resulted in the death of 8 persons.[4] Fire was confined to a single patient room and principally involved two plastic mattresses and two chairs with foam cushions. Heavy quantities of black smoke were produced by the fire prior to discovery. Two persons died in a New York office building fire in August, 1970.[5] Although the factors involved in this fire within a high-rise building are many, a report of the fire noted that despite a generally low order of combustibility, where there is ". . . the severe fire hazard caused by foamed plastic furniture, there is the recipe for conflagration."

Influence of Psychological and Physiological Factors

Psychological and physiological factors must be considered in addition to physical factors in planning exits. People cannot be expected to behave logically in the stress of fire conditions. Panic is contagious, and the danger is greater in a large crowd, as in a place of public assembly. Fear, rather than actual fire danger, is the main factor in panic. Fatal panics have occurred where there was no fire in a building, but people thought there was a fire. On the other hand, where people have had confidence in a building and its exits there have been orderly evacuations without panic even though actual danger was present. As long as people can keep moving toward a recognized place of safety, there is little danger of panic, but any stoppage of movement is conducive to panic. Once panic starts, exits may be quickly blocked.

Evacuation procedures and creation of areas of refuge within high-rise buildings in some cases contemplates movement upward within buildings. The effectiveness of this concept has not been fully evaluated in actual fire emergencies. A question exists because of the orientation of most people toward "escape." It is possible, in spite of instruction, occupants may attempt to evacuate a building in the conventional "down and out" approach.[6]

Under fire conditions, people are likely to try to leave a building by the same route by which they entered, neglecting alternate means of exit; thus all exits need to be conspicuously marked. It is also important that all exits from a building are used as a matter of daily routine so that occupants will be familiar with them. The Life Safety Code requires that in assembly occupancies the main exit (which also serves as the entrance) be sized to handle at least half of the occupant load.

Influence of Fire Protection Equipment

It is questionable practice to rely on fire extinguishment to the neglect of exits because of the possibility of both human and mechanical failures, and because loss of life may occur before fire fighting facilities can be effective. Manual fire fighting, however valuable, under no conditions can be accepted as an excuse for not providing proper exits.

Automatic sprinklers, where a complete standard system is installed, are sufficiently reliable so that they do have a major influence on life safety. In addition to providing an automatic alarm of fire, they quickly discharge water on the fire before smoke has spread dangerously. While automatic sprinklers should not be made the excuse for the neglect of safe exits, they are recognized in various ways by the Life Safety Code, including shortening permissible travel distance to exits, the use of interior finish of greater combustibility, and, in buildings used for health care, the use of combustible construction in situations where it would otherwise be prohibited. Sprinklers are particularly valuable in dealing with exit problems in existing buildings.

Automatic fire detection (fire alarm) systems (see Sec. 12, Chap. 2) have a valuable function in notifying oc-

cupants of fire so that they may escape promptly; however, they are not specified in the Life Safety Code to any great extent. They only provide warning and of themselves do nothing to stop the spread of fire. An automatic fire detection system is not a substitute for safe exits.

D. Definition of the Term "Exit"

The Life Safety Code includes the term "exit" in an overall definition of means of egress, i.e., a means of egress being a continuous path of travel from any point in a building or structure to the open air outside at ground level, and, consisting of three separate and distinct parts. They are: (1) the way of exit access, (2) the exit, and (3) the means of discharge from the exit.

An "exit access" is defined as that portion of a means of egress which leads to an entrance to an exit.

An "exit" is that portion of a means of egress which is separated from the area of the building from which escape is to be made by walls, floors, doors, or other means which provide the protected path necessary for the occupants to proceed with reasonable safety to the exterior of the building. It may comprise vertical and horizontal means of travel such as doorways, stairways, escalators, ramps, corridors, passageways, and fire escapes.

"Exit discharge" is that portion of a means of egress between the termination of the exit and the exterior of the building at ground level.

Figure 6-9C illustrates the relationship in a building of the three areas defined above.

The types of permissible exits are: doors leading directly outside or through a protected passageway to the outside; horizontal exits, smokeproof towers, interior stairs, and outside stairs and ramps; escalators that meet certain specific requirements; and moving walks. Elevators are not accepted as exits. See Figure 6-9D for illustrations of three common types of exit arrangements.

Exits are measured in units of 22-in. width. In 1914 the NFPA Committee on Safety to Life recommended this figure to the NFPA Annual Meeting as the average width of a man at shoulder height. It has been checked periodically since that time against national studies of the dimensions of the human figure.[7]

The placement of exits is a matter for judgment, because any specific requirement on this would place undue hardship on the designer in making maximum economical use of space. The Life Safety Code states that exits must be remote

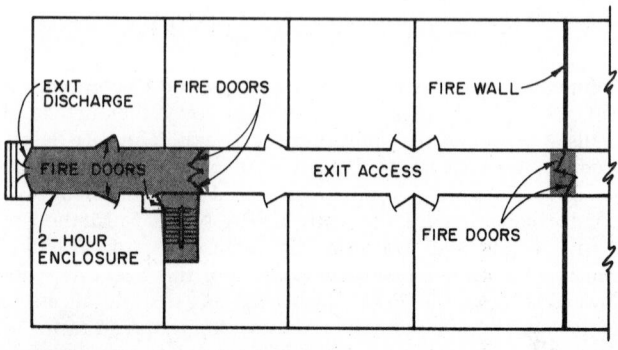

SHADED AREAS ARE EXITS

Fig. 6-9C. Plan view of the first floor of a multistory building showing the "exit access," the "exits," and "exit discharge" in a typical situation. The shaded areas are the exits, and openings to them from normally occupied spaces are limited to those necessary for access.

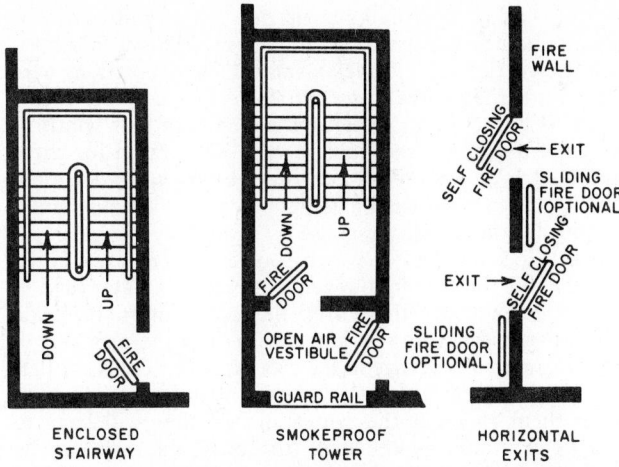

ENCLOSED STAIRWAY   SMOKEPROOF TOWER   HORIZONTAL EXITS

Fig. 6-9D. Plan views of types of exits. Stair enclosure prevents fire on any floor trapping persons above. Smokeproof tower is better, as opening to air at each floor largely prevents chance of smoke in stairway. Horizontal exit provides a quick refuge, lessens need of hasty flight down stairs. Horizontal sliding fire doors provided for safeguarding property values are arranged to close automatically in case of fire when open. Swinging doors are self-closing. Two wall openings are needed for exit in two directions.

from each other. The principle involved is to provide two exits, so located that occupants can travel in either of two opposite directions to reach an exit. This is important when it is necessary for them to leave a fire area and move toward an exit. If they must enter the fire area to reach an exit, it is doubtful whether they will be able or willing to do so.

The Access to an Exit

The access to an exit is that portion of a means of egress which leads to an entrance to an exit. The access to an exit may be a corridor, an aisle, a balcony, a gallery, a porch, or a roof. Its length establishes the travel distance to an exit—an extremely important feature of a means of egress, since an occupant might be exposed to fire during the time it takes to reach an exit. The average recommended distance is 100 ft, but this varies with the occupancy, depending on the fire hazard and the physical ability and alertness of the occupants (see Table 6-9B). The travel distance may be measured from the door of a room to an exit or from the most remote point in a room or floor area to an exit. In those occupancies where there are large numbers of people in an open floor area or where the nature of the business conducted makes an open floor area desirable, the travel distance is measured from the most remote point in the area to the exits. Conversely, in occupancies where there are only a few people in small cutoff areas or rooms (e.g., hotels and apartments) the travel distance is measured from the door of the room or area to the exits. The only exception to this rule is the office occupancy, where, because of the character of the occupancy and the low hazard of the contents, the travel distance is measured from the most remote point on a floor to the exits.

In most cases travel distance can be increased—up to 50 percent—if the building is sprinklered.

A dead end is an extension of a corridor or aisle beyond an exit or an access to exits that forms a pocket in which occupants may be trapped. Since there is only one access to an exit from a dead end, a fire in a dead end between an exit and an occupant prevents the occupant from reaching the exit. While traveling toward an exit in a smoke-filled

Table 6-9B. Summary of Life Safety Code Provisions for Travel Distances to Exits

Occupancy	Dead-End Limit, Ft	Travel Limit to an Exit, Ft	
		Unsprinklered	Sprinklered
Places of Assembly	N.R.*	150	200
Educational	20	150	200
Open plan	N.R.*	150	200
Flexible plan	N.R.*	150	200
Institutional			
New	30	100	150
Residential			
Hotels	35	100	150
Apartments	35	100	150
Dormitories	0	100	150
Lodging or rooming houses, 1- and 2-family dwellings	N.R.*	N.R.*	N.R.*
Mercantile			
Class A, B, and C	50	100	150
Open Air	0	N.R.*	N.R.*
Business	50	200	300
Industrial			
General, and special purpose	50	100	150†
High hazard	0	75	75
Open structures	N.R.*	N.R.*	N.R.*
Storage			
Low and ordinary hazard	N.R.*	N.R.*	N.R.*
High hazard	N.R.*	75	100
Enclosed parking garages	50	150	200
Aircraft hangars, ground floor	N.R.*	Varies ‡	Varies ‡
Aircraft hangars, mezzanine floor	N.R.*	75	75

* No requirement or not applicable.
† A special exception is made for one-story, sprinklered, industrial occupancies.
‡ See Paragraph 15-3111 of Life Safety Code for special requirements.

atmosphere an occupant may pass by the exit and be trapped in the dead end. Ideally, dead ends should be prohibited; but, for purposes of design latitude and effective utilization of space, dead ends are permitted in most occupancies, within reasonable limits.

The width of an access to exits should be at least sufficient for the number of persons it must accommodate (minimum: 28 in.). In some occupancies, the width of the access is governed by the character of the occupancy— for example, hospitals, where patients will be moved in beds; therefore, the corridors in patient areas must be wide enough for a bed to be wheeled out of a room and turned 90 degrees.

A fundamental principle of exit access is provision of a free and unobstructed way to exits. If the access passes through a room that can be locked or through an area containing a fire hazard more severe than is typical of the occupancy, the principles of exit access are violated.

The floor of an exit access should be level: if it cannot be level, small differences in elevation may be overcome by a ramp, large differences by stairs. Where only one or two steps are necessary to overcome differences in level in an exit access, a ramp is preferred because in a crowded corridor people may not see the steps or notice that persons in front of them have stepped up and may therefore trip and fall on the stairs.

The Discharge of an Exit

Ideally, all exits in a building should discharge directly or through a fire resistive passageway to the outside of the building; but in deference both to building owners and operators and to designers, the Life Safety Code permits a maximum of 50 percent of the exits in most occupancies to discharge into the street floor. The obvious disadvantage of this arrangement is that it is possible, if a fire occurs on the street floor, for people using the exit discharging to that floor to be discharged into the fire area. In some occupancies it is impossible to retreat up the exit to a floor above to gain access to another exit because, for security reasons, the doors in the stairway are locked on the inside except at the street floor. Therefore, if any exits discharge to the street floor, the Code requires: (1) that such exits discharge to a free and unobstructed way to the outside of the building, (2) that the entire street floor be sprinklered, and (3) that the street floor be separated from any floors below by construction having a 2-hr fire resistance rating.

Discharging an exit to the outside is not necessarily discharging to a safe place. If the exit discharges to a court, exit passageway must be provided from the court; if the exit discharges to a fenced yard, sufficient area must be provided to handle the expected occupant load far enough away from the building so that the occupants will not be exposed to fire in the building. If the exit discharges to an alley, the alley must be wide enough to accommodate the capacity of all the exits discharging to it, and any openings in the building walls bordering it should be protected to prevent fire exposure to occupants discharging through it.

When exit stairs from floors above the street floor continue on to floors below the street floor, occupants evacuating the building may miss the door to the street level and continue down the stairway and enter a floor below, completely missing the exit discharge. Therefore, the Life Safety Code recommends a physical barrier or some other effective means at the street-floor landing to prevent this.

Capacity of Unit of Exit Width

The capacity in number of persons of a unit of exit width varies with the occupancy—from 30 persons per unit of exit width for hospitals to 100 persons per unit of exit width for office buildings and assembly buildings for travel in a horizontal direction. For travel in an inclined direction, e.g., downstairs, the figures vary from 22 persons per unit of exit width in hospitals to 75 persons per unit of exit width in places of assembly (see Table 6-9C). The reason for these variations is to establish a consistent total evacuation time in different occupancies, based upon the physical ability, mental alertness, and response to discipline of the occupants. In occupancies in which people sleep or are housed for care, the time taken to reach exits will be greater than in other occupancies; therefore, the exits must be wide enough to prevent any waiting to get into the exit and to provide an area of refuge in the exit. It can be expected that in an assembly occupancy people will rush to the exits and reach them at about the same time, so they will have to wait before entering the exit (the expected rush can be partly overcome by requiring the main exit to provide at least 50 percent of the total required exit width, on the assumption that people will try to leave by means of the same door through which they entered).

The capacity of exits is used to establish a consistency of evacuation time on the basis of the rate of travel through a door of 60 persons per min and down a stairway of 45 persons per min per unit of exit width respectively. These figures were established by actual counts conducted in several separate studies.[8]

Occupant Load

Occupant load, or the number of people to be expected in a building at any time, for whom exits must be provided, is determined by dividing the gross area of the building or the net area of a specific portion of the building by the area in square feet projected for each person. The amount of floor area projected for each person varies with the occupancy (see Table 6-9C). These figures are based upon actual counts of people in buildings and review of architects' plans. In some situations the actual number of people in a building can be determined at the design stage—in which case this number should be used in the design of the exits. A typical example is an assembly occupancy in which fixed seating is installed. Counting the number of seats provided would obviously give a more accurate figure than multiplying a square-foot-per-person figure by the net floor area.

Computing Required Exit Width

To compute the required exit widths from the individual floors of a building is it necessary to follow these steps: (1) calculate the floor area (net or gross, whichever is applicable); (2) determine from the Life Safety Code the allowable number of sq ft per person; (3) divide the number of sq ft per person into the floor area to determine the number of people for which exits must be provided (occupant load) for that floor; (4) determine from the Life Safety Code the capacity of the type of exit(s) to be used for the occupancy being designed; and, finally, (5) calculate the number of units of exit width for each type of exit used based upon its capacity.

It should be pointed out that in a multistoried building, if X units of exit width are required from each floor, the stairways serving those floors do not need to be X times the number of floors served in units of exit width. The stairs need be only wide enough to serve each floor—but not less than the minimum width allowed by the Life Safety Code.

Street-floor exits may require special treatment, depending on the occupancy. Some occupancies require street-floor exits to be sized to handle not only the occupant load of the

Table 6-9C. Summary of Life Safety Code Provisions for Occupant Load and Capacity of Exits

Occupancy	Occupant Load	Capacity of Exits Number of Persons per Unit of Exit Width					
	Sq Ft per Person	Doors* Outside	Horizontal Exit	Ramp Class A	Ramp Class B	Escalator	Stairs
Places of Assembly	15 Net	100	100	100	75	75	75
Areas of concentrated use without fixed seating	7 Net						
Standing space	3 Net						
Educational		100	100	100	60		60
Classroom area	20 Net						
Shops and vocational	50 Net						
Institutional		30	30	30	30		22
Sleeping departments	120 Gross						
Impatient departments	240 Gross						
Residential	200 Gross	100	100	100	75	75	75
Mercantile		100	100			60	60
Street floor and sales basement	30 Gross						
Other floors	60 Gross						
Storage-shipping	100 Gross						
Business	100 Gross	100	100	100	60	60	60
Industrial	100 Gross	100	100	100	60	60	60

* Not more than three risers or 21 in. above or below grade.

street floor but also a percentage of the load of the exits discharging to the street floor from floors above and below. In addition, in those occupancies where floors above and/or below the street floor are permitted to have unenclosed stairs and escalators connecting them with the street floor, the exits must be sufficient to provide simultaneously for all the occupants of all communicating levels and areas. In other words, all communicating levels in the same fire area are considered as a single floor area for purposes of determining the required exit capacity. This can have considerable effect on the sizing of the street-floor exits.

It should also be pointed out exits should never decrease in width along their length of travel, and if two or more exits converge into a common exit, the common exit should never be narrower than the sum of the width of the exits converging into it.

Generally, the minimum number of exits is two. In certain situations, because of very low occupant load and low fire hazard, one exit may be permitted.

Dynamic Evaluation of Exit Design

Exit design may be evaluated on a dynamic basis using calculated evacuation times. Dynamic evaluation allows for the establishment of goals in terms of evacuation times and certain other key criteria.

For example, the General Services Administration (GSA) has established a goal oriented system approach to building fire safety which utilizes specific sets of goals for normal federal office type operations.[9] The established goals are as follows:

1. All occupants exposed to the fire environment must be able to evacuate to a safe area within 90 sec of alarm.

2. A portion of this time, not to exceed approximately 15 sec, can be involved in traveling in a direction toward the fire, e.g., dead-end corridor.

3. All occupants must reach an area of refuge within 5 min of downward vertical travel or within 1 min of upward vertical movement.

Further criteria established by the GSA for evaluation uses 3.5 fps as the rate of horizontal movement. Exit flow rates for level travel is calculated at 60 persons per min per 24-in. width; 45 persons per min per 24-in. width. down stairs and 40 persons per min per 24-in. width up stairs.

Fatigue is judged to become important after 5 min of travel in a downward direction or 1 min of travel in an upward direction and, therefore, becomes a "human factor" consideration impacting on design.

The time to exit from a building can be calculated using information and formulas contained within studies produced by the London Transport Board[2] and National Research Council of Canada. Mr. M. Galbreath, National Research Council of Canada, Division of Building Research, prepared Fire Research Note No. 8 entitled "Time of Evacuation by Stairs in Hi-Rise Buildings"[10] using data developed by a study conducted by the London Transport Board and a method designed in a British post-war building study.[11]

Calculations are possible based upon the number of people discharged per unit of exit width per min. The calculated evacuation time reflects:

1. The time required to fill the stairs with people.

2. The time during which additional people can enter the stairs from the upper floors.

3. The time required for all people remaining in the stairs to discharge to the outside.

The following calculation method results in the time for complete evacuation based upon the sum of the preceding intervals 1, 2, and 3:

$$T = \frac{N + n}{r \times u}$$

where

T = the time in min required for complete evacuation by stairs.

N = the number of people in the building above the first floor.

n = the number of people who can stand on the stairs at 3 sq ft per person or the number of people on the floor, whichever is less.

r = the rate of discharge of the stairs in people per unit exit width per min (see Table 6-9D).

u = the number of 22-in. exit units of stair width.

This calculation method assumes occupants will be uniformly distributed over the floor area. If, however, all occupants were located 100 ft from the stair, additional time would be required. In fact, an additional $\frac{1}{2}$ min evacuation time would be added to the total.

Further, it is necessary to determine the time required for the person located at the most remote point of the floor under consideration to reach the stair or exit. If the travel time for this person exceeds the time calculated for all persons to egress by stairs or other exits, this additional time interval becomes a factor in the total evacuation time.

The method of calculation described above provides guidance in terms of the minimum time necessary for evacuating a building under normal considerations. It is obvious loss of an exit stair due to contamination, artificial obstructions to exit paths, and the like could seriously affect evacuation times. From earlier discussions, it was noted when densities result in less than 7 to 8 sq ft per person, *forward motion* is significantly slowed and conditions conducive to panic may be created.

Table 6-9E records evacuation times calculated and provides a comparison to actual evacuation times measured as a result of drills conducted during nonemergencies.

E. Exit Facilities and Arrangements

The following kinds of exit facilities are covered in the Life Safety Code:

Doors

Doors should swing with exit travel except for small rooms. Vertical sliding or rolling doors are not recognized as exits. Panic hardware should be installed on exit doors in places of assembly and schools.

Where doors serve to protect exit facilities, as in stairway enclosures and smoke barriers, they must be kept normally closed to serve their function of stopping the spread of

Table 6-9D. Relationship Between Concentration of People on Stairs and Forward Movement[10]

Concentration of People on Stairs, sq ft per person	Forward Movement, ft per min	Resultant Discharge from Stairs, persons per unit exit width* per min.
2	0	0
2.5	53	39
3.0	75	45
3.5	82	43
4.0	94	43
4.5	106	43
5.0	117	43
5.5	129	43
6.0	139	43
6.5	143	40
7.0	147	39
7.5	150	37
8.0	152	35
8.5	154	33
9.0	156	31
9.5	157	30
10.0	158	29
11.0	158	26
12.0	158	24
13.0	158	22
14.0	158	21
15.0	158	19

* unit exit width = 22 in.

smoke, or, if open, must be closed immediately in case of fire. Ordinary fusible link operated devices to close doors in case of fire will function to stop the spread of fire, but do not operate to stop the spread of smoke, which can have fatal effects even if at relatively low temperature.

Persons who are ignorant or oblivious of fire hazards commonly block self-closing doors open, using hooks or wedges under the door to keep the door from closing. Doors are blocked open to provide ventilation, for the convenience of building maintenance personnel, to avoid accident hazard due to swinging doors, and for other reasons. In addition to the imposition of drastic penalties for blocking doors open, the following measures have been suggested to deal with this situation:

1. Use of smokeproof towers, which protect against smoke even if doors are open.

2. Doors normally closed, opened electrically or pneumatically upon the approach of persons to the door.

Table 6-9E. Time of Evacuation for Certain Existing Office Buildings[12]

Building No.	Height in Stories	Area of Exit Stairs per Floor, sq ft	Width of Exit Stairs, Unit Exit Width	Average Number of Occupants per Floor at Time of Survey	Evacuation Time Calculated by Formula, min	Evacuation Time in Practice Drill, min	Maximum No. of Occupants per Floor By NBC Provisions
1	7	857	10	61	2.1	$4\frac{1}{2}$	600
2	7	636	8	108	2.1	5	480
3	9	692	8	133	3.6	$4\frac{1}{2}$	480
4	9	408	4	111	6.0	$5\frac{1}{2}$	300
5	11	346	4	110	6.7	$6\frac{1}{2}$	240
6	11	150	4	100	5.8	$7\frac{1}{2}$	240
7	12	314	4	67	4.3	9	240
8	13	319	6	38	1.8	4	360
9	18	260	4	50	5.2	$7\frac{1}{2}$	240
10	22	160	2	80	20.0	incomplete	180

3. Doors normally closed, opened and held open manually by monitors, as in schools.

4. Doors normally open, but equipped with door closers and held open by magnetic hold-open devices which release and allow the doors to close on operation of an automatic sprinkler system, automatic fire detection system or smoke or other products of combustion detection devices.

There are qualifications and limitations applicable to each of the several methods, the most important of which is that in the event of failure of electric current, the door must close and remain closed unless manually opened for escape purposes.

Another major maintenance difficulty with exits is the door which is locked to prevent unauthorized access or for other reasons. The Life Safety Code specifies that all doors must be kept unlocked from the side from which egress is made at all times when the building is occupied. Types of locks which let people go out while not letting people go in are satisfactory, but even this type is not satisfactory when there is collusion between people in the building and those outside. Possible safe measures to prevent unauthorized use of exit doors include:

1. Automatic alarm to ring when door is opened.

2. Visual supervision (wired-glass panels and mirrors may be used where appropriate).

3. Automatic photographic devices to provide pictures of users.

Of the above, only the first two have been used to any material extent.

So-called exit locks, with a break-glass unit actuated by striking with the hand on a handle are not permitted by the Life Safety Code unless installed in conjunction with panic bars because they do not comply with the provision which reads: "A latch or other fastening device on an exit door shall be provided with a knob, handle, panic bar or other simple device, the method of operation of which is obvious, even in darkness."

Other types of break-glass locks, and electrical controls for releasing exits from a central point are prohibited, except where controls may be necessary as in prisons and mental institutions.

A single door in a doorway should not be less than 28 in. or more than 48 in. in width. To prevent tripping, the floor on both sides of the door should have the same elevation.

Exit Door Hardware (Panic Hardware)

The exit doors of occupancies such as schools, motion picture theaters, and places of assembly are normally equipped with what is popularly known as "panic hardware" or what more technically may be described as fire exit bolts. Basically these devices are designed so that they will facilitate the safe egress of people in case of an emergency when a pressure not to exceed 15 lbs is applied to the releasing device in the direction of exit travel. Such releasing devices are bars or panels extending not less than two-thirds of the width of the door and placed at heights suitable for the service required, not less than 30, not more than 44 in. above the floor.

Fire testing laboratories have tested and listed assemblies which are intended for mounting on or integral with outward swinging doors designed to meet the installation recommendations given in the Life Safety Code. Panic hardware also has been tested on fire doors to determine the fire resistance of the complete assembly.

Panic hardware is available for use on single and double doors with variations on rim-mounted hardware and for mortise and vertical rod devices.

Horizontal Exits

A horizontal exit is a way of passage from one building to an area of refuge in another building on approximately the same level, or a way of passage through or around a fire wall or fire partition to an area of refuge at approximately the same level in the same building that affords safety from fire or smoke. With a horizontal exit it is obvious that space must be provided in the area or building of refuge for the people entering it. The Life Safety Code recommends 3 sq ft per person. Horizontal exits cannot comprise more than half the total required exit width except in health care facilities where horizontal exits can comprise all but one-third the total required exit width. Horizontal exits are particularly applicable to health care facilities where evacuation of patients over stairs is slower than taking them through a horizontal exit to a safe area of refuge.

A swinging door in a fire wall provides a horizontal exit in one direction only; two openings, each with a door swinging in direction of exit travel are needed to provide horizontal exits from both sides of the wall. Where property safety requires fire doors on both sides of the wall, a normally open automatic, horizontally sliding door may be used on one side; a swinging door on the other.

Stairs

Exit stairs are arranged to minimize the danger of falling, as one person falling on a stairway may result in the complete blocking of an exit. Stairs must be wide enough so that two people can descend side by side; thus a reasonable rate of evacuation may be maintained, even though aged or infirm persons may slow the travel on one side. There should be no decrease in width along the path of travel; this may create congestion or, in a panic rush, a solid wedge of bodies blocking the exit.

Steep stairs are dangerous. Treads must be wide enough to give good footing. Avoid winding stair treads (winders) but provide landings to break up any excessively long individual flight. Good railings make for safer use of stairs, and stairs of unusual width should have one or more center rails.

Two classes of stairs are recognized in the Life Safety Code. They are Class A and Class B stairs and requirements for each class are given in Table 6-9F.

Stairways may be inside the building where the Life Safety Code generally specifies enclosures. They also may be outside if they comply with requirements for inside stairs and are arranged to avoid any handicap to their use by persons having a fear of high places, are not exposed to fire originating in the building, and, where necessary, are shielded from snow and ice. Outside stairs should not be confused with fire escape stairs (see Fig. 6-9E).

Construction details of stair enclosures involve the principles of limitation of fire spread. Doors on openings

Table 6-9F. Requirements for Class A and B Exit Stairs

Stair Requirements	Class A	Class B
Width, minimum	44 in.	44 in.*
Width inside hand rails, minimum	37 in.	37 in.
Tread, without nosing, minimum	10 in.	9 in.
Riser height, maximum	7½ in.	8 in.
Landing height, maximum	8 ft	12 ft
Maximum landing dimension in travel direction	44 in.	44 in.

* Thirty-six in. where total occupancy of all floors served by stairway is less than 50.

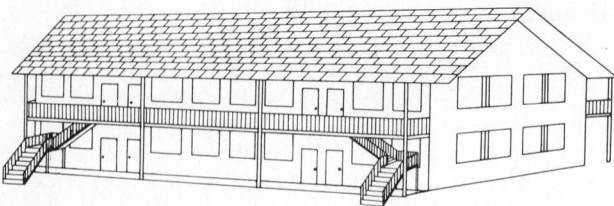

Fig. 6-9E.   An example of using outside stairs to provide direct exits to the outside for all rooms in a multistory building. There are no interior corridors through which smoke and flame could spread. This method has application in many types of occupancies, such as schools, motels, small professional buildings, etc. Note that there are two means of egress, remote from each other, from the second-story balcony.

from each story are essential to prevent the stairway serving as a flue. Stairway enclosures should in general include not only the stairs, but also the path of travel from the bottom of the stairs to the street, so that people are protected all the way out of the building (see Fig. 6-9F).

There is no objection to the use of wood for stairs in buildings that are low in height unless the building is of fire resistive construction.

Smokeproof Towers

Smokeproof towers are the safest form of stair enclosure recommended by the Life Safety Code. Access to the stair tower is only by balconies open to the outside air, so that smoke and fire will not readily spread into the tower even though the doors are accidentally left open.

Ramps

Ramps, enclosed and otherwise arranged like stairways, are sometimes used instead of stairways where there are

Fig. 6-9F.   Doors on stairway enclosures at left are open, and basement fire quickly extends up stairs, spreading to upper floors. Doors on stairway at right are closed, confining fire to basement and permitting safe use of stairway.

large crowds. They are required where differences in floor level would result in less than 3 steps of a stair. Ramps must have a very gradual slope to be considered safe exits.

Exit Passageways

A hallway, corridor, passage, tunnel, underflow passageway or overhead passageway may be designated as an exit component providing it is separated and arranged as per the requirements for exits.

The use of a hallway or corridor as an exit component introduces some unique considerations. The use of these spaces for purposes other than exiting may violate fundamental design considerations. For example, within an industrial situation, the use of a gasoline powered fork lift within a corridor designated as an exit component would violate the principles of exit design. The Life Safety Code specifies an exit enclosure should not be used for any purpose which could interfere with its value as an exit and specifically prohibits piping for flammable liquids and gases. Furthermore, penetration of the enclosure by ducts and other utilities may violate the protective enclosure.

Each opening in an exit enclosure introduces a point of weakness which could allow contaminants to spread rapidly into the exit preventing its use. Use of a corridor as an exit with the typical arrangement having numerous door openings could result in contamination of the enclosure as a result of a door failing to close and latch. Openings in exits enclosures should be limited to those necessary for access to the enclosure from normally occupied spaces. Therefore, openings to spaces such as boiler rooms, storage spaces, trash rooms, and the like, are considered unwise.

Fire Escape Stairs

Fire escapes should be stairs, not ladders. Fire escapes are at best a poor substitute for standard interior or outside stairs. Their principal use is to correct exit deficiencies of existing buildings where additional standard stairs cannot be provided.

The same principles of design apply as for interior stairs, though requirements for width, pitch, and other dimensions are generally less strict. The Life Safety Code gives the following criteria for fire escape stair design:

Fire escape stairs ideally extend to the street or ground level. When sidewalks would be obstructed by permanent stairs, or where it is desired to keep intruders out, swinging stair sections, designed to swing down with the weight of a person, may be used for the lowest flight of the fire escape stair. The area below the swinging section must be kept unobstructed so that the section can reach the ground. A counterweight should be provided for swinging stairs of the type balancing about a pivot; cables should not be used. Fire escapes terminating on balconies above the ground level, with no way to reach the ground except by portable ladders or jumping, are unsafe.

Many persons having a fear of high places are reluctant to use fire escapes. Design should, as far as possible, provide a sense of security as well as suitable railings and other details actually needed for safety. Fire escapes must be well anchored to building walls, and kept painted to prevent rust.

Access to fire escapes preferably is through doors leading from the main building area or from corridors; never through rooms the doors to which may be locked, except where every room or apartment has separate access to a fire escape. Although access to fire escapes preferably is by doors, windows may be used in which case sills should not be too high above the floor. Windows should be of ample size, and if insect screens are installed they should be of a type which can be quickly and easily opened. Fatalities have occurred in fires where exits were obstructed by screens.

Fire escapes in many fires have served as grills on which to roast helpless people as flames came out windows beneath. The best location for fire escapes is on exterior masonry walls without exposing windows with access to fire escape balconies by exterior type fire doors. Where window openings expose fire escapes, wired-glass windows in metal sash should be used. Where there is a complete standard automatic sprinkler system, the exposed hazard to fire escapes is minimized.

In northern climates, outside fire escapes are subject to obstruction by snow and ice. Roofs are sometimes provided, particularly for escapes serving theaters and places of assembly.

Escalators, Moving Walkways, and Elevators

Escalators, if enclosed like exit stairs and meeting the requirements for stairs as to tread width and riser height may be recognized as exits. They are, however, seldom so installed as to qualify as exits, and it is common to find installations with the hazard of unprotected floor openings (see Chap. 8 of this Section).

Moving walkways may also be used as means of egress if they conform to the general requirements for ramps if inclined, and passageways if level.

Elevators are not recognized as exits.

Ropes and Ladders

Ropes and ladders are not generally recognized in codes as a substitute for standard exits from a building. This is proper since there is no excuse for permitting their use except possibly in existing 1- and 2-family dwellings where it is economically impractical to add a secondary means of egress. In this case a suitable rope or chain ladder or a folding type metal ladder may be desirable. The homeowner should recognize, however, that aged, infirm, the very young, and physically handicapped persons cannot use ladders and that if the ladder passes near or over a window in a lower floor, flames from the window can prevent the use of the ladder or burn people using it.

Windows

Windows are not exits. They may be used as access to fire escapes in existing buildings if they meet certain criteria having to do with type of window and the distance of the sill from the floor.

Windows are required in rooms subject to student occupancy in schools unless the building is sprinklered and in bedrooms in 1- and 2-family dwellings that do not have two separate ways of escape. These windows are for rescue and ventilation and are required to meet criteria for size, method of operation, and height from the floor. The Life Safety Code also requires windows in bedrooms in hospitals, nursing homes, and residential custodial care facilities for the purpose of venting products of combustion and to provide fresh air to the occupant.

F. Exit Lighting and Signs

Exit Lighting

In buildings where artificial lighting is provided for normal use and occupancy, exit lighting and the lighting of access to exits is required to assure that occupants can quickly evacuate the building. The intensity of the lighting should be at a value of not less than 1-ft candle measured at the floor. It is desirable that such floor lighting be by lights recessed in the wall about 1 ft above the floor as such lights are then not likely to be obscured by smoke which might occur during a fire. In auditoriums and other places of public assembly where motion pictures or other projections are made, the Life Safety Code permits a reduction in this illumination for the period of the projection to values of not less than $\frac{1}{5}$-ft candle.

Emergency Lighting

The Life Safety Code requires emergency power for lighting of the means of egress based upon occupancy criteria. For example, emergency power is required within places of assembly, certain types of educational buildings, health care facilities, residential buildings with more than 25 rooms (hotels), or living units (apartments), dormitories subject to occupancy by more than 100 persons, Class A and B mercantiles, business buildings subject to occupancy by more than 1,000 people, parking garages, and underground and windowless structures subject to occupancy by more than 100 persons.

Well designed emergency lighting, using a source of power independent from the normal building service, provides the necessary illumination automatically in the event of interruption of power to normal lighting as a result of any failure. Failure of the public utility or other outside electric power supply, opening of a circuit breaker or fuse or any manual act including accidental opening of a switch controlling normal lighting facilities should result in automatic operation of the emergency lighting system.

Reliability of the exit illumination is most important. NFPA No. 70, the National Electrical Code, details recommended good practice in the installation of emergency lighting equipment. Battery-operated electric lights and portable lights or lanterns normally are not used for primary exit illumination, but they may be used as an emergency source under the restrictions imposed by the Life Safety Code. Luminescent, fluorescent or other reflective materials are no substitute for required illumination since they do not provide sufficient intensity of illumination to justify recognition as exit illumination.

Where electric battery-operated emergency lights are used, suitable facilities are needed to keep the batteries properly charged. Automobile type lead storage batteries are not suitable by reason of their relatively short life when not subject to frequent discharge and recharge. Dry batteries likewise have a limited life and there is danger that they may not be replaced when deteriorated due to age or exhausted by use.

Emergency lighting is so arranged that the necessary exit illumination will be automatically maintained in the event of failure of the normal lighting of the building with no appreciable interruption of illumination during the changeover. Where a generator is provided, a delay of up to 10 sec is considered tolerable. The normal procedure is to provide such emergency lighting for a period of at least $\frac{1}{2}$ hr. In certain occupancies, such as health care facilities, a period of 1 hr is recommended. The Life Safety Code requires hospitals have self-contained electric generating plants for emergency power supplies, not only for exit lighting but for emergency use in the event of failure of the public utility due to hurricanes, tornadoes, earthquakes, or other catastrophes. Where such emergency electric facilities are provided they may serve the purposes of emergency exit lighting as well as power supply to other critical areas of such buildings.

Exit Signs

All required exits and ways of access thereto must be identified by readily visible signs. The character of the occupancy will determine the actual need for such signs. In places of public assembly, hotels, department stores, and other buildings subject to transient occupancy, the need for signs will be greater than in a building subject to permanent or semipermanent occupancy by the same people. Even in permanent residence types of buildings, however, there is need for signs to identify exit facilities such as stairs which are not subject to regular use during the normal occupancy of the building. It is just as important that doors, passageways, or stairs which are not exits, but which are so located or arranged that they may be mistaken for exits, be identified by signs indicating either their actual character or the words "NOT AN EXIT."

Signs should be so located and of such size, color, and design to be readily visible and care taken not to have decorations, furnishings, or other building equipment located to impair the visibility of these signs or to detract from them.

Red is the traditional color for exit signs although green has also been used in some localities following the idea that traffic lights are green to indicate safety and red is used to signal stop. The Life Safety Code does not make any specific requirement for color on the assumption that either red or green will be used in most cases.

Signs reading "TO EXIT" or similar designations are frequently required in locations where the direction of travel to reach the nearest exit is not immediately apparent.

G. Alarm Systems

Alarm systems for the purpose of alerting occupants to leave the building are normally manually operated. The alarm sounding devices themselves should be distinctive in pitch and quality from all other sounding devices and the use of these devices should be restricted to evacuation purposes. It is, of course, very important that these devices be so distributed as to be effectively heard in every room of a building above all other sounds.

Visual alarm devices are sometimes used in buildings occupied by deaf persons. Such visual alarm devices should be provided in addition to audible alarms.

The proper maintenance of alarm systems is most important. Alarm systems should be under the supervision of a responsible person who will make proper tests at specified intervals and have charge of all alterations and additions to the systems.

H. Fire Exit Drills

General

Fire exit drills are essential in schools and are desirable in every type of occupancy to assure familiarity with exits and their orderly use. In occupancies such as hospitals, nursing homes, hotels, and department stores, drills are usually limited to an exercise of employees, without alarming patients, guests, or customers. Drills should be planned to get everyone out of the building or to a place of safety as promptly as consistent with orderly procedure. Fire fighting is always secondary to life safety, and, in general, fire fighting operations should not be started until people are out, except in cases where trained fire departments conduct rescue and fire fighting operations simultaneously.

Drills should be held at least once a month or oftener, but not at regularly scheduled periods. They should cover all shifts in an occupancy operated 24 hrs a day. Drills should be conducted without warning, and should simulate fire conditions.

School Exit Drills

School fire exit drills are an exercise in discipline, not speed, through reasonably prompt emptying of the building is important. No running or horseplay should be tolerated. Children should not be permitted to stop to put on wraps. No teacher should be permitted to remain in the building and no child should be excused from participating.

The drill should include a roll call by classes outside the building to make sure that no one is left behind. There should also be a routine for a complete check of the entire building, including toilet rooms, to make sure that no one is left behind. All exits should be used in drills, but routes should be varied from drill to drill and occasional drills held, simulating conditions when one exit cannot be used because it is blocked by fire or smoke. All drills should include provision to simulate calling the fire department.

I. Exit Maintenance

The provision of standard exits with adequate capacity does not guarantee the safety of the occupants in the event of need for rapid evacuation of any building. Exits which were not properly maintained have been responsible for loss of life. Property managements usually assign definite responsibility for maintenance of mechanical and electrical equipment, but fail to do so for the maintenance of exits. As a result it is all too common for inspection authorities to find stairways, otherwise safe, used for storage of materials during peak sales or manufacturing periods. In habitational buildings, rubbish, baby carriages and other obstructions are allowed to collect in stairway enclosures. Exit doors are often found locked or the hardware in need of repair. Doors blocked open or removed on openings into stairway enclosures are certain to permit rapid spread of smoke or hot gases throughout the building. Loose handrails and loose or slippery stair treads offer the dangerous probability that persons evacuating a building will fall in the path of others seeking escape. Maintenance of standard exits in safe operating condition at all times is of equal importance in the prevention of loss of life as safe construction and the safeguarding of fire hazards.

Bibliography

References Cited

[1] Fruin, J. J., *Pedestrian Planning and Design,* Metropolitan Association of Urban Designers and Environmental Planners, Inc., New York, 1971.

[2] London Transport Board, "Second Report of the Operational Research Team on the Capacity of Footways," Research Report No. 95, Aug. 1958, London.

[3] Abbott, J. C., "Fire Involving Upholstery Materials," *Fire Journal,* Vol. 65, No. 4, July 1971, p. 88.

[4] Lathrop, J. K., et al., "In Osceola: A Matter of Contents," *Fire Journal,* Vol. 69, No. 3, May 1975, pp. 20–26.

[5] Powers, W. R., "New York Office Building Fire," *Fire Journal,* Vol. 65, No. 1, pp. 18–23, 87.

[6] Phillips, A. W., "You and the High Rise Building Fire," Technology Report 74-1, 1974, Society of Fire Protection Engineers, Boston.

[7] Lakely, L. W., "Dimensions of the Human Figure," Cleveland Designers and Consultants, Inc., Cleveland, Ohio.

[8] "Design and Construction of Building Exits," Miscellaneous Publication M51, Oct. 10, 1935, National Bureau of Standards, Washington, D.C., pp. 30–37 (out of print).

[9] General Services Administration, "Building Firesafety Criteria," PBS P 5920.9 CHGE 2, Apr. 27, 1972, Washington, D.C.

[10] Galbreath, M., "Time of Evacuation by Stairs in High Buildings," *Ontario Fire Marshal,* Vol. 5, No. 2, First Quarter, 1969.

[11] Ministry of Works, Joint Committee on Fire Grading of Buildings, "Fire Grading of Buildings," Part III, "Personal Safety," Post-War Building Studies No. 29, 1952, Her Majesty's Stationary Office, London.

[12] Galbreath, M., "A Survey of Exit Facilities in High Office Buildings," Building Research Note No. 64, Oct. 1968, Division of Building Research, National Research Council, Ottawa, Canada.

NFPA Codes, Standards, and Recommended Practices (see the latest *NFPA Publications and Visual Aids Catalog* for availability of current editions of the following documents)

NFPA No. 101, Life Safety Code.

NFPA No. 102, Standard for Tents, Grandstands, and Air-Supported Structures Used for Places of Assembly.

Additional Readings

Stevens, R. E., "Designing Life Safety for Places of Public Assembly," *Fire Journal,* Vol. 61, No. 1, Jan. 1967, pp. 22–24.

——, "Designing Life Safety in Educational Occupancies," *Fire Journal,* Vol. 61, No. 2, Mar. 1967, pp. 24–25.

——, "Designing Life Safety in Institutional Occupancies," *Fire Journal,* Vol. 61, No. 3, May 1967, pp. 50–53.

——, "Scissors Stairs as Exits," *Fire Journal,* Vol. 59, No. 1, Jan. 1965, p. 40.

——, "Smokeproof Towers," *Fire Journal,* Vol. 60, No. 1, Jan. 1966, pp. 54–55.

——, "What is an Exit?" *Fire Journal,* Vol. 59, No. 6, Nov. 1965, pp. 44–45.

Chapter 10

SPECIAL STRUCTURES

Special structures constitute a variety of constructed items that are designed for very specific purposes. They also represent a departure from the norm, in terms of what is considered typical day to day uses or occurrences for most structures. Typical examples of special structures are towers, tunnels, bomb shelters, highway and railroad bridges, grandstands, tents, signs, mechanical parking garages, piers and water surrounded structures used for other than vessel mooring or cargo handling, and air-right structures. Because these structures represent unusual uses or solutions to design problems, they also represent unusual or special fire protection problems of design.

A. Towers

The major fire problems with towers are: (1) the difficulty of extinguishing fires that may occur high in the tower; (2) the limited means of egress for occupants of lookout or observation towers (this prompts the use of noncombustible materials throughout, and good fire prevention practices); and (3) vulnerability to exposure fires. Since most towers are built of unprotected steel or wood, a ground fire can result in ignition or structural failure, or both, of the tower. Towers are frequently appended or attached to other structures of lower height. In such cases, egress from the tower should be directly outside where possible. If this is not feasible, the exits of the building should be designed with consideration given to their use by occupants of the tower. Apart from fire damage, but extremely important from a life safety viewpoint, is the possibility of windstorm damage to towers. Where towers are used for living or sleeping purposes, such as a forest fire observation tower, the requirements of NFPA 101, Life Safety Code, for private dwellings are observed. See Section 8, Chapter 2 of this HANDBOOK for a discussion of typical dwelling design practices for life safety.

Water Cooling Towers

Functionally, a water cooling tower is a structure designed for the transfer of heat from water to air. This is accomplished by passing the water in small particles through the air where heat is removed from the water partly by an exchange of latent heat (heat required to pass from liquid to a gas) due to the evaporation of some of the water particles, and partly by a transfer of sensible heat (heat required to change the temperature). Figure 6-10A shows a cross section of a typical mechanical induced-draft water cooling tower and identifies some of its significant parts.

Construction of water cooling towers may be all metal, metal framed with wooden or plastic fillers and wooden or plastic drift eliminators, all wood (redwood is generally used) or ceramic. Some towers have a noncombustible exterior covering. Wood is used in cooling tower construction primarily because of its durability, the absence of corrosion problems, and economics both in the cost of the original material and for replacement.

Types of water cooling towers are atmospheric and mechanical draft. Mechanical draft towers are of two general types: force draft and induced draft. They may be further classified by design as counterflow and crossflow.

Contrary to a popular misconception, fire records of water cooling towers indicates that about two-thirds of the fires studied occurred while the tower was in operation. Despite what would appear to be the case, towers do have some relatively dry areas even when operating, particularly the induced-draft types.

The majority of cooling towers fires are caused by ignition from outside sources. Most common of these sources are sparks from welding and cutting (either on the tower or on adjacent structures), sparks from trash fires, incinerators, chimneys, and industrial stacks. Other causes include carelessly discarded smoking materials, lightning, and exposure fires.

Fires caused by the equipment in the tower originate from mechanical failures in gear reduction boxes and bearings, misaligned fan blades, or metal fatigue which can result in localized heating. Electrical breakdowns in motors, short circuits in wiring, and other electrical faults also account for many cooling tower fires.

In considering the possible fire hazard of a water cooling tower, the construction of the tower is a primary factor. Small towers (those of main structure not exceeding 2,000 cubic feet in volume) are generally completely noncombustible and therefore seldom a problem. Larger towers, however, generally contain considerable amounts of combustible materials and thus may constitute special fire prob-

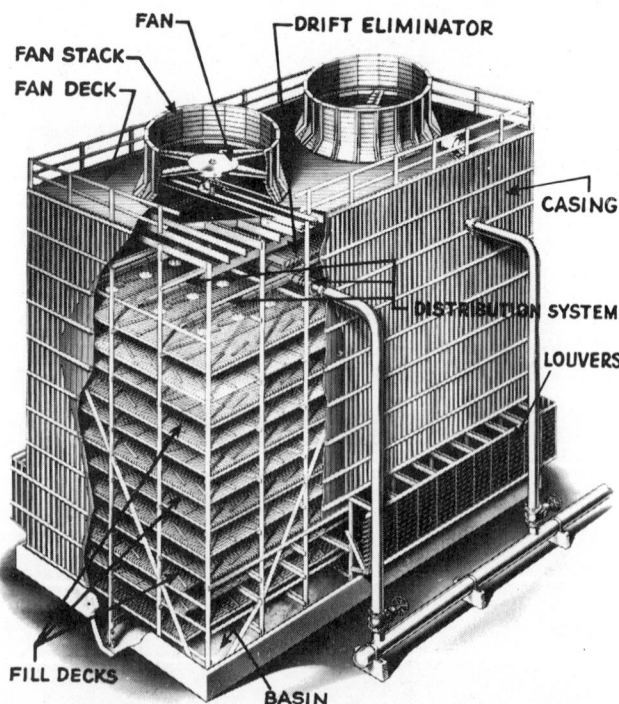

Fig. 6-10A. A typical mechanical, induced draft, counterflow, water cooling tower. Water is pumped to the distribution system where it is cascaded over the fill decks and collected in the basin at the base of the tower. The fan draws in air through the louvers and the casing of the tower. Drift eliminators minimize loss of water through the fan stacks.

lems. Towers on roofs, for example, may be inaccessible to regular fire fighting equipment; those in yard areas may require fencing and weed control or protection to prevent exposure damage to an adjacent building. Once the degree of hazard has been determined, any one or a combination of the following protection measures may be considered when dealing with essentially combustible towers:

1. Adequate separation from exposures
2. Noncombustible exterior coverings
3. Division of areas by fire partitions between cells
4. Automatic fire protection systems (deluge systems or dry pipe or wet pipe automatic sprinkler systems, the latter in warm climates only)
5. Automatic water spray systems (exterior of the tower only)
6. Hydrants and standpipes
7. Lightning protection.

The key element in a fire protection analysis is to provide a combination of prudent engineered tower design with sufficient consideration to automatic extinguishment plus good preventive maintenance; all directed at providing a high level of assurance that the fan deck, fan, and related motor and drive survive intact the effects of a fire incident. This is recommended for two reasons:

1. Considerable damage is done to the entire tower when the fan deck collapses dropping it and its equipments' substantial weight down through the tower during a fire.

2. Downtime of the tower is considerably lessened when replacement is required for only the louvers and fill deck material. This is critical since downtime on a cooling tower may cause downtime on a key, income producing manufacturing process.

Cooling towers, like other outside structures, must be designed and constructed to prevent damage from windstorms. Care also should be taken that the towers are not under or adjacent to high voltage wires or transformers.

Fire prevention involves the usual control of the fire causes previously discussed, plus a regular maintenance program. Scheduled checking of mechanical parts for overheating, excessive wear, inadequate lubrication, and the like is an essential part of this program.

Preventing fires and fire damage in water cooling towers is covered in detail in NFPA No. 214, Water Cooling Towers.

Television, Microwave, and Radio Transmitting Towers

Television and radio transmitting towers frequently have electronic equipment at heights that make fire fighting from the ground impossible. In such situations an automatic carbon dioxide halogenated agent, or dry chemical extinguishing system, with an interlock to cut off power to the electronic equipment, could be considered as practical protection (see Sec. 15, Chaps. 4, 5 and 6). In any case, it is good practice to have a means of shutting off the power to the tower from the ground.

Microwave towers, frequently located in remote areas, have equipment buildings near their bases for relays, standby generators and batteries. These buildings should be protected by automatic detection and extinguishing systems.

Airport and Railroad Control Towers

Airport and some railroad control towers present special problems because of the highly valuable, complicated electrical and electronic equipment normally installed therein. Automatic fire extinguishing equipment is usually justified by the importance of the tower equipment.

Forest Fire and Other Observation Towers

Forest fire and other observation towers should be of noncombustible construction throughout, not only because of the possibility of ignition of the base from a ground fire, but also to avert any fire in the upper structure of the tower. The problem of fire protection in these towers is especially important since, as pointed out previously, they are normally occupied by observation personnel.

B. Underground Structures

Underground Buildings

The inaccessibility of underground structures results in some unique fire problems. Primary among these are the venting of smoke and gases from fires, the difficulty in evacuating occupants, and the fire fighting handicaps. These problems are fundamental in all fire protection, but the solution of all of them in relation to underground structures has not been set down in any single standard. Furthermore, the inaccessibility of underground structures eliminates any thought of partial fire protection facilities that might suffice in an aboveground building where dependence is placed on public fire service. On the contrary, protecting occupants and property in underground structures prompts maximum utilization of good fire protection.

Following are some fire protection measures primary to underground structures. Many of these measures are also applicable to windowless buildings, since the only advantage such buildings have over underground buildings is that direct access for occupants to the outside can be provided. Windowless buildings provide the same problems of venting, and fire fighting and rescue as underground buildings. They are not intended to be all inclusive nor to eliminate the usual fire protection considerations typical of buildings.

Exits from underground buildings are provided for in NFPA No. 101, Life Safety Code. Those recommendations take into consideration the panic that may result when there is no direct access to the outside and no windows to permit fire department rescue and ventilation.

Automatic sprinkler systems, venting facilities, emergency lighting, and similar features are also recommended in certain conditions of occupancy and of construction and contents to assure orderly evacuation.

Automatic sprinklers should be installed in all such buildings because of combustible contents and concealed spaces even though construction may be noncombustible.

Venting facilities must be provided to exhaust smoke and fire gases from the buildings. Storage buildings may require extensive venting facilities, whereas buildings with low fire loading, noncombustible construction, and automatic sprinklers may be cleared of smoke through the ventilation system provided for normal changes of air.

Emergency lighting for safe evacuation should be required since artificial light is a necessity in underground buildings.

Minimum use of combustible construction, interior finish, and combustible contents will reduce fuel and fire loading, since fire severity is a critical factor to overcome.

Maximum division of areas limits fire extent and severity, and provides areas of refuge for occupants.

Manual fire fighting equipment, such as standpipe and hose systems and portable fire extinguishers, can provide quick extinguishment of fires when handled by trained personnel who may discover a fire in the incipient stage.

Drainage of water sprinkler discharge or from hose streams can be a serious problem in underground structures and therefore requires study in the early planning stages. If provisions for drainage are required for reasons other than fire protection, it may be possible to use one drainage system for all purposes, provided it is designed to handle the expected maximum flow.

Tunnels

Tunnels for automotive vehicles and tracked vehicles (trains and subways) present fire problems similar to those of underground buildings, except that the cargo of the vehicles using tunnels may present any of a number of hazards. The transportation of certain cargoes, such as high explosives through tunnels by automotive vehicles, is prohibited in some cities.

Because gasoline as an automotive fuel is commonly involved in automotive fires, handling the hazard of gasoline spill fires is a typical consideration in providing fire protection for tunnels.

Providing means for giving an alarm for fire in a tunnel is a primary consideration. This may be satisfied by fire alarm boxes or telephone stations spaced at intervals along the tunnel. This system can also be tied into the traffic control system so that incoming traffic can be stopped. Automatic sprinklers provide good protection for tunnels. In addition, an adequate water supply with hose connections should be provided on both sides of the tunnel. Supplemental portable fire extinguishers for handling small fires can be installed in wall cabinets for use by attendants and motorists.

Fire apparatus specially equipped to pull disabled vehicles from tunnels, to combat vehicle fires, and to extricate accident victims should be stationed at least at one end of the tunnel.

As with underground buildings, ventilation in tunnels is important to dissipate smoke and fire gases. The existing mechanical ventilation system may be satisfactory for emergency use if it is capable of handling the required volume to exhaust smoke and fire gases.

Low points in the tunnel should have suitable drainage to handle flammable liquid spills and water used for extinguishment.

See Section 17, Chapter 4, for further information on fire problems associated with subway tunnels.

Exit Tunnels

Exit tunnels, normally used for ingress to and egress from buildings, subway stations, and the like, involve primarily safety to life. Tunnels are commonly used to satisfy exit requirements for large industrial facilities. Detailed requirements for such tunnels are contained in NFPA No. 101, Life Safety Code; see also Section 8, Chapter 7 of this HANDBOOK.

Bomb Shelters

Shelters design to protect people from the effects of bombing, especially nuclear, are underground structures and therefore, are subject to the same general fire protection factors as other underground structures.

Areas of refuge designated as bomb shelters in buildings may be considered as temporary expedients; nevertheless, they should be chosen with care, and thought should be given to such matters as alternate means of egress, noncombustible construction, sprinklered areas, proximity to gas mains, water pipes, and other building services that may be damaged by explosion or fire resulting from bombing, and similar existing factors that could protect or unnecessarily expose people seeking refuge.

C. Bridges

Highway Bridges

Highway bridges, being susceptible to all types of traffic carrying hazardous cargoes, plus exposure from events occurring on the roadway or waterway they are spanning require provisions for limitation of fire damage through the use of fire resistive and noncombustible construction, and by the availability of fire fighting equipment, means to transmit emergency alarms, traffic control, and means for removal of disabled vehicles.

A fire resistive bridge would, of course, be the type of construction most effective against damage from an exposure fire, such as may be expected if the contents of a ruptured tank on a gasoline tank truck are ignited. An alternative design of lower fire resistance is noncombustible construction which will not burn and therefore would not be ignited but could suffer severe structural damage if exposed to sufficient heat (see Fig. 6-10B).

Fire alarm boxes or telephones spaced along a bridge provide means of notifying the fire department or bridge attendants of an emergency condition. As in tunnels, this system can be tied into a traffic control system to stop traffic from driving onto the bridge and to alert vehicles already on the bridge.

Since fire fighting is a necessity on bridges, adequate water supply from standpipes, preferably on both sides of the bridge or, on long bridges at intervals along its length, is good practice.

The location of apparatus to combat bridge fires can be a problem if a bridge is located in a rural area. It is desirable, however, that apparatus be stationed as near the bridge as possible. In addition to having fire fighting equipment, this apparatus should be designed to move disabled vehicles and should have the equipment needed for rescue.

Railroad Bridges

Railroad bridges are a fire problem because so many of them are constructed of wood, which usually has been

Fig. 6-10B. The damage that can be suffered by unprotected steel bridges from exposure fires is clearly demonstrated by this fire. A collision between a gasoline tank truck and another vehicle resulted in a fire that involved the contents of the 6,000-gal tank truck and trapped the driver. The unprotected steel of the bridge structure collapsed as flames from the burning gasoline reached the overhead spans. (Wide World Photos)

Fig. 6-10C. Fire fighters were forced to pull hose lines on hand cars across thousands of feet of track to fight a fire in this wooden trestle located in a remote area on Long Island, N.Y. Water around the trestle was too shallow for fire boats. High winds drove the fire rapidly through the wooden trestle and destroyed about 2,500 ft of the structure.

treated with a flammable wood preservative. There are two kinds of wooden bridges and trestles; open deck and ballast deck. The fire potential is considerably more severe in open deck design. A good many railroad bridges are located in remote areas and, therefore, if ignited are generally a complete loss (see Fig. 6-10C).

Wooden railroad bridges are subject to ignition by such sources as friction sparks and hot metal particles generated when brakes are applied on heavily loaded freight trains on steep downgrades, burning waste from overheated journal boxes, and exposure fires from burning grass and brush around supporting piles.

Some satisfactory fire retardant treatments are being used quite successfully on timbers for bridges; but wooden bridges, even when treated, should not be considered as an adequate substitute for fire resistive or noncombustible bridges.

Concrete walls or extended piers, spaced at intervals along the substructure of a wooden bridge, can serve as barriers to the spread of fire.

Fighting railroad bridge fires presents many problems, particularly in areas where bridges are not accessible to organized fire fighting facilities. Water casks at the approaches to bridges or located at intervals along their length for use by train crews is one method of providing minimal fire extinguishing capacity. Some railroads keep a magazine of explosives nearby to blow fire breaks in bridges if necessary. In other instances, preemergency planning calls for tearing down sections of platform-type bridges to stop the spread of fire.

D. Places of Outdoor Assembly

By "places of outdoor assembly" is meant amusement parks, athletic fields and stadiums, grandstands, tents, and similar places where crowds gather to watch an event or take part in recreational activities. There is also an open question as to what source documents adequately provide design guidance for partially enclosed stadii that have become popular as a half measure towards achieving a resemblance to an "astro" or "super" dome facility.

The frequency of fires in these places and the possibility of loss of life from fire and panic in any place where crowds congregate compel the consideration of providing adequate and accessible ways of escape, and of minimum good prac-

tice construction features to reduce the probability of fire spread. NFPA No. 102, Places of Outdoor Assembly, spells out in detail the recommendations on reasonable measures of safety to prevent loss of life. In the case of partially enclosed stadii, it may be of some guidance to further review NFPA 101, Life Safety Code.

The primary consideration is the provision for escape of people from a fire area to a place of refuge. This escape may have to be made through gates in a fence, from a grandstand, out of a tent, or from any confinement that restricts the passage of masses of people. Providing sufficient units of exit width to handle the capacity of the area established by a predetermined figure, based on square feet of floor or ground area per person, is the recommended method of assuring adequate escape means (see Chap. 9 of this Section). This assumes that the capacity will not be allowed to be exceeded and that the exits will be within a reasonable distance from all occupants of the area. It also assumes that the access to exits will be unobstructed and free from tent ropes, parked automobiles, and other obstructions. The area of refuge for occupants may be an open space, but access to the place of assembly for fire apparatus and other emergency vehicles is a necessity.

Exit requirements for grandstands and other places of outdoor assembly are less than for places of indoor assembly because venting of smoke is not so much of a problem. Placing a complete roof over a place of assembly confines smoke, and may increase panic hazard, calling for more exits for quicker evacuation.

The second consideration in a place of outdoor assembly is the construction. The temporary or portable nature of the structures generally used in such places and the false sense of complacency that may exist due to the open or partially open nature of the structures, whether fixed or portable, may result in construction weaknesses that accelerate fire spread.

Other typical features include temporary wiring, inadequate maintenance and poor housekeeping (particularly when exhibitions involving displays are present), use of considerable combustible materials (including decorations and flammable liquids), and the general lack of proper fire prevention practices.

A good supply of portable fire extinguishers as well as a reliable method of quickly communicating with the closest fire department and other appropriate emergency organizations are necessities.

Tents

Tents became a major concern to fire protection authorities following the disastrous circus fire in Hartford, Conn., on July 6, 1944, in which 168 lives were lost. This fire clearly demonstrated the need for flame resistant materials for tents in places of outdoor assembly (see Sec. 3, Chap. 2). Flame resistant material should be used for tents occupied for assembly, for tents housing animals, and for any tents within the area used by the public. Other tents where heating devices are used should also be of flame resistant material, as well as tarpaulins and decorative materials used in the area occupied by the public.

Tents are combustible, even though made of flame resistant material, and it is good practice to limit their number and size, and to keep them separated from each other and from other structures. The area around tents must be kept free of combustible material including vegetation. Combustible material used inside a tent should be kept to a minimum, and smoking in tents occupied by the public should be prohibited.

Fig. 6-10D. More than 5,000 people escaped without serious injury when fire occurred in this wooden grandstand at Louisville, Ky. The evacuation was not orderly, and several occupants received minor bruises in their haste to escape. A cigarette is believed to have fallen through a crack into a concealed space below the wood flooring where it ignited debris.

Grandstands

Grandstands are typical examples of structures found in places of outdoor assembly that constitute a safety-to-life problem. These structures, particularly the larger ones, should be built with adequate aisles, proper distance between rows of seats, strong railings, and other exit features to assure rapid and orderly evacuation to areas of refuge. Without them panic situation could develop in emergencies as depicted in Fig. 6-10D. They should also be designed to withstand predetermined deadweight and live loads, and wind load.

Since many grandstands are constructed in whole or in part of wood, basic fire protection principles of division of areas and separation for exposure protection apply. Long, combustible grandstands may be divided by fire partitions or may be built in small sections with adequate space between sections. They should also be away from other structures unless there is a fire partition between the grandstand and the other structure.

Frequently, the space underneath a grandstand is an area for storage of materials, and for concession booths, and becomes littered with refuse. This is not good practice, and the space should be kept clear of such activities.

Amusement Park Structures

Structures supporting amusement rides are generally built of wood, contain considerable electrical wiring, involve gear boxes for pulleys, and similar friction-producing machinery, and are usually poorly maintained. Life safety is the primary consideration in evaluating these structures; therefore, adequate and accessible means of escape in emergency conditions is vitally important. Fire prevention, noncombustible construction, exposure hazards, maintenance, and housekeeping are other factors to be considered.

E. Air-Supported Structures

An air-supported structure is a "balloon-like" shelter constructed of flexible-coated fabrics supported and stabilized against wind loads by a small amount of internal pressure (usually 1 to 1.5 in. of water pressure) supplied by continuously operated centrifugal fans (see Fig. 6-10E). There are no beams, columns, girders, or other structural members involved. Variations of the air-supported structure include

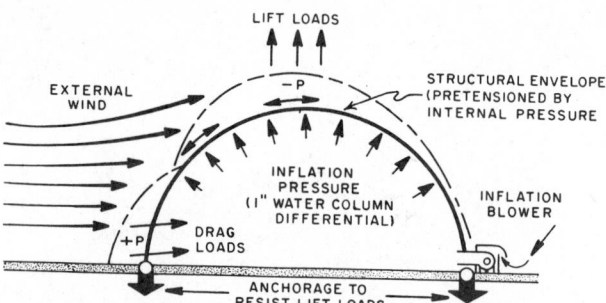

Fig. 6-10E. The aerodynamic and inflation loading of a typical single-walled, air-supported structure.

types which have air-inflated double-walled roof and side panels and a combination structure which is rib supported but in heavy wind is air supported.

The fabric used is a plastic coated synthetic fiber. The synthetic fiber will not absorb flame resisting solutions but the plastic coating can contain flame retardants. If the fan serving an air-supported structure fails, or if a hole is made in the fabric, as by heat from an exposure fire, it takes a relatively long time for the structure to deflate. Normal opening and closing of doors will not affect the structure. In fact, breather holes are provided in the skin for air changes.

F. Piers and Water-surrounded Structures

When piers or related structures surrounded by water are used for places of amusement, restaurants, or passenger terminals, they fall out of the "normal" use category (namely; mooring of vessels and handling of cargo) and fall into the "special" structure category. Of primary concern for these types of use is the question of life safety, since the operations listed above all involve the gathering together or assembling of people in large numbers in or on structures that may have limited egress facilities, due to the location or arrangement of the pier or water-surrounded structures.

On the question of good design practice for piers, the following recommendations are made when the pier extends more than 150 ft from the shore. Note that the 150-ft criteria arises from the recognized maximum travel distance requirement for the uses listed above as found in the Life Safety Code. Also note that these design approaches are considered equivalent.

1. The pier may be arranged to have two separate ways of travel to shore, as by two well-separated walkways or independent structures.

2. The pier deck may be designed to be of open, fire resistive construction resting on noncombustible supports.

3. If combustible construction is used for the pier deck, superstructure, and/or substructure, they should be protected by an automatic sprinkler system.

4. If the pier is completely open and unobstructed, it may be considered to be of generally safe arrangement if the minimum width is not less than 50 feet for piers up to 500 ft in length and, if the length is increased above 500 ft, a 10 to 1 ratio is maintained for the relationship of length to width.

Regardless of which of (1) through (4) above, either individually or jointly, are applicable to a particular pier, the minimum requirements of the Life Safety Code for providing means of egress also concurrently apply. These cover the number, arrangement, location, and protection of means of egress for the type of occupancy involved plus related questions of hardware, construction, and interior finish for the means of egress. In addition, further guidance for piers is given in NFPA 87, Piers and Wharves.

When a building or structure is completely surrounded by water, such as a typical lighthouse, oil drilling platform and related housing facilities (e.g., the now famous "Texas Towers"), several considerations must be given to life safety from fire. Either sufficient outside ground area, such as an island, is needed for refuge, or a fire resistive platform is constructed, again for refuge during a fire. This has to be coupled with a communication system and a means of transportation for evacuating the occupants from the refuge area. Such transportation will be limited to either boat or helicopter due to the obvious nature and location of these special structures. However, such a system of refuge, communication, and rescue is only as good as the preplanning and ready availability of the transportation on a standby basis. Delays imposed by either poor planning or intolerable weather conditions can lead to a disaster. Thus, such factors must be considered before the event and not in retrospect later on.

Permanently Moored Vessels

Where a sizable vessel is permanently moored and used as a restaurant, hotel, museum, or convention center, it is for all practical purposes like any permanently constructed building occupied for those purposes. Thus, the design practices found elsewhere in this HANDBOOK and in the National Fire Codes of the National Fire Protection As-

sociation are applicable based on the occupancy and use made of the permanently moored vessel.

G. Air-Right Structures

The economics of purchasing choice inner urban space, site preparation, demolition of existing structures, and the complex problem of foundation design and caisson construction, all without adversely affecting surrounding structures and without exceeding stringently applied cost limitations has led to a structure which either totally or partially solves many of those problems—the air-right structure.

The air-right structure is generally a facility constructed over existing rail lines, highways, or even other buildings. Its design, from a fire safety standpoint, is not unlike that that would be promulgated if it were isolated on its own site, with one key exception. The air-right structure is more likely to be adversely affected by an exposing event on or in the facility it is erected above. This is due to the fact that the exposure is in the vertical plane which is ideal for the heat transfer process to take place. Thus, normal good fire safety design practice must be followed, plus allowance for potentially severe fire exposure from the facility that it straddles. Much of the previous discussion of tunnels and bridges would apply to the air-right structure. Normal design guidance is found elsewhere in this text and in the NFPA National Fire Codes based on the occupancy of the structure.

Fig. 6-10F. Air air-right hotel and office building shown spanning an expressway and a two-track railroad right-of-way.

H. Other Special Structures

Signs

In general, outside signs on buildings are not a fire problem of very great seriousness because of the limited amount of combustibles involved in such signs and because of their location. Certain types of signs, such as those illuminated by neon tubing, may cause fires because of the wiring and transformers connected to them.

An outside sign may suffer considerable damage from wind and may expose other properties to damage if torn loose by wind. If a sign is of such size, construction and location as to be considered a fire hazard, it should be protected like any other structure; for example, automatic sprinklers may be installed.

A combustible sign attached to the exterior and covering a large percentage of one side of a fire resistive or noncombustible building may significantly change the fire safety considerations of the building. It is a fire exposure problem not generally contemplated in building design. A large sign can also be a hazard to fire fighters should it fall during fire fighting operations. For these reasons, some building codes limit the size and type of construction of combustible signs that can be installed on buildings.

Mechanical Parking Garages

The primary fire problem with mechanical parking garages is the open shaft through which automobiles are automatically transferred from floor to floor. The nature of the transferring equipment is such that installation practices seldom provide for enclosure. Since there are no occupants above the first floor, the open shaft is not a life safety factor, but like any open shaft it is conducive to fire spread. If the building is fire resistive, the open shaft may not be a serious problem. Otherwise, the shaft should be enclosed, or if that is not possible, should be protected by automatic sprinklers. However, recent fire tests conducted by the British at Boreham Wood[1] and by the American Iron and Steel Institute[2] in this country, have led to the conclusion that the potential exposing fire in partially open, above ground parking garages is sufficiently dissipated due to air movement through the structure to preclude the need for automatic extinguishment systems. This data would not necessarily apply to above ground enclosed garages nor to underground garages.

Bibliography

References Cited

[1] Butcher, E. G., Langdon-Thomas, B. J., and Bedford, G. K., "Fire and Car-park Buildings," Fire Note No. 10, 1968, Ministry of Technology and Fire Offices' Committee/Joint Fire Research Organization, London.

[2] "Automobile Parking Structures," a Building Code Modernization Bulletin, 2nd ed., 1971, American Iron and Steel Institute, New York.

NFPA Codes, Standards, and Recommended Practices (see the latest NFPA Publications and Visual Aids Catalog for availability of current editions of the following documents)

NFPA No. 87, Standard for the Construction and Protection of Piers and Wharves.

NFPA No. 101, Code for Safety to Life from Fire in Buildings and Structures.

NFPA No. 102, Standard for Tents, Grandstands and Air-Supported Structures Used for Places of Assembly.

NFPA No. 214, Standard on Water-Cooling Towers.

Additional Readings

Bond, H., "Underground Buildings," Fire Journal, Vol. 59, No. 4, July 1965, pp. 52–55.

Stevens, R. E., "Air Supported Structures," Fire Journal, Vol. 59, No. 10, Sept. 1965, pp. 42–44.

———, "Water Cooling Towers Will Burn," NFPA Quarterly, Vol. 50, No. 9, Oct. 1956, pp. 97–105.

Chapter 11

BUILDING CODES AND STANDARDS

The occurrence of fires and disasters which claim many lives and result in severe casualties and heavy property damage inevitably stirs the general public, professional groups, and governmental officials to take corrective action. Usually, the corrective action takes the form of municipal, county, state, or federal legislation. In the area of building construction the legislation is known as a building code.

A. Development

Building codes have been in existence since about 1700 BC when King Hammurabi established a law by which a builder could be executed if the house he built collapsed, resulting in the death of the owner. However, this discussion will be limited to the modern building codes as they developed through this century.

A building code is a law which sets forth minimum requirements for design and construction. These minimum standards are established to protect the health and safety of the general public and generally represent a compromise between optimum safety and economic feasibility. Although builders and building owners often establish their own requirements, the minimum standards must be met. Construction features covered include structural integrity, fire protection, life safety of occupants, mechanical and utility systems, and interior finish.[1]

There are two types of building codes. *Specification* codes spell out in detail what materials can be used, how large (or small) and how components should be assembled. *Performance* codes detail the objective to be met and establish criteria for determining if the objective has been met. The designer and builder are, thus, allowed freedom in selecting construction methods and materials as long as it can be shown that the performance criteria can be met. Performance-oriented building codes still embody a fair amount of specification-type requirements, but the provision exists for substitution of alternate methods and materials, if they can be proven adequate.

B. Building Codes and Fire Protection

The requirements contained in building codes generally have as their basis the known properties of materials, the hazards presented by various occupancies, and the experience gained by previous experiences, such as fire and natural disasters.[2] The promulgation of the modern building codes which are in use today began with the disastrous fire incidents which this country experienced at the turn of this century. Thus, it is understandable that building codes and fire protection are partners in alleviating the loss of life and property.

For instance, building codes usually establish fire limits in certain areas of the municipality. Only certain types of construction are allowed within the fire limits, thus restricting the conflagration potential of the more densely populated areas. Outside the fire limits, the restriction of certain construction types is relaxed, due to decreased population density, increased spacing between buildings, etc. Obviously, the establishment of fire limits approximates occupancy and use zoning.

Another example of the impact of building codes on fire protection and prevention is the establishment of height and area criteria. The criteria establish how big and how high a particular building can be, based on what the building will be used for. Unfortunately, these requirements vary considerably from one area to the next and are rather hit-or-miss. There is no nationally recognized standard for setting height and area limitations. NFPA No. 206M, Guide on Building Heights and Areas, serves as groundwork for establishing such criteria. The types of building construction, as delineated in Chapter 5 of this section, are an important factor in the establishment of height and area limitations.

Other requirements found in building codes which bear directly on fire protection include: enclosure of vertical openings, such as stair shafts, elevator shafts, and pipe chases; provision of exits for evacuation of occupants; requirements for flame spread of interior finish; and provisions for automatic fire suppression systems. Exit requirements found in most building codes are based on those found in NFPA No. 101, the Life Safety Code.

C. Toward Uniformity of Building Codes

As the development of building codes progressed, one factor became evident: requirements differed markedly from one jurisdiction to another. While far from being completely resolved, much has been done to provide greater uniformity among codes. As early as 1905 the National Board of Fire Underwriters (now the American Insurance Association) published a National Building Code. This code is periodically reviewed and revised, as necessary, and republished. In 1927 the International Conference of Building Officials promulgated the Uniform Building Code that has since been widely adopted on the West Coast and elsewhere. In 1945 the Southern Building Code Congress adopted a Southern Standard Building Code (now called the Standard Building Code) specifically to meet the needs of southern municipalities. In 1950 the Building Officials Conference of America (now the Building Officials and Code Administrators, International) published its Basic Building Code, adopted widely in the Northeast and Midwest.

Originally known as regional codes, all four of these model codes are frequently considered when a code revision is contemplated. Boundary lines for adoption today are much less significant. In fact, much effort has been expended through such organizations as the Joint Committee on Building Codes (composed of representatives of the organizations sponsoring the model codes and others concerned with the development of codes and standards) towards the elimination of differences between the model codes. Formed in 1949, the Joint Committee has since been renamed the Model Code Standardization Council, with code uniformity still the prime objective.

The regional model code agencies mentioned have supplemented their major effort with the development of other model codes and activities. These include fire prevention, housing, plumbing, one- and two-family dwellings, and swimming pool codes. Also included are plan examination and training programs, product approval, and publication of magazines. They also have provision for annual code revisions, developed through committee action and review of annual meetings.

The Council of American Building Officials was organized in 1972 as a more closely knit organization of representatives of the model code groups. The objective of the Council of American Building Officials is to seek uniformity while maintaining autonomy. One of the first accomplishments of this group was the publication of a jointly sponsored One- and Two-Family Dwelling Code.

Recognizing problems involved with each of the regional groups maintaining a product approval program, CABO recently organized a National Research Board to annually review applications for product recognition by participating organizations and to provide plant inspection for producers of fabricated parts and systems. This will provide a central point for product approval for those industries seeking a national market.

Another group organized to promote uniformity of building regulations and for other purposes is the National Conference of States on Building Codes and Standards. Organized in 1968, this group is an adjunct of the National Conference of States. As such, it is composed of official delegates from the various states with other membership classifications established through its by-laws. The NCSBCS operates with assistance from the National Bureau of Standards. It is concerned, among other things, with the achievement of uniformity among building codes and the improvement of the quality of building code administration. The NCSBCS works closely with the American National Standards Institute, the American Society for Testing and Materials, and the National Academy of Code Administrators.

The National Academy of Code Administrators, organized in 1970, is another step toward uniformity supported by BOCA, ICBO, SBCC, and NCSBCS. Its objective is the education and training of code administrators. Located in Washington, D.C., this organization publishes a Code Administration Review. Its membership is open to any interested person.

Finally, the Association of Major City Building Officials was formed in 1974. This group recognized code problems which are peculiar to large cities. Their objective is to define problem areas and seek their solutions.

D.　The Role of Standards in Building Codes

Many of the requirements found in building codes are based on the standards published by nationally recognized organizations. These are usually adopted into the building code by reference, thus keeping the building codes to a workable size and eliminating much duplication of effort. Such standards are also used by specification writers in the design stage of a building to provide guidelines for the purchasing agent. These outside standards also serve as product development incentives by specifying performance criteria.

Numerous NFPA standards are referenced by the model building codes and, thus, obtain legal status where these model codes are adopted. Notable examples of such NFPA Standards are NFPA No. 101, the Life Safety Code, NFPA No. 13, Standard for the Installation of Sprinkler Systems, and NFPA No. 30 Flammable and Combustible Liquids Code. A complete list of the NFPA codes and standards adopted by the various model building codes and the many

municipal codes is contained in the current issue of the *NFPA Publications and Visual Aids Catalog.*

Advisory construction and performance standards on products tested and listed by Underwriters Laboratories, Inc., are issued by that organization with many of them being submitted to the American National Standards Institute and approved as ANSI Standards. Similar standards are published by Underwriters Laboratories of Canada. The Canadian Standards Association is also a source for fire protection equipment and fire test standards. The Factory Mutual Engineering Corporation publishes a large number of standards designed to assist their assureds.

Numerous other national (ANSI) standards of varying applications in the fire protection field are prepared by governmental agencies and by other technical groups such as the National Bureau of Standards, (U.S. Department of Commerce), the General Services Administration (U.S. Government), various departments in the U.S. Department of Defense, the American Society of Mechanical Engineers, the American Society for Testing and Materials,[3] the Society of Automotive Engineers, and the American Water Works Association. Also, a number of trade associations issue standards that are of value in providing fire protection for structures. Among them are the American Gas Association, the Compressed Gas Association, the National Electrical Manufacturers Association, the Institute of Makers of Explosives, the National Automatic Sprinkler and Fire Control Association, the American Petroleum Institute, the American Concrete Institute, American Iron and Steel Institute, National Forest Products Association, American Society of Heating, Refrigerating and Air Conditioning Engineers, the Manufacturing Chemists Association, and the National Warm Air Heating and Air Conditioning Association.

E.　Reference Materials

At the end of this Chapter, in addition to the publications referenced in the text, there is a list of suggested reading material. Attention is called particularly to the three books at the top of the listing and to the publications of the three model code agencies and the National Fire Protection Association. The monthly or bi-monthly journals of these organizations as well as those of the American Society for Testing and Materials (*Standardization News*) and the National Association of Code Administrators (*Code Administration Review*) contain much information relative to the reasoning behind code requirements, standards development and proposed changes. Membership in these organizations is available to interested individuals and a journal subscription usually is included with the membership fee. The address of each is as follows:

American Society for Testing and Materials, 1916 Race Street, Philadelphia, PA 19106.

Building Officials and Code Administrators International, 1313 East 60th Street, Chicago, IL 60637.

International Conference of Building Officials, 5360 South Workman Mill Road, Whittier, CA 90601.

National Association of Code Administration (recently moved from Chicago to Washington. Street address unknown).

National Fire Protection Association, 470 Atlantic Avenue, Boston. MA 02210.

Southern Building Code Congress International, 3617 8th Avenue South, Birmingham, AL 35222.

Bibliography

References Cited

[1] Sanderson, R. L., *Codes and Code Administration*, Building Officials Conference of America, Inc., Chicago, 1969.

[2] *Ibid.*

[3] *ASTM Standards in Building Codes*, American Society for Testing and Materials, Philadelphia, 1973.

NFPA Codes, Standards, and Recommended Practices (see the latest *NFPA Publications and Visual Aids Catalog* for availability of current editions of the following documents)

NFPA No. 13, Standard for the Installation of Sprinkler Systems.

NFPA No. 30, Flammable and Combustible Liquids Code.

NFPA No. 101, Code for Safety to Life from Fire in Buildings and Structures.

NFPA No. 206M, Guide on Building Heights and Areas.

Additional Readings

Curless, M., "Codes, Standards and Fire Protection Engineering," MP 69-1, 1969, National Fire Protection Association, Boston.

Fire Protection Through Modern Building Codes, American Iron and Steel Institute, Washington, D.C., 1971.

Sanderson, R. L., *Readings in Code Administration*, 3 vols. Building Officials and Code Administrators International, Inc., Chicago, 1975.

Taylor, D. M., *A Guide for Codes Adoption and Codes Enforcement*, U.S. Department of Housing and Urban Development, Regional Office 4, Atlanta, 1974.

Chapter 12

FIRE HAZARDS OF CONSTRUCTION, ALTERATIONS, AND DEMOLITION OF BUILDINGS

Buildings, bridges, tunnels and other structures are more hazardous and more vulnerable to fire when under construction, regardless of construction type or construction method, than when completed. The hazards and vulnerability are even more pronounced in the case of alterations to existing structures, since normal operations are seldom curtailed during the alterations. Fires that are not discovered and extinguished in their incipient stages are likely to spread farther and more rapidly due to the absence or impairment of fire suppression and detection systems, lack of confinement, and heavier-than-normal concentration of combustibles. The results? Destruction of building materials stored on-site, lengthy delays in project completion, and, in the case of alterations, the possibility of staggering business interruption and, more important, loss of life.

Construction operations can be made reasonably safe by advance planning for contingencies in the project estimates and by providing necessary facilities and project responsibility once the project is begun. Responsibility should be increased and more widely delegated as construction proceeds. Necessary fire protection facilities should receive priority and should keep pace with the progress of the overall project. Essential considerations include: site preparation, temporary buildings and trailers, private and public fire protection, minimizing hazards inherent in construction operations, and coordination of permanent safeguards with progress schedules as work proceeds.

A.   Site Preparation

Most construction contracts require the removal of brush, trees, and debris from the site prior to the start of actual construction. However, few require that permanent roadways and installation of water mains and other underground work be completed prior to major construction activities, even though this would result in efficiency in the distribution of construction materials as well as the obvious benefits of adequate and readily available water supplies and improved access to the construction site by fire fighters. Instead, open trenches delay, if not completely prevent, access by fire fighting equipment. Temporary buildings and material storage areas indiscriminately surround the construction site. Little thought is given to topographical features of the site, such as railroad rights-of-way, water courses, embankments, to name a few. All of these place constraints on access to the site.

Advance planning demands that all of the above situations be foreseen and their adverse effects minimized. Also, due considerations must be given to the possibility of an exposure fire. Adequate access for fire apparatus should be provided on all sides of the construction site. Alternate access routes can provide access when operations require temporary blockage of principal roadways.

B.   Temporary Buildings and Trailers

Temporary buildings have always been commonplace at construction sites for storage of tools, equipment, and materials, as well as for field offices. Recently, the trend has been to replace the use of these temporary buildings with converted mobile homes and over-the-road freight trailers. Use of trailers eliminates the expense of erecting and dismantling the temporary buildings. Also, the trailers are inherently safer. It is still customary to build a saw shed for cutting lumber, however.

Both trailers and temporary buildings are subject to the same hazards. Extensive temporary wiring is more likely to be found in storage trailers. However, mobile field offices usually house various pieces of office equipment, such as typewriters, duplicating machines, etc., and use of extension cords and overloading of wall outlets is common. Unsafe heating systems are also commonplace, especially where space heaters are used. The greatest hazard comes from the heavy concentrations of combustibles. Field offices hold valuable, often irreplaceable, plans, blueprints, specification sheets, and project records. Storage of flammable liquids with combustible building materials adds to the fire hazard.

Finally, it is important to recognize that trailers and temporary storage buildings are often grouped together. This results in exposure fire hazards. Care in preliminary site planning can eliminate this hazard.

C.   Fire Protection During Construction

Normal buildings operations require considerable amounts of combustible building materials, forms, scaffolding, etc., which suggests the importance of protecting the project site against unauthorized entry. Security and the need for security personnel should be considered well in advance. Construction sites invariably demand an adequate number of well-trained and capable guards. Primary importance is given to fire detection and prompt notification of the public fire department. The availability of public fire protection must be evaluated and the need for a private fire brigade determined.

It is often mistakenly assumed that water supplies adequate for construction purposes are also adequate for fire fighting. Unless water is supplied from an adequate source, through permanent mains and hydrants (which are kept clear and well marked), it will not be adequate for fire fighting. In multistory structures or those in which permanent water supplies are either inaccessible or inadequate for fire fighting, temporary standpipe and hose systems should be installed to keep pace with the project. NFPA 241, Safeguarding Building Construction and Demolition Operations, gives guidance with respect to good fire protection practices to follow at building and renovation sites. For particularly hazardous operations, temporary automatic sprinkler protection should be considered.

A project fire warden having responsibility for compliance with common sense rules for fire prevention and protection is definitely advantageous. The project fire warden should also be responsible for coordination with the local fire department. He should also consult public fire officials in developing an emergency action plan and should inform them of any particularly hazardous operations or any phases of construction which render the structure particularly susceptible to fire. The fire warden should also be responsible for maintaining convenient and unobstructed emergency access routes. As mentioned previously, alternate routes are sometimes needed. The local fire department must be informed whenever the usual access routes are not available to it.

Recent economic developments have brought the unwanted prospects of shortages of various materials. This could lead to last-minute substitution of some materials without adequate review of the hazard potential of the substituted material. It is the responsibility of project management to insure that any substituted material is fully able to meet all the requirements set by the specifications.

D.   Hazards of Construction Operations

If the structure is built mostly or entirely of combustible materials, the possibility of total loss, in event of fire during construction, is inversely proportional to the precautionary measures taken. Heavy damage is also likely to occur to noncombustible or fire resistive structures during the construction phase, due, principally to the extensive use of wood forms, wood scaffolding, tarpaulins, and canvas (see Fig. 6-12A). Recently the use of heavy gage plastic film has begun to replace canvas (see Fig. 6-12B). The use of metal forms, fire retardant treated wood and canvas, and slow-burning plastic film reduce the hazard from this quarter. This is particularly important for large structures and tall buildings. Concrete should be poured as quickly as possible after erection of combustible forms and the forms should be removed as soon as the concrete has set, thus minimizing the amount of combustible material exposed at any one time. Where fire proofing is specified, it should be applied as soon as possible, thus affording fire protection to steel beams, girders, and columns early during the construction phase.

Consideration of necessary safeguards for construction hazards depends on the height and area of the structure, accessibility by fire fighters, available water supplies, and probable fire spread patterns. Some items ordinarily referred to as "common" hazards become significant hazards during construction operations. The most significant of these include:

Rubbish Collection and Disposal: Daily cleanup of scrap lumber, paper cement sacks, corrugated cardboard, and other debris not only removes the hazard, but also provides

Fig. 6-12A.   Combustible formwork is a constant source of danger to concrete buildings under construction. Here fire consumes wood formwork for cast-in-place floor and wall panels on a parking garage.

Fig. 6-12B.   Large sheets of plastic are sometimes used to enclose buildings under construction to confine heat. (Francis L. Brannigan)

more orderly working conditions. Most municipalities prohibit burning of scrap, so portable dumpsters are provided. These should be so located that a fire in one of them will present minimal exposure to the structure. Also, temporary water supplies and fire hose should be located nearby and ready for use.

Where burning of scrap is permitted, it should be done often enough so that fires are relatively small. Again, temporary water supplies and fire hose should be available.

Cutting and Welding Equipment: Improper use of cutting and welding apparatus and lack of proper safeguards are particularly hazardous. Careless use of plumbers' torches, especially at floor or wall penetrations, has been the cause of numerous fires. Increased use of glass-fiber reinforced plastic plumbing fixtures, combustible insulation, and combustible sound-deadening materials have contributed to the hazard. The obvious solution is to use noncombustible materials. Where combustible materials are used, extra precaution must be taken.

With proper protection and observance of safe working procedures, cutting torches, welding equipment, plumbers' torches, and other spark producing apparatus can be used with reasonable safety. NFPA No. 51B, Cutting and Welding Processes, gives guidance on good practices to follow (see also Sec. 4, Chap. 8 of this HANDBOOK).

Salamanders: Ignition of combustible material, such as canvas, wood forms, etc., by heating salamanders is commonplace. Use of these should be regulated and supervised. They should be kept clear of combustible materials.

Temporary Wiring: Construction projects ordinarily require considerable temporary wiring. All wiring should be installed and supervised by competent electricians. It is important for electricians to note that the use of aluminum and copper-clad aluminum wire requires special installation procedures. Disregard for these special procedures may lead to increased fire hazards not only during construction, but also after completion of the project. Temporary circuits, especially high voltage circuits, require substantial protection against physical damage from moveable equipment, etc.

Flammable Liquids: Careless storage and handling of flammable and combustible liquids are responsible for many construction project fires. Small quantities of gasoline used for motorized construction equipment should be handled in safety containers and stored in an isolated location. Bulk quantities of other flammable or combustible liquids should be stored and handled in a standard manner (see Sec. 3, Chap. 3). Paint rags, etc., should be disposed of in covered metal containers, since these are subject to spontaneous combustion.

Tar Kettles: Use of tar kettles involves the hazard of the fuel, heating of the material, and exposure to combustibles. They should only be used outdoors, away from combustible storage. They should never be used on a combustible roof. Wood fires should never be used for heating tar kettles. Should a fire occur, it is imperative to remember that water thrown into the tar kettle itself will result in frothing of the tar.

Roofing Mops: Roofing mops soaked in pitch or asphalt should never be left inside a building, near heating equipment, or near combustible materials. These mops are subject to spontaneous heating, regardless of what they are made of.

Explosives: Storage, handling, and use of explosives is usually regulated by law or ordinance. NFPA 495, Explosives Materials Code, specifies appropriate requirements (see also Sec. 3, Chap. 6 of this HANDBOOK).

Gasoline Powered Equipment: Gasoline powered equipment, such as air compressors, hoists, pumps, etc., should be so located that exhausts are well away from combustible material. Where used underground, or in other locations where it is necessary to pipe exhaust to the outside, at least 6 in. clearance from combustible material should be provided for the piping. Gasoline engines should be shut off during refueling operations. It is especially desirable that electrically driven or air-operated equipment be used in underground operations or beneath buildings.

Compressed Air Operations: Where construction operations are conducted under increased air pressure, as in tunnels and caissons, combustion is greatly accelerated, and particular precautions to prevent the ignition of combustible materials are necessary.

E. Permanent Safeguards

In most construction operations, the progress of the work toward completion gradually enhances the safety of the structure. As the need for combustible form work and scaffolding, materials storage, temporary buildings and trailers and other inherent hazards diminishes, they should be removed from the site.

Access to the structure by fire fighters is important. Installation of permanent stairways and stairway enclosures should be completed as quickly as possible. Likewise, firewalls and other essential features provided for confinement of fire should be installed as early as possible. Penetrations of fire resistive construction made for building services should be closed up immediately after the services are installed. Integrity of all fire cut-offs should be maintained.

Permanent standpipe and hose systems should be installed as construction work progresses. In buildings lacking automatic sprinkler systems, or those in which the installation of tanks and other equipment must wait for the completion of structural elements, standpipe and hose systems may provide the only certain source of water for fire fighting throughout the project. Where automatic sprinkler systems are to be a part of the permanent protection for a building, proper correlation of the work will provide water supplies for the system and prompt installation of sprinklers following the completion of the interior finish of the building. Blank gaskets used in flanges to permit sprinkler protection by sections as construction work is completed should be provided with lugs that are painted red to assure removal when the system is extended.

Permanent wiring systems should replace temporary wiring systems as rapidly as the removal of form work will permit. Permanent heating plants and temporary nonfired heat exchangers can often be used to supplant the more hazardous use of salamanders.

F. Fire Protection During Alterations

Alterations to an existing structure present even greater fire hazards as use of the structure is rarely curtailed while the renovations are being made. Thus, alterations require great vigilance on the part of owners, architects, contractors, and their personnel, since the existing structure is threatened not only by the hazards of the construction work, but also by the hazards of the occupancy. Life safety problems may be compounded too, as some means of egress may be blocked.

The greatest hazard is the removal of permanent barriers to fire spread without the provision of substantial temporary enclosures for floor and wall openings. Another hazard is the impairment of automatic sprinkler protection without preparation for its immediate restoration to service in case of fire. Cutting and welding are often carried out in concealed spaces with little or no protection of combustibles.

Finally, the replacement of elements of fire-rated construction demands that replacement of materials affords equivalent fire endurance.

G. Demolition

Demolition operations involve the same fire hazards and safeguards as construction and alterations, but with the significant differences that fire is usually important only from the point of view of life safety, exposure damage, and possible undue burden on the fire department. In fact, unwanted buildings are often burned deliberately under fire department supervision.

Bibliography

NFPA Codes, Standards, and Recommended Practices (see the latest *NFPA Publications and Visual Aids Catalog* for availability of current editions of the following documents)

NFPA No. 241, Safeguarding Building Construction and Demolition Operations.

NFPA No. 51, Standard for the Installation and Operation of Oxygen-Fuel Gas Systems for Welding and Cutting.

NFPA No. 51B, Standard for Fire Protection in Use of Cutting and Welding Processes.

NFPA No. 395, Standard for the Storage of Flammable and Combustible Liquids on Forms and Isolated Construction Projects.

NFPA No. 495, Code for the Manufacture, Transportation, Storage and Use of Explosives and Blasting Agents.

Other Publications

"Buildings Under Construction," FR 58-1, 1958, National Fire Protection Association, Boston, Mass.

Brannigan, Francis L., *Building Construction for the Fire Service*, National Fire Protection Association, 1971, 297 pp.

"Collapse of the Hotel Vendome, Boston, Mass.," *Fire Journal*, Vol. 67, No. 1, Jan. 1973, pp. 33–41.

Feld, Jacob, *Construction Failures*, J. Wiley & Sons, 1968, 399 pp.

Herbstman, Donald, "Fire Protection During Construction," *Fire Journal*, Vol. 64, No. 1, Jan. 1970, pp. 29–32, 89.

Juillerat, Ernest E., "The Menace of Abandoned Buildings," *Fire Journal*, Vol. 59, No. 1, Jan. 1965, pp. 5–10.

McKaig, Thomas H., *Building Failures—Case Studies in Construction and Design*, McGraw Hill Book Company, Inc., 1962, 261 pp.

Peterson, Carl E., "The Occupancy Fire Picture: Apartment Buildings Under Construction," *Fire Journal*, Vol. 63, No. 5, Sept. 1969, pp. 23–25.

Chapter 13

EVALUATING STRUCTURAL DAMAGE

There are two factors to be considered with respect to building components subjected to fire exposure. The first relates to the ability of the structure to withstand collapse during the actual fire. The second involves evaluation of structural damage after the fire has been extinguished. A decision must be made to either renovate or demolish the structure. Economic considerations generally determine the course of action to be taken.

Immediately after a fire is extinguished, the structure must be inspected for the possibility of imminent collapse. This is done on a gross basis by inspecting the major load bearing elements to determine if any major weaknesses are present. Distorted or partially collapsed bearing walls, columns which have been moved by temperature gradients to the point that loads are no longer supported axially, partial collapse of critical supports, and unsymmetrical loading are important aspects of post-fire inspection. Also, removal of lateral supports of flexural members either by the fire or by subsequent clean-up operations is of critical concern. Temporary shoring or lateral supports may be required after a fire.

If the building is to be renovated, the strength of the structural assemblies which were exposed to the fire must be determined. Assessment of damage will involve both evaluation of the structure as a unit and evaluation of specific structural members and assemblies. The evaluation should be conducted by a qualified engineer, as the influence of distortion and residual stresses may have a significant influence on load-carrying capacity.

The influence of temperature on the mechanical properties of structural materials is detailed in Chapter 7 of this Section. However, the question arises as to the "use ability" of the material after temperatures have cooled down to ambient. The evaluation of the structural behavior of steel, concrete, and wood is described below. A more detailed evaluation procedure and a case study of renovation is given in Chapters 12 and 13 of *A Complete Guide to Fire and Buildings* edited by E. W. Marchant.[1]

A. Steel

The use of several strength grades of steel in buildings and bridges is accepted in modern building codes and design standards. These different grades of steel include a wide range of strengths, but tensile and yield strengths of all are similarly affected by the temperatures that may be expected due to fires in buildings.

The behavior of beams or other members subject to bending stresses under fire conditions is complex. In a building fire, the steel temperature may vary considerably over a single cross section as well as along the length of a structural member. Information relating to the strength properties of steel at elevated temperatures has been derived from the results of tests on small specimens heated so that the entire specimen was at or close to the measured temperature. Conclusions relating to strength characteristics from such small-scale tests may not be applicable to steel structural members. Moreover, plastic action results in the redistribution of stresses in steel members loaded close to the design limit. This characteristic permits steel members

to sustain loads greater than those calculated to be safe on the basis of yield strength alone; therefore, the strength of a given steel member cannot be determined from isolated temperature data alone.

In a building fire, parts of the structure may have been exposed to heating followed by abrupt cooling by water from hose streams. This temperature change is usually less severe than what is accepted practice in heat treating of steel during manufacture. Tests performed on structural steel specimens taken from a building which underwent a fire during construction showed no significant loss of either yield or tensile strength. If a steel member shows no distortion due to heat or if it can be straightened, its physical properties are generally unchanged but connections between members should be checked for cracks around rivet or bolt holes.

Occasionally, steel exposed to a fire will have a somewhat roughened appearance due to excessive scaling and grain coarsening. The coarsening is caused by exposure of steel to temperatures around 1,600°F or higher. The steel will usually have a dark gray color, although other colors may be present if certain chemicals have been involved in the fire. Steel so modified is commonly called "burnt" steel. Members which have become burnt will usually be severely corroded as well and their suitability for further use is a matter for individual judgment.

Many instances have been reported where straightening of structural steel members distorted due to fire has been both feasible and economical. Following the McChord AFB fire in 1957 near Tacoma, Washington in which two aircraft hangars were seriously damaged, 1,486 structural steel members were either straightened or replaced in the steel frame. Of that number, only 46 members were replaced; the remaining 1,440 members were flame-straightened, using welding torches.

The use of cast iron as a structural material has all but ceased. One reason is that cast iron may fracture when heated and suddenly cooled. Fires in buildings may cause heated cast iron columns to collapse if they are struck by water from hose streams. Although rare in modern structures, cast iron columns may still be found in older buildings.

B. Concrete

In a fire lasting 1 to 2 hrs, concrete will be generally only moderately damaged, and so routine cutting and patching procedures will usually be adequate preliminary to repairs. In intense and lasting fires, such as may occur in large, heavily stocked warehouses and department stores, severe damage to concrete may be expected. In some cases of record, restoration entailed the removal of severely damaged areas and patching in areas less severely damaged. Experienced engineering judgment is required for evaluating the residual strength of those areas that are somewhere between moderately and severely damaged. For an example, one approach to the problem of evaluating the residual strength of apparently marginally damaged concrete structural units would be to refer the reader to "Prestressed Concrete Resists Fire," by C. Zollman and M. Garavaglin.[2]

A waiting period of perhaps several weeks should elapse after the fire has been extinguished before careful study of structural damage is initiated. This delay will allow any damage to the concrete to become more discernible such as cracking, layering, calcination and discoloration (a change from the natural gray color to pink or brown is indicative of heating to temperatures in excess of 450°F). The thickness of fire damaged concrete in structural members can be determined by chipping with a pick or geologist's hammer. Unsound concrete may be colored and will be more or less soft and friable. Sound concrete will give a distinctive ring when struck with a pick or hammer. Cored concrete samples for compressive strength tests and reinforcing steel for tensile strength determinations will enable a more close evaluation of the residual strength of damaged members. Load tests may be applied but only under the supervision of a registered structural engineer.

Two other methods for evaluating fire damage are worthy of mention, but each requires an experienced operator. These make use of the Schmidt hammer and the soniscope. The Schmidt hammer has a spring loaded plunger which is caused to strike the test surface by the release of a trigger. The rebound of the plunger is a measure of concrete strength. The rebound numbers should not be considered more than a qualitative evaluation of the concrete strength as there are several variables other than strength which may affect rebound numbers. The soniscope is an electronic device which has been used to gage the soundness of relatively heavy concrete sections, such as highway pavement slabs, bridge components, and dams. In operating principle a high frequency pulse is directed by an electronic sender through the section in question and is picked up by an electronic receiver. The speed at which the pulse travels through the section from sender to receiver, in feet per second, is a gage of the integrity of material in the pulse path. Severe exposure of heavy concrete sections to fire may cause "layering," that is, partial separation of the outer 1 to 2 in. of concrete of a building member from the interior mass. Such "layering" can absorb the full energy of the pulse, so interpretative experience is necessary. The device has been successfully used in conjunction with other methods in evaluating fire damage in at least one case.

A very complete report dealing with a survey of fire damage to a multistory reinforced concrete building and the subsequent repair procedure may be found in the paper "Fire Damage to General Mills Building," by J. Fruchtbaum.[3]

A very severe fire occurred in 1951 in an unsprinklered paper warehouse. This fire lasted for more than 44 hrs, and it is estimated that heat intensities of more than 1,600°F existed for 3 hrs or longer. Even after this very severe fire the structure was still standing and the concrete floors prevented the spread of fire and major water damage. An inspection of the structure after the fire showed that the concrete roof and columns appeared to have suffered little damage, except that the roof showed deflection up to a maximum of about $2\frac{1}{2}$ in. in a 20-ft span. When holes were cut through the roof, it was found that the concrete was calcined and had a light brown color in varying depths. This damaged concrete had almost no strength, and after a period of several weeks began to disintegrate. As a result, the portions of the roof slab that showed appreciable amounts of calcine were replaced. Many of the columns required removal of the concrete down to the reinforcing steel spiral, and, in some cases, calcining appeared inside the spiral. In these cases, the entire column was replaced. The column caps were replaced completely if more than one half of the column cap showed evidence of calcining. Reinforcing rods showed some reduction in tensile strength

but, mostly, were salvaged and reused, and downgraded to about three quarters of their original strength.

C. Wood

When wood structural members are subjected to fire, the ability to withstand the imposed loads is dependent to a degree upon the amount of cross sectional area remaining. The average rate of penetration of char when flame is impinged upon an exposed wood member is approximately $1\frac{1}{2}$ in. per hr. Beyond the char area to a point not more than $\frac{1}{4}$ in. away the structural properties of wood may be affected by its exposure to high temperatures. The degree of strength loss in this small zone adjacent to the char is not known exactly, but is presumed to be insignificant.

Fire tests made on two solid sawn wood joists, 4 in. by 14 in., nominal size, at the Southwest Research Institute[4] showed that after 13 min of fire exposure, there remained 80 percent of the original wood section, undamaged and available to carry the load. In another test of two 7 in. by 21 in. glued laminated beams, after 30 min fire exposure, 75 percent of the original wood section remained and continued to support the design load.[5]

The above tests, as well as actual fire experience, substantiates the fact that wood members will remain in place under fire conditions and continue to support design loads. It is usually in the larger or heavy timber members that char can be scraped clear and an evaluation can be made by a qualified engineer or architect to determine the remaining load supporting capacity of the wood member. This same process is true of smaller size members except that they usually have the benefit of protection by lath and plaster or gypsum wallboard. It can be said then that the strength of a wood member subjected to a prolonged period of fire intensity may be reduced by the loss of cross section which results in a corresponding change in deformation under a given load. After the char area has been removed, the remaining strength or load supporting capacity can be easily determined through proper design analysis.

Bibliography

References Cited

[1] Marchant, E. W. (Ed.), "A Complete Guide to Fire and Buildings," Barnes and Noble, 1973, New York, p. 268.

[2] Zollman, L. and Garavaglin, M., "Prestressed Concrete Resists Fire," Civil Engineering, December 1960, New York, pp. 36–41.

[3] Fruchtbaum, J., "Fire Damage to General Mills Building," Proceedings of American Concrete Institute, Jan. 1941, Detroit, Michigan.

[4] "Comparative Fire Tests on Wood and Steel Joists," Technical Report No. 1, 1961, National Forest Products Association, Washington, D.C.

[5] "Comparative Fire Tests of Timber and Steel Beams," Technical Report No. 3, 1961, National Forest Products Association, Washington, D.C.

Additional Readings

Dill, F. H., "Structural Steel After a Fire," Procedings of AISC, National Engineering Conference, Brown Palace Hotel, Denver, Colorado, May 5 and 6, 1960.

Bessey, G. E., "The Visible Changes in Concrete or Mortar Exposed to High Temperature," Part II, *National Building Studies,* Tech. Paper No. 4, Ministry of Technology and Fire Offices' Committee Joint Fire Research Organization (formerly Department of Scientific and Industrial Research), Building Research Station, Garston, Watford, Herts., printed at His Majesty's Stationery Office, London, 1950.

Parker, T. W. and Nurse, R. W., "Investigation of Building Fires: The Estimation of the Maximum Temperature Attained in Building Fires from Examination of the Debris," Part I, *ibid*.

"Notes on Repair of Damaged Buildings": Note 2—Repair of

Structural Steelwork Damaged by Fire, Nov. 1944, Ministry of Technology and Fire Offices' Committee Joint Fire Research Organization (formerly Department of Scientific and Industrial Research), Building Research Station, Garston, Watford, Herts., printed at Her Majesty's Stationery Office, London.

————, Note No. 13—"Reinforced Concrete Columns Damaged by Fire," Sept. 1945, *ibid*.

————, Note No. 19—"The Repair of Solid Concrete and Hollow-tile Floors Damaged by Fire," Sept. 1945, *ibid*.

————, Note No. 24—"Reinforced Concrete Beams Damaged by Fire," July 1946, *ibid*.

Smith, Peter, "Investigation and Repair of Damage to Concrete Caused by Formwork and Falsework Fire," Journal of the American Concrete Institute, Nov. 1963, pp. 1535-1565.

Troxell, G. E., "Prestressed Lift Slabs," Civil Engineering, Sept. 1965, New York, pp. 64-66.

SECTION 7

BUILDING SERVICES

Chapter 1

HAZARDS OF BUILDING SERVICES—INTRODUCTION

Section 7 provides detailed discussion on the hazards of building services. Generally, these building services are essential to the functional operation of a facility, but their needed presence also brings an increase in the potential of a fire occurring. Being essential services, their presence cannot be prohibited. Consequently, this requires that, in the true sense of risk management, their presence must be treated, from a fire protection engineering standpoint, to mitigate the increase in potential hazard to the facility.

To properly provide for the presence of these many building services, it is necessary to understand their general operating characteristics and the common elements of increased fire hazard they bring with them. This brief inductory chapter lists the variety of building services that must be considered in formulating overall fire protection and prevention plans for a building.

Electrical Systems and Appliances

Electrical appliances, which do not of themselves possess a fuel hazard, are subject to the many causes of fire of electrical origin. Chapter 2 provides further discussion on both electrical systems and appliances. This includes a discussion of the fire problems resulting from the use of electricity for lighting, heating, and power purposes; a general description of the elements of electricity to aid in understanding the text; a review of the electrical codes and standards used in the United States and Canada; and is followed by discussions on building wiring, design and protection; electrical household appliances; industrial and commercial appliances; electronic data processing equipment; electrical equipment for outdoor use; electrical equipment for use in locations exposed to moisture and noncombustible dusts; communications systems; emergency lighting equipment; special occupancy fire problems, including hazardous locations, theaters and assembly halls, motion picture studios, and motion picture projection booths; and the origins of electrical fires in buildings.

Heating Systems and Appliances

Another essential set of building services, heat-producing appliances and equipment pertaining to them, are one of the most prevalent causes of fire, as they operate at temperatures above the ignition temperatures of most common materials. In addition, combustion-type appliances involve the hazard of a fuel and the possible exposure of it to ignition sources.

Chapter 3 discusses fuels and methods of firing, heating appliances and their uses, heat distribution through duct systems and pipes, installation of heating appliances, chimney and vent connectors and chimneys, fireplaces, and venting systems.

Air Conditioning and Ventilating Systems

A necessary adjunct that goes hand in hand with heat-producing appliances, due to both need for "conditioned" air and for heat removal from a facility, is air conditioning systems and appliances and related air movement equipment. Chapter 4 discusses all types of duct systems for the movement of air and the potential hazard of their being the means for spreading fire and smoke through the building or area which they serve. Other potential fire hazards of duct systems and of air conditioning equipment are also the subject of this chapter.

Air Moving Equipment

Special occupancy needs requiring air moving equipment including all mechanical-draft duct systems, of both the pressure and exhaust types, for removal of dusts, vapors, and waste material and for the conveying of materials are discussed in Chapter 5. The hazards of such systems lie in the possibility of igniting flammable materials or vapors by sources such as sparks struck by fans or by overheated fan bearings, and in the part that such systems play in spreading fires through buildings.

These systems do, however, play an important role in fire protection because they remove materials that if allowed to accumulate could result in explosions, as from vapor-air mixtures; flash fires, due to such things as accumulations of lint; and general poor housekeeping conditions conducive to fires.

Refuse Handling Systems and Equipment

Refuse removal systems and their related equipment also perform a needed role in fire protection. Removal of combustible waste material from a facility reduces the potential of a fire originating due to either poor housekeeping practices or the unneeded accumulation of excessive quantities of combustible waste. Since these systems necessarily handle material that constitutes a fuel hazard, a malfunction of the system or its ancillary equipment could lead to fire propagation. Chapter 6 discusses typical refuse handling systems, related equipment and the primary elements of proper arrangement.

Miscellaneous Building Services

Chapter 7 contains information on a variety of building service equipment that does not fall into any other generic classification. Included are communication equipment and their introduction of fuel into a facility in the form of large quantities of low voltage wiring, usually clad in a combustible cover, e.g., PVC (polyvinyl chloride) that is not placed in conduit, but either located in open chases or haphazardly arranged above suspended ceilings or in concealed interstitial spaces. Also discussed in Chapter 7 are combustible piping for water circulation and waste removal, now widely used. They are also often located in open chases, above suspended ceilings, and in concealed interstitial spaces and, like noncombustible piping, they are often the cause of potential weakening of the fire resistance of a floor-ceiling assembly due to their penetration of the assembly in the form of "poke-through" construction.

Chapter 7 provides discussion on laundry chutes, elevators and dumbwaiters which represent the "other" vertical shafts often overlooked when determinations are made of a a facility's required fire protection needs. Finally, discussion is found in Chapter 7 on the subject of electric stairways and the hazard associated with their motive power.

Chapter 2

ELECTRICAL SYSTEMS AND APPLIANCES

This chapter is introduced by: (1) a discussion of the fire problems resulting from the use of electricity for lighting, heating, and power purposes; (2) a general description of the elements of electricity to aid in understanding the text; (3) a review of the electrical codes and standards used in the United States and Canada; and is followed by discussions on (4) building wiring design and protection; (5) electrical household appliances; (6) industrial and commercial equipment; (7) electronic computer equipment; (8) electrical equipment for outdoor use; (9) electrical equipment for use in locations exposed to moisture and noncombustible dusts; (10) communications systems; (11) emergency equipment; (12) special occupancy fire problems, including hazardous locations, places of assembly, theaters and similar locations, motion picture studios and similar locations, and motion picture projectors; and (13) the origins of electrical fires in buildings.

A. Fire Problems of Electrical Systems and Appliances

If properly designed, installed, and maintained, electrical systems for lighting, power, heating, and other purposes are convenient and safe, but if not installed and maintained in accordance with well established standards, they may introduce both fire and personal injury hazards. This has been recognized since electric power first came into general commercial use.

Electricity may become a fire hazard through arcing or overheating of electrical equipment. It presents a casualty hazard through burns or shocks (or falls, drowning, self-inflicted wounds with circular saws, etc., as a result of shock) when contact is made with live parts or with non-conducting metal parts that have been energized through fault conditions.

To minimize these hazards, only suitable and safe materials which have been tested and listed by a recognized testing laboratory should be used, provided testing and listing service is available for the type equipment in question. (Where there are no standards available for special equipment, arrangements usually can be made for testing on an individual basis.) Equipment should be installed in conformity with accepted standards. Such installations should then be maintained and used in accordance with the latest edition of NFPA No. 70, National Electrical Code (NEC).

When an electric circuit carrying a current is interrupted, either intentionally, as by a switch, or accidentally, or un-intentionally, as where a contact at a terminal becomes loosened, an arc or heating from the high-resistance connection is produced. The intensity of the arc and degree of heat depends in a great measure on the current and voltage of the circuit. The temperature may easily be such that any combustible material in its vicinity may be ignited.

An electric arc not only may ignite combustible material in its vicinity, such as the insulation and covering of the conductor, but it may also fuse the metal of the conductor. Hot sparks from burning combustible material and hot metal may be thrown about or fall and set fire to other combustible material.

When an electrical conductor carries a current, heat is generated in direct proportion to the resistance of the conductor and to the square of the current. The resistance of conductors used to convey current to the location in which it is used, or to convey it through the windings of a piece of apparatus (except resistance devices and heaters), should be as low as practicable. Metals, such as copper, silver, and aluminum are used for this purpose. In other instances, the heating effect of the current serves a useful purpose, as in electric heaters, pressing irons, soldering irons, and numerous other devices.

As a fire hazard, the heating of conductors used to convey current is negligible under ordinary circumstances. The NEC specifies the maximum safe current a conductor may carry without overheating (see Tables 7-2C through 7-2F). This depends upon the size of conductor and type of insulation. Where these specified currents are exceeded, or where a conductor is "overloaded," the generation of heat becomes a hazard in two ways: first, through deterioration of the insulation of the conductor, and second, through the excess heat generated. Apparatus or appliances which utilize an electric conductor as a heating element or which use the electric arc for the generation of heat are likely to be a fire hazard unless properly installed and used.

In many electrical installations, a method of reducing the degree of hazard is to provide an adequate degree of air circulation to prevent unsafe temperatures in the devices or equipment and premature breakdown due to overheating.

All standards governing the installation and maintenance of electrical equipment include requirements intended to prevent fires caused by arcing and overheating and to prevent accidental contact which may cause a shock and related casualties. In the installation, maintenance, and inspection or reinspection of electrical equipment, these primary sources of electrical hazards should be kept in mind.

B. Elements of Electricity

Volt (V): A unit of electrical pressure, or electromotive force which causes electricity to flow. The voltage of a circuit is not necessarily a measure of its fire or life hazard. A fine wire across the terminals of a dry cell battery (approximately 1.5 V) can produce a fire hazard by becoming "red hot" in the presence of a combustible material, and yet there is no shock hazard. Certain types of circuits may have very high voltages but such low current as to be incapable of passing sufficient current to injure a person even though a considerable "shock" may be experienced. This is because the source of supply, such as a transformer, does not have sufficient power, even at high voltage levels, to force a lethal current through the resistance of the skin, flesh, and vital organs. The ordinary house circuit at 115 V has sufficient voltage and current to present both fire and shock hazards.

Ampere: A unit of rate of flow of a current of electricity. The flow of electricity measured in amperes, depends upon the pressure in volts and the resistance in ohms. (In alternating current, there also exists, in most instances, an inductive reactance [induction] and a capacitive reactance [capacity]. The total effect of ohmic resistance and reactance is known in such ac circuits as impedance.)

Ohm: A unit of electrical resistance. The relation between volts, amperes, and ohms is expressed in Ohm's Law: $I = \dfrac{E}{R}$, or $R = \dfrac{E}{I}$, or $E = I \times R$, in which I = current in amperes, E = electromotive force in volts, R = resistance in ohms. Ohm's Law applies to direct current (dc); in alternating current (ac), the total impedance (Z) must be reduced to ohms (R) before this formula can be applied.

Watt (W): A unit of power. A current of one amp flowing under a pressure of one volt makes one watt. A 100-W electric light bulb rated at 110 V draws a current of about 0.9 amp and has a resistance of about 120 ohms $\left(R = \dfrac{E}{I}\right)$. A 115-V, 15-amp circuit can carry a load of $115 \times 15 = 1,725$ W. A kilowatt (kW) is 1,000 watts. A kilowatt-hour (kWh) is a unit of quantity (work) representing a power of 1,000 W or 1 kW continued for 1 hr. In heating devices, the rating in watts indicated the relative amount of heat produced (1 kW = 56.90 Btu per min).

Electrical Current

There are two kinds of electrical current: direct, referred to as "dc," and alternating, referred to as "ac."

Direct Current: This is a continuous flow of the same polarity, as in current from batteries or from direct current generators.

Alternating Current: The polarity of the current flow in this type of circuit is reversed periodically, creating a regular system of sine waves—going from zero to its maximum in a positive flow, then dropping to zero, going from zero to maximum in a negative flow, and back to zero, etc. A cycle equals two of these waves (alternations), one in each direction (for each polarity). In most ac circuits in the United States, there are 60 cycles per second, or 120 alternations (waves) per second.

Alternating current circuits are usually single- or three-phase. Some old two-phase circuits are in use, but most have been replaced with three-phase. (A "phase," constitutes one alternation of one cycle, and in electrical terminology a phase in a circuit is extended to include the winding itself within a transformer enclosure.) Single-phase current is supplied by 2-wire and by 3-wire circuits. Three-phase circuits may be either delta-connected or wye-connected. Two-wire or 3-wire, single-phase lighting and power circuits or 3-wire and 4-wire, 3-phase lighting and 3-phase power circuits may be derived from either a delta- or wye-connected system.

Four-wire, 3-phase circuits or three 2-wire, single-phase circuits may be derived from the wye-connected system, such as for lighting and receptacles. In this system, the voltage between each of the phases is the same, and the voltage from each phase to the neutral conductor is the same but lower than the phase-to-phase voltage. Hence both lighting and power loads may be served. The most common voltages for this system are 120/208 and 265/460-V (the latter is sometimes designated as 277/480-V).

Three-wire, 3-phase circuits may be derived from a 3-wire delta system for power circuits. In order to obtain a 4-wire delta system, however, which has no neutral point for a grounded neutral, the mid-point of one of the phase windings must be grounded, from which point the grounded neutral is derived. Single-phase, 2- and 3-wire circuits for lighting and small power receptacles, etc., may be derived

from the phase winding that is grounded. The voltage between each of these phase conductors and the neutral is usually 120, and between each of the three-phases it is 240, or 120/240 (of the type used for lighting). The third phase cannot be used for lighting, however, as the voltage between it and the neutral is 208. (Higher voltages than 240 are frequently used on 3-wire delta systems for power only.) Single-phase 120/240-V, 3-wire systems are also in common use.

The flow of electric current creates a magnetic force, and change in a magnetic field surrounding a system of wires produces an electric voltage which creates current flow; these facts are the basis of the electric motor and the generator. The electric motor also acts as an electric generator under some abnormal conditions. An electromotive force (voltage) is produced in the windings of generators. This EMF (electromotive force) is utilized in the windings of the motor to turn its rotor. The motor then builds up a counter EMF that restricts the flow of current from the power supply. This is why the starting current in a motor is about six times greater than it is after its counter EMF has built up after reaching full speed.

C. Codes and Standards

All electrical installations in the United States should be made, used and maintained in accordance with the National Electrical Code, the National Electrical Safety Code, and other standards which apply in special situations, e.g., NFPA No. 79, Electrical Metalworking Machine Tools; NFPA No. 75, Electronic Computer Equipment; and NFPA No. 76A, Essential Electrical Systems for Health Care Facilities. There are also special standards for electrical installations on shipboard, aircraft, mobile homes, recreational vehicles, and other vehicles.

National Electrical Code (NFPA No. 70, ANSI Standard C1)

The National Electrical Code, referred to hereafter as the NEC, provides for the practical safeguarding of persons and structures and their contents from hazards arising from the use of electricity. The NEC was first issued under its present name in 1897. It is revised every 3 yrs by the National Fire Protection Association under the aegis of a National Electrical Code Committee and combines the experience and judgment of all parties interested in the use of electricity.

National Electrical Safety Code (ANSI Standards C2.1, C2.2, C2.3, C2.4, and Supplements)

As interest increased in electrical safety in the United States, a need was felt for a code to cover the practices of public utilities and others when installing and maintaining overhead and underground electric supply and communication lines. Accordingly, a National Electrical Safety Code was completed in 1916. Currently this code is developed by a committee (C2) of the American National Standards Institute.

Canadian Electrical Code

The Canadian Standards Association currently sponsors and publishes the Canadian Electrical Code. This code establishes essential requirements and minimum standards for the installation and maintenance of electrical equipment for adoption and enforcement by electrical inspection departments throughout Canada and was prepared with due regard for the NEC and the National Electrical Safety Code. Its several parts are the Canadian equivalent of the NEC, the National Electrical Safety Code, and the standards of the Underwriters Laboratories, Inc., in the United States.

Lists of Inspected Electrical Equipment

Three pamphlets indicating electrical appliances and materials which have been examined and listed, entitled, *Hazardous Location Equipment List*,[1] *Electrical Appliance and Utilization Equipment List*,[2] and *Electrical Construction Materials List*[3] are published annually by Underwriters Laboratories, Inc. Devices and materials listed have been tested for use in accordance with the NEC and under the standards of Underwriters Laboratories, and the operation of these devices and materials are observed in use. The lists are published so that the names of manufacturers of designated devices judged to be designed and manufactured in compliance with these standards may be readily obtained. The sections of the NEC relating to the design and construction of appliances are but a partial outline. Underwriters Laboratories, Inc., has complete standards for most electrical fittings, materials, and equipment, including specifications for performance under tests and in service, and further details of design and construction. Other testing laboratories in the United States and Canada that test electrical equipment include the Factory Mutual System, the Electrical Testing Laboratories, and the Canadian Standards Association Laboratory. In testing equipment, some laboratories stipulate compliance with the NEC.

D. Building Wiring, Design and Protection

This section contains information on various types of building wiring and equipment, including panelboards and overcurrent protection; types of electrical conductors; identification of conductors, terminals, etc., how to calculate loads, and similar subjects.

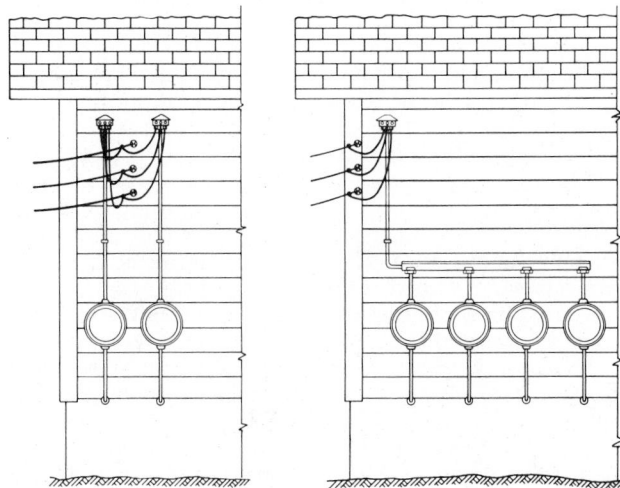

Fig. 7-2A. The diagram at left shows an installation in which two sets of service entrance conductors are tapped from one service drop, with meters mounted on the outside of the building. In the diagram at right, a set of main service entrance conductors is connected to the service drop and is carried through a trough and then through four sets of subservice entrance conductors to each service equipment. Here again the meters are on the exterior wall.

Service Entrance

Good practice requires that service entrance conductors comply in all respects with the detailed requirements of the NEC. See Figure 7-2A for typical arrangements of service entrance conductors.

Means are provided for disconnecting all conductors in the building from the service entrance conductors. The principle is to permit disconnection of all conductors of the service with no more than six operations of the hand (see Fig. 7-2B). The limitation is applicable to all of the service disconnecting means located in one place or "grouped." It does not include the services for fire pumps, emergency electrical systems, etc., which the NEC recognizes as being separate services for specific purposes.

The disconnecting means is either an inside or outside installation at a readily accessible location nearest the point of entrance of the service-entrance conductors. For each set of service-entrance conductors (or each sub-set) the disconnecting means consists of not more than six switches or six circuit breakers mounted in a single enclosure, in a group of separate enclosures, or in or on a switchboard.

Service-entrance conductors should be of sufficient size to carry the anticipated load. In general, a building or other structure served should be supplied by only one set of service drops (see Fig. 7-2A) or service lateral conductors, but additional services are permitted for fire pumps, emergency electrical systems, multiple occupancies, large capacities, large areas, and different classes of use.

Underground service conductors are protected against physical damage. Table 7-2A gives minimum cover requirements for protecting various types of conductors carrying 600 V or less. Table 7-2B gives cover requirements for conductors with circuit voltages over 600 V. (Cover is defined as the distance between the top surface of direct buried cable, conduit, or other raceways approved for the purpose or duct and the finished grade.)

Service-entrance conductors or underground service lateral conductors are insulated. However, a grounded service conductor may be without individual insulation or covering when it is part of a cable assembly having a moisture-and-fungus resistant outer covering. A grounded copper service-entrance or service lateral conductor may not have individual insulation or covering for direct burial where bare copper is judged to be suitable for the soil conditions.

Where accessible to other than qualified persons, service conductors of more than 600 V are installed in rigid conduit or as multi-conductor cable approved for the purpose. Where the cable conductors emerge from a metal sheath or raceway, the insulation is protected from moisture and physical damage by a pothead or other approved means. Where the voltage exceeds 15,000 V, between conductors the service should enter through metal-enclosed switchgear or a transformer vault conforming to NEC requirements.

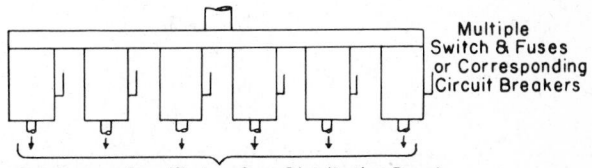

Multiple Switch & Fuses or Corresponding Circuit Breakers

Feeders to Specific Loads or Distribution Panels
One Example: To Load Center Panels in Apt. House

Fig. 7-2B. Typical layout for multiple disconnecting means. As explained in the text, the maximum number of switches is six and the principle is to permit disconnecting all conductors of the service with not more than six operations of the hand.

Table 7-2A. Minimum Cover Requirements, 0 to 600 Volts
(Table 300-5 of the NEC)

Wiring Method	Minimum Burial (Inches)
Direct Buried Cables	24
Rigid Metal Conduit	6
Rigid Nonmetallic Conduit	
Approved for Direct Burial	
without Concrete Encasement	18
Other Approved Raceways	18

Note: Raceways approved for burial only when concrete encased shall require a concrete envelope not less than 2 in. thick.

Table 7-2B. Minimum Cover Requirements, 600 V and Over
(Table 710-3 (b) of the NEC)

Circuit Voltage	Direct Buried Cables	Rigid Nonmetallic Conduit Approved for Direct Burial*	Rigid Metal Conduit
		INCHES	
Over 600–22KV	30	18	6
Over 22KV–40KV	36	24	6
Over 40KV	42	30	6

Unshielded cables shall be installed in rigid metal conduit or rigid nonmetallic conduit encased in not less than 3 inches of concrete.

* Listed by a nationally recognized testing agency as suitable for direct burial without encasement. All other nonmetallic systems shall require 2 inches of concrete or equivalent above conduit in addition to above depth.

Lightning Arresters—Building Wiring

Lightning arresters are not required at residential buildings, but they are required by the NEC for some industrial plants where supplied by an overhead circuit if thunderstorms are prevalent in the area. NFPA No. 78, Lightning Protection Code, does require the provision of lightning arresters on electrical service entrance conductors where the structure is provided with a lightning protection system. Lightning protection should be provided where lightning disturbances are prevalent for overhead circuits supplying Class I, II, or III hazardous locations (see Part L of this chapter for a description of these Classes). This protection should include lightning arresters, surge-protective capacitors, and the interconnection of all grounds.

Each lead-in from an outdoor antenna of radio and television receiving stations and amateur transmitting stations

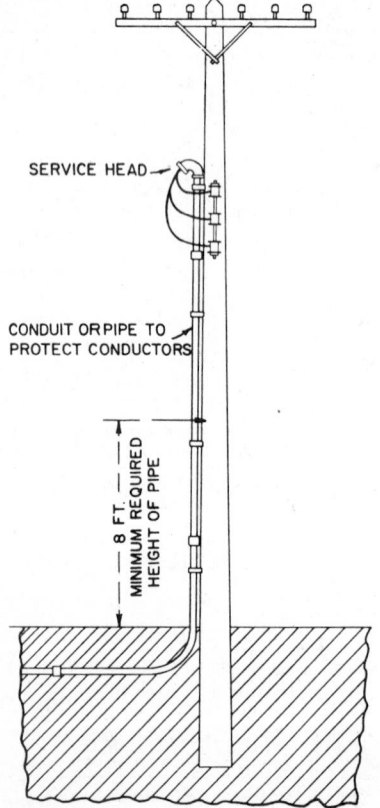

SERVICE HEAD

CONDUIT OR PIPE TO PROTECT CONDUCTORS

8 FT. MINIMUM REQUIRED HEIGHT OF PIPE

Fig. 7-2C. Here service conductors from the outside pole are carried underground from the overhead supply line. Note the service head to protect the conductors against entrance of water and that the point of connection of the service entrance conductors is below the level of the service head.

needs protection from lightning. Lightning arresters provide good protection, and they are recommended for many other types of service as well, especially in rural areas.

Grounding Requirements—Building Wiring

Dangerous voltages, which may be a fire hazard and a personal injury hazard, may be imposed on electrical distribution systems and equipment. Such potentials may be caused by lightning, inadvertent contact with a high-voltage primary system, breakdown of insulation, surface leakage due to dirt or moisture, or by a wire coming loose from its connection.

By grounding one conductor of the electrical circuit and then grounding all metals which may come in contact with a live conductor, a short circuit is formed if the ungrounded circuit conductor should become accidentally grounded. The short circuit current finds a path through the grounded conductor and causes the operation of the overcurrent devices in the ungrounded circuit conductor and eliminates the dangerous condition. The resistance of the fault path must be low enough to permit sufficient current flow to cause the prompt operation of the overcurrent devices. The NEC requires that where the secondary system is grounded at any point, a grounded conductor shall be run to each individual service. This is because the grounded conductor provides a lower impedance path for the fault current than would be provided by the earth on that part of the fault current circuit extending between the service equipment and the supply transformer. This requirement, therefore, assures a more rapid operation of circuit protective devices than the earth path previously relied upon.

Two wire dc systems operating at between 50 and 300 V generally are grounded. The neutral conductor of all three-wire dc systems also should be grounded.

Alternating-current systems of 50 to 1,000 V should be grounded where the system can be so grounded that the maximum voltage to ground on the ungrounded conductor does not exceed 150 V; where the system is nominally rated 480Y/277 volt, 3-phase, 4-wire in which the neutral is used as the circuit conductor; where the system is nominally rated 240/120 volt, 3-phase, 4-wire in which the midpoint of one phase is used as a circuit conductor, or where a circuit conductor is uninsulated as allowed by the NEC. Alternating-current circuits of less than 50 V should be grounded where supplied by transformers if the transformer supply system exceeds 150 V to ground; where supplied by transformers if the transformer supply system is ungrounded or where installed as overhead conductors outside of a building. Alternating-current systems of

1,000 V and over supplying portable equipment should be grounded. Where supplying other than portable equipment, such systems may be grounded and when such systems are grounded, they should comply with the applicable provisions of the NEC. Separately derived alternating-current systems that are required to be grounded should be grounded as specified in the NEC.

The metal enclosures of conductors (conduits, metal armor of cables, metal raceway, boxes, cabinets and fittings) should be grounded. The proper use of suitable ground detectors on ungrounded systems can provide additional protection.

The exposed noncurrent-carrying metal parts of fixed equipment likely to become energized under abnormal conditions are required by the NEC to be grounded as follows: (1) where supplied by means of metal-clad wiring, (2) in wet and damp locations and not isolated, (3) where within 8 ft vertically or 5 ft horizontally of ground or grounded metal objects and subject to contact by persons, (4) in a hazardous location, (5) where equipment is in contact with metal, and (6) where equipment operates with any terminal at more than 150 V to ground. The following fixed equipment should be grounded regardless of voltage: motors and motor controllers, electrical equipment of elevators and cranes, electrical equipment in garages and theaters, motion picture and projection equipment, electric signs, switchboard frames and structures supporting switching equipment and generators and motor frames in an electrically operated organ.

The NEC requires the grounding of exposed noncurrent-carrying metal parts of cord- and plug-connected equipment likely to become energized under any one of the following conditions: (1) when used in hazardous locations, (2) when used in wet or damp locations, and (3) when used where operated by persons standing on the ground or metal surfaces or where operated at more than 150 V to ground except guarded motors and in some isolated cases, the metal frames of portable, stationary, and fixed electrically heated appliances. The NEC also specifies grounding of particular cord- and plug-connected appliances in residential occupancies. They include refrigerators, freezers, air conditioners, clothes washers and dryers, dish washers, sump pumps, electrical aquarium equipment, portable, hand-held, motor-operated tools and appliances. The last named includes drills, hedge clippers, lawn mowers, wet scrubbers, sanders, and saws. An exception is that double insulation may be recognized as providing equivalent protection.

A metallic underground water piping system is required as the grounding electrode where it is available. Where the buried portion of the pipe is less than 10 ft long it should be supplemented by the use of an additional electrode of a type as specified in (1) through (4) below. Caution is needed to check such piping for insulating joints and nonconducting materials. Effective bonding should be provided around insulated joints and sections, and around any equipment that is likely to be disconnected for repairs or replacement.

Alternatives to underground water piping systems as electrodes are: (1) the metal frame of the building, if it is effectively grounded; (2) concrete encased steel reinforcing bar or rod systems of underground footings or foundations; (3) a continuous metallic underground gas piping system that is uncoated and electrically continuous; or (4) other local metallic underground systems or structures, such as a piping system and underground tanks. Finally, if none of the electrodes mentioned previously are available, the

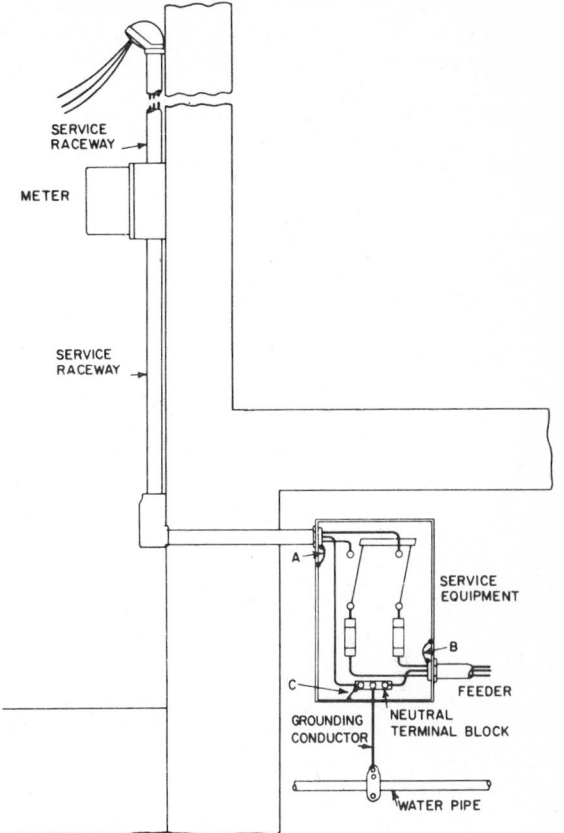

Fig. 7-2D. *Grounding at a typical small service (ac, single-phase, three-wire (115/230 V)). The service raceway is grounded through the metal of the box and this electrical connection is indicated at "A." The jumper shown is one of the methods employed to assure electrical continuity at service equipment. It is desirable, though not required, to connect the feeder raceway to the box in the same manner as the service raceway. Such a connection is indicated at "B." The service enclosure is itself bonded to the grounded neutral conductor at point "C." The meter box and the upper portion of the service raceway or cable are grounded through threaded connections to the meter box if conduit is used, or through connectors making threaded connections to the meter box if tubing is used. The meter box on the line side of the service equipment is usually grounded by connection to the grounded neutral and such ground would be required in case of nonmetallic service-entrance cable. The grounding connection shown is to an underground cold water piping system. The connection should be as required by the NEC.*

grounding electrode may consist of a concrete-encased, copper-wire electrode, a driven pipe or rod, or metal plate buried below permanent moisture level. Such made electrodes should be of an appropriate type as specified in the NEC. The interior metal cold water piping system should always be bonded to the service equipment enclosure, the grounded conductor of the service, the grounding electrode conductor where of sufficient size, or to the one or more grounding electrodes used (see Fig. 7-2D).

Panelboards and Overcurrent Protection—Building Wiring and Equipment

A panelboard has buses (with or without switches) and automatic overcurrent devices for the control and protection of light, heat, or power circuits. The buses are mounted in a cabinet or cutout box which is placed in or on a wall and is accessible only from the front.

A lighting and appliance branch-circuit panelboard is one having more than 10 percent of its overcurrent devices rated 30 amp or less and for which neutral connections are provided.

Because of the many electrical contacts at switches, fuses, circuit breakers, and terminals, considerable heat may be developed which may cause dangerous temperatures and unnecessary operation of overcurrent devices unless these contacts are maintained in good condition. To reduce further the heating and unnecessary operation, the branch-circuit conductors and the overcurrent devices of panelboards in industrial and commercial buildings where loads continue in operation for 3 hrs or more should be connected to loads not in excess of 80 percent of each branch-circuit overcurrent device and a total load not in excess of 80 percent of the rating of the panelboard. An exception is permitted for panelboards approved for continuous loads at 100 percent of their ratings.

Not more than forty-two overcurrent devices of a lighting and appliance branch-circuit panelboard are to be installed in any one cabinet or cutout box. This does not include the main overcurrent devices.

Panelboards installed in wet locations need weatherproof cabinets and are mounted so that there is at least ¼ in. of air space between the cabinet and the wall or other supporting surface. Special requirements of the NEC govern installation of panelboards in hazardous locations.

Panelboards equipped with snap switches rated at 30 amp or less should have overcurrent protection not in excess of 200 amp. (Circuit breakers are not classified as snap switches.)

Each lighting and appliance branch-circuit panelboard is required by the NEC to be individually protected on the supply side by not more than two main circuit breakers or two main sets of fuses with a combined rating not exceeding the rating of the panelboard. These mains may be either inside or outside the panelboard (see Figs. 7-2E and 7-2F).

There are two exceptions to this rule, as follows:

1. Where the overcurrent protective device for the feeder supplying the panelboard has a rating not in excess of the rating of the panelboard, an additional main (or a set of two mains) for the panelboard is not required, such as

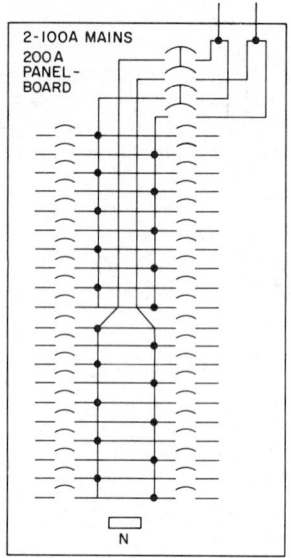

Fig. 7-2F. Two mains required.

where a distribution panelboard supplies the branch-circuit panelboard feeder through an overcurrent device with a rating not exceeding the rating of the branch-circuit panelboard (see Fig. 7-2G).

2. Where the panelboard constitutes the service equipment for an individual residential occupancy (including an apartment in buildings without individual occupancies above the second floor) individual protection is not required on the supply side of the panelboard other than for the supply of any bus within the panelboard that supplies one or more 15- or 20-amp branch circuits (see Fig. 7-2H).

Overcurrent Protection: Conductors and equipment are provided overcurrent protection for the purpose of opening the circuit if the current reaches a value which will cause an excessive or dangerous temperature in the conductor or conductor insulation. No feature of an electrical installation should have more careful attention and supervision. In general, an overcurrent device rated or set in accordance with the ampacity tables of the NEC should be installed in each ungrounded conductor of each circuit and for each feeder at the point where the conductor to be pro-

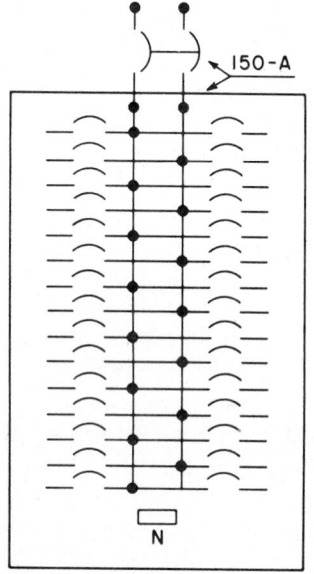

Fig. 7-2E. One main required.

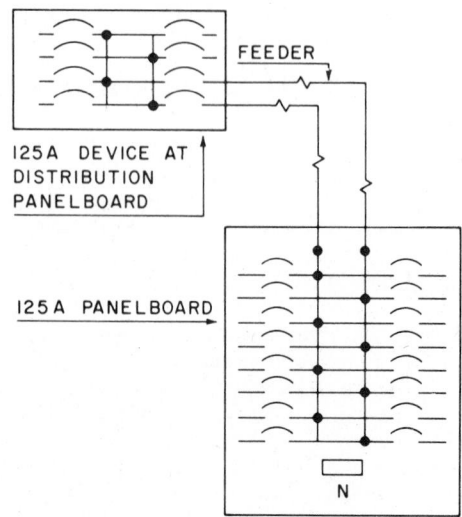

Fig. 7-2G. No mains required.

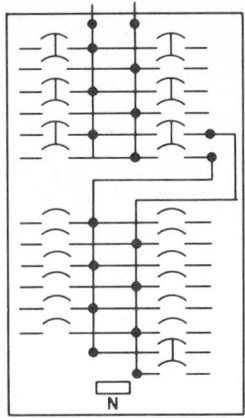

Fig. 7-2H. Circuit breakers rated at 30, 40, and 50 amp in the upper section. One is the main for lower section buses supplying 15- and 20-amp circuits. This arrangement is for an individual residential occupancy.

tected receives its supply. Exceptions for fixture wires, cords, taps, motor circuits, and remote control circuits are covered in the NEC. Tables 7-2C to 7-2F give the allowable ampacity of insulated copper and aluminum conductors under the conditions noted. These tables are identical with Tables 310-16 through 310-19 of the 1975 NEC.

Overcurrent Protective Devices

The most commonly used overcurrent protective devices for the protection of feeders, circuits, and equipment are fuses, circuit breakers, and thermal overload units. (Overcurrent and undervoltage relays, etc., are used on high voltage, high current systems.)

Plug Fuses: These consist of two basic types: (1) the ordinary Edison base type; and (2) the S type. Either of these may or may not be of the time-delay type.

The S type is so designed that tampering or bridging cannot usually be accomplished, or at least not without extreme difficulty. They are designed with adapters that fit the Edison base fuseholders. After an adapter has been properly installed, it cannot be removed without damaging the fuseholder. The adapters are designed to prevent the use of Edison base fuses in the fuseholder, to prevent the use of type S fuses of sizes 16 amp to 20 amp and sizes 21 amp to 30 amp from being used in an adapter designed for a lower rating, and to prevent the use of pennies and other bridging schemes. Edison base fuses of any size will fit Edison base fuseholders of any size.

Fig. 7-2I. A typical Edison base nonrenewable fuse, single element. (Bussmann Mfg. Div., McGraw-Edison Co.)

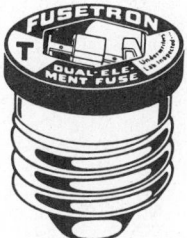

Fig. 7-2J. Another Edison base nonrenewable fuse, dual element. (Bussmann Mfg. Div., McGraw-Edison Co.)

Fig. 7-2K. A Type S nonrenewable fuse. The time lag type of fuse shown is acceptable but not required by the NEC. These fuses have been designed so that tampering or bridging can be done only with difficulty. The National Electrical Code specifies that fuse holders for plug fuses of 30 amp or less shall not be used unless they are designed to use this Type S fuse or are made to accept a Type S through use of an adapter. (Bussmann Mfg. Div., McGraw-Edison Co.)

Time-Delay Type Plug Fuses: Whether of type S or Edison base design, the time-delay type permit short-time current surges, such as small motor starting currents, without interruption of the circuit. These momentary surges are harmless. This makes it possible to use type S fuses in sizes small enough to give better protection than a nontime-delay type that must be oversized to allow for such surges. In the case of a short-circuit or high-current fault, however, the time-delay type will operate and clear the circuit as rapidly or even more rapidly than the nontime-delay type.

All types of plug fuses come in sizes up to 30 amp, but the time-delay type usually has a lower and a wider range. All types are rated at not over 125 V except on circuits derived from a grounded system having a maximum voltage to ground of 150 V. In other words, plug fuses could be used on a 208-V circuit or two in series on a 240-V circuit, where the voltage to ground is 120 V. A single fuse could also be used on a circuit where the voltage to ground is 120 V even though the phase-to-phase voltage is 240 V. A single fuse is not intended to be used, however, on a 240-V circuit where the voltage to ground from one of the phases is 208 V. Some representative plug fuses are shown in Figures 7-2I, 7-2J, and 7-2K.

Cartridge Fuses: These are of both the time-delay and the nontime-delay types. They are also of the one-time and the renewable-link types. When a one-time fuse "blows" the entire fuse must be replaced. But when a renewable-link fuse "blows," the fuse link can be replaced inside the same cartridge unless the cartridge also had been damaged by the fault or from charring.

Renewable-link fuses have two disadvantages: (1) the links can be doubled or tripled, etc., thereby defeating their purpose and usefulness; and (2) the links, upon replacement, can be left with loose connections. One-time fuses usually run cooler and are believed to provide better protection by most electrical engineers and electricians. Cartridge fuse ratings in the 0 to 600 amp range are divided into three basic groups: (1) not over 250 V; (2) not over 300 V; and (3) not over 600 V. Cartridge fuses in the 601 to 6,000 amp range at 600 V are classified into nine groupings. Cartridge fuseholders are designed to prevent, or to make it extremely difficult, to insert a fuse with a lower voltage rating or with a higher current rating than that for which the fuseholder was intended. There are specially designed cartridge fuses for voltages higher than 600 V.

Some representative cartridge fuses are shown in Figures 7-2L and 7-2M.

Table 7-2C.   Allowable Ampacities of Insulated Copper Conductors
(Table 310-16 of the NEC)
Not More than Three Conductors in Raceway or Cable or
Direct Burial (Based on Ambient Temperature 30°C, 86°F)

Size AWG MCM	60°C (140°F) TYPES RUW (14-2), T, TW, UF	75°C (167°F) TYPES RH, RHW, RUH (14-2) THW, THWN, XHHW, USE	85°C (185°F) TYPES V, MI	90°C (194°F) TYPES TA, TBS, SA, AVB, SIS, FEP, FEPB, RHH, THHN, XHHW†	110°C (230°F) TYPES AVA, AVL	125°C (257°F) TYPES AI (14-8), AIA	200°C (392°F) TYPES A (14-8), AA, FEP*, FEPB*	250°C (482°F) TYPES TFE (Nickel or nickel-coated copper only)
18	...	...	...	21	...	...	...	...
16	...	...	22	22	...	...	...	...
14	15	15	25	25‡	30	30	30	40
12	20	20	30	30‡	35	40	40	55
10	30	30	40	40‡	45	50	55	75
8	40	45	50	50	60	65	70	95
6	55	65	70	70	80	85	95	120
4	70	85	90	90	105	115	120	145
3	80	100	105	105	120	130	145	170
2	95	115	120	120	135	145	165	195
1	110	130	140	140	160	170	190	220
1/0	125	150	155	155	190	200	225	250
2/0	145	175	185	185	215	230	250	280
3/0	165	200	210	210	245	265	285	315
4/0	195	230	235	235	275	310	340	370
250	215	255	270	270	315	335	...	...
300	240	285	300	300	345	380	...	...
350	260	310	325	325	390	420	...	...
400	280	335	360	360	420	450	...	...
500	320	380	405	405	470	500	...	...
600	355	420	455	455	525	545	...	...
700	385	460	490	490	560	600	...	...
750	400	475	500	500	580	620	...	...
800	410	490	515	515	600	640	...	...
900	435	520	555	555	...	...	...	...
1000	455	545	585	585	680	730	...	...
1250	495	590	645	645	...	...	...	...
1500	520	625	700	700	785	...	...	...
1750	545	650	735	735	...	...	...	...
2000	560	665	775	775	840	...	...	...

These ampacities relate only to conductors described in Table 310-13 of the NEC.

* Special use only. See Table 310-13 of the NEC.

† For dry locations only. See Table 310-13 of the NEC.

‡ The ampacities for Types FEP, FEPB, RHH, THHN, and XHHW conductors for sizes 14, 12, and 10 shall be the same as designated for 75°C conductors in this Table.

For ambient temperatures over 30°C, see Note 13 of Notes to Tables 7-2C through 7-2F.

Notes to Tables 7-2C Through 7-2F

Ampacity. The maximum, continuous, ampacities of copper conductors are given in Tables 7-2C and 7-2D. The ampacities of aluminum and copper-clad aluminum conductors are given in Tables 7-2E and 7-2F.

1. Explanation of Tables. For explanation of Type Letters, and for recognized size of conductors for the various conductor insulations, see Sections 310-12 and 310-13 of the NEC. For installation requirements, see Sections 310-1 through 310-9 of the NEC, and the various Articles of the NEC. For flexible cords see Tables 400-4 and 400-5 of the NEC.

2. Application of Tables. For open wiring on insulators and for concealed knob-and-tube wiring, the allowable ampacities of Tables 7-2D and 7-2F shall be used. For all other recognized wiring methods, the allowable ampacities of Tables 7-2C and 7-2E shall be used, unless otherwise provided in the NEC.

3. Three-Wire Single-Phase Residential Services. For 3-wire, single-phase residential services, the allowable ampacity of Types RH, RHH, RHW, THW, and XHHW copper service-entrance conductors shall be for sizes No. 4-100 Amp., No. 3-110 Amp., No 2-125 Amp., No. 1-150 Amp., No. 1/0-175 Amp., and No. 2/0-200 Amp., and the allowable ampacity of Types RH, RHH, RHW, THW, and XHHW aluminum and copper-clad aluminum service-entrance conductors shall be for sizes No. 2-100 Amp., No. 1-110 Amp., No. 1/0-125 Amp., No. 2/0-150 Amp., No. 3/0-175 Amp. and No. 4/0-200 Amp.

4. Aluminum and Copper-Clad Aluminum Conductors. For aluminum and copper-clad aluminum conductors the allowable ampacities shall be in accordance with Tables 7-2E and 7-2F.

5. Bare Conductors. Where bare conductors are used with insulated

Table 7-2D. Allowable Ampacities of Insulated Copper Conductors
(Table 310-17 of the NEC)
Single Conductor in Free Air
(Based on Ambient Temperature of 30°C, 86°F)

Size AWG MCM	Temperature Rating of Conductor. See Table 7-2G								
	60°C (140°F)	75°C (167°F)	85°C (185°F)	90°C (194°F)	110°C (230°F)	125°C (257°F)	200°C (392°F)	250°C (482°F)	
	TYPES RUW (14-2), T, TW	TYPES RH, RHW, RUH (14-2), THW, THWN, XHHW	TYPES V, MI	TYPES TA, TBS, SA, AVB, SIS, FEP, FEPB, RHH, THHN, XHHW†	TYPES AVA, AVL	TYPES AI (14-8), AIA	TYPES A (14-8), AA, FEP*, FEPB*	TYPE TFE (Nickel or nickel-coated copper only)	Bare and Covered Conductors
18	....	....	....	25	....	....	....	...	....
16	....	....	27	27	....	....	...	...	....
14	20	20	30	30‡	40	40	45	60	30
12	25	25	40	40‡	50	50	55	80	40
10	40	40	55	55‡	65	70	75	110	55
8	55	65	70	70	85	90	100	145	70
6	80	95	100	100	120	125	135	210	100
4	105	125	135	135	160	170	180	285	130
3	120	145	155	155	180	195	210	335	150
2	140	170	180	180	210	225	240	390	175
1	165	195	210	210	245	265	280	450	205
1/0	195	230	245	245	285	305	325	545	235
2/0	225	265	285	285	330	355	370	605	275
3/0	260	310	330	330	385	410	430	725	320
4/0	300	360	385	385	445	475	510	850	370
250	340	405	425	425	495	530	...	...	410
300	375	445	480	480	555	590	...	...	460
350	420	505	530	530	610	655	...	...	510
400	455	545	575	575	665	710	...	...	555
500	515	620	660	660	765	815	...	...	630
600	575	690	740	740	855	910	...	...	710
700	630	755	815	815	940	1005	...	...	780
750	655	785	845	845	980	1045	...	...	810
800	680	815	880	880	1020	1085	...	...	845
900	730	870	940	940	....	....	...	...	905
1000	780	935	1000	1000	1165	1240	...	...	965
1250	890	1065	1130	1130	....	....	...	...	....
1500	980	1175	1260	1260	1450	....	...	...	1215
1750	1070	1280	1370	1370	....	....	...	...	....
2000	1155	1385	1470	1470	1715	....	...	...	1405

These ampacities relate only to conductors described in Table 310-13 of the NEC.
  * Special use only. See Table 310-13 of the NEC.
  † For dry locations only. See Table 310-13 of the NEC.
  ‡ The ampacities for Types FEP, FEPB, RHH, THHN, and XHHW conductors for sizes 14, 12, and 10 shall be the same as designated for 75°C conductors in this Table.
  For ambient temperatures over 30°C, see Note 13 of Notes to Tables 7-2C through 7-2F.

conductors, their allowable ampacities shall be limited to that permitted for the insulated conductors of the same size.

6. Mineral-Insulated, Metal-Sheathed Cable. The temperature limitation on which the ampacities of mineral-insulated, metal-sheathed cable are based is determined by the insulating materials used in the end seal. Termination fittings incorporating unimpregnated, organic, insulating materials are limited to 85°C operation.

7. Ultimate Insulation Temperature. In no case shall conductors be associated together in such a way with respect to the kind of circuit, the wiring method employed, or the number of conductors, that the limiting temperature of the conductors will be exceeded.

8. More Than 3 Conductors in a Raceway or Cable. Where the number of conductors in a raceway or cable exceed 3, the maximum allowable load current of each conductor shall be reduced as shown in the following table:

Number of Conductors	Percent of Values in Tables 7-2C and 7-2E
4 thru 6	80
7 thru 24	70
25 thru 42	60
43 and above	50

Where single conductors or multiconductor cables are stacked or bundled without maintaining spacing and are not installed in raceways, the maximum allowable load current of each conductor shall be reduced as shown in the above table.

Exception No. 1: When conductors of different systems, as provided

Table 7-2E. Allowable Ampacities of Insulated Aluminum and Copper-Clad Aluminum Conductors
(Table 310-18 of the NEC)

Not More than Three Conductors in Raceway or Cable or
Direct Burial (Based on Ambient Temperature of 30°C, 86°F)

Size	Temperature Rating of Conductor. See Table 7-2G						
AWG MCM	60°C (140°F)	75°C (167°F)	85°C (185°F)	90°C (194°F)	110°C (230°F)	125°C (257°F)	200°C (392°F)
	TYPES RUW (12-2), T, TW, UF	TYPES RH, RHW, RUH (12-2), THW, THWN, XHHW, USE	TYPES V, MI	TYPES TA, TBS, SA, AVB, SIS, RHH, THHN, XHHW*	TYPES AVA, AVL	TYPES AI (12-8), AIA	TYPES A (12-8), AA
12	15	15	25	25†	25	30	30
10	25	25	30	30†	35	40	45
8	30	40	40	40	45	50	55
6	40	50	55	55	60	65	75
4	55	65	70	70	80	90	95
3	65	75	80	80	95	100	115
2	75	90	95	95	105	115	130
1	85	100	110	110	125	135	150
1/0	100	120	125	125	150	160	180
2/0	115	135	145	145	170	180	200
3/0	130	155	165	165	195	210	225
4/0	155	180	185	185	215	245	270
250	170	205	215	215	250	270	. . .
300	190	230	240	240	275	305	. . .
350	210	250	260	260	310	335	. . .
400	225	270	290	290	335	360	. . .
500	260	310	330	330	380	405	. . .
600	285	340	370	370	425	440	. . .
700	310	375	395	395	455	485	. . .
750	320	385	405	405	470	500	. . .
800	330	395	415	415	485	520	. . .
900	355	425	455	455	. . .	. . .	. . .
1000	375	445	480	480	560	600	. . .
1250	405	485	530	530	. . .	. . .	. . .
1500	435	520	580	580	650	. . .	. . .
1750	455	545	615	615	. . .	. . .	. . .
2000	470	560	650	650	705	. . .	. . .

These ampacities relate only to conductors described in Table 310-13 of the NEC.

* For dry locations only. See Table 310-13 of the NEC.

† The ampacities for Types RHH, THHN, and XHHW conductors for sizes 12 and 10 shall be the same as designated for 75°C conductors in this Table.

For ambient temperatures over 30°C, see Note 13 of Notes to Tables 7-2C through 7-2F.

in Section 300-3 of the NEC, are installed in a common raceway the derating factors shown above shall apply to the number of power and lighting (Articles 210, 215, 220, and 230 of the NEC) conductors only.

Exception No. 2: The derating factors of Sections 210-22(c), 220-2(a) and 220-10(b) of the NEC, shall not apply when the above derating factors are also required.

Exception No 3: For conductors installed in cable trays, the provisions of Section 318-10 of the NEC shall apply.

9. Overcurrent Protection. Where the standard ratings and settings of overcurrent devices do not correspond with the ratings and settings allowed for conductors, the next higher standard rating and setting shall be permitted.

Exception: As limited in Section 240-3 of the NEC.

10. Neutral Conductor. (a) A neutral conductor which carries only the unbalanced current from other conductors, as in the case of normally balanced circuits of 3 or more conductors, shall not be counted in determining ampacities as provided for in Note 8.

(b) In a 3-wire circuit consisting of two phase wires and the neutral of a 4-wire, 3-phase wye-connected system, a common conductor carries approximately the same current as the other conductors and shall be counted in determining ampacities as provided in Note 8.

(c) On a 4-wire, 3-phase wye circuit where the major portion of the load consists of electric-discharge lighting there are harmonic currents present in the neutral conductor and the neutral shall be considered to be a current-carrying conductor.

11. Voltage Drop. The allowable ampacities in Tables 7-2C through 7-2F are based on temperature alone and do not take voltage drop into consideration.

12. Aluminum-Sheathed Cable or Copper-Sheathed Cable. The ampacities of Type ALS and Type CS cables are determined by the temperature limitation of the insulated conductors incorporated within the cable. Hence the ampacities of aluminum-sheathed cable or copper-sheathed cable may be determined from the columns in Tables 7-2C and 7-2E applicable to the type of insulated conductors employed within the cable.

13. Use of Conductors with Higher Operating Temperatures. Where the room temperature is within 10 degrees C of the maximum allowable operating temperature of the insulation, it is desirable to use an insulation with a higher maximum allowable operating temperature; although insulation can be used in a room temperature approaching its

Table 7-2F. Allowable Ampacities of Insulated Aluminum and Copper-Clad Aluminum Conductors
(Table 310-19 of the NEC)

Single Conductor in Free Air
(Based on Ambient Temperature of 30°C, 86°F)

Size	Temperature Rating of Conductor. See Table 7-2G							
AWG MCM	60°C (140°F)	75°C (167°F)	85°C (185°F)	90°C (194°F)	110°C (230°F)	125°C (257°F)	200°C (392°F)	
	TYPES RUW (12-2), T, TW	TYPES RH, RHW, RUH (12-2), THW, THWN, XHHW	TYPES V, MI	TYPES TA, TBS, SA, AVB, SIS, RHH, THHN, XHHW*	TYPES AVA, AVL	TYPES AI (12-8), AIA	TYPES A (12-8), AA	Bare and Covered Conductors
12	20	20	30	30†	40	40	45	30
10	30	30	45	45†	50	55	60	45
8	45	55	55	55	65	70	80	55
6	60	75	80	80	95	100	105	80
4	80	100	105	105	125	135	140	100
3	95	115	120	120	140	150	165	115
2	110	135	140	140	165	175	185	135
1	130	155	165	165	190	205	220	160
1/0	150	180	190	190	220	240	255	185
2/0	175	210	220	220	255	275	290	215
3/0	200	240	255	255	300	320	335	250
4/0	230	280	300	300	345	370	400	290
250	265	315	330	330	385	415	. . .	320
300	290	350	375	375	435	460	. . .	360
350	330	395	415	415	475	510	. . .	400
400	355	425	450	450	520	555	. . .	435
500	405	485	515	515	595	635	. . .	490
600	455	545	585	585	675	720	. . .	560
700	500	595	645	645	745	795	. . .	615
750	515	620	670	670	775	825	. . .	640
800	535	645	695	695	805	855	. . .	670
900	580	700	750	750	. . .	. . .	. . .	725
1000	625	750	800	800	930	990	. . .	770
1250	710	855	905	905	. . . .	. . .	. . .	. . . .
1500	795	950	1020	1020	1175	. . .	. . .	985
1750	875	1050	1125	1125	. . . .	. . .	. . .	. . . .
2000	960	1150	1220	1220	1425	. . .	. . .	1165

These ampacities relate only to conductors described in Table 310-13 of the NEC.

* For dry locations only. See Table 310-13 of the NEC.

† The ampacities for Types RHH, THHN, and XHHW conductors for sizes 12 and 10 shall be the same as designated for 75°C conductors in this Table.

For ambient temperatures over 30°C, see Note 13 of Notes to Tables 7-2C through 7-2F.

maximum allowable operating temperature limit if the current is reduced in accordance with the correction factors for different room temperatures as shown in the correction factor table, Table 7-2G.

14. Type MTW Machine Tool Wire. The ampacities of Type MTW wire are specified in Table 200-B of the Electrical Standard for Metalworking Machine Tools 1974 (NFPA Publication No. 79).

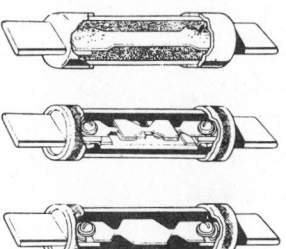

Fig. 7-2L. Three types of cartridge fuses: at top, an ordinary drop-out link renewable fuse; at center, a super-lag renewable fuse; and at bottom, a one-time fuse. (Bussmann Mfg. Div., McGraw-Edison Co.)

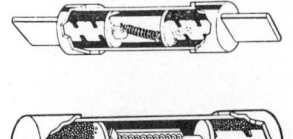

Fig. 7-2M. A dual element cartridge fuse, blade and ferrule type. (Bussmann Mfg. Div., McGraw-Edison Co.)

Table 7-2G.   Correction Factors Ambient Temps. Over 30°C, 86°F
(Table 13 of the NEC)

C°	F°	60°C (140°F)	75°C (167°F)	85°C (185°F)	90°C (194°F)	110°C (230°F)	125°C (257°F)	200°C (392°F)	250°C (482°F)
40	104	.82	.88	.90	.91	.94	.95	...	...
45	113	.71	.82	.85	.87	.90	.92	...	...
50	122	.58	.75	.80	.82	.87	.89	...	...
55	131	.41	.67	.74	.76	.83	.86	...	...
60	140	...	.58	.67	.71	.79	.83	.91	.95
70	158	...	.35	.52	.58	.71	.76	.87	.91
75	167	...	...	.43	.50	.66	.72	.86	.89
80	176	...	...	.30	.41	.61	.69	.84	.87
90	194	...	...	...	...	.50	.61	.80	.83
100	212	...	...	...	...	...	.51	.77	.80
120	248	...	...	...	...	...	...	.69	.72
140	284	...	...	...	...	...	...	.59	.59
160	320	...	...	...	...	...	...	...	.54
180	356	...	...	...	...	...	...	...	.50
200	392	...	...	...	...	...	...	...	.43
225	437	...	...	...	...	...	...	...	.30

Circuit Breakers: There are two basic types of breakers: (1) adjustable-trip and (2) nonadjustable-trip. The adjustable-trip type may be either air or oil immersed type. The setting of the trip point is adjustable between a minimum and a maximum range and is installed, usually, only on large installations having qualified operating and maintenance personnel. They are designed to trip when the current reaches that of the setting. The nonadjustable-trip type comes in a moulded case, making it impossible, or extremely difficult, to change its rating. It is of the inverse time type and designed so that the current has to exceed its rating (as is also true with all types of fuses) before it will trip. Nonadjustable-trip circuit breakers have standard ratings up to 1600 amp. Adjustable-trip types have no NEC stipulated maximum settings. Any circuit breaker that is intended to interrupt fault currents in excess of 10,000 amp is required to be so marked either on the breaker itself or on the label. Many of the adjustable-trip type are designed for very high voltages.

A representative nonadjustable circuit breaker is shown in Figure 7-2N.

Thermal Devices: Unless designed for the purposes, are not intended for protection against short circuits, but only for the protection of overload currents of a comparatively lower magnitude. An example is overcurrent protection for a motor where short-circuit protection is provided by the branch-circuit fuses or circuit breakers. For detailed requirements for motors and other equipment, see the applicable provisions of the NEC. In general, most motors should have overload protective devices having a rating not in excess of 125 percent of the full-load motor current. For some types of motors, the rating of the device should not exceed 115 percent of the motor full-load current. There are exceptions for some types of small motors.

Current-Limiting Overcurrent Protective Devices: These devices are provided in some installations where high current capacities are involved. They are designed so that when interrupting a specified current, the devices will consistently limit the short-circuit current in that circuit to a specified magnitude substantially less than that obtainable in the same circuit if the device were replaced with a solid conductor having comparable impedance (see Fig. 7-2O).

Ground-Fault Circuit-Interrupters (GFCIs)

Circuit breakers and fuses open a circuit and stop the flow of electricity when the flow is in excess of the ratings of the circuit breaker or fuse. Lighting and receptacle circuits are usually rated 15 or 20 amp. At times as little as 60 mA (milliamperes) can kill a normal healthy adult; thus the rating of lighting and receptacle circuits is high relative to the amount of current that could kill a person.

Ground-fault circuit-interrupters are devices which sense when current—even a small amount—passes to ground through any path other than the proper conductor. When

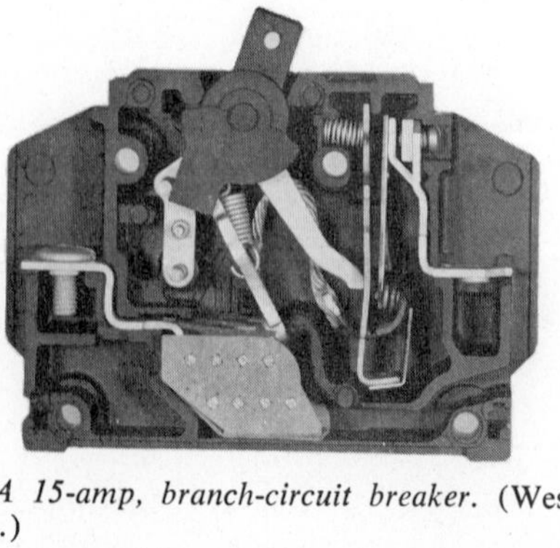

Fig. 7-2N. A 15-amp, branch-circuit breaker. (Westinghouse Electric Corp.)

Fig. 7-2O.   A current limiting overcurrent protection device.

this condition exists, the GFCI (ground-fault circuit-interrupter) instantly trips the circuit breaker stopping all current flow to the circuit and to a person receiving the ground fault shock.[4]

Simplicity of design is one reason for the reliability of the GFCI. Figure 7-2P shows a typical circuit arrangement of a personnel GFCI. Figure 7-2Q shows a GFCI unit. The incoming two-wire circuit is connected to a two-pole, shunt-trip overload circuit breaker. The loadside conductors pass through a toroidal coil onto the outgoing circuit. As long as the current in both load wires is equal the circuit functions normally. If one of the conductors becomes in contact with a grounded condition or passes through a person's body to ground an unbalanced current is established. This unbalanced current is picked up by the differential transformer, and a circuit is established through the sensing circuit to energize the shunt trip of the overload circuit breaker and quickly open the main circuit.

Present GFCIs are set to operate when line-to-ground currents reach 5 mA nominal. Even at trips of 5 mA, it should be clearly understood that instantaneous current will be higher, and any shock during the time the fault is being cleared will not feel comfortable. A shock at 5 mA is not pleasant either. The key to the ground-fault circuit-interrupter is the time-current characteristic. Trip-out time is about 1/40 of a second (25 milliseconds) when the fault reaches or exceeds 5 mA.

There are two classes of GFCIs—Class A and Class B. The Class A GFCI trips at 5 mA nominal and not at lower or higher values. The Class B GFCI trips at 20 mA nominal and not at lower or higher values, and is used only on swimming pool underwater lighting fixtures. The Class A GFCI is used where personnel protection against ground-fault is required or desired.

GFCIs at Construction Sites: Precautions must be taken to aid the efficient operation of GFCIs on construction sites. Most laboratory-tested appliances have 0.5 mA leakage or less under normal operating conditions; however, moisture and improper maintenance on portable hand-held tools, common at construction sites, can create conditions under which GFCIs can be expected to trip. Portable cords with standard cap and connector connections when dropped in water, such as puddles, can be expected to cause leakage currents (100 to 300 mA or greater) far in excess of GFCI trip currents. Motors with dirty brushes, carbon-tracking on commutators, or moisture in the windings contribute to leakage current.

A common sense approach to installing, using, and maintaining GFCI circuits would do much toward eliminating "nuisance tripping" at construction sites. Actually, tripping under any of the conditions mentioned previously is not "nuisance tripping," but merely a device performing its intended function. It has been shown that moisture is the major culprit in current leakage on wiring and equipment. Panelboards, receptacles, and cord caps and connectors in-

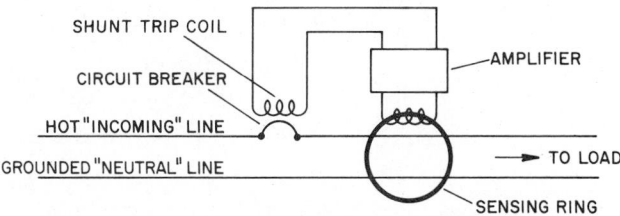

Fig. 7-2P. Circuit arrangement for a typical ground-fault circuit-interrupter for personnel protection. (I-T-E Imperial)

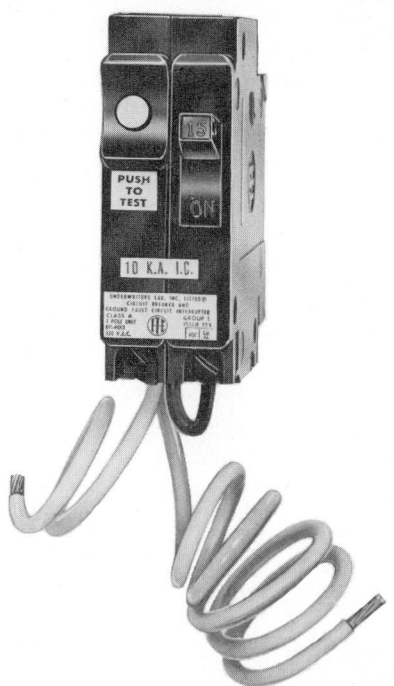

Fig. 7-2Q. A circuit breaker and ground-fault circuit-interrupter device. (I-T-E Imperial)

tended for dry locations should not be subjected to moisture conditions. Construction receptacles should be centrally located to enable cords of 150 ft or less to be used, with a sufficient number of circuits used to keep the number of tools on a circuit to a minimum. Receptacles should not be on the same circuit as lighting or other uses. Maintenance of all motors used on construction sites should be performed periodically.

GFCIs in Residential Occupancies: The danger of ground faults has become so widespread that the NEC requires GFCIs on all 120 V, single-phase 15- and 20-amp receptacle outlets installed outdoors and in bathrooms in residential occupancies. Receptacles located within 15 ft of the inside walls of swimming pools, fountains, and similar locations should be protected by GFCIs.

Ground-Fault Protection of Equipment

The need for protecting electrical installations against the damaging effects of ground faults has been recognized by the NEC. Ground-Fault Protection (GFP) of equipment is provided for solidly grounded wye electrical services of more than 150 V to ground, but not exceeding 600 V phase-to-phase for each service disconnecting means to open all ungrounded conductors of the faulted circuit. The maximum setting of the GFP should be 1,200 amp. This requirement of the NEC is aimed mainly at 480Y/277-volt services. The purpose is to prevent burndowns of such services where line-to-ground faults occur on the load side of any service disconnecting means rated 1,000 amp or more. Any disconnecting means rated less than 1,000 amp, such as the use of five 800-amp disconnecting means in lieu of a single 4,000-amp disconnect, would not require ground-fault protection.

Types of Wiring Methods and Materials

The NEC recognizes a number of standard wiring methods, some of which are suitable for general use and others suitable only for special purposes. The NEC limits the use

Fig. 7-2R. A Type UF sheathed cable. The insulated conductors are jacketed in parallel with a tough, weather-resistant PVC compound. (Plastic Wire & Cable Corporation)

of certain wiring methods. In some localities, local regulations restrict the use of some of the wiring methods recognized by the NEC. The following are the most widely used wiring methods: rigid metal conduit, rigid nonmetallic conduit, electrical metallic tubing, metal-clad cable, nonmetallic sheathed cable, surface metal and nonmetallic raceways, wireways, busways, underfloor raceways, and cellular metal floor raceways. All electrical conductors should be installed and maintained in accordance with NEC requirements, and none should be used for either temporary or permanent work which do not fully conform to these safety specifications.

Identification of Conductors, Terminals, Circuits, Branch Circuits

With few exceptions, all interior wiring systems have a grounded conductor which is continuously identified throughout. The identification for conductors of No. 6 and smaller (except for Type MI cable) should consist of an outer white or natural gray color. Insulated conductors larger than No. 6 should have similar identification or be identified by distinctive white marking at terminals during installation. Where conductors of different systems are installed in the same raceway, box, auxiliary gutter, or other types of enclosures, the grounded conductor of one system, if required, should have an outer covering of white or natural gray. Each other system grounded conductor, if required, should have an outer covering of white with an identifiable colored stripe (not green) running along the insulation or other and different means of identification. The grounded conductors of Type MI cable are identified by distinctive marking at the terminals during installation.

In general, the terminals of electrical devices to which a grounded conductor is to be connected are identified by being made of metal substantially white in color or have a metallic plate coating substantially white in color. In the case of screw-shell type lamp holders, the identified (white) terminal is the one that is connected to the screw shell. The terminals of lighting panelboards, of devices having a rating of more than 30 amp, of fixed appliances (except those which include a single-pole switch as an integral part), and of portable appliances need not be marked for identification.

The grounding conductor of a branch circuit is identified by a continuous green color or a continuous green color with one or more yellow stripes unless it is bare. Ungrounded conductors of different voltages should be of different color.

Lighting and Appliance Branch Circuits

A branch circuit is that portion of a wiring system extending beyond the final overcurrent device protecting the

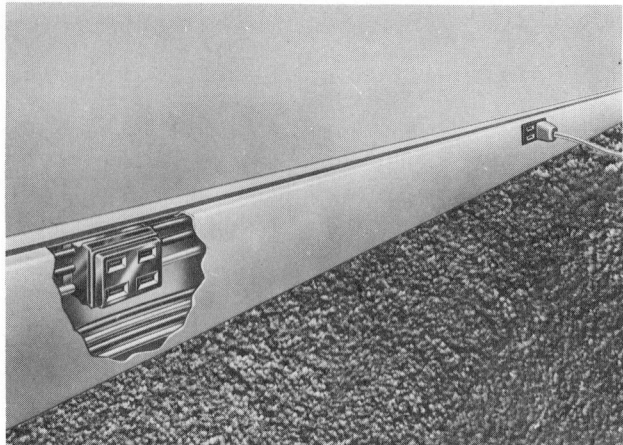

Fig. 7-2T. Installation of a typical metal raceway system showing an all-steel baseboard and a multioutlet system. (The Wiremold Company)

circuit. An appliance branch circuit is one supplying one or more outlets to which appliances are to be connected and which has no permanently connected lighting fixtures. A general purpose branch circuit supplies two or more outlets for lighting and appliances. An individual branch circuit is one which supplies only one utilization equipment.

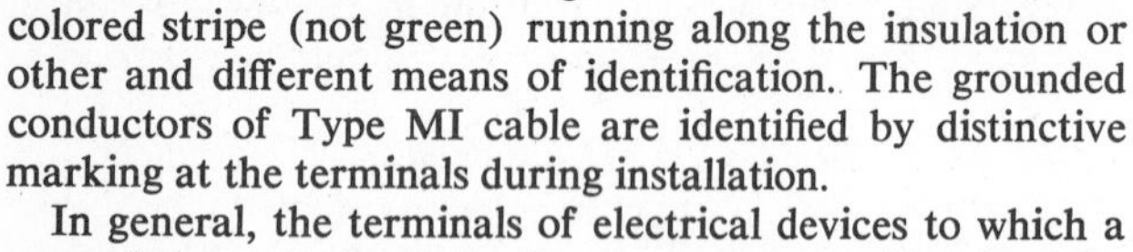

Lighting and appliance branch circuits are classified in accordance with the maximum permitted rating or setting of the overcurrent device, and the classification for other than individual branch circuits is 15, 20, 30, 40, and 50 amp. They may be two-wire or multiwire circuits.

The voltage to ground on branch circuits in dwellings supplying lampholders, fixtures, or standard receptacles of 15 amp or less rating should not exceed 150 V. The voltage between conductors may exceed 150 V in dwellings for permanently connected appliances, portable appliances of more than 1,380 watts, and portable motor-operated appliances of ¼ hp or greater rating.

The rating or setting of an overcurrent device should not exceed the carrying capacity of the circuit conductors (except that tap conductors, fixture wires, and cords are considered as protected by the circuit overcurrent device).

Receptacles rated at 15 amp connected to 15 or 20 amp branch circuits serving two or more outlets should not supply a total load in excess of 12 amp for portable appliances.

Fig. 7-2S. A typical metal-clad cable (Type AC) that is frequently referred to as "BX." Another type (ACL) has lead covered conductors and is often referred to as "BXL." (Both "BX" and "BXL" are trade names.) (General Electric Company)

Fig. 7-2U. The use of a surface metal raceway in a domestic kitchen installation. Frequent spacing of outlets eliminates interference from cords and reduces risk of injury. (The Wiremold Company)

Table 7-2H. Maximum Portable and/or Stationary Appliance Load to Receptacle
(Table 210-21 (b) (2) of the NEC)

Circuit Rating Amperes	Receptacle Rating Amperes	Maximum Load Amperes
15 or 20	15	12
20	20	16
30	30	24

Table 7-2I. Receptacle Ratings for Various Size Circuits
(Table 210-21 (b) (3) of the NEC)

Circuit Rating Amperes	Receptacle Rating Amperes
15	Not over 15
20	15 or 20
30	30
40	40 or 50
50	50

Receptacles rated at 20 amp and connected to 20 amp branch circuits serving two or more outlets should not supply a total load in excess of 16 amp for portable appliances.

The total load should not exceed 80 percent of the branch-circuit rating if motor-operated appliances are supplied or if in normal operation the load will continue for 3 hrs or more, as in store lighting and similar loads. Where the current drawn by resistance loads exceeds the motor-current rating, as in clothes dryers and similar appliances, branch-circuit conductors and overcurrent devices for individual branch circuits supplying such appliances should have a capacity of 125 percent of appliance nameplate ratings.

Lampholders, when connected to circuits having a rating of more than 20 amp, should be the heavy-duty type.

Receptacles, when connected to circuits having two or more outlets, should conform to the ratings in Tables 7-2H and 7-2I.

Individual branch circuits may supply any loads. Branch circuits having two or more outlets may supply only loads as follows:

Branch circuits are for lighting units or appliances rated at 15 and 20 amp. The rating of any one portable or stationary appliance is not to exceed 80 percent of the branch circuit ampere rating. The total rating of fixed appliances should not exceed 50 percent of the branch-circuit ampere rating when lighting units, portable or stationary appliances or both are supplied.

Branch circuits rated at 25 and 30 amp are to supply fixed lighting units with heavy duty lampholders in other than dwelling occupancies or appliances in any occupancy. The rating of any one portable or stationary appliance is not to exceed 80 percent of the branch-circuit ampere rating.

Branch circuits rated at 40 and 50 amp are to supply fixed lighting units with heavy duty lampholders or infrared heating units in other than dwelling occupancies, or fixed cooking appliances in any occupancy.

Receptacle outlets in dwelling occupancies, including guest rooms in hotels and motels, should be installed in every kitchen, family room, dining room, breakfast room, living room, parlor, library, den, sun room, bedroom, recreation room, or similar rooms.

In kitchen and dining areas a receptacle outlet should be installed at each counter space wider than 12 inches.

Receptacle outlets should, insofar as practicable, be spaced equal distances apart (see Fig. 7-2V). Most appliances and portable lamps are provided with flexible cords at least 6 ft in length and it is the intent of the NEC to place receptacle outlets around the perimeter of a room so that any appliance or lamp placed along the wall could be served by an existing outlet without the need for using an extension cord (see Fig. 7-2V).

Receptacles installed on 15 and 20 amp branch circuits should be of the grounding type and should be effectively grounded. This does not mean that all portable equipment must be of the grounded type (see the NEC for specific details on grounding of portables).

Calculation of Loads

The loads specified in the NEC provide a basis for calculating the expected branch circuit and feeder loads and for determining the number of branch circuits required. Where in normal operation the maximum load of a branch circuit will continue for 3 hrs or more (such as store lighting), the minimum unit loads specified should be increased by 25 percent.

The unit lighting loads in watts per square foot for various types of occupancies are given in the NEC. In determining the load, open porches and garages in connection with dwelling occupancies need not be included. Unfinished and unused spaces in dwellings need not be included unless adaptable for future use.

For lighting other than general illumination, for general use receptacles, for appliances, and for loads other than motor loads, the following minimum unit load should be included for each outlet:

Outlets supplying specific appliances and other loads   Amp rating of appliance or load served

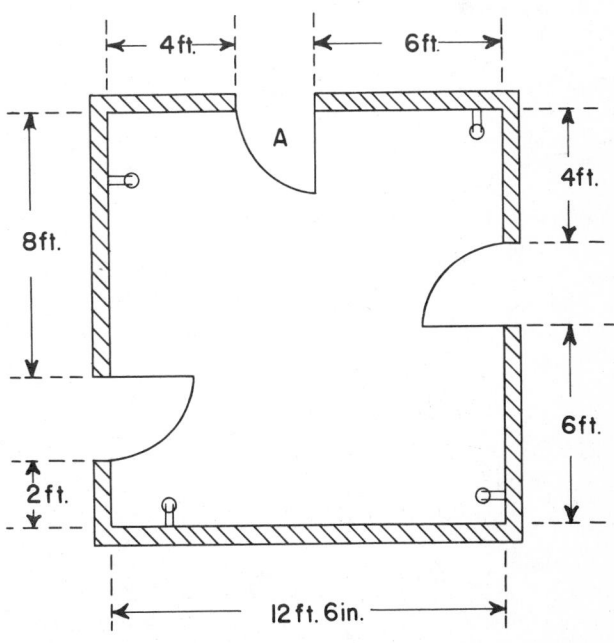

Fig. 7-2V. *Illustration of the requirements in the NEC on the placing of receptacles in dwelling occupancies. Receptacles should be installed so that no point along the floor line is more than 6 ft, measured horizontally, from an outlet.*

Table 7-2J. Lighting Load Feeder Demand Factors
(Table 220-11 of the NEC)

Type of Occupancy	Portion of Lighting Load to which Demand Factor Applies (wattage)	Demand Factor Percent
Dwellings—other than Hotels	First 3,000 or less at Next 3,001 to 120,000 at Remainder over 120,000 at	100 35 25
*Hospitals	First 50,000 or less at Remainder over 50,000 at	40 20
*Hotels and Motels —including Apartment Houses without provision for cooking by tenants	First 20,000 or less at Next 20,001 to 100,000 at Remainder over 100,000 at	50 40 30
Warehouses (Storage)	First 12,500 or less at Remainder over 12,500 at	100 50
All Others	Total Wattage	100

* The demand factors of this Table shall not apply to the computed load of feeders to areas in hospitals, hotels, and motels where the entire lighting is likely to be used at one time; as in operating rooms, ballrooms, or dining rooms.

Outlets supplying heavy-duty lampholders	600 volt-amperes
Other outlets*	180 volt-amperes

For receptacle outlets, each single or multiple receptacle is considered at not less than 180 volt-amperes.

Feeder Loads

Feeder conductors should have sufficient ampacity to supply the load served. The computed load of a feeder should not be less than the sum of all branch-circuit loads supplied by the feeder subject to the provisions of the NEC. In no case should the computed load of a feeder be less than the sum of the loads on the branch circuits supplied. Tables of demand factors for general illumination, for electric ranges and other cooking appliances, and for clothes dryers are found in the NEC. Table 7-2J shows how the demand factors may be applied to that portion of the total branch circuit load computed for general illumination.

An example of how to calculate the load in a single family dwelling is presented to illustrate the principles involved:

Using a dwelling which has a floor area of 1,500 sq ft (exclusive of unoccupied cellar, unfinished attic, and open

Table 7-2K. Optional Calculation for One-Family Residence
(Table 220-30 of the NEC)

Load (in W or VA)	Percent of load
Air conditioning and cooling, including heat pump compressors	100
Central electrical space heating	65
Less than four separately controlled electrical space heating units	65
First 10 W of all other load	100
Remainder of other load	40

* This provision is not applicable to receptacle outlets connected to the small appliance and laundry branch circuits as required for dwelling occupancies by the NEC.

porches) and a 12 kW range, the load may be computed as follows:

General Lighting Load: 1,500 sq ft at 3 watts per sq ft = 4,500 watts.

Number of Branch Circuits Required
General Lighting Load:
4,500 ÷ 115 = 39.1 amp; or three 15 amp, 2-wire circuits; or two 20 amp 2-wire circuits
Small Appliance Load: Two 2-wire 20 amp circuits
Laundry Load: One 2-wire, 20 amp circuit

Minimum Size Feeders Required

Computed Load	
General Lighting	4,500 watts
Small Appliance Load	3,000 watts
Laundry	1,500 watts
Total (without range)	9,000 watts
3,000 watts at 100 percent	3,000 watts
9,000 − 3,000 = 6,000 watts at 35 percent =	2,100 watts
Net Computed (without range)	5,100 watts
Range Load	8,000 watts
Net Computed (with range)	13,100 watts

For 115/230 V system feeders 13,100 ÷ 230 = 57 amp. Therefore, feeder size for total load may be selected on basis of 57 amp load.

Net computed load exceeds 10 kW so service conductors shall be 100 amperes.

An optional method of calculating the load for a one-family residence served by a 115/230 V, three-wire, 100-amp or larger service where the total load is supplied by one feeder or one service is to use the percentages in Table 7-2K.

Examples of branch circuit and feeder calculations for other buildings and occupancies are given in the NEC.

Flexible Cords

Flexible cords should be used only for pendants, wiring of fixtures, connection of portable lamps or appliances, elevator cables, wiring of cranes and hoists, for the connection of stationary equipment to facilitate its interchange, to prevent the transmission of noise or vibration, or to facilitate the removal or disconnection of fixed appliances for maintenance or repair. Flexible cord should not be run through walls, ceilings, or floors nor should it be concealed behind them, and it should not be attached to building surfaces or substituted for fixed wiring in a building or structure. It should be used only in continuous lengths without spliced or taped connections.

Flexible cords are made in many types for various kinds of service. The NEC gives a description, the ampacities, and the intended use of the various flexible cords now available. The ampacity of flexible cords is limited by type and gage of wire used. They should not be overloaded nor should the size be reduced where the gage is intended for mechanical strength.

Flexible cords are frequently subject to physical damage and rapid wear. Grounds or short circuits may occur if the insulation is damaged, and the resulting arc may ignite the insulation or nearby combustible material. If a conductor is exposed, there is danger of electric shock for any person handling the cord in the vicinity of any grounded metal object.

Replacement of flexible cords as soon as they show appreciable wear is of utmost importance.

Under current labeling practices by Underwriters Laboratories, Inc., only replacement cords carry the UL label; formerly the cords were labeled, and many consumers thought a label on the cord of an electrical appliance signified the appliance itself was investigated for safety. Cords on new appliances now do not carry the UL label so the consumer cannot be misled into assuming the appliance itself has been UL-investigated, which may not be the case.

Switches

Switches are required for the control of lights and appliances, and as the disconnecting means for motors and their controllers. To assure adequate illumination throughout livable areas of an occupancy, and to assure adequate illumination of exterior doorways, at least one wall switch for a lighting outlet is installed in dwelling-type occupancies in every habitable room, hallway, stairway, and attached garage and at outdoor entrances.

Switches are also used to isolate high voltage circuit breakers to facilitate maintenance operations. Switches may be of either the air-break type or the oil-break type. In the oil-break type the interrupting device is immersed in oil.

Air-break switches should be enclosed in metal boxes or cabinets and be externally operable. Service switches should plainly indicate whether they are open or closed and be of a type approved for service equipment.

A motor circuit switch, which is rated in horsepower, is capable of interrupting the maximum operating overload current of a motor of that horsepower at rated voltage. An isolating switch has no interrupting rating and should be operated only after the circuit has been opened by some other means.

The chief hazard is the arcing produced when the switch is opened. This hazard is somewhat greater with oil-break switches. If operated much beyond their rated capacity, or if the condition of the oil is poor or its level is not properly maintained, the arc may vaporize the oil, rupture the case, and cause a fire. However, the amount of oil is comparatively small (except in high voltage equipment) and if properly used and maintained, these switches present no hazard.

E. Electrical Household Appliances

Electric Heating Equipment: Electrical heating equipment is finding increasing use, and it is important that all such devices be tested and listed by recognized testing laboratories.

With fixed heating equipment, covered in the NEC, the protection of adjacent combustible material or combustible material which may be brought in contact with it should be given consideration, unless it has been found to be acceptable when installed in direct contact with such combustible material. Baseboard heaters listed by Underwriters' Laboratories, Inc., for example, have been investigated and found to incorporate suitable safeguards against fire hazards that might result from contact with draperies, furniture, carpeting, bedding, and the like, although discoloration or scorching but no glowing embers or flaming may result on adjacent materials.

Some electric air heaters may present fire hazards if they come in contact with combustible materials if they are covered or blocked in any manner. Space heating systems are not installed where exposed to severe physical damage unless adequately protected, nor in damp or wet locations unless approved for such locations. With portable equip-

ment, the design should be such that accidental tipping or upsetting will not start a fire. Portable heating equipment should be provided with a heat-resistant cord or heater cord approved for that purpose.

A heater installed in an air duct or plenum should be of a type approved for this purpose. The NEC covers installation of such heaters and such items as air flow reliability, problems of condensation, fan circuit interlock, limit controls, and location of disconnecting means. NFPA No. 90B, Warm Air Heating and Air Conditioning Systems, should also be referred to for details on central systems.

Electric Ranges, Wall-Mounted Ovens, and Counter-Mounted Cooking Units: Each of these devices needs a means for disconnection from all ungrounded conductors of the supply circuit, except that a separable connector or a plug and receptacle may serve as the disconnecting means for free standing household ranges. For such household ranges, a plug and receptacle connection at the rear base of the range, if it is accessible from the front by removal of a drawer, is considered satisfactory.

The frames of electric ranges, wall-mounted ovens, and counter-mounted cooking units served by a 120/240 V, single phase, 3-wire circuit or a 120/208 V circuit derived from a 3-phase, 4-wire supply may be grounded by connection to the grounded circuit conductors, provided the grounded circuit conductors are not smaller than No. 10 AWG. Grounding contacts of receptacles furnished as a part of equipment grounded to the neutral circuit conductor is bonded to the equipment which is so grounded. Where service-entrance cable having an uninsulated neutral conductor is used, the branch circuit is required by the NEC to originate at the service entrance equipment. All branch circuits supplying equipment which is grounded to the grounded circuit conductor should originate at the service equipment, except for ranges and dryers with an insulated grounded conductor.

The feeder loads for household electric ranges and other cooking appliances are calculated in accordance with the NEC.

Refrigerators: Fire problems principally are from deterioration in service of the fractional horsepower motors used on these devices and the possibility of overheating. Refrigerant coils and motors are susceptible to accumulations of lint and oily deposits so that cleanliness is the primary consideration in fire prevention. New devices have sealed motors not requiring oiling or maintenance, but overheating can result from improper use or inefficient cooling of the refrigerant due to coil dirt or damage. Ordinary household or commercial refrigerators should not be used to store flammable liquids. (Refrigerators for use in Class I, Group D hazardous locations are listed by Underwriters' Laboratories, Inc.) Noncurrent carrying metal parts of refrigerators and freezers which are likely to become energized need to be grounded under provisions of the NEC.

Room Air Conditioning Units: These have the same fire hazards as other motor-operated appliances. The exposed noncurrent-carrying metal parts should be grounded in accordance with the requirements of the NEC. If connected to a branch circuit which also supplies lighting units or other appliances, the total load of motor-operated, air-conditioning equipment is not to exceed 50 percent of the rating of the branch circuit, and should not exceed 80 percent of the rating of an individual branch circuit.

Incandescent Lamps: Incandescent lamps inherently possess the hazard of heating and igniting combustible material in contact with them. Under normal conditions, with incandescent lamps in approved lampholders and fixtures where properly guarded, the heating hazard is negligible, but if lamps are surrounded by or laid on combustible material, ignition of such combustible material may result. Table 7-2L presents information on surface and base temperatures of standard lamps in open sockets. The temperature measurements are all taken at an ambient temperature of 77°F. In most instances, where lamps are incorporated in various kinds of lighting equipment, the ambient temperature at which the lamps operate is higher; thus the surface temperatures of the bulbs are also higher. The bulb temperatures may be still further increased if the lamp is in a position other than that when operating vertically, base up. Figure 7-2W shows surface temperatures of 100-W A-19 and 500-W PS-35 lamps in various positions, but, again, these temperatures were measured in an ambient temperature of 77°F, and so where enclosed in fixtures, the temperatures will be higher. Conventional Christmas tree lamps of U.S. manufacture have approximate average bulb surface temperatures at the hottest spot of approximately 260°F for the blue and green colors, and somewhat lower for the white, red, and yellow colors.

The data in Table 7-2L was extracted from the *IES Handbook*, 4th ed., of the Illuminating Engineering Society and is used here with the permission of the Society. The reader is asked to bear in mind the above comments in the text regarding use of data in Table 7-2L and Figure 7-2W.

In locations where there are flammable vapors, gases, dusts, combustible fibers, etc., lamps in fixtures specially approved for the location should be used.

Electric Discharge (Fluorescent) Lamps: The operating temperature of a fluorescent tube is lower than that of the glass envelope of the incandescent lamp, but high voltage must be used in starting the lamp. This requires the use of transformers, reactors, capacitors, and switches, and the heat produced by this equipment must be taken into account and the equipment properly safeguarded.

Bulb temperatures on the surface of fluorescent lamps average between 100°F and 110°F over most of their length, since this is a requirement for efficient light production. There is a small area of higher bulb temperature directly above the cathode at each end of a fluorescent lamp which ranges from 120°F to 250°F, depending on the type involved.

Fluorescent lamps having an open-circuit voltage of more than 300 V, where installed in dwelling occupancies, ideally have no exposed live parts when lamps are being inserted, are in place, or are being removed.

Extreme care is required in mounting fluorescent lamp fixtures containing a ballast on combustible, low-density, cellulose fiberboard and materials of similar combustibility. Combustible, low-density, cellulose fiberboard includes sheets, panels, and tiles which have a density of 20 lbs or less per cu ft and which are formed of bonded plant fiber material, but does not include solid or laminated wood. Fixtures containing ballasts should not be mounted in contact with low-density, cellulose fiberboard unless they are specifically listed by testing laboratories for mounting in that manner, or, if not specifically listed, they should be spaced not less than $1\frac{1}{2}$ in. from the surface of the combustible material. The principal hazard is overheating of the ballasts from failure of capacitors or partial short circuits in the ballast windings. Integral ballast protection is now provided for fluorescent fixtures installed indoors.

Portable Hand Lamps: These lamps may constitute a fire and casualty hazard. Metal shell, paper lined lampholders are not designed to be used as portable lamps. The fire hazard may result from a defective or worn cord or from the breaking of a lamp. The casualty hazard may result from personal contact with bare spots on the cord or by contact with a live metal socket. Portable hand lamps ideally have a handle and where subject to physical damage or where the lamp may come in contact with combustible material, should have a substantial guard.

Portable hand lamps used in hazardous locations should be of a type specifically approved for the purpose (see Fig. 7-2X). Portables used on grounded surfaces or in damp or wet places should be grounded unless supplied through an insulating transformer with ungrounded secondary of not over 50 V. Since a portable hand lamp can and will be used on grounded surfaces, it is recommended that 3-wire cords be used on all such devices.

Television and Radio Equipment: Outdoor antennas and lead-in conductors should be of corrosion-resistant material and securely supported. They should not be attached to poles or similar structures carrying electric light or power wires or trolley wires. They should not cross over electric light or power circuits and should be kept well away from all such circuits so as to avoid the possibility of accidental

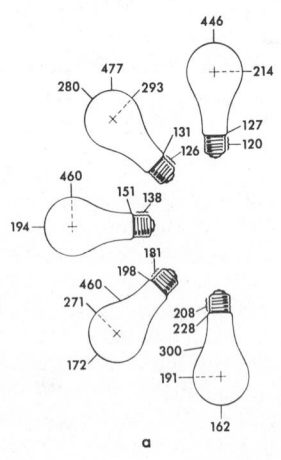

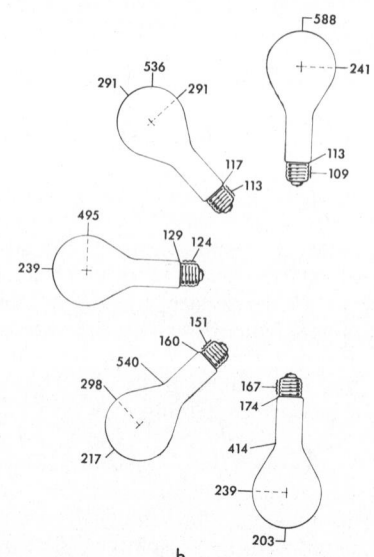

Fig. 7-2W.   Surface temperatures of lamps in various positions. At left is a 100-watt, A-19 lamp and at right a 500-watt, PS-35 lamp.

Table 7-2L. Surface and Base Temperature Data on Standard Lamps in Open Sockets

Watts	Bulb Size (Letter indicates shape [see figures below]. Number indicates largest diameter of bulb in eighths of an inch.)	Maximum Over-All Length (inches)	Approximate Initial Filament Temperature (°K)	Maximum Bare Bulb Temperature* (°F)	Base Temperature† (°F)
10	S-14 inside frosted or clear	3½	2420	106	106
25	A-19 inside frosted	3 15/16	2565	110	108
40	A-19 inside frosted and white	4¼	2740	260	221
40	S-11 clear	2 5/16	2800	570	390
60	A-19 inside frosted and white	4 7/16	2770	255	200
75	A-19 inside frosted and white	4 7/16	2840	275	205
100	A-19 inside frosted and white	4 7/16	2905	300	228
100	A-21 inside frosted	5 5/16	2860	260	200
150	A-23 inside frosted or clear or white	6 5/16	2885	280	210
150	PS-25 clear or inside frosted	6 15/16	2870	290	210
200	A-23 inside frosted white or clear	6 5/16	2895	345	225
200	A-25 clear or inside frosted or white	6 15/16	2895	295	165
200	PS-30 clear or inside frosted	8 1/16	2895	305	210
300	PS-25 clear or inside frosted	6 15/16	2935	400	235
300	PS-30 clear or inside frosted	8 1/16	2935	275	175
300	PS-35 clear or inside frosted	9⅜	2920	330	215
500	PS-35 clear or -inside frosted	9⅜	2945	415	175
500	PS-40 clear or -inside frosted	9¾	2945	390	215
1000	PS-52 clear or inside frosted	13 1/16	2995	480	235
1500	PS-52 clear or inside frosted	13 1/16	3040	510	265

* Lamp burning base up in ambient temperature of 77°F.

† At junction of base and bulb.

S—straight sides; A—standard line bulb with inside frost; PS—pear shape, straight sides.

Fig. 7-2X. A representative portable hand lamp of a type suitable for use in Class I, Group C and D locations. It has an aluminum guard and globe holder. (Stewart R. Browne Mfg. Co., Inc.)

contact. Lead-in conductors should be kept at least 6 ft from any conductor forming a part of a lightning rod system.

Masts and metal structures supporting antennas should be well grounded and each conductor of a lead-in from an outdoor antenna should be protected by an approved lightning arrester. Metal masts on buildings are required by NFPA No. 78, Code for Protection Against Lightning, to be bonded to the nearest lightning conductor (where available) and this is normally done with standard lightning conductors.

Fig. 7-2Y. A dangerous arrangement of a lightly supported television antenna in the proximity of power lines.

Radio interference eliminators and noise suppressors connected to power supply leads and devices intended to permit an electric supply circuit to be used in lieu of an antenna should be approved for the purpose.

Operating television sets develop considerable heat so that most cabinets housing such equipment are provided with ventilation openings at the rear and bottom. It is important not to install television receivers so as to cut off or significantly reduce the desired ventilation (as by recessing in a wall, bookcase, or the like) unless such receivers have been approved for the purpose.

Washers and Dryers: These devices need a means for disconnecting them individually from all ungrounded conductors of the supply circuit. A separable cord connector or an attachment plug and receptacle may serve as the disconnecting means.

Electric clothes washers and dryers are usually installed within reach of a person who can make contact with a grounded surface or object; consequently, to remove the danger of electric shock, the exposed, noncurrent-carrying metal parts of these machines should be grounded.

Accumulations of lint in dryers and in lint traps present a hazard if not periodically cleaned out.

Smoothing Irons: These appliances intended for use in residences are required by the NEC to be equipped with approved temperature-limiting means. The general use of automatic irons has greatly reduced the number of fires resulting from hot nonautomatic irons left in contact with combustible material. However, some hazard still remains

because satisfactory ironing of many fabrics requires a degree of heat sufficient to cause ignition if the iron is left in contact with combustible materials for a considerable period of time.

The NEC also requires that each smoothing iron intended to be applied to combustible material be provided with an approved stand which may be a separate device or a part of the iron. The use of such stands and the use of ventilated, noncombustible ironing boards also tend to reduce the fire hazard but are not a substitute for the only fully safe practice of disconnecting the iron when it is not in use.

In other than residences, irons and similar electrically heated appliances used in contact with combustible materials are required by the NEC to be provided with an integral temperature limiting device or with a signal device to indicate when the appliance is energized.

Electric irons should be provided with approved heater cord which should be properly maintained.

Electrically Heated Pads and Bedding: These are commonly made of fabrics having certain inherent fire and shock hazards which cannot be reliably guarded against by excellence in design and construction. The user must be warned by means of a marking on the appliance and by instructions packed with it against the common possible abuses which would increase the fire or shock hazard.

Because fabrics readily absorb moisture, pads listed by the Underwriters' Laboratories, Inc., (unless of the waterproof type) are provided with moisture resistant envelopes. This envelope should be examined frequently for signs of deterioration. Internal wiring, including the heating element, of electric bedding has waterproof insulation. These appliances are protected against high temperatures by thermostatic switches within the appliance, or by other means. Blankets are normally designed so that they may be laundered. Some are not constructed so as to be suitable for dry cleaning (as with Stoddard Solvent or Perchlorethylene) and are normally labeled "Do Not Dry Clean."

F.   Industrial and Commercial Equipment

Furnaces

Industrial furnaces generally employ transformers which may be either the dry type, askarel-insulated, or oil-insulated type. The NEC requires oil-insulated transformers of a total rating exceeding 75 kVA to be located in a fire-resistive vault. Oil-filled circuit breakers that control arc furnaces are subjected to unusually severe duty and unless frequently inspected and properly maintained, may fail with disastrous results. Circuit breakers on circuits operated at more than 600 V and which are used to control oil-filled transformers are located outside the transformer vaults. Vents on high voltage circuit breakers should be piped outdoors. Electric arc furnace circuits are also subject to high surge voltages, due to the nature of the operation, which can cause failure of the arc circuit breakers used. In these cases, shunt capacitors are installed in the circuit to prevent these high voltage surges.

Inductive and dielectric heat generating equipment employing high frequency alternating currents is in use in many heat treating processes. In order to eliminate both the personal and fire hazards of such equipment, construction and installation should comply with the special requirements of the NEC.

Other hazards of electric furnaces are similar to those of furnaces employing other means of heating (see Chap. 3 of this Section).

Motors

Motors are the cause of many fires. Ignition of the motor insulation or of nearby combustible material may be caused by sparks or arcs when the motor winding short circuits or grounds, or when brushes operate improperly. Bearings may overheat because of improper lubrication and sometimes excessive bearing wear allows the rotor to rub on the stator. Individual drive of machines of many different types sometimes makes it necessary to install motors in locations and under conditions which are injurious to motor insulation. Dust that can conduct electricity may be deposited on the insulation, or deposits of textile fibers, etc., may prevent the normal dissipation of heat. Motors should be cleaned and lubricated regularly. All motor installations should comply with the requirements of the NEC, which includes special rules for motors in hazardous locations (see Part L of this chapter).

Machine Tools

NFPA No. 79, Electrical Metal Working Machine Tools, covers the electrical equipment, apparatus, and wiring furnished as a part of an industrial metal-working machine tool, commencing at the place of connection of the supply providing the voltage is 600 V or less. The NEC covers the size and overcurrent protection of supply conductors to the tools and the nameplate data required on each.

The NEC contains requirements for general application, particularly regarding protection of several motors on one branch circuit. These special provisions apply only to metal-working machine tools which are defined as metal-cutting or metal-forming, power-driven machines, not portable by hand, used to remove metal or to press, forge, emboss, hammer, blank, or shear metal. These provisions of the NEC do not apply to other electrically powered manufacturing machines, such as woodworking or textile machinery, etc.

The electrical equipment of a modern machine tool may vary from a simple, single-motor drill press to large complicated multimotor, automatic machines, involving highly complex control systems and equipment. This latter type is generally especially designed and is factory wired. They incorporate many devices and safeguards to provide safety to life, safety from fire, reduction of machine lost time due to replacement of parts, safety to the machine tool itself, and safety to the work in process. To provide these safeguards, it is sometimes preferable to sacrifice deliberately a motor or other component rather than chance injury to the operator, the machine, or to the work. It is for this reason that the special provisions are contained in the NEC and the NFPA Electrical Metalworking Machine Tools standard.

Electrical equipment is subject to damage by oil, metal chips, coolants, and moving parts. The fixed wiring to the machines specified in the NEC generally should be conductors in rigid metal conduit or Type MI cable. Exceptions are connections to continuously moving parts which should be approved extra flexible, nonmetallic, covered, multiconductor cable having oil and moisture resistant insulation, and with a flame-retardant outer covering. In lieu of cable, individual conductors in flexible tubing may be used, the tubing and fittings being approved for the purpose and the conductors being resistant to oil and moisture. For flexible connections where small or infrequent movement is in-

volved, as at motor terminals, flexible metal conduit or liquidtight flexible metal conduit may be used.

Motor Control-Center Rooms

Automation in industrial plants has led to the development of what is sometimes called "motor control-center rooms." A number of large fire losses have occurred in such rooms, and the severity of them has been significantly influenced by the arrangement of the electrical wiring and equipment.

Automation of production machinery has greatly increased the use of motors and their related control circuits. This has resulted in grouping the motor control equipment in relatively large, compartmented, metal enclosures. These are especially designed, factory-built equipment, commonly referred to as "motor control centers." Usually they are located in large rooms, and electrical failures or fires in the motor control center have often resulted in the destruction of the equipment in many compartments of the center due to rapid temperature rise.

One of the principal reasons for the large losses has been that hundreds of multiconductor circuits have been installed stacked one above the other in cable trays. Heat from arcing or from a fire in the control center has the effect of raising the temperature of the air at the level of the cables in the control center rooms to the point where normally slow burning cables become readily combustible. A fire in such cables can shut down a process or an entire plant for weeks or even months.

The NEC limits the use and construction of cable trays, and these rules should be strictly followed where this type of support is used. "Cablebus," which is an assembly of insulated conductors mounted in spaced relationship in a ventilated metal protective supporting structure that includes fittings and conductor terminations, is also covered in the NEC.

The number of motor control centers in one room should be so limited or arranged that exposure of a large number of circuits or equipment to any one disturbance is avoided. Power circuit conductors, such as those handling continuous or long-time duty cycles to equipment requiring large conductors, should preferably be in a metallic conduit or armored cable as opposed to nonmetallic cable. Such power circuits should, as far as practicable, be run on separate supports or racks and not be intermingled with control and other low-power cables.

Motor control-center rooms should be of noncombustible construction, having a roof or ceiling not readily weakened by a major electrical disturbance or fire. In addition to normal ventilation, the room should be provided with emergency ventilation for removal of heat and smoke in event of a severe disturbance.

Fire protection for motor control-center rooms may consist of pre-action sprinkler systems, fixed water spray protection to cover exposed cables, thermostats to initiate an alarm at a central point in the event that abnormally high temperatures develop, a standard carbon dioxide flooding system on manual control, portable Class C extinguishers located at each entrance to the control room, and small hose connections with suitable hose and adjustable spray nozzles readily available near the control room.

Switchboards

Switchboards should ordinarily be installed in clean, dry locations. They should be under competent supervision and accessible only to qualified persons. Where it is necessary to install a switchboard in a wet location or outside a building, it should be enclosed in a weatherproof enclosure or cabinet. Ample space should be provided for maintenance operations, as stipulated in the NEC.

Open feeder conductors grouped at the rear of switchboards, as well as the instrument and control wiring, should have outer coverings which will not support combustion.

Circuit breakers and switches should have ample ratings for the maximum loads and ample interrupting capacity for the maximum short circuit currents. Contacts of switches and circuit breakers should be kept in good condition, and the oil in oil circuit breakers should be renewed periodically and kept at the proper level.

Capacitors

Capacitors may be insulated with a combustible liquid or a nonflammable liquid. Capacitors containing more than 3 gal of flammable liquid should be enclosed in vaults or outdoor fenced enclosures.

Capacitors are enclosed, located, or guarded so that persons cannot come into accidental contact or bring conducting materials into accidental contact with exposed energized parts, terminals, or buses associated with them. Capacitors should be provided with a means of draining the stored charge.

If no means were provided for draining off the charge stored in a capacitor after it is disconnected from the line, a severe shock might be received by a person servicing the equipment or the equipment might be damaged by a short circuit.

If a capacitor is permanently connected to the windings of a motor, the stored charge will drain off rapidly through the windings when the circuit is opened. Reactors or resistors used as discharge devices must either be permanently connected across the terminals of the capacitor or a device must be provided that will automatically connect the discharge devices when the capacitor is disconnected from the source of supply.

The residual voltage of a capacitor should be reduced to 50 V or less within one minute after the capacitor is disconnected from the source of supply. The discharge circuit should be either permanently connected to the terminals of the capacitor or capacitor bank, or provided with automatic means of connecting it to the terminals of the capacitor bank on removal of voltage from the line. Manual means of switching or connecting the discharge circuit should not be used.

Resistors and Reactors

Except when installed in connection with switchboards or control panels that are so located that they are suitably guarded from physical damage and accidental contact with live parts, resistors should always be completely enclosed in properly ventilated metal boxes. A resistor is always a source of heat, and when mounted on a wooden wall or partition, a thermal barrier should be required if the space between resistors and reactors and any combustible material is less than 12 in. The enclosing box should be grounded when located in any of the areas specified in the NEC.

Large reactors are commonly connected in series with the main leads of large generators or the supply conductors from high-capacity network systems to assist in limiting the current delivered on short circuit. Small reactors are used with lightning arresters, the object here being to offer a high impedance to the passage of a high-frequency lightning discharge and so to aid in directing the discharge to ground.

Another type of reactor, having an iron core and closely resembling a transformer, is used as a remote-control dimmer for stage lighting. Reactors as well as resistors are sources of heat and should therefore be mounted in the same manner as resistors.

Resistors and reactors should not be placed where exposed to physical damage. A thermal barrier should be required if the space between the resistors and reactors and any combustible material is less than 12 inches. Insulated conductors used for connections between resistance elements and controllers should be suitable for an operating temperature of not less than 90°C (194°F).

Motion Picture Projectors

Motion picture projectors of the professional type (employing 35 mm film having 5.4 perforations per inch on each edge) should be located in approved enclosures. Motor-driven projectors should be approved for the purpose as an assembly, or should be a listed projector with a listed lamp with the motors so designed or guarded as to prevent ignition of film by sparks or arcs. All professional projectors should have qualified operators.

Asbestos covered Type AA conductors or other types approved for a maximum operating temperature of 200°C (392°F) should be used on all lamps or other equipment where the ambient temperature at the conductors will exceeds 50°C (122°F).

Motor-generator sets, transformers, rectifiers, rheostats, and similar equipment for the supply or control of current to arc lamps on projectors should, if practicable, be located in separate rooms, but if placed in the projection room, should be so located or guarded that arcs or sparks cannot come in contact with film. No switches, overcurrent devices, or other equipment not normally required or used for projectors, sound reproduction, flood or other special-effect lamps or other equipment (except remote control switches for the auditorium lights or a switch for the motor operating the curtain at the motion picture screen) should be installed in such booths or rooms.

Conductors supplying outlets for arc projectors of the professional type should not be smaller than No. 8 and should be of sufficient size for the projector employed. Conductors for incandescent type projectors are to conform to normal wiring standards of the NEC.

Approved projectors of the nonprofessional or miniature type when employing only approved slow-burning film may be operated without a booth. Nonprofessional projectors designed for using the standard 35 mm film should be marked: "For use with slow-burning films only." Slow-burning film should have a permanent distinctive marker for its entire length identifying the manufacturer and the slow-burning character of the film stock.

Cranes and Hoists

Wiring methods for cranes and hoists should be metal raceways or Type ALS, Type CS, or Type MI cable, except that bare conductors may be used as contact conductors, open conductors may be used in short lengths at resistors, collectors, etc., flexible connections may be used where necessary to motors and similar equipment, and multiple conductor cable may be used for wiring to pendent push button stations. Where bare contact conductors are objectionable because of the presence of easily ignitible material, current may be conducted to a crane or hoist by means of a multiple cable on a cable reel with suitable take-up devices.

The allowable ampacities of conductors in raceways or cables used with short-time rated crane or hoist motors is somewhat greater than that of conductors for continuous duty installations. These higher values are given in the NEC.

Main contact conductors should be secured at the ends by means of approved strain insulators and so mounted on approved insulators that the extreme limit of displacement will not bring the conductor within less than $1\frac{1}{2}$ in. from the surface wired over. The insulating supports should generally be located not more than 20 ft apart, the conductors being not less than 6 in. apart (except for monorail hoists where a separation of not less than 3 in. may be used), but where necessary, intervals between insulating supports may be increased up to 40 ft with the separation between conductors increased proportionately. Bridge contact conductors should be kept at least $2\frac{1}{2}$ in. apart and if the span exceeds 80 ft, insulating supports should be placed at intervals of not more than 50 ft.

Monorail, tramrail, or crane runway tracks may be used as conductors of current for one phase of a three-phase alternating current power supply system provided the power is obtained from an insulating transformer, the voltage is not more than 300 V, the rail serving as a conductor is effectively grounded at the transformer, and the two other phase conductors are insulated.

Where a crane operates over readily combustible material, the resistors should be placed in a well ventilated cabinet of noncombustible material which will not emit flames or molten metal, or should be placed in a cage or cab constructed of noncombustible material which encloses the sides of the cage or cab from the floor to a point at least 6 in. above the top of the resistors.

Collectors should be so designed as to reduce to a minimum sparking between them and the contact conductors and when operated in rooms where easily ignitible fibers or materials producing combustible flyings are handled, manufactured, used, or stored, the installation should comply with the special requirements of the NEC.

All exposed metal parts of cranes, monorail hoists, and accessories (including pendent controls) are metallically joined together into a continuous electrical conductor so that the entire crane or hoist will be grounded.

Elevators, Dumbwaiters, Escalators, and Moving Walkways

Operating controls and signal circuits for this type of equipment should not exceed 300 V except that higher voltages may be used for alternating current frequencies of 25 through 60 Hz or for direct current provided the current in the system cannot, under any conditions, exceed 8 mA for ac or 30 mA for dc. The nominal voltage used for driving machine motors and machine brakes should not exceed 600 V, but higher potentials may be used for driving motors of motor-generator sets.

All live parts of electrical apparatus in the hoistways, at landings, in or on cars of elevators and dumbwaiters, or in the wellways or landings of escalators or moving walks should be enclosed to prevent accidental contact.

All wiring on panels, in raceways, and in or on cars, including the traveling cables, should have flame-retardant, moisture-resistant insulation, except that conductors to main circuit resistors should be flame-retardant and suitable for a temperature of not less than 90°C (194°F).

Traveling cables for operating, control, and signal circuits should be so suspended at the car and hoistway as to reduce the strain on the individual copper conductors to a minimum. They may have one or more nonmetallic fillers or a supporting filler of stranded steel wires with its own protective braid or cover. Cables exceeding 100 ft in length should have steel supporting fillers except where subject to excessive moisture or corrosive gases. Cables exceeding 100 ft in length which have steel fillers should be suspended directly by the steel fillers. Cables which have nonmetallic fillers should be suspended by looping the cables around the supports. The traveling cable supports should be so located as to reduce to a minimum the possibility of damage due to cables coming in contact with the hoistway or equipment. Where necessary, suitable guards should be provided to protect the cables.

To reduce the danger of electric shock, the following equipment should be effectively grounded in accordance with the grounding requirements of the NEC: (1) conduit, Type ALS cable, Type CS cable or Type AC metal clad cable attached to elevator cars; (2) the frames of all motors, elevator machines, controllers; (3) the metal enclosures for all electrical devices in or on the car or hoistway; (4) the frames of nonelectric elevators if accessible to persons and if any electrical conductors are attached to the car.

Equipment mounted on members of the structural metal frame of a building is considered to be grounded. Metal car frames supported by metal hoisting cables attached to or running over sheaves or drums of elevator machines are deemed to be grounded when the machine is properly grounded.

Where the source of power supply to elevator motors is incapable of absorbing electrical energy (as in some cases where alternating current is converted to direct current for the operation of direct current elevator motors) means should be provided to absorb a sufficient amount of the energy regenerated by the elevator motors under overhauling load conditions to prevent any elevator from attaining a speed of more than 125 percent of its rated speed.

Motor generators driven by direct current motors and used to supply direct current for the operation of elevator machine motors should be provided with speed limiting devices which will prevent the elevator from attaining at any time a speed of more than 125 percent of its rated speed.

Heating Cable

Underwriters Laboratories, Inc., has listed a number of heating cables for use within buildings. These devices are primarily designed to be used around water pipes to prevent freezing and to facilitate the flow of viscous liquids. One type of listed equipment has a cable which consists essentially of four parallel fusible resistant wire conductors with separate and overall insulation. This unit is produced in a special length for operation on nominal 115-V circuits. Another unit consists of a solid nichrome wire-heating element with an insulation of felted asbestos and varnished cambric and an overall lead sheath. It can be cut to any length depending on the surface area of the installation and the voltage rating of the branch circuit. The minimum length of the latter type cable for 110-V, 400-W circuits is 60 ft; for 220-V, 800-W circuits, 120 ft; and for 440-V, 1,600-W circuits, 240 ft. The cable is secured to the pipe by means of straps, and the pipe and heating cable are then encased with sponge felted asbestos pipe covering or its equivalent. Where the pipe passes vertically through flooring or where the pipe lines run along the floor level, the installation is protected by sheet steel not less than No. 10 USS gage. This protection should extend at least 4 ft above the floor.

Electrical space heating cables and for outdoor ice and snow-melting systems are covered in the NEC.

G. Electronic Computer/Data Processing Equipment

Electronic computer/data processing (ECDP) equipment has become a vital and commonplace tool for business, industry, government and research groups. Certain procedural steps require study before installing ECDP equipment and among them is a careful study of the protection given the equipment against fires of either accidental or deliberate origin. In addition to the hazards of fire from accidental causes, many computers and data processing installations have become prime targets for sabotage and arson.

Oftentimes, the strategic importance placed upon ECDP equipment by the user is vitally tied to uninterrupted operation of the system. Consequently, by the partial or entire loss of this equipment, an entire operation of vital nature could be temporarily paralyzed.

Not to be overlooked are the "one-of-a-kind" ECDP processing systems. These are the "custom-made" models that are designed to perform specific tasks. Replacement units for this type of equipment are not available and the probability of the existence of duplicate facilities, which could be used to perform vital operations in the event the "one-of-a-kind" system is partially or totally impaired by a fire, is remote.

Computer Rooms

Due to the high value of computer systems and the importance of their functional service, such systems are located in an area cut off by adequate fire-resistance-rated walls, floors, and ceilings from other portions of the building. Systems are not located above, below, or adjacent to areas where hazardous processes are located unless it has been established that adequate protective features are installed to protect the computer room and its contents. Normally computer rooms are of fire resistive construction with noncombustible interior finish. The whole theory is to locate such systems in areas to minimize the possibility of damage from fire, water, smoke, or heat exposure.

Raised floors are frequently required to house electrical wiring and to serve as air conditioning plenums. These floors, including the structural supporting members, are normally concrete, steel, aluminum, or other noncombustible material. Access sections or panels are provided in such raised floors so that all space beneath is readily accessible. Electric cable openings in floors are smooth to prevent damage to cables, and the openings in raised floors for cables or other uses are protected to minimize the entrance of debris or other combustibles beneath the floor.

Only the actual electronic computer equipment and such input-output or other auxiliary electronic equipment interconnected with the computer, or which must be located in close proximity to the equipment, is permitted within the computer room itself. All office furniture in the computer room is of metal. Unnecessary supplies of paper or other combustible material are strictly limited to the minimum needed for efficient operations (see Fig. 7-2Z).

Equipment

The construction of the computer equipment itself and the amount of combustibles used within the assemblies will determine, to a major extent, the amount of protection required. Preferably the design is such that fire in or about any one component or part will be confined to the immediate area of ignition. Equipment in this category normally includes automatic means to de-energize the circuits when a hazardous temperature condition develops.

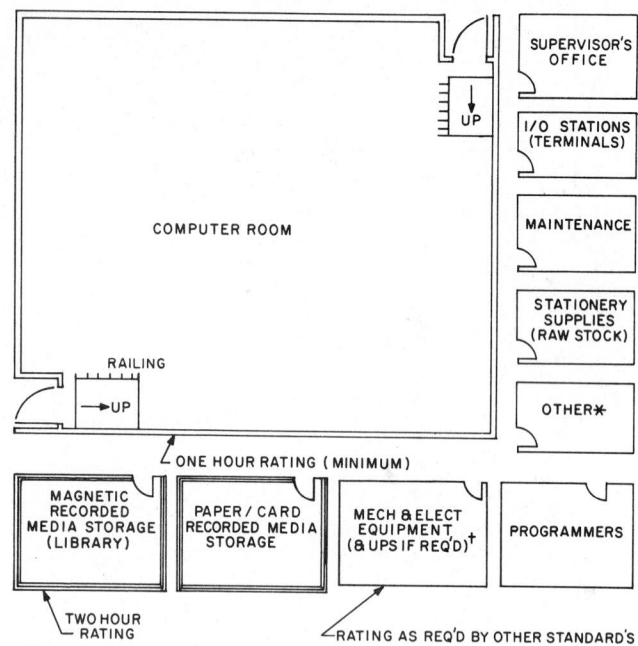

* OTHER: RECEPTIONIST, SECURITY STATION, COMMUNICATIONS
† UNINTERRUPTABLE POWER SUPPLY (MOTOR/GENERATOR OR SOLID STATE SYSTEMS)

Fig. 7-2Z.   A typical computer room layout.

Individual units of a system are housed in metal or noncombustible enclosures with suitable subdivisions to minimize the likelihood of a fire spreading from one section to another within the unit. The noncombustible enclosures are so designed that easy access is possible to interior sections in the event emergency or overheat conditions develop.

Air circulation through each unit is generally required for removal of the heat which is generated. A separate air conditioning system is provided for each computer area. Attention must be given to the effect of this air circulation and most particularly to the design of the air filters that are used to be sure that they will not burn or emit any smoke or objectionable products of combustion if attacked by flames. Any sound deadening material used inside computer equipment must be noncombustible. If oil is used in any component of a unit, it must have a high flash point characteristic and the container in which the oil is stored must be of a sealed construction with automatic pressure relief devices.

Emergency disconnects are provided as a part of the main electric service wiring supplying the electronic computer equipment. These emergency switches disconnect power to all electronic equipment in the computer area and to the air conditioning system serving the computers or the computer rooms, and one is located near the operator's console and another next to the main exit door. Service transformers are not permitted in the electronic computer rooms. The number of junction boxes in underfloor areas is kept to a minimum. No splices or connections are permitted in the wiring in the underfloor area except within approved junction boxes or approved type receptacles or connectors. Grouping of cables is arranged as to avoid serious multiple failures because of a fault or overheating in any one conductor.

Records

Unnecessary supplies of paper or other combustible material are strictly limited to the minimum needed for efficient operations.

The operation of most electronic computer systems involves obtaining, using, creating, and storing large amounts of records. These records fall into five basic types which need safeguarding in accordance with their importance and the difficulty involved in their replacement. The following are the five types:

1. Input Data: This is the raw or partially refined information to be entered into the computer system, either as memory for later use or for immediate use in the solution of a problem, development of a statistic or production of some other product.

2. Memory: This is information previously converted to language or symbols immediately recognizable to the computer equipment and held for future use. Memory may be on any media which can be directly read by the computer system.

3. Program: This is data, which may be on paper or punch cards or on photographic, magnetic, or electronic media used to direct the computer in the selection of the correct input or memory data for use, on how to use it, and as to the type of results to obtain. Also to be considered in this category are any diagrams or records which can be used to reproduce programs.

4. Output Data: This is the final product of the computer system and may consist of printed material or electronic data.

5. Engineering Records: These are plans, specifications, and other records which provide the engineering record of the construction, wiring, and arrangement of the computer system and its housing. Of particular importance may be records of modifications made following the original installation.

Records kept within the computer room are held to the minimum required for efficient operation. All other records are stored outside the computer room in accordance with good record protection practices. Those that are vital or important are stored in special record protection devices designed to safeguard this type of record (see Sec. 5, Chap. 4). Useful records are stored in metal files or cabinets, if they are paper-based or plastic.

Fire Protection

ECDP units are particularly susceptible to severe damage from fire and the accompanying heat and smoke. Any sustained temperature in excess of about 140°F can cause malfunctioning of some parts within electronic computer systems, and temperatures in the range of 300°F to 500°F can impair the reliability of system units, normally requiring replacement of the units. Smoke and acids produced by fire can also adversely affect the operation of computer equipment and magnetic components. Fire exposures (heat or steam, or both) that would not damage ordinary paper records may easily damage magnetic tapes. The best protection for records that are essential to the mission of the ECDP equipment, that are irreplaceable, or that would be needed immediately after the fire and could not be quickly reproduced, consists of storing duplicate records in separate areas not subject to the same fire.

For the protection of computer rooms and equipment, automatic sprinkler systems are installed if the computer room has any combustible structural components or if the computer housing or the structure itself is built all, or in part, of combustible material. To minimize water damage under these conditions to the electronic computer equipment, it is important that power be shut off prior to the application of water on the fire. If the facilities are under the supervision of a trained operator during all periods that the equipment is energized, the normal delay between the initial outbreak of the fire and the operation of a sprinkler system would provide adequate time for the operator to shut off the power by use of the emergency shutdown switches. In other instances, where a fire may operate sprinklers before discovery by personnel, a method of automatic detection should be provided to automatically de-energize the electronic equipment as quickly as possible.

Products of combustion or smoke-type detectors are provided in the air space below any existing combustible raised floor to sound an audible as well as visual alarm and to shut down all electric power passing under such raised floors. In cases where fire in an electronic computer can spread throughout or beyond the computer's housing, fixed carbon dioxide extinguishing systems conforming to NFPA No. 12, Standard for Carbon Dioxide Extinguishing Systems, or total flooding automatic Halon 1301 systems conforming to the requirements of NFPA No. 12A, Halogenated Fire Extinguishing systems may be required. These may be manually actuated when the equipment, during all periods when it is energized, is under the supervision of an operator or any persons familiar with the equipment. In all other instances, the extinguishing systems are provided with both manual and automatic actuating means. Automatic actuation of a carbon dioxide or Halon 1301 system is arranged to meet the requirements of NFPA No. 72D, Proprietary Protective Signaling Systems, with particular attention given in the choice of actuation means to assure detection, considering the air flows usually involved in electronic computer equipment and the small heat release under fire conditions. Manual carbon dioxide hand hose systems or portable fire extinguishers may be substituted for the fixed systems under certain conditions, which include constant supervision by a competent person during all periods that the equipment is energized, adequate accessible controls to shut down power and air conditioning, accessibility of interior sections of equipment for manual fire fighting, and an adequate supply of extinguishing agent available.

Portable carbon dioxide or Halon 1301 extinguishers are provided for electrical fires, and water-type extinguishers for ordinary combustible materials, such as paper and plastics.

Guidance on emergency procedures is given in NFPA No. 75, Protection of Electronic Computer/Data Processing Equipment.

H.   Electrical Equipment for Outdoor Use

Electrical equipment which is installed outside of buildings should be weatherproof in design, i.e., so constructed that exposure to the weather will not interfere with its successful operation, or it should be enclosed in weatherproof cabinets. These enclosures are designed to prevent moisture or water from entering and accumulating within them and, if mounted on a wall or other supporting surface, there should be at least $\frac{1}{4}$-in. air space between the box or cabinet and the supporting surface (see Part I of this chapter for information on enclosed and gasketed equipment).

Description of Devices

Electrical equipment suitable for outdoor use is tested by recognized testing laboratories. The tests encompass suitability of the materials used and the protective coatings for sunlight, rain, and snow; effects of heat and cold; provisions for grounding, etc. The term "raintight" as used in the NEC is applied to equipment so constructed or protected that exposure to a beating rain will not result in entrance of water. The term "weatherproof" as used in the NEC is applied to equipment so constructed or protected that exposure to the weather will not interfere with successful operation.

Rainproof, raintight, or watertight equipment can fulfill the requirements for weatherproof where varying weather conditions other than wetness, such as snow, ice, dust, or temperature extremes, are not a factor.

Electric Signs and Outline Lighting

Except for portable signs of the indoor type, signs and outline lighting equipment preferably are constructed of metal or other noncombustible material. Wood may be used for external decoration only if placed not less than 2 in. from the nearest lampholder or current-carrying part. Enclosures for outside use should be weatherproof. All steel parts of enclosures should be galvanized or otherwise protected from corrosion. Signs, troughs, tube terminal boxes, and other metal frames should be grounded in the manner specified in the NEC unless they are insulated from ground and from other conducting surfaces and are inaccessible to unauthorized persons. Signs of the portable incandescent or fluorescent lamp type in which the open circuit voltage does not exceed 150 V to ground are not required to be grounded.

Each electric sign (other than the portable type) and each outline lighting installation should be controlled by an external operable switch or circuit breaker (handle on outside of switch enclosure) which will open all ungrounded conductors and which will be suitable for the conditions of installation. The switch or breaker should be within sight of the sign or outline lighting installation unless it is capable of being locked in the open position.

The circuit, number of outlets, and transformers should be arranged in such a manner that the maximum load on a branch circuit conforms to the NEC which also contains detailed requirements for installation of conductors, transformers, electric-discharge tubing and its terminals and electrode receptacles, and switching arrangements.

Electric Fences

Wire fences with electrical connections to produce a shock when animals come in contact with them are widely used on farms. The animals, after experiencing a shock, learn to keep away from the fences. To avoid hazard to persons and to stock, the current and the time interval during which the current is on must be limited to values which will not cause fatalities or injuries to persons or animals, even though causing an unpleasant sensation of shock. Careful design of current supply equipment is accordingly essential. Fatalities have resulted from home-made equipments supplied from ordinary lighting circuits. The open circuit voltage need not be limited if the current is properly limited Underwriters Laboratories' Bulletin of Research No. 14[5] gives detailed information.

The output characteristics of some controllers are such that combustible material may be ready ignited when a grounded object occupies a position with respect to the energized fence as to produce an electric arc. To insure against the possibility of fire from such a cause, users should determine that the controller has been designed and tested with respect to this hazard.

Marina and Boatyard Wiring

Marina and boatyard wiring presents special outdoor electrical equipment wiring problems which are covered in the NEC. Metallic raceways and metallic boxes should not be depended upon for grounding; a continuous insulated copper conductor, not smaller than No. 12 AWG, should be provided for a grounding conductor from outlet boxes to the service ground. Wiring over and under navigable water should be subject to approval by the authority having jurisdiction.

I. Locations Exposed to Moisture and Noncombustible Dusts

Special electrical equipment is required for use where moisture and noncombustible dusts may be present. For years, the NEC referred to such equipment as "vaportight," but the Code dropped this term because of confusion in the field between equipment so designated and "explosion-proof" equipment. Many users assumed that "vaportight" equipment was safe to use in atmospheres containing flammable gases or vapors (Class I locations), combustible dusts (Class II locations), or easily ignitible fibers or flyings (Class III locations). To avoid this type of misunderstanding, the term "enclosed and gasketed" has been developed by Underwriters Laboratories for this type of equipment. The use of such equipment in hazardous locations or wet locations (as defined in the NEC) has not been investigated. Some inspection authorities permit enclosed and gasketed lighting fixtures in Class II, Division 2, and in Class III, Divisions 1 and 2, locations when marked to show the maximum voltage lamps permissible and which are stated by the manufacturers' data sheets that the temperature will not exceed 165°C (329°F). The NEC requires lighting fixtures to be marked for use in wet and damp locations when so used.

J. Communications Systems

Communications systems, including telephone, telegraph, fire and burglar alarms, watchman and sprinkler supervisory systems, operate with low voltages and currents, and if they are kept free from accidental contacts with higher voltage systems, they present no unusual hazards. However, if the power supply is from storage batteries of appreciable current rating, from the lighting system of a building, or from transformers (other than approved signaling transformers), special precautions should be taken with the wiring and equipment. Because of the importance of these systems, they should be properly designed and installed so as to give reliable service.

Signaling systems and communication systems should be installed in accordance with the requirements of the NEC. The Standards of the National Fire Protection Association identified as NFPA Nos. 71, 72A, 72B, 72C, 72D, 72E, 73, and 74 cover the proper electrical wiring and equipment for fire alarm services and cross reference the NEC since telephone communication circuits may be used for completing the fire protective circuits between the protected premises and fire alarm headquarters (see also Sec. 12, Chap. 2 of this HANDBOOK).

K. Emergency Systems

The requirements for an emergency system are given in the NEC. They cover the installation, operation, and maintenance of circuits, systems, and equipment intended to supply illumination and power in the event of failure of the normal supply or in the event of accident to elements of a system supplying illumination and power essential for safety to life and property where such systems or circuits are legally required by code or law.

Emergency systems are generally installed in places of

assembly where artificial illumination is required, such as hotels, theaters, sports arenas, hospitals and similar institutions subject to occupancy by large numbers of persons.

NFPA No. 101, Life Safety Code, should be consulted for specification of locations where emergency lighting is considered essential for life safety (see Sec. 6, Chap. 9 of this HANDBOOK). NFPA No. 76A, Essential Electrical Systems for Health Care Facilities, delineates minimum factors governing the design, operation, and maintenance of those portions of health care facility electrical systems where interruption in any degree would jeopardize the effective and safe care of hospitalized patients. The provisions in this standard do not supersede the recommendations in the Life Safety Code or the NEC, except that it does limit the type of alternate source of electrical power allowable for use to assure electric power continuity in health care facilities. The standard recognizes the progressively greater dependence being placed upon electrical apparatus for the preservation of life of hospitalized patients and is a guide to health care facilities in the selection of the electrical services for emergency supply to all lighting and power equipment considered essential, and for their design and maintenance.

The sources of electric current which should be used for emergency lighting equipment are: (1) a storage battery of suitable capacity, (2) a generator driven by some form of prime mover, (3) a second electric service widely separated electrically and physically from the regular service to minimize the possibility of simultaneous interruption of both services, or (4) connections on the line side of the main service if sufficiently separated from the main service to prevent simultaneous interruption of supply through an occurrence within the building or group of buildings served. The NFPA Health Care Facilities Standard stipulates that the alternate source of power be prime mover-driven generators or be a separate utility supply from the normal service. Means should be provided for automatically energizing emergency lights upon failure of the regular lighting system supply. For hospitals, the transition time from the instant of failure of the normal power source to an emergency generator source should not exceed 10 sec.

Audible and visual signal devices are provided where practicable to give warning of derangement of the emergency source, to indicate that the battery or generator is carrying load, and to indicate when a battery charger is functioning properly.

No appliances and no lamps other than those specified as required for emergency use are supplied by the emergency lighting circuits.

The emergency lighting system is so designed that the failure of any individual lighting element, such as the burning out of a light bulb, cannot leave any space in total darkness.

The emergency lighting circuit wiring is independent of all other wiring and equipment and does not enter the same raceway, box, or cabinet with other wiring except at transfer switches and exit lighting fixtures supplied from both the normal and the emergency sources.

It is good practice to test the complete system upon installation and periodically thereafter to assure its maintenance in proper operating condition. A written record should be kept of such tests and maintenance.

L. Special Occupancy Electrical Problems

This section discusses hazardous locations and other special problems requiring individual attention and for which the NEC has specific recommendations.

Hazardous Locations—General

Electric lights and motors are necessary or desirable in many locations which are hazardous because of the presence of flammable liquids, gases, dusts, or fibers. In these areas special electrical equipment is necessary for safety. The NEC divides hazardous locations into three classes depending upon the kind of hazardous material involved and divides each class into two divisions according to the degree or severity of the hazard. Also, for the purposes of testing and approval, various atmospheric mixtures of gases, volatile-liquid vapors, and hazardous dusts have been grouped on the basis of their hazardous characteristics. These classes, divisions, and groups are given in Table 7-2M.

Approved equipment is marked to show the Class, Group, and operating temperature, or temperature range, based on operation in a 40°C ambient, for which it is approved. The temperature range, if provided, is indicated by identification numbers, as shown in Table 7-2N. The identification numbers are marked on equipment nameplates.

For purposes of testing and approval, various atmospheric mixtures (not oxygen-enriched) have been grouped on the basis of their hazardous characteristics, and facilities have been made available for testing and approving equipment for use in the atmospheric groups listed in Table 7-2M. Since there is no consistent relationship between explosion properties and ignition temperature, the two are independent requirements.

The temperature markings specified in Table 7-2N are not to exceed the ignition temperature of the specific gas or vapor to be encountered.

For information regarding ignition temperatures of gases and vapors, see NFPA No. 325M, Fire-Hazard Properties of Flammable Liquids, Gases, Volatile Solids and Table 3-11A in this HANDBOOK.

Complete definitions of the several classes and divisions of hazardous locations and the kind of wiring and types of electrical equipment to be used in each are covered in detail in the NEC. In addition, NFPA No 70C, Hazardous Locations Classification, a compilation of material on hazardous locations extracted from other NFPA standards as well as from certain ANSI and ASHRAE standards, is a helpful guide. Rules applying specifically to commercial garages, aircraft hangars, gasoline dispensing facilities and service stations, bulk storage plants, finishing processes, and other areas containing flammable anesthetics are also covered in the NEC.

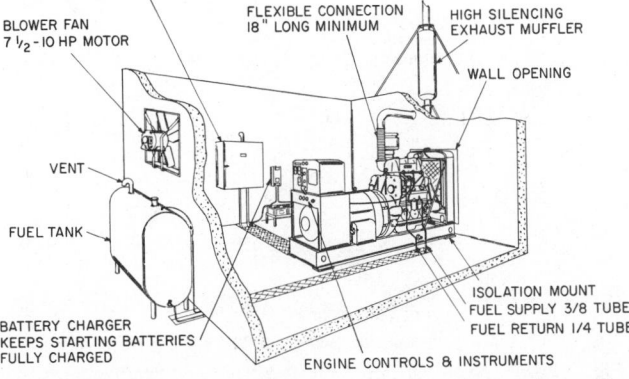

Fig. 7-2AA. Typical installation of a diesel-powered standby generator such as might be used for emergency light and power systems. (P & H Harnischfleger Corp.)

Table 7-2M. NEC Hazardous Locations Classifications (1975)

Class 1, Divisions 1 and 2	Chemicals by Groups
Group A Atmospheres Chemical acetylene	**Group D Atmospheres** Chemical acetone acrylonitrile

Group B Atmospheres
butadiene[1]
ethylene oxide[2]
hydrogen
manufactured gases containing
    more than 30% hydrogen
    (by volume)
propylene oxide[2]
	ammonia[3]
	benzene
	butane
	1-butanol (butyl alcohol)
	2-butanol (secondary butyl
	    alcohol)
	n-butyl acetate
	isobutyl acetate
	ethane

Group C Atmospheres
acetaldehyde
cyclopropane
diethyl ether
ethylene
unsymmetrical dimethyl
    hydrazine (UDMH 1,
    1-dimethyl hydrazine)
	ethanol (ethyl alcohol)
	ethyl acetate
	ethylene dichloride
	gasoline
	heptanes
	hexanes
	isoprene
	methane (natural gas)
	methanol (methyl alcohol)
	3-methyl-1-butanol
	    (isoamyl alcohol)
	methyl ethyl ketone
	methyl isobutyl ketone
	2-methyl-1-propanol
	    (isobutyl alcohol)
	2-methyl-2-propanol
	    (tertiary butyl alcohol)
	petroleum naphtha[4]
	octanes
	pentanes
	1-pentanol (amyl alcohol)
	propane
	1-propanol (propyl alcohol)
	2-propanol (isopropyl
	    alcohol)
	propylene
	styrene
	toluene
	vinyl acetate
	vinyl chloride
	xylenes

[1] Group D equipment shall be permitted for this atmosphere if such equipment is isolated in accordance with Section 501-5(a) of the NEC by sealing all conduit ½-inch size or larger.
[2] Group C equipment shall be permitted for this atmosphere if such equipment is isolated in accordance with Section 501-5(a) of the NEC by sealing all conduit ½-inch size or larger.
[3] For Classification of areas involving ammonia atmosphere, see Safety Code for Mechanical Refrigeration (ANSI B9.1-1971) and Safety Requirements for the Storage and Handling of Anhydrous Ammonia (ANSI K61.1-1972).
[4] A saturated hydrocarbon mixture boiling in the range 20-135°C (68-275°F). Also known by the synonyms benzine, ligroin, petroleum ether, or naphtha.

Class II, Divisions 1 and 2
Group E, Atmospheres containing metal dust, including aluminum, magnesium, and their commercial alloys, and other metals of similarly hazardous characteristics;
Group F, Atmospheres containing carbon black, coal or coke dusts which have more than 8 percent total volatile material (carbon black per ASTM D1620, charcoal, coal and coke dusts per ASTM D271) or atmospheres containing these dusts sensitized by other materials so that they present an explosion hazard.
Group G, Atmospheres containing flour, starch, or grain dust.

Class III, Divisions 1 and 2
Locations containing easily ignitible fibers or flyings such as cotton, rayons, sisal, hemp, jute, and other materials of similar nature.

Table 7-2N. Temperature Identification Numbers

Maximum Temperature Degrees C	Degrees F	Identification Number
450	842	T1
300	572	T2
280	536	T2A
260	500	T2B
230	446	T2C
215	419	T2D
200	392	T3
180	356	T3A
165	329	T3B
160	320	T3C
135	275	T4
120	248	T4A
100	212	T5
85	185	T6

Class I, Division 1: Locations in which (1) hazardous concentrations of flammable gases or vapors exist continuously, intermittently, or periodically under normal conditions, (2) hazardous concentrations of such gases or vapors may exist frequently because of repair or maintenance operations or because of leakage, or (3) breakdown or faulty operation of equipment or processes which might release hazardous concentrations of gases or vapors and might also cause simultaneous failure of electrical equipment. Motors and other rotating electrical machinery, lighting fixtures, switches, circuit breakers, and similar electrical equipment in these locations should be the explosion-proof type approved for Class I locations.

Class I, Division 2: Locations in which (1) volatile flammable liquids or flammable gases are handled, processed, or used, but are normally confined within closed containers or systems from which they can escape only in case of accidental rupture or breakdown or abnormal operation of equipment, (2) in which hazardous concentrations of gases or vapors are normally prevented by positive mechanical ventilation, or (3) which are adjacent to but not suitably cut off from Class I, Division 1 locations. In general, ordinary types of motors which do not have brushes, switch mechanisms, etc., may be installed in these locations, but motors which do have sliding contacts, switches, etc., should be the explosion-proof type approved for Class I locations. Lamps operating at dangerous temperatures

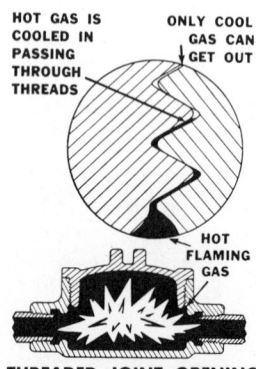

THREADED JOINT OPENING

Fig. 7-2BB. Explanation of the principle of "explosion-proof" equipment, indicating containment of hot gases within the enclosure. (Crouse-Hinds Company)

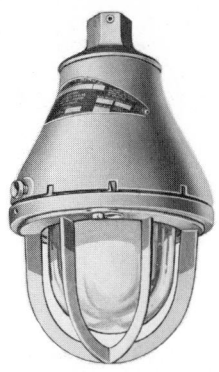

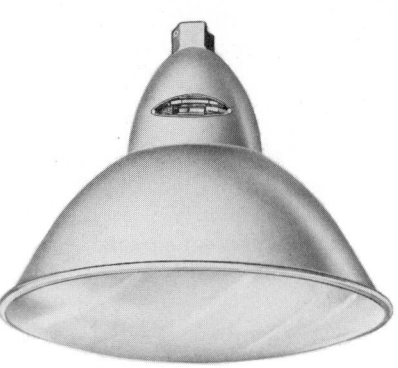

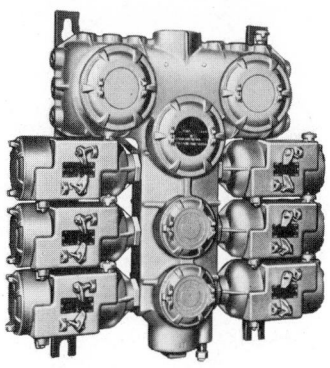

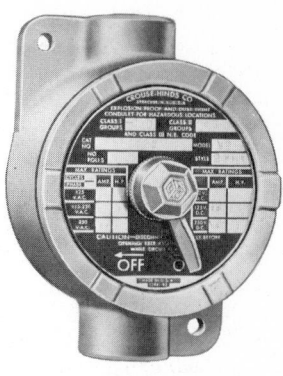

A lighting fixture for use in Class I hazardous locations (60-300 w). (Crouse-Hinds Company)

A dust-tight light fixture for use in Class II hazardous locations. (Crouse-Hinds Company)

An example of a panelboard for use in Class I hazardous locations. (Crouse-Hinds Company)

Tumbler switch for use in Class I and Class II hazardous locations. (Crouse-Hinds Company)

Fig. 7-2CC. REPRESENTATIVE LIGHTING FIXTURES FOR USE IN VARIOUS HAZARDOUS LOCATIONS.

Fig. 7-2DD REPRESENTATIVE SWITCHING AND PANELBOARD EQUIPMENT FOR USE IN VARIOUS HAZARDOUS LOCATIONS

should have approved explosion-proof enclosures. Units located where falling sparks or hot metal from lamps might ignite localized concentrations of flammable gases should have suitable enclosures. Switches, circuit breakers, and controllers intended to interrupt current in normal operation should either be explosion-proof, have their contacts in hermetically sealed chambers, or have contacts immersed in oil. Enclosures for electrical equipment which does not interrupt current may be of the general purpose type. Portable lamps shall be of the type satisfactory for use in a Class I, Division 1 location.

Class II, Division 1: Locations (1) in which combustible dust is or may be in suspension in the air continuously, intermittently, or periodically under normal operating conditions in quantities sufficient to produce explosive or ignitible mixtures, (2) where mechanical failure or abnormal operation might cause such mixtures to be produced and might also provide a source of ignition, or (3) in which dusts of an electrically conductive nature may be present. Motors should be of an enclosed type approved as dust-ignition-proof for Class II locations. Lighting fixtures, switches, circuit breakers, controllers, and fuses which are intended to interrupt current in normal operation should be provided with dust-ignition-proof enclosures approved for Class II locations. Maximum surface temperatures under actual operating conditions should not exceed 165°C (329°F) for equipment which is not subject to overloading, and 120°C (248°F) for equipment such as motors, power transformers, etc., which may be overloaded.

Class II, Division 2: Locations in which combustible dust will not normally be in suspension in the air, or will not be likely to be thrown into suspension by normal operation in quantities sufficient to produce explosive or ignitible mixtures, but also those where (1) deposits or accumulations of such dust may be sufficient to interfere with the safe dissipation of heat from electrical equipment, or (2) such deposits or accumulations of dust on, in, or in the vicinity of electrical equipment might be ignited by arcs, sparks, or burning material from such equipment. In general, self-cleaning, squirrel-cage textile motors or standard, open-type motors without sliding contacts, switches, etc., are satisfactory in many of these locations. Fixed lamps and lampholders should have enclosures designed to minimize the deposit of dust and prevent the escape of sparks, burning material, or hot metal. Switches, circuit breakers, con-

trollers, and fuses should be provided with tight metal enclosures designed to minimize the entrance of dust and to prevent the escape of sparks or burning material. The same temperature limits apply to Division 2 locations as to Division 1.

Class III, Division 1: Locations in which easily ignitible fibers or materials producing combustible flyings are handled, manufactured, or used. In general, motors in these locations should be of the enclosed type except that where only moderate accumulations of lint are present and cleaning and maintenance are satisfactory, self-cleaning, squirrel-cage, textile motors or standard, open-type motors without sliding contacts, switches, etc., may be installed; lamps and lampholders, switches, circuit breakers, controllers, and fuses should be provided with tight enclosures designed to minimize the entrance of fibers and to prevent the escape of sparks or burning material. Maximum surface temperatures under actual operating conditions should not exceed 165°C (329°F) for equipment which is not subject to overloading, and 120°C (248°F) for equipment such as motors, power transformers, etc., which may be overloaded.

Class III, Division 2: Locations in which easily ignitible fibers are stored or handled (except in process of manufacture). Motors should be of the enclosed type; lamps, lampholders, switches, circuit breakers, controllers, and fuses should have enclosures similar to those specified for Class III, Division 1 locations. The same temperature limits apply to Division 2 locations as to Division 1.

Equipment for Use in Hazardous Locations

Equipment for use in Class I hazardous locations, as defined in the NEC, is sometimes referred to as "explosion-proof" equipment. The basic design criterion for Class 1 equipment is that it withstands internal explosions of flammable-gas or vapor-air mixtures. In other words, it is recognized that surrounding flammable-gas or vapor-air mixtures will, under certain conditions, enter the enclosure of this equipment and that there is the possibility of their ignition within the enclosure. To prevent the propagation of flame to the outside surrounding atmosphere, which may likewise contain flammable vapor-air mixtures, the enclosures of this equipment must: (1) arrest flame at joints or other openings to the outside; (2) be strong enough to resist (without rupture or serious distortion) the internal pressure; and (3) the temperature of the enclosure must not increase enough to ignite the surrounding gas or vapor. The various gas or vapor-air mixtures vary considerably with respect to (1) the propagation of flames through joints of such assemblies; (2) the pressure developed within the enclosure following ignition; and (3) the ignition temperature of the gas or vapor-air mixture. Thus, equipment is listed for use in the various Groups indicated in Table 7-2M.

Equipment for use in Class I hazardous locations must also be designed to operate under full load conditions without developing surface temperatures above the ignition temperature of the flammable gas or vapor in which they are intended to be used.

As an alternate to "explosion-proof" motors and generators—equipment approved for use in Class I locations—it is permissible to use either of the following two designs:

(1) Totally enclosed equipment supplied with positive-pressure ventilation from a source of clean air with discharge to a safe area, so arranged to prevent energizing the machine until ventilation has been established and the enclosure purged with at least ten volumes of air, and also arranged to automatically de-energize the equipment when the air supply fails.

(2) Totally enclosed inert-gas-filled equipment supplied with a suitably reliable source of inert gas for pressurizing the enclosure, with devices provided to assure a positive pressure in the enclosure, so arranged as to automatically de-energize the equipment when the gas supply fails.

When either of these two designs are used, no external surface of the motors, generators, or other rotating electrical machinery should have an operating temperature (in degrees Celsius) in excess of 80 percent of the ignition temperature of the gas or vapor involved as determined by ASTM test procedure D2155-69. Appropriate devices are also to be provided to detect any increase in temperature of the equipment beyond its design limits and then to automatically de-energize the equipment; this equipment should be approved for the location in which it is installed.

NFPA No. 496, Purged and Pressurized Enclosures for Electrical Equipment, provides information for the design of purged enclosures for the purpose of eliminating or reducing within the enclosure a Class I hazardous location (gases or vapors in air in quantities sufficient to produce explosive or ignitible mixtures). Protective measures include supplying an enclosure with clean air or an inert gas at sufficient flow and positive pressure to achieve an acceptable safe level of the atmosphere and to maintain this safe level.

Another alternate is the use of "intrinsically safe" equipment and wiring—this is equipment and wiring incapable of releasing sufficient electrical energy under normal or abnormal conditions to cause ignition of a specific hazardous atmospheric mixture. NFPA No. 493, Intrinsically Safe Process Control Equipment for Use in Hazardous Locations, is the standard covering this subject.

In many cases, the amount of "explosion-proof" equipment required can be reduced, through the exercise of ingenuity in the layout of electrical installations, by locating much of the equipment in nonhazardous areas. The extent of the hazardous areas is normally defined by the codes and standards relating to the storage and handling of the specific liquids, gases, or solids.

Equipment for use in Class II and Class III hazardous locations presents a somewhat different problem because such equipment is designed to be dust-ignition-proof for Class II, Division 1, and for some Class II, Division 2, locations, and to be totally enclosed with telescoping covers for some Class II, Division 2, locations and for Class III loca-

tions. It is thus not intended to resist internal explosions of dust-air mixtures. Such equipment is tested in specific dust-air mixtures (as also outlined in Table 7-2M) to determine that the enclosures are dust-ignition-proof for Class II locations and that overheating does not occur when the device is blanketed with dust or lint and flyings.

Garages, Commercial (Repair and Storage)

The NEC requirements on this subject apply to locations used for the servicing and repair of passenger automobiles, buses, tractors, trucks, etc., in which flammable liquids or flammable gases are used. NFPA No. 88B, Repair Garages, and 88A, Parking Structures, should also be consulted in connection with further classifications of garages and the fire protection recommendations applying thereto. The specific hazardous areas in these garages are defined in the NEC.

Aircraft Hangars

Where aircraft containing gasoline, jet fuels, or other flammable liquids are stored or serviced, the specific hazardous areas are as defined in the NEC. Reference should also be made to NFPA No. 409, Aircraft Hangars, for guidance on the construction and protection of these structures.

Service Stations

This occupancy group includes locations where gasoline or other volatile flammable liquids or liquefied petroleum gases are transferred to the fuel tanks or auxiliary fuel tanks of self-propelled vehicles. Such facilities normally have dispensers (or dispensing pumps). Other facilities normally found at service stations include lubritoriums, service and repair rooms, air compressor rooms, toilet facilities, and offices.

Reference should be made to NFPA No. 30, Flammable and Combustible Liquids Code, as well as the NEC for information on the hazardous areas and other guidance on fire safety at such locations.

Bulk-Storage Plants (Flammable Liquid)

Where gasoline or other volatile flammable liquids are stored in tanks having an aggregate capacity of one carload or more and from which such products are distributed, the hazardous areas are as defined by the NEC and in the NFPA Flammable and Combustible Liquids Code, which also contains many informative guides to the safe construction and utilization of bulk storage plants.

Paint Spray Booths and Areas, etc.

The NEC applies to hazardous locations where paints, lacquers, or other flammable finishes are regularly or frequently applied by spraying, dipping, brushing, or by other means and where volatile flammable solvents or thinners are used, or where readily ignitible deposits or residues from such paints, lacquers, or finishes may occur. Further information regarding safeguards for finishing processes are contained in NFPA No. 33, Spray Applications, and NFPA No. 34, Dip Tanks Containing Flammable or Combustible Liquids. Hazardous areas with respect to flammable vapors are defined in the NEC.

Flammable Anesthetics

In hospitals and other locations where flammable anesthetics are or may be administered to patients (such as cyclopropane divinyl ether, ether chloride, ethyl ether, and ethylene), special rules apply. The NEC defines the anesthetizing (hazardous) area as any area in which it is intended to administer any flammable or nonflammable inhalation agent. It includes operating rooms, delivery rooms, emergency rooms, and anesthetizing rooms, and other areas when used for induction of anesthesia with flammable or nonflammable anesthetizing agents. In a flammable anesthetizing location the entire area is considered to be a Class I, Division 1 location extending upward to a level 5 ft above the floor.

For further information on the subject of flammable anesthetics, reference should be made to NFPA No. 56A, Inhalation Anesthetics.

Places of Assembly, Theaters, and Similar Locations

In places of assembly, theaters, and similar locations where numbers of people congregate, it is important that the electrical equipment be properly designed and installed. The general rules of the NEC as well as its special requirements for these occupancies should be followed in installing the equipment. NFPA No. 101, Life Safety Code, is the source to consult for information on use of emergency lighting (see also Sec. 6, Chap. 9 of this HANDBOOK).

Motion Picture Studios and Motion Picture Projectors

Special rules are also given in the NEC to cover electrical installations in motion picture studios, exchanges, factories, laboratories, stages, or areas of buildings in which work is done on professional cellulose nitrate film. This includes wiring on stages, sets, dressing rooms, viewing, cutting, and patching tables, and film storage vaults. Motion picture projectors are covered under NEC recommendations on electrical services for professional and nonprofessional projectors.

M. Origins of Electrical Fires in Buildings

In the United States, electrically caused fires in buildings, during the year 1973, were the source of almost 16 percent of the fires and over 13 percent of the total dollar loss. This is the most common cause of fire. In dollar costs of damages, electrical fire losses are number 1.[6]

Electrical fires are caused by arcing and overheating as discussed in Part A of this chapter. The International Association of Electrical Inspectors has standardized in nine broad categories to report electrical fires on a nationwide basis. These are shown in Table 7-20.

In even broader terms, these could be divided into four categories, as follows:

Worn-out or "Tired" Electrical Equipment Fires: This phrase indicates equipment actually worn out in service or wires having served a full and useful purpose for a period of years, which have deteriorated from service, thereby resulting in a fire.

"Tired" equipment is responsible for the largest percent of the electrical fires of known cause. The leading item within this category is the electrical motor. Also included in "tired" equipment fires are blazes caused by worn-out wires, television sets, lamp and other appliance cords, fixtures, and heated appliances.

Aging of electrical equipment results in the deterioration of insulation and, in some cases, corrosion or fatigue of the wires themselves.

Improper Use of Approved Equipment: Equipment which has been tested and listed by a nationally recognized laboratory rarely causes a fire if properly used in accordance with this listing and replaced when over-age.

Many of the fires of known cause are the result of using listed equipment. improperly.

"Improper use of approved equipment" indicates that although the equipment itself complies with safety standards of recognized testing laboratories, fires have occurred because such equipment is used under conditions not covered by its listing—i.e., use of No. 16 lamp cord for extension lights in hazardous locations.

There are three of the most prominent offenders in the group of misused equipment fires. First are the fires caused by the improper use of heated appliances; second, the

Table 7-20. Origin of Electrical Fires (Trend Over Two-Year Period)*

Origin	No. of Fires 1973	Percent of Total 1973 (227 Cities)	Percent of Total 1972	Percent Increase or Decrease
1. Cords	494	6.568	7.689	−1.121
2. Christmas decorations	30	0.399	0.513	−0.114
3. Heating appliances and incandescent lamps	787	10.465	10.064	+0.401
4. Motor windings (not integral with appliance)	415	5.518	6.021	−0.503
5. Transformers	124	1.649	1.682	−0.033
6. Radios (tape recorders, reproducing equipment)	56	0.745	0.783	−0.038
7. TV sets	443	5.890	7.253	−1.363
8. Miscellaneous wires, devices, and appliances	3924	52.172	53.017	−0.845
9. Electrical origin (no other details reported and others not specified)	1248	16.594	12.978	+3.616
TOTAL	7521	100	100	

* Based upon data compiled for 1973 appearing in the Sept./Oct. 1974 issue of *IAEI News*. For more up-to-date statistics see the current Sept./Oct. issue of the *IAEI News*.

Table 7-2P. Location of Electrical Fires

Location	Percentage*	
Outside Buildings	4	
Lightning		2
Cables		2
Inside Buildings	93	
Meters (defective)		—
Panelboards		1
Wires		15
Transformers (neon sign, etc.)		3
Terminal Equipment		12
Fixtures			6
Outlets			2
Switches, lamps, receptacles, sockets			4
Cords		9
Christmas Tree Wiring		—
Appliances		52
Motors			30
Heated tools, appliances,			
except residential irons			9
Television sets			6
Neon signs			3
Radio sets			2
Residential irons			1
Electric welder sparks,			
and other appliances			1
Miscellaneous Electrical Equipment	3	
Total	100	

* A dash indicates that the percentage is about ½ of 1 percent.

improper use of electrical motors; and third, the improper use of lighting cords.

Accidental Occurrence: Some electrical fires of known origin are the result of an accidental misuse or oversight on the part of people who operate the equipment. These fires are caused by such occurrences as clothes left in contact with lamps, dropping materials into electric equipment accidentally, heated appliances left on unintentionally, etc.

Defective Installations: Many of the electrical fires of known cause are the result of defective installations. Defective installations are those installed in a manner not acceptable under the National Electrical Code—i.e., a fractional horsepower motor automatically started which does not have overcurrent running protection as recommended by the Code.

The causes of a large percent of all electrical fires were never determined. Usually, this is due to the destruction of evidence so that the cause of the electrical failure cannot definitely be determined even though the fire was believed to have been the result of failure in an item of electrical equipment.

Earlier IAEI surveys indicate that in about 65 percent of the electrically caused fires, enough evidence remains to determine which factor was responsible. A five-year study was made of 39,392 electrical fires as reported by electrical inspectors from 237 U.S. cities.[7] Table 7-2P indicates the distribution of the percentage of the causes as a result of that study. (Since then, methods have improved as indicated in Table 7-2O.)

Bibliography

References Cited

[1] Hazardous Location Equipment List, Underwriters Laboratories, Inc., Chicago, published annually with bimonthly supplements.

[2] Electrical Appliance and Utilization Equipment List, Underwriters Laboratories, Inc., Chicago, published annually with bimonthly supplements.

[3] Electrical Construction Materials Lists, Underwriters Laboratories, Inc., Chicago, published annually with bimonthly supplements.

[4] "Why You Need More Protection Against Electrical Hazards Today, and How You Get It," I-T-E Imperial Bulletin 2.1.2-4A, Nov. 1973, I-T-E Imperial, Spring House, Penn.

[5] "Electric Shock as It Pertains to the Electric Fence," UL Bulletin of Research No. 14, Dec. 1939, Underwriters Laboratories, Inc., Chicago.

[6] "Fires and Fire Losses Classified, 1973," *Fire Journal*, Vol. 68, No. 5, Sept. 1974.

[7] "What Causes Electrical Fires," NFPA *Quarterly*, Vol. 53, No. 3, Jan. 1960, pp. 274–277.

NFPA Codes, Standards, and Recommended Practices (see the latest *NFPA Publications and Visual Aids Catalog* for availability of current editions of the following documents)

NFPA No. 12, Standard on Carbon Dioxide Extinguishing Systems.

NFPA No. 30, Flammable and Combustible Liquids Code.

NFPA No. 33, Standard for Spray Application Using Flammable and Combustible Materials.

NFPA No. 34, Standard for Dip Tanks Containing Flammable or Combustible Liquids.

NFPA No. 56A, Standard for the Use of Inhalation Anesthetics (Flammable and Nonflammable).

NFPA No. 70, National Electrical Code.

NFPA No. 70A, Electrical Code for One- and Two-Family Dwellings.

NFPA No. 70B, Electrical Equipment Maintenance.

NFPA No. 70C, Hazardous Locations Classification for Electrical Equipment and Wiring Methods.

NFPA No. 70L, Model State Law Providing for Inspection of Electrical Installation.

NFPA No. 71, Standard for the Installation, Maintenance and Use of Central Station Protective Signaling Systems.

NFPA No. 72A, Standard for the Installation, Maintenance and Use of Local Protective Signaling Systems.

NFPA No. 72B, Standard for the Installation, Maintenance and Use of Auxiliary Protective Signaling Systems.

NFPA No. 72C, Standard for the Installation, Maintenance and Use of Remote Station Protective Signaling Systems.

NFPA No. 72D, Standard for the Installation, Maintenance and Use of Proprietary Protective Signaling Systems.

NFPA No. 72E, Standard on Automatic Fire Detectors.

NFPA No. 73, Standard for the Installation, Maintenance and Use of Public Fire Service Communications.

NFPA No. 75, Standard for the Protection of Electronic Computer/Data Processing Equipment.

NFPA No. 76A, Standard for Essential Electrical Systems for Health Care Facilities.

NFPA No. 76CM, Manual for the Safe Use of High-Frequency Electrical Equipment in Hospitals.

NFPA No. 77, Recommended Practice on Static Electricity.

NFPA No. 78, Lightning Protection Code.

NFPA No. 79, Electrical Standard for Metalworking Machine Tools.

NFPA No. 88A, Standard for Parking Structures.

NFPA No. 88B, Standard for Repair Garages.

NFPA No. 101, Life Safety Code.

NFPA No. 409, Standard on Aircraft Hangars.

NFPA No. 497, Electrical Installation in Electrical Plants.

NFPA No. 501A, Standard for Mobile Home Parks.

NFPA No. 501B, Standard for Mobile Homes.

NFPA No. 501C, Standard for Recreational Vehicles (Travel Trailers, Motor Homes, Truck Campers, Camping Trailers).

NFPA No. 501D, Standard for Recreational Vehicle Parks.

NFPA No. 513, Standard for Motor Freight Terminals.

Chapter 3

HEATING SYSTEMS AND APPLIANCES

Heat-producing appliances and associated equipment are among the most prevalent causes of fire, since they operate at temperatures above the ignition temperature of many common materials. In addition, combustion-type appliances may involve the hazard of accumulated combustible mixture, the discharge of unburned fuel, and possible exposure of fuel to ignition sources. Electrical appliances, on the other hand, while not possessing a fuel hazard, are subject to the many causes of fire of electrical origin (see Chap. 2 of this Section).

This chapter discusses fuels and methods of firing (Part A), heating appliances and their uses (Part B), heat distribution through duct systems and pipes (Part C), installation of heating appliances (Part D), chimney and vent connectors (Part E), and chimneys, fireplaces, and venting systems (Part F).

A. Fuels and Methods of Firing

Combustion may be defined as a chemical reaction between a fuel and oxygen with evolution of heat and light. In a heat-producing device it is necessary that this reaction be continuous so a balance will be established between the rate at which oxygen or air fuel is supplied, and the rate at which heat and the products of combustion are removed. Complete combustion takes place when all of the fuel is oxidized by the air supplied to it. The air that is left over after complete oxidation is called excess air. If only enough air is supplied for complete combustion, perfect combustion is the result, under suitable conditions, an impracticality in commercial heat-producing appliances. All such appliances, therefore, operate with some excess air.

Air for combustion is supplied in two ways: (1) primary air is introduced through or with the fuels, and (2) secondary air is supplied to the combustion zone; that is to the zone where flames are present. In some cases all of the air is supplied as primary air while in others only part is supplied as primary air, the balance being furnished as secondary air.

Incomplete combustion in a fuel burning device can produce hazardous carbon monoxide. It also indicates poor efficiency since the fuel is obviously not being completely oxidized, and its total heating value is not being obtained.

Incomplete combustion usually results from inadequate air supply, insufficient mixing of air and gases, or a temperature too low to produce or sustain combustion.

Solid Fuel—Coal

Coal is the principal solid fuel used in heat-producing appliances. There are a number of types of coal, each having widely different characteristics, although in many cases there is no distinct line of demarcation between them; thus, the qualities of one type can overlap those of another. Pulverized coal systems, however, require the use of coals having characteristics within the specific range of the coal handling and coal burning equipment.

Coals of all types consist chemically of carbon, hydrogen, oxygen, nitrogen, sulfur, and a mineral residue called ash. There are two methods of analysis used to determine the composition of coal. The proximate analysis method determines the composition by mechanical processes, while the ultimate analysis method separates coal into its chemical constituents by chemical processes.

The calorific values of coal may be determined either in the laboratory with a bomb calorimeter or by Dulong's formula, which gives values accurate to within 2 percent. Dulong's equation is:

$$\text{Btu per lb} = 14{,}544C + 62{,}028 \left(H - \frac{O}{8}\right) + 4050S$$

in which C, H, O, and $S =$ proportion by weight of the carbon, hydrogen, oxygen, and sulfur respectively in a pound of coal as determined by ultimate analysis.

The seven principal types of coal used in heat-producing appliances are:

Anthracite: A clean, dense, hard coal. It burns with a minimum of smoke and has a minimum dust hazard during handling.

Semianthracite: A coal having a higher volatile content than anthracite but not as hard.

Bituminous: This includes many types of coal with different properties depending on where they are mined. It gives off considerable smoke and soot if improperly fired. Bituminous coal may be subject to spontaneous ignition under some storage conditions and has a dust hazard during handling.

Semibituminous: A dusty soft coal that tends to break up. It may be subject to spontaneous ignition under some storage conditions. It normally produces less smoke than bituminous coal.

Subbituminous: A coal subject to spontaneous ignition under some storage conditions. It burns with very little smoke and soot.

Lignite: A coal having a woody structure and, normally, a high moisture content. It is subject to spontaneous ignition under some storage conditions. It burns with little smoke and soot.

Coke: A product of the destructive distillation of coal; the type of coke produced is determined by the coal used, and the temperatures and time of distillation. Petroleum coke is produced from the destructive distillation of oil.

The Combustion of Coal

When coal is burned in a firebox, oxygen in the air passing through the grate (primary air) unites with the carbon in the lower portion of the fuel bed, called the oxidation zone, to form carbon dioxide. Some of this carbon dioxide is then reduced to carbon monoxide in the upper part of the fuel bed, called the reduction zone. Gases liberated from the fuel bed are carbon monoxide, carbon dioxide, nitrogen, and some oxygen. Oxygen from the air admitted over the fuel bed (secondary air) combines with some of the carbon monoxide to form carbon dioxide. When fresh coal is applied to the fire, moisture is driven off as steam and the hydrocarbon gases are distilled, combined with oxygen, and burned above the grate in what is called the distillation zone.

Methods of Firing Coal

Coal is fired either by hand or automatically by stokers or pulverized coal burners.

There are many acceptable hand-firing methods. With high volatile coals, the objective is to leave a suitable bed of glowing fuel to ignite the gases as they are driven off from the fresh coal charge; otherwise the gas may accumulate and when finally ignited, do so explosively. Anthracite and other low volatile coals can be spread evenly over the fuel bed. The only feature of a hand-fired furnace that can be automatic is the draft regulation. Draft can be controlled by a room thermostat, by steam pressure, or by water temperature. But, as with any hand-fired solid fuel, the fire is continuous and overtemperature conditions are difficult to control unless there is attendance.

Mechanical Stokers: These are classified according to their coal burning capacities, and they range from those that handle 10 lbs per hr to those handling over 1,200 lbs per hr. A stoker feeds fuel to the combustion chamber and usually supplies air for combustion under automatic control. There are four basic types of stokers: (1) underfed, (2) overfed, (3) traveling and chain grate, and (4) spreader with fired grate or continuous ash discharge.

Underfed stokers move the coal by screw conveyor or by rams (see Fig. 7-3A). Overfed stokers feed the coal pneumatically or by rotors. Spreader stokers similarly feed coal by rotors or paddles and discharge onto stationary or traveling grates. Stokers may feed from hoppers or directly from bins. They are equipped with fueling controls that either change the firing rate or stop the fuel altogether. Some stokers are equipped with a control that will stop the feeding of fuel if the fire goes out.

Pulverized Coal Systems: These are of two general types: (1) the direct-fired or unit system and (2) the storage or bin system. In the direct-fired system (see Fig. 7-3B), raw coal is fed directly to a pulverizer where it is pulverized, mixed with air, and blown to the burners. In the storage system (see Fig. 7-3C), coal is delivered to a raw fuel bin and then passed through a raw fuel feeder to a pulverizer where it is reduced to a powder and dried (usually with flue gas). From the pulverizer, the coal is gathered in a cyclone collector where it is fed by gravity to a pulverized-fuel pump that delivers it to a pulverized-fuel bin. The pulverized coal is then taken from the bin by a fuel feeder and delivered to the burners.

Basically, there are two types of firing. In one type, the furnace firebox serves as the mixing chamber for the air and fuel. In the other type, the burner nozzles have their own air supplies and involve an accurate air and fuel metering method. The tangential burner (air and coal directed from corners of the burner tangent to a circle in the center of the burner) is an example of the first type, whereas vertical and horizontal burners are examples of the second type. In any case, the objective is the combustion of the fuel in a minimum of furnace volume with as low an amount of excess air as possible.

The equipment for pulverized-fuel systems is designed to

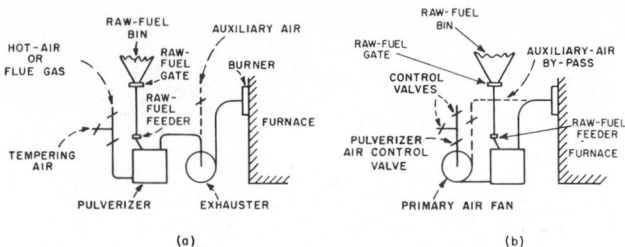

Fig. 7-3B.   Direct-fired pulverized coal systems.

withstand most internal explosions that may be expected with coal dust and air mixtures. Portions of systems are valved, and the various components equipped with interlocks and other safeguards to prevent conditions that could result in fires and explosions. NFPA No. 60, Standard for the Installation and Operation of Pulverized Fuel Systems, discusses the design of systems and the many safeguards required. (See also Section 4, Chapter 10 for information on pulverization equipment.)

Storage of Coal

Coal is stored on the ground or on a floor in a bin that does not contain foreign materials (leaves, pieces of wood, etc.); these bins should not contain steam or hot water pipes, and the floor and walls preferably are noncombustible. Coal dropped any considerable distance may result in excessive breakage. Piles should be limited in height and area, the limits established to be based on the amount of coal demand with no more than about 50 tons in any one bin. More detailed information on precautionary measures to take for coal subject to spontaneous ignition and heating is found in Section 3, Chapter 5.

Solid Fuels—Miscellaneous

Miscellaneous solid fuels include: wood (logs, scrap lumber, etc.), wood waste from lumber and paper mills (sawdust, shavings, bark, etc.), hogged fuel (sawmill refuse run through a disintegrator or "hog" to form uniform chips or shreds), charcoal, briquets, peat, bagasse, and a host of other combustibles, such as tanbark, wet bark, straw, city refuse, paper, etc. The methods of firing these fuels are not described in detail because they vary so much with the type of device and the nature of the particular fuel.

Liquid Fuel—Fuel Oils

This discussion principally concerns fuel oil used in heat-producing appliances and equipment. Chapter 3 of Section 3 gives general information on flammable and combustible liquids and their storage and handling.

Fuel oil, like other petroleum products, is made up of varying compounds of hydrocarbons. Even the same grade of fuel oil will vary as to its chemical composition, depending on such factors as the type of crude oil used and the refining process employed.

Types of Fuel Oil: Historically, fuel oils fall into two classes: (1) distillate fuel oils, and (2) residual fuel oils. As the terms imply, a distillate fuel oil was originally derived from the distillation of crude oil, while residual fuel oil was the residue left after this distillation process. Fuel oils derived solely from the distillation process were known as "straight run."

With the development of better refining processes, distillation has become obsolete. Modern practice employs various methods to secure more finished products out of a single barrel of crude oil. Fuel oils obtained from these newer processes are known as "cracked" oils, and practically

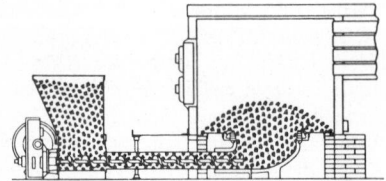

Fig. 7-3A.   One type of underfed coal stoker.

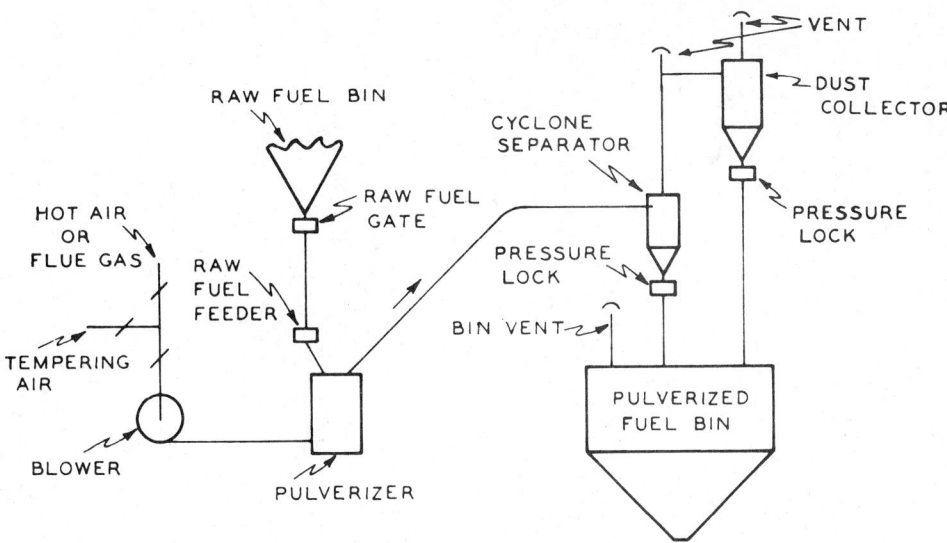

Fig. 7-3C. Storage system for pulverized coal (vented air discharged to atmosphere).

all petroleum products on the market today are obtained by this "cracking" process.

No. 1 and No. 2 fuel oil, as well as those fuels commonly known as kerosine, range oil, furnace oil, star oil, and diesel oil, may still be broadly classed as "distillates," and No. 4, No. 5, and No. 6 oil (as well as Bunker C) as "residuals." (No. 3 fuel oil, a former intermediate grade, is no longer standard.)

Due to the variety of fuel oil quality and general performance characteristics, it has been found desirable to lay down certain quality limitations. Oil burners are constructed (and subsequently tested and listed by testing laboratories) for a specific grade or grades of fuel oil. For example, burners listed by Underwriters Laboratories, Inc., have the grade or grades of fuel oil which may be used in each inscribed on the UL listing mark applied to the unit (see Figs. 7-3D and 7-3E). It is important that only the proper grade or grades of oil be used in each burner for safety as well as efficiency reasons. Specifications for fuel oil are outlined by the American Society for Testing and Materials in their Specifications for Fuel Oils, ASTM D396, and in Canadian Government Specification 3-GP-28 (see Table 7-3A).

Caloric Values of Fuel Oils: Table 7-3B gives the calorific values for the various grades of fuel oil (further identified by their weight per gallon).

Method of Firing Fuel Oil

An oil burner is a mechanical device that converts a fuel from the liquid state to the vapor or gaseous state and then combines the gaseous fuel with air in controlled quantities for combustion. Two methods, vaporization and atomization, are employed for the preparation of fuel oil for combustion. The air needed for combustion is supplied by natural or mechanical draft. Ignition is accomplished manually or by means of an electric ignition system, a gas pilot, or an oil pilot. Operation may be continuous, modulating with high-low flame, or intermittent. While most burners operate from automatic temperature or pressure sensing controls, some simpler types are operated manually.

Oil burners may be classified in several different ways, i.e., by application, by type of vaporizer or atomizer, by firing rates, etc. They are divided into two major groups, residential types and commercial-industrial. Vaporizing burners and atomizing burners having capacities of not more than 7 gph (gallons per hour) are considered residential types and are intended to be used with oil fuels not heavier than No. 2. The major portion of residential-type burners currently being produced are the pressure atomizing burner, commonly referred to as the gun type. However a substantial number of other types, subsequently described in this chapter, are still in service.

Vaporizing Burners: These include the sleeve type, the pot type, and the vertical rotary wall-flame type.

Sleeve-type burners (see Fig. 7-3F) have application in residential type heating and cooking stoves. They are ignited manually and regulated manually by a valve that controls oil flow to the burner, except that in some wick types the height of the flame is regulated by raising and lowering the wick. Fuel consumption varies from 2 to 10 gal of range oil per day.

Fig. 7-3D. Listing mark used on oil-fired furnaces listed by Underwriters Laboratories, Inc. Note that the grade of oil satisfactory for use in the device appears at the bottom of the marker.

Fig. 7-3E. Listing mark used on oil burning stove listed by Underwriters Laboratories, Inc. Note that the grade of oil satisfactory for use in the device appears at the bottom of the marker.

Table 7-3A. Detailed Requirements for Fuel Oils*

Grade of Fuel Oil	Flash Point, deg F (deg C) Min	Pour Point, deg F (deg C) Max	Water and Sediment, percent by volume Max	Carbon Residue on 10 percent Bottoms, percent Max	Ash, percent by weight Max	Distillation Temperatures, deg F (deg C) 10 percent Point Max	90 percent Point Min	90 percent Point Max	Saybolt Viscosity, sec Universal at 100°F (38°C) Min	Universal at 100°F (38°C) Max	Furol at 122°F (50°C) Min	Furol at 122°F (50°C) Max	Kinematic Viscosity, centistokes At 100°F (38°C) Min	At 100°F (38°C) Max	At 122°F (50°C) Min	At 122°F (50°C) Max	Gravity, deg. API Min	Copper Strip Corrosion Max	Sulfur, percent Max
No. 1: A distillate oil intended for vaporizing pot-type burners and other burners requiring this grade of fuel	100 or legal (38)	0§	trace	0.15	—	420 (215)	—	550 (288)	—	—	—	—	1.4	2.2	—	—	35	No. 3	0.5 or legal
No. 2: A distillate oil for general purpose domestic heating for use in burners not requiring No. 1 fuel oil	100 or legal (38)	20§ (—7)	0.05	0.35	—	—	540§ (282)	640 (338)	(32.6)#	(37.93)	—	—	2.0§	3.6	—	—	30	—	0.5§ or legal
No. 4: Preheating not usually required for handling or burning	130 or legal (55)	20 (—7)	0.50	—	0.10	—	—	—	45	125	—	—	(5.8)	(26.4)	—	—	—	—	‖
No. 5 (Light): Preheating may be required depending on climate and equipment	130 or legal (55)	—	1.00	—	0.10	—	—	—	150	300	—	—	(32)	(65)	—	—	—	—	‖
No. 5 (Heavy): Preheating may be required for burning and, in cold climates, may be required for handling	130 or legal (55)	—	1.00	—	0.10	—	—	—	350	750	(23)	(40)	(75)	(162)	(42)	(81)	—	—	‖
No. 6: Preheating required for burning and handling	150 (65)	—	2.00**	—	—	—	—	—	(900)	(9000)	45	300	—	—	(92)	(638)	—	—	‖

* It is the intent of these classifications that failure to meet any requirement of a given grade does not automatically place an oil in the next lower grade unless in fact it meets all requirements of the lower grade. This table reprinted from ASTM D-396-69. See complete specification ASTM D-396-69.

† Outside U.S. the sulfur limit for No. 2 shall be 1.0 percent.

‡ Legal requirements to be met.

§ Lower or higher pour points may be specified whenever required by conditions of storage or use. When pour point less than 0°F is specified, the minimum viscosity shall be 1.8 cSt (32.0 sec, Saybolt Universal) and the minimum 90 percent point shall be waived.

‖ The 10 percent distillation temperature point may be specified at 440°F (226°C) maximum for use in other than atomizing burners.

Viscosity values in parentheses are for information only and not necessarily limiting.

** The amount of water by distillation plus the sediment by extraction shall not exceed 2.00 percent. The amount of sediment by extraction shall not exceed 0.50 percent. A deduction in quantity shall be made for all water and sediment in excess of 1.0 percent.

Table 7-3B. Characteristics of Fuel Oil

No.	Weight (lbs per gal)	Calorific Value (Btu per gal)
1	6.9–6.7	137,000–132,900
2	7.3–6.9	141,800–135,800
4	8.2–7.2	153,300–140,600
5	8.4–7.8	155,900–148,100
6	8.6–7.9	157,300–149,400
6 low sulfur	8.1–7.4	150,000–142,000

Pot burners (see Fig. 7-3G) may be ignited manually or more generally by a pilot flame. The oil is fed through a constant-level device with capacities for the natural draft type ranging from 0.9 to 1.5 gph. Natural draft pot burners have applications similar to sleeve-type burners. Forced draft pot burners have increased efficiency and may be used in central heating furnaces and boilers. The larger sizes may burn up to 2.5 gph fed through a constant-level device.

Vertical rotary wall-flame vaporizing burners are designed to be used in residential-type boilers and furnaces for central heating. Each unit consists of a vertical motor, a blower, an oil distributor, and a vaporizing ring. Oil is propelled radially from the motor-driven distributor out to the vaporizing ring. Vaporization occurs at the ring and the vapor mixes with air from the blower which also is driven by the vertical motor. Ignition is either by an electric spark or a gas pilot. Fuel is fed by gravity through a constant-level device with consumption ranging from 0.75 to 7 gph.

Atomizing: These burners have a wide variety of applications and include high and low pressure types, horizontal rotary cup types, and air and steam atomizing types, the latter used primarily for commercial and industrial applications. High pressure, gun-type burners consist of a motor, oil pump (with integral or separate pressure regulating and shut-off valve), strainer, fan, ignition transformer, nozzle, and electrode assembly (see Fig. 7-3H). The motor-driven pump draws oil from the supply tank and delivers it to the nozzle at pressure of from 100 to 300 psi. The nozzle atomizes the oil into fine particles and swirls it into the combustion chamber as a cone-shaped spray. Air from the fan, also driven by the motor, is blown through a tube surrounding the nozzle-electrode assembly passing through

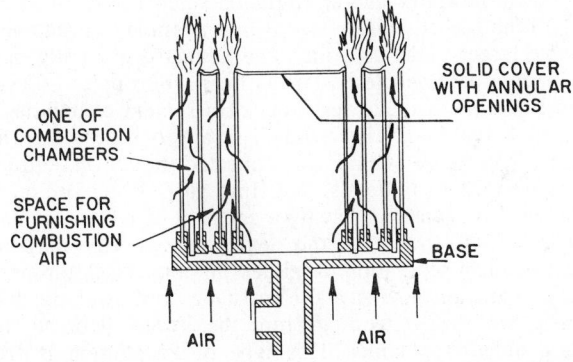

Fig. 7-3F. A sleeve-type burner which consists essentially of a flat, cast iron or pressed steel base having two or more interconnecting grooves. Perforated metal cylindrical sleeves are placed in the grooves so that the space between the inner two sleeves and the outer two sleeves becomes a combustion chamber. The space between the second and third sleeves is for the purpose of furnishing combustion air. Covers with annular openings usually are placed on top of the sleeves. Sleeve burners may or may not employ wicks in the annular spaces in the base depending upon the make and type of burner.

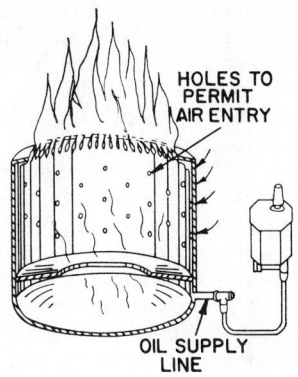

Fig. 7-3G. A vaporizing pot-type burner. The oil is introduced into the bottom of the burner and is continually vaporized by the heat of the fire. The holes on the side permit primary air and secondary air to enter the burner where they mix with the oil vapors for proper combustion. The primary air is mixed with the oil vapors before combustion takes place and the secondary air is supplied to complete the combustion process. At full fire the velocity of the vapors and the amount of air required result in the flame burning only at the top of the burner.

vanes which give the air a whirling motion opposite to that of the atomized oil thus creating an intimate mixture of air and oil. The mixture is ignited by an electric spark, gas pilot, or oil pilot. The ignition system may be intermittent in which case the ignition means is "on" all the time the burner is firing or the ignition may be interrupted shortly after the main burner flame has been established. These burners are made in capacities ranging from 0.5 to 50 gph for application boilers, heating furnaces, and other appliances. They are generally designed to burn No. 2 oil although some of the larger sizes are made for No. 4 oil.

The industrial version of the high pressure burner, known as the mechanical atomizing burner, is a high capacity burner for use with large boilers and industrial furnaces. The high pressure nozzle is mounted in an air register (wind box) attached to the appliance being fired. Separate fan and pump sets supply air and fuel respectively. The heavier oils are usually used in these burners.

The low pressure gun burner is similar but differs from the high pressure gun burner in two ways. First, the burner includes an air pump to supply compressed air for atomization, and second, the oil and air are delivered to the nozzle at pressures of 15 psi or less. Atomization is accomplished by delivering to the nozzle through separate conduits mea-

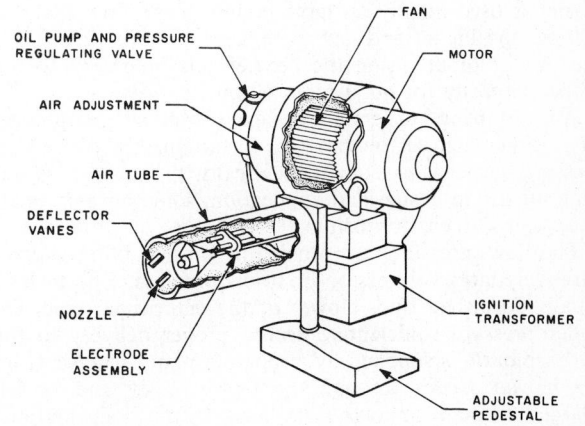

Fig. 7-3H. A high pressure atomizing oil burner. (National Oil Fuel Institute, Inc.)

sured volumes of air and oil, intermixing these in the nozzle and then releasing this mixture as fine particles of oil mixed with air. Secondary air to complete the combustion process is supplied by the blower as in the high pressure gun burner. Also the size ranges, ignition, and fuel used are as described for the high pressure gun burner.

The horizontal rotary cup oil burner atomizes the oil by spinning it in a thin film from a horizontal rotating cup and injecting high velocity primary air into the oil film through an annular nozzle which surrounds the rim of the cup. The atomizing cup and primary air fan are mounted on a horizontal main shaft which is motor driven at a constant speed of from 3,450 to 6,000 rpm, depending upon the size and make of burner. The oil is fed to the cup at rates controlled by metering devices from an oil pump which may be included in the burner assembly or in a separate pump set. Secondary air for combustion is supplied from a separate fan set forcing air through the burner wind box. The introduction of secondary air by means of natural draft is not recommended. Ignition is accomplished by an electrically ignited gas- or oil-burning pilot. The main burner and wind box assembly is arranged for mounting on the appliance being fired and the burner is hinged so that it can be swung away from the firing position for easy access for servicing. These burners are used for firing boilers and furnaces and may be used singly or as multiple units on a single appliance. They are made for firing rates of from 5 to 300 gph. No. 2 fuel may be used with some of the smaller sizes but No. 4, 5, or 6 is generally used with the larger sizes.

In the steam atomizing burner atomization is accomplished by the impact and expansion of steam. Oil and steam flow in separate channels through the burner "gun" to the nozzle where the steam and oil mix before being discharged through an orifice into the combustion space. The spray of atomized oil and steam forms a hollow cone. Combustion air, supplied by a forced draft fan, passes through the directing vanes of the air register (wind box), through the burner throat, and into the combustion space. The vanes give the air a spinning motion and the burner throat directs the air into the cone-shaped spray where intimate mixing of air and oil takes place. Full-load oil pressure at the burner inlet is usually from 100 to 150 psi and the steam pressure is kept at about 25 psi greater than the oil pressure. Where steam is not available for start-up, compressed air may be used. Some designs permit the use of a mechanical atomizing nozzle for start-up when neither steam nor compressed air is available. This type of burner is used mainly on large boilers generating steam at 100 psi and higher and having capacities above 12,000,000 Btu per hr input, using the heavier oils preheated to the proper viscosity for good atomization.

Air atomizing burners are designed to utilize compressed air at either high or low pressure for atomization. The high pressure burner is practically identical with the steam atomizing burner in design and application, some burners operating well with either medium.

The low pressure air atomizing burner utilizes comparatively large volumes of air at low pressure, 5 psi or less, usually furnished by a blower of the centrifugal type. Oil under pressure sufficient to secure proper delivery to the burner nozzle is supplied by a separate pump set. Air from the blower passes through the burner body and is discharged through annular slots between the body and the nozzle tip, where it meets at an angle the film of oil issuing from the tip. The impact of the air stream upon the oil film produces a fine mist which is projected into the combustion

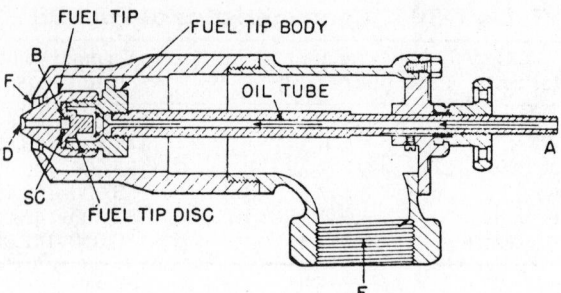

Fig. 7-3I.   A low-pressure air-atomizing burner. Nomenclature: **A**—oil inlet, **B**—oil slots, **D**—oil discharge orifice, **E**—air inlet, **F**—air discharge orifice, and **SC**—swirl chamber.

space. These burners may be fired with light or heavy oil and are usually manually lighted. They are most often used to fire industrial heating and processing furnaces.

Combination oil and gas burners which combine the features of certain oil burners with provisions for burning gas have been developed, which permit the operator to choose either fuel as circumstances may dictate.

Figure 7-3I illustrates a low-pressure air-atomizing burner.

Fuel Oil Storage

Detailed provisions for the installation of fuel oil tanks and related piping are set forth in NFPA No. 31, Standard for the Installation of Oil Burning Equipment, hereinafter referred to as the NFPA Oil Burning Equipment Standard. This Standard covers the installation of tanks underground, unenclosed and enclosed inside buildings, and outside aboveground. The installation requirements in NFPA No. 31 for fuel oil tanks differ slightly from the requirements for tanks given in NFPA No. 30, Flammable Liquids Code, which covers liquids having a wider range of flash points and which are used in a variety of locations for a variety of reasons.

Unenclosed Tanks in Buildings: For many years the NFPA Oil Burning Equipment Standard limited the maximum capacity for unenclosed fuel oil tanks to 275 gal. This figure was largely based on the fact that it was the largest size tank that could be taken in and out of the doors and up and down the stairs leading to the basements of most dwellings in the United States. As it is now possible to install and remove larger tanks as a unit, the Standard currently permits individual unenclosed tanks of capacities up to 660 gal (550 Imp gal) in the lowest story or basement of buildings. Two such tanks may be installed in any one area but the aggregate capacity of tankage connected to any one burner is not more than 660 gals (550 Imp gal). If separation is provided for each tank having a capacity of not more than 660 gal (550 Imp gal) the aggregate capacity may be greater. Such separation is either an unpierced masonry wall or partition having a fire resistance rating of not less than 2 hrs, and extending from the lowest floor to the ceiling above the tanks. This type of installation is frequently found in multiple unit housing where each family has its own heating system.

If located above the lowest story or basement of a building an unenclosed tank should be no larger than 60 gal (55 Imp gal) capacity.

All unenclosed tanks inside buildings should be located not less than 5 ft from any fire or flame either in or external to any fuel burning appliance. Furthermore they should not obstruct quick and safe access to any utility service meter, switch panel, and shut-off valve.

Corrosion of Tanks: Internal corrosion of unenclosed fuel oil tanks, caused by electrolytic action of water on the steel, has been a major problem. Corrosion and subsequent tank leakage have actually been more of a nuisance than a fire hazard. Fire can occur, however, when a burner is located in a pit in the basement and oil from a leaking tank enters the pit. In order to correct the cause of corrosion, two generally accepted procedures are recommended. One method is to slope the tank to one end and take the burner oil supply line from the bottom of that end. In this way, water is not permitted to accumulate in the bottom of the tank. As the water is only that which has been entrained in minute quantities in the oil that comes from condensation inside the tank, the quantity is so small that it is no problem to the safe operation of the burner. The second method is to use a small amount of an alkaline solution as an additive to the oil itself or to add a small amount of the solution at periodic intervals directly into the tank.

Enclosed Tanks in Buildings: Tanks larger than 660 gal (550 Imp gal) capacity may be installed in buildings provided the tanks are within an enclosure constructed of walls, floor, and top having a fire resistance rating of not less than 3 hours with the walls bonded to the floor. Any opening into the enclosure is required to have a noncombustible sill or ramp at least 6 in. high and the opening must be provided with a self-closing fire door for a Class A location. The top and walls of the enclosure are to be independent of building construction except that an exterior building wall having a fire resistance rating of not less than 3 hrs may serve also as a wall for the tank enclosure. Installation of tanks in this manner is found only in commercial and industrial buildings.

Outside Aboveground Tanks: Tankage not in excess of 1,320 gal (1,100 Imp gal) may be installed outside aboveground in built-up areas. The tanks may be adjacent to buildings but should be away from the line of adjacent property. Not more than one tank or two tanks having an aggregate capacity of not more than 660 gals (550 Imp gal) should be connected to one oil burning appliance. For details covering the installation of these and larger outside aboveground tanks see NFPA No. 31.

Underground Tanks: Tanks built to conform to the NFPA Oil Burning Equipment Standard, are installed with foundations and coverings, also specified in the Standard, for the location selected, outside or under buildings. The Standard also gives special precautions to take relative to building foundations, protection against traffic, e.g., vehicle movement over the buried tanks, and for areas subject to flooding (see the NFPA Flammable and Combustible Liquids Code for additional information on protecting tanks containing flammable liquids in locations that may be flooded). Underground tanks should not be placed closer than 1 ft from the nearest line of adjoining property that may be built upon. All connections to underground tanks, as well as to enclosed tanks inside buildings, are made only through the top of the tank. Underground tanks need to be vented to the open air and provided with a means for gaging.

Centralized Oil Distribution Systems: A system of piping through which oil is supplied from a central tank or tanks may be employed under certain conditions to serve a number of buildings, mobile homes, recreational vehicles, or other structures. For details covering such systems see the NFPA Oil Burning Equipment Standard.

Fill and Vent Pipes: Underground tanks and tanks larger than 10 gal capacity inside buildings have fill and vent pipes terminating outside of buildings. Vent openings and vent pipes are of ample size to prevent abnormal pressure during filling but not smaller than 1¼-in. pipe size for 550 gal (500 Imp gal) and correspondingly larger for tanks having greater capacity. In addition to provision for normal venting, outside aboveground tanks also have some form of construction or device to relieve excessive internal pressure that may be caused by an exposure fire. All connections to underground tanks and tanks inside buildings are made through the top of the tank except the supply connection to an unenclosed inside tank having a capacity not exceeding 660 gal (550 Imp gal) and the cross connection permitted between two unenclosed inside tanks having an aggregate capacity of not more than 660 gal (550 Imp gal). Gaging devices are desirable, but on inside tanks they must not allow oil or vapor to be discharged into the building.

Small Capacity Tanks: There are several types of small tanks used with cooking appliances and room heaters. An auxiliary tank of not over 60 gal capacity may be provided between the burner and the main fuel supply tank. An unenclosed supply tank of not more than 10 gal capacity for an individual appliance is permitted provided it is placed not less than 2 ft from a source of heat either inside or outside the appliance being served, and provided that the temperature of the oil in the tank will not exceed 25°F above room temperature at the maximum firing rate.

Integral tanks are furnished by manufacturers as a component part of some oil burning appliances, e.g., kerosine and oil stoves. Stoves with integral tanks (not over 5 gal capacity) operate on the gravity or barometric feed principle. The oil in the tank reservoir and in the burner are at the same level. As the oil level drops due to burning, oil runs into the reservoir from the tank, either because a float drops and opens a valve (gravity feed) or because air enters the tank through the cap and allows oil to enter the reservoir until it covers the air opening (barometric feed).

The NFPA Oil Burning Equipment Standard contains specific provisions on supply tanks for kerosine and oil stoves, portable kerosine heaters, and conversion range oil burners.

Liquid Fuels—Miscellaneous

Alcohol and gasoline are used for some heat-producing appliances and equipment to a limited extent. Alcohol stoves and torches, and gasoline torches are examples. NFPA No. 393, Recommended Good Practice for the Construction, Maintenance and Use of Gasoline Blow Torches and Plumbers' Furnaces, should be referred to for guidance on handling these fuels. The NFPA Flammable and Combustible Liquids Code gives additional basic data on the safe storage practices for these liquids.

Gas Fuels

Generally, gas-fired heat-producing devices and equipment use natural gas, liquefied petroleum gas, liquefied petroleum gas-air mixture, or mixtures of these gases. Natural gas is the most commonly used gas fuel in the United States, especially since gas transmission pipeline systems have been extended to supply most areas of the country. There also has been in recent years a tremendous growth in the use of liquefied petroleum gas-fired heating devices, particularly in sparsely settled areas of the United States and Canada. A number of other flammable gases are used as fuel in many industrial processes for special purposes.

Natural gas consists principally of methane and some ethane, propane, butane, and small amounts of carbon dioxide and nitrogen. Fuel gases can be made in a variety of ways from coal, or by the "cracking" of oils. It goes through cooling, scrubbing, and purifying processes prior to distribution. Liquefied petroleum gases are largely propane, propylene, butane and butylene, or mixtures of these gases. Details on the fire hazard properties of these gases will be found in Section 3, Chapter 4.

Typical calorific values of various gases as fuel are given in Table 3-4B. Various procedures for sampling, analysing, measuring, and testing gaseous fuels are outlined in thirteen ASTM Standards which have been compiled in one publication, ASTM Standards on Gaseous Fuels.[1]

Methods of Firing Fuel Gases

Air is mixed with gas at the burner of a gas-fired heating device, or they are premixed. To accomplish effective mixing under different conditions, a wide variety of types and sizes of burners are used. Every burner is designed to transform the potential energy of the fuel gas into useful heat which can be absorbed in the most effective manner.

Injection (Bunsen) Type Burners: Practically all residential type and commercial gas appliances and some industrial gas-fired appliances use injection type gas burners. This type of burner employs the energy of a jet of gas to inject primary air for combustion into the burner and mix it with the gas. This mixing occurs before the gas reaches the burner ports or point of ignition. Figure 7-3J shows a typical injection type gas burner.

Nonaerated Burners: In the nonaerated or luminous flame burner only air externally supplied at the point of combustion is depended on for the burning of the gas; the flame produced is without any premixing of air with the gas.

Catalytic Burners: Another type burner is the catalytic burner that permits combustion of the gas at temperatures well below the normal ignition temperature of fuel gas-air mixtures.

Power Burners: In a power burner, either gas or air or both are supplied at pressures exceeding the line pressure of the gas and atmospheric pressure for the air. The added pressure is applied at the burner. A burner for which air for combustion is supplied by a fan ahead of the appliance is commonly designated as a forced draft burner. A premixing burner is a power burner in which all or nearly all of the air for combustion is mixed with the gas as primary air (air which mixes with the gas before it reaches the burner port or ports). A pressure burner is supplied with an air-gas mixture under pressure (usually from 0.5 to 14 in. of water and occasionally higher).

Figure 7-3K illustrates some of the types of industrial appliance gas burners.

Changing from one kind of gas to another may cause serious problems unless the appliance is designed for such change. Appliance designs certified by the American Gas Association Laboratories are tested for satisfactory performance with one or more gases as requested by the manu-

facturer. These include natural, manufactured, and mixed gases, as well as liquefied petroleum gas and LP-Gas-air mixtures. The specific gas or gases with which an appliance may be used is marked on the appliance. Such appliances may be converted in the field to any one of the marked gases, but such conversion may require some interchange of parts and may involve some element of hazard unless carefully done by experienced, qualified personnel.

Gas mixing systems (see Fig. 7-3L), consisting of apparatus for premixing gas and air used in industrial burners, are installed only in well-lighted and adequately ventilated sections of buildings where they are readily accessible for repairs, and where no spark-producing equipment or other sources of ignition are in the vicinity. A gas mixer presents appreciable hazard because it delivers a gas-air mixture within the explosive range. Provisions are made for venting explosions because of the possibility of the ignition of an explosive gas-air mixture in the apparatus. Flashback arresters approved for the gas are provided between the piping system and the mixing apparatus and at the burners.

Appliance and Piping Installation

Installation, alteration, and repair of gas appliances and gas piping should be done only by men fully experienced in this work. Provisions outlined in NFPA No. 54, National Fuel Gas Code, provide necessary guidance. Gas should be turned on only after the system has been thoroughly tested

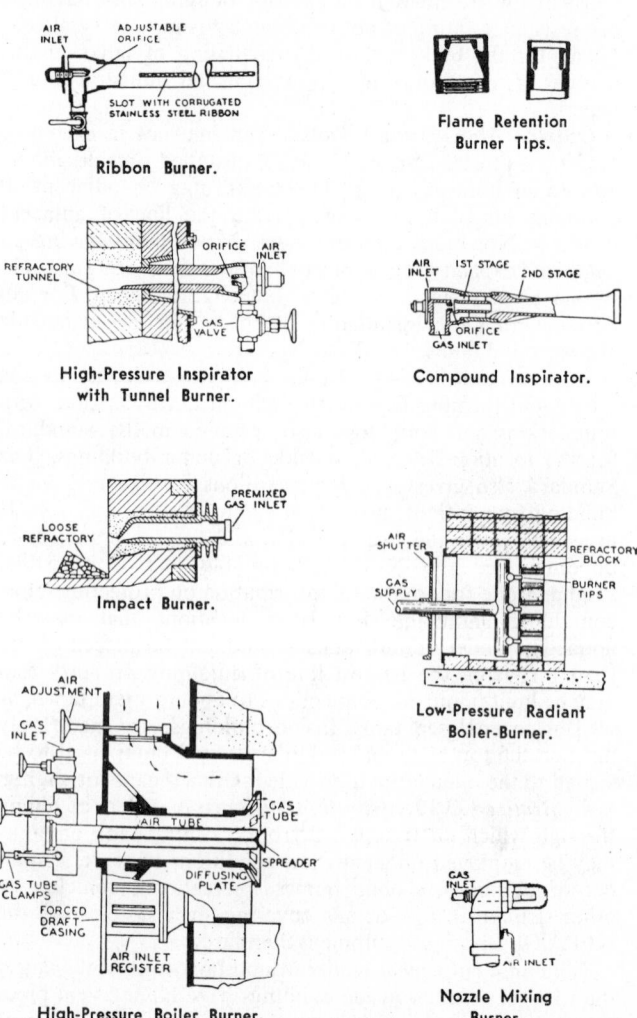

Fig. 7-3K.　Types of industrial appliance gas burners.

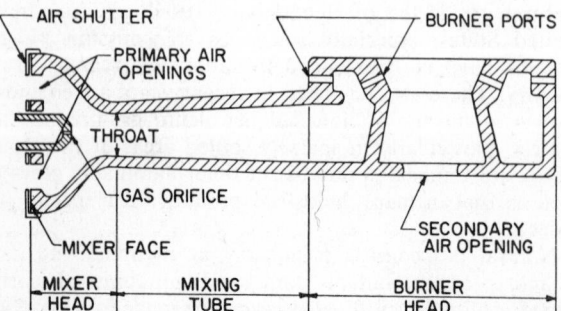

Fig. 7-3J.　A schematic view of a typical injection type burner.

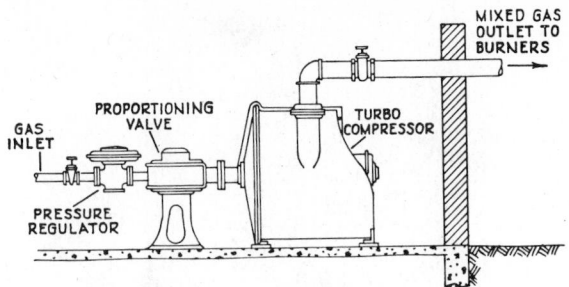

Fig. 7-3L. High-pressure gas mixer with turbo compressor.

to be certain there is no leakage. Any air remaining in piping is a hazard because a "slug" of air reaching a burner will extinguish the flame, and when gas again flows, unburned gas will escape and possibly form an asphyxiating or explosive atmosphere.

The uncontrolled flow of unburned gas into any gas appliance could form an explosive gas-air mixture. Safeguards to prevent this are of major importance, particularly in industrial and other large gas burning devices. Without safeguards, unburned gas may flow to accumulate in fire boxes or ovens at the time of lighting, or when the gas pressure fluctuates. If the pressure is reduced below a certain point, the flame may be extinguished, and with a subsequent return of normal pressure unburned gas might continue to flow. An increase in pressure may increase the velocity through the burner to a rate in excess of that of flame propagation, so that the flame will be forced away from the burner. A number of automatic devices are available to safeguard against this hazard, and are commonly found on the larger installations.

Storage of LP-Gas at Consumer Sites

Details on the storage of LP-Gas at locations where liquefied petroleum gas-fired heat-producing devices and equipment are in service are covered in Section 3, Chapter 4.

Controls for Fuel Burners

The uncontrolled flow of unburned fuel into appliances and other fuel fired equipment can lead to serious consequences. In the case of firing with pulverized coal, gas, or oil, a combustible mixture could accumulate within the confines of the appliance or equipment. If ignited it could result in an explosion. To guard against the discharge of unburned fuel or improper mixtures of fuel and air, certain controls are required for all fuel burners.

Primary Safety Controls: These controls are necessary to cause the fuel to be shut off in the event of ignition failure or unintentional flame extinguishment. Except for pot and sleeve type vaporizing burners, shutoff is accomplished by means of a primary safety control, or in the case of gas appliances having inputs of 400,000 Btu per hr or less, an automatic gas ignition device. Both of these types of controls sense the presence or absence of flame and cause the fuel to be shut off in the prescribed period of time upon ignition or flame failure. All fuel to the burner should be shut off, an exception is that in the case of gas appliances for use only with natural or manufactured gas or a mixture of the two and having inputs not over 400,000 Btu per hr, the fuel to the pilot burner is not required to be shut off. These controls usually include provision for starting, initiating, and timing automatic ignition systems, if provided, and stopping operation of the burner in response to changes in demand (room thermostat, process controller, etc.). Controls for commercial and industrial burners may provide for

a purge period during which time a flow of air through the appliance is established for an interval prior to initiating fuel flow. Furthermore the control does not permit main burner fuel to be admitted until the control has proved the existence of the ignition flame.

The discharge of unburned oil from pot and sleeve type vaporizing burners is prevented by a constant level value or by barometric feed, each of which maintains a predetermined level of oil in the burner below any point of overflow. See the NFPA Oil Burning Equipment Standard for an explanation of barometric feed.

Air-fuel Interlocks: If safe operation of a burner is dependent on forced or induced draft fan or air compressor for supplying combustion air, an interlock is needed to shut off fuel in case of air supply interruption.

Atomizer-fuel Interlock: In an oil burning system where air, steam, or other means for atomization can be interrupted without stopping oil delivery to the burner, an interlock should be provided to immediately shut off the oil upon failure of the atomizing means.

Pressure Regulation and Interlocks: Gas burners and pressure type oil burners require uniform fuel pressure to burn the fuel safely and efficiently. Pressure regulators are employed to maintain uniform fuel pressures. In situations where fuel pressure fluctuations may be expected, pressure interlocks are provided which shut off the fuel to the main burners if the pressure is too low or too high for safe operation.

Oil Temperature Interlock: Oil burners requiring heated oil for satisfactory operation are equipped with a low oil temperature switch which prevents the burner from starting or shuts down the burner if the oil temperature falls below the required minimum.

Manual Restart: The control system of a burner not equipped to provide safe automatic restarting after shutdown should be arranged to require manual restarting after any control function to extinguish the burner flame.

Remote Shutoff: Providing a method for manually stopping the flow of fuel at a location remote from the burner is good practice. With electrically powered equipment this may be accomplished by an identified switch in the burner supply circuit, placed near the entrance to the room where the burner is located. A valve in the fuel supply line operable from a location reached without passing near the burner may also be used.

Safety Shutoff Valves: Safety shutoff valves are to prevent the abnormal discharge of fuel. They should be constructed so that they cannot be readily restrained or blocked in the open position. Such valves should close upon being de-energized regardless of the position of any damper operating lever or reset handle. Electrically-operated valves should not depend upon being energized to close and pressure-operated valves should close upon failure of the operating pressure.

Safety Control Circuits: Safety control ac circuits are of the two-wire type with one side grounded, not exceeding nominal 120 V and be protected with suitable fuses or circuit breakers. All switches should be in the "hot" ungrounded line. With such a circuit accidental grounding of the circuit will not cause a required safety control to be bypassed.

Appliances and equipment fired with fuel burners require some additional controls to avoid excessive pressure, temperature, or other abnormal conditions. Such controls are covered in Part B of this Chapter.

Appliances listed by nationally recognized testing agencies are equipped with all the required safety controls. The application of controls to fuel burning systems assembled in the field or intended for specific applications should be entrusted only to people specializing in this work. The standards pertaining to fuel-burning equipment referenced in the bibliography at the end of this chapter include specific information on controls which are essential to safe operation of the fuel-burning equipment.

Safety controls are generally preset by the manufacturer or the installer. Any alteration of these settings or bypassing any safety control could lead to serious consequences. When replacing a faulty control a like model and setting are advisable.

Electricity

The generation of heat with electricity involves two basic electrical properties: resistance and induction. The methods by which heat is developed utilizing these properties and an electrical current are discussed in Section 2, Chapter 1.

Units of Electrical Heat: Heating calculations for electrical heating are expressed in kilowatt power requirements. One kwh equals 56.9 Btu per min.

Controls: Automatic regulation of the electrical input (usually through proportional-type step controllers) allows heaters to be energized and deenergized in increments small enough to prevent excessive total operation of all heaters whenever temperature drops.

Method of Installation: The installation of all electric heating systems should be made in accordance with the recommendations of NFPA No. 70, the National Electrical Code. (See also Sec. 7, Chap. 2 of this HANDBOOK.)

Types of Electrical Heating Appliances

Most electrical heating appliances for heating small rooms and for other small heating jobs involve resistor heating elements which are usually one or more metal-alloy wires, nonmetallic carbon rods, or printed circuits. Resistor heating is used in radiators, unit heaters, convectors, central hot water systems, central warm air heating systems, and panel-type radiant heat installations for walls, floors, and ceilings. Resistor heating also is used for household electrical appliances, such as stoves, irons, toasters, etc.

For industrial ovens and furnaces, see Section 4, Chapter 5 of this HANDBOOK.

Fig. 7-3N. *A low-pressure gas-fired steam boiler.* (Bryant Mfg. Co.)

B.   Heating Appliances and Their Application

Central heating appliances, room heating and cooking appliances, and miscellaneous heat-producing devices, fired by the various fuels and methods discussed in Part A of this chapter are described in the following pages. Industrial heat producing equipment is described in Section 4.

Central Heating Appliances

Boilers: These are either of the steam or hot water types and are constructed of cast iron or steel. The ASME Boiler and Pressure Vessel Code defines low pressure boilers (for low pressure steam heating, hot water heating, and hot water supply) as those steam boilers that operate at pressures not exceeding 15 psi, and hot water boilers as boilers that operate at pressures not exceeding 160 psi and temperatures not exceeding 250°F.[2] The ASME Boiler Code also covers the construction of power boilers, locomotive boilers, and miniature boilers.

Boilers are equipped with safety devices to prevent overpressure conditions. Automatically fired boilers also have controls that will shut off the burner or electric heating elements under low-water conditions and when a predetermined pressure or temperature has been reached.

The fire problems of boilers involve their mountings and clearances to combustibles. Explosions due to unburned fuel accumulations in the firebox or due to over-pressure conditions could rupture fuel lines thus contributing to the potential for subsequent fire or explosion damage.

Warm Air Furnaces: The residential types currently installed in the United States are usually equipped with circulating fans, filters, and other features which make them in effect air conditioning systems (see Chap. 4 of this Section).

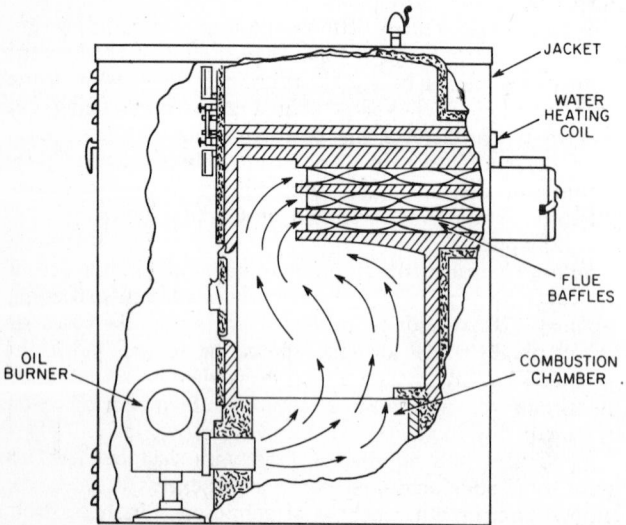

Fig. 7-3M. *An oil-fired steam boiler.* (National Oil Fuel Institute, Inc.)

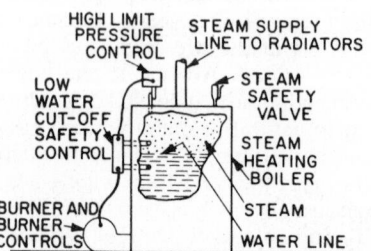

Fig. 7-3O. *Essential features of steam boilers.* (National Oil Fuel Institute, Inc.)

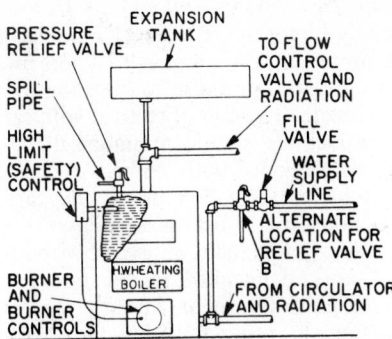

Fig. 7-3P. *Essential features of hot water boilers.* (National Oil Fuel Institute, Inc.)

Central Warm Air Furnaces are of the following types:

1. Gravity—depends primarily on circulation of air by gravity.

2. Gravity with integral fan—fan is an integral part of the furnace construction and is used to overcome internal resistance to air flow.

3. Gravity with booster fan—fan does not restrict flow of air by gravity when fan is not operating.

4. Forced air—equipped with fan which provides the primary means of circulating air (see Fig 7-3Q).

Forced air type central warm air furnaces may be classified according to the direction of air flow through them as horizontal, upflow, or downflow.

Gravity furnaces are floor mounted and can heat only spaces above them, whereas forced air furnaces may be floor mounted or suspended and may be found on most any floor of a building, including the attic and roof.

Automatic controls, called high limit controls, which cannot be set above prescribed temperature limits, shut off the fuel or electric supply whenever the air in the furnace warm air plenum, or at the beginning of the main supply duct—at a point not affected by radiated heat—reaches 250°F or less, depending on the type of furnace and its installation. Some furnaces used only with special duct systems are factory equipped to permit temperatures above 250°F at the inlet of the supply ducts.

With downflow furnaces and in some cases with horizontal furnaces there is a possibility that upon fan failure, reverse air flow will occur. This may be prevented by the installation of a secondary limit control in the return air plenum.

In automatically operated forced air type furnaces, a fan control energizes the fan motor at plenum temperatures between 90°F and 130°F, and stops the fan at about 15°F below the cut-in point. The fan control and high limit con-

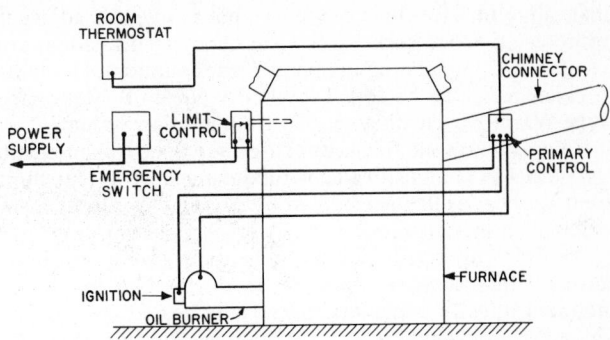

Fig. 7-3R. *Control wiring schematic, oil-fired gravity warm air furnace. (Certain primary controls are mounted on the burner assembly.)* (National Oil Fuel Institute, Inc.)

trol are sometimes combined in a single unit. With automatic coal stoker firing, a room thermostat, once it is satisfied, will shut down the stoker and fan, but temperatures could continue to build up. Therefore, furnaces equipped with automatic stokers require an over-run control to start the fan when a specified temperature is exceeded. A manual disconnect switch, if installed, should shut down the fan and stoker simultaneously. The object of these requirements is to keep temperatures reasonable in the supply ducts and consistent with the type of installation made.

On thermostatically controlled warm air, hand-fired solid-fuel burning furnaces, limit controls include: (1) a barometric draft control to limit the draft to a maximum of 0.13 in. of water or the maximum prescribed by the manufacturer, whichever is lower, and (2) an automatic damper regulator connected to the limit control (maximum setting 250°F), which will operate the check damper and the ash pit damper. This regulator will automatically check the furnace in case of a power failure or when the limit temperature has been reached, whether or not power is available. If the furnace has a fan to circulate the air, it should be equipped with an over-run control to start the fan when a specified temperature has been reached.

Furnaces supplying heated air to under-floor crawl spaces used as plenums should have limit controls that cannot be set higher than 150°F to start the air circulating fan whenever the temperature in the bonnet reaches that amount.

Many furnaces are factory-equipped with the required controls. If the controls are furnished separately, the furnace and control manufacturers' instructions are the guides to installation.

Under some conditions of operation, plenums of warm

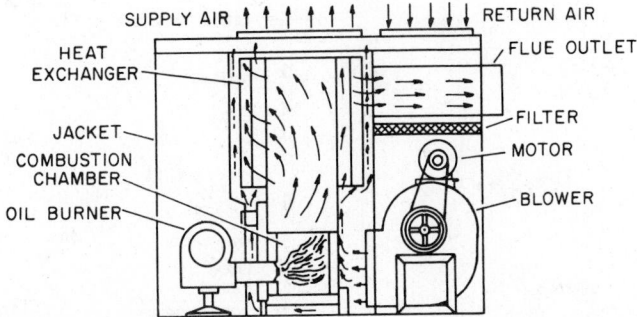

Fig. 7-3Q. *An oil-fired forced air furnace.* (National Oil Fuel Institute, Inc.)

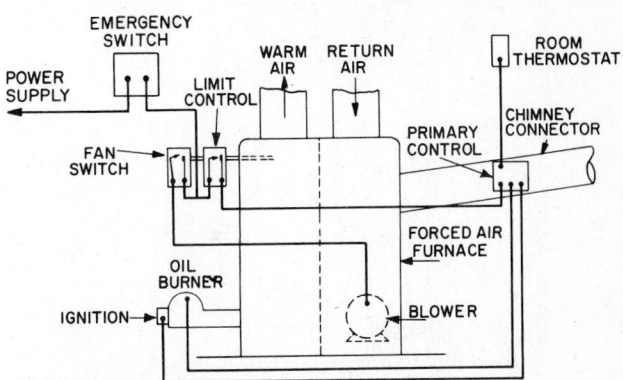

Fig. 7-3S. *Control wiring schematic, oil-fired forced warm air furnace. (Certain primary controls are mounted on the burner assembly.)* (National Oil Fuel Institute, Inc.)

air heating furnaces may become so hot as to ignite adjacent unprotected woodwork; thus clearances or insulation are necessary. Complete requirements for installation of systems in residences may be found in NFPA No. 90B, Residence Type Warm Air Heating and Air Conditioning Systems.

Central warm air furnaces cause fires due to inadequate clearances to combustible construction, lack of proper limit controls, heat exchanger burned out, and other causes associated with lack of servicing and maintenance.

Pipeless Furnaces: These are essentially gravity warm air furnaces that are not connected to ducts. The furnace is mounted directly under the space to be heated, and all the air heated in its outer jacket is discharged through a register above the heat exchanger. Some types obtain the air to be heated from another jacket around the discharge register; others take cold air through openings in the bottom of the outer furnace jacket. These furnaces are used for heating small homes, small one-story mercantile properties, and similar structures.

Pipeless furnaces may produce dangerously high temperatures, particularly if the air circulation is restricted; for example, if the register in the floor of a small hallway heats adjoining rooms by air circulating through opened doors, the temperature of the entire hall may be raised to a dangerous degree if the doors are closed tightly at a time when the furnace is in full operation. Fires also have occurred through the ignition of clothing left to dry above a central floor register.

It is good practice to equip automatically-fired pipeless furnaces with limit controls.

Floor Furnaces: Both oil and gas fired, are principally designed so they may be installed in combustible floors (see Fig. 7-3T). They should not be installed in combustible floors, however, unless they have been listed for such use by one of the nationally recognized testing laboratories.

Temperature limit controls are provided on floor furnaces to shut off the fuel supply when the temperature of the discharged air reaches a predetermined level.

The NFPA Fuel Burning Equipment Standard and NFPA No. 54, National Fuel Gas Code, give detailed installation recommendations for floor furnaces. The provisions in each Standard are generally similar in content with respect to placement, bracing, support, clearance, and accessibility of the furnaces. Part D of this chapter discusses clearances in greater detail.

Accessibility for installation, maintenance, and inspection is especially important. Clearances should be sufficient, not only for protection of combustible floors and walls (see Part D of this chapter), but also to keep the furnace casing and piping connected to it out of contact with earth or damp materials. The location should minimize the possibility of the furnace being flooded with water. All these conditions are often difficult to meet, but unless they are met, floor furnaces may constitute a fire hazard.

In auditoriums, public halls, or assembly rooms, floor furnaces should not be installed in the floor of any aisle, passageway, or exitway. Floor furnace registers may become hot enough to cause burns under some conditions; thus in dwellings registers should not be located in passageways to bathrooms where persons would be likely to step with bare feet. Users should be warned against covering registers or placing clothing on them to dry.

Wall Furnaces: These are self-contained indirect-fired gas or oil heaters installed in or on a wall. They supply heated air directly to the space to be heated, either by gravity or by a fan through grilles on openings or boots in the casing supplied by the manufacturer. The furnaces may be of the direct vent type or are vent- or chimney-connected depending on the fuel.

Standards for gas and oil appliance installations respectively, give details for proper location and mounting of these devices, and Part D of this chapter discusses clearances in greater detail.

Limit controls on wall furnaces limit outlet air temperature. Furnaces equipped with a fan but not with limit controls are tested for maximum temperatures developed with the fan stopped and the filters, if any, blocked to air passage.

The fire problems with recessed wall furnaces are similar to those encountered with any warm air furnace, except floor furnaces, which have fire problems peculiar to themselves. Wall furnace installations are shown in Figures 7-3U and 7-3V.

Duct Furnaces: These furnaces are installed directly in ducts of some warm air and air conditioning systems and depend on air circulation from a blower not furnished as a part of the furnace. They may be oil- or gas-fired, or electrical, and are equipped with a limit control to shut off the fuel supply at excessive temperatures.

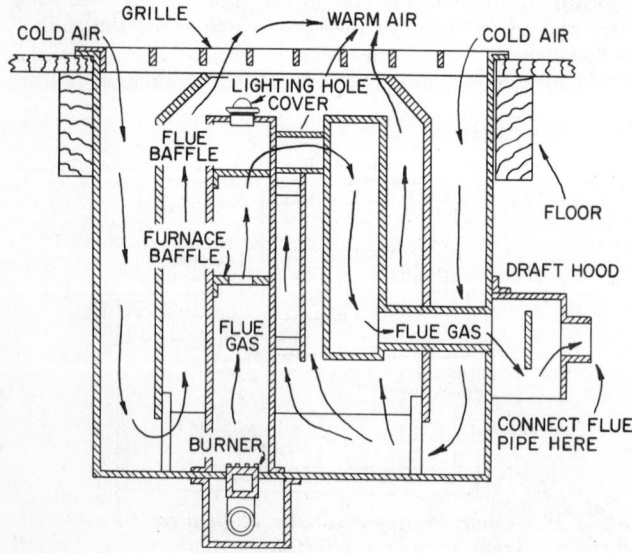

Fig. 7-3T. A typical floor furnace. (John Zinc Burner Co.)

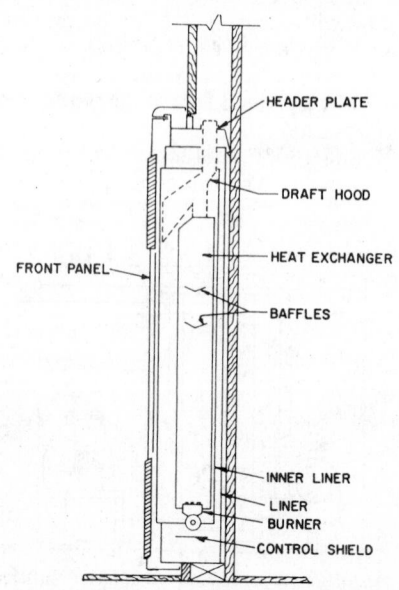

Fig. 7-3U. Typical gas-fired wall furnace.

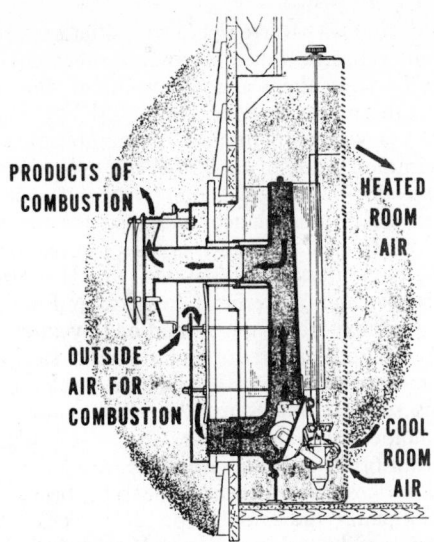

Fig. 7-3V. Gas-fired wall furnace with sealed combustion chamber for installation in an exterior wall. Air for combustion is taken directly from the outside. (Stewart-Warner Corp.)

When duct furnaces are used in conjunction with refrigeration coils in a combined heating and cooling system, the furnace should be located upstream from the refrigeration coil or parallel with it. This is to prevent condensation from corroding the furnace. There are, however, furnaces made of corrosion resistant material which may be installed downstream from the refrigeration coil. When the furnace is located upstream from the refrigeration coil, the coil should be designed so that excessive pressures and temperatures will not develop in the coil.

Further information on recommendations for installation of duct furnaces can be found in NFPA No. 31 (oil-fired devices), NFPA No. 54 (gas-fired devices), NFPA No. 90A (air conditioning and ventilating systems), and NFPA No. 90B (residence-type warm air and air conditioning systems). A duct furnace installation is shown in Figure 7-3W.

Warm Air Heating Panels: These are used in low temperature systems to circulate warm air through plenums or chambers which have one or more surfaces exposed to the space to be heated. NFPA No. 90B gives recommendations for the use, construction, and installation of these panels.

Radiant Heating: This is a type of heating utilizing panels of hot water piping or electric heating elements which usually operate at moderate temperatures. The panels are embedded in plaster walls or ceilings, or in cement floors. Hot water or electrical equipment in radiant systems should conform to standard installation practices as do other types of heating. The NEC contains specific recommendations on the installation of electrical space heating equipment.

Heat Pump: This is a term applied to a type of heating system in which refrigeration equipment is used in such a manner that heat is taken from a heat source and given up to the conditioned space when heat service is wanted, and is removed from the space and discharged to a heat sink when cooling and dehumidification are desired. These systems frequently have supplemental heating units, and in such cases the units are equipped with an interlock to prevent the unit from operating unless the indoor air circulating fan on the system is running. The units also have temperature limit controls. Hazards are those that come from power and refrigeration equipment, and heat units, if the last-named are part of the system.

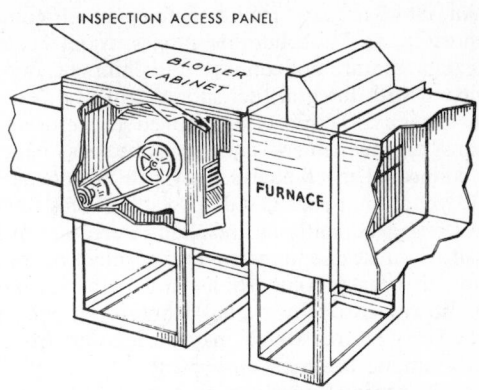

Fig. 7-3W. A duct furnace installation.

Unit Heaters: These are classed as self-contained, automatically controlled, chimney- or vent-connected air heating appliances having an integral means for circulation of air and which may be of the floor mounted or suspended type. These heaters are also equipped with temperature limit controls. As the term "unit heater" is used in NFPA Standards, it is intended to cover appliances used in heating non-residential properties; thus excluding room heaters, floor furnaces, and similar devices. More specifically, a unit heater is an appliance consisting of a combination of heating element and fan housed in a common enclosure and placed within or adjacent to the space to be heated. Unit heaters as described should not be confused with heat exchangers which are equipped with fans to circulate heated air. In the latter type, hot water or steam is piped from a heating unit to the heat exchanger in the area to be heated.

Unit heaters may be designed for connection to a duct system. When so installed, they may be considered as central heating furnaces and should be provided with the same safeguards. A typical unit heater is shown in Figure 7-3X.

Room Heating and Cooking Appliances

A room heater differs from a central heating furnace in that it is designed for direct heating of the space around it. It has no external heating pipes or ducts. Room heaters fall into two general types: circulating and radiant. A circulating heater is designed to change heat of combustion to convective heat by the circulation of air heated by contact with the heating surfaces.

A stove with openings in its outer jacket to permit direct radiation from the heating surfaces is classified as a radiant type from a safety point of view. Radiant heaters also include those types designed to transfer heat of combustion primarily by direct radiation.

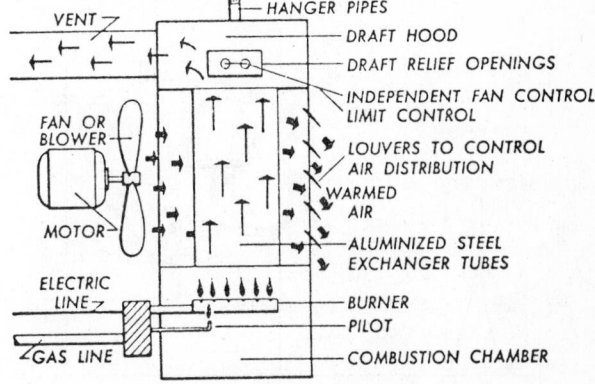

Fig. 7-3X. Typical gas-fired unit heater.

Kerosine Stoves: These may be defined as self-contained, self-supporting, kerosine burning ranges, room heaters, or water heaters that are not connected to chimneys but which are equipped with integral fuel supply tanks not exceeding 2 gal in capacity. Terms often applied to kerosine room heaters are "cabinet heaters" and "space heaters." Since they are not connected to chimneys, they can be moved rather easily but yet are not considered "portable." This feature of kerosine stoves frequently has resulted in creation of severe fire and life hazards due to improper placement of the stoves in relation to nearby combustibles and paths of exitways. Kerosine stoves listed by testing laboratories incorporate fire protection features which may be missing from those not listed. Among the more important features of "listed" stoves are the types of construction materials, primary control valves, and drip pans used in them.

Portable Kerosine Heaters: These are similar in hazard to kerosine stoves as they are not connected to a chimney, but the hazard in their use is increased by their even greater portability and subsequent misuse and misplacement. Unfortunately, the majority of portable kerosine heaters sold in the United States and Canada are not laboratory tested. Heaters that are tested incorporate fire safety features not included in others such as special types of latching devices, and integral sheet metal trays under the burners to catch oil drips. They usually employ wick-type burners integral with the oil reservoir.

Conversion Range Oil Burners: These consist essentially of a single or double sleeve-type burner assembly, regulating valves, and an oil supply assembly with a suitable supporting stand and seamless connecting tubing. A thermal valve located in the burner compartment of the stove adjacent to the burner is installed in the oil supply line (see Fig. 7-3Y).

Range oil burners, found most frequently in the northeastern section of the United States, are designed to burn kerosine, range oil, or similar fuel. They are primarily for installation only in stoves or ranges originally designed to use solid fuel. Range oil burners should not be mistaken for conversion oil burners of the vaporizing pot type designed for conversion of central heating appliances.

Coal and Wood Burning Stoves: While essentially radiant-type room heaters, these stoves warrant special attention because of their record as a fire cause, particularly in fires involving loss of life in dwellings. The poor fire record of coal and wood burning stoves may be due primarily to the fact that they are not given the constant attention they require when in operation. The necessity of frequent stoking involves much regulating of draft limiting devices to prevent overheating. Changes in outdoor conditions which affect chimney draft also can occur at times when a stove is

unattended, and an overtemperature situation from rapid burning may result. Since stoves can become red hot, clearances between them and combustibles should be kept at the maximum specified in Table 7-3F. "Freshening" a solid fuel fire with a flammable or combustible liquid is another common cause of fatal fires and explosions.

Gas-fired Room Heaters: These are self-contained gas burning air heating appliances intended for installation in the space being heated. Many types of room heaters are used, e.g., circulators, coal baskets, fireplace inserts, gas logs, radiant heaters, overhead heaters, and wall heaters. These heaters may be of the vented or unvented type. Unvented type heaters should not be installed in sleeping rooms or in rooms generally kept closed nor in any location in institutions such as homes for the aged, sanitariums, convalescent homes, orphanages, etc.

Restaurant-type Cooking Appliances: These include a variety of devices, such as ranges, deep fat fryers, steamers, broilers, hot plates and griddles, portable ovens, and others. These devices, like other heat-producing devices, require careful installation to avoid overheating of adjacent combustibles. Some of them result in accumulations of grease which adds to the fire hazard. The NFPA National Fuel Gas Code contains recommendations on the installation of gas-fired restaurant cooking appliances. Ventilation of fixed restaurant cooking equipment is covered in NFPA No. 96, Vapor Removal from Cooking Equipment (see also Chap. 5 of this section).

Miscellaneous Heat-producing Devices

There are so many miscellaneous heat-producing devices that it is unrealistic to treat each individually in this text. Certain basic principles apply to all of them, however, including provision for adequate clearances to combustibles, venting products of combustion, adequate air for combustion and ventilation, safeguarding against the hazard of the fuel by proper burner controls, proper storage and handling of the fuel, and safeguarding the heat-producing device by safety controls.

Testing laboratories tests and lists many miscellaneous types of heat-producing appliances, such as direct-fired heaters, incubators, lanterns, forges, torches, etc.

Salamanders: These are typical miscellaneous portable heating devices. They are used on construction jobs and in unheated buildings. Too frequently a salamander consists of only a metal drum with some holes punched in it for draft, and wood scrap and other construction waste materials are used in it as fuel. They present an acute spark hazard, and as they are not chimney connected, there is the hazard of carbon monoxide poisoning. Crude salamanders of this type, and gas- and oil-fired salamanders that have not been tested and listed by a nationally recognized laboratory, should not be used.

Underwriters Laboratories, Inc., and the American Gas Association Laboratories test and list portable gas- and oil-fired heaters, such as salamanders. An alternate to using salamanders is to carry heated air indoors through flexible ducts from a heating unit located outdoors. NFPA No. 58, Storage and Handling of Liquefied Petroleum Gases, has extensive material on the use of LP-Gas fired portable heaters.

Servicing Fuel-burning Appliances

When servicing or adjusting appliances, it is important to observe the manufacturer's recommended settings of blower pulleys or blower motor speed controllers and that the maxi-

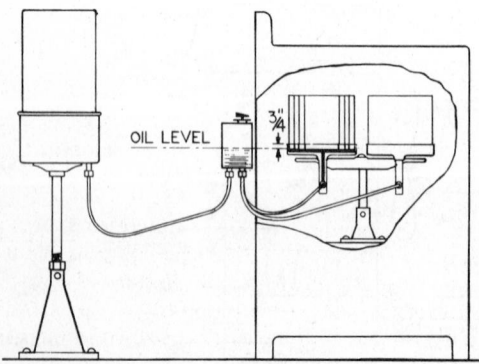

Fig. 7-3Y. Typical installation of conversion range oil burner.

mum and minimum input of the appliances not be altered by the use of burner nozzles or orific spuds other than recommended in the manufacturer's instructions.

C.   Distribution of Heat by Ducts and Pipes

Warm Air Distribution Systems

Warm Air Supply Ducts: Warm air ducts are installed with clearances as given in Table 7-3C. They are substantially constructed of metal or of Class 0 or Class 1 or 2 duct materials* and are properly supported and protected against injury. In single family residences where a listed or unlisted automatically fired forced air or gravity system equipped with a 250°F limit control, or a steam or hot water heat exchanger with steam not over 15 psi and hot water not over 250°F is used, ducts that are 3 or 6 ft beyond the bonnet, depending on whether the furnace is listed or unlisted, may be of Class 0 or Class 1 or 2 duct materials.

When ducts are encased in not less than 2 in. of concrete in a floor slab, the fire safety requirements are inherently met except that the provisions listed above apply to ducts within 2 ft of the furnace plenum or to a vertical connection to a riser or register.

Supply Air Plenums: It is common practice in some localities to use the crawl space in a basementless one-story single family house as the supply plenum for warm air heating systems. These systems utilize a downflow furnace that discharges hot air through directional ducts into the crawl space. An opening cut in the floor of each room of the house and covered with a grill serves as the supply register. The hazards of these systems include: use of combustible construction as a plenum, use of the crawl space for storage, presence of a large enclosed combustible area with no limitations of fire spread and with direct openings to every room of the house, and the possibility of reverse flow in the downflow furnace (the cold air return then becomes the supply duct). NFPA No. 90B gives specific recommendations and limitations applying to the use of under floor space as supply plenums, and it should be consulted for detailed guidance.

Vertical ducts, risers, boots, or boxes that enter floors, partitions, or enclosures constructed of combustible material require clearances to be maintained as follows:

1. When installed within 3 ft of plenums of furnaces requiring clearances for horizontal ducts within, but not over, 3 ft of the plenum as given in Table 7-3F, the clearances are the same as that above the plenum.

2. When installed within 6 ft of the plenums of furnaces requiring clearances of from 2 to 6 in. above the plenums, the clearance around ducts, risers, boots, or boxes is the same as that required above the plenum.

3. When installed within 6 ft of plenums of furnaces requiring 18 in. above the plenum, the ducts are so arranged that heated air must travel at least 6 ft from the closest primary heating surface and change direction equivalent to at least one 90° turn before entering such floor, partition or enclosure.

* NOTE: Duct materials are tested and listed by Underwriters Laboratories, Inc., in accordance with UL Standard No. 181, Air Ducts, and are classified by the Laboratories as Class 0, 1, or 2 which are defined as follows:
Class 0—Air duct materials having a fire hazard classification of zero (flame spread and smoke developed).
Class 1—Air ducts that have a flame-spread rating of not over 25 without evidence of continued progressive combustion and a smoke-developed rating of not over 50.
Class 2—Air ducts that have a flame-spread rating of not over 50 without evidence of continued progressive combustion and a smoke-developed rating of not over 50 for the inside surface material and not over 100 for the outside surface material.

Table 7-3C.   Installation Clearances for Horizontal Warm Air Ducts

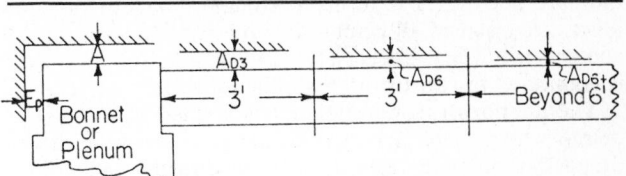

A—Clearance above top of casing, bonnet. plenum, or appliance determined by Table 7-3G.
A_{D3}—Clearance from horizontal warm air duct within 3 ft of plenum.
A_{D6}—Clearance from horizontal warm air duct between 3 and 6 ft of plenum.
A_{D6+}—Clearance from horizontal warm air duct beyond 6 ft of plenum.
E_P—Clearance from any side of bonnet or plenum.

If A Equals	A_{D3} Equals	A_{D6} Equals	A_{D6+} Equals	E_P Equals	Method of Firing
1	1	0	0	1	Automatic oil, comb. gas-oil, or gas
2	2	0	0	2	Automatic oil, comb. gas-oil, or gas
6	6	6	0	6	Automatic oil, comb. gas-oil, or gas
6	6	6	1*	6	Automatic stoker fired†
18	18	6	1	18	Any fuel or control.

* Clearance A_{D6+} to be maintained to a point where there is a change in direction equivalent to 90 degrees or more.
† Furnace must be equipped with limit control that cannot be set higher than 250°F and must also have a barometric draft control operated by draft intensity and permanently set to limit draft to a maximum intensity of 0.13 in. water gage, otherwise clearances should be as indicated for any fuel.

The requirements of paragraphs (1) and (2) above may be waived if the duct changes direction equivalent to at least two 90° turns before entering the floor partition or enclosure.

In systems requiring 18 in. above the plenum, the ducts, risers, boots, and boxes must have $\frac{3}{16}$-in. clearance where they pierce combustible floors or be of double wall construction with a $\frac{3}{16}$-in. air space. This requirement also applies to vertical ducts and risers of these systems in walls, partitions, or other combustible concealed space, unless the ducts or risers are covered with a cellular-type noncombustible insulation at least $\frac{1}{8}$ in. thick.

Registers: To prevent development of excessive heat in the duct system, one register or grill must be installed without a shutter and without a damper in the duct to it, except in the case of automatic oil- or gas-fired systems with approved temperature limit controls or systems in which case dampers and shutters are so designed that they cannot shut off more than 80 percent of the duct area.

Where registers are installed in the floor over the furnace, as in pipeless furnaces or floor furnaces, the register box is constructed with a double wall with an air space of not less than 4 in. between walls. Furnaces with a cold air passage around the warm air passage comply with this requirement.

Return Air Ducts and Plenums: Return air is best conducted to the furnaces and duct heaters through continuous ducts. Return ducts need not be of the same materials as supply ducts except those portions directly over the heating surface or within 2 ft of the outer casing or jacket of the furnace or duct heater. However, they are not made of materials more combustible than 1-in. (nominal) wood boards. Under floor spaces may be used for return ducts from rooms directly above, but such spaces are used only if they are not over 2 ft in depth from the bottom of floor joists, are clean of all combustible material and are tightly and substantially enclosed. No vertical stack for return air is connected to registers in more than one floor.

The interior of combustible ducts is lined with metal at points where there is danger from incandescent particles dropped through a register, such as directly under floor registers and at the bottom of vertical ducts.

Air Filters: Air filters are of a type which will not burn freely or emit large volumes of smoke or other objectionable products of combustion. Only liquid adhesive coatings with a flash point of 350°F or higher (Cleveland open cup tester) are acceptable. Filters are not installed in ducts of heating systems unless the system design calls for such installation. Otherwise the filters may restrict the flow of air and cause dangerous overheating.

Heating Panels: The NFPA Warm Air Heating and Air Conditioning Standard recommends that heating panels be used only with automatically fired gas or oil burning or electric forced warm air systems or systems equipped with steam or hot water heat exchangers.

Panels used with automatically fired forced warm air systems are of noncombustible material or at least of material with a flame spread rating of not over 20.

Where the warm air supply is from a steam or hot water heat exchanger, the panels may be made of material not more flammable than 1-in. (nominal) wood boards. No one panel should serve more than one story of a multistoried building.

Steam and Hot Water Pipes

The temperature of steam varies with the pressure. For example, at atmospheric pressure the temperature of steam is 212°F, while at 25 psig its temperature is 267°F. Other values of temperature of saturated steam at various pressures are given in Table 7-3D.

Water at high temperature and pressure is also used for heating and for hot water systems. In such systems, the system pressure must always exceed the pressure at the saturation temperature to prevent the water from flashing to steam. This means that the pressure in high temperature hot water systems must exceed the values shown in Table 7-3D at the specific temperature at which the system

Table 7-3D.   Temperature of Saturated Steam

Gage Pressure psi*	Temperature °F	Gage Pressure psi	Temperature °F
0	212.0	35	280.6
1	215.4	40	286.7
2	218.5	45	292.3
3	221.5	50	297.7
4	224.4	75	320.0
5	227.1	100	337.8
6	229.6	125	352.9
7	232.3	150	365.9
8	234.7	200	387.9
9	237.0	300	421.7
10	239.4	400	448.2
11	241.5	500	470.1
12	243.7	600	488.8
13	245.8	700	505.6
14	247.8	800	520.3
15	249.8	900	534.0
20	258.8	1000	546.4
25	266.7	1500	597.6
30	274.1	2000	636.8
		3211	706.1†

* Zero gage pressure corresponds to an absolute pressure of 14.696 psi.

† Critical point, from Keenan's Tables.

Note: Superheated steam has a higher temperature than saturated steam at the same pressure, depending upon the degree of superheat.

operates. Most systems operate at temperatures between 250° and 430°F.

A steam pipe or pipe carrying water at 212°F or above may in the course of time produce charcoal from any wood in contact with it (see Sec. 3, Chap 1). Charcoal is subject to spontaneous heating (see Sec. 3, Chap 5).

Recommended clearances for steam and hot water pipes and radiators are given in Table 7-3E.

Radiators and pipes should not be used as racks for drying purposes. Where radiators are placed in window recesses or concealed spaces, such spaces should be lined with noncombustible material, have ample air circulation, and be kept clean.

D.   Installation of Heating Appliances

Any source of heat is a potential fire hazard unless it is arranged to prevent the possibility of dangerous temperatures developing in adjacent combustible materials. Because of the possibility that wood and certain other combustible materials may ignite at temperatures far below their usual ignition temperatures after long and continued exposure to

Table 7-3E.   Installation Clearances for Steam and Hot-Water Pipes and Radiators

Description	Clearances
A. Hot-water pipes and radiators supplied by automatically fired gas, gas-oil, or oil burning boilers equipped with limit control that cannot be set to permit a water temperature above 150°F.	None
B. Hot-water and steam pipes and radiators supplied with hot water at not more than 250°F, except as permitted in A above, and with steam at not over 15 psig.	1 Inch*
C. Steam pipes carrying steam at pressures above 15 but not over 500 psig.	6 Inch

* At points where pipes emerge from a floor, wall or ceiling, the clearance at the opening through the finish floor boards or wall or ceiling boards may be not less than ½ in. Each such opening shall be covered with a plate of noncombustible material.

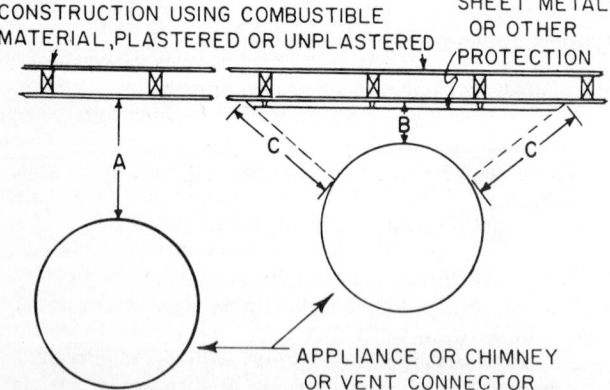

CONSTRUCTION USING COMBUSTIBLE MATERIAL, PLASTERED OR UNPLASTERED

SHEET METAL OR OTHER PROTECTION

APPLIANCE OR CHIMNEY OR VENT CONNECTOR

*Fig. 7-3Z. Extent of protection required to reduce clearances. **A** equals the required clearance with no protection, specified in Table 7-3G. **B** equals the reduced clearance permitted in accordance with Table 7-3F. The protection applied to the construction using combustible material shall extend far enough in each direction to make **C** equal to **A**.*

relatively moderate heat, and to provide a factor of safety, it is good practice to install heat-producing appliances in such a manner that under conditions of maximum heat (long and continued exposure), the temperature of exposed combustibles will not exceed dangerous limits (see Sec. 3, Chap. 1). This is done by providing clearance between the appliance and combustibles. Adequate clearances for various types of heat-producing devices to prevent exceeding this maximum temperature in exposed combustibles have been determined by testing laboratories and through field experience. Table 7-3F gives recommended clearances, including a reasonable factor of safety, around and above residential, commercial, and industrial heat-producing appliances. The term "listed appliance" which appears in the paragraph under the title of Table 7-3F, refers to appliances that have been tested by laboratories, and the proper clearances for them, as determined by tests, are published in a listing. The recommended clearances are also indicated either on the appliance or in the manufacturer's installation manual included with the appliance.

Recognized laboratories that test, and list, appliances and related equipment are the Factory Mutual Engineering Corporation, Underwriters Laboratories, Inc., Underwriters Laboratories of Canada, and American Gas Association Laboratories.

Modifications of Clearances: The clearances given in Table 7-3F are intended to provide reasonable protection for exposed surfaces, assumed to be of considerable area, against assumed conditions of continuous operation of heat-producing appliances at maximum temperatures. The specified clearances therefore have some factor of safety. There are in existence hundreds of thousands of installations where the clearances are less than specified without fires having occurred. Careful operation of the devices in many such cases has limited temperatures to below the maximum. Yet every year there are thousands of heating plant fires when cold weather forces long operation at maximum temperatures. An important contributing factor is probably the thorough drying out of exposed wood under such circumstances.

The clearances specified for locations where a connector goes through a combustible partition are roughly 2½ times the diameter of the connector.

It is not sufficient to install heating appliances so that during their normal operation adjacent combustible materials will not be exposed to dangerous temperatures; clearances and protection should be designed for safety when the heating device is operated at the maximum temperature of which it is capable. Some provision for ventilation or air circulation or other method of cooling is necessary to dissipate heat.

In large rooms a suitable clearance between a heating appliance and combustible material is all that is necessary to prevent ignition. In small rooms or poorly ventilated spaces, particularly where the size of the heating device is large in proportion to the room, dangerous temperatures may be built up no matter how great the clearance unless some provision is made for cooling by air circulation. It is not good practice to put appliances in confined spaces, such as alcoves or closets, unless they have been designed and tested for that type of service. The clearances specified for them are observed regardless of whether the enclosing walls are combustible or noncombustible.

Table 7-3G together with Figure 7-3AA shows methods by which clearances may be reduced by the installation of protection between the heat-producing device and combustible material. This information has particular value in correcting existing situations of inadequate clearance where it would be impractical to move the heat-producing appliance.

Limitations of Insulation

Insulating material is often appropriate protection if used with a proper understanding of its limitations. The insulation may be used on the heating appliance or on the exposed surfaces of walls or combustible material, but its value under such circumstances should be determined by tests.

Many heat-producing appliances have built-in insulation which makes it safe to reduce the clearances to combustible material that would otherwise be required.

Insulation alone is not sufficient, however, for no matter how thick the insulation, long continued heat may eventually penetrate it unless the heat is in some manner conducted away before it reaches the combustible material which the insulation is designed to protect. (See discussion of heat transfer, Sec. 2, Chap. 1.)

Long continued temperatures cause many fires under apparently safe conditions. Figure 7-3AA shows specific cases of fires caused under conditions which the layman, at least, would consider safe. Solid masses of brick or concrete or plaster finish may be as bad as no protection at all. Safety lies either in entirely noncombustible surroundings, or in so placing and supporting heat-producing devices that ample ventilation is secured.

Metal or Insulating Sheet Material As Wall Surface Protection: If the air space between heating appliances and combustible material is necessarily small, a barrier of metal or heat retardant material should be installed in such a manner as to leave air space between it and the heat radiating surface on one side and between it and the combustible material on the other (see Table 7-3G). The air currents set up by this means will prevent the combustible material from attaining a dangerous temperature with a lesser clearance than otherwise necessary.

Metal sheets tend also to distribute the heat, preventing in some measure its building up at one location.

Mountings

The limitations of masonry, concrete, metal, and other materials as insulating mediums apply particularly to the under side of stoves, heaters, boilers, furnaces, and other similar heat-producing appliances. Table 7-3H gives a list of various mountings for various classes of heat-producing appliances.

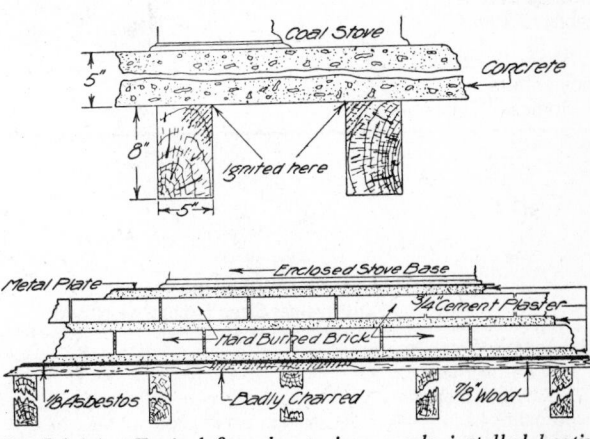

Fig. 7-3AA. Typical fires due to improperly installed heating appliances.

BUILDING SERVICES

Table 7-3F. Standard Installation Clearances, Inches, for Heat-Producing Appliances
(See Note 1.)

These clearances apply unless otherwise shown on listed appliances. Appliances should not be installed in alcoves or closets unless so listed. For installation on combustible floors, see Note 2.

Residential Type Appliances For Installation In Rooms Which Are Large (See Note 3)		Above Top of Casing or Appliance	From Top and Sides of Warm-Air Bonnet or Plenum	From Front See Note 4	From Back	From Sides
Boilers and Water Heaters						
Steam Boilers—15 psi	Automatic Oil or	} 6	—	24	6	6
Water Boilers—250°F	Comb. Gas-Oil					
Water Heaters—200°F	Automatic Gas	6	—	18	6	6
All Water Walled or Jacketed	Solid	6	—	48	6	6
	Electric	6	—	18	6	6
Furnaces—Central						
Gravity, Upflow, Downflow, Horizontal	Automatic Oil or	} 6^5	6^5	24	6	6
and Duct. Warm-Air—250°F Max.	Comb. Gas-Oil					
	Automatic Gas	6^5	6^5	18	6	6
	Solid	18^6	18^6	48	18	18
	Electric	6^5	6^5	18	6	6
Furnaces—Floor						
For Mounting in Combustile Floors	Automatic Oil or	} 36	—	12	12	12
	Comb. Gas-Oil					
	Automatic Gas	36	—	12	12	12
	Electric	36	—	12	12	12
Heat Exchanger						
Steam—15 psi Max.		—				
Hot Water—250°F Max.		1	1	1	1	1
Room Heaters						
Circulating Type	⌠Oil or Solid	36	—	24	12	12
Vented or Unvented	⌡Gas	36	—	24	12	12
	⌠Oil or Solid	36	—	36	36	36
Radiant or Other Type	⌡Gas	36	—	36	18	18
Vented or Unvented	⌠Gas with double metal or ⌡ceramic back	36	—	36	12	18
Radiators						
Steam or Hot Water	Gas	36	—	6	6	6

Ranges—Cooking Stoves Vented or Unvented					Firing Side	Opp. Side
		See Note 7				
	Oil	30	—	—	9 · 24	18
	Gas	30	—	—	6 · 6	6
	Solid—Clay lined Firepot	30	—	—	24 · 24	18
	Solid—Unlined Firepot	30	—	—	36 · 36	18
	Electric	30	—	—	6	6

		Above Top of Casing or Appliance	From Top and Sides of Warm-Air Bonnet or Plenum	From Front	From Back	From Sides
Clothes Dryers						
Listed Types	Gas	6	—	24	6	6
	Electric	6	—	24	0	0
Incinerators		See Note 10				
Domestic Types	—	36	—	48	36	36

Low Heat Appliances Any and All Physical Sizes Except As Noted		Above Top of Casing or Appliance See Note 8	From Top and Sides of Warm-Air Bonnet or Plenum	From Front	From Back See Note 8	From Sides See Note 8
Boilers and Water Heaters						
100 cu ft or less						
Any psi Steam	All Fuels	18	—	48	18	18
50 psi or Less						
Any Size	All Fuels	18	—	48	18	18

Table 7-3F.   Standard Installation Clearances, Inches, for Heat-Producing Appliances (Continued)

Low Heat Appliances Any and All Physical Sizes Except As Noted		Appliance				
		Above Top of Casing or Appliance See Note 8	From Top and Sides of Warm-Air Bonnet or Plenum	From Front	From Back See Note 8	From Sides See Note 8
Unit Heaters						
Floor Mounted or Suspended—Any Size	Steam or Hot Water	1	—	—	1	1
Suspended—100 cu ft or less	Oil or Comb. Gas-Oil	6	—	24	18	18
Suspended—100 cu ft or less	Gas	6	—	18	18	18
Suspended—Over 100 cu ft	All Fuels	18	—	48	18	18
Floor Mounted Any Size	All Fuels	18	—	48	18	18
Ranges—Restaurant Type						
Floor Mounted	All Fuels	48	—	48	18	18
Other Low-Heat Industrial Appliances						
Floor Mounted or Suspended	All Fuels	18	18	48	18	18

Commercial-Industrial Type Medium-Heat Appliances		Appliance				
		Above Top of Casing or Appliance See Note 9	From Top and Sides of Warm-Air Bonnet or Plenum	From Front	From Back See Note 9	From Sides See Note 9
Boilers and Water Heaters Over 50 psi Over 100 cu ft	All Fuels	48	—	96	36	36
Other Medium-Heat Industrial Appliances All Sizes	All Fuels	48	36	96	36	36
Incinerators All Sizes		48	—	96	36	36
High-Heat Industrial Appliances All Sizes	All Fuels	180	—	360	120	120

NOTES TO TABLE 7-3F

1. Standard clearances may be reduced by affording protection to combustible material in accordance with Table 7-3G.

2. An appliance may be mounted on a combustible floor if the appliance is listed for installation on a combustible floor, or if the floor is protected in an approved manner. For details of protection reference may be made to the Code for the Installation of Heat-Producing Appliances, obtainable from the American Insurance Association (NBFU), 85 John Street, New York, N.Y. 10038, or Part 6 of the National Building Code of Canada published by the National Research Council, Ottawa, Canada.

3. Rooms which are large in comparison to the size of the appliance are those having a volume equal to at least 12 times the total volume of a furnace and at least 16 times the total volume of a boiler. If the actual ceiling height of a room is greater than 8 ft, the volume of a room shall be figured on the basis of a ceiling height of 8 ft.

4. The minimum dimension should be that necessary for servicing the appliance including access for normal maintenance, care, tube removal, etc.

5. For a listed oil, combination gas-oil, gas, or electric furnace this dimension may be 2 in. if the furnace limit control cannot be set higher than 250°F or this dimension may be 1 in. if the limit control cannot be set higher than 200°F.

6. The dimension may be 6 in. for an automatically stoker-fired forced warm-air furnace equipped with 250°F limit control and with barometric draft control operated by draft intensity and permanently set to limit draft to a maximum intensity of 0.13 in. water gage.

7. To combustible material or metal cabinets. If the underside of such combustible material or metal cabinet is protected with asbestos millboard at least ¼ in. thick covered with sheet metal of not less than No. 28 gage the distance may be not less than 24 in.

8. If the appliance is encased in brick, the 18 in. clearance above and at sides and rear may be reduced to not less than 12 in.

9. If the appliance is encased in brick the clearance above may be not less than 36 in. and at sides and rear may be not less than 18 in.

10. Clearance above the charging door should be not less than 48 in.

The testing laboratories indicate in their listings whether the appliances tested may be installed on combustible or noncombustible floors. In some cases there is a statement on the appliance itself to the effect that it may be installed on a combustible floor. If, however, no such indication appears, it is advisable to check the listing for the particular appliance.

Air for Combustion and Ventilation

In most locations, combustion-type, heat-producing appliances have ample sources of air for efficient combustion apart from ventilation required to prevent undue temperature rises. In basements of dwellings, for example, sufficient air comes in through the cracks around doors and windows.

In rooms which are relatively tight, such as furnace and boiler rooms, means to supply air for combustion and ventilation must be provided. There is no universally accepted formula for calculating the size of openings necessary to provide adequate air for combustion and ventilation because there are so many variables involved: such as, tightness and size of the furnace or boiler room, and the operation of exhaust fans and other equipment that would affect the static air pressure in the building. Both the NFPA Oil Burning Equipment Standard and National Fuel Gas

Table 7-3G. Clearances, Inches, with Specified Forms of Protection*

Type of Protection — Applied to the combustible material unless otherwise specified and covering all surfaces within the distance specified as the required clearance with no protection (see Fig. 7-3Z). Thicknesses are minimum.	36 in. Above	36 in. Sides and Rear	36 in. Chimney or Vent Connector	18 in. Above	18 in. Sides and Rear	18 in. Chimney or Vent Connector	12 in. Above	12 in. Sides and Rear	12 in. Chimney or Vent Connector	9 in. Above	9 in. Sides and Rear	9 in. Chimney or Vent Connector	6 in. Above	6 in. Sides and Rear	6 in. Chimney or Vent Connector
(a) ¼ in. asbestos millboard spaced out 1 in.†	30	18	30	15	9	12	9	6	6				3	2	3
(b) 28 gage sheet metal on ¼ in. asbestos millboard	24	18	24	12	9	12	9	6	4				3	2	2
(c) 28 gage sheet metal spaced out 1 in.†	18	12	18	9	6	9	6	4	4				2	2	2
(d) 28 gage sheet metal on ⅛ in. asbestos millboard spaced out 1 in.†	18	12	18	9	6	9	6	4	4				2	2	2
(e) 1½ in. cement covering on heating appliance	18	12	36	9	6	18	6	4	9				2	1	6
(f) ¼ in. asbestos millboard on 1 in. mineral fiber bats reinforced with wire mesh or equivalent	18	12	18	6	6	6	4	4	4				2	2	2
(g) 22 gage sheet metal on 1 in. mineral fiber bats reinforced with wire or equivalent	18	12	12	4	3	3	2	2	2				2	2	2
(h) ¼ in. asbestos cement board or ¼ in. asbestos millboard	36	36	36	18	18	18	12	12	9				4	4	4
(i) ¼ in. cellular asbestos	36	36	36	18	18	18	12	12	9				3	3	3

* Except for the protection described in (e), all clearances should be measured from the outer surface of the appliance to the combustible material disregarding any intervening protection applied to the combustible material.

† Spacers should be of noncombustible material.

Code as well as other standards pertaining to heat-producing appliances (see bibliography at end of this chapter) include specific recommendations on how the air required for combustion and ventilation is to be supplied.

For certain laboratory-tested appliances, notably oil burning appliances for installation in alcoves and closets, the minimum size is specified for an opening to the heater room or space necessary to provide enough air for the operation of the unit.

Clearances for Servicing

Quite apart from the need to provide clearances between combustible materials and heat-producing appliances as previously discussed, is the necessity for clearance for servicing and maintenance. Lack of servicing and maintenance can result in fires. If lack of space around an appliance makes accessibility difficult, the appliance, or at least some parts of it, will be neglected. This same reasoning applies to appliances located in out-of-the-way places and places difficult to reach. Typical of such installations are suspended furnaces and furnaces in attics and underfloor crawl spaces.

E. Chimney and Vent Connectors

Chimney and vent connectors are specifically the pipe or breeching used to connect heating appliances with the chimney or vent. Principal requirements are that the connectors be short, well-fitted and supported, pitched up towards the chimney, and have adequate clearance to combustible material.

Connectors preferably are made of noncombustible corrosion resistant material, such as steel or refractory masonry. They must be capable of withstanding the flue gas temperature produced by the appliance and be of sufficient thickness to withstand physical damage. Connectors for appliances installed in attics are Type B or Type L vent systems for gas appliances with draft hoods or of Type L material for oil appliances suitable for Type L vents. For other appliances allowed in attics, a chimney is directly attached to the appliance.

Table 7-3I gives the construction for single wall metal pipe connectors. Use of heavier metal than called for in the table will increase the life of connectors. Slip joints should lap 2 in. and be fastened with sheet-metal screws, rivets, or other satisfactory means to prevent separation.

Masonry connectors or breechings preferably are made of refractory material equivalent in resistance to heat and erosion to high duty fire brick (ASTM C106, Type A) not less than 4½ in. thick.

Connectors for gas appliances having draft hoods may be constructed of material having resistance to corrosion and heat not less than that of No. 28 gage galvanized steel, or they may be of Type B or Type L vent material.

Connectors of Type L material may be used with gas, oil, and solid fuel-burning residential type appliances including residential-type incinerators.

Good engineering methods are used to size connectors. As an alternative, the effective area of a connector for a single appliance can be not less than the area of the appliance flue collar. A connector or manifold serving two or more appliances has an effective area equivalent to the combined area of the appliance flue collars or individual con-

Table 7-3H.   Floor Mountings for Heat-Producing Appliances

Type of Mounting	Required for the Following Types of Heaters and Furnaces
(a) No Floor Protection: Combustible floors.*	Residential-type central furnaces so arranged that the fan chamber occupies the entire area beneath the firing chamber and forms a well-ventilated air space of not less than 18 in. in height between the firing chamber and the floor, with at least one metal baffle between the firing chamber and the floor. Low heat appliances (see Table 7-3M for examples) in which flame and hot gases do not come in contact with the base, on legs which provide not less than 18 in. open space under the base of the appliance, with at least one sheet metal baffle between any burners and the floor. Other appliances for which there is evidence that they are designed for safe operation when installed on combustible floors.
(b) Metal: A sheet of metal not less than No. 24 U.S. Gage, or other approved noncombustible material, laid over a combustible wood floor.*	Heating and cooking appliances set on legs or simulated legs which provide not less than 4 in. open space under the base. Ordinary residential stoves with legs. Residential ranges with legs. Residential room heaters with legs. Water heaters with legs. Laundry stoves with legs. Room heaters with legs.†
(c) Asbestos and Metal: A sheet of ¼-in. asbestos covered with a sheet of metal not less than No. 24 U.S. Gage, laid over a combustible floor.*	Heating furnaces and boilers in which flame and hot gases do not come in contact with the base and which are set on legs which provide not less than 4 in. open space under the base. Residential-type incinerators with 4 in. legs. Counter-type gas burning appliances with 4 in. legs.
(d) Asbestos Millboard and Metal: A sheet of ⅜-in. asbestos millboard covered with a sheet of metal not less than No. 24 U.S. Gage, laid over a combustible floor and extending at least 6 in. beyond the base on all sides.‡	Floor mounted restaurant-type cooking appliances set on legs which provide not less than 8-in. open space under the base. Restaurant ranges on legs.
(e) Hollow Masonry: Hollow masonry not less than 4 in. in thickness laid with ends unsealed and joints matched in such a way as to provide free circulation of air through the masonry.	Downflow furnaces.
(f) Hollow Masonry and Metal: Hollow masonry not less than 4 in. in thickness covered with a sheet of metal not less than No. 24 U.S. Gage, laid over a combustible floor. The masonry will be laid with ends unsealed and joints matched in such a way as to provide a free circulation of air from side to side through the masonry.‡	Heating furnaces and boilers in which flame and hot gases do not come in contact with the base: Floor mounted heating and cooking appliances. Residential stoves without legs. Residential ranges without legs. Room heaters without legs. Water heaters without legs. Laundry stoves without legs. Residential-type incinerators. Restaurant ranges on 4-in. legs. Other low heat appliances on 4-in. legs. Medium heat appliances on legs which provide not less than 24 in. open space under the base.
(g) Two Courses Masonry and Plate: Two courses of 4-in. hollow clay tile covered with steel plate not less than ³⁄₁₆ in. in thickness, laid over a combustible floor. The courses of tile will be laid at right angles with ends unsealed and joints matched in such a way as to provide a free circulation of air through the masonry courses.‡	Heating furnaces and boilers in which flame and hot gases come in contact with the base. Restaurant ranges. Other low heat appliances.

* Where an appliance is mounted on a combustible floor, and solid fuel is used or the appliance is a domestic type incinerator, a sheet of ¼-in. asbestos covered by a sheet of metal not less than No. 24 U.S. Gage will be required extending at least 18 in. from the appliance on the front or side where ashes are removed. (The sheet of asbestos may be omitted where the protection required under the appliance is a sheet of metal only.) For residential type incinerators the protection must also extend at least 12 in. beyond all other sides. If the appliance is installed with clearance less than 6 in. the protection for the floor should be carried to the wall.

† Floor protection for radiating type gas burning room heaters which make use of metal, asbestos or ceramic material to direct radiation to the front of the device should extend at least 36 in. in front when the heater is not of a type approved for installation on a combustible floor.

‡ Where an appliance is mounted on a combustible floor, and solid fuel is used or the appliance is a residential type incinerator, a sheet of ¼-in. asbestos covered by a sheet of metal not less than No. 24 U.S. Gage will be required extending at least 18 in. from the appliance on the front or side where ashes are removed. (The sheet of asbestos may be omitted where the protection required under the appliance is a sheet of metal only.) For residential-type incinerators the protection must also extend at least 12 in. beyond all other sides.

Table 7-3H.   Floor Mountings for Heat-Producing Appliances (Continued)

Type of Mounting	Required for the Following Types of Heaters and Furnaces
(h) **Fire-Resistive Floors, Extending 6 in.:** Floors of fire-resistive construction with noncombustible flooring and surface finish and with no combustible material against the underside thereof, or on fire-resistive slabs or arches having no combustible material against the underside thereof. Such construction will extend not less than 6 in. beyond the appliance on all sides, and where solid fuel is used, it will extend not less than 18 in. at the front or side where ashes are removed.	Floor mounted heating and cooking appliances. Residential-type room heaters. Residential-type water heaters.
(i) **Fire-Resistive Floors Extending 12 in.:** Floors of fire-resistive construction with noncombustible flooring and surface finish and with no combustible material against the underside thereof, or on fire-resistive slabs or arches having no combustible material against the underside thereof. Such construction will extend not less than 12 in. beyond the appliance on all sides, and where solid fuel is used, it will extend not less than 18 in. at the front or side where ashes are removed.	Heating furnaces or boilers. Restaurant-type cooking appliances. Residential-type incinerators. Other low heat appliances.
(j) **Fire-Resistive Floors Extending 3 ft:** Floors of fire-resistive construction with noncombustible flooring and surface finish and with no combustible material against the underside thereof, or on fire-resistive slabs or arches having no combustible material against the underside thereof. Such construction will extend not less than 3 ft beyond the appliance on all sides, and where solid fuel is used, it will extend not less than 8 ft at the front or side where ashes are removed.	Medium heat appliances and furnaces. (See Table 7-3M for examples.)
(k) **Fire-Resistive Floors Extending 10 ft:** Floors of fire-resistive construction with noncombustible flooring and surface finish and with no combustible material against the underside thereof. Such construction will extend not less than 10 ft beyond the appliance on all sides, and where solid fuel is used, it will extend not less than 30 ft at the front or side where hot products are removed.	High heat appliances and furnaces. (See Table 7-3M for examples.)

nectors. Linings, if used, should not reduce the required area of the connector.

A connector is made as short and straight as possible by locating the appliance as close as practicable to the chimney or vent. The horizontal run of an uninsulated connector to a natural draft chimney or vent, serving a single appliance, is not more than 75 percent of the height of the vertical portion of the chimney or vent above the connector, unless part of an engineered system. Connectors serving two or more appliances must be engineered to prevent failure of the draft in one or more of the appliances.

A connector to a masonry chimney extends through the chimney wall to the inner face or liner but not beyond, and should be firmly cemented to masonry. A thimble may be used to facilitate removal of the connector for cleaning, in which case the thimble should be permanently cemented in place (see Fig. 7-3BB).

It is best to avoid sharp bends or other construction features in connectors that could create excessive resistance to the flow of flue gases. Devices that could obstruct the flow should not be installed in connectors, chimneys, or vents unless the devices are specifically required, such as heat reclaimers, draft regulators and safety controls. A manual damper is never used in a connector serving stoker-fired, gas, and liquid fuel-burning appliances.

The entire length of a connector should be readily accessible for inspection, cleaning and replacement. Connectors should be cleaned periodically and inspected to see if the metal is rusted or damaged.

Two or more fuel-burning appliances may be connected to a single chimney or vent provided sufficient draft is available for safe combustion of each appliance and removal of all combustion products safely to the outdoors. Gas and oil appliances so connected are equipped with automatic controls to shut off the fuel in the event of flame failure.

Connectors Through Combustible Partitions: Connectors

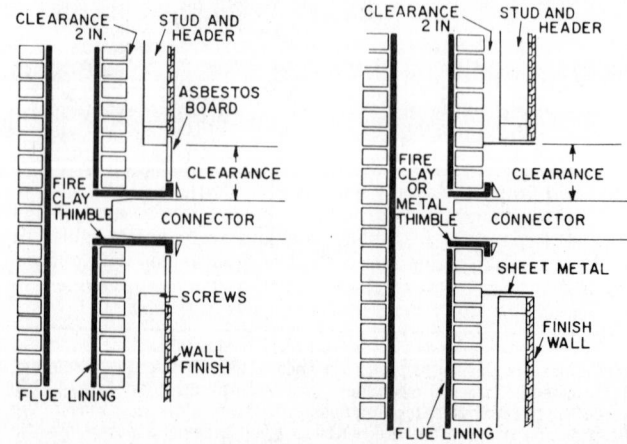

Fig. 7-3BB.   Two methods of installing chimney connectors for domestic stoves, heaters, furnaces, and boilers where the connector must pass through a combustible finish wall. Sheet metal may be used in place of the asbestos board shown or the portion of finish wall shown may be plaster on metal lath.

Table 7-3I. Construction of Connectors

Type of Appliance	Diameter, Inches	Galvanized Sheet Metal Gage	Lining
Residential and Low Heat Appliances	10 or less	24	—
	10 to 12	22	—
	14 to 16	20	—
	16 and over	16	—
Medium Heat Appliances* and Commercial and Industrial Incinerators	up to 12	16	—
	12 to 14	16	2¼-in. fire brick
	14 to 16	14	2¼-in. fire brick
	16 to and inc. 18	12	2¼-in. fire brick
	over 18	10	4½-in. fire brick
High Heat Appliances	up to 14	16	4½-in. fire brick
	14 to 16	14	4½-in. fire brick
	16 to and inc. 18	12	4½-in. fire brick
	over 18	10	4½-in. fire brick

* Connectors for appliances producing low flue gases and connectors not over 10 in. diameter and 8 ft long may be insulated flue tile or other suitable construction without fire brick lining, if located in the appliance room.

from medium or high heat appliances should never be run through combustible partitions or walls. A connector should never pass through a floor or ceiling into an attic or other concealed space before entering a chimney because heat does not dissipate readily from such spaces, combustible materials can be placed near the connectors, and dangerous deterioration of the connector can go undetected. Table 7-3J indicates methods by which connectors for residential-type and low heat oil-, gas-, and solid-fired-appliances may be arranged to pass through combustible partitions (see also Fig. 7-3CC). If the arrangements shown in Table 9-1J are not used, the combustible material must be cut away from the connector to provide the clearances that are shown in Table 7-3K.

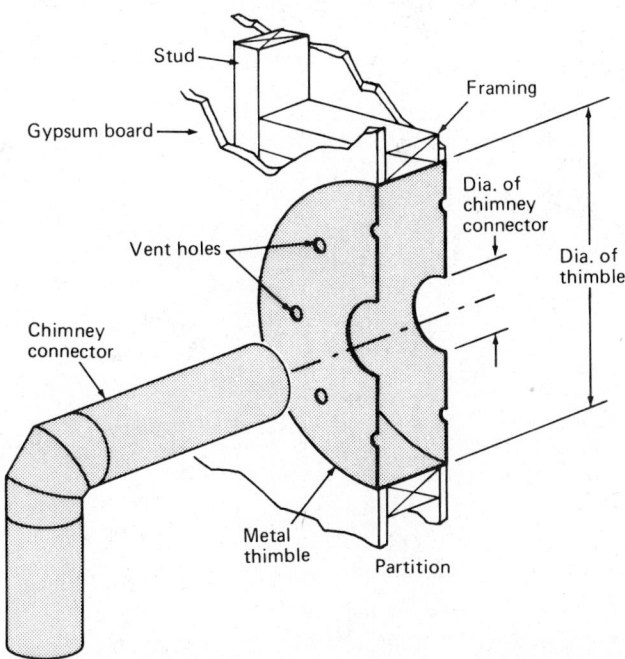

Fig. 7-3CC. A ventilated metal thimble is one permissible method of installing a chimney connector through a combustible partition wall.

Table 7-3J. Connectors Through Combustible Partitions

1. Listed Gas Appliances with Draft Hoods (Col. I, Table 7-3L). Oil Appliances listed for Type L Vents (Col. III, Table 7-3L)	Type B or Type L Vent Material for gas appliances, Type L for oil appliances. Installed with listed clearances or single wall metal pipe guarded by ventilated metal thimble at least 4 in. larger in diameter than the pipe.
2. Other low heat appliances	Ventilated metal thimble at least 12 in. larger in diameter than connector, or a metal or burned fire clay thimble in brick or other fireproofing material extending at least 8 in. on all sides beyond thimble.
3. Medium and high heat appliances	Not permitted.

Clearances to Combustible Material: Recommended clearances to combustible material for chimney and vent connectors for various types of heat-producing appliances are given in Table 7-3K. When connectors pass through combustible partitions, the clearances given in Table 7-3K may be reduced if protection is provided in accordance with Table 7-3J. Reductions in clearances for other situations may be allowed as indicated in Table 7-3J.

Appliances to be Chimney or Vent Connected

Oil: All oil-fired appliances are to be chimney-connected or connected to Type L vents except direct-fired heaters, listed kerosine stoves, and portable kerosine heaters.

Solid Fuels: All solid fueled appliances are chimney connected.

Gas: Gas appliances required to be vented by being connected to chimneys or vents include:

1. Central heating appliances, including steam and hot water boilers, warm air furnaces, floor furnaces, and wall furnaces.

2. Unit heaters and duct furnaces.

3. Incinerators.

4. Water heaters with inputs over 5,000 Btu per hour, except as indicated in (6) and (7) below in the list of gas burning appliances not requiring vents.

5. Built-in domestic cooking units listed and marked only as vented units.

6. Room heaters listed onlyl for vented use. Room heaters listed as "vented and unvented" units may be installed unvented subject to approval of the authority having jurisdiction.

7. Appliances equipped with gas conversion burners.

8. Other listed appliances which have draft hoods supplied by the appliance manufacturer.

9. Unlisted appliances, except as provided under the following item (9).

The following gas burning appliances do not require vents:

1. Listed ranges.

2. Built-in domestic cooking units listed and marked as unvented units.

3. Listed hot plates and listed laundry stoves.

4. Listed domestic clothes dryers, except those installed in mobile homes.

5. Listed water heaters with inputs not over 5,000 Btu per hr.

6. Automatically controlled instantaneous water heaters which supply water to a single faucet which is attached to and made part of the appliance.

Table 7-3K. Chimney Connector and Vent Connector Clearances from Combustible Materials

Description of Appliance	Minimum Clearance, Inches (See Note 1)
RESIDENTIAL AND BUILDING HEATING APPLIANCES	
Columns I and II, Table 7-3M	
Single-Wall Metal Pipe Connectors	
Gas Appliances Without Draft Hoods	18
Electric, Gas, and Oil Incinerators	18
Oil and Solid-Fuel Appliances	18
Unlisted Gas Appliances With Draft Hood	9
Boilers and Furnaces Equipped With Listed Gas Burner and With Draft Hood	9
Oil Appliances Listed as Suitable For Use With Type L vent	9
Listed Gas Appliances With Draft Hoods. See Note 3	6
Type L Vent Piping Connectors	
Gas Appliances Without Draft Hoods	9
Electric, Gas, and Oil Incinerators	9
Oil and Solid-Fuel Appliances	9
Unlisted Gas Appliances With Draft Hoods	6
Boilers and Furnaces Equipped With Listed Gas Burner and With Draft Hood	6
Oil Appliances Listed as Suitable for Use With Type L Vent	(See Note 2)
Listed Gas Appliances With Draft Hoods	(See Note 3)
Column I, Table 7-3M	
Type B Gas Vent Piping Connectors	
Listed Gas Appliances With Draft Hoods	(See Note 3)
COMMERCIAL AND INDUSTRIAL HEATING APPLIANCES	
Low-Heat Appliances	
Column III, Table 7-3M	
Single-Wall Metal Pipe Connectors	
Gas, Oil, and Solid-Fuel Boilers, Furnaces, and Water Heaters	18
Ranges, Restaurant Type	18
Oil Unit Heaters	18
Unlisted Gas Unit Heaters	18
Listed Gas Unit Heaters With Draft Hoods	6
Other Low-Heat Industrial Appliances	18
Medium-Heat Appliances	
Column IV, Table 7-3M	
Single-Wall Metal Pipe Connectors	
All Gas, Oil, and Solid-Fuel Appliances	36

Note 1: These clearances apply except if the listing of an appliance specifies different clearance, in which case the listed clearance takes precedence.

Note 2: If listed Type L vent piping is used, the clearance may be in accordance with the vent listing.

Note 3: If listed Type B or Type L vent piping is used, the clearance may be in accordance with the vent system listing.

The clearances from connectors to combustible materials may be reduced if the combustible material is protected in accordance with Table 7-3G.

7. A single, listed, booster-type (automatic instantaneous) water heater when designed and used solely for the sanitizing rinse requirements of a National Sanitation Foundation Class 1, 2, or 3 dishwashing machine, provided that the input is limited to 50,000 Btu per hour, the storage capacity is limited to 12.5 gal, and the heater is installed with the draft hood in place with proper clearances, and in an unaltered condition in a commercial kitchen having a mechanical exhaust system.

8. Listed refrigerators, except those installed in mobile homes and recreational vehicles.

9. Counter appliances.

10. Room heaters listed for unvented use.

11. Other appliances listed for unvented use and not provided with flue collars.

12. Specialized equipment of limited input such as laboratory burners or gas lights.

When any or all of the appliances listed in items (5) to (9) above as not requiring vents are installed so that the aggregate input rating exceeds 30 Btu per hr per cu ft of room or space in which they are installed, one or more of them is vented so that the aggregate input rating of the remaining unvented appliances does not exceed the 30 Btu per cu ft figure. When the room or space in which they are installed is directly connected to another room or space by a doorway, archway, or other opening of comparable size, which cannot be closed, the volume of the adjacent room or space may be included in the calculations.

Vents

Type B Gas Vents: These are laboratory-tested, factory-built components used to vent gas appliances with draft hoods and other types of gas appliances specifically designed to be used with Type B gas vents. They are not used for venting the following:

(a) Vented wall furnaces designed to be used with Type BW gas vents,

(b) Incinerators,

(c) Appliances which may be converted readily to the use of liquid or solid fuel,

(d) Combination gas-oil burning appliances,

(e) Appliances listed for connection to chimneys only.

Type BW Gas Vents: These are laboratory-tested, factory-built components that are used with gas wall furnaces having capacities not greater than that of Type BW gas vents. See Fig. 7-3DD.

Type L Vents: These are laboratory-tested, factory-built components that are used only with oil appliances designed to be used with them and with gas appliances listed as suitable for Type B gas vents.

Single-Wall Metal Pipe Vents: These vents are constructed of sheet copper not lighter than No. 24 B&S gage or of galvanized iron not lighter than No. 20 galvanized sheet

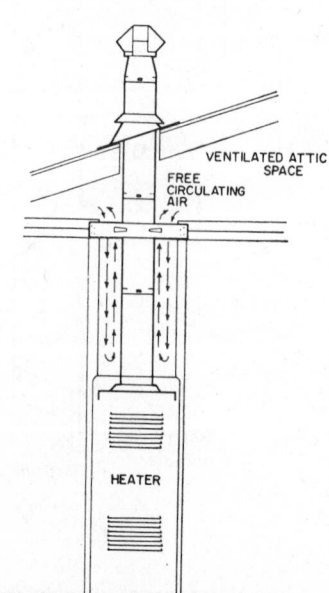

Fig. 7-3DD. Type BW vent installation on a wall furnace. (Metalbestos Div. Wallace-Murray Corp.)

gage. They may be used to vent gas appliances and to vent incinerators used outdoors, such as in open sheds, breezeways or carports.

Installation of Vents

Types B, BW, and L Vents: Installations are made in compliance with the terms of their laboratory listings and the manufacturer's instructions; making certain that the required clearances are maintained.

Single Wall Metal Pipe: The use of single wall metal pipe is restricted to runs directly from the space in which the appliance is located through the roof or exterior wall to the outside. The pipe is not to originate in any attic or concealed space, and is not to pass through any attic, inside space nor through any floor or ceiling. The minimum clearances from combustible material for single wall metal pipe connectors are given in Table 7-3K. Where a single-wall metal pipe passes through an exterior wall constructed of combustible material, the pipe is protected at the point of passage as described in Table 7-3J. If the pipe passes through a roof constructed of combustible material it is protected at the point of passage as specified for connectors in Table 7-3J. If the appliance the roof vent serves is a gas appliance suitable for use with a Type B gas vent, protection is by a noncombustible, nonventilating thimble not less than 4 in. larger in diameter than the pipe and extending not less than 18 in. above and 6 in. below the roof with annular space open at the bottom and closed at the top.

Venting Capacities: The venting capacities of various sizes of gas vents, chimneys, and single-wall metal pipe used for venting gas appliances are given in tables in the NFPA National Fuel Gas Code. The Code also contains data which may be used to calculate the size of vents required under various circumstances and to establish configurations of venting arrangements. Good engineering methods may also be used.

Termination of Vents: Vents and chimneys should extend high enough above buildings and other obstructions so that the wind from any direction will not result in a positive pressure in the vent or chimney. Details on this and other features of vents, and chimney and vent connectors for

gas appliances are given in the NFPA National Fuel Gas Code and the NFPA Chimneys, Fireplaces and Vents Standard (see also Figs. 7-3EE and 7-3FF).

Firestopping: Vents that pass through floors of buildings requiring the protection of vertical openings are enclosed within walls having a fire resistance rating of not less than 1 hr if the vents are in a building less than four stories in height and not less than 2 hrs if located in a building four stories or more in height. (See Table 7-3L.)

Draft Hoods

A draft hood is a device built into an appliance, or made a part of the vent connector from an appliance, which is designed to (1) assure the ready escape of the flue gases in the event of no draft, back draft, or stoppage beyond the draft hood; (2) prevent a back draft from entering the appliance; and (3) neutralize the effect of stack action of the chimney or gas vent upon the operation of the appliance.

Draft hoods are an important safety feature of gas appliances and are generally required on all vented appliances except incinerators, dual oven-type combination ranges, appliances with sealed combustion chambers, and units designed for power burners or for forced venting.

F. Chimneys and Fireplaces

Chimneys are classified into three types: (1) factory-built, (2) masonry, and (3) metal (smokestacks). Table 7-3M is a tabulation of types of heating appliances showing which of the three types of chimneys can be used with each appliance.

Factory-built Chimneys

Factory-built chimneys are rapid in warmup, efficient draft producers, and simple to install. They may be defined as chimneys that are factory made and tested and listed by a nationally recognized testing agency as suitable for use for the elimination of waste products of combustion from solid or liquid fuel burning appliances, gas incinerators, and gas appliances. As factory-built chimneys are tested against

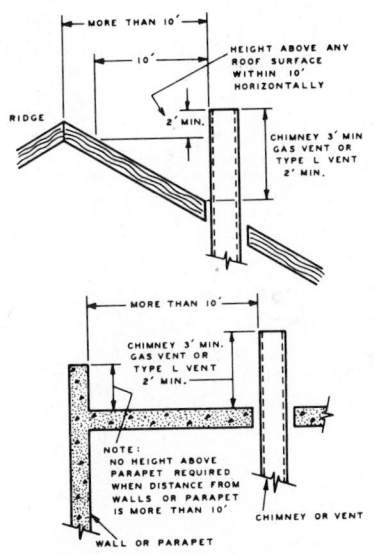

Termination more than 10 ft from ridge, wall or parapet.

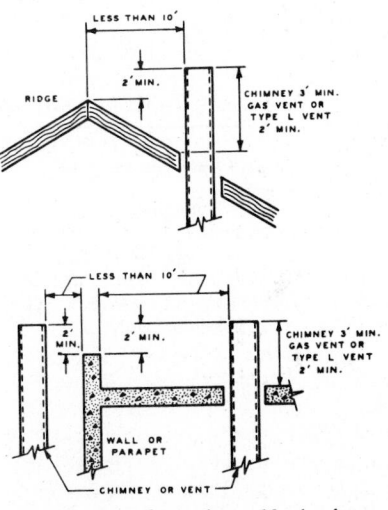

Termination less than 10 ft from ridge, wall or parapet.

Fig. 7-3EE. Termination of vents and chimneys above buildings.

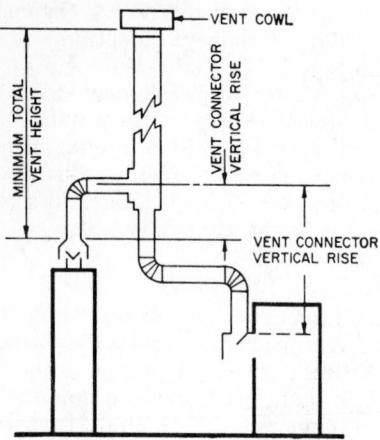

Fig. 7-3FF. Typical Type B multiple appliances vent system. (AGA Laboratories)

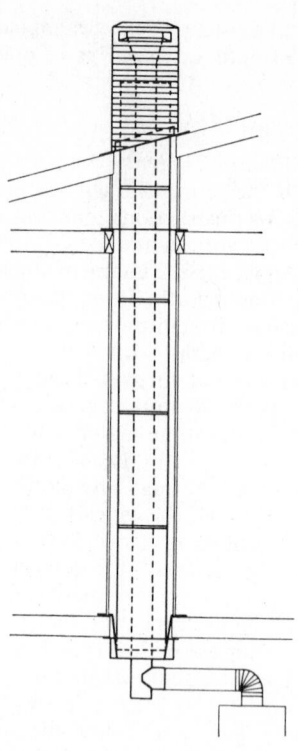

Fig. 7-3GG. A typical factory-built chimney. (Metalbestos Div., Wallace-Murray Corp.)

safety standards, they have an added assurance of fire safety over masonry chimneys which are subject to the know-how and ability of available labor and are not tested, except perhaps for a smoke test. Laboratory tests of factory-built chimneys are conducted on the basis of their size, kind, and height, and the minimum clearance required between them and combustible construction. To determine the minimum clearance to combustibles, factory-built chimneys are tested at 1,000°F to reach equilibrium temperatures on the chimney parts and test enclosure, at 1,400°F for 1 hr, and at 1,700°F for 10 min to simulate soot burnout.

Other advantages of factory-built chimneys are:

1. They heat up quickly and it is not necessary to operate the appliance at forced draft for long periods to warm up the great mass of chimney. This not only results in greater safety but more efficient operation of the equipment.

2. Soot problems are minimized because of the quick warmup of the inner walls of factory-built chimneys. Tarry products condense on cold chimney walls—not on hot inner liners.

The clearances to be maintained from combustible material as determined by testing laboratories are given on each section of the chimney. A typical factory-built chimney is shown in Figure 7-3GG.

Masonry Chimneys

Defective masonry chimneys are one of the leading causes of fires in buildings. Chimneys must always be made safe, even if it requires rebuilding them. If chimneys leak in a smoke test or are found to be charring surrounding combustibles, replacement is advised. Wood or other combustible material must have a minimum of 2-in. clearance from the outer masonry surfaces of chimneys for residential type and low heat appliances and 4 in. for chimneys for medium heat appliances.

Chimney Inspection: Chimneys can be inspected for flaws, debris, broken tile, or unlined sections, by lowering a flashlight on a string from the top or with a mirror poked into connector and cleanout openings. If mortar has begun

Table 7-3L.   Venting System Selection Chart

TYPE OF VENTING SYSTEM			
Type B—Gas	Type BW—Gas	Type L—Oil	Single Wall Metal Pipe
Column I	*Column II*	*Column III*	*Column IV*
All listed gas appliances with draft hoods such as: 1. Central furnaces. 2. Duct furnaces. 3. Floor furnaces. 4. Heating boilers. 5. Ranges. 6. Built-in ovens. 7. Vented wall furnaces listed for use with Type B vents. 8. Room heaters. 9. Water heaters. 10. Horizontal furnaces. 11. Unit heaters.	1. Vented wall furnaces listed for use with Type BW vents only.	1. Low temperature flue gas appliances listed for use with Type L vents. 2. Gas appliances shown in Column 1.	1. Incinerators used outdoors, such as in open sheds, breezeways or carports. 2. Gas appliances shown in Column 1. 3. Listed residential and low heat gas appliances without draft hoods and unlisted residential and low heat gas appliances with or without draft hoods.

Table 7-3M. Chimney Selection Chart

Chimneys for Residential Type Appliances	Building Heating Appliances	Chimneys for LOW HEAT Appliances — Industrial Type Low Heat Appliances	Chimneys for MEDIUM HEAT Appliances[1]	Chimneys for HIGH HEAT Appliances[3]
1. Factory built (low heat). 2. Masonry (residential).	1. Factory built (low heat). 2. Masonry (low heat type). 3. Metal (smokestack).	1. Factory Built (industrial low heat type). 2. Masonry (low heat type). 3. Metal (smokestack).	1. Factory built (medium heat type). 2. Masonry (medium heat type). 3. Metal (smokestack).	1. Masonry (high heat type). 2. Metal (smokestack).

TYPES OF APPLIANCES TO BE USED WITH EACH TYPE CHIMNEY

Column I	Column II	Column III	Column IV	Column V
A. Residential type appliances, such as: 1. Ranges. 2. Warm air furnaces. 3. Water heaters. 4. Hot water heating boilers. 5. Low pressure steam heating boilers (not over 15 psig). 6. Domestic incinerators. 7. Floor furnaces. 8. Wall furnaces. 9. Room heaters. 10. Fireplace stoves. B. Fireplaces.	A. All appliances shown in Column I. B. Nonresidential type building heating appliances for heating a total volume of space exceeding 25,000 cubic feet.* C. Steam boilers operating at not over 50 lb per sq in. gage pressure; pressing machine boilers.	All appliances shown in Columns I and II, and appliances such as: 1. Annealing baths for hard glass (fats, paraffin, salts, or metals). 2. Bake ovens (in bakeries). 3. Boiling vats, for wood fibre, straw, lignin, etc. 4. Candy furnaces. 5. Coffee roasting ovens. 6. Core ovens. 7. Cruller furnaces. 8. Feed drying ovens. 9. Fertilizer drying ovens. 10. Fireplaces, other than residential type. 11. Forge furnaces (solid fuel). 12. Gypsum kilns. 13. Hardening furnaces (below dark red). 14. Hot air engine furnaces. 15. Ladle drying furnaces. 16. Lead melting furnaces. 17. Nickel plate (drying) furnaces. 18. Paraffin furnaces. 19. Recuperative furnaces (Spent materials). 20. Rendering furnaces. 21. Restaurant type cooking appliances using solid or liquid fuel. 22. Rosin melting furnaces. 23. Stereotype furnaces. 24. Sulphur furnaces. 25. Tripoli kilns (clay, coke and gypsum). 26. Type foundry furnaces. 27. Wood drying furnaces. 28. Wood impregnating furnaces. 29. Zinc amalgamating furnaces.	All appliances shown in Columns I, II and III, and appliances such as: 1. Alabaster gypsum kilns. 2. Annealing furnaces (glass or metal). 3. Charcoal furnaces. 4. Cold stirring furnaces. 5. Feed driers (direct fire heated). 6. Fertilizer driers (direct fire heated). 7. Galvanizing furnaces. 8. Gas producers. 9. Hardening furnaces (cherry to pale red). 10. Incinerators, commercial and industrial type. 11. Lehrs and glory holes. 12. Lime kilns. 13. Linseed oil boiling furnaces. 14. Porcelain biscuit kilns. 15. Pulp driers (direct fire heated). 16. Steam boilers operating at over 50 lb per sq in. gage pressure except pressing machine boilers. 17. Water-glass kiln. 18. Wood-distilling furnaces. 19. Wood-gas retorts.	All appliances shown in Columns I, II, III, and IV and appliances[2] such as: 1. Bessemer retorts. 2. Billet and bloom furnaces. 3. Blast furnaces. 4. Bone calcining furnaces. 5. Brass furnaces. 6. Carbon point furnaces. 7. Cement brick and tile kilns. 8. Ceramic kilns. 9. Coal and water gas retorts. 10. Cupolas. 11. Earthenware kilns. 12. Glass blow furnaces. 13. Glass furnaces (smelting). 14. Glass kilns. 15. Open hearth furnaces. 16. Ore roasting furnaces. 17. Porcelain baking and glazing kilns. 18. Pot-arches. 19. Puddling furnaces. 20. Regenerative furnaces. 21. Reverberatory furnaces. 22. Stacks, carburetor or superheating furnaces (in water gas works). 23. Vitreous enameling ovens (ferrous metals). 24. Wood carbonizing furnaces.

* Nonresidential type building heating appliances for heating a total volume of space not to exceed 25,000 cubic feet may be connected to chimneys for residential type appliances.

Note 1: Appliances otherwise classed as high heat appliances may be considered as medium heat appliances if not larger than 100 cubic feet in size.

Note 2: When such appliances are larger than 100 cubic feet in size, and other furnaces classified as high heat appliances in accordance with nationally recognized good practice.

Note 3: Continuous operating equipment of the counter current type may not require the type of flue indicated by general types of appliances.

to fall away from between the bricks, openings may be expected to develop all the way through the chimney wall. If an ice pick or other sharp instrument can be pushed all the way through, rebuilding is indicated. Chimney tops are the most likely portions to require rebuilding.

Construction of Chimneys: The quality of workmanship in a chimney may make the difference between a safe and an unsafe chimney. All masonry chimneys are best built from the ground up, and wholly supported on masonry footings or self-supporting fire resistive construction. None of the weight of a chimney is carried by anything except its proper foundation.

Chimney walls should be thick enough for structural stability and have the minimum thicknesses required for walls and flue linings based on the classification of appliances to be connected to the chimney (see Table 7-3N).

No changes should be made in the size or shape of a chimney flue lining near where it passes through a roof for a distance of 6 in. above or below the roof joists or rafters. Chimneys should be capped with noncombustible weatherproof material.

A chimney which is part of a wall of a building should be properly bonded to the building wall. In a wall less than 12 in. in thickness, corbelling is acceptable where it projects equally on both sides of the wall. Aside from this exception chimneys may not be in brick walls corbelled more than 6 in. from them, nor can such corbelling exceed 1 in. for each course of brick.

If there are more than two flues in a chimney, the flues should be divided with masonry wythes at least 4 in. wide so that there are not more than two adjacent flues not separated by wythes. Joints in adjacent flue linings should be staggered.

Flues and Flue Linings: The thicknesses of flue linings are specified in Table 7-3N. Flue linings are made of fire clay or other refractory clay capable of withstanding the action of flue gases and resisting without softening or cracking the temperatures to which they will be subjected (1,800°F as a minimum).

Two or more chimney connectors may be joined to make a single chimney connection provided that the connectors and the chimney flue are of sufficient size to serve all the appliances or heater units thus connected. A heating appliance connector should not be connected to the chimney of an incinerator of the apartment house type which has rubbish chutes opening into the chimney.

Wood Framing Around Chimneys: Wood framing is kept at least 2 in. away from the chimney walls but the space between the chimney and wood framing should be firestopped. Chimneys serving commercial or industrial type incinerators should be at least 4 in. from combustible material.

Height of Chimneys

The height of a chimney, regardless of its type, is based primarily upon three things: (1) the stack effect necessary to provide sufficient draft, (2) the avoidance of down-drafts due to wind, and (3) the possibility of sparks from the chimney igniting the roof covering. Table 7-3N lists the heights above roofs and portions of the building within certain distances of the chimney as recommended in NFPA Standards.

Fireplaces

A spark screen should always be provided for a fireplace and dampers, if any, should be of a type which may be operated from outside the fireplace.

Table 7-3N. Construction of Masonry Chimneys

	Thickness in Inches (Minimum)		Termination Above Roof, Feet
	Walls	Lining	
RESIDENTIAL TYPE APPLIANCES (*Table 7-3M, Column I*)			
Solid masonry units or reinforced concrete with fire clay lining extending 8 in. below connector or above throat of fireplace	4	5/8	3 2 ft from any portion of building within 10 ft
Rubble stone masonry with similar lining	12	5/8	
LOW HEAT APPLIANCES (*Table 7-3M, Columns II and III*)			
Solid masonry units or reinforced concrete with fire clay lining extending 8 in. below connector or above throat of fireplace	8	5/8	3 2 ft from any portion of building within 10 ft
Rubble stone masonry with similar lining	12	5/8	
MEDIUM HEAT APPLIANCES (*Table 7-3M, Column IV*)			
Solid masonry units or reinforced concrete with fire brick lining laid in fire clay mortar, lining extending 2 ft below and 25 ft above connector entrance to chimney	8	4½	10 ft. higher than any portion of building within 25 ft
Rubble stone masonry with similar lining	12	4½	
HIGH HEAT APPLIANCES (*Table 7-3M, Column V*)			
Double Walls:			
Outer wall of solid masonry units or reinforced	8		20 ft higher than any portion of building within 50 ft
Air space	2		
Inner wall, total thickness 8 in., of solid masonry units or reinforced concrete with fire clay brick lining laid in fire clay mortar	3½	4½	
INCINERATORS			
Residential Type—same as for low heat appliances			
Chute Fed			
Combined hearth and grate area 7 sq ft or less			
Clay or shale brick with fire brick lining for 10 ft above roof of combustion chamber	4	4½	Same as for low heat appliances
More than 10 ft above roof of combustion chamber with fire clay flue liner	8	5/8	
Combined hearth and grate area over 7 sq ft			
Clay or shale brick with fire brick lining for 40 ft above roof of combustion chamber	4	4½	10 ft higher than any portion of roof within 25 ft
More than 40 ft above roof of combustion chamber with fire clay flue liner	8	5/8	
Commercial or Industrial Types			
Clay or shale brick lined with fire brick full height	8	4½*	Same as for chute fed
Reinforced concrete or metal		4½*	

* Incinerators specially designed to produce low flue gas temperatures may be lined with fire clay flue liner.

Factory-built Fireplaces and Fireplace Stoves: Factory-built fireplaces consist of a fire chamber, chimney sections including the roof assembly, firestopping, and other parts to complete the installation. Each component is preassembled and does not require field construction. A fireplace stove (Franklin stove) is a solid fuel burning stove having part of its fire chamber open to the room and intended to be connected to a chimney. Both types of appliances have been fire laboratory tested.

The fireplaces can be installed on any floor and the chimney extends vertically through the roof. Portions of the chimney that may be exposed in living quarters or storage areas should be enclosed to avoid the possibility of personal contact with and damage to the chimney. The fireplace stoves can be installed where a chimney is available in the same manner as a conventional stove.

The fireplaces and fireplace stoves that have been laboratory tested are designed to be placed directly upon and adjacent to combustible building construction. The installation should be strictly in accordance with the terms of the listing and the manufacturer's instructions.

The NFPA Chimneys, Fireplaces, and Venting Systems Standard recommends that hearth extensions for factory-built fireplaces and fireplace stoves be of noncombustible material at least ⅜ in. thick. Hearth extensions can be placed directly on combustible flooring.

Masonry Fireplaces: These fireplaces are constructed of solid masonry or of reinforced portland or refractory cement concrete. If a lining of firebrick at least 2 in. thick, or an equivalent, is provided in the fireplace, the total thickness of it back and sides, including the lining, may be not less than 8 in. Otherwise the back and sides ought to be at least 12 in. thick.

Steel fireplace units incorporating a firebox liner of not less than ¼-in. thick steel and an air chamber may be installed with masonry to provide a total thickness at the back and sides of not less than 8 in., not less than 4 in. of which is to be solid masonry.

A hearth should extend in front of and beyond each side of the fireplace opening. If a fireplace is elevated above or overhangs a floor, the hearth extension includes the area under the fireplace. Brick, concrete, stone, or tiles, the latter properly supported with no combustible material against the underside of them, are good materials for hearth extensions. Wooden forms or centers used during construction are to be removed when construction is completed.

All wood beams, joist, and studs are trimmed away from fireplaces. Headers supporting trimmer arches at fireplaces are not less than 20 in. from the face of the chimney breast. Trimmers are not less than 6 in. from the inside face of the nearest flue liner. No woodwork is placed within 4 in. of the back face of a fireplace (see Fig. 7-3HH) nor is it within 6 in. of the fireplace opening, except that if it is above and projecting more than 1½ in. from the face of the opening, the distance is less than 12 in.

Firestopping

Noncombustible firestopping is required between the masonry of chimneys and fireplaces and wooden joists, beams or headers. The principal points at which firestopping is required are shown in Figure 7-3HH.

The best firestopping material for chimneys is a 1-in. thickness of mortar or plaster on strips of metal lath or wire fabric laid across the space between floor headers and the chimney wall. Filling the space between wooden floor

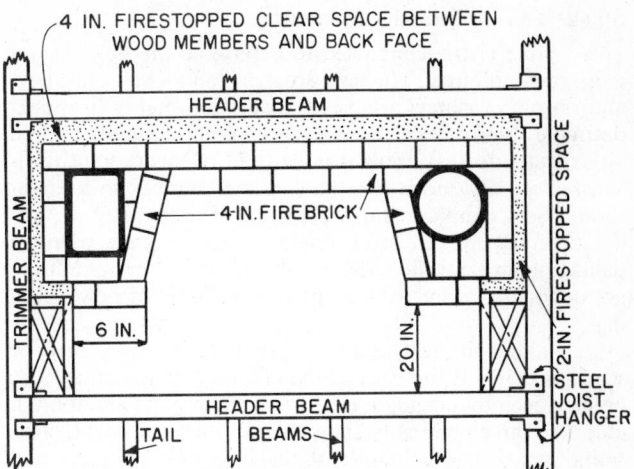

Fig. 7-3HH. Floor framing around a fireplace, when the fireplace opening is 6 sq ft or larger.

beams and chimney walls with mineral wool or other loose noncombustible material, or filling the open space around the chimney between the ceiling and attic floor level may introduce a hazard because they restrict air circulation to the extent that the chimney at the floor or attic levels will not be normally cooled. Under conditions of long continued high flue temperatures, ignition of the woodwork is a likelihood.

Chimney Fires

The burning of soot and other accumulations in a chimney is characteristic of what is called a chimney fire as opposed to a fire in which the chimney itself is defective. A common but unsafe method of getting rid of soot and incrustations is to burn them out.

Chimney fires can be extinguished by water used sparingly from a spray nozzle to prevent spalling of the hot brickwork and cracking of the lining, and to prevent damage from dirty water running out of the chimney.

Excessive soot accumulations or continually smoking chimneys are an indication of improper design of the heating appliance or chimney, the use of unsuitable fuel, or improper operation. Soot deposits will be minimized when the heating appliance is so operated as to produce complete combustion of the fuel, and chimney wall temperatures are maintained sufficiently high to prevent condensation of products of combustion in the chimney. The same factors that produce satisfactory and efficient operation of heating devices will minimize soot deposits.

One cause of prolific soot accumulation in chimneys is improper stoking of handfired heaters burning bituminous coal. Portions of the coal are volatilized but the temperature and air at the surface of the fuel bed are not sufficient to assure combustion. Another common cause of soot accumulation is the use of green firewood.

Dampers of the types which regulate the draft by admitting cold air to the smokepipe, commonly referred to as "barometric" dampers, tend to increase soot deposits by cooling the smoke and thus promoting condensation of tarry products on the chimney walls. In general, soot accumulations will be greater where the operation of a heating appliance is intermittent and the chimney walls have time to cool between operations than when the appliance is in continuous operation.

Smoke Test for Masonry Chimneys

A smoke test is conducted to determine the tightness of a masonry chimney. The tests are made on all new chimneys and on old chimneys whenever inspection makes it appear desirable. Many brick masons say that all chimneys should be expected to leak. This is not true if the workmanship is satisfactory. A smoke test showing the chimney to be tight should be a condition for acceptance of a chimney.

Care must be exercised in conducting smoke tests to avoid damaging interior finishes. Smoke tests of new chimneys are conducted prior to final interior finishing of new buildings.

In making the test, a fire of paper, tar paper, straw, or wood is made at the base of the chimney. Smoke may also be produced by placing a mixture of three parts ammonium chloride, three parts potassium chlorate, and one part lactose (milk sugar) in a container at the base of a chimney and lighting it. Once the smoke starts passing up the chimney in a dense column, the outlet at the top is tightly blocked by laying a wet blanket over it. Smoke will then appear at points of leakage.

Metal Chimneys

Metal chimneys may be used to serve fuel-burning equipment of all kinds. They may be located outside or inside buildings except not inside dwellings. The metal must be adequate thickness with sections properly joined (riveting, welding, etc.) and constructed in accordance with good engineering practices. They are supported on substantial foundations of masonry, concrete, or noncombustible material. The foundation is independent of building construction and designed to transfer the load directly to the ground.

Sheet steel for the walls of chimneys ought to be not less than indicated in Table 7-3O.

If a metal chimney must pass through a combustible roof, a ventilating thimble of galvanized sheet metal or other corrosion resistant metal (see Fig. 7-3II) is required.

Metal chimneys terminate above the roof at an elevation as specified for masonry chimneys in Table 7-3N, and where necessary they are braced at least every 20 ft or otherwise substantially and securely supported.

Spark Arresters on Chimneys

Spark arresters are required in a variety of situations on chimneys in dwellings and other buildings, on industrial chimneys, and on chimneys on refuse burners. They are particularly called for where there are combustible roofs, lumber storage, and similar conditions. Although arresters cannot entirely eliminate the spark hazard, they may abate

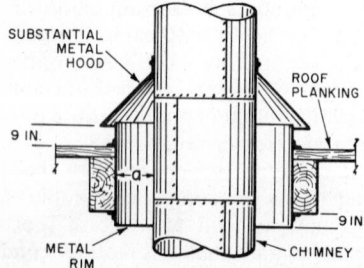

Fig. 7-3II. Arrangement of a metal chimney through a wooden roof. For chimneys serving residential-type or low heat appliances, dimension "a" should be at least 6 in. For chimneys serving medium heat appliances, dimension "a" should be at least 18 in.

Table 7-3O. Metal Thickness for Chimneys

Mfrs. Std. Gage No.	Area (sq in.)
16	Up to 154
14	154 to 201
12	201 to 254
10	Larger than 254

the hazard where combustible rubbish is burned and where there may be sooty deposits in chimneys from which flying brands may originate.

Metal chimneys for medium heat appliances producing flue gases having a temperature above 1,000°F, measured at the entrance to the chimney, and chimneys for high heat appliances preferably are lined with suitable firebrick. Metal work is painted—galvanized metal is seldom used.

If an interior chimney extends through any story of a building above that in which the appliance connected to the chimney is installed, the chimney is enclosed in the upper stories within a continuous enclosure constructed of noncombustible material. The enclosure extends from the ceiling of the appliance room to or through the roof so as to maintain its integrity as an enclosure. A fire resistance rating of not less than 1 hr is required if the building is less than four stories in height and not less than 2 hrs if the building is four stories or more in height.

Clearances around metal chimneys are established with the following in mind: the distance from combustible material, room required for inspection and maintenance, and the possibility of people coming in contact with and being burned by the chimney, particularly if the chimney is near an exit or walkway. Recommended minimum clearances for chimneys for residential type, low heat and medium heat appliances are given in Table 7-3P. Clearances for high heat appliances are based on good engineering practices.

Table 7-3P. Clearances for Metal Chimneys

Description	Clearances, Inches Kind of Appliances Served	
	Residential Type and Low Heat	Medium Heat
Interior Chimneys		
To combustibles	18	36
To enclosure	12	12
Exterior Chimneys		
To combustibles	6	24
To door, windows, and walkways	24	24
Interior and Exterior		
To noncombustible building walls		
Over 18 in. diam.	4	4
18 in. or less diam.	2	2

SI Units

The following conversion factors are given as a convenience in converting to SI units the English units used in this chapter.

1 Btu	=	1.055 kJ
1 Btu per hr	=	0.293 W
1 in.	=	25.400 m
1 ft	=	0.305 m
1 psi	=	6.895 kPa
$\frac{5}{9}$(°F − 32)	=	°C
1 gal	=	3.785 litres

Bibliography

References Cited

[1] ASTM Standards on Gaseous Fuels (Parts 23, 24, 25, and 26), American Society for Testing and Materials, Philadelphia, 1974.

[2] "Heating Boilers," Section IV, *ASME Boiler and Pressure Vessel Code,* American Society of Mechanical Engineers, New York, 1974.

NFPA Codes, Standards, and Recommended Practices (see the latest *NFPA Publications and Visual Aids Catalog* for availability of current editions of the following documents)

NFPA No. 30, Flammable and Combustible Liquids Code.

NFPA No. 31, Standard for the Installation of Oil Burning Equipment.

NFPA No. 54, National Fuel Gas Code.

NFPA No. 58, Standard for the Storage and Handling of Liquefied Petroleum Gases.

NFPA No. 60, Standard for the Installation and Operation of Pulverized Fuel Systems.

NFPA No. 70, National Electrical Code.

NFPA No. 85, Standard for Prevention of Furnace Explosions in Fuel Oil- and Natural Gas-Fired Watertube Boiler Furnaces with One Burner.

NFPA No. 85B, Standard for Prevention of Furnace Explosions in Natural Gas-Fired Multiple Burner Boiler-Furnaces.

NFPA No. 85D, Standard for Prevention of Furnace Explosions in Fuel Oil-Fired Multiple Burner Boiler-Furnaces.

NFPA No. 85E, Standard for Prevention of Furnace Explosions in Pulverized Coal-Fired Multiple Burner Boiler-Furnaces.

NFPA No. 86A, Standard for Ovens and Furnaces.

NFPA No. 86B, Standard for Industrial Furnaces.

NFPA No. 86C, Standard for Industrial Furnaces Using a Special Processing Atmosphere.

NFPA No. 89M, Manual on Clearances for Heat Producing Appliances.

NFPA No. 90A, Standard for the Installation of Air Conditioning and Ventilating Systems.

NFPA No. 90B, Standard for the Installation of Residence Type Warm Air Heating and Air Conditioning Systems.

NFPA No. 96, Standard for the Installation of Equipment for Removal of Smoke and Grease-Laden Vapors from Commercial Cooking Equipment.

NFPA No. 97M, Standard Glossary of Terms Relating to Chimneys, Gas Vents and Heat Producing Devices.

NFPA No. 211, Standard for Chimneys, Fireplaces and Vents.

NFPA No. 255, Method of Test of Surface Burning Characteristics of Building Material.

NFPA No. 393, Recommended Good Practice for the Construction, Maintenance and Use of Gasoline Blow Torches and Plumbers' Furnaces.

Additional Readings

"American National Standard for Gas Utilization Equipment in Large Boilers," ANSI Z83.3, 1971, American Gas Association Laboratories, Cleveland, Ohio.

ASHRAE Handbook and Product Directory, "Applications," 1974; "Systems," 1973; "Equipment," 1972; American Society of Heating, Refrigerating and Air-Conditioning Engineers, Inc., New York.

"Clearances and Insulation of Heating Appliances," UL Bulletin of Research No. 27, Feb. 1943, Underwriters' Laboratories, Inc., Chicago.

"Fireplaces and Chimneys," Farmers Bulletin No. 1889, U.S. Department of Agriculture, Washington, D.C.

"Gas Vent Tables," Research Report No. 1319, Dec. 1960, American Gas Association Laboratories, Cleveland.

Hale, R. A., and Bissell, L. P., "Wood Fuel for Home Burning," *Forestry Notes,* a University of Maine Cooperative Extension Service Information Sheet on Forest Conservation, Nov. 1973.

Havens, David, *The Woodburners Handbook,* Media House, Portland, Me., 1973.

"Industrial Control Equipment," UL Bulletin of Research No. 58, Sept. 1964. Underwriters Laboratories, Inc., Chicago.

Orton, Vrest, *The Forgotten Art of Building a Good Fireplace,* 2nd ed., Yankee Press, Inc., Dublin, N. H., 1974.

"Performance of Type B Gas Vents for Gas-Fired Appliances," UL Bulletin of Research No. 51, May 1959, Underwriters' Laboratories, Inc., Chicago.

Perry, E. H., "A Field Survey of Gas-Appliance Venting Conditions, Part II," Research Report No. 1267, March 1957, American Gas Association Laboratories, Cleveland.

Perry, E. H., and Verderber, J. J., "Vent Cowl Performance and Location," Research Report No. 1362, Nov. 1963, American Gas Association Laboratories, Cleveland.

"Primary Safety Controls for Gas and Oil-Fired Appliances," UL 372, 2nd ed., 1971. Underwriters Laboratories, Inc., Chicago.

"Recommended Rules for Care and Operation of Heating Boilers," Section VI, ASME Boiler and Pressure Vessel Code, American Society of Mechanical Engineers, New York, 1974.

Reed, H. L., "A Field Survey of Gas Appliance Venting Conditions," Research Report No. 1243, American Gas Association Laboratories, Cleveland.

Reineke, L. H., "Wood Fuel Combustion Practice," Report No. 1666-18, Reaffirmed, May 1961, U.S. Department of Agriculture, Forest Products Laboratory.

Reineke, L. H., "Wood Fuel Preparation," U.S. Forest Service Research Note EPL-O90, Jan. 1969, U.S. Department of Agriculture, Forest Service, Forest Products Laboratory, Madison, Wis., in cooperation with the University of Wisconsin.

"Sizing of Vent Pipe and Chimneys for Gas Appliances," Research Report No. 1300, June 1960, American Gas Association Laboratories, Cleveland.

"Specifications for Fuel Oils," D 396-73, American Society for Testing and Materials, Philadelphia, 1974.

"Using Coal and Wood Stoves Safely, A Hazard Study," NFPA HS-8, National Fire Protection Association, Boston, 1974.

"Wood Fuel and Wood Stoves," No. R1279, June 1942, U.S. Department of Agriculture, Forest Service, Forest Products Laboratory, Madison, Wis., in cooperation with the University of Wisconsin.

Chapter 4

AIR CONDITIONING AND VENTILATING SYSTEMS

The term "air conditioning" has been defined by the American Society of Heating, Refrigerating, and Air Conditioning Engineers as: "Air conditioning is the process of treating air so as to control simultaneously its temperature, humidity, cleanliness, and distribution to meet the requirements of the conditioned space." The use of air conditioning and ventilating systems invariably, except for self-contained units, involves some use of ducts for air distribution. Likewise, the use of ducts invariably presents the possibility of spreading fire, fire gases, and smoke throughout the building or area served. This and other potential hazards of air conditioning and ventilating systems are the subjects of this chapter.

Details on safeguarding against the hazards of duct systems are presented in NFPA 90A, Air Conditioning and Ventilating Systems Standard. Also, the bibliography at the end of this chapter contains additional references from which much useful information may be obtained. Finally, the recent interest in providing smoke control systems in buildings is discussed in *Part H* of this chapter, as well as in NFPA 90A.

A. System Types and Operation

The several types of air conditioning systems include: (1) systems in which air is filtered or washed, cooled and dehumidified in summer, and heated and humidified in winter; (2) systems where air is filtered, cooled, and dehumidified; (3) systems where air is filtered, heated, and humidified. Figure 7-4A depicts a typical arrangement of the various components of a central air conditioning system. A ventilating system simply supplies or removes air by natural or mechanical means to or from a space. The air may or may not be conditioned.

Referring to the typical recirculation type of central air conditioning system depicted in Figure 7-4A, a fresh air intake duct connects directly to the system's return duct. From this point, the mixture of fresh and recirculated air passes through the air conditioning equipment. The air is subjected to several operations in this equipment, including filtration or cleaning, heating or cooling, and humidification or dehumidification. The conditioned air is then circulated

throughout the area served via the duct system (see Fig. 7-4B). The process is continuous. Those systems which do not recirculate any air take all of their make-up air directly from the outside. A building may contain more than one system, not necessarily of the same type.

B. Location of Equipment

Fans, heaters, filters, and associated equipment that make up the air conditioning unit for a central system are preferably located in a room cut off from the rest of the building area by walls, floor, and floor-ceiling assembly providing a minimum one hour fire resistance rating. This arrangement prevents a fire involving the equipment from immediately spreading to adjacent areas of the building. Also, such an arrangement prevents access to the equipment by unauthorized persons. Ideally, service rooms housing air conditioning equipment are protected by automatic sprinkler equipment. At the least, smoke or heat detectors, or both should be provided and arranged to initiate an alarm and shut down the air conditioning system. No combustible storage should be allowed in the equipment room.

C. Fresh-air Intakes

The location selected for the fresh-air intakes of a system is critical, since fire, fire gases, or smoke originating outside the building can easily be drawn in through these intakes and then be spread throughout the building. Where such a hazard may exist, protection can be provided by the installation of fire doors or dampers at the intakes that are controlled by fire and smoke detectors.

When considering the location of exterior fresh-air intakes, thought should be given to the possibility of sparks or other products of combustion from an exposing fire chimney, or incinerator stack, being drawn into the system. Consideration should not be limited to adjacent buildings or

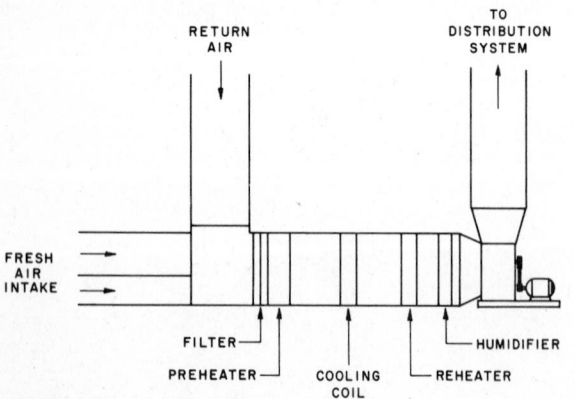

Fig. 7-4A. Typical arrangement of the component parts of a central air conditioning system.

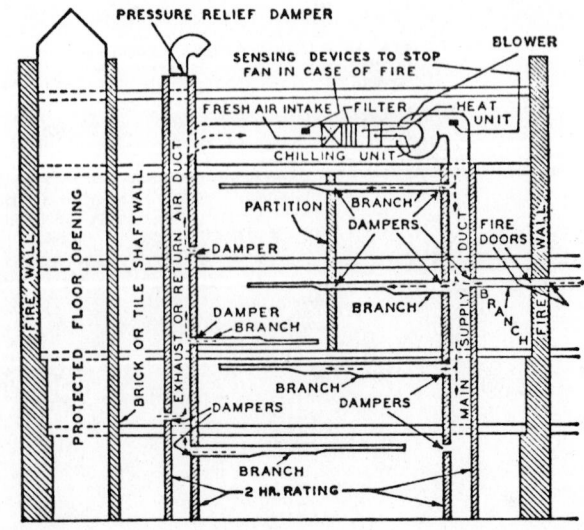

Fig. 7-4B. Typical installation of air conditioning system in building.

combustible storage. The possibility of fire from a different section of the same building or an adjoining building is a factor which must be considered in selecting the location of fresh-air intakes.

All air intakes are provided with screens of corrosion-resistant material not larger than $\frac{1}{2}$-in. mesh, to prevent any material from entering the system. Proper maintenance includes periodic removal of any accumulated rubbish or other waste from the immediate vicinity of the intakes. It should be noted that some fresh air intakes are fitted with a filter which is subject to the same hazards mentioned in Part F, Air Filters and Cleaners. These should be protected and maintained accordingly.

D.   Air Cooling and Heating Equipment

Air cooling equipment presents two basic classes of hazards: those of the electrical equipment and those of the particular refrigerant used. Fire experience is generally good where the cooling equipment is properly installed and maintained. Installation of all electrical equipment should follow both the manufacturer's recommendations and NFPA No. 70 National Electrical Code.

In general, the refrigerant poses a toxicity problem and, in a few cases, a combustibility hazard (see Sec. 4, Chap. 12). Even some of the halogenated hydrocarbon refrigerants used in most systems are slightly flammable. The greatest problem associated with refrigeration units is the explosion hazard due to pressurization of the refrigerant. Recommendations for the installation of mechanical refrigerating equipment are contained in the *Safety Code for Mechanical Refrigeration* issued by the American Society of Heating, Refrigerating, and Air Conditioning Engineers.[1] Construction of pressure vessels is covered by the *Unfired Pressure Vessel Code* of the American Society of Mechanical Engineers.[2]

Hazards of air heating equipment depend on the mode of heating used. Installation and protection of heating systems are covered in more detail in Chapter 3 of this Section.

E.   Air Filters and Cleaners

The types of air filters and cleaners used in air conditioning and ventilating systems fall into three general categories: fibrous media unit filters, renewable media filters, and electronic air cleaners. The first two are true filters; the last is a static precipitator. Air filters and cleaners pose a potential hazard due to their function of removing entrained dust and other particulate matter from the air stream. This material builds up on the filter media or precipitator collection plates and, if ignited, may burn producing large volumes of smoke. The smoke and other combustion gases can be circulated throughout the building by the air handling system, thus posing a direct threat to life safety. Not to be overlooked are the possibilities that filter media may be coated with a combustible adhesive or may itself be combustible.

Underwriters Laboratories, Inc., lists two classes of filter media:[3]

Class 1: Filters which, when clean, do not contribute fuel when attacked by flame and which emit only negligible amounts of smoke.

Class 2: Filters which, when clean, burn moderately when attacked by flame and/or which emit moderate amounts of smoke.

Both of these classes include renewable (washable and reuseable) media and replaceable (disposable) media.

Class 1 filter media is preferred, particularly for systems serving places of assembly, such as theaters, auditoriums, department stores, etc. Class 1 filter media is also the obvious choice for systems serving occupancies whose contents are easily susceptible to smoke damage; however, any filter media, if not cleaned or replaced regularly, may become hazardous due to accumulation of combustible dust, etc.

Fibrous Media Unit Filters

Fibrous media unit filters are placed into the air stream and remain there until the pressure drop across the filter reaches some critical point, due to the build-up of entrained material. At this point, the filter is either removed, cleaned, and reinstalled or simply discarded and replaced with a new filter. Fibrous media unit filters are of either the viscous impingement type or the dry media type, the latter being more popular now.

The viscous impingement type of filter is characterized by flat or pleated panels of relatively coarse fiber mats. Porosity of the panel is high. The fibers are coated with an adhesive which traps any material entrained in the air stream. The mats are $\frac{1}{2}$- to 4-in. thick, 1 and 2 in. being most common. This type of filter is most effective when air velocity ranges from 250 to 700 fpm (feet per minute). Most of these unit filters are ready for replacement when the pressure drop reaches 0.5 in. of water. The renewable panels must be washed with steam or a hot detergent solution, then recoated with fresh adhesive.

Dry media unit filters are flat or pleated panels of relatively fine fibers, usually $\frac{1}{2}$- to 2-in. thick. As their name implies, these filters have no adhesive coating. Porosity is not as great as for the viscous impingement type; hence particulate removal is greater, depending on fiber size and porosity. These filters are most effective with an air velocity of 90 to 250 fpm. Pressure drop rise to as much as 2.0 in. of water before replacement is necessary. Disposable dry fibrous media unit filters, particularly of the deep pleated design, are fast becoming the standard for large central air conditioning systems. The dry media classification of air filters also includes membrane and high efficiency types which are used to ultra-clean air for clean rooms and similar areas.

Renewable Media Filters

Renewable media air filters can more accurately be termed "moving curtain" air filters, since they operate in exactly such a fashion. The media, whether viscous-coated or dry, is supplied on a large roll, and extends across the air stream. As the dust load builds up, pressure drop increases to a point where a pressure switch activates a motor drive which feeds fresh media across the air stream and winds the dirty media onto a take-up spool. Generally, controls are provided that de-energize the drive motor when the media supply is almost exhausted, thus preventing the media from being completely wound onto the take-up spool. A signal indicates that a fresh roll is needed. Operating velocities range from 200 to 500 fpm with the dry media types requiring the lower velocities. Filter thicknesses vary from $\frac{1}{2}$ to $2\frac{1}{2}$ in.

Some renewable viscous impingement filters are of permanent design. The media is in the form of an endless belt, one part of which passes through a reservoir where the dust load is removed and fresh adhesive added. Proper maintenance includes periodic removal of precipitated dirt and dust from the reservoir. This type is not so common now.

Electronic Air Cleaners

Electronic air cleaners utilize the principle of electrostatic precipitation to remove entrained dust and particulate matter. There are several types of electronic air cleaners, but their basic operation is the same. Entrained particles in the air stream pass through intense, nonuniform electrostatic fields and, due to electric polarization, are collected either on a filter media supported on a charged gridwork or on charged plates. In some units, equipment is provided to preionize the particulate matter.

Special Industrial Filters and Air Cleaners

There are many situations in industrial applications of air cleaning that involve more than the usual filtering and cleaning methods previously cited. Exhaust systems for flammable vapors, dusts, and other materials in suspension require equipment for recovering the suspended material. (Exhaust systems are covered in Chapter 5 of this Section.)

Air cleaning to limit contamination and pollution is of growing concern to industry and public health authorities. Whatever the reason for specialized air cleaning, and whatever the type of equipment used, the selection and protection of the equipment are of concern as the fire hazards are the same as for more common types of air cleaning equipment.

One current industrial application of air filtering is in clean rooms where HEPA (high efficiency particle air) filters are used to filter the atmosphere. These filters must pass an operational efficiency test of 99.97 percent efficiency with 0.3 micron particles. The filters are tested and labeled by Underwriters' Laboratories, Inc., in accordance with *High Efficiency Air Filter Units,* UL 586.[4] The fire hazards of and protection for clean rooms are discussed in detail in a *Fire Technology* article.[5]

Protection for Air Filters and Cleaners

Fire in the filters or air cleaning equipment can release copious quantities of smoke or fire gases that can be distributed by the air handling equipment throughout the area served. Adequate protection to minimize the possibility of such an occurrence must be designed into and around the air conditioning system.

Some means is necessary to prevent smoke and fire gases from being distributed by the main supply fan to all areas served by the system. To accomplish this, detectors are located in the main supply duct, downstream of the filters or air cleaner, to sense smoke or particles of combustion. The detectors are interlocked so as to immediately shut down the entire air conditioning system upon activation. The detectors also control the operation of smoke dampers located in the main supply and return ducts, thus isolating the entire air conditioning section of the system.

Automatic extinguishing systems are recommended for fire suppression within the enclosure of the air filtration or cleaning equipment. The extinguishing agent may be water, inert gas, or dry chemical. Operation of the extinguishing system can be independent or can be triggered by the smoke or particles of combustion detectors.

With specific regard to viscous impingement filters, the adhesive used should have a flash point of not less than 325°F, (via Pensky-Martens Closed Tester.)[6] Also, combustible adhesives should be stored in a safe location, remote from the equipment room housing the air conditioning equipment.

Fire protection always includes facilities for manual fire fighting. This usually takes the form of portable fire extinguishers. Fans, motors, pumps, control circuits, etc., all point out the need for carbon dioxide extinguishers. However, dry chemical extinguishers would be more suitable for use on filters, especially the viscous impingement type, since the chemical powder would readily adhere to the coated media. The obvious solution is to provide both types.

A final word in connection with electronic air cleaners. The operational voltage and amperage of such equipment is lethal. Therefore, interlocks are provided on every access door and panel so that the equipment is immediately shut down if any one of them is opened. An alarm should also be incorporated into this safety interlock circuit.

F.   Ducts

Ducts are to an air conditioning or ventilating system what pipes are to a water system; a means of distribution. Unfortunately, in fire situations, the ducts may transport deadly smoke and products of combustion instead of breatheable air. If proper design and installation precautions are not taken, smoke, fire gases, heat, and even flame can spread throughout the area served by the duct system. The usual result in such a situation is panic among the occupants. Exit halls used as plenums, lack of smoke detection activated control equipment in the system, and lack of adequate smoke dampers in appropriate walls, ceilings, or partitions can lead to tragic situations.

Duct Construction

Ducts may be fabricated of metal, masonry, or other noncombustible material. The thickness of materials used in metal ducts of various sizes and methods of bracing, reinforcing, and hanging are covered in the duct manuals of the Sheet Metal and Air Conditioning Contractors National Association (SMACNA)[7] and the Guide and Data Book, Equipment of the American Society of Heating, Refrigerating, and Air Conditioning Engineers (ASHRAE).[8] SMACNA also publishes manuals on the installation of glass fiber ducts.[7]

Underwriters Laboratories, Inc. tests and lists duct materials in accordance with its *Standard for Factory-Made Air Duct Materials and Air Duct Connectors,* UL181.[9] This standard sets limits on such characteristics as flame spread and flame penetration. Materials are classified as follows:

Class 0: Material having flame spread and smoke developed ratings of zero.

Class 1: Material having a flame spread rating of not over 25, with no evidence of continued progressive combustion, and a smoke developed rating not over 50.

Class 2: Material having a flame spread rating of not over 50, with no evidence of continued progressive combustion, and a smoke developed rating of not over 50 for the inside surface and not over 100 for the outside surface.

In addition to the above, Class 0 and Class 1 materials must pass a 30-min flame penetration test and Class 2 materials must pass a 15-min flame penetration test.

The NFPA Air Conditioning and Ventilating Standard specifies only Class 0 or Class 1 duct materials for use in systems over 25,000 cfm capacity. The standard also gives other mandatory provisions for duct linings and coverings, duct tapes and bands, as well as limitations on the use of flexible duct connectors which must pass through walls, partitions, floors, or ceilings intended to afford fire resistance or smoke control.

Duct Installation

Ducts, by their very nature, provide excellent means for transferring heat, fire gases, and flame, thus resulting in the

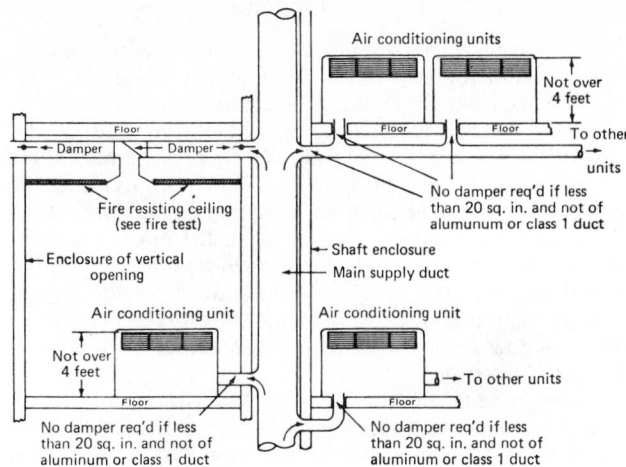

Fig. 7-4C. Typical fire damper requirements and examples of locations where dampers are not required.

spread of fire from one area to another. In addition, at some point or another, a duct will pass through a wall, partition, floor, or ceiling which is designed specifically to provide fire resistance. Literally, a hole has been poked through a fire-safe design. Theoretically, of course, the duct fills the opening. But, if the installation has been made without proper regard for firestopping, this is not valid. Also, under severe fire exposure, the duct will eventually collapse, creating an opening in the fire barrier. Figure 7-4C illustrates typical fire damper locations.

In the gages commonly used, some sheet metal ducts may protect an opening in a building construction assembly for up to 1 hr, if properly hung and adequately firestopped. Therefore, ducts passing through fire barriers having a rating of up to 1 hr of fire resistance can be assumed to present no extraordinary hazard. If the wall, partition, ceiling, or floor is required to have a fire resistance rating of more than 1 hr, a fire damper is required to properly protect the opening. Where it is necessary for a duct to pierce a fire wall, an automatic-closing fire door suitable for a Class A opening (see Sec. 6, Chap. 8) is required to properly protect the opening. The NFPA Air Conditioning and Ventilation Standard provides comprehensive recommendations and requirements for the location of fire doors and fire dampers in rated assemblies.

Fire Dampers

Fire dampers are tested and listed for use in air conditioning and ventilating ducts by Underwriters Laboratories, Inc., in accordance with NFPA No. 252, Standard Method of Fire Tests of Door Assemblies. Such dampers have a $1\frac{1}{2}$-hr fire protection rating. These dampers include single-blade, multi-blade, and interlocking blade types, actuated by fusible links. Most fire dampers are designed for vertical installation; some can be installed horizontally as well.

G.   Smoke Control—Passive

Smoke Dampers

Smoke dampers are required in air conditioning or ventilating ducts which pass through required smoke barrier partitions. The NFPA Air Conditioning and Ventilating Standard, requires smoke dampers to operate automatically upon detection of smoke and must function so that smoke movement through the duct is halted. Basically, they simply

interrupt air flow through the duct. The Standard permits the use of fire dampers for smoke control purposes. Obviously, a fire damper used thus must be modified to function by a smoke detection device, not a fusible link. The Standard also permits use of motorized air control dampers as smoke dampers, in which case smoke detection triggers an override of all other control functions and the motor drive closes the damper. Smoke dampers do not have to meet the requirements of fire dampers. Although there are no currently accepted criteria for air leakage past closed smoke dampers, designers should select dampers which exhibit minimum leakage, especially where the damper will provide both air control and smoke control.

Smoke Detectors

Smoke detectors are installed in all air conditioning or ventilating systems over 15,000 cfm capacity. Further, smoke detectors for use in ducts must include features in their design specifically for this purpose. Smoke detectors may shut down the air conditioning or ventilating system, sound alarms, operate smoke control dampers, activate fire suppression equipment, or initiate active smoke control functions (see Part H). Preference is for detectors whose sensitivity is adjustable, thus minimizing false alarms due to incidental dust or other particulate matter.

Smoke detectors are located in the main supply ducts, downstream of air filters or air cleaners, and in the main return ducts prior to exhausting from the building or joining the fresh air intake ducts. Smoke detectors at these locations are primarily intended to prevent smoke circulation throughout the entire area served by shutting down the air handling system. Also they prevent circulation of smoke from a fire in the air filters or air cleaners. Due to dilution effects of air picked up from various branch return ducts, these smoke detectors cannot be expected to reliably provide "early warning" smoke detection. For this reason, additional smoke detectors may be provided; for example, in the main branch return duct from each floor or major area division. Such detectors could also be tied in to a zoned fire alarm system; however, such an arrangement is not a substitute for a smoke detection system for building protection.

H.   Smoke Control—Active

The preceding material covered passive control of smoke and fire gases—control designed to prevent products of combustion from moving out of the area of its source. It is an inescapable fact that attempts to completely confine smoke and fire gases are seldom successful. Recognizing this, smoke movement in high-rise buildings and its threat to life safety, has been the object of much investigation.[10, 11] The discussion of modes of smoke movement, their causes, and effects are outside the scope of this chapter (see Sec. 2, Chap. 5). However, worthy of note, i.e., high-rise buildings do present several unique problems: excessive evacuation time, inability of conventional fire equipment (aerial ladders, "snorkels", and monitor nozzles) to reach upper floors, and the reinforcement of existing upward air flow patterns within the building via vertical shafts (stack effect).

In view of the increasing trend towards high-rise buildings, it becomes attractive to utilize the air conditioning or ventilating system for smoke control and removal in case of fire. Tests have been conducted on the feasibility of pressurizing emergency exit stairwells and elevator shafts to prevent smoke migration from the fire floor to other parts of a building during evacuation.[12] Another approach recommends venting of the fire floor and pressurization of the rest of the building.[13]

The supply air units of the building air conditioning or ventilating system can be utilized to pressurize exit stairwells, elevator shafts, or refuge areas within the building. It is doubtful, however, that the supply units alone will be able to accomplish such a task without the aid of auxiliary pressurization fans. Return or exhaust units of the air handling system will probably be unsuited for venting of the fire area, unless they are specifically designed to handle hot fire gases for extended periods of time.

Some reevaluation of power requirements for fan units will be necessary, since protected areas will have to be pressurized to a minimum of about 0.15 in. of water, to counter the pressure buildup in the fire area as a result of thermal expansion.[14] Electrical services to these emergency systems will have to be well protected from the effects of a fire. These systems must be tied into an emergency electric generator. The appendix of the NFPA Air Conditioning and Ventilating Standard provides guidelines for designers who wish to provide active smoke control systems for buildings.

I. Fans, Controls, Etc.

The fan unit should not in itself present undue hazard, if properly installed and firmly supported on a rigid foundation. It should also be readily accessible for cleaning, servicing, and lubrication. Fans should be provided with excess vibration switches, wired to sound an alarm and initiate system shutdown when bearing failure is imminent.

Fan motors installed inside ducts or plenums need protective devices to cut off power before temperatures reach a point where smoke may be generated. Most fractional horsepower motors have over-temperature protective devices. Thermal overload relays are recommended for fan motors of one horsepower or larger.

Electric wiring to all components should follow NFPA No. 70, National Electrical Code. All electrical equipment should be listed by a recognized fire testing laboratory.

All air conditioning or ventilating systems need manual shutoffs for use in case of fire or other emergency. This shutoff should be well identified and located where it is readily accessible, such as near building exits. In systems of 2,000 to 15,000 cfm capacity, it is good practice to provide automatic shutoff controls triggered by thermostatic devices in the same locations as recommended for smoke detectors (see Part G). A setting of 136°F for the thermostatic device in the return air stream and a setting of 50°F above maximum operational temperature for the device in the supply stream are recommended.

J. Unit Air Conditioners

The term "unit air conditioner" is a rather loose one. It may include any factory-produced unit serving one room or area. Such units do not involve the hazard of spreading fire from floor to floor or area to area as do ducted systems. However, if improperly designed, installed, or maintained, they may involve the other hazards associated with larger systems. For example, any window-sill type unit can overheat through failure of its thermal relay. This could lead to ignition of wire insulation or filter media and the fire could spread to curtains or the wood sash of the window. Defective wiring could lead to the same condition. The greatest problem involving these units is that they are too frequently plugged into outlets on branch circuits not designed to carry so great a load or already heavily loaded. This practice directly violates principles of the National Electrical Code.

K. Maintenance

Maintenance and cleaning are of utmost importance to safe operation of any air conditioning or ventilating system. Filters must be changed or cleaned as frequently as necessary. Ducts, particularly on the return side of the system are cleaned out periodically to prevent hazardous accumulations of combustible dust and lint. Evidence of any form of wiring or electrical equipment defect is checked out immediately and rectified, if needed. Repairs on ducts or equipment casings which require welding or cutting should be protected by complete shutdown of the system and thorough cleaning of the area to be worked on. If possible, the duct section to be repaired should be isolated from the rest of the system.

Proper maintenance includes periodic testing of all fire protection devices, including fire suppression equipment, smoke control dampers, alarms, and even vibration switches on fans. A program should be established for regular testing. If such testing is outside the function of regular maintenance staff, it should be contracted to an outside agency.

SI Units

The following conversion factors are given as a convenience in converting to SI units the English units used in this chapter.

$$1 \text{ in.} \quad = 25.400 \text{ mm}$$
$$1 \text{ ft} \quad = 0.305 \text{ m}$$
$$\tfrac{5}{9}\,(°F - 32) = °C$$
$$1 \text{ cfm} \quad = 0.283 \text{ m}^3/\text{min}$$

Bibliography

References Cited

[1] "Safety Code for Mechanical Refrigeration," No. 15-70, 1970 ed., American Society of Heating, Refrigerating and Air Conditioning Engineers, New York.

[2] "Unfired Pressure Vessel Code," Sec. VIII, 1974 ed., American Society of Mechanical Engineers, Inc., New York.

[3] "Standard for Air Filter Units," UL900, 2nd ed., Aug., 1971, Underwriters Laboratories, Inc., Northbrook, IL.

[4] "Standard for High Efficiency Air Filter Units," UL586, 3rd ed., July 1971, Underwriters Laboratories, Inc., Northbrook, IL.

[5] Keigher, Donald J., "Clean Rooms—Another Fire Protection Problem," Part I, *Fire Technology*, Vol. 3, No. 4, Nov., 1967, pp. 261–271.

[6] "Standard Method of Test for Flash Point by Pensky-Martens Closed Tester," D 93, 1972 ed., American Society for Testing and Materials, Philadelphia, PA.

[7] "Duct Manual, Fibrous Glass Construction Manual for Ventilating and Air Conditioning Systems," 3rd ed., 1972, "Low Velocity Duct Construction Standard," 4th ed., 1969 and, "High Velocity Duct Construction Standard," 2nd ed., 1969, Sheet Metal and Air Conditioning Contractors National Association, Inc., Arlington, VA.

[8] "Guide and Data Book, Equipment," 1972 ed., American Society of Heating, Refrigerating, and Air Conditioning Engineers, Inc., New York.

[9] "Standard for Factory-Made Air Duct Materials and Air Duct Connectors," UL181, 4th ed., 1974, Underwriters' Laboratories, Inc., Northbrook, IL.

[10] McGuire, J. H., "Smoke Movement in Buildings," *Fire Technology*, Vol. 3, No. 3, August, 1967, pp. 163–174.

[11] Hutcheon, N. B. and Shorter, G. W., "Smoke Problems in High-Rise Buildings," ASHRAE Journal, Vol. 10, No. 9, September 1968.

[12] Koplon, N. A., "Report of the Henry Grady Fire Tests," City of Atlanta Building Department, Atlanta, GA, January, 1973.

[13] McGuire, J. H. and Tamura, G. T., "The Pressurized Building Method of Controlling Smoke in High-Rise Buildings," National Research Council of Canada, Division of Building Research, Technical Paper No. 394 (NRCC 13365), Ottawa, September, 1973.

[14] "Multi Protection Design," Preliminary Draft, December 1973, Defense Civil Preparedness Agency, Washington, D.C., p. 264.

NFPA Codes, Standards, and Recommended Practices (see the latest *NFPA Publications and Visual Aids Catalog* for availability of current editions of the following documents)

NFPA No. 70, National Electrical Code.

NFPA No. 90A, Standard for the Installation of Air Conditioning and Ventilating Systems.

NFPA No. 252, Standard Methods of Fire Tests of Door Assemblies.

Additional Readings

"Air Conditioning" Fire Hazard Study, Fire Record Bulletin HS-7, 1967, National Fire Protection Association, Boston.

Capron, J. J. and Wilson, J. A., "Fire Hazard of Fibrous Glass Ducts—An Evaluation," *Fire Technology,* Vol. 2, No. 1, Feb. 1966, pp. 24–36.

Factory Mutual Engineering Corporation, "Air Conditioning Systems," *Handbook of Industrial Loss Prevention,* 2nd ed., McGraw-Hill, New York, 1967, pp. 10–1, 10–6.

Stevens, R. E., "Fire Dampers in Air Conditioning Ducts," *Fire Journal,* National Fire Protection Association, Vol. 59, No. 4, July, 1965, pp. 44–45.

Tamura, G. T., "Computer Analysis of Smoke Control with Building Air Handling Systems," National Research Council of Canada, Division of Building Research, Research Paper No. 534 (NRCC 12809), Ottawa, September, 1972.

Chapter 5

AIR MOVING EQUIPMENT

Air moving equipment (AME) includes all mechanical-draft duct systems, of both the pressure and exhaust types, for removal of dusts, vapors, and waste material and for the conveying of materials. The hazards of such systems lie in the possibility of igniting flammable materials or vapors by sources such as sparks struck by fans or foreign material (rocks or tramp metal) or by overheated fan bearings, and in the part that such systems play in spreading fires through buildings.

These systems do, however, play an important role in fire protection because they remove materials that if allowed to accumulate could result in explosions, as from vapor-air mixtures; flash fires, due to such things as accumulations of lint; and general poor housekeeping conditions conducive to fires.

Details on the installation of air moving equipment are given in NFPA No. 91, Blower and Exhaust Systems for Dust, Stock, and Vapor Removal or Conveying, and NFPA No. 96, Removal of Smoke and Grease-Laden Vapors from Commercial Cooking Equipment.

A. Fundamentals of Air Moving Systems

Fundamentally, air moving equipment is designed to carry away the material given off from a process or operation. This requires an air velocity ("capture velocity") at the place of generation of the material to be exhausted sufficient to overcome other forces acting on the material. These forces involve the size and shapes of particles, their specific gravity, the gravitational force and inertia given the particles as a result of the process or operation, and outside effects such as air currents. Usual "capture velocities" are in the range of 50 to 2,000 fpm.

Basic Design Considerations

Ideally, equipment producing dusts or vapors is enclosed so that the full benefit of the air velocity in the exhaust system can be utilized without interference from outside air currents. Generally, this is not possible and the design of a suitable hood, canopy, or other suction inlet is neces-sary (see Figs. 7-5A, B, C, and D) to suit various situations and to provide the best exhaust with the least air velocity. On a dip tank, for example, where vapors are to be exhausted, lateral slots around the periphery of the tank or a side hood are used where an overhead hood would interfere with the work. If the process involves vapors that are lighter than air, or if it is a "hot" process and advantage can be taken of a thermal up-draft, a canopy or hood is generally the most effective. Complete removal of the material to be exhausted is the objective, avoiding pockets where vapors may accumulate and preventing deposits of condensed material in and around equipment. Dissimilar materials should not be handled through a single exhaust system where the intermingling or contact of one type of material with another would create a fire or explosion hazard in the duct system.

Duct Construction and Installation

Ducts for air moving equipment are made of sheet metal or other noncombustible material of sufficient structural stability to remain rigid. They are substantially supported with hangers. Special materials are required where corrosive materials are handled. Joints are made tight to avoid leakage, and laps in joints are made with the inner lap in the direction of air flow. Fittings are designed to minimize friction losses and to avoid air pockets. A typical example is the tapered transformation fitting used for reducing duct sizes. Here the angle of taper is kept to 30° maximum. Numerous hand holes should be provided in the duct system to provide accessibility for inspection and cleaning.

Materials moved in air moving systems are divided into three classes. They are:

Class I: Includes nonabrasive applications such as paint spray, woodworking, pharmaceutical and food products, discharge ducts from dust collectors.

Class II: Includes nonabrasive materials in high concentrations; low pressure pneumatic conveying of moderately abrasive materials; and highly abrasive materials in light concentrations. Typical examples are conveying of chemicals and wood dusts; exhaust of foundry shakeouts and

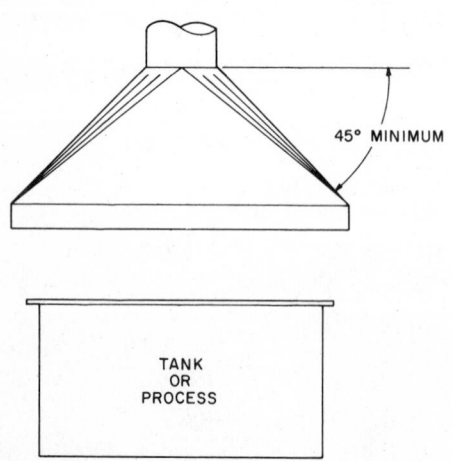

Fig. 7-5A. Canopy hood. (American Conference of Governmental Industrial Hygienists)

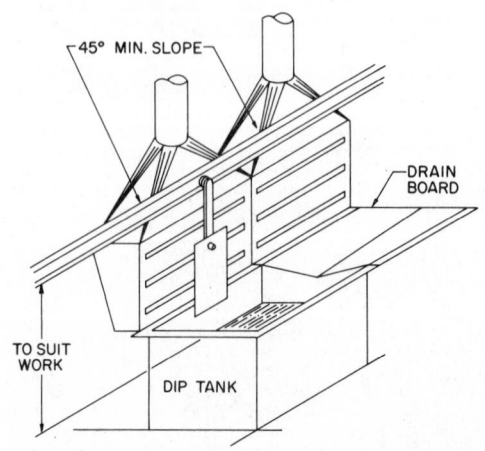

Fig. 7-5B. Side hood, such as used for dip tanks. For best results the drainboard should be enclosed as a drying tunnel. (American Conference of Governmental Industrial Hygienists)

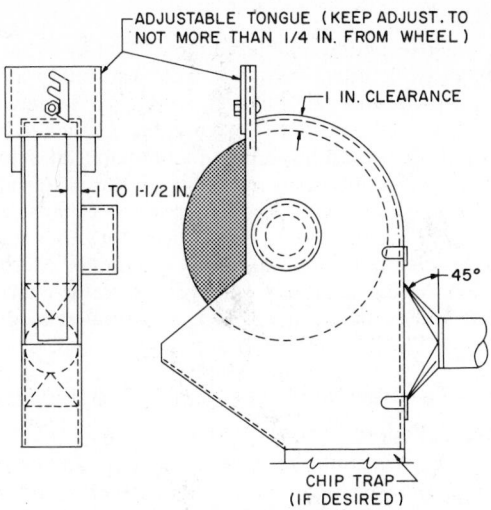

Fig. 7-5C. Grinder wheel hood. (American Conference of Governmental Industrial Hygienists)

sand-handling systems; grain dusts; coal crushing and screening and grinding; buffing and polishing.

Class III: Includes all highly abrasive materials in moderate to heavy concentration and moderately abrasive materials in heavy concentrations such as low pressure conveying of tobacco; exhaust systems from sand and grit blasting, abrasive cleaning operation, rock and ore screening, crushing dryers and kilns; fly ash from boiler stacks.

The class of material moved in a system governs the thickness of metal used in construction of ducts of various diameters. (See Table 7-5A)

For Class II or Class III materials, all sheet metal elbows, wyes and bends are made from materials at least two gages heavier than is required for straight duct-work of the same diameter, except that for No. 14 gage and heavier, the elbows and straight duct-work may be of the same gage.

More detailed requirements for duct construction and design based on the material being handled are dealt with later in this chapter.

Preferably, ducts run directly from the equipment or process served to the outside. Running ducts through fire walls, piercing floors, or extending them through attics or other concealed spaces is not good practice. If a duct must pierce a fire wall, an installation of fire doors is recommended. Fire dampers, as used in air conditioning systems (see

Table 7-5A. Minimum Gages for Ducts Constructed of Sheet Steel

Diameter of Straight Ducts (in.)	U.S. Standard Gage for Steel Duct		
	Class I	Class II	Class III
Up to 8	24	22	20
Over 8 to 18	22	20	18
Over 18 to 30	20	18	16
Over 30	18	16	14

Chap. 4 of this Section), are generally not suitable for installation in exhaust ducts because they obstruct the flow of materials through the duct resulting in accumulation on the damper which must be cleaned off periodically. If a duct passes through a wall or floor, the space around the duct is sealed with noncombustible material.

Clearance of ducts from combustible material and combustible construction is a factor requiring consideration of the material passing through the duct. If the gases in a duct are at elevated temperatures or if there is probability of fire occurring in the duct, clearances are increased to meet those conditions to avoid ignition of exposed combustibles, and if temperatures run higher than 900°F the duct should be lined with refractory material.

Design and Selection of Fans

The common types of fans used in blower and exhaust installations are centrifugal and axial flow. There are variations in design in each of these two general classifications (see Fig. 7-5E). A straight blade centrifugal fan is suitable for exhausting large particles of materials as it will not clog and the blades will withstand considerable abrasion. Propeller fans will move large volumes of air but only against small resistance. Such a fan could not operate efficiently against the friction a duct would introduce and therefore is not suitable for installation in a duct of any appreciable length.

The general fire protection features of fans to consider include: (1) noncombustible construction, (2) remote control to shut down the fan in case of fire, (3) accessibility for maintenance, and (4) structural quality to assure minimum wear and to overcome distortion and misalignment caused by structural weakness or overloading. When exhausting

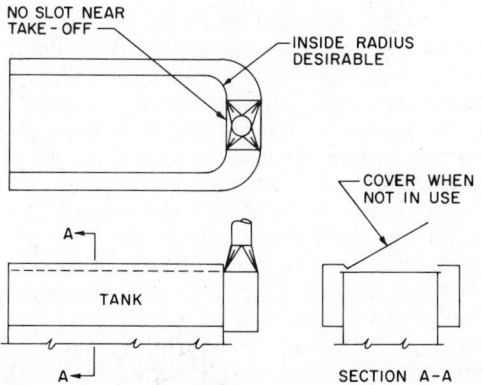

Fig. 7-5D. Slot exhaust such as used for solvent degreasing tanks. (American Conference of Governmental Industrial Hygienists)

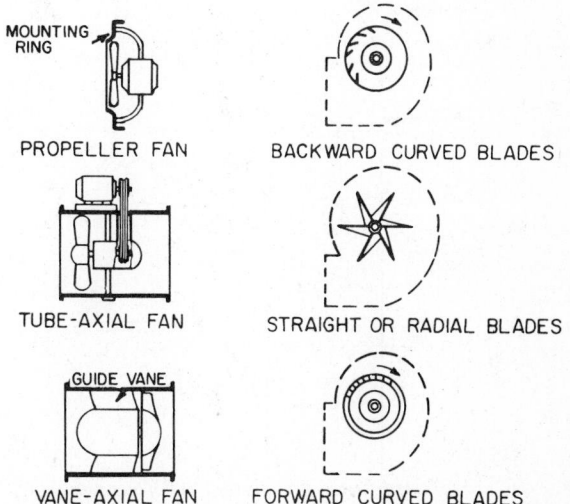

Fig. 7-5E. Types of fans suitable for use in exhaust systems. (American Conference of Governmental Industrial Hygienists)

flammable solids or vapors, there is a possibility of ignition from a spark struck when the blade hits the housing due to misalignment. This possibility of friction sparks is minimized by using a fan and fan housing of nonferrous material.

Fire Extinguishing Systems

The number of fires that originate in and spread through ducts justifies the need of automatic extinguishing systems installed in ducts handling flammable or combustible materials. Such systems may be automatically or manually controlled. Several of the extinguishing systems discussed in Section 15 are satisfactory for this purpose.

When an extremely flammable material is involved, it may be advisable to install a deluge system (see Sec. 14, Chap. 3) actuated by heat responsive devices. Sprinklers or nozzles or other types of extinguishing systems may be coated or covered to protect them, and may also have to be cleaned regularly to keep them free of deposits.

Manual Extinguishing Equipment

Portable fire extinguishers of appropriate type (see Sec. 16) or small hose with spray nozzles are helpful where fires may occur in ducts. This is true even where fixed pipe extinguishing systems have been provided.

Explosion Venting

Explosion relief vents provide protection to prevent or minimize damage to duct systems used for conveying materials which may form an explosive mixture with air. The vents should lead by the most direct practical route to the outside of the building. See Figure 7-5F for a suggested relief vent for a duct turn.

Explosion Prevention

Section 15, Chapter 7, of this HANDBOOK gives information on how inerting or explosion suppression equipment may be effectively used to prevent serious pressure ruptures of air moving equipment ducts and associated vapor or dust collecting equipment. The use of suppression and inerting systems is limited by the configuration of the equipment and the physical and chemical properties of the material being handled. Details concerning these systems are given in NFPA No. 69, Explosion Prevention Systems.

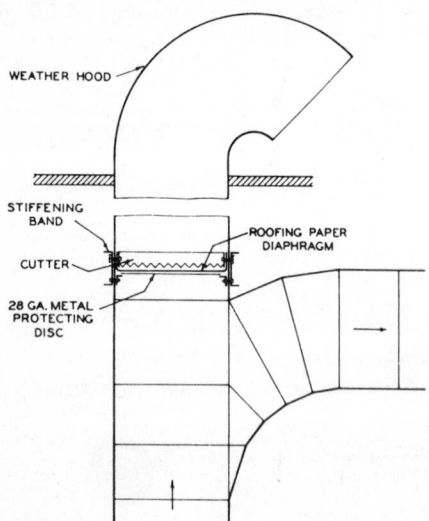

Fig. 7-5F. Suggested form of explosion relief vent suitable for use at duct turns. The thin metal protecting disc shown beneath the rupture diaphragm serves to prevent abrasion of the diaphragm, and upon operation of the device will blow free.

Static Electricity

The passage of flammable vapors, dusts or other materials through a duct results in the generation of static charges on the duct. If a charge is allowed to accumulate on an electrically insulated portion of a duct system, it could discharge to an adjoining duct section, at a joint for example, and result in the ignition of the material being conveyed in the system. For this reason, exhaust systems carrying flammable vapors, dusts, gases, or other materials should be electrically bonded and grounded. Methods of achieving the elimination of dangerous static charges are discussed in Section 5, Chapter 5, and treated in detail in NFPA No. 77, Static Electricity.

B. Special Consideration for Specific Uses

Flammable Vapors

Due to the possibility of ignition of flammable vapors in a duct system resulting in a fire or an explosion, precautions must be taken to eliminate ignition sources. Using a single system to exhaust flammable vapors as well as to exhaust particles from spark-producing processes is obviously dangerous. Similarly drawing different vapors which individually may not be flammable but which as a mixture may be hazardous into a single exhaust system is extremely poor practice. For example, if perchloric acid vapors were drawn into a system that was exhausting organic materials, fire and explosion could result as perchloric acid acts as an oxidizing agent at elevated temperatures. It is important that vapors be withdrawn from the rooms or equipment in which they are generated and taken directly to the outside of the building. Processes generating flammable vapors are best located along an outside wall of the building to facilitate efficient vapor removal.

When flammable vapors cannot be readily picked up at a specific source, general ventilation through a system of suction ducts with inlets to the room or area may be employed. As suction inlets have but little directional effect beyond a few inches from the face of the inlet, they preferably are located to best produce a sweeping or purging effect that will tend to avoid pockets in which vapors may accumulate. An air inlet supply properly located in relation to the point where vapors are generated and openings for exhaust ducts will aid in dilution and removal of vapors. The ventilation system should provide sufficient air movement to maintain the vapor concentration below the lower explosive limit in the area where vapors are being liberated. If vapors are toxic, it may be necessary to maintain concentrations well below those required from the standpoint of flammability.

NFPA No. 86A, Standard for Ovens and Furnaces, gives procedures to follow when calculating the volume of air per minute necessary to dilute flammable vapors below their lower flammable limit. Information on this subject is also given in Section 4, Chapter 5 of this HANDBOOK.

Where heavier-than-air vapors or mixtures are handled, exhaust openings located near the floor line generally will be more effective. Conversely, for vapors or mixtures lighter than air, exhaust openings located near the top of the room, hood, or enclosure will be more effective. Caution in evaluating the specific gravity of vapors is necessary where other than normal temperatures and pressures exist.

Ducts: Ducts for systems handling flammable vapors need to be structurally capable of withstanding some degree of fire exposure. Where there is a possibility of condensation of vapors, continuously welded joints in the ducts prevent leakage. Recommended gages of steel for various sizes of ducts handling flammable vapors are given under Class I of Table 7-5A.

Since flash fires or explosions can occur in ducts, they are preferably installed where readily accessible and away from combustibles. Ducts should never be installed in a wall or ceiling. Duct systems exhausting flammable materials should terminate outside where the vapors cannot be ignited and where they will not form deposits on the building or other structures that might create a hazardous situation. An enclosure is sometimes used around the discharge end of a duct to prevent deposits on exposed property. These enclosures should be sprinklered.

Frequent cleaning of ducts and enclosures, if any, will minimize the intensity of a fire in duct systems and prevent possible spontaneous heating of deposits subject to this phenomenon.

Fire Extinguishing Equipment: Systems suitable for handling flammable vapors include fixed pipe systems and portable extinguishers for the application of water, dry chemical, or inert gas, as conditions warrant.

Fans: All fans are of a type suitable for moving vapors and air. If the vapor contains a material which may condense and build up on the fan blades, this possibility should be provided for and can be minimized by the selection of a fan with backward curved blades.

Both the fan and the fan housing should be of nonferrous construction.

Electrical Equipment: All equipment which may be exposed to flammable vapors should be of a type specified by the National Electrical Code for such a location.

Ventilation of Kitchen Cooking Equipment

Exhaust systems for restaurant equipment present a troublesome problem due to condensation of grease in the interior of the ducts. Grease accumulations may be ignited by sparks from the stove, or more often by a small fire on the stove due to overheating of cooking oil or fat in a deep fat fryer or on a grill. If there were no grease accumulation in the duct, fires on stove tops often could be extinguished, or be allowed to burn out, without causing appreciable damage. Fires occur frequently in frying because cooking oils and fats are heated to their flash points, and may reach their self-ignition temperatures by accidental overheating, or be ignited by spills on the stove top. Details of a typical kitchen range exhaust system are shown in Figure 7-5G.

Fans should be selected to exhaust the required quantity of air against all calculated friction losses.

Grease Removal Devices: All exhaust systems for kitchen cooking equipment require a means for removing grease. These may be grease extractors, grease filters, or other grease removal devices, such as special fans designed to remove grease vapors effectively and to provide a fire barrier. Grease filters, including frames, or other grease removal devices should be constructed of noncombustible materials.

Ducts: The following is a summary of factors to be considered in designing a good duct system for commercial cooking equipment:

1. Design the system to minimize grease accumulations with a minimum air velocity of 1,500 fpm through any duct.

2. Arrange ducts with ample clearance from combustible materials to minimize the danger of ignition in case of fire in the duct.

3. Use ducts of substantial construction (not lighter than No. 16 Manufacturers Standard Gage steel or No. 18 Manufacturers Standard Gage stainless steel) with all

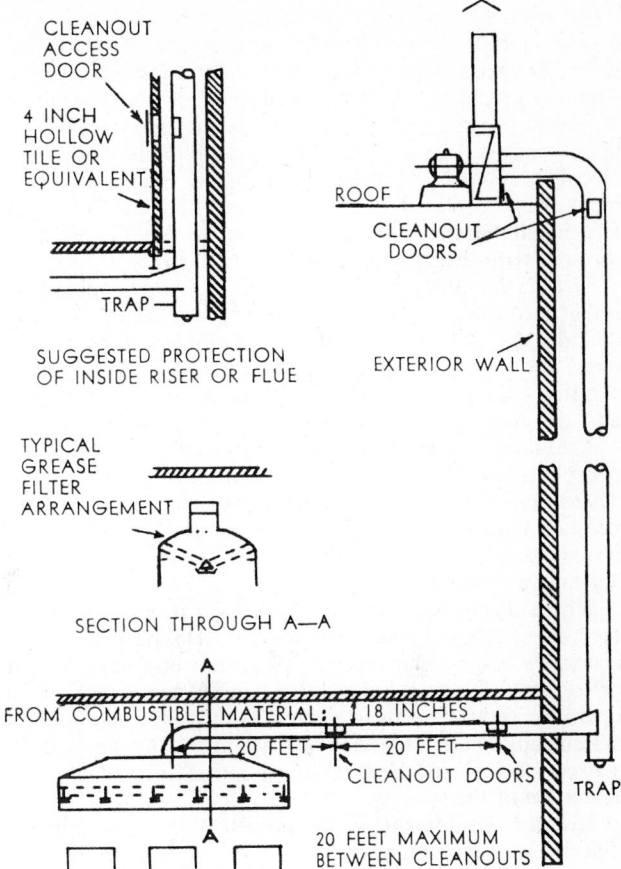

Fig. 7-5G. Typical kitchen range exhaust system arrangement, showing vertical riser outside the building. If necessary to locate riser inside the building it should be enclosed in a masonry shaft.

of the seams and the joints having a liquidtight, continuous external weld.

4. Separate systems—no connection with any other ventilating or exhaust systems.

5. Lead ducts directly outside the building without dips or traps.

6. Provide openings for inspection and cleaning. Do not install damper in any duct system unless required as part of a grease extractor or an extinguishing system.

Cleaning of Ducts: Clean ducts are essential to fire safety. Cleaning is likely to be neglected because it is a difficult and unpleasant job. The use of flammable solvents for cleaning is dangerous. Satisfactory cleaning results have been obtained with a powder compound consisting of one part calcium hydroxide and two parts calcium carbonate. This compound saponifies the grease or oily sludge, thus making it easier to remove and clean. Proper ventilation must be provided and safety precautions taken if cleaning is done inside the duct or fan housings.

Spraying of duct interiors with hydrated lime after cleaning is a fire prevention method in commercial use. This tends to saponify the grease, and may facilitate subsequent cleaning but does not provide any permanent fireproofing effect.

Electrical Equipment: Manual control of the fan motor should be provided near the motor and also near the hood. In addition, it is desirable to have automatic shutdown of the motor by a heat-sensitive device in the hood close to the outlet.

All electrical equipment which may be exposed to fumes, grease, or heat should be installed in accordance with National Electrical Code requirements for those conditions. Fixtures should not be installed in ducts or hoods used for removal of cooking smoke or grease-laden vapors or located in the path of travel of such exhaust products unless specifically designed and tested for such use. Electrical equipment may be placed outside the path of fume travel by locating it on the outside of the hood with illumination through tight-fitting glass panels in the hood.

Fire Extinguishing Equipment: For sizeable cooking installations, this equipment may consist of fixed pipe carbon dioxide, dry chemical, foam-water sprinkler or spray systems, or automatic sprinklers, supplemented by portable alkaline type (sodium bicarbonate or potassium bicarbonate) dry chemical extinguishers.

Acidic base extinguishing materials, such as ammonium phosphate base multipurpose types, impede saponification. Therefore, if the cooking equipment being protected involves exposed liquefied fat or oil in depth, such as fat fryers, extinguishers employing these extinguishing agents are not recommended.

Where fixed extinguishing systems (except automatic sprinklers) are installed, they should: (1) have a readily accessible means of actuating the system in a path of exit or egress, (2) be arranged for simultaneous automatic operation of all systems in a single hazard area upon operation of any one system, and (3) automatically shut off all sources of fuel and heat to all equipment protected upon operation of the system.

Exhaust Equipment in Dwellings: Fire protection requirements for ventilation of kitchen cooking equipment for dwellings generally are not as stringent as those for commercial and industrial occupancies. Some dwelling kitchen exhaust systems discharge through a duct to the outside. Another type is the wall mounted fan that is installed in an exterior wall and discharges directly outdoors. Still another type utilizes filters to remove grease and discharge the air back into the room.

Where ducts are provided, they should lead directly outside the building, have tight joints, and be provided with means of accessibility for cleaning. Kitchen exhaust duct systems should never discharge into the building, always outside. As with any kitchen exhaust system, periodic cleaning is essential. If filters are not the type that can be washed, they should be replaced when necessary.

Corrosive Vapors and Fumes

Frequently corrosive vapors must be exhausted from a process. The degree of expected corrosion is the governing factor in the construction of the ducts. In some cases a heavier gage metal may be sufficient. Other situations may be handled with protective coatings. Occasionally, however, the degree of corrosiveness is so extreme that a special lining is required. Stainless steel and asbestos cement have been used very successfully in some cases. Plastic lining may be used for vapors that are flammable as well as corrosive, provided that such lining has a flame spread rating of 0 when tested in accordance with NFPA No. 255, Surface Burning Characteristics of Building Materials.

Plastic duct systems may be used only if the vapors are nonflammable and the plastic has a flame spread rating of 25 or less and a smoke developed rating of 50 or less. Automatic fire protection is also necessary at the hood, canopy, or intake to plastic duct systems.

A duct system of plastic materials for a typical industrial exhaust system is shown in Figure 7-5H, and a duct system for a typical laboratory fume hood exhaust system is shown in Figure 7-5I.

Dust Collecting and Stock and Refuse Conveying Systems

These systems consist of suction ducts and inlets, air moving equipment, feeders, discharge ducts and outlets, collecting equipment, and vaults and other receptacles, designed to collect powdered, ground, or finely divided material.

Collecting and conveying systems may constitute an important part of the operations of a plant, deliver fuel to boilers, contribute to the safe operation of a plant, or perform some other essential function. These systems have inherent hazards when the material being handled is in finely divided form and is combustible or explosive. For all these reasons it is of primary importance to have the design, construction, and operation conform to recognized standards. The general recommendations given in the first part of this chapter should be observed as well as the following more specific ones.

Fans: Systems conveying combustible dust should be arranged so that the fan is on the clean air side of the collector, that is, the system operates under suction, and dust collecting equipment is installed to remove the dust from the air stream before it reaches the fan. This prevents combustible dust from passing through the fan where it may be ignited. If such an arrangement is not possible and the fan is between the dust-producing equipment and the collector, the blades and spider of the fan and the fan housing should be made of nonsparking material with ample clearance between the blades and the housing. Fan bearings and motors should be outside of casings unless the fan and motor assembly are designed and tested for use in the dust atmosphere present.

Magnetic Separators: As with flammable vapor conveying systems, combustible dust collecting systems should not be connected with processes which may produce sparks. If there is a possibility of particles of ferrous materials entering the collecting systems, magnetic separators of the permanent magnetic or the electromagnetic types, safely arranged, can be installed at points where combustible materials which contain ferrous particles enter the system. After collection, the dust passes into rooms or bins. These places of collection should be of noncombustible construction and provided with explosion vents terminating outside of the building.

Ducts: For conveying dusts or stock ducts should be constructed of metal. The recommended gages of metal used for various sizes are given in Table 7-5A. Changes in direction in the duct system should be made with long bends or elbows. This minimizes accumulations of solid particles at the turns.

The following are some general design techniques recommended for ducts conveying dusts and other solid materials:

1. Every duct should be kept open and unobstructed throughout its length.

2. Not more than two branches should connect to any section of the main suction duct.

3. Connect branch ducts to the top or side of the main duct at an angle not exceeding 45° inclined in the direction of air flow.

4. Keep main suction and discharge ducts as short as possible.

5. Flexible duct sections should not restrict airflow, and be as short as possible.

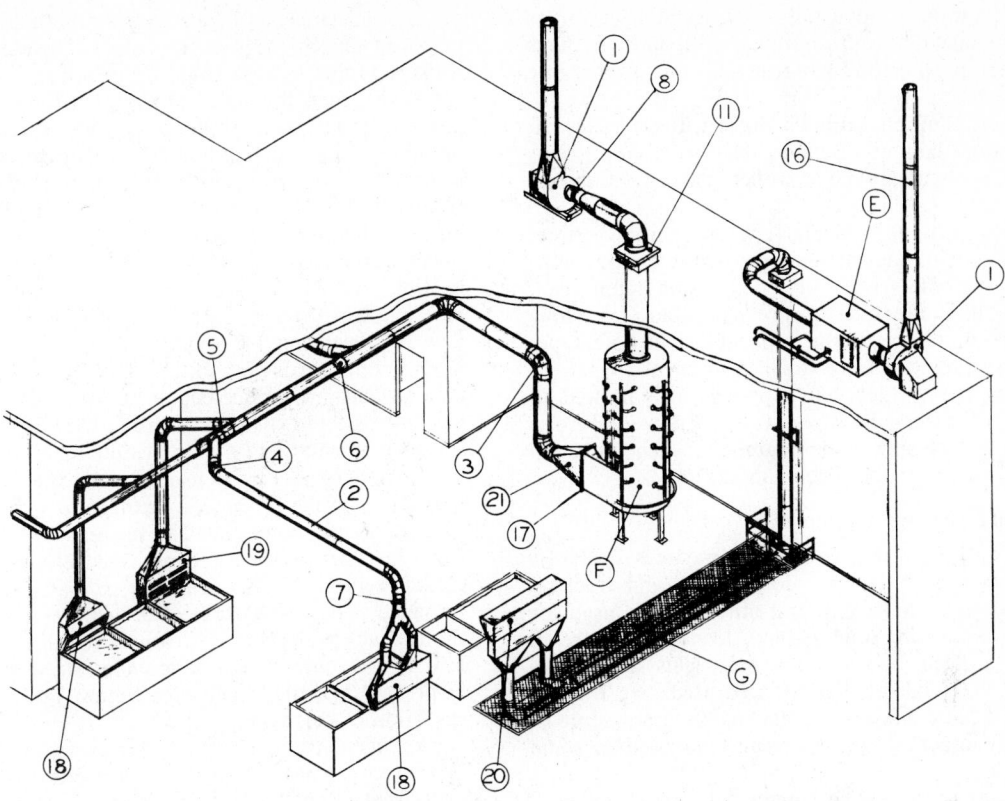

Fig. 7-5H. Exhaust system for one-story building occupied by various type fume hoods with vertical type fume scrubber and service trench. (For nomenclature, see below right.)

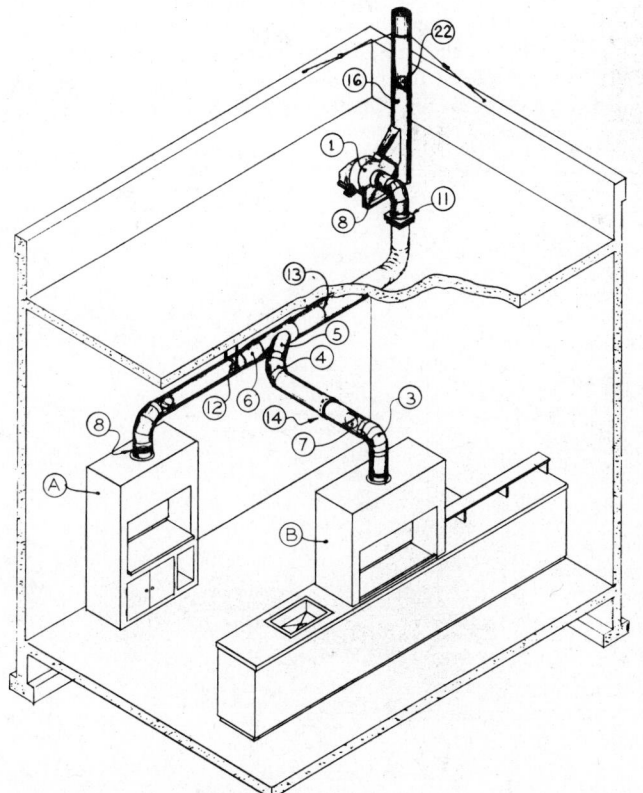

I. Equipment
    A. Cabinet type laboratory fume hood
    B. Bench type laboratory fume hood
    C. Filter box for special or high efficiency filters
    D. Shaft
    E. Horizontal type fume scrubber
    F. Vertical type fume scrubber
    G. Service pit or trench

II. System Components
    1. Air Moving Equipment (Centrifugal type exhaust fan)
    2. Horizontal duct section
    3. 90° Elbow
    4. Elbow (less than 90°)
    5. Lateral Entry
    6. Transition
    7. Manual Balancing Damper
    8. Flexible Connection
    9. Fire Damper
    10. Access Door
    11. Counterflashing
    12. Duct Hanger
    13. Circumferential Girth Joint (Butt Welded)
    14. Bell end duct seam
    15. Weather Cap
    16. Fan discharge stack
    17. Flanged duct connection
    18. Open face tank exhaust hood (updraft)
    19. Slotted face tank exhaust hood (updraft)
    20. Open face tank exhaust hood (downdraft)
    21. Round to rectangular (or square) Transitional Fitting
    22. Gravity operated backdraft damper

Fig. 7-5I. Rooftop exhaust system for one-story building occupied by a cabinet type laboratory fume hood and bench type laboratory fume hood. (For nomenclature, see above right.)

6. Systems handling combustible dusts should, as far as practicable, be outside of the building with branch ducts from each floor passing through the wall and discharging into the main duct outside.

7. Do not add additional branch ducts without redesigning the system, or blank off disconnected or unused portions of the system, without providing orifice plates to maintain required airflow.

Explosion Prevention: Particularly where ignition sources are difficult to control, inerting may be used to create a safe atmosphere within the system, or an explosion suppression system may be used effectively to prevent explosions. However, there are limitations to the applicability of both types of systems. Inerting generally is only practical for essentially closed systems. Explosion suppression is limited to those materials that can be successfully protected. Efforts to suppress explosions in some materials, such as metal dusts, for example, have not been successful.

Separating and Collecting Equipment

Separating and collecting equipment includes cyclones, condensers, wet type collectors, cloth screen and stocking arresters, centrifugal collectors, and other devices used for the purpose of separating solid material from the air stream in which it is carried, and hoppers, bins, silos, and vaults for collecting the solid material so separated. See Figures 7-5J, 7-5K, 7-5L, and 7-5M for typical examples of some of this equipment and how sprinklers may be used in some types.

Separating and collecting equipment is designed to withstand anticipated explosion pressures, allowance being made for explosion relief vents. This equipment should be constructed of steel or enclosed in steel and located outside the building. To avoid collapse of equipment which could result in an explosive dust cloud, equipment should be well supported on steel, masonry, or concrete. Equipment and discharge ducts should be well separated from combustible construction and unprotected openings into buildings.

Collectors which must be located indoors and which can-

not be constructed of sufficient strength to withstand anticipated explosion pressures can be located near outside walls to facilitate explosion relief venting.

Gravity feed through tightly fitted ducts is the best arrangement for delivering stock from separators, cyclones, or other collection equipment to storage receptacles. Delivery ducts from cyclone collectors should not convey refuse directly into the fireboxes of boilers, furnaces, refuse burners, incinerators, etc.

Where processes produce very fine dusts or where combustible metal dusts are being handled, wet collectors provide efficient dust control. Dust is removed by passing the flow of air through a water curtain and is collected as a sludge submerged in water. Except where combustible metal dusts are collected, these wet collectors generally have no fire or explosion hazards. (See Sec. 3, Chap. 9 for further information on combustible metal dusts.)

Where refuse is to be used as fuel, the discharge system from the storage receptacle or intermediate feed bin to the furnace should be designed to prevent a flashback from the furnace. This may be accomplished either by means of a choke feeder or choke conveyor so that a positive cutoff is provided. The installation of a steam spray in the duct to the furnace which blows steam in the direction of the fuel flow is recommended as it provides an added safety factor in preventing a flashback. See Figure 7-5J for a typical installation of this type.

The installation of screw conveyors or rotary feeds at appropriate points in stock or dust conveying systems has been used to good advantage in many plants as a means of introducing a "choke," which, by filling the conveyor with the material being conveyed, stops the spread of a flash fire. Also by introducing an explosion vent, the pressure of an explosion may be relieved and its progress stopped. This combination has many times kept small fires or explosions from becoming large and disastrous.

High Efficiency Air Filter Units: Particulate air filter units are intended for removal of very fine particulate matter (i.e., to remove not less than 99.97 percent of 0.3 micron

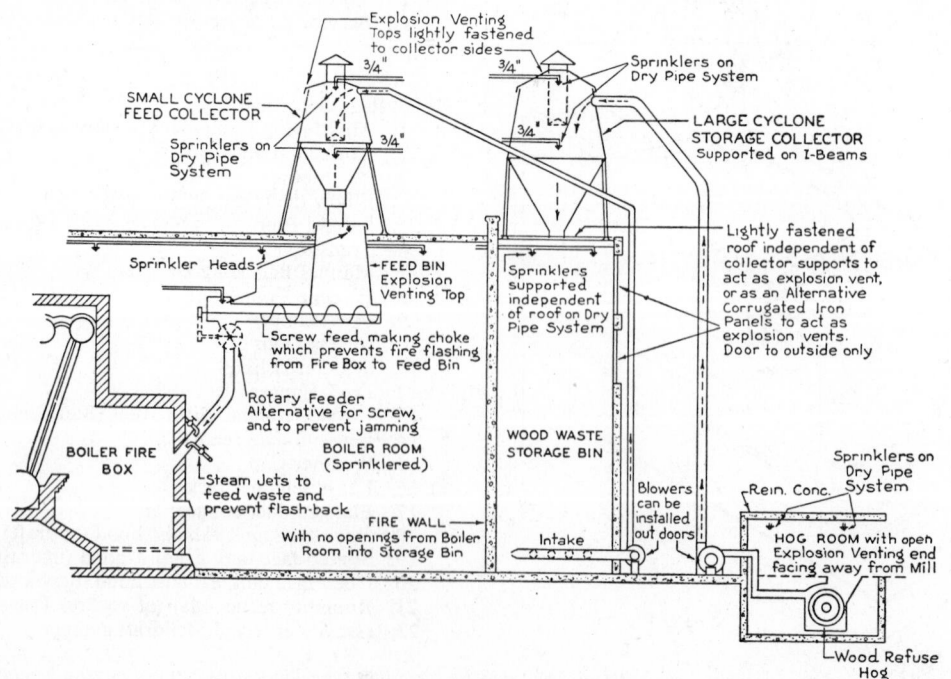

Fig. 7-5J.   Suggested arrangement for wood waste firing of boiler to minimize explosion and fire hazard.

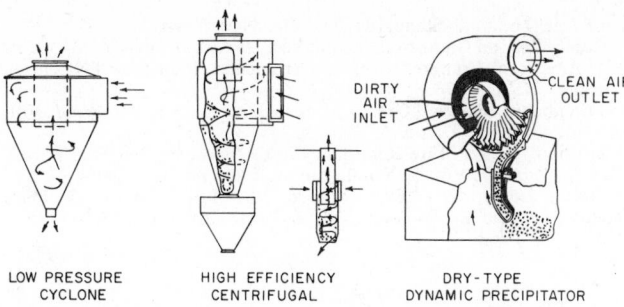

LOW PRESSURE CYCLONE　　HIGH EFFICIENCY CENTRIFUGAL　　DRY-TYPE DYNAMIC PRECIPITATOR

Fig. 7-5K. Examples of typical types of dust collecting equipment. (American Conference of Governmental Industrial Hygienists)

diameter particles) from the air of industrial and laboratory exhaust systems. The Atomic Energy Commission requires high efficiency filters for filtering air exhausted from spaces where radioactive materials are handled.

This requirement is met by filter units which consist of a filter medium of glass fiber, glass asbestos fiber, or equivalent inorganic material. The adhesive used is combustible but contains a self-extinguishing additive. Fire of sufficient temperature and duration to melt glass fibers can damage the filter at points of contact. However, exhaust of filtered air will continue through the undamaged area.

The AEC installs large banks of these filters, limits the number in a fire area to 100, and protects them with automatic sprinklers.

Fire Extinguishing Systems: Cloth-screen or bag-type dust collectors used for collection of fine dusts present a

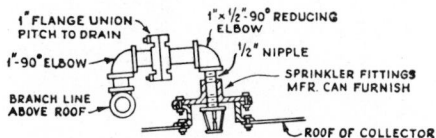

DETAIL "A"

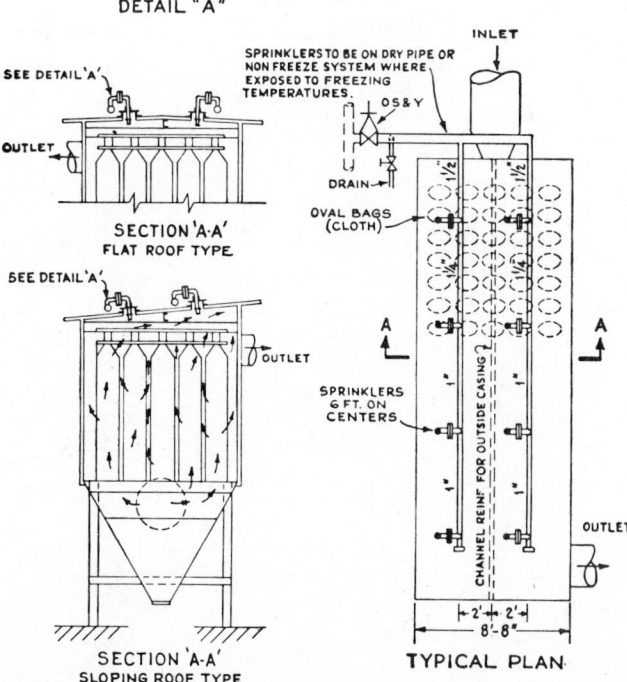

Fig. 7-5L. Typical sprinkler protection for a bag type dust collector.

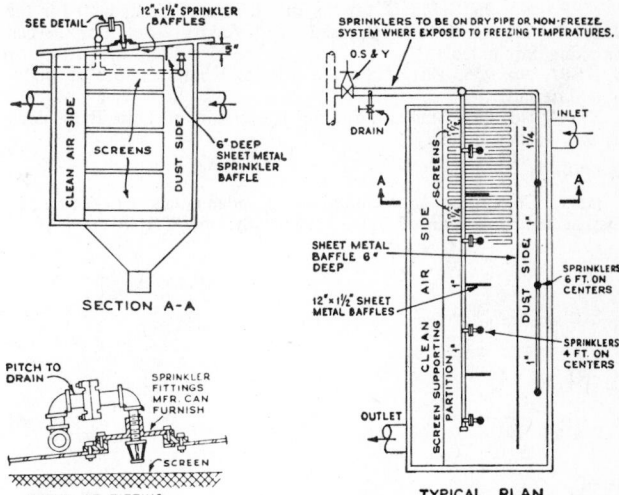

Fig. 7-5M. Typical sprinkler protection for a screen type dust collector.

special problem even where the dust is noncombustible because of the use of a combustible fabric. Automatic sprinkler protection may be needed where cloth dust collectors are important for continuity of production or where they provide exposure to other property. Figures 7-5L and 7-5M show typical layouts of sprinkler protection for cloth dust collectors.

Equipment of large volume in which pulverized stock is stored or may accumulate, such as bins, dust collectors, etc., should be protected by automatic sprinklers. Automatic carbon dioxide, dry chemical, halogenated agent, or water spray extinguishing systems can be used effectively in dust collecting systems. Inert gas may be effectively used to create safe atmospheres in conveying systems.

SI Units

The following conversion factors are given as a convenience in converting to SI units the English units used in this chapter.

$$1 \text{ in.} = 25.400 \text{ mm}$$
$$\tfrac{5}{9}(°F - 32) = °C$$

Bibliography

NFPA Codes, Standards, and Recommended Practices (see the latest *NFPA Publications and Visual Aids Catalog* for availability of current editions of the following documents)

NFPA No. 61A, Standard for Manufacturing and Handling Starch.
NFPA No. 61B, Standard for Prevention of Fire and Dust Explosions in Grain Elevators and Bulk Grain Handling Facilities.
NFPA No. 61C, Standard for the Prevention of Fire and Dust Explosions in Feed Mills.
NFPA No. 61D, Standard for the Prevention of Fire and Dust Explosions in the Milling of Agricultural Commodities for Human Consumption.
NFPA No. 63, Fundamental Principles for the Prevention of Dust Explosions in Industrial Plants.
NFPA No. 65, Standard for the Processing and Finishing of Aluminum.
NFPA No. 68, Guide for Explosion Venting.
NFPA No. 70, National Electrical Code.
NFPA No. 77, Recommended Practice on Static Electricity.
NFPA No. 86A, Standard for Ovens and Furnaces, Design, Location, and Equipment.
NFPA No. 91, Standard for the Installation of Blower and Exhaust Systems for Dust, Stock and Vapor Removal or Conveying.

NFPA No. 96, Standard for the Installation of Equipment for the Removal of Smoke and Grease-Laden Vapors from Commercial Cooking Equipment.

NFPA No. 255, Test of Surface Burning Characteristics of Building Materials.

NFPA No. 654, Standard for the Prevention of Dust Explosions in the Plastics Industry.

Additional Readings

ANSI Committee on Ventilation, "Fundamentals Governing the Design and Operation of Local Exhaust Systems," ANSI Z9.2-1971, American National Standards Institute, New York.

Committee on Industrial Ventilation, *Industrial Ventilation,* 13th ed., American Conference of Governmental Industrial Hygienists, Lansing, Mich., 1974.

Levenback, George, "Grease Fires in Kitchens," *Fire Journal,* Vol. 66, No. 4, July 1972, pp. 69–72.

Siconolfi, C. A., "Fire Retardancy in Chemical Process Ductwork," *Fire Technology,* Vol. 5, No. 3, August 1969, pp. 217–224.

Smith, Edwin E., "Evaluation of the Fire Hazard of Duct Materials," *Fire Technology,* Vol. 9, No. 3, August 1973, pp. 157–170.

Chapter 6

REFUSE HANDLING SYSTEMS AND EQUIPMENT

A. Domestic Incinerators, Refuse Storage, and Compactors

Prompt and efficient disposal of collections of refuse and trash is axiomatic to good fire prevention. Although the general run of refuse generated in the course of daily activity is rarely in itself a source of ignition (smoldering smoking materials excluded), its presence in any amount can only serve to provide fuel to fires originating from other sources. This chapter discusses the systems and equipment available for handling and disposing of refuse in a way that minimizes its hazard potential.

Domestic Incinerators

Domestic incinerators, used primarily in one- and two-family dwellings, are classified as gas appliances. The gas is simply an ignitor, and the refuse itself is the prime fuel. If the unit is designed to be smoke and odor free, temperatures in the combustion chamber must be over 1,100°F and will normally run about 1,500°F. This temperature is reduced by introducing dilution air as it enters the chimney connectors; however, temperatures in the chimney connector can be well over 1,000°F. Plastics, rubber, floor tiles, etc., have high heating values and can produce temperatures in excess of 1,500°F if put in an incinerator without mixing with other household wastes.

Clearances to combustibles are very important factors, particularly with the chimney connector, the most hazardous element of a system. At least 48 in. clearance is required above the charging door of a domestic incinerator. However, the clearance can be reduced to 24 in. if exposed combustible surfaces are protected with sheet metal not less than No. 28 manufacturers standard gage spaced out 1 in. on noncombustible spacers. Side and rear clearances from the chimney connector are 12 in. and 18 in. respectively. These may be reduced as given in Table 7-3G.

The incinerator should be placed as close to the chimney as possible to reduce the hazard of the hot chimney connectors and to avoid heat loss which could seriously affect the draft and thus the operation. When the chimney connector penetrates a combustible wall, it is protected with a ventilated thimble not less than 12 in. in diameter.

Domestic incinerators are never connected to a gas vent. They may be vented through a masonry chimney or a factory-built chimney. In some cases, such as breezeways, open sheds, or carports, No. 20 galvanized pipe may be used, if proper clearances, as given in the NFPA No. 82, Standard for Incinerator and Rubbish Handling, hereinafter referred to in this chapter as the NFPA Incinerator and Rubbish Handling Standard, are observed.

Chimney servicing incinerators terminate above roofs at heights as given in Figure 7-3FF.

A frequent problem with all combustion appliances is meeting the requirement for proper air supply. It is usually assumed that air leakage into one- and two-family dwellings will be adequate; however, this is only true if the incinerator is unenclosed or, if enclosed, has adequate ventilation to the outside or to areas receiving infiltrated air. It is best practice to have a direct opening to outside air of a diameter at least equivalent to the chimney diameter.

The most common domestic incinerators have a capacity of 1.5 bushels or 3,712.5 cu. in. or slightly less than three supermarket bags or about three days of waste. Larger sizes are also available. A typical domestic incinerator is shown in Figure 7-6A.

Normal household wastes are best stored in the incinerator and burned when the capacity is reached. Storage of rubbish within the incinerator eliminates the undercounter storage fire hazard. A typical four-member family will burn rubbish two to three times each week.

The greatest problem occurs not with normal garbage and waste but with large collections of waste, such as old floor tiles or scrap rug etc., after a floor covering or remodeling installation or any situation where quantities of waste are developed. This material cannot be burned en masse since the heat release is very great and will produce both smoke and flashbacks that could prove dangerous. Exceedingly high temperatures occur in the fire box and chimney connector.

Plastics, such as bottles, wrappers, drinking cups, etc., never are burned alone; they are best mixed in small quantities with daily refuse. High heat release materials, such as foamed plastics should be disposed of by other means.

Aerosol cans and other flammable or combustible liquids must never be incinerated due to explosion hazards.

Refuse Storage

The most common container for primary refuse storage in dwellings and apartment units is the brown paper supermarket bag, usually stored in an under-counter cabinet along with a supply of extra bags. Such storage can be a fire hazard, particularly since ash trays with their "snuffed out" contents might be emptied here. The hazard can be reduced by utilizing a metal container, with an inside measurement slightly greater than the bag measurement (usually $12 \times 17 \times 7$ in.), with a tight-fitting metal cover to contain the bag, thus reducing the exposure of fire that may occur.

Domestic Compactors

The kitchen compactor has come into wide use for dwelling and apartment unit primary refuse storage. This appliance reduces the fire hazard of stored refuse by retaining it in a metal container under compaction. Units are of the undercounter and movable types. It is important that the

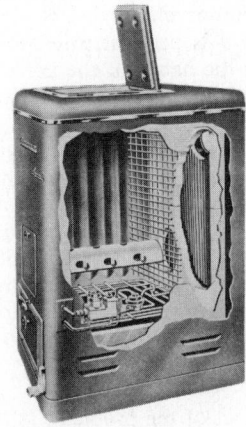

Fig. 7-6A. A typical gas-fired domestic incinerator. (Calcinator Corp.)

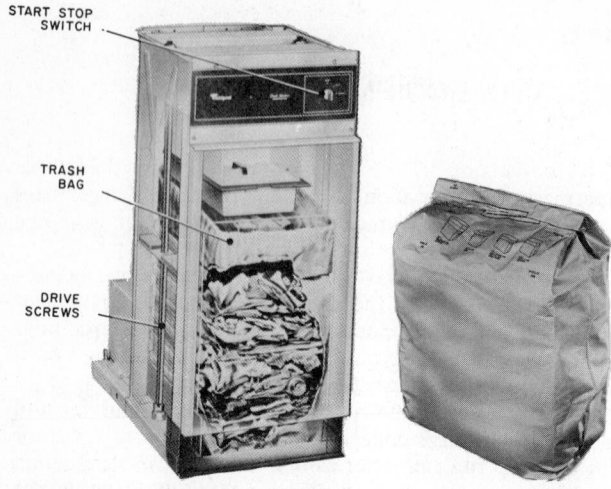

Fig. 7-6B. A domestic compactor unit. Trash is compacted and retained in the unit in the bag, shown at right, that when full holds a week's normal household trash for the average family of four. (Whirlpool Corp.)

door can be opened and refuse removed easily in the event of equipment failure. Figure 7-6B illustrates a typical domestic compactor.

B. Gravity and Laundry/Linen Refuse Chutes

General access gravity chutes for refuse handling are installed in apartment buildings and other multi-story residential buildings. These chutes may be considered storage areas since they accidentally can become clogged during use or clogged due to inadequate design, presenting a fire and smoke hazard should ignition occur.

Large scale use of refuse chutes became popular in the middle 1920s to service incinerators such as the flue fed units which used the chute as a chimney.[1] Air pollution laws, however, are, for all practical purposes, removing incineration as a method of waste disposal in apartment buildings and replacing that method with compactors. Refuse chutes for the most part are now being utilized to service compactors.

Chute Diameter

It is not completely clear how the first criteria for chute size were developed; however, it was evident that clogging could be caused by many strange and often very simple objects, such as baby mattresses, umbrellas, and cardboard boxes. To prevent clogging minimum chute size requirements were established; however, it is prudent to examine the volume and type of usage and the habits of the users of a refuse chute before accepting the minimum sizes allowed by standards. The size of a typical refuse package and its relationship to the chute govern both chute and service opening dimensions. A kitchen compactor, for example, may produce a package measuring $16 \times 16 \times 9$ in., and to accommodate such a package, a 36-in. diameter chute having 289 sq in. service opening doors is recommended. Chutes for use with domestic compactors need impact-resistant linings and have a substantial impact surface at the bottom of the chute.

Service Opening Size

Chute diameter is only one aspect of the problem. If the chute door were allowed to be of unlimited size, it is obvious

that a chute could be clogged very rapidly. A relationship of one third the cross-sectional area of the chute was established as a suitable door size, with a maximum of 168 sq in. This latter restriction was later removed, since it limited package size. Under current standards, any package size is acceptable as long as the door size is not more than one third the cross-sectional area of the chute.

The one third door-chute relationship avoids the "piston effect" that results when packages are so large that they create a positive pressure under the falling package (see Fig. 7-6C). This pressure can be sufficient to push contaminated air from the chute into living areas. In apartment buildings this becomes a nuisance, transmitting odors and vermin into living areas. In hospitals or other health service buildings it may also force contaminated air into living areas.

Refuse Chute Doors

The chute service opening must also have a fire rating and meet other specific requirements to prevent or reduce the escape of flame or dispersion of chute air into living areas by natural building air pressures and other forces. The NFPA Incinerator and Rubbish Handling Standard requires that general access chute service openings be equipped with fire-rated hopper-type doors that are self-closing self-latching, and bottom-hinged.

Chute Enclosures

The floor openings through which a chute passes require fire-rated protection as well as the chute service openings and the enclosures around them in order to maintain the fire integrity of the whole chute system. Metal chutes provide no fire resistance rating and must rely upon fire-rated walls for protection of the chute and floor opening. See Section 6, Chapter 8 for methods of protection of floor opening such as presented by refuse chutes. The NFPA Life Safety Code contains requirements for enclosures for chutes.

Recognition is given, however, to the fire rating of masonry chutes, since the walls of the masonry chute enclose with the floor openings within fire resistant walls. If a masonry chute penetrates a floor without closing the opening entirely, the space between the floor and the chute is filled with material equivalent to the floor in fire resistance.

Service Opening Enclosures

For many years it was general practice to put chute service openings in public corridors for convenience sake. How-

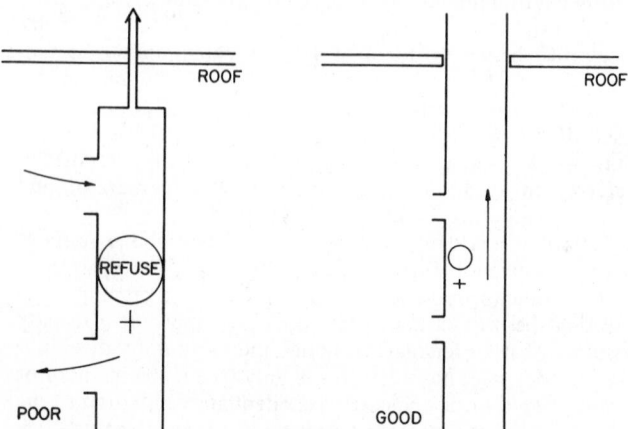

Fig. 7-6C. The piston effect created by a large falling package in a refuse chute is illustrated at left. A smaller package size (right) allows chute air to be displaced as the package falls.

ever, aside from the problems of unsightliness and poor sanitation, fire hazards were seriously increased, and the fire integrity of the building reduced. The refuse chute became an avenue to transmit fire from floor to floor or from chute to floor. Fatalities occurred when chute fires spilled into corridors cutting off the means of escape.

Now the NFPA Incinerator and Rubbish Handling Standard requires every service opening to be located in a room or compartment separated from other parts of the building by an enclosure having 1-hr fire-rated wall and ceiling assemblies with the opening into the enclosure protected by fire doors suitable for Class B openings. The self-enclosing fire door is not necessary if the building has sprinkler protection.

Refuse Chute Roof Terminations

Refuse chutes to their full size extend at least 4 ft above the roof and are open to the atmosphere. It is good practice to install a cap to eliminate either downdrafts or aspiration (updrafts) due to wind action and to avoid entrance of undesired items.

Natural Building Pressures—Air Movement in Buildings

Natural building pressures are air movement are the forces acting upon a building, due solely to the difference in temperature between the inside and the outside of the building.[2] During the heating season, cold, heavy outside air presses down and into a building, while the warm inside air is forced upward. If we were to open a window on a lower floor, air would flow in. (This "stack effect", which accounts for most of the natural air movement in buildings under normal conditions, is discussed in more detail in Section 2, Chapter 5.)

These same forces are also to be observed at work on the refuse chute. Air enters the lower floors and is discharged on the upper floors if the top is closed. The entire process is reversed during the air-conditioning season, when the heavy inside air flows down and out the lower floors, with warm air entering the upper floors. The problem areas of odor and smoke migration are now quite evident.[3]

If the top of the chute is opened, all flow is into the chute, with a downflow in summer and an upflow in winter. The

current practice of using a brown paper bag or plastic bag as the household refuse container minimizes the upflow of light particles. The open top also provides a vent for smoke when a chute fire occurs.

Chute Construction

Chutes are made of steel masonry, or factory-built chimney sections that have been laboratory-tested for use with incinerators. Aluminum chutes, once very common, have very limited capacity to withstand heat.

While chutes are installed as straight and plumb as possible, a 15° offset from the vertical is permitted with the allowable offset at the chute's termination.

Sprinklers for Chutes

The NFPA Incinerator and Rubbish Handling Standard requires that a chute be sprinklered or capable of containing fire and venting products of combustion. Thus, masonry chutes or chutes made of laboratory-test, factory-built medium-heat appliance chimney sections are not required to be sprinklered. Metal chutes require sprinklers at the top and at every other floor (NFPA No. 13, Installation of Sprinkler Systems, contains specific requirements for sprinkler installation in chutes). A good practice is to locate sprinklers where they can be inspected and maintained and yet be out of the reach of vandals and beyond the range of falling refuse.

Chute Terminal Room Enclosure

The chute terminal room or bin where the refuse is stored is subject to many potential ignition sources. The walls, ceilings, and floor of the room or bin are required to have a fire resistance rating equivalent to that required for the chute. Openings into the enclosure are protected by fire doors suitable for Class B openings.

Sprinklers in Chute Termination Rooms: Termination rooms require not only fire resistance, but sprinklers. These requirements are in recognition of the seriousness of fires in refuse, which are generally difficult to control by ordinary means because of the large amount of smoke evolved and the consequent difficulties in fire fighting. Automatic extinguishment of such fires in the incipient stage is of prime importance.

Limited Access Gravity Chutes

These chutes are used primarily in hospitals and health care installations or any other multistoried building for disposal of refuse and handling of laundry and linen where only authorized personnel may use them. Ideally, the individuals involved are aware of the effects of air movement in buildings and will close the door to the enclosure around the chute opening before the service entrance to the chute is actually opened. (It is for this reason that the door may be side-hinged and without the hopper device that closes off the chute.) Unfortunately, this practice is not always observed; thus the most desirable situation is one which has a double door system at entrances to the chute. The outer door allows charging of material with the inner door closed. The inner door discharges the material into the chute when the outer door is closed.

The primary storage in an area serviced by a limited access chute is usually a metal wastebasket. Waste is removed from the basket and placed into a larger bag carried on a cart. This larger bag varies in size but is substantially larger than the conventional supermarket bag; thus it requires a large door to the chute. No maximum door size has been established for limited access chutes; the size is simply

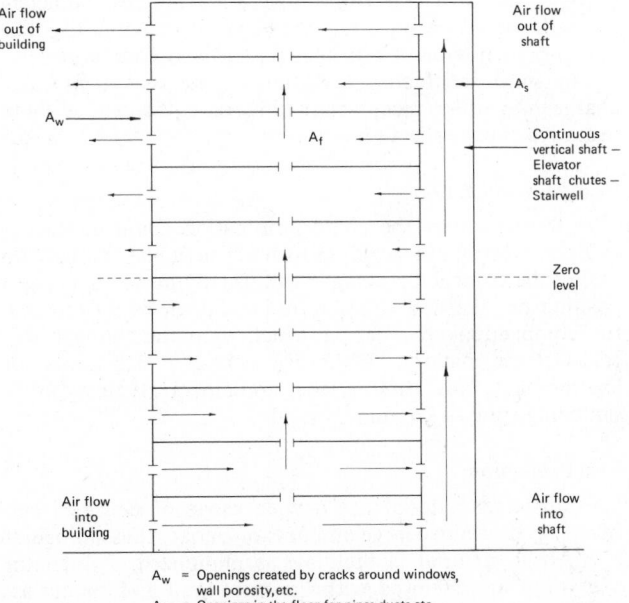

A_w = Openings created by cracks around windows, wall porosity, etc.
A_f = Openings in the floor for pipes ducts, etc.
A_s = Shaft openings

Fig. 7-6D. An air flow pattern in a heated multistory building.

limited to one third the cross-sectional area of the chute. Some designers, recognizing that large plastic bags are common and require a large door, have allowed the door to be the same size as the chute. Unfortunately, this can force air into living areas by the positive pressure in front of the large plastic bag "plugs" of falling refuse. Openings of this size should not be used unless the chute is evacuated from the bottom with sufficient air flow and negative pressure to convey the material down and to avoid air exit from the chute as the package falls.

C.   Pneumatic Laundry/Linen and Refuse Chutes

This type of refuse or linen handling chute system is usually found in hospitals or other health care buildings; however, it could be used for any size or class of building. These chutes operate under a negative pressure of about 17 in. of water with speeds of about 60 mph for packages being carried along in them; therefore, most of the building air movement and fire safety problems are avoided. Figure 7-6E is a diagrammatic view of a building-wide pneumatic chute system.

The service entrances, or charging stations, may be in the same area as the chute itself and each consists of a compartment with an outside door which is opened to place refuse or linen into it and an inner door that is sequenced electrically allowing only one door on the system to be opened at a time; thus only one package is in the system at a time. In the event of clogging, the fuel load would be very low.

A pneumatic chute does not depend upon gravity as the moving force but upon high velocity moving air aspirated at the top of the chute and exhausted at its termination. The chute may, therefore, be designed horizontally, vertically and may even go up at an angle depending upon the characteristics of the system and blower. The minimum chute diameter is 16 in. With this fact in mind, the most practical fire safety requirement is the location of fire dampers at any point where the pneumatic chute system penetrates a fire-rated floor and ceiling assembly, fire wall, or other fire rated enclosure.

The chute termination hopper should be sprinklered and the chute termination room enclosed in walls, floor and ceiling assemblies with a minimum fire resistance rating of 1 hr.

Linen chutes conform to the same criteria as refuse

chutes. It is possible to use one chute to convey both linen and refuse. When this is done, a combination charging station with separate linen and refuse entrances is used.

Combined Pneumatic-Gravity Chute Systems

This type of system commonly used in apartment buildings, utilizes a conventional general access gravity chute to feed a collecting chamber which in turn feeds a pneumatic conveyor. The collecting chamber is the most vulnerable point and must be adequately sprinklered or otherwise protected to contain fire. It should have easy access in event of fire.

D.   Refuse Compactors

Current air pollution laws are such that incinerators of any type are banned, for all practical purposes, from apartment buildings and many other uses. Compactors are taking their place as the prime rubbish handling system.

There are a number of different configurations for compactors; however, the basic elements are similar. In many installations refuse chutes are used in conjunction with compactors.

Chute Termination Bin

Most refuse chutes do not feed directly into the compactor but into a small storage chamber, chute connector, or impact area that is usually large enough to store small quantities of refuse. This can create a potential fire hazard that can be minimized by installing sprinklers and providing access doors of sufficient size to allow access in the event of fire. If a compactor is charged manually from a large bin with an open top, the bin need not be sprinklered. It is sufficient to rely on the sprinklers protecting the compactor room for protection.

The nature of the bottom closure of a storage bin or area and its ability to be opened under fire conditions deserves attention. If, for instance, there is equipment failure, refuse will not only build up into the chute termination chamber but also into the chute. In the event of a fire and sprinkler discharge the weight of soggy refuse could become excessive and jam simple slide devices. Sufficient strength should be built into these closure devices to allow opening them without breakage under these conditions.

The most satisfactory situation is one that allows discharge into other receptacles, bins, or equipment without excessive chute collection.

Compaction Chamber

As refuse enters the chute termination chamber it activates an electric eye which in turn activates the compaction cycle. The compactor plunger will usually move to its open position or otherwise allow refuse to fall or be moved into the compaction chamber at which time the plunger will compact the material. There are a variety of systems for loading bags, bins, cars or other containers. At this point a sanitizing spray is commonly used.

Fire Protection

Compacted material has a wide range of densities and can burn to produce large amounts of smoke; thus storage of compacted material in buildings is minimized. Compactor operations are enclosed with fire-rated wall and ceiling assemblies with fire doors suitable for Class B openings. Automatic sprinklers are also required in compactor rooms.

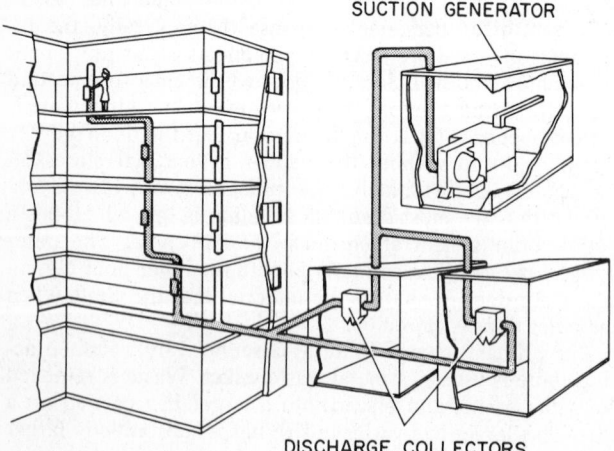

SUCTION GENERATOR

DISCHARGE COLLECTORS

Fig. 7-6E. A diagrammatic representation of a building-wide pneumatic chute system.

Types of Compactors

There are four types of compactor systems. They are:

The Bulkhead Type Compactor: This type of unit compacts refuse in a chamber against a bulkhead. When a compacted block is ready for removal a bag may be installed and filled with the compacted block. The block may be cylindrical or rectangular.

Extruder Type: Refuse is compacted by forcing refuse through a cylinder that has a restricted area. These forces, coupled with the forward driving force, compact the material and extrude it into a "slug." This is broken off and bagged or placed in the container. It is also used to feed refuse into incinerators, the slug maintaining a positive seal. An extruder type is illustrated in Figure 7-6F.

Carousel Type Bag Packer: Material is compacted into a container in which a bag has been inserted. Various configurations are used; some utilize a compaction chamber from which the compacted plug is pushed into the bag. Others use a cylinder that is inserted into the bag. This cylinder acts as a compaction chamber. Upon compaction the cylinder is removed while the compacting head holds the material in place.

Container Packers: Refuse is compacted directly into a bin, cart, or container. When full, the container can be either manually or mechanically removed from the compactor and compaction area. Small containers that are light enough to be removed from the building with speed or which have an opening into which a fire hose may be placed need no further fire protection.

Larger containers which cannot be manually moved and which require special vehicles for handling should be provided with 1½-in. fire department hose connections at the top to permit flooding of the container in event of fire. They should be constructed so that they can be opened with simple tools to reach the burning contents for fire fighting.

E. Incinerators

Although current air pollution laws are such that apartment building incineration is practically being replaced by compactors; hospitals and other institutional and commercial buildings are exempt because of hazardous health conditions that exist in the handling of contaminated or specialized wastes.[4]

Hospital waste consists of both pathological wastes and general hospital waste. In some cases pathological wastes are mixed with general wastes; in others, separate incinerator units are utilized.

All incineration processes consist of several basic elements: a means to get air into the unit, a primary combustion chamber that physically holds the refuse, a settling chamber that reduces velocity to allow settling of particles, and a secondary combustion chamber that burns the vapors and gases.[5, 6] Incinerators may be constructed of bricks and mortar with liners of castable or any other refractory material that will resist differences and conditions involved, and may have a variety of shapes. The differences between incinerators will depend upon how air is introduced and how much is supplied. If an incinerator were to burn with less air than required for theoretical combustion pyrolysis would occur with a production of vapors and gases, the temperature depending upon the amount of air supply. At exactly theoretical air these vapors and gases would burn to produce the highest temperatures. As air is increased above theoretical requirements, the dilution lowers the temperatures. If all smoke and most odors are to be consumed, the tem-

*Fig. 7-6F.   The sequence of operation of an extruder-type refuse compactor. Refuse falling from the chute (**A**) trips a sensor and starts the compacting cycle. The ram moves forward (**B**) to let refuse fall into the compactor chamber and then moves forward (**C**) with more than 40,000 lbs of force to force the refuse through a system of restrictors that compacts the refuse and pushes it out of the machine.*

peratures must be above 1,100°F assuming good mixing of vapors and air. Glass fuses at temperatures above 1,800°F and deposits undesirable slags. Thus, conventional incinerators were designed for 100 percent excess air that diluted temperatures to about 1,500°F, a temperature above the smoke consuming temperature, but below the slagging temperature. When air is provided at or slightly above theoretical requirements temperatures can go over 3,000°F depending upon the material burned.

Charging Devices

The control of combustion is the prime factor governing differences between incinerators. Control cannot be maintained if a door must be opened to charge the unit, unless of course a batch operation is involved. Manual charging depends upon the ability to regulate the rate of feed. If overcharging occurs, the incinerator may not accommodate it; thus, mechanical feeding devices are needed to charge incinerators for controlled combustion if air pollution laws are to be met. It is now general practice that all incinerators have mechanical feeding devices or are batch operated. Charging devices are usually of the ram feed type similar to compaction units. The fire safety requirements are also similar.

Storage bins servicing charging devices are sprinklered and have access doors for fire fighting.

Fire Protection

An incinerator is enclosed within a room separated from other parts of the building by fire-rated walls, ceiling and floor assemblies. Fire doors suitable for Class B openings are installed at incinerator room openings. Automatic sprinkler protection for incinerator rooms is recommended.

Conventional Incinerators

These units are designed to provide 100 percent excess combustion air that is pulled into the combustion chamber primarily through open ports by the chimney draft.[7] The primary combustion chamber temperature will vary from 1,100°F or less to 2,500°F depending upon how much air is provided, the burning rate of the refuse, its heat release, the amount charged, and the Btu input of the primary burner.

The secondary combustion chamber must provide good mixing with temperatures over 1,100°F to consume smoke. They usually range from 1,400°F to 2,500°F.

Settling chambers represent a change in direction to allow particulates to be collected.

Air is introduced through a barometric damper to reduce chimney temperatures to the 1,600° to 1,800°F range.[8] An exception to that range is in pathological waste incineration. Temperatures can be 2,500°F or more. A conventional type of commercial and industrial incinerator is illustrated in Figure 7-6G.

Conventional incinerators are often field fabricated of brick and mortar, most having a steel encasement. However, the walls are not completely airtight and the air port velocities are subject to variation. Infiltration through the walls and other entrances often exceeds the 100 percent excess air design criteria, and in some instances has been found in actual test to be 200 percent and more, a condition that reduces temperatures, increases smoke, and generally does not meet air pollution code requirements.

The amount of air entering the unit obviously affects the velocity through the unit. At 100 percent excess air the settling chamber and its velocities may allow proper settling; but, as the velocities increase due to infiltration more particulates are carried into the chimney. It is therefore necessary with most conventional units to incorporate a gas washing device that utilizes water in a variety of forms to assist in particulate removal. A pressure loss and chimney temperature loss are created by these devices which must be overcome by utilizing a draft inducer, as a supplement to the natural draft.

Chimney temperatures for general waste are up to 1,800°F; thus chimneys suitable for medium heat appliances (see Tables 7-3M and 7-3N) and breechings, as specified in the NFPA Incinerator and Rubbish Handling Standard, are used. A chimney is also designed for natural draft conditions to allow proper exhaust in the event of a power failure to a draft inducer required if a gas washing device is used.[9] A bypass is installed around the inducer to allow venting of the combustion products into the chimney under these circumstances.

Pathological incinerators usually with temperatures in the 2,000°F + range require high heat chimneys.

Controlled Air Incinerators

This class of incinerators utilizes blowers to force air into the combustion chambers placing the unit under positive pressure. Doors and feeding devices must have tight seals to avoid smoking.

Many units are charged with mechanical feeding devices for continuous burning. Manual loading requires a batch operation and does not allow feeding the unit without disrupting the burning process.

Controlled air incinerators can be classified into three basic groups, (1) those burning with close to theoretical air, (2) those burning with medium amounts of theoretical air

(30 percent), and (3) those burning with 100 percent excess air. In all cases there is no air infiltration as the units are designed with a steel shell and positive air blowers. Velocities are maintained within the variable limits of the refuse burned. Low velocities stir up less particulates and entrain less for exhaust to the atmosphere. High temperatures in controlled air units consume smoke and other airborne materials; thus, gas washing devices are usually not required.

Pathological wastes are frequently mixed with general hospital wastes without problems in these units. When pathologicals are burned separately, high Btu input burners maintain the temperature level.

A typical unit utilizing air just under theoretical requirements in the primary chamber will produce temperatures in the 2,500°F + range. This will increase to well above 2,500°F, as slightly more air is introduced in the secondary chamber. The secondary chamber is small since the length of time the material must stay at these high temperatures to be consumed is short. A section of the chimney usually acts as the secondary chamber.[10]

It is essential in these units to use special refractories in this combustion zone of the chimney and these should be supplied by the manufacturer to avoid serious refractory loss or structural damage.

At some point above the combustion chamber additional air is introduced into the chimney to reduce the temperature further. High heat chimney construction (see Tables 7-3M and 7-3N) is used up to the point where temperature is at or below 1,800°F, the usual working temperatures for medium heat chimneys.

If these units are used within a building, care must be taken to provide wide clearances to the high temperature portions of the chimney. It is desirable to locate these units away from sensitive areas such as operating rooms. If chimneys pass through fire-rated shafts it will in all probability be necessary to pass outside air in the area between the chimney and the enclosing walls. This will require an intake at the shaft bottom. If this is done the intake duct must be protected with a proper fire-rated enclosure to insure fire integrity of the building.

A medium air unit has a larger secondary chamber to accommodate the extra air. An air intake above the secondary chamber cools the chimney to a reasonable temperature.

Primary chamber temperature may be up to 2,500°F; however, secondary temperatures are usually in the 1,800°

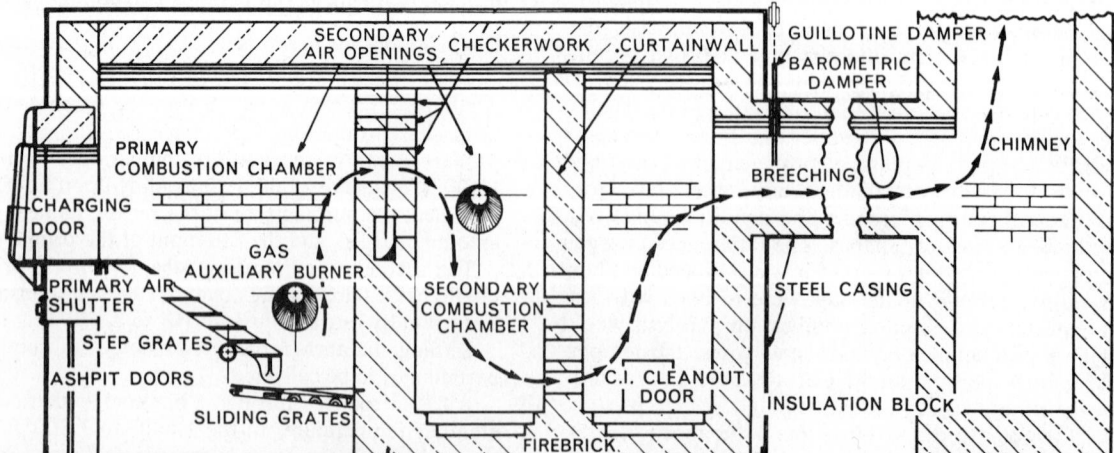

Fig. 7-6G. The basic design and nomenclature of a conventional commercial and industrial incinerator.

to 2,400°F range with chimney temperatures at or below 1,800°F. Medium heat chimneys may be used on these units.

A 100 percent excess air unit has a large secondary combustion chamber to accommodate the extra air. Temperatures in the primary chamber are 1,600° to 2,500°F with secondary chamber from 1,400° to 2,500°F and a chimney temperature of 1,800°F. Medium heat chimneys may be used on these units.[11]

Pyrolytic Incineration

This is another form of controlled air incineration where the air in the primary combustion chamber is well below theoretical requirements.[12] A destructive distillation, rather than combustion, takes place with the distilled vapors passing into a secondary chamber or fume incineration section where excess air is introduced to combust the distillation products. Exit temperatures are dependent upon the amount of air introduced into the secondary combustion chamber or into the chimney. Most units operate at a 1,800°F chimney temperature; however, these units must be checked with the manufacturer to determine the temperature involved, if a proper chimney section is to be made. There are many instances where the distilled fumes may be utilized to supplement fuel requirements using special burner adapters or direct introduction into conventional boilers.

Chimneys for Incinerators

Chimney requirements for individual incinerators vary according to the temperatures involved as has been discussed earlier in this chapter. The NFPA Incinerator and Rubbish Handling Standard stipulates that incinerator chimneys service incinerators only. The practice of exhausting incinerators into chimneys for other appliances is avoided because:

1. Incinerators operate under positive pressure and could force combustion products into the other appliances.

2. The burning rate of refuse is variable thus if a high heat release, rapidly burning material is charged, there can be a sudden surge in pressure and temperature that will not only force combustion products into the other appliances, but could shut off the flow of products from the appliance.

3. Boiler chimneys may not be medium heat chimneys suitable for the high temperatures associated with incinerators thus a fire liability may exist.

4. Some boiler chimneys become wet with condensed flue acids and moisture. This may enter porous materials slowly over a long period of time. If the chimney is suddenly subject to rapid heating and high temperatures, spalling can take place.

5. Flue gases from incinerators are always acid and will vary in intensity depending upon the amount of fire retardant plastics in the mix. A blow back of these acid fumes into boilers or other connected appliances could cause considerable corrosion as they condense upon tubes, burners, and other metallic parts.

6. The blow back situation occurs primarily when the refuse mass burns at a higher than normal rate and when the heat release expands the gases at a more rapid rate. Pressure is produced. If this occurs in a multiple connection the blow back will be through the areas of least resistance, thus through the connected appliance. This effect usually has a high acid concentration in the combustion products since plastics are the prime high heat release, high combustion rate materials.

Shredders

There are some instances where a more uniform feed to an incinerator is required or where refuse must be transferred over a distance before storage. It is good practice to sprinkler the feed bins for shedders, and if they are serviced by chutes, arrangements must be made to bypass the shredder since shredders have frequent periods of repair. All bypass areas and storage areas are sprinklered and enclosed within fire-rated rooms with fire doors suitable for Class B openings. The discharge from shedding devices also requires sprinkler protection.

SI Units

The following conversion factors are given as a convenience in converting to SI units the English units used in this chapter.

1 in. $= 25.400$ mm
1 sq in. $= 645.160$ mm^2
$\frac{5}{9}$(°F $- 32$) $=$ °C

Bibliography

References Cited

[1] Schulz, Joseph F., "Standards for Refuse-Handling in Apartment Houses," *Fire Journal*, Vol. 68, No. 2, Mar. 1974, pp. 82–86.

[2] Tamura, G. T. and Wilson, A. G., "Building Pressures Caused By Chimney Action and Mechanical Ventilation," paper presented at the ASHRAE 74th Annual Meeting, Minneapolis, Minnesota, June 26–28, 1967.

[3] Tamura, G. T. and Wilson, A. G., "Natural Venting to Control Smoke Movement in Buildings Via Vertical Shafts," paper presented at the ASHRAE Annual Meeting, Kansas City, Missouri, June 28–July 1, 1970.

[4] Keiser, E. R., "Incineration of Refuse—State of the Art," *Public Works*, April 1971, pp. 77–79.

[5] Corey, R. C., *Principles and Practices of Incineration*, Wiley-Interscience, New York, 1969.

[6] Cross, Frank L., *Handbook of Incineration*, Technomic, Westport, Conn., 1972.

[7] Incinerator Standards, Incinerator Institute of America, Falls Church, Va., Nov. 1968.

[8] "Guidebook for Industrial and Commercial Gas-Fired Incineration," American Gas Association, Inc., New York.

[9] Ellison, William, "Wet Scrubbers Popular for Air Cleaning," *Power*, Feb. 1971, pp. 62–63.

[10] Theoclitus, Gregory, et al., "Concepts and Behavior of the Controlled Air Incinerator," *Proceedings*, 1972, National Incinerator Conference, ASME, New York.

[11] Lewis, Michael F., "Controlled Air Incineration of Industrial Solid Waste," paper presented to National Industrial Solid Waste Management Conference, Mar. 25, 1970.

[12] Milkovich, Joseph J., "What's Happening to Pyrolysis," *Pollution Engineering*, Jan. 1972.

NFPA Codes, Standards, and Recommended Practices (see the latest *NFPA Publications and Visual Aids Catalog* for availability of current editions of the following documents)

NFPA No. 13, Standard for the Installation of Sprinkler Systems.
NFPA No. 30, Flammable and Combustible Liquids Code.
NFPA No. 31, Standard for the Installation of Oil Burning Equipment.
NFPA No. 54, Standard for the Installation of Gas Appliances and Gas Piping.
NFPA No. 58, Standard for the Storage and Handling of Liquefied Petroleum Gases.
NFPA No. 82, Standard on Incinerators and Rubbish Handling.
NFPA No. 89M, Manual on Clearances for Heat Producing Appliances.
NFPA No. 97M, Standard Glossary of Terms Relating to Chimneys, Gas Vents, and Heat Producing Appliances.
NFPA No. 101, Life Safety Code.
NFPA No. 211, Standard for Chimneys, Fireplaces and Vents.

Additional Readings

"Incinerator Testing Bulletin T-6," Incinerator Institute of America, New York, June 1967.

Puglisi, E. A. and Loftus, "Air Pollution, Incineration, and the Construction Industry, Part II," *Incinerators Construction Review*, Oct. 1969, pp. 4–12.

Schulz, J. F., "Incineration Air Pollution and Apartment Buildings," *Comfort Engineering*, Winter 1966/67 issue.

Chapter 7

MISCELLANEOUS BUILDING SERVICES

This chapter gives information on building services not covered elsewhere in this Section. Discussion will cover both fire protection and fire prevention features and considerations. With few exceptions, standards or codes do not outline design or performance requirements for the miscellaneous building services to be covered. Some guidance is found in the NFPA No. 101, Life Safety Code and NFPA No. 70, National Electrical Code. Regardless of the depth of code guidance given, considerations should be taken in facility design to account for these items which are frequently overlooked in proper design and during fire inspections.

The building services discussed in this chapter are: communications (Part A), elevators, escalators, moving walks and dumbwaiters (Part B), plumbing (Part C), and service chutes and chases (Part D).

A. Communications

In this age of need for instantaneous data with constant updating, communications are vital to almost any type of operation. For example, some operations depend almost entirely on telephone service, such as a telephone order operation or a multifaceted computer network tied to terminals throughout the world. Loss of access to communication equipment or loss of the equipment itself can have devastating implications on the profitability and viability of an operation. The dual problem associated with the installation and protection of the communication equipment is the fact that the equipment often introduces combustible fuel loading into an otherwise ideal fire safe configuration in the building; and that often the installation of the equipment leads to serious reductions of the structural compartmentation originally designed into the facility.

There are various types of communications used in buildings, such as the public phone system, private phone systems, audible voice page, light or tone page, and radio. The most common system is the telephone. In a large complex the location, construction, and protection of the cable entrance enclosure in a building must be an enclosure free of fire hazards and located in a secured area, because unauthorized tampering, deliberate sabotage, or fire could "kill" the entire telephone service. Underground service lines feeding a building should be identified for excavation purposes and overhead communication lines should not be located above or near hazardous operations subject to fire or explosion.

Most communication equipment utilizes electrical service of "low voltage" (50 volts or less) which exempts the wiring from being placed in conduit. Although the communication service is low voltage, ringing circuits are usually 110 V dc. In addition the wiring is usually polyvinyl chloride (PVC) clad wires wrapped in sizeable bundles and placed in vertical chases that, as enclosures, have minimal fire resistance.

The wiring has been shown to contribute significant fuel in fires, even when classed as PVC "self-extinguishing" wire. The bundling together of the wire in close proximity in vertical shafts open throughout leads to potentially serious fire spread problems and provides a fuel in a most ideal configuration for continued burning. (See Part D, Service Chutes, and Section 6, Chapter 8, for further discussion on

protection of vertical utility chases). Usually the wiring enters the floor in communication rooms and is mounted on combustible panels arrayed in close proximity to one another. This means that the communication room frequently contains an extremely high fuel loading, sometimes quantum levels above the surrounding occupancy. This hazard is often unrecognized. Fires originating in these rooms both can overcome the less than substantial partitioning enclosing the room allowing fire to spread on the floor of origin; and can also spread rapidly up the open vertical shaft to other communication rooms providing for a multifloor fire. Good practice considers automatic fire extinguishment, fire resistive compartmentation, and protection of both the communication room and the vertical shafts in order to correctly deal with a communication system installed throughout a building in typical fashion.

Communications systems are important during an emergency so that personnel in authority can communicate to the people in the buildings. This is particularly critical in a high rise structure where the occupants either cannot evacuate the building or must be advised of areas of refuge or alternative egress routes to take. Emergency communications systems should be supplied from a reliable standby electrical power supply.

B. Elevators, Escalators, and Dumbwaiters

People conveyances in multistory buildings are essential for a building to function, yet they in turn can contribute to fire fatalities. Concern has been raised in recent years based on the substantial evidence that elevators are a contributing factor in fire deaths in high rise buildings. For design and construction details of enclosures for elevators, escalators, and dumbwaiters, refer to Section 6, Chapter 8.

Elevators

Elevator doors on new installations are required to have a fire protection rating, but they are of little value to people in an elevator car when the elevator stops and opens its doors at a floor involved with fire or filled with smoke and fire gases. There are a number of ways in which this can happen:[1]

1. A passenger already in a car presses a button for the fire floor unaware of the ongoing fire.

2. A person on the fire floor attempting to evacuate presses both the up and down call buttons in order to quickly get away from the fire. This is done to stop the first car available. Often there is not enough time to wait for the elevator and occupants will continue onward and escape via the nearest stairway. This does not prevent the elevator car from stopping in response to the activated call button. Under these circumstances a given car can stop at the fire floor twice, once in the up mode and then again in the down mode. So the original passenger, if fortunate to enter during the up mode, may return to the fire floor from which he was seeking escape. By this time the fire has more than likely had a chance to have grown in intensity and the elevator, by stopping may fatally expose all passengers in the car.

3. During a fire, the call button unit with all its com-

ponents and wiring may become deformed, deteriorated, and destroyed by the intense heat. In so doing, a "call" for the elevator is registered. This situation occurs on mechanical as well as on electronic touch buttons. Laboratory tests have shown that this happens between 450° and 500°F.

Elevator manufacturers have not made call buttons operated by the heat of a finger. Some manufacturers use mechanical buttons operated by slight pressure, others use electronic buttons operated without pressure, but by the completion through the person of a circuit to ground. This is not to say that a flame applied directly on an electronic touch button or creating an ionized field in the surrounding atmosphere will also operate the call button. A fire test conducted at 30 Church Street in New York City found that electronic touch buttons could be activated when exposed to dense products of combustion (smoke) over a significant period of time under certain conditions.

Both the National Bureau of Standards and the ANSI A17.1 Committee, responsible for the National Elevator Code, took a systems approach to the fire problems associated with elevators and in 1969 recommended "Special Emergency Service." It requires that by operation of a key switch in the lobby all elevators in a group immediately disregard all activated call buttons, return nonstop to the main lobby, open their doors, and remain at the lobby until manually activated. Some of the more recent elevator recall systems combine the key operated switch with an automatic smoke detection system utilizing detectors at each floor lobby. Elevators are either manually or automatically recalled depending on which mode operates initially. This is being required in many building code provisions for high rise buildings.

The immediate return of all elevators is so essential to life safety that all cars in the up mode are stopped and reversed to return to the lobby. Cars in the down mode continue but will not stop at any intervening floor.

Among some of the more significant reasons that elevators are brought to the lobby and not stopped at the nearest floor are:

1. The hatchway may become filled with smoke.
2. The nearest floor may be involved in fire.
3. Firemen at the lobby can quickly ascertain that all elevators are accounted for and none are stuck in the hoistway requiring rescue.
4. The elevators are essential for use by fire fighters in rescuing occupants, deploying equipment and men, and initiating a coordinated fire attack.

After all elevators have returned nonstop to the lobby and people evacuated, it is preferable that they be shut down, because the elevators and their equipment are not presently designed to operate while exposed to fire and its elevated temperatures. Five potential areas of elevator failure due to fire exposure are:

1. Hoistway walls and doors that have limited fire resistance capability.
2. Essential electric controls that are subject to shutdown because of blown fuses and tripping of circuit breakers due to short circuits caused by flames, heat, and water.
3. A main elevator controller in a machine room at the top of the shaft(s) that may not function reliably or stop altogether due to heat and smoke rising in the hoistway.
4. Hoist cables that may part or lose strength if exposed to severe fire and heat and drop an elevator car on its "safety."
5. A main elevator power supply that may fail or be deliberately disconnected during fire fighting operations.

If elevators are shut down completely by a master key in the lobby, certain designated cars can be used by fire fighters for moving equipment to upper floors of a high rise to fight fire. The National Elevator Code has provisions that permit designated elevator cars to be operated by a special key switch inside the car for independent service, stopping for car calls only. This is a trade-off relationship where fire fighters must assume a severe risk in using the elevator to quickly move equipment and men. It is good practice for the designated cars to be powered by an emergency generator supply.

Fire Prevention

Oil, trash, debris, etc., should be continually cleaned up and removed from elevator pits, particularly those associated with hydraulic elevators. Oil soaked rags and other combustible material should be removed from the elevator equipment room. Only listed solvents and degreasers should be used in maintaining and cleaning elevator equipment, particularly in the hoistways.

Sprinkler Protection

Provisions are outlined in NFPA No. 13, Installation of Sprinkler Systems, for sprinklers in elevator shafts.

Any outside openings leading into the shaft should be marked with a large sign marked "SHAFT WAY" at each opening. This is a safeguard for anyone entering this opening who would otherwise be subject to falling down the shaftway.

Stalled Elevators—Rescue Operations

Proper procedures are needed for rescuing passengers from stalled elevators due to power failures, electrical malfunctions, fire, etc. For suggestions to prepare fire fighters for the removal of passengers from stalled elevators, the American Insurance Association's Special Interest Bulletin No. 55, is a good reference.

In the final analysis, the prime emphasis in safety plans of any building containing elevators should be placed on an education program based on this message: NEVER USE ELEVATORS AS EMERGENCY EXITS! This is true for either an electrical or fire emergency.

Escalators

Floor cutoff requirements for escalators are given in NFPA No. 101, Life Safety Code, and sprinkler protection requirements are described in the NFPA Sprinkler Standard. See also Section 6, Chapter 8, of this HANDBOOK for information on protecting floor openings.

An important factor in fire prevention is keeping oil, grease, and dust cleaned up at the drive motor and sprocket ends. If possible, escalators should be placed on a maintenance service contract with a vendor who would be responsible for periodic cleaning.

Escalators used as a means of egress should be arranged so that they can operate *only* in the direction of egress. During exiting, a stopped escalator may present severe tripping hazards at the floor entrance and floor exit due to the nonuniform arrangement of the first and last few treads and risers. If the evacuation plan calls for use of escalators, efficient crowd control is required to avoid serious pile-ups and potential panic. The NFPA Life Safety Code gives guidance on methods of protection of openings for escalators used as required exits.

Moving Walks

The same fire protection features as described above for escalators would apply to moving walkways, plus one additional factor, the combustible belt. A moving walkway can be considered as essentially the same as a large conveyor belt with the potential of spreading the fire either by the belt itself or by movement of burning items along the length of the belt.

Dumbwaiters

Dumbwaiters do not present the same problem as elevators from a passenger standpoint, but they are another version of an open vertical shaft requiring a floor cutoff or enclosure. Dumbwaiters can be responsible for moving smoke throughout a building. In addition, dumbwaiters used to move large quantities of mail or supplies have receiving rooms on each floor which can contain a high combustible loading. Consideration should be given to providing automatic fire extinguishment and a fire resistive compartment around substantial receiving rooms.

NFPA No. 101, Life Safety Code; NFPA No. 80, Standard for Fire Door and Windows; and Section 6, Chapter 8, contain information on design and construction requirements of the shaft and dumbwaiter car.

C.   Plumbing

Plumbing fixtures and piping have not been a fire hazard other than during installation, until the widespread use of plastic pipe. Full scale tests have been conducted on typical plumbing installations using ABS plastic (acrylonitrile-butadiene-styrene) for drains, waste and vent pipes, and fittings. These laboratory tests indicated that ABS plastic drains, waste and vent pipe, and fittings, if separated from other plastic pipe arrays, do not significantly contribute to the spread of fire.[2, 3] Such pipe located in a chase provides less of a fire spread potential than if located above a suspended ceiling arrayed with or in close proximity to other combustible fuel. When used as part of a fire resistive assembly, the plastic pipe may prove to have a detrimental effect.

A fire report has been documented where a polypropylene plastic vent spread a fire vertically in both directions as well as horizontally. In addition, the dripping plastic while being pyrolized dropped onto and ignited combustible material.[4]

A good feature of plastic plumbing versus copper plumbing with solder joints, is that a hot open flame is not required during installation. However, most of the solvent cements used to join plastic pipe joints are flammable and give off combustible vapors. Precautions are necessary in using these solvents during installation. Care should be used to avoid a significant quantity of vapor being given off during installations; and all materials used to install the pipe, including additional cement and rags used to clean the joints, should be removed from the facility on a daily basis.

D.   Service Chutes and Chases

Most multistory buildings will have at least one type of vertical chute (or chase) constructed for essential building services. From fire protection design, life safety, and fire prevention inspection standpoints, the vertical openings are either frequently overlooked or are given insufficient fire protection. Because chutes and chases can be a contributing factor in spreading smoke, fire gases, heat, and water damage throughout a building, plus, in the process, exposing essential building services, consideration must be given to proper arrangement, elimination of combustible loading in the chute, and automatic extinguishment. Refer to Section 6, Chapter 8, for design and construction details for protecting openings such as for chutes and chases.

Mail Chutes

Mail chutes have been in existence for nearly a century, and there has been little concern about fire problems with them. This may be attributed to the small floor openings they require, ranging from around 22 for letter drops, to 112 sq in. for bundle chutes. They are also normally capped off at the top thus minimizing any significant stack effect. Heights range to as high as the number of floors in the building. (There is an accumulation of over 430 stories of mail chutes in the World Trade Center in New York City.)

The observation glass-metal inspection and removable panels, etc., in mail chutes are specified by the U.S. Postal Service; however, there are no fire resistance rating requirements for chute enclosures at this time.

Fires have been reported in mail chutes, but they have been contained to the receiving container. Mail chutes are available that are designed to eject a cigarette dropped into the mail slot. The cigarette will be ejected back out on the floor. It is important that the chute is capped or sealed off at the top to minimize any flue effect. Consideration is being given to designing a fire damper with a fusible link at each floor into the mail chutes.

Trash Rubbish Chutes

Trash and refuse disposal is discussed in Chapter 6 of this Section.

Laundry or Linen Chutes

Installations of laundry or linen chutes frequently are found in large hospitals and hotels. These chutes when not properly designed or protected have contributed to spreading the fire through other portions of the building. Every opening into the enclosure should be protected by a self-closing fire-rated assembly. Laundry and linen chutes have hazards similar to that of rubbish chutes and should be designed accordingly (see Chapter 6 of this Section). For specific construction, enclosure and protection requirements refer to the NFPA Incinerator and Rubbish Handling Standard.

Pipe or Utility Chases

Utility chases for piping and wiring are very common in multistory buildings, because the utilities must be carried to each floor, and it is more convenient and economical to run them in a common location. This provides a vertical shaft running from the basement up through the entire building, because water, sanitary, electricity, and telephone services are usually provided on each floor.

These utility shafts have contributed to the spread of fire and smoke with loss of life and property. Fire studies have shown some of the main weaknesses include (1) poor shaft construction, (2) unsatisfactory access doors, and (3) combustible pipe insulation and jackets.[4] The solution to limit the spread of fire and smoke through chases is to fill in solidly with noncombustible material (preferably the same material as the floor construction) at each floor level. All pipes, etc. passing through the fire-smoke stop should be completely filled in around the pipe or sleeve with a noncombustible grouting material and no pipe insulation carried through the chase fire stop.

If this is not possible, fire doors or access doors that have been listed by an independent fire testing laboratory for the protection of openings are recommended for the openings in utility chases. Panels of combustible material or noncombustible panels attached to combustible frames are never used to close such openings.

Bibliography

References Cited

[1] Figiel, Walter J., "The Control of Elevators During a High Rise Building Fire," *Elevator World,* July 1972, pp. 8–14.

[2] Bletzacker, R. W. and Birle, J. G., "Standard ASTM Fire Endurance Test and Hose Stream Test on Duplicate Non-Load Bearing Acrylonitrile-Butadiene-Styrene (ASB) Plumbing Wall Assemblies," Building Research Laboratory Report No. 5473, April 1973, The Ohio State University, Columbus, Ohio.

[3] Troxell, George E., "Fire Tests of Plastic Vents and Drain Pipes," *Fire Journal,* Vol. 60, No. 4, July 1966, pp. 52–57.

[4] Stevens, Richard E., "Utility Shafts for Piping and Wiring," *Fire Journal,* Vol. 61, No. 4, July 1967, pp. 22–23.

NFPA Codes, Standards, and Recommended Practices (see the latest *NFPA Publications and Visual Aids Catalog* for availability of current editions of the following documents)

NFPA No. 13, Standard for the Installation of Sprinkler Systems.
NFPA No. 72E, Standard on Automatic Fire Detectors.
NFPA No. 80, Standard for Fire Doors and Windows.
NFPA No. 82, Standard on Incinerators and Rubbish Handling.
NFPA No. 101, Life Safety Code.
NFPA No. 211, Standard for Chimneys, Fireplaces and Vents.
NFPA No. 251, Standard Methods of Fire Tests of Building Construction and Materials.
NFPA No. 252, Standard Methods of Fire Tests of Door Assemblies.

Additional Readings

American Society of Mechanical Engineers, "Safety Code for Elevators, Dumbwaiters, Escalators and Moving Walks," ANSI 17.1, American National Standards Institute, New York, 1971.

American Society of Mechanical Engineers, "Evacuation of Passengers from Stalled Elevator Cars," A17 Guide, American National Standards Institute, New York, 1973.

"Bimonthly Fire Record, Apartment Building-Vertical Opening," *Fire Journal,* Vol. 59, No. 5, Sept. 1965, p. 47.

"Bimonthly Fire Record, Elevator Fire," *Fire Journal,* Vol. 66, No. 4, July 1972, p. 62.

"Bimonthly Fire Record, Office Building," *Fire Journal,* Vol. 60, No. 4, July 1966, pp. 48–49.

Chandler, Lee T., "Automatic Recall of Elevators by Smoke Detectors in High Rise Buildings," *Fire Journal,* Vol. 68, No. 6, Nov. 1974, pp. 79–82.

Juillerat, E. E., "New Mexico State Hospital Fire," *Fire Journal,* Vol. 62, No. 1, Jan. 1968, pp. 5–9.

Juillerat, E. E. and Gaudet, R. E., "Fire at Dale's Penthouse Restaurant," *Fire Journal,* Vol. 61, No. 3, May 1967, p. 9.

———, "Three Hotel Fires," *Fire Journal,* Vol. 60, No. 3, May 1966, pp. 38–41.

Powers, Robert W., "New York Office Building Fire," *Fire Journal,* Vol. 65, No. 1, Jan. 1971, pp. 22–23.

———, "Office Building Fire 919 Third Avenue New York City," *Fire Journal,* Vol. 65, No. 2, March 1971, p. 7.

Sears, A. B., "Another Home for Aged Fire: Ten Killed," *Fire Journal,* Vol. 65, No. 3, May 1971, p. 7.

Skilling, Gerald B., "The Case for Evacuating High Rise Buildings," *Fire Journal,* Vol. 66, No. 3, May 1972, p. 32.

Stone, Walter R., "Fire Fatal to Three in Residential Care Facility," *Fire Journal,* Vol. 67, No. 5, Sept. 1973, p. 22.

Watrous, L. D., "Fatal Hotel Fire-New Orleans," *Fire Journal,* Vol. 66, No. 1, Jan. 1972, p. 7.

———, "Fire in a High Rise Apartment Building," *Fire Journal,* Vol. 63, No. 3, May 1969, p. 11.

———, "High Rise Fire in New Orleans," *Fire Journal,* Vol. 67, No. 3, May 1973, p. 9.

Willey, A. E., "Fatal Flammable Liquid Elevator Shaft," *Fire Journal,* Vol. 67, No. 4, July 1973, pp. 62–63.

———, "High Rise Building Fire-Sao Paulo, Brazil," *Fire Journal,* Vol. 66, No. 4, July 1972, p. 107.

———, "Tae Yon Kak Hotel Fire-Seoul, Korea," *Fire Journal,* Vol. 66, No. 3, May 1972, p. 12.

SECTION 8

THE HAZARDS OF OCCUPANCIES

Chapter 1

ASSESSING LIFE SAFETY FROM FIRE IN BUILDINGS

When a building is designed, there are many factors that must be considered in order to result in an economical structure that best satisfies the needs of the owner. Much study is given to such factors, one of the most important of which is the life safety of the building's occupants from fire. If, during the initial planning of buildings, more consideration were given to the life safety of the future occupants, safer buildings would be designed.

Many times buildings are in advanced design stages before local fire safety codes are consulted; for the most part, local fire safety codes set forth minimum requirements that do not deal with all types of situations. Therefore, to assure that a building's owner will have a safe building, it is necessary to include fire safety features during the initial design stages. All too often building owners take it for granted that architects and designers will automatically include such features.

Other important factors to be considered during the planning of a building are: (1) the people who will occupy the building, (2) the activities of the people in the building, (3) the kind and severity of fire that might occur in the building, and (4) the inherent design features of the building that could affect life safety should fire occur. While this chapter deals primarily with the life safety of people, property protection is also vitally important and is dealt with in other chapters of this HANDBOOK.

To assist in the planning of fire safe buildings, the NFPA has developed a decision tree (see Sec. 6, Chap. 2) from which can be selected an economical, predetermined level of life safety. To use the decision tree when selecting a system that best suits a particular building, preliminary analysis of factors about the building and its proposed use must be made in order to choose the appropriate route for making a cost analysis and calculating probabilities of success. Also of assistance when designing fire safe buildings is NFPA No. 101, Code for Safety to Life from Fire in Buildings and Structures, hereinafter referred to in this chapter as the NFPA Life Safety Code. The NFPA Life Safety Code covers construction, protection, and occupancy features to minimize danger to life from fire, smoke, fumes, or panic before buildings are evacuated. The Code specifies the number, size, and arrangement of exit facilities sufficient to permit prompt escape of occupants from buildings or structures in case of fire or other conditions that are dangerous to life.

A. People Factors

In most cases, people are what the designers of buildings are attempting to protect when they include fire safety features in their designs. Although the state of the art of designing buildings for safe evacuation is reasonably well understood (see Sec. 6, Chap. 1), human characteristics (as influenced by the following items) are an important consideration; for example, the design of means of egress is largely governed by human characteristics. Important human characteristics that need to be considered in building design for safety from fire are as follows:

1. Physical and mental characteristics.
2. Age.
3. Agility.

4. Decision-making capabilities.
5. Awareness.
6. Training.
7. Special knowledge and beliefs.

As each occupancy group of buildings is discussed in this section, mention will be made of applicable human characteristics as they pertain to the design of the occupancy for life safety. The discussions will be based largely on studies of fire incidents contained in NFPA files, although some behavioral patterns are evidenced in situations other than fire. Fire, like any emergency, may exemplify the behavior.

Not included in the list of characteristics (since it is not a characteristic but the result of a situation) is people control. This is a factor which becomes important in occupancies such as schools and certain industries. It has been demonstrated that during fire emergencies evacuation will be orderly and rapid when the people involved have been exposed to disciplinary control and training. There will be little likelihood of panic, and people so trained will be able to deal with the unexpected.

Rubin and Cohen in their study of Occupant Behavior in Building Fires[1] state that "an examination of the information concerning the needs of occupants in fire emergencies (as opposed to insuring a degree of structural integrity for the building) indicates that the scientific information base is woefully inadequate." This statement rightfully points out an area needing much research and study. There are, however, some interesting and pertinent papers that are worthy of review which provide a better understanding of the characteristics that affect human behavior in emergencies (see Bibliography at end of this chapter).

One study conducted in Great Britain by Peter G. Wood[2] draws conclusions from data collected from 1,000 fire incidents involving more than 2,000 people. Mr. Wood points out three general types of reaction to fire, as follows (in order of frequency):

1. Concern with evacuation of the building either by oneself or with others.
2. Concern with fire fighting or at least with containing the fire.
3. Concern with warning or alerting others, either individuals or the fire department.

Wood states that "the most frequent courses of action were, in fact, directed solely to one end; either leaving the building or fighting the fire." Because Mr. Wood's study is the most comprehensive and pertinent of its kind known, a synopsis of his findings is presented as follows:

In general the majority of people appeared to have behaved in what might be considered an appropriate fashion, although some 5 percent of the people did something which was judged to "increase the rise." There was little evidence of true "panic."

The actions taken were considered sequentially and the most frequent first actions were, in order: (1) some fire-fighting action, (2) contact fire department, (3) investigate fire, (4) warn others, (5) do something to minimize the danger, (6) evacuate oneself from the building, and (7) evacuate others from the building. These 7 classes of action describe almost 80 percent of the first actions taken.

The effect of other variables upon first action taken was as follows:

The more serious a person considered a fire to be, the more likely that he would immediately leave the building and the less likely that he would attempt to fight the fire.

Familiarity with the layout of building did not affect whether or not a person attempted to immediately leave the building. People who were less than completely familiar with the building were more likely to try and save personal effects.

The more frequently people had been trained or instructed in what to do in a fire, the more likely they were to raise the alarm or organize evacuation as a first action. In other respects frequency of training did not affect first action taken.

People who had been previously involved in a fire incident were no more likely to contact the fire department than those who hadn't. They were, however, more likely to fight the fire or minimize the risk in some way. They were less likely to immediately leave the building.

Women were more likely to take the following first actions: (1) warn others, (2) immediately leave the building, and (3) request assistance and evacuate their families.

Women were less likely to take the following first actions: (1) fight the fire, or (2) minimize the risk.

An increasing proportion of people from age 10 to 59 fought the fire.

Evacuation of the Building

Men were less likely to leave the building than women. They were, moreover, more likely to return into the building if they did leave.

People were more likely to leave the building if they didn't know any means of emergency escape.

People were more likely to leave the building when smoke was present. They also returned more frequently when smoke was present.

People were less likely to leave the building if they had been previously involved in a fire incident. They were, moreover, more likely to return into the building.

People who had never received training were more likely to leave the building. People who had received training at least once a month were less likely to leave.

The time of occurrence of the incident did not affect whether or not people left the building.

People were more likely to leave the building if the smoke spread beyond the room of origin. The greater the smoke density the more likely that people would leave the building.

Differences in people's familiarity with the layout of the building did not affect which exit they used. The more familiar people were with the building, the more frequently they returned into the building.

The more extensive the smoke spread, the more frequently exits other than normal were used.

People returned to the building more frequently when members of their immediate families were present.

Movement through Smoke

In incidents where smoke was present, 60 percent of the people attempted to move through it. Nearly 50 percent of these people moved 10 yd or more.

Men were more likely to move through smoke than women. They were also more likely to move greater distances.

Knowledge of a means of escape did not affect whether or not a person moved through smoke. However, people who stated they did know a means of escape were more likely to move more than 15 yd through smoke.

Previous involvement in a fire incident did not affect whether or not people moved through smoke. However, people who had been previously involved tended to move greater distances.

The more familiar a person was with the layout of the building, the more likely that person would be to attempt to move through smoke. Familiarity did not, however, affect how far a person moved.

The frequency with which a person had received training or instruction on what to do in a fire did not affect whether or not that person attempt to move through smoke. People who had never received training were less likely to move as great a distance through smoke as those who had.

People were more likely to attempt to move through smoke if the incident occurred during the day than if it occurred at night. People involved in night-time incidents were, however, more likely to move further through smoke.

B. People Activities

Another important factor to be considered during the planning of a building is the type of activities that people in the building will be performing. A study of these activities should alert architects and designers to conditions that require specific attention, particularly when studied with the human characteristics listed in Part A of this chapter. For example, if an occupant is in a building to perform office work, it may be assumed that such a person's mental characteristics, decision-making capabilities, and awareness are not unusual. If, however, the person is a paraplegic, physical and agility characteristics must be considered. Similarly, the activity of sleeping presents special considerations that are typical of residential and institutional occupancies. There are many other activities performed in these types of occupancies, each of which should be studied. In some occupancies, people activities combined with human characteristics present very special situations requiring more life safety measures than for other occupancies. A study of the activities of people is helpful in analyzing the kind and severity of fire that might occur in a building. This point will, however, be largely confined to those activities which involve known hazards, since in many occupancies there are so many activities performed that the results of a study would be inaccurate if only a few activities were studied. As evidenced by the causes of fires in one- and two-family dwellings (see Chap. 2, this Sec.), activities in such occupancies are extremely varied. In comparison, at a fireworks plant where employees are working on firecrackers, the kind and severity of fire that might occur is quite evident from the activity.

People activities are clues to situations that should be considered in the life safety design of a building. For example, in addition to the many fire hazards normally involved in restaurant operations, eating in a restaurant is a people activity that might involve situations like crowded conditions with inadequate aisles to reach exits, loose chairs to be thrown during escape, blocking of exits with tables or equipment, locking of exits to keep customers from leaving without paying, and other situations typical of restaurants. Clues to such situations should guide the architect or designer so that the building design results in space utilization that mitigates as much as possible the situations that can occur in restaurants. This type of design must also take into consideration the hazards inherent in restaurant operation (e.g., kitchen hazards such as deep fat fryers).

The preceding example is simply indicative of the kind of people activity that should be considered by the designer, the code writer, fire protection engineer, and anyone else involved in life safety from fire in buildings. People activity is an important factor to the designer. Its importance as a determinant in designing for life safety from fire should not be minimized.

C. Kind and Severity of Fire

Predicting the kind and severity of fire that may occur in a building is important in the early design stages because such a prediction influences decisions on how to manage both the fire and the exposed occupants in the future. Throughout this HANDBOOK there is information on the fire characteristics of materials including ignition temperatures, flash points, softening points, calorific value, rate of burning, flame spread, smoke developed, and other characteristics that should be studied before one attempts to predict the kind and severity of fire that may occur in a building space. There is also information on equating fire loading (lbs of combustibles per sq ft of floor space) to fire severity in terms of time of expected duration. Fire loading is only one of the parameters that should be considered when predicting the kind and severity of a fire that may occur. All of the characteristics previously mentioned should be studied, and it should be pointed out that there are variables within some of those characteristics (e.g., variation of ignition temperature with size of specimen, size and shape of specimen, affect on rate of burning, etc.).

Since the type of ignition source can have a relationship to the kind of fire, a review of fire ignition sequences for various occupancies is appropriate. (For more detailed information concerning fire ignition sequence, see Section 2 of this HANDBOOK.) Also, it is appropriate to review the fire experience in the occupancy under consideration. Such reviews often reveal situations that some building designers do not believe can happen; the expression "there is nothing to burn here" has often been shattered by fire experience.

The activities and behavior of people also hold clues as to the kind and severity of fire that might occur. For example, the janitor of a school is charged with, amongst other things, keeping the building clean. When he piles all the furniture together so that he can sweep the floor, the kind and severity of fire that would occur if that furniture were ignited would be quite different than if the furniture had been arranged for classroom use.

It should be recognized that behavioral patterns in some cases appear to be inherent in some occupancies; e.g., it is common in hotel fires for guests to pay little attention to fire alarms, and for employees to investigate a reported fire situation and to attempt to fight the fire, usually unsuccessfully. Notifying the fire department appears to be a last resort, and by the time the department has been notified enough time has elapsed for the fire to become severe.

D. Building Design Features

One of the fundamentals of building design is to provide a structure that will be so designed and arranged as to best suit its intended purpose. Before any design is started the designer should spend time determining his clients' needs, and more specifically in determining the kinds of activities that will be performed in the building. The building must provide for the most efficient utilization of the space possible, and it must provide an environment that will result in efficiency for the people who will occupy it. Because of these facts, it should be recognized that buildings for certain types of activities result in inherent design features that are important to consider when life safety protection for the building is considered. Shopping centers with malls, for example, have specific inherent features that tax the fire protectionist. They shelter under one roof (and hence become single buildings) many different hazards. Since merchants are interested in displaying merchandise in order to attract customers into their stores, each store will either have large glass windows between the mall and the store or store fronts that open onto the mall. Thus, a fire in one store will undoubtedly vent itself into the mall to endanger the people and other shops that open onto the mall. If the facility is more than one story in height, it can be expected that the design will involve atrium arrangements in the mall so that occupants of the mall can see as many store fronts as possible. Vertical separation, therefore, is not possible.

Because many of the stores in shopping malls are relatively small, they usually have only one means of egress out of the store: by way of the mall. This can lead to undesirably long travel distances to exits. With multiple stores or other occupancies all under one roof, separation between occupancies, while attainable, is difficult to maintain and must extend into a roof space common to all the occupancies.

This rather brief analysis of one type of structure has been presented to point out inherent fire problems that include separation between occupancies, vertical openings, travel distance to exits, and possible hazard extremes under one roof. This kind of analysis can pinpoint the problem areas inherent in building design that must be recognized before a system for life safety from fire is selected.

Probably one of the most definitive examples of inherent building design features affecting life safety from fire is the "high rise" building. High rise has been variously defined, but it is generally agreed that three things are inherent in a high rise building: (1) the fire must be fought from inside the building, (2) evacuation of the building is impractical because of the time necessary for evacuation, and (3) the "stack effect" is significant. All three of these factors must be considered when designing the life safety system for a "high rise" building. In addition, a high rise building may contain several occupancies presenting various degrees of fire hazards. Typical of such a situation would be a building (starting from grade level) containing a parking garage, offices, mercantiles, and apartments on the lower floors, with an assembly occupancy (restaurant) on the top floor. It can be expected that such complex structures will become increasingly more common.

Other typical examples of types of building design affecting life safety are:

1. Large undivided industrial buildings where compartmentation becomes impractical and travel distance to exits can become excessive.

2. School buildings of open and flexible plan layouts where, again, compartmentation is impractical and access to exits may be varied and obstructed.

3. "Astrodome" structures where large numbers of people must be quickly evacuated in fire emergencies.

4. Hotel exhibition halls that involve heavy fire loading and numerous ignition sources.

5. Windowless buildings that make entrance for fire fighting and rescue difficult.

Although the preceding list could be longer and more varied, these examples should serve to emphasize the importance of assessing the inherent design features of a building when selecting a system for life safety from fire.

Bibliography

References Cited

[1] Rubin, A. I. and Cohen, A., "Occupant Behavior in Building Fires," National Bureau of Standards, U.S. Department of Commerce, Washington, D.C., Feb. 1974.

[2] Wood, P. G., "The Behavior of People in Fires," Fire Research Note No. 953, Nov. 1972, Department of the Environment, Building Research Establishment, Fire Research Station, Borehamwood, Herts, England.

NFPA Codes, Standards, and Recommended Practices (see the latest *NFPA Publications and Visual Aids Catalog* for availability of current editions of the following document)

NFPA No. 101, Code for Safety to Life from Fire in Buildings and Structures.

Additional Readings

Bryan, J. L., "A Study of the Survivor Reports on the Panic in the Fire at the Arundel Park Hall in Brooklyn, Maryland, on January 29, 1956," unpublished investigation.

Galbreath, M., "A Survey of Exit Facilities in High Office Buildings," Building Research Note 64, 1968, Division of Building Research, National Research Council, Ottawa, Canada.

Glass, A. J., "Mass Psychology," *Proceedings of Workshop on Mass Burns,* 1960, National Academy of Science, Washington, D.C.

Stevens, R. E., "For Architects and Builders: 'People' Factors in Building Design," *Fire Journal,* Vol. 63, No. 4, July 1969, pp. 31–32.

———, "For Architects and Builders: A System for Life Safety from Fire," *Fire Journal,* Vol. 64, No. 1, Jan. 1970, p. 80.

Chapter 2

RESIDENTIAL OCCUPANCIES

For fire protection purposes a residential occupancy is one in which sleeping accommodations are provided for "normal residential purposes." As a result, a residential occupancy grouping includes all buildings and facilities designed to provide sleeping accommodations, with the exception of health care occupancies and penal facilities. Health care occupancies (hospitals, nursing homes, residential custodial care facilities, etc.) and penal occupancies (prisons, detention homes, etc.) are not included in the traditional definition of a residential occupancy since the sleeping accommodations for these types of facilities are not for "normal residential purposes."

This chapter deals with five different classifications of residential occupancies: hotels, apartment buildings, dormitories, lodging or rooming houses, and one-and two-family dwellings.

A. General Life Safety Requirements

In assessing the degree of fire safety and life safety hazards represented by residential occupancies, it is necessary to determine what these facilities have in common that enables them to be so classified. The definition of residential occupancies centers around the fact that sleeping accommodations are found within each and every facility for "normal residential purposes". This means that this group of occupancies is responsible for the housing of each and every individual in this country for the largest part of a given day. Unfortunately, while these occupancies are inhabited, most of the occupants are asleep and consequently not readily aware of their surroundings nor the events that they may portend.

This condition of unawareness due to sleeping is reflected in the appalling life safety statistics that apply to residential occupancies under conditions of fire. In the United States most deaths from fires in residential occupancies are the result of fires that initiate in the pre-dawn hours. Thus, the most important factor to be considered in the fire and life safety design aspects of residential occupancies is the production of a viable environment that protects the individual, for the most part, from events occurring both outside his own control and during a period of time when he may not be aware of them. Obviously, even in this type occupancy, it is impossible to anticipate fire and life safety design criteria that will protect the individual from careless acts such as smoking in bed or smoking and drinking heavily prior to retiring to bed.

It must be recognized that the Model Building Codes and NFPA No. 101, Code for Safety to Life from Fire in Building and Structures, hereinafter referred to in this chapter as the NFPA Life Safety Code, have more than adequately dealt with the question of residential occupancy design in the public sector. Since our codes and laws are structured to provide a level of public safety, these documents have developed reasonably stringent requirements for hotels, apartment buildings, dormitories, and lodging or rooming houses. However, since one- and two-family dwellings are not considered in the public sector, the level of codification of design criteria for dwellings in the area of fire protection is notably less stringent. Again, this is

further reflected in the fire statistics quoted in the previous paragraph.

B. NFPA Life Safety Code Requirements

The NFPA Life Safety Code requirements contained in this chapter are common to all residential occupancies. In developing means of egress arrangements and design, it is necessary to determine the occupant loading for a particular facility. For residential occupancies it is recognized that an occupant load of one person per 200 sq ft gross floor area, or the maximum probable population of any room or section under design consideration, should be utilized for determining exit width. The notable exception to this criteria is the one- or two-family dwelling where such population loadings are neither expected nor anticipated. In assessing these occupant loads in other than dwellings, the NFPA Life Safety Code requires that open mezzanines and balconies be reviewed in the assessment and their potential occupant load assigned to the floor directly below the mezzanine or balcony for exit width and design requirements. In addition, the following requirements are placed on exit design in relationship to occupant loading. Doors, including three-stair risers (21 in.) above or below ground level, Class A ramps (see Sec. 6, Chap. 9), and horizontal exits are assigned the capacity of 100 persons per unit of exit width (22 in.). Stairs and all other types of exits not listed in the previous sentence are assigned an occupant capacity of 75 persons per unit of exit width (22 in.).

Because the locking of doors in occupied residential occupancies prevents expedient egress, the NFPA Life Safety Code contains a strict prohibition against the locking of any door in any means of egress in all residential occupancies. This Code requirement is obviously not recognized in hotel or motel rooms occupied on a transient basis and in permanent domiciles in dwellings or apartment buildings where common practice is to lock doors against ingress and egress on a nightly basis for security purposes. Although the popular trend towards use of "deadbolt" locks or "double cylinder" locks that require key operation from the inside as well as from the outside has solved normal security requirements for residential occupancies, such use has greatly increased the potential of loss of life during fire emergency conditions. Recent fire events have led to multi-death disasters when keys could not be located or operated quickly enough. This has resulted in the reassessment of the types of locking hardware considered suitable for both security and fire safety needs in residential occupancies. The NFPA Life Safety Code has always required that locks, when installed, should not prohibit egress from a building nor should they require other than a simple type device (knob, push bar, etc.) for operation to release the latch while exiting. These requirements again would lead to a prohibition, for life safety purposes, of any locking device requiring the use of a key, or the complex operation of several devices (a knob and pushbutton, or a knob and slide bar) to obtain egress.

C. Hotels

Hotels are considered to include buildings or groups of buildings under the same management in which there are 15 or more sleeping accommodations for hire, primarily by transients (with or without meals), whether designated as hotels, motels, inns, clubs, or by any other name. Apartment hotels are also classified in this category because they are potentially subject to transient occupancy.

Hotels represent several types of occupancies housed under one roof. These include ballrooms, assembly or exhibition halls, and restaurants. This is in addition to the normal sleeping room facilities that constitute the majority of a typical hotel occupancy. The treatment from a fire and life safety standpoint of ballrooms, assembly or exhibition halls, and restaurants, is dealt with elsewhere in this chapter and in other sections of this HANDBOOK. In recognition of the inherent design considerations of these particular occupancies, the NFPA Life Safety Code contains special requirements developed for public assembly occupancies. The Code directs designers and enforcing officials to apply these requirements when designing or arranging these particular areas within a hotel facility.

Exit Details

In recognition of the fact that many hotel occupancies provide numerous small shops or meeting rooms as an adjunct to the hotel occupancy, there is a general NFPA Life Safety Code requirement that small rooms having a capacity of less than 50 persons can be permitted to have a single exit if the rooms are arranged with an outside door at street or ground level. This arrangement is permitted only if the room is designed so that the travel distance within the room to the door is no more than 50 ft from all parts of the room. In furtherance of the fact that hotels are also arranged to house a variety of rooms and facilities that are not open to the general public, such as mechanical equipment rooms, storage rooms, and service operations (other than kitchens which are considered part of the hotel occupancy), the NFPA Life Safety Code allows for exit arrangements that are appropriate to these actual occupancies rather than a more stringent exit design based on the assumption that the public would not occupy these spaces. Finally, hotel occupancies are designed so that stairways are not cascaded but are permitted to be a constant width throughout the facility, with that width designed to accommodate the maximum population of the largest floor. Consequently, the NFPA Life Safety Code states that the same stairway or other exit required to serve any one floor may also serve other floors. This is done with the strict prohibition that no inside open stairway, escalator, or ramp may serve as a required egress from more than one floor. This last prohibition is borne out by the rather poor hotel life safety fire experience that centers around traditional old hotel designs incorporating the use of one sizable open monumental stair or several open stairways (as in the LaSalle Hotel Fire in Chicago and the Winecoff Hotel Fire in Atlanta, both in the 1940s).

Exit Capacity and Arrangement

Since hotel occupancies are those that house the most transient occupants who, unfortunately, are the least familiar with the facility, it is expected that during a fire condition occupants will attempt to evacuate through the hotel's main entrance. This reaction represents human nature and the reliance on subconscious conditioning during panic situations which causes people to use only those egress paths that they are familiar with. In recognition of this, the NFPA Life Safety Code requires capability, on an exit width basis, for the intermingling of occupants from the upper floors of a hotel with the occupants of the various public occupancy sections of the hotel usually located near

and around the main entrance. This leads to the following exit width requirements which deviate from the general width requirements previously discussed:

1. One unit (22 in.) of exit width is required for each 100 persons of street floor occupant load capacity for doors and other level exits. This includes those that are three-stair risers above or below ground level.

2. One unit of exit width (22 in.) is required for each 75 persons of street floor capacity for stairs or other exits requiring descent to ground level. This is in recognition of the common practice of arranging for meeting rooms on the second floor or balcony (mezzanine) areas directly above the main lobby of hotels.

3. One and one-half exit units (34 in.) of door width are required for each two units (44 in.) of exit width of required stair capacity from upper hotel floors that discharge through the street floor.

4. One and one-half exit width units (34 in.) of door capacity are required for each two units of required stair capacity from lower floors that discharge through the street floor of the hotel.

The minimum number of exits required for hotel occupancies is not less than two. These exits must be accessible from every floor, including the floors located below the floor of exit discharge and occupied for public purposes (the one exception being the conditions listed earlier in this chapter under the general discussion of residential occupancies). The maximum acceptable travel distance for exits for hotel occupancies is 100 ft from the door of any room. In recognition of the popular concept of exterior exit access routes found in many motel designs, the maximum travel distance of exits in those cases may be increased to 200 ft. In further recognition of the capabilities of automatic sprinkler protection, the maximum travel distance is permitted to be 150 ft in facilities equipped with automatic sprinkler protection. This is also permitted for partial sprinkler applications where the 150 ft travel distance is recognized for only that portion of the building equipped with automatic sprinkler protection if that portion of the building is separated from the remainder of the facility by construction having a fire resistance rating of not less than one hour for buildings of three stories or less in height, and two hours of fire resistive construction for buildings of four or more stories in height.

From every point in sizable open areas within a hotel and from the entrance door to individual rooms, exit access must be provided so that exits can be reached from at least two different directions. There is allowance for up to 35 ft of common exit travel (dead-end) from door entrances or from any point in an open area. This allowance permits a small degree of dead-end or pocketing of corridor arrangements in the allowable travel distance within open areas.

In recognition of the review of recent fire experience in hotel occupancies where the entrance door to a sleeping room was left open in a fire emergency condition contaminating the remainder of the corridor and exposing the remainder of the hotel occupancy on that floor to the fire, the NFPA Life Safety Code now requires that all doors between guest rooms and corridors be self-closing. This requirement applies to new and existing hotel construction. It is perhaps the single most important requirement from a fire safety standpoint (since the requirements for enclosing open stairs) because the presence of a door closer provides assurance that the high level of compartmentation, via the room walls, present in each guest room will be permitted to function as a barrier to both fire and smoke spread for the majority of fire incidents in a hotel. It also assures that the corridor area and related vertical shafting that is ancillary to the corridors will remain relatively free of smoke and products of combustion for the early stages of a fire in a room, allowing ease of egress for occupants immediately exposed by the fire and ease of ingress for fire fighting forces.

Again, in recognition of typical hotel design practices, at least half of the required number of units of exit width from upper hotel floors, exclusive of horizontal exits designed within the various floors, must lead directly to and discharge to the street or lead through a yard, court, or passageway with protected openings separated from all parts of the interior of the building, and discharged to the exterior. The NFPA Life Safety Code permits only a maximum of 50 percent of the exits to discharge through areas on the floor of exit discharge (street floor) under strict requirements. These requirements are:

1. Such exits must discharge to a free and unobstructed way to the exterior of the building which is readily visible and identifiable from the point of discharge from the exit.

2. The floor of discharge into which the exits discharge is provided with automatic sprinkler protection, and any other portion of the level of discharge with access to the discharge area is provided with automatic sprinkler protection or separated from it in accordance with the traditional requirements for enclosure of exits (see Sec. 6, Chap. 9). NOTE: There is recognition in this particular requirement that stairs may discharge into vestibules or foyers of less than 10 ft in depth from the exterior of the building, and less than 20 ft in length, where the foyer is separated from the remainder of the level of discharge by construction providing protection equivalent to wired glass in steel frames, and that the foyer is used only for means of egress purposes.

3. The entire area on the floor of discharge is separated from areas below by construction having a minimum of 2 hrs of fire resistance rating.

Exit Illumination, Marking, and Emergency Lighting

Every public space, hallway, stairway, or other means of egress in hotel occupancies is required to have illumination in accordance with the NFPA Life Safety Code. This includes the establishment of a minimum value of illumination of 1 footcandle for all elements of the means of egress, as measured at the floor. This illumination must be continuously present at all times and, where the occupancy of the hotel exceeds 25 rooms, emergency lighting is required as a backup system in case of failure of the primary power supply. This requirement for emergency lighting is waived in hotels having less than 25 rooms, each room of which has direct access to the outside of the building at ground level (as in motels). In addition, every exit access door from public hallways or corridors on floors with sleeping accommodations must have illuminated exit signs. Where corridors meander or provide less than an obvious indication as to the direction to follow to obtain access to an exit, directional exit signs are also required.

Protection of Vertical Openings

The vertical openings in hotels are required to be protected as outlined in the discussions of mercantile occupancies in Section 6, and this Section, Chapter 5, of this HANDBOOK. As is traditional, unprotected vertical openings that connect not more than three floors (one of which is the street floor) for hotel occupancy may be permitted. Further, in recognition of the numerous existing hotel facilities in this country which may not meet the requirements for protection of vertical openings, the authority having jurisdiction may permit unprotected vertical open-

ings to continue in existence if the facility has complete automatic sprinkler protection and the exits and exit access areas are protected and safeguarded against fire and smoke within the building, or where the condition exists such that every individual guest room has direct access to an exterior exit without passing through any public corridor.

Any required exit stair that is arranged to pass through the lobby or other open space to reach the outside of the building must be continuously enclosed to the lobby level. Floors below the floor of exit discharge that are used only for storage, heating equipment, or purposes other than a hotel occupancy are not permitted to have unprotected openings to the hotel occupancy floors. This provision is required to prevent exposing hotel guests to hazardous areas.

Protection of Guest Rooms

In recognition of the importance that the individual guest room wall construction plays in the compartmentation (confining) of fire spread, all new hotels are required to have 1-hr fire resistance ratings for the corridor walls. This requirement is waived if the hotel is equipped throughout with an automatic sprinkler system. In addition, each guest room is required to have a door of a minimum fire protection rating of at least 20 min providing further compartmentation. The authority having jurisdiction may continue to accept existing 1¾-in. solid bonded wood core doors that are in use. Again, in recognition of the more notable hotel fire disasters that have occurred in this country, transoms cannot be installed in partitions of sleeping rooms in new buildings. Further, in existing buildings, transoms must be fixed in the closed position and covered or otherwise protected to provide a fire resistance rating at least equivalent to that of the wall in which they are installed. All other openings in corridor partitions, other than door openings, are prohibited in hotel occupancies.

Interior Finish

Interior finish requirements for hotel occupancies have been divided into two categories: one for existing hotels, and the second for new hotels. In existing Class A, B, or C interior finish is permitted in individual guest rooms, other rooms, lobbies, and corridors (not used as required exit access). Class A or Class B interior finish is permitted in lobbies and corridors used as exit access and in exits. In new construction, or where new interior finish is applied to existing construction, up to Class C interior finish is permitted only in individual guest rooms and other rooms not classified in the previous sentence. Only Class B interior finish or better is permitted in exits, lobbies, and corridors. In both new and existing hotels the requirements for interior finish for the areas occupied as places of assembly (ballrooms, meeting rooms, exhibition halls, and restaurants) must be as per the requirements discussed in Chapter 4 of this Section.

Alarm Systems

An alarm system (at least of the manual activation type) is required in any hotel accommodating 15 or more guests. Only in hotels that are not over three stories in height, and arranged such that each guest room has direct access to the outside (as in motels), is this requirement for the alarm system waived. It is further required that the sounding devices for the alarm systems be of sufficient noise-generating capability to arouse occupants within the vicinity of the sounding device. Further, an alarm-sending station should be installed at the hotel desk or other recognized central control point that is under continuous supervision by hotel employees. These requirements for sending stations may be waived where there exists either automatic sprinkler protection for the facility or automatic fire detection systems which can activate the sending stations notifying the occupants of fire.

Isolation of Hazardous Areas

In addition to the prohibition of unprotected vertical openings between hazardous areas and hotel public occupancy floors, any room that contains high pressure boilers, refrigerating machinery, transformers, or other service equipment subject to possible explosion must not be located directly under or directly adjacent to exits. These rooms must be effectively isolated, and in some cases provided with automatic sprinkler protection in accordance with the design criteria that is appropriate for the occupancy in question. As a minimum, a hazardous area must be separated from other parts of the hotel by construction having at least a one-hour fire resistance rating, with all communicating openings to be protected by approved automatic or self-closing fire doors with a rating appropriate to the one-hour fire resistive wall construction. Or, each area shall be equipped with automatic fire protection (generally taken to be an automatic sprinkler system). Where the hazard is deemed severe by the authority having jurisdiction, it is essential that both the fire resistive construction and automatic extinguishing system be provided. For hotel occupancies, areas requiring isolation and protection (but not necessarily limited to such areas) include boiler and heater rooms, laundries, repair shops, and rooms or spaces used for storage of combustible supplies and equipment in quantities that are of hazardous volume.

Building Service Equipment

The air conditioning systems normally found within hotel occupancies must be designed in accordance with NFPA No. 90A, Air Conditioning and Ventilating Systems; NFPA No. 90B, Warm Air Heating and Air Conditioning Systems; and NFPA No. 91, Blower and Exhaust Systems, Dust, Stock, and Vapor Removal or Conveying.

D.   Apartment Buildings

Apartments are considered to include buildings containing three or more living units with independent cooking and bathroom facilities, whether designated as apartment house, tenement, garden apartment, or by any other name.

Since apartment building occupants are, for the most part, transient in nature (though the average stay is measured in months rather than days), apartment buildings can be considered as hotels for fire protection purposes but, as a minimum, should meet the requirements for one- and two-family dwellings as discussed in Part B, this Chapter. Thus, it is generally recognized in fire protection practice that if an apartment building is arranged as per the requirements for hotels (see Part A of this Chapter), then the facility has achieved an acceptable minimum level of fire safety. Further, it is generally recognized in fire protection practice that if each individual living unit within an apartment building is arranged as per the minimuum requirements for one- and two-family dwellings, then an acceptable level of life safety has been achieved. As a middle-ground position that recognizes the unique characteristics of apartment building occupancies, the following requirements may be met to assure that the facility has achieved a level of life safety (though not as stringent as for hotel occupancies) that is truly applicable to apartment occupancies and which,

as a result, is more stringent than the requirements for one- and two-family dwellings.

Exit Detail

The discussion of exits for hotel occupancies is appropriate for apartment occupancies and contains all information considered pertinent to the proper arrangement of an apartment facility with the following exceptions, necessary in order to achieve the middle-ground design position. First, every living unit in an apartment facility must have access to at least two separate exits. However, due to the popularity of "garden" apartment design, the NFPA Life Safety Code recognizes the following three parameters which provide alternative design arrangements that do not require every living unit to have access to at least two separate exits:

1. Any living unit having an exit directly to the street or yard at ground level or by way of an outside stairway, or an enclosed stairway with fire-resistance rating of one hour or more, serving that apartment only and not communicating with any floor below the floor of exit discharge or other area not a part of the apartment served.

2. Any apartment building of any height with not more than four living units per floor with a smokeproof tower or an outside stairway as the exit, immediately accessible to all apartments.

3. Any building not more than three stories in height with no floor below the floor of exit discharge or, in case there is such a floor, with the street floor construction of at least one-hour fire resistance provided the following conditions are met: (a) a stairway is provided that is completely enclosed by a partition having a fire resistance rating of at least one hour with self-closing fire doors protecting all openings between the stairway enclosure and the building, (b) the stairway does not serve any floor below the floor of exit discharge, and (c) all corridors serving as access to exits have at least a one-hour fire resistance rating.

4. There is not more than 20 ft of travel distance to an exit from the entrance door of any living unit.

Exit arrangements, exit access, and travel distance as discussed for hotels in Part A of this Chapter is appropriate for apartment design. This includes the requirement on common path of travel (dead-end corridor arrangement). In addition, exits and exit access must be so located that it will not be necessary to travel more than 50 ft within an individual living unit to reach the nearest exit, or to reach an entrance door of the apartment which provides access through a public corridor to an exit on the same floor level. Further, within any individual living unit it will not be necessary to traverse stairs more than one story above or below the floor level of the apartment to the nearest exit or entrance door. Finally, the entrance door to any apartment must be arranged to be within 100 ft of an exit, or within 150 ft in a building protected throughout by an automatic sprinkler system. Again, in recognition of the recent compilation of fire experience that shows that the apartment door left open during a fire emergency provides the greatest degree of exposure to the remaining occupants of the building, the NFPA Life Safety Code requires self-closing doors between apartments and corridors in both new and existing construction.

The arrangement of exit discharge as discussed for hotels in Part A of this Chapter is considered the acceptable exit arrangement for apartment buildings.

Exit Illumination and Exit Signs

Within apartment buildings, every public space, hallway,

stairway, or other means of egress must have illumination in accordance with the NFPA Life Safety Code. This includes the maintaining of a minimum value of 1 footcandle measured at the floor for each component of a means of egress. Further, any apartment building with more than 25 living units is required to have an emergency lighting system as a backup to the normal illumination system. Exit signs are required only in apartment buildings that are, of themselves, required to have more than one exit.

Protection of Vertical Openings

Again, the discussion of protection of vertical openings as within hotels is appropriate to apartment buildings. In recognition of those apartment designs that permit only one exit, there is a strong prohibition against unprotected vertical openings in any building or "fire section" that is provided with only one exit.

Interior Finish

As with hotels, apartment building interior finish requirements differ between new and existing facilities. In existing apartment buildings, Class A, B, or C interior finish is permitted in all spaces with the exception of exits which are restricted to only Class A or Class B interior finish. For new apartment construction, or where new interior finish is applied in existing facilities, up to Class C interior finish is permitted only within individual living units. Up to Class B interior finish only is permitted in exits, lobbies, corridors, and public spaces of new construction or where new interior finish is applied to existing construction.

Alarm and Detection Systems

Alarm systems are not required in apartment buildings that are less than three stories high, that have less than 12 apartment units, that are protected by an automatic sprinkler system, or that are provided with a complete automatic fire detection system.

In the 1973 Edition of the NFPA Life Safety Code a tentative interim amendment requires that an approved smoke detector to be installed in every living unit within an apartment building. In lieu of this requirement the building may be provided with an automatic fire extinguishing device in every habitable room. Further, it is recommended that the automatic smoke detector is to be installed in the corridor area directly adjacent to the sleeping rooms of the apartment with an alarm-sounding device capable of arousing occupants from sleep. In multilevel apartment units (which became increasingly popular in the late 1950s) it is recognized that the unprotected vertical openings represented by the stairs that traverse the multilevels in such apartments had to be provided with additional smoke detection units in order to, as quickly as practical, pick up incipient fires that could quickly spread toxic products of combustion throughout the dwelling occupancies. In the case of multilevel apartment units, some design and application consideration should be given to providing detectors both in hallway areas adjacent to bedrooms at the top of unprotected stairways that traverse multilevels in apartments, and in the building service equipment areas (furnace room, basement, laundry room, etc.).

Hazardous Areas

Hazardous areas in apartment buildings are required to be separated from other parts of the facility by construction having a fire resistance rating of at least one hour. Communicating openings must be protected by approved automatic or self-closing fire doors of suitable fire protection rating for the wall which they penetrate. Hazardous areas for apartment buildings are generally recognized to be the following: boiler and heater rooms, laundries, repair shops, and rooms or spaces used for storage of combustible supplies and equipment in quantities deemed hazardous by the authority having jurisdiction. It is generally considered acceptable fire protection practice for the enclosure protection provided by the one-hour fire resistance construction to be omitted if automatic fire extinguishing systems are provided. However, where the hazard is considered "high," both the fire resistance enclosure and automatic fire protection may be required for the hazardous area. The statistical analysis of typical apartment fires shows that many fires initiate in spaces housing equipment or facilities similar to those listed earlier in this paragraph. It should be recognized that the NFPA National Fire Codes and other sections in this HANDBOOK provide additional guidance and criteria for the arrangement of building service equipment, including that equipment used for air conditioning and ventilation.

E.   Dormitories

Dormitories are considered to include buildings where group sleeping accommodations are provided in one room or in a series of closely associated rooms under both joint occupancy and single management for persons who are not members of the same family group. Typical examples are college dormitories, fraternity houses, military barracks, and ski lodges, with or without the provision of meals and related cooking. The fire and life safety provisions for hotels, as discussed earlier in this chapter, provide a suitable minimum level of fire and life safety not only for hotels, but for apartment and dormitory occupancies. Consequently, if the recommendations listed for hotels are followed, further discussion and consideration of the fire and life safety arrangements of dormitories is unnecessary. Also, in the case of a dormitory that is divided into suites of rooms with one or more bedrooms opening into a living room or study that opens into a common corridor serving a number of other suites, as is popular in modern dormitory design, it is recognized that the facility both approximates and should be classed and treated as an apartment building. When dormitories are so arranged, the provisions for apartment buildings discussed in Part C of this Chapter are suitable for obtaining a minimum level of fire and life safety. Thus, further discussion or provisions for dormitories is unnecessary, with one exception that recognizes the nature of the arrangement of dormitories and their subsequent population characteristics. That exception is the mandatory requirement of a manual fire alarm system in all dormitories not equipped with automatic sprinkler systems or automatic fire detection systems.

In lieu of the above recommendations for arranging a dormitory as either a hotel or an apartment building from a fire and life safety standpoint, the guidelines in the following paragraphs are recommended as an alternative system for providing a minimum level of fire and life safety for dormitories.

Exit Arrangement

The exit arrangements discussed for hotels in Part C of this Chapter are also applicable to dormitories. However, the occupant load for determination of minimum widths of exits is altered to reflect the population characteristics of dormitories. As such, each street floor exit door for a dormitory should be of sufficient width to provide one unit

(22 in.) of exit width for each 50-person occupant load capacity of the street floor, plus one unit (22 in.) for each unit width of required stairway that discharges through the street floor. Again, exits should be arranged so that it is not necessary for an occupant to travel more than 100 ft from any point within the dormitory to reach the nearest door or stair. This distance is permitted to be increased to 150 ft in buildings that are protected by automatic sprinklers. In addition, there is a prohibition limiting travel to no more than a one-story flight of inside, unenclosed stairs for existing purposes.

Where dormitories are not arranged according to the provisions outlined for hotels or apartment buildings, their exits should be arranged to allow for access to two separate and distinct exits from any sleeping room or open dormitory sleeping area. This access should be to exits that are located in different directions with no common path of travel. It is recognized that one means of exit may be accepted where the room or space in the dormitory is subject to occupancy by not more than 10 persons and, further, where the room or space has a door that opens directly to the outside of the building at the street or ground floor level, or that opens to an outside stairway.

Exit Illumination and Marking

Dormitories must have exit illumination according to the NFPA Life Safety Code. This includes a minimum value of 1 footcandle of illumination for all components of the means of egress, with that value of illumination measured at the floor level. Where dormitories have an occupancy load of greater than 100 persons, they are further required to have emergency lighting, again in accordance with the NFPA Life Safety Code. As such, the emergency system provides a secondary source of power for illuminating means of egress during emergencies and blackout conditions. Only when the population of a dormitory is more than 100 persons does the Life Safety Code call for exit and directional signs.

Protection of Vertical Openings

Vertical openings in dormitories are, in general, required to be protected per the traditional fire protection requirements found in most building codes and in the NFPA Life Safety Code. These requirements are discussed in Sec. 6, Chap. 8, and in Chap. 5 of this Section of this HANDBOOK.

In general, this leads to a requirement of 2 hrs of fire resistive construction providing an enclosure around vertical openings that penetrate four or more stories in height. Construction is also limited to noncombustible materials in new buildings. Also, in new construction, vertical openings that penetrate three stories or less are required to be of one-hour fire resistance. Generally, existing buildings, regardless of height, are permitted to continue to have, as a minimum, $\frac{1}{2}$ hour of fire resistance to provide an enclosure around vertical openings. The authority having jurisdiction can require compliance to the requirements for new construction if it is felt that the protection in existing buildings is insufficient.

In existing dormitories that are not more than two stories in height (of any type of construction), it is recognized that unprotected vertical openings may be permitted if the building is protected by an automatic sprinkler system. If every sleeping room or area used for sleeping purposes has direct access to an outside exit (negating the necessity of passing through any corridor or other space exposed to an unprotected vertical opening) and the dormitory is equipped

with an automatic fire detection system, unprotected vertical openings may be permitted by the authority having jurisdiction.

Interior Finish

Interior finish in dormitories is restricted to Class A or Class B in exits, lobbies, and corridors. All other areas are permitted interior finish having a flame spread rating up to 200 (Class A, B, or C) in any other area not named in the previous list.

Alarm System

The mandatory requirement for dormitory alarm systems is discussed in Part D of this Chapter.

Building Service Equipment

The NFPA National Fire Codes and Section 7 of this HANDBOOK discuss the proper arrangement of protection of building service equipment such as that for air conditioning or ventilation. If the design requirements previously outlined for hotels or apartment buildings are followed for dormitories, the necessary requirements for isolation and protection of hazardous areas will be met. The alternative approach to life safety, as discussed in this section, does not require isolation or protection of hazardous areas. However, transoms are prohibited from being installed in partitions of sleeping rooms in new buildings. And, like hotels, existing building transoms must be fixed in the closed position and must be covered or otherwise protected to provide a fire resistance rate equivalent at least to that of the corridor wall in which they are installed. This provides a tighter degree of compartmentation, and the sleeping rooms are isolated from the corridors by substantial construction. It also assists in controlling the spread of products of combustion into the individual dormitory sleeping rooms from the corridor area, or from spaces that expose the corridor area.

F. Lodging or Rooming Houses

Lodging or rooming houses include buildings that rent separate sleeping rooms for a total accommodation of 15 persons or less on either a transient or permanent basis, with or without the provision of meals, but potentially without separate cooking facilities for individual occupants. Since lodging or rooming houses are of a relatively low population loading, they are more akin on a fire and life safety basis, except for transiency, to the hazards and potential exposures experienced in one- and two-family dwellings. As a result, as a minimum, every lodging or rooming house must comply with the requirements to be listed in Part G of this Chapter. However, since the occupant loading represents a number greater than normally found in most one- and two-family dwellings, the following additional requirements for lodging or rooming houses are contained in the NFPA Life Safety Code. It should be noted that these requirements are provided to achieve a level of fire and life safety that is higher than that of the one- and two-family dwelling, but appreciably less than the levels discussed in the preceding parts of this chapter on hotels, apartments, and dormitories.

Exit Arrangement

In a lodging or rooming house it is required that every sleeping room above the street floor must have access to two separate means of exit, at least one of which must consist of an enclosed interior stairway, an exterior stairway, a fire escape, or a horizontal exit. All required exits must be arranged to provide a safe path of travel to the outside of the facility without traversing any corridor or similar space that would be exposed to an unprotected vertical opening. In lodging or rooming houses that are protected by sprinkler systems (in existing facilities only), it is deemed permissible to allow traversing of unprotected vertical openings in order to achieve egress from the facility. In a lodging or rooming house, any sleeping room that is located below the street floor is required to have direct access to the outside of the building.

Alarm System

The only other requirement for lodging or rooming houses is that of a manual fire alarm system. A manual fire alarm system is required in all cases, except where the facility is provided with an automatic sprinkler system or an automatic fire detection system.

G.   One- and Two-family Dwellings

One- and two-family dwellings include dwellings in which each living unit is occupied by members of a single family, with rooms rented to outsiders, if any, not accommodating more than three persons.

As mentioned earlier in this chapter the residential occupancy, as a generic class, accounts for the vast majority of deaths due to fire in this country. More specifically, the one- and two-family dwelling occupancy provides for almost all of the residential fire deaths. This is not unusual in two respects. The first reason is that the vast majority (over 80 percent) of the population of the United States resides in one- and two-family dwellings. This leads to the obvious conclusion that since this is where the greatest potential exposure to fire exits, this is where the greatest statistical number of fire deaths can be expected. The second reason is that a review of the NFPA Life Safety Code requirements coupled with Building Code requirements show that the dwelling occupancy, because it represents the private sector which is generally not as stringently treated by codes and fire safety requirements as the public sector, is required to achieve a very minimal level of fire and life safety. Traditional good fire protection practice, such as the requirement of fire resistive or noncombustible construction, the limitation of interior finish, the protection of vertical openings, the provision of either automatic sprinkler protection or automatic fire detection, plus the generally accepted requirement of two remote, distinct exits that are reachable by separate paths, although recognized for public occupancies, are not, for the most part, to be found in existing residential occupancies.

A recent review of the state-of-the-art of dwelling design has led to the recognition of a need for complete coverage by either an automatic detection system or an automatic sprinkler system for most dwelling occupancies, or, as a minimum, at least for the hazardous areas within a dwelling. In the 1973 Edition of the NFPA Life Safety Code a tentative interim amendment requires an approved smoke detector to be installed in every dwelling unit. In lieu of this requirement the building may be provided with an automatic fire extinguishing device in every habitable room. Further, it is envisioned that the automatic smoke detector would be installed in the corridor area directly adjacent to the sleeping rooms of the dwelling occupancy with an alarm-sounding device capable of arousing occupants from sleep. In split level units, as well as multiple story dwellings with open stairs, it is recognized that the unprotected

vertical openings represented by the stairs that traverse the multilevels had to be provided with additional smoke detection units in order to detect incipient fire that could quickly spread toxic products of combustion throughout the dwelling. In multilevel dwelling units, consideration should be given to providing detectors in hallway areas adjacent to bedrooms, at the top of unprotected stairways that traverse multilevels in dwellings, and in the building service equipment areas (furnace room, basement, laundry room, etc.).

However, as one views the requirements in the NFPA Life Safety Code, it is apparent that even the requirement of a "means of egress" (a defined term in the Code hinging on building construction of a minimum fire resistance to both enclose and separate a required exit from the remainder of the facility) is not found in a dwelling unit. Rather, the requirement when applied to a dwelling is on a "means of escape" which is not based on fire resistance for either enclosure or separation of dwelling exits. Further, dwelling occupancies are permitted to rely on a window of a specified size as the second means of escape. No other occupancy in the NFPA Life Safety Code is recognized as being properly arranged where reliance is made on a window as a means of escape. These provisions recognize realistic design in the use of dwellings where a trade-off has been made that greatly favors the aesthetic and utilitarian requirements of the space with a lessened recognition of the potential fire and life safety hazards represented by the dwelling occupancy.

Exit Arrangement

In any dwelling of more than two rooms, every room used for sleeping, living, or dining purposes must have at least two means of egress, at least one of which must be a door or stairway providing a means of unobstructed travel to the outside of the building at the street or ground level. In addition, there is a prohibition against the use of rooms or spaces being occupied for living or sleeping purposes when they are accessible only by a ladder, folding stairs, or through a trapped door.

A window designated as an exit from a sleeping room must be capable of being opened from the inside without the use of tools; the current state-of-the-art requires the window to provide an opening of not less than 22 in. in its least dimension and 5 sq ft in area. Further, for ease of use and as a compromise to other requirements for child safety, the bottom of the opening shall not be more than 4 ft above the floor. These requirements are waived if the sleeping room has two doors providing separate ways of escape, or one door that leads directly outside the dwelling. Recent tests conducted by the San Diego Fire Department have resulted in a recommendation that minimum dimensions and area of the window be changed as follows: (Note that these dimensions were developed by using a fire fighter who was equipped with a full "turn out" outfit including an air support cylinder mounted on his back.) The outside window must be openable from the inside without the use of tools and, further, the window must provide a clear opening of not less than 20 in. in width, 24 in. in height, and 5.7 sq ft in area. It is also recommended that the bottom of the opening shall not be more than 44 in. above the floor, which is a reduction of 4 in. from previous requirements.

A further prohibition in the NFPA Life Safety Code is against permitting any path of travel for exit purposes to the outside from any room from passing through another room or apartment not under the immediate control of the occupant of the first room or his family, nor through a bathroom or other space subject to locking. There is a minimum requirement that the exit access for sleeping rooms to the outside to be at least 3 ft in width. However, interior doors providing a means of exit are currently required to be not less than 24 in. in width. To avoid entrapment during emergency conditions, the NFPA Life Safety Code requires that every closet door latch must be such that children can open the door from the inside of the closet. This is in recognition of the fact that children will seek refuge from a fire either under a bed or in a closet. A similar requirement is placed on bathroom door locks so that they can be opened from the exterior of the bathroom during an emergency condition, even when in the locked position.

Interior Finish

Existing dwellings may have interior finish of Class A, B, C, or D ratings, allowing materials of up to 500 flame spread rating (Class D materials are not permitted in any public occupancy). New dwellings are restricted to up to Class C material (Class A, B, or C) which would put an upper limit of 200 flame spread rating on interior finish materials in new construction. This is a considerable tightening of the interior finish requirements in dwellings, and hopefully will lead to an improvement in the fire and life safety record in these occupancies. A sound recommendation would be to limit to 200 the flame spread rating for interior finish in all dwellings.

Building Service Equipment

The only other provision of the NFPA Life Safety Code for one- and two-family dwellings is that no stove or combustion heater shall be located or arranged so that it blocks escape in case of a fire arising from the malfunctioning of the stove or heater. This leads to a prohibition of placing of stoves or heaters in the immediate vicinity of the means of egress from the room or space in which the heater is located and, more importantly, prohibits the use of these devices in locations directly adjacent to the means of egress for the dwelling.

H. Mobile Homes

A special form of what can be classified as a residential occupancy is the mobile home. These homes are distinguishable insofar as they are factory-assembled structures, transportable in one or more sections. Highway transport normally requires a special permit as mobile homes are conventionally 8 ft or more in width and range from 32 to 80 ft in length.

Each mobile home is built on a permanent chassis and is designed principally to be used as a dwelling unit when placed on stabilizing devices (which may be piers and footers rather than permanent foundations) and when connected to the required utilities.

Mobile home construction (body and frame design); plumbing systems; heating, cooling and fuel-burning systems; and electrical systems have been built to a special standard because of their uniqueness. NFPA No. 501B, Standard for Mobile Homes (ANSI A119.1), has been the guiding document since 1968. Earlier NFPA and ANSI Standards date back to 1940 and 1963 respectively. Forty-six states have adopted the NFPA/ANSI Standard for Mobile Homes (as of June 1975) to regulate their utilization in those states, and concerned federal agencies (such as the Federal Housing Administration and the Veterans Administration) have utilized the Standard in connection

with purchases of mobile homes under loan programs administered by those agencies. The national testing laboratories have based their approvals of mobile homes on this Standard, and major industry groups have made it a condition of membership that manufacturers comply with the provisions of the Standard.

A companion Standard to the Mobile Homes Standard is NFPA No. 501A, Standard for Mobile Home Parks, (ANSI A119.3) which is designed to assure the proper installation of mobile homes whether on private property or in mobile home parks. Special provisions in this Standard cover land utilization, lot facilities, windstorm protection methods, mobile home accessory buildings and structures, permanent buildings in the park, plumbing systems, electrical systems, fuel supply systems, and fire safety considerations.

Mobile homes were initially designed to fill the need for low cost, single-family housing. Low cost is achieved by standardization of components, by mass production, by the use of economically viable materials for the intended function, and by avoiding the necessity, because the home is built on a chassis, of permanent foundations. Mobile homes are designed to be transportable as a unit so that they can be moved from time to time at the convenience of the owner. Gradually mobile homes have increased in width and length from the minimums of 8 by 32 ft to as wide as 14 by 80 ft, with some so designed as units that they can be joined at the site to form "double-wides" or even "triple-wides" and thus to become sizable homes. Some unintended uses have developed, such as employing mobile homes as multi-family occupancies, as dormitories, and as multi-story structures. The basic mobile home also is used as temporary banks or offices, as field offices at construction sites, and for a host of other purposes. Mobile homes basically are not designed for such uses and where so utilized need special attention from a firesafety viewpoint. One of the major uses of mobile homes has been for emergency housing, such as following windstorm and flood disasters, and in this application have served a unique and vital function.

Some communities place special barriers through zoning and taxation regulations to keep mobile homes out of built-up areas. This had led to the development of mobile home parks in unincorporated areas or in areas remote from other sections of a community which might be affected by allowing mobile homes to be used in areas that might depreciate adjoining property values. Mobile homes have found particular acceptance by young families because of their low cost and by retirees who find them especially desirable because of low maintenance and low taxation, and the transportability of such homes is a decided advantage to such groups.

The Mobile Homes Standard is unique in that it crosses many standards disciplines now and as historically practiced in the United States. Normally there are separate building codes, separate plumbing codes, separate heating codes, and separate electrical codes governing the construction of any building. The Mobile Homes Standard incorporates all these disciplines into one document so that the manufacturers, the testing laboratories, the enforcing officials, the dealers, and the consumers can have in one source all the essential requirements. In order to permit innovation and utilization of new materials, the Standard is basically a performance-type Standard, although it contains many very specific requirements for health and safety.

From a firesafety viewpoint, the Mobile Homes Standard requires that interior finish be regulated as to its flame spread characteristics, and in certain areas of the home as regards combustibility. Firestopping is required in concealed wall and partition spaces. At least two exterior doors are required, arranged to provide a means of unobstructed travel to the outside. The width of doors is specified as is the ability to operate locking mechanisms from the inside to facilitate egress. Every room designed expressly for sleeping purposes, unless it has an exterior door to the outside, is required to have at least one outside window of such size to permit emergency egress, with the window openable without the use of special tools. Smoke detectors are mandated to protect each sleeping area to warn the occupants of any fire condition that might develop within the mobile home.

Where LP-Gas is used for heating or cooking, these containers are limited as to size, number, and location. The containers are restricted as to location so they will be mounted on the "A" frame of the mobile home or in a vented compartment vaportight to the inside of the mobile home and accessible only from the outside. Stiff requirements are included to assure secure mounting of the containers so they will not jar loose, slip, or rotate while the home is in transit. Special provisions are included to protect shutoff valves on containers while the mobile home is in transit, in storage, or while being moved. LP-Gas regulators are required to be connected directly to the container shutoff valves or mounted on adjacent support brackets connected to the valve by listed high-pressure connectors. LP-Gas safety relief devices are required, and the discharge from these devices is regulated as to proximity to any opening in the mobile home. Gas piping systems are also regulated in detail as to allowable pressures, piping materials, routing, sizing, anchoring, and the provision of shutoff valves. Appliance connectors cannot run through walls, floors, ceilings, or partitions and specific gas piping leakage tests are specified which the manufacturer must perform before delivering.

Where oil is used as the heating fuel, specific requirements are included with regard to oil tanks, fill and vent pipes, liquid level gages, and shut off valves. Materials for oil piping systems are specified as to size, type of joints couplings, grading, hangers, and tests for leakage.

Perhaps one of the most unique features of the Mobile Homes Standard concerns the installation of heat-producing appliances. Especially noteworthy and unique is the requirement that all fuel-burning appliances (except ranges, ovens, illuminating appliances, clothes dryers, solid fuel-burning fireplaces and solid fuel-burning fireplace stoves) be installed to provide for complete separation of the combustion system from the interior atmosphere of the mobile home. Combustion air inlets and flue gas outlets are required to be listed or certified as components of the appliance. The required separation may be obtained by the installation of direct vent systems (sealed combustion systems) or by the installation of the appliance within enclosures so as to separate the appliance combustion system and venting system from the interior atmosphere of the mobile home.

Any forced air appliance and its return-air system cannot allow a negative pressure to be created to affect either its or any other appliance's combustion air supply, nor act to mix products of combustion with circulating air. Other requirements with regard to heat-producing appliances include special provisions relating to solid fuel-burning fireplaces or fireplace stoves. Circulating air duct materials are specified as to their size and air-tightness. Duct materials are regulated as to their design and combustibility. Special

provisions are included for registers and grills and additional special requirements for the use of ducts in expandable or multiple mobile home connections.

The latest edition of the Standard also pays significant attention to energy conservation measures regarding heat loss and heat gain as influenced by the design of the mobile home (the so-called thermal envelope area) and the design of heating system components. The manufacturer must affix a certificate to the interior of the mobile home that is readily visible indicating that the mobile home has been thermally insulated to conform to the requirements of the Mobile Homes Standard and that the heating equipment has a capacity to maintain an average 70°F temperature in the home when the outdoor temperature is at a specified level. The country is divided into zones to facilitate matching energy conservation requirements to temperature gradients. Limits are imposed on air infiltration through windows and doors as well as through wall and ceiling cavities.

The Mobile Homes Standard also includes specific requirements with regard to electrical installations. It concentrates on those provisions which differ from provisions applicable to all buildings under the National Electrical Code. Identical provisions are included in the NEC (Article 550) to those in the Mobile Homes Standard so that coordination is maintained in both of the nationally recognized documents. Some of the special features have to do with the compactness of mobile homes, the fact that they are factory assembled, the lighter construction techniques commonly used, the under-chassis wiring requirements, the wiring of expandable and dual units, the need for outdoor outlets, the need for bonding of sometimes extensive amounts of non-current carrying metal parts, and the grounding of services and appliances.

Windstorm Damage

Windstorm damage to mobile homes has been an item of special concern. The Mobile Homes Standard specifies that the roof framing be securely attached to wall framing, the walls to the floor structure, and the floor structure to the chassis to secure and maintain continuity to resist wind overturning and sliding as imposed by designed wind loads. The country is again divided into areas, this time on the basis of where hurricane force winds are anticipated, and the wind loads vary for the different zones, being higher of course for the hurricane zones. The manufacturer is required to indicate when the home is built to meet what the Standard designates as "hurricane zone resistive mobile homes."

Additional provisions in the Mobile Homes Standard relate to support and anchoring systems which will resist overturning and lateral movement of the mobile home. For single-wide mobile homes specifications are given for the minimum number of ties required per side, the spacing of those ties, and other special provisions. The strength of the ties is also specified as well as the resistance of the ties to weathering when exposed to the atmosphere. Additional provisions in the Mobile Home Parks Standard cover the construction and location of footers, piers, anchoring equipment (including ties, ground anchors, concrete slabs and tensioning devices), and deal with such special problems as frost heave.

I. Recreational Vehicles

Recreational vehicles are vehicular-type units primarily designed as temporary living quarters for recreational camping or travel. They either have their own motive power or are mounted on or drawn by another vehicle. The basic entities are the travel trailer, the camping trailer, the truck camper, and the motor home. There are several variations of these recreational vehicles, and the industry is constantly developing new equipment to meet the demands for leisure time use by the public interested in travel and camping.

The automotive features of recreational vehicles, in general, are covered by federal motor vehicle safety standards. The federal standards do not, however, currently apply to plumbing, heating, and electrical systems in recreational vehicles or to materials of construction relating to interior walls, partitions, ceilings, exit facilities, and fire protection. NFPA No. 501C, Standard for Recreational Vehicles (ANSI A119.2), is the Standard that concentrates on plumbing, heating, electrical, and firesafety and life safety considerations. The Recreational Vehicles Standard's requirements for the installation of fuel-burning appliances are similar to those found in the Mobile Homes Standard insofar as it provides for complete separation of the combustion system from the interior atmosphere. This applies to all types of fuel-burning appliances used in recreational vehicles except ranges, ovens, and illuminating appliances. Attention is likewise given to the ventilation and combustion air systems, clearances between heat-producing appliances and adjacent surfaces, circulating air system ducts and their sizing, duct supports, registers, and grills.

Electrical systems also are covered in the NFPA Recreational Vehicle Standard as well as in the NEC (Article 551). The bulk of the provisions relate to the electrical equipment and materials required in a recreational vehicle for connection to a wiring system nominally rated 115 V (two wires with ground) or a wiring system nominally rated 115/230 V (three wires with ground). Other special requirements cover low voltage systems (other than circuit supply lines subject to federal or state regulations), combination electrical systems for connection to a battery or direct current supply which may also be connected to a 115 V source, and generator installations.

Fire and life safety requirements in the Standard cover interior walls, partitions and ceilings, exit facilities, and

stipulate that each recreational vehicle equipped with fuel-burning appliances or an internal combustion engine shall be provided with a listed portable fire extinguisher with a specified minimum rating.

In order to facilitate proper use of recreational vehicles, another Standard, NFPA No. 501D, Recreational Vehicle Parks (ANSI A119.4), has been developed. The intent of this Standard is to provide minimum construction requirements for parks designed primarily for use by owners of recreational vehicles. Attention is devoted to park design and construction, recreational vehicle stand construction, environmental health and sanitation, fuel gas systems and storage of flammable and combustible liquids, the electrical systems, and firesafety.

SI Units

The following conversion factors are given as a convenience in converting to SI units the English units used in this chapter.

$$1 \text{ sq ft} = 0.0939 \text{ m}^2$$
$$1 \text{ footcandle} = 10.764 \text{ lx}$$
$$1 \text{ in.} = 25.400 \text{ mm}$$
$$1 \text{ ft} = 0.305 \text{ m}$$
$$\tfrac{5}{9}(°F-32) = °C$$

Bibliography

NFPA Codes, Standards, and Recommended Practices (see the latest *NFPA Publications and Visual Aids Catalog* **for availability of current editions of the following documents)**

NFPA No. 90A, Standard for Air Conditioning and Ventilating Systems.

NFPA No. 90B, Standard for Warm Air Heating and Air Conditioning Systems.

NFPA No. 91, Standard for Blower and Exhaust Systems, Dust, Stock, and Vapor Removal or Conveying.

NFPA No. 101, Code for Safety to Life from Fire in Buildings and Structures.

NFPA No. 501A, Standard for Mobile Home Parks.

NFPA No. 501B, Standard for Mobile Homes.

NFPA No. 501C, Standard for Recreational Vehicles.

NFPA No. 501D, Standard for Recreational Vehicle Parks.

Chapter 3

HEALTH CARE OCCUPANCIES

Development of criteria for life safety from fire within health care occupancies is based upon concepts that are related to the abilities of occupants to escape during fire emergency. Health care occupancies may be divided into two general categories that reflect this occupant characteristic. These two categories are:

1. Buildings housing occupants who are "mobile"—buildings from which rapid escape is possible.

2. Buildings housing occupants who must be "defended in place"—buildings from which rapid escape is impossible because of building size, or because occupants are physically restrained, or because occupants have impaired physical or mental capabilities.

A. Occupant Characteristics

Buildings housing assembly and educational facilities are typical of buildings considered to house "mobile" occupants. Occupants in such buildings are considered to be alert, awake, and in possession of normal physical capabilities.

Hospitals, nursing homes, residential-custodial care facilities, detention and correctional facilities, and in some cases high rise office buildings, are considered typical examples of occupancies and structures (or both) in which rapid escape is not possible and, therefore, in which occupants must be "defended in place."

B. Health Care Facilities

Health care facilities are those occupancies used for purposes such as medical or other treatment or care of persons suffering from physical or mental illness, disease, infirmity, and for the care of infants, convalescents, or aged persons. Health care facilities provide sleeping accommodations for occupants and are typically occupied by persons who are mostly incapable of self-preservation because of age, physical, or mental disability. In some cases, buildings housing occupants with mental disabilities are equipped with security measures which limit freedom of movement.

Fire safety for health care facilities poses a significant problem, the solution to which lies first in the recognition of the entirety of the problem. Then, personnel—health care facility and fire service—must be indoctrinated in the steps necessary for resolution of the problem. One significant part of the problem is combustible loading.

For a variety of reasons, including the hazards of cross infection, personnel shortages, and the possible financial savings involved in not processing and packaging items for reuse, disposable one-use items have entered the modern hospital scene in large volumes. Gloves, gowns, drapes, bedpans, tubing, anesthesia masks and bags, and even surgical and anesthesia instruments are available in disposable form. The economies of bulk purchasing result in severe overcrowding of receiving and storage facilities never intended for such use. The items themselves and their packaging generate large volumes of highly combustible trash. The result is heavy combustible loading in many hospital areas such as central stores, central supply, and trash receiving and holding areas. The NFPA Committee on

Hospitals has recognized the problem of combustible loading, and the Sectional Committee on Combustible Solid Supplies in Hospitals has drafted a proposed standard covering this problem. Provisions include ionized particle detectors, sprinkler protection and fire doors for storage rooms and trash receiving areas, and recommendations for the minimization of the volume of these items kept within the hospital premises.

C. NFPA Life Safety Code Requirements

Modern therapeutics has dictated the need for three types of inhospital care: intensive, general, and ambulatory. Given proper directions, the ambulatory patient—except under severe fire or smoke conditions—can make his own way to safety. Patients under general care may be transported on stretchers or wheel chairs with some difficulty. Generally, while horizontal movement and some vertical movement is possible, evacuation from the building is not. The patient who is undergoing intensive care is usually connected to a variety of therapy, monitoring, and drainage devices. Movement for even short distances can be accomplished only with great difficulty; evacuation is impossible without seriously jeopardizing the patient's survival.

In these respects, the hospital resembles a ship at sea or a high rise building. It is far better to keep the fire from the patient than to remove the patient from the fire. Thus, hospital design and operation must incorporate methods by which fires may be detected early, contained, and fought rapidly and successfully. Early alarm, containment, horizontal evacuation, and rapid extinguishment are essential: they require careful consideration in hospital design as well as operation.

NFPA No. 101, Code for Safety to Life from Fire in Buildings and Structures, hereinafter referred to in this Chapter as the NFPA Life Safety Code, is often used to establish minimum criteria for life safety from fire within health care facilities. The NFPA Life Safety Code sets forth fire safety criteria for health care facilities based upon the following general principles:

1. Fire resisting construction.
2. Subdivision of spaces (compartmentation).
3. Protection of vertical openings.
4. Provision of adequate means to egress.
5. Provision of exit marking, exit illumination, and emergency power.
6. Limits on the use of interior finish materials.
7. Fire alerting facilities.
8. Smoke control mechanism.
9. Protection of hazardous areas.
10. Adequate protection of building service equipment.

Application

The NFPA Life Safety Code recognizes the need for a total building system in the development of reasonable safeguards for the protection of occupants. A careful blending of fire limiting techniques is essential. Exits within health care facilities play a somewhat lesser role in the total fire defense system than is typical for other types of occupancies. As a fundamental design factor, safety to life should not be dependent upon any single safeguard, the failure of which would result in an unacceptable exposure to occupants.

Chapter 10 of the NFPA Life Safety Code deals with health care facilities; it is unique among standards in that it has a section dealing exclusively with minimum criteria for existing buildings. Retroactive application of standards is considered reasonable and necessary in those cases where a threat to life is apparent. The NFPA Life Safety Code recognizes that provision of equivalent but different systems is possible and may be permitted provided that such alternative arrangements will secure equivalent safety to life as would have been achieved by compliance with the Code.

D. Building Construction

Since occupants must be defended in place, health care facility construction becomes an important factor, especially in the design of multistory buildings. Preferably, buildings should be constructed of noncombustible materials capable of resisting fire effects and maintaining structural rigidity.

Buildings two or more stories in height should be constructed of noncombustible materials with major structural members possessing at least two hours fire resistance. Buildings designed with materials which either burn or support combustion, although less desirable, may be safely used. Since these buildings contribute to their own destruction by providing fuel for fire, special consideration and precautions are necessary. Provision of an automatic sprinkler system is considered essential as a portion of the "total" fire defense system.

Evaluation of the effect of building materials during fire should include consideration of smoke generating capabilities. When exposed to fire, cellulosic materials provided with fire retardants sometimes exhibit tendencies toward unusual smoke generation. The use of plastic construction materials is becoming more common, and the result of their exposure to fire is sometimes the generation of large quantities of contaminants compared to fire size.

Subdivision of Building Spaces

Separation of Patient Sleeping Rooms: Recognizing in some cases that it may not be possible to remove occupants of health care facilities during fire, sleeping rooms should be isolated from all other building spaces by one hour fire rated construction. Partitions should be constructed continuous from the floor slab to the underside of the floor or roof above through any concealed spaces such as those above suspended ceilings. Doors providing access to such rooms should be of a type possessing at least a 20-min fire protection rating. The doors should be equipped with a positive latch capable of maintaining the door in the closed position during fire exposure. The door should be installed in a steel frame with glazing (720 sq in.—maximum) limited to wired glass installed in steel frames. (See Fig. 8-3A for typical floor plan for a health care facility.)

Any penetration of such partitions by building service equipment should be protected to maintain the one hour fire rated separation. All spaces around piping and ducts should be tightly sealed with a noncombustible material providing adequate fire resistance, and capable of retarding smoke transfer. Transfer grills should not be used within such doors or partitions.

The effect of duct penetrations of such partitions should be carefully evaluated. Considerations include the effect of metallic versus nonmetallic ducts, location of openings, purpose of the duct system, direction of air flow, inter-

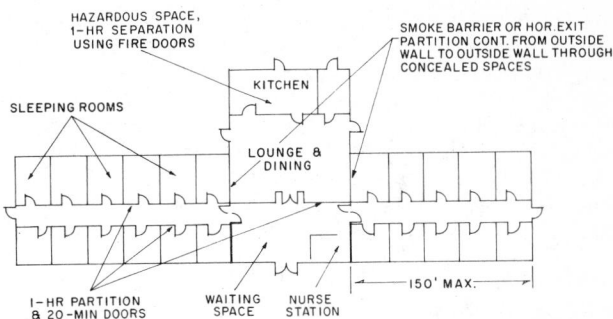

Fig. 8-3A. Typical floor plan for a health care facility.

connected spaces, control features, and general arrangement of the air handling system.

Smoke Barriers: Every floor used by in-patients for sleeping or treatment should further be subdivided by partitions capable of retarding the transfer of smoke. A horizontal exit, when constructed to satisfy the additional criteria imposed upon construction of smoke stop barriers, may be used as a desirable alternate to a smoke stop partition. To minimize the number of occupants exposed by a single fire, the uninterrupted corridor length should be limited to a maximum of 150 ft. Additionally, the maximum area of any smoke compartment should be limited to less than 22,500 sq ft and no dimension of length or width greater than 150 ft.

Partitions designed to restrict the spread of smoke should be constructed to provide a fire resistance rating of at least one hour. The partitions should be constructed from outside wall to outside wall complete through any concealed spaces; for example, between a suspended ceiling and the floor slab above. Openings in such partitions should be limited to those required for egress purposes, and such openings should preferably be limited to corridors, lobbies, or other public spaces.

Corridor openings should be protected using a pair of swinging doors with each leaf arranged to swing in a direction opposite from the other. Such doors should possess a minimum fire protection rating of 20 min with vision panels limited to wired glass not exceeding 720 sq in. in steel frames. The meeting edges of the doors should be sealed as tightly as possible to minimize smoke transfer using rabbets, bevels, or an astragal. The minimum width of each door leaf in a hospital or nursing home should be 44 in. The doors should be maintained in the closed position at all times, unless held open by an electrical device and arranged to close upon operation of the building alarm system, by actuation of a local smoke detector installed near the door, or by operation of either an automatic fire detection system or an automatic extinguishment system.

Ducts penetrating smoke barriers should be equipped with fire dampers arranged to close by operation of smoke detectors located within the areas from which the duct takes suction.

Protection of Vertical Openings

The tendency of fire and fire-produced contaminants to spread vertically within a building should be recognized. Special effort is required to minimize this effect and to prevent fire on one level from threatening occupants above. Limiting fire effects to a portion of a single floor becomes especially important within health care facilities.

The NFPA Life Safety Code recognizes the importance of this feature and requires, except in the case of the fully sprinklered facility, that all shafts be enclosed with materials to provide fire resistance of not less than two hours. Openings in shaft walls should be limited to those necessary to the purpose of the shaft.

In the design of partitions enclosing vertical shafts, consideration should be given to the varying durability of materials. In those spaces where partitions may be subject to mechanical injury, materials used to provide floor to floor separation should possess sufficient resistance to damage to maintain the required fire resistance.

Exit Design

Under the time limit and stresses imposed by fire emergency, vertical evacuation of occupants within a health care facility is, at best, difficult and time consuming. Health care facilities should be designed with the consideration that horizontal movement of patients is of primary importance.

Horizontal passageways and doors opening into corridors and rooms used for sleeping or treatment purposes should be of sufficient width to facilitate the horizontal movement of occupants, even in beds. Even under favorable staff to patient ratios, relocation of patients is a relatively slow process. The NFPA Life Safety Code recognizes these difficulties and establishes criteria for the protection of exit access routes to minimize exposure to persons during early stages of fire.

Exit access corridors should be separated from all other areas within the building by partitions designed to provide a fire resistance of one hour. Doors in such partitions should have a minimum 20-min fire protection rating, and should be equipped with a positive latch of a type suitable for keeping the door tightly closed under fire conditions. Glazing in doors and partitions is limited to a wired glass type installed in steel frames and of limited size. Corridors should be at least 8 ft in unobstructed width. Doors leading to sleeping rooms, diagnostic and treatment areas, such as X-ray, surgery, and physical therapy, and all doors between these spaces and required exits should be at least 44 in. wide.

Subject to certain protection criteria, a few spaces may be open to the corridor without separation recognizing functional requirements of health care facilities and fuel load limits typically associated with such spaces. For example, waiting spaces of limited size may be open to corridors used for exit access providing direct supervision is available by staff, and also providing an electrically supervised smoke detection system is provided to monitor conditions within the space. Nursing stations may be open to the corridor as may be space for doctors and nurses, charting, communications, and clerical areas. This judgment is based upon the minimal fuel loads normally associated with such spaces, coupled with the nearly constant supervision by staff.

All other spaces containing materials or contents capable of producing a fire or contaminants of sufficient quantity to prevent use of exit access corridors should be isolated by fire resisting partitions. For example, lounge spaces typically equipped with combustible furnishings, sometimes using carpeting as a floor finish, possess sufficient combustibles to create such an exposure. The use of electrical devices (such as television sets) and smoking practices in lounges can result in ignition possibilities, thus compounding the problem in such spaces.

Exits within health care facilities are limited to doors leading directly to the outside of the building, interior stairs and smoke proof towers, ramps, horizontal exits, outside stairs, and exit passageways. Exits involving horizontal travel are the preferred type.

Horizontal Exits: Horizontal exits are commonly employed in health care facilities. Partitions used as horizontal exits and smoke barriers should be constructed to provide the fire resistance required for exits, and, in addition, should satisfy the criteria for smoke barriers. Door openings should preferably be limited to corridors or public spaces. The most desirable arrangement of mechanical systems is one in which the partitions forming the horizontal exit are not penetrated. When penetration by utilities occurs, such as piping, the space around the piping should be tightly filled with noncombustible materials to preserve the fire resistance of the partition. Where ducts penetrate such partitions, fire dampers should be provided, preferably arranged to operate by smoke detectors placed in the areas from which the duct takes suction.

Since a horizontal exit contemplates the transfer of occupants from one side of a partition to the side opposite the fire, adequate space must be available to "store" occupants after movement. At least 30 net sq ft per occupant should be available on each side of the horizontal exit for the total number of occupants in adjoining compartments.

Interior Stairs: Interior stairs should be designed to satisfy the criteria for Class A stairs. Stairs should be suitably enclosed with fire resistive materials, and stair openings should be limited to those necessary for access and discharge purposes.

Exit Features

Since occupants will be slow to move to the exits and some storage of occupants may be necessary, exit capacities are specified on a relatively low "flow rate" basis. The capacity of exits providing travel by means of stairs is limited to 22 persons per unit of exit width, whereas the capacity of doors or horizontal exits where travel involves level passageways is indicated at 30 persons per unit of exit width.

Limits placed on the distance of travel reflect the anticipated slow movement. Travel distance should normally not exceed the following limits:

1. Between any room door intended as exit access and an exit should not exceed 100 ft.

2. Between any point in a room and an exit should not exceed 150 ft.

3. Between any point in a sleeping room or suite and an exit access door of that room or suite should not exceed 50 ft.

Facilities should further be arranged to limit travel in a direction toward the fire (dead-end) to less than 30 ft.

Elevators are recognized as having special significance in health care facilities for the movement of people. Elevators may be looked upon as a supplementary facility, but are not counted as constituting a portion of required exit facilities.

Exit Marking and Exit Illumination

All exits should be identified by a readily visible sign. Where access to exits is not immediately visible to occupants, access routes should also be marked with suitable signs.

Illumination of the entire means of egress must be continuous at all times the building is occupied. Illumination should include access routes required to reach exits, the entire path within exits, and the point of exit discharge. In some cases, normal street lighting is considered adequate for illumination of exit discharge. However, consideration should be given to the possibility of power failure and conditions resulting therefrom.

Emergency power is required for illumination of the means of egress and exit marking. Illumination for the means of egress in hospitals should be supplied by the Life

Safety Branch of the hospital electrical system as described within NFPA No. 76A, Standard for Essential Electrical Systems for Health Care Facilities. Luminescent, fluorescent, or reflective material should not be used as a substitute for any required illumination.

Emergency power supplies should be capable of maintaining illumination with no appreciable interruption during the changeover from normal to emergency power. Where a generator is provided, a delay of not more than 10 sec is usually allowed. Emergency lighting systems should be arranged to provide necessary illumination automatically in the event of any interruption of normal lighting, such as any failure of a public utility or any outside electric power supply, opening of a circuit breaker or fuse, or any manual act including accidental opening of a switch controlling normal lighting facilities.

Interior Finish Materials

The initial growth of fire may be significantly affected by the materials used as interior finishes within a building. Combustible interior finish materials such as low density fibreboard ceilings and "plastic" carpeting have been significant factors in multideath fires.[1,2] The relative hazard of any interior finish is usually judged on the basis of tests conducted in accordance with NFPA No. 255, Method of Test of Surface Burning Characteristics of Building Materials, commonly referred to as the Tunnel Test.

Materials of interior finish on walls and ceilings within the means of egress and any room is limited to Class A materials (flame spread rating of less than 25). Class B materials (flame spread rating between 25-75) are considered tolerable in individual rooms having not over four persons.

Floor finish materials have in the past typically been excluded from the requirements for interior finish materials. The justification for such an exemption was based upon favorable experience and the assumption that limited exposure would exist during actual fires at the floor level. A fire on January 9, 1970 in the Harmer House Convalescent Home, Marietta, Ohio resulted in a significant change in philosophy.[2] Thirty-two people died in the fire where carpeting equipped with a foam rubber backing material was judged to play a significant role. Floor finish materials are now generally limited, based upon fire safety quality in health care facilities.

Some carpet, when tested by itself, demonstrates a certain capability to limit flame spread and smoke generation. The same carpet, when applied over an underlayment, when tested may produce entirely different, and considerably less desirable, flame spread and smoke development characteristics. Therefore, for test purposes, floor finish materials such as carpet, when to be applied over an underlayment, should be tested as an assembly, using the underlayment as a part of the test assembly, including adhesives where applicable. Floor finish materials, including carpets, must be Class A or B throughout health care facilities. These requirements may not be increased to permit a higher flame spread material in buildnigs equipped with automatic sprinklers.

In many occupancies it is considered reasonable to use a higher class of interior finish in buildings equipped with automatic sprinkler systems. This practice is not considered prudent within health care facilities.

Fire Alerting

Every building should be equipped with an electrically supervised, manually operated fire alarm system. When actuated, the fire alarm system should be designed to sound throughout the facility internal audible alarm devices which can be heard above ambient noise levels in all portions of the building. The fire alarm system should be designed to automatically transmit an alarm to the fire department.

Actuation of any fire detection or fire suppression system provided within a building should automatically actuate the building alarm system.

Alarm systems, including detection components, should be provided with an emergency power supply and should be designed in accordance with NFPA No. 72A, Standard for the Installation, Maintenance, and Use of Local Protective Signaling Systems.

The operation of any alarm activating device should automatically, without delay, provide general alarm indication and control functions. Pre-signal systems are considered undesirable and are generally not considered suitable. Systems utilizing a zoned design and coded signal have certain desirable characteristics.

Fire Suppression

Many authorities believe the most practical and most reliable approach to life safety in health care facilities is attained through the use of automatic fire suppression. Automatic sprinkler systems respond automatically to a fire challenge and provide an automatic alarm on actuation.

The automatic sprinkler system has a proven record of life safety extending for nearly 100 years. A person in contact with the fire origin may still be seriously threatened in a sprinklered environment. However, persons in adjoining spaces—and in a number of cases during actual fire incidents, persons within the same room—have been adequately protected against fire effects by automatic sprinklers.[3]

An automatic sprinkler system should be designed in accordance with NFPA No. 13, Standard for the Installation of Sprinkler Systems. Operation of the automatic sprinkler system should automatically sound the building fire alarm. The sprinkler system and components should be electrically supervised to assure reliable operation. Electrical supervision should include gate valve tamper switches providing a local alarm at a constantly attended location when the valve is closed. In the case where a single water supply is provided by a connection to city mains, a low pressure monitor should be included. If pressure tanks are provided as the primary source of water, air pressure and water level and temperature should, additionally, be supervised. In the case where fire pumps are provided to boost system pressure, electrical supervision should include loss of pump power, pump running indication, low system pressure, and low pump suction pressure.

Protection of isolated areas where six or less sprinklers are required may be provided by connections to the building's domestic water supply system. The water supply should have proven hydraulic capability to provide not less than .15 gpm per sq ft of floor area throughout the entire enclosed area. An indicating shut-off valve should be provided at an accessible location between the sprinklers and the connection to the domestic water supply. Waterflow indication and alarm is recommended, as is gate valve tamper supervision.

Portable fire extinguishers are required to be provided within all buildings. Portable fire extinguishers in conjunction with small hose lines provide building occupants an opportunity to control fire during early stages. In all cases, the fire department should be notified prior to or simultaneous with occupant fire fighting efforts. Delayed alarms to fire departments have resulted in fires growing to large scale which, in turn, threatens occupants prior to fire department notification and arrival.

Smoke Control

Every patient sleeping room should be provided with an outside window or door arranged and located to permit opening from the inside without the use of tools, keys, or special knowledge. The window or door will permit venting of products of combustion during fire. The window may provide access to fresh air during fire emergency where a patient is forced to remain in his room.

Substitution of a specially designed mechanical system suitable for smoke control and exhaust purposes is considered a desirable alternate to the outside window where permitted by the authority having jurisdiction. Special forced air systems, or in some cases, adaptation of conventional building air handling systems, may permit venting of products of combustion early in the fire ignition sequence. Further, through the use of such systems, it may be possible to create a pressure differential across physical barriers (floors or partitions) to prevent smoke transfer. The effectiveness of fire partitions designed to restrict the transfer of fire and fire produced contaminants may be significantly improved by the use of such systems. Many authorities believe a partition may only be effective to limit smoke when designed in conjunction with a pressure barrier to "plug" holes and openings in the barrier which result from functional criteria involved with building design and pedestrian, and mechanical utility systems.

Where adaptation of the building air handling system is contemplated for smoke removal, the design should be as required within NFPA No. 90A, Standard for the Installation of Air Conditioning and Ventilating Systems. Due consideration should be given to alternate power supplies and electrical supervision of critical system components.

Protection of Hazardous Areas

Areas housing contents judged to be hazardous with respect to contents normally associated with health care facilities should be adequately safeguarded to minimize the exposure to occupants in the event of fire. Hazardous areas such as boiler and heater rooms, laundries, kitchens, repair shops, and the like, should be separated by 1-hr fire rated construction with openings to such rooms protected by listed fire doors. Where the hazard is judged as severe, automatic sprinkler protection should be provided in addition to the separation. Spaces judged as requiring both separation and extinguishment are soiled linen rooms, paint shops, rooms or spaces (including repair shops and trash collection rooms) used for the storage of combustibles, supplies, and equipment in quantities judged hazardous.

Laboratories should be protected and separated from other building spaces in accordance with NFPA No. 56C, Standard for Laboratories in Health Related Institutions.

Cooking equipment should be arranged and protected in accordance with NFPA No. 96, Standard for the Removal of Grease Laden Vapors from Commercial Cooking Equipment.

Hospitals typically contain a number of hazardous operations which must be suitably safeguarded to minimize the effect of fire. Flammable liquids stored and used within laboratory spaces should be safeguarded in accordance with NFPA No. 56C, Standard for Laboratories in Health Related Facilities. Flammable liquid storage and use within repair shops and finishing areas should be in accordance

with NFPA No. 30, Flammable and Combustible Liquids Code.

A number of unique exposures exist within operating rooms, especially those handling flammable anesthetics. NFPA No. 56A, Standard for Inhalation Anesthetics, should be consulted for the design of such spaces. NFPA No. 76A, Standard for Essential Electrical Systems for Health Care Facilities, should be reviewed for criteria involved with essential electrical systems including local underground electrical circuits provided for each operating room. Isolated circuits should be equipped with monitors to indicate possible leakage or fault currents to ground. Conductive flooring is required. Also, the resistance of conductive floors should be checked at regular intervals with a record maintained of such inspections. All electrical equipment within operating rooms, below the 5-ft level, should be of a special type suitable for use within hazardous spaces.

Nitrous oxide and oxygen is piped through hospital spaces typically from a central distribution point. These gases will not burn; however, they significantly accelerate the combustion process. Special precautions are necessary and are detailed in NFPA No. 50, Standard for Bulk Oxygen Systems at Consumer Sites, NFPA No. 56B, Standard for Respiratory Therapy, and NFPA No. 56F, Standard for Nonflammable Medical Gas Systems (see also Sec. 5, Chap. 7 of this HANDBOOK).

Building Service Equipment

Building service equipment should be installed and maintained in accordance with appropriate NFPA Standards in order to minimize the probability of such equipment serving as a source of fire exposure to building occupants.

Special consideration should be given to the design and installation of heating and air conditioning systems. Rubbish chutes have been an important factor in a number of fires,[1] and due regard should be given to the design of rubbish and linen chutes (including pneumatic systems).

Portable heating devices are judged as being unsafe within patient occupied portions of health care facilities. Heating devices should be designed and installed to prevent ignition of combustible materials. Approved suspended unit heaters may be used, except in means of egress and patient sleeping areas, provided such heaters are located high enough to be out of the reach of persons using the area.

Combustion and ventilation air for boilers, incinerators, or heater rooms should be taken directly from, and discharged directly to, the outside.

Operating Features

Inadequate control of smoking practices is a leading cause of fire in health care facilities.[4] Adoption and enforcement of suitable smoking regulations is essential to minimize the likelihood of fire. Smoking should be prohibited in any room, ward or compartment where flammable liquids, combustible gases, or oxygen is being used or stored. Such areas should be posted with suitable signs. Smoking by patients under sedation or not considered responsible should be prohibited. Metal containers with self-closing cover devices should be available in all areas where smoking is allowed. Window draperies and curtains should either be of noncombustible material, or rendered and maintained flame retardant. Such curtains should be capable of passing both the large and small scale tests stipulated in NFPA No. 701, Standard Method of Fire Tests for Flame Resistant Textiles and Films.

Furnishings, decorations, and other objects should not be located so as to obstruct exits or exit access routes. Combustible decorations which could contribute to rapid initial growth of fire should be prohibited.

Exits and mechanical devices provided to control or limit the effects of fire should be adequately maintained to assure reliable operation. Inspections and periodic tests as required should be performed to verify satisfactory performance.

In those facilities in which locking of exits is required, adequate staff should be maintained. Such staff should be equipped with keys to release and direct occupants away from the fire area to a place of safety during emergency.

Care should be exercised during the construction of additions and during repair operations to assure no reduction in life safety results from such activities to persons occupying the existing building. It should further be recognized that adequate preventive maintenance for mechanical systems, including tests and periodic inspections, are necessary to assure reliability of operation.

E. Emergency Planning

Each health care facility should have a fire safety and evacuation plan. All facility personnel must become familiar with this plan. Additionally, personnel must be indoctrinated, by lectures and demonstrations, of the use and limitation of fire extinguishers and hose cabinet lines. They must understand some of the other details of proper fire response such as how to sound an alarm, move or evacuate patients, and contain the fire. Appendix E of NFPA No. 56A, Standard for Inhalation Anesthetics, and Appendix D of NFPA No. 56B, Standard for Respiratory Therapy, can be of immeasurable help in orienting health care facility personnel. Each facility should have a safety officer whose prime responsibility is recognition of hazards, who also acts as liaison with the fire service, and who arranges for training of personnel. While indoctrination of hospital personnel is straightforward and may be accomplished "on the job," orientation of members of the fire service in hospital problems is relatively more difficult.

Copies of the fire safety and evacuation plan should be available to all personnel, with specific instructions for key (supervisory) personnel in the event of fire. All employees should have periodic training to assure readiness, with respect to their obligations under the emergency plan. A copy of the plan should be readily available and posted for reference.

Emergency drills should include transmission of a fire alarm signal and simulation of emergency fire conditions to such an extent as is possible without jeopardizing the well-being of occupants. Drills should be conducted at least quarterly on each shift to familiarize personnel with signals and emergency action. At least twelve drills should be held every year, with drills being varied to test the alertness of all shifts. The preferable arrangement is to conduct the drills on an unannounced basis, using conventional fire alarm facilities. The use of the building alarm equipment during drills provides an operating test verifying that such facilities are performing normally.

The fire safety and evacuation plan should include the following fundamentals:

1. Training in the use of alarm and alarm equipment.
2. Transmission of alarm to the fire department.
3. Details as to isolation of fire.
4. Evacuation practices for all areas.
5. Preparation of building spaces for evacuation.
6. Fire extinguishment practices.

Emphasis during drills should be placed upon immediate notification of the fire department upon discovery of fire. Many fires have grown to large scale, prior to fire department operation, owing to delayed alarms. This feature should be emphasized during all drills.

SI Units

The following conversion factors are given as a convenience in converting to SI units the English units used in this chapter.

1 sq in. = 645.160 mm^2
1 sq ft = 0.0929 m^2
1 in. = 25.400 mm
1 ft = 0.305 m
1 gpm = 3.785 litres/min

Bibliography

References Cited

[1] Juillerat, E. E., Jr., "The Hartford Hospital Fire," NFPA Quarterly, Vol. 55, No. 3, Jan. 1962, pp. 295–303.
[2] Sears, A. B., Jr., "Nursing Home Fire," Fire Journal, Vol. 64, No. 3, May 1970, pp. 5–9.
[3] Boettcher, E. N., M.D., "Hospital Fire Defense: People and Sprinklers," Fire Journal, Vol. 61, No. 4, July 1967, pp. 93–96.
[4] NFPA Fire Record Department, "Hospitals: A Fire Record," Fire Journal, Vol. 64, No. 2, Mar. 1970, pp. 14–27.

NFPA Codes, Standards, and Recommended Practices (see the latest NFPA Publications and Visual Aids Catalog for availability of current editions of the following documents)

NFPA No. 72A, Standard for Installation, Maintenance, and Use of Local Protective Signaling Systems.
NFPA No. 76A, Standard for Essential Electrical Systems for Health Care Facilities.
NFPA No. 101, Code for Safety to Life from Fire in Buildings and Structures.
NFPA No. 220, Standard Types of Building Construction.
NFPA No. 251, Standard Methods of Fire Tests of Building Construction and Materials.
NFPA No. 255, Method of Test of Surface Burning Characteristics of Building Materials.

Additional Readings

Burgun, J. A., "The Structural Needs of Health Care Facilities," Fire Journal, Vol. 66, No. 2, Mar. 1972, pp. 55–58.
Darcy, Sister Mary C., "Partners in Hospital Protection," Fire Journal, Vol. 64, No. 4, July 1970, pp. 19–21.
Eggleston, L. A., "Fire Tests in a Hospital Room," Project No. 3-2947-350, June 25, 1971, Southwest Research Institute, San Antonio, Texas.
"Nursing Home Fires and Their Cures . . . ," National Fire Protection Association, Boston, 1972.
Palmer, R. T., "Emergency Planning for Hospitals," Fire Journal, Vol. 63, No. 2, Mar. 1969, pp. 36–41.
Project Corridor: Fire and Life Safety Research, Western Fire Journal, North Highlands, Calif., 1974.
Stickney, C. W., "Oregon Life Safety Study of Institutional Care Facilities," Office of State Fire Marshal, Division of Department of Commerce, Salem, Ore., June 1971.

Chapter 4

EDUCATIONAL AND ASSEMBLY OCCUPANCIES

NFPA No. 101, Code for Safety to Life from Fire in Buildings and Structures, hereinafter referred to in this chapter as the NFPA Life Safety Code, defines educational occupancies as including all buildings used for gatherings of groups of six or more persons for purposes of instruction, such as schools, universities, colleges, and academies. Also included are part-time day schools, nursery schools, kindergartens, day care facilities, and other schools whose purpose is primarily educational, even though the students are of preschool age. It excludes facilities in which instruction is incidental to some other occupancy; in such cases the requirements of the other occupancy are applied. It does include child day care facilities.

Assembly Occupancies are broadly defined in the NFPA Life Safety Code to include: structures designed and constructed exclusively for religious services, auditoriums (with fixed or loose chair seating); theatres (both legitimate and motion picture); ballrooms and meeting rooms; restaurants and cocktail rooms; sports arenas (fully enclosed) and field houses; exhibition halls; and passenger terminals (for air and surface transportation).

A. Educational Occupancies

Population Characteristics

Life safety hazard in educational occupancies varies with the physical properties of the facilities and the age groups housed. Younger children require safeguards not necessary for more mature occupants. The NFPA Life Safety Code makes such differential provisions by limiting kindergarten and first grade rooms to only the floor of exit discharge, and second grade rooms to not more than one story above the level of exit discharge. In a panic situation kindergarten and first grade children would be endangered on stairs. Also, in day care facilities the height at which different age groups may be housed in buildings of various construction types is tabulated. Building codes have similar limitations based on age and type of building construction.

Occupancy Hazards

The hazards in elementary or grammar schools are relatively low, except where a building has serious construction deficiencies. Such buildings should be evaluated to see whether automatic protection or other means are available to compensate for construction deficiencies, or whether the building is unfit for school use. Junior and senior high schools have greater hazards such as shops, laboratories, and home economics areas. These facilities are required to be separated from academic areas by construction having a fire resistance rating of at least 1 hr.

Educational Facilities for the Handicapped

The necessity for accommodating physically and mentally handicapped students with normal students is a fairly recent development that affects school design. Several states have already adopted the requirement that handicapped students must be educated with normal students. This presents a minor problem in one-story buildings where level exiting is possible. However, in multistory buildings it may be necessary to provide horizontal exits and refuge areas in order not to have to rely on stairs and elevators for evacuation of occupants during emergencies. Such possibilities should be investigated by those planning educational facilities before proceeding with designs. The authority having jurisdiction should check to see that proper provision is made for accommodating physically and mentally handicapped students.

General Design Considerations

Conventionally constructed schools with double loaded corridors have a potential life safety hazard in that corridors can become untenable if not properly protected. *Operation School Burning*, No. 1[1], and *Operation School Burning*, No. 2[2], demonstrate the necessity for the closing of room-to-corridor doors in order to reduce corridor contamination by smoke and heat. Many building codes require automatic-closing or self-closing doors.

Schools with conforming exterior exits from all student-occupied rooms represent a good design.

Flexible and Open Plan Design

Newer school design concepts include flexible plan and open plan buildings. Flexible plan structures differ from conventional school buildings in that corridor construction may not comply with the NFPA Life Safety Code; they may have unprotected noncombustible walls and partitions which are capable of being rearranged from time to time as educational methods or other factors change the desirable arrangement of spaces.

Openings between rooms and corridors must be provided with proper doors. When these are omitted, the provisions for open plan schools apply.

The advantage claimed for flexible plan buildings is the ability to modify spaces without excessive cost. The NFPA Life Safety Code permits such changes only after a new space arrangement is approved by the authority having jurisdiction. Stairways and other vertical openings must have enclosures as required by Chapters 5 and 6 of the NFPA Life Safety Code. Travel distance to exits is limited to 150 ft, and where this is exceeded a complete automatic extinguishing system must be provided. Flexible plan buildings have all the life safety hazards of conventional buildings plus the lack of fire rated compartmentation.

Open plan buildings delineate spaces and corridors by use of movable fixtures or low height (5 ft. high max.) partitions.

The life safety hazard in these buildings is increased by the omission of features which can confine fires to a single space long enough to permit evacuation. The compensating factor is the ability of occupants to observe the entire area and detect fire in its incipient stage. Since the occupants are awake and alert, their natural faculties serve as excellent fire and smoke detectors. Early detection makes evacuation or extinguishment possible.

Protection of Hazardous Areas

Areas such as shops, laboratories, home economics, food preparation sections of cafeterias, storage rooms, and stages must be separated from academic areas by construction having a fire resistance rating of at least 1 hr. Stages require noncombustible separations having a fire resistance rating of 2 hrs.

Means of Egress Arrangement

School authorities should be cautioned to avoid creating circuitous access to exits when fixtures are rearranged. Exit access dimensions must be maintained at least equal to those in schools with corridors.

Multistory open plan buildings create additional life safety problems. Interior stairways must be enclosed, thus frequently obstructing clear view of all portions of a floor.

In buildings whose plan dimensions necessitate stairways not at the building periphery, exit passageways at the level of discharge become necessary in order to continue stair enclosures to exit discharges. Such enclosures further obstruct an overview of the floor.

Many layouts locate stages, auditoriums, and libraries at approximately midfloor, thus obstructing overall view of a floor. Such layouts have exiting problems when large areas, such as auditoriums, are enclosed, especially when these are located above the level of exit discharge. Such facilities should preferably be located around the perimeter of the building.

Travel distance to exits must not exceed 150 ft unless the building is equipped with a complete automatic extinguishing system complying with Chapter 6 of the NFPA Life Safety Code; it may then be increased to 200 ft.

Except in fully sprinklered buildings, all rooms subject to student use require a door to the exterior at grade or opening on a conforming balcony. In lieu thereof, an openable window may be provided for ventilation; below the fifth floor, such windows must provide a clear opening which will permit possible rescue. It sometimes may be safer to remain in a room, other than the fire room, provided that heat may be vented and fresh air supplied for the occupants, until rescued.

Interior finish of Class A or B may be used for areas other than corridors. Corridors must have Class A interior finish. Fixtures and low height partitions may have Class C interior finish. In one-story buildings exposed surfaces of heavy timber structural members may be permitted.

Very few schools are actually designed as completely open plan buildings. Hybrid designs pose difficult problems in providing adequate life safety from fire.

Any room occupied by more than 300 persons in an open or flexible plan design must have one of its exit accesses through a separate means of egress, which in effect constitutes a separate atmosphere. Where three or more means of egress are required, not more than two of them may enter the same means of egress. This is one of the most effective life safety provisions of the NFPA Life Safety Code.

The separate atmosphere concept should actually be applied to all buildings in order to provide maximum life safety. However, practical limitations presently limit the application.

An approved fire alarm system is required for all educational buildings.

Colleges and Universities

Colleges and universities encompass most types of occupancies. Life safety hazards vary between relatively low hazard classroom buildings and high hazard laboratories. Each building or portion thereof requires treatment commensurate with the hazards of use; thus the NFPA Life Safety Code in its entirety must be applied using good judgment. The occupancy classification of each building shall be based on the real nature of activities it will house. In addition to the NFPA Life Safety Code, some areas may require the application of other NFPA Standards. In some, the materials handled may require extinguishing systems other than water type.

Buildings may be entirely or partially windowless, in which case the NFPA Life Safety Code requirements for special structures are applicable. Automatic extinguishing must be provided, and provisions made to ensure smoke venting in the event of fire. Emergency lighting and power are important in windowless buildings and in buildings subject to use after daylight hours.

Due to the high cost of land or its nonavailability, colleges and universities are frequently housed in high rise buildings. Such buildings should be provided with horizontal exits rather than relying on stairs, since total evacuation is impractical. These buildings should incorporate the safeguards specified for other high rise structures.

Schools for students where daily attendance is constant (through grade 12) must have fire drills as specified in the NFPA Life Safety Code. At the college and university levels, drills involving students are impractical: it is almost impossible to have all students participate because they arrive and leave at different times and on different days, and conducting drills would necessitate daily drills at different hours. Therefore, students and faculty members should be given a prepared plan for behavior during emergencies, and should be examined to determine that they have familiarized themselves with such instructions. A public address system is an excellent tool for advising all of the occupants as to appropriate procedures during emergencies.

Fire alarm provisions are desirable in individual buildings for use together with public address systems. Campuswide alarms should be avoided at the college or university level.

Day Care Facilities

Day care facilities are described in the NFPA Life Safety Code. It should be recognized that the care at such facilities may also be provided during the night as well as during the day, and that the life safety hazard is increased where sleeping facilities are provided.

The NFPA Life Safety Code classifies these facilities according to the number of persons cared for in a facility. Where care is provided for more than 12 recipients, facilities are classified as day care centers; where care is provided for 7 to 12 recipients, facilities are classified as group day care homes; where care is provided for 6 or less, facilities are classified as family day care homes. The NFPA Life Safety Code also groups recipients by age: 0 to 3 yrs, 3 to 5 yrs, and 6 yrs and older.

Each type of facility has its own requirements and its own hazards. Children younger than 3 yrs of age may need to be carried out in an emergency, children 3 to 5 yrs of age most likely can be led out; those over 6 yrs of age are capable of being directed, as are school children during fire drills.

The NFPA Life Safety Code establishes minimum ratios of staff to care recipients. Day care facilities must not be permitted to operate with fewer staff than the established minimum. Reduction of staff seriously increases the hazard to life safety.

Day care facilities may operate 24 hrs a day in order to provide care for dependents of people who work at night. These facilities are the most hazardous, and in some the staff can be found to be napping instead of keeping alert for an emergency. In group day care homes that care for persons over 3 yrs of age, the minimum staff ratio is 1:10. This results in only 1 staff member, who usually goes to bed when the care recipients are asleep. For the same reason, the situation in family day care homes may be even worse. The authority having jurisdiction must be alert to such staff deficiencies, and must carefully check to see that at least all prescribed safeguards (especially detection and alarm devices) are present on the premises prior to permitting use of the premises for day care purposes.

The Department of Health, Education, and Welfare's Bureau of Child Development Services publishes a document[3] that includes the NFPA Life Safety Code requirements. The document is of importance to enforcing authorities, as other regulations contained therein interact with fire safety.

Adequate fire evacuation plans should be established by the authority having jurisdiction together with the facility operator. Drills should be conducted to evaluate the staff's knowledge of recommended procedures. In day care facilities it may be advisable to assist the authority having jurisdiction by training certain personnel to make frequent inspections between those routine inspections made by the regularly established authorities.

In all educational occupancies good housekeeping is basic to safety to life from fire. In educational occupancies student work is often displayed loosely attached to classroom walls. This practice should be discouraged, and when permitted the displayed material should not exceed 20 percent of the wall area unless the material is flame resistant or noncombustible. Such materials should never be permitted in the means of egress.

Where closed-circuit television is used as part of the instructive curriculum, proper wiring provisions are necessary. Receivers may not be so located as to impair exit access or be subject to inadvertent mislocation.

No room subject to student occupancy may be locked against egress. Doors from rooms which accommodate more than 100 occupants, and all exterior doors (except classroom to exterior), must not have a latch or lock unless the door is equipped with proper panic hardware.

Day care facilities with sleeping provisions require smoke detectors as set forth in the NFPA Life Safety Code. These must be periodically inspected for proper functioning.

Where an educational or day care facility is located in a building which houses other occupancies, proper separations must be provided. Where exits are common to mixed occupancies, their capacity must be sufficient for the combined occupant load.

Where the authority having jurisdiction is satisfied that no simultaneous use will occur, he may permit exit capacity as required for the maximum occupant load of an individual occupancy.

The NFPA Committee on Safety to Life at this writing (1975) is presently considering the expansion of the NFPA Life Safety Code to include provisions for similar day care facilities for adults. In many aspects similar requirements are applicable to all age groups. However, since the necessity for this type of adult care usually involves persons who have handicaps that make them incapable of self care, the subject is still under study.

B. Assembly Occupancies

The diverse uses of assembly occupancies present a common life safety hazard; namely, high density occupant

load. No other occupant use permits a population based on a minimum of 3 sq ft per person in waiting areas, 7 sq ft per person in dance halls and other dense occupancies, and 15 sq ft per person in dining areas. Further, on a day-to-day basis, some assembly occupancies such as theatres and restaurants are fully occupied while in partial or total darkness. These conditions, high density plus unusual occupancy practices coupled with general unfamiliarity of the facility, are conducive to panic when an emergency condition occurs.

C. NFPA Life Safety Code Requirements

The NFPA Life Safety Code prescribes compensatory measures in order to minimize the danger of panic. These comprise required seating arrangements, aisle widths and spacing, plus exit access ways and exits. In addition, separation of areas which are deemed most likely to be subject to fire from other occupancies and from the audience or patron seating area, are dealt with in the NFPA Life Safety Code. Also, provisions for emergency lighting in the event of failure of the normal energy source supplied to the building are mandated.

Occupancies with Fixed Seating

Two types of acceptable fixed seating arrangements are permitted: conventional and continental. Conventional seating comprises arrangements with close row-to-row spacing and is limited to a maximum of 14 seats to a row. Continental seating which encompasses larger row spacing permitting the between-the-row spaces to function as an efficient conduit for occupant flow, accomplishes better access to exits than does the conventional type. It also permits more seats in prime viewing areas (up to 49 per row) and greater comfort for occupants, especially in the normal traffic to and from seats. Its use should be encouraged wherever possible.

Where loose chairs are used in lieu of fixed seating, they are required to be bonded together as set forth in Chapter 17 of the NFPA Life Safety Code. This is required in order to avoid haphazard chair arrangements which can impair exit access. Many chair manufacturers produce chairs with interlocking features. They require no tools to join or separate the chairs and permit ordinary vertical stacking for storage.

Alarm and automatic extinguishing provisions are required in certain areas. However, due to the danger of panic if an alarm is sounded in a darkened theater or auditorium, the NFPA Life Safety Code specifies that the alarm must sound only in the manager's office or such similar location. In a theater with a stage, the alarm must also sound in all auxiliary theater areas and rooms. A public address announcement is both recommended and used to advise occupants regarding evacuation.

Stages

The NFPA Life Safety Code prescribes special safety features for stages and their auxiliary rooms. These features are extremely important, and should be rigorously enforced both during construction and during the subsequent operation of the facility. Most serious theater fires (as with the 1903 Iroquois Theater Fire in Chicago) have originated behind, above, or below a stage.

Modern stages assume many forms: traditional stages are situated almost entirely behind the proscenium wall; thrust stages project into the audience a distance equal to their extension behind the proscenium wall; and arena stages may be completely detached from the proscenium wall, as in theaters in the round. These require special planning in order to provide a level of safety comparable to the conventional stage.

Many new stages store and handle scenery horizontally, thereby eliminating the necessity for a high scene loft and gridiron. The use of a rigid asbestos curtain to separate such stages from the audience seating area is impractical. The NFPA Life Safety Code now provides an acceptable alternate means, combining automatic detection and extinguishment for providing the desired protection.

Motion Picture Projection

Where motion pictures are projected with direct light, proper projection booths must be provided. When safety film (usually cellulose acetate) is used, the NFPA Life Safety Code prescribes the required construction and arrangement, including signs limiting the booth to the use of safety film only. Where cellulose nitrate film is to be projected, the Code refers to NFPA No. 40, Standard for the storage and Handling of Cellulose Nitrate Motion Picture Film.

Restaurants and Nightclubs

Many restaurants, cocktail lounges, and nightclubs are located atop high rise buildings. Some of these facilities revolve to give patrons a panoramic view in all directions. Such facilities need careful scrutiny when plans are submitted to the authority having jurisdiction for approval. The number of required exits for the assembly occupancy may exceed that which is required for an office building or hotel beneath the assembly occupancy. The assembly exits must continue in a protected exit until they reach an approved exit discharge without decreasing in width or number in the direction of egress.

Usually a rotating rooftop facility is smaller than the building on which it is supported; when stairs occur at the ends of the supporting building, the exit enclosures must be continuous from the rooftop area to the exit discharge. Since a minimum of two exits are required for the assembly area, it may be impossible to adequately separate them within the stationary portion of the revolving area. This important detail is frequently overlooked, thus creating a serious hazard.

Acceptable Seating Arrangements for Restaurants and Nightclubs: Restaurants and cocktail lounges must provide proper access to exits. Regulation of table and chair layouts is important since the number and widths of exits may be of no avail if access to them is blocked or seriously impaired by an improper fixture arrangement.

Facilities at which drinking and dining occur during or between live presentations on a full stage frequently violate the requirement for proper access to exits. The enforcing authority should insist on receiving fixture layouts for approval, and should strictly enforce adherence to the approved layouts.

Cooking Equipment

The NFPA Life Safety Code references standards such as NFPA No. 96, Standard for the Installation of Equipment for the Removal of Smoke and Grease-Laden Vapors from Commercial Cooking Equipment, in order to reduce the danger of fire in cooking areas. Today there is widespread use of "display cooking" which provides no fire resistance rated separation between food preparation areas and dining areas. Strict adherence to the referenced standard is, therefore, a must.

Operating Features

Chapter 17 of the NFPA Life Safety Code regulates operating features. These are extremely important for the protection of building occupants. Many large fatality fires in assembly occupancies have resulted from neglect of the requirements of this chapter. The authority having jurisdiction must familiarize himself with these requirements as well as those in NFPA No. 1, Fire Prevention Code, and should make the requirements known to the person or persons responsible for the facility. Tableside cooking, flambé cooking, and flaming sword devices should be discouraged. They are permitted with the restrictions set forth in Chapter 17 of the NFPA Life Safety Code.

The use of open flame devices is regulated by the NFPA Life Safety Code. Promiscuous use of such devices has been a contributing cause of fires and should be prohibited, except as expressly permitted by the Code.

Meeting Facilities, Convention Facilities and Sports Arenas

Ballrooms and meeting rooms are actually multipurpose rooms. They may be used for dining, dancing, or as assembly areas. There are requirements applicable to each use.

Where large areas are provided with movable subdividing walls or partitions, each subdivision must provide proper exit accesses and exits. This is frequently overlooked in planning such facilities. The authority having jurisdiction should study submitted plans to ensure that the arrangement can meet the egress requirements.

Sports arenas and field houses usually have fixed seating accommodations for more than 10,000 persons, plus a large area for indoor athletic contests and other uses. They also have locker and shower rooms, storage areas for equipment, and a few incidental offices. The greatest hazard occurs when such buildings are used as exhibit areas for trade shows. Where such use occurs, the structure and protective features must comply with the special provisions for exhibition halls as set forth in the NFPA Life Safety Code, including removal from the display and seating area of all packing material to separated storage areas. There is some further guidance given for large areas in NFPA No. 102, Standard for Tents, Grandstands, and Air-supported Structures.

Large meetings and conventions are frequently held in sports arenas, and loose chairs are set up in the area usually set aside for athletic activities. Chair arrangement and bonding along with aisle widths and spacing must conform to the NFPA Life Safety Code. Exits should be provided based on the fixed seating capacity plus the largest number of loose chairs which may be permitted under the NFPA Life Safety Code.

Exhibition Halls

Exhibition halls are large assembly areas which are suitable for many uses. They are sometimes combined with sports arenas. The NFPA Life Safety Code makes special provision for these structures.

Special diligence with inspections and control of the arrangement of displays or chairs must be exercised in order to ensure unimpeded access and that travel distance to exits is not exceeded. Some jurisdictions require all trade shows or exhibitions to file layouts of displays and seating for approval well in advance of the use date.

Separate areas or buildings are required for the storage of packing materials needed for transporting displays, and for surplus quantities of literature. The importance of rigid enforcement of the requirement to immediately remove such materials from the display or seating areas and storing them in approved rooms or buildings cannot be over-emphasized. An outstanding example of this hazard is the McCormick Place fire in Chicago. Displays and booths of flimsy construction should be treated with a flame retardant to reduce their ease of ignition.

Any exhibition building whose area exceeds 15,000 sq ft must have a complete, automatic, supervised sprinkler system complying with NFPA No. 13, Installation of Sprinklers. The authority having jurisdiction must consider the ceiling height of such areas in order to determine whether open heads and deluge valves will be necessary to ensure that water is applied over the fire area. High ceilings can produce many design problems that would tax an ordinary sprinkler system design.

Passenger Terminals

Passenger terminals are treated on a special basis since only general rules can be written for their regulation. Densely populated areas are localized such as at departure or arrival gates.

The principal life safety hazard is due to the infrequent use of emergency exits. People usually arrive and depart the terminal at certain locations which may entail excessive travel distance from dense population centers.

Modern multilevel terminals result in large portions being located below grade. These must be treated as underground or windowless structures for which the NFPA Life Safety Code provides specific guidance.

Exit Hardware

Exits from all assembly areas with an occupant load of 100 or more persons must have doors without a latch or lock, unless the doors are equipped with panic hardware. The authority having jurisdiction must make frequent inspections to ensure the nonuse of chains, padlocks, or other devices which may negate panic hardware. Chained and padlocked exit doors have been responsible for many fatalities in assembly occupancies.

Interior Finish and Furnishings

Interior finish is an important part of life safety in assembly areas. The NFPA Life Safety Code specifies that the interior finish in all means of egress in all places of assembly shall be Class A (flame spread 0-25). Requirements for interior finish in the general assembly areas may be Class B (flame spread 26-75), or better, in Class A and Class B places of assembly. Class C places of assembly may have Class C interior finish (flame spread 75-200), or better, in the general assembly areas.

Drapes, hangings, and other decorative materials must be flameproofed if not of noncombustible material. Inadvertent ignition of these items has been responsible for panic in densely occupied spaces such as at the 1942

Cocoanut Grove fire in Boston. Proper treatment of such materials must be evidenced by dated certificates usually issued by state licensed applicators.

Employee Training

The NFPA Life Safety Code requires employees and attendants of places of public assembly to be schooled and drilled in their duties in case of fire, panic, or other emergency in order to be of greatest service in effecting orderly exit of assemblages. This is of major importance, but is frequently neglected as demonstrated during fires in these occupancies.

When the following conditions are avoided, places of assembly can be safely occupied: (1) overcrowding, (2) blocking or impairing exit accesses and illegally locking exits against egress, (3) storing combustibles except in authorized locations, (4) using open flame without proper precaution, and (5) using combustible decorative material.

SI Units

The following conversion factors are given as a convenience in converting to SI units the English units used in this chapter.

1 sq ft = 0.0929 m²
1 ft = 0.305 m

Bibliography

References Cited

[1] *Operation School Burning: Official Report on A Series of School Fire Tests Conducted April 16, 1959, to June 30, 1959, by the Los Angeles Fire Department,* National Fire Protection Association, Boston, 1959.

[2] *Operation School Burning, No. 2: Official Report on a Series of Fire Tests in an Open Stairway, Multistory School Conducted June 30, 1960 to July 30, 1960 and February 6, 1961 to February 14, 1961, by the Los Angeles Fire Department,* National Fire Protection Association, Boston, 1961.

[3] U.S. Department of Health, Education, and Welfare, Office of Child Development, Bureau of Child Development Services, DHEW Publication No. (OCD) 73-1053, U.S. Government Printing Office, Washington, D.C.

NFPA Codes, Standards, and Recommended Practices (see the latest NFPA Publications and Visual Aids Catalog for availability of current editions of the following documents)

NFPA No. 1, The Fire Prevention Code of the National Fire Protection Association.
NFPA No. 40, Standard for the Storage and Handling of Cellulose Nitrate Motion Picture Film.
NFPA No. 96, Standard for the Installation of Equipment for the Removal of Smoke and Grease-Laden Vapors from Commercial Cooking Equipment.
NFPA No. 101, Code for the Safety to Life from Fire in Buildings and Structures.
NFPA No. 102, Standard for Tents, Grandstands, and Air-Supported Structures.

Chapter 5

MERCANTILE OCCUPANCIES

Mercantile occupancies are considered to be those facilities involved in the display and sale of merchandise. Typical examples are supermarkets, department stores, drugstores, auction houses, and shopping centers. This chapter deals with: (1) the life safety and related fire safety hazards presented by the typical mercantile occupancy located within its own individual facility, jointly in the same building with other similar occupancies, and with these facilities located on isolated individual sites or in congested urban areas; and (2) the growing trend towards covered mall shopping centers, including the fire and life safety concerns associated with these facilities.

A. Occupancy Characteristics

With the exception of employees, a mercantile occupancy is a public occupancy in every sense of the word. The general public usually visits a mercantile occupancy with the intention of viewing and purchasing merchandise offered for sale. Because zoning restrictions usually require that the many varied stores of mercantile occupancies be located away from residential areas, and because such stores require potential customers to circulate amongst a maze of wares, it is almost a prerequisite that such customers be highly mobile. Thus, even the elderly, the handicapped, and most of the children utilizing these occupancies are ambulatory. From an exiting and life safety standpoint, being ambulatory carries many significant implications. These implications are further discussed in Section 6, Chapter 9 of this HANDBOOK. What is essential in this chapter is the recognition that life safety design for mercantile occupancies is based on the assumption that in an emergency the occupants can quickly evacuate either the immediate fire area, the entire facility, or both.

Another consideration that bears an impact on life safety design is the public's general unfamiliarity with the facility being visited. During an emergency event this unfamiliarity leads to a usual evacuation practice of the majority of the public converging on the "main entrance" in an attempt to leave the premises. This illustrates the fact that the only egress facilities the public has knowledge of are the few they come in frequent contact with, and these facilities, unfortunately, are the "main entrances." This reliance by the public on one egress route as a means of evacuation is reflected in the requirements contained in NFPA No. 101, Life Safety Code, hereinafter referred to in this chapter as the NFPA Life Safety Code.

B. NFPA Life Safety Code Requirements

The document most commonly used to develop the minimum criteria for life safety from fire within mercantile occupancies is the NFPA Life Safety Code. As previously stated in this HANDBOOK, the NFPA Life Safety Code sets forth fire safety criteria for public occupancies, including mercantile occupancies, based upon the application either jointly or separately, of the following fire protection design elements:

1. Fire resisting construction.
2. Provision of automatic sprinkler protection.
3. Protection of vertical openings.
4. Provision of adequate exit facilities.
5. Provision of exit marking, exit illumination, and emergency power.
6. Limits on the use of interior finish materials.
7. Fire alerting facilities.
8. Protection of hazardous areas.
9. Adequate protection of building service equipment.

Application

As mentioned at the beginning of this chapter, mercantile occupancies are assumed to contain ambulatory or mobile occupants who can quickly evacuate when presented with a fire emergency situation. As a result, the primary emphasis in fire protection design is the provision of adequate exit facilities coupled with an additional element of design that recognizes the convergence and mixing of occupants from various levels of a mercantile occupancy at and around the main entrance of a store during an evacuation, plus the requirement of automatic sprinkler protection when stores are permitted to be of a substantial size—generally larger than 30,000 sq ft GLA (gross leasable area)*—and are further expected to be stocked throughout with combustible merchandise.

In addition, the observance of automatic sprinkler requirements for stores of certain types of construction over a certain size both in the Model Building Codes in the United States and, to a certain extent in the NFPA Life Safety Code, has led to a good life safety record for mercantile occupancies. A review of the large loss-of-life fires in stores (those in which there were twelve or more fire deaths) shows only five such events within the United States since 1900. Of those, four directly resulted from explosions—either natural gas, LP-Gas, sewer gas leakage, or gunpowder. The remaining event, the collapse of a wall during a fire in New York City, caused the deaths of twelve fire fighters.

In the United States, in an effort to avoid conflagrations similar to the ones that destroyed portions of many cities in the late 19th century, the Model Building Codes became more stringent in their requirements for both the construction and automatic fire protection of mercantile stores located within urban areas. This stringency is further reflected in the automatic sprinkler requirements of the NFPA Life Safety Code. Although the efforts of the Model Building Codes may have been primarily directed at property protection, the ultimate effect of both the Building Codes and the NFPA Life Safety Code has been the remarkable life safety record of American stores. This record is not reflected outside the United States. There have been sizable loss-of-life fires in stores in France, Columbia, Belgium, and Japan, the latter two countries having had major fires that occurred as recently as the late 1960s and early 1970s. These sizable loss-of-life fires involved nonsprinklered mercantile occupancies.

---

* Gross leasable area is the total floor area designed for tenant occupancy and exclusive use, expressed in sq ft measured from center lines of joint partitions and exteriors of outside walls.

C. Building Construction

The coupling of strict zoning requirements with the strict building code requirements that were promulgated to prevent large conflagrations has led to most sizable stores in the United States being of fire resistive construction and, because these stores are sizable, the additional requirement of an automatic sprinkler system. The NFPA Life Safety Code does not specify levels of building construction for mercantile occupancies; however, it does require total sprinkler protection in all of the following types of mercantile occupancies:

1. In all one-story buildings over 15,000 sq ft GLA.
2. In all buildings over one story in height and exceeding 30,000 sq ft GLA.
3. Throughout floors below the street floor exceeding 2,500 sq ft GLA when used for the sale, storage, or handling of combustible goods and merchandise.

Thus, most building codes require a high level of fire resistance or automatic sprinkler protection, or both, for any typical, large department store that is found in a congested urban area. Less sizable stores and stores that are less than two stories in height may not be covered under these strict building code requirements, but the NFPA Life Safety Code does provide further guidance. Thus, it is only the relatively small stores that are either less than 15,000 sq ft GLA if one story in height, or less than 30,000 sq ft GLA if over one story in height, that are not required to meet either stringent construction requirements or the provision of an automatic sprinkler system. These stores represent corner grocery stores or combined mercantile-dwelling occupancies, neither of which presents a severe threat to life safety nor a significant threat to property protection.

Protection of Vertical Openings

Most sizable department stores suffer from a variety of vertical penetrations that potentially weaken the vertical system of fire barriers represented by the floor and ceiling slabs. These vertical penetrations consist of a combination of sizable stairways, elevator shafts, and, all too frequently, numerous escalator openings. The NFPA Life Safety Code requires a stringent level of protection for these vertical openings when they occur in mercantile occupancies and when they consist of the required exits. With the exception of the "special" systems designed to protect escalator openings not comprising required exits, the traditional protection of vertical openings by two hours of fire resistive construction, when the mercantile occupancy is four stories or more in height, applies to the mercantile occupancy. When less than four stories in height, the vertical requirements for fire resistive construction are one hour, and in existing buildings the requirements for vertical openings are reduced to one-half hour of fire resistive construction.

However, the requirements for "special" protection of escalator openings apply to both new and existing mercantile occupancies. A choice of four equivalent protection systems is given under the NFPA Life Safety Code for escalators: (1) the sprinkler-vent method, (2) the spray nozzle method, (3) the rolling shutter method, and (4) the partial enclosure method. Specific design details for each of these systems are found in the NFPA Life Safety Code. The design principles involved include automatic detection, automatic extinguishment, and/or the use of compartmentation either through automatic closing devices or in-place fire resistive construction. The function of any one of the four systems is to prevent the potential spread of

fire and related products of combustion vertically through these rather sizable openings (see Sec. 6, Chap. 8).

In recognition of the traditional "open" design of mercantile stores that was prevalent in the United States before the turn of the century through the period shortly after World War II, the NFPA Life Safety Code recognizes the following exceptions to the traditional protection of vertical openings cited in the preceding paragraph. For Class A stores (those stores having an aggregate GLA of 30,000 sq ft or more, or utilizing more than three floor levels for sales purposes), which under the Code would generally be required to be protected throughout by an automatic sprinkler system, the following additional arrangements for unprotected vertical openings are permitted:

1. Openings may be unprotected between any two floors, such as open stairs or escalators between the street floor and the floor below, or open stairs to the second floor or balconies (mezzanines) above the street floor. However, there is a prohibition for allowing simultaneous unprotected vertical openings to the levels above and below the street floor unless a sprinkler system is present.
2. If a sprinkler system is present, no more than three floor levels may be penetrated by an unprotected vertical opening. These three floor levels must be arranged so that the street floor level constitutes one of the floors that is penetrated by the unprotected vertical opening.
3. Again, if a sprinkler system is present, one additional floor may be penetrated by an unprotected vertical opening; i.e., one floor in addition to the three levels previously discussed, if that floor is not used for sales purposes.

For Class B stores (those stores having not less than 3,000 sq ft nor more than 30,000 sq ft aggregate GLA, or utilizing balconies, mezzanines, or floors above or below the street floor level for sales purposes), the following additional arrangements for unprotected vertical openings are permitted:

1. Vertical openings may be unprotected between any two floors, such as open stairs or escalators between street floor and the floor below, or between the street floor and mezzanine or second floor. However, there is again a prohibition for simultaneous unprotected vertical openings above and below the street floor unless automatic sprinkler protection is provided.
2. If a sprinkler system is present, unprotected vertical openings are permitted between any two floor levels involving the street floor level as one of the two levels penetrated by the unprotected vertical opening. With this arrangement, unprotected vertical openings are permitted between the street floor and the floor below the street floor, and between the street floor and the second floor, including any intermediate balcony or mezzanine.
3. In any existing Class B store, the NFPA Life Safety Code permits all floors to have unprotected vertical openings if an automatic sprinkler system is present throughout the building.

For Class C stores (those stores having 3,000 sq ft GLA or less and used for sales purposes on the street floor only), the following additional arrangements for unprotected vertical openings are permitted:

1. Openings may be unprotected between the street floor and balcony.
2. In existing Class C stores only, openings may be unprotected between the street floor and the floor below, or the second floor not used for sales purposes.

A review of Section 6 of this HANDBOOK and the NFPA Life Safety Code will reveal additional conditions concerning the protection of vertical openings, and the exceptions permitted for unprotected vertical openings. These conditions are reflected against known fire experience which indicates that unprotected vertical openings are a primary means of rapid spread of fire in building fires. In summation, the standard design practices permitted under current fire protection technology evolves into a general prohibition of unprotected vertical openings. There is a recognition that up to three communicating floor levels without an enclosure may be permitted under stringent conditions contained within the NFPA Life Safety Code. Because these arrangements of unprotected vertical openings involve the use of the street floor as one of the penetrated floors, the majority of exceptions that evolve around unprotected vertical openings are limited to openings in close proximity to the street or ground floor. As mentioned herein, escalators that serve as required exits for a mercantile occupancy must be enclosed in the same manner as exit stairs. Also, the four "special" systems previously discussed only apply to escalator openings that do not constitute an exit.

Exit Design

Under the NFPA Life Safety Code, the design of exits for mercantile occupancies evolves around the assumption that the occupants of the building are mobile, ambulatory, and capable of vertical evacuation up or down through a building as well as horizontal evacuation within a floor experiencing a fire emergency. Consequently, the first tenet of exit design (the provision of not less than two exits remote from each other) is followed in the arrangement of mercantile occupancies by the requirement of not less than two exits from each and every floor. However, there are no requirements for the cascading or widening of stairs to handle the simultaneous evacuation of all floors. The assumption in this design is that a fire event in most mercantile occupancies will require the immediate evacuation of one floor (that experiencing the fire) followed closely thereafter by a staged evacuation of the remainder of the building. For these reasons the Code permits any stairway, escalator, outside stair, or ramp that serves two or more upper floors in a mercantile occupancy to serve any other upper floor. The basis for this is that the width of stair necessary to handle the greatest occupant load on any floor is sufficient to handle each and every floor. The same conditions apply to stairs or other exits serving floors below the street floor. However, the following prohibitions are made: namely, for any upper floor, no inside open stairway, escalator, or ramp may serve as a required egress facility for more than one floor; for any floor below the street floor, all required exits must be independent of any open stairways between the street floor and the floor below it.

The NFPA Life Safety Code goes further and recognizes that due to the arrangement of a facility it is possible for several floors to constitute the street floor due to changes in topography. When the NFPA Life Safety Code is applied in such cases, each and every floor that has the capability of permitting direct outside exit shall constitute a street floor for the previous definitions and Code requirements discussed. This is also in line with the discussion at the beginning of this chapter dealing with the public's familiarity with the street floor entrance as the primary egress facility during a fire emergency.

Means of egress in mercantile occupancies are restricted to interior stairs, smokeproof towers, outside stairs, horizontal exits, ramps, and escalators. Fire escapes are no longer recognized, the exception being that existing facilities equipped with fire escapes may continue to receive credit for the fire escapes if the authority having jurisdiction considers such an arrangement to be satisfactory.

Recognizing the large number of occupants that can be found in most mercantile occupancies during a sales day, the NFPA Life Safety Code assigns the following capacity to exit components for mercantile occupancies:

1. Doors including those leading to the outside of the building at the ground level or three risers above or below the ground level—100 persons per unit of exit width (as discussed previously in other sections of this HANDBOOK, a unit of exit width constitutes 22 in.).

2. Class A or Class B interior stairs, smokeproof towers, or outside stairs—60 persons per unit of exit width.

3. Escalators—the same requirements as stairs if qualifying as required exits.

4. Horizontal exits—100 persons per unit of exit width.

The NFPA Life Safety Code, recognizing the traditional mercantile design which involves a large open main floor area surrounded by open balconies or mezzanines, with interior stairs, either open or enclosed, all converging in the vicinity of the main entrance, requires sufficient street floor exit doors to accommodate such an intermingling of occupants attempting to exit. Thus, exit doors for the street floor must be arranged to meet the following conditions:

1. One unit (22 in.) of door width for each 100 persons of occupant capacity of the street floor, plus

2. One and one-half units (34 in.) of door width for each two units (44 in.) of required stairways discharging through the street floor from floors above, plus

3. One and one-half units (34 in.) for each two units (44 in.) of required stairways discharging through the street floor from floors below, plus

4. One and one-half units (34 in.) for each two units (44 in.) of escalator width discharging through the street floor, where escalators qualify as required exits or as a means of access to required exits, and

5. If ramps are used instead of stairways, street floor doors shall be provided on the same ratio as for stairways, with door width appropriate to the rated discharge of ramps.

The preceding conditions are based on the fact that people moving horizontally to egress a building can travel one and one-third times faster than they can move vertically up or down a set of stairs. Consequently, the same width of door opening onto a horizontal plane will accommodate one and one-third times as many people as the same width of stair, which is why only one and one-half units of exit width are required for each two units of stair width discharging onto the street floor from either above or below the street floor. The provision that allows the tradeoff of one and one-half units for each two units is in addition to the door capacity needed to handle the population expected to be found on the street level. Thus, the NFPA Life Safety Code makes allowances for the convergence of many levels of occupants on a simultaneous basis in and around the main exit on the street floor of sizable mercantile occupancies.

The only exception to the preceding occurs in small Class C stores where, if no part of the Class C store is more than 50 ft from a street door, a single exit may be permitted.

In further recognition of the merchandising practices of mercantile occupancies where merchandise is arranged so that the public visiting a store must circulate among many aisles, the NFPA Life Safety Code requires that the total width (on an aggregate basis) of all aisles leading to each exit shall be equal to the required width of the exit. In addition, for ease of egress, the minimum width of any aisle must not be less than 28 in. in a mercantile occupancy. In Class A stores, the NFPA Life Safety Code goes further and requires at least one aisle of 5 ft minimum width leading directly to an exit.

Also, in recognition of the general public's reliance on main exits as the primary means of egress from mercantile facilities, the NFPA Life Safety Code recognizes that if the primary, and often the only, means of customer entrance is through an exterior wall of the building, then regardless of all foregoing conditions for intermingling, at least two-thirds of the required exit width for the entire facility must be located in that exterior wall.

Finally, in recognition of the increasing popularity of checkout stands and their associated railings and barriers, the NFPA Life Safety Code requires that at least one half of all the required exits for a mercantile facility be arranged so that it is not necessary to pass through such potential obstructions.

Occupant Load

In order to arrange a mercantile occupancy according to the foregoing paragraphs on exit design, it is essential to know what the NFPA Life Safety Code recognizes as the potential occupant load for a mercantile occupancy. The minimum exit widths including doors, stairs, and escalators are based on occupant load. Under the Code, the street floor is assigned an occupant load of one person for each 30 sq ft of gross floor area. Where a street floor is deemed not to exist because it does not meet the definition of a street floor (namely, any store or floor level accessible from the street or from outside the building at ground level with the floor level at the main entrance not more than three stair risers above or below ground level at these points, and so arranged and utilized as to qualify as a main floor), then the principal floor of entrance for the store is considered to be the street floor. As mentioned in previous paragraphs, when more than one floor is directly accessible to the exterior, all such floors are considered as street floors for purposes of exit design and for occupant load.

Recognizing the common practice of establishing bargain basements in the sales floors below the street floors (such floors being by nature as popular as the main floor in terms of public congregation), the loading of one person per 30 sq ft of gross floor area is assigned to all sales floors below the street floor. Upper sales floors are assigned the occupant load of one person for each 60 sq ft of gross floor area. Floors or sections used only for offices, storage, and shipping, and not open to the general public, are assigned an occupant load of one person for each 100 sq ft of gross floor area. Floors or sections used for other than mercantile purposes are required to be assigned an occupant load based on the requirements stated elsewhere in this section, and also in Section 6, Chapter 9, for the particular occupancy involved. Occupant loading and egress arrangements for covered malls are covered in Part D of this chapter.

Travel Distance to and Discharge from Exits

The maximum acceptable travel distance to exits is 100 ft, with an allowance of up to 150 ft travel distance for mercantile occupancies that are protected by automatic sprinkler systems. The presence of automatic sprinkler protection also permits up to one half of all required exit units of stair widths, escalators, and ramp widths to discharge from upper floors through the main street floor area, and from floors below the street floor up and through the main floor with the following prohibitions:

1. Not more than one half of the required units of exit from any single floor considered separately discharge through the street floor area.

2. The exits are enclosed per the discussion of protection of vertical openings to the street floor.

3. The distance of travel from the termination of the enclosure for the stair, escalator, or ramp to an outside street door is not more than 50 ft.

4. The street floor doors provide sufficient units of exit width to serve exits discharging through the street floor in addition to the street floor itself. This is once again in recognition of the expectation that the general public will attempt, for the most part, to exit down through the main street floor and out the main street floor exits.

Doors

In general, doors for mercantile occupancies are expected to be of the hinged, swinging type that swing in the direction of exit travel. The one exception to this is small Class C mercantile occupancy doors that may swing inward if they serve only the street floor area. If revolving doors are used, they can constitute part of the required number of exit units for a street floor only, and should not be used at the foot or top of stairs located at the floor of exit discharge. Under the provisions of the NFPA Life Safety Code, revolving doors receive credit as constituting one-half unit of exit width for each revolving door.

Exit Marking, Exit Illumination, and Emergency Power

Every mercantile occupancy is required to have exit illumination and exit signs that meet the provisions of the NFPA Life Safety Code. These include a minimum value of illumination of one footcandle measured at the floor for each part of the means of egress, and the arrangement of adequate exit signs and/or directional exit signs indicating the proper path of egress from each and every point within the floors of occupancy. Also, sizable mercantile occupancies (Class A and Class B stores) shall have emergency lighting facilities to provide backup assistance to the exit illumination system, should the normal utilities fail.

Interior Finish

Interior finish within mercantile occupancies is limited to the following components. The interior finish of exits in all mercantile occupancies must be Class A or Class B. This allows materials of up to 75 flame spread rating to be used in all exits. In sizable mercantile occupancies (Class A and Class B stores), interior finish of the ceiling material must be Class A or Class B (up to 75 flame spread) unless a sprinkler system is present. Where sprinkler protection is provided, the ceiling material may be permitted to be Class C (up to 200 flame spread). The permissible construction for the exposed surface of walls in Class A and Class B stores is restricted to Class A, Class B, or Class C interior finish materials (up to 200 flame spread). Further, in any mercantile occupancy, exposed portions of structural members complying with the requirements for heavy timber construction may be permitted (see NFPA No. 220, Standard Types of Building Construction). Laminated wood, if provided, must not delaminate under the influence of heat. Class C stores are permitted to have Class A, B, or C interior finish (up to 200 flame spread) throughout the store, with the exception of the exit construction previously discussed.

Alarm System

Only Class A and Class B stores are required to have a

manual fire alarm system. If an automatic fire detection system or an automatic sprinkler system is provided in Class A and Class B stores, the manual fire alarm system is not required. There are no fire alarm system requirements for Class C stores.

Automatic Sprinkler Protection

The automatic sprinkler protection requirements of the NFPA Life Safety Code are discussed under "Protection of Vertical Openings" in Part C of this chapter.

Protection of Hazardous Areas

In recognition that the hazardous areas used for heating, air conditioning, or maintaining the mercantile facility will, in many cases, provide the source of ignition for mercantile occupancy fires, the following requirements are imposed on areas housing such occupancies:

1. Any area used for general storage, boiler or furnace rooms, fuel storage, janitor closets, maintenance shops including woodworking and painting areas, and kitchens must be separated from the remainder of the mercantile occupancy by construction having a fire resistance rating of not less than one hour.

2. All openings into these areas must be protected by self-closing fire doors of suitable rating for installation in fire resistive construction of one hour. These requirements are waived in mercantile facilities that are protected by automatic extinguishing systems.

3. Any areas that house high hazard content are required to be isolated by fire resistive construction and protected by automatic sprinkler protection.

Building Service Equipment

The protection of air conditioning, ventilating, heating, cooking, and other building service equipment that may be expected to be found in mercantile occupancies are discussed in other sections of this HANDBOOK and in the related NFPA National Fire Codes.

This protection is in addition to the isolation of the hazardous areas housing this equipment. The only additional NFPA Life Safety Code requirements for the arrangement of building service equipment is the recognition that elevators cannot serve as required means of exit, and that where mercantile occupancies are located in facilities that are more than three stories in height, or more than three stories above the street floor, any automatic elevators used for the vertical mode of transportation must be arranged for fire emergency use by the fire fighting forces. This involves the use of a key operation to transfer automatic elevator operation to a manual mode and to automatically return the elevator to the street floor for use by members of the fire service. This carries with it the requirement that the elevators in mercantile occupancies be located for free and ready access by the fire department.

Self-service Stores

In addition to the foregoing requirements for mercantile occupancies, since self-service stores involve an arrangement of checkout stands, barriers, turnstiles, and the use of wheeled carts for the carrying of merchandise by the customers, caution must be taken to prevent the obstruction of means of egress by either the checkout facilities or the arrangement of shopping carts.

Open-air Mercantile Occupancies

Where open-air mercantile operations such as open-air markets, gasoline filling stations, roadside stands for the sale of farm produce, or other types of outdoor mercantile operations are utilized, it is necessary that they be arranged to permit free and unobstructed ways of travel allowing prompt escape from any point of danger or emergency for occupants. This includes the strict prohibition against dead-end corridors or dead-end paths that might cause persons to be trapped due to display stands, adjoining buildings, fences, vehicles, or other obstructions.

Combined Mercantile and Residential Occupancies

For the many corner grocery store operations where dwelling units have been combined with mercantile occupancies, the NFPA Life Safety Code requires that the dwelling units have exit arrangements other than through the mercantile occupancies. Multiple-dwelling occupancies are prohibited above mercantile occupancies, with the following exceptions:

1. Where the residential occupancy and its exits are separated from the mercantile occupancy by construction having a fire resistance of at least 1 hr, or

2. Where the mercantile occupancy is protected throughout by automatic sprinklers, or

3. Where an existing building with not more than two dwelling units above the mercantile occupancy is protected by an automatic fire detection system.

D. The Covered Mall Shopping Center

Much of the preceding discussion of population characteristics, behavior of occupants, need for proper aisle width and merchandising arrangement, means of egress arrangement, etc., also applies to covered mall individual mercantile occupancies. (See also Part D of Chap. 1 of this Section.)

The commonly accepted definition of a covered mall is "a covered or roofed interior area used as a pedestrian way, and connecting buildings or portions of a building housing single and/or multiple tenants." In a relatively short period of time, the covered mall shopping center has come into prominence as a modern-day retail marketplace. Today most shopping centers of any significant size under construction or in the planning stage are of this type. Many existing shopping centers that have malls open to the elements are having such malls enclosed in an effort to "catch-up" with this relatively new retail merchandising concept. In addition to the typical suburban covered mall shopping center where parking and landscaping surround the building, many covered malls are being planned and built in urban areas in conjunction with parking decks, office buildings, hotels, recreational facilities, and public or private people-mover systems.

Since the advent of covered mall shopping centers, the application of existing building codes has been an ongoing problem to architects, owners, developers, and building officials. However, until very recently, many of the model building codes did not consider the covered mall shopping center to be a unique type of mercantile occupancy worthy of special attention. When such special attention was finally given, it was often misdirected by those architects, owners, and developers most intimately involved in the design and development of covered mall shopping centers. Such persons often failed to identify the many and varied complexities of these buildings. Once this has been remedied, the requirements for safety, health, and welfare can be reconciled with the requirements for retail merchandising, economics, and construction which bear so heavily on the degree of success attained by the shopping center.

In order to provide a more definitive context, regional

enclosed mall shopping centers in excess of 750,000 sq ft in area are primarily referenced herein. This range suggests projects containing two or more department stores plus a multiplicity of various types of smaller retail occupancies. With certain qualifications, the same conclusions can then be applied to smaller projects and to urban projects as well.

Design of Covered Mall Shopping Centers

The covered mall shopping center is generally conceived and designed as essentially one building comprised of from one to as many as six sizeable department stores plus an assemblage of smaller specialty retail shops, all of which are interconnected and intercommunicable by means of a covered, climate-controlled, public pedestrian way. The complex may also include other occupancies incidental to the primary use, such as movie theaters, bowling lanes, ice arenas, project management offices, and other customer service areas to which access is similarly provided by means of the covered mall.

The project may be designed as one level or multilevel, depending upon such factors as topography, the size of the land parcel, and the number and size of the department stores and retail shops. The vast majority of suburban projects built in the United States are either one- or two-level centers, with the occasional introduction of a partial mezzanine level.

When the project is designed as a two-level center, the topography of the parking lot surrounding the building is usually shaped to provide grade access to each level of the department stores and the mall shops. This is done to equalize customer flow on both levels so that one level has no advantage over the other as far as sales exposure to customer traffic is concerned. The "two-level" shopping center is distinguished from the "two-story" shopping center in this important respect. (See Fig. 8-5A.) The covered mall proper is designed primarily to serve the

requirements for occupant egress, maximization of tenant sales, and promotional activities. The storefronts occurring along the pedestrian "public street" of the mall are usually designed to encourage unrestricted customer flow and traffic control from the mall to the individual shops, as well as to the department stores. This system of customer traffic flow and traffic control is the essence of the merchandising concept employed in covered mall shopping center design.

The types of storefront closures ideally suited to the requirements for maximizing customer traffic flow and security are those that are capable of being fully recessed, such as rolling overhead grilles, side coiling grilles, and horizontal sliding doors. Since the ambient temperature in the mall is the same as in the tenant space, the storefront closure need only satisfy the requirement for security when the store is closed for business and unoccupied.

The Development Process—Interjection of Fire Protection Needs

The developer is essentially the manager of the project and the spearhead of the development process. In addition, he may have an equity interest in the project either as a partner or as the sole owner. The developer's organization could include any one or all of the following disciplines in addition to the administrative or management function: market research, leasing, architecture, construction, property management, environmental, legal, and accounting.

The developer proposes a building site to the owner(s), key department stores, and tenants after extensive investigation in connection with market research, demographics, traffic studies, public utilities, topographical configuration, zoning requirements, subsoil conditions, building codes, local fire safety codes, environmental and any other considerations that could have some bearing on the final selection of a building site. In concert with these investigations, fire protection needs are interjected when preliminary

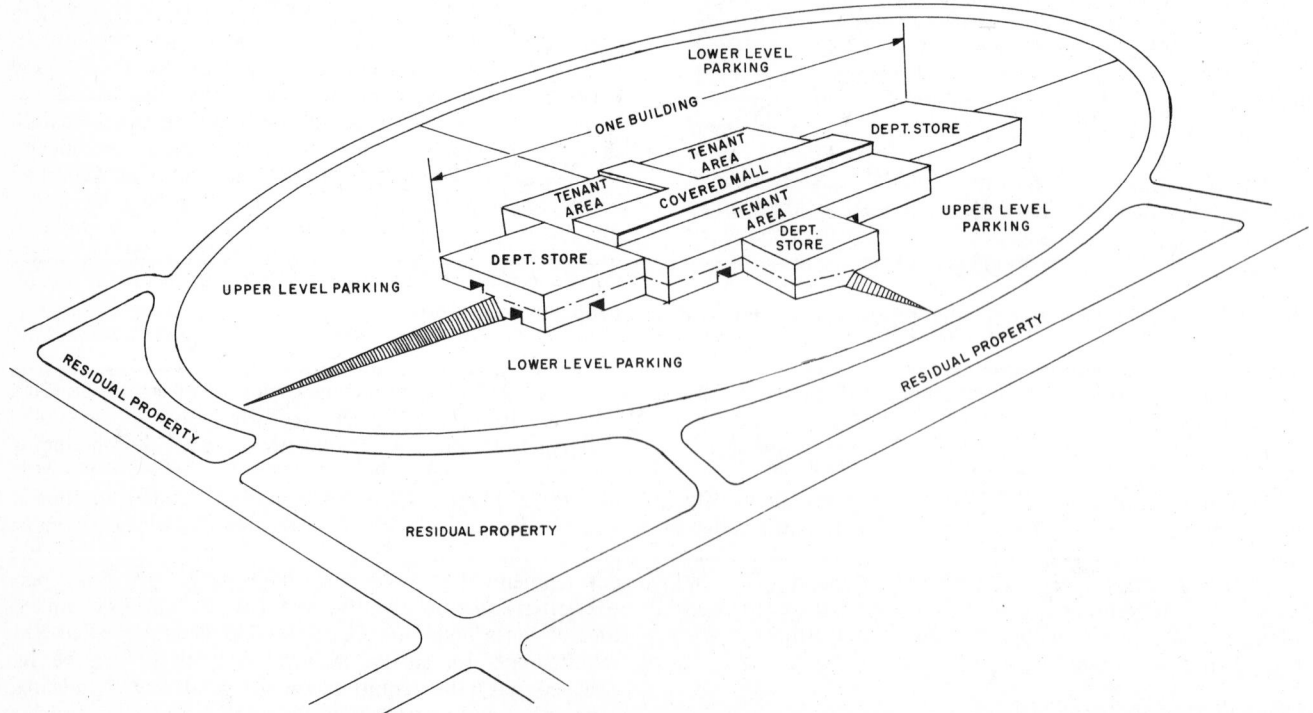

Fig. 8-5A. Many shopping centers today are purposefully designed (and merchandised) to provide an equal distribution of customer flow on all levels.

site plan feasibility studies are prepared by the developer's planning staff to determine the general building configuration indicating the relationship of department stores to each other and to the tenant and mall areas. In addition, roadway geometrics are defined both on-site and off-site, in conjunction with the parking area and landscape design.

Occupant Allowance Requirements

Many covered mall shopping centers are constructed by a "fast track" construction procedure so that the ultimate ratio of sales space to storage space for tenant stores is not known at the time construction is started. In simple terms, fast tracking is a phased construction procedure which allows construction to proceed upon completion of the construction documents for any given phase of the work. Hence, a projection must be made regarding occupant load in order to determine beforehand the required units of exit width.

Many model codes, including the NFPA Life Safety Code, require that the occupant load be calculated on the basis of one occupant per 30 sq ft of "first floor" area and basement sales areas (if planned), plus one occupant per 60 sq ft of "other upper sales floors." The occupant load for stock or storage space not open to the public is calculated on the basis of one occupant per 100 or 300 sq ft, depending upon the particular code being used. Whether or not the covered mall proper is assigned an occupant load depends upon how it is designed to function.

The projected occupant load is usually arrived at by empirical means. That is, an assumption of the ratio of sales area to storage area for tenant space is made based on past experience, or the occupant load for tenant space can be determined on the basis of car count as in the following example. When considering a building complex of 1,000,000 sq ft GLA comprised of three department stores of 200,000 sq ft each and 400,000 sq ft GLA of tenant space:

1. An adequate parking ratio for a shopping center of this size is 5.0 cars per 1,000 sq ft GLA, or 5,000 cars total. The Urban Land Institute Technical Bulletin 53 is presently being considered for revision downward from 5.5 to 5.0 cars per 1,000 sq ft GLA.

2. Assume that all 5,000 parking spaces are occupied and that every car contains 4 passengers, which is $1\frac{1}{2}$ passengers more than the national average of 2.5 persons per car for peak shopping periods such as back-to-school, Christmas, and Easter seasons. This increase of 60 percent is more than adequate to allow for drop off customers, public transportation, and walk-in traffic.

3. The occupant load for the shopping center would be 20,000 persons. This translates into one occupant per 50 sq ft for the department store area and the tenant GLA.

Although the car count method of determining occupant load has proven through experience to be reasonable and workable for large suburban regional shopping center developments, it is not recognized in the NFPA Life Safety Code. The car count method could be applied to urban shopping centers as well, depending, of course, to some extent on the particular market area being considered in relation to the proximity of walk-in customer traffic generators, such as apartment buildings, private residences, public transportation, and to a lesser degree office buildings.

The Covered Mall Proper—A Systems Approach

In addition to the typical one-level covered mall design, the covered mall may be designed as a multilevel space serving multilevel tenant areas and department stores.

Although the vast majority of suburban shopping centers built in the United States are either one- or two-level centers with the occasional introduction of a partial mezzanine level, multilevel shopping centers are becoming more commonplace in urban areas as a result of urban redevelopment programs.

In most cases, two-level covered malls are designed for visual intercommunication of the levels by means of openings in the floor of the upper level. Visual intercommunication of the levels wherever practicable is important in maximizing exposure of storefronts and merchandise to customer traffic. The floor areas between openings in the upper level serve as bridges which promote cross-mall shopping convenience for the customer.

Negotiations between the department stores and the owner (who may also be the developer, if he has an equity interest in the project) are conducted concurrently to determine the number of department stores, their size, general configuration, and their location on the site with respect to the covered mall and tenant space. It is generally known at this point whether or not the department stores will own in fee or lease from the landlord that portion of the property on which their store will be built plus the property supporting their parking requirement. In either case, the department stores are usually responsible for the design and construction of their own stores up to the mall and/or sidewalk curb line surrounding their store, although the department stores may negotiate to have the developer assume this responsibility.

The developer is responsible for the design and construction of the covered mall areas and the building shell housing tenant areas, the parking areas and related roadways, and the proprietary utility systems. Like department stores, a tenant may negotiate to have the developer design and construct his store within the tenant building shell. The negotiations between the developer and the department stores may include certain cost-shared items, such as parking lot construction, road work, utility systems, landscaping, and other items that relate to the total project, even though the developer bears the direct responsibility for construction.

As stated earlier, a great many covered mall shopping center projects are constructed by the fast track construction procedure. With this procedure, foundation and structural steel drawings and specifications are completed and contracts awarded. While the structural work takes place in the field, architectural, mechanical, and electrical plans and specifications are prepared for phased bidding with contracts awarded in a similar manner. In summary, the fast track construction process allows the developer to open the shopping center for business and thereby capitalize his considerable investment in the shortest possible time, saving himself as many as twelve months in some projects of the magnitude under discussion.

Everything about the shopping center is not known, even to the developer, at the time construction is started. For example, the final architectural treatment of the exterior and interior spaces may be determined only to the extent permitting the structural elements to be designed. The location of tenant demising walls may not be known since lease negotiations with prospective tenants may not commence until after the superstructure has been erected. Mechanical, electrical, and fire protection systems are designed for main distribution only with branch distribution added to the construction documents when the tenant's space is defined by lease agreement.

The mechanical intercommunication between levels is accomplished by means of stairs, escalators, elevators, and

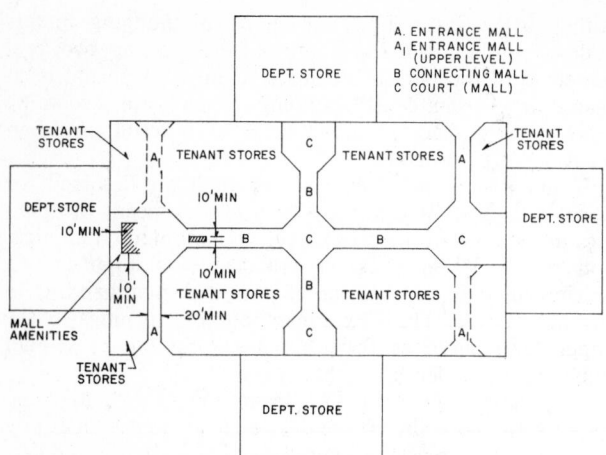

Fig. 8-5B. *Typical two-level shopping center (lower level).*

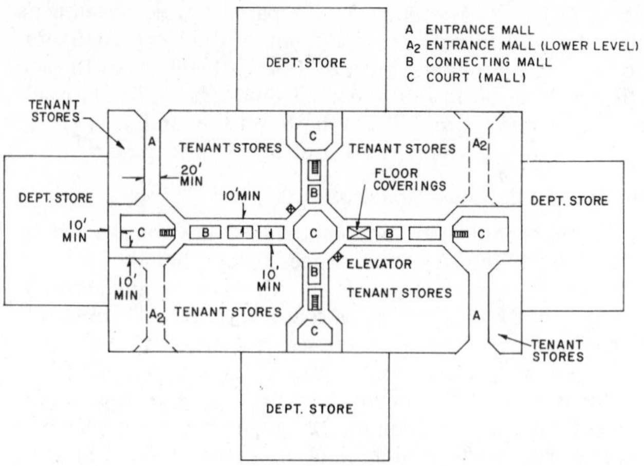

Fig. 8-5C. *Typical two-level shopping center (upper level).*

ramps. Any one or all of these vertical transportation modes can be employed in multilevel shopping centers. Convenient and appropriate vertical transportation for the elderly and the handicapped should not be overlooked in the overall design of the covered mall. (See Fig. 8-5B and Fig. 8-5C.)

Basically, the covered mall may be considered in either of two ways:

1. As a way of exit access from the connected buildings.

2. As a pedestrian way permitting an increase in the distance of travel from each of the tenant stores to a mall exit.

In the first instance, the entire complex is treated as one building or one compartmented department store, as it were, where the covered mall is treated simply as an extension of the sales space. The covered mall is considered in terms of exit access, as an aisle common to the various tenant stores and joining the exit access aisles of the tenant stores to mall exits. This treatment, in terms of the NFPA Life Safety Code, leads to the strict application of all design factors discussed in the first part of this chapter. In the second instance, a systems design is offered where the mall is considered to offer a higher degree of life safety if all of certain minimum conditions of the system are met:

The covered mall shall be at least of sufficient clear width to accommodate egress requirements for mercantile buildings, but in no case less than 20 ft wide in its narrowest dimension: The minimum width dimension of 20 ft has particular significance in terms of exit access and should not be construed as a requirement to provide minimum separation between storefronts on opposite sides of the covered mall. The need for separation per se in a covered mall shopping center that is protected by an automatic sprinkler system is not substantiated by the history of recorded accounts of exposure fires involving mercantile as well as various other types of occupancies.

The excellent performance of automatic sprinklers in connection with exposure fires as documented by Mr. Harry Marryatt in his book *"Automatic Sprinklers in Australia and New Zealand, 1886–1968,"* together with the sprinkler performance data compiled by the NFPA, is compelling enough to mitigate almost any reasonable doubt regarding an additional requirement for separation over and above the minimum 20 ft width requirement for exit access.

The foregoing notwithstanding, the width of the covered mall connecting courts at entrances to department stores is generally found to be well in excess of the 20 ft minimum

in order to provide for the amenities described earlier, and at the same time provide for an aggregate of 20 ft of exit access. (See Fig. 8-5D.)

In practice, one is more likely to find the entrance malls to be designed for the minimum width. Since stores located on either side of entrance malls do not lie along the direct path to department stores (commonly called "anchor stores" or "magnet stores" because of their greater customer attraction), such stores do not enjoy as much customer exposure as those located along connecting malls. As a result, stores on opposite sides of the entrance mall are brought closer together by eliminating any mall amenities which in themselves are not likely to generate traffic, thereby maximizing convenient cross-mall customer shopping. The minimum mall width of 20 ft is entirely compatible with this merchandising concept and does not impose an unreasonable burden upon developers nor merchants as has been shown by countless applications of this minimum width requirement in shopping centers throughout the United States.

The covered mall shall be provided with an unobstructed exit access on each side of the mall floor area of not less than 10 ft in clear width, parallel and adjacent to the mall storefront. Such exit access shall lead to an exit having a minimum of three units of exit width: The purpose of the requirement of 10 ft of clear exit access is

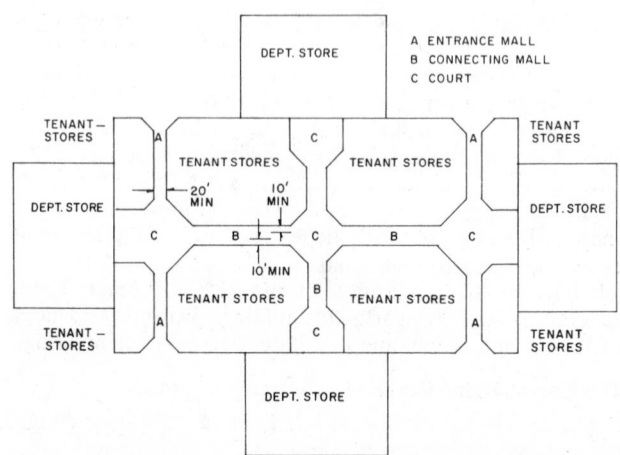

Fig. 8-5D. *Typical one-level shopping center.*

to provide a higher degree of safety in the covered mall commensurate with its use as a continuation of exit access from the tenant stores. Safe, continuous, and unobstructed exit access from each tenant store is provided at the same time recognizing the need to allow for the owner's merchandising and operational requirements for the mall amenities.

The minimum requirement of 10 ft of clear exit access parallel and adjacent to the mall storefronts relates directly to the minimum mall width of 20 ft. None of the mall amenities mentioned earlier may encroach upon this minimum dimension of 10 ft. The net effect of this requirement is to preclude the installation of any of the mall amenities in areas of the coveerd mall that are a minimum of 20 ft in width. In practice thus far, this requirement has proved to be reasonable and workable in terms of life safety and has the added advantage of not being unduly restrictive nor burdensome to developers.

The minimum requirement for terminating mall exit access in not less than three units of exit width relates to the minimum requirement for at least one aisle in Class A stores (30,000 sq ft or greater in area) to be 5 ft in width.

The units of exit width from the covered mall need only satisfy the calculated occupant load based on all of the connected tenant occupancies. It is not necessary to provide units of exit width from the covered mall commensurate with the minimum mall width which would necessarily result in wall-to-wall doors, unless the calculation of the occupant load together with the number and location of mall exits so dictates.

The covered mall and all buildings connected thereto shall be provided throughout with an electrically supervised automatic sprinkler system in accordance with NFPA requirements: It is a generally accepted fact that the single most effective way of protecting life and property from the ravages of fire is by means of an electrically supervised automatic sprinkler system. Sprinkler performance data, as referenced earlier, gives rise to objective scrutiny of long standing "accepted" code requirements. For example, accounts of sprinkler performance published in recent years have brought into question the need to provide current established levels of "fireproofing" of steel structural members when the building is protected by an electrically supervised sprinkler system.

Considerable data attesting to the effectiveness of sprinkler systems in the protection of life and property would strongly suggest that perhaps current levels of "fireproofing" of steel structural members is unjustified in terms of cost-benefit when the building is protected by an electrically supervised sprinkler system, at least in the context of one- and two-level covered mall shopping centers. Another example is the imposition of additional building code restrictions on buildings in fire districts even when such buildings are protected by sprinkler systems.

Originally, fire districts were established to prevent, or at least minimize, the possibility of conflagration primarily in older, more highly congested urban areas. This resulted in the placement of added restrictions on the building area, building height, the separation of buildings, and construction type without due regard for the effectiveness of sprinkler systems. Recently, model codes have recognized this problem by eliminating many of the unwarranted fire district restrictions.

Walls dividing stores from each other shall extend from the floor to the underside of the roof deck or floor deck above. No separation is required between a store and the covered mall: The purpose of this requirement is to confine the spread of fire and smoke to the place of origin by inhibiting the passage of fire and smoke through ceilings and over the tops of tenant demising walls into adjacent occupancies. Model codes call for such walls to be constructed of noncombustible materials. In practice, tenant demising walls are usually constructed of metal studs and drywall.

In effect, tenant demising walls represent a form of compartmentation to the extent that no separation is provided at the storefront. A requirement for separation at the storefront would defeat the merchandising purpose of the covered mall which is to optimize unrestricted customer flow between the covered mall and the tenant store. With this form of compartmentation in concert with an electrically supervised automatic sprinkler system, the need for any additional "firewall" building code requirement becomes highly questionable. Accounts of fires in shopping centers where this configuration was in evidence tend to support the theory that any additional "firewall" requirement is unnecessary.

The covered mall shall be provided with smoke control in accordance with NFPA requirements: Under fire conditions, any build-up of smoke in a tenant store could ultimately find its way into the covered mall due to the open storefront configuration. Effective means of smoke control in the covered mall proper are essential in order to assure its continuous use as a smoke-free primary way of exit access.

In addition to the foregoing, certain conditions of exiting should be present in *all* covered malls regardless of how the covered mall is considered. These conditions of exiting are as follows:

1. Every floor and every store (except class C stores less than 50 ft deep) of a covered mall must have no less than two exits located remote from each other.

2. No less than one-half the required exit widths for each store greater than 3,000 sq ft in area connected to a covered mall shall lead directly outside without passage through the mall.

3. Every covered mall must be provided with unobstructed exit access parallel to and adjacent to the connected buildings. This exit access must extend to each mall exit.

4. Exits from the covered mall must be arranged so that the length of travel from any mall-store entrance to an exit shall not exceed 200 ft.

Conclusion

All of the items discussed in this chapter have been put into practical application in many stores and many covered mall shopping centers throughout the United States, and have answered the requirement for life safety without imposing burdensome or unreasonable restrictions on developers and the merchandising needs of covered mall shopping centers.

In addition to the NFPA Life Safety Code, other model codes are presently being revised in an effort to codify requirements for covered mall shopping centers. This effort can turn out to be a blessing or a curse, depending upon how successfully the life safety concern is in harmony with the retail merchandising purpose of the covered mall shopping center.

There exists the possibility of over-reaction in the formulation of code requirements, especially when the building type being considered is not fully understood in all of its important aspects. The revision of existing code requirements that have proved to be unreasonably restrictive or unfounded in terms of any real threat to life safety, practicability in application, and cost-benefit should be pursued in much the same way as the efforts that are being made to rectify potentially dangerous life safety situations in buildings by the adoption of more restrictive and yet reasonable code language.

SI Units

The following conversion factors are given as a convenience in converting to SI units the English units used in this chapter.

1 sq ft   = 0.0929 m²
1 footcandle = 10.764 1x

1 in.   = 25.400 m
1 ft   = 0.305 m

Bibliography

NFPA Codes, Standards, and Recommended Practices (see the latest *NFPA Publications and Visual Aids Catalog* for availability of current editions of the following documents)

NFPA No. 101, Code for Safety to Life from Fire in Buildings and Structures.
NFPA No. 220, Standard Types of Building Construction.

Additional Readings

Marryatt, H. W., *Fire: Automatic Sprinkler Performance in Australia and New Zealand, 1886–1968*, Australian Fire Protection Association, Melbourne, Australia, 1971.

Chapter 6

BUSINESS OCCUPANCIES

Business occupancies are broadly defined as those facilities involved in the conduct of financial, managerial, technical, and similar work in the management of business, commerce, and services. Business occupancies traditionally involve management processes remote from operations concerned with the production of raw materials such as:

1. Manufacture or any other mechanism of processing or adding value to materials.
2. Servicing and repairing of property or equipment.
3. Transporting or warehousing of such materials.

Typical business occupancies include: office facilities of all types; computer and other data processing operations; information and other public contact activities (excluding mercantile operations); banking and similar financial institutions; and facilities for the handling and maintenance of records and files.

A. Occupancy Characteristics

Historically business occupancies have been considered to be low hazard types of occupancies. In general, they are relatively free of high potential special hazard occupancies and activities. The hazard or risk that is present is normally associated with the common ignition sources arising from heat, light, and power as well as from a high level of personal activities and the support activities commonly associated with business occupancies such as eating facilities, parking facilities, and retail operations. Business occupancies frequently have high concentrations of persons during the business hours. While such concentrations are not as dense as the population loads associated with assembly occupancies, they may be heavily distributed throughout a large building at densities approaching the 100 sq ft of gross floor area per person specified for such occupancies by NFPA No. 101, Code for Safety to Life from Fire in Buildings and Structures, hereinafter referred to in this chapter as the NFPA Life Safety Code. This figure was developed by the NFPA Committee on Safety to Life and reported in the annual reports of that Committee to the National Fire Protection Association in the years 1915–1917. These figures are still in use. Some question as to their continued validity has been raised. It is possible that some additional insight into the current use of office facilities will be indicated by the office building fire load studies that are presently being conducted by the National Bureau of Standards and referenced later in this chapter.

Business occupancies can often have high concentrations of value. This occurs particularly with automatic data processing equipment and financial institutions actually handling money or other negotiable instruments. Business occupancies, particularly the aggregate of related groups, can also have a critical impact on business interruption, continuity of services, or fulfillment of essential missions. Distributed throughout business occupancies are also items of special or critical importance including computers and other automatic data processing equipment, communication networks, and vital and important records and accounts.

B. Ignition Sources

Fires in business occupancies normally result from common hazards, with the most frequent probable sources occurring from smoking and smoking materials, electrical machines and related office equipment, and torches and other open flame devices used by those doing welding, cutting, or burning in maintenance and alterations operations. The most commonly expected initial fuels are furniture, paper, other working materials used in the conduct of business, and occasionally the finish or insulation. In business occupancies there is frequently a massive flow of paper and similar materials, and a particular concern must be directed to trash and waste paper collection, storage, and disposal.

C. Fire Loads

Fire load studies have been made on several occasions. Most current practices are based on the fire load studies conducted in the late 1920s and early 1930s and reported in documents of the National Bureau of Standards BMS 92 (1942) and BMS 149 (1957).[1] Generally these measurements were taken in the type of businesses existing at that time and usually involved not only wooden desks, but often wooden cabinetry and file cases. The values reported from those early studies included the combustible materials involved in the flooring, interior finish, and trim as well as the furniture, equipment, and working materials. These studies showed concentrations of combustibles ranging from 0 to 86 psf of floor area. General design practice since that time has been based on ranges usually between 20 and 30 psf. These figures have been extensively challenged as being outdated and representative of the type of furnishings no longer used. Additional fire load studies have been made since that time. The most important of these related to business occupancies is a continuing program instituted by the National Bureau of Standards and the Building Research Advisory Board, presently being funded on large scale by the U.S. General Services Administration. This study, expected to be completed in 1976 or 1977, is targeted to involve the evaluation of over 10,000 rooms in approximately 100 buildings. Initial pilot studies have indicated results of approximately those shown in Figure 8-6A.

In recent years there has been an increasing tendency to upgrade the aesthetics and appearance of many business occupancies. In numerous cases this has led to increased use of foam and plastic cushion materials. In addition, there has been a significant increase in the use of the high impact type of plastics for the housing of business machines and equipment. These impinge significantly on the probable fire conditions in office occupancies. The general fire load of office or business occupancy types of problems can be classified broadly, based on the predominant type of furniture or equipment. Where combustible interior finish becomes involved, it must be considered as significantly increasing the fire risk problem in any of the following general categories: steel furniture, wooden furniture, plastic

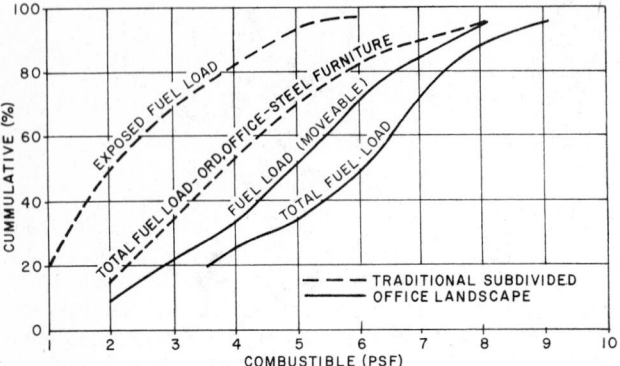

Fig. 8-6A. Chart developed from data derived from two separate pilot studies. In one case, labeled "Traditional Subdivided," a study was made of a government building where the majority of the furniture was modern steel furniture and the building was subdivided into separate rooms. This study is reported in detail in "Techniques for the Survey and Evaluation of Live Floor Loads and Fire Loads in Modern Buildings," National Bureau of Standards Science Series No. 16.[2] The solid line represents a separate study made of an "Office Landscape" arrangement where a large area was operated without partitions, subdivided by privacy dividers approximately 4 ft high, and following some of the modern concepts which eliminate closed drawers or containers for fuel. In this latter arrangement all movable fuel load is exposed to potential ignition.

materials, data processing communication materials, and storage files.

Steel Furniture

Steel furniture has a low probability of fire development (dependent almost entirely upon exposed combustibles exterior to the steel furniture) and a low potential fire severity.

Wooden Furniture

Wooden furniture contributes to the increased probable rate of fire buildup. The principal difference between businesses containing wooden furniture and businesses containing metal furniture is the inability of wooden file cabinets, wooden bookcases, and wooden desks to prevent their contents from entering the fire, particularly as the fire advances in size or when the total room involvement occurs (flashover).

Impact of Plastics

All modern occupancies contain some plastic materials. Plastics can become a controlling factor, greatly increasing the fire risk when they represent large concentrations (such as cushioning on couches, case goods, or basic furniture elements). Plastics are particularly suspect when used as containers housing other combustible materials (wastebaskets, desks, cabinets, or similar containers). The potential total rates of heat release and fire development of some plastics is quantum levels higher than that of ordinary cellulosic combustible (wood, paper, etc.) so that any concentration can result in a significant increase in the probability of serious, dangerous, spreading fire.

Data Processing and Communications

Data processing and communication centers represent mass concentrations of importance and value. They frequently also represent considerable concentrations of plastic materials commonly in combination with large quantities of paper and significant amounts of electrical energy.

Special protection is considered necessary for each such installation. (See also Sec. 5, Chap. 4, and Part G of Sec. 7, Chap. 2, this HANDBOOK.)

Files

Almost all businesses generate and store files. The problems and hazards of files that are essential records or files that are relocated to record centers are covered elsewhere in this HANDBOOK. In business occupancies, files maintained in steel file cabinets do not represent an increase in fire risk. Where files are stored or maintained on open or partially open mechanisms, they represent massive increases in the fire potential. Files maintained on magnetic media or microfilm can also represent such increases in fire potential, particularly when contained in thermoplastic cassettes, cases, and reels. The thermoplastic most commonly used is polystyrene.

D.   Construction

Business occupancies can be located in any type of construction. In addition, this occupancy is found in a mix with any other type occupancy, due to the need for an "office" or "office space" with all types of occupancies. This type of occupancy is frequently located in dwellings, warehouses, factories, and all other types of buildings where it is possible to provide light and heat and locate a desk or other working space. There is, however, a common type of building specifically developed for business purposes. This may be called an office building, bank, or "commercial" building. Although such buildings are located in concentrated business districts and in separate locations throughout any community, they are most frequently located in high value districts. Such buildings are permitted by codes to be of any height, and a large percentage of such office or related business functions are located in high-rise buildings.

Office and similar business type buildings can generally be divided into two classes. The older (pre 1945) structures, particularly the taller multistory buildings, are usually built of heavy fire resistive construction of either masonry and tile, brick arch, or steel frames encased in concrete or other fire resistive masonry. These buildings tend to be divided into compartments with a regular pattern of corridors and exits separating the occupancies into individual suites that are further separated by substantial walls of tile or other masonry material. Generally all offices or other spaces have openable, usually double-hung, windows. Such buildings are normally relatively "loose" in terms of development of stack effect. As constructed, such buildings usually have few voids, relatively low use of power, and few penetrations between floors. Serious fires occasionally occur in such buildings, usually due to readily identifiable factors such as open stairwells or combustible interior finish. In most cases, however, fire in such buildings are confined to the room or space of origin, with little impact outside of that area.

In recent years the general style of building construction has changed, and the modification of many older buildings has also caused them to approach the newer designs in terms of style, appearance, and firesafety problems. In the newer buildings lighter-weight types of construction have been used, and instead of the massive heat sink provided by the old-style, substantial masonry construction, lightweight steel or similar framing has been protected by "fireproofing" material. This protects the frame, but provides no heat sink or other method of assisting in mitigating the impact of the fire energy. Various types of block construction and open unpartitioned space have become common, with the loss of the value of inherent compartmentation that was formally traditional to this type of building. Suspended ceilings and additional utilities for air conditioning, power, and illumination, have caused the creation of numerous void spaces between floors and vertical passes, "poke throughs," and other penetrations of the floor deck system. Modern business operations and other needs have greatly increased power demands. Building perimeters have been made as tight as possible in an energy conservation mode, and fixed sealed windows are now common to such facilities. Even where operable windows are used, they are designed to be difficult to operate and to be as tight as possible. The resultant effect is to create a specially controlled environment. In normal nonemergency situations this is beneficial to the economy and comfort of the building. Under fire conditions, however, it can cause large areas to participate in and contribute to a dangerous and possibly lethal fire environment.

E.   Fire Control Design Approaches

The control of fire impact in business occupancies is viewed as involving three major phases, in sequence: the second phase is conditional on the first, and the third phase is conditional on both the first and second. In order of sequence these phases are:

Prevention of Fire Ignition: It is axiomatic that there can be no harm from fire if there is no fire. Building design considerations related to the prevention or avoidance of fire initiation all relate to keeping sources of ignition (energy) away from sources of fuel.

Control of Fire Size and Rate of Growth: Since it is functionally impossible to reasonably avoid all fires, it is necessary to design buildings on the basis that a fire may occur. The designer, however, has many capabilities of designing to limit the maximum or expected potential of the fire and its products both in rate of growth and ultimate size. His ability to control this potential (or "design the fire") is determined by: (1) the potential energy inherent to the fire situation (controlled by the amount, type, position, and arrangement of combustibles in the construction of the building and in the furniture and furnishings and other materials brought in by the occupants), (2) physical confinement as provided by the basic structural integrity of the building and all of the compartments and subdivisions within it, and (3) suppression or termination of the fire through fire extinguishing or other energy removal systems by manual or automatic means.

Protection of That (or Those) Exposed: When a fire occurs, that which is imminently involved in the fire environment itself is completely threatened, and its protection is essentially controlled by its ability to withstand or delay the destructive impact of fire. In general, this is referred to as salvage value. For all practical purposes, humans have no capability of surviving any period of time of actual involvement in the chemical reaction of fire. Other materials have different capabilities, and in some instances special protective measures can be taken to enhance the potential salvage. This is particularly important in the case of records protection where fire survivability and salvage can be highly determined by equipment design. Where the exposed (particularly humans) can either remove themselves or be promptly removed from the advancing danger of fire, or where the fire limitation design prevents the advancement

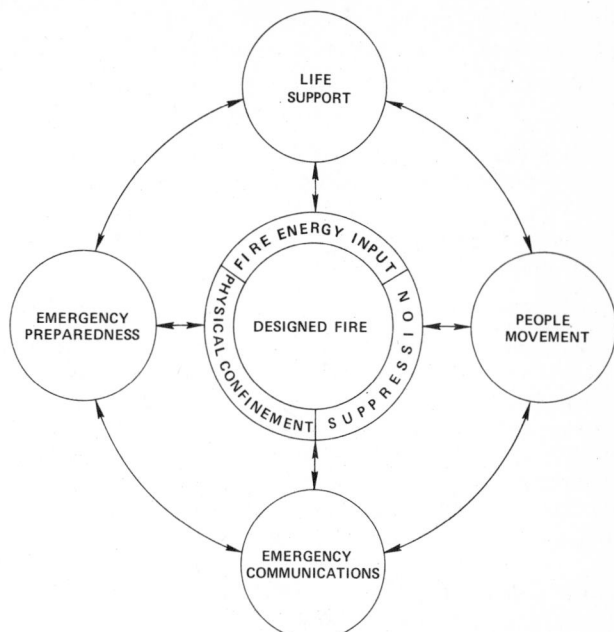

Fig. 8-6B.   The elements of firesafety design.

of the actual fire beyond a predesigned limit, protection of people and property can be designed by: (1) the provisions of the necessary elements, including life support capabilities, (2) people and personnel movement arrangements (means of egress) to move them from the area of danger to areas of safety, (3) emergency communications and control to direct people and control mechanical and electrical equipment, and (4) appropriate training and consideration of the capabilities and limitations of people during the design planning. The firesafety design elements that are intended to limit fire and protect that which is exposed to fire are shown in Figure 8-6B.

F.   Ignition Prevention

Ignition prevention may be divided into two general areas: ignition from within a structure, and ignition from without.

Ignition from Within a Structure: This design approach participates in elimination of ignition sources through the control of the special and common hazards such as power, heating, cooking, and other flame and energy sources. In general, these areas have been highly codified in documents such as the National Electrical Code and various other codes and standards, most of which are issued by the NFPA. The designer has little control over ignition sources that may be casually brought in by the occupants; even so, his planning can have a very significant impact on the presence of fuel, particularly incoming and outgoing materials. It is important that building designers consider the receiving of materials, their transportation through buildings, staging and storage areas, and particularly the total system for the collection, staging, and removal of trash (see Sec. 7).

External Ignition: External ignition may come from an external fire source, that radiates energy onto the building. Exposure protection requirements reflect this potential hazard. The basic mechanism for the transportation of energy from a fire external to a building onto the building's exterior or through openings into the building, is radiant energy. The requirements for protection of fire from external ignition sources are covered in NFPA No. 80A, Standard for Protection from Exposure Hazards.

G.   Energy Control

Since the common essential factor in producing fire energy is combustible fuel, anything related to reduction in the total fuel will impact as reduction in the total fire potential. There are, however, additional factors relevant to the impact of the fuel load in its occupancy.

Effects of Steel Containers on Fuel Load

Since the furnishings in a typical business building are often steel, it is important to understand the confining effects that a substantial steel container (such as a filing cabinet or desk) has in reducing the potential of the combustible materials contained in it. Table 8-6A has been developed from data published by the National Bureau of Standards in BMS 92, and clearly shows the value of steel containers in reducing the fire potential of combustibles.

Table 8-6A.   Effects of Steel Containers on Fuel Load

Effective Impact of Ordinary Combustible Materials in Steel Containers

Container	Part of Combustibles in Containers		
	Less than $\frac{1}{2}$	$\frac{1}{2}$ to $\frac{3}{4}$	More than $\frac{3}{4}$
Backed and Partitioned Shelving	75%	75%	75%
Shelving with Doors and Transfer Cases	60%	50%	25%
Filing Cabinets and Desks	40%	20%	10%
Fire Resistive Records Storage Equipment Rated at 1 Hr or More	0%	0%	0%

Other Factors Affecting Fuel Load

In addition to the gross fuel in a structure and the impact of steel containers, recent testing and modeling of fires has indicated additional factors which relate to the impact of fuel in a space particularly relevant to the rate of burning and the resultant rate of release of energy. As of this date, technical data on these factors and their impacts are sketchy and should be considered only for making gross determinations. The following generalized statements, however, can be used and are helpful in comparing changes in traditional occupancies where considerations of new materials, new configurations, or new forms of materials are involved.

1. The larger the exposed surface area of combustible, the faster the rate of fire development.

2. The higher the percentage of space occupied by combustible material versus the total space available, the more likely and faster the development of fire.

3. The higher the surface flame spread rating of any material, the more rapid the development of fire.

4. Combustibles on a ceiling contribute to flame spread and fire development more than those on a wall.

5. Combustibles near a wall or ceiling contribute more to fire development than those away from the walls and ceiling.

6. The combination of combustible walls and ceilings and proximity of combustible materials, particularly in a corner arrangement, contribute more to the development and spread of fire than the same materials in other positions in the room.

7. Various materials have various inherent rates of heat release when burning. The higher the rate of heat release of the material, the more rapid the development.

Space and Environment Factors Impacting on Initial Fire Growth

While fuel is the single most important factor, and in the very first stages of fire is the completely controlling factor, the surrounding environment becomes significantly involved in, and a controlling factor of, fire development as soon as fire size grows to involve an energy interplay with materials other than the initially ignited items, or as soon as the rate of burning develops a demand for oxygen larger than that which can be supplied by the immediate surrounding atmosphere. It is obvious that a given small amount of fuel (for example, a 10-lb bag of wastepaper towels) will produce an entirely different type of fire exposure if it is ignited in a large open space (such as a parking lot outside the building) than if it is burned in a small confined space (such as in an elevator). The same differences hold true in larger-scale instances involving larger quantities of fuel. Principal impacting factors are:

The Geometric Dimensions of the Space, Particularly Height: The dimensions of the room or space are important because of the impact the room, ceiling, and walls have on the extension of flame and thereby the development of a fire radiating surface. The most important dimension is ceiling height. The term ceiling height in this instance means the distance from the level of the burning material to the ceiling. Normally this is the distance from floor or desk height to the ceiling. In those instances where combustibles are stacked to high levels, however, it can well be the distance from the top of the stack to the ceiling. When the developing flame column strikes a barrier such as a wall or ceiling, it flares or mushrooms to produce a larger total flame surface area with a high probability of rapid engulfment placing the entire volume in fire, even when the initiator is a small fuel force.

Ventilation: In the initial stages of burning, ventilation is important primarily in its impact in changing the volume of air and, therefore, the equivalent volume of space. Should the fire reach a flashover condition (see below), ventilation becomes a primary controlling factor in the same manner that a damper controls fire in a solid fuel furnace. In the initial stages, the ventilation rate is controlled by the movement of air through ducts, doorways, open windows, etc. In the post-flashover stage it is reasonable to assume that the windows in the compartment of origin will be broken, and that the ventilation rate will be essentially determined by the window area. The report of a task group, Panel Three, "Fire Propagation and Movement," presented at the 1971 GSA International Conference on Firesafety in High-rise Buildings, provides a conceptual overview of the relationship of the factors involved in both fuel and environment.

Flashover

In business occupancies a critical factor in fire impact and risk is flashover. In many business occupancies the fuel levels are such that flashover will not take place in every condition, or will require extended times of fire build-up to reach the flashover stage. Fire builds up through a development stage where the intensity of heat radiation produced and the quantity and temperature of heated gases

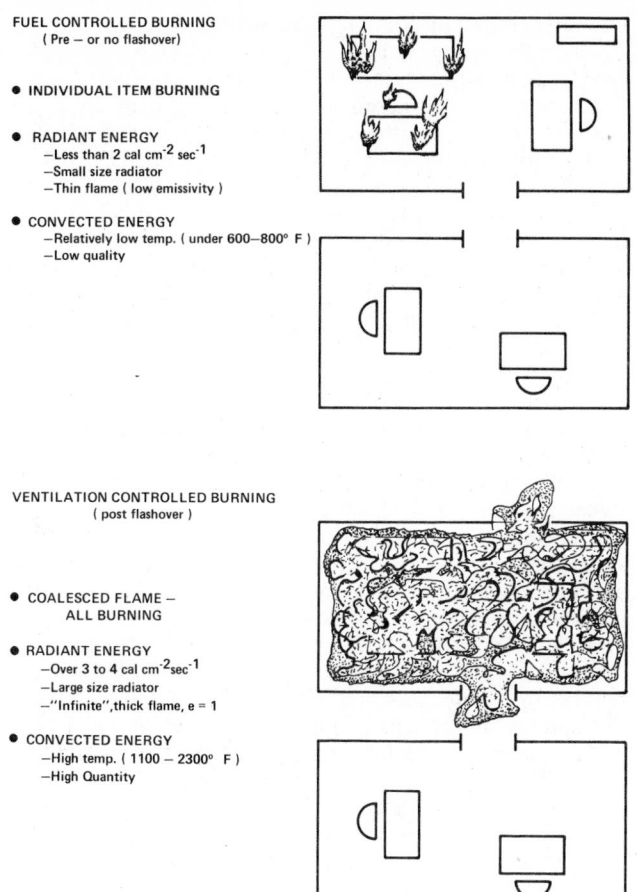

FUEL CONTROLLED BURNING
(Pre — or no flashover)

● INDIVIDUAL ITEM BURNING

● RADIANT ENERGY
—Less than 2 cal cm^{-2} sec^{-1}
—Small size radiator
—Thin flame (low emissivity)

● CONVECTED ENERGY
—Relatively low temp. (under 600—800° F)
—Low quality

VENTILATION CONTROLLED BURNING
(post flashover)

● COALESCED FLAME —
ALL BURNING

● RADIANT ENERGY
—Over 3 to 4 cal cm^{-2}sec^{-1}
—Large size radiator
—"Infinite",thick flame, e = 1

● CONVECTED ENERGY
—High temp. (1100 – 2300° F)
—High Quantity

Fig. 8-6C.   Flashover: (above) fuel controlled burning, and (below) ventilation controlled burning.

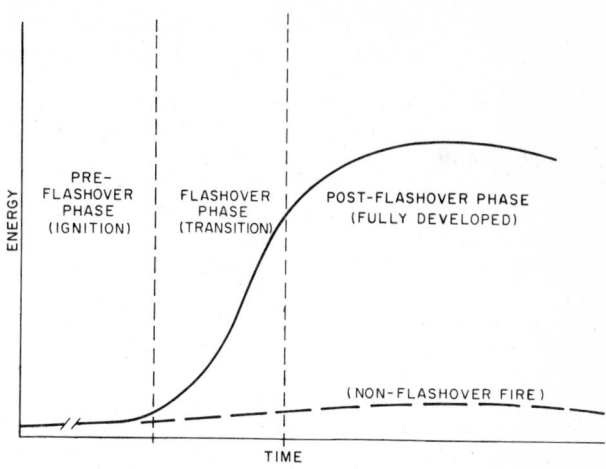

Fig. 8-6D.   Three-phase fire intensity course.

are relatively low, to a point (controlled by the fuel and environmental factors) which frequently involves a sudden and dramatic change (often called flashover) where simultaneous ignition of many items or a large area takes place. At this point the radiation level can more than double, major quantities of high temperature gases are produced, the area of involvement is grossly increased, and the actual flame becomes all encompassing and not directly identifiable with individual items of fuel. (See Fig. 8-6C.) From a practical standpoint the situation will either be one of fuel and environmental conditions in which the fire will pursue its entire course and terminate without reaching a fully developed or flashed over stage, or a situation in which the fire will persist to the point of full development. For design purposes there is no "in between" stage.

Fire Intensity

Fire intensity is a measurement of the level of energy produced by a fire. The level of fire intensity will vary through the course of the fire. Fires that do not flashover, however, normally pursue their entire course at a low intensity level. Fires that do flashover will normally follow a three-phase intensity course as diagrammed in Figure 8-6D. The first phase of such a fire is the pre-flashover phase and approximates that of a low intensity fire. At the point of flashover, the intensity rises dramatically and is primarily controlled in its ultimate height by either the total amount of fuel available or the amount of ventilation. Normally the greater the ventilation, the higher the intensity but the shorter the period of duration of this high intensity.

Fire intensity is the measurement determiner of the ability of fire effects to transmit radiated or convected heat across the various corridors, aisles, and other open spaces in sufficient quantity to ignite the combustible materials. In situations where there is not enough fuel or appropriate environmental conditions to develop a full intensity or flashover fire, and there is not a continuity of combustible to move a flame, fire will not normally spread from its immediate area of origin. Where conditions are such that flashover occurs, however, ignition can readily be transmitted through open spaces that are totally free of other combustibles. Of special concern has been data, reinforced by fire experience, that demonstrates massively higher levels of fire intensity in rooms or spaces which are lined with combustible finish, as compared with fire situations in rooms or spaces identical in all other features except for the combustible lining. Intensity levels have been reported as capable of doubling under such conditions. This impact of combustible lining on fire intensity is felt to have been a factor in the tragic high-rise fires in São Paulo, Brazil.

Relationship of Fire Load and Environmental Factors to Fire Severity

Fire severity is a measurement of the total energy impact of a fire. As such it is the principal factor in determining the ability of building members, barriers, and other materials to withstand the impact of fire and hold their shape and form. Fire severity is essentially the integration of the area under the fire intensity curve. On this basis it can be assumed that unless there is flashover there is virtually no fire severity. Fire severity is, therefore, controlled by the same factors that control fire intensity. Of these factors the ones most impacting on the post-flashover energy level and total duration are: (1) the total amount of fuel available; (2) the ventilation or rate at which air can be fed to this fuel; and (3) the thermal properties of the enclosure. (See Section 6, Chapter 8 for details of fire severity, standard time temperature curve, and other aspects of fire severity.)

Surface Flame Spread

Any continuous or nearly continuous path of combustible materials can act as a fuse train carrying fire from one place to another. The characteristics of the material(s) involved, its position, and the fire initiating environment that it is exposed to, govern both the extent and speed at which such combustibles can spread fire across their surface. Flame spread rates are specified in all building codes

and in the NFPA Life Safety Code. The impact of interior
finish is further discussed in Section 6, Chapter 6. Consideration of the impact of interior finish is critical to
business occupancies. In those business occupancies where
the fuel load is light, the presence of highly combustible
decorative finish, acoustic material, thermal insulation,
etc., can be the principal determiner of the extent of fire
involvement and the fire severity and intensity. It can be
axiomatically stated that the lesser the hazard of the
occupancy the more critical the hazard of the finish.

H.   Physical Confinement

The classic combustible loading (light to moderate total
load) and the arrangement usual in office and other business
occupancies makes physical confinement an important
factor in design for fire safety. In the older traditional types
of buildings with offices and other work areas subdivided
by substantial partitions (even where traditional fire ratings
were not necessarily achieved), the separation of the
buildings by fire-resistive floors and building frames with
vertical openings properly and effectively cut off resulted
in a natural type of subdivision that limited the maximum
probable size of fire and controlled the "risk" with an
historical record of high efficiency. Modern architectural
and aesthetic trends towards open office landscaping,
atriums, and other related vertical openings reduce the
inherent potential for limitation of fire "risk." Where open-
ness is involved, other measures such as control of the
fuel, or, more importantly, provisions for early suppression or termination of any fire, becomes much more
important. Extensive discussion of fire resistance, fire doors,
and other aspects of providing substantial subdivided
structures are covered elsewhere in this HANDBOOK and
are, therefore, not detailed in this Section. The principal
elements that are to be achieved by any physical confinement mechanism, however, must include the following:

1. The barrier to fire advance must stay structurally
sound, must stay in place, and must be able to carry its
own weight as well as the imposed live and dead weight
load that may be placed upon it.

2. The barrier must resist the thermal transfer of
conducted heat.

3. The barrier must prevent flame transmission through
openings that may be present at the start of fire, or that
may develop in any way throughout the course of fire
exposure.

I.   Fire Suppression (Extinguishment)

All fires eventually terminate either by consuming all of
the available fuel (burning themselves out), or through
some type of automatically or manually applied suppression
action. To the degree that suppression systems function,
they either mitigate or eliminate the impact of the fire—
usually by terminating or otherwise interfering with the
combustion process, and occasionally by cooling or otherwise protecting the exposed building elements and contents.

Fire Suppression by Water

While there are a number of means of extinguishing fires,
the extinguishing agent usually involved in attacking a fire
in buildings is water. Water extinguishes fire by removing
Btu from the heat source. When water is applied to a fire
in a manner where the heat removal at least equals the
rate at which the heat is being produced, the fire is controlled and prevented from spreading. When the heat
absorption increases to the level that actually results in the
cooling of the fuel material, the fire is extinguished.

Fire Suppression by Automatic Sprinkler Systems

The principal automatic response suppression system
used in buildings today is the automatic sprinkler system.
The ability of the automatic sprinkler system to apply
relatively small quantities of water promptly and directly
to the fire area generally produces the most effective use
of water. This ability is one of the principal reasons for
the automatic sprinkler system's outstanding record in
preventing serious fire damage. The sprinkler system is also
an effective remover of Btu and can be used as a reinforcing
method to control potential Btu release from a fuel load
occupancy where the potential fire energy exceeds the
actual fire resistive capabilities of the structure.

Other Types of Automatic Extinguishing Systems

Other automatic extinguishing systems that can be used
where applicable are water deluge systems, carbon dioxide
and other gas systems based on oxygen reduction, halogenated gas systems, high expansion foam systems, and
dry chemical systems. When selecting any extinguishing
system it is necessary to include the initial cost, the cost
effectiveness of the installation, the potential damage from
fire and fire extinguishing actions in case of ignition, the
possible need for long soaking periods or reserved supplies,
the reliability of the entire system, and the inspection,
preventive maintenance, and other services required to keep
the system in operating condition. All of these factors
come together in the following four parameters which determine the worth of any automatic extinguishing system:

Coverage: Some systems can be applied reasonably to an
entire facility. Others are best designed for small rooms
or even individual pieces of equipment.

Activation: Critical in any automatic extinguishing
system is both the probability the fire will activate it and
the probable size of the fire including the amount of "risk"
or damage which has occurred or developed by the time
activation occurs. Both the type of detector and detector
arrangements are critical factors in this aspect.

Extinguishing or Fire Controlling Capabilities: Given
that the fire extinguishing system is placed in automatic
operation and is discharging its extinguishing agent in the
manner intended, the probable eventual size of the fire,
damage done, and total impact are the major determiners.
Each system has its own characteristics and capabilities.

Reliability: All of the preceding functions are subject to
the mechanical, electrical, and other features of the total
system to supply, initiate, and deliver the extinguishing
media. All systems have some degree of unreliability. The
degree can be controlled and a very high level of
reliability achieved through careful design and good
maintenance. Different types of systems have varying inherent reliability characteristics. The more complex the
system, the larger the use of electrical or electronic interlocks and connections, the greater the number of valves,
and usually the greater the reliability problem.

Manual Systems

In addition to automatic systems, various types of manual
arrangements for applying extinguishing agents to fires are
available and important in building design. Manual systems,
however, only represent part of a total extinguishing
system. Such systems are of value only if they are properly
placed into service in time of need. In order for any manual
system to be effective, there must first be an initiation of
alarm in order to initiate the system; second, the people
who will operate the system must have safe access to the
point where the necessary extinguishing or control action

will take place; third, the equipment must be proper, readily available, and in good condition; and finally, the devices and equipment must have the capability of effectively attacking a fire of a probable size that will be encountered. Manual equipment includes the following:

1. Hand fire extinguishers are generally located at convenient points in the building. These are a traditional first fire attack device. While they are expected and generally mandated by law, they are of minimum value and extremely limited capability in office type buildings.

2. In many communities small diameter hose is hung from standpipe locations for intended use by occupants. In other communities such hoses are not provided in business occupancies, usually because of the lack of capability of occupants to safely and properly handle the hose and cope with the problems involved in maintaining the hose in good fire service condition.

3. The manual extinguishing systems having the most significant impact are those based on the needs of the professional fire department. From a business occupancy designer's standpoint, in order to properly function and optimize the capabilities of the department it is necessary to consider factors that will:

(a) Notify the fire department as promptly as possible following ignition.

(b) Provide the fire department ready and safe access through the building.

(c) Provide information and data on the building and on the on-going fire incident, including data on people and activities.

(d) Provide a prompt, direct, and safe internal means of travel from the building entry to the area from which a fire attack can be launched.

(e) Give a safe position for launch of the fire fighting attack.

(f) Provide internal communications between the fire command position and those attacking the direct fire front.

(g) Include a capable water supply with outlets and connections meeting the fire fighting needs, located convenient to a point of safe attack.

(h) Coordinate the building's fire suppression requirements with the fire fighting practices and techniques of the local fire department.

(i) Insure the fire fighter a reasonable degree of safety. Particularly important in fire fighting is the avoidance of entrapment due to dangerous conditions that would not be apparent to the responding officer in charge. Most important to avoid are the potentials of detonation and other explosions plus structural collapse or failure that can occur without reasonable advanced indications of danger.

J. Life Risk and Property Risk Determiners

Prior discussion in this chapter has related to those factors which control the size and extent of the fire and its direct products and effects. The fire and its effects, of course, are the principal controlling factors that determine harm to both life and property. To a large degree the extent of property damage is identical to the extent of fire growth. Even in the area of fire growth there is frequently a large degree of recovery of value of property after a fire. The duration of the fire as well as the characteristics of ease of damage or resistance to damage of the material can have a major impact on the degree of salvage. It is seldom possible to remove property in the face of an oncoming fire; therefore, the prime mechanism of safeguarding property from fire is to stop the advance of fire before it reaches the property. Obviously any fire protection features or other arrangements which either prevent the initiation of fire or limit its size help to protect both life and property. Humans, however, have significantly less resistance to fire than even the most sensitive machinery or valuable records. Humans cannot sustain even brief moments of actual involvement in flame. They are particularly susceptible to the toxic fumes and gases which can result from fire. Humans must be considered not only as the most valuable, but also the most easily harmed item in the building. Normally, however, the occupants of business facilities are ambulatory and free to move, and can escape from fire with proper warning, means of emergency movement to safety, maintenance of reasonable life support (control of smoke), and knowledge or training in what to do in case of fire. For a detailed discussion on means of egress, see Section 6, Chapter 9.

SI Units

The following conversion factors are given as a convenience in converting to SI units the English units used in this chapter.

1 sq ft	$= 0.0929 \text{ m}^2$
1 Btu	$= 1.055 \text{ kJ}$
1 lb	$= 0.454 \text{ kg}$
$\frac{5}{9}(°F - 32)$	$= °C$
1 gal	$= 3.785 \text{ litres}$

Bibliography

References Cited

[1] "Fire Resistance Classifications of Building Constructions," Report No. BMS 92, Oct. 7, 1942, National Bureau of Standards, Washington, D.C.; "Combustible Contents in Buildings," Report No. 149, July 25, 1957, National Bureau of Standards, Washington, D.C.

[2] "Techniques for the Survey and Evaluation of Live Floor Loads and Fire Loads in Modern Buildings," NBS Science Series No. 16, June 1, 1966, National Bureau of Standards, Washington, D.C.

NFPA Codes, Standards, and Recommended Practices (see the latest *NFPA Publications and Visual Aids Catalog* for availability of current editions of the following documents)

NFPA No. 70, National Electrical Code.

NFPA No. 80A, Recommended Practice for Protection of Buildings from Exterior Fire Exposures.

NFPA No. 101, Code for Safety to Life from Fire in Buildings and Structures.

Chapter 7

INDUSTRIAL OCCUPANCIES

The potential for loss of life from a fire in an industrial occupancy is directly related to the fire hazard risk of the industrial operation or process. Fire records show that the majority of industrial fires that result in multiple fire deaths are the result of: (1) flash fires in highly combustible contents, or (2) explosions involving combustible dusts, flammable liquids, or gases.

Although annual industrial fire losses constitute a high percentage of the total national fire loss from a property standpoint, such fires have not, as a general rule, resulted in extensive life loss. A number of favorable operating features common to industrial occupancies contribute to this. Continued emphasis on good exit design and day-to-day attention to industrial safety and training programs can help to continue this trend.

A. General Design Considerations

One of the major elements of an industrial building occupancy life safety system is the widespread utilization of automatic sprinkler protection. Originally developed for industrial property protection, the automatic sprinkler has also been largely responsible for an excellent life safety record in industrial occupancies. This record has been recognized and further extrapolated by fire protection engineers and fire authorities as evidenced by the recent widespread adoption of automatic sprinkler systems specifically designed for life safety protection in buildings with extensive life safety exposure. Automatic sprinkler protection in industrial occupancies has been a principal factor in life safety through control of fire spread. Limitation of fire size by operation of sprinklers provides sufficient time for safe evacuation of personnel exposed to fire. The extent of contribution of the automatic sprinkler in industrial occupancy life safety can only be fully evaluated when it is recognized that the industrial plant includes a wide severity of fire risk due to a variety of processes and product related hazards. (For further discussion on fire protection engineering of industrial processes, see Section 4 of this HANDBOOK.)

Population Characteristics

Occupants and employees of industrial buildings are generally ambulatory and fully capable of quick response to fire situations, as well as being able to rapidly exit once properly alerted. To capitalize on this employee capability, many industrial plants include life safety measures in their emergency preplanning. A well thought out preplan provides a valuable tool for helping to prevent loss of life. Provisions which should be included in the emergency preplan include measures for alerting employees, identification and posting of exit routes, establishing of group assembly areas for evacuees outside the building, plus procedures for determining if all employees have safely exited. Responsibilities are usually established in the preplan to insure that necessary tasks to facilitate safe exiting of the building are accomplished. The preplan should be routinely evaluated by simulated fire exercises and fire drills. It is only through such drills that weaknesses in the preplan can be recognized and the plan modified.

Modern Design Practices

Although life safety experience in industry has been relatively good, a major problem may be emerging with the trend to construct larger industrial plants housing hazardous operations. The introduction of new materials, such as extensive quantities of plastics, has increased the need for additional life safety measures to help insure employee safety from fire. The modern industrial building has compounded the life safety exposure to employees from fire. Compared with industrial buildings of the early twentieth century, the modern industrial complex places a larger number of employees in a more complex and increasingly hazardous environment. This trend has increased the need for industrial management to concentrate on life safety principles not only during design but during day-to-day plant operations.

B. Fire Brigades

Most industrial firms include in the employee training program an orientation in the use of first aid fire fighting equipment such as in-plant standpipes, hose, and fire extinguishers. Industrial training of this type, where fully utilized, has resulted in a major reduction in fire loss and loss of life. Although first aid fire fighting measures are primarily a property protection measure, there is also a significant life safety benefit. In any fire situation where fire progress is checked through effective employee action, employee life safety is also provided. If fire spread is restricted to the incipient stages, there is no life safety exposure of major significance. (For a more extensive discussion of industrial fire brigades, see Sec. 10, Chap. 3.)

C. NFPA Life Safety Code Requirements

To a great extent, NFPA No. 101, Life Safety Code, hereinafter referred to in this chapter as the NFPA Life Safety Code, was developed from a review of past catastrophic events resulting in an approach to building design and operations which, if properly applied, reduce the potential for loss of life from fire. Industrial buildings of modern design have not, as yet, accumulated a major loss of life experience from fire. When fully incorporated, the measures in the NFPA Life Safety Code are sufficient to insure against major loss of life from industrial plant fires.

In order to properly arrange the exit facilities of an industrial occupancy, the plant life safety risk should be fully evaluated. From this evaluation, the exit facilities and protection for employees from the effects of fire can be properly designed to insure the necessary degree of employee life safety.

D. Industrial Occupancy—the Risk to Life Safety

In order to properly design exit facilities for an industrial plant, the occupancy must first be classified for relative degree of fire and life safety risk. Operations involving low or ordinary hazard materials, processes, or contents are classified as general industrial occupancies for exit planning purposes. Where high hazard materials, processes, or contents are housed in the building, the occupancy is classified as a high hazard industrial occupancy. Examples of a general industrial occupancy include electronic and metal fabrication operations, textile mills, automobile assembly operations, steel mills, and clothing manufacturing operations. It should be noted that incidental high hazard operations, such as a paint spray booth or flammable liquid storage room in a low or ordinary hazard occupancy, do not classify the entire building as a high hazard occupancy. Examples of a high hazard occupancy include paint and chemical plants, explosives manufacturing, grain or other combustible dust handling operations, plus any operation involving extensive quantities of flammable or hazardous materials.

Occupancy classification is necessary because the same life safety risk does not occur in all industrial occupancies. Once so classified, the exit facility design can be made using the basic design principles set forth in the NFPA Life Safety Code.

Some low and ordinary hazard industrial operations involve the use of extensive machinery or equipment which occupies a majority of the available floor space. In such instances the entire building need not be evaluated for exit purposes, since there are few people in the building. In a special purpose building, exits need only be provided for the actual number of employees in the structure.

E. Means of Exit Design Requirements

Requirements in the NFPA Life Safety Code for arrangement of means of egress in industrial occupancies include many of the features required in any structure. The travel distance to an exit in a general industrial occupancy is 100 ft, except where the building is completely protected by an automatic sprinkler system. With automatic sprinkler protection, travel distance may be increased to 150 ft.

In large industrial buildings, the 150 ft travel distance may not be possible without major renovations in building arrangement, especially in large volume structures. In such cases, exit facilities consisting of exit tunnels, overhead passageways, or travel through fire walls utilizing horizontal exits will provide the necessary safeguards. In unusual situations the use of additional precautions may be permitted to allow for increased travel distance of up to 400 ft. In such cases, the contents should be limited to low or ordinary hazard in a general industrial or special purpose occupancy. Additional provisions required for increased travel distance should include, as a minimum, the following:

1. Only one-story buildings should be considered.
2. Interior finish should be limited to Class A or B.
3. Full emergency lighting should be provided in the building.
4. An automatic sprinkler or other automatic fire extinguishing system should be installed and be fully supervised for malfunctions, closed valves, and water flow or operational alarm.
5. Smoke and heat venting or other engineered means to limit spread of fire and smoke is necessary. The system design should insure that employees will not be overtaken by heat or smoke within 6 ft of floor level before reaching the exits.

In high hazard industrial occupancies the travel distance to an exit is reduced to 75 ft. The shorter travel distance insures that employees can reach the exit rapidly when exposed to fire in hazardous materials or processes. A common path of travel of 50 ft to two separate exits in a general

industrial occupancy is allowed. There is no allowable common path of travel in a high hazard industrial occupancy. Regardless of size, every high hazard occupancy is required to have at least two separate and remote exits.

Illumination of the Means of Egress

Emergency lighting has become more important in industrial occupancies, particularly with the increasing popularity of windowless structures encompassing large floor areas. Equally important is illumination of the means of egress, especially in emergency conditions. Where a building is only occupied in daylight hours and the means of egress is fully illuminated by means of skylights, windows, or other means of natural lighting, the normal electrical illumination may be waived. In special purpose industrial occupancies where routine human habitation is not the case, exit illumination and emergency lighting may also be omitted.

F. Protection for Life Safety in Industrial Occupancies

As a general rule, vertical openings are fully enclosed in industrial occupancies. The enclosure may be omitted from vertical openings which are not used for exit purposes in buildings with low or ordinary hazard contents protected by an automatic sprinkler system. Another exception to the requirement for enclosure of openings is in specially designed industrial buildings housing operations, processes, or equipment requiring openings between floors. Should this be the case, each floor connected by the openings should be provided with exits, such as enclosed stairways, which are fully protected from obstruction by fire or smoke in the interconnecting floors.

Due to the size and complexity of most industrial structures, a fire alarm system is a necessity to insure prompt and effective action. The fire alarm system should alert responsible persons in a continuously manned location so that positive steps are promptly taken to start fire fighting, employee evacuation, shutdown of hazardous processes, and other action as needed to limit the fire and life safety hazard. In high hazard occupancies, the fire alarm system should also sound an alarm to immediately notify employees to evacuate the building.

High hazard industrial occupancies present a unique fire control problem and a severe life safety hazard. High hazard industrial occupancies, operations, or processes should have automatic extinguishing systems or other equally effective protection, such as explosion venting or suppression, to minimize the life safety hazard. The protection system should be sufficient to allow occupants to escape before being exposed to a fire or explosion.

In general industrial occupancies with less than 100 persons, or 25 persons normally above or below the street level, the fire alarm system may be waived.

Bibliography

NFPA Codes, Standards, and Recommended Practices (see the latest *NFPA Publications and Visual Aids Catalog* for availability of current editions of the following documents)

NFPA No. 6, Recommendations for Organization of Industrial Fire Loss Prevention.
NFPA No. 8, Recommendations for Management Responsibility for Effects of Fire on Operations.
NFPA No. 27, Standard for Private Fire Brigades.

NFPA No. 63, Fundamental Principles for the Prevention of Dust Explosions in Industrial Plants.

NFPA No. 101, Code for Safety to Life from Fire in Buildings and Structures.

NFPA No. 601A, Standard for Guard Operations in Fire Loss Prevention.

Reference Cited

Industrial Fire Brigades Training Manual, National Fire Protection Association, Boston, 1968.

SECTION 9

PUBLIC FIRE PROTECTION

Chapter 1

FIRE DEPARTMENT ORGANIZATION

The purpose of this section is to provide a discussion of the various elements that comprise public fire protection, starting with a brief history of the organization of fire departments. Historically, there were no reliable references to fire protection organizations until civilizations were well advanced.

A. History of the Organization of Fire Departments

Presently there are many types of public fire department organizations in existence, and most public fire protection is normally, although not necessarily, a function of local government; i.e., town, city, municipality, county, organized fire district, state, or province. The organization and objectives of public fire departments vary according to resources available, and range from simple to complex. Today, there are approximately 25,000 fire departments in the United States and Canada.

Public fire departments have evolved from five kinds of community effort toward fire protection:

1. Establishment of a night watch service.
2. Drafting of fire prevention regulations and appointment of fire protection officers.
3. Efforts to salvage building contents from loss by fire.
4. Appointment of fire fighting officers and personnel.
5. Organization of voluntary fire fighting companies.

Early Fire Protection and Fire Regulations

Possibly the first organized fire protection occurred when Augustus became ruler of Rome in 24 B.C. A "vigile" or watchman service was created, and regulations for checking and preventing fires were issued. Night patrolling and night watch forces were the principal services, and some of the vigiles had duties more like those of police or soldiers than fire fighters. It is clear from the history of that period, however, that fires were a major problem and that the vigiles were provided with fire fighting tools and equipment (buckets, axes, etc.).

One of the earliest recorded fire protection regulations came about in the year 872 in Oxford, England, when a curfew was adopted requiring that fires be extinguished at a fixed hour in the evening. After 1066 William the Conqueror established a general curfew law in England. This law appears to have been enforced not only as a fire prevention measure, but also as a means of preventing revolt.

Probably the first enactment on a fire prevention subject not related to buildings was initiated in 1566 in the city of Manchester, England, when an ordinance requiring the safe storage of fuel for bakers' ovens was put into effect. A Parliamentary Act in 1583, the first state action in England, forbade tallow chandlers to melt tallow in dwelling houses. After the London fire in 1666 a complete code of building regulations was adopted; however, commissioners to provide enforcement were not appointed until 1774.

On a world-wide basis, the early development of public fire protection regulations and types of public fire department organizations closely parallel those of Great Britain and the American Colonies, as described in the following material.

Fire Brigades in Great Britain

Great Britain did not provide statutory authority to units of local government for night or other watchmen with fire apparatus until 1830. Blackstone's *History of the British Fire Service*[1] mentions only two cases where the subject came up in England before the establishment of civil police forces. One was during the British Civil War in 1643 when a company of fifty women was organized to patrol the town of Nottingham at night.

In England, fire insurance companies were started primarily as a result of the London fire in 1666. The insurance brigades formed by the insurance companies were without statutory authority or obligations, and the insurance company offices, not the government authorities, decided where the brigades would be located. In London in 1833 the insurance office fire brigades were consolidated into the London Fire Engine Establishment, which was taken over by the Metropolitan Fire Brigade in 1865.

It was not until Edinburgh's Fire Brigade establishment came into being in 1824 that public fire services began to develop modern standards of operation. A surveyor named James Braidwood was appointed chief of the brigade. He selected eighty part-time aids between the ages of 17 and 25 years, and required regular drills and night training. Braidwood wrote the first comprehensive handbook on fire department operation in 1830. His handbook included some 396 standards and explained, for the first time, the kind of service a good fire department should perform.

Fire Protection in Early America

Following a disastrous fire in 1631, the town of Boston adopted the first fire ordinance in the New World. The ordinance prohibited thatched roofs and wooden chimneys, and was enforced by the "board of selectmen." In 1648 New Amsterdam appointed five municipal "fire wardens" with general fire prevention responsibilities. This is often considered to be the origin of the first public fire department in North America.

In 1679, as a result of a conflagration that destroyed 155 principal buildings and a number of ships in Boston, building laws were adopted requiring stone or brick walls for buildings and slate or "tyle" roofs for houses. The 1679 conflagration also led to the establishment of the first paid municipal fire department in North America, if not in the world. Boston imported a fire engine from England and employed twelve fire fighters and a fire chief. From the start, Massachusetts adopted the practice of using paid municipal firemen on a call basis as contrasted with the unpaid volunteer fire companies that were later organized in other colonies.

Colonial communities required each householder to keep two fire buckets and, upon the ringing of church bells, to report to the scene of fires where lines formed to pass water from wells or springs. When fire engines were obtained, companies were organized to man the engines. As late as 1810, Boston citizens were subject to a $10 fine for failure to respond to alarms with their buckets. The laws in a number of states still impose penalties on citizens who refuse to assist in fighting fires upon orders from fire officers.

Fire wardens were appointed in Boston in 1711. With the members of their staffs, fire wardens responded to fires and supervised citizen bucket brigades. By 1715, Boston had six fire companies with engines of English manufacture.

Mutual Fire Societies: The first of a number of mutual fire societies was formed in Boston in 1718 when some of the more affluent citizens organized to assist each other in salvaging goods from fires in their homes or places of business. Their equipment was a bag in which to collect valuables, a screw driver, and a bed key. The bed key was an important tool, for with it beds could be disassembled and brought outside a burning building. About a century later, these fire societies became inactive when fire insurance became available to the more prosperous citizens. The mutual fire societies are often considered to have been the forerunners of the salvage corps.

Salvage Corps: After the principal cities of the United States organized paid fire departments with steam engines in the latter half of the nineteenth century, insurance interests formed salvage corps to reduce water damage at fires. While the insurance salvage corps did much to develop the techniques of salvage work, improved fire fighting procedures plus the increased expense of operation led to their disbandment. Today, public fire departments handle most salvage operations at fires.

Growth of Paid Departments: Lack of discipline in the ranks of volunteer fire fighters coupled with resistance to the introduction of steam pumping engines led to the organization of paid fire departments in the larger cities. Following serious disorders at fires, a paid fire department with horsedrawn steam pumpers was placed in service in Cincinnati on April 1, 1853. In 1855 two steamers were delivered to New York City, but the volunteer fire fighters would not use them. Ten years later the "Metropolitan Fire Department," using steamers, replaced New York's volunteers.

Early Fire Apparatus and Equipment

Most of the basic fire fighting tools and apparatus currently employed were developed and placed in service in the latter half of the nineteenth century, although some developments in the earlier part of the century foreshadowed the later progress.

First mention of the use of an engine capable of taking suction was in New York City in 1806. With the introduction of suction engines, fire cisterns were constructed in various parts of cities and towns much in the fashion that hydrants are now distributed. Primitive fire hydrants on public mains began to be installed in the 1830s and 1840s. Prior to that time there were some wooden water pipes with plugs at intervals which could be removed to obtain water for fire fighting. However, because hydrants were unreliable and were supplied by 3- or 4-in. mains, cisterns long remained a principal source of water for fire engines.

Fire Hose: The use of fire hose was a comparatively late development in fire fighting. Boston imported a few short lengths of leather hose from England in 1799. This permitted advancing the nozzle (which for 120 years had been mounted directly atop the pump) somewhat closer to the fire. Within a few years leather fire hose was being manufactured in Philadelphia, and hose reels were gradually added to fire department equipment.

In 1871, $1\frac{1}{2}$-in. fire hose was placed in service in Boston. Wovenjacketed rubber-lined hose was introduced to replace leather hose, and expansion ring couplings with clear waterways replaced the old couplings. Interest in hose thread standardization followed the fires in Chicago and

Boston in 1871 and 1872, but no significant progress was made until the NFPA was given the job of thread standardization following the Baltimore fire of 1904. The dimensions of the National (American) Standard for $2\frac{1}{2}$-in. hose threads were selected because 70 percent of the existing threads could be recut to the standard. In 1877 the Boston fire department repair shop installed water pressure relief valves on all fire engines, and shutoff nozzles were issued to fire companies so that for the first time hose operators could control water damage.

Apparatus: Boston, Detroit, and New York City had self-propelled steam fire engines in service in the 1870s, and steam fireboats were introduced in 1873. The first aerial ladders went into service in 1873 and could be extended to 97 ft. As a result of several accidents, the wooden "big stick" was generally limited to 85 ft and was equipped with ladder pipes. These ladders were manually raised. By 1882 water towers were in service for providing powerful streams on the upper floors of buildings. Spring-assisted aerial ladders came into use in 1905, and the power operated 100-ft metal aerials were introduced in the mid-1930s. The "Babcock" chemical engines, introduced about 1873, provided fast fire attack with $\frac{3}{4}$-in. hose. The Babcock hose thread became the standard booster hose thread.

By 1910 the introduction of automobile fire apparatus was well underway, and in 1914 the first NFPA standard on automotive fire apparatus was adopted. Pumper pressure-volume ratings were standardized at 120 psi net pump pressure, which was the case for some 40 years until the present 150 psi rating was established. The introduction of automotive fire apparatus gradually eliminated the separate chemical and hose wagons in many fire departments because each pumper could carry its own ancillary equipment. However, a number of fire departments replaced the hose wagon with a second pumper, greatly improving the efficiency of their engine or pumper companies.

Hydraulic Studies: Of lasting significance were the studies of fire service hydraulics by John R. Freeman, published in 1889 and 1891, and the studies by Boston city engineer William Jackson in 1893. Freeman measured flows from nozzles, friction losses in fire hose, and suggested the standard 250 gpm fire stream. His recommendations led to the almost immediate adoption of 3-in. fire hose by most of the leading fire departments. Jackson conducted detailed tests of pumper performance, water tower operation, and practical fireground layouts with both $2\frac{1}{2}$-in. and 3-in. hose using various sizes of nozzles, resulting in improved fire fighting procedures.

Alarm and Extinguishing Systems: A fire alarm telegraph system was installed in Boston in 1851, and by the time the telephone was introduced in 1887 fire alarm systems were in widespread use. By the end of the nineteenth century automatic detection and alarm systems and automatic sprinkler systems were becoming increasingly common and were adding to the efficiency of fire departments.

Duty Systems and Training

Until World War I, paid members of fire departments worked a continuous duty system with only limited amounts of time off. By World War II, most paid fire departments had adopted some form of the two-platoon system which made allowances for additional days off and reduced the average number of hours worked per week. The hours worked per man has continued to decline, although in most cities the hours worked per week are still greater than in private industry or other lines of municipal employment. Although many fire fighters still continue to work 24-hour duty shifts, federal legislation implemented in 1975 is expected to have a significant impact on the working hours of fire fighters.

In 1889 the Boston Fire Department established the first drill school where probationary men were required to complete thirty days of basic training, and uniform company drills were established. New York City established a school for training fire fighters in the use of "pumper" or scaling ladders and related equipment. This was followed by the establishment of an engineers' school for the training of pump operators. Today most departments provide some degree of training for personnel.

In 1914 New York City established a "Fire College" for advanced officer training, and during that same year the first state fire school was organized in North Carolina. In 1925 Illinois and Iowa started state fire schools for the training of volunteer fire fighters. By 1950 most states were providing systematic fire service training. In 1937 Oklahoma A & M College (now Oklahoma State University) initiated a two year college program in fire protection. The initial objective of the program was to provide trained individuals for the fire service; however, the emphasis was later shifted to the industrial and insurance aspects of fire protection. Currently, there are approximately 200 to 250 institutions in the United States offering two year programs in fire protection. Two four-year programs (the University of Maryland and Illinois Institute of Technology) offer a full curriculum in fire protection engineering.

Post World War II Developments

Two of the most significant advances since World War II have been the widespread adoption and use of adjustable spray nozzles and radio communications.

Fire attack techniques have been improved through the use of preconnected attack lines and turret nozzles. Larger water tanks on pumping apparatus, and larger pumper-tankers have increased the efficiency of departments operating in locations that are remote from water sources. The increased availability and use of large diameter hose of lightweight construction has enabled fire departments to move larger volumes of water with greater efficiency.

In 1960, elevating platform apparatus was introduced into the fire service. To date there has been widespread acceptance of this type of apparatus. One manufacturer has designed an elevating platform capable of extending to 150 ft.

More recent developments include: the use of computers for record keeping, plotting, and assisting in dispatching; pumpers designed to allow nozzle operators to control the rate of flow from the nozzle; telescopic booms mounted on standard pumpers; and water additives that reduce friction loss in hose streams, thus allowing greater amounts of water to be moved through smaller diameter hose lines at normal operating pressures.

Developments in personal protective equipment for the fire fighter have been, and are continuing to be, made. Examples are protective clothing made from noncombustible materials, improved design of breathing apparatus, and newly designed head protection.

Many fire departments have recognized the need for better and stronger fire prevention and building codes, increased fire prevention, and public education activities. Good fire investigation is also receiving more emphasis.

B. Fire Department Objectives

The foundation of any organization is a set of sound objectives that provide both purpose and direction to the organization. Fire departments, as organizations, are no exception, and must establish valid objectives in order to perform effectively. The traditional objectives commonly accepted by most fire departments are:

1. To prevent fires from starting.
2. To extinguish fires.
3. To prevent loss of life and property when fire starts.
4. To confine fire to the place where it started.

These objectives, whether documented or implied, are likely to be the only objectives of many fire departments. All four are presented here as broad, general statements that are not definitive in terms of achievement or performance. To be more meaningful, objectives should be performance oriented.

Each fire department, regardless of size, should develop a set of performance objectives that specify goals to be achieved, the results expected, and the period of time required for achievement. The following material explains a system for developing performance objectives and their related enabling objectives. The procedure for developing objectives and the examples given are a brief overview, given for illustrative purposes. Those desiring to use this concept are advised to consult specific texts on the subject of management by objectives.

Developing Performance Objectives

The first step in developing performance objectives is to determine the purpose of the organization and why it exists. This should be done not only for the department as a whole, but for each operating division or section. When determined, these items should show the relationship between the department and each of its operating divisions, and the relationship between the divisions. An example of how this may be done is to make lists with standard headings such as: "The Fire Department exists for the purpose of," "The Fire Suppression Operations Division is currently responsible for," "The Fire Prevention Division is currently responsible for," etc.

The next step is to develop a list of responsibilities. Each operating division should be asked to develop a list of its current responsibilities and activities. The responsibilities listed should be specific. Once complete, this list should indicate where there is overlapping or where there are deficiencies in areas of responsibility. This information may be listed in tabular form, as in the following example. The example shows only two operating divisions. Additional headings should be provided for each operating division within the department.

The Fire Suppression Operations Division is currently responsible for:	The Fire Prevention Division is currently responsible for:
1. Suppressing Fires	1. Fire Prevention Code Administration
2. Rescue	2. Building Plans Review
Current Activities Are:	Current Activities Are:
1. Pre-fire Planning	1. Public Fire Prevention Education
2. Training	2. Inspections of all Educational Occupancies

The third step is to write a series of statements that describe desired goals. These statements should be expressed in terms that describe definite and measurable goals, and should describe in detail what the department or division would like to achieve. It is important that the statements developed be realistic and achievable. Statements that extend beyond the scope or resources of the department may be meaningless unless they are properly labeled as long-range goals. Most departments or operating divisions should prepare not one, but a series of statements. Following are two examples of such statements:

1. Fire Suppression Operations Division—Each company will conduct an inspection of all target hazards in their first duty area.

2. Fire Prevention Division—Design and develop a fire prevention curriculum and resource material for implementation at the third grade elementary level.

Once the divisions have determined their desired goals, an evaluation should be made by comparing what is currently being done with what has been proposed. This comparison might indicate the need for a decision concerning present status and desired goals. Perhaps the extra effort needed to achieve the desired goals may not be productive, and in many cases there might be gaps between present and desired levels of performance. It is in these areas that priorities should be assessed in order to establish realistic objectives. For example, in the Fire Prevention Division example, the stated goal is the designing and developing of a fire prevention curriculum for third grade elementary school students. Assuming that there is currently a fire prevention program at the third grade level and that there are other goals desired by the Fire Prevention Division, it may not be feasible to channel resources into this effort at this time; the third grade curriculum might well be terminated or set aside as a long-range goal.

In the example for the Fire Suppression Operations Division, the stated goal is that all companies will conduct inspections of all target hazards in their first due area. Are the companies currently doing this? If not, and if it has been decided that all companies will accomplish this goal, then enabling objectives that explain *how* to achieve this goal must be established in order for it to become a performance oriented objective.

Enabling objectives must be measurable, a standard of performance established, and a definite period of time set. If the enabling objectives are not expressed in quantitative terms, they will be of little value since there will be no means of measuring the performance necessary to achieve the overall objectives or goals.

The chart on page 9-4 illustrates one method of listing the steps for the Fire Suppression Operations Division to achieve its desired objective, and shows how objectives are subdivided when more than one division is involved.

Management by Objectives

Once specific objectives have been established, consideration should be given to the possibility of developing a more functional operating system than the current one. This requires that the specific steps necessary to achieve results must be identified, the problem areas determined, details of what is going to be done must be planned, and a time sequence programmed. It is important that time deadlines be set at various points so that programs and procedures may be monitored and schedules met.

To establish a possibly more efficient operating system, it should first be determined whether or not the present system has the capacity to do what is desired. Based on this decision, changes in the present system may be necessary. For example, using the previous Fire Suppression Operations Division as an example, if it has been decided that all companies are to conduct inspections of target hazards in their first due area, the following questions might be asked:

1. Does the present system have the capacity to do this?
2. Have the fire fighters been trained in inspection techniques?
3. If not, what training is required?
4. Does the training division have the time and resources to conduct this training?
5. How long will the training take?

The answers to the preceding questions will help fill any existing gaps in the present system, and will help to identify key areas that need to be improved.

Next, specific enabling objectives for any changes and improvements should be written. The enabling objectives should be expressed in terms of how these changes and improvements are to be accomplished, and should be used as the basis for revising the present operating system or for establishing a new system.

Before the overall program can be completed, objectives for individual positions within the system must be developed. These objectives must also be specified in terms that are performance oriented, measurable, and a time limit should be established for their completion. In this way each individual will know what is expected and the amount of time allowed for completion.

Examples of two individual objectives for the Fire Suppression Inspection Project involving more than one division are as follows:

1. Fire Suppression—Each company officer will arrange for and ensure that the target hazards in each first due area are inspected starting in January of the next calendar year. Each company will submit weekly progress reports on the inspections completed, and the completed inspection forms. All inspections will be completed prior to the last day of March.

2. Training—The training officer will design and develop a training course for suppression personnel on the techniques of inspecting target hazards. The training course will include all items necessary for the identification of potential hazards and recommendations for their elimination based on the fire prevention code and nationally recognized good practices. Progress reports on course development will be submitted weekly to the chief of training. All work will be completed prior to the last day of October.

Finally, it is necessary to continuously monitor results at timed intervals as specified in the objectives. Monitoring provides an opportunity for evaluation, and shows what is happening. There may be instances during evaluation when it becomes evident that some of the objectives that have been established are not realistic and may require change. Also, because some objectives may be above or below the capacity of the department, they may require change.

The process of managing an operating system by the use of performance objectives is not static. If good objectives are established, the process is dynamic and continuously changing. Constant feedback, realignment, changing, and adding objectives is required.

C. Fire Protection Organizations

The laws of most states and provinces in North America usually provide for the establishment of public fire protection organizations by local agencies of government, or establish special local agencies for providing fire protection. Normally it is the responsibility of local government to provide adequate fire protection, and the framework within which such protection operates.

Types of Organizations

The types of public fire protection organizations in existence are widely varied. One of the most common types found in most large municipalities is the public *fire department,* a department of municipal government, with the head of the department directly responsible to the chief administrative officer of the municipality.

Less common is a *fire bureau,* usually a division of a department of public safety. In this type of organization the public safety department head must divide his time between several important functions, including police and fire service.

The *county fire department,* an increasingly important type of fire force, has gained considerable acceptance in metropolitan areas. In this type of organization numerous small suburban municipalities can enjoy the benefits of a large, professionally administered public fire department with its staff and service facilities which, ordinarily, few small communities could individually afford. Frequently, this begins with a county fire prevention office and a fire communications system.

Another type of public fire service organization is the *fire district,* organized under special provisions of state or provincial law. It is, in effect, a separate unit of government, having its own governing body composed of commissioners or trustees, and is commonly supported by a district tax levy. Usually, it is organized following a favorable vote of the property owners in the proposed district. The fire district may include portions of one or more townships or other governmental subdivisions. Its fire force is frequently termed a "fire department," although in many cases it is the only department operated by that unit of government.

A fifth common type of fire-protection authority is the *fire protection district* which in some states is a legally established, tax-supported unit for the purpose of contracting for fire protection from a nearby fire department or even from a voluntary fire association. This type of organization provides the equivalent of municipal fire protection for rural or suburban areas that might find it difficult to maintain their own experienced and effective fire fighting forces. The fire protection district is often a means of providing a source of extra income and special rural fire apparatus for the small municipal fire departments that contract to supply fire protection.

An early type of public fire service organization is the *volunteer fire company* or *association* that raises its own funds by public activities and subscriptions, frequently with contributions of funds or equipment from interested units of government. Many voluntary fire associations maintain excellent equipment and stations, and also serve as centers for various community activities. Often, volunteer organizations prefer to retain their independence from government, especially when purchasing equipment, although in some instances the activities of independent fire organizations are coordinated through special associations and governmental advisory boards. It is not uncommon for several volunteer companies to join in providing fire protection for a sizeable municipality.

D. Fire Department Personnel

It is estimated that there are at least 185,000 paid personnel and more than one million call or volunteer personnel serving in the United States and Canadian Fire Services. The chief distinction between paid and call or volunteer personnel is that paid personnel are assigned regular periods of duty and are compensated on a regular basis. Call or volunteer personnel are not normally required to be available except for meetings, drills, and fires, and may or may not receive compensation for their services.

While most cities and towns of appreciable size, especially in the northeastern part of the United States, employ only paid personnel, some cities utilize auxiliary personnel to supplement their regular force. Other cities and towns may use combinations of paid, call, or volunteer personnel. Some communities maintaining their own fire departments may have a paid chief, officers, and apparatus operators, but rely upon call or volunteer personnel to provide the staffing balance necessary for efficient fire fighting operation. Other communities may use paid personnel only during normal daytime working hours and rely on call or volunteer personnel during the night.

The combinations of personnel utilized—paid, call, or volunteer—are strictly the choice of the community: what might work well for one community might not work well for another. There are a number of factors worthy of consideration that can influence the type of personnel utilized within a fire department. These factors are: (1) the financial resources of the community, (2) the availability of call or volunteer personnel, (3) the frequency of fire incidents, (4) the area served, and (5) the type of department preferred by the community.

Frequently the financial resources of many smaller communities will dictate that the department be composed entirely of volunteer personnel. Since salaries normally consume a large percentage of the fire department budget, the finances available may only be sufficient to purchase apparatus and equipment. Other communities with adequate financial resources may or may not elect to implement a fully paid service. This decision may be based on one or a combination of the factors described in the remainder of this Part of this Chapter.

Call or Volunteer Personnel

In some cases where the community is desirous of or in need of fire protection, there may not be a sufficient number of persons willing or able to serve in a volunteer capacity. This requires that the community finance the operation of either a fully paid or partially paid department. A situation of this type is probably most evident in the rapidly growing urban communities surrounding major metropolitan areas. Originally, these outlying areas were composed of small communities that provided a climate suitable for volunteer departments. As times changed, however, and these communities started to experience rapid growth rates in terms of population, housing, and ancillary services, the demands for fire protection services grew accordingly. The original nucleus of volunteers were unable to meet the increased demand or to recruit new members: often, persons moving into these areas did not care to serve as volunteer or call members of the fire department. Many residents commute out of the community on normal work days and are unavailable for fire department participation. Therefore, many of these once volunteer fire departments have undergone an evolutionary process and have added the services of paid officers, paid fire fighters, and paid fire prevention personnel.

Effect of Frequency of Incidents on Personnel Selection

The frequency with which the department responds to incidents will have a determining effect on the type of personnel chosen to staff the department. A department that responds to a large number of incidents each year will tend to inhibit a full volunteer operation unless the department has a large membership and the workload can be apportioned equally. There are no set figures on the number of incidents that require paid personnel. The determination must be made locally based on the ability of the department to perform at an acceptable level. It is reasonable to assume that when the number of incidents increases beyond the level that the volunteers are capable of handling, the members will request a change.

Area Served by Personnel

The area served is another factor that will have an effect on the staffing of the department. Large, congested, heavily populated areas are likely to produce an increased need for fire department services. Again, this would tend to inhibit the volunteer operation. More sparsely settled areas normally yield a fewer number of incidents, and therefore fewer demands on the department.

Type of Department Personnel Preferred by the Community

Communities often have preferences as to the type of staff members they wish to have serve in their fire departments. The preference may be based on one or several of the previous factors, or on entirely different reasons. In some instances the volunteer fire department serves as a focal point of community activity, and the community is satisfied with the level of service provided. It is the community that ultimately must decide on the type of personnel to be utilized within the department.

There are many fire departments—paid, combination, and volunteer—that provide an acceptable level of service to their respective communities. The success of their operations is not dependent upon whether the personnel are salaried or not, but upon the individual and collective ability to perform and to accomplish departmental objectives. There are no simple guidelines that set forth the requirements as to the type of personnel to be utilized. The decision is one that must be made at the local level following a careful analysis of all pertinent factors.

E. Fire Department Structure

Fire departments, like other organizations, are comprised of a group of people working together in a coordinated effort to achieve a common set of objectives (see Part B, this Chapter). In order for a department to function effectively, it must have an organizational plan that shows the relationship between the operating divisions and the total organization. An organizational plan does not preclude the necessity for active leadership; it merely provides the means by which the organization can be managed effectively. Organizational charts showing typical structures of small, medium, and large fire departments are shown in Figures 9-1A, 9-1B, and 9-1C.

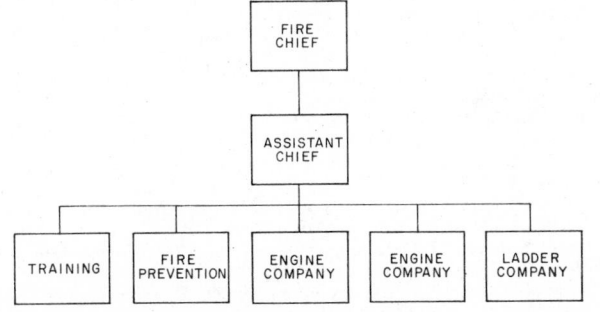

Fig. 9-1A. Typical organizational structure of a small fire department.

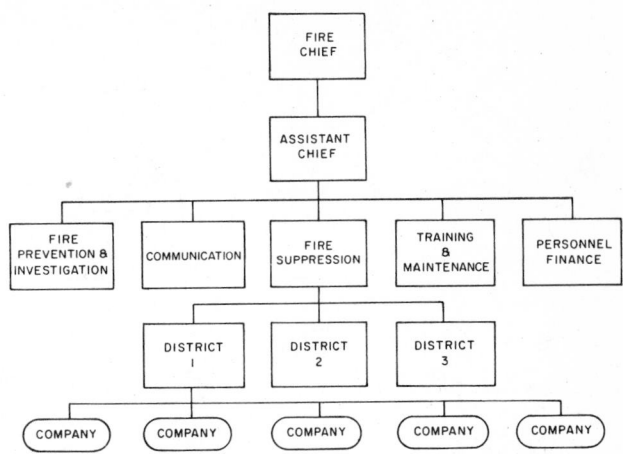

Fig. 9-1B. Typical organizational structure of a medium-sized fire department.

Principles of Organization

There have been many books written on organization and organizational principles. Although it is impossible to list all of these principles, the several that are generally applicable to fire department organizations are briefly described in the following material.

One of the first and most basic principles is that the work should be divided among the individuals and operating units according to a well arranged plan. The plan should be based on the individual functions that must be performed, such as fire prevention, training, communications, etc.

The next principle is that as the department increases in size and becomes more complex, there is an increased need for coordination. Small departments are simple organizations that allow frequent personal contact among individuals, thus little need for extensive coordination. However, as departments increase in size and become more complex they require more extensive coordination of the operating units in order to achieve their objectives.

Another principle is that lines of authority must be established. Each individual should know his relationship to the total organization, and each operational unit or division must know its relationship to the total organization. In many cases individuals are given the responsibility of performing certain tasks, but are not given the authority to make some of the decisions necessary to complete the tasks. This will restrict the performance of the organization since such individuals will need to constantly consult their immediate supervisors when decisions have to be made. When responsibility is assigned, authority must also be granted.

Unity of command in departmental structure is of prime importance in that an individual receiving conflicting orders from several superiors is likely to become confused and inefficient, while an individual receiving orders from only one superior will perform more efficiently. Also, the capacity to efficiently supervise becomes limited if there are too many individuals reporting to one supervisor. Supervisors having too many persons directly reporting to them tend to become involved in details, thus leaving themselves little time for additional managerial and supervisory duties.

Line Functions

Line functions in fire departments normally refer to those activities directly involved with fire suppression operations, and fire suppression directing officers are primarily considered to be line officers. This does not mean, however, that

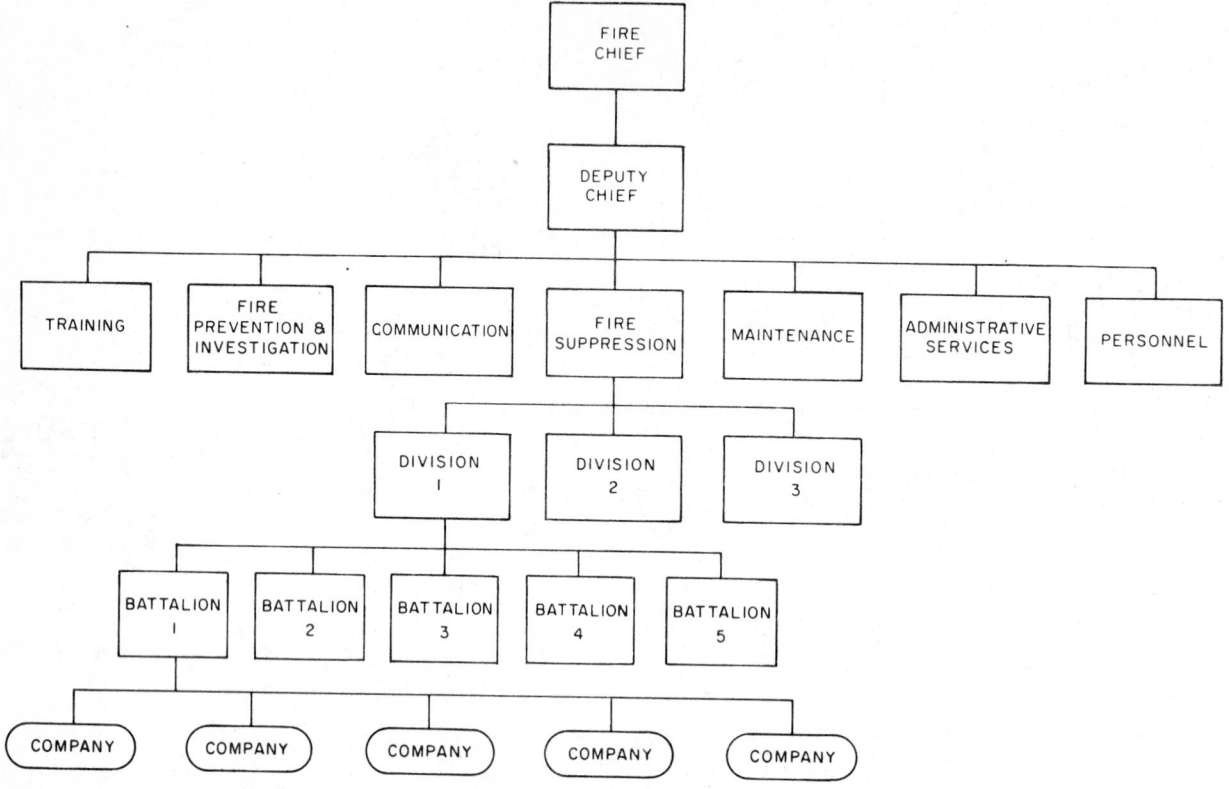

Fig. 9-1C. Typical organizational structure of a large fire department.

they do not have other functions. As these officers are promoted to higher levels within the department, their line responsibilities may be equally divided with staff responsibilities. At the highest officer levels within the department, line responsibilities diminish while staff responsibilities increase.

Staff Functions

Staff functions are those activities that do not involve fire fighting. When the department is divided into divisions or bureaus such as fire prevention, training, communications, maintenance, and personnel, a staff officer will usually be assigned to supervise each such division. Staff officers are normally not involved in line functions.

Organizational Plans

The manner in which fire departments are organized is dependent upon the size of the department and the scope of its operations. Organizational plans are designed to illustrate or show the relationship of each operating division to the total organization. It is essential that each fire department have an organizational plan that reflects the current status of the department. Some departments find projected plans useful for budgetary and planning purposes. A good plan is essentially a blueprint of the organization.

SI Units

The following conversion factors are given as a convenience in converting to SI units the English units used in this chapter.

1 in. = 24.4 mm
1 ft   = 0.305 m
1 psi = 6.895 kPa
1 gpm = 3.785 litre/min

Bibliography

References Cited

[1] Blackstone, G. V., "The Insurance Fire Brigades," *A History of the British Fire Service,* Routledge and Kegan, London, 1957.

NFPA Codes, Standards, and Recommended Practices (see the latest *NFPA Publications and Visual Aids Catalog* for availability of current editions of the following documents)

NFPA No. 4, Standard for Organization for Fire Services.
NFPA No. 4A, Standard for the Organization of a Fire Department.
NFPA No. 1001, Standard for Fire Fighter Professional Qualifications.

Additional Readings

Bennis, W. G., *Changing Organizations,* McGraw-Hill, New York, 1966.
Blau, P. M. and Scott, R. W., *Formal Organizations,* Chandler Publishing Co., San Francisco, 1964.
Caplow, Theodore, *Principles of Organization,* Harcourt Brace & World, Inc., New York, 1964.
Ditzel, P. C., *Firefighting,* Van Nostrand Reinhold Co., New York, 1969.
Etzioni, Amitai, *Modern Organizations,* Prentice-Hall, Englewood Cliffs, N.J., 1964.
Hickey, Harry E., *Public Fire Safety Organization: A Systems Approach,* National Fire Protection Association, Boston, 1973.
Holbrook, Donald, *An Unlikely Firemaster,* National Fire Protection Association, Boston, 1968.
Holzman, Robert S., *The Romance of Firefighting,* Harper & Brothers, Publishers, New York, 1956.
Kimball, Warren Y., *Fire Department Terminology,* National Fire Protection Association, Boston, 1970.
————, *Operation of Small Community Fire Departments,* National Fire Protection Association, Boston, 1968.
Kogan, Herman and Cromie, Robert, *The Great Fire: Chicago 1871,* G. P. Putnam's Sons, New York, 1971.
Likert, Rensis, *The Human Organization: Its Management and Values,* McGraw-Hill, New York, 1967.
Morriss, John V., *Fires and Firefighters,* Random House, New York, 1955.
Strong, Charles S., *Roll the Red Wagons,* Dodd, Mead & Co., New York, 1969.

Chapter 2

ADMINISTRATION AND MANAGEMENT

The fire service has many unique management problems. It requires a distinct team spirit; it has a need for a strong disciplinary influence due to the need for concerted and instant reaction on the fireground; it requires a high quality of leadership from its officers; it has a continuing training demand; it requires an extremely wide range of technical competence; it has a labor/employer relationship not comparable to that in other occupations; it requires an ability to deal with the public under both minor and major crisis situations. The fire service is not profit oriented, and has an obscure productivity pattern. It is a major consumer of tax dollars, uses costly equipment, is heavily dependent on manpower, and at present has no satisfactory means of measuring effectiveness in relation to cost. Despite these problems, the fire service has generally performed well for many years.

Almost all fire departments were administered by means of clearly defined organizational structures long before systems techniques were applied to industry and business houses. A system of task allocation to engine and ladder crews was developed whereby each man on the apparatus performed certain functions, in sequence, so that the team operated in action as a coordinated unit without duplication of effort or confusion. Step-by-step functions were determined for over 50 years in processes that are now termed "human engineering" and "factors application." Although only a part of the possible measurement of cost effectiveness, the fact that only about 20 percent of the fires dealt with result in a loss exceeding $500, and only about 500 out of one million fires extended to a loss exceeding $250,000, is significant testimony to the effectiveness of the fire service and its management.

A. Function of Management

The operation of a fire department is normally a function of local government (in the case of a fire district possibly the only function) which supports the service and is responsible for the level of service rendered. As with any governmental or business operation, this involves three major areas of responsibility: (1) fiscal management, (2) personnel management, and (3) productivity.

In general, fiscal management practices follow those used by the government agency supporting department and includes budgeting, cost accounting, personnel costs including payroll, and purchasing or procurement costs. The degree to which these factors are a direct responsibility of fire department management varies depending upon the practices of local government.

Fire departments utilize persons with specialized skills who are organized into various operational and staff units. Fire department management is involved to some degree in the recruitment, selection, and promotion of personnel needed to fill various positions in the organization. Very largely, these matters are governed by law, by personnel agencies including civil service authorities, and by direct decisions of the governmental agency operating the fire department. The assignment of available personnel to positions provided in the budgeted organizational structure, and supervision of personnel performance normally are the direct responsibility of the fire department management, although frequently certain assignments are governed by work contract agreements.

Productivity is the most difficult ingredient in the fire department service for management to measure. The basic objective is the protection of life and property. Modern practice involves two major activities: (1) control of hazards to minimize fire losses and to prevent fires, and (2) dealing with actual fires and emergencies to keep suffering and losses at a minimum. It is difficult to assess the number of fires and suffering that have been prevented by fire department activities except that experience has demonstrated that lack of effective fire prevention and control measures invites disastrous experiences. Likewise, the fact that most fires are suppressed with minimum losses and injuries does not indicate conclusively that an adequate level of fire department service has been provided because experience shows that major fires and emergencies often arise from combinations of circumstances beyond the immediate control of fire department management but which must be dealt with effectively to protect the public. It is imperative that fire department management be concerned with maintenance of reasonable standards of organization based upon local and national fire loss experience. Fire department management is responsible for maintaining highly trained and efficient operational units to perform assigned tasks both in the prevention and suppression of fires.

B. Personnel

Normally, the recruitment of personnel is seldom a paid fire department responsibility except in those cases where there is no local governmental personnel agency. Fire districts and volunteer departments recruit their own members.

It is the responsibility of fire department management to notify the personnel agency of vacancies which exist in the organization and to request the number of persons needed to fill these vacancies. In connection with recruitment, fire department management has three responsibilities. The first is to recommend to the personnel agency appropriate recruitment standards. So that staffing by competent persons such as those included in NFPA No. 1001, Standard for Fire Fighter Professional Qualifications, hereinafter in this chapter referred to as the NFPA Fire Fighter Qualifications Standard, be followed in order to obtain persons physically and mentally qualified to do the work. The second is to provide the basic training necessary for the new personnel so they can properly perform their assigned duties. The third is to certify after providing the basic training that the new members are ready for appointment as permanent fire fighters, or where individuals prove unable to perform satisfactorily, to recommend that their services be terminated before permanent appointment.

Selection of personnel must meet local, state, and federal standards. U.S. Courts have ruled previously that there must be no discrimination in hiring practices. Some rulings prohibit residency requirements for recruitment, although fire department rules of employment may stipulate that because of the emergency nature of the work employees must reside within a reasonable distance of the community. One court decision has ruled out examinations that require knowledge of fire department practices and equipment prior to appointment and in-service probationary training. Many states have adopted, or are in the process of adopting, minimum fire fighter qualifications standards.

The NFPA Fire Fighter Qualifications Standard is designed to be nondiscriminatory in that requirements are based upon performance criteria to do required tasks after appropriate instruction by qualified fire department instructors. Job-related tasks are set forth as performance objectives that are required of fire fighters. The Standard describes levels of competence based upon subsequent ability to do the work with decreasing levels of direct supervision.

In most jurisdictions applications for employment as fire fighters are obtained from a municipal personnel or civil service agency. In at least two states recruitment is handled by a state civil service commission. In either system, the fire department is furnished with a certified list of persons eligible for probationary appointment. Age requirements for appointment vary from a minimum of 18 years to a maximum of 35 years of age.

Fire Fighter Qualifications

With the cost of manning each position on fire apparatus round-the-clock ranging from $50,000 to $90,000 annually, it is imperative that all persons employed in the fire service be fully qualified and capable of efficiently performing the wide range of services necessary to the protection of life and property. Many states have enacted legislation establishing commissions on fire fighter standards which require that all personnel employed by fire departments must satisfactorily complete required basic training before being given permanent employment.

In 1970 the Joint Council of National Fire Service Organizations consisting of ten national organizations directly involved in various aspects of the fire service recommended that national fire service professional qualification standards for fire fighters be developed through NFPA committee procedures. The Joint Council established a National Professional Qualifications Board to supervise a nationally coordinated continuing professional development program for the fire service of the United States. The Board has nine members of whom two each are nominated by the International Association of Fire Fighters, the International Association of Fire Chiefs, and the National Fire Protection Association, and three by the Joint Council, collectively. The Board agreed that the desired professional qualifications standards should be developed through the NFPA standards making system, and that the secretariat for the committees and the Board would be provided by the NFPA staff. The Board reviews all draft standards before these are submitted to NFPA for final adoption.

In accordance with the objectives outlined, the NFPA has established four technical committees composed of peer-group representatives, each charged with developing specific areas of the fire service qualification standards. These are: Committee "A" Fire Fighter Qualifications Committee, Committee "B" Fire Inspectors and Investigators Qualifications Committee, Committee "C" Fire Service Instructors Qualifications Committee, and Committee "D" Fire Service Officers Qualifications Committee. These committees began the development of professional qualifications standards in their assigned subject areas early in 1973. It was recognized that of first priority was the Fire Fighter Professional Qualifications Standard, designated NFPA No. 1001, because standards for fire officers, training officers, and fire pre-

vention personnel are related to this base. This standard received final adoption at the NFPA Fall Meeting in Seattle in November 1974. These standards cover entrance requirements including medical examination, and three levels or grades of fire fighter qualifications known as Fire Fighter I, II, and III. Throughout the standards, levels of numerical ascending sequence have been used to denote increasing degrees of responsibility.

Fire Fighter I, at the first level of progression, has demonstrated the knowledge of and the ability to perform the objectives specified for that level, and works under direct supervision. Fire Fighter II, at the second level of progression, has demonstrated the knowledge of and the ability to perform the objectives specified for that level, and works under minimum direct supervision. Fire Fighter III, at the third level of progression, has demonstrated knowledge of and ability to perform the objectives specified and works under minimum supervision but under orders. The standards for officers cover various specified levels of officer qualifications and responsibilities including company level, and chief officers of various grades including specified assistant chiefs and departmental management chiefs. For more details concerning these levels, see Chapter 3, this Section.

All of the standards are expressed in measurable performance or "behavioral" objectives covering both required knowledge and demonstrated skills. The standards are prepared for use as a basis for nationally standardized examinations by authorized agencies, and are available for adoption by federal, state, and local authorities in the United States.

The establishment of standards and testing procedures do not, in themselves, ensure that all personnel will achieve the required level of competency, and the NFPA Fire Fighter Qualifications Standard is a professional qualifications standard and not a training standard. Training programs are necessary to prepare members of the fire service to acquire the skills and knowledge necessary to achieve the terminal performance objectives set forth for each grade. However, training should not be merely random but should be organized to prepare trainees to meet the specified levels of performance which should be demonstrated by performance testing as envisioned in the standard. (See Chapter 3, this Section.)

The U.S. Supreme Court decisions based upon constitutional prohibition of sex discrimination in employment has caused some women to apply for fire fighter jobs and has resulted in considerable publicity. Again, there is no place in the standards for discrimination. In connection with both racial and sexual discrimination, courts have ruled that height and weight requirements are discriminatory. However, candidates must demonstrate their ability to perform the required duties.

Fire fighting requires a major degree of physical strength, and an important factor is the interdependence of fire fighters on each other in fire suppression and rescue operations. If there is a great disparity of physical strength and endurance between members of a crew, then an unreasonable burden and strain is placed on those with most strength and stamina. This is not only dangerous to the fire fighter, but also adversely effects performance in the protection of the public.

In some jurisdictions the services of the fire department training division may be utilized in testing recruits and also in conducting promotional examinations. In all such cases, recognized standards such as the NFPA Fire Fighter Qualifications Standard should be followed carefully so that the results will not be subject to valid charges of discrimination, and so that the qualifications essential to the work will be tested adequately.

Promotional Practices

In the vast majority of fire departments, promotions to various officer ranks are made from personnel serving in the next lower rank or ranks. Promotional procedures are designed to take into account technical qualifications for the particular rank and fire department experience. It is essential that examination procedures in the civil service be fully competitive and nondiscriminatory. In general, as with initial appointments, promotional procedures are administered by personnel departments or by state or local civil service authorities. Usually such authorities employ the advice of persons who are experienced and knowledgeable about the particular job classification, including advice from fire chiefs, fire fighter organizations, and technical consultants. Normally, such advice includes guidance as to the relative weights to be given to the results of written examinations covering the technical qualifications, and to experience based upon seniority in prior grade. In some systems performance ratings are included, but these have tended to be vehicles for various forms of discrimination even though such discrimination may have been quite unintentional. Some supervisor's tend to be much more demanding than others when rating performance, and their subordinates often have less favorable performance grades than those of other employees who may actually be less qualified. For this reason performance ratings should be used sparingly in the promotional process. If performance has not been satisfactory, the matter should have been dealt with prior to the promotional process.

Some promotional practices also include an oral interview as part of the process. Again, this can easily become a vehicle for discrimination on the basis of race, color, or mannerisms, and few such oral interviews are scientifically designed or are professionally administered. Too often they have been vehicles by which an administration selects and rewards its friends and adherents. Therefore, increasing emphasis is being given to having candidates for promotion examined in writing regarding the required technical knowledge. A good outline of subject areas normally included in the duties of company officers and of chief officers of various grades is included in NFPA No. 4, Standard for the Organization for Fire Services. At this writing the NFPA Committee on Fire Officer Qualifications is preparing a detailed performance standard covering the qualifications that should be expected of fire officers of the various ranks. As this will require individuals to measure up to stated levels of professional competence that can be demonstrated by knowledge and performance, it should replace some of the less professional means of evaluating officer candidates.

The fire department administration, as an arm of the municipal administration, does have an important role to play in the promotional process. First, it must advise the personnel agency as to the qualifications required in any job or rank to be filled where such qualifications have not been previously established. Secondly, when a list of successful candidates for promotion is received from the personnel agency, it should advise the promoting authority regarding the promotions to be made. Usual practice is to fill vacancies from the top of the promotional list, except where the head of the fire department specifies in writing valid reasons for rejection of an individual. Such reasons might be a record of serious disciplinary problems including disobedience of written orders, frequent bad judgment when performing assigned duties, a record of conflicts with other employees, and other major personality defects. While such problems might not be serious enough to warrant severance from the present level of employment, they do indicate that the particular candidate, although technically qualified, would be less preferable than another candidate on the list. Personnel records should be available to substantiate any such reasons for rejection.

In a number of fire departments a specified number of years in prior grade is required before promotion. However, where there are not enough candidates in the next lower grade to make a competitive list, the examination may be opened to personnel in the lower ranks who have the required period of service.

Some fire departments include educational requirements such as a community college fire science certificate for all officers, or a college bachelor degree for chief officers. However, the majority base promotion on competitive examinations open to all members who have the required length of service, although educational credits may be included in the promotional process.

Personnel Records

A complete record must be maintained for each individual member of the fire department. Such records cover all pertinent facts of each member's fire service career from probationary appointment through retirement. If there is no personnel agency, the individual's record should contain the original application for employment or a copy. It contains all assignments, transfers, promotions, commendations, and records of disciplinary action. It is well for the record to include information on any special skills possessed by the individual which may be useful to the department, as well as education background including "fire science" courses and other courses completed that may be of value to the service. Dates of appointment and promotions are important because of the role played by seniority in fire department operations, and most fire departments maintain a seniority roster that includes all members from date of original appointment. Date of permanent appointment, the notation of date of qualification as a professional fire fighter under state or local standards, should be shown on the individual's record.

In addition to the general record of an individual's service, a training file should be maintained as covered in NFPA standards. This will show training periods and subjects in which the individual has received instruction such as apparatus operator, first aid, emergency medical technician, and fire instructor.

A medical history must be kept of each member, showing absences due to sickness and service connected injuries. The maintenance of the medical history may be the responsibility of the fire department medical examiner or "surgeon." Service connected injuries are important not only as they involve the safety record of the fire fighting occupation, but because they affect the pension rights of the individual. Nonservice connected injuries and sickness are in a different category, and fire fighters generally are allowed a specified amount of sick leave without loss of pay. However, by law, heart and lung problems are assumed to be service connected.

Duty records must be carefully maintained. Usually these begin with the daily company report prepared by the company officer on duty, and account for every individual assigned to the command indicating those on duty, off duty, on sick leave, on injured leave, or detailed to another command. Company reports are forwarded through the district or platoon chief who may be responsible for balancing the strength of the operating units if this responsibility is not assigned to a personnel officer.

Vacation schedules must be maintained. Usually individual members receive varying amounts of vacation, from two to four or more weeks depending upon the length of individual service, and may be entitled to additional leave sometimes including "lieu days" for holidays worked.

Individual payroll and work records are essential and must conform to federal requirements governing hours of work and overtime for fire fighters, as well as applicable state laws. In usual budgeting practice each rank or grade has a given budgetary or account number which is related to the basic annual, daily, and hourly rate of pay based upon a specified average number of hours worked per week. Very frequently there are step-grades within each rank based upon longevity in the rank, and often step-grades for longevity of service beyond the length of service required for the minimum pension. In addition, members are paid a daily or hourly rate for acting in a higher capacity, and are paid overtime for time worked filling in on other shifts for absent members or when called back or when held on duty because of fires and emergencies. In some fire departments there is a pay differential giving increased compensation for duty on the night shifts. All of these factors must be correctly recorded in payroll records.

Federal regulations specify time and one-half pay for overtime of all fire fighting personnel (full-paid or part-paid) beyond the permitted average work week. In some states the state law specifies time and one-half pay for working in excess of 40 or 42 hours per week. In other locations the straight rate is used for regular overtime not involving call back. Where off-duty members are called or respond to alarms as call fire fighters, a minimum overtime rate is specified. All such work, both regular assignments and overtime assignments, must be carefully recorded for payroll purposes. This includes the response and payment of part-time call fire fighters. Usually, the maintenance of such payroll records are the responsibility of the fire department administrative or fiscal officer, or an executive deputy chief, although the actual payroll generally is handled by the municipal accounting or finance department which issues the pay checks.

As with other payroll accounts in business, payroll records and payment checks must show deductions for state and federal income taxes, pension payments, social security taxes where applicable, local union dues check-offs, and contributions to charities authorized as payroll deductions. The employer must file the required tax records for each individual with the appropriate state and federal agencies, and furnish a copy of the annual record to each employee.

From the administrative point of view all payroll costs are charged against the authorized budgeted salary appropriation, except that it is usual to have a separate overtime account—especially in fire departments where it is official policy to maintain a stipulated minimum level of manning on duty through the use of overtime personnel. This allows the administration to evaluate the cost of overtime versus employing additional fire fighters for each shift.

C. Manning Practices of Fire Departments

With the standard 42-hour average work week (4 platoons), usually 2.5 fire fighters per 1,000 population protected are needed to provide 0.5 men on duty per 1,000 persons protected, or 4 men on duty for each 8,000 population. At this level of manning, a population of 24,000 is required to have a dozen officers and men on duty. Communities of less population would need off-shift response on first alarms or call fire fighters to provide a standard minimum first alarm manpower response. Chief officers and

their aides who perform regular fire duty are included in the manpower ratio, but chiefs do not count toward required fire company manning; also, allowances must be made for company officers who regularly act as relief chiefs.

Fire departments still operating on the 3-platoon system and where members have the same amount of time off from their regular shifts require 75 percent as much manpower as with the 4-platoon or group system. Thus 1.875 fire fighters per 1,000 population are needed to maintain 0.5 men on duty per 1,000 persons protected, assuming the same amount of vacation and sick leave absences.

A 1974 study of 25 fire departments working the 42-hour work week in a major metropolitan area showed a median strength of 3.0 fire fighters per 1,000 population. This provides an average of 12 officers and men on duty for 20,000 population. Where fire departments operate ambulances or rescue squads additional personnel are needed in order to maintain basic fire company manning. In some of the smaller communities the manpower ratio per population protected may be relatively high because of the need for sufficient on-duty personnel for effective initial attack and rescue operations, especially in "bedroom communities" where call personnel are not readily available daytimes and where there are substantial values to be protected that may be more significant than population ratios in determining the manpower to be provided.

Not only in suburbs, but in many core cities the fire departments must protect substantial concentrations of values that exceed the average values related to populations. For example, a core city of 80,000 persons may be the business center for an area of 500,000 persons as well as housing a high percentage of the low-income groups. The number of high-rise and large-area structures that must be protected and the frequency of alarms for fires and emergencies should be considered in determining the fire department manpower that should be on duty.

Where manpower levels are substantially below those levels previously listed, it is often found that there is an inadequate distribution of fire stations so that many response distances are excessive, that engine and ladder companies are undermanned, that there is a deficiency in ladder company or other types of truck company coverage, and that there is a deficiency in the distribution of chief officers. Some cities have organized manpower squads to supplement weak fire companies. In general, this is an unsatisfactory solution to the manpower needs because squads crews usually do not arrive in time to assist the first arriving companies which are unable to properly perform initial evolutions. Squad or rescue companies are a valuable supplement to properly manned engine and ladder companies but not as a substitute for such needed companies.

Some very large fire departments may operate with a lower relative strength per 1,000 population than cities of a more average size, because with high population densities they have sufficient companies to provide needed coverage while handling working fires. For example, a large city fire department may operate one engine company per 15,000 to 20,000 population and still have a large number of well distributed fire companies, whereas a city of 30,000 persons could not be properly protected with only two engine companies.

In many cases mutual aid companies provide an important part of the needed coverage by fire companies. Relatively few communities are large or wealthy enough to meet all of their potential fire company requirements with regularly assigned on-duty forces. Even large cities are making increased use of regularly assigned mutual aid response.

Often this is a practical matter as companies from neighboring fire departments may be much nearer to a fire location than some of the local fire companies.

Frequently it is impossible for small cities to fully man all of the fire companies needed for proper distribution of companies throughout the community as necessary for the handling of working fires. In many cases the population density and the values protected per square mile are relatively low. In such communities some engine companies may respond with only three men on duty, and ladder trucks with only two men. Such low levels of manning must be backed up promptly by off-shift or call response, or by multiple alarm response to fires that could be handled with a standard first alarm response. In some cases additional apparatus may be assigned to respond to off-set deficient company manning. Some fire departments elect to man more fire companies than needed for basic coverage, but to assign additional companies to each alarm. In communities of large areas with relatively low concentrations of value this may be an acceptable arrangement. However, in general, a minimum of 4 men on duty, including an officer, should be provided for each engine company where there is no assigned off-shift or call response on first alarms.

Part-paid, part-call, and volunteer fire departments are very common, even in some sizeable communities. At last count there were 507 paid fire departments with 22,045 full-paid members assisted by 30,192 paid on call or volunteer members. This does not include numerous volunteer departments with less than five full-paid members.

Public Fire Department Manning

In past years assignment of personnel for fire apparatus manning was poorly managed. A given number of officers and men, generally from 4 to 7 depending upon the supposed importance of the particular company, was assigned to each shift of each company with the hope that a sufficient number would be available to man the apparatus at all times. On-duty manning of fire companies varied with members on vacation, sick, injured, or due to rotating days off. When fire company on-duty strength fell below the level deemed the minimum for effective operations, a member was detailed from another company when possible, and in some cases companies were put out of service to keep others operating. Within a short period of days a given fire company might respond to alarms with anywhere from 3 to 6 men and with or without an officer. There was little attempt to equate company manning with work to be performed and ability to perform standard fireground evolutions. Operating efficiency varied considerably. However, fire fighter labor was relatively cheap so that wasteful and inefficient personnel practices were tolerated. Work weeks were extremely varied and many were difficult to administer on an efficient basis due to the practice of having a long nominal duty period for each shift or platoon, but reducing this by granting rotating days off to various members.

Faced by high personnel costs, modern management cannot tolerate such haphazard operations and inefficiency. The current approach has been to determine the essential positions in the fire fighting force that must be covered 24-hours a day and 365 or 366 days per year, and the total number of duty tours involved. With 24-hour shifts there is one duty tour per position per day. With 10-14 hour or similar tours of duty, there are two per day or 730 or 732 per year. The daily pay scale for each rank is determined whether a position is filled by the regularly assigned personnel or by members "acting" to cover absences.

For example, it is determined that a minimum force of

58 officers and men of the various ranks should be on duty at all times. With a standard 42-hour nominal average work week, working day and night shifts, each shift or group is on duty 182 or 183 times during a 365 day year (average 182.5 duty shifts per platoon). With 58 officers and men on duty, this requires 42,340 individual tours of duty per year. From review of fire department records it is found that with vacations, sick and injured leave, and other contractural absences, the individual members of the fire fighting force average not 182.5 but 146.5 tours of duty per year. The required 42,340 tours of duty divided by 146.5 tours worked per man shows that rather than 232 officers and men (4 shifts x 58 positions) 289 members actually are needed in the fire fighting force or 72 men per platoon to cover the normal absences that must be anticipated. Even with vacations carefully scheduled so that only one man from each shift of each company will be absent at any given time, there may be times due to sickness or injury when off-duty men must be used on an overtime basis; this is less expensive than carrying more relief men on the roster than required to maintain normal minimum manning. Overtime will be required when members are called back for major fires and emergencies; budget allowances should be made for this.

Years ago, it was customary to allow 10 percent for absences from assigned shifts due to vacations and sickness. Now the figure commonly is 20 percent or more. Vacations have been increased and work contracts provide for various other compensated absences from duty. An important factor has been the increase in injured leave resulting from reduced on-duty manning and increases in the number of alarms answered per company. With the reduction in work hours many cities have both reduced the number of fire companies maintained and the level of company manning on duty. At the same time, the number of fires and alarms has increased significantly in most fire departments so that runs per company have doubled or tripled. Thus, individuals on duty are exposed to much more potential injury than when there were more and stronger manned fire companies. The injury potential is increased further if chief officers are slow in calling additional fire companies to working fires. Accordingly, in some fire departments where minimum company manning has been reduced to 4 men, the work contract requires the dispatching of an additional fire company to alarms for structural fires to provide a safer minimum manpower level for initial fire attack.

The example given of a fire department requiring 58 officers and men on duty is based upon minimum effective manning of 8 engine and 4 ladder or platform companies grouped in 2 fire districts commanded by an on-duty chief with aides. The minimum manning for all companies is not less than 4 men on duty including the company officer. Two-engine companies operate hose trucks requiring operators, and two others operate water tankers in suburban areas also requiring an extra apparatus operator on duty. In addition, a 5-man minimum is maintained with two ladder companies in districts of high life hazard and more than average fire duty. To distribute the needed relief personnel, the platoon roster for each company carries one additional man above the minimum that must be maintained, and one relief officer is assigned to each district headquarters.

In a number of fire departments the minimum manning levels are not absolute. At times when there is an unusual amount of absence, stations housing more than one company may be allowed to operate one man below the normal minimum rather than to pay overtime unless the company minimum strength is specified by contract or city ordinance.

In general, a nominal 42-hour work week requires not 4

but 5 men per position. Thus, a 20-man company is needed to maintain an average of 4 men on duty. As this does not provide for 2 members being away from their shift at one time, details between companies, or overtime, may be needed from time to time.

With a fire department operating on the old 3-platoon system with 24-hour duty tours, each platoon covers 122 tours in 366 days (a leap year). To have 58 officers and men on duty requires a total of 21,208 tours. It is found from the records that the average member works 98 tours per year. Thus, 21,208 + 98 requires 216 officers and men, or 72 for each of the 3 platoons. However, with a 54-hour maximum work week permitted under federal labor law, each member working an average of more than 54 hours in each 4 week cycle would get 2 hours of time-and-one-half pay per week, except possibly when the work cycle is broken by absences.

Where 5 man minimum company manning is desired with the regular 42-hour work week, most fire companies have 24 officers and men assigned to the 4 duty shifts, and about every fourth company may have 28 men assigned. In some fire departments where more of the vacations are scheduled in summer months, a 4-man minimum may be maintained in the summer and a 5-man minimum company strength maintained in the winter. However, most fire departments prefer to maintain minimum manning year round rather than attempt to man for seasonal trends. If additional manning is needed during severe winter storms, this is done on a temporary overtime basis and thus does not add too significantly to the annual personnel budget, but is a part of the overtime account.

Minimum Manning: During recent years an increasing number of fire departments have established "minimum manning" levels for each fire company or each duty shift. In many fire departments it is policy not to operate engine or ladder companies with less than four men on duty, including an officer. In some cases, because of the population and values protected per company and the work load, the minimum established is five men on duty per company. Where a company member is sick or injured while another member is on vacation and no spare manpower is available to cover the absence, it is the policy to employ an off-duty member of the company on an overtime basis to maintain the essential minimum manning.

Even though state and federal labor laws or contract requirements may require payment of time and one-half for such overtime work, administrators often find it more economical to use personnel on overtime to cover absences from duty which exceed the average allowed for in the organization manning tables rather than to maintain additional men on each duty shift of each fire company to cover abnormal amounts of absence. However, in the past the manning tables of many fire departments made no allowance for covering scheduled absences, and fire companies were allowed to run shorthanded, thus seriously compromising their operating efficiency. Also, in a number of cases there has been a failure to allow for the usual amount of sickness and injury. On the average throughout the United States almost 50 percent of the fire fighters receive injuries annually which result in loss of time from duty. In one large busy fire department, an average of one member of each fire company is on injured leave at any given time; therefore, the manning tables necessarily include approximately 4 additional fire fighters per 100 employed just to cover anticipated injuries. Calculations should also include men on terminal leave and new recruits assigned to a specified period of basic training. Otherwise, the overtime costs may exceed the cost of having the needed number of men per shift.

Mandatory minimum manning levels for fire companies are advantageous both to the public and for the safety of personnel. Decisions by labor boards and by at least one court have found that minimum manning agreements or ordinances are reasonable requirements for the protection of the public and of personnel. A number of small fire departments which do not attempt to maintain minimum on-duty company manning have established a minimum for the duty shift while employing off-duty personnel to maintain their predetermined minimum effective strength, taking into account the apparatus that must be operated from the several fire stations before off-shift or call fire-fighters can arrive to assist.

Work Schedules: Work weeks for fire fighters average from 40 to 56 hours. In 1974 Congress amended the Fair Labor Standards Act to extend the Act's minimum wage, overtime, equal pay, and record-keeping requirements to most public agency employees, including fire and police departments. Only departments with less than 5 paid or part-paid employees are exempted. Pursuant to the Act, the Administrator of the Wage and Hour Division of the U.S. Department of Labor issued definitions and rules for what constitutes a work period. The work week used in the rules may be the average number of hours worked in a cycle not to exceed 28 days. The law requires payment of time and one-half for all hours worked in excess of that allowed. The rules require a progressive reduction in the average hours worked per week without payment of overtime from 60 hours on January 1, 1975 to 54 hours effective January 1, 1977; prior to January 1, 1978, the Secretary of Labor will determine whether the maximum hours allowed should be further reduced. The rules state that sleeping time of fire fighters on duty in fire stations is to be counted as part of the work time.

The limitation of fire fighters' average work week to 60 hours unless overtime was paid effective January 1, 1975 affected slightly under 7 percent of the nation's fire fighters who, prior to that time, had duty schedules averaging from 62 to 96 hours per week. Two-thirds of these were members of fire departments in communities having populations under 50,000, mostly located in the South and Southwest.

As of January 1973, 46.1 percent of the nation's fire fighters worked 54 hours or less, and 44.1 percent worked 55 to 58 hours. These figures do not include staff personnel, most of whom have long been on a 40-hour work week. Prior to the application of the Fair Labor Standards to fire fighters, most fire departments in the Northeast and in some other areas were working a 42-hour 4-platoon system. New York State had mandated a 40-hour work week. Practically all fire departments in Canada have had a 42-hour work week for a number of years.

At this writing the maximum number of hours in the average work week permitted without overtime was reduced to 58 hours. This affected some 2.9 percent more of the country's fire fighters. On January 1, 1977 when the number of hours that may be worked without overtime is scheduled to be reduced to 54 hours, an additional 44.1 percent who have been working a 56-hour week will be affected. In almost all cases, all other municipal workers have been working at least 16 hours less per week than these fire fighters. Thus, the Act will affect 53.9 percent of the country's fire fighters who were working excessive hours without overtime compensation prior to January 1, 1975.

Most fire departments working an average of more than 50 hours per week have used a 24-hour tour of duty. Most fire departments working 48 hours per week or less have day and night shifts. Most popular is the 10-hour day shift and 14-hour night shift; this plan varies from twelve 12-hour shifts to eight 16-hour shifts. The 54-hour average work week limitation scheduled to be effective January 1, 1977 does not necessarily mean that a 56-hour 3-platoon system will not be permitted. Many fire departments, where law requires a 40-hour week or payment of overtime, work a 42-hour 4-platoon schedule by paying 2 hours of overtime. Often this is considerably less expensive than hiring additional personnel, and better teamwork is maintained by keeping crews together on a regular 4-shift basis.

From time to the municipal administrators who are not knowledgeable about fire department operations have suggested that fire fighters be assigned to a 5- to 8-hour day, 40-hour per week work schedule similar to the police. This is neither practical nor desirable. On-duty police manning properly varies with time of day and day of week as required by needs for traffic control, patrolling, details, etc. Fire fighting is a team effort with the team including platoon chief officers, company officers, apparatus operators, and fire fighters working together on a regular basis. Serious fires occur at any hour of the day or night, and any day of the week; thus, constant uniform manning is essential as is provided by either the 3 or 4-platoon systems. These are readily scheduled in seven 24-hour or fourteen 10- and 14-hour tours of duty per week with either the 42-hour or 56-hour average work week. This may include a 40-hour pay week or a 54-hour pay week with 2 hours of overtime. When the 168-hour calender week is divided by 8-hour tours, this requires 21 work shifts which cannot be scheduled on a uniform basis with even platoons. To implement an 8-hour schedule, company officers would regularly be paid as acting chiefs, and fire fighters would be paid as acting company officers (in addition to usual vacation coverage); all semblance of platoon teamwork and assigned responsibility would be completely destroyed with no advantage to the community or to the employees, and generally with increased cost. In most instances where the 8-hour schedule has been proposed, it has appeared only as a bargaining weapon to counter employee demands for better compensation; invariably it has been rejected.

In the entire United States there are only about two dozen fire departments using an 8-hour work shift. With a few exceptions these are places with volunteer departments which employ a few paid men five days per week, while the volunteers are engaged at their regular employment.

In establishing the maximum work weeks for fire fighters, the government has recognized its responsibility for sharing the cost. Every city and town receives an annual governmental "revenue sharing" grant to help with municipal expenses; these funds are being increased. The Federal Revenue Sharing Act specifically mentions "fire protection" as an authorized use for these substantial funds. Many municipalities regularly allocate the funds toward their fire department personnel budget.

One effect of the federal rules governing maximum hours worked by fire fighters is that overtime must be paid when men are called back to assist at major fires or to cover fire stations if the overtime worked exceeds the permissible average work week. Experience in a number of states which previously have required payment of time and one-half for overtime indicates that call-back is far less common than when fire fighters' labor was free whenever an "emergency" such as a multiple alarm occurred. Where previously all off-duty personnel or an entire off-duty shift was recalled, present practice is to contract for a standby force sufficient to man reserve apparatus when needed with perhaps a maximum of a dozen men being on call at any given time.

Also, the requirement for overtime has resulted in improved mutual aid arrangements because on-duty companies from nearby departments can respond much faster than off-shift local personnel, and overtime costs are kept down. However, many small fire departments rely heavily upon off-duty response on an overtime basis. Usually, a minimum of 2 and often 4 hours overtime pay is guaranteed for each response. Where alarms for structural fires are not too frequent, it may be much more economical for a small municipality to contract for overtime response than to provide full on-duty fire company manning around the clock. For example, a typical small fire department with 9 officers and men on each duty shift may contract to have one off-shift respond to first alarms for structural fires. If proper records are kept (which are required for payroll purposes), the department would be credited under the insurance grading schedule with having 3 additional men responding, and there would be additional credit for mutual aid response and for additional off-shift response to multiple alarms.

It is poor management not to arrange for regular off-shift response when needed. Some fire departments, rather than pay overtime, call in rural and suburban volunteer companies. This practice often results in delays in getting needed manpower, and these outside companies generally operate their own apparatus rather than provide the men needed on the first alarm companies. Some work contracts require that local off-duty personnel must be called whenever non-scheduled outside response is called to a fire.

Manning of Volunteer Fire Departments

A substantial part of the population of both Canada and the United States is in communities that cannot support a fully paid or even a partly paid fire department. Therefore, volunteer fire departments are essential to providing needed public fire protection throughout vast areas of both countries. According to the 1970 U.S. Census, 73.5 percent of the nation's population is located in urban communities. However, the Census classification of "urban" includes all places of 2,500 or more people. Only 46 percent live in communities large enough to support a paid fire department with a recommended minimum of a dozen fire fighters on duty. Many of these communities are in metropolitan areas that are served by county rather than municipal fire departments, or they cover such extensive territory that it is necessary to operate a number of fire stations and fire companies so that concentrations of paid on-duty manpower are not possible. At the last count, approximately 10 percent of the fire departments in the United States served communities having populations of 10,000 or more, approximately 18 percent protected communities having populations of from 2,500 to 10,000, and over 72 percent of the fire departments served communities having populations under 2,500, or served the needs of rural areas.

The fire departments of small communities are manned almost entirely by volunteers. Even if a town of 2,500 inhabitants had as many as 3 paid fire fighters per 1,000 population, which is considerably above the average, there would be only 2 men on each duty shift so that full-paid fire departments would not be feasible unless there were very large industrial or institutional values to protect. A population density in the order of 5,000 persons per square mile is required to support a single adequately manned paid fire company within a 1½-mile radius of a fire station. Such population densities are found in principal metropolitan and urban areas. However, the average population density per square mile in the United States is 57 persons per square mile. This average does not provide enough people to support a paid fire department, and at least half of the total national population resides in areas of relatively low population densities. However, a density of 57 persons per square mile results in over 700 persons living within the allowable 4-mile response radius of a volunteer fire department. Moreover, assuming an average number of alarms per 1,000 persons protected, there are not enough fire and emergency calls to justify fully paid fire departments in over 90 percent of the local jurisdictions of the country. Thus, it is likely that the volunteer service will be required for many years to come, and fire administrators in such areas should be responsible for seeing that their communities have well-trained and well-equipped volunteer fire departments.

In most small communities, volunteer fire departments are operated on a "neighbor-help-neighbor" basis in which fire department members, except possibly fire station custodians and sometimes a few paid men on duty, get no compensation other than possibly some reimbursement for personal expenses and uniforms. To replace this free community labor with minimum manning by fully salaried personnel would involve an added national fire protection cost of approximately $3 billion per year. Various states have recognized the contribution made by their volunteer fire fighters by enacting protective legislation and by providing state-wide training programs and facilities.

On receipt of an alarm, members of most volunteer fire departments report to assigned fire stations from which they respond with apparatus. In order to provide a minimum effective working crew, many such fire departments require that the first piece of apparatus must not respond with less than three members. A minimum volunteer fire company response to an alarm should be four members. Usually this requires a volunteer fire company membership of at least twelve men where there are no paid members assigned to the company.

Fire department administrators should periodically review response records to determine that sufficient active fire company members are available to respond at all times of the day or night, and where necessary should recruit and train additional personnel to provide the required minimum response. All essential staff positions in a well-organized all-volunteer fire department are covered by assigned volunteer officers. However, in many jurisdictions paid fire prevention and training officers are provided by the county or other larger unit of government.

Where a community can afford paid apparatus operators on duty, response to alarms is faster and efficiency is increased. The on-duty drivers take the apparatus to the fire, and the volunteers notified by radio go directly to the fire thus saving, on the average, about 3 minutes in arrival time. The paid apparatus operator normally is in charge of the apparatus and of the fire station, but volunteer officers direct the fire fighting. One difficulty with this arrangement is that there are few, if any, opportunities for advancement for paid personnel. This discourages paid personnel from studying to qualify for more responsible positions. Paid apparatus operators usually also serve as company clerks, keeping attendance and other records required by management.

With the increasing legal and technical responsibilities of the fire chief as the principal fire protection officer of a community, the time when the fire chief was elected annually by the volunteer membership on a more or less honorary basis should be passing. Where this practice is still followed, it is common to have a paid fire officer responsible for management and in charge of paid personnel. However, this tends to be a compromising position. It is preferable to have a paid chief of department as the municipal fire depart-

ment administrator, even if the volunteer companies elect their own officers—including chief officers.

Where there are three or more fire companies operating with paid apparatus operators, there should be a paid fire captain on duty in charge of each shift who is also in command at fires in the absence of superior officers and who directs the paid personnel in their assigned duties. With the standard 4-platoon system, this type of organization requires a force of approximately 20 paid men plus the chief, and is found in communities in the 8,000 to 12,000 population range. Normally, the off-duty paid men should be expected to respond with their companies on an overtime basis to alarms for structural fires, especially in "bedroom communities" where the attendance of volunteers may be below average on weekdays. There have been numerous incidents where response of volunteer companies has been seriously delayed or deficient on weekdays.

An important step in the development of a part-paid, part-volunteer fire department is provision of one or more additional paid men on each shift. This permits the handling of still alarms, including many emergency calls, without calling out the volunteer members; it also provides hosemen and laddermen for fast initial fire attack before most of the volunteers and off-duty paid members arrive. The ability to handle still alarms without volunteer assistance can be important in moderate sized communities where too many calls for what prove to be trivial fires can result in a poor attendance record for volunteer companies. Many volunteers consider it unreasonable to be required to answer more than one or two alarms per week in addition to required attendance at drills.

A mistake made in a number of communities is to operate completely separate paid and fire organizations covering the same districts. The partly manned paid companies generally arrive first, but their operations are seriously restricted by lack of manpower. The volunteer companies arrive later, and operate with their own equipment under separate officers rather than assist with the fire attack already underway.

In the absence of minimum effective on-duty strength, sufficient volunteers or on-call members should be assigned to each fire company to permit fully efficient operation of the apparatus. Administrators should not tolerate friction between paid and volunteer personnel. Relationships and command should be clearly set forth in the rules. Volunteer companies should have their own meeting rooms and facilities, and the paid members should have the necessary quarters and facilities.

An arrangement that works quite successfully is to have the first responding pumper manned by a paid operator, the officer, and, where manpower permits, an additional firefighter. This force is supplemented by additional personnel assigned to respond on call. The second due engine may be manned by a fully volunteer company, or it may have a paid operator to take the apparatus to the fire where it is joined by the volunteer company under its officers. The ladder truck has a paid operator assigned, but is manned at the fire by a volunteer company. This sort of arrangement permits a reasonably effective initial fire attack quickly backed by volunteer members. In many cases complaints of paid personnel about serious undermanning are due to the fact that, because of poor organization, they get no assistance at fires from volunteers who do not even train with the assigned apparatus operators, but hold completely separate drills. In all cases there should be but one fire department in any jurisdiction, operating under a clearly defined and unified chain of command.

In a number of part-paid fire departments, the paid members have complained about being under the command of volunteer officers whom they felt lacked the needed experience and qualifications. All fire officers, whether elected or appointed, should meet the NFPA qualifications for the rank they hold. Countless volunteer officers have qualified to meet the technical standards for their duties. When a paid apparatus operator is assigned to operate the apparatus of a volunteer fire company, he should work under the orders of the volunteer officer of that company on the fireground. When both paid and volunteer captains respond to an alarm, the rules normally provide that the paid officer is in overall command in the absence of a chief officer. It is important that administrators make clear the respective roles and duties of all members, paid and volunteer.

Paid Call Fire Fighters

Hundreds of fire departments in small communities use fire fighters who have no regular shift duty in the stations, but are paid for response to alarms and drills. In some cases such members are loosely termed "volunteers," but under federal labor rules as well as local fire department rules and, as such, are considered paid employees of the fire department and, as such, are subject to the requirements of federal wage and hour regulations. The paid on-call members may also be employed by other municipal agencies, in which case the time spent on fire department duty may affect their overtime status. In most cases call fire fighters are local businessmen and tradesmen who are willing to be fire fighters on a part-time basis. Call fire fighters are expected to meet the same standards of performance as full-paid members of the same rank, but may not be assigned as apparatus operators where there are sufficient full-paid operators on shift duty.

There are various methods used in determining compensation for call fire fighters. In many departments they receive the same hourly wage for the rank they hold as do employees who work regular duty shifts. Time is based upon attendance at fires and training sessions, with a minimum hourly rate specified for response to alarms. Often upon reaching a mandatory retirement age, they also receive a pro-rated pension based upon years of service and hours of duty as call fire fighters. Another method of compensation is to have a fixed annual salary, based on rank, from which deductions are made for excessive numbers of unexcused failures to respond with their assigned companies. Many fire chiefs arrange to excuse members known to be at their regular employment, except in the case of multiple alarm fires; chiefs should have the authority to dismiss members who frequently fail to respond to fires and assigned training sessions. Still another method of compensation is to make an annual appropriation for call fire service based upon past experience, and designed to approximate the hourly wage rate for fire fighters. This is divided on a regular basis amongst the call members as determined by individual attendance at fires and training sessions so that members responding most faithfully receive the largest compensations. A fire department, whether fully volunteer or partly paid, should pay for members' insurance and workmen's compensation where required by law.

It is important that accurate records be kept in the personnel files for all call and volunteer members. Individual service records should be kept for all volunteers and call members, as well as for full-paid members. Also, response and attendance records are essential for volunteer and call members. Normally, to be credited with attendance at an alarm, the members on call should report within not over 10 minutes after their apparatus responds. Fire chiefs should not tolerate volunteer and call members who wait for a radio report of a "working fire" before responding to join their unit. Members who are habitually late in arriving should be replaced. Volunteer members should be furnished with night turnout suits so that they will lose no time in getting dressed to respond.

In a number of cases senior call and volunteer fire fighters who cannot respond regularly to first alarms are assigned to man reserve apparatus or to pilot mutual aid fire companies when serious fires occur. Other senior call members may be assigned to cover the alarm desk when all of the paid apparatus operators are out of quarters.

The keeping of accurate response records of volunteer and call members has enabled many fire chiefs to secure the provision of additional paid personnel on regular shift duty. In numerous cases municipal officials have believed that because they had the names of several hundred volunteers on the roster, the fire department had ample manpower; frequently, fire chiefs have had to sound multiple alarms to get more paid drivers to the scene to man hose lines due to lack of attendance by volunteers. This has often resulted in serious delays and extension of fires which should have been more readily controlled. Where such situations persist, additional paid personnel on shift duty may be required.

Chief Officers

All fire departments should have at least one deputy fire chief who is responsible for the department in the absence of the chief officer, and who assists in overall operational command at fires. In some small paid fire departments the deputy chief is in command of one of the regular work shifts while platoon captains are in charge of the other work shifts, thus performing dual roles as company officers and duty shift commanders. A better arrangement is to have a platoon chief in charge of each duty shift. The platoon chief is in overall command of the department during his tour of duty. He supervises the various fire companies through their officers, and responds to all alarms for structural fires and other working fires in a command car and not on the apparatus; he is also in charge of operations. He has authority to call off-shift help when needed, or to request additional mutual aid assistance. The senior platoon chief or deputy chief is in charge of the department in the absence of the fire chief unless there is a higher ranking administrative deputy chief designated for this responsibility.

Three, or at the most four, fire stations are the number that can be properly supervised by a single chief officer on duty. For effectively coordinated operations at fires, the assigned chief officer should arrive with the companies he is expected to direct. Where the territory served by a chief is too large, the chief will be late arriving at many fires. Also, the frequency of alarms in each area must be considered so that when the first due chief officer is on a prior call, another chief can quickly "fill in" at the second fire. In many cases isolated districts served by as few as four fire companies (engine, ladder, etc.) should be under the command of a district fire chief.

In paid fire departments with 5 to 8 fire stations, a frequent arrangement is to divide the department into two operating districts or commands. The platoon chief (who may be a deputy chief or an assistant chief) is in direct charge of one district as well as in overall charge of the department, and a district or battalion fire chief who is subordinate in rank is in charge of the other district. Each chief is in charge of the fire companies, and in charge at first alarms in his assigned district except that the platoon chief assumes overall command when he arrives at major fires prior to the arrival of the chief of department. A more desirable arrangement is to have a district or battalion chief on duty in each district working under the platoon or shift deputy fire chief. This makes it possible for both a district fire chief and the platoon chief to respond to major fires and target hazards while one district chief is available for other fires and emergencies. Normally, all fires which require the response of more than the basic first alarm response should have at least two chief officers assigned for proper tactical control. (See the NFPA books *Fire Attack 1* and *Fire Attack 2*.[1])

A minimum of one district fire chief should be on duty for each 8 fire companies or major fraction thereof; but, with the normal distribution of fire stations and companies, an average of at least one chief officer on duty for each 6 fire companies (such as 4 engines and 2 ladders) is a desirable arrangement to permit close supervision and quick response and supervision at fires. In areas of very high fire frequency, additional chief officers may be needed. In some cases a relief chief is provided on each shift to cover districts in which serious fires are in progress.

Large fire departments which have numerous districts or battalions commonly group these into divisions commanded by division deputy or assistant fire chiefs. In such cases there may not be an overall platoon chief for the work shift, but instead an administrative deputy chief at headquarters in charge of the fire fighting division.

Normally, where there is one, or more, chiefs on duty with each work shift, the chief of department does not respond on first alarms except possibly to target hazards because of his staff and administrative responsibilities. Where there are both deputy and district fire chiefs on duty, the chief of department (or acting chief of department) does not respond regularly before a third alarm except in situations where his presence may be required, such as at fires involving loss of life.

In some fire departments the command structure also includes a designation of specified fire captains as "task force commanders" in charge of a group of fire companies usually responding together from a given fire station. This may help provide better coordinated operations than where chief officers must deal directly with a larger number of small company units.

Chiefs' Aides

One of the positions most important to fire department efficiency is that of chiefs' aides or assistants. Aides are experienced officers or fire fighters who are assigned to work directly as assistants to various chief officers rather than as members of a company team. Aides are administrative assistants in the operation of the command; generally they operate the command car, they handle and channel most fireground radio communications with the alarm center, and assist their chief in numerous other ways including helping to size-up a fire and in directing placement of fire companies as determined by the chief. As chief officers must prepare hundreds of fire, personnel, and inspection reports while answering alarms and supervising administration of companies in their districts, a competent assistant is essential to efficient management and operations. In some fire departments the aides justly receive added compensation for this demanding work.

Fire Officers

Every fire company or similar fire fighting unit should be under the supervision of a qualified company officer both when in quarters or when responding to alarms, or when making in-service inspections. Fire companies with paid drivers and call fire fighters may have a qualified call officer, but in such part-paid departments at least one paid on-duty officer should immediately respond to alarms and should supervise the on-duty personnel when other company officers are not available.

In many fire departments all company officers hold the rank of fire captain, and there is a captain assigned to each duty shift of each fire company. A more common arrangement is to provide both captains and lieutenants. In some fire departments each fire company has one fire captain who works on one of the duty shifts, with lieutenants being in charge of the company on other shifts. The captains are assigned between the companies on the various shifts so that each shift or platoon will have its share of captains on duty. The captains also are used as relief chiefs when one or more of the chiefs on the duty platoon are absent, although many fire departments have some relief chiefs to cover a normal amount of absence. Another arrangement is to assign one fire captain on duty in each fire station with lieutenants in charge of other companies in the station on each shift. The captain is station commander and coordinator of operations in the absence of a chief officer. A lesser number of fire departments also have the rank of "sergeant." Sergeants actually are third-grade officers who are in charge of work shifts in their assigned companies. They do the work of lieutenants, but rank below lieutenants in the chain of command both in quarters and on the fireground.

Assignment of Paid Apparatus Operators

One of the most serious organizational faults of part-paid, part-volunteer fire departments has been the practice of assigning paid drivers to too many volunteer companies serving the same area. For example, a fire department may have 15 to 20 paid men on duty in 8 or 10 closely grouped volunteer fire company stations operating a dozen or more pieces of apparatus. No serious fire fighting or rescue operation can be carried out until volunteers arrive. Often, volunteer attendance is poor during the daytime making it necessary to sound a second or third alarm to get a dozen paid men to a fire which should be handled with a first alarm response. In some cities this situation has led to total elimination of the volunteer fire companies. The proper arrangement is to assign the available paid personnel to strategically located stations from which they can respond in effective strength.

Some fire departments designate apparatus operators as "engineers," with status intermediate between fire fighters and company officers. Most fire departments find it desirable to qualify all fire fighters as apparatus operators because they do not have enough personnel on duty with each company to maintain a separate classification, although certain members are designated as "first-drivers" or operators when on duty with their assigned shifts.

D. Labor Relations

The vast majority of paid fire department employees of all ranks below chief of department in both the United States and Canada are members of local unions. Most of the local unions are affiliated with the International Association of Fire Fighters (IAFF) which in turn is affiliated with the American Federation of Labor and Congress of Industrial Organizations (AFL-CIO), and with the Canadian Federation of Labor. IAFF also is affiliated with the Public Employees Department of AFL-CIO. In addition, most of the locals are affiliated with the various state and provincial federations of fire fighters.

In the earlier days of fire department unions, of chief concern were matters such as reduction in excessive work weeks, increase in wages, and improvements in vacations and pension plans. The problem of work weeks has been resolved in many areas. Much effort is now devoted to keeping pay scales comparable to increases in the cost of living and to improvements in working conditions, including compensation for working out of grade. Of special concern is the maintaining of safe manpower levels. In many communities the reduction in hours of work (which was long enjoyed by the police and all other public employees) resulted in drastic reductions in fire company strength to a point considered hazardous to the personnel on duty. Many work contracts have a health and safety clause, and increasingly provisions are being included for maintaining a specified minimum fire company strength on duty or a specified minimum total on-duty strength.

Most work contracts have provisions whereby either party can appeal grievances (alleged violations of contract) to an impartial fact-finding body under provisions of state law. The fact-finder or arbitrator may be nominated by the state and accepted by both sides, or the case may be heard by a state labor board or panel including representatives of both management and labor. In most cases the findings are advisory and not binding, but generally are supported by public opinion.

E. Budgeting

Except in the case of a fire district, the fire department budget is a portion of the municipal budget. There is a departmental account number that is broken down into various categories, each category having specified sub-numbers. On the average, approximately 95 percent of the fire department budget is allocated to payroll. This tends to be a fixed charge resulting from the pay scale negotiated in the current contract with the local fire fighters' union. This means that out of each $1,000,000 expended, only about $50,000 of the fire department budget is concerned with operating expenses. This 5 percent (or possibly 6 percent) must cover such operating expenses as heat and light for the fire stations, fuel for the fire apparatus and other vehicles, maintenance supplies, minor equipment including breathing apparatus and fire fighting tools, office supplies, repairs to buildings and grounds, etc. While fire hose should be replaced on a schedule, it is often replaced as part of a capital improvement.

Fire apparatus costs normally run from 1 percent to 2 percent of payroll costs. Some fire departments include an apparatus replacement allowance in the budget, but unfortunately this is an item that is too regularly cut with the result that apparatus replacement is included in a capital improvement fund financed by municipal bonds. While this reduces the fire department annual budget, it ultimately results in higher taxes due to interest costs. However, such decisions are made above the level of the fire department administration. New fire stations usually are included in a capital improvement budget separate from the fire department budget, although occasionally these are financed by federal revenue sharing funds. Pension payments to retirees are usually paid out of a separate municipal account and commonly amount to from 33 to 40 percent of the current fire department budget.

In large fire departments there may be separate budget accounts for staff divisions such as fire prevention, maintenance, and signal or alarm systems, although frequently the latter is handled by a different municipal department.

Expenditures are charged against specific items in the line budget, and the remaining balance is shown after each expense deduction. Usually the department head or staff division superintendents have authority to make emergency transfers of funds between line categories; transfers between major categories can be made only upon authorization of the municipal management or finance officer.

In recent years a new concept in budgeting has developed in the U.S. Bureau of the Budget and is being used in several cities. This concept is called PPB, or planned performance budgeting. The concept was that rather than merely approving annual operating budgets, budgets should be constructed and planned over a period of years to achieve planned performance objectives. The idea had some appeal for large units of government having departments and agencies spending hundreds of millions and even billions of dollars. However, even in such cases use of this concept is limited by the fact that agency appropriations must be approved annually by legislative authorities subject to political influences and demands that fluctuate with changes in economic and social conditions such as welfare costs, educational costs, pressures of inflation, and the international food and fuel situations. Thus, actual appropriations tend to follow political realities far more than budgetary theories.

In the case of the vast majority of fire departments, budgeting consists almost entirely of the cost of manning and operating fire companies rather than concepts about performance. Because of costs and limited financial resources, most fire departments are operating fire companies that are deficient in manpower. Departments also are deficient in the number of companies needed to provide reasonably effective coverage of their territories. Programmed budgeting is admirable if properly applied and not subject to arbitrary destruction by contingencies.

The public could be better served if fire department budgets were increased on the basis of values and populations protected. In many cases less than half as many fire fighters are on duty protecting much greater values than was the case a quarter century ago. Although employees benefit by improved wages and hours as a result of improved "productivity" and efficiency of fire companies, there are levels of service below which it is not prudent to go just to put dollars ahead of the safety of lives.

Fire department administrators are required to submit their budget estimates for the coming fiscal year by a specified time. Usually the budgets are submitted to a finance officer or finance committee, and department heads are interviewed on specific items in order to justify each. Although salary total is likely to be governed by contract with the employees, estimates must be included covering all ranks and including overtime costs. Quite often the actual salary scale is not negotiated prior to submission of the budget, but municipal administrators commonly make a percentage allowance for increases they hope will be accepted in negotiations. When a departmental budget has been approved by the city administration, it must be approved by the city or town council; in some municipalities it must be approved by the financial town meeting. With some municipal charters the council can reduce, but cannot add to, the budget. This is to guard against political pressure on the administration. Once approved, the budget takes effect at the beginning of the fiscal year. If not approved in time, it is customary to permit expenditures at the same rate as the previous year. As indicated, all expenditures must be made against specified items in the budget. Normally there is a set amount above which expenses cannot be incurred without competitive bidding under purchasing department procedures.

F. Planning and Research

Planning for the future needs of a fire department is a management responsibility, but one that is often neglected because of the pressures of current problems.

Planning: As a part of financial planning, some jurisdictions require all department heads to submit estimates of projected capital equipment needs for five years in advance. A few larger fire departments in growing communities have planning staffs engaged in the planning of new fire stations for developing areas, and for the replacement and possible relocation of old stations. Plans also may be made for replacement of apparatus. In the vast majority of communities planning is far less sophisticated. City administrations tend to heed citizens' demands for better protection of areas remote from existing fire stations, and the fire department may be consulted as to a suitable location. Not uncommon is the practice of employing outside consultants to recommend relocation and consolidation of fire stations. Also quite common are fire department annual reports that recommend various improvements. In numerous instances the initiative and drive for needed improvements, including new apparatus and stations, come from the local fire fighters' union.

It would appear desirable for all fire departments to have regularly scheduled planning sessions presided over by the fire chief or his executive assistant, with participation by officers responsible for the various staff services. Perhaps the greatest problem might be lack of incentive where it appears that there will be no support from the municipal management for any projects, however desirable, that may require additional expenditures. The fact should not be overlooked that most municipalities have a planning board or other official planning agency which often has considerable resources, including federal funds and information, that could be of value to the fire department planning effort. Regular contact should be maintained by the fire department administration and the planning agency. All too often this has not been the case, and fire protection requirements have not been adequately considered in city planning.

Research: In the fire service the term "research" has had considerable lip service; few fire departments, however, are staffed or financed so as to support any significant research activity. Exceptions are some of the larger fire departments such as New York City, Los Angeles, and Boston. Limitation in research is due largely to the fact that most fire departments are relatively small organizations which do not have sufficient personnel to meet their on-going obligations for furnishing fire protection. True research into efficient equipment design generally is beyond the capability of most fire departments, and even of the majority of fire equipment suppliers as this is a relatively small volume competitive business with little margin for research and development. In recent years a major part of the engineering effort of fire apparatus builders has been devoted to meeting the increasingly demanding vehicle safety standards of the U.S. Department of Transportation. Some improvements have been made in various features of fire apparatus design, but not on a uniform or planned research basis.

Planning for resource allocation and resource utilization tends to be seriously restricted by lack of funds and personnel to meet even basic operational needs. For the years immediately following World War II the rapid growth in

school populations preempted most municipal funds, and fire department needs, considered to be a lower priority, were postponed. As school populations leveled off, welfare costs became of major importance and assumed a priority over the needs of fire departments. Increases in fire department budgets not due to inflation were largely associated with reduction of excessive work weeks. Since 1960 the populations of the great majority of core cities decreased significantly, while their fire problems and welfare costs soared. Thousands of people moved to suburban communities where new schools had to be built and sewer and water systems established. Again, fire protection was not a high priority item. This was especially true because the more established residents of suburban areas were accustomed to virtually free volunteer fire department service, and were reluctant to assume costs for paid fire department personnel needed to protect greatly increased populations of newcomers. In hundreds of such communities, fire apparatus still responds with only one or two fire fighters; for any serious fire fighting, reliance is placed upon off-shift response and mutual aid. Fire prevention efforts are at least equally undermanned. Hopefully, recommendations of the National Commission on Fire Prevention and Control will result in the development of local fire protection programs that will overcome existing deficiencies, thus resulting in future fire protection that is more realistic.

One area in which fire department research can readily pay off is in fire record analysis utilizing programs such as the UFIRS (uniform fire incident reporting system) developed by the NFPA in cooperation with a selected group of fire departments. Properly utilized fire prevention efforts can be directed against the hazards shown to be most dangerous and significant at any given period, and results of programs can be effectively analyzed.

Research has been used in a number of instances to help determine optimum locations for fire stations. However, a principal difficulty is that all areas of a community must be covered within reasonable response distances, and considerable judgment and experience is required when considering the many variables such as population densities, valuations at risk, fire frequency and severity, and the number of fire companies required in a given area to apply the required fire flow and to maintain coverage during fires. These requirements may be at variance with any optimum location for a given fire station. A number of research studies have placed considerable emphasis upon the arrival time of the nearest fire company, rather than the total fire protection requirements of the area. Arrival times may be of less significance than time required for actually getting to work at a fire, particularly in large high-rise structures or shopping centers. One experienced fire department research chief has cautioned that research must be under the direction of experienced fire officers if it is to be practical and is not to lead to false conclusions. A problem may be so oversimplified for computer analysis by data processing specialists that dangerously false results are obtained. Hopefully, in the years ahead professional research techniques can be applied under the guidance of fire officers; too often the professional fire officers have been under administrative orders to merely supply the data to persons not competent to evaluate fire department needs, following which city administration has used such data to justify a dangerous reduction in the level of protection.

Fortunately, the fire service is not without competent research resources. The NFPA Research Division has many on-going projects designed to be of direct help and benefit to fire departments. IAFF operates a Research Department which is available to assist its local affiliates with problems on request. Additionally, there are several private research groups which utilize fire service personnel as technical advisors.

G.   Records and Reports

A records system should be provided to supply the fire chief and other administrative officers with data indicating the effectiveness of the department in preventing and fighting fires insofar as practicable to facilitate management of the department. It is essential to maintain complete records of all fires and inspections. The records system should provide data on fire department activities which the fire chief should make to city officials and to the public. The fire chief should specify the records to be kept and methods of gathering data. A records retention and disposal system should be employed. All records should be examined in light of their usefulness. Too often there is an accumulation of old records that are no longer needed.

A typical list of fire department management reports and records is as follows:

TYPICAL MANAGEMENT REPORTS AND RECORDS*

GENERAL MANAGEMENT
   Report on Each Alarm by District Chief (consolidates data on operations and investigations)
   Fire Record Journal (chronological list of alarms and fires)
   Consolidated Daily Report (where used)
   Consolidated Monthly Report
   Annual Report

FINANCIAL MANAGEMENT
   Inventory Records (stock records kept by each company or bureau of the department to which land, buildings, furniture, apparatus or equipment is assigned)
   Purchase Records (requisitions, invitations to bid, quotations, purchase orders, reports on goods received)
   Budgetary Control Records
   Payroll Records

PERSONNEL MANAGEMENT
   Company Record of Personnel Attendance
   Department Daily Summary of Personnel Attendance
   Master Personnel Record on Each Member

PUBLIC RELATIONS
   Daybook Record of Programs and Activities

WATER SUPPLY
   Company Records of Hydrants and Cisterns
   Company Records of Sprinklers, Standpipes and other Private Fire Protection
   Daybook Record of Activities of Fire Department Water Officer or Bureau (including reports of water supply interruptions)
   Record of Fire Flow Tests
   Plans of Public Water Systems
   Plans and Files on Static Water Sources

FIRE PREVENTION INSPECTION AND EDUCATION
   Company Daily Summary of Inspections Made
   Company Record of Individual Properties
   Bureau Daily Summary of Inspections Made
   Bureau Daybook Record of Inspection and Educational Activities
   Bureau Record of Individual Properties

FIRE FIGHTING AND EMERGENCY SERVICE MANAGEMENT
   Company Daybook or Journal (chronological record kept at company watch desk as source of entries in company records)
   Company Run Report
   Report on Each Alarm by District Chief (includes consolidation of data on operations of all companies and service units responding to each alarm)

FIRE INVESTIGATION
   Report on Each Alarm by District Chief (includes data for classification of alarm and results of chief's investigation)
   Investigation Bureau Report on Each Alarm Investigated
   Loss Summaries for Consolidated Management Report
   Record of Insurance Losses
   Record of Estimated Uninsured Losses
   Name File of Properties and Persons Involved in Alarms

TRAINING
   Company Record of Training Sessions at Station
   Daybook of Training School Activities
   Records of Training Courses (including attendance and grading of participants)

COMMUNICATIONS
   Daily Summary of Alarms Received
   Radio Log
   Daybook Record of Work on Communications System (including disposal of trouble signals)
   Reports of Tests Specified for Communication Equipment
   Record Card on Each Public Fire Alarm Box
   Record or File on other Communications Equipment
   Plans of Wiring
   Record of Installation, Maintenance Repair, Replacement or Removal.

BUILDINGS AND APPARATUS MANAGEMENT
   Periodic Reports Required from Companies and Bureaus on Tests of Assigned Apparatus and Equipment (covers motor fire apparatus, hose and other items of equipment)
   Records Kept by Companies and Bureaus of Maintenance Work Performed on Assigned Apparatus and Equipment
   Shop Reports of Tests of Apparatus and Equipment
   Shop Records of Maintenance and Repairs of Apparatus and Equipment (including cost data)
   Record of Maintenance of Each Parcel of Land
   Record of Maintenance of Each Building

H. Public Information and Community Relations

As a public agency supported by public funds the fire department needs all of the public support it can get. Moreover, understanding and cooperation by the public is required to make fire prevention programs fully effective.

---

* Suggested forms for certain of the management records and reports enumerated are illustrated in the text, Municipal Fire Administration, published by International City Management Association, 1140 Connecticut Ave., N.W., Washington, D.C. 20036.

Accordingly, public information and community relations programs are an important activity of concern to fire department management.

In a good public information program it is important to develop and to maintain procedures whereby the public is kept informed of important developments and newsworthy items of information regarding all types of departmental activities and programs. Properly prepared press releases should be issued on all such programs and items of general interest. Relations with the news media should be cordial, and representatives of the media should be given all possible cooperation. This is not always easy because hundreds of suburban fire departments are located in communities that depend largely upon a metropolitan press, and items that might be of interest to local citizens may not be newsworthy for the entire region served by press, radio, and TV stations. However, there are usually local weekly papers or local area editions of metropolitan papers which do have local correspondents who can be kept informed of fire department activities. The amount of publicity obtained by fire departments seems to vary greatly in different geographical areas. In some areas citizens are traditionally interested and involved in local governments and in their fire departments, while in other areas fire departments are not considered to be news and greater efforts must be made to get the fire stories to the public. In general, those communities where citizens regularly participate in town affairs seem to give fire departments better support than communities with largely transient populations which leave local government almost entirely to professional administrators who only see the fire department as an expense. Communities with substantial numbers of low income residents subject to fire dangers often are most concerned with the adequacy of fire department services.

Normally, public information programs are of direct concern to the head of the fire department who makes many personal contacts and who often holds memberships in various civic groups in the community, and who often knows newsmen and editors on a personal basis. It is important that newsmen be given information promptly (while it is still news) when emergencies occur. Most fire departments have rules that only the officer in charge at a fire or emergency should give out information. This is to avoid conflicting and inaccurate statements which may be misleading or may compromise the results of subsequent or on-going investigations of fires.

Some large fire departments have a designated public information officer who is assigned to give the press all possible cooperation and information. In smaller fire departments, this function is usually one of the duties performed by the fire chief or, in cases where fires are under investigation, by the fire marshal.

Community relations should be a year-round activity and should embrace the various seasonal fire prevention programs such as Fire Prevention Week, Clean-up Week, etc. Often, both the fire prevention bureau staffs and the training division staffs are utilized for such activities. In some fire departments the community relations program is coordinated by the fire prevention bureau as a logical part of its program of public education.

Many fire departments have a community relations unit or speakers' bureau available to address various civic and church groups. These bureaus are often sponsored by the fire fighters' local which donates the necessary time, thus eliminating the problem of paying required overtime for official duty beyond the specified work week. Educational films are available concerning the nature of the fire fighters'

job. IAFF conducts an annual Press Awards Contest in which cash prizes are given to representatives of the various news media (press, radio, TV, and press photographers), and prizes are awarded to representatives from both the metropolitan press and the small community press.

I. Intergovernmental Relations

Fire departments are but one agency of local government, and much of their success depends upon their working relationships with other local, state, and federal agencies. Some of the more important contacts are mentioned here.

Building Department: Proper construction and arrangement of buildings is essential to a sound fire protection program. Increasingly, state laws and local ordinances, or agreements between fire and building departments, are requiring written approval by the head of the fire department concerning specified fire protection features before building permits can be issued. Also, close cooperation is needed between these departments to control serious fire hazards which commonly are present while buildings are under construction before the required fire resistance features have been installed. In small communities the fire chief generally must handle this assignment, but in most well organized fire departments it is one of the important responsibilities delegated to the fire prevention bureau.

Police: Cooperation between the fire and police departments is essential. Regular police response to fire alarms is necessary to control traffic and crowds. Police often are first at the scene of a fire or emergency and should have basic training in what to do and what not to do at fires. All too often there have been serious delays in notifying the fire department of fires because police did not follow proper procedures or did not give fire alarms a priority over routine police messages. This includes notifying fire departments of traffic accidents where fire department service is required to assist in rescues or to control fire hazards. Police cooperation also is needed in many fire investigations, particularly where there may be criminal law violations; in some jurisdictions members of the fire prevention bureau staff have special police powers. In most jurisdictions police operate under the direction of the senior fire officer in charge on the fireground.

Water Department: Adequate water supplies including the hydrant service are essential for fire fighting and are the responsibility of the water department or division. A knowledgeable fire officer should be assigned to maintain liaison with the water authority. Water counts equally with the fire department in the ISO grading schedule. All too often water authorities have little knowledge of the fire flow requirements of the fire department in various areas and types of property. Thousands of fire hydrants have been improperly set because water crews did not understand the proper location and setting of hydrants as required for efficient fire fighting. In some communities the fire department is responsible, by ordinance, for determining the location and setting of hydrants. It is important that all hydrants be serviced regularly and after each use, especially in cold weather; the fire department should promptly report all hydrants used to the water department. Some fire departments maintain a list of hydrants in each fire company inspection district with flow data on each hydrant. Hydrants should be properly marked for flows and painted for nighttime visibility. In many fire departments the liaison with the water authority is one of the responsibilities of the training division.

Personnel Department: Members of fire departments are

public employees, and as such their recruitment and promotion often involves cooperation with the personnel agency which in some jurisdictions is responsible for conducting entrance and promotional examinations. Commonly the fire department executive officer or executive secretary or chief training officer would be assigned to maintain liaison with the personnel office.

Finance Department: The fire department gets most of its money from the finance department, and fire department fiscal business must be conducted under the procedures of that department. Although some fire departments have finance officers, liaison with the finance department is usually handled by fire chiefs or their executive officers.

Purchasing: All purchases exceeding stipulated amounts must be made according to specifications, and usually with competitive bidding by the purchasing department. Close liaison is necessary to assure that specifications are properly drawn to meet fire department needs, and that when bids are opened any proposals that deviate from specifications are rejected. This may be handled directly by the fire chief or by his executive officer, or by the chief of apparatus and equipment.

Data Processing: Increasingly, fire departments are utilizing electronic data processing for keeping fire records, payroll records, and for statistical analysis. Each fire department should have persons knowledgeable in the use of data processing. It may be desirable to have one officer appointed as coordinator of this work, but commonly there would be an administrative committee in the fire department which would include representatives of plans and research (where provided), administration, fire prevention, and fire suppression. This same committee may also be involved in long range planning.

J. Procurement of Equipment and Supplies

In most municipalities, procurement of fire department equipment and supplies is done through purchasing departments. Items that are common to all departments may be requisitioned from the purchasing agency and charged to the appropriate fire department account. Where items are of a specialized nature such as fire apparatus or fire fighting tools and equipment, purchasing specifications must be prepared by the fire department, approved by the purchasing department, and advertised for bids. In preparing specifications for such items as fire apparatus and fire hose, current NFPA recommended practices should be followed. (For further details on fire department specifications, see this Section, Chapter 4.) The fire chief with the advice of his apparatus and equipment superintendent should be the determining factor concerning whether or not proposals submitted by bidders adequately meet specifications. In many jurisdictions law requires that a contract be awarded to the lowest responsible bidder. However, quite frequently bidders take exceptions to various details in the specifications or offer substitutes so that judgment must be exercised as to whether or not such proposals meet the intent of the specifications. If they do not, the bids should be rejected; but if the proposals conform to the specifications and are within the appropriation or budget item, the contract is awarded. Upon delivery, new equipment should be tested in accordance with the provisions of NFPA standards.

When emergency purchases must be made, it is customary to require estimates from several suppliers. If the amount involved is small and funds are available in the appropriate budget item, the fire chief can authorize the expenditure. If funds are not available in the fire department budget, authorization and funds must be obtained from the municipal management or finance officer.

All fire department supplies are inventoried and kept under lock to be issued only on requisition by the supply officer. Some large fire departments have a supply department. More commonly, office and fire station supplies are kept in a headquarters storage area, and maintenance supplies are kept in a stock room in the fire department shop. Regular annual inventories are required from fire officers covering all items issued to the various fire companies and fire stations. Usually a senior captain is designated as station officer or station commander responsible for all station supplies and equipment.

K. Resource Allocation and Utilization

The principal resource of a fire department is its highly trained personnel. The vast majority of personnel and man-hours are assigned to the fire fighting division, and possibly 2 percent to 3 percent of the personnel are assigned full-time to the fire prevention bureau. Thus, for most effective resource allocation, maximum use must be made of the fire fighting personnel. This is done by careful time utilization schedules assigning appropriate allocations of work periods to apparatus and equipment maintenance, fire service training, and scheduled inspections. Such programs require close coordination between the chiefs of the fire fighting, training, and fire prevention bureaus or divisions. In well-managed fire departments, at least half of the routine fire prevention inspections are made by fire companies in their assigned inspection districts. Time utilization studies in some fire departments have shown that undue amounts of time were being wasted on common janitorial duties that could be done more cheaply under contract, or by less skilled labor. Another common waste is the lack of adequate secretarial and clerical service, office equipment, and transportation for fire prevention inspectors, many of whom have to spend a great deal of time on routine report writing and filing. Some large fire prevention bureaus do not have clerks or secretaries, and in the majority of smaller fire departments such staff services are almost always inadequate. This situation can be corrected in large measure by employing the technically qualified line officers as staff personnel on an overtime basis. Many of these officers have fire science certificates or appropriate college degrees and would welcome an opportunity to perform staff work on designated off days. Under the usual platoon systems, each officer is on day duty only about two days per week. Rather than work at outside odd jobs, many would prefer an opportunity for professional staff work in the fire department. In many cases only the fire chief is available on a regular basis to handle all staff duties, and accordingly many of the management functions outlined in this text tend to be neglected. Personnel are not fully utilized when the talents of highly trained officers are neglected because of the necessity for assigning most of them to command operational units. In the past, one of the difficulties has been that many fire chiefs had no training or experience in staff and business management and did not know how to delegate responsibilities.

Currently, changes in attitudes plus newly acquired management skills are rapidly compensating for past deficiencies, and many fire chiefs now have competent assistants and staff officers to assist in performing management functions. Considering the fact that 20 percent or more of all fire department personnel are officers, there should be ample technically qualified managerial help available even in a small fire department for good staff services that can contribute to maximum efficiency and productivity.

Bibliography

References Cited

[1] Kimball, W. Y., *Fire Attack 1* and *Fire Attack 2,* National Fire Protection Association, Boston, 1966.

Additional Readings

Anderson, D. L., ed., *Municipal Public Relations,* International City Managers' Association, Chicago, 1966.

Bahme, C. W., *Fireman's Law Book,* 4th ed., National Fire Protection Association, Boston, 1967.

Banovetz, E. E., ed., *Urban Government: A Reader in Administration and Politics,* 2nd ed., The Free Press, New York, 1969.

Barnard, C. I., *The Functions of the Executive,* Harvard University Press, Cambridge, Mass., 1968.

Beck, A. D., Jr. and Hillmar, E. D., *A Practical Approach to Organization Development through MBO-Selected Readings,* Addison-Wesley Publishing Co., Reading, Mass., 1972.

Bellows, Roger; Gilson, T. O.; and Odiorne, G. S., *Executive Skills: Their Dynamics and Development,* Prentice-Hall, Englewood Cliffs, N.J., 1962.

Bennis, W. G., *Changing Organizations,* McGraw-Hill, New York, 1966.

Bormann, E. G., et al., *Interpersonal Communications in the Modern Organization,* Prentice-Hall, Englewood Cliffs, N.J., 1969.

Brown, F. G., and Murphy, T. P., eds., *Emerging Patterns in Urban Administration,* Lexington Books, Lexington, Mass., 1970.

Clark, R. T., *Compulsory Arbitration in Public Employment,* Public Employee Relations Library, No. 37, Public Personnel Association, Chicago, 1963.

Cutlip, S. M. and Center, A. H., *Effective Public Relations,* 4th ed., Prentice-Hall, Englewood Cliffs, N.J., 1971.

Dale, Ernest and Michelon, L. C., *Modern Management Methods,* World Publishing Company, Cleveland, 1966.

Dale, Ernest and Urwick, L. F., *Staff in Organization,* McGraw-Hill, New York, 1960.

Drucker, P. F., *The Effective Executive,* Harper & Row, New York, 1967.

Fordyce, J. K. and Weil, Raymond, *Managing with People: A Manager's Handbook of Organization Development Methods,* Addison-Wesley, Reading, Mass., 1971.

Hatry, Harry and Cotton, John, *Program Planning for State, County, City,* George Washington University, State-Local Finances Project, Washington, D.C., 1967.

Hayel, Carl, *Organizing Your Job in Management,* American Management Association, New York, 1960.

Heisel, W. D.; Padgett, E. R.; and Harrell, C. A., *Line-Staff Relationships in Employee Training,* International City Managers' Association, Chicago, 1967.

Hughes, C. L., *Goal Setting: Key to Individual and Organizational Effectiveness,* American Management Association, New York, 1973.

Hickey, H. E., *Public Fire Safety Organization,* National Fire Protection Association, Boston, 1973.

———, *Successful Public Relations,* National Fire Protection Association, Boston, 1974.

Koontz, H. O., *Appraising Managers as Managers,* McGraw-Hill, New York, 1971.

Kraemer, K. L., *Policy Analysis in Local Government: A Systems Approach to Decision Making,* International City Managers' Association, Washington, D.C., 1973.

La Patra, J. W., *Applying the Systems Approach to Urban Development,* Dowden, Hutchinson & Ross, Inc., Stroudsburg, Penna., 1973.

McGregor, Douglas, *The Professional Manager,* McGraw-Hill, New York, 1967.

Miller, E. C., *Objectives and Standards: An Approach to Planning and Control,* American Management Association, New York, 1966.

Morgan, J. S., *Practical Guide to Conference Leadership,* McGraw-Hill, New York, 1966.

Nigro, F. A., *Management Employee Relations in the Public Service,* Public Personnel Association, Chicago, 1969.

Odiorne, G. S., *Management by Objectives: A System of Managerial Leadership,* Pitman Publishing Corp., New York, 1965.

Ottoson, John, *How to Use Statistics,* National Fire Protection Association, Boston, 1974.

Parker, J. K., *Introduction to Systems Analysis,* Management Information Service Reports, No. 298, International City Managers' Association, Washington, D.C., 1968.

Post-Entry Training in the Local Public Service: With Special Reference to Administrative, Professional, and Technical Personnel in the United States, International City Managers' Association, Chicago, 1963.

Sagoria, Sam, ed., *Public Workers and Public Unions,* Prentice-Hall, Englewood Cliffs, N.J., 1972.

Sasso, C. O., *Coping with Public Employee Strikes: A Guide for Public Officials,* Public Personnel Association, Chicago, 1970.

Schaenman, P. S. and Swartz, Joseph, *Measuring for Protection Productivity in Local Government,* National Fire Protection Association, Boston, 1974.

Starrett, P. F., *Mass Communications for Local Officials,* Arizona State University, Institute of Public Administration, Tempe, Ariz., 1970.

Stieber, Jack, *Public Employee Unionism: Structure Growth, Policy,* Brookings Institution, Washington, D.C., 1973.

Terry, G. R., *Principles of Management,* 6th ed., Richard D. Irwin, Inc., Homewood, Ill., 1972.

Vance, J. E., *Information Communication Handbook: Policies for Working with the Media for Public Officials, Citizens, Business and Community Groups,* published by the author, St. Paul, Minn., 1973.

Wall, N. L., *Municipal Reporting to the Public,* International City Managers' Association, Chicago, 1963.

Wellington, H. H. and Winter, R. K., Jr., *The Unions and the Cities,* Brookings Institution, Washington, D.C., 1972.

Chapter 3

FIRE DEPARTMENT OPERATIONS

The majority of fire department resources—including personnel, equipment, facilities, and support services—are committed to fire suppression efforts. The basic function of fire suppression operations is that of suppressing fires and performing related duties once a fire occurs. This, however, should not be their only function. For example, the majority of personnel within the department are assigned to fire suppression duties at locations throughout the community where they can also perform invaluable service by aiding in the fire prevention effort through in-service inspection activities, pre-fire planning, training, and other related assignments.

A. Organization for Fire Suppression

Chapter 1 of this Section illustrates the typical fire department organization and how the fire suppression operation relates to the total organization. The basic tactical unit of fire suppression is the company. Each company is normally composed of one or more pieces of apparatus and a complement of personnel under the supervision of a company officer. Typical fire companies are engine, ladder, and rescue. Two other types of tactical companies are manpower squads and task forces; although not widely accepted, these two types of tactical companies have proven successful in communities that use them.

Engine Company: Engine companies normally comprise the largest number of companies within any fire department. The basic unit of apparatus is the triple combination pumper, although there are variations. Some departments prefer the two-piece engine company concept which may either consist of two triple-combination pumpers or one triple-combination pumper and a hose wagon specifically designed to respond with a pumper. There are advantages and disadvantages to each concept. The merits of each concept must be considered by the department that is contemplating change in view of their own particular situation and method of operation.

Engine company operations may involve all aspects of fire fighting, particularly in smaller departments that don't have ladder companies. In larger departments, engine company operations become more specialized and involve only such suppression operations as initial fire attack, interior and exterior fire fighting, water supply, and rescue.

Ladder Company: The basic unit of apparatus of ladder companies may either be the aerial ladder or the aerial platform. In either case, the apparatus provides the capability to place fire fighters at elevations necessary to effect rescue and ventilation.

Ladder company operations involve the placement of ladders for rescue, ventilation, and use by engine company personnel in advancing hose lines. In addition to rescue and ventilation, ladder companies are also assigned the tasks of forcible entry, salvage, and overhaul. In some departments not having rescue companies, ladder companies are assigned all nonfire related rescue operations.

Rescue Company: Some fire departments utilize the services of a rescue company or companies within their operations to perform most non-fire related rescues and assist at fire incidents. Personnel trained in all phases of rescue are assigned to a special vehicle equipped to perform most rescue tasks. The tasks performed by rescue companies are widely varied and normally include both fire and non-fire related activities.

Manpower Squads: There are a number of fire departments that have implemented the use of "manpower squads," "flying squads," or "tactical control units" to supplement the normal complement of assigned fire fighters at working incidents, or to augment assigned companies during peak periods of response activity. In some instances these special units consist of personnel assigned to a vehicle that is used for transportation only, or a pumper, or ladder, and respond to all working fires or selected fires within the department's response area; also, they supplement assigned companies during peak alarm periods.

Task Forces: Another concept that has been used successfully by several fire departments is the task force. This concept consists of several pieces of apparatus, a complement of personnel, and a task force commander. A basic task force may consist of two engines and one aerial ladder, plus personnel including an officer in command. The Los Angeles City Fire Department has utilized the task force concept for several years. The principal advantage of the task force concept is that with several pieces of apparatus and a complement of personnel, the task force commander has the flexibility to utilize the optimum combination of personnel and equipment to accomplish assigned tasks.

Multicompany Operations

As the number of companies within a fire department increases, it becomes necessary to provide some means of coordinating multicompany operations and providing routine supervision and administration of company activities.

Battalions-Districts: The method most commonly used to coordinate multicompany operations is to assign a specified number of companies to a battalion or district. The number of companies assigned should be based on good management practices that allow for proper span of control and take into account geographical considerations.

Battalions or districts are normally commanded by a chief officer. The battalion or district officer is responsible for all suppression operations, and administrative and supervisory duties within his command.

Divisions: Large metropolitan fire departments that have a number of battalions or districts must, for obvious reasons, provide some means of command, administration, and supervision. This is done by assigning a number of battalions or districts to a particular division under the supervision of a division commander.

The tactical units, battalion or district, and division commanders comprise the majority of the fire suppression forces within the fire department organization. There are variations according to the needs of a particular community. Other support functions are necessary within any fire department to assure continued operation and provide the necessary administrative needs on a day to day basis.

Tactical Operations

Tactical operations are the basic means employed by fire

suppression forces to cope with fire incidents. There are several tactical operations that may or may not be employed at each fire incident and at times there may be several tactical operations being carried out simultaneously during multicompany operations at fires. In some instances the situation may dictate only one tactical operation. Regardless of the number of operations needed it is essential that each individual, depending upon company assignment, be trained in carrying out these operations.

Size-up: One of the most important tactical operations that precludes any physical activity is the mental process of size-up. This is a continuous mental evaluation of the situation and all related factors that may determine the success or failure of the fire ground operation. This mental evaluation should begin as soon as companies are alerted; it should be continuous throughout the incident. Size-up should not be limited only to the fire ground commander, but should be practiced by each fire fighter and officer involved with the incident.

Rescue: Rescue is the first and most important consideration at any fire incident, and may preclude any attempts at extinguishment until the rescue operation is complete. Rescue operations may be simple, requiring only one or two men, or may require resources beyond the capabilities of the entire alarm assignment. Rescue operations may be compounded by the time of the incident, the occupancy, the height, and the construction of the structure. Rescue is the only acceptable reason for exposing fire fighters to otherwise unnecessary risks.

Exposures: The failure to adequately protect exposed structures often leads to large loss fires that extend beyond the building of fire origin. The problem of exposure protection may be compounded by closely spaced buildings, combustible construction, the type of occupancy, the lack of fire department access, and the lack of fire department resources. Exposure protection is a vital and necessary tactical operation, and should be anticipated. Exposure protection should commence as soon as possible to prevent the extension of fire to exposed structures.

Confinement: The confinement of fire to its area of origin is often a complex operation because it first requires locating the fire. Heavy smoke conditions will cause such a delay. All avenues of possible fire travel must be explored. The concept of surrounding the fire (over, under, and around) once it is located, is necessary for successful confinement. Additional factors that influence the success or failure of confinement operations are the type of fuel involved, the location of the fire, construction features of the building, the presence of built-in fire suppression systems, and the availability of fire department resources.

Extinguishment: The problems associated with confinement, such as the type of fuel involved, the location of the fire, and the degree of involvement, are generally applicable to extinguishment operations. Extinguishment may involve only one or two hand lines, or require the use of master streams. In some instances the use of special extinguishing agents may be required. Often the success of extinguishing operations will depend upon the availability of fire department resources to apply water in sufficient quantities where needed.

Ventilation: Ventilation operations are the planned and systematic removal of heat, smoke, and fire gases from the structure. In some cases it may be necessary to commence ventilation prior to rescue in order to protect occupants from combustion products and heat until rescue operations can be completed. Also, it may be necessary to provide ventilation for visibility and tenability during rescue oper-

ations. Ventilation is also mandatory during confinement and extinguishment to aid in locating the fire and provide better working conditions for fire suppression personnel.

Salvage: Salvage operations are activities conducted by fire suppression personnel to minimize damage to the structure and contents due to heat, smoke, flame, and water. Salvage is an integral part of tactical operations and should commence as soon as possible to prevent additional damage to both structure and contents.

Overhaul: Overhaul operations are those that are required to completely extinguish the fire, to place the structure in a safe condition, and to aid in determining the fire ignition sequence. Overhaul may involve only a few personnel for a short period of time, or large numbers of personnel over an extended period of time. Extensive overhaul may require the use of special pieces of equipment beyond what is normally provided by the fire department. It is important that extensive overhaul not be commenced prior to a thorough investigation to determine the cause of the fire. Once the investigation is complete, overhaul should continue to insure that the premises are left as safe as possible, and that all fires are extinguished.

Nontactical Operations

There are additional tasks performed by fire suppression personnel that are not tactical operations, but are equally important. These are pre-fire planning, fire prevention activities, and training.

Prefire Planning: Prefire planning is a necessary task that should involve all fire suppression personnel on a continuous basis. It is a course of action against a probable fire, and is based on the collective experiences of those involved in the planning process, known or existing conditions, the relation of cause and effect, and reasonable expectancy. The following steps are part of the pre-fire planning process:

1. Information Gathering—Collecting pertinent information at the selected site that might affect fire fighting operations, such as building construction features, occupancy, exposures, utility disconnects, fire hydrant locations, water main sizes, and anything else that would be pertinent if a fire should occur.

2. Information Analysis—The information gathered must be analyzed in terms of what is pertinent and vital to fire suppression operations, a plan formulated, and put into a usable format that can be used on the fire ground.

3. Information Dissemination—All companies that might respond to each prefire planned location should receive copies of the plan so that they become familiar with both the plan and the pertinent factors relating to it.

4. Class Review and Drill—Each company that might be involved at the pre-planned location should review the plan on a regular schedule. Periodic drills with all companies involved should be scheduled on the property if possible.

Prefire plans are necessary for all target hazards and special risks, but need not be developed for occupancies such as single-family dwellings or other smaller occupancies since a standard operating procedure should be sufficient. Prefire planning is a necessary adjunct to tactical operations, and if used, should aid in operational efficiency, reducing fire losses, and help provide an optimum level of fire protection.

Fire Prevention: The participation of fire suppression personnel in fire prevention activities is as necessary as their participation in tactical operations. Because the majority of the fire department's resources are committed to suppression activities and are systematically distributed throughout the protected area, it is important that these resources be committed to fire prevention efforts. Good fire department objectives can provide the proper approach for involvement in fire prevention activities. Departments that are committed to a comprehensive fire prevention and inspection program can utilize fire suppression personnel on a regular basis for routine inspections within their first due response area, and reserve fire prevention personnel for follow-up inspections, enforcement, and special technical inspections. The total involvement of all personnel, particularly those assigned to suppression activities, should not only decrease the incidence of fire, but will demonstrate maximum utilization.

Training: It is essential that a portion of the duty time of the fire suppression forces be devoted to training. Training activities provide the opportunity to develop the skills and knowledge necessary to implement tactical operations. The elements of good training are discussed in detail in Part F of this Chapter.

Strategy and Tactics

The success of any fire suppression operation or major emergency that is the responsibility of the fire department is dependent upon how efficiently and effectively the department's resources are managed for any given situation. It is the responsibility of the officer in charge, or the fire ground commander, to manage the department's resources and deploy units in a coordinated manner to achieve maximum benefit. The management of resources at emergency incidents is dependent upon the type of incident, the associated conditions, resources available, and the evaluation made by the fire ground commander.

The management of fire department resources at emergency incidents normally employs the concepts of fire suppression strategy and tactics.

Suppression Tactics: Tactics are the methods or operations employed by the tactical units (companies, task forces, etc.) to achieve objectives such as rescue, confinement, extinguishment, ventilation, salvage, overhaul or other tasks as assigned by the fire ground commander.

Suppression Strategy: Strategy is the method employed by the fire ground commander to coordinate the tactical units (engine and ladder companies) and the management of additional resources, if required, to successfully control the incident or emergency.

Risk Potential

A detailed knowledge of the potential fire problem in any area protected is necessary not only in planning resources, responses, and locating facilities, but also for dealing with incidents when they occur. This knowledge is essential to effective suppression activities. It is critical in the decision-making process at the time of arrival when the fire officer is called upon to make an instant, often irrevocable decision, which may affect the lives of not only his personnel, but also the lives of the general public. The fire officer must commit personnel and apparatus based on a number of choices. Apart from obvious and visible indicators of the fire situation, the fire officer needs an appreciation of the way fire can be expected to behave in any given situation. In determining risk potential, factors similar to the following should be considered:

Life Risk: Are the occupants likely to be active, physically capable, able to help themselves, or are they likely to be infirm, aged, bedridden, handicapped, or otherwise unable to take any action towards self-rescue? Are the occupants likely to be awake or asleep and, therefore, more prone to being trapped? Are there a large number of persons con-

centrated together and, therefore, liable to present a multiple rescue problem (with a possible panic condition), or is the density of occupants limited?

Contents: Are the contents highly flammable, likely to give off considerable heat in relation to amount (high fire load), are they liable to explode, produce dense smoke rapidly, etc, or are they generally incombustible? Are the contents in quantity or limited, are there generally low fire loadings with an isolated group of high fire loadings, and where is such an isolated high load located? Are the contents themselves liable to promote rapid flame spread and flashover (independent of interior surface finishes)?

Construction: Is the construction fire resisting and likely to maintain structural integrity, or is it unprotected and liable to fail early in the operation? Are the interior finishes liable to cause rapid flame spread and extension of fire? Is the building compartmented with fire walls and doors that can be taken into account in determining course of fire suppression activity? Are there openings in floors, walls, ducts, shafts, etc? Is the building old, or has it been remodeled with possible resultant weaknesses? Are there structures that present a situation in which a developed fire is virtually impossible to control by standard fire hose streams, due mainly to release of heat and the reach limitations of hose streams? Are there buildings of excessive height that directly affect fire fighting strategy in three principal ways: one, because of the height limitations of hose streams; two, more often by the need for additional manpower on the upper floors of multistoried buildings; or three, heat release is greater than applied water can absorb?

Built-in Protection: Are there sprinklers which might restrict growth and spread of fire? Are there fire doors, compartments, etc? Are there other fire protection arrangements which would mitigate fire effect?

Time: Are there occupants who are alert and would discover a fire soon after its inception? Or, are occupants asleep or, perhaps is there no one present? Is there a smoke or fire detection system? Is the system connected to the fire department or a central station system? Is the risk some distance from a fire station? Are there railroad crossings, heavy traffic patterns, or other restrictions on speed of response? Are there any other factors that would delay discovery, alarm, or response?

Suppression Resources: What is the availability of water or other extinguishing agents? Will there be problems regarding entry or access? What demands for manpower may be created? Is special apparatus required? Will there be rescue problems? Will there be a need for a large amount of breathing apparatus, foam, etc? Are there any other factors affecting the fire department response or action? Will there be a need for support services, e.g., police, ambulances, etc?

In summary, prefire planning is essential to ascertain risk potential, but additionally, an in-depth understanding of the dynamics and behavior of fire, building construction, human reactions and the properties and hazards of materials is necessary if the fire officer is to make rapid and sound decisions on the fire ground.

The combination of being aware of the layout and occupancy of buildings, industrial plants, and other hazards in the area, together with the technical knowledge of fire, makes for an understanding of the risk potential which can take some of the uncertainties out of fire suppression activities and fire ground decision making.

In assessing risk potential, whether for prefire planning or when dealing with incidents, all of the factors in Table 9-3A should be considered individually and collectively. For

Table 9-3A. Interrelated Factors Affecting Risk Potential

1. Life Risk	Handicapped, sleeping, concentrated, etc.
2. Contents	Readily combustible, extremely hazardous, quantities, disposition, etc.
3. Construction	Type, age, condition, compartmentation, height, extent, exposures, interior finishes, etc.
4. Built-in Protection	Sprinklers, fire doors and walls, smoke detection, etc.
5. Time	Delayed alarms, long distances, traffic, etc.
6. Suppression Resources	Water, apparatus, equipment, manpower, etc.

example, in the case of an old wood-frame nursing home having no alarm or sprinkler system and located some distance from a fire station, the factors from Table 9-3A that should be considered are 1, and 3 through 6.

This type of semi-analytical approach can be expanded and used for almost any risk: it can be used for planning resources, response levels, and preparing action plans. It can also be used to develop training exercises using group reaction techniques that help prepare officers and officer candidates to think in terms of a systematic assessment for fire ground decision making.

Transportation Incidents

Road: Incidents involving road transportation may range from a simple car engine fire to the fully involved tank truck carrying hazardous materials. Such incidents often involve simultaneous fire and rescue operations in which speed is invariably an essential element. Extreme caution is required in handling any truck fire until the exact nature of its contents is known. A large amount of hazardous materials is moved daily by road, and there have been a number of cases where fire fighters have been killed or injured when dealing with what appeared to be a simple fire situation that, too late, was found to involve extremely hazardous materials.

Rail: As with road transportation, a wide range of cargoes are carried by rail; in any fire involving rail cars, extreme caution is required. Until the nature of the cargo can be determined, fire fighters should assume a highly defensive posture. Means of identifying cargo is by labels or placards on the product or car respectively, and by the manifests or waybills carried in the locomotive or caboose. Services such as "Chemtrec" (a 24-hr emergency advice service provided by the Manufacturing Chemist's Association—toll free telephone no. 800-424-9300), or contact with the railroad concerned might assist where positive identification cannot be made on the scene or when other advice or assistance is required. Often, mixed cargoes are involved which may seriously compound the risk.

Air: Aircraft crashes may occur on or off airfields and invariably present a fire and rescue problem. In order to carry out rescue, fire department action has to be rapid and effective. There are several good sources of information on dealing with aircraft accidents, including: NFPA No. 402, Standard Operating Procedures, Aircraft Rescue and Fire Fighting; NFPA No. 403, Standard for Aircraft Rescue and Fire Fighting Services at Airports and Heliports; NFPA No. 406M, Standard for Aircraft Rescue and Fire Fighting Techniques for Fire Departments Using Conventional Fire Apparatus; and IFSTA (International Fire Service Training Association) No. 206, Aircraft Fire Protection and Rescue Procedures.

Marine: Fires on waterborne vessels can generally be categorized as follows: (1) engine space or room, (2) accommodations, and (3) cargo space. Vessels range from small pleasure boats through barges, cargo carriers, warships, cruise ships, and super tankers. All categories present differing problems that require a thorough knowledge of ship construction, design, stability, and the special techniques of shipboard fire fighting. In the case of cargo ships, the nature of the cargo may vary from inert materials through general combustibles to highly flammable and explosive materials. As with any other transportation fire, restraint is required until positive identification of the materials involved is made. The ship's manifest is usually available from the ship's master.

Generally, fire departments with port facilities are trained in dealing with shipboard fires. Such training is of extreme importance, as marine fires cannot be handled in the same way as shore fires. Another important factor is the need to interact with the Port Authorities, the Coast Guard, and the master of the vessel concerned. The division of authority and responsibility is often unclear and should be clarified at the time of the incident, or before, if possible.

Some basic factors to consider are: stability, which may be affected by application of water; premature ventilation, which may greatly increase the loss; the possible obstruction of waterways or port facilities should the vessel capsize or founder; ability to deal with fire away from wharfside; use of ships' built-in extinguishing systems to the absolute maximum; and fire spread through bulkheads.

Much will depend on a proper determination of the exact location, extent of fire, and materials involved. Until this has been done, action should be limited to layout of hose lines and other preparations in readiness to deal with the fire once a final decision has been made as to course of action.

Transportation incidents differ from structural fires or fires at industrial plants in that they may occur in any part of a fire department's area of protection. It is, therefore, difficult to pre-plan action on a precise basis; nevertheless, a plan of action should be developed which can be applied to any possible location where the incident might occur. The following guidelines are reprinted from NFPA Technical Information Bulletin No. 1-74, "Hazardous Materials Transportation Accidents":

> Extreme caution in dealing with fires involving tank trucks or tank cars is necessary due to the many hazardous materials carried, the difficulty of identification of contents under accident conditions, and the extreme danger presented by possible explosion within a short time following the accident. An unduly high number of fire fighter deaths and injuries have occurred at such incidents.

> Unless there are overriding requirements to rescue or protect persons who either cannot be evacuated or the number of whom is such that immediate and rapid evacuation is impossible, the fire department should keep out to a safe distance. If, for rescue or life protection purposes, it is decided to commit fire personnel to action, such action should be carried out with maximum resources so that the desired effect will be achieved. Fire fighters must be provided with full protec-

tive clothing and equipment, be covered by water spray, use large, long reach hose streams directed at all points of flame impingement on tanks, set up unattended monitors, and withdraw. (Water supplies must be capable of prolonged and sustained operation.)

Tanks have exploded with devastating effect, minutes after involvement. The effects are: (1) flash ground fire, (2) blast, (3) missile effect of rocketing tanks and large fragments of metal (not necessarily in the line in which tanks are lying), and (4) fire ball, a large rising ball of flame, expanding and radiating heat.

No guaranteed safe distances can be given as fragments have been known to travel 5,000 ft. Generally, however, an evacuation area of at least 3,000 ft in all directions is recommended as the absolute minimum.

Mutual Aid and Major Emergencies

There is always the possibility of fire and "disaster" problems that may exceed the capacity of the local fire fighting forces. For this reason, fire departments traditionally have rendered mutual assistance in times of need. Mutual-aid plans have been developed to establish procedures for calling and sending help between fire departments so that each party to the agreement will know what is expected. Mutual-aid plans may include the following functions: (1) immediate joint response of several fire departments to alarms of fire from high risk properties, (2) response from the communities to alarms adjacent to the boundaries between fire department areas, (3) covering of vacated territories by outside departments when the resources of the local department are engaged to the extent that its ability to furnish adequate protection for subsequent fires has been reduced, (4) provision of additional units to assist at major fires that may be too great for the local department to handle efficiently, and (5) the provision of specialized types of fire fighting equipment not available in adequate quantity locally.

True "mutual aid" is a relationship in which each member is prepared to render assistance to the parties of the agreement. In many places there are programs of "outside aid" whereby communities or individual properties known to be deficient in fire fighting resources contract in advance for certain fire fighting assistance in case of need. In some instances the contract covers basic first alarm response, and in other cases additional assistance for fighting major fires. Both in the case of "mutual aid" and "outside aid," definite agreements should be made in advance in line with the legal requirements governing fire department operations outside its normal jurisdiction.

It should be recognized that mutual aid tends to have deficiencies. The parties to the plan may only give help to the extent that they feel they can do so without seriously reducing the local protection, although the better plans provide effective coverage for all districts dispatching apparatus. Each local department may have its own operating methods, and types of equipment, so that maximum coordination may be hampered. This is far less serious than formerly, due to state fire training programs, large scale exercises, and fire officer command schools and conferences.

The advent of nuclear weapons, as well as experience with large-scale natural disasters, has focused attention upon the importance of plans and organizational procedures for systematically mobilizing fire forces for large-scale operations. In some states in the United States the emergency organization and methods to be followed are prescribed by state law. Experience in many major peacetime disasters has shown that, for successful disaster operations, it is imperative that formulated plans allow fire departments to function within the scope of their normal organizational and command procedures.

B. Fire Prevention

Fire prevention encompasses all of the means used by fire departments to decrease the incidence of uncontrolled fire. The fire prevention methods employed by fire department personnel involve a combination of engineering, education, and enforcement. Good engineering practices can do much to provide built-in safeguards that help to prevent fires from starting; such practices also help to limit the spread of fire should it occur. Education is the method used to instruct and inform groups and individuals of the dangers of fire and its possible effects. Enforcement is the legal means of correcting deficiencies that pose a threat to life and property. Enforcement is implemented when other methods fail. In addition, fire investigation aids fire prevention efforts by indicating problem areas that may require additional educational efforts or legislation to correct deficiencies.

In the United States, the full value of fire prevention was not realized until fire departments and agencies began to compile meaningful information concerning the causes and circumstances of fires. Such information caused the more progressive departments to initiate more effective fire prevention efforts in addition to maintaining their fire fighting forces. Currently, the results of such efforts are being more clearly defined every year. In 1973, fire prevention received its greatest endorsement when the National Commission of Fire Prevention and Control reported on the fire problem in America. Throughout the report, top priority was given to the necessity for increased fire prevention activities in reducing fire loss.

Organization for Fire Prevention

In the Dominion of Canada there is a Dominion Fire Commission and provincial fire commissioners for the various provinces. In the United States, although certain branches of the federal government conduct research and gather data concerning the fire problem, no national governmental agency has been created to maintain a fire fighting or fire prevention force. Most states have offices at the state level to oversee certain phases of fire protection. The chief administrator at the state level is usually called the state fire marshal.

State Fire Marshal: The makeup of state fire marshal offices differs from state to state. Most receive their authority from the state legislature and are answerable to the governor, a high state officer, or a commission created for that purpose. In some states the fire marshal's office may be a division of the state insurance department, state police, state building department, state commerce division, or other state agency. Few are organized as separate agencies.

State or provincial agencies normally function in those areas that go beyond the scope of the municipal, county, or fire district organizations. Local fire protection organizations are sometimes granted the authority to act as agents for the state in stipulated areas of inspection, enforcement, and investigation.

Chief of Fire Prevention or Local Fire Marshal: The laws of the county, municipal, or fire districts delegate the responsibility and authority of fire prevention to the fire chief or fire department head. Provision is then made for him to delegate this authority to an individual or division, depending on the size of the department. The individual or head of the division should be a high ranking chief officer and should also function as a staff officer to the fire chief. This division of the fire service is normally called the fire prevention bureau, and its top officer is chief of fire prevention or local fire marshal. Where size permits, the bureau is divided into subdepartments of inspections, investigations, and public education. These subdepartments are then headed by subordinate chiefs.

Fire Inspector or Fire Prevention Officer: The term fire inspector or fire prevention officer has different meaning depending on department classification. Sometimes the two titles are the same and denote the position responsible for conducting fire inspections assigned to the fire prevention bureau. In bureaus not large enough for three subdepartments, the fire inspector is also responsible for conducting fire investigations and performing public education duties.

Fire Protection Engineer: The complexity and magnitude of fire protection problems make the services of fire protection engineers very desirable. While most of their work is done on a consulting basis, some public fire protection agencies have recognized the need for full-time staff engineers.

Fire Prevention Operational Tasks

Plans Review: This service is now legally mandatory for many fire prevention agencies. It provides the fire service with its best opportunity to see that fire protection standards are met prior to construction. Plans review must be followed up with on-site inspections to ensure that the fire protection provided for in the plans is not overlooked in construction.

Inspections: Fire department inspections fall into four general categories. Occupancies to be inspected in the first three inspection categories include places of public assembly, educational, institutional, residential (not interior of dwellings), mercantile, business, industrial, manufacturing, and storage. The four general categories are:

1. Inspections required by law are usually conducted by members of the fire prevention bureau. These inspections include all buildings and premises with the exception of the interiors of private dwellings. Inspections are made for the purpose of seeking out those conditions that violate the fire code, and that are liable to cause fire or endanger life and property. Emphasis is also placed on those conditions of interest to fire officers for pre-fire planning and training purposes.

2. Fire inspections conducted by fire companies that supplement inspections of the fire prevention bureau. Before performing inspection work, fire fighters should receive proper training and be granted the authority to conduct inspections as fire prevention officers. These inspections are normally conducted in the fire company's first due area. The fire prevention bureau provides assistance where needed in obtaining compliance to company recommendations.

3. Inspections made by fire company personnel for the purpose of pre-fire planning and training. Emphasis is also placed on conditions that violate the fire code, and that are liable to cause fire or endanger life. Conditions that require more than on-the-spot correction are usually referred to the fire prevention bureau.

4. Home inspections conducted by fire companies. The fire fighters are received into the homes voluntarily by the occupants. The recommendations made are not mandatory. If definite code violations are found, an effort should be made to have the hazard corrected through proper department channels of authority.

In June 1967 the Supreme Court of the United States made a landmark decision affecting inspections and right of entry.[2] This decision has not affected fire inspectors of public or private commercial establishments to a very large degree. The decision does point out, however, that in those rare cases where a businessman might insist on a warrant before his business can be inspected, it is best to obtain the warrant.

Public Education: Public education and training are necessary tools in fire prevention. If the public is to take the initiative in helping to solve the fire problem, it must be made aware of the problem; should the fire service fail to provide adequate knowledge and motivation, lack of public concern may result. The purpose of the public fire service makes it a logical organization for helping to educate the general public. Also, individual organizations can provide effective campaigns that help to draw attention to particular problems.

Seasonal Activities: The four seasons of the year present a natural time table that is often used as the basis for informative education programs of interest to the general public. Public education programs include National Fire Prevention Week, Operation EDITH, and Sparky's Junior Fire Department Programs. Many materials supplied by the National Fire Protection Association are used in public education programs.

Special Interest Groups: Special interest groups with information needs similar to those of the general public, but different enough to require individual programs, include educational, industrial, institutional, residential, high-rise, civic, service, professional, and commercial groups. There are many ways to reach such groups. For example, the media looks for public service information that will be of interest to their viewers, readers, and listeners; educational groups are interested in lesson plans that can be added to study programs.

Public education must be constantly up-dated and upgraded in order to maintain public interest and support. Failure to be up-to-date in an educational approach to fire prevention often results in the loss of excellent opportunities for communicating vital information to special interest groups as well as to the general public.

Fire Prevention Codes: Many well-meaning fire prevention recommendations receive voluntary public acceptance and compliance. However, a fire prevention code that has been adopted into law is essential for any successful fire prevention program. The major objective of any successful code is to provide a reasonable degree of safety to life and property from fire.

The Insurance Service Organization publishes its recommended fire code, and several building code organizations have written, or are in the process of writing, fire codes for use in conjunction with their own building codes. The National Fire Protection Association has also developed NFPA No. 1, Fire Prevention Code.

Some states and local governments have adopted the 15 volumes of the National Fire Codes of the NFPA; these fire codes are often considered to be the country's most authoritative codes.

Public Information: At times there is certain information that the general public needs to know immediately, and time does not permit its dissemination by means of regular public education channels. It may be information about a particular fire problem that suddenly appears, such as hazardous toys or garments, a particular need of the fire service, or a large fire that is in progress and of concern to the public. Some departments have officers on their staffs who serve as public information officers; in the absence of such officers, information is usually handled by the fire prevention bureau.

Consultation: The general public looks to the public fire service for answers to its fire problems. Because fire prevention covers such a broad area and reaches so many people, consultation services are necessary. Fire prevention officers must be capable of explaining fire codes to professional people such as architects and engineers who may be experiencing fire codes for the first time when they file their plans for review, as well as being able to explain to children the dangers of playing with matches.

Records and Reports: Records and reports of fire prevention activities should be clear and concise. Every time an inspector or fire prevention officer visits a location, information about that location is included in a record or a report. The occupancy file of each building visited should include a complete history of the building site, building plans, specifications (where possible), permits issued for the use, storage, and handling of hazardous materials, inspection reports, and fire incidents.

Photography: The inclusion of photography in records and reports is invaluable. A photograph, properly taken and identified, is one of the best ways to fully illustrate conditions to persons such as the city attorney, owner of the building, chief officer, judge, or jury. Photographs and detailed reports can help eliminate much argument as to actual conditions at the time of exposure. Photography is also useful for educational purposes. Many departments have full-time photographers and complete camera and laboratory equipment and facilities.

C. Fire Ignition Sequence Investigation

Most fire departments were organized to provide for the immediate urgency of fighting fires, and few were set up to develop and compile comprehensive, in-depth information on the number of fires occurring by location and occupancy, the fire ignition sequence or causative factors, the time of day or week of occurrence, the room or floor in which the fire occurred, and similar information that is basic to any effective evaluation of a fire problem.

While it has long been recognized that fire prevention is one of the major concerns of all fire department personnel, a point that has not been as well recognized is that comprehensive investigation of fires and all the factors influencing or contributing to the fire ignition sequence or communication of fire is the very foundation on which fire prevention is built. Without the extensive and detailed information obtained from these factors, it is impossible to develop the most effective regulatory codes, standards, inspection and suppression procedures, and similar actions designed to prevent or control fire.

A fire protection duty of equal importance to comprehensive investigation is the accurate *reporting* of such investigations. This duty has seldom been recognized as an essential part of fire protection, the result being that fire departments and fire protection interests have, in the past, often depended upon unreliable projections and reports in order to effect corrective efforts involving building and fire prevention codes and standards, to point up special fire protection problems, to judge the magnitude of the problem, or to determine whether or not there is a problem.

There is increasing interest and recognition of the need for improvements in both fire ignition sequence investigation and fire loss reporting by all public agencies, from the national level down to the smallest volunteer department. Coupled with this increased recognition is the fact that there is now available informational guidelines and standards to assist in the development of fire loss investigation techniques and reporting systems. Fire ignition sequence investigation and fire loss reporting are important functions in the operation of fire departments. For further details on both, see Chapter 4 of Section 1, in this HANDBOOK.

Fire Loss Reporting

NFPA No. 901, Standard for Uniform Coding for Fire Protection, hereinafter in this chapter referred to as the NFPA Uniform Coding Standard, establishes uniform language, methods, and procedures for fire loss reporting and coding. This system is designed so that all information can be coded for electronic or manual data processing.

The use of electronic data processing is essential if meaningful and readily retrievable fire loss data is to be collected. The almost unlimited capability of data processing allows for the input of great volumes of individual reports covering all sections of a large jurisdiction, as well as details of reported information relating to the factors and combinations of factors influencing the ignition sequence or communication of fire. By electronic means, the nation's approximately 1,200,000 fire service personnel can now more effectively find, evaluate, and compile fire ignition sequence information. By pinpointing problems, suggesting answers, and eliminating the misdirection of effort and expenditures of the fire protection dollar, analysis of this type of information will lead to fire prevention programs that have a major effect on fire suppression procedures, structural and fire protection codes, manufacturers and equipment dealers, and on all other areas of fire protection.

Legal Aspects

Accurate determination and reporting of the fire ignition sequence is in the public interest. This is indicated by the broad powers given most fire marshals in rights of entry for fire inspection and investigation, fire marshal's hearings, rights of subpoena of any records or persons who may have information as to the fire ignition sequence, etc. These powers have been upheld by most courts of law. Such powers are invaluable in establishing and corroborating ignition sequence of fire, and such authority should be honored when utilized by members of the fire service when performing their duties.

Such broad powers are not generally applicable, however, to criminal investigations, and since arson is a felony, these rights do not apply to fire investigation after the fire ignition sequence has been established as arson. These rights may also tend to become diffused when a recognized police agency conducts fire ignition sequence investigations in cases where the ignition sequence is not immediately established. For this reason, it is usually advantageous to maintain some distinction between civil actions involving fire ignition sequence and criminal investigations of arson.

Relationship with Other Investigation Agencies

More effective results are usually produced in both fire investigation and suppression of arson by establishing areas of primary responsibility in arson detection and arson investigation. It should be recognized that the *detection* of incendiary or arson fires along with all other fire ignition sequences is the responsibility of the fire service. This is due to the fact that fire service personnel normally have the best or perhaps the only opportunity to observe fire behavior, analyze the fire scene, and preserve evidence, etc.

Since all state laws establish arson as a felony, after the fire service determines the ignition sequence of a fire to be arson, then that sequence must be further investigated. At the arson investigation phase the police authorities normally have primary responsibility, much the same as for other felonies occurring within their jurisdiction. In many areas of the United States, particularly at the state level or in larger cities, state and municipal laws give fire authorities the power to perform the police function of arson investigation.

Both areas of responsibility—fire detection and fire investigation—are highly technical and specialized. Close coordination of detection and investigation efforts, along with a recognition of the necessity for overlapping in these two general areas, is essential. Often, additional information obtained from interrogations or other aspects of the criminal investigation will corroborate and strengthen the fire ignition sequence factors, and in some cases change the fire ignition sequences altogether.

Should a suspect be apprehended and charged, it is again the primary responsibility of the fire service to prove the corpus delecti of arson, i.e., that the fire was willfully and maliciously caused.

Case Development

When developing an arson case, the following three elements must be established:

1. That there was an actual charring or destruction by fire.

2. That the ignition sequence of the fire was the result of willful and malicious design or intent.

3. That the suspect or an agent of the suspect had the opportunity to cause the fire.

An established motive is of great value in an arson case, although motive is not, from a legal standpoint, considered as an essential element of arson: in fact, many incendiary fires might be classified as being without motive. It should also be considered that in the presentation of an arson case, each of the three preceding elements must be established to the satisfaction of the court in the order presented before the next element may be determined.

Probable Cause

When evaluating a fire scene, it is necessary to work toward developing probabilities with the understanding that absolute certainty is seldom possible, and that probability suffices to govern belief and action. After assembling as many of the fire ignition sequence factors or conditions as possible, several ignition sequence possibilities are usually considered. It is advisable to work from the most probable possibilities while keeping known facts in mind. Thus, a probability that fits most of the known conditions will usually be found.

Burn patterns or combustion characteristics of commonly involved materials have many exceptions and variables. These patterns should not be construed as positive indications when considered individually. A number of burn patterns, such as similarities in finger prints, will usually give a highly probable indication of the time-temperature and other fire ignition sequence factors.

Some indicators have much more value than others, but all must be considered in light of their probative value. There should be no reluctance to establish probative values; actually, even so-called direct evidence has a probative

value and is rarely absolute and positive by itself. All evidence must be weighed or considered for its probative value.

Preliminary Investigation

There are many conditions and situations that a fire fighter should note on the way to, and at the time of, a fire, such as autos and persons in the area, color and intensity of the fire and smoke, number of fires, and direction of fire travel. Although most fire fighters are familiar with these, there are often some items that are easily overlooked, such as noting the description of vehicles and persons traveling in the opposite direction. It is also important, where possible, to note the license numbers of vehicles and the names of persons at or near the scene of the fire at the time of arrival. Persons at the scene seldom volunteer information and will often leave before the fire fighting job is completed. Full names of all persons who may have information, or may have been in a position to have information, should be obtained. Information supplied by such persons can be valuable in corroborating items such as point of origin, time of burning, and actions of occupants in both accidental and arson fires. It is important to determine whether doors and windows were locked, unlocked, or open, and if forced open by fire fighters, which ones, and in what condition they were at the time they were forced open.

When the fire is out, guards should be posted and all persons (including unnecessary fire fighters and policemen) should be excluded from the area—especially the point of origin—until the cause has been established or the investigator has taken charge.

In making investigations there are several exceptions or reservations to usually accepted procedures; for example, for years fire departments have been taught to reduce fire loss and create good public relations by thoroughly cleaning the premises and leaving everything in good order. Such action can actually make investigation more difficult as many thousands of fire ignition sequences, both incendiary and accidental, have been eliminated by such hasty cleanup action. A basic rule of fire investigation is to not overhaul or disarrange the premises in any way other than as necessary for controlling or blacking out the fire. It is always preferable to make a preliminary investigation at the point of origin, since walking on or moving any of the burned debris in any way can alter or destroy evidence. In nearly all cases there is little additional loss if the room or area encompassing the point of origin is not cleaned out, since this area is usually the most heavily damaged by the fire and only minimal salvage is possible.

Fire Scene Analysis

In fire ignition sequence investigation, it is helpful to analyze the ignition sequence by establishing five basic factors essential to the occurrence of a fire: (1) the place the fire started or the point of origin, (2) the initial material to become ignited, (3) the source of ignition, (4) the time, and (5) temperature factors. The most probable fire ignition sequence or the act or omission of an act that brought these factors together in a manner resulting in fire is then developed by combining the available information from as many of the essential fire ignition sequence factors as can be determined, and relating this fire scene information to information obtained from occupants, witnesses, or any other source. The act or omission of an act that combines ignition sequence factors into fire is generally referred to as "fire ignition sequence."

In many fires not all of the ignition sequence factors can be determined. However, some of the factors can be developed and are valuable as partial information. Even when only one factor, such as point of origin, is determined, such information can be combined with readily determined information like occupancy, time, place, and date to help determine the ignition sequence or focus the direction of further investigation. This is particularly so when combined with many other such fire incidents in a broad-based fire reporting system. An additional advantage of analyzing fire ignition sequence by determining essential factors is that such practice aids in coordinating and expediting fire loss reporting and data processing since national fire loss reporting standards, such as the NFPA Uniform Coding Standard, are structured to approach fire losses by component elements of origin, materials ignited, source of ignition, etc.

Point of Origin

The first step in most fire investigations is to determine point of origin as closely as possible. Because time-temperature information is necessary to the development of all other ignition sequence factors and particularly to point of origin, the type of fire that has occurred should be considered in terms of fire temperature and burning time.

When developing time-temperature factors, they should be broken down into periods prior to discovery of the fire and from the time of alarm to blackout—or up to the point when there is no further active or free flaming combustion. With the development of the fire time and temperature factors, the point of origin factor will usually be developing simultaneously, and effort should be made to define the point of origin as closely as possible. Point of origin is always determinable, and in most cases can be determined easily and quickly.

As well as being the first step in fire scene analysis, developing a point of origin is also the most important step since, when point of origin can be accurately pinpointed, many of the other ignition sequence factors become more clearly indicated and the majority of possible factors can be eliminated.

Burn Patterns

In determining the time-temperature factors leading to the point of origin, many burn patterns, combustion characteristics, or what might be termed "fire tracks," are used to determine direction of burning or fire travel, fuel consumption, and the time and temperature of fire exposure. Heat signs will be found on nearly all commonly involved combustible materials such as window glass, wood, plastics, aluminum, etc.

Points of origin are much more easily established after reconstruction of the fire scene. Occupants can assist in locating the position of furniture and in giving details as to the types of materials that were in the area. If occupants are not available, someone familiar with the occupants might remember details of content arrangement. The direction of heat flow can then be followed by checking for deepest charring, indications of highest temperature, duration of heat, and comparison of similar objects exposed to similar heat conditions. Temperatures at certain spots are indicated by the condition of metal, glass, wood, plastics, etc. Since heat flows up whenever possible, a general rule of thumb is to look for the lowest point of deep char as the point of origin, bearing in mind the many exceptions.

Once the room or area of origin has been established, the level of origin within the room should be determined by examining the bottom side of shelves, ledges, moldings, and furniture. All sides of the legs, arms, and framework of reconstructed furniture should be examined. It is important

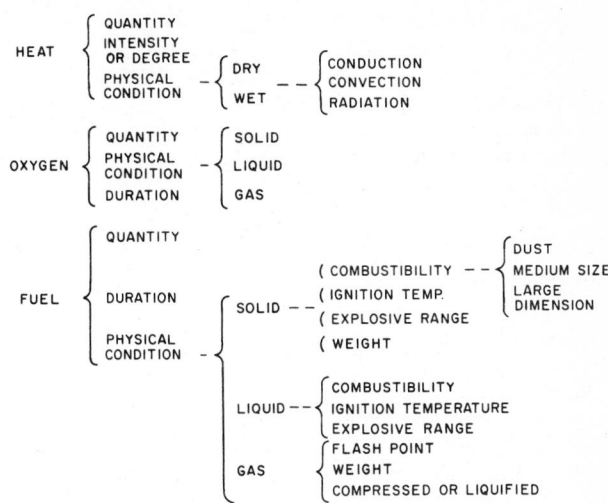

Fig. 9-3A.   Expansion of fire triangle.

to carefully clean the floor at the point of origin, examining and keeping aside *all* objects. Next, the floor and/or rugs should be swept as clean as possible for examination of burn patterns. The floor and lower areas of the room will produce the most clues since this is the "living area"; most of the equipment and contents are near floor level, the actions of the occupants are conducted near floor level, and most materials will drop to floor level during a fire.

To assist in arriving at the point of origin and ignition sequence, it is helpful to examine and analyze the heat patterns and burning characteristics of the involved materials and equipment. Many variables can be seen if we consider the fire triangle and expand it to include some additional factors. (See Fig. 9-3A.)

When checking for the fire ignition sequence at the point of origin, it is advantageous to use the "layer checking" technique. Before any material is moved or shoveled out, notes should be made and the layers or strata of material should be examined carefully. This can lead to a picture of the sequence of materials burned at the point of origin. For example, a set fire could be indicated by charred newspapers found at the floor beneath charred drapery fabric, particularly if the papers would not normally be in that area or if the dates on them were different from the present date.

Fires caused from low-temperature or nonflaming heat sources are probably the most deceiving. Some examples are cigarettes, light globes, steam pipes, electric irons, soldering irons, electric blankets, heating pads, and spontaneous ignition. In order to understand the manner and probability of ignition from low temperature heat sources in the area of 800°F in usual everyday conditions, several factors must be considered. Besides the combustibility of the fuel there is the insulation factor created by density and depth of fuel, the duration of exposure to the heat, the flashpoint, the ignition temperature, and the explosive range or limits of flammability. When heat as low as 250°F is applied to cellulose materials (such as wood) for a long period of time, pyrophoric carbon is formed. Carbon absorbs oxygen rapidly and has a tendency to self-heat. The tendency to self-heat becomes an important factor when large quantities of carbon are involved. Conditions of this type are encountered when light globes or steam pipes have rested against heavy timbers for long periods of time and considerable depths of carbon having much lower ignition temperatures than wood are formed. The depth of pyrophoric carbon with its self-heating tendency combined with the heat of the electric bulb or steam pipes is known to have caused fires at temperatures as low as 250°F. Although such fires are a rare occurrence, such conditions are usually indicated during a fire investigation by a large charred-out section several inches in depth at the base, or point of origin, of the fire. Evidence of a slow-generating fire will also be indicated.

Fire Scene Evidence

It is obvious that evidence of fire ignition sequence and any factors influencing the communication of fire cannot normally be reduced to just a few items. Actually, the entire fire scene can be considered as evidence.

Some of the items at the fire scene will have greater value than others. These items usually are at or near the point of origin, and are generally factors that, by pointing out or corroborating other indicators, help to establish one or more of the fire cause factors. In determining what evidence to remove from the scene for more extended analysis and/or for later corroboration of conclusions, it will usually be these same indicators or samples of them that provide information on burning time and temperatures, initial materials ignited, and source of ignition.

All fire ignition sequence evidence should be photographed before removal and immediately tagged or marked by the officer removing the evidence, indicating the officer's name or initials, date, type of evidence, and where the evidence was located. Also, if evidence is of any material or intrinsic value, a receipt should be given to the owner.

In order to preserve the continuity of possession, it is preferable that evidence stays in possession of the officer removing it; if possession is transferred, a written record should so indicate.

Just as every effort should be made to determine the factors leading to the ignition sequence or communication of fire, so should extra effort be given to preserving all evidence leading to such conclusions. Often, the most effective means of preserving fire cause evidence is with ample and clear photographs.

In summary, the following can be considered as a fairly effective general guide for investigation of the fire scene:

1. Review structural exterior and fire suppression and timing.
2. Reconstruct as much as possible.
3. Establish approximate burning time and temperatures.
4. Determine path of heat travel and point of origin.
5. Evaluate combustion characteristics of all materials involved.
6. Compare similar materials and situations.
7. Fit known facts to various possibilities.
8. Corroborate information from occupants and witnesses.

D.   Communications

Fire department communications consists of three main areas:

1. The means for receiving notification of emergencies from the public.
2. The means for alerting and dispatching apparatus and personnel.
3. The communications necessary for emergency and routine business.

(See Section 12, Chapter 1, for a description of municipal fire alarm systems and hardware.)

Dispatch Procedures

NFPA No. 73, Public Fire Service Communications Standard requires that a distinctive tone signal be trans-mitted before transmission of a verbal alarm of fire. In many fire departments using both radio and wired circuits for dispatching, the radio message preceeds the message on the metallic circuit so that noise and confusion in the fire stations incidental to response will not hinder receipt of voice instruction which is confirmed subsequently on the wired circuit. However, in some fire departments the wired dispatch circuit is treated as primary with specific instructions being given to responding units by radio. A difficulty sometimes experienced with this procedure is that where a fire is near the station, officers trying to contact the communications office by radio are delayed by repeated dispatch announcements.

In order to limit radio traffic, rather than use the radio dispatch circuit, some communications systems using coded signals on wired circuits make it a practice to give still or local alarms to the units involved by means of fire department telephone. Where wired voice circuits are provided, these circuits are used for transmission of both still or local alarms and alarms requiring a standard first alarm response. Where apparatus normally assigned to respond to alarms is not available, the operators must send the next nearest available companies—usually those assigned to second alarm response at the same location. The NFPA Public Fire Service Communications Standard requires that an alarm of fire, including requests for multiple alarms, must be transmitted to the proper fire department companies over the required dispatch circuits. Also, it requires that the first arriving fire company at the location of the alarm must give a brief preliminary report to the communications center on the conditions observed. Some fire departments also require periodic progress reports from the officer in charge at a fire including an estimate of the time that apparatus will be held at the scene. Companies returning from a fire report their availability to the operator. If ready for further response, they may report from the fire scene.

Fire dispatching can be greatly facilitated where data processing equipment is used to maintain constant status of available companies, to provide directory assistance to fire alarm operators and units in the field, and to maintain records of alarms.

Staffing

Fire dispatching requires specially trained operators who are familiar with the operations of the fire department and its equipment. Operators should be capable of conducting the required tests of the system unless other qualified persons are assigned to this work. The NFPA Public Fire Service Communications Standard gives guidance as to the minimum number of operators that should be on duty. For systems receiving less than 600 alarms per year, alarms not automatically retransmitted must be received and retransmitted to the fire force by a competent person who may be the house watch at a fire station, a member of another department, or a designated person employed by the local telephone company. Where a fire fighter on watch responds with the apparatus, means must be provided to transfer service to another municipal office such as the police department when the watch desk is uncovered. Hundreds of communities no longer have supervised local telephone exchanges, and the nearest supervising operator many miles away may be totally unfamiliar with the local fire department or community. In such cases, the fire phone number may be arranged to ring in a number of locations where appropriate action can be taken to dispatch fire apparatus. This may be the situation in volunteer fire departments having no regular watch service at the central fire station. Increasingly, small fire departments are being served by regional fire alarm offices which can be properly equipped and staffed.

Where the number of fire alarms is more than 600 and less than 2,500 per year, at least one trained alarm operator must be on duty at all times. Where there are more than 2,500 alarms per year, at least two trained operators must be on duty at all times with additional operators provided as warranted by the traffic. Additional operators should be provided as needed for periods of peak work loads such as brush fire seasons, times of civil unrest, and when major fires are in progress. In addition to transmitting alarms of fire and dispatching apparatus to emergencies, operators must handle the radio traffic, operate the telephone equipment, maintain records and logs, and provide directory service. Frequently, they also have to conduct the numerous periodic equipment tests called for in the NFPA Public Fire Service Communications Standard. In a busy alarm office there should be a senior or principal operator in charge of the shift who usually directs movements of apparatus, at least two operators at the alarm console, and a radio dispatcher. Where the alarm office handles emergency ambulance dispatching, it is often desirable to maintain a separate console staffed by one or two operators as needed.

Information Retrieval and Storage

An important part of a communications office operation is to have immediately available any information that may be needed in dispatching assistance to fires and emergencies. A considerable part of an operator's time is spent in maintaining directories and data files that are typed either on a visible index or as input into a data bank. Included in the data files are a complete index of all streets and ways, giving house numbers for cross streets, the area or alarm box code number which may be from the master map, the first alarm assignment, and units to be dispatched on still alarms. These directories include all target hazards such as schools, hospitals, industrial and business buildings, and the phone numbers of persons and organizations (such as utility companies) to be contacted to provide needed assistance during emergencies. Also recorded are data and phone numbers of fire departments participating in mutual aid operations. (In many cases the fire radios of adjoining fire departments are monitored and fire departments of adjoining communities may also receive alarms over metallic circuits, even where they are not served by the same communications office.)

The use of electronic data processing equipment makes information retrieval much more rapid, and it is possible to program and retrieve considerably more data than is quickly available by more conventional means. Readouts available to the operator on signal of an alarm location from the keyboard may include data on construction, hazards, inspection information, and even prior fire experience. In addition, data concerning each alarm can be entered into the permanent records and provide complete statistical data on fire experience such as provided under the NFPA "Uniform Fire Incident Reporting System" (UFIRS).

Reports and Records

The NFPA Public Fire Service Communications Standard and NFPA Standard No. 4, Organization for Fire Services, indicate the reports and records which must be maintained by the fire alarm or communications office. These include: a daily summary of alarms received and transmitted, a radio log, a daybook record of work on the system, reports of tests specified for communications equipment, a record card for each alarm box, a record or file on other communications equipment, plans of wiring, and record of installation, maintenance, or removal of equipment. In addition, an annual report of operations summarizing statistics is required from the superintendent. In some communities, management may require a monthly report as well as copies of the daily report. The daily journal of the communications center should show what operators are on duty on the various tours and who is in charge.

In all fire alarm offices a complete radio log is required by FCC rules. Operators at the radio base station in the communications office are required to control traffic on the assigned frequencies and follow FCC rules. In addition, all incoming and dispatch messages must be recorded with time indication. Both radio and telephone alarm messages are tape recorded with playback features provided to substantiate messages when necessary.

Fire Station Alerting Systems

Standard No. 73 requires that when watch is maintained at all times in fire stations, instruments on all dispatch circuits and the department telephone shall be located in the vicinity of the watch desk or console which usually is in a fire station watch room. Alarm instruments need not be located elsewhere in the station except as necessary to alert all fire fighters but it is common to have speakers and alarm bells or tappers throughout the station. At the watch desk are located controls for the house gong or bell used to alert fire fighters for response to alarms of fire and also control for the house lights which light all areas of the station when fire fighters are turned out for an alarm. There is a call bell used to summon individual members or to make coded announcements. Controls for electrically operated doors may also be operated from the watch desk. In some systems the house bell, lights, and station doors are operated from the communications center when apparatus is due to respond at times when house watch is not maintained. Maps of the area served, fire department running cards indicating order of response to various alarms, and usually a board showing first alarm assignments for companies in the station also are posted in the watch room. At some stations, controls are provided for traffic warning lights outside of quarters. Chalkboards or other equipment is provided to record alarms received and other information that may later be transferred to the company journal.

Where stations are manned entirely by call or volunteer fire fighters and alarm box numbers are not sounded on outside air horns on the dispatch circuit, the communications center may sound the fire station sirens either by a metallic circuit or by radio signal.

E. Maintenance of Fire Department Equipment

The maintenance of fire department apparatus and equipment at peak operating efficiency is one of the primary responsibilities of the fire department administrator, and should be of concern to every member of the department. The safety of both the public and fire department personnel, as well as fire fighting efficiency, depend in considerable measure on the effectiveness of the maintenance program. When properly cared for, fire apparatus is expected to give years of reliable service. The adequacy of a fire department's maintenance program is an important gage of an efficient organization. Each fire department needs a clearly established policy concerning maintenance responsibilities and routines to avoid possible equipment failures during operations.

Ideally, every fire department should have an officer assigned as chief or superintendent of equipment, or a chief master mechanic. In small fire departments this may be a part-time job. Such an officer should keep the chief administrator informed as to the condition and status of the equipment, the equipment needs of the department, and should assist in preparing specifications for the procurement of new items of equipment following accepted standards.

The fire department maintenance officer should maintain a complete record of every piece of apparatus and equipment. This record should show all repairs and servicing, along with cost of labor and parts. The periodic servicing, testing, and lubrication of all apparatus should be under his direction. Service tests of pumping engines should be conducted annually with records maintained of the tests. These periodic tests should be compared with the original performance of the equipment. Service tests should be also conducted on other equipment such as ground and aerial ladders and elevating platforms. Tests should be conducted in accordance with NFPA No. 193A, Standard for Fire Department Ground Ladders, and NFPA No. 193B, Standard for the Care, Maintenance, and Testing of Fire Department Aerial Ladders and Elevating Platforms.

Some fire departments maintain service vehicles and crews that check and service apparatus in quarters, and respond to fires to oversee mechanical equipment operation and emergency repair. Other departments have maintenance personnel, on call 24 hours a day, who respond only to major fires. Some small fire departments without full-time maintenance personnel have one or more fire fighters serving as part-time mechanics in addition to their duty as fire fighters.

Maintenance of fire apparatus and equipment should be a continuous operation. Insofar as possible, routine maintenance should be preventive, with all minor repairs made promptly. This will help eliminate many costly repairs. For example, a frequent cause of major breakdowns has been failure to change oil and lubricate apparatus on a scheduled basis. Since fire apparatus is subject to frequent starting and relatively high speed operation with cold engines, this maintenance procedure becomes even more critical if the apparatus is to be dependable and expected to last. Road mileage for heavy apparatus is seldom high, but crankcase oil is subject to rapid dilution, deterioration, and sludge accumulation unless the crankcase is drained, flushed, and refilled regularly.

It is important that there be a definite policy in every fire department as to what constitutes apparatus repair, and who performs each function. In general, repair consists of fixing or adjusting equipment that is either broken or not operating properly. In-service maintenance is concerned with keeping all items at a peak state of efficiency. The apparatus operator has an important role in the in-service maintenance program, but is seldom expected to make repairs. For example, it is not the usual function of the apparatus operator to adjust the ignition system of an engine. That is the responsibility of the maintenance division.

A large part of routine apparatus maintenance is the responsibility of the assigned apparatus operators under the direction of their company officers. This should be carried out on a daily and weekly basis following check lists or report forms. Among the items for which apparatus operators are responsible are: keeping the fuel tank full, checking oil level in the engine, checking batteries, maintaining tire pressure at the specified level, maintaining water level in the radiator, keeping apparatus water tanks full, and checking all lights. All items needing repair should be reported immediately through proper channels. When repairs are needed, the work should be completed without avoidable delay. The parts used most often should be in stock or readily available. Parts should be inventoried and ordered by the manufacturer's number. The maintenance or service manuals delivered with each piece of apparatus should be on file and used as guides.

Apparatus taken out for repairs or maintenance should be replaced by reliable, properly equipped reserve apparatus. Every fire department should have at least one reserve pumping engine in good condition and ready for use. The insurance grading schedule calls for at least one reserve pumper for each eight pumpers in service or major fraction thereof, but in any case not less than one. Where reserve apparatus is also used by the off-shifts to respond to fires, a higher ratio of reserve to first-line apparatus should be provided. Some fire departments have a reserve fleet of from 25 to 33 percent of their first-line equipment. Reserve ladder trucks, rescue trucks, and ambulances also are important where fire departments operate such equipment.

While the insurance grading schedule calls for one reserve ladder truck for each five ladder trucks in service, many smaller fire departments maintain at least one reserve ladder truck by retaining an old ladder truck when a new one is obtained.

Minor equipment or appliances also need routine maintenance and servicing. In a fire department, all items of equipment should be inspected on a periodic basis and repaired or replaced as needed.

Every fire department should have a repair and servicing facility commensurate with its needs to take care of apparatus and equipment, including fire hose. The necessary power tools for maintenance should be provided. Repairs other than minor must not be made on the apparatus floor of a fire station. Such practices disrupt normal operations and impose potential accident and fire hazards. This is particularly true of a station area that contains the alarm dispatch center or quarters for personnel. A repair shop area should be properly cut off from the operating areas of a fire station if the area is not located in a separate building.

The fire department shop should be well lighted, have needed work benches, ample power outlets, and jacks and hoists as needed to handle heavy equipment. The shop should meet all fire protection standards for a repair garage, and areas used for painting should be properly protected. There should be an office for the officer in charge of maintenance, an adequate and secure stock room for parts, and suitable toilet and washroom facilities. A shop facility should include a section or area where fire hose and couplings can be properly repaired. Large fire department maintenance shops generally also have an equipment repair section. Where a fire department has a fleet of chief officer and staff cars, it is convenient to have a separate section equipped as a small car shop.

In a moderate sized fire department having ten or more fire companies, a minimum sized repair shop should be capable of handling at least two major pieces of fire apparatus simultaneously, including an aerial ladder or elevating platform truck. This is important so that routine servicing of apparatus can continue while another piece of apparatus is laid up for repairs that require appreciable time while parts are being obtained or serviced. Garage space should be provided for maintenance vehicles. In some cases pump testing equipment is provided at the shop, and in other fire departments these facilities are at the fire department training center.

In some communities repair of apparatus is assigned to a municipal service garage. This arrangement may be satisfactory if a regular fire apparatus repair and service section is provided and staffed by persons qualified for the specialized nature of this work. Such personnel must be available on a 24-hr basis to take care of maintenance needs at fires and emergencies, and a proper supply of needed parts must be maintained. Unfortunately, many fire departments find that their equipment repair and servicing has a very low priority in a municipal shop, often coming after garbage trucks, police vehicles, and various other city vehicles. Often, mechanics do not have the necessary time or skills to carry out a proper fire department maintenance program.

Regardless of whether repairs and servicing are done by fire department mechanics or by another agency, there should always be a fire department maintenance officer reporting to the fire chief; the fire department maintenance officer is responsible for the complete equipment maintenance program. Where work has to be sent out to private repair garages, this work should be done to the satisfaction of the fire department maintenance officer or master mechanic. In some cases it is advisable to send apparatus to an apparatus manufacturer for major repairs or rebuilding.

The maintenance officer should prepare an annual report to accompany the fire chief's annual report. This report should indicate the condition of the apparatus and equipment, work done, and cost of repairs.

Unfortunately, there are no standards covering the proper staffing of a fire department maintenance operation. However, administrators should keep in mind that this is an essential round-the-clock service. Maintenance personnel are entitled to vacations and sick leave, as are other fire department employees. A desirable minimum maintenance staff would consist of a chief master mechanic assisted by two mechanics. This provides a minimum of two men on regular weekday duty at all times, with at least one man available on 24-hr call. It also permits the assignment of one man to check apparatus in the stations as needed while shop work continues. Additional personnel time is also necessary where fire department maintenance personnel are required to deliver supplies. Also, where fire department maintenance personnel are responsible for maintenance of fire department buildings, additional personnel will be needed.

In small fire departments, at least one full-time, qualified, maintenance mechanic should be provided when the hourly overtime rate for conducting a complete fire department maintenance program on a part-time basis approaches the cost of having a full-time man. In small fire departments where there is only one regular mechanic, arrangements should be made to provide qualified assistance as needed.

F. Training

Fire departments are unable to obtain the services of trained personnel and must, therefore, provide all necessary instruction and training themselves. The level of performance demonstrated by a department is usually a good indication of the type, quantity, and quality of the training provided. For example, training programs in small departments may consist of only basic fire fighting instruction, while large departments may provide comprehensive training programs for all levels of personnel.

In addition to departmental training programs, most states provide some type of fire service training that, depending upon the state, ranges from basic fire fighter training to fire department management programs. Nationally, large city and county fire departments tend to have training facilities and full-time training staffs. The training divisions of some fire departments, having added research responsibilities to their training facilities, have come to be known as research and training divisions. In the larger fire departments, training takes two forms: the first is continuous in-service training conducted by the company officer on a daily basis; the second is an annual refresher of from one to five days at a fire training center. Officer training may be conducted on an annual basis at a fire college or a staff and command school.

Large cities often have deputy chiefs in charge of training, with staffs made up of personnel from various ranks within their departments; middle-sized communities tend to have district chiefs or captains in charge of training, with minimal additional personnel (including fire fighters having specialized expertise). Small communities may have a captain or lieutenant in charge of training, with the authority to assign other officers as needed during certain periods of the year.

The training of call or volunteer fire fighters is usually the responsibility of the chief or deputy chief. In some call or volunteer departments, an officer is designated as the training officer.

Training Objectives

The goal of any fire department training program should be the provision of the best possible training for each person within the department, regardless of rank, so that each person will perform at acceptable performance levels. Ideally, training program courses should have their own instructional objectives, a list of enabling objectives showing how the instructional objectives can be reached, and stated methods that explain how anticipated or desired behavioral changes can be measured.

State Fire Training Programs

State fire training agencies are normally headed by a state director of fire training. Many state fire training programs operate under the umbrella of an educational agency within the state (usually vocational or occupational education), or under the auspices of a state university or college. In some states the director is responsible for both informal training and college level courses, while in other states there is a separate community or junior college coordinator.

In some states the state director of fire training operates under other state agencies such as the state fire marshal's office, the state department of public safety, the state civil defense agency, or the state department of community affairs. In Delaware, the state fire training program operates under a commission appointed by, and reporting directly to, the governor.

Recently some states have established state fire protection personnel standards and education commissions. These commissions are appointed by the governor and consist of representatives from fire service organizations within the state as well as engineers, members of the insurance industry, and citizens at large. The commissions report directly to the governor, and their relationship to state fire training programs varies in that some commissions work directly with the state training agency supplying the supportive services for the commission while others, having their own staffs, function independently.

Some state directors of fire training have no full-time instructors, while others have a small cadre of full-time senior instructors or supervisors who, in addition to their teaching functions, may be responsible for: assigning and supervising part-time field instructors, developing instructional outlines, developing and producing audio-visual training aids and props, and monitoring the required records associated with a state program. State programs may also provide services such as training of recruit fire fighters for departments that employ only a small number of fire fighters at one time and lack the training facilities, personnel, and resources to conduct their own training programs. Additionally, state programs provide training for specialists within the service, conduct seminars on material of current interest and importance, and serve as a valuable reference and informational service.

Fire Service Organization Training Programs

Each of the major fire service organizations sponsors conferences and seminars as a part of its annual meeting, or separate seminars on material of current importance. Examples include the "Symposiums on Occupational Health and Hazards of the Fire Service" conducted by the International Association of Fire Fighters, the "Seminars on High-Rise Fires" conducted by the National Fire Protection Association, and the annual meetings of the National Fire Protection Association, the International Association of Fire Chiefs, and local and state fire service organizations.

Utility Company and Private Agency Training Programs

At the local and regional levels, programs are available from: the major utility companies (gas and electrical companies), from state agencies (forestry, public safety, and civil defense), and from private agencies that interact in various ways with the fire service. Many such privately sponsored training programs can be considered public education training programs.

College Training Programs

Since the early 1960s there has been a rapid increase in the number of two-year college level fire science programs in the United States. Most programs are offered by community and junior colleges either on a full-time or part-time basis. In most cases an associate degree is awarded upon successful completion of the program, and some institutions award certificates for partial completion.

College level fire science programs are usually designed to supplement, but not replace, fire training provided by fire departments and state training agencies. The curriculum design for many such programs emphasizes the arts and sciences and special courses in fire protection subjects that are beyond the scope of basic fire training programs; courses requiring manipulative skills such as hose, ladders, etc., are not incorporated into college level fire science programs.

Training Levels

Efforts of the National Professional Qualifications Board for the Fire Service are helping to produce nationally accepted, standardized levels of rank within the fire service. At present few major differences exist within the ranks of fire fighter or of fire officer. Levels of training for other fire service personnel are, in most cases, nonexistent, although training courses do address the general specialized classification. The following material presents examples of the types of training that could be applied to the various levels and ranks of fire service personnel.

Fire Fighter: Fire fighter training should be performance oriented (see Part B, Chap. 1 of this Sec.), continuous, and repetitive in order to obtain and maintain proficiency within the three generally accepted levels, and to afford progression from level to level. Entry or recruit level training should be specified in terms of meeting performance objectives. Performance levels should meet the needs of the department. The recruit fire fighter should be able to demonstrate the knowledge of, and ability to perform, the objectives specified for Fire Fighter I in NFPA No. 1001, Standard for Fire Fighter Professional Qualifications, and should be able to work under direct supervision. In-service fire training should help maintain the skills and proficiency developed at the Fire Fighter I and II levels, and should help to upgrade these skills so that the individual will be able to demonstrate a knowledge of, and an ability to perform, the objectives specified for the next higher level. In-service training should be formal, well planned, and continuous. It should consist of daily training within the company and frequent refreshers at a fire training facility. Advanced training for the Fire Fighter III level should be mandatory. These fire fighters are often required to function as officers, and should be prepared to advance to the rank of officer as vacancies occur. Training to meet the requirements of the first supervisory officer level should be made available at the Fire Fighter III level along with training in fire prevention and instructing.

Special courses in a variety of subjects should be available to all fire fighters. Subjects common to all levels such as hazardous materials, inspection and prevention practices, water safety, arson, etc., can be covered in special seminars. Subjects common to certain geographical areas such as high-rise fire fighting, wildland fires, and maritime fire fighting can be covered in special training sessions. Emergency medical personnel can be trained and certified by means of special courses. Special courses should be available for fire prevention bureau personnel, fire alarm dispatchers, aircraft crash and rescue fire fighters, marine company personnel, mechanics, and clerical personnel.

Officer Training: Officer training courses in strategy and tactics, fire suppression, fire ground command, and how to cope with major emergencies can best be taught at fire academies where provisions can be made to observe the handling of personnel. Courses in the humanities, liberal arts, technology, engineering, and business administration are best dealt with through college programs. Following is an outline of the suggested training that could be applied at the officer levels:

1. Company officer is usually the first officer level. The training at this level should include advanced training in fire suppression, building construction, hazardous materials, safety principles, chemistry, report writing, fire prevention, protection systems, leadership, and interpersonnel relations.

2. Intermediate officer levels may include the rank of captain or district chief, and assignments may include station commander, district commander, or assignment to a specialized area such as training, inspection, fire prevention, arson, etc. Training at this level should include technical mathematics, physics, fire protection systems planning, major emergency planning and control, community relations, press relations, leadership, and prefire planning.

3. Chief officers require highly specialized technical skills and administrative ability. When an officer reaches this level he should be trained in the political sciences, public administration, government relations, planning and forecasting future needs, writing specifications, management information systems, and labor relations. In addition to college courses available in these subject areas, it is highly advantageous for chief officers to participate in short courses and seminars aimed at specific interest areas.

Fire Prevention Personnel Training: This type of personnel requires specialized training in a number of areas. In the past many of the personnel assigned to fire prevention bureaus have had to learn through experience due to limited specialized training. Training should include fire safety, public education, portable and fixed extinguishing systems, building codes, fire prevention regulations and codes, ordinances and laws, community relations, press relations, public speaking, fire investigation, and plans examination. Advanced training for those responsible for a fire prevention bureau should include the advanced sciences, program planning, analysis of fire records, and courses in leadership, administration, and supervision.

Instructor Training: Programs for state field instructors are provided by state fire training programs. These programs vary in length from 6 to 250 hours, and few are given or required at the college level. Following are suggested instructor level training descriptions:

1. A Fire Instructor I should have the ability to teach from prepared lesson plans using prepared visual aids. A program of study that meets these standards should include courses in motivation, lesson preparation, lesson presentation, handling students, educational psychology, and the use of all types of visual aids and props.

2. A Fire Instructor II should have the ability to develop lesson plans, procure and develop visual aids, design training aids, and prepare and review examinations. Subjects taught at this level should include lesson plan development, audio-visual program design, testing and measurements, and developing performance objectives.

3. A Fire Instructor III should have the ability to design overall programs and supervise personnel. Subjects taught at this level should include performance analysis, program design, scheduling techniques, specification preparation, scheduling and evaluation techniques, personnel supervision, and program budget preparation.

4. A Fire Instructor IV (usually the State Director of Fire Training or the head of a municipal training division) should have the ability to administer a training program. Subjects taught at this level are in many cases identical to those at the Chief Officer level. Additional subjects would be similar to those required by the administrative head of an educational agency.

Fire Investigation Personnel Training: A solid foundation as a fire fighter or in fire behavior should be mandatory, and experience as a fire inspector should be a prerequisite for appointment as a fire investigator. Training should include specialized training in the areas of interrogation techniques, conducting investigations, report writing, criminal behavior, characteristics of fire travel, and criminal law. Certain portions of this curriculum are generally available in police science courses. Local and national arson seminars permit personnel to keep abreast of current developments.

Communications Personnel: Training for communications personnel can be divided into the following two areas:

1. Personnel working as dispatchers should receive training in listening, communications, use of telephone and recording equipment, radio procedures, fire alarm procedures, dispatching and movement of apparatus, and information retrieval.

2. Personnel assigned to the fire alarm division should be trained in electronics circuitry, fire alarm installation and maintenance, and radio repair.

Apparatus Maintenance Personnel: These persons should have strong backgrounds in automotive truck repair. In many departments the personnel responsible for repairing apparatus are civilian employees, while the head of the maintenance division is a fire officer. First echelon maintenance should be the responsibility of the driver/operator; the maintenance division may be responsible for their training, including driver training. Most engine and transmission manufacturers have regional training centers. Fire apparatus maintenance personnel can attend sessions at these centers and can learn new techniques or participate in refresher courses. Pump or apparatus manufacturers can be requested to provide maintenance training for their equipment.

Training Records and Reports

Recent court decisions regarding job-related examinations have placed additional importance on training records and personnel evaluations. Training records and reports are probably most important at the entry or recruit level where training examinations are necessary and personnel evaluations must be conducted. Whether from examinations or evaluations, such records and reports should be discussed with the individual concerned. It is good practice to have such reports signed by the individual concerned to indicate that they have reviewed them.

There are no standard training record forms. Each department or agency must develop its own. Sample forms may be found in several of the publications listed in the Bibliography at the end of this chapter. Training records should be clear and concise, and should document a fire fighter's advancement. The content of records and reports are particularly important when personnel are evaluated for pay increases and promotions.

G. Emergency Medical Service

In addition to their regular fire suppression services, many fire departments provide ambulance service. Ambulance service often includes emergency medical service and minimal patient treatment as well as transportation to the nearest medical facility.

In recent years, there has been increased interest and activity in emergency medical service. Some departments have elected to provide this additional service, while others have been required by local government to assume such responsibility. The quality of emergency medical service has shown marked improvement.

One of the greatest stimuli for the increased interest and activity in emergency medical service has been federal involvement requiring higher standards for patient care and the upgrading of training and equipment. Also, the medical community has shown an increased interest in this type of medical service.

Fire department communications systems are basically the same as citizen access and dispatching systems and can be successfully used for emergency medical service. It has been found that because fire fighters are emergency service oriented, they can be easily trained to provide emergency medical care.

At present, there are two basic types of emergency medical service categories in fire departments—emergency medical technician and paramedic. Both categories require special training. In most cases the emergency medical technician undergoes a minimum of 81 hours of training, including in-hospital training, in a standard course that is taught or supervised by professional medical personnel. The paramedic may receive up to 1,000 hours of training, a majority of which are in-hospital training. Paramedics are trained in administering drugs and intravenous solutions, and in other medical techniques, under a doctor's supervision. In order for the paramedic to function effectively under a doctor's supervision while in the field, some rather extensive and sophisticated communications systems have been developed.

Bibliography

NFPA Codes, Standards, and Recommended Practices (see the latest *NFPA Publications and Visual Aids Catalog* for availability of current editions of the following documents)

NFPA No. 9, Standard for Training Reports and Records.

NFPA No. 13E, Standard for Fire Department Operations in Protected Areas.

NFPA No. 197, Training Standard on Initial Fire Attack.

NFPA No. 295, Standard for Wildfire Control by Volunteer Fire Organizations.

NFPA No. 73, Standard for Public Fire Service Communications.

NFPA No. 402, Standard Operating Procedures, Aircraft Rescue and Fire Fighting.

NFPA No. 403, Standard for Aircraft Rescue and Fire Fighting Services at Airports and Heliports.

NFPA No. 406M, Standard for Aircraft Rescue and Fire Fighting Techniques for Fire Departments Using Conventional Fire Apparatus.

Additional Readings

Bahme, C. W., *Fire Officer's Guide to Extinguishing Systems*, National Fire Protection Association, Boston, 1970.

———, *Fire Officer's Guide to Dangerous Chemicals*, National Fire Protection Association, Boston, 1972.

———, *Fire Officer's Guide to Emergency Action*, National Fire Protection Association, Boston, 1974.

Brannigan, F. L., *Building Construction for the Fire Service, a Fire Officer's Guide*, National Fire Protection Association, Boston, 1971.

Bond, Horatio, ed., *NFPA Inspection Manual*, 3rd ed., National Fire Protection Association, Boston, 1970.

The Fire Fighters' Responsibility in Arson Detection, National Fire Protection Association, Boston, 1971.

Fire Officer's Guide to Breathing Apparatus for the Fire Service, rev. ed., National Fire Protection Association, Boston, 1975.

Fire Protection Guide on Hazardous Materials, 5th ed., National Fire Protection Association, Boston, 1973.

Grant, R. W., *Public Fire Safety Inspections*, National Fire Protection Association, Boston, 1967.

Kimball, W. Y., *Fire Attack 1*, National Fire Protection Association, Boston, 1966.

———, *Fire Attack 2*, National Fire Protection Association, Boston, 1968.

———, *Fire Service Communications for Fire Attack*, National Fire Protection Association, Boston, 1972.

Layman, Lloyd, *Attacking and Extinguishing Interior Fires*, National Fire Protection Association, Boston, 1955.

———, *Fire Fighting Tactics*, National Fire Protection Association, Boston, 1953.

Lyons, P. R., *Fire Officer's Guide to Elevating Platforms and Aerial Towers*, National Fire Protection Association, Boston, 1974.

Morse, H. N., *Legal Insight*, National Fire Protection Association, Boston, 1973.

Operating Fire Department Pumpers, a Fire Officer's Guide, National Fire Protection Association, Boston, 1974.

Operating Aerial Ladders, a Fire Officer's Guide, National Fire Protection Association, Boston, 1974.

Page, J. O., *Effective Company Command*, National Fire Protection Association, Boston, 1974.

———, *Handling Hose and Ladders*, National Fire Protection Association, Boston, 1969.

Storey, T. G., "FOCUS: A Computer Simulation Model for Fire Control Planning," *Fire Technology*, Vol. 8, No. 2, May 1972, pp. 91–103.

Tobin, E. T.; Davis, J. B.; and Mandt, Conrad, "Automated Forest Fire Dispatching—a Progress Report," *Fire Technology*, Vol. 5, No. 2, May 1969, pp. 122–129.

The following additional readings are published by the Internatonal Fire Service Training Association, Stillwater, Okla.

Forcible Entry
Ground Ladder Practices
Fire Hose Practices
Salvage and Overhaul Practices
Fire Stream Practices
Fire Apparatus Practices
Fire Ventilation Practices
Fire Service Rescue and Protective Breathing Practices
Fire Service First Aid Practices
Fire Prevention and Inspection Practices
Fire Service Practices for Volunteer Fire Departments
Fire Service Training Programs
Water Supplies for Fire Protection
Aircraft Fire Protection and Rescue Procedures
Ground Cover Fire Fighting Practices
The Fire Department Officer
Fire Department Facilities, Planning, and Procedures
Fire Service Instructor Training
Leadership in the Fire Service
IFSTO Source Material References Guide

Section 9

Chapter 4

FIRE DEPARTMENT FACILITIES, APPARATUS, AND EQUIPMENT

Facilities, apparatus, and equipment comprise those items, in addition to personnel, that enable a fire department to function and fulfill its assigned objectives. This section discusses these three categories.

A. Facilities

Facilities may include buildings or space for administration, housing of personnel and equipment, communication, training, maintenance, and supply. In some smaller organizations all of these functions may be contained in one building. Larger organizations, however, may require several facilities in different locations. Apparatus and equipment are the means by which fire department personnel achieve assigned tasks.

Administrative Offices

Administrative offices may be located in an office building of local government, such as city hall or county courthouse, at a fire headquarters building, or a central fire station. Administrative offices should include space for the administrative head of the organization plus staff personnel. This may include offices for such activities as fire prevention, fire investigation, planning and research, budget, and personnel. The size and space requirements will be dictated by the size of the organization.

When planning new offices, expansion of existing offices, or new administrative offices, consideration should be given to the activities that occur within each office. Offices that are frequented by the public should be easily accessible, and arranged so that the general public does not have to pass through other offices or quarters. Separate entrances may be desirable for staff personnel. Ample storage space should be provided for the filing and storage of records and reports.

When fire investigators are assigned there should be separate rooms for interviewing witnesses and suspects, as well as secure storage rooms for the preservation of evidence. If frequent staff meetings are held or the department operates under a board or commission, it may be desirable to have a large meeting room. This room can also serve as an operations center for the department during major emergencies, if properly equipped with communications equipment. In addition to the building, there should be ample parking space for the public, assigned personnel, and department vehicles.

Fire Stations

Determining fire station locations is one of the most significant factors in planning any fire station. When planning for new fire stations or relocating existing stations, several factors should be considered to provide the best possible protection in terms of coverage to the area and response time.

Determining Location: The area to be protected by the proposed station is the most important factor in determining station location. Some areas in the community will contain higher risk potentials than others, such as those containing primarily business, industrial, mercantile, institutional, and multifamily residential occupancies. In some instances it may not be desirable to locate a station in a high risk area. The station should therefore be located within a reasonable

response distance on the perimeter. Distribution should provide a concentration of companies for response into high risk areas without depleting other areas of the community should a second fire occur. In other areas that contain an equal risk throughout, such as residential, stations should be equidistant from all parts of the area. Where stations are staffed by volunteer fire fighters consideration must be given to locating them in or near areas where those fire fighters live and work in order to facilitate quick response.

Topographical features of a community may also affect fire station locations, and the total number of stations required. Communities that are divided by natural and manmade barriers such as rivers, mountains, limited access highways and railroads may limit response routes and require additional stations. Heavily traveled and one way streets are undesirable for fire station locations because of access and limiting response routes. Stations that are located in outlying areas close to community boundaries reduce response areas except when the community is anticipating annexation. Coordination with community or regional planning agencies can provide valuable information in terms of growth potential and land use when planning new fire station locations.

Fire department records can also provide valuable information for plotting fire station locations. Fire experience may indicate specific areas of high rate of incidence. Response times may also prove useful. Computers are currently being used in some communities to aid in plotting fire station locations. This is not the answer for all communities since a valid data base must be established before computers can be utilized. (See Fig. 9-4A for a plot plan for a typical district station for urban and suburban services, and Fig. 9-4B for a plot plan for a typical rural station. See Fig. 9-4C for elevation and plan view of a typical urban fire station, and Fig. 9-4D for elevation and plan view of a typical rural fire station.)

Site of Structure: Once the location has been determined, the site of the structures on the location must be determined. The station should be set back far enough to permit a paved ramp in front of the building so that apparatus can be cleaned prior to parking inside. The site should also allow sufficient parking for personnel. Parking and traffic patterns on the site will differ for volunteer and paid personnel. Additional space should be provided for outside training activities.

Design Features of Fire Stations: The size of fire stations should be compatible with the maximum anticipated number of personnel and pieces of equipment that will be assigned. Construction details should emphasize three important aspects: maintenance, traffic patterns within the station, and fire protection features. All portions of the station should be designed so that it is easy to clean and maintain. Stations that require extensive amounts of time for cleaning and maintenance reduce departmental productivity in terms of prefire planning, fire prevention, and training. Stations that require frequent painting are also costly in terms of maintenance. Traffic patterns within the station should receive careful consideration. The design must consider the ease with which personnel can reach the apparatus room from all parts of the building with a minimum of confusion.

Fire protection features are an item that must not be

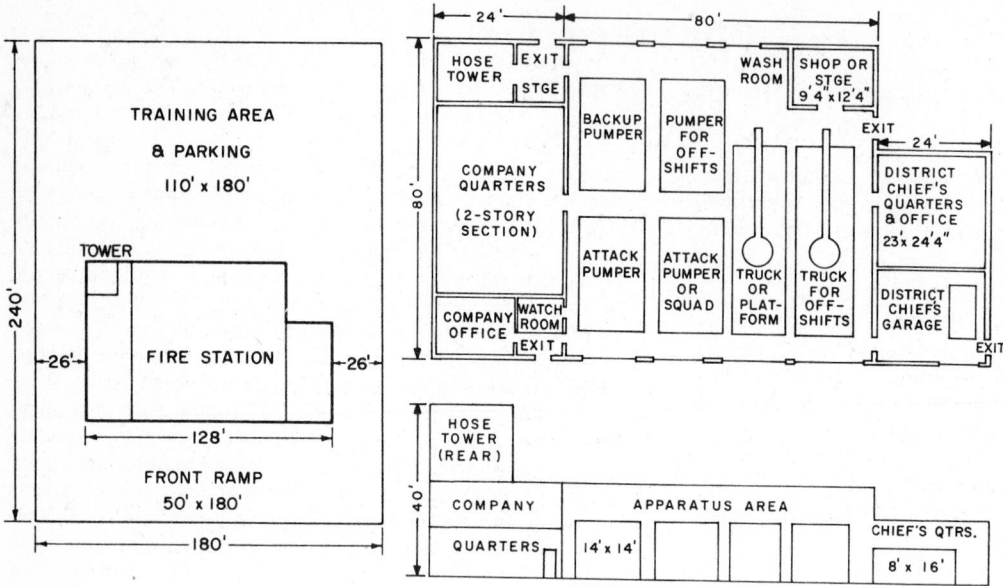

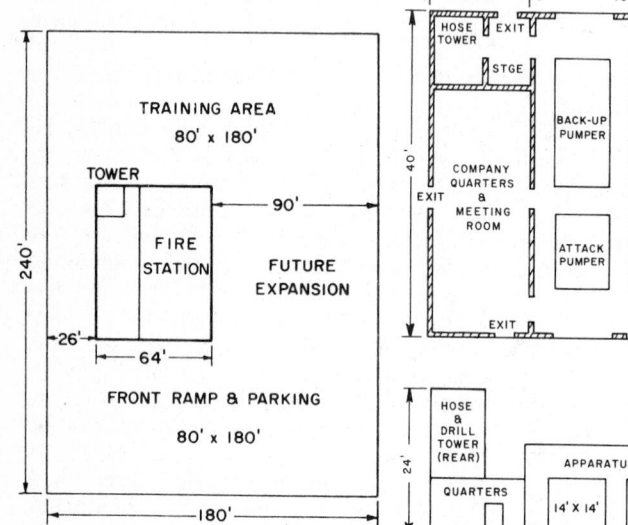

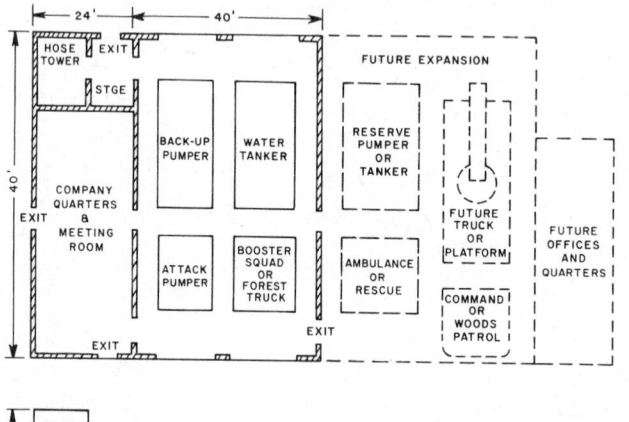

Fig. 9-4A (left). Plot plan for a typical district fire station for urban and suburban services. Minimum recommended plot size is 43,200 sq ft.

Fig. 9-4C (right). Elevation and plan view of a typical urban fire station.

Fig. 9-4B (left). Plot plan for a typical rural fire station. Minimum recommended plot size is 43,200 sq ft.

Fig. 9-4D (right). Elevation and plan view of a typical rural fire station.

overlooked. Since fire stations contain all the hazards normally found in a garage, assembly hall, dormitory, and school, protection from these hazards should be included in the building design. This includes fire detection devices, fire suppression devices, and proper exits plus other local building code requirements.

Based on safety considerations it is preferable that fire stations be only one story high. However, because of lot size and economics, two stories may be necessary. Basement areas should be avoided, particularly under apparatus floors, since this tends to add materially to the cost because of the weight that must be supported. Apparatus room floors should be of concrete slab construction with care taken to avoid a slick finish. Painted concrete floors are generally unsatisfactory, and if color is desired it would be preferable to add it to the finish layer of the floor. Some departments utilize steel treads or runners under the apparatus, but these are expensive. Air entrained concrete should be used to avoid salt damage. The floor should be pitched for adequate drainage, but not so steeply that the apparatus will roll toward the doors when the brakes are off. Drains across the front of the apparatus room are sometimes installed to permit washing the salt off the apparatus in the winter.

Apparatus room doors should be wide and of more than ample height. They should open vertically, and if power operated should be able to be raised manually in the event of a power failure. Power operated door controls should be provided at each door and at the watch desk. All doors should be capable of being opened simultaneously from the watch desk but, unless there is ample visibility from the watch desk, should only be closed from controls at the door. It should be kept in mind that doors with large glass areas may lead to high heat losses and require larger heating facilities. Doors opening into the apparatus room should be provided between the apparatus room and the rest of the building.

Heating and Ventilating: The heating and ventilating system should be adequate and installed in accordance with appropriate standards of the National Fire Protection Association. The system must have the ability to recover rapidly after the apparatus responds to a winter alarm and the doors are not immediately closed. Fuel storage should be outside the structure, and the inside filling of fuel oil tanks should be avoided.

Adequate ventilation of the apparatus room should be provided to avoid concentrations of carbon monoxide during the usual engine warmup, drilling or servicing which may be done. Exhaust hoses or mechanical ventilation equipment should be provided.

Electrical facilities should be adequate and installed in accordance with the National Electrical Code provisions for garages. Service receptacles should be closely spaced, especially in the apparatus room and maintenance areas. Drop leads, suitably protected, may be desirable near the apparatus.

Battery charger loads should be handy to the apparatus position, preferably with the cable on self-retracting reels. Battery chargers should be so located that when used the leads do not present a hazard to men attempting to board the apparatus to respond to an alarm. Emergency power of sufficient capacity should be provided to operate all necessary station services, including alarm devices and equipment.

In addition to the water services usually provided for a public building of this type, consideration should be given to facilities for refilling department tankers and apparatus booster tanks. While in good weather this can be done outside, it may be desirable to have water hose leads suspended over each apparatus position for quick refilling during cold weather. In rural areas, water cisterns or tanks near the station may be desirable.

Training Area: A separate classroom for use as a training area is preferable, but if not feasible the meeting hall should be planned with training in mind. Training facilities should include a wall mounted chalkboard, a projection screen, shades to darken the room, book shelves, etc.

Watch Desk: The point at which alarms are received within the station should be in the form of a desk arrangement with wall space for maps, schedules, and instructions, and with ample space for the necessary radio equipment, alarm control devices, floor controls, and traffic signal controls. The area should be as soundproof as possible, and should allow clear visibility of the entire apparatus room. A desirable location is near the front entrance to the station, the point where visitors may enter and seek information.

An apparatus room should be located with consideration given to its location relative to the remainder of the building. It is preferable that the floor area be unobstructed by columns or projection of other rooms into this space. Ample space must be provided to permit work around apparatus, changing of hose, and to permit free movement when responding to alarms. Additional space is needed for clothing racks and hose storage, if not provided in separate rooms. Multitrack stations require a minimum width of 20 ft per track. Single track stations should be at least 24 ft wide. Depth is dependent upon the number of pieces of apparatus to be housed, but ample space must be provided front and rear to permit routine maintenance, ease of response, and repacking of hose.

Stations should have adequate office facilities for all officers assigned. This includes both company officers and battalion or district chiefs. Dormitories, locker rooms, washrooms, kitchen, and recreation rooms are also required when full time personnel are assigned. The storage of equipment and supplies, and storage of fuel for apparatus and hose drying are additional considerations for fire stations.

Training Facilities

Training facilities are a definite prerequisite to the meaningful training of fire service personnel. Much training can be done without formal facilities; however, certain areas of training become more meaningful and productive when carried out at facilities designed especially for training purposes. Throughout the country, one can find many types of facilities ranging from the low cost, self-designed, and self-constructed facility to those designed by architects and constructed by professional contractors. The sizes, shapes, and varieties range from a ladder tower constructed of telephone poles and lumber with 3 floors and pitched roofs for a cost of less than $1,000, to a complete fire academy facility which can cost up to $6,000,000. It is the intent of this part of this chapter to list the advantages and disadvantages of each type, to emphasize the safety features regardless of the type, and to point out as many types as possible to those considering the new facilities. New constraints imposed on the fire service by the environmental protection laws, which dictate air and water pollution standards, must also be considered.

Many existing training facilities are underused and understaffed. The original intent in constructing such facilities was honorable and creditable. Some fire departments and other agencies are constrained by budget limitations and cannot provide adequate training facilities. Thus, many facilities are unused for great periods of time. Those interested in constructing a facility are advised to explore the use of existing training facilities within the immediate area, or to enter into an agreement with other contiguous communities and share both the expense and use of such a facility.

The sharing of facilities is becoming more common today, in view of the current austerity program affecting fire department budgets. A pioneer in this field is the Joint Powers Training Center in California, constructed by the cities of Fountain Valley, Seal Beach, Westminster, and Huntington Beach. Through the combined efforts of the mayors, city managers, and fire chiefs of these four cities, an agreement was reached for the construction and operation of a central fire training facility and fire training system.

In the past 10 years, the number of fire training facilities throughout the country has increased as more fire administrators have focused on the values of training. Those considering the construction of a facility are advised to arrange on-site visitations at existing facilities prior to the selection of, or in the company of, the architect selected to design the facility. Within a radius of 100 miles of Washington, D.C., there can be found no fewer than six such facilities, each of which has its own characteristics, strengths, and weaknesses. Within these facilities are found most variations of major importance to the design and construction of training facilities.

Utilization of a training facility must be considered at a very early stage. A utilization plan is an important factor in the budget justification. County, regional, and state training facilities are considerably more difficult to plan for than a local or municipal facility. In planning utilization, it is desirable that the exact length and content of the curriculum and the frequency that courses will be attended be known. Deducting periods when the facility will not be used, such as during the winter months in areas affected by snow and ice and during holiday and vacation periods, can help establish a utilization formula.

Location: Careful and detailed consideration concerning the location of a training facility is necessary, because once the commitment is made and ground is broken it is almost impossible to change locations. Such changes are extremely costly. Factors involved when considering locations for training facilities regardless of jurisdiction include:

1. Land selected for the construction of a training facility

should be remote from all types of occupancy, although accessibility must be a careful consideration for state, regional, and county facilities.

2. Topography is important, and flat land is most desirable for economic reasons.

3. Water in adequate quantities is an absolute necessity for training purposes, and drainage considerations are important.

4. Electricity should be available in adequate quantity.

Design Features of Training Facilities: The designs of training facilities are varied and numerous. The intended use of the facility must be projected in detail before the actual design is finalized. Experience is important, and assistance from persons experienced in the scheduling and operation of training facilities should be sought before final decisions are made.

There are two basic design concepts for training centers. One concept is that all essential features of a training facility, i.e., ladder tower, forcible entry area, smoke house, burn building, and draft pits be incorporated into one building. The second concept that has been advanced in recent years is that of having separate buildings or areas for each of the major functions carried out at the training facility. The disadvantage of this concept is that the cost is greater than a building that contains all features under one roof. The advantages are that evolutions being performed in a specific building or area do not interfere with those being carried out in other buildings or areas. If adequate land is available when the facility is being designed, it is easy to incorporate a buffer zone of trees or other natural barriers between each operational area or building.

In the design stages, consideration must also be given to water supply, drainage, oil and water separation, and in general any element that could or will be affected by the environmental protection laws.

Essential Features of Training Facilities: There are many essential features that must be included when planning a training facility. Again, intended use dictates which features will be incorporated and the space requirements for each feature. The size of municipal fire departments is usually stable when training facilities are being considered. Communities experiencing growth should anticipate future needs during the planning stage. Communities that are annexing land or protecting contiguous unincorporated areas should consider future increased demands which may be placed on such a facility. Safety should be a prime consideration in the planning of all facilities. Some of the essential features common to most training centers include:

1. An adequate amount of space for the administration area.

2. Storage space for paper and office supplies, as well as clean rack storage for printed material used by instructors and students.

3. Library facilities.

4. Audio visual and training aid facilities, as well as an audio-visual laboratory, viewing and listening areas, and space for the storage and maintenance of all audio-visual equipment.

5. Classrooms, to include careful consideration of adequate lighting.

6. Apparatus storage must be taken into consideration, even if only on a temporary basis. Space to accommodate at least one pumper with adequate room for an instructor and students is minimal, and an exhaust system to carry the exhaust from the apparatus to the outside is mandatory.

7. Towers, preferably constructed of masonry, with enclosed interior stairways and exterior fire escapes are desired, including a dry standpipe system with an outlet at

each floor, windows of varied styles and sizes, window openings, doors, both flat and pitched roofs, skylights, and cutout panels within the roofs, floors and partitions, safety railings at any openings, and elevator shafts to simulate high rise occupancies.

8. Fire buildings, frequently called burn buildings, with at least two stories and a basement, provisions for movable partitions to change the configuration of the interior, windows with steel casings and wired glass, exterior doors, and stairways and bulkheads of adequate size.

9. Adequate space for storage, maintenance, and recharging of breathing apparatus is essential.

10. Areas for flammable liquid fire fighting training consisting of both props and pits.

11. Underground storage space for fuel supplies for training operations, large enough to accommodate from 1,000 to 10,000 gal.

12. Flammable gas training facilities with specially constructed tanks having extra safety features that simulate actual fire conditions. These tanks are equipped with relief valves and other safety and warning features that confront students with the reality they will experience on the fireground.

13. Drafting pits, both for training purposes and for the annual testing of pumpers. Design features should include proper baffles to prevent swirling and air entrapment when water is returned to the pit. Also, provisions must be made for filling and draining the pit.

14. Driver training facilities, consideration of increasing importance in all training programs.

15. Areas for rescue training. (In certain sections of the country, fire fighters are trained in tunneling and shoring techniques at the fire training facility, while in other sections this type of training is carried out at Civil Defense training facilities.)

16. Control towers from which all fire operations can be observed. The tower should be high enough to provide a clear view of the entire facility, and two-way selective communications to each individual building or area on the site is desirable along with an adequate public address system. It should also have controls for lighting and power to the individual facilities on the training ground.

17. Personnel needs such as cafeterias, dining facilities, and locker and shower facilities for instructors and students. Most training centers have the administrative, classroom, storage, and apparatus housing area in one complex, and the remaining buildings and areas located throughout the site. In these cases the central facility should be designed so the students can enter directly into the locker and shower area to clean or change before entering other sections of the building. The necessity of dormitory accommodations must be considered in regional and state training facilities.

Communications Center

The most important aspect of fire department communications is the facility where calls for assistance are received and action is taken. Large communities may require one large center and possible satellite centers to handle message loads, while smaller communities may require only a watch desk located in a fire station. In addition to receiving calls for assistance, the alarm center must be capable of handling all radio communications for the department, keeping a continuous record on the status of all companies, handling communications to each station, maintaining current files and maps of streets, and must have the personnel resources for the required record keeping.

The design of communications centers should focus on the operations room where all calls and alarms are received, and from which all alarms are transmitted to companies or stations. A desk or console may be provided which is occupied by the dispatcher or dispatchers on duty. Console design must be functional so that all necessary operations can be performed efficiently. The operations room may contain all equipment necessary for the receipt of tolerance calls from the public, receipt of alarms from street boxes, a department telephone switchboard if necessary, radio transmitting and receiving equipment, tone alerting equipment, and computer terminals and video display units, if used.

Equipment requirements are dictated by the size of the operation and the type of services that are provided. Centers in communities that have community wide alarm systems require space for alarm equipment and standby batteries. Space is also required for radio and telephone equipment. If computer assisted dispatching is used or anticipated, additional space is required.

Maintenance Facilities

Facilities for maintenance and repair work should be provided for all types of fire department equipment if cost effectiveness can be demonstrated. It may be more economical for some departments to contract with outside agencies, thereby reducing overhead costs for seldom used services. If outside agencies are used, there should be explicit agreements that fire department needs will receive top priority.

Some larger departments maintain specialized shops for all types of maintenance and repair such as apparatus, ladder, alarm equipment, breathing apparatus, and radio equipment. The need for such facilities is dictated by the demand for service. New or additional facilities should be cost effective.

Some departments use mobile vans that are equipped to perform a specified level of maintenance at the station requiring less time for apparatus out of its response area.

B. Apparatus

To a considerable measure, a fire fighting organization is built around the apparatus and equipment used for suppressing fires. The efficiency of its operation is often dependent upon the nature and adequacy of this apparatus. This chapter contains information on the standards and procurement policies that should be followed in acquiring equipment and apparatus.

In North American practices, the basic fire fighting vehicle is a diesel or gasoline driven truck that carries a rather extensive assortment of tools and equipment for fighting fires. Such equipment may include a pump, hose, water tank, ladders, and various portable tools and appliances. The amount and capacities of the various fire fighting components carried varies in accordance with the intended service of the particular vehicle, generally taking into account performance standards which can be measured by tests. NFPA Standard No. 19, Standard for Automotive Fire Apparatus, hereinafter in this chapter referred to as the NFPA Automotive Fire Apparatus Standard, which also has been adopted by the Insurance Services Office and the International Association of Fire Chiefs, is designed to facilitate procurement in accordance with the various components required and specified by the purchaser. In Canada, generally similar standards are developed through the Canadian Insurer's Advisory Organization, and certification tests on apparatus are conducted by Underwriters Laboratories of Canada.

The NFPA Automotive Fire Apparatus Standard is arranged in chapters that deal with the various components of a given piece of apparatus; the Standard also gives details of procurement, provisions applicable to all types of apparatus, and the performance requirements for each type of apparatus. Fig. 9-4E shows some of the automotive apparatus that can be purchased by specifying appropriate chapters and provisions of the Standard.

The size of pump and the amount of water, hose, and equipment carried will vary with the intended type of service such as municipal, suburban, and rural. In general, the largest pumps are provided to protect areas requiring application of large fire flows such as industrial districts. Pumps of 1,000 or 1,250 gpm capacity are popular for general municipal service, and 1,000 or 750 gpm pumps are common in rural and suburban service. The once popular 500 gpm rating is very seldom specified.

In many fire departments it has been found desirable to supplement units equipped primarily for hose-stream service with other vehicles that provide a large variety of tools and equipment such as ladders, forcible entry tools, generators, lights, and rescue equipment. Such units are variously termed "ladder trucks" or "squad trucks," depending upon the primary type of equipment carried.

On the fireground, pumping apparatus must be positioned for the efficient application of hose streams. Other apparatus may be placed for convenient use of the equipment. Ladder, squad, and rescue trucks should have their own regularly assigned crews who can utilize their equipment effectively while pumper companies are getting streams into service.

About one-third of the work at an average fire involves the use of tools and equipment in duties classed as "truck" and "rescue" work. Apparatus suitably equipped for such service should be available at all structural fires and at emergencies such as highway fires and accidents. While pumping engines, squad trucks, and rescue trucks may carry

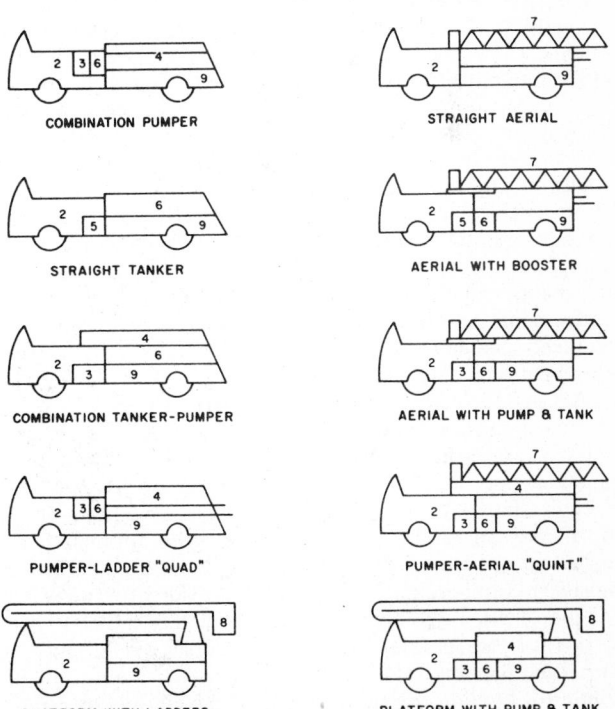

Fig. 9-4E. Some of the types of automotive apparatus that can be purchased by specifying appropriate chapters and provisions of NFPA No. 19, Standard for Automotive Fire Apparatus. The numbers on the drawings identify the location of various components of the apparatus: i.e., 2-chassis; 3-pump; 4-hose body; 5-booster pump; 6-water tank; 7-aerial ladder; 8-elevating platform; and 9-equipment carried.

considerable equipment, the larger aerial ladder and elevating platform trucks commonly transport additional equipment not usually found on other apparatus. Both of these types of apparatus provide vehicle-supported, power-operated equipment to provide access above the normal reach of manual ladders and capable of effective elevated stream service.

A very wide variety of combinations of fire fighting equipment are provided on automotive fire apparatus. Besides combinations of pump, hose, and water tank commonly termed a "triple combination," it is not uncommon to provide a booster pump and small stream equipment on ladder trucks or an elevating platform, or a water tower on a pumping engine. Various desired combinations can be obtained by specifying the desired provisions from the various chapters of the NFPA Automotive Fire Apparatus Standard. When fire apparatus is equipped with long ground ladders and other usual ladder truck equipment in addition to the usual pumping engine equipment, the apparatus is referred to as a "quadruple combination" or "quad." If a power-operated aerial ladder or elevating platform is added, such apparatus is termed a "quint." However, there tends to be a decrease in operating efficiency and capability if too many functions are to be performed by one unit of apparatus.

Increasingly, apparatus is being designed for functional performance as desired by individual fire departments. Initial fire attack capability for pumpers is being improved not only with the addition of preconnected hose lines, but frequently with the addition of elevated stream equipment. Pumpers often are built with considerable compartment space for emergency equipment, and may serve as combination rescue-pumpers.

Provisions Applying to All Types of Apparatus

Chapter 1 of the NFPA Automotive Fire Apparatus Standard is devoted to "provisions applying to all types of apparatus." This chapter covers vehicle design including load carrying capacity, engine design, cooling system, lubrication system, fuel system, and exhaust system. It covers the electrical system and devices including power supply, batteries, starting devices, ignition system, and lights. Vehicle components such as braking system, suspension and wheels, the apparatus body—including the components such as steps and handrails, the driving compartment, and the metal finish and painting. The chapter calls attention to thirty subjects on which special provisions to meet specific local needs may be included in purchase specifications.

Altogether, the NFPA Automotive Fire Apparatus Standard calls attention to 115 options that should be considered as "special provisions" to make the apparatus suitable for local needs when writing fire apparatus specifications. For example, requirements for fighting large brush fires in southern California are quite different from those occasioned by fire fighting in below zero weather in northern Minnesota. The Standard provides for desirable standardization of many items for which a uniform performance measurable by tests is desirable, but allows the necessary flexibility to meet local needs that could not be supplied by one assembly-line type of production. Such differences include rated pump capacity, water tank capacity, length of aerial ladders, height of elevating platforms, and over 100 other important design features.

Fire Apparatus Engines

Engines may be either diesel or gasoline types, as the purchaser may specify. Fuels other than diesel or gasoline, such as LP Gas, are acceptable if they meet the intent of the NFPA Automotive Fire Apparatus Standard. The Standard does not contain any minimum size for the engine because the size of the engine must be chosen to correspond with the conditions of service and design of apparatus. With the possible exception of large capacity pumps, the size of engine usually is determined by the carrying capacity of the vehicle rather than the power requirements of the pump, and the road tests are designed to prove that the engine is of adequate size.

The carrying capacity of a vehicle is one of the most important, but least understood, features of a vehicle. Under the NFPA Automotive Fire Apparatus Standard it is the responsibility of the apparatus manufacturer to provide GAWR and GVWR adequate to carry a 1,200 lb personnel weight, a full water tank, the specified hose load, plus a miscellaneous equipment allowance of 1,000 lbs for pumpers and water towers, and 2,500 lbs not including ladders for aerials and elevating platforms. (GAWR is the value specified by the vehicle manufacturer as the loaded weight on a single axle system, and GCWR means the value specified by the manufacturer as the loaded weight of a combination vehicle such as a tractor-trailer unit. GVWR is the value specified by the manufacturer as the loaded weight of a single vehicle, and is the sum of the weights of the chassis, body, cab, equipment, water, fuel, crew, and all other loads.) All vehicles are designed for "rated GVWR" or maximum total weight which should not be exceeded by the apparatus manufacturer, or by the fire department after the vehicle is placed in service. Too many fire departments have seriously overloaded apparatus by adding more equipment weight than the vehicle was designed to carry. There are a number of factors included in the GVWR, such as the springs or suspension system, the rated axle capacity, the rated tire loading, and the weight distribution between the front and rear axles. One of the critical factors is the size of the water tank. Water weighs about $8\frac{1}{3}$ lbs per U.S. gal. A value of 10 lbs is often used when estimating the weight of a full tank, making $2\frac{1}{2}$ tons for a full 500 gal tank. The improper distribution of weight between front and rear wheels can make a vehicle difficult to control, and may require tires of different sizes to carry the load. Overloading not only affects the handling characteristics, but undoubtedly results in increasing maintenance problems with transmissions, clutches, and brakes.

Compliance with Federal Standards

Since the passage of the National Traffic and Motor Vehicle Safety Act of 1966, the federal government has adopted motor vehicle safety standards applicable to all manufacturers of vehicles, including fire trucks. This legislation is enforced by DOT (U.S. Department of Transportation). Under these standards it is unlawful to sell a truck not in compliance with the current federal standards. Manufacturers cannot accept specifications which would make them perform unlawfully, delete required items, or include items that are illegal. As fire apparatus is complex and may require considerable lead-time between the signing of a contract and delivery, the federal regulations provide that in the case of fire apparatus, standards applicable at the time of contract shall be those complied with provided that the delivery of the apparatus takes place within two years.

Additional requirements are placed upon apparatus and engine manufacturers based upon the Clean Air Act enforced by the EPA (Environmental Protection Agency). Engines cannot be modified once approved by EPA. These standards have resulted in changes in engine performance, and often require the use of larger engines than were previously used in order to obtain the same vehicle performance.

Electrical Power for Apparatus

A major requirement for reliable fire apparatus is to have sufficient electrical capacity for the vehicle and its components. Electricity is essential to reliable starting of the apparatus under all conditions of temperature and weather. Emergency warning lights and sirens impose a heavy electrical demand, with radios and speakers as an added load. In addition, hose reels, pump controls, and other items of equipment may be operated electrically. An electro-mechanical siren alone may require about 300 amps to start it rolling, and 100 amps to keep it rolling. The radio takes additional amperage depending upon equipment, and the standard light load is about 40 amps. Much of the equipment must perform when the apparatus is at a fire with the engine off or idling.

The NFPA Automotive Fire Apparatus Standard permits either dual or single battery systems, but dual batteries are recommended. Capacities are required to be not less than 120 amp-hr rating at a 20-hr discharge rate for gasoline engines, and 200 amp-hr rating at 20-hr discharge rate for diesel engines. It is not acceptable to attempt to meet battery requirements with two small batteries of dissimilar size and age as these will not charge or discharge at an equal rate, nor have equivalent reliability and power. The standard stipulates that when a dual battery system is supplied, each battery shall be of the capacity required for a single battery system.

The NFPA Automotive Fire Apparatus Standard requires provision of an electric alternator (alternating current generator) and rectifier equipment of sufficient output to meet the vehicle electrical requirements. If 110-v power is required, a separate 3-phase transformer or rectifier unit should be provided in connection with the alternator to produce 110 v dc at special outlets. These outlets can be used to supply floodlights of suitable size. Portable tools and other electrically driven equipment supplied from these outlets must be designed for dc operation or have universal motors as alternators produce current at frequencies varying from 80 to 160 cycles per second; ac motors designed only for 60-cycle current will soon burn out.

Where a dual battery system is provided it is important that each battery be maintained at peak efficiency, and that polarized receptacles be provided for charging.

Apparatus Equipped with a Fire Pump

Chapter 2 of the NFPA Automotive Fire Apparatus Standard covers provisions applying to apparatus equipped with a fire pump. The most common basic fire fighting vehicle is termed a "pumper" or "pumping engine." This chapter includes sections on design and performance of the pump, construction requirements, operating controls and devices, and suction and booster hose, which may be supplied with the pumper. The design requirements include the rated capacity to be specified, the suction capability, and the engine capability. Construction requirements cover the construction of the pump and the pump suction inlets and discharge outlets. At least one gated suction inlet is required. Normally this is a 2½-in. inlet unless a larger size is specified. Many fire departments specify two or more gated pump inlets so that the full capacity of the pump can be supplied through feeder lines from hydrants, or by a pumper relay when the apparatus is operating as an attack engine near a fire or is being used to supply heavy stream equipment in a

relay. The section of the Standard on operating controls covers the pump operator's position and various controls for the pump including the engine controls, the priming device, and pressure gages and tachometer.

A section on suction hose and booster hose sets forth their requirements, if specified. Hard suction hose is not required to be carried, unless specified, if suitable suction hose is available for testing because many pumpers serve in areas where high pressure water supply systems exist and there is no opportunity for drafting at the fireground. Some fire departments use different types and sizes of preconnected hose lines in lieu of booster hose. Pumpers designed for use as water supply engines at hydrants or at draft do not require booster hose. However, provision must be made for some apparatus to carry small hand line equipment for initial fire attack and mopping up operations.

Standard sizes of fire pumps for installation on apparatus are: 500, 750, 1,000, 1,250, 1,500, 1,750, and 2,000 gpm (U.S.), or in Canada 416, 625, 833, 1,040, 1,250, 1,458, and 1,666 gpm (Imperial). Normal truck chassis and power train generally provide ample power for 1,000 gpm and larger pumps; thus, a decreasing percentage of smaller size pumps are sold. Relatively few are of the 500 gpm rating which was popular years ago when commercial engines were less powerful.

Rated pumping capacity is determined at 150 psi net pump pressure with the pump tested at draft, and preferably with a vertical lift not exceeding 10 ft, as pumps designed for general fire service tend to be somewhat less efficient at very high lifts. Nevertheless, the pump should be capable of drafting at a 10 ft lift. Where pumps are to serve at locations having altitudes above 2,000 ft, the NFPA Standard calls for the purchaser to specify the altitude so that the necessary performance requirements including engine power and suction capability can be met.

The performance requirements for acceptance which a fire pump must meet are covered in detail in Chapter 10 of the NFPA Automotive Fire Apparatus Standard which deals with tests. These tests include a hydrostatic test to be conducted by the manufacturer, and certification that the vehicle has been operated for 2 hrs (run-in) before delivery. A 3-hr certification test is also required. The purchaser may specify that the certification test be conducted by engineers of Underwriters Laboratories Inc., or by other capable testing agencies. ULT bulletin "Subject 822" covers the test procedures in much detail. The certification test includes a 3-hr test at draft during which the pump must deliver its rated capacity for 2 hrs at 150 psi net pump pressure followed by two ½-hr periods during which 70 percent of rated capacity is delivered at 200 psi, and 50 percent of rated capacity at 250 psi. The apparatus is then given a 10 min overload test discharging rated pump capacity at 165 psi to demonstrate reserve engine power. Automatic pump pressure controls are to be tested with the pump discharging at 90, 150, and 250 psi. A vacuum test is conducted to prove the ability of the pump to hold a vacuum with the primer off and discharge outlets uncapped. Where the apparatus has a water tank, the specified rate of flow from tank to pump must be maintained for at least 80 percent of the rated tank capacity for tanks of 300 gal capacity or larger. The minimum specified tank to pump flow rate is 250 gpm, but is increased to 500 gpm where a pumper has a water tank in excess of 750 gal capacity.

Hose Bodies

Chapter 3 of the NFPA Automotive Fire Apparatus Standard contains provisions applying to apparatus equipped with a hose body. A standard hose body for pumpers has at least 55 cu ft of space and is designed to carry a minimum of 1,500 ft of 2½-in. hose, and 400 ft of 1½-in. hose. Standard hose capacity for a pumper-ladder truck is 40 cu ft and is designed to carry 1,000 ft of 2½-in. hose, plus 400 ft of 1½-in. hose.

Many fire departments specify at least 2,000 ft carrying capacity for 2½-in. or larger hose, and a capacity for 800 to 1,000 ft of 1½-in. hose. Increasingly, fire departments are specifying that the hose body be divided to permit laying of two or more lines of large diameter hose, and two or more lines of 1½-in. hose. In some cases the compartments for attack hose (hose used to transport water from the apparatus to the fire) run across the apparatus so that the hose may be stretched from the side of the apparatus.

With the larger capacity pumpers now commonplace, additional hose capacity is required to move the larger volumes of water. A convenient way to relate needed hose capacity to pumper discharge requirements is on the relative water carrying capacity of various sizes of hose at normal operating pressures, as follows: 250 gpm for 2½-in. hose, 400 gpm for 3-in. hose, 500 gpm for 3½-in. hose, 650 gpm for 4-in. hose, and 1,000 gpm for 5-in. hose. Thus, to move 500 gpm 1,000 ft requires 2,000 ft of 2½-in. hose. (Relatively small increases in flow may be obtained by higher discharge pressures, especially in short lines.) Many pumpers in rural and suburban areas carry at least 2,000 ft of big line in a split load. Unless hose laying apparatus is arranged to lay multiple lines or large diameter hose is provided, considerable time and manpower may be required when flows above 250 gpm per pumper are needed.

Increasingly, fire departments are using hose of diameters larger than the nominal 2½-in. size. Care should be taken to specify hose carrying capacity needed—larger hose requires more space on the apparatus; also, size of hose reels must be specified whether for booster hose or for larger hose. Normally, hose reels are equipped with a power rewind.

Booster Pumps

Chapter 4 of the NFPA Automotive Fire Apparatus Standard applies to apparatus equipped with a booster pump. The term "booster pump" applies to pumps of less than 500 gpm rated capacity. Normally, these pumps are not subject to certification tests by Underwriters Laboratories, inc. When equipment was developed to supply small hose on fire apparatus to replace the former chemical tanks, the equipment consisted of a small tank of water at zero psi pressure and a permanently connected pump of about 30 gpm capacity which took suction from the tank and supplied ¾-in. hose. There were no other discharge connections, but commonly 2½-in. hose inlet was provided to replenish the tank supply as was the case with many chemical engines. Later, additional suction and discharge connections were added.

Booster pumps used predominantly for fighting grass fires and other small fires usually are capable of supplying one or two reels of 1-in. booster line and have a capacity of up to 100 gpm at pressures not exceeding 250 psi. Often pumps for use on grass fires are designed to be operated when the apparatus is in motion. This feature is called "pump-and-roll."

When one or two lines of 1½-in. hose are to be supplied, a capacity of 250 gpm at 150 psi is desirable. For predominantly structural fire fighting a standard fire pump is required. There is little excuse for failure to provide at least the 500 gpm minimum for structural fire fighting because the apparatus motor generally has ample power for the job.

When working pressures exceeding 250 psi are desired in a small pump, the pump discharge capacity should be at least 50–60 gpm at the specified pressure. In some cases this small volume, high pressure characteristic is specified as an additional capability for a fire pump meeting standard pressure-volume characteristics.

Years ago when most booster lines discharged approximately 15 gpm in a straight stream using ¾-in. hose, very high pressures for small stream service became popular. Poorly informed fire fighters had the mistaken notion that "high pressure" contributed to fire extinguishment. Tests demonstrated that the heat absorption necessary for the cooling and extinguishment of fires was due entirely to the volume of water discharged in spray form, and that excessive pressures not only were unnecessary but much of the high pump pressure was lost due to high friction losses in the small diameter hose used.

Small booster pumps can be powered by power-take-off units attached to SAE 6-bolt openings on the chassis transmission. Larger booster pumps usually are driven by 8-bolt PTOs, flywheel PTOs, or by separate engines. Purchasers should indicate the volume and pressure desired of booster pumps, and the tests to be conducted. Pumping tests should demonstrate the pump capacity and pressure, the engine capability, the suitability of pump controls, engine controls, and suction capability if applicable. All tests should be conducted in accordance with the NFPA Automotive Fire Apparatus Standard.

Water Tanks

The majority of fire trucks equipped with a pump also carry a water tank. The tank is used to supply water to the pump for initial fire attack hose streams before hydrants or suction sources may be brought into use. The NFPA Standard requires a minimum water tank capacity of 300 gal for pumpers and 150 gal for ladder trucks or elevating platforms for which water tanks are specified. Most new pumpers have water tanks larger than 300 gal.

Chapter 5 of the NFPA Automotive Fire Apparatus Standard deals with water tank construction, tank connections (including a capped fill opening of not less than 5-in. diameter), tank overflow, and venting. It also covers special provisions for tanks used for mechanical foam or water additive agents. The chapter also specifies flow rates from tanks to fire pumps and to booster pumps. For tanks of 300 to 750 gal capacity, a 250 gpm flow rate is specified (up to the capacity of the booster pump when that is smaller) to permit immediate fire attack with one 2½-in. hose line or several smaller streams, and also for fast unloading of water carriers. For tanks of over 750 gal capacity, a flow rate to the pump of 500 gpm is required. All rates of flow between the water tank and the pump shall be maintained for 80 percent of the tank capacity, unless otherwise specified.

Mobile Water Tank Apparatus

In rural districts and in outlying districts of cities where hydrant distribution is not complete, supplemental water tank apparatus, defined as "mobile water supply apparatus" is commonly provided. Such apparatus is covered in Chapter 5 of the NFPA Automotive Fire Apparatus Standard, and may have a permanently installed pump or a portable pump for tank filling and discharge. Suitable hose and fire fighting tools for accomplishing intended tasks should be carried on the vehicle.

Normally, mobile water supply apparatus is supplemental to fire department pumpers. A 1,000 gal tank capacity is recommended. Larger tanks require heavier vehicles and may limit the mobility of apparatus on rural roads and bridges. The efficiency of mobile water supply apparatus in transporting water to fires depends upon the over-the-road mobility, the ability to quickly unload water at a fire, and the ability to quickly refill the tank to transport additional water. Under the standard a $2\frac{1}{2}$-in. gated connection is required to permit rapid filling of the tank which must be baffled and vented. Tests have shown that tankers meeting these standards can provide pumpers at a fire with enough water to maintain a 100 gpm fire flow using a water supply source a mile distant.

Many rural fire departments use large "nurse" tankers as a portable reservoir to supply pumping engines at a fire. In some cases, the large tankers are kept supplied by a shuttle of the smaller mobile tankers. The capacity of the large tankers may be 5,000 gal or more. To meet the requirements of the standard and DOT regulations, where tankers of 1,500 gal capacity or larger are specified, either tandem rear axles, semitrailer construction, or both, may be needed. A truck chassis with tandem rear axles is suggested for mobile water supply apparatus of from 1,500 to 2,000 gal and for tanks over 2,500 gal a semitrailer chassis with tandem trailer axles is needed. A maximum water tank capacity of 4,800 U.S. gal or 20 tons of water is recommended. Power brakes and power steering are important considerations in design of mobile water supply apparatus, and experienced truck drivers are needed for safe operation of large tank vehicles.

Aerial Ladders

Aerial ladders have been in use by fire departments for gaining access to upper floors and roofs of buildings for more than a century. The first aerials were manually operated before spring assist and air hoists were introduced. These were followed by the present hydraulic hoists and ladder controls powered by the truck engine. The more reliable steel or aluminum truss construction has replaced the wooden beams used in the earlier aerial ladders.

Chapter 6 of the NFPA Automotive Fire Apparatus Standard covers provisions applying to apparatus equipped with an aerial ladder. The chapter is divided into three main sections dealing with the aerial ladder and its equipment, control devices, and the type of vehicle chassis to be used. Once an aerial has been positioned and stabilized, one man has full control of all operations of the ladder; the ladder is independent of the integrity of the building on fire.

Common sizes of aerial ladders are 65, 75, 85 and 100 ft, and the user must specify the length wanted and whether a single chassis vehicle or a tractor-drawn vehicle is to be provided. In recent years the formerly popular 65-ft aerial has been specified less frequently for ladder trucks. The 85- and 100-ft aerials have become increasingly popular due to increased height of buildings and because of the advantages of greater horizontal reach when fighting fires. Aerial ladders up to 150-ft can be purchased. In some cases the shorter aerial ladders are provided as a useful addition to a combination attack pumper. The length of an aerial is measured by a plumb line from the top rung to the ground, with the ladder fully extended at its maximum elevation. The NFPA Automotive Fire Apparatus Standard requires a minimum width of 18 in. at the narrowest point of the ladder.

A detachable ladder pipe is standard equipment for an aerial ladder, and is used to provide elevated fire stream service. When supplied by 3-in. hose up the ladder, 600 gpm is the practical maximum which can be supplied in normal operations. Tips provided with the ladder pipe are $1\frac{1}{4}$, $1\frac{3}{8}$, and $1\frac{1}{2}$ in., and a 500 gpm spray nozzle.

Section 6-2 of the NFPA Automotive Fire Apparatus Standard deals with control devices for aerial ladders. An operator's position is required from which controls are operable. Usually controls are grouped at a pedestal. The operator's position must be such that the operator's line of sight coincides with the axis of the ladder when it is in any position. Lighted and clearly marked control devices are provided: to immobilize the vehicle; transfer power to the ladder mechanism; stabilize the vehicle; lock in and release the ladder from its bed; control elevation, rotation, and extension of the ladder; indicate the angle of elevation and the load limit; and control the engine for operation of the ladder. Complete details on safe use of aerial ladders are included in the *NFPA Fire Officer's Guide to Operating Fire Department Aerial Ladders.*

Elevating Platforms and Aerial Towers

Fire trucks with hydraulically operated elevating platforms are widely used, and are covered in Chapter 7 of the NFPA Automotive Fire Apparatus Standard. Some of these are on trucks that also carry ground ladders and other equipment for ladder company service, while the smaller sizes may be mounted on attack pumpers.

Platform apparatus are of two principal designs: with one, the platform is mounted on an articulated boom which travels in an arc as desired by the operator; with the other, the platform is mounted on an extendable or telescopic boom much in the fashion of an aerial ladder.

Platform equipment is available with booms designed for maximum extension from about 50 to 90 ft, and some have been built to reach heights of 125 ft. Under the standard the nominal height of a platform assembly is measured by a plumb line from the top surface of the platform to the ground, with the platform raised to its maximum elevation. It is important in selecting platforms for reach and elevation under fireground conditions to obtain from the manufacturer charts showing reach under recommended operating conditions. The articulated boom design provides its maximum horizontal reach at approximately half of its maximum elevation. The telescopic extendable boom of the same nominal length generally permits somewhat greater horizontal reach at higher and lower elevations. The telescopic type often has the added feature of an extending ladder attached to the boom which provides access to and from the platform, while elevated, which is not the case with the articulated boom.

Both designs provide stable platforms with dual controls located both on the platform and at the turntable. The latter control is overriding. The NFPA Automotive Fire Apparatus Standard requires that the platform be able to handle a payload of at least 700 lbs in all recommended operating positions. An advantage of either type is that the platform can be moved quickly from window to window for fire fighting or rescue. The Standard specifies that the platform must be capable of reaching its maximum elevation, extension, and a rotation of 90° within 150 sec.

Both types of platforms are designed to give water tower service that is superior to that provided by ladder pipes. The NFPA Standard requires that the platform turret or turrets be capable of rotation through at least 45°, while ladder pipes are limited to a horizontal rotation of 15°. Also, the mobility of the platform permits the operator to quickly change the turret location as desired. The apparatus must be designed so that regardless of the position of the platform and the direction of the stream, the equipment can be operated safely while discharging 750 gpm through a $1\frac{3}{4}$-in. tip; many platforms are built to handle 1,000 gpm discharge. Standard nozzle tips for platform turrets are $1\frac{3}{8}$, $1\frac{1}{2}$, and $1\frac{3}{4}$ in., and a 500 gpm spray nozzle. Some platforms have two turret nozzles.

As with aerial ladders, the standards cover operating mechanisms, platforms and equipment, control devices including platform and engine controls, load limitations, and turret nozzle operations. Detailed information of efficient and safe use of various types of platform apparatus is contained in the *NFPA Fire Officer's Guide on Elevating Platforms and Aerial Towers.*

Water Towers

The success of elevating platforms on the fireground during the decade of the 1960s was a prelude to the use of hydraulically operated water towers designed to apply large flows on a fire from effective heights and positions. Such water towers have proven to be very useful and have been widely accepted as an important type of equipment in both large and small communities. Years ago in the larger cities water towers were used to deliver elevated streams from a fixed tower described as a nozzle mounted on a vertical standpipe. These require much time to get into operation. Modern water towers have a much greater flexibility and are designed to discharge from 300 to 1,000 gpm or more in either a straight stream or spray, to move the boom and nozzle under the control of the operator from lowest position to maximum height, and to extend horizontally for the best application of water.

Many of the newer water towers are mounted on attack pumpers permitting the pump operator to supply the pressure and volume needed for the tower stream. In many cases the initial operation is from the apparatus water tank while hose lines are being placed in service to supply the apparatus. Some towers are mounted on hose trucks permitting the equipment to lay its own supply lines from pumpers, or form high pressure fire mains.

Water towers, like elevating platforms, may be of either articulated or telescopic boom design. As with earlier water towers, maximum heights specified may be from 55 to 75 ft with the smaller size designed for mounting on standard pumpers or hose trucks. The telescopic type may be equipped with a ladder extending the full length of the boom.

Chapter 8 of the NFPA Automotive Fire Apparatus Standard covers water tower apparatus. Except for the lack of the platform feature, the water tower capability called for in the Standard is similar to that of platform turret nozzles. The tower is mounted on a turntable or pedestal to permit rotation in either direction through 360°, and can rotate with the nozzle in operation at rated capacity. All controls are grouped at the control station adjacent to the turntable, and the operator has full control of the pressure, volume, and stream pattern. Additional details are contained in the *NFPA Fire Officer's Guide on Elevating Platforms and Aerial Towers.*

Chief Officers' Vehicles

Each paid fire department and many volunteer fire departments find it essential to provide automotive transportation for staff command officers above the fire company level. In the larger fire departments, sizeable fleets of automobiles are maintained. Automobile transportation is necessary for chief officers, fire prevention officers and inspectors, training officers, communications officers, etc. Some fire departments follow the practice of paying a mileage allowance for the use of private cars. This is not a very good arrangement

because efficient public service is better performed by public owned vehicles, especially where response to emergencies may be involved. Inadequate transportation in staff agencies often results in wasted staff time.

All fire department vehicles used to respond to fires and emergencies, including automobiles, must be equipped with warning lights and sirens, and radio communications facilities with the emergency networks on which the department operates, including mutual aid frequencies. The vehicles should carry protective clothing and equipment for the officers and for their aides, directories containing pertinent information on properties in the area served, water distribution plans, and reference books to hazardous materials. The cars normally carry a portable fire extinguisher and a first aid kit.

Many cities provide district or battalion fire chiefs with station wagons in which the necessary equipment is mounted for ready access. Reserve cars are needed not only to cover vehicles undergoing mechanical repair, but for use of off-shift officers when recalled to duty to cover vacated districts.

Generally, these cars respond to more alarms and acquire more mileage than the apparatus of individual fire companies, and a replacement program should be followed. In busy districts cars may be used for fire duty for 2 or 3 years before being placed in reserve or assigned to staff work.

Floodlight Trucks or Trailers

These units have a generator of 5,000 w rating or larger, generally driven by its own engine. They may carry floodlights and various power tools. These units provide extra generating capacity that can be used at fires and at emergencies involving interruption of normal power sources. They supplement the emergency lighting and power equipment carried on fire apparatus. Pigtail grounded adapters for both two-wire and three-wire services are required as part of the emergency electrical equipment.

Because of the necessity for operating fire department emergency electrical equipment under conditions of extreme wetness, it is important that properly installed and grounded three-wire services be provided for generator and lighting units.

Specialized Apparatus

There is a wide diversity of fire apparatus designed for special types of service. These units should be designed with the rigors of fire duty in mind and should conform to the general vehicle standards set forth in Chapter 1 of the NFPA Automotive Fire Apparatus Standard. Many fire departments operate squad or rescue trucks carrying emergency equipment to supplement that carried on pumpers and ladder trucks. Many of the rescue trucks are enclosed to provide shelter for first aid and emergency work during inclement weather.

Another specialized type is the forest fire truck. Generally these are smaller vehicles, frequently with all-wheel drive, and equipped with a small water tank, booster hose, forestry hose, a small capacity pump, and a number of portable water type extinguishers and various hand tools for fighting wildland fires. When operated by municipal fire departments, the forest or brush fire trucks may have 500 or 750 gpm front mounted fire pump, and a 500 gal water tank. The apparatus may respond to structural fires for initial fire attack in the district served and may also be equipped for fighting highway fires.

A few cities still have salvage trucks equipped with twenty or more waterproof covers and other equipment used to reduce water damage. This supplements the salvage equipment carried on pumpers, ladder trucks, and squad trucks. Years ago insurance underwriters operated salvage corps in a number of cities; with the reduction of water damage at fires through improved fire fighting methods and better internal protection, all of these have been disbanded except the Fire Patrol in New York City.

Fireboats

Fireboats come in various sizes and types in accordance with local needs, and vary from large tugs to fast jet-propelled fire-rescue craft. A number of cities maintain fleets of fire fighting vessels. Some of these are operated by fire departments, and some by port authorities. Navy and Coast Guard vessels also are equipped for fire fighting service.

Among the principal services of fireboats are: (1) protection of vessels in the harbor, (2) protection of piers, pier-sheds, and cargoes along the waterfront, (3) protection of yachts and houseboats in basins and marinas, (4) marine rescue from all types of water accidents, and (5) serving as pumping stations for providing large flows at fires within reach of hose supplied by the boats. They also may provide a valuable emergency source of water for fire protection should an earthquake or other accident interrupt the normal supply. Some fire departments operate hose trucks or "fireboat tenders" out of fireboat stations. Such trucks carry a mile or so of large diameter hose to permit utilization of fireboat pumping capacity at shore fires along the waterfront. In harbors subject to freezing, fireboats should be equipped for ice breaking.

The selection as to size, type, pumping capacity, and equipment carried by fireboats should depend upon the type of service expected by the vessel or vessels. The NFPA pamphlet "Fireboats" suggests equipment and pumping arrangements for various classes of service. Fireboats must carry much of the same equipment as pumpers, ladder trucks, and rescue vehicles on land. They need foam-making capability, and should carry quantities of special extinguishing agents such as carbon dioxide.

Pumping capacity for individual fireboats varies from 500 gpm for very small craft to 10,000 gpm or more for larger vessels. Pumping capacity is rated at 150 psi discharge pressure as with motor pumpers. Some small jet-powered fire boats rely upon jet pumps to supply the vessel's fire main. These may develop substantial volumes at pressures adequate to supply turret nozzles attached to the fire main, but may find it difficult to provide the pressure needed to supply the hose streams needed to fight ship fires or fires ashore unless additional pumps are provided to meet standard pressure requirements.

Where fireboats are intended for the protection of wharf frontage, the Insurance Grading Schedule recommends that pumping capacity be at least half of the fire flow required for the district protected, but at least 5,000 gpm. The schedule also recommends fireboat protection within $1\frac{1}{2}$ miles of areas having an occupied wharf frontage of at least one mile.

Where fire protection is required for yacht basins and where water rescue service must be provided, time is of the essence and boats should be berthed as near the area of anticipated need as practicable. In addition to the life hazard from boat fires and explosions, the values involved with closely berthed yachts can be considerable.

In some cities waterfront areas have tended to present some of the most serious fire hazards because of substandard construction, large undivided areas, and hazardous storage. Lumber, packaged materials, chemicals, and flammable liquids often are stored and handled in bulk. Wharf sheds may lack fire divisions, and fires may extend between wharf decks and the water presenting troublesome problems of access, particularly in tidewater areas. In some fire departments fireboat crews include scuba divers trained in underwater recovery and in fighting fires under piers.

The best fireboat protection may be at a disadvantage where piers are structurally weak, lack automatic sprinkler protection, are without draft curtains or underpier firestops, and lack skylights or other means for venting roofs. Manning of fireboats varies from 3 fire fighters on the smaller fire-rescue craft, to a full fire company of 5 or 6 fire fighters plus a licensed marine crew for the larger vessels. A licensed marine crew consists of a pilot with the required papers for the waters served by the vessel, a marine engineer, and one or two assistants. The assigned fire company would have the same officers and manning provided for an engine company ashore in the same district.

The smaller fireboats do not require a licensed marine crew provided that qualified fire fighters are assigned as operators. It is essential that these operators complete the U.S. Coast Guard course for power boat operators, and know the rules that must be observed for all vessels. It is also essential that each fireboat carry proper papers for navigation of the waters in which it is to serve. Fireboats need radar as well as radio communications to enable them to operate safely under all conditions of weather and, at times, in heavy smoke. In many cases protective breathing equipment is essential for fireboat crews.

Where fireboats are used relatively infrequently, the cost of manning these vessels has been a problem for fire department administrators. In some instances this has been partially resolved by berthing the fireboat adjacent to a land fire company. The problem with this arrangement is that many waterfront fires require simultaneous operations from both land and water, and it is necessary to train personnel from covering companies to man the vessel when the assigned company is out of quarters. The most practical solution where the economics of the situation do not permit proper manning and maintenance of a large fireboat has been replacement of the vessel with a more modern type requiring less crew and lower maintenance costs.

At some ports fireboats are owned and operated by port authorities. This arrangement has sometimes resulted in poor coordination of fire fighting operations between the fireboat crew and land fire companies. It is important that control of fire fighting operations be under the direction of the chief officer at a fire so that personnel will not be endangered by powerful fireboat streams directed into areas where hose crews and truck crews are working.

In a number of locations fireboats furnish valuable fire protection for various island and resort communities not readily accessible to land fire apparatus.

Airport Crash Trucks

Specialized apparatus is required for aircraft rescue and fire fighting service at airports. In many cities such equipment is manned by fire department companies. In others it is maintained and operated by an airport authority.

An aircraft fire frequently demands immediate attack with foam and other extinguishing agents capable of overcoming intense flammable liquid fires. Under NFPA Standards, to be of significant value in saving lives it is considered that the apparatus should have a capability of establishing a rescue path to a burning plane in not over 90 sec after arrival of the equipment.

The NFPA Committee on Aviation and its sectional committees have issued NFPA 402, Standard Operating Procedures, Aircraft Rescue and Fire Fighting, NFPA 403, Aircraft Rescue and Fire Fighting Services at Airports and Heliports, and NFPA 406M, Guide for Aircraft Rescue and Fire Fighting Techniques for Fire Departments Using Structural Fire Apparatus and Equipment. The NFPA Committee on Aviation, through its Sectional Committee on Aircraft Rescue and Fire Fighting, has prepared NFPA No. 414, Standard for Aircraft Rescue and Fire Fighting Vehicles. Because of off-highway performance needs, the vehicle weight of crash trucks should be distributed equally over all wheels. Greater axle and chassis clearances of the road are needed than for standard fire apparatus, as well as high acceleration characteristics. The NFPA Standard calls for a drive that provides multiplication of torque from the engine flywheel to the wheels of the vehicle. Positive drive to each wheel is required to negotiate soft ground, snow, and ice. The positive wheel drive can be provided by torque proportioning or no-spin differentials, or by means of other automatic devices that assure that each wheel (rather than axle) is driven independently.

Three types of vehicles are covered: (1) major fire fighting vehicles with gross weights of 8 or more tons, (2) light rescue vehicles with gross weight under 4 tons, and (3) water tank vehicles. The lighter vehicles are for carrying rescue tools and small capacity extinguishing equipment intended to reach the emergency site quickly to get rescue operations started before the heavier apparatus arrives. Heavy crash trucks are equipped with turret nozzles to control flammable liquid fires around a plane, and supplementary supplies of carbon dioxide and dry chemical. Crash trucks utilize a combination of extinguishing agents with capacities and discharge rates to support about 5 min of continuous protection before arrival of back-up apparatus. Airport crash apparatus should include a small rescue vehicle which can also serve as a command car, and a nurse tanker carrying additional water and extinguishing agents. Efforts to make crash trucks suitable for fighting fires in hangars and other airport structures should not detract from their primary mission.

Numbers of personnel assigned to man airport crash trucks vary according to the apparatus provided and the aircraft using the facility, and the distribution of air traffic over a 24-hr period. During flight operations sufficient personnel are required to immediately operate both a light rescue vehicle and at least one major crash truck. Apparatus should be located and manned so that response can be made to any area of the airport and extinguishing agent application initiated within three min of the sounding of the alarm. Additional units should have qualified operators assigned, but may be manned by trained airport personnel who respond to an emergency upon call.

Apparatus Procurement Policies

The responsibility for procurement of fire apparatus and equipment should rest with the agency operating the fire department, whether that be a municipality, fire district, or private industry. In some cases, procurement is a cooperative measure in which a larger unit of government contributes to the cost of providing fire apparatus for fire department organizations serving in its territory. In a few cases, state governments contribute to local fire apparatus costs.

When the fire department is an agency of municipal government, it is the responsibility of the latter to provide all of the public fire fighting equipment. Providing the necessary monies is the responsibility of the appropriating fiscal authorities, but the actual selection of the equipment should be the responsibility of the fire department management responsible for fire protection. The chief administrative officer of the fire department (aided by his staff of technical specialists, including the master mechanic) should keep the municipal administrator informed regarding the age and condition of equipment, and should prepare current specifications consistent with applicable national standards covering items ready for replacement. In autonomous volunteer fire departments there may be a purchasing committee appointed to handle procurement of apparatus. In municipalities, actual purchase is usually handled through a municipal purchasing department. The purchasing department should not try to tell the fire department what type of fire apparatus it should use, but should see that required procurement procedures such as open competitive bidding are followed.

The Appendix of the NFPA Automotive Fire Apparatus Standard, contains helpful suggestions covering the writing of specifications, studying of proposals, awarding of contracts, and acceptance of apparatus.

In general, the buying and replacement of fire apparatus should be a regular item of the fire department capital budget. In most cases, except for accidents, the requirements can be planned and funded on a long-range basis. Systematic apparatus replacement provides the fire department with reliable apparatus at all times. Improvements in automotive and fire apparatus design can be introduced, maintenance costs become more favorable, and increased operating efficiency and equipment reliability will be sustained.

The normal life expectancy for first-line fire apparatus will vary from city to city, depending upon the relative amount of use of the equipment and the adequacy of the maintenance program. In general, a 15-year life expectancy has been considered normal for first-line pumping engines. In fire departments where ladder trucks make substantially less responses to alarms than engines, a planned first-line service of 20 years for ladder trucks may be warranted. Some fire departments operate pumping engines with reasonable efficiency up to 20 years, although obsolescence will make the older apparatus less desirable even if it is mechanically functional. In some types of service, including areas of high fire frequency, a limit of 12 years for first-line service may be all that is reasonable. The older apparatus may be maintained as part of the required reserve as long as it is in good condition, but in almost no case should much reliance be placed if it exceeds 25 years of age.

Some fire departments follow a policy of assigning new apparatus to the busiest fire companies for a few years, and then reassign it to less busy companies to average out the work load over the life of the apparatus. With 2-piece engine companies, a newer machine may be assigned as the initial attack apparatus, with an older engine used mainly for water supply operations.

To achieve these objectives, a fire department with 15 first-line pieces of apparatus may schedule replacement of one unit per year with 5 or 6 of the older apparatus kept as reserve. A fire department with 5 first-line engines may schedule replacement of an engine each 3 years with three older engines being kept as a reserve. A department with 2 ladder companies plus one reserve ladder truck may schedule replacement of ladder trucks on an 8-year cycle so that none of the trucks, including the reserve, will exceed 24 years of age.

The cost of new fire apparatus varies according to the type, size, and special equipment provided. At this writing properly equipped pumpers meeting NFPA Standards and federal regulations range from $45,000 to $65,000 or more, plus cost of special features provided. Aerial ladder and platform trucks commonly cost from $60,000 to over $100,000, depending upon the equipment carried. However, the cost of good apparatus is normally between 1 and 2 percent of the cost of properly manning it in a paid fire department. While costs have increased due to inflation and also due to requirements of federal highway safety standards, fire protection needs are an authorized use for federal revenue sharing funds, and many municipalities are utilizing part of these funds to procure needed fire apparatus as well as for meeting part of their fire department personnel budgets.

All specifications for purchase of municipal fire apparatus should be based upon the requirements of the latest edition of the NFPA Automotive Fire Apparatus Standard, as applicable to the type of apparatus desired. These standards include basic provisions that will provide a complete, well-engineered fire fighting vehicle. Apparatus manufacturers are geared to provide equipment that meets the Standard.

Acceptance Tests and Requirements

Acceptance tests are designed to demonstrate that apparatus will perform as specified in the purchase contract. Tests should be performed prior to delivery or within 10 days after delivery. Tests should be conducted by the manufacturer's representative in the presence of such person or persons as the purchaser may have designated in the delivery requirements. Normally, the fire chief or his designated representative is the acceptance authority, exercising this authority following satisfactory completion of tests and inspections for compliance with the purchase specifications.

The acceptance tests and requirements for fire apparatus and its various components are given in Chapter 10 of the NFPA Automotive Fire Apparatus Standard. Applicable to all types of apparatus are the road tests designed to prove that the apparatus has ample power for the intended service. Road tests are conducted with apparatus fully loaded with men, hose, water, and the equipment specified to be carried. From a standing start, through the gears, the vehicle must attain a true speed of 35 mph, within 25 sec for pumpers and within 30 sec for heavier apparatus such as tank trucks, aerials, and elevating platforms. It shall also accelerate from 15 to 35 mph in 30 sec without moving the gear selector. This demonstrates that the vehicle has the necessary "pick-up" to operate safely and efficiently in traffic. The vehicle must attain a top speed of 50 mph, or a higher speed where specified. The required brake performance shall also be tested. While the tests mentioned demonstrate power needed to negotiate grades found in most communities, any special ability to climb very steep grades may be tested if specified.

The pump tests including certification tests have been outlined earlier in this text. If a pump test conducted by the manufacturer is desired at point of delivery, this must be conducted as the purchaser has specified. In all cases with a pump, the manufacturer must supply with delivery a copy of: (1) the engine manufacturer's certified brake horsepower curve showing the maximum no-load governed speed, (2) a record of pumper construction details as indicated on a form in the NFPA Automotive Fire Apparatus Standard, (3) the pump manufacturer's certification of suction capability, (4) the pump manufacturer's certification of hydrostatic test, and (5) the certification of inspection by a nationally recognized testing agency (usually Underwriters Laboratories, Inc.).

A test plate is required at the pump operator's position giving the rated discharge and pressures together with engine speed determined by the manufacturer's test for the unit, and the no-load governed speed of the engine as stated on a certified brake-horsepower curve.

Tests are conducted to see that the water tank has at least the capacity specified and gives the flow rate specified.

Structural strength of an aerial ladder is tested by its ability to lift 200 lbs on the free end of the main section of the ladder. An operations test demonstrates ability to raise and extend the ladder to full height with 90° rotation in 60 sec after the truck is set for operation.

The stability test for elevation platform apparatus includes rotating a complete 360° with 150 percent of the manufacturer's rated payload on the platform with the platform at maximum horizontal reach. The operational test consists of extending the platform to full height and a 90° turn within 150 sec. All such tests must be completed smoothly without undue vibration. The apparatus must also comply with the turret nozzle discharge requirements. For water towers the full extension with 90° rotation must be completed within 120 sec after the vehicle is set. Tests also are required to demonstrate required water delivery and other specified features.

C. Equipment Carried on Apparatus

The NFPA Automotive Fire Apparatus Standard, includes listings of equipment and appliances needed with fire apparatus. These lists of ancillary equipment for major apparatus categories are arranged in three groupings. Chapter 9 of the Standard lists equipment which the apparatus manufacturer is required to furnish with each type of apparatus unless otherwise specified in special provisions. The Appendix to the Standard contains additional equipment lists, including lists of equipment normally carried on each type of apparatus but not necessarily purchased with apparatus, and additional equipment needed for each class of service (engine, truck, rescue, etc.) but not necessarily carried on each piece of apparatus of a given type.

Apparatus must be equipped with the tools necessary to accomplish fire ground operations. Where apparatus is delivered with only the minimum items of equipment, other equipment must be appropriated as needed. The latest edition of the NFPA Automotive Fire Apparatus Standard should be consulted for up-to-date equipment lists. These lists are generally used when evaluating fire department equipment.

Equipment Carried on Pumpers

Pumping engines carry a wide assortment of tools and equipment needed to make them self-sustaining fire fighting units. An important feature is fire hose of various sizes. This includes large diameter supply hose for supplying the pump from a hydrant and, where needed, hard suction hose for drafting. Pumpers normally carry from 1,200 to 2,000 ft or more of large diameter hose (2½- to 5-in. sizes) which may be used either for long supply lines or for supplying water to nozzles. Small hose is needed either for streams supplied from the apparatus water tank or for reducing the larger lines when small streams are needed. Normally, 400 to 1,000 ft of 1½-in. hose is carried for this service. If hose reels are provided, 200 to 300 ft of 1 in. or larger hose may be carried on each reel.

Pumpers carry a wide selection of nozzles for use with the various sizes of hose. Nozzles come with 1-in. and 2½-in. fittings, and may be a combination spray and straight stream type, or separate spray and solid stream tips may be carried.

A portable monitor nozzle with suitable tips enables the pumper to utilize its capacity with a minimum number of fire fighters, and provides a large volume fire stream with greater reach than that obtained from smaller nozzles. Such equipment should be carried on each pumper company. A pumper also should carry a distributor nozzle for use in cellars or fires in concealed spaces, and possibly a bayonet nozzle for partition or ceiling fires.

For effective use of hose equipment, various tools and fittings are necessary, including: hydrant adapters; a suction hose strainer when suction hose is carried; 2½-in. siamese connections for combining flows from two lines into one ; 2½-in. wye connections for supplying two hose lines from one; a wye connection reducing from 2½-in. to two 1½-in. outlets; 2½-in. gate valves; adapters for any nonstandard threads; double male and double female connections to permit reversing of hose lays; spanners for 1½-in. and 2½-in. hose; hose clamps; hose straps or rope hose tools; hose jackets for burst hose; and a hose hoist.

Fire departments may not require all of the above items on each piece of apparatus. Where a 2-pump operation is used, supply and control of hose streams may be performed at the engines without use of hose clamps, hose jackets, and siamese and wye connections. Some fire departments having numerous preconnected 1½-in. hose lines may have no occasion to use a reducing wye connection. Where wyes are used, each outlet should be gated to permit control of individual lines. Siamese connections should either be gated or have clapper valves.

The pumper should carry an assortment of minor truck tools including a 14-ft roof ladder, a 24-ft extension ladder, a short pike pole or ceiling hook, fire axes, a clawtool, a crowbar, rope, and bolt cutters. Where a pumper serves a district having buildings more than two stories high and there is no ladder truck in the station to which the pumper is assigned, a 35-ft extension ladder should be carried in lieu of the 24-ft extension ladder.

It is recommended that a pumper carry a number of salvage tools, including: at least two salvage covers, a salvage runner, sprinkler stoppers, brooms, shovels, squeegees, buckets, and possibly a smoke ejector. Rescue and emergency equipment carried on pumpers includes: a standard first aid kit, self-contained breathing apparatus for each fire fighter assigned (but at least two units), and wool blankets. Pumper lighting and power equipment includes: electric hand lanterns, floodlights or spotlights, and preferably a portable electric generator or an alternator serving power outlets. In addition to the preceding hose and nozzle equipment, the pumper carries portable extinguishers and often other special extinguishing equipment. For rural service, a portable fire pump should be carried plus possibly rakes, hay forks, long-handled pointed shovels, and about ¼ dozen back-pack water type extinguishers.

Equipment Carried on Ladder Trucks

The amount of space available on pumpers necessarily is limited by space requirements for hose and water tanks. Most fire departments generally provide a number of ladder trucks operated as separate fire companies. These companies are termed "ladder trucks" because of the prominence of the long ladders, but the ladders form only a part of the large inventory of equipment carried.

Among the tools carried on a ladder truck are: axes of both the flat-head and pick types; crowbars; door openers; pike poles of varying lengths from 6 to 16-ft; scoop and plain-type shovels; ⅝-in. and ¾-in. rope; pitchforks; sledges; battering ram; bolt cutters; wire cutters; 10- and 20-ton hydraulic jacks; hydraulic or air-powered spreaders; power

saw and blades; block and tackle; pull-down hooks; gas and water shutoff wrenches; oxyacetylene cutting outfit; compressed air or hydraulic cutters; bale hooks; and a tool box with an assortment of hand tools.

Ladder trucks also carry a considerable amount of "rescue" equipment, and truck company crews normally are responsible for search and rescue while pumper companies are getting water on a fire. Rescue equipment includes: at least 6 sets of breathing apparatus plus spare cylinders for each unit; a 24-unit first aid kit; four blankets; two litters or stretchers; a resuscitator (with spare cylinders) capable of caring for two patients; a body bag; and a life net. Pompier belts or ladder belts should be carried to permit ladder men to tie-in when working on a ladder. Some ladder trucks carry single spar "pompier" or scaling ladders. In a few cases a life gun used for projecting a life-line is carried in areas where it may be needed in outdoor rescues from places of difficult access. A ladder truck is often equipped either with a hydraulically operated aerial ladder, or elevating platform or aerial tower.

A ladder truck should also be equipped for salvage service with ten salvage covers 12 ft × 18 ft; two roof covers; a syphon or small portable dewatering pump; four squeegees; four mops; mop wringers; four brooms; heavy plastic tape; rolls of tarpaper or heavy plastic sheeting for "boarding up"; two padlocks and keys; claw hammer and nails; heavy duty staples; smoke ejector of at least 5,000 cfm capacity; smoke deodorant; 12 assorted sprinkler heads; sprinkler wrenches for upright and pendent sprinkler heads; and sprinkler stoppers or wedges. It is also useful to carry a 2-wheeled "hand-truck" for moving heavy objects.

Ladders: A standard complement of ladders for ladder trucks as required by Standard No. 19 consists of 163 ft of ground or portable ladders: one 40-ft extension, one 35-ft extension, one 28-ft extension, one 20-ft single ladder with roof hooks, one 16-ft single ladder with roof hooks, one 14-ft extension, and one 10-ft callapsible ladder. Ladders must be constructed to meet the performance requirements of NFPA No. 193, Standard for Fire Department Ladders, Ground and Aerial.

In ordering a ladder truck, careful consideration should be given to the ladder needs of the area served. Manually raised extension ladders more than 40-ft long are generally not required, because aerial ladders and elevating platforms provide adequate emergency access to upper floors and roofs. Other considerations are that additional manpower is required to raise longer ladders, and space available for ladders on combination ladder trucks and on platform trucks is limited.

However, some fire departments do need more and longer ladders, especially where there are areas of apartment and tenement structures that cannot be reached by aerial ladders. Such fire departments often specify and use from 300 to 400 ft of ladders for ladder trucks. This usually involves one or two 50-ft extension ladders, or a 45- and 55-ft extension ladder, an additional 35-ft extension ladder, and 25- and 30-ft single or wall ladders in addition to the required ground ladder load. It is unconscionable to have a first-due ladder truck arrive at a building where numerous rescues must be made from upper floors without an ample number of ground ladders capable of reaching above the third floor.

Ladder Loads and Safety Tests: Loads that fire ladders are designed to support vary according to the length and type, and are shown in the NFPA Fire Department Ladders Standard.

Load limitations are based on use of the ladder supported at the top end against a building, with the butt of the ladder at a distance not to exceed one-third of the ladder length away from the building (approximately a 70° angle), and preferably with the butt of the ladder placed a quarter of the ladder's length away from the building (approximately a 75° angle). These angles are measured from the horizontal with the ladder in the raised position. At angles less than these, the loads on the ladder should decrease accordingly.

The NFPA Fire Department Ladder Standard calls for a thorough inspection of all ladders at least annually, and at any time the ladder is suspected as being unsafe. Inspections are for discovering defects and to determine when testing should be accomplished. The tests are designed to show that the ladder is safe for continued use under the conditions for which it was originally designed. If tests are to be performed, the test procedures must be carefully observed to ensure that ladder damage does not occur. Ladders also should be given visual inspections as outlined in the Standard to detect loose rungs, loose belts and rivets, defects in welds, cracks, splintering, breaks, discoloration, and other signs of possible weakness that might warrant testing to determine whether the ladder is safe to use or needs repair. Over the years fire fighters and members of the public have been killed or injured by failure of ladders that were either overloaded or were used when in an unsafe condition.

Combination Apparatus

In many communities combination apparatus for both pumper and truck service is useful. It may be desirable to provide small stream equipment on ladder trucks, especially in districts where they may arrive at fires before a pumper company. This situation may occur when the first-due engine is at another fire and the ladder company must wait for a covering engine to arrive. In some cities with low pressure water systems the engines always have to connect directly to hydrants, and small stream equipment on ladder trucks is used for initial fire attack. Even where ladder companies do not normally operate hose streams, a large capacity pump on an aerial ladder or platform truck may be useful for boosting pressure to elevated streams. Also, the additional pumping capacity can be credited by the insurance grading personnel toward off-setting a deficiency in the required pumping capacity.

It is not practical to expect one vehicle to provide all of the operational capabilities needed on the fireground. However, a pumper-truck combination may be used as the initial fire attack apparatus in a response group or task force. Positioned close to the building on fire, the apparatus provides preconnected attack lines plus essential ladder and truck tools, while other pumping engines supply water from hydrants and other sources. Often an aerial ladder or elevating platform is provided on such combination apparatus. Good manning is needed for effective use of such combination apparatus even if manpower is assigned to supporting apparatus. Where apparatus is used simultaneously for both engine and ladder truck service, the insurance graders credit this fire company as $\frac{1}{2}$ engine company and $\frac{1}{2}$ ladder company. Where a single vehicle is provided for both types of service, the NFPA Automotive Fire Apparatus Standard recognizes that it must carry a minimum amount of both types of equipment because of space and load limitations. Care must be taken to avoid having an overloaded piece of apparatus, or one with inadequate hose-carrying capacity or an undersized water tank.

Fire Extinguishers

At least two approved portable fire extinguishers are required as basic equipment on all fire apparatus. The variety selected must be suitable for use on Class A, B, and C fires. The minimum sizes called for are: 20 BC rating in dry chemicals, 10 BC rating in carbon dioxide, and 2 A rating in water type extinguishers. Generally dry chemical fire extinguishers are more effective on outside fires than carbon dioxide types. Portable fire extinguishers can often be used effectively in conjunction with water spray nozzles on flammable liquid fires. Vaporizing liquid extinguishers are objectionable because of toxic vapor generation resulting from their use, and consequently are not recommended.

For grass and brush fires most fire departments carry water-pump type extinguishers. The NFPA Automotive Fire Apparatus Standard calls for 6 such units (back-pack type) on each pumper in suburban and rural service, and 4 such portable extinguishers on mobile water supply apparatus. Soda-acid fire extinguishers are seldom used. It is recommended that fire apparatus lacking a water tank and pump be provided with several water-type extinguishers in addition to Class B and C types. The "stored pressure" Class A extinguisher is generally used because it is economical and easily rechargeable.

Foam and Water Additive Equipment

The potential for serious flammable liquid fires has caused many fire departments to provide various types of foam making equipment, or other agents which are more effective than plain water. Often built-in proportioners and foam tanks are specified for new pumpers. In other cases foam making nozzles and portable foam making or generating equipment and foam supplies are carried on the apparatus. Increasingly, new pumpers are being equipped to use an aqueous film forming additive to seal off the surface of flammable liquid fires and smother the fire.

"High expansion" foam is often used as a dual purpose extinguishing agent. Such foams are provided with foam-to-water expansion ratios varying from 100 to 1 up to 1,000 to 1. It is carried and used for the control of flammable liquid fires and spills, and also as an agent for rapid "flooding" of fire areas which present difficult access for hose crews. Less time is required to fill a basement area with high expansion foam than when using water in its usual form, and damage tends to be far less after a fire is extinguished. Its function when used on Class A fires is to quickly exclude oxygen, reduce smoke, and introduce rapid cooling. For effective use as a flooding agent there should be suitable openings to apply the foam and to provide ample ventilation to permit displacement of air, smoke, and gases so that the foam may flow freely. Fire extinguishment is generally successful even though in some applications it may be difficult to contain sufficient foam to completely smother a fire.

Forcible Entry Tools

Ordinarily structural fire fighting cannot be carried out entirely successfully without entering the building or the part of the structure where the fire occurs. Fire apparatus carry a variety of tools for gaining access to locked or closed areas. This equipment permits fire fighters to gain entrance through doorways and windows and to open walls, partitions, ceilings, or roofs to uncover hidden fire or to perform ventilation procedures. Some fire companies carry patented forcible entry tools that have special features.

The use of hydraulic or air-powered spreaders is common because more leverage is obtained than what can be supplied manually. Frequently a heavy door can be sprung with these tools without permanent damage. Such tools also are useful in freeing persons trapped in elevators, wrecked vehicles, and by machinery.

An important aspect of forcible entry is access through

costly tempered glass doors where there is no alternate path for entry. Often, an effective method of entry with the least damage is to drive out the lock cylinder. Special tools are available for this purpose.

Radio Equipment

Every fire department vehicle should be equipped with a 2-way radio capable of operating on the frequency or frequencies used to dispatch the apparatus, and a fireground communications channel. The NFPA Automotive Fire Apparatus Standard makes provision for specifying a weather-proof radio equipment compartment. It is highly desirable to provide radio loud speakers, both inside and outside the vehicle cab, that can be heard above the usual noise on the fireground so that messages can be received by personnel away from the apparatus. A loudspeaker and frequently a radio phone is provided at the pump operator's position, as well as the usual hand set and speaker in the cab.

Every fire company as well as chief officers' vehicles should carry at least one portable 2-way radio to provide communications when away from the vehicle at fires or during inspections. This is important in avoiding delays in getting fire fighting equipment into service and relaying operational instructions after locating a fire in a large area structure, such as an apartment house, shopping center, or industrial property. The radios in fire chiefs' vehicles should be equipped to monitor the various frequencies as well as having the capability of being locked in on a frequency specified by the communications center for particular operations.

Fire chiefs' vehicles may also be equipped to send and receive hard-copy messages (which may be associated with computerized dispatching and recording) and also may have facilities for receiving visual displays of information, including maps and fire hazard data that may be transmitted from the communications center.

Electric Lights and Generators

Each fire apparatus should carry a minimum of two hand lights or lanterns. In addition, each officer needs an electric light for work in a smoke-filled building. Such equipment should be carried on the vehicle to which the officer is assigned. Wet cell batteries can be kept fully charged by battery charging equipment in the fire house. Electric lanterns can be carried on a belt. Lights facilitate operations and help to reduce injuries.

The fire service is often faced with the need to provide electric power at fires and emergencies. Power demands may include: (1) power to operate fire apparatus and its appurtenances, (2) power to operate tools and lights on the fireground, (3) emergency power to maintain essential services such as communications, and (4) emergency power for temporarily replacing essential community services. This demand may be met in several ways: by the provision of generating equipment, transformers, and outlets as part of a vehicle's electric system; by portable generators on fire apparatus; by special "lighting trucks" or mobile generator units; and by standby generators at locations such as fire stations and communication centers.

A portable generator of at least 2,500 watt rating with three portable floodlights and six 50-ft lengths of electric cable on a reel or reels is required for every ladder truck. Such equipment should be carried on pumpers and squad trucks where ladder trucks do not regularly respond. Portable generators capable of generating either direct or alternating current should be investigated. Where smoke ejector

fans and equipment other than lights are to be served, a 3,500-watt or larger generator is desirable.

Generators may be mounted on apparatus and arranged for automatic starting, but should also be capable of being removed from the apparatus. Some fire apparatus carry two generators so that one can be dropped off where needed, while the other provides the required electrical capacity on the unit. Sometimes one portable generator and one generator driven by the apparatus engine are provided.

When power tools, such as heavy-duty cutting tools, are supplied by generators, individual circuits should be furnished with each circuit protected by circuit breakers, so that if a tool should stall it will not stall or damage the generator while operating other equipment. Electric cables, fittings, and lights should be the heavy-duty waterproof types that can be used safely without danger of shock or damage when immersed. A common error is using conductors that are too small to carry the load required to operate appliances efficiently. Many fire departments provide large capacity conductors serving a multiple outlet to which individual appliances can be attached near the point of use.

Portable Pumps

Portable pumps for fire department service are covered in NFPA No. 191, Standard for Fire Department Portable Pumping Units, except for special types for forest fire service which are covered in the NFPA No. 295, Equipment and Organization for Fighting Forest, Grass, and Brush Fires. Such pumps are too small in capacity to be of much value either for fighting structural fires or for filling and discharging fire department tankers.

Portable pumps for fire department service are generally of the centrifugal type. They are grouped in categories based upon the pressure-volume characteristics that make them suitable for various classes of work. Small streams at high pressure are intended mainly for grass and brush fire work. Pumps delivering relatively large volumes at low pressures can serve as a supply pump for fire trucks where the water supply source is beyond the reach of suction hose. They also may be used as a dewatering pump. Fairly large volume flows at higher pressures are considered valuable in hilly areas where ordinary portable pumps do not develop sufficient pressure to overcome elevation or "head."

The NFPA Automotive Fire Apparatus Standard recommends that both pumpers and water tank apparatus serving rural areas carry a portable pump. In selecting portable pumps, fire departments should be careful to obtain models which will give the needed flow characteristics at a safe, continuous engine speed. The user should obtain from the manufacturer or supplier the discharge-pressure curve for the model selected.

D. Protective Equipment for Fire Fighters

The NFPA Automotive Fire Apparatus Standard requires that each pumper (engine company) carry at least two pieces of self-contained breathing apparatus (National Institute of Occupational Safety and Health approved), and that each ladder truck carry six pieces of self-contained breathing apparatus (NIOSH approved). The laws of some states require that approved protective breathing apparatus be provided for all fire fighters exposed to smoke and gases from fires and emergencies.

Respiratory Protective Equipment

NFPA No. 19B, Standard for Respiratory Protective Equipment for Fire Fighters, provides that: "all fire fighters exposed to smoke and gases from fires and emergencies where such gases may be released shall be provided with suitable self-contained breathing apparatus," and that "only self-contained breathing apparatus approved by the National Institute of Occupational Safety and Health shall be considered as meeting the provisions of this Standard." Breathing apparatus carried on fire department apparatus requires self-contained equipment having ½-hour minimum service life.

There are three approved types of breathing apparatus for fire department use: (a) self-contained open circuit "demand" or "pressure-demand" types containing one or more cylinders of respirable air, (b) closed circuit breathing apparatus using a chemical as the source of respirable oxygen, and (c) closed circuit compressed oxygen breathing apparatus.

For some fifty years following World War I, many fire departments provided and used mask equipment consisting merely of a face mask attached to a canister containing chemicals designed to filter out a limited amount of the products of combustion. These masks did not supply the oxygen needed to support life, and a number of fatalities and serious injuries resulted from their use. In many cases it was not practical for fire fighters or fire officers to judge the degree of danger involved in working in contaminated oxygen deficient atmospheres. Accordingly, in 1971 on recommendation of the Sectional Committee on Respiratory Equipment for Fire Fighters, the NFPA adopted Standard No. 19B which makes approved self-contained breathing apparatus mandatory. The Standard also requires that fire department officials shall have respiratory protective equipment inspected at regular intervals, preferably weekly, but not less than monthly, and shall arrange for immediate replacement of equipment not providing the degree of protection indicated in the Standard.

From time to time various types of respiratory devices lacking NIOSH approval have been offered to the fire service in the United States. Some deficiencies of such devices include: protection only for a very limited period of time; the absence of a full face piece; and construction unsuitable for rugged conditions of fire service masks. Their use and maintenance is contained in the *NFPA Fire Officer's Guide on Breathing Apparatus for the Fire Service*.

"Demand" masks consist of a facepiece connected by tube to a regulator or pressure reducing valve which is connected to a pressure tank of air or oxygen. It also has a pressure gage and the necessary harness. The tank is intended to provide 30 min protection to the average wearer. The period may be shorter for men of above average breathing capacity, or when worn during heavy exertion. The mask is popular in areas where masks are used frequently. Recharging is relatively inexpensive, and many fire departments maintain their own recharging equipment. Additional cylinders are carried on fire apparatus for use as needed.

Masks of the type that use canisters to generate oxygen were developed for the U.S. Navy. These masks are fairly light in weight (13.5 lbs). The canister is not activated until the seal is broken and the wearer has exhaled into the mask to start the oxygen generating reaction. After use, the canister should be punctured on both sides and at the bottom, and immersed in water so that the canister will not continue to generate oxygen after it has been discarded.

Another type of self-contained breathing apparatus used by fire departments is an oxygen rebreathing or oxygen regeneration type. This "mask" has a cylinder supplying oxygen to the wearer through a pressure reducing valve,

and a container of chemicals to remove carbon dioxide from the exhaled air. A breathing bag operates as an admission valve in conjunction with the cooler and regenerator. A mouthpiece, or facepiece with inhalation, exhalation, salivatrap, and release valves and tubes, connects to the cooler. In this apparatus, the process of inhalation operates the valve, admitting oxygen into the breathing bag and cooler. Exhaled air passes through cardozide to absorb carbon dioxide and then goes to the cooler where it is enriched by fresh oxygen and then rebreathed. It is necessary to clear the mask of excess nitrogen every 15 to 20 min used, by opening a release valve and exhaling to the outside atmosphere. This type of equipment must only be used by trained rescue workers experienced with the equipment.

Use of Breathing Apparatus: Protective breathing equipment should be used only after thorough training with the specific type of equipment available for use and practice in working under restricted breathing and visibility conditions. Fire fighters wearing masks should not work alone and should be under supervision of officers. Masks should not be donned by men who have been subjected to heavy exertion and smoke. The use of masks does not protect an individual against excessive heat, gases, and poisons that attack the body through the skin.

Some breathing equipment is equipped with an audible warning signal to warn the user when the air or oxygen supply is low. When this alarm sounds wearers should leave the contaminated area immediately. Fire fighters have been overcome when they removed their masks too soon or because of difficulty in breathing when a canister or air supply was becoming exhausted. Generally, a wearer is safer (if getting any air at all) to leave the mask on until he reaches a safe atmosphere or receives help.

When feasible, lifelines should be used to indicate the path of escape. If it is necessary to descend into manholes or cisterns, lifelines must be fastened to the men.

Special caution is necessary in the use of breathing apparatus in pressurized atmospheres not only because of the increased hazard of fire and explosions, but because the period of protection may be reduced by the higher pressure. Another problem exists when fires are difficult to reach and the time required to get to the fire and return to outside air utilizes most of the respirable air of the equipment. Some fire departments have large wheeled air cylinders arranged for such situations. Two-hr self-contained masks are also available.

A number of fire departments have scuba (self-contained underwater breathing apparatus) designed for their own purposes. Fire department air or oxygen masks should not be used for underwater work.

Training in the use and care of protective breathing apparatus is part of basic fire fighter training. Confidence in the equipment, as well as knowledge of its practical limitations, should increase with use.

Resuscitators

It is recommended that fire department ladder trucks and rescue trucks carry at least one resuscitator capable of caring for two patients (plus spare oxygen cylinders). Such equipment should also be carried on engine companies where such companies are assigned to answer rescue calls in their districts. In NFPA 1001, Standard for Fire Fighter Professional Qualifications, all fire fighters are required to hold certificates of completion of advanced first aid training. This training includes the ventilation of victims either by physical or mechanical means. Some states by law require that all fire department and police personnel be trained in cardiopulmonary resuscitation (see Chapter 2, this Section for fire department emergency medical technician and paramedic qualifications). Correct techniques for care and use of resuscitation equipment as well as manual means of resuscitation are covered in the *NFPA Fire Officer's Guide on Breathing Apparatus for the Fire Service.*

Smoke Ejectors

Smoke ejectors are required equipment on ladder trucks and on other apparatus used for performing ventilation service. The smoke ejector commonly used has a 16-in. diameter and is rated at 5,000 cfm at 1,750 rpm. There are also 24-in. ejectors which are rated up to 11,750 cfm. Both ac and dc meters are available with explosion-proof features and the ability to operate on a 110 v or 220 v optional. In fire department operations smoke ejectors are often used for pulling out smoke and gases as well as for blowing in fresh air. At serious fires it is not unusual to use a number of smoke ejectors at various locations to move the desired quantity of smoke and air.

An important use of smoke ejectors is to reduce smoke damage from minor fires. Prompt use helps prevent soot particles from settling, and when used in connection with vacuum equipment most soot may be removed. Some fire departments also use ejector fans to spray deodorants after a fire. (See the NFPA booklet, titled "Open Up!" covering fire department ventilation procedures.)

When ejectors are used to remove concentrations of combustible gases, explosion-proof equipment will be required. Suggestions for successful use include: (1) having an adequate power supply and conductors to operate ejector meters efficiently, (2) placing fans at openings in a manner to blow out so the fumes will travel the shortest possible distance, (3) placing fans as high as possible in openings using secure hooks and other supports as needed, (4) using prevailing wind when possible, (5) closing openings around the equipment as necessary so smoke will be drawn through the fan (some departments have folding covers designed to block openings around the equipment), (6) opening doors and windows to establish cross ventilation, and (7) removal of screens and other obstructions likely to block the movement of air.

Life Nets

A rescue item commonly carried on ladder trucks is the life net or jumping net. Most nets consist of heavy canvas supported by a folding metal frame and springs, and containing a pad to soften impact. A few fire departments also carry rope jumping nets for use in confined places where limited space or obstructions preclude use of the large circular metal rimmed nets.

Lives have been saved with life nets from heights as great as 8 stories, but for practical purposes 3 or 4 stories is considered to be the maximum height at which nets may be used with reasonable safety. A manually held net is of little practical value for extreme heights from which some would-be suicides threaten to jump; these nets impose great danger to the personnel holding them. Few fire companies have sufficient men to hold a net effectively, even for persons jumping from the third or fourth floors. If a net is to be used, adequate manpower must be utilized.

In using a net it is important for the jumper to land sitting down to avoid severe injuries. Fire fighters are trained to hold nets with elbows at sides, hands, chest, or neck high, left foot forward, and with eyes directed toward the person jumping. A danger is that when a net is opened,

panicstricken persons may jump before the net is properly positioned. The net should not be opened directly below the jump site. Many fire officers consider the net a "last resort item" and generally, in most places where a net can be used effectively, a ladder can be placed as quickly by fewer men and with greater safety.

Life Guns

A life gun designed to shoot a rope line to persons in distress is an item of equipment occasionally carried on ladder or rescue trucks. One type of gun, powered by a .30-06 cartridge, has a launcher that permits variations in distance from 100 to 650 ft using a $\frac{1}{16}$-in. nylon line with a 180-lb tensile strength. Primarily, the life gun is used in water rescues (such as for persons stranded on rocks from overturned boats), and to rescue persons from cliffs or canyons. Fire fighters need extensive practice to use the equipment efficiently.

Protective Clothing for Fire Fighters

Fire fighters should not enter burning buildings or buildings that have been subjected to appreciable fire damage unless wearing full protective clothing, including fire helmets. It is the responsibility of the authority operating the fire department to provide clothing and equipment for all fire fighting personnel. This is preferably done through direct procurement by the fire department, but may be done by providing personnel with allowances for clothing and equipment that meet fire department standards and specifications.

At a minimum, protective equipment should include a suitable helmet, a protective coat, boots, and gloves, all of which should be properly sized for the individual wearer. Some fire departments provide a full turnout suit with trousers of material and construction comparable to the protective coat. Protective clothing is designed to protect the wearer from heat and cold, as well as from abrasions. It should also be water-repellant, light in weight, and easy to put on.

Boots used by fire fighters should have protective insoles designed to guard against foot punctures, and toe caps to protect against impact injuries. Most fire fighters use ¾-length boots which can be pulled up above the knees when required. Short "bunker boots" are used with turnout suits. All boots should have straps to facilitate rapid use in donning when an alarm is received.

E. Hose, Couplings, and Nozzles

Fire hose is the vital link between the water supply and nozzles used to project streams on the fire. Hose must be rugged and dependable, capable of carrying water under substantial pressures, and yet flexible and sufficiently easy to handle. Hose is an important item in a fire department budget. Selection of the proper grades and types of hose, and maintenance to assure maximum useful life are of concern to fire department management. These two chief factors are covered in detail in NFPA No. 196, Standard for Fire Hose, and NFPA No. 198, Standard for the Care of Fire Hose. Aside from unavoidable mechanical injury at fires, dependability and length of life of hose rest on three factors: (1) the quality and suitability of the hose purchased, (2) the care with which it is handled at fires, and (3) the maintenance and care of hose in quarters. Under average fire conditions and with proper care, hose should be serviceable for a minimum of 10 years unless subject to damage in use. There is no reason for discarding hose at the end of 10 years if it is in good condition and passes annual service tests.

Types of Fire Hose

Fire hose is manufactured in the following principal sizes measured by the internal diameter in inches: $\frac{3}{4}$, 1, $1\frac{1}{2}$, $2\frac{1}{2}$, 3, $3\frac{1}{2}$, 4, $4\frac{1}{2}$, 5, and 6. The internal diameter of the hose waterway principally determines the flow delivered at a given expenditure of pressure energy. For example, two lines of 3-in. hose carry as much water as three lines of the nominal $2\frac{1}{2}$-in. size; one line of $3\frac{1}{2}$-in. hose carries approximately as much water as two $2\frac{1}{2}$-in. lines.

Fire hose is made with a number of different forms of construction in accordance with the intended type of service. Most fire hose has an interior rubber tube or lining to provide a smooth, watertight conductor and one or more jackets to provide the strength to withstand the intended pressure, and to protect the tube against damage from abrasion. Certain types of hose also have a protective cover.

Various types and sizes of hose used for fire protection purposes are described in the NFPA Fire Hose Standard. The Standard indicates the tests that should be met for the types and sizes of hose to be purchased. These types include: (1) woven-jacket, rubber-lined hose, (2) relay supply hose, (3) booster hose, (4) suction hose, and (5) special types including unlined fire hose, forestry hose, and covered woven-jacket rubber-lined hose.

Woven-jacket, Rubber-lined Fire Hose: Fire departments, both public and industrial (brigades), are most familiar with woven-jacket rubber-lined fire hose. The rubber lining may be natural or synthetic, or a combination of these materials. Jackets may be single or multiple woven. Single jacket hose is intended for use at industrial yard hydrants and at standpipes where it will not get hard usage. Multiple-jacket hose is used by public fire departments because service conditions require the additional protection provided by the extra jacket or jackets.

For many years the woven jacket was made entirely of cotton fibers. In recent years much of the hose that has been manufactured has had cotton warp or lengthwise threads, and synthetic fiber filler or circumferential cords. The synthetic filler thread adds strength, reduces weight, and results in a more flexible hose that is easier to fold into a hose bed. Hose also is made of all-synthetic fiber jackets. This hose is lighter in weight than cotton-jacket hose, considerably more flexible, and a greater amount can be carried on apparatus or on standpipe racks. Both the all-cotton and cotton-synthetic jacket hose are subject to mildew, although both are available from manufacturers in treated form that retards the formation of mildew.

The common trade sizes for single-jacket rubber-lined hose are $1\frac{1}{2}$ and $2\frac{1}{2}$ in., and for multiple-jacket rubber-lined hose $1\frac{1}{2}$, $2\frac{1}{2}$, 3, $3\frac{1}{2}$ and 4 in. Hose in certain other sizes, or hose with high hydrostatic and burst pressure characteristics, can be obtained for special applications.

The $1\frac{1}{2}$-in. hose is particularly applicable to inside fire fighting for ease in handling and for initial fire attack where appropriate. A larger back-up line is always recommended.

More $2\frac{1}{2}$-in. fire hose is carried on fire apparatus than any other size. It is used to provide standard 250 gpm hose streams from hand lines, and also in multiple lines to supply master streams. Dual $2\frac{1}{2}$-in. lines are used to supply flows of from 500 to 600 gpm.

The 3-in. and $3\frac{1}{2}$-in. hose are used as supply lines to supply large stream devices including ladder pipes. Many fire department pumpers carry short lengths of large diameter woven-jacket rubber-lined hose for supplying the pump from hydrants. Frequently such hose is preconnected to a pump inlet. Sizes used include $4\frac{1}{2}$-, 5-, and 6-in. diameters.

Relay Supply Hose: In addition to the double-jacket rubber-lined fire hose designed to withstand rugged service (including high pump discharge pressures), many fire department pumpers carry a lighter-weight large diameter fire hose having a single synthetic jacket. This hose is used to supply pumps from hydrants, or in relays between a pump at a water source and a pump at a fire. Such large diameter hose is available in 4-, $4\frac{1}{2}$-, 5-, and 6-in. diameters. It is furnished with a lining and frequently has a protective synthetic cover.

Suction Hose: Hard suction hose has a rubber lining and layers of fabric reinforcement with a spiral wire set in rubber between the reinforcement layers to prevent collapse of the hose when drafting water with pressure in the hose below atmospheric pressure. Usually the hose is furnished in 10 ft lengths, and the common sizes are 4 to 6 in. Smaller sizes are available for special applications such as for supplying portable fire pumps. The use of hard suction hose is not recommended when supplying pumps from hydrants if other suitable large diameter hose is available. The NFPA has issued no performance standards for hard suction hose other than the requirement that such hose be able to withstand hydrostatic pressure of 200 psi to guard against damage from pressure surges.

Booster Hose: Originally, booster hose was developed as "Chemical Engine Hose." Many fire department pumping engines and other fire apparatus are equipped with one or two reels, each carrying 200 to 300 ft of this hose which has an inner rubber tube, a reinforcement consisting of fabric wrapping(s) or braid(s), and an outer rubber cover. Sizes ordinarily used by fire departments are $\frac{3}{4}$ and 1 in., with the latter size being preferred because it carries approximately twice as much water at a given pressure. Booster hose has a usual proof pressure of 400 psi, but 800 psi or higher proof pressure is required for high pressure pumps.

Special Types of Hose: Unlined fire hose consists of a tube of fabric, the threads of which swell after being wet, thus closing the spaces between the threads to make the tube watertight. This hose, usually made of linen yarn and available in $1\frac{1}{2}$- to $2\frac{1}{2}$-in. sizes, is designed primarily for fire protection installations at inside standpipes and similar places where it can be kept dry. It should never be wet, except for use at a fire. Its friction loss characteristics are approximately double that for lined fire hose of the same size.

Hose used by forest services usually is 1 to $1\frac{1}{2}$ in. with a single woven jacket, either lined or unlined. The lined hose is used extensively. The unlined hose is preferred where it must be back-packed by fire fighters to the point of use. Again, the lower friction loss with a given size is an advantage of the lined hose, and takes much less time for water to reach the nozzle through a long line of lined hose. (See Chapter 5, this Section, for details on friction loss in fire hose.)

Covered, woven-jacket, rubber-lined hose in various sizes is used extensively in locations where the extra protection afforded by the coating or cover is required.

Diameter and Length of Hose: The NFPA Fire Hose Standard requires that hose shall have an internal diameter not less than the trade size of the hose, except that for $2\frac{1}{2}$-in. hose the internal diameter shall be not less than $2\frac{9}{16}$-in. unless otherwise specified, and the hose shall be in lengths averaging not less than 50 ft. No nominal 50-ft lengths shall be less than 48 ft, except that the length from which the burst test piece was taken may be 47 ft. Many fire departments specify that relay supply hose be delivered in 100-ft lengths to reduce the cost and weight of couplings in long water supply lines. No nominal 100-ft length shall be less than 98 ft, except that the length from which the burst test piece was taken may be 97 ft.

Hydrostatic Pressure Tests

Acceptance Pressure: Consideration of the "acceptance pressure" to which a hose shall be tested is important. Damage to the hose from pump pressures seldom exceeds 200 psi, and hose meeting 400 psi pressure is commonly specified. Fire departments that may have to use high pump pressures for heavy streams, for supplying standpipes, or for pumper relays, commonly specify that fire hose must pass a 600 psi pressure test. The higher pressure test also automatically requires higher pressures in the other hydrostatic tests called for in the NFPA Fire Hose Standard. Some fire departments specify 600 psi pressure to obtain hose which they believe will better withstand hard usage over a period of years.

Burst Test: The NFPA Fire Hose Standard specifies that a 3-ft sample taken from each lot of hose shall be subjected to a "burst test." For multiple-jacket fire hose, the sample should not burst at a pressure at least 50 percent greater than the required pressure. Thus, hose specified for 400 psi pressure must pass a 600 psi burst pressure test, and a sample of 600 psi pressure hose must withstand a 900 psi burst test. Some purchasers have thought mistakenly that they were buying 600 psi pressure hose because a sample of the hose passed a 600 psi pressure burst test. The pressure is determined by testing each length of hose to the specified pressure. The higher burst pressure indicates that the pressure tests will not damage the hose because of its lighter single-jacket construction. The NFPA Fire Hose Standard requires relay supply hose to meet only a 400 psi pressure test and a 600 psi burst test for the $3\frac{1}{2}$- to $4\frac{1}{2}$-in. sizes, and only 300 psi pressure and 500 psi burst test for the 5- and 6-in. diameters which are used chiefly for supplying pumpers from hydrants. Industrial fire departments (brigades) using fire department type pumpers quite commonly use the double-jacket fire hose. However, where the hose may be subject to damage by chemicals or abrasive materials when used, it is common to specify a special protective coating.

The burst test on the 3-ft sample is conducted by subjecting the hose to hydrostatic pressure increasing at a rate not less than 300 psi nor more than 1,000 psi per min while lying either straight or curved on a surface having a radius of 27 in. The pressure is increased until a burst occurs or the maximum pressure of the apparatus is reached. The hose must not burst at a pressure less than the burst pressure specified.

Kink Test: In addition to the pressure test for each length of hose and the burst pressure test on a 3-ft sample, the NFPA Fire Hose Standard requires that a full length of hose shall withstand a required hydrostatic pressure while kinked, without rupturing or breaking any thread in the jackets. The purpose of the kink test is to ensure that the hose will withstand actual conditions met on the fireground. Where hose is laying straight, the warp threads that run lengthwise are not stressed; under kink conditions which occur commonly at fires, these threads are highly stressed.

Other Fire Hose Tests: In addition to the hydrostatic tests, the NFPA Fire Hose Standard specifies tests of elongation, twist, warp, and rise, to prove that the hose is suitable for the intended service. For hose diameters up to $2\frac{1}{2}$ in. inclusive, when tested at 300 psi for single-jacket hose, and at 400 or 600 psi for multiple-jacket hose, or 8 percent for

multiple-jacket hose. Initial measurement is taken at 10 psi pressure.

The hose when tested to proof pressures must not twist more than a specified number of turns per 50 ft. In all cases any final twist must be to the right to tighten the couplings. The twist test does not apply to relay supply hose. No twisting is permitted between inner and outer jackets.

When tested to specified proof pressure, the hose must not warp more than 20 in. in 50 ft from the center line drawn between couplings, and no rise from the test table is permitted for multiple-jacket hose. A rise of 4 in. is permitted for single-jacket $2\frac{1}{2}$-in. hose, and 7 in. for the smaller single-jacket hose. The warp and rise tests do not apply to relay supply hose.

Unless otherwise specified, all tests are conducted with the couplings to be delivered, and couplings are examined for leakage, distortion, or movement during the tests.

Examination of Hose for Compliance

For compliance with the NFPA Fire Hose Standard, hose examinations and tests should be made under standard conditions, and the record made generally available through publication by organizations properly equipped and qualified for experimental testing and inspection of hose at factories. Many fire departments and other purchasers specify that a test report be furnished for each individual length of hose purchased, and that the test report include notation regarding the attachment and condition of couplings.

Purchasing fire hose by specification alone does not ensure the obtaining of the desired quality and proof pressure. To assure this, there must be definite tests performed under each item of the specifications, conducted in a standard manner by persons qualified in this work. Visual inspection alone does not detect inferior or defective lengths of hose. The cost for the testing service is nominal as compared with the investment involved in purchasing hose and the importance of reliability and suitability of intended service. In many cases money is saved by purchasing tested and listed fire hose that is constructed to meet the performance tests specified, thus helping to assure a long reliable service under anticipated conditions of use.

To help obtain hose that meets the requirements of the NFPA Fire Hose Standard, a fire department should indicate the number of feet and nominal size of hose, number of jackets, the type of jacket fiber wanted, and whether mildew treatment is wanted for cotton or part-cotton jackets.

Care, Maintenance, and Use of Fire Hose

To be reliable, fire hose should always be cared for properly. It should not be used for other than fire fighting service, except in emergencies and with the approval of fire department officials. Burst hose at a fire may cause serious injury to fire fighters and other persons, and may mean loss of time in bringing a fire under control. The proper use, care, and maintenance of various types of fire hose is the subject of the NFPA Fire Hose Standard.

Care of Woven-jacket Rubber-lined Hose: With the exception of booster hose and hard suction hose, most of the fire hose carried on fire department apparatus is of woven-jacket, rubber-lined construction. Hose carried on fire apparatus should be loaded in such a way that air can circulate. Where apparatus serves in areas subject to frequent rain and snow, the hose compartments should be protected by removable decks fitted with waterproof tarpaulins or covers extending downward over the rear opening of the hose body. Such covers, providing air space over the hose, also protect the hose from the direct rays of the sun when fire apparatus is out of quarters during inspection and training periods.

Where hose is installed at yard hydrants at industrial plants, it should be kept in well-ventilated hose houses in such a way that air can circulate and excessive heat avoided. Details of such hose houses are covered in NFPA No. 24, Standard for Outside Protection.

In order to prevent damage and permanent set to the rubber tube, hose should be removed from the apparatus or hose house at least quarterly and reloaded in a different position. It is considered desirable to also run water through the hose at least quarterly. When hose has been charged with water, whether at fires or drills or for servicing, it should be replaced on the apparatus by spare hose so that the required amount will be available for fire fighting while the hose that has been used is being cleaned and dried. Whether hose jackets are of cotton or synthetic construction, the hose should be cleaned and dried after use to remove possible abrasive or contaminating materials, and to protect the hose compartment of the apparatus against rust or water damage.

Care of Hose at Fires: When used for fighting fires, fire hose is subject to severe strains, pressure surges, and mechanical injury. Care should be taken to lay hose so that injury will not result from contact with sharp or rough objects at fires insofar as possible. Too often hose is treated as though it were rugged water pipe instead of a flexible tube protected only by the fabric jacket. Vehicles should not be driven over hose lines. Where it is necessary for fire department vehicles to cross, hose bridges should be used where possible; however, it is desirable to detour all nonemergency traffic from the fire area. When it is necessary to hoist lines, mechanical injury can be avoided and the task made easier by use of hose rollers. When hose lines are extended up ladders, the hose should be supported by hose rope tools placed so as to take the strain off couplings.

Pressure surges are a principal cause of damage to fire hose. Shut-off nozzles should be opened and closed slowly because sudden closing of nozzles can cause severe pressure surges or shock waves which are unpredictable and can be extremely damaging both to hose and to pumping apparatus. Pressure relief devices on pumping engines should always be used to control sudden increases in pressure. In pump operation it is preferable to reduce pressure at the pump when convenient to do so before shutting nozzles as this avoids pressure surges which may occur even where the engine governor or relief valve is functioning properly.

The usual required relief valves or pressure governors are designed to protect the discharge side of the pump. When water is relayed from a pump at a water source to a pump at a fire, special precautions should be taken to prevent damaging pressure surges. If not provided as part of the pumping apparatus, some form of relay relief valve should be attached to the inlet or "suction side" of the pump near the fire to which the relay hose line is to be attached. The lower the setting of this relief valve on the inlet of the receiving pump, the greater the protection to the hose supplying the relay.

In cold climates care should be taken to prevent water from freezing in or on the hose. Once water is turned on, some water should be left running through the hose until the line is no longer needed. During freezing weather it is common practice to place the nozzle out of a window and, by "cracking" the valve, keep water moving through the hose while overhaul is in process because moving water does not freeze readily. Sharp bends should be avoided in any hose in or on which ice has formed, as frozen hose can be damaged by such bends. Care must be used in chopping ice from hose after a fire. After hose which has been frozen has been dried it should be service tested.

Care must be taken to avoid the burning of the hose at woods and grass fires. As fire is knocked down and the nozzle is advanced, the hose often comes in contact with hot spots or rekindled fire unless care is exercised. An advantage of unlined hose in forestry service is that water seeping from the hose helps to protect it against such damage.

Care of Hose after Fires: When hose has been returned to quarters it should be laid out where it can be swept and washed as needed. Some fire departments have machines for this purpose. It is important to remove dirt and other foreign material from the jackets. A scrub brush and mild soap and water may be used, but frequently a small hose is used for washdown purposes. (Figs. 9-4F and 9-4G show typical hose washing and drying machines.) Fresh clean hose should be loaded on the apparatus to replace the hose that has been used, except for rubber-covered booster hose which merely needs to be wiped clean as it is rerolled on the reel.

After cleaning to remove grime and contaminants, hose should be thoroughly dried. There are three approved methods of drying cabinets. Where drying cabinets are used, sufficient number should be provided to properly service the hose. Normally, not less than two cabinets of 500-ft hose capacity will be needed for each fire station. Some fire departments have a central hose depot that cares for all hose, and supplies fresh clean hose to the fire stations as needed. When hose has been thoroughly dried, it should be removed from the drying equipment, rolled for storage, and placed on storage racks ready for use. (See Fig. 9-4H for typical commercial fire hose storage rack.)

Fig. 9-4F. A commercially available hose washing machine. (Circul-Air)

Fig. 9-4G. A commercial hose drier. (Circul-Air)

Fig. 9-4H. Typical commercial rack for storing fire hose. (Circul-Air)

Size	Identification No. of Length		FIRE DEPARTMENT HOSE RECORD				
Kind		Brand		Cost per foot		Date of Purchase	
Manufacturer			Vendor			Guarantee	
Date in Service	Co. No.	Length Tested			Out of Service		Couplings	Remarks

Date in Service	Co. No.	Date	Pressure	O.K. or Failure	Date	Reason	Couplings	Remarks

Fig. 9-4I.   One type of hose record card.

Hose Records

Good hose records are necessary in order to keep accurate data on hose performance. These records may be kept in a book or on printed card forms. They include the fire department's record of its complete hose inventory, and a record of use of hose by the individual fire fighting units to which it is assigned. Upon delivery and acceptance, each length of hose is given an identification number. This is used to record its history throughout its service life, and ultimately shows the reason the hose was condemned and removed from service. Such records enable fire department administrators to determine the cost-effectiveness of the various sizes and types of hose in service, the work to which hose is subjected, service tests, repairs, and other pertinent data. If hose falls within the guarantee period, this will be indicated.

Each length of hose should be identified by an assigned code number corresponding to the fire department hose record. The number may be stenciled on the hose near the coupling, taking care to use an ink or paint that will not be deleterious to the hose. Or the number may be stamped on the bowl or swivel of the coupling. Coupling bowls may be damaged by improper number stamping. The proper procedure is to insert a special steel plug with rounded edges into the end of the expansion ring. One sharp blow from a sharp steel numbering die should then stamp the coupling.

Some fire departments color code the couplings, as well as various other tools, to identify the fire company to which the equipment is assigned. This enables each company to readily identify and pick up its own hose and equipment used at a fire. Where mutual aid operations are frequent, each length of hose should be stenciled with an identification of the fire department owning the hose.

Each fire company may be required to keep a hose record book. This shows when each length of hose is put on particular apparatus, when it is removed after use, and whether used for fires or drills. When hose has been removed from the apparatus for use at fires or drills and so recorded, it is not necessary to make a scheduled hose change except for the required service tests. Where apparatus has several hose compartments, the compartment from which hose was last removed may be marked with chalk indicating that change of hose is not required for that compartment. However, if hose has not been changed within three months and a compartment has been partly unloaded at a fire, it may be desirable to reload the entire compartment after a fire so that hose at the bottom of the load will not be neglected.

Responsibility for maintaining the required hose records should be spelled out in departmental rules or orders. The hose shop or maintenance division should keep a hose work report. Records should indicate the age of the hose, the vendor, the fire company to which it was assigned, and also the cause of failure or reason for condemning an individual length of hose. (See Fig. 9-4I for typical hose record card.)

Service Tests for Fire Hose

Reliability of fire hose is essential to good fire department service. Service tests should be conducted on each length at least annually and after repairs, or at any time that hose has had hard usage and its condition is suspect. NFPA No. 198, Standard for the Care, Maintenance, and Use of Fire Hose, includes recommended service test procedures and includes a typical annual hose test record form. The Standard calls for service test pressures of 250 psi for 400 psi proof hose and of 350 psi for 600 psi proof hose.

The development of test pressures as high as 250 psi introduces a serious accident potential unless recommended procedures are followed. Where test pressure is in excess of 250 psi, testing must be limited to a single coupled length and extra care must be taken to see that all air is bled from the hose before allowing pressure to rise. The hose must be tested on a surface that permits the hose to elongate freely and is supported in such a way that curvatures other than normal warping does not occur.

Service pressure tests may be conducted either with a hose testing machine or by use of fire department pumpers. The NFPA Fire Hose Care and Maintenance Standard details both methods. In most fire departments it is more practical and convenient to schedule hose tests for fire companies so that each company will test its own hose, using its pumper to supply the pressure. It is important to use a hose test gate valve with a $\frac{1}{4}$-in. opening to permit test pressure to be maintained after the hose has been filled and the valve closed, but which doesn't permit a pressure surge should the hose burst while testing.

The required service testing of hose to at least 250 psi is an important consideration in the underwriters' grading of a fire department which also requires that necessary test records be maintained. Following are recommended test procedures using a fire department pumper:

1. Lay out hose to be tested in lines of convenient length. Make sure that lines are straight without kinks or twists. Record identifying numbers of lengths to be tested.

2. Connect a fire department pumper at a suitable location to provide the water and pressure for testing.

3. Connect lines to be tested to gated outlets of the pumper. Attach shutoff nozzles to the far end of the lines. Secure both ends of the hose. Support the line being tested

with a rope hose tool at a point 10 to 15 in. from the hose butt coupled to the pumper discharge port.

4. Secure the nozzle (or hose back of it) to avoid possible whipping or other uncontrolled reaction.

5. In attaching hose to pumper use a hose test gate which will prevent an excessive pressure surge should hose burst during test.

6. With test gate valve and nozzle open, fill hose with water at a pressure not exceeding 100 psi. After line is charged and all air has been exhausted from the hose, close the nozzle slowly and close the test gate valve at the pumper.

7. Check all couplings for leakage and tighten couplings with spanner where necessary. Mark hose at each end of couplings with crayon or pencil. This is to determine whether there is any coupling movement during the test.

8. With test gate valve closed, raise the pressure slowly to 250 psi and hold test pressure for 5 min. During this time, walk down the line and inspect for coupling leaks or pin holes. Never straddle hose under pressure. Except as necessary to inspect couplings, keep a distance of at least 15 ft from the hose.

9. After 5 min, reduce pumper to idling speed, close hydrant, disengage pump, and open drain valve on pumper to reduce pressure in line under test. When pressure drops below 100 psi, open nozzle slowly to finish relieving pressure, close gates, and disconnect lines.

10. Observe marks placed on hose back of couplings. If couplings have moved during test, the length of hose should be sent to shop for resetting of coupling. The identifying number of the length should be marked on the record card and the hose tagged to indicate what the defect is. Burst lengths should be tagged and taken out of service.

11. Hose records should be marked to indicate the condition of each length tested.

12. After testing, hose should be properly drained and dried.

Unlined Fire Hose

Unlined hose designed for standpipe use is intended for first aid fire protection purposes only. It should never be wet except for use at a fire, after which it should be discarded and replaced with new hose. This makes it uneconomical for most industrial fire protection use, and single-jacket rubber-lined hose is commonly recommended for hose attached to standpipe outlets in industrial properties. The lined hose has the advantages of lower friction loss at a given flow, it does not cause water damage from seepage, it can be used to supply spray nozzles and other shutoff nozzles, and it can be reused after service when properly cleaned and dried.

Unlined hose usually is stored on a rack or reel and used on standpipes inside of buildings. Warm dry air does not affect it, but moisture can cause rapid deterioration unless the hose has been treated to resist rot and mildew. Valves must be kept in good condition so that there will be no leakage. Hose must be protected from condensation on the standpipes.

The hose end attached to the standpipe should be tested periodically by slightly twisting the hose at the valve connection and giving a sharp pull. Hose stored on a rack or reel should be given a careful examination at least once a year. If a hydrostatic test appears desirable, a 3-ft section may be cut from the hose for testing and the remaining hose recoupled. The service test pressure for this hose need not exceed the pressure that will be supplied at the standpipe outlet. The yarns of unlined fire hose are highly absorptive because their function is to quickly absorb water

and expand to hold water when in use. The yarns will lose effectiveness if impregnated with liquids other than water. The hose must not come in contact with oil, grease, or corrosive chemicals. Care must be taken to keep polish which may be used on racks or couplings from coming in contact with the hose. Where enclosed in approved hose cabinets, no polish should be necessary. (For further details on unlined hose for standpipe use, see NFPA No. 14, Standard for Standpipe and Hose Systems.)

Unlined forest fire hose should be treated to inhibit mildew. Mildew treatment which conforms to U.S. Forest Service Specification No. 182 for cotton forestry hose, and No. 183 for linen forestry hose, should give the maximum amount of mildew resistance that can be obtained with these hose jackets. The hose must be cleaned and dried thoroughly after use. In the absence of a hose washing machine, hose should be washed with a scrubbing brush using water and mild soap, followed by thorough rinsing. When thoroughly dry, hose should be stored in a cool, dry room where air will circulate, out of contact with damp floors or walls.

Fire Hose Connections

Screw Threads and Gaskets: NFPA No. 194, Standard for Screw Threads and Gaskets for Fire Hose Connections, covers 10 sizes of threaded connections, from ¾ to 6 in., used in fire protection. The Standard gives the dimensions for screw thread connections, gages, gaskets, gasket seats, and the size of the threaded connections. These standards apply to: fire hose couplings, suction hose couplings, relay supply hose couplings, fire pump suctions, discharge valves, fire hydrants, nozzles, adaptors, reducers, caps, plugs, wyes, siamese connections, standpipe connections, sprinkler connections and all other hose fittings, connections, and appliances that connect to or with fire pumps, hose, and or hydrants.

These threaded connections are defined as the "American National Fire Hose Connection Screw Thread," abbreviated throughout the NFPA Standard as "NH" (also known as NST and NS). Each of the 10 standard sizes is designated by specifying in sequence the nominal size of the connection, the number of threads per in., and the thread symbol as follows:

.75-8 NH	3.5-6 NH
1-8 NH	4.0-4 NH
1.5-9 NH	4.5-4 NH
2.5-7.5 NH	5.0-4 NH
3-6 NH	6.0-4 NH

The need for standard fire service connections is most apparent during mutual aid operations. When hose couplings, nozzles, and other equipment do not conform to standards, it becomes necessary to use adaptors, thus adding complications and confusion to fire fighting operations. Equally important, standard hose fittings are more readily available and can generally be obtained at a more favorable price than where nonstandard fittings are specified. This is important to business and industry as well as to public agencies such as the fire department and water utility. Moreover, most nonstandard threads are very poorly defined, and often new purchases are not fully compatible with earlier equipment. The Appendix of NFPA Standard No. 194 gives suggestions for the use of adapters to connect NH standard and nonstandard threads.

Standard fire service connections are a proper and essential objective in the national interest. Some states have laws supporting fire hose thread standardization. A 1965 survey by the NFPA showed that nearly ¾ of U.S. fire departments were using NH 2½-in. threads, and a very much higher percentage were using NH threads on 1½-in. and booster hose. Since that date, standardization programs have been carried out in a number of states and individual communities. Conformity with the NFPA Standard results in fire fighting equipment that is intended to be serviceable, economical, easily assembled, and that provides maximum effectiveness in fire fighting operations.

There are a number of screw threads which give the appearance of compatibility with the NFPA Standard; however, what often appears a good connection when lines are not pressurized may be loose, cross-threaded, or improperly mated connections that have a tendency to fail when hose lines are charged. This both impairs fire fighting operations and presents a serious hazard to personnel. Gaskets are an essential feature of fire hose coupling standards because hose connections use swivel or "female" fittings which must provide a tight waterway when connected to the opposing thread.

Fire Hose Couplings: Couplings of standard alloy, machined in a normal manner, weigh about 5 lbs for the 2½-in. size and 1⅜ lbs for the 1½-in. size. Drop forge couplings, weighing somewhat less, have had acceptance in the fire service. They are relatively hard, and thus cannot be reused as readily as a normal coupling of softer metal which can be re-expanded.

For high pressure (800 psi working pressure) ¾- or 1-in. booster hose suppliers may use a patented coupling in which hose is secured into a coupling bowl with a threaded fitting rather than a smooth expansion ring. Such couplings also are available for some other sizes of fire hose. Attaching couplings requires a considerable degree of skill and experience. Couplings can be cracked and damaged by application of too much pressure with the expander, but if insufficient pressure is applied, the coupling may not hold. Also, the correct size expansion ring must be used for the type of hose and coupling bowl diameter. Unless a fire department uses a large amount of hose and has a mechanic skilled and experienced in attaching couplings, this work should be done by the manufacturer of the hose or by a local coupling supplier who has the trained personnel and equipment necessary.

It is desirable to use new couplings with new hose. Where hose must be recoupled, couplings should be checked for the number of times they have been previously expanded before reusing them. Reattaching couplings too many times may cause them to be overstressed so they will not hold properly when water pressure is applied. Over-expansion causes the wall of the bowl to become weak. When a coupling has been expanded several times, the diameter of the bowl may become so enlarged that a standard expansion ring does not hold.

Care should be taken by fire fighting personnel to avoid dropping couplings on hard surfaces as this may damage the couplings. It is important that vehicles not be driven over couplings. This can cause couplings to become "out of round." Couplings "out of round" should be repaired by a person experienced in this work and having the needed equipment. Otherwise, it is better to replace the coupling.

After use, coupling threads and swivels should be examined and repaired as necessary, and maintained so they can easily be made up by hand. A good practice when loading hose on apparatus is to examine each coupling before it is connected to the load; any hose with defective couplings should be set aside for repair. As a general rule, couplings should have no oil or grease applied, as oil may damage the hose. If dirty, couplings should be cleaned in a pail of water.

Some fire departments are equipped with dies and other tools for chasing and refurbishing couplings. Coupling gaskets should be renewed as needed. This is one of the items to be checked when hose is being reloaded or changed. Gaskets that project into the waterway should be replaced.

Suction Hose Connections: NFPA Standard No. 19 specifies the size of suction hose normally needed to permit pumpers to pass capacity tests at draft. In some fire departments prescribed test sizes are kept only at the shop. Where hard suction hose is carried on the apparatus, a standard 4½- or 5-in. size may be provided for all pumpers.

Until the standard for pumper supply hose threads was developed in 1955, each pump manufacturer furnished thread dimensions of his own choosing so that different makes of pumps could not use the same suction hose. Purchasers should specify that all threaded connections on apparatus and equipment comply with NFPA No. 194, Standard for Screw Threads and Gaskets for Fire Hose Connections.

Small capacity portable fire pumps and mobile water supply apparatus that meet the provisions of the NFPA Automotive Fire Apparatus and Portable Pumping Units for Fire Department Service Standards generally carry 2½-in. suction hose with standard threads. However, certain portable pumps may use 2½- or 3-in. suction hose depending upon the rated capacity of the pump. Pumpers used in rural service should carry additional suction hose where needed to take advantage of suction sources.

Hydrant Outlets and Outlet Threads: A standard fire hydrant for fire department service should have at least one large outlet for pumper supply and two outlets for 2½-in. hose. As most pumping engines in municipal service are rated to deliver at least 1,000 gpm, it is desirable that water mains be capable of delivering at least this quantity to individual hydrants at a residual pressure of 20 psi while a group of hydrants in the vicinity of the fire are supplying the fire flow required for the area. Otherwise, it is often necessary to run supplemental supply lines from pumpers at other hydrants to properly supply pumps nearest a fire. Cities using pumpers of more than 1,000 gpm rated capacity may need stronger hydrant supplies in areas requiring relatively high fire flows. Even 750 gpm pumpers frequently are able to use upward of 1,000 gpm where high pump discharge pressures are not required.

The hose threads provided on hydrant outlets are properly of concern to the fire department. Whatever the size of supply hose used, each pumping engine is required to carry adapters to permit the connection of the engine supply hose thread to the local hydrant outlet threads. Adapters are needed to permit connection of hose both to large hydrant outlets ("steamer connection") and 2½-in. outlets. A reducer is used to make the latter connection where the supply hose is larger than 2½ in. In most cities the large hydrant outlets are equipped with 4½-in. NH threads, although some areas, including California, use a 4-in. NH hydrant outlet.

A single 2½-in. outlet cannot provide enough water for capacity operation of pumpers unless hydrant residual pressures remain relatively high. Even where two 2½-in. outlets are used to supply a pumper, the flow is considerably less than that provided from a single 4½-in. outlet at the same pressure. Cities make a mistake when they fail to provide pumper outlets on hydrants on low pressure water systems. The more critical the water supply problem, the greater the importance of an efficient waterway. A few cities use 5-in. pumper supply outlets.

Coupling Adapters and Reducers: Adapters are used to

make connection between different types of couplings or couplings having threads other than NH threads. The NFPA Screw Threads and Gaskets for Hose Connections Standard contains specifications for adapter threads. In some cases building standpipes have been installed with plumbing pipe thread rather than the proper NH fire protection thread. In such cases the fire department must have adapters to attach its hose to the standpipe. Some fire departments require that an adapter be tied to each standpipe outlet not equipped with fire department thread. Where fire departments respond on mutual aid to areas that still have not standardized their hose threads, adapters must be carried, or the adapters may be provided by the host fire department.

Reducers are carried to permit connection of smaller sizes of hose to larger diameter hose or outlets. Reducing wyes are commonly carried on pumpers to permit the supplying of several 1½-in. lines from one 2½-in. line or outlet. The smaller outlets should be gated. Most 3-in. fire hose is fitted with 2½-in. reducing couplings so that it can be used interchangeably with 2½-in. hose and fittings.

Nozzles

The minimum number of hand nozzles to be carried on various pieces of fire apparatus is indicated in the equipment lists in the NFPA Automotive Fire Apparatus Standard. Choice of nozzles for each class of service is left to the individual fire department. Spray and straight-stream nozzles for 1-, 1½-, and 2½-in. hose, and for large streams, are available in types with various flow characteristics.

The size of nozzle orifice, whether solid-stream tip or spray type, determines the flow discharged at a given nozzle pressure. Fire department pumping engines have rated capacities based upon 250 gpm increments, and a flow of 250 gpm is designated as a "standard fire stream." This is the flow from a 1⅛-in. nozzle tip used on a 2½-in. hand line at normal operating pressure. This standard stream can be supplied through a long line utilizing the full amount of hose carried on most pumpers. Years ago, with small capacity under-powered pumpers, it was often necessary to use small nozzle tips on long lines of hose. Now, a 1-in. tip flowing approximately 200 gpm is the smallest size recommended for a 2½-in. hand line. Some large city fire departments regularly use a 1¼-in. tip on hand lines. These tips can be supplied by 2½-in. hose where lines from pumpers are relatively short.

Fire department nozzles for 1½-in. hose normally are designed to discharge approximately 100 gpm. Nozzles for 1-in. hose generally discharge in the 20 to 30 gpm range.

With spray nozzles, a wide variety of types and flows are available in nozzles fitting various size hose connections. It is important that the user select nozzles having the desired characteristics for the intended class of service. Some early types of spray or "fog" nozzles for 2½-in. hose provided relatively small flows; where still used, they should be replaced with modern types.

Spray nozzles for hose streams are of three general types:

1. Open nozzles having a fixed spray pattern, usually attached to shutoff valves.

2. Adjustable nozzles which provide variable discharges and patterns with adjustments from shutoff to straight stream, and from narrow to wide angle spray.

3. Combination nozzles in which either a solid stream or a fixed or adjustable spray and shutoff are selected by a control valve.

Nonadjustable spray nozzles have fixed angles of spray and usually are attached to shutoff valves. Generally, these are recommended for use on electrical fires to avoid the possibility of inadvertently applying a straight stream. Nonadjustable nozzles having a wide spray angle (90° to 180°) and a fine short-range spray are effective for Class B (flammable liquids) fires when attached to applicators, usually 6, 10, or 12 ft long, for close-up application.

Adjustable spray nozzles make it possible for the user to adjust the cone of spray from a straight stream to wide angle while the stream is in use. Some of these nozzles have predetermined settings for angles of spray. In some nozzles the discharge varies considerably as the spray angle is changed.

Other adjustable spray nozzles are designed to give a practically constant discharge rate for the straight-stream and spray angles. These types of nozzles are popular with fire departments because the friction loss characteristics in the hose and nozzle pressures remain constant with the selected orifice setting. Usually such nozzles are capable of adjustment for full and partial rated flows. Combination spray nozzles usually consist of nonadjustable spray nozzle and a separate straight-stream nozzle opening with a valve operable by the user to give the desired type of stream or to shut off the nozzle.

Very high pressure spray nozzles are designed to deliver small flows at pressures in the 400 to 800 psi range at the pump. This equipment, designed for fire department use, is supplemental to standard apparatus. Either separate high-pressure pumps or extra-pressure stages on volume pumps are required. Water is delivered to these nozzles through ¾-in. high pressure hose carried on reels. The quantity of water delivered is usually 25 to 30 gpm. Spray nozzles are widely used on standpipe hose for first aid fire protection, and are available in both 1- and 1½-in. sizes.

Use of Hose Spray Nozzles: In the majority of fire departments, nozzles used for initial attack on fires using 1-, 1½-, and 2½-in. hand lines are of the adjustable spray type. Such nozzles are suitable for fires in ordinary combustibles, on flammable liquids, and both inside and outside of buildings, including grass and brush fires. They can also be used on fires in transformers and other electrical equipment. (See Sec. 13, Chap. 1 for discussion of conductivity of hose streams.) In general, the discharge ratings for fire department spray nozzles are based upon discharge at 100 psi at the base of the nozzle.

Where long range and penetration of streams into burning materials is desired, the solid stream nozzle tips are generally used. Solid stream nozzles may also be used where debris in water being drafted may clog a spray nozzle, or when extremely cold temperatures may result in a freezing problem with spray equipment.

Master Stream Equipment: The rated capacity of pumping apparatus cannot be utilized to best advantage unless nozzles are available with which to apply the desired fire flow. Unfortunately, it has not been uncommon to find pumpers of 1,000 gpm and larger capacity carrying only hand line nozzles. Often, the tips carried are too small to provide standard streams from hand lines; thus, only a small percentage of the available pumping capacity can be utilized in applying needed fire flow.

Full pump capacity can be most effectively employed through master stream appliances. Preferably, every pumper should carry a portable master stream appliance. In many fire departments such nozzles are preconnected on pumpers for fast initial attack on serious fires.

Master stream nozzles, whether portable or permanently connected to fire apparatus, should have nozzle tips and hose thread connections as specified in the NFPA Screw Threads and Gaskets for Fire Hose Connections Standard.

In addition to the solid stream tips, each such device should be provided with a large capacity spray (fog) nozzle. The Standard covers two types of master stream devices. These are monitor nozzles rated under 1,250 gpm, and those rated over 1,250 gpm but less than 3,000 gpm. For both classes all inlet connections (other than connections piped permanently to a pump) must be fitted with internal swivel connections having standard thread, and at least one of which shall be the 2.5-7.5 NH thread.

The discharge ends of master stream devices designed to discharge from 350 to 1,250 gpm must have the 2.5-7.5 NH thread for attaching nozzle tips or spray nozzles. If stacked tips are used, one of these tips may have the 1.5-9 NH standard thread. Discharge ends of stream devices designed to discharge in excess of 1,250 gpm, but less than 3,000 gpm, must have the 3.506 NH standard thread for attaching nozzle tips or spray nozzles. However, such large capacity appliances shall be provided with a reducer fitting, 3.5-6 NH female x 2.5-7.5 NH male.

Nozzle tips and spray nozzles designed to discharge flows between 350 and 1,250 gpm must have 2.5-7.5 NH standard thread for internal thread. Nozzle tips and spray nozzles designed for flows above 1,250, but less than 3,000 gpm at standard operating pressures, must have the 3.5-6 NH standard fire hose thread for the internal entrance thread. Discharging ends and nozzles for large stream devices over 3,000 gpm must be designed so that all inlet and outlet threads are the NH standard thread.

Standard tip sizes (diameters of orifices in inches) for stream devices rated under 1,250 gpm are: $1\frac{3}{8}$ (500 gpm), $1\frac{1}{2}$ (600 gpm), and $1\frac{3}{4}$ (800 gpm). For the devices rated over 1,250 but less than 3,000 gpm, standard tip sizes are: $1\frac{3}{4}$ (800 gpm), 2 (1,060 gpm), and $2\frac{1}{4}$ (1,350 gpm). The flows indicated are approximate and vary with the square root of nozzle pressure.

Some fire departments using portable stream devices designed for under 1,250 gpm discharge prefer the lighter-weight devices equipped with only two 2½-in. inlets because of convenience in operation with available equipment and manpower. Normally, a 1½-in. solid stream tip discharging 600 gpm is the largest that can be supplied efficiently with two 2½-in. lines, unless lines are relatively short.

In 1956 the NFPA Committee on Fire Department Equipment tested various types of large stream devices, including ladder pipes, available to fire departments. The results published by the NFPA in 1957 showed flows obtained with the various sizes of tips supplied with the nozzles and the pressure losses in the nozzles occasioned by these flows. After the tests, several manufacturers announced model changes to reduce pressure losses in stream devices; some nozzles incapable of efficiently handling 600 gpm were withdrawn from the market. The maximum size tip recommended for a ladder pipe supplied by 3-in. hose on the ladder is 1½ in. which discharges 600 gpm at 80 psi.

SI Units

The following conversion factors are given as a convenience in converting to SI units the English units used in this chapter.

1 in.	= 25.400 mm
1 ft	= 0.305 m
1 lb	= 0.454 kg
1 psi	= 6.895 kPa
1 gal (U.S.)	= 3.785 litres
1 cu ft	= 0.283 m^3
1 gpm	= 3.785 litres/min

Bibliography

NFPA Codes, Standards, and Recommended Practices (see the latest *NFPA Publications and Visual Aids Catalog* for availability of current editions of the following documents)

NFPA No. 4, Organization for Fire Services.

NFPA No. 4A, Recommendations for Organization of a Fire Department.

NFPA No. 14, Standard for the Installation of Standpipe and Hose Systems.

NFPA No. 19, Standard for Automotive Fire Apparatus.

NFPA No. 19B, Standard on Respiratory Protective Equipment for Fire Fighters.

NFPA No. 24, Outside Protection.

NFPA No. 73, Standard for the Installation, Maintenance, and Use of Public Fire Service Communications.

NFPA No. 191, Specifications for Portable Pumping Units for Fire Department Service.

NFPA No. 193, Standard on Fire Department Ladders, Ground and Aerial.

NFPA No. 194, Standard for Screw Threads and Gaskets for Fire Hose Connections.

NFPA No. 196, Standard for Fire Hose.

NFPA No. 198, Standard for the Care, Maintenance, and Use of Fire Hose (Including Couplings and Nozzles).

NFPA No. 295, Standard for Wildfire Control by Volunteer Fire Departments.

NFPA No. 402, Standard Operating Procedures, Aircraft Rescue and Fire Fighting.

NFPA No. 403, Recommended Practice for Aircraft Rescue and Fire Fighting Services at Airports and Heliports.

NFPA No. 406M, Guide for Aircraft Rescue and Fire Fighting Equipment: Techniques for Fire Departments Using Structural Fire Apparatus and Equipment.

NFPA No. 412, Standard for Evaluating Foam Fire Fighting Equipment on Aircraft Rescue and Fire Fighting Vehicles.

NFPA No. 414, Standard for Aircraft Rescue and Fire Fighting Vehicles.

NFPA No. 1001, Fire Fighter Professional Qualifications.

Additional Readings

Fire Officer's Guide to Breathing Apparatus for the Fire Service, rev. ed., National Fire Protection Association, Boston, 1975.

Fire Officer's Guide to Operating Aerial Ladders, National Fire Protection Association, Boston, 1974.

Fire Officer's Guide to Operating Fire Department Pumpers, National Fire Protection Association, Boston, 1974.

Fitzsimmons, James A., "Allocation of Emergency Ambulances to Fire Stations," *Fire Technology*, Vol. 9, No. 2, May 1973, pp. 112–118.

Guild, Richard D. and Rollin, Jess E., "A Fire Station Placement Model," *Fire Technology*, Vol. 8, No. 1, Feb. 1972, pp. 33–44.

Handling Hose and Ladders, National Fire Protection Association, Boston, 1969.

Hudiburg, E. and Stump, L. M., editors, *Source Material, Reference Guide 1974*, 1st ed., Fire Protection Publications, Oklahoma State University, Stillwater, Okla., 1974.

Hudiburg, E. and McCoy, C. E., *Fire Department Facilities, Planning and Procedures*, 2nd ed., Fire Protection Publications, Oklahoma State University, Stillwater, Okla., 1970.

Kimball, W. Y., *Effective Streams for Fighting Fires*, National Fire Protection Association, Boston, 1961.

Lyons, P. R., *Fire Officer's Guide to Elevating Platforms and Aerial Towers*, National Fire Protection Association, Boston, 1974.

Mitchell, Phillip S., "Efficient Allocation of Fire Department Resources—Part I," *Fire Technology*, Vol. 7, No. 3, Aug. 1971, pp. 237–242.

Chapter 5

FIRE STREAMS

This chapter on fire streams is included in this section on public fire protection systems insofar as the use of hose streams and nozzles is essentially a fire fighting function and the principal tool of the fire fighting service. For further information on water supply requirements for fire protection, water distribution systems, water supply facilities, fire pumps, testing water supplies, and hydraulics, see Section 11 of this HANDBOOK.

The development of effective fire streams for fire suppression involves the flow of water through various types, diameters, and lengths of fire hose, and the discharge from various sizes and types of nozzles. Other related factors such as loss of pressure due to elevation and various appliances such as gates and wyes, etc., also have an effect on fire streams.

A. Nozzle Selection

An effective fire stream requires the use of a nozzle capable of delivering water in the most effective form and at a rate necessary for extinguishment or control of a particular fire. There are principally two types of nozzles: solid stream nozzles and spray nozzles. Each has advantages and disadvantages.

Solid Stream Nozzles

Solid stream nozzles are identified by size, the size being taken from the inside diameter of the top of the nozzle. Size is expressed in inches and/or fractions. As it leaves the nozzle, the stream produced is a solid, compact stream with little spray. Solid streams have the ability to reach long distances and can penetrate areas and materials that might not otherwise be reached by other types of streams.

Formulas for calculating the discharge from solid stream nozzles as well as tables listing the discharge for various size nozzles at different pressures can be found in Section 11, Chapter 6 of this HANDBOOK.

Spray Nozzles

Spray nozzles are classified by their rates of discharge. They produce broken streams of water particles in a definite pattern that is determined by the nozzle used. Most spray nozzles have adjustable patterns ranging from 60 degrees to straight streams. All spray nozzles are rated in gpm discharge with 100 psi at the base of the nozzle. Some spray nozzles have an adjustable gallonage feature. A recent innovation has been the introduction of the constant pressure nozzle.

There is no easy means for calculating the discharge from spray nozzles since there is no reliable way to determine the nozzle diameter. Flow rates, if not known, can be obtained from the manufacturer or from manufacturers' literature.

B. Friction Loss in Fire Hose

The flow of water in fire hose follows the same general principles as the flow of water in piping, with minor variations. These variations are due to the expansion and elongation of hose under pressure, the effects of hose couplings, and hose construction.

Friction loss in fire hose is defined as that part of total pressure that is used to overcome friction while forcing water through the hose. This may be expressed as:

$$\text{Friction Loss} = \text{Engine Pressure} - \text{Nozzle Pressure}$$

There are four principles which govern friction loss in fire hose. These are:

1. Friction loss varies directly with the length of the hose.
2. Friction loss varies approximately with the square of the velocity of the water flowing.
3. For a given velocity, friction loss varies inversely as the fifth power of the hose diameter.
4. For a given velocity, friction loss is nearly independent of pressure.

Friction loss in fire hose can be obtained in one of three ways. The first is by the use of friction loss tables showing the loss per 100 ft at various flows. The second is by calculation. The third is by field testing.

Calculating Friction Loss for 2½-in. Hose

The most commonly accepted formula for determining friction loss in 2½-in. hose is:

$$FL = (2Q^2 + Q)L$$

where FL = friction loss per 100 ft of hose
Q = flow rate, hundreds of gpm
L = length of hose, hundreds of ft

With flows of 100 gpm or less, the formula should be changed to:

$$FL = (2Q^2 + \tfrac{1}{2}Q)L$$

There are variations to the formula shown. The comparison of various formulae are shown in Table 9-5A.

Table 9-5A. Friction Loss through 100 ft of 2½-in. Hose at Various Flows According to Several Formulas

Flow, gpm	Friction loss, psi				
	Kimball $1.82Q^2L$	Gaskill $1.9Q^2L$	Purington $2Q^2L$	Theobald $2.4Q^2L$	Underwriters $(2Q^2 + Q)L$
100	1.82	1.9	2.0	2.4	3.0
200	7.28	7.60	8.0	9.60	10.0
300	16.4	17.1	18.0	21.6	21.0
400	29.1	30.4	32.0	38.4	36.0

Calculating Friction Loss in Hose Other than 2½ in.

To calculate friction loss in fire hose with a smaller or larger diameter than 2½-in. hose, the conversion factors shown in Table 9-5B may be used.

Friction losses in small diameter rubber or rubber-lined fire hose, in rubber-lined hose, and rubber-lined hose for heavy streams from single or siamesed lines are shown in Tables 9-5C, 9-5D, and 9-5 E.

Table 9-5B.   Conversion Factors for Calculating Friction Loss in Fire Hose with a Smaller or Larger Diameter than 2½-in. Hose

	FACTORS				
Diameter	Divide By	Multiply By		Divide By	Multiply By
Single Lines			Siamesed Lines of Equal Length		
¾-in. chemical hose	.0029	344	2–2½-in.	3.6	.28
1-in. chemical hose	.011	91	3–2½-in.	7.75	.129
1¼-in. rubber lined hose	.025	40	2–3-in.	9.35	.107
1½-in. rubber lined hose	.074	13.5	1–3-in. and 1–2½-in.	6.1	.164
1¼-in. unlined linen hose	.0157	63.6	2–2½-in. and 1–3-in.	11.5	.087
1½-in. unlined linen hose	.039	25.6	2–3-in. and 1–2½-in.	15.0	.067
2-in. unlined line hose	.16	6.25			
2½-in. unlined linen hose	.47	2.13			
2-in. rubber lined hose	.34	2.94	Standpipes		
3-in. rubber lined hose	2.6	.385	4 in.	7.5	.133
3-in. hose with 2½-in. couplings	2.5	.4	5 in.	22.00	.045
3½-in. rubber lined hose	5.8	.172	6 in.	52.00	.019
4-in. rubber lined hose	11.0	.09			
4½-in. rubber lined hose	19.5	.051			
5-in. rubber lined hose	32.0	.031			

Table 9-5C.   Friction Losses in Rubber-Lined Fire Hose for Heavy Streams from Single or Siamesed Lines*

(Pounds per square inch per 100 ft of hose)

Flow in Gpm	2 Lines of 2½-In. Siamesed	2½-In. and 3-In. Siamesed	2 Lines of 3-In. Siamesed	3 Lines of 2½-In. Siamesed	3-In. Hose	3½-In. Hose
400	10.1	5.9	3.9	4.7	14.1	6.3
420	11.1	6.5	4.2	5.2	15.4	6.9
440	12.0	7.1	4.6	5.6	16.8	7.5
460	13.0	7.7	5.0	6.1	18.2	8.1
480	14.1	8.3	5.4	6.6	19.7	8.8
500	15.2	9.0	5.9	7.1	21.2	9.5
520	16.4	9.6	6.3	7.7	22.7	10.3
540	17.5	10.4	6.7	8.3	24.3	11.1
560	18.7	11.1	7.2	8.9	26.0	11.9
580	19.9	11.9	7.7	9.5	28.0	12.7
600	21.2	12.7	8.2	10.1	29.9	13.4
620	22.5	13.5	8.7	10.7	31.6	14.2
640	23.8	14.2	9.3	11.4	33.5	15.0
660	25.3	15.1	9.9	12.0	35.5	15.9
680	26.9	15.9	10.5	12.7	37.5	16.8
700	28.3	16.8	11.0	13.4	39.5	17.7
720	29.9	17.7	11.6	14.1	41.4	18.7
740	31.5	18.6	12.2	14.8	44.0	19.7
760	33.0	19.5	12.8	15.6	46.1	20.7
780	34.6	20.4	13.4	16.4	48.3	21.7
800	36.2	21.5	14.1	17.2	50.1	22.7
820	38.0	22.5	14.8	18.0	—	23.8
840	39.9	23.6	15.5	18.7	—	24.9
860	41.5	24.5	16.1	19.5	—	26.0
880	43.2	25.6	16.8	20.4	—	27.1
900	45.0	26.7	17.5	21.2	—	28.2
925	47.2	28.1	18.4	22.3	—	29.7
950	49.6	29.5	19.3	23.4	—	31.2
975	52.3	30.9	20.2	24.5	—	32.7
1000	55.1	32.4	21.2	25.8	—	34.3
1100	—	38.5	25.2	31.0	—	41.0

* Based upon tests of 2½-in., 3-in., and 3½-in. fire hose conducted by the National Board of Fire Underwriters in 1909.

Table 9-5D. Friction Losses in Rubber-Lined Fire Hose
(Pounds per square inch per 100 ft of hose)

Flow in Gpm	2½-In.*	2¾-In.† (3-In. couplings)	3-In.‡ (2½-In. couplings)	3-In. (3-In. couplings)	Flow in Gpm	2½-In.*	2¾-In.† (3-In. couplings)	3-In.‡ (2½-In. couplings)	3-In.* (3-In. couplings)
100	2.5	1.7	1.2	1.2	290	19.9	11.9	8.4	7.7
110	3.2	2.1	1.4	1.4	300	21.2	12.7	9.0	8.2
120	3.9	2.4	1.6	1.6	310	22.5	13.5	9.7	8.7
130	4.5	2.8	1.9	1.8	320	23.8	14.3	10.3	9.3
140	5.2	3.1	2.1	2.0	330	25.3	15.2	10.9	9.9
150	5.8	3.6	2.5	2.3	340	26.9	16.2	11.6	10.5
160	6.6	4.0	2.9	2.6	350	28.4	17.1	12.3	11.0
170	7.4	4.5	3.2	2.9	360	30.0	18.0	13.0	11.5
180	8.3	5.0	3.6	3.2	370	31.5	18.9	13.7	12.2
190	9.2	5.6	3.8	3.5	380	33.0	19.8	14.4	12.8
200	10.1	6.1	4.0	3.8	390	34.6	20.7	15.2	13.4
210	11.1	6.7	4.4	4.2	400	36.2	21.7	16.0	14.1
220	12.0	7.2	4.5	4.6	420	39.9	24.0	17.7	15.4
230	13.0	7.8	5.3	5.0	440	43.2	25.9	19.4	16.8
240	14.1	8.5	5.8	5.4	460	46.8	28.1	21.3	18.2
250	15.3	9.2	6.2	5.9	480	50.8	30.5	23.1	19.7
260	16.4	9.9	6.8	6.3	500	55.1	33.1	25.0	21.2
270	17.5	10.5	7.3	6.7	—	—	—	—	—
280	18.7	11.2	7.8	7.2	—	—	—	—	—

* The losses shown for nominal 2½-in. hose (actual 2 9/16-in. waterway) and for 3-in. hose are based upon tests conducted in 1909 by the National Board of Fire Underwriters.

† Losses for 2¾-in. hose with 3-in. couplings are based upon tests by the Oakland, California, Fire Department. The 2¾-in. hose with 3-in. couplings, while widely used in the San Francisco Bay area, is not a nationally recognized standard fire hose. Three-inch hose should be equipped with 2½-in. couplings to be considered a standard size.

‡ Losses for 3-in. hose with standard 2½-in. couplings are based upon tests by the NFPA Fire Service Department in cooperation with the Boston Fire Department.

Table 9-5E. Friction Losses in Small Diameter Rubber or Rubber-Lined Fire Hose
(Pounds per square inch per 100 ft of hose)

Flow in Gpm	¾-In. (Booster)	1-In. (Booster)	1½-In. (Lined standpipe & lined forestry)	1½-In. (Good quality fire dept. hose)	2-In.*
10	13.5	3.5	0.5	0.3	0.1
15	29.0	7.2	1.0	0.7	0.3
20	50.0	12.3	1.7	1.2	0.4
25	75.0	18.5	2.6	1.9	0.6
30	105.0	26.0	3.6	2.5	0.9
35	140.0	35.0	4.8	3.4	1.2
40	180.0	44.0	6.1	4.3	1.5
45	—	55.0	7.6	5.4	1.9
50	—	67.0	9.2	7.1	2.3
60	—	—	13.0	9.2	3.2
70	—	—	17.3	12.3	4.3
80	—	—	22.0	15.6	5.4
90	—	—	27.3	19.5	6.9
100	—	—	33.0	25.5	8.3
120	—	—	47.0	33.0	11.7
150	—	—	70.0	50.0	17.5
200	—	—	—	—	29.9

* The 2-in. hose is not recognized as a standard size but is used in some fire departments as a "leader line" because it is relatively easy to handle and carries more water at a given pressure than 1½-in. hose.

C. Large Diameter Hose

With the introduction of lightweight, large diameter hose, fire departments have been able to move large quantities of water with greater efficiency. The reason for the increased efficiency is based on the principle that as the diameter of the hose increases the loss due to friction becomes less. Table 9-5F shows the inside diameter vs. the area in square inches of various sizes of hose. Note that one 5-in. hose line has the same area as four 2½-in. lines.

Table 9-5G illustrates the friction loss of large diameter hose at various flows. Note that the friction loss for 100 ft

Table 9-5F.   Inside Diameter vs. Area

Hose Diameter	Area in In.²
2½	4.9
3	7.0
3½	9.6
4	12.6
5	19.6
6	28.3

of 2½-in. hose flowing 250 gpm is 15.2 psi, and that the same friction loss for 5-in. hose is for a flow of 1,500 gpm.

Table 9-5G.   Friction Loss of Large Diameter Compared with 2½- and 3-in. Hose
(—FRICTION LOSS—psi/100 ft)

Flow GPM	Hose Inside Diameter (Inches)					
	2½	3	3½	4	5	6
200	10.1	3.9	1.8	.82	.28	.12
250	15.2	5.9	2.7	1.4	.47	.18
300	21.2	8.2	3.7	1.9	.66	.24
400	36.2	14.1	6.3	3.3	1.1	.42
500	55.0	21.2	9.5	5.0	1.7	.62
700	——	39.5	17.7	9.6	3.3	1.2
800	——	50.5	22.7	12.4	4.3	1.7
1000	——	76.5	34.3	19.2	6.6	2.6
1100	——	91.5	41.0	23.0	7.9	3.0
1200	——	——	——	28.5	9.5	3.5
1500	——	——	——	41.5	14.5	5.7
2000	——	——	——	75.0	26.0	12.0

D.   Master Streams

Master streams consist of any variety of heavy streams formed by siamesing two or more large hose lines into a single heavy stream device. Master streams are commonly operated at 80 to 100 psi nozzle pressure, and are capable of producing flows ranging from 500 to several thousand gpm depending upon the device used. Several devices are used to produce master streams. The most commonly used devices are turret pipes and monitors, deluge set, and ladder pipe.

Turret Pipes and Monitors: Turret pipes are master stream devices mounted on a pumper or fire boat and directly connected to the pump. A monitor is the same as a turret pipe except that it is controlled by wheel operated gears.

Deluge Set: A portable device normally carried on fire apparatus for producing master streams. Consists of a large nozzle, a supporting base, and a two-, three-, or four-way siamese inlet.

Ladder Pipe: A heavy stream nozzle attached to an aerial ladder and usually supplied by a 3-in. hose. Table 9-5H shows the pressures required at the base of the ladder to supply ladder pipes.

E.   Effective Range of Fire Streams

Much of the fundamental data now employed in hydraulic work in fire protection was developed in a series of extensive investigations by John R. Freeman in 1888 and 1889.[1] Some of the results of Freeman's work are shown in Fig. 9-5A. Considerable data have also been obtained by numerous tests conducted by leading testing laboratories and from studies by other NFPA members.

Mr. Freeman's contributions to fire protection engineering through these investigations may be summarized briefly as follows:

1. Fire stream tables in use prior to his investigations underestimated nozzle discharges by 15 to 20 percent. Freeman developed new tables.

2. Measurements of discharge of water under pressure, as, for example, the delivery of a pumping engine, may be made with accuracy through nozzles.

3. The distribution of velocity was found to be uniform throughout the cross section of jet from the best nozzles, except in the immediate vicinity of the walls of the orifice.

4. Streams from more than 40 different nozzles were compared and showed that the smooth conical nozzle gave the best results of any tried. Nozzles with a convergence designed to produce a uniform acceleration of the stream were found to possess no advantage over the smooth cone type, and ring nozzles and undercut ring nozzles were definitely inferior. From these results, Freeman outlined the principal features of the standard "Underwriter" playpipe and nozzle found in many hose stations in private properties.

5. The character of the internal surface of fire hose was found to affect the loss of pressure by friction to a much greater degree than was generally supposed. This prompted great improvements in the manufacture of hose, the development of standard specifications for fire hose, and the making of accurate tests on friction losses in fire hose.

6. Recommendation was made for the use of 3-in. hose by fire departments and elsewhere because of the very much greater carrying capacity due to lower friction losses (as compared with 2½-in. hose).

Freeman also defined what he considered to constitute a good solid stream. He pointed out that the extreme limit at which a jet can be called a good fire stream is not sharply defined, but is to a considerable extent a matter of judgment. In viewing a given stream, he found difficulty in saying within 5 ft or 10 ft, exactly where the stream ceased to be good. In securing the results given in Table 9-5I covering the effective range of fire streams for 1-in. to 1½-in. nozzles, he classed as good those streams which at the limits named, had the following characteristics:

1. Had not lost continuity by breaking into showers of spray.

2. Appeared to shoot nine-tenths of the whole volume of water inside a circle 15 in. in diameter and three-quarters of it inside a 10-in. circle, as nearly as could be judged by the eye.

3. Would probably be stiff enough to attain height or distance in fair condition, even if a fresh breeze were blowing.

4. With no wind blowing, would enter a room through a window opening and strike the ceiling with force enough to spatter well.

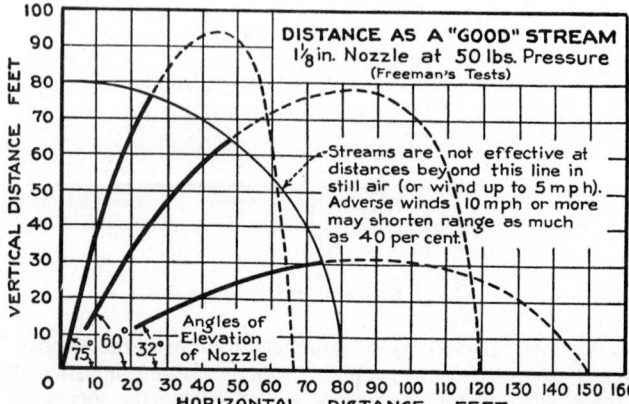

Fig. 9-5A.   Effective range of a fire stream from 1⅛-in. nozzle.

Table 9-5H. Pressures Required at Base of Ladder to Supply Ladder Pipes*
(80 psi nozzle pressure. Where spray nozzles are used, add 20 psi)

Flow in Gpm	Nozzle Tip (In.)	Elevation of Pipe Above Ground	50-Ft Lines on Ladder (from Siamese)				
			2½ In.	3 In.	Two 2½ In.	3½ In.	Two 3 In.
400	1¼	35	123	112	110	108	107
		50	130	119	117	115	114
500	1⅜	35	132	115	112	110	108
		50	139	122	119	117	115
600	1½	35	140	120	116	112	109
		50	147	127	123	119	116
700	1⅝	35	157	125	119	114	111
		50	164	132	126	121	118
800	1¾	35	173	130	123	117	112
		50	193	137	130	124	119
			100-Ft Lines on Ladder (from Siamese)				
400	1¼	35	141	119	115	111	109
		50	148	128	122	118	116
		65	154	132	128	124	122
		80	161	139	135	131	125
500	1⅜	35	160	126	120	115	111
		50	167	133	127	122	118
		65	173	139	133	128	124
		80	180	146	140	135	131
600	1½	35	175	135	126	119	113
		50	182	142	133	126	120
		65	188	148	139	132	126
		80	195	155	146	139	133
700	1⅝	35	—	145	133	123	116
		50	—	152	140	130	123
		65	—	158	146	136	129
		80	—	165	153	143	136
800	1¾	35	—	155	141	128	119
		50	—	162	148	135	126
		65	—	168	154	141	132
		80	—	175	161	148	139

* Pressure required to move water from pumper to base of ladder must be added. Where pressures above 200 psi are required at base of ladder, ladder figures are omitted as impractical of attainment. Data based upon tests by Boston Fire Department in cooperation with NFPA.

Table 9-5I. Effective Range of Solid Fire Streams
Showing the distance in feet from the nozzle at which streams will do effective work with a moderate wind blowing. With a strong wind, the reach is greatly reduced. Vertical distances are with nozzle elevated 60° to 75°; horizontal distances with nozzle elevated 30° to 35°.

	SIZE OF NOZZLE								
	1-In.		1⅛-In.		1¼-In.		1⅜-In.		1½-In.	
Pressure at Nozzle	Vertical Distance, Ft	Horizontal Distance, Ft	Vertical Distance, Ft	Horizontal Distance, Ft	Vertical Distance, Ft	Horizontal Distance, Ft	Vertical Distance, Ft	Horizontal Distance, Ft	Vertical Distance, Ft	Horizontal Distance, Ft
20	35	37	36	38	36	39	36	40	37	42
25	43	42	44	44	45	46	45	47	46	49
30	51	47	52	50	52	52	53	54	54	56
35	58	51	59	54	59	58	60	59	62	62
40	64	55	65	59	65	62	66	64	69	66
45	69	58	70	63	70	66	72	68	74	71
50	73	61	75	66	75	69	77	72	79	75
55	76	64	79	69	80	72	81	75	83	78
60	79	67	83	72	84	75	85	77	87	80
65	82	70	86	75	87	78	88	79	90	82
70	85	72	88	77	90	80	91	82	92	84
75	87	74	90	79	92	82	93	84	94	86
80	89	76	92	81	94	84	95	86	96	88
85	91	78	94	83	96	87	97	88	98	90
90	92	80	96	85	98	89	99	90	100	91

Note: Nozzle pressures are as indicated by Pitot tube. The horizontal and vertical distances are based on experiments by Mr. John R. Freeman. *Transactions* Am. Soc. C.E., Vol. XXI.

It is interesting to note that for interior fire fighting with solid streams, it was desired to use pressure to effect break-up of the stream by impact against parts of the structure to improve the heat-absorbing quality of the stream. This is now done by various features of nozzle design, as with spray-type nozzles, but sufficient pressure must be retained to carry the jet of water the desired distance and to effect penetration of deep-seated fires.

Water in good quantity could be thrown much farther than the limits indicated by Freeman, but, beyond the limit set, it tends to be in the form of a spray easily carried away by drafts. Streams may be considered "fair" for distances about 15 percent greater than "good" streams.

Reach of streams from small nozzles may be of importance in protecting exposures at rural fires. Accordingly, the NFPA, with the cooperation of the District of Columbia Fire Department, conducted studies of the reach of small solid streams, with a group of fire department officers serving as judges. The findings published in the NFPA book, *Operating Fire Department Pumpers*[2], show the following effective ranges of small streams: $\frac{1}{4}$-in. tip at 40 psi, 30 ft; $\frac{5}{8}$-in. tip at 70 psi, 60 ft; and $\frac{3}{4}$-in. tip at 80 psi, 70 ft. With the $\frac{1}{4}$-in. tip, the stream began to break badly above 50 psi, and with the $\frac{5}{8}$-in. tip, 70 psi was the maximum effective pressure for these small solid streams.

The adverse effect of wind is of great importance in determining the effective range of a fire stream. In adverse winds of about 10 mph or more, the effective range of the fire stream may be shortened as much as 40 percent, although a favorable wind may assist fire fighters in carrying water toward the fire. Skillful fire fighters may thus make use of natural drafts in fighting fires.

Figures 9-5B and 9-5C give the results of tests made at the General Electric Company plant in Lynn, Mass., by the Associated Factory Mutual Fire Insurance Companies to determine the effective range of large streams from monitor nozzles.

Figures 9-5D and 9-5E give the results of tests made in 1939 and 1940 by the Chicago Fire Department in cooperation with the National Board of Fire Underwriters. In these tests, the element of judgment in determining the distances at which the streams were "good" was handled by a committee of six judges making night observations with the aid of powerful searchlights directed through the streams. This method was followed to secure more accurate results than would be possible in ordinary daylight observations.

The NFPA Committee on Fire Department Equipment has conducted several series of studies on the reach and

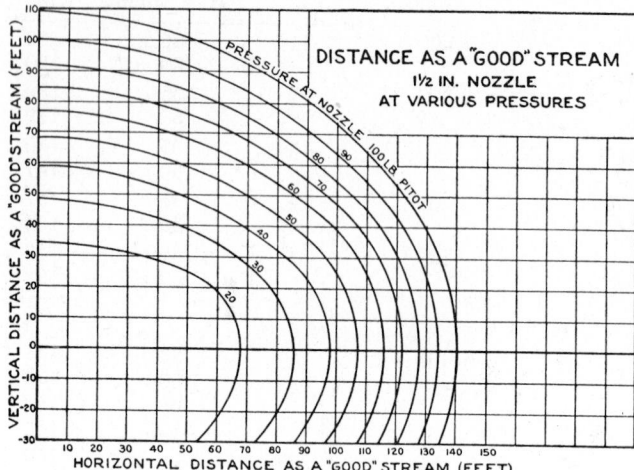

Fig. 9-5C. Results of Factory Mutual tests made to determine effective range of large streams from 1½-in. monitor nozzles.

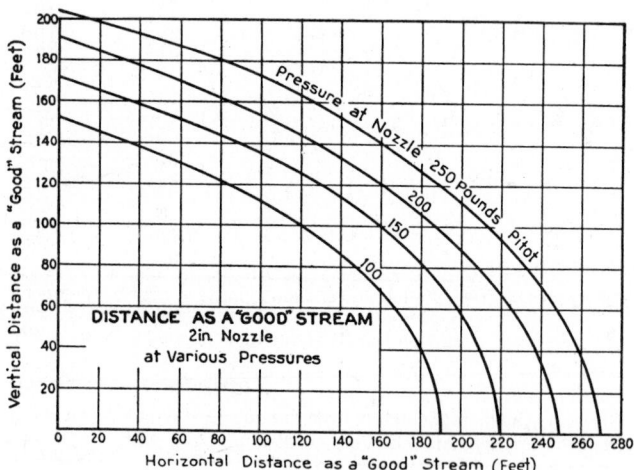

Fig. 9-5D. Results of Chicago Fire Department tests on 2-in. nozzles.

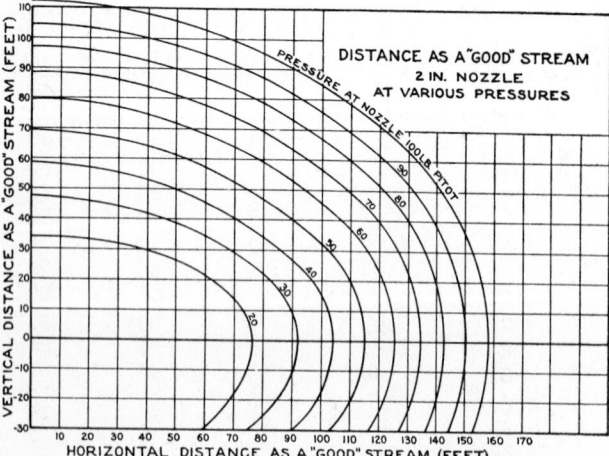

Fig. 9-5B. Results of Factory Mutual tests made to determine effective range of large streams from 2-in. monitor nozzles.

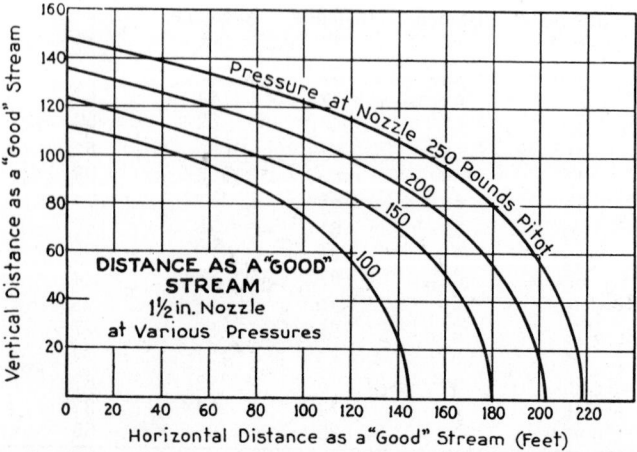

Fig. 9-5E. Results of Chicago Fire Department tests on 1½-in. nozzles.

characteristics of streams from various types of portable spray nozzles which included photographing streams at predetermined pressures and with carefully measured flows against a standard backdrop. The results of these studies conducted at Elmira, N.Y., and at the University of Maryland, College Park, Md., have been published by the NFPA.

The effective reach of the stream of many spray nozzles depends upon adjustment of the spray pattern by the operator. With many nozzles, adjustment toward a straight stream necessary to obtain greater reach reduces the orifice opening with corresponding reduction in nozzle discharge, although "constant flow" nozzles are now available. Frequently, the discharge from spray nozzles is considerably less than that of nozzle tips normally employed for solid streams from the same size of hose, even though the spray nozzles used by fire departments are normally operated at relatively high nozzle pressure.

F.   Reaction Forces in Hose Lines and Nozzles

When water is discharged from a hose line there are two reaction forces acting upon the line: one is hose line reaction, and the other is nozzle reaction. Both contribute in varying degrees to the total reaction that is present in any hose nozzle flow configuration. For purposes of simplicity, each is treated separately in this chapter.

Hose Line Reaction

Reaction forces occur in fire lines when the direction of water flow is changed by a bend in the hose. Between the hydrant and nozzle, the velocity is constant in the hose and the acceleration is zero as shown by the equation $Q = av$ where Q is rate of flow, a the cross-section area, and v the average velocity.

In the nozzle, a decreases and v increases until the stream has left the orifice. Once in the air, the velocity is retarded by wind forces, gravity, and friction.

Figure 9-5F illustrates a typical hand line situation where enough push must be applied at the bend to resist the reaction force F_3. There is no problem where the hose bends off the ground.

Figure 9-5G is a chart by which values of the reaction F_3 in pounds can be directly determined. To obtain reactions in other sizes of hose, Figure 9-5G includes a table of conversion factors.

Example: What is the reaction at a 55° bend in 1½-in. hose if the pressure were 100 psi?

Solution: On the deflection angle side, move horizontally from 55° to intersection with the 100 psi curve. From there go down vertically to the reaction scale and read 450 lbs. From the table, note that the factor for 1½-in. hose is 0.36. Multiplying 450 by 0.36, the answer is 162 lbs.

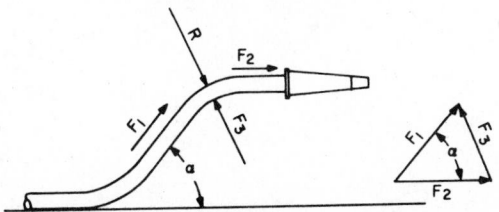

Fig. 9-5F.   Reaction in a Hose Line. α = Deflection angle at bend. F_3 = Resultant of forces F_1 and F_2 = Reaction in pounds. R = Force needed to hold hose against F_3.

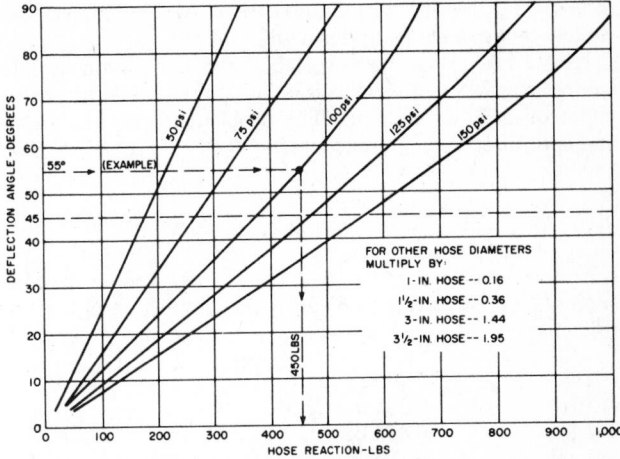

Fig. 9-5G.   Reaction forces in 2½-in. hose. (See table within the graph for conversion factors to use in calculating reaction forces in hose of other diameters.)

Nozzle Reaction

Water that is discharging from a nozzle produces a reaction that is opposite the flow of water and is known as nozzle reaction. As flow and pressure are increased, the greater the reaction. Nozzle reaction of solid stream nozzles may be calculated by means of the following formula.

$$NR = 1.5d^2p$$

where NR = nozzle reaction in lbs
d = diameter of the nozzle in in.
p = nozzle pressure in psi

Another formula that may be used for both solid stream and spray nozzles is:

$$NR = gpm \sqrt{P} .0505$$

where NR = nozzle reaction in lbs
gpm = gpm
P = nozzle pressure

G.   Reaction Forces in Ladder and Tower Streams

The reaction of heavy streams, either solid or spray, discharged from ladder pipes, platform booms, and towers can easily cause serious problems, such as leverage effects of large magnitude, and displacement of centers of gravity. Thus the stability of the whole structure could be threatened; likewise a sudden loss of pressure when a hose line bursts or a pump stops may cause a whipping effect.

A ladder pipe or other large stream from a ladder (including 2½-in. hand lines) should always be operated in line with the main beams or trusses. Ladders have little resistance to torsional effects. The Committee on Fire Department Equipment recommends that ladder pipes be incapable of horizontal travel and in any event, that maximum horizontal movement of the pipe must not exceed 15°. Rotation of the ladder turntable is the correct way to rotate the stream from ladder pipes. Also, care should be used in elevating and lowering the stream because this changes the direction of the thrust on the ladder mechanism. The fly ladder should not be raised or lowered while a ladder pipe is discharging and under no circumstances should the vehicle be moved with the ladder pipe discharging. All such streams should be gated to permit movement of the ladder and vehicle without shutting down the pump.

Because there are many variable forces acting on mobile ladders or towers in service, it is quite impractical to devise tables of specific reactions. The problem is one of design, and careful operating procedures.

SI Units

The following conversion factors are given as a convenience in converting to SI units the English units used in this chapter.

1 in.	= 25.4000 mm
1 ft	= 0.305 m
1 lb	= 0.454 kg
1 psi	= 6.895 kPa
1 gal (U.S.)	= 3.785 litres
1 gpm	= 3.785 litres/min

Bibliography

References Cited

[1] Freeman, J. R., *Transactions of the American Society of Civil Engineers*, Vols. XII and XXIV.

[2] Lyons, P. R., *Operating Fire Department Pumpers*, 4th ed., National Fire Protection Association, Boston, 1974.

Additional Readings

Bonadio, G. E., *Fire Hydraulics*, Arco Publishing Co., New York, 1958.

Casey, J. F., ed., *Fire Service Hydraulics*, 2nd ed., Reuben H. Donnelley Corp., New York, 1970.

Erven, L. W., *Techniques of Hydraulics*, Glencoe Press, Beverly Hills, 1972.

Hudiburg, Everett, ed., *Fire Stream Practices*, 5th ed., International Fire Service Training Association, Stillwater, Okla., 1972.

Kimball, W. Y., *Effective Streams for Fighting Fires*, 1st ed., National Fire Protection Association, Boston, 1961.

———, *Fire Stream Fundamentals*, National Fire Protection Association, Boston, 1966.

Purington, Robert, *Fire Fighting Hydraulics*, McGraw-Hill, New York, 1974.

Vennard, J. K., *Elementary Fluid Mechanics*, 4th ed., John Wiley and Sons, New York, 1961.

Chapter 6

EVALUATION AND PLANNING OF PUBLIC FIRE PROTECTION

A. Evaluation

An evaluation of public fire protection must take into account a number of factors such as: what there is to burn, the life hazard that exists, fire frequency, climatic conditions, demographical and geographical factors, and a basic consideration of just what role a public fire department is expected or required to play in providing public fire protection to the jurisdiction. Failure to adequately consider each of these factors can lead to a large loss fire. The provision of fire protection can never be expected to make up for the deficiency or lack of built-in fire protection systems.

Rural Fire Protection

The principal difference between rural and suburban fire departments and urban fire departments is that the former must give more attention to water supply problems, even though this factor is important in the operations of both. Rural fire department operations and apparatus embrace not only fire fighting requirements, but the provision of water for fire fighting. Rural fire apparatus must have large water tanks to permit effective initial attack on fires while supplementary water supplies are being brought into action. Supplementary water supplies include suction sources on or adjacent to rural properties (see Section 11, Chapter 3), and mobile water supply apparatus for transporting water from more distant sources. Often, rural fire departments use apparatus and hose to relay water from sources up to 2,000 ft from the emergency scene, and will transport water where the distances are greater. Initial response of pumpers, tankers, and auxiliary apparatus should be commensurate with the fire fighting requirements of the property in question. It is possible, as more modern highways are constructed and maintained and as new fire apparatus are available, to bring substantial fire fighting forces to an emergency scene in rural areas in time to be effective in properly planned and executed initial fire attack operations. Few rural properties are now located in areas too remote to enjoy some level of rural fire protection. These properties must depend entirely on their own private fire protection and any help they might be able to obtain from forestry agencies or more distant fire departments.

Minimum standard protection for a rural area would include a pumper with a large water tank and a mobile water supply apparatus on an initial alarm. Properly designed water supply apparatus should be able to transport water at a sustained rate of 100 gpm from a suction source one mile from the fire. If larger hose is required to provide adequate fire protection services, additional tankers must be used or suction sources within reasonable distance of the possible emergency scene must be developed. Rural apparatus should carry 3½ in. or larger lay-in hose for providing adequate water supply at the fire scene. It is always advisable to lay large diameter fire hose from the water supply source as close to the emergency scene as possible in order to avoid extensive friction loss. At the emergency scene large diameter hose is often wyed into smaller hand lines. Other pieces of equipment such as rescue and aerial ladder apparatus should be provided as needed to carry out the mission of the fire department. Generally, there is not an extensive need for elevated master streams in rural operations, and normal ladder truck equipment for rescue, forcible entry, ventilation, and salvage type operations must be carried on the other pieces of apparatus.

Often, to be even minimally effective, the initial responding apparatus should be capable of reaching the emergency scene within 10 min of the sounding of the alarm. This apparatus should be capable of extinguishing small fires, or possibly preventing the extension of fires to other structures. When there is no public or organized private fire protection agency, any fire that is beyond the control of portable extinguishing equipment (extinguishers, garden hose, etc.) may be expected to burn until all fuel in a given fire area has been consumed. Minimum levels of fire protection —— while serving to confine fires to isolated properties —— leave much to be desired from the point of view of the property owner who suffers the loss, and the fire department whose morale is often affected by its inability to successfully hold the average fire.

Urban Fire Protection

In urban areas the inadequate response to initial alarms can be a major factor in fire losses due to the clustering of people and the increased exposure to the fire problem. The number of simultaneous fire fighting operations that must be conducted also dictates the amount of manpower and equipment needed to provide effective fire fighting operations. In all but the smallest structural fire, several operations must be carried on simultaneously and frequently; fire attack must be made from several points. This cannot be accomplished by the crew of a single fire apparatus. Multiple apparatus must be positioned relative to the various facets of the job to be done, and adequate extinguishing capacity must be brought to bear in order to cope with the combustible involved.

In its simplest terms, structural fire fighting involves simultaneous operation of three units under a chief officer: (1) a pumper company to make a fast initial fire attack, (2) a pumper to provide adequate water supply for the operation, and (3) a company to handle rescue, ventilation, salvage, and various other truck type services. At large structure fires additional fire fighting personnel are needed to cover the various points of fire attack and, in some cases, various functions can be handled more efficiently by specially trained crews such as rescue companies, salvage companies, etc., operating from specially equipped apparatus.

In a light hazard residential district, the minimum effective initial alarm response should consist of at least 3 pieces of apparatus, 2 of which should be equipped to conduct pumping and water supply operations, with the remaining piece equipped for truck type operations. Each piece should carry the necessary emergency tools and appliances to perform the designated operation. The manpower required for reasonably satisfactory operation of this equipment would be 12 fire fighters and a chief officer. A more efficient use of the equipment could be made with a minimum response of 15 fire fighters and officers (12 fire fighters, 2 company officers, and 1 chief officer).

Table 9-6A. Evaluation of Fire Department Response Capability

High Hazard Occupancies (Schools, hospitals, nursing homes, explosive plants, refineries, high rise buildings, and other high life hazard or large fire potential occupancies)

At least 4 pumpers, 2 ladder trucks, 2 chief officers, and other specialized apparatus as may be needed to cope with the combustible involved; not less than 24 fire fighters and 2 chief officers.

Medium Hazard Occupancies (Apartments, offices, mercantile and industrial occupancies not normally requiring extensive rescue or fire fighting forces)

At least 3 pumpers, 1 ladder truck, 1 chief officer, and other specialized apparatus as may be needed or available; not less than 16 fire fighters and 1 chief officer.

Low Hazard Occupancies (One, two or three family dwellings and scattered small businesses and industrial occupancies)

At least 2 pumpers, 1 ladder truck, 1 chief officer, and other specialized apparatus as may be needed or available; not less than 12 fire fighters and 1 chief officer.

Rural Operations (Scattered dwellings, small businesses and farm buildings)

At least 1 pumper with a large water tank (500 or more gal), one mobile water supply apparatus (1,000 gal or larger), and such other specialized apparatus as may be necessary to perform effective initial fire fighting operations; at least 6 fire fighters and 1 chief officer.

Additional Alarms

At least the equivalent of that required for Rural Operations for second alarms; equipment as may be needed according to the type of emergency and capabilities of the fire department. This may involve the immediate use of mutual aid companies until local forces can be supplemented with additional off-duty personnel.

Commercial, industrial, and mercantile areas generally require an additional piece of pumping apparatus in response to the initial alarm. If high life hazard type property such as schools, hospitals, nursing homes, etc. are involved, at least four pumping apparatus, two aerial ladder trucks, and 2 chief officers should be considered a minimum response on initial alarms.

To be effective, the required fire fighting units—upon the sounding of an initial alarm—should be located as to arrive in time to operate as an effective fire fighting unit following planned tactical procedures. Often, the task force type of concept where units are housed and respond together as a tactical unit may prove to be the most efficient fire fighting operation, even though a slight increase in response time is necessary for some areas of the first alarm district. Increased efficiency can often outweigh this slight increase in response time. A minimum task force unit should consist of 2 pumping engines, a ladder truck, and a chief officer.

In evaluating the adequacy of fire department protection in any given area, major consideration must be given to the ability of the fire department to handle efficiently any work load that may be reasonably anticipated. This requires an evaluation of the possibility of several simultaneous working fires, weather factors that may contribute to the spread of fire or the delay in response, and other demographical or geographical conditions that might affect the frequency of fire occurrence and the response time of initial fire fighting units. Where fire frequency is such that any fire company may expect 2 or 3 working fires a day, or where structures to be protected require a heavy initial response, closer spac-

ing or increased personnel requirements of individual fire companies may be necessary. The number of minor fire fighting type operations such as emergency rescue operations and grass, brush, rubbish, and automobile fires, may also require heavier than normal manning of equipment and closer spacing of fire companies. Major structural fires may result when the normal first alarm coverage in a district is depleted through covering these other emergencies, and structural fire fighting forces are inadequate. Manning fire apparatus at a level far below minimum may require the fire company to operate the equipment less effectively. This factor also has an adverse effect on the number of required fire companies for various alarms, since additional fire companies must be dispatched to the scene of an emergency in order to provide adequate manpower to deal with the emergency. It is also difficult to obtain effective team work and coordination with undermanned crews. Some fire departments have attempted to solve this problem by supplementing their crews with part-time or volunteer fire fighters, or by providing off-duty fire fighters with radios and paying them for overtime when they respond to a fire. The on-duty men make the initial fire attack and holding action while the off-duty men provide the additional manpower needed for efficient fire fighting operations, but not immediately. Efficiency is definitely lost and increased fire losses can be expected with this arrangement. Such protection should not be relied on to adequately take the place of the required manpower and equipment.

Manpower requirements are not merely a matter of numerical strength but are based on the establishment of a well trained and coordinated team necessary to utilize complicated and specialized equipment under the stress of emergency conditions. A general practice should be to avoid attempting to operate more fire companies than can be effectively manned even if some response distances must be somewhat increased. The effectiveness of pumper companies must be measured by their ability to give required hose streams and service quickly and efficiently. NFPA No. 197, Training Standard on Initial Fire Attack, should be used as a guide in measuring this ability. Oftentimes a fire company of less than 4 men may not be able to apply half as much water in a given time with their equipment as a 4 or 5 man company. Seriously undermanned fire companies generally are limited to the use of small hose streams until additional help arrives. Oftentimes, this action may be totally ineffective in keeping a small fire from becoming a large fire.

Consideration must also be given to maintaining an adequate concentration of additional forces to handle multiple alarm fires while still providing minimum fire protection coverage for the other areas under the protection of the fire departments. Off-shift personnel may be used to man adequate for routine fires but inadequate for major emergencies, arrangements should be made to supplement the fire protection coverage by calling back the off-shift personnel and promptly calling for mutual aid from nearby fire departments. Off-shift personnel may be used to man reserve apparatus or to relieve or supplement men on the fire ground. Fire companies not dispatched or utilized on the fire scene should be distributed throughout the remaining area of the jurisdiction to keep response time to other alarms to a minimum. Reserve apparatus should be properly maintained and equipped, and when placed in service should be manned to a degree commensurate with standard fire apparatus manning. Since it may take up to a half hour or more to place reserve units in service with manpower recalled in an emergency, these reserve units should not be completely relied upon to provide an adequate level of fire protection services.

In cases where several fire departments occupy adjacent or contiguous territories, arrangements should be made for joint response along common boundaries and for assistance in covering vacant fire stations at times of major fires. Mutual aid or mutual response should not be relied upon to always provide assistance in major emergencies since there could be times when local commitments will prevent their giving the anticipated assistance. This type of assistance does not reduce the responsibility of each jurisdiction for having adequate facilities to handle normal fire protection needs. It must also be assumed that teamwork and tactical efficiency will be somewhat less than what would be expected of equal units under a united command.

In the past it was common practice to relate the number of pumping engines, pumping capacity and other apparatus manpower requirements to the population to be protected. With the industrialization of many areas and the construction of commercial shopping centers in residential areas, it is possible that concentrations of value requiring substantial fire fighting forces may be needed in areas of small or large population. Persons having the responsibility for providing public fire protection must be prepared to cope with the fire potential wherever it may be. It is common practice to base fire department response requirements on the fire flow in gpm that may have to be applied. A good rule of thumb is to provide one pumper company (plus supporting units) for each 500 gpm that may be needed.

Some argue that it is not the public responsibility to provide adequate fire protection to the high hazard risk that should have built-in fire protection systems. However, failure to attempt to provide fire protection for large taxable values on which the economy of a community may be based would place some municipal officials in an untenable position and subject them to extreme criticism even though fire protection experts may consider that certain properties present hazards beyond the scope of effective fire protection by manual fire fighting. The minimum fire force that could be considered reasonably ample for any small community would be two pumpers, a ladder or squad truck, an auxiliary pumper or brush fire fighting vehicle, and possibly a tanker for use in areas where hydrant water supplies are limited. Where necessitated by fire frequency or response distances, additional pumpers and ladder trucks may be needed. Reserve apparatus is desirable not only to permit the repair of first line equipment, but to provide additional fire fighting units during major emergencies.

The municipal grading schedule of the ISO (Insurance Services Office) is often used as a guide for evaluating the public fire defenses. While it may give some standard of comparison of the municipality's ability to cope with fire emergencies, it must be remembered that this is an insurance underwriting tool and is used by insurance companies to evaluate the insurance company's financial risk in insuring a particular property or class of properties in a given jurisdiction.

Time has been another factor often utilized in the evaluation of public fire protection. It is generally considered that the first arriving piece of apparatus should be at the emergency scene within 5 min of the sounding of the alarm. The old adage says, "the first 5 min of any fire is the determining factor as to whether that fire will remain a small fire or become a large fire." If time is to be used in evaluating procedures, delays in the sounding of an alarm must be minimized or eliminated, and time cannot become the all important factor at the expense of safety. Time is a factor that must be reckoned with and considered in all planning for providing public fire protection, but it should not become the only factor and judge of public fire protection.

B. Insurance Grading Schedule

The "Grading Schedule for Municipal Fire Protection"[2] is published and copyrighted by the Insurance Services Office.* The schedule provides a yardstick for ISO insurance grading engineers in classifying municipalities with reference to their fire defenses and physical conditions. Gradings obtained under the schedule are used throughout the United States in establishing base rates for fire insurance purposes. A similar schedule is used in Canada by the Insurers' Advisory Organization to evaluate municipal fire defenses in that country.

The Insurance Grading Schedule originally was developed by the National Board of Fire Underwriters and was continued by its successor, the American Insurance Association, prior to the organization of ISO. It has had a profound influence upon the level of municipal fire protection provided in many communities. While ISO never assumes to dictate the level of fire protection services provided by a municipality, reports of surveys made by its Municipal Survey Office generally do contain recommendations for correcting any serious deficiencies found, and over the years have been accepted as guides by many municipal officials in planning improvements in their services. It is generally appreciated that removal of deficiencies can result in a more favorable fire insurance classification which has certain economic rewards as well as a general satisfaction that the community is providing its citizens with an improved level of service, or is holding a favorable classification where already obtained. While from time to time communities may want to employ independent consultants to evaluate their fire departments, water supplies, and building regulations, the fact is that over the past sixty odd years underwriters' surveys have provided a uniform measurement of municipal fire defenses involving many millions of dollars of engineering time and talent at no cost to the local communities which may choose to follow the recommendations. It has been observed, for example, that American communities enjoy the most adequate and reliable water systems in the world. This has been due in large measure to the engineering evaluations and recommendations of underwriter survey teams.

The Municipal Grading Schedule is subject to change with the state of the art and references in this text are to the 1974 edition. With the organization of ISO, application of the Grading Schedule has tended to be more uniform throughout the country. Under NBFU and AIA the larger communities, generally those over 40,000 population, were surveyed directly by teams of engineers from the national organization while smaller communities generally were graded by state or regional rating associations some of which used their own systems of grading municipal fire defenses. Most of the latter now have been consolidated into regional ISO offices insofar as municipal surveys are concerned although state associations have essential functions in filing rates and performing other duties as may be required by law.

The Grading Schedule is based upon a deficiency point system with a possible 5,000 points of deficiency representing a community totally unprotected against fire. The 5,000

* Available from Insurance Services Office, 160 Water St., New York, N.Y. 10038.

Table 9-6B. Relative Class as Determined by Points of Deficiency

Points of Deficiency	Relative Class of Municipality
0– 500	First
501–1,000	Second
1,001–1,500	Third
1,501–2,000	Fourth
2,001–2,500	Fifth
2,501–3,000	Sixth
3,001–3,500	Seventh
3,501–4,000	Eighth
4,001–4,500	Ninth#
More than 4,500	Tenth*

A ninth class municipality is one (a) receiving 4,001 to 4,500 points of deficiency or (b) receiving less than 4,001 points but having no recognized water supply.

* A tenth class municipality is one (a) receiving more than 4,500 points of deficiency, or (b) without a recognized water supply and having a fire department grading over 1/55 points, or (c) with a water supply and no fire department, or (d) with no fire protection.

points are divided into 10 classes, and every 500 points eliminated places the community in a more favorable class. Table 9-6B shows the relative class as determined by points of deficiency. However, a ninth class municipality may be one receiving 4,001 to 4,500 points of deficiency, or receiving less than 4,001 points but having no recognized water supply. A tenth class municipality may be one receiving over 4,500 points of deficiency, or without a recognized water supply, or with a water supply but no fire department, or without a water supply with a fire department grading over 1,755 points, or no fire protection at all. In many rural areas there are subclasses of Class 9 recognizing the value of properly organized and equipped rural fire departments serving communities without a recognized water supply. Such fire departments are required to have stipulated water tanker capacity as well as pumping engines.

The 5,000 possible deficiency points are divided between 4 main subject areas or features. Water supply and fire department each account for a possible 1,950 points, or 39 percent. Fire service communications account for another 450 points, or 9 percent. Fire safety control, including fire prevention and building regulations, counts for 650 points, or 13 percent. Where there is a divergence of more than 500 points between water supply and the fire department, additional deficiency points may be assessed on the grounds that a good water supply requires an adequate fire department to apply it in fire fighting, and a good fire department without an adequate water supply is less effective. If either of these essentials is lacking, up to 900 additional deficiency points may be charged.

Water Supply

It is important to understand that a principal basis for the Grading Schedule's evaluation of fire protection is the ability to provide needed "fire flow" of water measured in gpm. In years past schedule requirements were based largely upon population protected which, while having some validity, was not entirely equitable because some of the smaller communities may contain properties with serious fire potentials that could require large flows of water, whereas a larger community might not require as much water to control its fires. An example might be a very large unsprinklered shopping complex in a suburban residential community. In both water supply and fire department service, reliability factors get considerable attention in the schedule.

Required fire flow is the rate of flow needed for fire fighting to confine a major fire to the buildings within a block or group. The determination of this flow depends upon construction, occupancy, size of buildings, and exposure hazards. Required flow is determined for each section of a municipality and may vary from a minimum of 500 gpm to a maximum of 12,000 gpm for a single fire. Where consideration must be given to simultaneous fires, an additional 2,000 to 8,000 gpm is required. Actual flow tests are made in each section of the municipality and the results obtained are compared with the flow required in each neighborhood to deal with the hazards found.

For purposes of grading under the standard, a "basic fire flow" is used which is indicative of the quantities of water needed for handling fires in important districts. Among the items considered under water supply are: adequacy of supply works; reliability of source of supply; reliability of pumping capacity and of power supply; the condition, arrangement, operation, and reliability of system components; adequacy and reliability of mains and their installation; arrangement of the distribution system; distribution of hydrants and their size, type, installation, and condition; and various miscellaneous factors.

A minimum recognized water supply for grading purposes must be able to deliver at least 250 gpm for 2 hours, or 500 gpm for 1 hour for fire protection plus consumption of water at the maximum daily rate. Any water supply which cannot meet this requirement is not graded, and the full 1,950 deficiency points are assigned.

Fire Department

Items considered under the fire department include: pumpers, ladder trucks, distribution of companies and types of apparatus, pumper capacity, design and condition of apparatus, number of officers, manning, master and special stream devices, equipment for pumpers and ladder trucks (including elevating platforms), hose and its condition, training, response to alarms, fire operations, special protection such as fireboats, and miscellaneous factors.

A minimum recognized fire department under the schedule must have a permanent organization under applicable state and local laws, and be headed by one person responsible for the operation of the department. There must be sufficient membership to provide a response of at least 4 members to alarms, with training conducted for all active members. There must be at least one piece of suitable fire apparatus with housing and maintenance for the apparatus. Means must be provided for 24-hr receipt of alarms and immediate notification of members. Any fire department that cannot meet these requirements is not graded, and a full 1,950 deficiency points are assigned.

Under the schedule the number of engine and ladder companies must be at least equal to the number required for the basic fire flow. Engine and ladder companies must be located so that travel distances for first due, for first alarm companies, and for the maximum number of companies needed to apply required fire flows meet recommended travel distances. Structural conditions and hazards in the municipality may call for more companies than needed to apply basic fire flow. The probability of simultaneous fires, the number and extent of runs, and the need for placing additional companies in service or for relocating companies during periods of high frequency of alarms are factors considered. Consideration is given to providing protection for all areas during multiple alarms and simultaneous fires.

Where the required fire flow is 4,500 gpm or less, response

distance for the first due engine company must be not over 1½ miles, except that it may be 2 miles in residential districts of 1- and 2-family dwellings not requiring over 2,000 gpm fire flow, and 4 miles where such dwellings have an average separation of 100 ft or more. For flows of from 5,000 to 8,500 gpm inclusive, the first due engine should be within 1 mile, and for flows of 9,000 gpm or more the distance is ¾ mile.

The first due ladder company should be within 2 miles for flows of 4,500 gpm or less, but may be 3 miles for residential districts of 1- and 2-family dwellings and 4 miles where such dwellings have an average separation of 100 ft or more. Where there are less than 5 buildings of a height equal to 3 or more stories, a ladder company may not be required. Where required fire flow is from 5,000 to 8,500 gpm, the first due response distance for ladder trucks is reduced to 1½ miles, and where the required flow is 9,000 gpm or more the first due ladder should be within 1 mile.

Standard first alarm response is 2 engines and 1 ladder company for flows not exceeding 8,500 gpm, except that for flows of less than 2,000 gpm only one engine may be required, and ladder coverage may not be required for flows of 3,500 gpm or less if there are less than 5 buildings of a height requiring such service.

For flows of 9,000 gpm and above, the first alarm response should be 3 engines and 2 ladders. Response distances for the second due engine should be within 4 miles with fire flows of under 2,000 gpm, within 2½ miles for fire flows of from 2,000 to 4,500 gpm, 2 miles for flows from 5,000 to 6,500 gpm, and 1½ miles for flows between 7,000 and 8,500 gpm. Where 3 engines are required, these should be within 1½ miles. Where 2 ladders are required on first alarms, these should be within 2 miles.

Maximum multiple alarm response and response distances also are specified for the various fire flows. In general, one engine company is required for each 1,000 gpm fire flow through 7,000 gpm. At higher flows, additional engine companies are required up to 15 for 12,000 gpm. Maximum multiple alarm response distances for engines vary from 3 miles for 3 engines to 5 miles for 15 engines. In general, the response on each multiple alarm should duplicate the first alarm response.

A second ladder company within 2½ miles is required for multiple alarms with fire flows of 5,000 to 6,500 gpm, a third ladder company should be within 3½ miles for flows of 7,000 to 8,500 gpm, and on up to 7 ladders within 5 miles for 12,000 gpm.

It should be appreciated that these response requirements are a rather conservative minimum standard. Many fire departments will exceed these because pre-fire planning indicates need for additional companies because of life hazard or in order to run hand lines to control fires inside of buildings rather than application of maximum fire flow to merely confine fires as envisioned under the schedule. Levels of manpower on responding companies often influence the number of companies assigned to respond to various alarms. The basic purpose of the Grading Schedule is to confine fires to groups of buildings involved to avoid conflagrations, and it does not demand the same level of service that many communities choose to provide.

Under the schedule there should be at least one reserve pumper for every 8 pumpers or major fraction in service, but not less than one. This is essential to permit proper maintenance. Fully equipped reserve pumpers manned by designated off-shift or volunteer members are considered as increasing the pumpers in service and may equal up to one in-service pumper if manned on first alarms, and ½ an

in-service pumper if manned on specified multiple alarms; however, credit cannot exceed ⅓ of the required number of pumpers. Where the requirements for manning reserve pumpers have not been met, equipped reserve pumpers may be credited the same as outside aid.

Pumpers responding on automatic mutual aid within 5 miles of the municipal limits may be credited not to exceed ⅓ of the pumpers required. This credit requires a detailed mutual aid system with scheduled assignments and proper training and communications. Credit allowed may not reduce the point charge by more than 75 percent, except that where there is a central communications center dispatching all companies the reduction may be up to 90 percent. Consideration also is given to outside aid available within 15 miles, and depending upon various factors deficiencies may be reduced by not more than 33 percent for such available response. Similar credits are allowed for response of ladder companies responding on scheduled mutual aid and outside aid, and for reserve ladders manned by off-shift personnel. However, deficiencies charged for an inadequate number of ladder trucks is only half that for pumpers.

Pumping capacity must be not less than the basic fire flow, and additional capacity may be needed. From the response assignments in the schedule it appears that 1,000 gpm pumpers are assumed to be standard, although credit is given for smaller capacity pumps and also for available pumps on other apparatus. Where simultaneous fires are likely, the pumper capacity must not be less than the total flow requirements for the simultaneous fires. Pumper capacity is taken as that demonstrated by test and not merely that specified in purchasing contracts. In the absence of proper test data, the credit for pumper capacity may be reduced.

Fire Department Officers

There must be a chief officer in charge of the department. For more than 2 companies there must also be an assistant or other officer above company rank who is in charge in the absence of the chief. For over 8 companies there must be sufficient battalion or district fire chiefs to provide one on duty for each 8 companies or major fraction thereof. For less than 12 companies the assistant chief may serve as a battalion or district chief. The preceding is a very conservative requirement. Many fire departments provide a district fire chief on duty for each 5 or 6 companies in order to give prompt supervision of fire companies at fires and to cover simultaneous alarms. Most fire departments with 5 or more companies provide a chief officer on each duty shift, although not required under the schedule.

There must be a company officer on duty at all times with each required engine, hose, or ladder company. The company officers are credited in the company strength. Two call or volunteer officers are considered equivalent to one full paid officer, up to ⅓ the number of paid officers required.

Manning Standards

Standard manning is 6 men on duty for each required engine and ladder company, including the officer and 5 men for hose companies where pumps are not required. Where companies operate special apparatus, additional manning may be needed. Years ago from 5 to 7 men were considered standard manning, depending upon the type of company and the hazards of the district served. Today with the greater mobility of radio-equipped apparatus and the fact that serious hazards are found in all parts of the community and not just in a central district, a uniform manning is considered desirable. The 6-man standard level of company manning is a practical requirement based upon the work that must be done by engine and ladder companies. Where fewer men are provided, it is often necessary to obtain additional manpower from other companies.

While the standard calls for a 6-man level of company manning, credit is given for chiefs' aides who participate in fire fighting. Credit also is given for manpower responding on other units, such as rescue squads and fire department ambulance crews, to the extent that these assist in fire fighting, but not to exceed credit of one man per company. Credit is given also for the regular response of off-duty or volunteer fire fighters. In the schedule, 3 off-duty or volunteer members are counted as equal to one paid man on duty, up to $\frac{1}{2}$ of the required on-duty strength. Thus a fire company with 3 men on duty and 9 off-duty or volunteer members assigned to respond can be counted as a full 6-man crew. However, records of such off-duty response must be kept for both day and night alarms to substantiate the actual value of such manning. If proper records are not kept, call or volunteer response may be taken on the basis of 6 men on call equaling one on duty. In many small fire departments, small outside fires may be handled by the paid men on duty on still alarms without call assistance, but full standard response should be made immediately to all alarms for structural fires and other alarms that present a hazard to life and property.

Under the schedule a fully volunteer or call department with no paid men on duty ready to immediately answer alarms but with good call response would be charged 40 points of deficiency, as compared with an identical fire department having standard 6-man fire companies on duty or the equivalent under the schedule. This amounts to only 80 percent of all the possible deficiency points in a municipal grading. This would appear to be a small deficiency as compared with the advantage of immediate response by on-duty fire companies. If the volunteer or call department has paid apparatus operators on duty, the deficiency might be only 20 points out of 5,000 in the grading, all other things being equal.

Manpower responding on automatic mutual aid is credited up to $\frac{1}{2}$ of the required strength, but may not reduce the point charge by more than 75 percent or 90 percent as may be applicable. Credit also is given for outside aid, but may not reduce the point charge remaining after automatic aid and off-shift response credit has been applied by more than 33 percent. Credit also is given for off-shift response based upon past experience when called.

Deficiency charges are determined by comparing the total required manning of the fire companies being graded with the on-duty strength of these companies as determined by the schedule. Any deficiency divided by the number of companies equals the average deficiency per company. An average deficiency per company of one man results in only 10 points, two men 20 points, three men 40 points, four men 80 points, and five men 160 points. Thus, a fire department that maintains 5 men on each required engine and ladder company assisted by rescue squads, ambulance crews, and chiefs' aides may not be considered deficient in manpower under the standard. Likewise, a fire department that has an average on-duty manning of 3 men per required company plus response of off-duty or call men may not be considered deficient if the record of response is satisfactory. Thus, the manpower requirements are flexible and reasonable. Places that should expect poor grading on manpower are those with 2- and 3-man engine companies and 1- or 2-man ladder companies without satisfactory arrangements for prompt response of off-shift members or other men on call

and without well-scheduled automatic mutual aid. Such departments obviously are too badly undermanned to effectively apply required fire flow when serious fires occur. On the other hand, a small community requiring 2 engines and a ladder and having 6 paid men on duty supplemented by good off-shift and call response plus automatic mutual aid may have a minimum deficiency charge for manning.

Fire Service Communications

As fire service communications are an essential element in the fire defenses of any community, the Grading Schedule evaluates the following: the communications center; the communications center equipment and current supply; fire alarm boxes; alarm circuits and facilities including current supply at fire stations; material, construction, condition, and protection of circuits; fire department radio; fire department telephone service; conditions adversely affecting use and operations of facilities; fire alarm operators; and the handling of alarms. While alarm boxes are not required in residential districts, a credit of up to 20 points is given for such boxes depending upon coverage.

Determination of deficiencies under the various communications items are based upon the degree of compliance with the intent of applicable provisions of NFPA No. 73, Standard for Public Fire Service Communications. This Standard is discussed in further detail in Chapter 3 of this Section of the HANDBOOK.

Some persons in the fire service have often felt that the Grading Schedule placed undue emphasis on water supply at the expense of the fire department. In earlier editions of the schedule this may, to some extent, have been true. However, in recent editions items under fire department control including fire service communications and control of hazards amount to up to 58.5 percent of the 5,000 possible deficiency points. The one area in which water supply still has an advantage over the fire department service is the requirement that without a recognized water system, no community can have a classification better than Class 9. Hundreds of fire departments serving areas without water systems are organized to exceed the minimum requirements for fire flow from water systems by using fleets of tankers, and by the use of large diameter water supply hose supplied from pumpers at suction sources prepared and maintained by the fire department. With the water supply equipment responding with the attack pumpers, no delay is involved. Many rural fire departments believe that their ability to apply required fire flow should be recognized because it has proven successful in the control of major fires, including fires in communities recognized as having inadequate water supplies.

C. Planning

The following information has been extracted in whole and in part from "America Burning," the report of the National Commission on Fire Prevention and Control[1], and is considered appropriate for inclusion in this portion of the HANDBOOK.

Planning

Fire protection has been largely a local responsibility, and for good reasons it is destined to remain so. Each community has a set of conditions unique to itself, and a system of fire protection that works well for one community cannot be assumed to work equally well for other communities. To be adequate, the fire protection system must respond to local conditions, especially to changing conditions. Planning is the key: Without local-level planning, the system of fire protection is apt to be ill-suited to local needs and lag behind the changing needs of the community.

Excellent fire protection (for example, in the form of automatic extinguishing systems) lies within technical grasp, and certainly lies within the resources of most communities to provide. Even with considerable public support, this protection would require many years to accomplish. In the meantime, in every fire jurisdiction (whether a municipality, county, or region) standards aiming at a significant increase in fire protection must be set. Among the concepts to be defined:

Adequate Level of Fire Protection: The question of "adequacy" addressed itself not only to day-to-day normal needs, but to major contingencies that can be anticipated and to future needs as well. What is needed is a definition of "optimal" protection—in contrast to "minimal" protection, which fails to meet contingencies and future needs, and "maximal" protection, which is more than the community can afford.

Reasonable Community Costs: Fire, both as threat and reality, has its costs: property losses, deaths, injuries, hospital bills, lost tax revenues, plus the costs of maintaining fire departments, paying fire insurance premiums, and providing built-in fire protection. Each community must decide on an appropriate level of investment in fire protection. Some costs beyond the public's willingness to bear should be transferred to the private sector (as when buildings over a certain size or height or with a certain occupancy are required to have automatic extinguishing systems).

Acceptable Risk: A certain level of losses from fire must be accepted as tolerable simply because of limited resources of the community. Conditions that endanger the safety of citizens and fire fighters beyond the acceptable risk must be identified as targets for reduction.

Consideration of these matters helps to determine what functions and emphasis should be assigned to the fire department, other municipal departments, and the private sector, both now and in the future. It helps to define new policies, laws, or regulations that may be needed. Most important, consideration of these matters makes clear that fire safety is a responsibility shared by the public and private sectors. Because the fire department cannot prevent all fire losses, formal obligations fall on owners of certain kinds of buildings to have built-in fire protection. For the same reason, private citizens have an obligation to exercise prudence with regard to fire in their daily lives. But prudence also requires education in fire safety, and the obligation to provide that education appropriately falls in the public sector, chiefly the fire department. The public sector (again, chiefly the fire department) also has an obligation to see that requirements for built-in protection in the private sector are being met.

A fire department, then, has more than one responsibility. Nor are the responsibilities just mentioned exhaustive. At least 8 important functions for fire departments can be identified:

Fire Suppression: Fire fighters need proper training and adequate equipment for saving lives and putting out fires quickly, and also for their own safety.

Life Safety-paramedical Services: Capabilities needed during fires and other emergencies include first aid, resuscitation, and possibly paramedical services. (By "paramedical services" we mean emergency treatment beyond ordinary first aid, performed by fire service personnel under supervision (through radio communication, for example) of a physician.)

Fire Prevention: This includes approving building plans and actual construction, inspecting buildings, their contents, and their fire protection equipment, public education, and investigating the causes of fires to serve as a guide to future priorities in fire prevention.

Fire Safety Education: Fire departments have an obligation to bring fire safety education not only into schools and private homes, but also into occupancies with greater than average fire potential or hazard to people, such as restaurants, hotels, hospitals, and nursing homes.

Deteriorated Building Hazards: In coordination with other municipal departments, fire departments can work to abate serious hazards to health and safety caused by deteriorated structures or abandoned buildings.

Regional Coordination: Major emergencies can exceed the capabilities of a single fire department, and neighboring fire jurisdictions should have detailed plans for coping with such emergencies. But effectiveness can also be improved through sharing of day-to-day operations—as, for example, an area-wide communication and dispatching network.

Data Development: Knowledge of how well a fire department is doing, and of how practices should change to improve performance, depends on adequate record-keeping.

Community Relations: Fire departments are representative of the local community that supports them. The impression they make on citizens affects how citizens view their government. Volunteer departments dependent on private donations must, of course, also be concerned with their community relations. Moreover, since fire stations are strategically located throughout the community, they can serve as referral or dispensing agencies for a wide range of municipal services.

As communities set out to improve their fire protection, it is not the fire department alone they must consider. The police have a role in reporting fires and in handling traffic and crowds during fires. The cooperation of the building department is needed to enforce the fire safety provisions of building codes. The work of the water department in maintaining the water system is vital to fire suppression. In the realm of fire safety education, the public schools, the department of recreation, and the public library can augment the work of the fire department. Future development and planning will influence the location of new fire stations and how they will be equipped.

These are just the obvious examples of interdependence. So seemingly trivial a matter as the manner in which house numbers are assigned and posted can affect the ability of fire departments to respond quickly and effectively to emergencies.

Master Planning

Fire protection is only one of many community services. Not only must it compete for dollars with other municipal needs, such as the education system and the police department, but, in planning for future growth, the fire protection system must take into account the changes going on elsewhere in the community. For example, if a slum area is to be torn down and replaced with high-rise apartment buildings, that will change the fire protection needs of the area. Changes in zoning maps will also change the fire protection needs in different parts of the community.

To cope with future growth, local administrators are turning increasingly to the concept of *master planning* of municipal functions. Such plans include an examination of existing programs, projection of future needs of the community, and a determination of methods to fill those needs. They seek the most cost-effective allocations of resources to help assure that the needs will be met.

A major section of a community general plan of land use should be a *Master Plan for Fire Protection,* written chiefly by fire department managers. This plan should, first of all, be consistent with and reinforce the goals of the city's overall general plan. For example, it should plan its deployment of manpower and equipment according to the kind of growth, and the specific areas of growth, that the community foresees. It should set goals and priorities for the fire department. Not only is it important to set objectives in terms of lives and property to be saved, but also to decide allocations among fire prevention inspection, fire safety education, and fire suppression as the best way to accomplish the objectives.

Having established goals, the plan should seek to establish "management by objectives" within the fire department. This operates on the principle that management is most effective when each person is aware of how his tasks fit into the overall goals and has committed himself to getting specific jobs done in a specified time.

Because fire departments exist in a real world where a variety of purposes must be served with a limited amount of money, it is important that every dollar be invested for maximum payoff. The fire protection master plan should not only seek to provide the maximum cost-benefit ratio for fire protection expenditures, but should also establish a framework for measuring the effectiveness of these expenditures.

Lastly, the plan should clarify the fire protection responsibility for other groups in the community, both governmental and private.

Devising a Fire Protection Plan

The following can serve as guidelines to fire department administrators for developing and presenting a master plan for fire protection:

Phase I

1. Identify the fire protection problems of the jurisdiction.

2. Identify the best combination of public resources and built-in protection required to manage the fire problem, within acceptable limits:
   (a) Specify current capabilities and future needs of public resources;
   (b) Specify current capabilities and future requirements for built-in protection.

3. Develop alternative methods that will result in trade-offs between benefits and risks.

4. Establish a system of goals, programs, and cost estimates to implement the plan:
   (a) The process of developing department goals and programs should include maximum possible participation of fire department personnel, of all ranks;
   (b) The system should provide goals and objectives for all divisions, supportive of the overall goals of the department;

(c) Management development programs should strive to develop increased acceptance of authority and responsibility by all fire officers, as they strive to accomplish established objectives and programs.

Phase II

1. Develop, with the other government agencies, a definition of their roles in the fire protection process.

2. Present the proposed municipal fire protection system to the city administration for review.

3. Present the proposed system for adoption as the fire protection element of the jurisdiction's general plan. The standard process for development of a general plan provides the fire department administrator an opportunity to inform the community leaders of the fire protection goals and system, and to obtain their support.

Phase III

In considering the fire protection element the governing body of the jurisdiction will have to pay special attention to:

1. Short- and long-range goals,
2. Long-range staffing and capital improvement plans,
3. The code revisions required to provide fire loss management.

Phase IV

The fire loss management system must be reviewed and updated as budget allocations, capital improvement plans, and code revisions occur. Continuing review of results should concentrate on these areas:

1. Did fires remain within estimated limits?
2. Should limits be changed?
3. Did losses prove to be acceptable?
4. Could resources be decreased or should they be increased?

SI Units

The following conversion factors are given as a convenience in converting to SI units the English units used in this chapter.

1 gal (U.S.) = 3.785 litres
1 gpm = 3.785 litres/min

Bibliography

References Cited

[1] National Commission of Fire Prevention and Control, *America Burning: The Report of the National Commission on Fire Prevention and Control,* Government Printing Office, Washington, D.C., 1973.

[2] *Grading Schedule for Municipal Fire Protection,* Insurance Services Office, New York, 1974.

NFPA Codes, Standards, and Recommended Practices (see the latest *NFPA Publications and Visual Aids Catalog* for availability of current editions of the following documents)

NFPA No. 4, Organization for Fire Services.

NFPA No. 4A, Recommendations for Organization of a Fire Department.

NFPA No. 73, Standard for Installation, Maintenance and Use of Public Fire Service Communications.

NFPA No. 197, A Training Standard on Initial Fire Attack.

SECTION 10

ORGANIZATION FOR PRIVATE PROTECTION

Chapter 1

FIRE RISK MANAGEMENT

Often, in order to remain competitive in today's market, industries operate with some conditions and processes which are not completely fire safe. However, in order to provide a reasonably safe place for employees to work, the law requires industry to eliminate fire hazards where possible and to minimize those which it cannot eliminate. The program of identification, evaluation, and control of those hazards which might result in fire is known as fire risk management. While the responsibility for fire risk management is delegated amongst the various management echelons of an industry and the ultimate accountability rests with top management, the operation of a fire safe facility requires the cooperation of all employees.

A. Management Echelons

Industrial management can be divided into the following three categories, each of which makes important contributions to the fire risk management program: (1) top management—the board of directors and company officers, (2) general management—facility managers, department heads, and related staff managers, and (3) direct management—the supervisors and foremen who direct each phase of the operation.

In smaller industrial organizations the owner may perform the functions of all three categories and, although he may not be required to handle as many and as complex problems as the larger management groups, it is necessary that he exercise the same judgments but without the benefit of the experience of others and often without the background experience afforded by specialized training. Other facilities (such as schools) operate with their levels of management identified by different titles; however, the responsibility and accountability remain the same with all types of organizations.

B. Top Management

Members of top management establish policy, make major financial decisions, decide what product or service will be provided, and establish production levels. The role of top management in fire risk management is administrative. Based on information furnished them by general management, they decide the level of protection to be maintained, the percentage of risk to be insured, and the acceptable operating risk.

An efficient top management requires periodic progress reports on the status of the fire risk management program. These reports are obtained either through regular management channels or directly from the fire risk manager.

C. General Management

General management is responsible for providing top management with adequate information with which to make decisions and establish policy. They make recommendations which influence company policy, and they are accountable for the implementation and success of such recommendations. To best accomplish this, their function includes:

1. Making the site selection.
2. Planning the facility.
3. Directing the facility construction.
4. Planning production processes and facility layout.
5. Developing a fire insurance program.
6. Conducting community relations programs.
7. Providing guidance for direct management.

This chapter will discuss only those parts of the preceding functions which affect the fire risk management program. The title "fire risk manager" is used in reference to those persons in industrial management who are responsible for directing the fire risk management program. (Such persons may also be known by a variety of other titles, depending upon the organization.) The fire risk manager or his counterpart may be assigned to any one of an industrial organization's departments. While it is not necessary to assign the fire risk management function to a specific department, it should be assigned to a department having enough time to adequately fulfill the obligation. The position of fire risk manager is important in management organization, and should be classified high enough to permit an equable working relationship with the facility manager and other members of general and direct management.

In some industries, fire risk managers may also be responsible for employee safety management, property insurance management, and security management. For example, one large central management organization brought together a diversified group of component companies and plants and assigned an administrative vice president to handle fire risk management and a number of related functions. Under the administrative vice president came the fire risk manager who, in turn, supervised four assistant managers assigned to insurance, fire protection, safety, and security. Specific duties of the fire risk manager are detailed in Chapter 2 of this Section.

Generally, in industrial fire risk management situations, the facility manager depends on the fire risk manager to see that fire risk management policies are carried out in the following areas of shared responsibility:

1. Making the Site Selection. The fire risk manager should determine if the area under consideration has:
   (a) Adequate water supply to fulfill protection requirements in addition to providing needs
   (b) Severe exposure to natural hazard; i.e., tornado, flood, earthquake, or heavy snow
   (c) Extraordinary exposure from adjacent facilities
   (d) Acceptable response from support forces
   (e) Impediments to response by support forces; i.e., lift bridges, railroad crossings, or heavily traveled highways
   (f) A social environment subject to disorder or high incidence of crime

2. Planning the Facility. Fire risk management areas of concern to be considered during the planning stage are:
   (a) Use of fire resistant materials
   (b) Limit size of open areas by use of fire walls, fire doors, etc.
   (c) Provision of adequate emergency exits
   (d) Provision of physical protection; i.e., automatic sprinklers, hydrants, etc.

(e) Provision of access routes for fire protection vehicles

3. Directing the facility Construction. Fire risk management personnel should participate in:

    (a) Advising contractor personnel of fire risk management policies; should have authority to enforce compliance

    (b) Acceptance tests of all fire protection equipment

4. Planning Production Processes and Facility Layout. Fire risk management personnel should participate in consideration of processes which require:

    (a) Isolation for fire control or limiting exposure of other operations

    (b) Special protection systems

    (c) Limited access

    (d) Special exit facilities

5. Developing a Fire Insurance Program. Fire risk management personnel should participate in development of the insurance program by:

    (a) Furnishing the insurance manager with information on fire risk management which might be required by the carrier

    (b) Providing an escort for insurance representatives making facility inspections

    (c) Furnishing the insurance manager with immediate reports of impairment of protection systems

    (d) Furnishing the insurance manager with reports of all fires or explosions

6. Conducting Community Relations Programs. The fire risk manager should assist the facility manager or his public relations manager in publicizing the facility's fire risk management policies. This type of publicity can help build a favorable company image. The community has an interest in a facility's fire safety planning both from the standpoint of employee safety and because of the possible economic impact which would result from the loss of earnings by employees.

7. Providing Guidance for Direct Management. The fire risk manager and his staff must provide sufficient information and guidance to the direct management group to permit them to successfully comply with fire risk management policies.

D. Direct Management

Direct Management is that level of management which trains and supervises employees in the day-by-day operation of the facility. Members of direct management are responsible for applying the programs and procedures developed at the general management level for compliance with company policy.

Unless the members of direct management adequately perform their function, the fire risk management program cannot produce satisfactory results.

It is the direct manager who:

1. Trains hourly personnel in their participation in the fire risk management program.

2. Works with the fire risk manager and his staff to select employees for the private fire brigade and other program assignments.

3. Works with the fire risk manager and his staff to establish priorities for inspection, test, and maintenance of fire protection equipment.

4. Inculcates into the personnel they supervise a fire conscious attitude and respect for the fire risk management program.

5. Insists that aisles to all fire protection equipment and means of egress be kept open and free from tripping hazards.

6. Works closely with the fire risk manager and his staff to assure that new equipment or processes in his area are adequately protected before startup.

7. Reports all occupancy changes in his area which may effect any phase of the fire risk management program.

8. Works with the fire risk manager and his staff to assure that fire exit drills are held regularly; should a simulated emergency be used, the fire risk manager and his staff assure that it is realistic for the operation.

9. Assumes responsibility for a personnel count after each facility evacuation to assure that all employees have been accounted for.

10. Assumes interim command of emergency action when a fire occurs in his area.

Every industry or institution will have certain problems which are of individual concern. The guidelines in this chapter are general and basic, and are intended to emphasize the need for assigning responsibility and planning programs. The idiosyncracies of each operation should become apparent during the fire risk evaluation and, from that evaluation, a good fire risk management can plan the proper control measures.

Bibliography

NFPA Codes, Standards, and Recommended Practices (see the latest *NFPA Publications and Visual Aids Catalog* for availability of current editions of the following documents)

NFPA No. 6, Organization of Industrial Fire Loss Prevention.
NFPA No. 7, Management Control of Fire Emergencies.

Chapter 2

RESPONSIBILITIES OF THE FIRE RISK MANAGER

It is the responsibility of the fire risk manager to represent the facility manager in all areas of risk evaluation, fire prevention, and fire control. Although the fire risk manager may delegate some of these responsibilities to others, he is ultimately accountable to the facility manager for the success of the fire risk management program. In the absence of a fire risk manager, the facility manager must accept these responsibilities himself.

The scope of the fire risk manager's responsibility can be said to include the entire range of subject matter of this HANDBOOK. Some of his major responsibilities are:

1. Evaluation of loss possibilities.
2. Provision of systems and procedures for fire risk control.
3. Counsel with the facility engineering, maintenance, and planning departments.
4. Counsel with operating and service departments.
5. Establish standards and specifications for all items of equipment which are a part of the fire risk management program.
6. Interpretation of laws, codes, and NFPA and related standards applicable to fire risk management.
7. Organization of the private fire brigade and its training.
8. Scheduling periodic inspections of fire protection equipment.
9. Assist general management with public agency contact.
10. Assist general management with insurance contacts.
11. Assume administrative command of fire control operations.
12. Provide detailed reports of loss from fires and other emergencies.

A. Evaluation of Loss Possibilities

The fire risk manager should make an evaluation of the likelihood of fire occurring in any part of each piece of property, and the extent of its spread. He may receive advice from insurance and other outside advisers, but this advice does not take the place of his own evaluation of possibilities of fire and other disasters.

The general objective of loss evaluation should be to establish a proper basis for procedures to be followed by persons in individual properties or groups of properties. Following are some of the specific objectives:

1. To lessen loss potential by anticipating possibilities and instituting appropriate procedures.
2. To promote the fastest and most effective reaction of the personnel of all protective agencies, private and public, in dealing with an emergency.
3. To reestablish normal conditions with as little confusion and as promptly as possible.
4. To lessen the chances of the same type of emergency occurring more than once.
5. To secure better public relations by obvious preparation for emergencies.
6. To give people with responsibilities for dealing with fires and other disasters a sense of having taken all possible steps to meet likely situations.

Two specific figures are useful for the appraisal of the fire problem. The first figure is the largest percentage of the property value likely to be affected by fire, heat, smoke, and water damage. This figure shows the extreme possibilities of loss of physical plant facilities as, for example, with normal protection out of service. The second figure is the probable loss. This involves a figure smaller than the first, and takes into account the facilities for fire fighting and limiting the spread of fire.

Similar calculations can be made not only for fire potential but for the effects of other disaster factors. These are physical factors capable of appraisal. From them management can get a better basis for estimating the less tangible factors of loss of life, loss of profit, and other losses from interruption of use of the property.

Work Sheets for Loss Evaluation

Data for loss evaluation should be collected on work sheets in sufficiently abridged form so that it can be considered by top management. The operating departments (and particularly a loss-prevention staff agency) will present detailed information concerning loss; the corporation's insurance adviser will also provide loss information. Managers of each division of the company should be expected to summarize loss information possibility on work sheets for his own use, and to furnish the substance of this information to the fire risk manager. From such compilations the fire risk manager should, in turn, present top management officials with applicable loss possibility information on the operations of the corporation or enterprise as a whole.

The starting point for the flow of this management information on loss possibilities should be in the form of a work sheet prepared for each operating department, plant, or property. A suggested form for a work sheet would start with a list of buildings or operating units. Such a list would not attempt to show every building, and would simply ignore small buildings and small operating units that could hardly affect major operations of the enterprise. For each of these buildings or units, the following information should be shown:

Approximate Area: This figure can be expressed in thousands or millions of square feet. Its purpose is to show the maximum area that could be involved in a fire. This is usually the area between fire walls or within substantial open space separations.

Roof Construction: The type of roof is often the most important factor determining whether there is a serious building loss probability or not. The roof assembly should be described so that it can be determined whether the roof is substantially noncombustible or not. In unsprinklered buildings, a wooden roof deck or any metal roof deck with sufficient asphalt to provide adequate adhesion for wind resistance produces the likelihood of complete destruction of the building in the event of fire, a risk that management should, in most cases, consider unreasonable.

Occupancy: The loss possibilities are always very much more in buildings where automatic sprinklers are not provided for protection of combustible contents. Experience of the enterprise itself will determine the degree to which it has been found that sprinklers reduce the loss in any particular occupancy. Where there is no detailed experience on this point, it is often fair to assume that average losses in sprinklered buildings with adequate water supplies and all sprinklers in service will be one-tenth of those in unsprinklered buildings.

Approximate Value of Building and Contents: For this purpose it is not necessary to have exact figures, but simply figures close enough to show the magnitude of loss possibility.

Relative Importance of the Building: A final part of the work sheet is for notations about the relative importance and hazards of occupancy of the building in question. These should report the processes to which the building is devoted, or the materials stored in the building, particularly if these present any special problems which management must keep in mind (such as the relation of the operations in the building to other operations). Notes can be made under this heading about salvage and replacement problems in the event of loss of the building and other significant features of the building or unit under consideration.

B.   Provision of Systems and Procedures for Fire Risk Control

It is understood that the fire risk manager will not have the responsibility for all procedures which affect risk management. He must, therefore, design his procedures so that they can be correlated with other management procedures. Typical systems and procedures would be an engineering design review, a work order review, a hot work permit procedure, or notification of equipment impairment.

C.   Counsel with the Facility's Engineering, Maintenance, and Planning Departments

The facility manager should require that the property's engineering, maintenance, and planning departments work closely with the fire risk manager. He should specify that as soon as a new process layout is contemplated, the engineering and planning departments should consult with the fire risk manager. The managers of these departments should be required to know the fire risk control standards that have been adopted, and should apply them in changes and in all new designs of property.

Maintenance department management should be required to integrate facility maintenance procedures with fire risk procedures in order to prevent placing the property in jeopardy by shutting off services which affect fire control equipment. Examples would be the shutting of control valves to protective water supplies, or the shutting off of electric power to fire pumps. A high priority should be established for maintenance affecting fire control equipment, and advance notice of any impairment should be given to the fire risk manager so that he can provide alternate protection.

Valve Supervision

It is essential that all valves controlling water supplies to automatic sprinklers, hydrants, standpipes, and other fire protection equipment be maintained in a wide open position. It is the responsibility of the fire risk manager to know the condition of these valves at all times, and a system should be set up so that he is notified whenever a valve is closed. Valves are maintained in an open position by one of three methods: sealing, locking, or protective signalling systems.

Sealing: Valves are sealed by placing a wire through a movable part of the valve (wheel or shaft nut) and a fixed part of the valve, and securing the two ends of the wire with a seal (see Fig. 10-2A). Seals do not prevent the operation of a valve, but tend to discourage tampering by unauthorized persons. A broken seal is an indication that the valve has been operated or tampered with, and thus should be checked to be certain that it is open, and then resealed. (Sealing and tagging systems are described in NFPA No. 26, Supervision and Care of Valves Controlling Water Supplies for Fire Protection.)

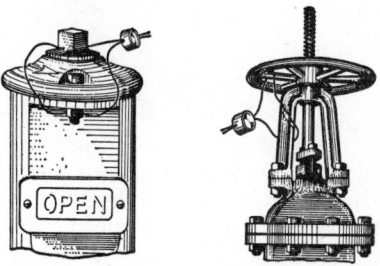

Fig. 10-2A.   Methods of sealing valves.

Locking: Valves are locked in the wide open position by padlocks, with or without chains or cables, so that they cannot be operated (see Fig. 10-2B). These sturdy securing devices are resistant to breakage, except by heavy bolt cutters. The distribution of keys is restricted to only those persons directly responsible for the fire protection system.

Fig. 10-2B.   Methods of locking valves.

Protective Signaling Systems: Valves are equipped with a device arranged to electrically transmit a signal whenever the valve is operated. These signals are transmitted through circuits to a location on the premises under the control of the plant proprietary system (see NFPA No. 72D, Installation, Maintenance, and Use of Proprietary Protective Signaling Systems), or to a location remote from the premises under the control of the local fire department or an organization whose function is to furnish such service (remote or central station system (see NFPA No. 71, Installation, Maintenance, and Use of Central Station Protective Signaling Systems and NFPA No. 72C, Installation, Maintenance, and Use of Remote Station Protective Signaling Systems).

Valve Operation: A procedure should be established so that the fire risk manager receives notification of the pro-

Fig. 10-2C. Shut valve with tag attached.

posed closing of any valve which affects the fire protection as far in advance of such closing as possible, so that adequate precautionary measures may be planned. If an emergency valve closing is necessary, the fire risk manager should be notified immediately. This information should be transmitted to the proper authority. A red tag should be attached to the valve to indicate that it is shut (see Fig. 10-2C), and a card or other device should be conspicuously displayed as a reminder to the person responsible for the fire protection equipment that the valve is closed. When the valve is opened, the red tag is removed and the fire risk manager should notify the proper authority that normal protection has been restored.

Work by Outside Contractors: When work on the property is to be done by an outside contractor, the facility manager should require the engineering department to contact the fire risk manager to determine exactly what special requirements must be met by the contractor. These requirements will vary with the job, and ordinarily they would include such items as: possible isolation of the contractor's work site; notifying the contractor of special hazards to be encountered in the operations (processes or stored materials at or near the job site); the possible hazard his work might present to the plant equipment, property, and personnel; smoking requirements; use of hot work permits; control of contractor's employees and vehicles on the property; movement and storage of construction equipment and materials as far as fire loss prevention is concerned; and waste disposal by the contractor.

D. Counsel with Operating and Service Departments on Matters of Fire Risk Management

The facility manager should require general and direct managers of operations and service departments to ensure that their equipment and structures are maintained in a condition which will help to minimize fire loss. It should also be the responsibility of these managers to make sure that the necessary elements of risk management are integrated with operating instructions on all standard or repetitive operations, and that through training and follow-up these instructions are observed.

The fire risk manager must provide operations managers with adequate information to assure that the training being presented is consistent with fire risk management policies and procedures. Other responsibilities of the operating managers with which the fire risk manager should assist are:

1. Selecting certain people from his department for assignment to duties on fire squads (first-aid fire fighters) and providing opportunities for all able-bodied people in the building to practice the use of the portable fire extinguishers provided. (It is often convenient to plan such practice when extinguishers are recharged in annual tests.)

2. Providing instruction to employees or other people assigned to special tasks for day-to-day fire loss prevention and for emergencies (what to do with processes and machinery that operate continuously; the procedure for safeguarding important records, stock, or finished products).

3. Preventing overcrowding of stock or workers. (Aisle space sufficient to permit orderly evacuation of people in the building, and easy access for fire fighting should be maintained on all floors and rooms in his department.)

4. Working out details of a plan for evacuation of people in his department (see Chapter 4 of this Section). He should appoint wardens for each floor and room, and other personnel (such as monitors, exit guards, and room searchers) to assure success of exit plans.

5. Informing new employees and new occupants of departmental practices which have been adopted for fire risk management, and keeping all of them constantly aware of these practices. (Not only must rules be posted, but supervisory employees must be held responsible for informing those under their direction. The department head should also make frequent checks to see that specific practices are actually being observed.)

6. Seeing that practice drills, including fire exit drills, are held under conditions simulating actual fire emergencies. (Drills should be arranged as frequently as called for in plant rules and should be executed properly.)

The fire risk manager and the direct manager of each area share responsibility for assuring that each employee knows what to do when a fire alarm sounds. Every occupant, whether man or woman, should know something about the equipment provided for fire protection, as well as what he can do to help prevent fires. Specifically, this knowledge includes:

1. His place in any plan established for evacuation of the building in case of emergency. Such plans are essential where the safety of occupants depends on prompt and orderly evacuation in case of fire or other emergency; where the number of people in one room or area would crowd aisles, doors, or stairways; or where there are materials or processes which would make a quick-spreading fire probable.

2. How to use the portable fire extinguishers and hand hose provided. By prefire planning, each occupant should know whether he is to help fight the fire or get out.

3. Some idea of the use of other protective equipment. Every occupant should know that water to extinguish fires comes from the sprinkler system, and that stock must not be piled so close to sprinkler lines that it prevents good distribution of water from sprinklers on a fire in the piled material. He should also know that fire doors must be kept operative, and not obstructed by stock piles, tools, or other objects.

4. How to give a fire alarm and how to operate private fire alarm boxes and street boxes in the public alarm system.

5. Where smoking in the property is permitted, and where, for safety reasons, it is prohibited.

6. The housekeeping routine. Disposal of wiping rags and waste, handling of packing materials, and other measures for orderliness and cleanliness throughout the property.

7. Hazards of any special process in which, as an employee, he may be engaged.

The fire risk manager should work closely with general management to see that special safeguards against fire are observed whenever a plant is vacated or temporarily idle. The term "vacated plant" refers to a property where normal operations will not be resumed. Most or all of the production equipment is removed from a vacated plant. An "idle plant" is a property where normal operations have been temporarily interrupted. Both protective equipment and production facilities are maintained serviceable.

The special safeguards against fire for vacated and idle plants should include:

1. Shutting down hazardous processes and leaving the plant clean.

2. Provision for necessary plant maintenance and guard forces.

3. Periodic inspections of fire protection equipment to assure that all of it is in proper operating condition.

4. Notification to the chief of the public fire department that there is a shutdown.

5. Review of the prearranged plan for receiving and directing the public fire department and its alteration to meet any new conditions that may be imposed by the shutdown.

Establish Standards and Specifications for Equipment

Even though the procurement of equipment may be the responsibility of others, the fire risk manager should establish standards and specifications which will assure that such equipment complies with the requirements of recognized testing laboratories, and is acceptable to the authority having jurisdiction.

Interpretation of Applicable Laws, Codes, and NFPA and Related Standards

The facility manager should make clear that the fire risk manager has the responsibility for providing interpretations of laws, codes, and standards applicable to fire risk management, and should make available to him the legal guidance required to fulfill his assignment.

Organization of the Private Fire Brigade and Its Training

This subject will be treated in detail in Chapter 3, "Private or Industrial Fire Brigades," of this Section.

E.   Scheduling Periodic Inspections of Fire Protective Equipment

Although some of the equipment inspection and testing may be assigned to others (maintenance or security departments), the fire risk manager should establish inspection schedules, the type of inspections to be made, and the routing of inspection reports. It is also the responsibility of the fire risk manager to see that these inspections are properly carried out.

Only general advice can be given as to the frequency with which various details of the fire protection equipment of a particular property should be inspected. Figures 10-2D and 10-2E show a sample inspection form designed for general industrial use. These can be adapted for use in other types of properties. Inspections should also be made to assure good housekeeping, and the proper attention to special hazards (see NFPA Inspection Manual[1]).

The fire risk manager, or members of his staff, should make personal inspections of the equipment on the following list:

1. Every control valve on the piping supplying water for fire protection, particularly those to automatic sprinkler systems (Sec. 14, Chap. 6). Valve inspections should be recorded showing whether each valve is open or closed, sealed or unsealed, and including notes about conditions to be remedied.

2. Hydrants (Sec. 11, Chap. 2).

3. Hose house and fire station equipment (Sec. 15, Chap. 1, Sec. 11, Chap. 2, and Chap. 3 of this Section).

4. Fire pumps (Sec. 11, Chap. 4).

5. Water tanks for fire protection (Sec. 11, Chap. 3).

6. Special types of protection.

In addition to these general items of protective equipment, a list of items to be checked should be made building by building, floor by floor, department by department. On these items, the fire risk manager may be able to require department or tenant area managers to make necessary day-to-day inspections and reports. A fire risk management staff man should make periodic supplementary inspections of these items. For each building and department the list should include such things as the following:

1. Fire extinguishers (Sec. 16, Chap. 2 and 3).

2. Small hose (Sec. 15, Chap. 1).

3. Fire doors (Sec. 6, Chap. 11).

4. Special hazards, special types of protection, special routines for fire safety.

Various inspections require a daily, weekly, or other periodic check. A convenient routine is to provide a card for each item to be checked. This is kept at the location to be examined, and inspectors are required to make the necessary periodic observations and record them on the card. The card entries should show date, time, and by whom the observation was made.

It is not enough for management to specify periodic checks. The men assigned to the checks must be made to feel that if the matter is important enough to be recorded, it must be done correctly; but if not, it does not need to be done at all. The fire risk manager should review these records and periodically summarize them for the facility manager.

F.   Assist General Management with Public Agency Contacts and Public Relations

During his daily operations, the fire risk manager will come into contact with representatives of those public agencies who have the responsibility for the fire protection and law enforcement of the community. He should not, however, depend on these contacts to firmly establish the company's relationship with them. As early as possible in the facility's organization, the fire risk manager should make official visits to the headquarters of these public agencies. Arrangements should be made for their personnel to visit his facility, and its operation should be explained in detail. If there are areas or processes which may present a life hazard or special problem to emergency control personnel, these should be pointed out and plans for their protection discussed. In order to establish a mutual understanding of operating practices, public agency representatives should be introduced to appropriate members of the facility's general management.

Generally, public announcements regarding an emergency are made by the facility manager or a member of his public relations staff. It is, therefore, imperative that the fire risk manager report the following information to them as early as possible:

| SAMPLE ONLY | NO ONE BLANK CAN BE DESIGNED TO FIT ALL CONDITIONS. USE THIS BLANK AS A BASIC GUIDE IN DEVELOPING YOUR OWN FORM. ITEMS THAT DO NOT APPLY CAN BE OMITTED. OTHER ITEMS CAN BE EXPANDED AS DESIRED, AND NEW ITEMS CAN BE ADDED. FOR ASSISTANCE, CONSULT THE NEXT FACTORY MUTUAL ENGINEER WHO VISITS YOUR PROPERTY. |

FIRE-PREVENTION INSPECTION

| INSTRUCTIONS TO INSPECTOR: | FILL OUT FORM WHILE MAKING INSPECTION. SEND COMPLETED FORM TO YOUR SUPERVISOR FOR NECESSARY ACTION. REPORT SHOULD BE HELD FOR REVIEW BY THE NEXT FACTORY MUTUAL ENGINEER. |

PLANT	LOCATION	DATE

VALVE INSPECTIONS
INSPECT LOCKED VALVES AT LEAST MONTHLY.   INSPECT ALL UNLOCKED VALVES AT LEAST WEEKLY.

ALL INSIDE AND OUTSIDE VALVES CONTROLLING SPRINKLERS OR FIRE PROTECTION WATER SUPPLIES ARE LISTED BELOW. CHECK CONDITION OF VALVE AS FOUND. PHYSICALLY "TRY" GATE VALVES INCLUDING NONINDICATING AND INDICATOR POST GATE VALVES. DO NOT REPORT A VALVE OPEN UNLESS YOU PERSONALLY HAVE TRIED IT. FM APPROVED PIVA'S (POST-INDICATOR-VALVE ASSEMBLIES), IBV'S (INDICATING BUTTERFLY VALVES) AND STANDARD OUTSIDE SCREW & YOKE VALVES DO NOT HAVE TO BE TRIED BUT SHOULD BE VISUALLY CHECKED AT CLOSE RANGE.

NO.	VALVE LOCATION	AREA CONTROLLED	OPEN	SHUT	LOCKED	SEALED
1						
2						
3						
4						
5						
6						
7						
8						
9						
10						
11						
12						
13						
14						
15						
16						
17						
18						
19						
20						

THE FACTORY MUTUAL VALVE SHUT TAG SYSTEM IS USED TO GUARD AGAINST DELAYED REOPENING OF VALVES. FACTORY MUTUAL RED TAGS SHOULD BE USED EVERY TIME A SPRINKLER CONTROL VALVE IS CLOSED. WHEN THE VALVE IS REOPENED THE 2 INCH DRAIN SHOULD BE FLOWED WIDE OPEN TO BE SURE THERE IS NO OBSTRUCTION IN THE PIPING. THE VALVE SHOULD THEN BE RELOCKED.

WERE ANY VALVES OPERATED SINCE THE LAST INSPECTION	Yes ☐ No ☐
WERE FACTORY MUTUAL RED TAGS USED	Yes ☐ No ☐
WAS THE VALVE REOPENED FULLY AND A FULL FLOW 2 IN. DRAIN TEST MADE BEFORE THE VALVE WAS RELOCKED OR RESEALED	Yes ☐ No ☐

COMMENTS:

Fig. 10-2D.   Front of Factory Mutual inspection blank.

INSPECT THESE ITEMS AT LEAST WEEKLY

SPRINKLERS

Auto-Matic Sprinklers	ANY HEADS DISCONNECTED OR NEEDED Yes ☐ No ☐		OBSTRUCTED BY HIGH PILING	Yes ☐ No ☐
	HEAT ADEQUATE TO PREVENT FREEZING (NOTE BROKEN WINDOWS, ETC.) Yes ☐ No ☐	Water Pressure	LB. AT YARD LEVEL	

COMMENTS

DRY PIPE VALVES

	No. 1	No. 2	No. 3	No. 4	No. 5	No. 6	No. 7	No. 8
VALVE ROOM PROPERLY HEATED	Yes ☐ No ☐	Yes ☐ No ☐	Yes ☐ No ☐	Yes ☐ No ☐	Yes ☐ No ☐	Yes ☐ No ☐	Yes ☐ No ☐	Yes ☐ No ☐
AIR PRESSURE	Lbs.	Lbs.	Lbs.	Lbs.	Lbs.	Lbs.	Lbs.	Lbs.

WATER SUPPLIES

FIRE PUMP	TURNED OVER Yes ☐ No ☐		GOOD CONDITION Yes ☐ No ☐	
	AUTO. CONTROL TESTED Yes ☐ No ☐		FUEL TANK FULL Yes ☐ No ☐	
	PUMP ROOM PROPERLY HEATED AND VENTILATED Yes ☐ No ☐		PRIMING TANK FULL Yes ☐ No ☐	
TANK OR RESERVOIR	FULL Yes ☐ No ☐		HEATING SYSTEM IN USE Yes ☐ No ☐	
	TEMPERATURE AT COLD WATER RETURN (SHOULD BE 42°F MINIMUM)		CIRCULATION GOOD Yes ☐ No ☐	

MFL WALL FIRE DOORS	CONDITION	OBSTRUCTED Yes ☐ No ☐	BLOCKED OPEN Yes ☐ No ☐

OTHER ITEMS

INSPECT THESE ITEMS AT LEAST MONTHLY

MANUAL PROT

EXTIN-GUISHERS	CHARGED Yes ☐ No ☐	ANY MISSING	ACCESSIBLE Yes ☐ No ☐	ATTENTION NEEDED (Give Location)
INSIDE HOSE	IN GOOD CONDITION Yes ☐ No ☐		ACCESSIBLE	Yes ☐ No ☐
YARD HYDRANTS & HOSE	CONDITION NO. 1 NO. 2		NO. 3 NO. 4	NO. 5 NO. 6
	HYDRANTS DRAINED Yes ☐ No ☐		REMARKS:	

OCCUPANCY

GENERAL ORDER & NEATNESS	GOOD Yes ☐ No ☐		COMBUSTIBLE WASTE REMOVED ON SCHEDULE (PROMPTLY) Yes ☐ No ☐ COMBUSTIBLE DUST, LINT OR OIL DEPOSITS ON CEILINGS, BEAMS OR MACHINES Yes ☐ No ☐ DESCRIBE AREAS NEEDING ATTENTION INCLUDING YARD:	
ELECT. EQUIP.	DEFECTS NOTED Yes ☐ No ☐ SAFETY CANS USED Yes ☐ No ☐			
FLAM. LIQUIDS	EXCESSIVE IN MFG AREAS Yes ☐ No ☐		DRAINAGE OBSTRUCTED Yes ☐ No ☐ VENT FANS ON Yes ☐ No ☐	
SMOKING REGULA-TIONS	LOCATIONS WHERE VIOLATIONS NOTED			
CUTTING & WELDING	PERMITS ISSUED FOR ALL C&W OPERATIONS Yes ☐ No ☐		LISTED PRECAUTIONS TAKEN Yes ☐ No ☐	
STORAGE	WELL ARRANGED Yes ☐ No ☐		AISLES CLEAR Yes ☐ No ☐	
	ADEQUATE SPACE BELOW SPRINKLERS Yes ☐ No ☐		CLEAR OF LAMPS, HEATERS Yes ☐ No ☐	

DOORS AT CUT-OFF WALLS	CONDITION	OBSTRUCTED Yes ☐ No ☐	BLOCKED OPEN Yes ☐ No ☐

Sprinkler Alarms	TESTED Yes ☐ No ☐	OPERATION SATISFACTORY (IF "NO" - COMMENT BELOW) Yes ☐ No ☐

OTHER ITEMS

INSPECTED BY:		DATE
REVIEWED BY:	TITLE	DATE

Fig. 10-2E. Back of Factory Mutual inspection blank.

1. The probable cause of the emergency.
2. An extent of damage estimate.
3. The number of employees involved.
4. Expected duration of the condition.

This report should be as complete and factual as possible. The facility manager can then decide how much information should be made public.

A factual report issued by the manager informs the public and dispels rumors.

G.   Assist General Management with Insurance Contacts

If top management decides that a part of the company's risk is to be shared with insurance carriers, this makes available to the fire risk manager a team of engineers to call upon for advice and guidance. While an industry should not expect the insurance company to carry the entire responsibility for the fire risk management program, generally both the broker and the carrier have on their staffs engineers who are qualified to give advice on any phase of industrial construction or operation.

The property insurance manager is usually a member of the general management group. To ensure the best results from the insurance program, the property insurance manager and the fire risk manager should closely coordinate their work. In order to provide adequate coverage at acceptable rates, the insurance carrier will need to make a comprehensive risk evaluation of the facility and maintain a program of periodic inspection. The fire risk manager and his staff can furnish much of the information required for risk evaluation, and should also furnish escort for facility inspection by insurance representatives.

Because of his own inspection program, the fire risk manager is aware of what equipment requires operation for test by maintenance personnel to avoid controversy with the facility's union. By scheduling such testing in advance, he can minimize cost and loss of time. His participation in the insurance program will also give the insurance representative an opportunity to evaluate the risk management program. If it is an effective program, it can be a strong influence in securing more favorable rates. To expedite the insurance manager's handling of claims, the insurance manager should be supplied with copies of the risk manager's emergency control and fire loss reports to the facility manager.

H.   Assume Administrative Command of Fire Control Operations

Generally, the local fire chief has command of all fire control activities in his community. However, if the fire risk manager has established good liaison with local fire officials, the direction of fire control within the facility can be a joint effort.

Most fire officials realize that they cannot keep themselves as current with property and process changes as someone who is spending full time on the premises. They welcome the assistance of the risk manager in evaluating the fire and planning a method of attack. The risk manager should be constantly available to the official in charge of the fire control effort in order to ensure immediate and qualified response to questions regarding occupancy or construction of areas adjacent to the fire zone which may be threatened by fire spread.

Prompt action by the fire risk manager and his organization can make the difference between a minor incident and a total loss. The fire risk manager should assume full command until the local fire department arrives and follows their prearranged plan.

I.   Provide Detailed Reports of Loss from Fires or Other Emergencies

The fire risk manager should keep the facility manager advised during the course of an emergency so he can make administrative decisions and handle public announcements. Information should be compiled by on-the-spot assessments and should be as complete as conditions will permit. Unless he has been authorized to do so he should not make statements to members of the press or other media.

When the emergency is over, the fire risk manager should, as quickly as possible, prepare a preliminary damage report. This report should contain:

1. Cause, if known.
2. Estimated damage.
3. Major injuries or death of employees.
4. Estimated time required for restoration of operations.

The time required for the preparation of a final report will depend on how soon detailed information can be supplied by the responsible departments. This report should amplify or correct the estimates submitted in the preliminary report. It should also contain recommendations to prevent recurrence of the incident. A limited number of photographs which clarify or emphasize sections of the report may be included with the report. Copies of the report should be given confidential status, and distribution should be limited to those persons designated by top management as having a "need-to-know."

Bibliography

References Cited

[1] Bond, Horatio, ed., *NFPA Inspection Manual*, 3rd ed., NFPA, Boston, 1970.

NFPA Codes, Standards, and Recommended Practices (see the latest *NFPA Publications and Visual Aids Catalog* for availability of current editions of the following documents)

NFPA No. 26, Standard for the Supervision and Care of Valves Controlling Water Supplies for Fire Protection.

NFPA No. 71, Standard for the Installation, Maintenance, and Use of Central Station Protective Signaling Systems.

NFPA No. 72C, Standard for the Installation, Maintenance, and Use of Remote Station Protective Signaling Systems.

NFPA No. 72D, Standard for the Installation, Maintenance, and Use of Proprietary Protective Signaling Systems.

Chapter 3

PRIVATE OR INDUSTRIAL FIRE BRIGADES

For many industrial facilities, fire protection is chiefly a matter of calling the public fire department of the community in which the facility is located. However, public fire departments are usually designed for the protection of their surrounding communities rather than for providing protection for institutions or industrial plants, especially for large facilities. Thus, many industrial facilities find it necessary to establish private or industrial fire brigades.

A. Facility Relations with the Public Fire Department

For those facilities dependent on public fire department protection, the facility manager (or the fire risk manager) must work out with the public fire department chief an arrangement whereby the public fire department's work will be most effective. Often, this is merely a matter of the facility having the means to promptly notify the public fire department of a fire or other emergency, and seeing to it that the public fire department's access to the property is promptly possible. No matter how "self-sufficient" a fire risk manager might feel his property is, he should never ignore the potential of the public fire department and, unless there has been prior agreement as to their respective responsibilities, the chief of the public fire department, rather than the manager himself, might be considered the one responsible for dealing with a fire at the facility. This is because of a principle of common law in which very broad authority is given a fire department in case of fire.

If the property houses operations and processes that are fairly straightforward, no serious complications are likely to develop when an outside agency like the fire department is brought into the property to assist in controlling a fire.

In some industrial plants the processes are very complicated. The plant may have hazards involving certain materials, or certain processes, that involve factors an outside agency could not be expected to know about; or the process layout may be such that the only person or persons who know what the situation is at a given time are the operating superintendent and his staff people. A mercantile occupancy may have especially damageable merchandise; an institution such as a mental hospital or jail may have custodial problems. In cases like these, fire fighting must have management guidance. Fire risk management and the fire department should be in agreement as to the details each will handle in an emergency.

The fire risk manager should make sure that the chief of the public fire department understands the situation, and that he will let the directions of the operating manager on duty guide the actions of members of the public fire department during the fire or emergency. No competent fire officer would try to deal with a situation within a property which the plant manager or shift superintendent could better handle. Concerning such situations, the fire risk manager should make sure that an understanding with the public fire department is clear and firm.

In such a property, the fire risk manager or shift fire official is the only person to whom fire fighting direction should be assigned. Only these people would know exactly the possibilities of controlling a fire in which the fire control procedure might not be the usual business of throwing water, but might involve the operation of valves and equipment to shut down a particular process or to transfer materials from one container to another or from one section of the property to another.

Public Fire Department Mobilization

Some properties are located where not one, but several, public fire departments may respond in case of fire. In some cases, these departments may respond because of an explosion, smoke, or flames that are visible for long distances. A management problem is to make sure that such fire department responses will not be haphazard, but will follow a plan the public fire departments have agreed upon in advance.

If the fire departments of several municipalities are working together at one fire, it is important that the respective officers have a clear understanding of their relationships with each other; that is, they should have formal, mutual aid agreements.

The fire risk manager should deal with the chief of the public fire department having jurisdiction in the community where the property is located, and through him with the other public fire departments. If there is no public fire department in the area where the property is located, the management usually has no ready way to deal with haphazard public fire department response to a plant emergency. The problem is complicated if the plant site extends over more than one political subdivision.

If the facility is located outside the limits of the fire department's jurisdiction, an understanding must be reached regarding response procedure. Following are some questions that need to be considered:

1. Are there existing laws or ordinances which give the local fire chief the authority to enter into agreements for extra-territorial protection?

2. What manpower and equipment is available for commitment to service outside the legal jurisdiction?

3. What is the facility's legal liability for fire department personnel and for the personnel of other fire departments responding as part of their mutual aid agreements?

Every facility manager should encourage his community and neighboring communities to have the best possible fire protection they can afford. Small-unit fire departments are both expensive and inefficient as compared to fire departments organized in a large fire district. The facility that is located in a community with a relatively small fire department, or one with only a few companies and a few officers, does not have as much to depend upon as it would if the plant were dealing with a large outside fire department with many companies and broadly experienced officers who have good staff technical services to assist them.

Strong, well-staffed fire department organizations could be set up in county areas by encouraging the establishment of large fire districts. A good fire department service can be obtained for many small cities by simply combining adjoining cities into a large enough fire district to support a first-rate, large fire department with adequate officers and technical staff services, standard equipment, and practices.

A private fire brigade's function is to provide a force of

fire fighters, specifically for the needs of the property, whose members are better acquainted with the property and its problems than are the members of any outside public fire department.

B. Private Fire Brigade Organization

Every property should provide an organization to deal with fires and related emergencies when they occur. The fire risk manager should evaluate the potential magnitude of a fire emergency within the property, or of an exposure fire and the availability of fire fighting assistance from a public fire department, to determine the nature of the organization to be provided. (See NFPA No. 7, Management Control of Fire Emergencies.)

In its most simple form, this organization would consist of the manager of the facility assisted by selected personnel. In properties where more persons are available, they should be organized as a team, or teams, to function as a private fire brigade. The availability of fire fighting assistance from a public fire department or a private fire department may affect the nature of the private fire brigade organization. These do not necessarily take the place of a private fire brigade in parts of a large property. Individual fire brigades may respond to alarms in all areas of a property, or each geographical or functional area may have a separate fire brigade organization according to the needs of the property. The organization should be such that a fire brigade is on duty on each working shift and at periods when the plant is shut down or idle.

The equipment that must be put into service at a fire will determine the number of men required for each operating unit or company into which the brigade is organized, and the total number of men needed in the brigade. Operating units or companies may be composed of two or more men to operate a specific item of equipment, or of a larger group to perform more complicated operations. Each company should have a leader and each brigade should have a chief. Where the fire risk manager does not himself perform them, he should assign a fire risk management staff man to perform the duties directly associated with the fire risk manager's responsibility for loss prevention. From the duties for each, note that the functions of the fire risk manager and the duties of the chief of a fire brigade are not the same.

The fire risk management staff man, acting for the fire risk manager, or the fire risk manager himself, should: (1) provide equipment and supplies for the fire brigade or brigades, (2) establish the size and organizational structure of the fire brigades, (3) see that the brigades are suitably staffed and trained, and (4) select the fire brigade chiefs. Fire brigade chiefs should have administrative and supervisory abilities. A fire brigade chief should have duties including the following:

1. Periodic evaluation of the equipment provided for fire fighting. He should be responsible for setting in motion necessary procedures for replacing missing equipment or correction of inoperative equipment. He should also call to the immediate attention of the fire risk manager, or his fire risk management staff man, any situation likely to reduce the effectiveness of fire fighting operations.

2. Provision of plans of action to meet possible fire situations in the plant subject to approval of the facility manager and the fire risk manager.

3. Periodic review of the brigade roster and preparation of recommendations that additional members be selected, appointed, and made available to keep up the roster.

4. Preparing the plan for training members of the brigade and other employees.

Enough assistant chiefs should be appointed to cover the chief's position around the clock. Their rank, one to another and to the chiefs, should be established to provide for succession in the event of absence.

Members of the fire brigade should consist of persons who have met qualifications appropriate for fire brigade work at the particular property. Its membership should consist of the necessary personnel for fire fighting teams and certain operating and maintenance personnel.

To qualify as a member of the fire brigade, individuals should be available to answer alarms and to attend required training sessions. A prearranged schedule for availability should be established to prevent conflict of duties and to cover absences such as regular off-duty periods, vacations, and sickness.

Minimum physical requirements should be established. A periodic physical examination is desirable. Employees with heart, lung, back, sight, and hearing ailments or deficiencies should not be accepted. Members of the brigade should have appropriate identification (such as a card or badge) in order to gain assistance in reaching the plant in an emergency, and for identification by plant guards for movement within the plant or parts of it where fire brigade duties have to be performed.

Mutual Aid

If the facility is located in an area where there are other industries, the fire risk manager may wish to enter into a mutual aid agreement with them. While such agreements are usually beneficial to both facilities, some precautions should be observed.

1. Clearance should be received from the company's legal counsel before a written agreement is signed.

2. Only such manpower and equipment should be committed to the program as can be released without jeopardy to the safety of the facility.

3. Assurance should be obtained from the insurance manager that all liability is adequately covered.

4. All fire brigade members should be aware of their obligations under the agreement.

5. Fire brigade members should be trained in the handling of special hazards to be found at the other facilities involved in the agreement.

6. A list of all manpower and equipment should be maintained at a central location to minimize the number of calls required to request assistance.

7. The local fire department should be aware of the agreement and, if possible, should be a part of the organization. Some fire departments are willing to serve as the record center. All assistance calls are handled by their communications system.

8. Activation of the mutual aid program should not delay an alarm report to the public fire department.

Training

A schedule of training should be established for members of the brigade. Members should be required to complete a specified program of instruction as a condition to membership in the brigade. Training sessions should be held at least monthly.

Members of the brigade should be instructed in the handling of any and all of the fire and rescue apparatus provided. The training program should be adapted to the purpose of the particular brigade. It should include fire fighting with portable fire extinguishers, the use of hose lines, ventilation of buildings, salvage operations, and performing related rescue operations. The training program should keep up with problems presented by new fire hazards in the property and new fire extinguishing equipment and methods provided for its protection.

Assistance in setting up and training the fire brigade can be obtained from outside agencies. Among these are the municipal fire departments, state fire schools, state educational extension services, state fire marshals' departments, state insurance inspection bureaus, colleges, and any other agency where fire service training is given. Members of the brigade should be afforded opportunities to improve their knowledge of fire fighting and fire prevention through attendance at meetings and special training classes, where available.

Where the number of men participating in the fire brigade training program warrants such arrangement, a special space or room in the property for fire brigade use should be available for that part of a training program requiring lectures or classroom instruction. Training aids such as books, literature, and films should be kept at such a location. The provision of a space or room for members of the brigade is one way in which membership in the brigade can be made attractive.

Practice drills should be held to check the ability of members to conduct the operations they are expected to perform with the fire equipment provided. Drills should occasionally be held under adverse weather conditions to work out special procedures needed under these conditions. During drills, equipment should be operated whenever possible. For example, portable extinguishers should be discharged, respiratory protective equipment should be operated, and water should be turned into hose lines. Under the control of the chief and leaders of companies, practice drills should always be carried out at a moderate pace with emphasis on effectiveness rather than speed. This should assure proper technique and safe operation, as required, at a fire.

At the conclusion of practice drill, equipment should be promptly placed in readiness to respond to a fire call.

Introduction to Fire Protection,[1] an NFPA training course, furnishes guidelines for training both industrial fire brigade members and their command officers. NFPA No. 27, Private Fire Brigades[2] and the NFPA *Industrial Fire Brigade Training Manual*[3] provide additional information on the organization and training of industrial fire brigades.

Fire Methods

When any fire, abnormal heat, or smoke is detected, employees should be instructed to give an immediate alarm. Under all ordinary circumstances, where there is an organized public fire department, it should be notified without delay. There are situations when a property that is maintaining a fully equipped professional fire force is located in a municipality having a part-time or volunteer department. In such situations, the town department may be considered as a reserve or backup for the private department. Normally, the first private fire brigade officers to arrive should ascertain whether a public alarm has been turned in; supervise operations pending the arrival of public fire officials; put men to work on the fire; and direct previously selected men to attend to the salvage, which would include covering stock and preventing water damage.

In sprinklered properties officers of any private fire brigade should assign personnel to the sprinkler valves to make sure that they are open and operating, and to see that the fire pump has been started. Caution: Too many hose streams should not be used, as this may deplete the water supply and the pressure for sprinkler systems. In sprinklered buildings, streams from 1½-in. hose will prove adequate and advantageous.

The fire chief or person in direct charge of the system should be the only person to authorize the closing of any sprinkler valve (or other valve) that controls water for fire apparatus.

Procedure After Fire

After a fire, all fused sprinklers should be replaced at once with the proper types of sprinklers, and protection restored as quickly as possible. Spare sprinklers should be readily available for this purpose.

Immediately after any fire, all water main and sprinkler valves should be carefully examined to see that no valves have been accidentally closed. Covering stock and other salvaging operations should be continued.

Fire extinguishers that have been used in fighting a fire should not be rehung on brackets, but should be placed on the floor in order to direct attention to the fact that they need recharging. Patrolmen should cover the property for quite some time after a fire has been extinguished to make sure that it does not rekindle.

The fire risk manager should conduct an investigation as to the cause of the fire, and should take steps to prevent similar fires in the future. A written report should be made of each fire (see Chapter 2 of this Section).

C.   Private or Industrial Fire Brigade Equipment

In properties that have well-planned fire protection, principal dependence for fire control is placed on automatic sprinkler systems and on extinguishing systems for special hazards. The private or industrial fire department's operations usually include spreading waterproof covers, seeing that floor drains are open, and restoring protection after the fire. Hose streams may have to be used on fires in stock stored in yards in some properties, or to protect exposure from fires in neighboring buildings.

Certain duties in the periodic inspection and maintenance of plant fire equipment, both fixed and portable, may be assigned to members of the fire brigade. However, the fire risk manager or his fire loss prevention manager should establish the necessary schedules for such work, should assign those duties to specific personnel, should see that these inspections and maintenance operations are carried out, and should see that reports are filed with management. In any plant, employees in each work area (not members of the fire brigade) should be encouraged to be constantly on the alert for conditions which would adversely affect fire protection, such as missing fire extinguishers, blocked fire doors, etc., to complement the periodic overall plant inspections made by members of the fire brigade.

Storage space for the fire brigade equipment should be provided so that it can be promptly obtained for use and properly maintained. This may also be a convenient location at which to provide for reference a posted plan of water mains serving the property with all section controls, sprinkler valves, hydrants, and fire alarm boxes shown and numbered.

The fire risk manager or the fire brigade chief should maintain a list of equipment available in the property which might be useful in fire brigade work, but which is not in the custody of the fire brigade. This includes such items as portable lighting equipment, power saws and other cutting tools, portable pumps, air-moving equipment, electric motors for replacement purposes, tarpaulins, and roofing material. The list should show where each item of equipment is usually located, and the name of the department, or person, in whose custody it may be found. An up-to-date list of equipment, and service agencies from which equipment or assistance may be needed, together with phone numbers, should be kept.

Equipment Check List

The brigade should be provided with a variety of equipment and tools in such numbers as to enable it to perform the service for which it was organized. This equipment should include items additional to the fixed or portable equipment provided in buildings and yards. Following is a list of the principal categories of equipment which should be considered by the fire risk manager and the fire brigade chief when choosing equipment for the brigade.

1. Portable fire extinguishers.

2. Hose and hose accessories, including hydrant wrenches, hydrant valves, rope tools or hose straps, rope, combination shutoff nozzles, gated wyes, double female hose couplings, and hose spanners.

3. Portable lighting equipment, including portable electric generators, hand lanterns, and a supply of extra batteries.

4. Forcible entry tools, including axes, saws, plaster hooks and pike poles, claw tools, door openers, and crowbars.

5. Ladders, consisting of a selection of sufficient length for the work required.

6. Salvage equipment, including salvage covers, brooms, and squeegees.

7. Rescue and first-aid equipment. The exact equipment provided should be governed by the extent to which members of the brigade have been trained in its use. It may include first-aid kits and resuscitation equipment—inhalator, resuscitator, or modification of these devices with spare cylinders of gas where used.

8. Spare and replacement equipment. This should include items which it is practical to have members of the fire brigade replace. The exact items should be determined in consideration of their availability otherwise, and their relative importance. These items should include fusible links for fire doors, and automatic sprinkler heads.

9. Personnel protective equipment, including helmets, coats, waterproof mittens, and rubber boots. Pompier belts or rope tools and respiratory protective equipment may be included, depending on the extent to which members are trained in their safe and effective use. The number of each item which should be provided should be determined by the number of members of the brigade who will be required to use such items of equipment at one time.

10. Transportation facilities. The brigade should have transportation equipment as needed for its particular work. In some properties small trucks for inside use, or motor trucks for outside use, may be desirable. (See NFPA No. 19, Standard for Automotive Fire Apparatus.)

Bibliography

References Cited

[1] *Introduction to Fire Protection*, NFPA, Boston, 1974.
[2] NFPA No. 27, Standard for Private Fire Brigades.
[3] Bond, Horatio and Kimball, Warren Y., *Industrial Fire Brigade Training Manual*, 4th ed., NFPA, Boston, 1968.

NFPA Codes, Standards, and Recommended Practices (see the latest *NFPA Publications and Visual Aids Catalog* for availability of current editions of the following documents)

NFPA No. 7, Standard for Management Control of Fire Emergencies.
NFPA No. 19, Standard for Automotive Fire Apparatus.

Chapter 4

TRAFFIC AND EXIT DRILLS

During a fire or an emergency there is the problem of seeing that people with essential duties are able to move to locations where they are needed to assist in protection measures. Often, an additional pedestrian traffic problem is imposed in that it is sometimes necessary to quickly and efficiently evacuate people.

A. Traffic

Emergency traffic control is divided into two categories: (1) external—on public streets and highways, and (2) internal—inside private property.

External Traffic

The traffic direction on public streets and highways is usually the responsibility of the law enforcement agency having jurisdiction over the area in which a facility is located. Occasionally, a facility is located in an area where the local law enforcement agency is inadequately staffed to provide traffic control. In such a situation, a facility may wish to furnish some control by supplying private security personnel or guards to help assure the safety of employees.[1, 2] This should be done only after consultation with, and authorization by, the appropriate law enforcement agency.

Regardless of who controls the outside traffic, it is essential that employees in the fire risk management program be able to move to the location of their assignment.

Many large companies provide members of their emergency control forces with identification which has been cleared by both the local law enforcement agency and Civil Defense. This allows their passage through roadblocks, generally established for traffic control, into emergency or disaster areas. This identification may also be used for emergency admittance to restricted areas inside the facility.

Outside traffic planning should also include a primary and an alternate approach route for fire equipment and other emergency vehicles.

Internal Traffic

Without prior arrangements, most police departments will not enter private property to control traffic. If a private security force is maintained, traffic control for both general and emergency movement is assigned to them. If there is no security force, operating personnel should be assigned and trained to control both pedestrian and vehicular traffic.

One person should be assigned to the entrance designated for use by fire department and other emergency control forces, to direct them to the fire scene. In a large facility it may be advisable to have an employee accompany them to the scene in order to minimize lost time.

If the facility is constructed with underpasses, overpasses, tunnels, or overhead piping across access drives, the fire department should be invited to bring in their largest piece of equipment to assure that there is sufficient clearance to admit it.

Personnel should also be assigned and trained to isolate the emergency scene. Only emergency personnel should be permitted in the area. This precaution will prevent personal injury exposure to unnecessary personnel, and hampering of the emergency control effort.

B. Exit Drills

Federal law now requires industrial facilities to provide and properly identify adequate emergency exits and access routes to them. (Occupational Safety and Health Act, Subpart E—Means of Egress.) Similar requirements are made for schools, public assembly facilities, etc., by the laws, codes, and ordinances of State and local governments.

Provision of exit facilities is not enough to assure personnel safety. Exit drills are essential in order to obtain effective use of exits. They are required in schools, and are commonly practiced in institutions and in industrial occupancies where life hazard from fire is high. Some form of exit drill organization is highly desirable in all cases to make sure that someone will be in charge of evacuating occupants, and to avoid confusion between fire fighting and evacuation. Necessary functions include checking exits to make sure they are available, selection of evacuation route, control of traffic, search for stragglers, check of occupants after they are outside the fire area, and control of the return to the building when it is safe. A most important decision is the time when it is necessary to evacuate; in case of doubt, the building should always be evacuated.

Responsibility for planning exit or evacuation drills is generally assigned to the fire risk manager and his staff. Plans should be discussed with both general and direct management to assure their understanding and cooperation. If there is no fire risk manager, the plant manager may assume the responsibility or he may assign it to some member of his staff.

All employees should be advised of the evacuation signal and the exit route they should follow. They should be instructed to shut off equipment immediately upon hearing the signal, and report to a predetermined assembly point. In large facilities primary and alternate routes should be established and all employees should be trained in the use of either route.

When employees are assembled, the direct manager of each area should account for all personnel under his supervision. In the event that some employees are not accounted for, this fact should be reported to the fire risk manager or his counterpart so that search and rescue efforts can be initiated. Only trained search and rescue personnel should be permitted to re-enter an evacuated area.

After each exit drill a meeting of the responsible managers should be held to evaluate the success of the drill and to work out details that might have been faulty or misunderstood.

Timing of drills will depend to some extent on the nature of the operation; generally, drills conducted a few minutes before the lunch break have been found to minimize loss of time and production. Frequency of drills should be determined by the degree of hazard involved in the operation, and by the complexity of shutdown and evacuation procedures.

If a facility does not maintain a security organization with responsibility for daily inspection of emergency exits and designated evacuation routes, one employee in each area should be given the assignment. Maintenance of doors, panic hardware, exit lights, etc., should be given high priority to assure that repairs will be made without delay. For further details on concepts of egress design, see Section 6, Chapter 9 of this HANDBOOK.

Bibliography

[1] NFPA No. 601, Standard for Watchman or Guard Instructions and Duties.

[2] NFPA No. 601A, Standard for Guard Operations in Fire Loss Prevention.

SECTION 11

WATER SUPPLIES FOR FIRE PROTECTION

Section 11

Chapter 1

WATER SUPPLY REQUIREMENTS FOR FIRE PROTECTION

This chapter gives information on the quantities of water needed for fire protection purposes. The components of a water system are discussed in other chapters in this section. No distinction is made for ownership of a system, whether public or private, as quantities of water needed for fire protection are not based on ownership of the system but rather on experience and engineering analysis of fire protection requirements for the property to be protected. Supply requirements for automatic sprinklers or other fixed systems using water are discussed in appropriate chapters of Sections 14 and 15.

A. The Two Uses of Water Systems

Water systems designed today for municipal use have dual functions; they supply potable water for domestic consumption, and they supply water for fire protection. Domestic consumption means more than just water for human consumption. It includes water used for sanitation, industrial processes, lawn sprinkling, air conditioning and similar water-consuming purposes. Sometimes industrial sites will provide separate systems for supplying process water and water for fire protection. Any dual-purpose system must be able to supply enough water for fire protection while at the same time meet the maximum anticipated consumption for other purposes.

B. Rates of Consumption

There are three rates of consumption that are considered in designing water systems. They establish a base to which required fire flows can be added in designing a system or determining its adequacy. The rates are:

1. Average daily consumption—the average of the total amount of water used each day during a 1-year period.

2. Maximum daily consumption—the maximum total amount of water used during any 24-hour period in a 3-year period. (Unusual situations which may have caused an excessive use of water, such as refilling a reservoir after cleaning should not be considered in determining the maximum daily consumption.)

3. Peak hourly consumption—the maximum amount of water that can be expected to be used in any given hour of a day.

The maximum daily consumption is normally about 1.5 times the average daily consumption. The peak hourly rate will vary from two to four times a normal hourly rate. The effect these varying consumption rates will have on the ability of the system to deliver required fire flows will vary with the system design. But both maximum daily consumption and peak hourly consumption should be considered to ensure that water supplies and pressures do not reach dangerously low levels during these periods, and that adequate water will be available in the event of a fire.

C. Water for Fire Fighting

Historically, water systems for cities and towns were developed with needs other than fire protection in mind. However, it was found that in a large city which had to have a lot of water for drinking, sanitation, and other purposes, there was usually sufficient water to provide a useful supply for fire fighting purposes. On the other hand, waterworks designed on the basis of ordinary water needs of a small city would be able to deliver only a fraction of the water which might be needed for fire fighting.

All this led to inquiries into the cost in a given city for a waterworks that could provide water for fire fighting purposes as well as for other uses. A number of distinguished engineers associated with individual waterworks examined the problem and their findings were discussed in technical papers presented at engineering society meetings. Papers by J. Herbert Shedd (1889),[1] J. T. Fanning (1892),[2] and Emil Kuichling (1897)[3] should be consulted for details of the discussions in which standards now followed in American and Canadian waterworks practice developed (Table 11-1A).

Table 11-1A. Estimates of Fire Flow

Populations Thousands	Number of Fire Streams Required Simultaneously				
	Shedd 1889	Fanning 1892	Freeman 1892	Kuichling 1897	NBFU 1910
1			2–3	3	4
4		7		6	8
5	5		4–8	6	9
10	7	10	6–12	9	12
20	10		8–15	12	17
40	14		12–18	18	24
50		14		20	26
60	17		15–22	22	28
100	22	18	20–30	28	36
150		25		34	44
180	30			38	48
200			30–50	40	48

Sources (these authorities define streams slightly differently as described in accompanying text, but the streams were of the order of 200 gpm to 300 gpm):

Shedd, J. Herbert, discussion on a paper by Sherman, William B., *Ratio of Pumping Capacity to Maximum Consumption.*[1]

Fanning, J. T., *Distribution Mains and the Fire Service.*[2]

Kuichling, E., *The Financial Management of Water Works.*[3]

Freeman, John R., *The Arrangement of Hydrants and Water Pipes for the Protection of a City Against Fire.*[4]

Figures furnished by National Board of Fire Underwriters, and presented in a paper by Metcalf, Leonard, et al.[5]

The Number of Hose Streams

The starting point for considering the cost of water for fire protection was an estimate of the number of hose streams that a fire department might need for fire fighting. This was usually estimated on the basis of the central portion of the city where the largest buildings were located and where there was the greatest building congestion. The number of streams was found to be related, in a very rough way, to the population. Shedd's proposal, the first, was on the basis of hose streams discharging 200 gpm. He suggested that a community of 5,000 population, as a rule, would need about five such streams and that the needs of other cities could be graduated up to thirty streams in a city of 180,000. Fanning proposed streams requiring about 54 psi pressure as the basis. His figures were of the same general order as Shedd's, beginning at seven streams for a community of 4,000 and going up to twenty-five streams for a city of 150,000.

Kuichling suggested a formula where the number of streams required would be the square root of the population in thousands multiplied by a factor of 2.8. There were arithmetical differences as to how these estimates worked out for individual cities, but they were of the same general order (Table 11-1A). Most important, they did provide a basis from which the waterworks designers could make some estimates of the cost factors which fire demands imposed on various details of the system.

During this period of consideration of waterworks design features to provide fire protection, the most important paper on the subject, *The Arrangement of Hydrants and Water Pipes for the Protection of a City Against Fire*, was presented (1892) by John R. Freeman.[4] He had done the fundamental work on flow of water through hose and nozzles, so he was able to pin down the definition of a standard fire stream to one with a discharge of 250 gpm at 40 to 50 psi pressure. He said that the relationships suggested by Shedd and Fanning between population and the number of streams required were of the right order, but he did not think the needs of individual cities could be quite so definitely pinned down. He suggested two to three streams as a minimum at 1,000 population graduated up to thirty to fifty at 200,000 (Table 11-1A). Most significantly, he warned: "Ten streams, or as large a proportion thereof as the financial consideration will permit, may be recommended for a compact group of large, valuable buildings, irrespective of a small population."

Engineering: Distributing Network, Hydrant Spacing, Storage

Freeman noted a fundamental difference in purpose between a system designed for supplying ordinary water needs and one for water for fire protection. Fire draft required concentration of the water, whereas domestic draft was a matter of distribution.

Freeman sought to secure recognition of the fact that if a water system was to supply fire protection needs, the distribution system should be designed to concentrate the needed amounts of water. Small pipes were sufficient for distribution, but larger ones were needed for concentration of supply to fire streams. He suggested 6-in. diameter pipe as the minimum for residential districts, and he noted that 8-in. pipe was adequate only where it formed part of a network of distributing pipes whose intersections were not far apart.

Another important point Freeman made was that hydrants should be placed where they could concentrate streams at specific blocks or groups of buildings to be protected rather than on an arbitrary basis of a certain number of feet apart on the street mains. His work on hose streams had shown how long hose lines reduced the water that can be delivered promptly on a fire. He therefore suggested a working rule for hydrant spacing of 250 ft between hydrants in compact mercantile and manufacturing districts, and 400 to 500 ft in residential districts. These working rules can still be used as guides for good design. (Hydrant spacing is discussed in greater detail in Chapter 2 of this Section.)

Freeman further insisted that fire supply should be in addition to maximum domestic consumption and laid the foundation for eventual recognition of this principle. He also indicated how much water should be stored in standpipes or elevated reservoirs in the application of the principle. He expressed the judgment that flow for all of the hose streams required should be supplied from a reliable source, such as an elevated storage reservoir, for a period of not less than 6 hrs during a period when the system was also furnishing maximum demands for domestic and other uses. His judgment also was that to supply the combined fire and domestic needs in a system provided with reliable pump capacity, a 1-hr supply in a standpipe or elevated reservoir would be acceptable.

The Insurance Grading Schedule

As early as 1889, the NBFU (National Board of Fire Underwriters) began to make fire protection surveys of municipalities. This work was intensified in 1904 after a conflagration in Baltimore. Today the larger cities countrywide and the smaller communities in all but seven states are surveyed by the ISO (Insurance Services Office), successor to the NBFU. The survey includes an evaluation of a municipality's water system in all its details, and a map is usually prepared of the system itself. Actual hydraulic tests are made to determine the fire flow available in various parts of the community.

From the examination of the water supply, as well as other factors affecting fire defenses, the community is provided with recommendations expressing an engineering judgment on what the community should consider in its decisions on its public fire protection program. Engineers use as a yardstick the latest edition of ISO's *Grading Schedule for Municipal Fire Protection*,[6] that considers a municipality as a whole, and no longer places more emphasis on protection for downtown districts than on other important districts as did earlier editions of the grading schedule. (For a more complete discussion of the insurance grading schedule see Section 9, Chapter 6.)

D.   Fire Protection Requirements in Water Systems

The capacity of a water system is determined by the total amount of water it must furnish. This is the sum of: (1) water required for domestic or industrial uses, and (2) water required for fire service. In small towns, the requirements for fire protection exceed other requirements.

In North American cities, a public water system is expected to furnish water for a great variety of purposes. In individual cities, there may be a heavy industrial demand, but demands for air conditioning and lawn sprinkling are examples of regular uses which can also affect the required capacity of the system. The adequacy of a public water system for fire protection cannot be taken for granted. These other demands on the system must be determined to estimate their effects on the capacity of the system for fire protection.

A joint report (1951) of committees of the American Society of Civil Engineers, the American Water Works Association and others,[7] suggested that the maximum general service demand on a waterworks system be taken as the peak hourly demand during a test year. This, they noted, was the only figure which can fairly be compared with the maximum fire flow requirement.

Evaluating System Capacity

ISO engineers evaluate the ability of a water system to meet the maximum daily consumption rate plus the needed fire flow. In most large cities, the peak hourly rate exceeds the maximum daily consumption rate plus fire flow, and therefore, is the controlling factor in system design. However, in the smaller communities the reverse is true with the maximum daily consumption rate plus fire flow being the controlling factors. For many years water consumption has been increasing in most municipalities resulting in increased peak hourly rates. One result of this trend has been an increase in the number of municipalities in which the peak hourly rate controls design.

Pressure Characteristics of Systems

The pressure for which systems are normally designed reflect several practical considerations. They attempt to provide pressures that are adequate for water supplies both for domestic consumption and for fire protection. If either type of service demands special ranges of pressure, they too can be provided. Pipe and related fittings and methods of using them will allow almost any desired range.

San Francisco, for example, has a separate system, designated the "high pressure system," under the control of the fire department. All of the pipe is extra-heavy cast iron, tar-coated and lined, and tested on installation and repair to 450 psi. Two steam-operated pump stations can pump water from San Francisco Bay into the system, and 20,000 gpm at 250 psi can be delivered to most of the principal mercantile district. San Francisco provided this system primarily because an earthquake might put the regular public water system out of service. A number of other cities have provided similar "high pressure" systems.

Modern motorized fire department pumping apparatus make heavy streams and high pressures available from ordinary water systems where adequate volume is provided. Cities that formerly had separate systems of fire mains, operating at so-called high pressures, now generally have these operating at what would be normal public water pressures. They retain the advantages of an extra system of water mains.

Public water systems reflect a compromise on the question of pressures. Pressures in the range of 65 to 75 psi are best in most systems. This range is adequate for ordinary consumption in buildings up to about ten stories. It will provide sufficient water for automatic sprinkler systems in buildings of four to five stories. Where pressures of this order are provided, there is a reasonable margin to make it relatively easy to compensate for local fluctuations in draft at various times.

It is generally recommended that a minimum residual pressure of 20 psi be maintained at hydrants when delivering the required fire flow. Pumpers can be operated where hydrant pressures are less, but with difficulty. Where hydrants are well distributed and of the proper size and type (so that friction losses in the hydrant and suction line may not be excessive), it may be possible to set 10 psi as the minimum pressure. Sufficient suction pressure should be maintained to prevent developing a negative pressure in the street mains, which might result in the collapse of the mains or other water system components, or back-siphonage of polluted water from some interconnected source. The use of residual pressures of less than 20 psi is not permitted by most state health departments.

Pressures in a public water system may be considered excessive as they approach 150 psi. As pressures increase, they tend to cause leaks in domestic plumbing, and special attention is required to restrain the mains in the ground. Pipe and fittings used in the ordinary public water system are designed for maximum working pressures of 150 psi. This does not mean that it is good practice to run pressures up that high. Pressure-reducing valves can be used in some sections of a system where the topography would produce excessive pressures, and individual water services to buildings may require pressure reducing valves to keep the pressure on domestic piping at safe levels.

Systems for Higher Elevations

When water must be supplied to an area of a community on high ground, the usual practice is to provide a separate water distribution system for the elevated section so that a normal range of pressures is provided. In such cases, the elevated area should be provided with its own water storage facility, and pumps may be provided to boost the water from the rest of the system. Likewise, the upper stories of a high building should be provided with water systems in the building itself. These systems will have the same requirements as for an area on a hill. A very tall building would have to be divided into a number of pressure zones. Zones of more than twelve stories tend to get outside the normal pressure ranges. In any case, each pressure zone must have storage of water in amounts needed for the sprinkler service or hose streams to be provided, and a system of pumps so that each zone is supplied from the zone below. Care should be taken to ensure that the pumps will be able to operate even during times of power failures.

E. Calculating Fire Flows

For many years the NBFU formula (see Table 11-1A) was commonly used as a guide in determining the fire flow required in the downtown business districts of municipalities. The formula

$$G = 1020 \sqrt{P} \ (1 - 0.01 \sqrt{P})$$

gave the fire flow, G, in gallons per minute as a function of the population, P, in thousands.

In making fire protection surveys, the fire flow requirements in the sections of the municipalities outside the downtown business district were estimated by the engineers of the NBFU and insurance bureaus.

As cities became more decentralized, the formula based on population became less reliable as a guide for the fire flow needed in the downtown district. In addition, it became more apparent that a guide to engineering judgment was needed for the other sections of the cities. In 1948, a paper by A. C. Hutson,[8] assistant chief engineer of the NBFU, provided some specific suggestions for estimating fire flow requirements in these sections.

The latest developments in estimating fire flow requirements are found in the *Guide for Determination of Required Fire Flow*[9] published by ISO in 1972. It provides guidance for estimating fire flow requirements in all parts of a municipality. The basic formula in the guide is:

$$F = 18 \, C \, (A)^{0.5}$$

where F is the required fire flow in gallons per minute, C is the coefficient related to the type of construction, and A is the total floor area of the building considered.

The values for C are: 1.5 for wood frame construction, 1.0 for ordinary construction, 0.8 for noncombustible construction, and 0.6 for fire resistive construction. Interpolation is used if the type of construction does not fall into one of the four categories.

To the result obtained by application of the formula, a credit or surcharge is applied for occupancy, a credit for complete automatic sprinkler protection when provided, and a surcharge for exposures.

The maximum fire flow required is 12,000 gpm for any one location. The practical reason for this top figure is that manual fire fighting methods using men with hose streams and heavy stream appliances are not likely to develop a larger supply considering the general arrangement of buildings and the availability of hydrants. However, the possibility of a second simultaneous fire in the largest cities is considered, for which an allowance of 2,000 to 8,000 gpm additional may be made. This sets a practical maximum fire flow demand of 20,000 gpm for any city.

For groupings of one-family and small two-family dwellings not exceeding two stories in height, the short method of determining required fire flow given in Table 11-1B may

Table 11-1B. Fire Flows for Groups of Dwellings

Exposure Distances Feet	Suggested Required Fire Flow* Gallons per minute
Over 100	500
31 to 100	750–1,000
11 to 30	1,000–1,500
10 or less	1,500–2,000†

* Where wood shingles could contribute to spreading fires, add 500 gpm.
† If the buildings are continuous use a minimum of 2,500 gpm.

be used. The required fire flow should be available with consumption at the maximum daily rate (see Part B of this chapter). The number of hours during which the required fire flow should be available varies from 2 to 10 hours as indicated in Table 11-1C.

Table 11-1C. Duration of Required Fire Flow (U.S. Gallons)

Gallons per minute	Million gallons per day	Duration hours	Gallons per minute	Million gallons per day	Duration hours
1,000	1.44	2	4,500	6.48	4
1,250	1.80	2	5,000	7.20	5
1,500	2.16	2	5,500	7.92	5
1,750	2.52	2	6,000	8.64	6
2,000	2.88	2	7,000	10.08	7
2,250	3.24	2	8,000	11.52	8
2,500	3.60	2	9,000	12.96	9
3,000	4.32	3	10,000	14.40	10
3,500	5.04	3	11,000	15.84	10
4,000	5.76	4	12,000	17.28	10

There are fires where quantities of water in excess of the required fire flow are used. Water supplies of 50,000 gpm or greater have been used in fire suppression, but to design systems capable of delivering flows of that magnitude in the average community for a possible unusual situation is not good economic practice.

F. Adequacy and Reliability of Supply

The adequacy of any given water system can be determined by engineering estimates. The source, including storage facilities in the distribution system, must be sufficient to furnish all the water that combined fire and domestic needs may call for at any one time. Arrangement of the supply works and details of the pumping facilities may limit the adequacy of the supply or affect its reliability. The various components of a water system are discussed in other chapters of this Section.

In a "pumping" system, a common arrangement is to have one set of pumps that takes suction from wells or from a river, lake, or other body of water. If the water does not have to be filtered, the pumps may discharge directly into the distribution system. Where filtration is necessary, the pumps take suction from the primary source and discharge the water into settling reservoirs and filter beds. After processing, the water flows to clear water reservoirs from which a second set of pumps takes suction and discharges the water directly into the water main system. Unfortunately, failure of any part of the equipment may put the supply works out of commission. This is usually taken care of by duplication of units and by arrangement of the plant so as to facilitate repairs.

In considering the reliability of the supply works, features taken into account include: minimum yield, frequency and duration of droughts, condition of intakes, earthquakes, floods, forest fires, ice formations, silting up or shifting of river channels, and absence of watchmen where needed or the possibility of physical injury to them. Reliability is also affected by reservoirs out of service for cleaning and interdependence of parts of waterworks. The condition, arrangement, and reliability of individual units of plant equipment, such as pumps, engines, generators, electric motors, fuel supply, electric transmission facilities and similar items are also factors. Pumping stations of combustible construction are subject to destruction by fire unless equipped with automatic sprinklers.

Duplication of pumping units and storage facilities, and arrangement of mains and distributors so that water may be supplied to them from more than one direction, are measures that can assure continuous operation. The importance of duplicate facilities is shown by the frequency of their use.

G. Future Requirements for Determining Fire Flow

The amount of water needed to control and extinguish a fire in a given property cannot be established currently in precise terms. Differences in fire fighting tactics and variations in conditions which may exist at the time of a fire, as compared with the conditions existing when fire flow requirements were established, are variables that cannot be adequately measured at the present time. Better fire experience data basis should make it possible to tailor fire flows more specifically to conditions that might be expected at the time of a fire. Better analysis may indicate a need to increase fire flow beyond what is presently required, or it may result in a water system design based upon a balance between the risk involved and the economics of maintaining the water system.

The Role of Codes and Ordinances

Fire prevention codes can effectively limit hazards and ignition sources within buildings which in turn will not only help to limit the number of fires, but the size of fires through the control of combustibles in a fire area. A good building code further reduces the chance for a serious fire by requiring construction materials and building assemblies which will contain a developing fire to a given area. These two factors alone will reduce considerably the amount of water needed for fire fighting. Zoning ordinances that establish distances between properties can be effective in controlling exposure situations.

The Role of Fire Detection and Extinguishing Systems

The increased use of automatic extinguishing systems, whether they use water or some other agent, will affect the quantities of water required. However, until more widespread use is made of early warning systems and automatic extinguishing systems, it will not be possible to equate the effect of these systems to required fire flow. Consideration is now given in the ISO *Guide for Determination of Required Fire Flow* for the presence of automatic sprinklers.

Water supply requirements are just one factor in a complex system that in total determines what the potential for a fire is, how extensive the fire will be, and the measures needed to suppress it. Research will someday equate all these factors and permit establishing fire flows on the basis of sound, thoroughly researched, and documented principles.

SI Units

The following conversion factors are given as a convenience in converting to SI units the English units used in this chapter.

1 ft   =   .305 m
1 psi = 6894.757 Pa
1 gpm =   3.785 litres/min

Bibliography

References Cited

[1] Shedd, J. Herbert, discussion on a paper by Sherman, William B., "Ratio of Pumping Capacity to Maximum Consumption," *Journal of New England Water Works Association*, Vol. 3, 1889, p. 113.

[2] Fanning, J. T., "Distribution Mains and the Fire Service," *Proceedings of the American Water Works Association*, Vol. 12, 1892, p. 61.

[3] Kuichling, E., "The Financial Management of Water Works," *Transactions of the American Society of Civil Engineers*, Vol. 38, 1897, p. 16.

[4] Freeman, John R., "The Arrangement of Hydrants and Water Pipes for the Protection of a City Against Fire," *Journal of the New England Water Works Association*, Vol. 7, 1892, p. 49.

[5] Metcalf, L., Huichling, E., and Hawley, W. C., "Some Fundamental Considerations in the Determination of a Reasonable Return for Public Fire Hydrant Service," *Proceedings of the American Water Works Association*, Vol. 31, 1911, p. 55.

[6] *Grading Schedule for Municipal Fire Protection*, Insurance Services Office, New York, 1974.

[7] "Fundamental Considerations in Rates and Rate Structures for Water and Sewage Works," a joint report of Committees of the American Society of Civil Engineers and the Section of Municipal Law of the American Bar Association and of Representatives of the American Water Works Association, National Association of Railroad and Utilities Commissioners, Municipal Finance Officers Association, Federation of Sewage Works Association, American Public Works Association, and Investment Bankers Association of America (reprinted from Ohio State Law Journal, Spring, 1951), ASCE Bulletin No. 2, American Society of Civil Engineers, New York, 1951. See also parts of the report presented in "Water Works Revenue for Fire Protection," *NFPA Quarterly*, Vol. 45, No. 1, July 1952, p. 93.

[8] Hutson, A. C., "Water Works Requirements for Fire Protection," *Journal of the American Water Works Association*, Vol. 40, No. 9, Sept. 1948, p. 936. Also reprinted in Special Interest Bulletin No. 266, National Board of Fire Underwriters (now American Insurance Association), New York, May 4, 1948.

[9] *Guide for Determination of Required Fire Flow*, Insurance Services Office, New York, June, 1972.

Additional Readings

Babbit, Harold E., and Doland, James J., *Water Supply Engineering*, 6th ed., McGraw-Hill, New York, 1962.

Blake, Nelson M., *Water for the Cities*, Syracuse University Press, Syracuse, 1956.

Carl, Kenneth J., Young, Robert A., and Anderson, Gordon C., "Guide for Determining Fire Flow Requirements," *American Water Works Association Journal*, Vol. 65, 1973, pp. 335-344.

Carl, Kenneth J., and Anderson, Gordon C., "The 1973 Grading Schedule for Municipal Fire Protection," *American Water Works Association Journal*.

Fair, G. M., Geyer, J. C., and Okum, D. A., *Water and Wastewater Engineering, Water Supply and Wastewater Removal*, Vol. 1, John Wiley & Sons, New York, 1966.

Hudiburg, Everett, and McCoy, Carl E., ed., *Water Supplies for Fire Protection*, 2nd ed., Fire Protection Publications, Oklahoma State University, Stillwater, 1971.

Engineering and Design—Water Supply for Fire Protection, Office of the Chief of Engineers, Department of the Army, Washington, D.C., 1958.

Chapter 2

WATER DISTRIBUTION SYSTEMS

This chapter discusses the components that make up a distribution system for water transfer from some supply source to a point of use for fire protection purposes. The principles are the same whether the distribution system is owned by a municipality, a public utility, or whether it is a privately owned system providing water to a single property.

Fire protection distribution systems on private property should be kept separate from systems used for domestic services and process-use water. The latter systems, because of unknown reliability of system components and conditions affecting their use, could fail when needed in a fire.

Combined fire and domestic systems do not provide satisfactory fire service; however, they may be tolerated where all of the following conditions are met:

1. The domestic use is small relative to the fire needs,
2. The water is clean and noncorrosive,
3. Means of readily controlling domestic lines are provided,
4. Expense of separate systems may not be warranted.

Powerful water supplies for industrial processes are sometimes available, e.g., chemical works, paper mills, and distilleries. These supplies should be connected to the fire protection underground system so that they are readily available for fire purposes. The arrangements employed, however, should be such that it is not possible to take fire supplies for domestic use, nor to introduce any danger of pollution to a potable supply.

The domestic supply may be connected to the fire system by a number of methods, among them the following:

1. Through a single check valve (when no danger of pollution is present),
2. Through special double check valves (when permitted by health regulations),
3. By a line discharging into a gravity tank or fire pump suction tank above the water line, an arrangement that avoids any chance of flow from a fire line to a domestic supply.

Fire extinguishment for certain commodities may require the application of water for hours or even days. Examples are straw yards at paperboard mills and wastepaper stock and pulpwood piles at paper mills. In such cases, it is obviously important that the substantially inexhaustible water supplies used for manufacturing be drawn on for fire use.

A. Sources of Supply

Sources of water supply fall into two general divisions: surface supplies and ground water supplies.

Surface Supplies

Surface supplies are further divided into lake and river supplies and impounded supplies. They are largely dependent upon rainfall directly. When the source is limited, the quantity available in the supply will vary considerably between wet and dry weather.

Lake supplies, if they are large enough, provide a reliable source of water under most conditions; however, supply intakes from lakes in temperate climates can suffer from ice hazards. There are several kinds of ice which may be injurious to an intake structure or crib. They are anchor ice, which forms on the bottom of lakes; frazil ice, which forms in intermediate depths and in flowing water; and surface ice. If surface ice is present, the other two types of ice normally will not form. If there are a number of ports designed in the intake structure and velocities are maintained carefully, the danger of completely clogging the intake of a supply is relatively small. However, sometimes the demand is not large enough to warrant an expensive intake structure, particularly if the only demand is for fire protection purposes.

If either anchor or frazil ice does start to clog an intake, it requires a relatively small change in temperature to free it. There are some intakes designed with a grid which is in essence a heating coil. In such a case, all that is required is to turn on power, which in turn will heat the intake element sufficiently to keep it free from ice. This method has been found economical in a number of locations, since it requires power a relatively small number of times per year, and then only for periods of short duration. If the intake is designed so that there is a continuous temperature recording, the imminence of the formation of anchor or frazil ice can be predicted.

A river can also be a reliable source of supply if it is large enough not to be seriously affected by prolonged drought periods. A river can be susceptible to ice hazard, scouring of the bottom, changing of the channel, and silting. Before a river intake is constructed, a careful study of the stream bottom, its degree of scour, how much surface ice is formed and whether or not it jams must be made. An intake can easily be destroyed by an ice jam, or the entire liquid flow of a river may be stopped by ice. Provision must be made in the design of the intake to make sure that it can withstand the forces which will act upon it during times of flood, heavy silting or ice conditions.

An impounded supply is one in which water from a stream or river is dammed or otherwise diverted to a natural storage basin.

Occasionally, in newly developed supplies, and in order to protect downstream riparian owners, only flood water can be taken from a flowing water supply and held in a storage basin. This type of catchment is coming into use as good reservoir sites are not necessarily peculiar to stream courses. If any area which would provide good storage facilities can be found and procured off a stream course, then pumping or diverting flood waters from a stream or streams may be the economical plan.

An impounded supply has one advantage over a river; it affords a continuity of supply during times when there might be a low stream flow.

Ground Water Supplies

Ground water supplies fall into two general groups, wells and springs. A spring is merely a well outcropping to the surface; a water-bearing strata or aquifer that intersects the surface of the earth. At another location a well might penetrate to the same strata and obtain the same water. Flowing wells are a type of artesian well in which the hydrostatic head is acquired by virtue of the fact that the source of the water-bearing strata is at a higher elevation than the point at which the flowing well is developed or drilled. Excessive use of artesian supplies always results in diminution of the head to a degree that in many areas where there was once a high hydrostatic head, flowing wells have either ceased to exist or nearly so.

Ground water supplies are less susceptible to radical changes due to lack of direct dependency upon rainfall. There is some time lag between periods of drought and the time that it is noticed in a well supply. However, the time lag between a period of drought and its noticeable effect on a well field is also reflected upon restoration of a well field. In other words, there may be some months after the beginning of a drought before a well supply is noticeably affected, but on the other hand, it will take some months after rainfall starts before restoration of a well field is attained.

Selection of Supply

The selection of a source of supply in some cases is limited to just one type. However, in some cases there is a choice of supplies, and the source should be selected which gives the desired quantity of water with the least mechanical operation and most reliability. The most desirable source would be that from a controlled water shed into a large impounded lake where it would flow by gravity to the distribution system. This type of supply is available in some locations, but it is impossible in others. A dependable source, capable of producing the necessary quantities of water needed for fire protection for the required duration under any and all conditions must be selected.

B.   Types of Systems

There are two basic types of water distribution systems; gravity flow systems and pumping systems; however, most water systems are a combination of the two types.

Gravity System

A true gravity system is the most reliable system as there is no machinery which can malfunction. Water is impounded at some point sufficiently elevated from the distribution system to allow it to flow into the distribution system and the elevation head provides sufficient working pressures at the needed points to provide water for fire protection.

Pumping System

When water cannot be obtained at an elevation sufficient to provide working pressures from the elevation head, it is necessary to provide pumps on the system. These pumps are normally located at the source of supply and are used to develop the pressure needed to overcome friction loss in the system and provide working pressures. Chapter 4 of this Section covers fire pumps and outlines the principles of pumps and pumping stations whether they are private or public systems. Public systems sometimes have water treatment facilities associated with the pumping station but it is not the intent of this HANDBOOK to discuss water treatment.

Combination Systems

Often associated with pumping systems are water storage facilities. These provide for storage of water during times of least demand and provide additional quantities of water during times of peak demand.

The storage can be so arranged that the pumps supply the water storage facility directly and water flows to the distribution system from the facility. The storage facility can also be located at a remote location within the dis-

tribution system, and water can be pumped directly into the distribution system with any excess automatically dumping into the storage facility. The more water which can be maintained in storage, the more reliable a system can be considered as water flowing from a storage facility is the same as a gravity system and any failure of a pump or its prime mover will not affect this water from being available for fire protection purposes.

C.   Supply Conduits, Aqueducts, Pipelines

Two terms used to describe the conveyor of water from the source of supply to the distribution system are "conduit" and "aqueduct." A conduit is an enclosed pipe capable of withstanding pressure while an aqueduct is either a closed tube or an open trench, canal, or channel in which water flows but which has no pressure on the side except that caused by the weight of the water. Aqueducts are not designed to withstand pressure other than atmospheric.

Pipelines

Pipelines are designed to withstand pressure and to distribute water to the point of use. Three classes of pipelines, or distribution mains, in a large system are:

1. Primary feeders consisting of large pipes with relatively wide spacing which convey large quantities of water to various points of the system for local distribution to the smaller mains;

2. Secondary feeders forming the network of pipes of intermediate size which reinforce the distributor grid within the various panels of the primary feeder system and aid the concentration of the required fire flow at any point; and

3. Distributors consisting of a gridiron arrangement of small mains serving the individual fire hydrants and blocks of consumers.

As a means of reliability, two or more primary feeders should run by separate routes from the source of supply to the high value districts of the city. Similarly, secondary feeders should be arranged as far as possible in loops so as to give two directions of supply to any point. This practice increases the capacity of the supply at any given point and assures that a break in a feeder main will not completely cut off the supply.

Secondary feeders should generally be installed in built-up areas not over 3,000 ft apart.

Where water systems are divided into pressure zones, water can often be transferred from one zone to another by operating valves or by using fire department pumpers to pump from the hydrants in one zone to hydrants in the other. The same sort of thing can be done between the water systems of adjoining communities or between a private system and the public system. Private systems at institutions, industrial plants, etc. sometimes can provide substantial amounts of water to tide over an emergency. The systems can be connected, but the valves are normally kept closed. By written agreement, the terms can be stipulated under which one system will supply the other in an emergency. Health regulations should be observed in all cases so nonpotable sources are not connected to a public system.

The Size of Pipe

No pipe less than 6 in. diameter is recommended for fire service and 6-in. pipes should only be used when they are looped in a gridiron where no leg is more than 600 ft in length. In congested districts it is recommended that distributors should be not less than 8 in. and interconnected within every 600 ft. On principal streets and for all long lines, the distributors should be 12 in. or larger.

The cost of a line of pipe includes such factors as trenching (sometimes with piling), laying the pipe, backfilling, and testing. All of these factors are present regardless of the size of pipe used. To them is added the cost of the pipe delivered on the job. It is usually good business, therefore, to install pipe for fire protection which is one or more sizes larger than the bare minimum might require. Stepping up the pipe only one size will often nearly double the possible flow. The figures in Table 11-2A show the relative capacity of pipe obtained by increasing sizes above 6 in.

Table 11-2A. Comparison of Pipe Capacity

Size of Pipe, Inches	Relative Capacity
6	1.0
8	2.1
10	3.8
12	6.2
14	9.3
16	13.2

In laying out a system, it is also important to consider the probable development of an area and to plan, in a general way at least, protection for the ultimate development of the area, and then to install that part of the system for which there is immediate need. The same planning should be used for private systems. Figure 11-2AA shows a layout for a large industrial plant with a gravity tank and fire pump. The future development idea is shown.

The actual size of pipe needed is determined based on the volume of water needed (domestic consumption plus fire flow), and hydraulic gradient in the area. Calculations of water flow in pipe are covered in Chapter 6 of this Section.

Another way to show advantages of larger pipes is to indicate the better performance of four sizes of pipes by comparing their friction loss characteristics under a simple range of fire demands (see Table 11-2B).

Table 11-2B. Friction Loss in Cast-iron Pipe
Figures given are for 15-year-old unlined cast-iron pipe.
(C = 100)

Flow Gallons per minute	Loss per 1,000 Feet of Pipe Pounds per square inch			
	6-inch	8-inch	10-inch	12-inch
500	14.4	3.5	1.2	0.49
1,000	52.0	12.8	4.3	1.78
1,500	110.0	27.1	9.1	3.76

Arrangements of Pipe Systems

Pipe systems are arranged in loops wherever possible. This allows hydrants and other connections to be fed from at least two directions and greatly increases the possible delivery of water without excessive friction loss.

In private water systems where lines supply hydrants only and where there are adequate pressures for good streams at the hydrants, it is general practice to use 6-in. pipe to supply two-outlet hydrants, and 8-in. or larger pipe under the following conditions:

Dead end mains: If more than one hydrant is to be supplied or the distance is more than 500 ft.

Looped mains: If two hydrants are to be supplied on a loop with over 1,500 ft of pipe.

If three hydrants are to be supplied on a loop with over 1,000 ft of pipe.

If four or more hydrants are to be supplied.

Where pressures are low, or where three outlet or four outlet hydrants only are installed, pipes should be larger.

Internal Condition of Pipe Systems

In the course of time the internal cross section of cast-iron pipe may be reduced or its interior surface roughened because of tuberculation, incrustation, or sedimentation. Incrustations may be due to: (1) tubercular-corrosion or rust, (2) chemical constituents of the water, or (3) growth of biological or living organisms. Deposits in all kinds of pipe may be due to: (1) sediments such as mud, clay, leaves, or vegetable decay, or (2) foreign matter other than sediment.

The existence of serious trouble can generally be detected by careful flushing tests. Flushing of the system will remove ordinary sediment. Operation of valves will sometimes show presence of sediment or corrosion. Local water conditions are taken into account in establishing a regular procedure of flushing and testing. Pipes can be cleaned by the use of a scraper or rotating auger. The cleaning device can be pulled through the pipe by a cable or forced through by water pressure.

Use of tees instead of ells, and crosses instead of tees in an underground system, makes it possible to inspect and clean mains without breaking into the piping.

D. Types of Pipes

Underground pipe and fittings for fire protection should be suitable for the working pressures and the conditions under which the pipe is to be installed. Pipe is mostly installed without blocks in flat-bottomed trenches with tamped backfill and a cover of about 5 ft. In this case, pipe designed for about 125 psi working pressure (150 psi maximum) is appropriate. Classes of pipe for working pressures above 150 psi are often used where the greater resistance of heavier and thicker pipe is desired, as for example, in unstable or corrosive soils or in locations difficult of access in event of leaks or breaks. Steel or reinforced concrete pipe is advantageous in difficult situations, such as under railroad tracks, in areas with heavy industrial machinery, in earthquake areas, or where steep slopes or unstable soil conditions are encountered. For ordinary conditions, cast-iron, ductile-iron and asbestos-cement pipe are preferred because they give satisfactory performance and can be installed at low cost for labor and engineering supervision. Usual maximum working pressures are 100, 150, and 200 psi for asbestos-cement; 100, 150, 250 and 350 psi for cast-iron; and 150, 200, 250, and 300 psi for reinforced concrete.

Pipe and fittings used for underground fire service mains should be listed or approved by a recognized testing laboratory.

Asbestos-cement Pipe

Asbestos-cement pipe is particularly well adapted for locations where ferrous types without special protective linings or coverings would be obstructed or weakened by actively corrosive waters, by soil conditions, or by electrolysis. Where asbestos-cement pipe must be buried in highly acid or alkaline soils, coatings can be provided that will protect the pipe from soil conditions.

Asbestos-cement pipe is made of a mixture of asbestos fiber and cement and is acceptable when manufactured in accordance with AWWA C400-1972, Specifications for Asbestos-cement Water Pipe. Where the maximum pressures to be encountered do not exceed 150 psi, Class 150 pipe can be used. Pressures in excess of 150 psi but not over 200 psi require Class 200 pipe. AWWA C400 does not cover pipe in classes higher than 200.

The usual joint for asbestos-cement pipe is an asbestos-cement sleeve into which a specially shaped rubber gasket is inserted in a circumferential groove near each end of the sleeve. When making the joint, the tapered ends of the pipe are forced into the sleeve, compressing the rubber gaskets to make a tight joint. Another method is to use an asbestos-cement sleeve, which is forced over roll-on rubber gaskets so arranged that the gaskets, in their final position, are properly located on each side of the joint to form a water-tight connection (Fig. 11-2A). Cast-iron fittings are used in asbestos-cement pipelines.

Extra precautions must be taken at bends, tees, etc., to prevent the pipe from moving and opening up joints.

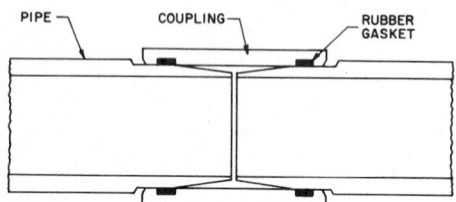

Fig. 11-2A.   Coupling for asbestos-cement pipe.

Cast-iron Pipe

Cast-iron pipe made in accordance with ANSI A21.6-1970, ANSI A21.8–1970, or an equivalent specification is acceptable. In these specifications, the pipe designation (150, 200, 250, etc.) represents maximum working pressure. Table 11-2C gives dimensions and weights for pipes of Thickness Class 22, which is designed for standard laying conditions. The complete specifications have additional data on pipe sizes, weights, pressure classes and thickness classes for other laying conditions. Pipe should be selected on the basis of maximum working pressure and the laying condition.

There are several acceptable types of joints. The most common are: (1) poured bell-and-spigot, (2) standardized mechanical, and (3) single-gasket push-on. All these joints are essentially bell-and-spigot and depend on friction between the parts and surrounding earth fill to prevent separation (see Figs. 11-2B, 11-2C, and 11-2D).

Poured Bell-and-Spigot Joints: These joints are started with a ring packing of jute or other material and caulked with lead. Special joint compounds are available which require no caulking. They are practical in large installations where they may effect a saving over lead joints.

When using bell-and-spigot pipe and fittings, changes in grade or direction should never be made by shifting the pipe in the joints. This would result in uneven packing and caulking, and such joints are likely to leak. Only a very slight variation from normal is tolerable.

"Lead wool," which is lead divided into fine shreds, and also lead wire are sometimes used for caulking joints in wet trenches where a joint cannot be poured. These joints are more expensive than the usual lead joint and must be caulked very firmly. At best, they are not as strong as the ordinary jute and melted lead joint and should be used only in special cases or for repairs.

Precaulked pipe has a built-up joint consisting of oakum and lead with a system of iron wedges imbedded in lead in the center of the joint. The lower half of this joint is ready caulked, and when the pipe is laid properly, it is necessary to caulk only the upper half of the joint.

Standard Mechanical Joints: These are joints in which a rubber ring gasket is held in place by a follower ring bolted to the bell. A mechanical joint provides for a limited amount of flexibility; a ball and socket joint of similar design provides a little more. Because of the flexibility, pipe with these joints is often selected for lines across bridges. The line is placed in position, and the bolts are then carefully tightened with special short wrenches to avoid excessive bolt tension and possible breakage of pipe. Where the strength of joints depends largely on the bolts, some protection against corrosion, such as a coating of asphalt, should be provided.

Push-on Joints: The push-on joint is made up by seating a circular rubber gasket of special cross section in the valve and then forcing the spigot end of the pipe past the gasket to the bottom of the valve socket. No packing or caulking is required.

Specifications for mechanical joints and push-on joints are covered by ANSI A21.11-1972.

Table 11-2C. Standard Dimensions and Weights of Cast-iron Pipe*

Nominal Size In.	Outside Diameter In.	Class 150 (150 Psi)		Class 200 (200 Psi)		Class 250 (250 Psi)	
		Thickness In.	Weight per 18-ft Laying Length† Lbs	Thickness In.	Weight per 18-ft Laying Length† Lbs	Thickness In.	Weight per 18-ft Laying Length† Lbs
4	4.80	0.35	290	0.35	290	0.35	290
6	6.90	0.38	460	0.38	460	0.38	460
8	9.05	0.41	655	0.41	655	0.41	655
10	11.10	0.44	870	0.44	870	0.44	870
12	13.20	0.48	1,125	0.48	1,125	0.52	1,215
14	15.30	0.51	1,410	0.55	1,510	0.59	1,610
16	17.40	0.54	1,700	0.58	1,815	0.63	1,960
18	19.50	0.58	2,050	0.63	2,210	0.68	2,370
20	21.60	0.62	2,430	0.67	2,610	0.72	2,785
24	25.80	0.73	3,415	0.79	3,665	0.79	3,665

* ANSI A21.6-1970. Based on standard laying conditions (5 ft-cover, flat-bottomed trench and tamped backfill).
† Includes bell.

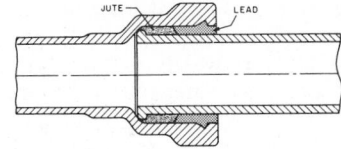

Fig. 11-2B. A bell-and-spigot lead joint.

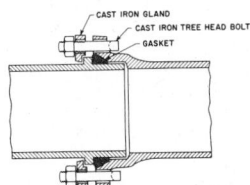

Fig. 11-2C. A standardized mechanical joint using anchoring fittings.

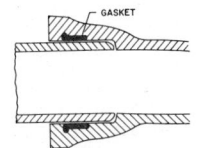

Fig. 11-2D. A push-on joint.

Table 11-2D. Standard Dimensions and Weights of Ductile-iron Pipe*

Nominal Size, In.	Outside Diameter, In.	Working Pressure, Psi	Thickness, In.†	Weight per 18-ft Laying Length,‡ Lbs
4	4.80	350	0.29	240
6	6.90	350	0.31	380
8	9.05	350	0.33	535
10	11.10	350	0.35	700
12	13.20	350	0.37	885
14	15.30	350	0.36	1,005
16	17.40	350	0.37	1,185
18	19.50	300	0.38	1,370
20	21.60	250	0.39	1,560
24	25.80	250	0.41	1,975

* ANSI A21.51-1972. Based on standard laying conditions (5-ft cover, flat-bottomed trench and tamped backfill).
† Minimum available.
‡ Includes bell.

Ductile-iron Pipe

Ductile iron has the corrosion resistance of cast iron and approaches the strength and ductility of steel. Grade 60-42-10 ductile iron (minimum: tensile strength 60,000 psi, yield strength 42,000 psi, 2 percent elongation in 2 in.) is used for water pipe in conformance with ANSI A21.51-1971.

Table 11-2D gives the minimum available thicknesses for ductile-iron pipe 4 to 24 in. in diameter. Ductile-iron pipe is made with push-on and mechanical joints.

Cast-iron fittings are used with ductile-iron pipe. Coating or cathodic protection is not needed, except where extremely corrosive conditions exist. Lined pipe is recommended for all new or replacement installations of cast-iron or ductile-iron pipe to offset the corrosive action of water. Portland cement is extensively used for lining. Coal-tar enamel linings are available but less common. A large percentage of all cast-iron pipe is cement-lined at the foundry. Cement lining should conform to ANSI A21.4-1971, Cement-mortar Lining for Cast-iron Pipe and Fittings.

Steel Pipe

Steel pipe of suitable wall thickness and manufacture, when lined and coated, is acceptable for fire service, both for underground mains and for supply lines in tunnels and buildings. Because of its high tensile strength, steel pipe is particularly suitable where it may be exposed to earthquake shock or to impact from railroad tracks, highways, drop-forge equipment, etc. The greater strength of steel is also advantageous in unstable soil or on steep slopes.

Steel pipe should conform to AWWA standards, either C202-1964, Mill-type Steel Water Pipe, or C201-1966, Fabricated Electrically Welded Steel Water Pipe. Approximate dimensions and weights are given in Table 11-2E.

Mill pipe is made from hot or cold strip, plate, or solid rounds by a more or less continuous process wherein the pipe itself moves during the making and finishing operations. Fabricated pipe is made from plates or sheets by electric fusion welding to form cylinders.

Steel pipe joints are welded, made with flanges or mechanical couplings (see Fig. 11-2E). Welding should conform to AWWA C206-62, Field Welding of Steel Water Pipes. If pipelines are to be welded in tunnels or buildings, suitable precautions against fire are essential. Expansion joints may be needed in long runs of pipe in tunnels. Hangers and supports should conform to good engineering practice and applicable standards.

Table 11-2E. Recommended Minimum Dimensions and Weights of Steel Pipe for Fire-protection Mains

Nominal Diameter In.	Outside Diameter In.	For Welded Joints		For Flexible Couplings or Threaded Joints	
		Minimum Wall Thickness In.	Weight per Ft Lbs	Minimum Wall Thickness In.	Weight per Ft Lbs
6	6.625	0.188	12.9	0.219	15.0
8	8.625	0.188	16.9	0.239	21.4
10	10.750	0.188	21.2	0.250	28.0
12	12.750	0.188	25.1	0.281	37.4
14	14.000	0.239	35.1	0.281	41.2
16	16.000	0.250	42.0	0.312	52.4

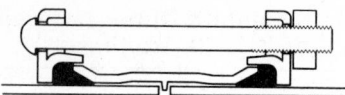

Fig. 11-2E. A steel mechanical coupling for plain-end steel pipe.

Reinforced Concrete Pipe

Several designs of pipe of concrete and steel 24 in. and larger in diameter are available. Concrete pipe is often used on long conduits and aqueducts but it is not normally used in distribution systems. A "nonprestressed" design is a steel cylinder with one or two steel-cage reinforcements encased in concrete. A "modified prestressed" design is a steel cylinder with a spirally wound steel rod reinforcement prestressed to provide a slight initial tension in the cylinder and concrete lining. "Prestressed" designs consist of a concrete-lined cylinder or steel cylinder helically wrapped under tension with a high tensile strength wire. External coatings are cement mortar.

Reinforced concrete pipe should be manufactured in accordance with AWWA C300-1972, Standard for Reinforced Concrete Water Pipe—Steel Cylinder Type, not prestressed; AWWA C302-64, Standard for Reinforced Concrete Water Pipe—NonCylinder Type, not prestressed.

Pipe Corrosion

Water is corrosive to cast-iron, ductile iron, and steel pipe. The initial rate of corrosion for steel pipe may be more rapid than for cast or ductile iron, but after several years exposure there is little difference.

External corrosion of buried iron and steel pipe is the direct result of complicated electrochemical reactions. Soil containing metallic salts, acids, or other substances in combination with moisture causes iron ions to separate from the pipe. The mass of the metal at the pipe surface is diminished, and the pipe becomes pitted or corroded. Iron or steel pipe should not be installed under coal piles, in cinderfill, or wherever acids, alkalies, pickling liquors, etc., can penetrate the soil.

Stray electric currents from external sources may reach and follow buried pipelines to locations where the resistance to ground is less than that of the pipeline. Ionization then occurs at points where the current leaves the pipe, producing an effect similar to that of soil corrosion.

When stray electric currents are suspected, the extent and origin should be determined by professional ground surveys. If the stray currents cannot be eliminated or diverted, the pipe, if not yet seriously corroded, can be protected by bonding all the joints and by providing direct low-resistance metallic ground connections.

Cathodic methods are widely used for the external protection of iron and steel water mains. Cathodic protection is a technique of imposing direct electric current from a galvanic anode to the buried pipeline. In many instances cathodic protection is more economical than coating and wrapping.

Internal protection against corrosion is by linings and coatings. The coatings should conform to AWWA C104-71, Cement-mortar Linings for Cast Iron Pipe and Fittings for Water; AWWA C203-66, Coal-tar Enamel Protective Coatings for Steel Water Pipe; or AWWA Standard C205-71, Cement-Mortar Protective Lining and Coating for Steel Water Pipe.

A smooth lining is necessary to minimize loss of carrying capacity. Buried piping needs a coating to protect against soil corrosion. An outside coating may be applied in the field if desired, but it is practical only on large jobs. Exposed piping should be painted or otherwise protected as required by atmospheric conditions. Nuts and bolts of buried joint assemblies are heavily coated. Any damage resulting to lining or coating should be thoroughly repaired.

Fittings

Fittings used should be appropriate for the same range of working pressures as the pipe with which they are used. A single class of cast-iron fittings for sizes 3 to 12 in. is now used generally. These are for working pressures of 250 psi. Cast-iron fittings (bends and tees) are used with asbestos-cement pipe. They have bells designed to be used with the asbestos-cement gasket-type joint.

Cast-iron and steel fittings for underground water lines for fire protection are listed or approved by recognized testing laboratories. Cast-iron fittings usually carry the identifying marks of the manufacturer and are marked with the working pressures for which they are designed. Ductile-iron fittings are marked "ductile" or "DI". They are defined by a standard of the AWWA for cast-iron fittings (AWWA C110-71). This standard covers fittings from 250 psi in sizes 12 in. and less, and for both 150 and 250 psi in larger sizes through 48 in.

E.　Rules for Laying Pipe

The depth of cover to provide protection against freezing will vary from about $2\frac{1}{2}$ ft in the southern states to about 10 ft in northern Canada. As there is normally no circulation of water in fire protection mains, they require greater depth of covering than do public mains. The $2\frac{1}{2}$-ft minimum should always be maintained to prevent mechanical damage. Depth of covering should be measured, from top of pipe to ground level, and due consideration should always be given to future or final grade and nature of soil. A greater depth is required in a loose, gravelly soil (or in rock) than in compact or clay soil. A safe rule to follow is to bury the top of pipe not less than 1 ft below the lowest frostline for the locality.

Placing pipes over raceways or near embankment walls should be avoided. Keep mains back a sufficient distance from the banks of streams or raceways to avoid any danger of freezing through the side of the bank. Where mains are laid in raceways or shallow streams, care should be taken that there will be running water over the pipe during all seasons of frost; a safer method is to bury the main 1 ft or more under the bed of the waterway.

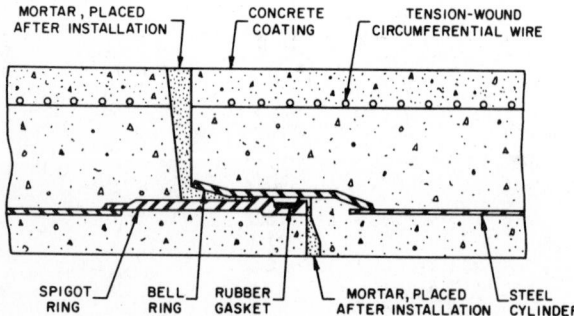

Fig. 11-2F. A reinforced concrete pipe joint.

Protection Against Breakage

In general, it is advisable to avoid running pipe under buildings. Where mains necessarily pass under a building, the foundation walls can be arched over the pipe. Pipes passing under building walls with ground floors at grade are buried to the same depth as outdoors. Pipes under basement floors below grade may require less depth but in no case should the cover be less than 2½ ft.

Any pipe that passes through a wall or foundation must be protected from fracture. This is done by keeping a clear 2-in. annular space around the pipe and sealing it with coal tar or asphalt (see Fig. 11-2G).

Special care is necessary in running pipes under railroad tracks, highways, large piles of iron, and under buildings housing heavy machinery that is likely to fall, and activities which could subject the buried pipes to shock or vibration. Where subject to such breakage, pipes should be run in a covered pipe trench or be otherwise properly guarded. While flanged cast-iron pipe with metallic gaskets is sometimes used under buildings, it is not recommended because of its lack of flexibility, higher cost and difficulty of repairs.

The loads to which pipe is subjected and the means of dealing with these various loads are in the various AWWA pipe and installation manuals (see Bibliography).

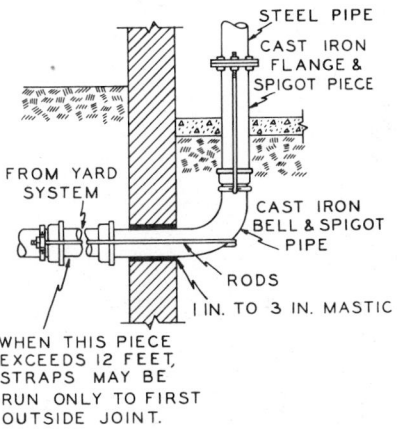

STEEL PIPE
CAST IRON FLANGE & SPIGOT PIECE
FROM YARD SYSTEM
CAST IRON BELL & SPIGOT PIPE
RODS
1 IN. TO 3 IN. MASTIC
WHEN THIS PIECE EXCEEDS 12 FEET, STRAPS MAY BE RUN ONLY TO FIRST OUTSIDE JOINT.

Fig. 11-2G. A common arrangement of pipe is through a foundation to feed a sprinkler or standpipe riser. The anchorage of the horizontal run is determined by soil conditions. In some cases, as in earthquake areas, considerable flexibility is desirable in this run and the first two joints outside the building. Often the run is brought into the building with the first joint of a flexible type, particularly if the pipe openings through foundation and floors are sealed with grouted concrete instead of mastic. The anchorages shown would be the usual ones.

Care in Laying Pipe

Pipes should be clean inside when put in trenches, and open ends should be plugged when work is stopped, to prevent stones or dirt from entering.

Pipes are supported throughout their length and not by the bell ends only. Superior support is obtained where the bottom of the trench is shaped to fit the pipe. If ground is soft or of a quicksand nature, special provision must be made for supporting pipe. For ordinary conditions of soft ground, longitudinal wooden stringers with cross ties will give good results. A reinforced concrete mat 3 or 4 in. thick in the bottom of the trench can also be used. In extreme cases, the stringers and cross ties or concrete mat may have

to be supported on piles. The most important aspect of laying pipe, though, is to follow the manufacturer's instructions for trench preparation, maximum deflection and method of joining.

Anchorage

Most conventional pipe joints are not designed to resist forces tending to pull them apart. Joints are expected to be kept in place by the soil in which the pipe is buried. It is necessary to determine, by tests in case of doubt, that a particular soil will actually do this. In unsatisfactory soils, trenches may have to be excavated below the final pipe level and filled to the pipe grade with soil suitable to give the pipe an even bearing throughout its length.

In considering anchorages, it is necessary to keep in mind the loads that are considered in the choice of pipe used for fire protection. Pipe thicknesses specified for fire protection in AWWA standards are for a specific condition, i.e., a flat-bottomed trench with tamped back filling and approximately 5 ft of cover. When other trench conditions are encountered, such as greater depth or soil with poor bearing features including muck or soft sand, it may be necessary to consider the additional loads that are imposed on the pipe.

Forces acting on pipe laid in the ground that must be considered, among others, are: (1) internal static pressure of the water, (2) water hammer, (3) load from the backfill, and (4) load and impact from passing trucks and other vehicles. Static pressure and backfill loads are always present. Water hammer loads are considered separately from impact loads of passing vehicles on the theory that simultaneous action of the two would be incidental. The thickness designated for the various pressure classes of pipe tends to reflect possible water hammer loads. Design methods for various kinds of pipe and thickness specified are explained in the AWWA pipe fitting standards and manuals. Anchorages are needed to take care of additional loads due to water hammer and other forces. Trenches, which have to be unusually wide or deep, impose additional loads which may affect the choice of pipe thickness for the particular installation.

To prevent joints in cast-iron pipes from coming apart, they should be securely braced or clamped unless anchoring fittings or locked joints are used. Typical methods of anchoring joints at elbows, tees and bends, and plugs at blanked openings are shown in Figures 11-2H to 11-2O. Clamps and rods and other steel fittings at anchors should be protected against corrosion by a thick covering of asphalt.

Thrust Blocks

It is also necessary to consider the loads imposed by water moving in the pipe. This is why at bends, tees, and pipe ends, and wherever the piping changes direction, the pipe assembly must actually bear on a surface that will resist the loads imposed. Anchoring or locking joints with standard pipe clamps and rods should be employed to resist forces wherever the soil alone does not or may not provide stability. In the case of asbestos-cement pipe, cast-iron fittings are used since the pipe is not designed to carry compression forces imposed by clamp and rod assemblies. Thrust blocks are used to keep the pipe assemblies in place. For assemblies of pipe 16 in. and larger, the soil conditions may require thrust blocks as well as anchoring or locking joints or rod-and-clamp reinforcement.

The usual thrust block is made of concrete and is placed between the fitting and the trench wall. A typical mix would be one part cement, two parts washed sand, and five parts

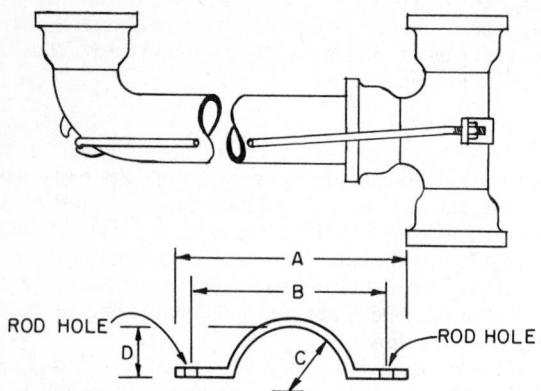

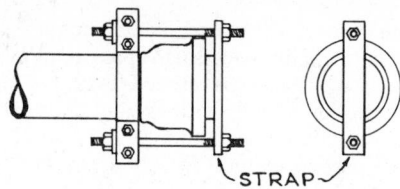

Fig. 11-2K. A plug for the bell end of a pipe. The strap holding the plug in the pipe is $\frac{3}{4}$ in. thick and $2\frac{1}{2}$ in. wide. The length of the strap is the same as for Dimension A for tee straps given in Figure 11-2H, and the distance between centers of rod holes is the same as Dimension B.

Fig. 11-2H. Strap for bend anchor to tee. Straps shall be $\frac{5}{8}$ in. thick and $2\frac{1}{2}$ in. wide for pipe diameters 4, 6, 8, and 10 in., and 3 in. wide for 12-in. pipe. Rod holes shall be $\frac{1}{16}$ in. larger than rods. Dimensions in inches for straps are suitable either for mechanical joint or bell and spigot fittings.

Other Dimensions (inches)

Pipe	A	B	C	D
4	$12\frac{1}{2}$	$10\frac{1}{8}$	$2\frac{1}{2}$	$1\frac{3}{4}$
6	$14\frac{1}{2}$	$12\frac{1}{8}$	$3\frac{9}{16}$	$2\frac{13}{16}$
8	$16\frac{3}{4}$	$14\frac{3}{8}$	$4\frac{21}{32}$	$3\frac{29}{32}$
10	$19\frac{1}{16}$	$16\frac{11}{16}$	$5\frac{3}{4}$	5
12	$22\frac{5}{16}$	$19\frac{3}{16}$	$6\frac{3}{4}$	$5\frac{7}{8}$

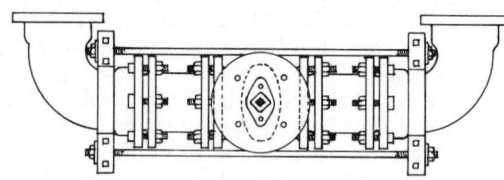

Fig. 11-2L. A general form of an anchor for indicator post valves. A mechanical joint pipe is illustrated.

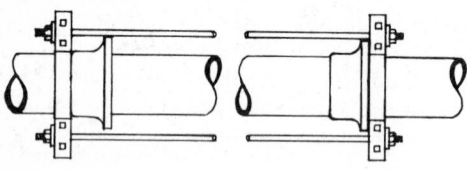

Fig. 11-2I. Anchor rods for bell-and-spigot pipe. When distances between bells is less than 12 ft, the next length of pipe is also anchored.

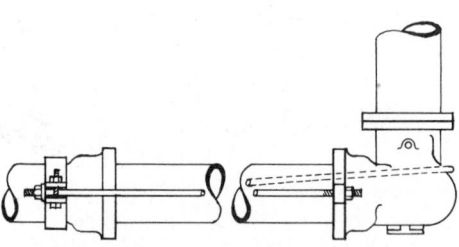

Fig. 11-2M. Hydrants are connected with a double spigot connection anchored as illustrated. Anchor fittings and locked joints are often more convenient alternatives for rodded anchors. When the hydrant does not have lugs, the anchor rods are arranged as indicated by the dotted lines.

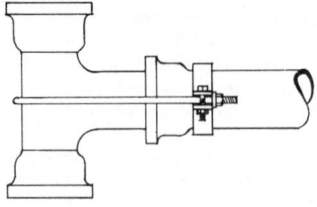

Fig. 11-2N. An anchor at a spigot end of a tee fitting.

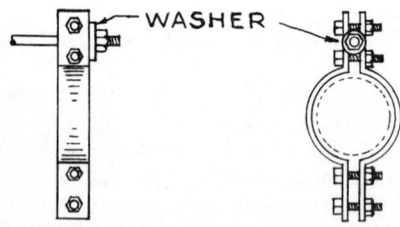

Fig. 11-2J. Clamps for bell-and-spigot pipe and short-body fittings. Clamps are $\frac{1}{2}$ in. by 2 in. for 4-in. and 6-in. pipe; $\frac{5}{8}$ in. by $2\frac{1}{2}$ in. for 8- and 10-in. pipe, and $\frac{5}{8}$ in. by 3 in. for 12-in. pipe. Bolt holes are $\frac{1}{16}$ in. larger than the bolts. Rods are $\frac{3}{4}$ in. in diameter for 4- 6- and 8-in. pipes, $\frac{7}{8}$ in. for 10-in. pipe, and 1 in. for 12-in. pipe. Washers may be cast iron or steel, round or square. Dimensions for cast iron washers are $\frac{5}{8}$ in. by 3 in. for 4-, 6-, 8-, and 10-in. pipes, and $\frac{3}{4}$ in. by $3\frac{1}{2}$ in. for 12-in. pipe. Dimensions for steel washers are $\frac{1}{2}$ in. by 3 in. for 4-, 6-, 8-, and 10-in. pipe and $\frac{1}{2}$ in. by $3\frac{1}{2}$ in. for 12-in. pipe. Holes are $\frac{1}{8}$ in. larger than the rods.

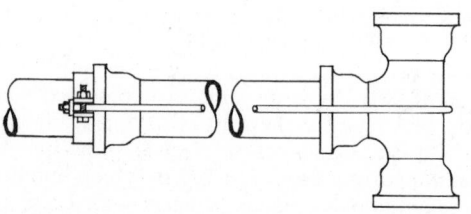

Fig. 11-2O. An anchor at a bell end of a tee fitting. If the distance between joints is less than 12 ft, rods should also be run to a clamp on the next bell.

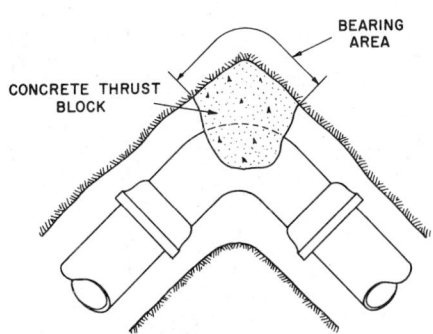

Fig. 11-2P. A thrust block at a one-quarter bend.

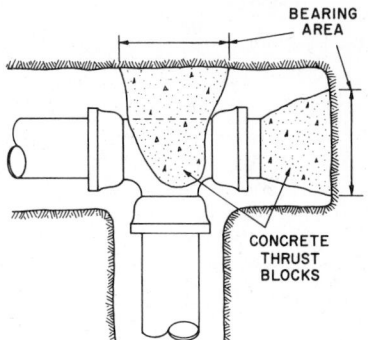

Fig. 11-2Q. A thrust block at a tee and plug.

washed gravel. In soils with good bearing characteristics, a small amount of hand digging behind the fitting will make a good bearing possible with a minimum of concrete. In soft, unstable soils, the soft material may have to be removed and ballast added to provide the needed bearing. Thrust blocks may be tied to foundations where these are of sufficient size to provide a bearing.

A thrust block under a hydrant or valve to prevent upward movement in the newly laid soil would require rods bent over the bells to hold the valve or hydrant to the block. Blocks under hydrants should be located so as not to prevent the hydrant from draining properly. About a barrel of small stones dumped alongside the thrust block is needed to provide a place where water from the hydrant barrel may drain without washing away bearing surfaces.

Table 11-2F gives bearing areas for thrust blocks to be used with various sizes of cast iron, ductile iron, and asbestos-cement pipe. There is, however, the practical difficulty of accurately measuring the surface of a lump of concrete dumped into a trench and determining within a square foot or two just how much bearing surface is being provided. It is better to err on the generous side when pouring a thrust block. Thrust blocks are shown in Figures 11-2P and 11-2Q.

Table 11-2F. Area of Bearing Face of Concrete Thrust Blocks

	Sq Ft			Sq Ft		
	Cast-iron and ductile-iron			Asbestos-cement		
Nominal size, in.	$\frac{1}{4}$ Bend	$\frac{1}{8}$ Bend	Tees, Plugs, Caps, Hydrants	$\frac{1}{4}$ Bend	$\frac{1}{8}$ Bend	Tees, Plugs, Caps, Hydrants
4	3	2	3	3	2	3
6	7	4	5	7	4	5
8	11	6	8	12	6	8
10	17	9	12	19	10	13
12	24	13	17	27	15	19
14	32	18	23	37	20	26
16	42	23	30	47	26	33
18	53	29	37	68	36	48
20	65	35	46	84	46	29
24	92	50	66	122	61	86

Basis: 2,000 psf soil resistance.
　　　250 psi water pressure.
Correction factors for other soils: soft clay　　　4
　　　　　　　　　　　　　　　　　sand　　　　　　2
　　　　　　　　　　　　　　　　　sand and gravel　1.33
　　　　　　　　　　　　　　　　　shale　　　　　　0.4

Testing

All pipelines, of whatever material, should be subjected to hydrostatic test, either by sections as completed or as a whole after completion. Such testing is usually done after the trench has been partially backfilled.

Asbestos-cement Pipe: In asbestos-cement pipelines, leakage and pressure tests are usually made at the same time over a period of at least 1 hr. After the pipeline is completed, it is filled with water, allowed to stand 24 hrs and then subjected to hydrostatic test. The test pressure is usually 1.5 times the operating pressure, and the test is made on sections before backfilling is completed. Allowable leakage is set by AWWA standard; it ranges from 0.71 gph (gallons per hour) per 100 couplings on 4-in. pipe at 50 psi pressure to 13.5 gph per 100 couplings on 36-in. pipe at 225 psi pressure. The data in AWWA C603-65 are based on a standard pressure of 150 psi and a leakage of 30 gpd (gallons per day) per mile of pipe per inch of pipe diameter for 13-ft pipe lengths.

Cast-iron Pipe: The usual procedure for testing cast-iron pipe is to fill each valved section of the pipeline slowly until all air is expelled. Then the pressure is brought up to the test level to determine if any leakage exists at joints. When joints do show evidence of leakage, they should be recaulked, otherwise adjusted or repaired as required.

All new cast-iron piping is tested hydrostatically at not less than 200 psi for 2 hrs or at 50 psi in excess of the maximum static pressure when the maximum static pressure is in excess of 150 psi. Leakage in piping is measured at the specified test pressure by pumping from a calibrated container.

New cast-iron pipe laid with rubber gasketed joints should have no leakage at the joints. Unsatisfactory amounts of leakage usually result from twisted, pinched or cut gaskets; however, some leakage might result from small amounts of grit or small imperfections. Leakage at the joints should not exceed 2 quarts per hour per 100 joints irrespective of pipe diameter. The leakage should be distributed over all joints. If leakage occurs at a few joints the installation of those joints should be considered unsatisfactory and repairs made.

New cast-iron pipe laid with caulked lead or lead-substitute joints should have little or no leakage at the joints. Any joint having leakage or more than a "slight drip" or "weeping" should be repaired. Leakage should not exceed 1 oz (liquid measure) per hour per inch of pipe diameter per joint. The leakage should be distributed over all joints. If leakage occurs almost entirely at a few joints, the installation should be considered unsatisfactory and necessary repairs made. The amount of allowable leakage may be increased by 1 fluid ounce per inch of valve diameter per hour for each metal seated valve in the test section.

Backfilling

Earth should be well tamped under and around pipes (and puddled where possible) to prevent settlement or lateral movement, and should contain no ashes, cinders, or other corrosive materials. Where the ground in which the pipe is laid is partly or wholly cinder-fill, care should be taken that about a foot of cinder-free dirt be put in the trench below the pipe and no dirt containing cinders be used in backfilling around the pipe. Cinders stimulate galvanic actions which may cause the pipe to fail in a relatively short period. There are similar considerations in occupancies where salt or other industrial wastes, e.g., from cattle sheds, packing operations and chemical plants, might seep into the ground.

Rocks should not be rolled into trenches nor allowed to drop on pipes. In trenches cut through rock, backfilling is normally entirely of earth. In any case, earth should be used under and around pipe and at least 2 ft above it.

Flushing

After a system of underground pipe for fire protection has been completed and before it is permanently filled with water, the entire system is thoroughly flushed out under pressure through hydrants or other outlets. Mains supplying sprinkler systems are flushed at the following rates: 6-in. pipe, 750 gpm; 8-in., 1,000 gpm; 10-in., 1,500 gpm; and 12-in., 2,000 gpm.

During flushing, the valves to any inside sprinkler or standpipe equipment are closed to avoid the washing of stones or other debris into the inside system. Branches from the outside system are flushed before they are connected to sprinkler or standpipe risers.

F. Hydrants

The most important features of good hydrants for fire protection are:

1. Normal diameter of bottom valve opening at least 4 in. for two 2½-in. or larger outlets, 5 in. for three 2½-in. or larger outlets, and 6 in. for four 2½-in. or larger outlet hydrants. Hydrants having a bottom valve less than 4 in., or outlets less than two 2½ inches, are not approved or listed by recognized testing laboratories. The connection between a water main and a hydrant is not less than 6 in. diameter.

2. The net area of the hydrant barrel is not less than 120 percent that of the valve opening.

3. A liberal-sized waterway and small friction loss. With the hydrant discharging 250 gpm through each 2½-in. hose outlet, the total friction loss of the hydrant must not exceed 2 psi for two-outlet hydrants, 3 psi for three-outlet hydrants and 4 psi for four-outlet hydrants.

4. A drip valve of noncorrosive construction.

5. A uniform-sized pentagonal operating nut measuring 1½ in. from point to flat at the base and $1\frac{7}{16}$ in. at the top.

Types of Hydrants

Hydrant bonnets, barrels, and foot pieces are generally made of cast iron with internal working parts of bronze. Valve facings vary and may be leather, rubber or a composition material. Hydrants are available with various configurations of outlets.

Probably one of the most common types has two 2½-in. outlets and one large pumper outlet. However, hydrants are available with up to six individual 2½-in. outlets and with two or more pumper outlets with or without individual 2½-in. outlets.

There are two types of fire hydrants in general use today. The most common is the base valve (dry barrel) type where

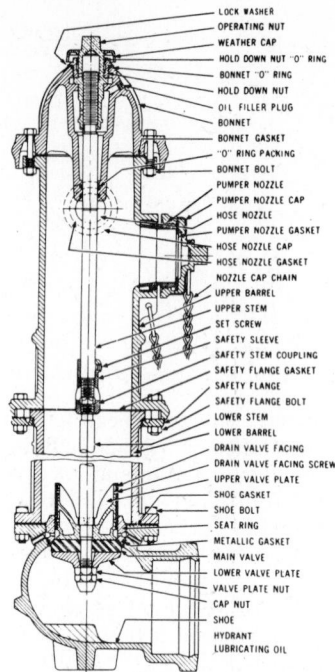

Fig. 11-2R. A base valve or "dry barrel" hydrant with nomenclature identified. When installed, the valve is below the frost line. This type of hydrant is also known as a "frost proof" hydrant. (Mueller Co.)

the valve controlling the water is located below the frost line between the foot piece and the barrel of the hydrant (see Fig. 11-2R). The barrel on this type hydrant is normally dry with water being admitted only when there is a need. A drain valve at the base of the barrel is open when the main valve is closed allowing residual water in the barrel to drain out. This type of hydrant is used whenever there is a chance

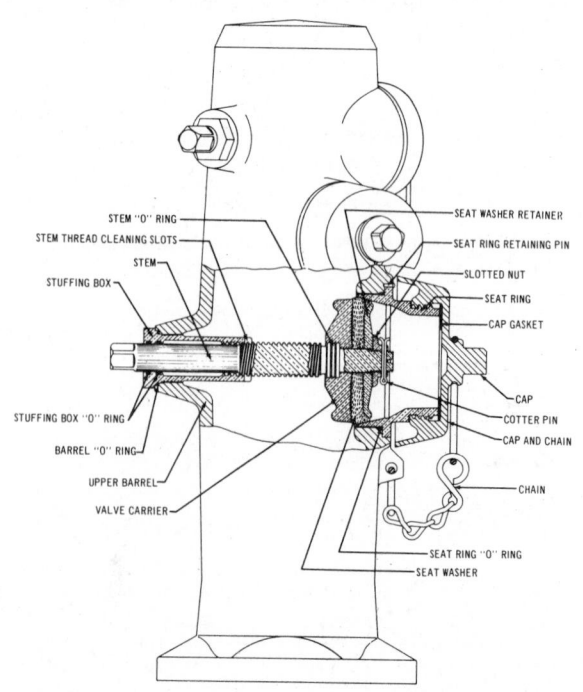

Fig. 11-2S. A wet barrel or "California" hydrant used where freezing is not encountered. There is a compression valve at each outlet. (Mueller Co.)

weather conditions will go below freezing as the valve and water supply are installed below the frost line.

The other type of hydrant is the wet barrel (California) type which is sometimes used when weather conditions are such that there is no danger of freezing. These hydrants usually have a compression type valve at each outlet but they may have one valve in the bonnet that controls the water flow to all outlets (see Fig. 11-2S).

Location

Hydrant spacing is now determined by fire flow demand under the ISO *Grading Schedule for Municipal Fire Protection*. Table 11-2G gives the average area per hydrant for each fire flow. However, this must be tempered with engineering decision. In no area should hydrant spacing exceed 800 ft between hydrants. In closed built areas, 500 ft between hydrants is more realistic. Hydrants should be located as close to an intersection as possible with intermediate hydrants along the street to meet the area requirements.

Where hydrants are located on a private water system and hose lines are intended to be used directly from the hydrants, they should be so located as to keep hose lines short, preferably not over 250 ft. At a minimum, there should be enough hydrants to make two streams available at every part of the interior of each building not covered by standpipe protection. They should also provide hose stream protection for exterior parts of each building using only the lengths of hose normally attached to the hydrants. It is desirable to have sufficient hydrants to concentrate the required fire flow about any important building with no hose line exceeding 500 ft in length. (The term "fire flow" is explained in Chapter 1 of this Section.)

For average conditions, hydrants normally are placed about 50 ft from the buildings protected. Where that is impossible, they are set where chance of injury by falling walls is small and from which men are not likely to be driven by smoke or heat. In crowded mill yards, hydrants usually can be placed beside low buildings, near substantial stair towers,

Table 11-2G.   Standard Hydrant Distribution

Fire Flow Required Gpm	Average Area per Hydrant Square feet
1,000 or less	160,000
1,500	150,000
2,000	140,000
2,500	130,000
3,000	120,000
3,500	110,000
4,000	100,000
4,500	95,000
5,000	90,000
5,500	85,000
6,000	80,000
6,500	75,000
7,000	70,000
7,500	65,000
8,000	60,000
8,500	57,500
9,000	55,000
10,000	50,000
11,000	45,000
12,000	40,000

Source: *Grading Schedule for Municipal Fire Protection,* Insurance Services Office.

or at corners formed by masonry walls which are not likely to fall.

Hydrants that must be located in areas subject to heavy traffic need protection against damage from collision. Two examples are parking lots of shopping centers and mill yards.

Setting of Hydrants

Hydrants are set plumb with outlets about 18 in. above the ground (18 in. above the floor in hose houses). When hydrants are placed before grading is completed, the final grade line and accessibility should be considered. Most hydrants have a grade line indicated on the barrel of the hydrant.

Drainage is necessary in "frostproof" hydrants and can be provided by excavating a pit about 2 ft in diameter and 2 ft deep below the base of the hydrant and filling it compactly with coarse gravel or stones placed around the bowl of the hydrant to a level of 6 in. above the waste opening. If the drip valve of the hydrant is below ground water level, it may be plugged to exclude ground water. In that case, water remaining in the hydrant after use should be pumped out to prevent freezing.

The bowl of a hydrant should be secured to the next preceding bell with anchoring or locking joints or rods and clamps, or securely anchored by means of concrete backing. Manufacturers furnish hydrants with lugs cast on the bell to facilitate strapping (see Fig. 11-2M).

Maintenance and Testing

Well-designed and installed hydrants present a minimum of maintenance difficulties. The dry barrel hydrant, for example, has a small drain near the base of the barrel arranged to permit water to drain out of the barrel when the main valve is shut. When the main valve is open, this drain is closed. If this drain is working properly and the main valve is tight, the difficulty of freezing of water in the barrel is avoided. Occasionally situations are found where ground drainage is unsatisfactory or where ground water may stand at dangerous levels. In those cases drains may be closed entirely and hydrant barrels pumped out periodically.

The use of salt or salt solutions to prevent freezing is not recommended because of their corrosive effect and limited usefulness. If anti-freeze is used in hydrant barrels, it should be of a noncombustible type.

Suggestions for detecting freezing in hydrants include:

1. Sounding by striking the hand over an open outlet. Water or ice shortens the length of the "organ tube" and raises the note.

2. Try turning hydrant stem. If frozen solidly, the stem will not turn. If only slightly bound by ice, placing a hydrant wrench on the nut and tapping smartly may release the stem. Blows should be moderate to prevent breaking valve rod.

3. Lowering a weight on a stout string into the hydrant. It may strike ice or come up wet, showing water in the barrel.

Probably the most satisfactory method of thawing a hydrant is by means of a steam hose. In many plants, steam is available for that purpose. A thawing device in which steam may be rapidly produced is also standard equipment of many fire departments. In either case, the steam hose is introduced into the hydrant through an outlet and pushed down, thawing as it goes.

Sometimes quicklime is placed in the hydrant barrel with hot water. This is effective but requires thorough flushing of the hydrant.

A major item of periodic maintenance is a check for leaks in (1) the main valve when hydrant is closed, (2) the drip valve when the main valve is open but outlets capped, and (3) the mains near the hydrant. Stethoscope-like listening devices are available to make these checks. Maintenance routines provide for an operating test, repair of leaks, and pumping out of the hydrants where necessary. Threads of the outlet, caps, and valve stem should be lubricated with graphite. Hydrants should be kept well painted but care should be taken in painting to prevent accumulations of paint from preventing easy removal of caps or operation of valve stems.

Uniform Marking of Fire Hydrants

Color coding hydrants based on fire flow available from them is of substantial value to water and fire departments. A test of an individual hydrant does not give as complete and satisfactory results as group testing, but such a test has sufficient value to make it worthy of adoption as a start in the right direction. The colors are understood to signify only the capacity of the individual hydrant as tested and not group hydrant effect.

NFPA No. 291, Uniform Marking of Fire Hydrants, recommends that hydrants be classified as follows:

Class	Flow	Color of bonnets and nozzle caps
A	1000 gpm or greater	Green
B	500 to 1000 gpm	Orange
C	Less than 500 gpm	Red

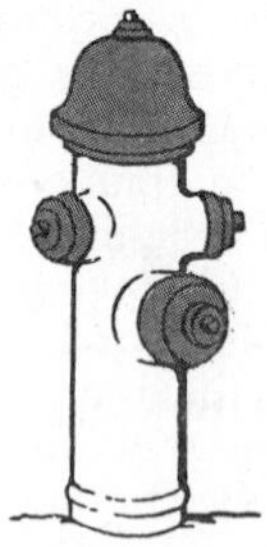

Fig. 11-2T. Shaded areas are color-coded to show the hydrant's flow capacity.

Capacities are rated by flow measurement and tests of individual hydrants at a period of ordinary demand. Rating is based on 20 psi residual pressures when initial pressures are over 40 psi. When initial pressures are less than 40 psi, residual pressures are at least half the initial pressure.

The capacity-indicating color scheme provides simplicity and consistency with colors used in signal work for safety, danger and intermediate conditions. Barrels of all public hydrants are normally chrome yellow except in cases where another color has already been adopted.

Within private enclosures marking of private hydrants is at the discretion of the owner. Private hydrants on public streets are painted red to distinguish them from public hydrants.

Location markers for flush hydrants carry the same color background for class indication with such data stenciled or painted thereon as may be necessary.

G.   Control Valves for Distribution Systems

Water distribution systems require valves at strategic locations and intervals to control flow as circumstances dictate. Gate valves, with or without indicating posts, and check valves are the two types of controlling valves used in supply systems.

Required features for listed and approved valves and indicator posts are:

For Gate Valves:

1. Stems of bronze having a minimum tensile strength of 32,000 psi.

2. Stuffing boxes having good-sized packing space.

3. Gland and bonnet opening, bronze-lined, and valve capable of being repacked under water pressure.

4. Yokes bolted on bonnets in valves larger than 4 in.

For Check Valves:

1. Large clearances between moving parts and valve body.

2. A clapper which moves entirely out of the waterway.

3. Bronze-to-bronze bearings having large wearing surfaces.

4. Valve of the straightaway type and iron body valve having a waterway equal to the area of the pipe.

For Indicator Posts:

1. A uniform flange to suit all sizes of gate valves.

2. Interchangeable operating stems.

3. Adjustable and interchangeable target plates.

4. Uniform sized square operating nut measuring $1\frac{1}{4}$ in. square by 1 in. high.

Gate Valves

Gate valves of the nonindicating type are provided in distribution systems to allow small segments to be shut off for repairs or extensions without reducing protection over a wide area. Such valves are normally a nonrising stem type which requires a key wrench to operate. A valve box is located over the valve to keep dirt from the valve and to provide a convenient access point for the valve wrench to the valve nut (see Fig. 11-2U).

Good practice dictates that valves are provided so that no single accident, break, or repair will necessitate shutting down a length of pipe greater than 500 ft in high value districts or greater than 800 ft in other sections, and so that flow may be maintained through other arterial mains.

Where a connection for fire protection is taken from a public system, the water utility customarily installs a control valve between the street main and the line to the private connection for fire protection. This valve is a service valve of the nonindicating type so that the water utility employees

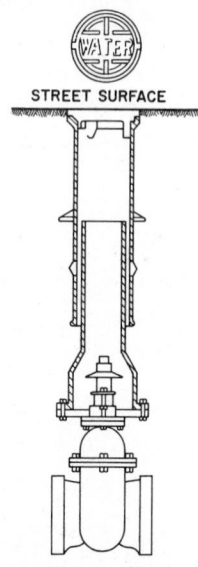

Fig. 11-2U.   A nonindicating-type gate valve for underground installation.

do not have to enter a private property to shut off the service. This valve is seldom operated and is provided principally as a convenience during installation of the rest of the private connection and for occasional use if extensions or repairs of either system are undertaken.

A water utilities' ability to operate promptly gate valves in the distribution system is important. It enables damaged areas in the system, or damaged facilities or equipment, to be cut off to prevent loss of water and to maintain service in areas unaffected by the damage. A well-run water utility has records of where all valves are located and has procedures for inspecting and operating each valve not less than once a year. Too many water utilities do not have such records, nor do the valves get frequent enough inspection and test operation.

Indicating Valves

The first valve in the fire line on private property is a valve of the indicating type. It may be one of three kinds: (1) underground gate valve with indicator post attached, (2) underground butterfly indicating type with post and (3) O. S. & Y. (outside screw and yoke) gate valve in a pit.

(The type of underground gate valve commonly used in domestic and industrial water lines which requires a key wrench to operate it should be avoided in fire lines. The difficulties of finding such valves, of getting up cover plates, and of locating a key wrench that will fit are determinants to its use. If used, underground gate valves should open counter-clockwise and have the same size nut on all valve stems. The valve locations are clearly marked on nearby buildings.)

Indicator posts can carry advantageously a metal plate showing what they control. Painting building names or numbers on them is always advisable. The proper direction to turn for opening should be shown. Posts often are locked in the open position to prevent tampering. Lock shackles should, however, be brittle so that locks can be removed readily if they are frozen and keys will not work. Posts should preferably have a handle, wheel, or wrench attached. Typical indicator post type valves are shown in Figure 11-2V.

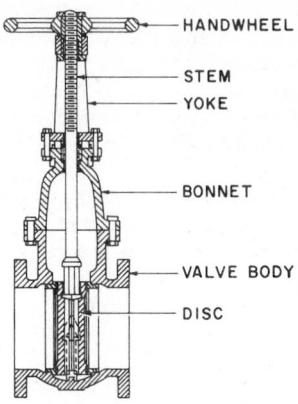

Fig. 11-2W. A typical outside screw and yoke (O.S. & Y.) valve. The spindle on the valve stem indicates whether the valve is open or shut.

O. S. & Y. gate valves, if underground, should be in pits. Important junction points often warrant the use of pits to cover several valves. Indicating valves are used on all shut-offs. They are universally used on inside piping as they show the position of the gates at a glance. They are commonly strapped or otherwise sealed open. For a recommended sealing procedure, see Section 10, Chapter 2. Where O. S. & Y. gate valves are in pits, a metal sleeve with upper end closed may be slipped over the valve stem to keep off dirt. An O. S. & Y. gate valve is shown in Figure 11-2W.

Check Valves

Next to this main control valve inside the property, a check valve is installed. Except where the check valve can be inside a building, it must be installed in a pit, even when the main control valve is a conventional buried valve with an indicating post. The check valve also needs to be accessible so the size of the pit, the arrangement of its manhole and ladder, and the size of working space around the valve or valves in the pit should be provided with an eye to convenient access (see Fig. 11-2X).

The purpose of a check valve is to allow water to flow from a public system to a private system but not from a private system into the public system. This arrangement also permits water at higher pressures in a private system

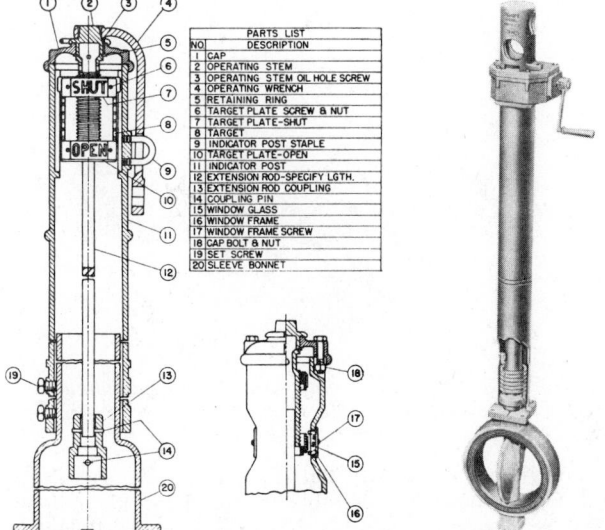

Fig. 11-2V. Details of a standard indicator post for gate valves are shown at left. Practically all manufacturers of valves furnish standard valves, and their catalogs should be consulted for details of each. At right is a post indicating valve of the butterfly type. (Henry Pratt Co.)

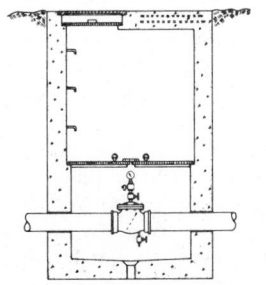
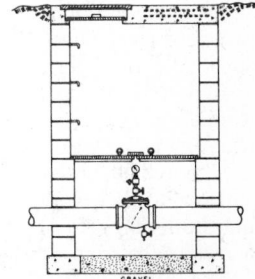

REINFORCED CONCRETE
Most substantial design. Appropriate where there is ground water.

CONCRETE BLOCK ASSEMBLY
A design which can be used where there is good ground drainage.

Fig. 11-2X. A valve pit is usually provided for a check valve (as shown) and for O.S. & Y. gate valves, meters, and other equipment on underground mains. Pit should be about 5 ft sq for one check valve. Clearance should be preferably 18 in. around all valves and equipment in the pit. Pits are as deep as necessary to conform to the location of the pipe in which the valve is located.

than the normal pressures in the connecting public water mains in case of fire. Higher pressures can be provided in a private system through its own fire pumps, where these are provided, or by fire department pumpers when they pump through the fire department connections on automatic sprinkler systems and standpipe systems in buildings or on a private yard system.

Check valves also are installed at the base of gravity tanks and in the private or fire department pump connections. The check valves at these points assure flow of water one way only.

Connections between potable and nonpotable water systems should be avoided. Where one water system must be separated positively from another, an air gap is provided so that backflow cannot occur. An example of an air gap is where water from one system is supplied through a pipe which discharges into a tank above the level of the water in the tank. Such an arrangement does not allow the receiving water system to have the advantage of the pressures available in the supplying system. With a connection through a check valve, practically all of the pressure in the supplying system may be available.

Double Check Valves

Commercial type single check valves normally close tightly. However, they may leak, particularly if not given periodic care. Unless there is some question of the safe quality of the water involved, a small flow from leaks in check valves in private systems would not affect the water in the public system. For situations where there is some question of leaks, double check valve equipment is available. (Double check valves are required for certain situations by the regulations of some departments of health.) Check valves in double installations are made with bronze working parts and rubber facings so that they will have tight seats. For each connecton, two of these valves are installed in series, thus increasing the efficiency, as the probability that both will leak at the same time is extremely remote. The two check valves are installed between valves in a pit where they are readily accessible for examination. In addition, the valves are provided with pressure gages and test cocks so arranged that the tightness of each check valve may be verified in a few minutes.

Figure 11-2Y shows a typical double check valve installation in a pit. The Bronze checks for this type of installation are made in 4-, 6-, 8-, and 10-in. sizes. To keep the cost of the equipment at a minimum, 6-in. valves may be used on 8-in. connections and 8-in. valves on 10-in. connections by using taper reducers. Such an arrangement will not materially increase friction loss because the section of reduced size is short.

When the two check valves are bolted together, an 18-in. space is provided between clappers, which is sufficient to prevent any ordinary material found in a pipe line from holding both clappers open at the same time. To improve further the efficiency of the equipment, a filling piece of pipe or spacer from 3 ft to 5 ft long installed between the check valves is advised where space is available.

Back-flow Preventers: Figure 11-2Z shows a backflow preventer assembly which is intended to maintain pressure between two check valves at less than the supply pressure in the pipe line. The assembly consists of two independently acting approved check valves interspaced by an automatically operated pressure differential relief valve. In case of leakage at either check valve, the relief valve operates to maintain the pressure between the check valves at less than supply pressure. There is some loss of head in such backflow

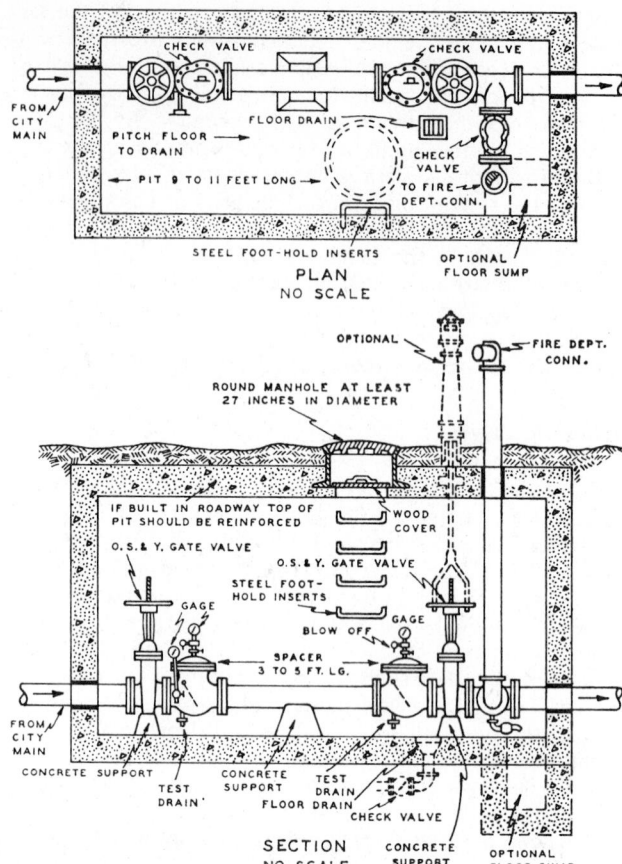

Fig. 11-2Y. Plan and section views showing the arrangement of double check valves in a connection for fire protection from a public water system. Indicating valves of the "butterfly" type designed for fire service may be used in place of the gate valves illustrated.

Fig. 11-2Z. A backflow preventer assembly for installation between two independently acting check valves. (Hersey-Sparling Meter Co.)

preventers, but there may be situations where sacrificing some loss of head is preferable to sacrificing all of it as would be necessary with an air gap separation. Backflow preventers are available for 8-, 10-, and 16-in. pipe lines.

Location of Valves

Opinions vary on how many valves should be used in a system of underground mains. More plants have probably been destroyed on account of a sectional control valve being shut than because a large part of the system was out of commission by reason of too few sectional valves. Nevertheless, the modern tendency is to make fairly liberal use of valves. Well-established principles shown in Figure 11-2AA are:

1. City supply check valve (and meter, if required) between indicating valves so it can be repaired without affecting city or plant systems.

2. Pump check valve between pump and indicating valves so that the latter can be used to shut off the connection to the system when making check valve and pump repairs.

3. Pit No. 1, in addition to the main water supply valve, contains three sectional valves, two (G and H) to take care of present loop and one (J) for a short branch supplying a small detached building. The branch will ultimately be part of a second loop. There should be a loop valve on each side of every valuable water supply so as to permit cutting off a part of the loop without cutting the water supply off altogether. Best practice requires that post indicators be attached to valves in pits, with the posts cemented into the concrete tops.

4. Indicator posts E and F are sectional control valves to cut loop (in connection with valves C and G) into four sections. In large or complicated underground systems, it is recommended that indicator posts controlling risers to sprinklers or standpipes be painted a different color from sectional control valves. Generally, not over six hydrants or indicator posts should be located between section valves.

5. Individual repair valves must always be provided where hydrants are connected to a water main of primary importance.

It is an element of weakness not to have a number of men know the location of all valves, especially sectional repair valves, and exactly what the various valves control. In event of a break in the underground system or the abandonment of a flowing hydrant during a fire, it is essential that the water be promptly shut off to protect the supply to other hydrants or sprinkler connections. Handling valves correctly and rapidly at time of fire, especially at night and under snow conditions, requires accurate knowledge. The recommended practice of painting section valves a color

different from that of valves in sprinkler lines is helpful in identifying valves that are grouped.

Familiarity with valves and their locations is best accomplished in the following manner:

1. By obtaining an accurate map and making a study of the valve system, recording in tabular form the valve or valves necessary to cut off each hydrant and post indicator (and, of course, piping to or near them), and listing the hydrants and post indicators also affected.

2. By putting this data in notebook form for convenient study and reference, and for use by the municipal fire department if needed.

3. By making officers of the plant fire department study and learn the conditions.

4. By holding drills in which it is assumed that breaks in piping have occurred.

5. By posting in plant fire department headquarters the facts regarding any interruptions of the system, and also notifying the department officers of the facts.

Maintenance and Testing

It is good testing policy to operate underground valves at least once a year during nonfreezing weather. More frequent operation may accelerate leakage of stuffing boxes. It is good practice to oil or grease valves annually.

Check valves should be checked and tested for tightness monthly, particularly where double check valves are used to prevent back flow between potable water and yard systems. The test drains and gages provide a means for determining where a leak may exist. Even though found tight when tested periodically, check valves should be thoroughly cleaned at regular intervals, preferably once a year so that they will remain tight.

Where there are several sets of check valves in fire connections from public mains, only one set of check valves should be overhauled and cleaned at a time, the others being left in service.

H. Meters for Fire Connections

Fire flow meters are devices capable of measuring small and large flows with a minimum loss of head for heavy

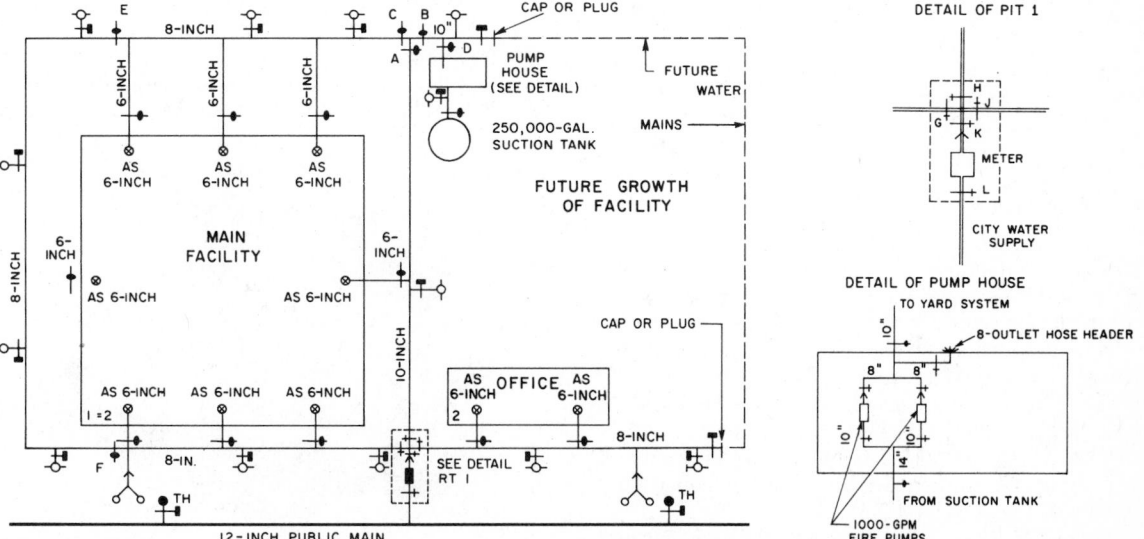

Fig. 11-2AA. Water piping for fire protection of an industrial site. Typical details shown are: connections to public mains and supplies for private fire pump, looped water mains, sectional control valves (lettered), and hydrants.

demands. They are offered in two types: (1) detector check valve-type meters that detect only small rates of flow and (2) so-called full registration meters that measure the entire flow throughout the line in which they are installed. Meters of types other than the fire flow type have been found to be unsatisfactory for fire protection water supplies.

Detector Checks

These devices consist of a check valve with a weighted clapper in the main passage and a disc meter in a bypass around the check. In operation the smaller flows pass through the disc meter in the bypass and are accurately registered. Disc meters may be furnished up to 3 in. in size to serve specific needs. For heavy flows the check valve opens and a free unmetered waterway is provided. Beyond the point where the weighted check valve lifts, the bypass meter registers only a small part of the flow. In many situations the detector checks should give the water works the assurance desired as to the proper use of water.

Figure 11-2BB shows a representative detector check valve.

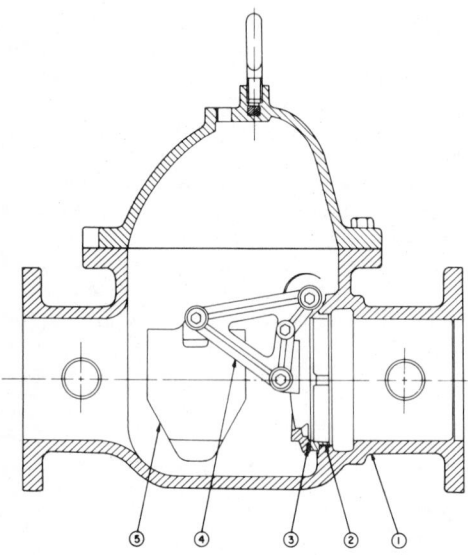

Fig. 11-2BB.   A detector check valve. Photo shows view from top of weighted check valve and meter in bypass. Section view shows clapper in closed position. (The Viking Corporation)

Full Registration Meters

These devices are of three general types, each produced by a different manufacturer, and they have been designed for small friction loss with large flows and for a main passageway practically unobstructed when open. The three types are: (1) proportional type meters, (2) meters of the displacement type in a bypass and (3) turbine-type meters.

Proportional Type, Hersey Detector Meter, Model FM: This meter is a special meter of the compound type in which a "proportional meter" and an automatic valve in the main line of the meter are combined with a disc or compound meter in a bypass (see Fig. 11-2CC).

In the Model FM, the smaller flows pass through and are measured by the bypass meter. When the demand for water reaches a rate of flow which causes a difference in pressure

Fig. 11-2CC.   A detector meter of the proportional type. (Hersey-Sparling Meter Company)

of 4 psi in the bypass, the automatic check valve opens and provides a practically free waterway through the main line. When water begins to flow through the line in which the automatic valve has opened, it is slightly retarded by a restricting orifice placed a little upstream from the automatic valve, and a part of the water is diverted through a metering unit. This diverted flow is a fixed percentage of the total flow through the restricting orifice. The metering unit is calibrated to record the total quantity through the line, the sum of the readings of the bypass meter and the main line metering unit gives the total flow.

Displacement Type, Neptune Trident Protectus Meter: This meter has all of the working parts in one casing. A disc meter is installed in a bypass on one side and a current meter on the other side of the main waterway. Small flows pass through the disc meter and are recorded when the check valve is closed. With larger flows the main check valve opens and gives a free waterway. The opening of the check valve stops the flow through the disc meter and opens the bypass to the current meter so that the flow through the open waterway is measured proportionately. The sum of the readings gives the total flow (see Fig. 11-2DD).

Turbo Type, Rockwell W-2000 Turbo Meter: This meter is based on the turbine principle of measurement. The meter is composed of two principal assemblies, the main case and the measuring chamber. The main case contains the flow straightening vane assembly. The measuring chamber includes rotor, adjusting vane, pulse amplifier chart and terminal strip for attaching the connecting cable. The function

Fig. 11-2DD.   A fire flow meter of the displacement type. (Neptune Meter Company)

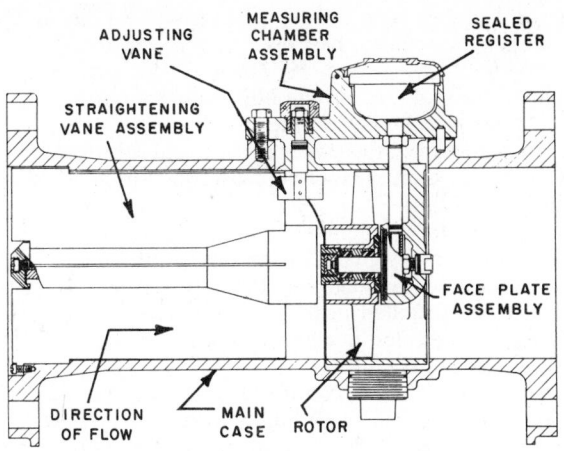

Fig. 11-2EE. A fire flow meter of the turbo type. (Rockwell Mfg. Co.)

of a printed circuit card is to electronically count revolutions and transmit intelligence to a register. The meter should be installed with a 6-in. Rockwell strainer placed immediately upstream of the meter. If the strainer is not used, a minimum of 15 diameters of straight pipe must be immediately upstream of the meter to assure valid registration (see Fig. 11-2EE).

Friction Loss in Fire Flow Meters and Detector Check Valves

The standard specifications for cold water meters adopted by both the American Water Works Association and the New England Water Works Association limit the friction loss for fire flow meters to 4 psi at rated flow capacities. Table 11-2H gives friction loss values for the three currently available types of fire flow meters.

Friction loss values for meters of the disc, current and compound type that are used commonly in waterworks systems for general purposes are relatively high and not suited for fire protection purposes. AWWA limits their friction loss values to 20 psi.

Detector Check Valves: The friction loss in detector check valves listed and approved by recognized testing laboratories is less than 3 psi for the following flows:

Size (in.)	Flow (gpm)
4	750
6	1,500
8	3,000
10	4,500
12	6,500

The pressure required to open the clapper is less than 20 psi.

I. Connection Between Public and Private Water Systems

Connections from public water systems for fire protection are for the purpose of providing water supply to the following:

1. Automatic sprinkler systems.
2. Standpipes for hand hose or fire department use.
3. Open sprinklers.
4. Yard systems with private hydrants.
5. Fire pumps.
6. Private storage reservoirs or tanks for fire protection.

A fundamental principle is that piping systems from which water is used for fire shall be independent, within the property, of systems for domestic and industrial service. Special conditions where this is not the case are rare and may be dealt with individually.

In public water systems, economics favor a single water system for combined fire use and domestic service. In private properties it is economically practicable to have separate systems, and the advantages of a definite, dependable supply, free from interruptions of service inevitable in a domestic system, strongly favor the established practice.

Occasionally a property will have two sources of water supply for fire protection, one from the public supply, the other from a private source, many times nonpotable. When this happens, adequate measures must be taken to prevent the public water supply from becoming contaminated. Means of achieving this have been discussed previously in this chapter. Some communities do not allow any direct connection and as such separate systems must be maintained if two supplies are required or desired with an air gap between the two systems.

Table 11-2H. Friction Loss in Fire Flow Meters
Compiled from data supplied by manufacturers

Meter Name and Type	Size of Meter Inches	Loss of Pressure Caused by Meter Pounds per Square Inch							
		Gallons per Minute Flowing							
		250	500	750	1000	1250	1500	2000	2500
Proportional Type (Hersey-FM)	4	2.2	1.9	4.0					
	6	3.8	2.7	1.4	1.8	2.2	2.9	3.9	
	8	3.0	3.7	1.9	1.0	0.8	0.8	1.3	2.2
	10	1.6	3.6	4.0	3.7	2.6	1.4	0.8	1.1
Differential Type (Trident Protectus)	4	2.2	2.0	3.9					
	6	2.9	1.9	1.8	1.8	1.8	1.8	2.2	3.3
	8	3.2	1.8	1.5	1.5	1.5	1.6	1.8	2.2
	10	3.0	2.3	1.8	1.3	1.2	1.1	1.1	1.2
Turbo Type (Rockwell W-2000 Turbo)	6	0.2	0.3	0.6	0.85	1.2	1.6	3.5	

Charges for Connections for Fire Protection

The question of annual stand-by charges for connections from a public water system to fire protection piping may be controversial largely because the nature of automatic sprinkler systems is not always understood by public officials. Whatever charges are made should be based on actual cost to the utility and not on possible value of the installation to the customer. Annual charges for connections to fire protection piping are often established in water rate schedules for the sole purpose of obtaining additional revenue.

Although many waterworks, both public and private, make no stand-by charge for connections for fire protection, there are no objections to charges that fairly reflect actual cost to the waterworks of the connection including necessary pits, valves, and meters. There could be costs to the waterworks for amortization of costs of its part of the connection and for its maintenance and inspection. However, it is usual to charge for the installation when it is made, and if repairs, maintenance, and inspection are charged for when done, there is little other cost involved.

Since water for fire fighting is paid for on a community basis through taxes, it is almost universal practice to make no charge to property owners for the water actually used in the extinguishment of fire or for authorized fire flow testing.

Control of Connections During Fires

The safe location of control valves for connections for fire protection is important so that they may be shut off promptly after water extinguishing systems have put out the fire, or to conserve water and pressure if pipes have been broken.

Sprinkler systems have outside indicating valves where yard space is available. This is the preferable arrangement. In many city properties having no yard space, valves are installed in a stair tower or other well cut-off area. Sometimes the control valves are located outside the area protected as, for example, on the other side of a fire wall. In a relatively few instances dependence must be placed on the accessibility of the valve on the connection to the street main.

Experience has shown that in practically all fires, sprinkler control valves on private property have been adequate to serve their intended use and allow prompt and safe control of fire protection.

Control of Water Waste

There are a number of conditions under which flow of water from private fire protection equipment other than for fire or testing purposes may occur. These are:

1. Leakage
2. Wrongful use, such as wetting down roofs, watering lawns, or waste through ignorance
3. Emergency use
4. Theft

Fire protection equipment should be inspected several times a year, to assure that the systems will be kept free from material leakage or unauthorized connections. Maintenance rules enforced by inspection authorities tend to discourage wrongful uses of these systems. These are further enforced in many places by fire department inspections, which are made to assure that valves controlling extinguishing systems and other fire supplies are kept open and that hose and other equipment are not used for any purpose other than that intended. Occasional inspections by waterworks inspectors are desirable.

In cases where inspections alone are not a sufficient safeguard against water waste, a plan involving the securing of valves and outlets has been successfully used. (For securing methods see Sec. 10, Chap. 2.) In such cases all sprinkler drains, hydrants and hose outlets are sealed by the water utility which may require:

1. A report from the owner when a seal is broken.
2. A notice from the user before testing through hydrants or sprinkler drains.
3. Payment of a nominal charge for resealing.

As a further safeguard, indemnity to the water utility may be secured by requiring the user to file a bond or deposit to be forfeited in the event of willful or persistent violation of the rules or abuse of the fire service furnished by the water utility.

The simplest cases of control of water waste to deal with are fire connections in single buildings such as those serving:

1. One or more standpipes for hand hose or fire department use.
2. Automatic extinguishing systems only.
3. Combined automatic sprinkler systems and standpipes.

In connections of these types, any regulation on the part of a water utility (for the ostensible purpose of preventing water waste) which involves an excessive annual charge or a costly meter installation, may impose an expense to the property owner so large as to discourage the installation of extinguishing systems or standpipes. This affects particularly a class of property—small industrials and mercantiles—in which the bulk of current fire losses occur, and which greatly needs the protection.

Ordinarily inspections, or at most a valve securing procedure, will give adequate protection to the utility. In extreme cases, special action may be taken by a utility against any individual violator. In adopting any procedure to apply to all users of private fire protection, the relative unimportance of a very small amount of water improperly used, as against the greater public good in the extensive installation of automatic sprinklers and other private fire equipment, should be considered.

Fire protection connections which serve several buildings with extinguishing systems and standpipes, or, in addition, a yard system with private hydrants, fire pump and tank supplies, may introduce a slightly more difficult problem of water waste control. In general, inspection of sealing procedures will suffice, and both may be appropriate in some cases. Where meters are employed on fire connections, the extent to which they reduce pressures and obstruct or reduce flows must be determined.

SI Units

The following conversion factors are given as a convenience in converting to SI units the English units used in this chapter

1 in.	= 25.400 mm
1 ft	= 0.305 mm
1 psi	= 6.895 kPa
1 gpm/sq ft	= 3.785 litres/min m²

Pipe Sizes (nominal)*

in.	mm
4	100
5	125
6	150
8	200
10	250
12	300
16	400
20	500

* Rounded off for convenience of use.

Bibliography

NFPA Codes, Standards and Recommended Practices (see the latest *NFPA Publications and Visual Aids Catalog* for availability of current editions of the following documents)

NFPA No. 24, Standard for Outside Protection.

NFPA No. 26, Standard for the Supervision and Care of Valves Controlling Water Supplies for Fire Protection.

NFPA No. 291, Recommendations for Uniform Marking of Fire Hydrants.

NFPA No. 292M, Water Charges for Private Fire Protection.

Other Codes and Standards

AWWA Handbooks, and Standards, American Water Works Association, 2 Park Avenue, New York, NY 10016 (see also USASI A21 listings).

AWWA C201, Standard for Fabricated Electrically Welded Steel Pipe, 1966.

AWWA C202, Standard for Mill-type Steel Water Pipe, 1964.

AWWA C203, Standard for Coal-Tar Enamel Protection Coatings for Steel Water Pipe, 1966.

AWWA C205, Standard for Cement-Mortar Protective Lining and Coating for Steel Water Pipe, 1971.

AWWA C300, Standard for Reinforced-Concrete Water Pipe—Steel Cylinder Type, Not Prestressed, 1964.

AWWA C301, Standard for Reinforced-Concrete Water Pipe—Steel Cylinder Type, Prestressed, 1964.

AWWA C302, Standard for Reinforced-Concrete Water Pipe—Noncylinder Type, Not Prestressed, 1964.

AWWA 303, Standard for Reinforced-Concrete Water Pipe—Steel Cylinder Type, Pretensioned, 1970.

AWWA C400, Standard for Asbestos-Cement Water Pipe, 1972.

AWWA C401-64, Standard Practice for the Selection of Asbestos-Cement Water Pipe, 1964.

AWWA C500, Standard for Gate Valves for Ordinary Water Works Service, 1971.

AWWA C502, Standard for Fire Hydrants for Ordinary Water Works Service, 1964.

AWWA C503, Standard for Wet-Barrel Fire Hydrants for Ordinary Water Works Service, 1970.

AWWA 506, Standard for Backflow Prevention Devices—Reduced Pressure Principle and Double Check Valve Types, 1969.

AWWA C600, Standard for Installation of Cast Iron Water Mains, 1964.

AWWA C603, Standard for Installation of Asbestos-Cement Water Pipe, 1965.

AWWA C703, Standard for Cold Water Meters—Fire Service Type, 1970.

Canadian Government Specification, Canadian Government Specification Board, National Research Council, Ottawa, Ontario.

No. 34-GP-la, Specification for Pipe; Asbestos-Cement, Pressure, 7 March 1957.

ULC Standards, Underwriters' Laboratories of Canada, 7 Crouse Road, Scarborough, Ontario.

No. C-246, Hydrants, January 1958.

No. C-262 (a), Inside Screw Valves for Underground Work, March 1950.

No. C-312, Swing Check Valves for Fire Protection Service, Nov., 1964.

No. C-789, Indicator Posts, June 1966.

No. C-888, Steel Pipe for Underground Water Service, May 1950.

UL Standards, Underwriters' Laboratories, Inc., 207 East Ohio Street, Chicago, IL 60611.

No. 107, Asbestos-Cement Pipe and Couplings, April 1973.

No. 246, Hydrants for Fire Protection Service, May 1973.

No. 262, Gate Valves for Fire Protection Service, May 1973.

No. 312, Swing Check Valves for Fire Protection Service, 1964.

No. 385, Play Pipes for Water Supply Testing, May 1973.

No. 789, Indicator Posts for Fire Protection Service, May 1971.

No. 888, Steel Pipe for Underground Water Service, Oct. 1972.

No. 194, Performance of Gasketed Joints for Cast Iron Pressure Pipe and Fittings, May 1973.

No. 753, Alarm Accessories for Automatic Water Supply Control Valves for Fire Protection Service, July 1971.

American National Standards Institute, Sectional Committee A21. (This committee is sponsored jointly by American Gas Association, American Society for Testing and Materials, American Water Works Association, and New England Water Works Association.) The following Manuals and Standards are published by American Water Works Association, 2 Park Avenue, New York NY 10016:

AWWA C101-67, ANSI A21.1—1967, Standard for Thickness Design of Cast Iron Pipe.

AWWA C150-71, ANSI A21.50—1971, Standard for the Thickness Design of Ductile-Iron Pipe.

AWWA C104-71, ANSI A21.4—1971, Standard for Cement-Mortar Lining for Cast Iron Pipe and Fittings for Water.

AWWA C106-70, ANSI A21.6-1970, Standard for Cast Iron Pipe Centrifugally Cast in Metal Molds, for Water and Other Liquids.

AWWA C108—1970, ANSI A21.8—1970, Standard for Cast Iron Pipe, Centrifugally Cast in Sand-Lined Molds, for Water and Other Liquids.

AWWA C110-71, ANSI A21.10-71, Standard for Cast-Iron Fittings, 2 in. through 48 in., for Water and Other Liquids.

AWWA C111-72, ANSI A21.11-72, Standard for Rubber Gasket Joints for Cast-Iron Pressure Pipe and Fittings.

AWWA C151-70, ANSI A21.51-71, Standard for Ductile-Iron Pipe, Centrifugally Cast in Metal Molds or Sand-Lined Molds, for Water or Other Liquids. American National Standards Institute Sectional Committee B16 (This committee is sponsored jointly by the Mechanical Contractors Association of America, Manufacturers Standardization Society of the Valve and Fittings Industry and the American Society of Mechanical Engineers). The following Standards are published by the American Society of Mechanical Engineers, 345 East 47th Street, New York, NY 10017.

ANSI B16.1-1967, Cast-iron Pipe Flanges and Flanged Fittings, 25, 125, 250 and 800 lb.

ANSI B16.5-1973, Steel Pipe Flanges and Flanged Fittings, 150, 300, 400, 600, 900, 1500 and 2500 lb., Including Reference to Valves.

U.S. Federal Supply Service, General Services Administration, the following Federal Specifications published by U.S. Superintendent of Documents, Washington, DC 20402.

No. SS-P-351C, Pipe, Asbestos-Cement, August 12, 1968.

No. SS-P-381, A(z), Pipe; Pressure, Reinforced Concrete, Pretensioned Reinforcement (Steel Cylinder Type), May 3, 1972.

No. SS-P-385A(1), Pipe, Steel (Cement-Mortar Lining and Reinforced Cement-Mortar Coating), February 27, 1968.

No. WW-P-406D, Pipe, Steel (Seamless and Welded) (For Ordinary Use), February 8, 1973.

No. WW-P-421C, Pipe, Cast-Iron, Pressure (For Water and Other Liquids), Sept. 11, 1967.

No. WW-P-521F, Pipe Fittings, Flanged Fittings, and Flanges, Ferrous and Steel (Screwed and Butt-Welded), 150 Pound, November 22, 1968.

U.S. Interdepartmental Screw-Thread Committee, Screw-Thread Standards for Federal Services, U.S. Superintendent of Documents, Washington, DC 02402, National Bureau of Standards Handbook H28. Part I, Unified and Unified Miniature Screw Threads, 1970. Part II, Pipe Threads, including Dryseal Pipe Threads; Gas Cylinder Valve Outlet and Inlet Threads; Hose Couplings, including Fire-Hose Coupling Threads; and Hose Connections for Welding and Cutting Equipment, 1966.

Additional Readings

AWWA Committee on Financial Aspects of Fire Prevention and Protection, A Business-like Approach to Fire Protection Changes, New York, AWWA, 1971.

Angele, G. J., "Backflow Prevention and Cross-Connection Control," *American Water Works Association Journal,* Vol. 62, No. 6, June 1970.

Babbit, Harold E., Cleasby, John L., and Doland, James, J., *Water Supply Engineering,* 6th ed., McGraw-Hill, New York, 1962.

Blake, Nelson M., *Water for the Cities,* N.Y., Syracuse University Press, Syracuse, 1956.

Engineering and Design—Water: Distribution Systems, Washington, D.C., Office of the Chief of Engineers, Department of the Army, January 31, 1963.

Factory Mutual Engineering Corporation, *Handbook of Industrial Loss* Prevention, Chapter 18, "Public Water Systems" 2nd ed., McGraw-Hill, New York, 1967.

Ibid., Chapter 15, "Underground Fire Service Mains."

FM Loss Prevention Data Sheets, Cross Connections, DS 3-3, 1971; Underground Fire Service Mains, DS 3-33, 1970; Water Demand for Private Fire Protection, DS 3-26, 1974; Factory Mutual System, Norwood, Mass.

Fair, G. M., Geyer, J. C., and Okum, D. A., Water and Wastewater Engineering, Vol. I, Water Supply and Wastewater Removal, John Wiley & Sons, New York, 1966.

Handbook of Cast Iron Pipe, Cast Iron Pipe Research Association, Chicago, 1952.

King, Reno C., ed., *Piping Handbook,* 5th ed., McGraw-Hill, New York, 1967.

"Meter Manual," AWWA M6, 1962, American Water Works Association, New York.

Peckworth, Howard F., *Concrete Pipe Handbook,* American Concrete Pipe Association, Chicago, March 1965.

Sweitzer, Robert J., *Basic Water Works Manual,* American Concrete Pressure Pipe Association, Chicago, 1958.

Chapter 3

WATER STORAGE FACILITIES AND SUCTION SUPPLIES

Water storage facilities and suction supplies, in a broad sense, encompass all bodies of water available as sources of supply whether contained by man-made or natural barriers. Elevated or ground level storage tanks of metal, wood, or rubberized fabric are examples of man-made storage facilities. Rivers, ponds, and harbors are examples of natural "storage" facilities that can be used as suction supplies. This chapter contains information on the design and installation of water storage facilities and the ways and means that surface and ground water supplies can be used for fire protection.

Open bodies of water, such as reservoirs created by damming streams, are sometimes used in private fire protection to supplement public water supplies or to furnish the primary source of water for fire protection in instances where public supplies are insufficient in volume or pressure, or both, or where they lack dependability. Such arrangements are, however, feasible only in special situations. The most common method is to use elevated gravity tanks or ground level suction tanks with fire pumps. Pressure tanks, with their limited capacity, may be used where storage requirements are relatively small.

A. Storage Tanks (Gravity and Suction)

Tanks for fire protection preferably are not used for any other purpose. The frequent filling of a tank, which is necessary when the water is used for manufacturing or other purposes, is objectionable because the tank then becomes a settling basin, resulting in a large accumulation of sediment in the bottom. When water is drawn from the tank, the sediment also is drawn into the yard and fire extinguishing system piping, and may cause obstruction.

In the case of a wooden tank, the varying water level, with alternate drying and wetting of the lumber, may appreciably shorten the life of the tank; with a steel tank more frequent painting is required, which means not only greater expense, but more time out of service.

Another important consideration involving dual purpose tanks is the water available at the time of the fire. The tank will not be full except at very rare times as domestic and industrial consumption would be constantly drawing it down. It is possible that as the industry supplied by the tank grows, the normal water level would drop lower and lower. If a fire should occur several years after the tank was installed, insufficient water at insufficient head would be available.

Location

A gravity tank supported on an independent steel tower with foundations placed in the ground rather than on a building is the preferable arrangement. The location chosen should, if possible, be such that the tank will not be subject to fire exposure from adjacent buildings. If lack of yard room makes this impracticable, the exposed steelwork is then suitably fireproofed. Fire proofing, when necessary, should include steelwork within 20 ft of combustible buildings or openings from which fire might issue.

When the tank or supporting trestle is to be placed on the

walls of a new building, the latter should be designed and built to carry the maximum loads.

Suction tanks preferably are located so as to minimize yard piping. The pump house is generally placed close to the tanks to minimize suction piping. The tanks should not be located so as to be exposed to fires in combustible construction or fires issuing from windows.

Design for Earthquake Resistance

Storage tanks can be designed to give satisfactory resistance to earthquakes. In an earthquake, the motion of the earth sets up a whip-like action in elevated tanks that produces stresses beyond those provided for in a design which allows only for ordinary dead, live, and wind loads.

One method of earthquake resistant design allows an extra 10 percent horizontal load factor for elevated tanks. This theory was given a practical test in May 1940, when an earthquake struck the Imperial Valley area in southern California. There were eight steel gravity tanks in the affected area for the municipal water systems. Two, designed with this extra 10 percent horizontal load factor, stood up without damage. After the earthquake, four towers not so designed were in dangerous condition because the stresses set up by the earth's motion stretched or broke the brace rods, especially near the top of the tower. Two of the tanks succumbed to the earth's motion and collapsed completely.

Suction tanks are affected less by earthquakes than are elevated tanks; however, consideration must be given to their support and foundation. Pipe connections between the supplies and the pumps must be specifically designed for earthquake protection.

Tank Capacities

It is usually economical to install a gravity tank of sufficient capacity and at such height that it can be connected directly into the fire protection system, thus furnishing a supply both for hose streams from hydrants as well as for automatic fire extinguishing systems. This means that a capacity of 30,000 gallons (gal) and installation with the bottom of the tank at least 75 ft above the ground are minimum values when the tank is to supply hose lines from hydrants. Capacities of less than 30,000 gal for gravity tanks are acceptable only in special cases. For unsprinklered buildings, where hose streams are relied on for protection,

Table 11-3A.   Standard Sizes of Gravity Tanks

Steel Tanks			Wooden Tanks		Standard Heights of Towers or Gravity Tanks*
Gallons			Gallons		
5,000	40,000	200,000	5,000	40,000	75 ft
10,000	50,000	300,000	10,000	50,000	100 ft
15,000	60,000	500,000	15,000	60,000	125 ft
20,000	75,000		20,000	75,000	150 ft
25,000	100,000		25,000	100,000	
30,000	150,000		30,000		

* Distance to bottom capacity line.

Table 11-3B. Common Sizes of Steel Pump Suction Tanks (Gallons)

50,000	150,000	400,000
75,000	200,000	500,000
100,000	250,000	750,000
125,000	300,000	1,000,000

Table 11-3C. Capacities of Cylindrical Tanks

Diameter Ft	Gals per Ft of Depth	Gals in Hemispherical Bottom	Gals in Ellipsoidal Bottom
11	711	2,610	1,300
12	846	3,390	1,590
13	993	4,300	2,150
14	1,152	5,370	2,690
15	1,322	6,610	3,310
16	1,504	8,020	4,010
17	1,698	9,620	4,810
18	1,904	11,400	5,710
19	2,121	13,400	6,720
20	2,350	15,700	7,830
21	2,591	18,100	9,070
22	2,844	20,900	10,400
23	3,108	23,800	11,900
24	3,384	27,100	13,500
25	3,672	30,600	15,300
26	3,972	34,400	17,200
27	4,283	38,500	19,300
28	4,606	43,000	21,500
29	4,941	47,800	23,900
30	5,288	52,900	26,400

the bottom of the tank is at least 40 ft above the highest building, but not less than 75 ft above the ground.

Gravity and suction tanks are generally erected in standard sizes (see Tables 11-3A and 11-3B). The capacity required is determined by the intended use of the tank and is specified in the number of U.S. gallons available from the tank. (The capacities of cylindrical tanks of various diameters are given in Table 11-3C.)

Steel gravity tanks with suspended bottoms are customarily erected on towers with four columns for capacities from 50,000 to 200,000 gal inclusive, six for capacities from 200,000 to 300,000 gal inclusive, and eight for tanks over 300,000 gal.

Construction of Tanks

Gravity tanks are usually built of wood or steel and supported on steel towers. Reinforced concrete towers are sometimes used, and tanks can also be placed directly on top of the structures they are supplying. Concrete has also been used for the tank shells themselves in a few cases. Typical gravity tanks are shown in Figures 11-3A and 11-3B.

A satisfactory installation is obtained by designing and installing a tank and all its equipment in accordance with NFPA No. 22, Water Tanks for Private Fire Protection, referred to hereafter in this chapter as the NFPA Water Tank Standard. That standard gives full requirements for construction materials, loads, unit stresses, details of design, foundations, accessories, and workmanship. Welding of towers should conform to the Code for Welding in Building Construction of the American Welding Society.[1]

Steel for tanks and towers should conform to the specifications referenced in the NFPA Water Tank Standard. Chief among them is the AWWA Standard for Steel Tanks, Standpipes, Reservoirs, and Elevated Tanks[2] which gives guidance on the thickness of steel plates to be used in the tanks and the welding practices to follow in their fabrication. Other standards referenced in the Water Tank Standard

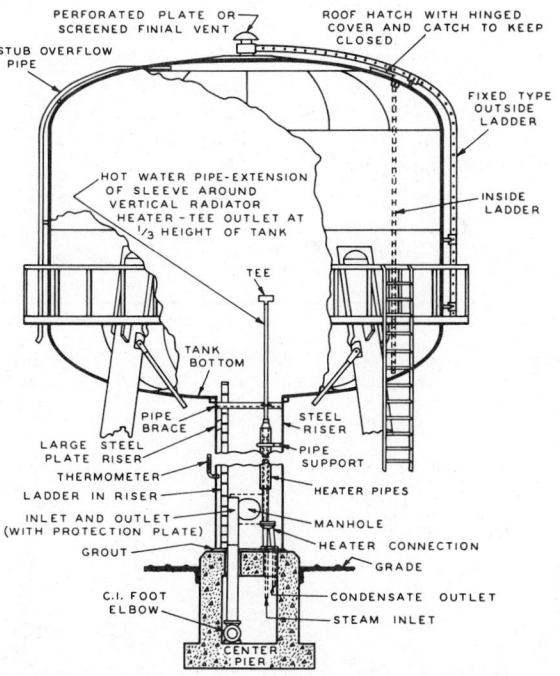

Fig. 11-3A. A typical tower-supported double ellipsoidal tank.

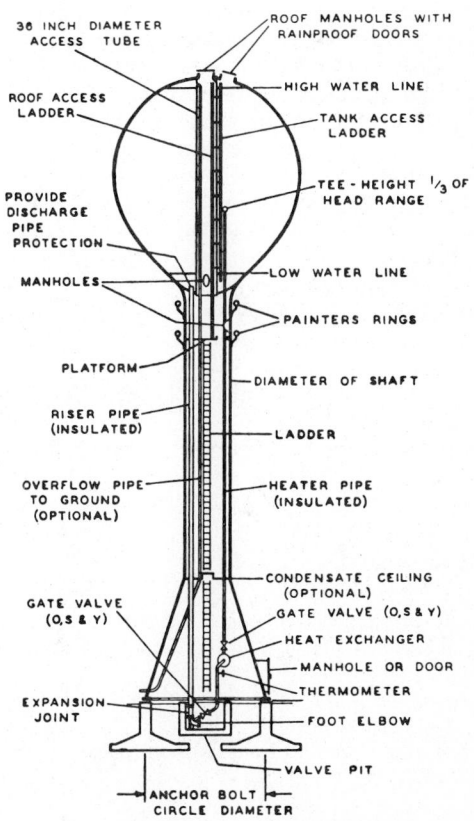

Fig. 11-3B.   A typical pedestal tank.

Table 11-3D. Unit Loads in Steel Tanks and Towers

	Load in Lbs	
	Tank	Tower
Dead Load:		
Steel, unit weight per cu ft	490	490
Concrete, unit weight per cu ft	144	144
Live Load:		
Water, weight per cu ft	62.4	—
Snow (slopes less than 30°) per sq ft of horizontal projection	25	—
Any 10 sq ft area on roof	500	500
Balcony, concentrated load to any 10 sq ft	1,000	1,000
Wind Load:*		
Vertical plane surfaces, per sq ft	30	30
Cylindrical surfaces, per sq ft of vertical projection	18	18

* The wind loads above are for 100 mph and should be increased in hurricane areas.

cover steel shapes, plate materials, bolts, anchor bolts and rods, forgings, castings, reinforcing steel, and filler material for welding.

Wood tank materials are also specified in the NFPA Water Tank Standard. The type of wood suitable for tanks, how it is processed, and its dimensions are given. References are also given for hoop materials and design.

Unit loads and unit stresses for steel tanks and towers are given in Tables 11-3D and 11-3F and working stresses for timber for wood tanks are given in Table 11-3E.

Steel tanks, as well as towers, are riveted or welded. Unfinished bolts may be used in field connections of nonadjustable tension members carrying wind stress only, and field connections of compression members and grillages in towers supporting tanks of 30,000 gal or less capacity.

In assembly and erection, plates are bolted firmly together before riveting. Drift pins preferably are not used for bringing parts together and are never used to enlarge unfair holes.

No waste material, such as boards, roofing, paint cans, etc., are left in the tank or in the space at the top of the tank after its completion, as it may get into water and obstruct the piping.

Tanks should be promptly put in service after completion. Wooden tanks may be damaged by shrinkage if left empty.

B. Tank and Tower Foundations

The following are principles of good foundations for tanks and tank towers.

Foundations in the Ground

Material: Concrete foundations are built of concrete with compressive strength of not less than 3,000 psi. The cement and aggregates should conform with the current American Concrete Institute Building Code Requirements for Reinforced Concrete (ACI 318).[3] The maximum aggregate size for unreinforced concrete in 3 in. and $1\frac{1}{2}$ in. for reinforced concrete.

Steel or wood pump suction tanks are set upon crushed stone, sand, or concrete foundations. For good soil conditions, at least 4 in. of crushed stone or sand is suggested. The material is saturated with oil and laid on moistened and compacted gravel after removing soft surface. Special consideration, outlined below, must be given for poor soil conditions.

A concrete ring wall at least $2\frac{1}{2}$ ft deep and 10 in. thick should surround the tank foundation. This type of ring normally projects 6 in. above grade and includes reinforcing steel equal to 0.25 percent of the cross-sectional area. If the ring wall is outside of the tank shell, asphalt flashing is installed between the tank and the ring wall at the ground level.

For poor soil, an 8-in. reinforced concrete slab with a concrete ring wall directly beneath the tank sides and extended below the frost line is advised. For tanks of riveted construction, a $1\frac{1}{2}$-in. layer of a dry mixture of sand and cement can be placed on top of the concrete slab. For tanks of welded construction, no sand cushion is needed on the concrete slab. Piles can be used in addition to the reinforced concrete slab when soil conditions are very poor.

Form: The tops of foundations are level and at least 6 in. above ground. The bottoms of foundation piers for towers are located below the frost line, and in the case of piers, at least 4 ft below grade resting on thoroughly tamped soil or rock.

Piers: Pier foundations may be of any suitable shape and many be either plain or reinforced concrete. If supporting a tower, their center of gravity preferably lies in the continued center of gravity line of the tower column or is designed for eccentricity. The height of piers should not be less than the mean width. The top surface should extend at least 3 in. beyond the bearing plates on all sides and is generally chamfered at the edges.

Table 11-3E. Working Stresses for Timber (Select Grade)
Allowable Stress—psi

Species	Bending		Compression	
	In Extreme Fiber	Horizontal Shear	Perpendicular to Grain	Parallel to Grain (short columns)
Cedar, western red	900	80	200	700
Cedar, northern and southern white	750	70	175	550
Douglas fir (Western Washington and Oregon)	1,600	90	345	1,175
Douglas fir (Western Washington and Oregon), dense grade	1,750	105	380	1,290
Douglas fir (Rocky Mountain type)	1,100	85	275	800
Pine, southern yellow	1,600	110	345	1,175
Pine, southern yellow, dense	1,750	120	380	1,290
Pine, white, sugar, western white, western yellow	900	85	250	750
Pine, Norway	1,100	85	300	800
Redwood	1,200	70	250	1,000
Spruce, red, white, Sitka	1,100	85	250	800

Table 11-3F. Unit Stresses per Sq. In. in Steel Tanks and Towers

Kind of Stress	Tank	Tower
Tension:		
On net section, rolled steel	15,000 lbs	—
Anchor bolts	15,000 lbs	—
Axial tension on net section, rods and structural steel shapes	—	15,000 lbs
Compression:		
Axial compression, gross section of columns and struts of structural shapes:		

$$\frac{P}{A} = \left\{ \frac{18,000}{1 + \dfrac{L^2}{18,000r^2}} \right\} \text{ or } 15,000 \text{ psi, whichever is the smaller.}$$

For tubular columns and struts:

$$\frac{P}{A} = XY, \text{ in which } X = \left\{ \frac{18,000}{1 + \dfrac{L^2}{18,000r^2}} \right\} \text{ or } 15,000 \text{ psi, whichever is the smaller.}$$

and (1) $Y = \dfrac{2}{3}\left(100\,\dfrac{t}{R}\right)\left\{2 - \dfrac{2}{3}\left(100\,\dfrac{t}{R}\right)\right\}$

(2) $Y =$ Unity (1.00) for values of $\dfrac{t}{R}$ equal to or greater than 0.015.

In the foregoing formulae, the symbols have the following meanings:
P = total axial load in pounds,
A = cross sectional area in square inches,
L = effective length in inches,
r = least radius of gyration in inches,
R = radius of the tubular member to the exterior surface in inches,
t = thickness of the tubular member in inches: minimum allowable thickness $\frac{1}{4}$ inch.
All circumferential joints in tubular sections should be butt joints either welded for complete penetration or riveted with butt straps on both sides.

Kind of Stress	Tank	Tower
Compression in short lengths	—	18,000 lbs
The maximum permissible slenderness ratio L/r for compression members carrying weight or pressure of tank contents	—	120
The maximum permissible slenderness ratio L/r for compression members carrying loads from wind or earthquake only	—	175
The maximum permissible slenderness ratio L/r for columns carrying roof loads only	—	175
Bending:		
Tension on extreme fibers, except column base plates	15,000	15,000
Column base plates	20,000	20,000
Compression on extreme fibers of rolled sections, and plate girders and built-up members for values of:		
$\dfrac{ld}{bt}$ not in excess of 600	15,000	15,000
$\dfrac{ld}{bt}$ in excess of 600	$\dfrac{9,000,000}{\dfrac{ld}{bt}}$	$\dfrac{9,000,000}{\dfrac{ld}{bt}}$

In the above l is the unsupported length and d the depth of the member; b is the width; and t the thickness of its compression flange; all in inches; except that l shall be taken as twice the length of the compression flange of a cantilever beam not fully stayed at its outer end against translation or rotation.

Kind of Stress	Tank	Tower
Pins, extreme fiber	22,500	22,500
Cast steel	11,250	11,250
Shearing:		
Rivets	11,250	11,250
Pins and turned bolts in reamed or drilled holes	—	11,250
Unfinished bolts	—	7,500
Webs of beams and plate girders, gross section	—	9,750
Cast steel	—	7,325
Tank plates and structural connection materials	—	11,250
Bearing:		
Rivets, single shear	24,000	24,000
Rivets, double shear	30,000	30,000
Turned bolts in reamed or drilled holes, single shear	—	24,000
Turned bolts in reamed or drilled holes, double shear	—	30,000
Unfinished bolts, single shear	—	15,000
Unfinished bolts, double shear	—	18,750
Expansion rollers and rockers (pounds per linear inch) where d is the diameter of roller or rocker in inches	—	600d
Pins	—	24,500
Contact area of milled surfaces	—	22,500
Contact area of fitted stiffeners	—	202,00

Note: When wind or earthquake loads are considered in calculating stresses, the permissible working unit stresses may be increased 25 percent, provided that the resulting section is not less than that required for dead and live loads alone. Wind and earthquake loads need not be considered simultaneously. For stresses due to a combination of wind or earthquake with other loads, and for wind and earthquake stresses only, the above working unit stresses may be increased 25 percent; however, in the design of concrete foundations the increase may be 33.3 percent. Wind and earthquake loads need not be considered simultaneously.

Anchorage: The weight of piers are sufficient to resist the maximum net uplift that occurs with the tank empty and when there are wind loads on the structure. The wind should be considered blowing from any direction. The weight of earth directly above the base of the pier may be included in the calculations.

Anchor bolts are arranged to securely engage a weight that is at least equal to the net uplift with the tank empty and with the wind blowing from any direction. Their lower ends should preferably be hooked or fitted with anchor plates.

Anchor bolts should be accurately located with sufficient free length of thread to fully engage their nuts. Expansion bolts are not acceptable. The minimum size of anchor bolts should be 1¼ in.

Grouting and Flashing: Bearing or base plates should have complete bearing on the foundation or be laid on cement grout to secure a complete bearing. The stressed portion of anchor bolts should not be exposed except where necessary. If the stressed portions of anchor bolts must be exposed, they are protected from corrosion by encasing them in cement mortar unless they are accessible for complete cleaning and painting. If structural shapes, plates, and bolts enter or are supported by masonry or concrete, the joint between the metal and masonry or concrete should be flashed with asphalt. (This does not refer to base plates under columns.)

Soil Bearing Pressure: The design soil bearing pressure and corresponding depth of foundation must be determined by subsurface investigation and by review of foundation experience in the vicinity. Such investigations include test borings made by or under the supervision of an experienced soils engineer or soils testing laboratory, and to the depth necessary to determine the adequacy of the support (usually a minimum of 20 to 30 ft).

Foundations: The foundations should be designed to carry the maximum loads without excessive settlement. If wooden piles are used above permanent low ground water level, they should be protected as specifications of the American Wood Preservers' Association.[4]

Foundations should not be constructed over buried pipes or immediately adjacent to existing or former deep excavations unless the foundation bases go below the excavation.

Center Pier: In addition to the weight of the water in a large plate riser, the weight of the column of water directly above the riser in the tank, and the weight of the steel plate, the center pier should be considered as supporting a hollow cylinder of water in the tank. If the hemispherical or ellipsoidal bottom is rigidly attached to the top of the large riser by a flat horizontal diaphragm plate, the radius of the hollow cylinder of water is determined as specified under large risers discussed elsewhere in this chapter.

C.   Tank Towers

Steel is generally used for the construction of tank towers. Details on the specific types of steel used in tanks is found in the NFPA Water Tank Standard.

Both live loads and dead loads are considered when designing towers. The dead load is an estimate of the weight of the structure and all its fittings. The live load is considered as the weight of the water when the tank is filled and overflowing. Consideration also is given to temporary loading in the form of ice and snow during construction and after construction.

The weight of the water in the riser is not considered when figuring loads unless the riser is suspended from the tank bottom. If the riser is used to support the tank bottom, the entire weight supported by the riser is considered including the weight of the water.

Additional loads to consider are wind, balcony, and earthquake. Wind loads are based on 30 psi for vertical plain surfaces and 18 psi over the vertical projection of cylindrical surfaces. These loads are applied to the center of gravity of the projected areas. The balcony load consists of the weight of the balcony railing and ladder material and, if exposed, the weight of snow. Earthquake loading must be designed specifically for local conditions.

Ladders and Balconies

Ladders on both the outside and inside of tanks with convenient passage from one ladder to the other are part of a tank's equipment. These ladders are for ease of access for inspection and maintenance of the tank exterior and interior surfaces. Materials for construction of the ladder must be compatible with the tank and tower materials. Ladders more than 20 ft long are equipped with a cage or other safety device designed to protect the climber.

Balconies and walkways are recommended for towers over 20 ft high for the convenience of inspection and maintenance activities. Normally the balconies are not less than 24 in. wide and walkways not less than 18 in. wide. Railings, at least 36 in. high, provide protection for personnel. Balconies and walkways, as are the ladders, are made of materials compatible with the tank and tower materials.

Tower Construction

During field erection the columns of towers should be built on thin metal wedges which, after the structure is completed, are driven to equal resistance so that all columns will be loaded equally. The spaces beneath the base plates and the anchor holes then are completely filled with cement mortar which should consist of one part portland cement to three parts clean sand. After the mortar has set, any remaining spaces under the base plates should be filled with neat cement grout. Joints between steel and mortar are flashed with asphalt.

Sections of structural members for towers preferably are symmetrical, and built of standard structural shapes or of tubular sections. Structural shapes are designed with open sections to permit the painting of all surfaces exposed to air or moisture and subject to corrosion. Tubular sections of columns and struts are airtight.

D.   Tank Heating Equipment

Adequate heating of tank equipment ranks next to structural design in importance. An ice plug in a riser pipe may make the tank water unavailable in case of fire and may break the pipe. Ice in or on tank structures has been the direct cause of collapse in several cases. The heating system must therefore be reliable and allow convenient and economical operation to 50°F. On the other hand, overheating can be seriously detrimental to wooden tanks and to the paint in steel tanks and is to be avoided.

Determination of Heater Capacity

To prevent freezing in any part of tank equipment during the coldest weather that may occur, the heating system must replace the heat lost from the tank and piping when the temperature of the coldest water is just safely above the freezing point and the mean atmospheric temperature for one day is at its lowest for the locality being considered. (See Fig. 11-3C for lowest one-day mean temperatures.)

Tables 11-3G and 11-3H show the heat losses from tanks

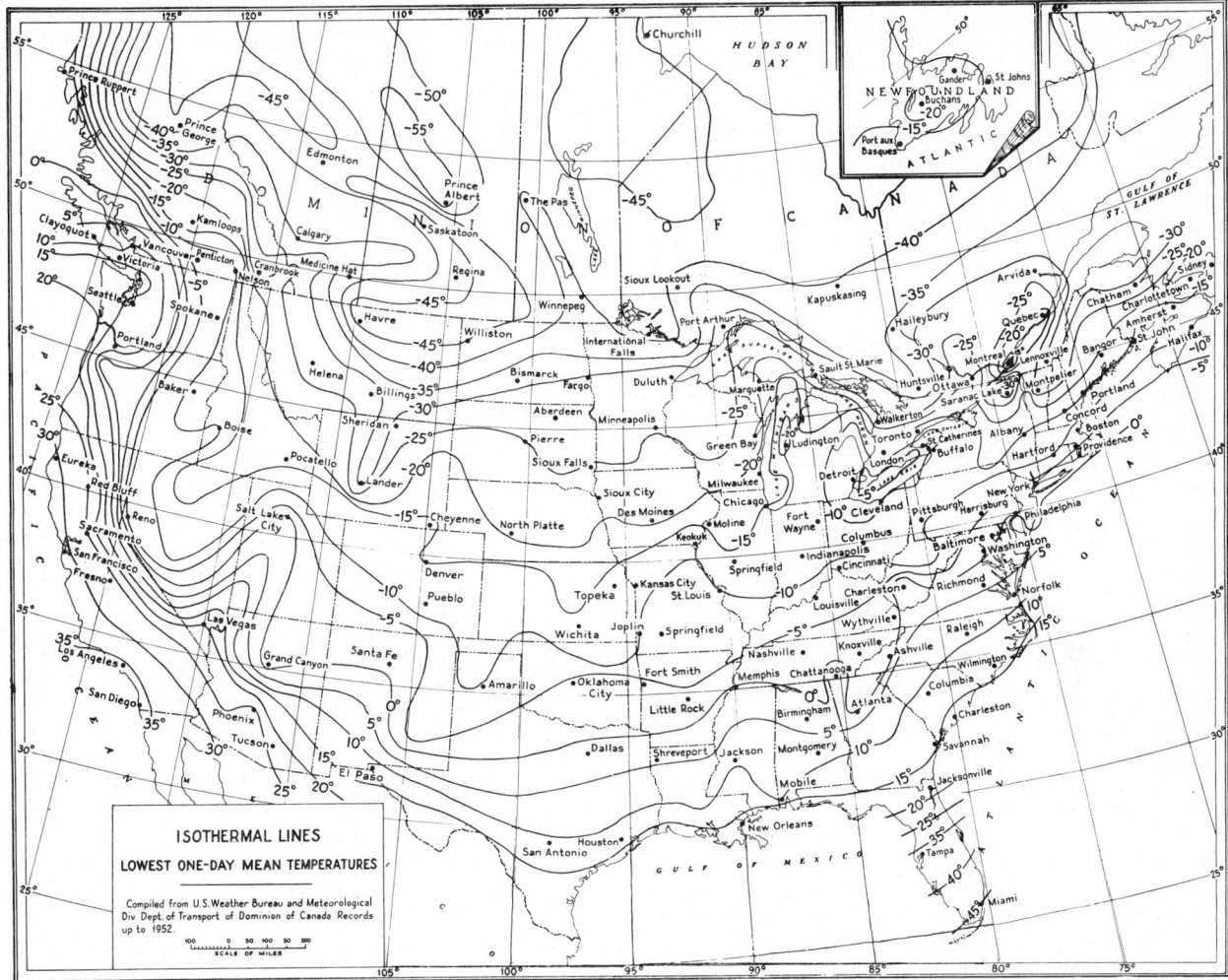

Fig. 11-3C. Isothermal lines—lowest one-day mean temperature. (Compiled from U.S. Weather Bureau Records)

of common sizes exposed to various atmospheric temperatures. The following paragraph is an example of the method used to determine required heating capacities for various types and sizes of tanks:

Question:

What heater capacity would be needed for a 75,000-gal steel tank at Duluth, Minn.? Answer—By interpolating from Figure 11-3C, the lowest mean temperature for one day at Duluth is −28°F, and by interpolating from Table 11-3H it is found that the heat loss at −28°F for a 75,000-gal steel tank is approximately 659,000 Btu per hr.

Answer:

The answer then is a heater capable of delivering 659,000 Btu per hr under field conditions.

Selection of Heating Method

The selection of a heating method depends upon many factors, such as tank height, material of construction, size and shape of tank and riser, and lowest temperature of exposure, just to name a few. The recommended methods of heating are covered in detail in the NFPA Water Tank Standard.

There are three basic methods of heating tank water: (1) gravity circulation of hot water, (2) steam coils inside tanks, and (3) direct discharge of steam into the water.

Gravity Circulation of Hot Water

Heating by gravity circulation is dependable and economical if correctly planned. Cold water received through a connection from the discharge pipe or from near the bottom of a suction tank or standpipe is heated and rises through a separate hot-water pipe into the tank. Steam, coal-burning or oil heaters are ordinarily used; gas heaters or electric heaters are also satisfactory.

A steam heater ordinarily consists of a cast-iron or steel shell through which water circulates by gravity around steam tubes or coils of brass or copper.

A steam heater should be located in a valve pit, heater-house, or in a nearby building at or near the base of the tank structure. When the tank is over a building, the steam heater preferably is located in the top story.

Heater Thermometer: The convenience of a gravity system is that it permits observation of the temperature of the coldest water at a thermometer located in the cold water return pipe near the heater. Failure to provide an accurate thermometer at this point or to observe it and keep it registering between 42 and 50°F is to risk freezing the equipment. A recording thermometer, with a sensitive bulb inserted in the cold water return, is a desirable accessory. The charts can be reviewed daily for more careful operation of the heating system.

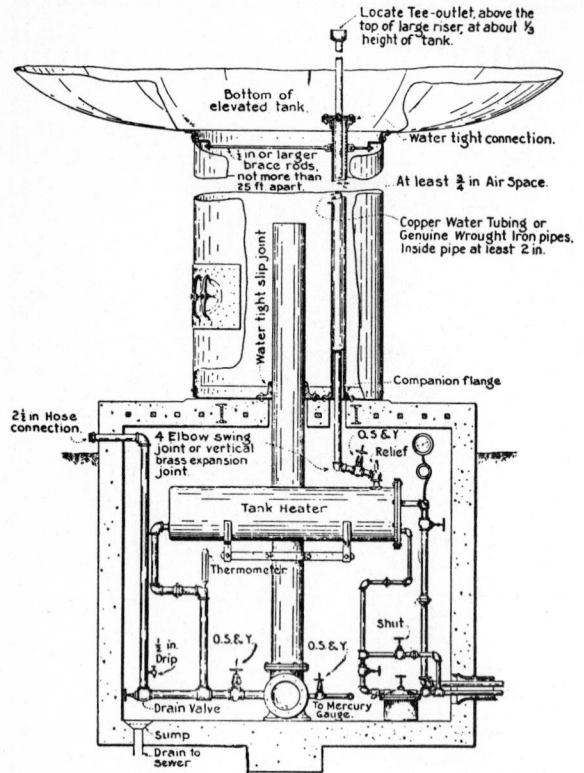

Fig. 11-3D. Arrangement of a circulating heater in a valve pit for a tank with a large riser.

(Water has its maximum density at 39.2°F. When the temperature of the water falls below 39.2°F, there is a water inversion so that the warmer water settles to the bottom of the tank while the colder water rises. Therefore, if the circulation heater is to be fully effective, sufficient heat must be provided so that the temperature of the coldest water will be maintained safely above 42°F.)

Water Circulating Pipes: The size of pipe used for the circulation of heating water is given in Table 11-3I. Pipe is either copper water tubing or made of genuine wrought iron or brass (85 percent copper) throughout. The hot water discharges into the tank through a tee fitting at the end of the hot water pipe at a height about one-third up from the bottom of the tank. The return pipe connects into the discharge pipe at a point that guarantees circulation throughout the portion of the discharge pipe subject to freezing. A typical arrangement of a circulating heater and piping in a valve pit is shown in Figure 13-3D.

Steam Coils Inside Tanks

Steam coils inside the tank do not permit convenient observation of water temperatures and have other faults which make them unsuited for heating elevated tanks, except occasionally in the South where only intermittent heating is necessary. This method may, however, be used for heating suction tanks and standpipes with flat bottoms supported near the ground level if coils are submerged continuously. The coil consists of at least 1¼-in. brass or copper pipe, pitched to drain, supplied with steam at not less than 10 psi pressure through a pipe of sufficient size to furnish the required quantity of steam from a reliable source.

Direct Discharge of Steam

Steam from a reliable supply is blown directly into the tank water through a pipe that enters the tank through the bottom, and extends to above the maximum water level and then returns to a point 3 or 4 ft below the normal fire service level. An air vent and check valve in the pipe above the surface of the water keeps the water from siphoning back down the steam line. This method is employed where the lowest mean temperature for one day is 5°F or above.

E.   Tank Equipment and Accessories

A complete installation of a gravity or suction tank includes the necessary pipe connections, valve enclosures, and

Table 11-3G.   Heat Loss from Standpipes and Steel Suction Tanks

Thousands of British thermal units lost per hour when the temperature of the coldest water is 42°F

To determine capacity of heater needed, find the minimum mean atmospheric temperature for one day from the Isothermal Map, Figure 11-3C, and note the corresponding heat loss below.

Atmospheric Temperature Deg. F	Tank Capacities—Thousands of Gallons							
	100	150	200	300	400	500	750	1,000
35	85	114	135	175	206	238	312	380
30	121	162	193	248	294	340	445	542
25	161	216	257	330	393	453	594	722
20	202	271	323	414	493	568	745	907
15	245	329	391	502	597	689	904	1,099
10	290	389	463	595	707	816	1,071	1,302
5	337	452	539	691	822	949	1,244	1,514
0	388	521	620	796	947	1,093	1,434	1,744
− 5	441	592	705	905	1,076	1,241	1,628	1,981
−10	498	669	797	1,023	1,216	1,403	1,841	2,239
−15	557	748	891	1,143	1,360	1,569	2,058	2,503
−20	619	830	989	1,270	1,510	1,742	2,286	2,781
−25	685	920	1,096	1,406	1,673	1,930	2,532	3,080
−30	752	1,010	1,203	1,545	1,837	2,119	2,781	3,383
−35	825	1,108	1,320	1,694	2,015	2,325	3,050	3,710
−40	898	1,206	1,437	1,844	2,193	2,531	3,320	4,039
−50	1,059	1,422	1,694	2,175	2,586	2,984	3,915	4,762
−60	1,229	1,651	1,966	2,524	3,002	3,463	4,544	5,528

Table 11-3H. Heat Loss from Elevated Tanks

Thousands of British thermal units lost per hour when the temperature of the coldest water is 42°F

To determine capacity of heater needed, find the minimum mean atmospheric temperature for one day from the Isothermal Map, Figure 11-3C, and note the corresponding heat loss below.

Atmospheric Temperature Deg. F	Wooden Tanks—Capacities in Thousands of Gallons								
	10	15	20	25	30	40	50	75	100
35	8	10	11	13	14	19	21	28	33
30	11	14	16	19	21	27	31	40	49
25	15	20	21	25	28	36	42	54	65
20	19	25	27	32	35	46	54	69	83
15	24	31	34	39	44	57	66	85	102
10	28	36	40	46	51	68	78	100	121
5	33	43	47	54	60	78	92	117	142
0	38	49	53	62	69	90	106	135	164
−5	43	56	61	71	79	103	120	154	187
−10	49	63	69	80	89	116	136	174	211
−15	54	71	77	89	100	130	153	195	236
−20	61	79	86	99	111	145	169	217	262
−25	68	87	95	110	123	160	188	240	291
−30	74	96	104	121	135	176	206	264	319
−35	81	105	115	133	148	193	226	289	350
−40	88	114	125	144	162	210	246	317	382
−50	104	135	147	170	190	246	290	372	450
−60	122	157	171	197	222	266	307	407	490

Atmospheric Temperature Deg. F	Steel Tanks—Capacities in Thousands of Gallons								See Note Below
	30	40	50	75	100	150	200	250	
35	43	51	59	77	92	120	145	168	69
30	62	72	83	110	132	171	207	242	192
25	82	96	111	146	175	228	275	323	340
20	103	120	139	183	220	287	346	405	506
15	125	146	169	222	267	347	419	491	692
10	147	172	200	263	316	411	496	582	893
5	171	200	233	306	367	478	577	676	1,092
0	197	231	268	352	423	551	664	779	1,309
−5	224	262	304	400	480	626	755	884	1,536
−10	253	296	344	452	543	707	853	1,000	1,771
−15	283	331	384	506	607	790	954	1,118	2,020
−20	314	368	427	562	674	878	1,059	1,241	2,291
−25	348	407	473	622	747	972	1,173	1,375	2,568
−30	382	447	519	683	820	1,068	1,288	1,510	2,860
−35	419	490	569	749	900	1,171	1,413	1,656	3,174
−40	456	534	620	816	979	1,275	1,538	1,803	3,494
−50	538	629	731	962	1,154	1,503	1,814	2,126	4,186
−60	624	730	848	1,116	1,340	1,745	2,105	2,467	4,936

Note: For each lineal foot of uninsulated riser 4 ft in diameter, add the number of Btu's in this column to the total Btu heat loss at the different temperatures for the various tank capacities.

Table 11-3I. Sizes of Circulating Pipes

Minimum One-Day Mean Temp	Size in Inches of Circulating Pipes Required for Elevated Steel Tanks. Tank Capacity (U.S. Gallons)									
Deg. F	15,000	20,000	25,000	30,000	40,000	50,000	60,000	75,000	100,000	150,000
10	2	2	2	2	2	2	2	2	2	2½
5	2	2	2	2	2	2	2	2	2	2½
0	2	2	2	2	2	2	2	2	2½	2½
−5	2	2	2	2	2	2	2	2	2½	2½
−10	2	2	2	2	2	2	2	2½	2½	2½
−15	2	2	2	2	2	2	2½	2½	2½	3
−20	2	2	2	2	2	2½	2½	2½	2½	3
−25	2	2	2	2	2½	2½	2½	2½	3	3
−30	2	2	2	2	2½	2½	2½	2½	3	3
−35	2	2	2	2½	2½	2½	2½	3	3	3
−40	2	2	2	2½	2½	2½	2½	3	3	3

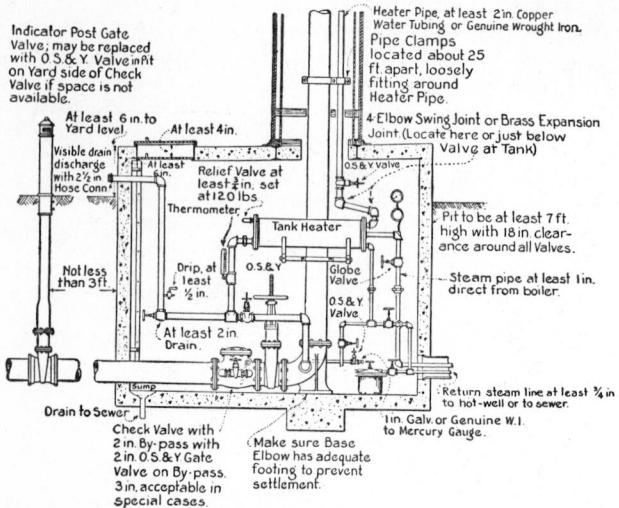

Fig. 11-3E. Valve pit and tank connection at the base of a riser.

where appropriate for the particular tank, such features as a frostproof casing for the riser.

Valve Pits

Ordinarily, a pit 7 ft deep and 6 ft by 9 ft inside is large enough to house the necessary valves, tank heaters, and other fittings. Details of the construction of the pit and its arrangement, including clearance around equipment, waterproofing, manhole and ladder, and drainage, should conform to the recommendations given for valve pits in Chapter 2 of this Section. A typical valve pit is shown in Figure 11-3E.

Valve Enclosures

The tank heater and other fittings are sometimes installed in an enclosure above grade. In such a case, the indicating valve and the check valve are generally placed in the horizontal pipe below the frost line in a small pit heated sufficiently to maintain a temperature of at least 40°F during the most severe weather.

The enclosure may be of concrete, brick, cement plaster on metal lath, or any other noncombustible material with suitable heat-insulating properties. The roof is constructed to be strong enough to support the frostproof casing and other loads without excessive deflection.

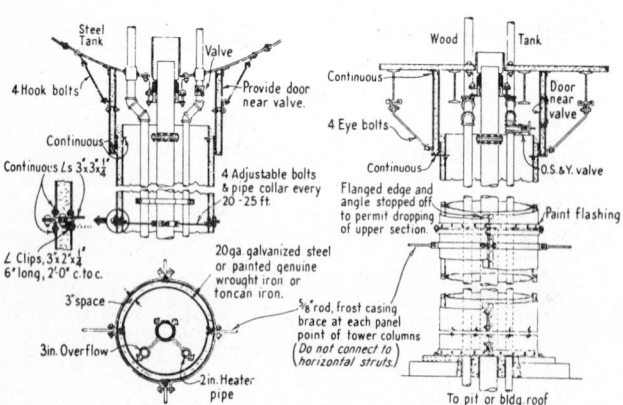

Fig. 11-3F. Suggested insulated metal frostproof casings.

Frostproof Casings

Except in the case of a large steel riser, a frostproof casing around all exposed tank piping in localities where the lowest mean atmospheric temperature for one day as shown by the isothermal map (Fig. 11-3C) is 20°F or lower. Tank piping subjected to temperatures below freezing within unheated buildings must also be adequately protected. Noncombustible frostproof casings are used where there is the danger of serious fire exposure.

Frostproof casings are often built as shown in Figures 11-3F and 11-3G. Fire stops are installed in all spaces in wooden casings, about 6 ft and 10 ft above the base of the casing, except for prefabricated casings when the lower fire stop may be at the base of the casing. Treating the lumber used in wooden frostproof casings with a suitable preservative, such as sodium fluoride, creosote, or zinc chloride, is advised to prevent rotting. Details on the construction of frostproof casings are found in the NFPA Water Tank Standard.

Large Risers

Large steel plate riser pipes 3 ft or more in diameter, without frostproof casings, are often desirable. The fire hazard and upkeep of the frost casing are thereby avoided, the ex-

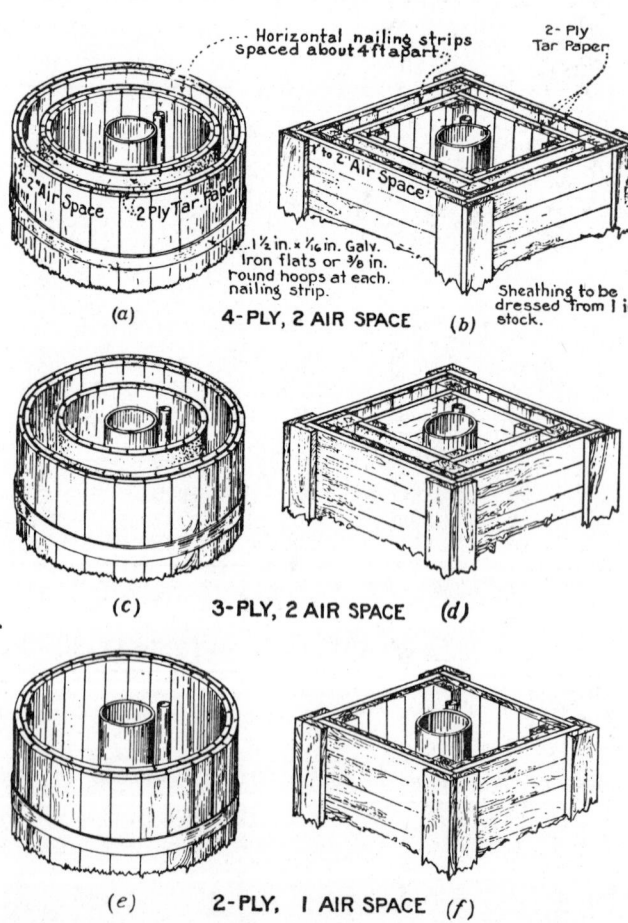

Fig. 11-3G. Six wooden frostproof casings. Casings (a) and (b) are recommended for localities where the lowest atmospheric temperature shown by the Isothermal Map (Fig. 11-3C) is −20°F or lower; (c), (d) for temperatures −20°F to 0°F; (e), (f) for temperatures of 0°F to 20°F. Heat transmission per square foot, per hour, per degree difference in temperature: (a), (b), 0.137 Btu; (c), (d), 0.17 Btu; (e), (f), 0.294 Btu.

pansion joint in the discharge pipe is eliminated, and it is not necessary to have a walkway to reach the valves. When the tank is on an independent tower, a concrete valve pit at the base of the discharge pipe and the pier are usually built as a single unit to support the riser (see Figure 11-3B). On the other hand, the larger valve pit at the base of the rise makes the first cost more than for equipment with small risers.

Water Level Indicators

The mercury gage is the most reliable water level indicator for tanks. One constructed as shown in Figure 11-3H is recommended to indicate the depth of water in the tank. A dependable, closed-circuit, high and low water electrical alarm is a suitable substitute for the mercury gage in certain installations.

The mercury gage normally is installed in a heated room, such as a boiler room, engine room, or office, where it will be readily accessible without likelihood of damage for reading, testing, and maintenance.

The gage is accurately installed so that, when the tank is filled to the level of the overflow, the mercury level is opposite the "FULL" mark on the gage board. The procedures for installing and testing mercury gages are given in detail in the NFPA Water Tank Standard.

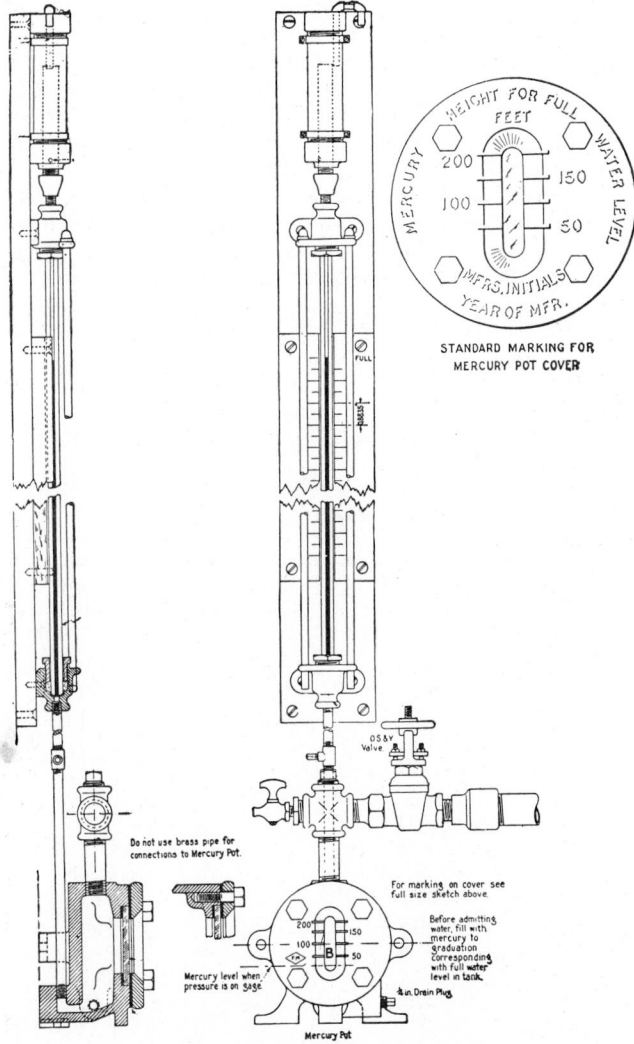

Fig. 11-3H. A mercury gage.

Overflow Pipes

The overflow pipe located at the top capacity or high water line of the tank, is preferably not less than 3 in. in diameter. When dripping water or a small accumulation of ice is not objectionable, the overflow may pass through the side of the tank near the top. The pipe should be extended not more than 4 ft, with a slight downward pitch to discharge beyond the balcony and away from the ladders.

When a stub pipe is undesirable, the overflow pipe can be extended down through the tank bottom and inside the frost-proof casing or steel-plate riser, discharging through the casing near the ground or roof level. The section of the pipe inside the tank is of brass except in the case of tanks with steel-plate risers, when overflow pipes $3\frac{1}{2}$ in. or larger may be of extra-heavy wrought iron or of flanged cast-iron pipe.

Cathodic Protection

Cathodic protection can be an effective alternative to interior painting for the prevention of interior corrosion in steel tanks (except pressure tanks). Cathodic protection is effective only on surfaces that are submerged most of the time. Other surfaces inside the tank are painted.

Internal corrosion is caused by galvanic current flowing from numerous local anodic areas of the tank shell, through the water to adjacent cathodic areas. Cathodic protection counteracts this process by passing sufficient direct current from an outside source (anodes suspended in the water) to the tank shell to keep the whole of the interior wetted surfaces of the tank at a negative potential. Low-voltage direct current is supplied from a rectifier. Frequent and regular checking of the ammeter and voltmeter readings is advisable to determine whether the electrical system is functioning.

Aluminum anodes, which are in common use, require renewal annually. In unheated tanks ice may damage the anodes in winter, and early servicing in the spring is necessary. Broken parts of the anodes are removed from the tank.

For heated tanks, anodes of fine platinum wire (which is not deteriorated by the electric current) are sometimes used, but the cost is considerably greater than for aluminum anodes.

F. Embankment-supported Rubberized Fabric Suction Tanks

Embankment-supported rubberized fabric tanks (ESRF) can be used as suction tanks for fire protection. The NFPA Water Tank Standard contains details on construction, installation, and maintenance of ESRF tanks.

ESRF tanks are available in sizes of 20,000 and 50,000 gal, and in 100,000 gal increments up to 1 million gal. The tank is generally a composite of a reservoir liner with an integral flexible roof and is designed to be supported by earth on all four sides. The material for construction of ESRF tanks is a nylon fabric coated with an elastomer compounded to provide abrasion and weather resistance. Support for the tank is provided by a specifically prepared excavation and earthen berm, or both.

Preparation of the installation site is critical to the reliability of an ESRF tank. The normal procedure is to make a shallow excavation approximately the size of the bottom of the tank. The excavated earth is then graded to form the berm, or embankment, for the upper sides of the tank. The exterior of the berm is graded to allow for rain and snow drainage, and the interior graded to match the contour of the tank including rounded corners. Grading must also take into account the pipe connections to the tank. ESRF tanks

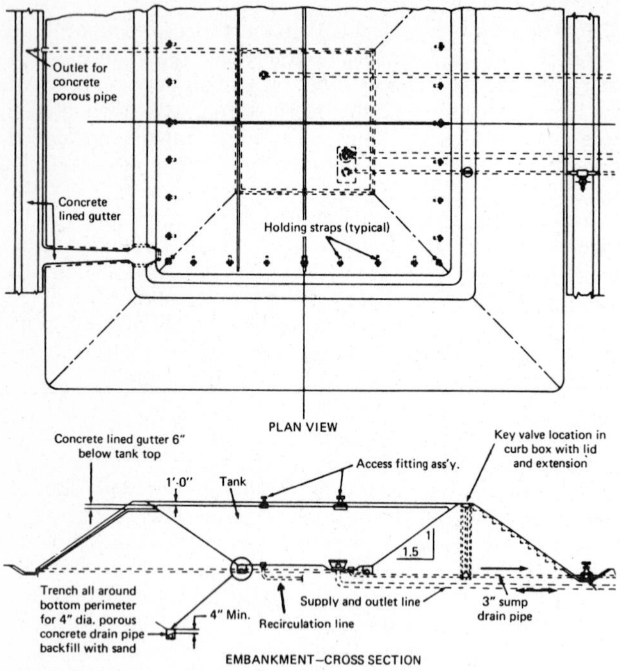

Fig. 11-3I. Typical installation details of an embankment-supported rubberized fabric tank including fittings.

may also be placed underground with the top of the tank at grade level, or they may be placed above ground where the earthern berm provides the entire support.

When the excavation meets the shape requirements of the tank to be installed, a 6-in. layer of sand or clean soil is spread over a 3-in. underlayment of pea gravel on the floor of the tank excavation, providing a firm base with good drainage. All sharp objects must be carefully removed before the tank is installed.

Tanks are shipped to the site fully constructed. They are laid in the foundation and all connections are made. After the tank is filled, a coating is applied to the exposed surface to protect it from the atmosphere. (See Fig. 11-3I for a typical ESRF installation.)

As with other types of storage tanks, water temperature in ESRF tanks is maintained at not less than 42°F. An acceptable method of providing heat is a water recirculation systems with a heat exchanger. When the ambient temperature drops below 42°F, a thermostat activates a pump which draws water from the tank through an inlet-outlet fitting and pumps the water back into the tank through a recirculation fitting located in the bottom of the tank diagonally opposite from the inlet-outlet fitting.

G. Pressure Tanks

Pressure tanks are used for limited private fire protection services, such as sprinkler systems, standpipe and hose systems, and water spray systems. They are sometimes used in connection with fire pumps and gravity tanks for quicker discharge. The tanks are located at as high an elevation as possible.

Tank capacity is considered as the total contents, both air and water, not including dished ends. For light-hazard occupancies only, the tank may have a minimum capacity of 3,000 gal (2,000 gal of water), but the tank capacity ordinarily should be at least 4,500 gal (ordinary hazard occupancies). Tanks for this service generally are not over 9,000 gal capacity. For larger supplies more than one tank would be employed. (See Tables 11-3J and 11-3K.)

The tank is normally kept two-thirds full of water, and an air pressure of at least 75 psi maintained. As the last of the water leaves the pressure tank, the residual pressure shown on the gage should not be less than zero, and should be sufficient to give not less than 15 psi pressure at the highest water-supplied automatic extinguishing system discharge device under the main roof of the building.

Air for pressure tanks is supplied by compressors capable of delivering not less than 16 cfm of free air for tanks of 7,500 gal total capacity, and not less than 20 cfm for larger sizes. The compressors are located in the tank house.

Relationship of Air Pressure and Volume in Tanks

The volume of air in the tank at any time varies inversely with the pressure:

$$\frac{P_1}{P_2} = \frac{V_2}{V_1}$$

Table 11-3J. Capacities of Horizontal Pressure Tanks

Tanks Two-Thirds Full

Diameter Tank in Inches	Height from Bottom in Inches	Height Above Center in Inches	Gallons Capacity per Foot of Length	Diameter Tank in Inches	Height from Bottom in Inches	Height Above Center in Inches	Gallons Capacity per Foot of Length
66	41¾	8¾	118	82	51¾	10¾	182
67	42¼	8¾	122	83	52½	11	187
68	43	9	126	84	53	11	191
69	43¾	9¼	129	85	53¾	11¼	196
70	44¼	9¼	133	86	54½	11½	201
71	45	9½	137	87	55	11½	205
72	45½	9½	141	88	55¾	11¾	210
73	46¼	9¾	145	89	56¼	11¾	215
74	46¾	9¾	149	90	57	12	220
75	47½	10	153	91	57½	12	225
76	48	10	157	92	58¼	12¼	230
77	48¾	10¼	161	93	58¾	12¼	235
78	49¼	10¼	165	94	59½	12½	240
79	50	10½	169	95	60	12½	245
80	50½	10½	174	96	60¾	12¾	250
81	51¼	10¾	178				

Table 11-3K. Typical Dimensions of Horizontal Pressure Tanks of Standard Sizes

Approx. Gross. Cap. in Gals	Approx. Net Cap. ⅔ Full	Inside Diam. in Inches	Inside Length in Feet	Approx. Wt. of Water in Lbs. ⅔ Full
3,000	2,000	60	20.2	16,670
3,000	2,000	66	17.0	16,670
3,000	2,000	72	14.2	16,670
4,500	3,000	66	25.4	25,000
4,500	3,000	72	21.3	25,000
4,500	3,000	78	18.2	25,000
6,000	4,000	72	28.2	33,340
6,000	4,000	78	24.2	33,340
6,000	4,000	84	21.0	33,340
7,500	5,000	78	30.3	41,670
7,500	5,000	84	26.2	41,670
7,500	5,000	90	22.7	41,670
9,000	6,000	84	31.4	50,000
9,000	6,000	90	27.3	50,000
9,000	6,000	96	24.0	50,000

Note: 4,500 gals gross capacity is the minimum ordinarily accepted for pressure tanks for automatic sprinkler systems.

In the above table the length of the tank has been figured as though the ends were flat instead of dished.

The actual length of tanks of the above capacities and diameters will therefore be a trifle greater.

Pressures are absolute pressures, not gage pressures, as used in the above general formula. Let us apply this formula to the special condition which exists in a tank used to supply water for sprinklers. Except where there is danger of air lock it is desirable to have 15 psig pressure in the tank when the last water leaves. Thus,

P_2 = residual pressure required + atmospheric pressure,

$$= \quad 15 \text{ psi} \quad + \quad 15 \text{ psi}$$

$$= \quad 30 \text{ psi}.$$

Since at this condition the tank is full of air,

$$V_2 = 1.$$

If the tank is at or above the top line of sprinklers, the tank will be normally kept ⅔ full of water, so,

$$V_1 = \tfrac{1}{3}.$$

Therefore,

$$P_1 = P_2 \times \frac{V_2}{V_1} = 30 \times \frac{1}{\tfrac{1}{3}} = 30 \times 3 = 90 \text{ psi}.$$

The corresponding gage pressure would be 90 psi minus the atmospheric pressure, 15 psi, or 75 psi.

If the tank is below the top line of sprinklers, P_2, the required residual pressure would be increased 0.434 psi for every foot of head represented in the distance between the base of the tank and the highest sprinkler. If we call this head H, we have

$$P_1 = P_2 \times \frac{V_2}{V_1} = (30 + 0.434H) \frac{V_2}{V_1}.$$

Gage pressure to be carried in tank would be $P_1 - 15$ or

$$(30 + 0.434H) \frac{V_2}{V_1} - 15.$$

For a tank ⅓ full of air $\frac{V_2}{V_1} = 3$, and gage pressure would be

$$3(30 + 0.434H) - 15 = 75 + 1.30H.$$

For a tank ½ full of air $\frac{V_2}{V_1} = 2$, and gage pressure would be

$$2(30 + 0.434H) - 15 = 45 + 0.87H.$$

Air Lock

A condition known as air lock can occur when a pressure tank and a gravity tank are connected into a sprinkler system through a common riser, if the gravity water pressure at the gravity tank check valve is less than the air pressure trapped in the pressure tank and the common riser by a column of water in the sprinkler system, after water has been drained from the pressure tank. For instance, if the pressure tank is kept two-thirds full of water with an air pressure of 75 psi, and a sprinkler opens 35 ft or more above the point where connections from both tanks enter the common riser supplying the sprinkler system, the pressure tank drains, leaving an air pressure of 15 psi balanced by a column of water of equal pressure (35-ft head) in the sprinkler system, and the gravity tank check valve is held closed unless the water pressure from the gravity tank is more than 15 psi (35-ft head).

Air lock can be prevented by increasing the volume of water and decreasing the air pressure in the pressure tank, so that little or no air pressure remains after water has been exhausted. For example, if the pressure tank is kept four-fifths full of water, with an air pressure of 60 psi, the air pressure remaining in the tank after water has been drained is zero, and the gravity tank check valve opens as soon as the pressure at that point from the pressure tank drops below the static head from the gravity tank.

Air lock may be conveniently prevented in new equipment by connecting the gravity tank and pressure tank discharge pipes together 40 ft or more below the bottom of the gravity tank (see Fig. 11-3J).

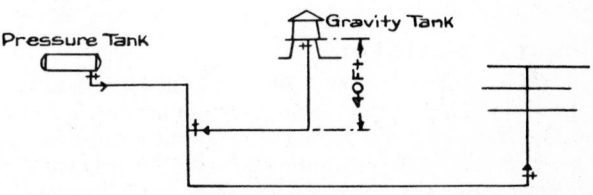

Fig. 11-3J. A gravity tank and a pressure tank showing how risers are connected to avoid air lock.

Construction of Pressure Tanks

Standard pressure tanks are constructed in accordance with the Rules for the Construction of Unfired Pressure Vessels, of the American Society of Mechanical Engineers (ASME) Boiler and Pressure Vessel Code, Section VIII,[5] with modifications given in the NFPA Water Tank Standard. Important modifications are a minimum hydrostatic test at 150 psi and a test for tightness.

Tanks are located in substantial noncombustible housings unless they are within a heated room in a building. A tank room is large enough to provide free access to all connections, fittings, and manhole, with at least 3 ft clearance around the valves and gages and at least 18 in. around the rest of the tank. The distance between the floor and any part of a tank is at least 3 ft.

The interiors of pressure tanks are inspected at 3-yr intervals to determine if corrosion is taking place and if repainting or repairing is needed. When necessary, tanks are scraped, wire-brushed, and repainted with an approved metal-protective paint. Relief valves are tested at least once each month.

Provisions should be made to drain each tank independently of all other tanks and have the sprinkler system drained by a pipe not less than $1\frac{1}{2}$ in. in diameter.

The filling supply or pump should be reliable, and capable of replenishing the water to be maintained in the tank against the normal tank pressure in not more than 4 hrs.

H.   Natural and Man-made Suction Facilities

Piped systems have advantages which make them a first choice for a water supply for fire protection, but there are situations where other water may be available more conveniently or at less expense. Examples are groups of property in suburban or farm areas or at resorts which are not near a community with a piped water system for fire protection. In many of these locations, however, there is water available for fire protection in natural bodies: the ocean, lakes and ponds, and rivers and streams. Cisterns or tanks can be used for storage at locations distant from natural water sources or where such water is not available. Water that is provided for other uses in fairly large quantities, such as the stock tanks on a farm, may prove very useful for fire protection if the tanks are kept full. Conversely, small ponds in parks and swimming pools are not particularly good sources of emergency water because of difficulties in the competing use of these for their regular purposes.

For water sources such as those mentioned, a general term "suction supplies" has come to be used to distinguish these supplies from the conventional public water systems for fire protection. Static suction supplies must, in general, be used where they are found. While there have been instances where water in suburban, farm, and forest situations has been used to provide effective fire streams at very long distances, it should be kept in mind that laying long hose lines (of more than 750 to 1,000 ft) seldom makes it possible to provide good protection due to the time required to lay the long lines and the greater difficulty in operating them.

Ground Tanks and Cisterns

If no hydrant on a water system is available, one way to get the amount of water required for fire fighting would be to store it in underground tanks or cisterns at or about the locations where hydrants normally would be installed. The fire department pumper would get water from a connection on the tank or by dropping a suction hose into the tank. The tanks and cisterns are filled from domestic water sources

too small for fire fighting and the water does not have to be changed so frequently as to present serious difficulties.

Static water supplies are of obvious value in suburban, farm, and forest areas, but they are equally important for emergency conditions in cities. Before the present public water systems were developed, some cities provided underground reservoirs or cisterns for fire protection. When water was needed for fire fighting, a pumper suction hose was simply dropped through a manhole. Some of these cisterns can be found still in use. Notable are those of San Francisco. Chicago is another city which has kept street cisterns in service. Even though San Francisco has a regular water system and a separate system of high pressure mains, it has been considered prudent, because of the threat of earthquake, to keep in service over 100 cisterns, mostly 75,000-gal capacity each which are provided under the streets in the central section of the city. Some of the oldest cisterns have brick walls. Newer ones are reinforced concrete.

Rivers and Ponds

Rivers and ponds are important auxiliary water sources. The fact that the water from these sources is in sight does not assure that it can be used for fire fighting. It is often necessary to provide suitable approaches so that automotive fire apparatus can get near enough to the water without becoming mired. A cleared space and some fill in many cases will provide access to a good water supply. These sources must be studied to determine that the water is available in all seasons, and to select the best when there are a number of possible spots for an approach to avoid miring apparatus, need of too long suction pipes, and other foreseeable difficulties. The locations are recorded and mapped and given periodic attention in much the same manner that hydrants are kept in operating condition.

At such locations it is usually necessary to provide a basin or cistern into which water can flow and into which the pumper suction strainer can be placed. Such containers can be arranged with a screen or weir so that large objects will not get into the basin and interfere with the suction strainer. In some places a permanent suction pipe and strainer can be installed. The details of such an arrangement are the same as those for a fire pump operating under a lift. The suction pipe should be laid with enough cover so there is no need of protection from freezing. It can be connected at the top to a hydrant with one or more pumper suction connections.

Small Streams and Brooks

Where water supply comes from a brook or stream, it is usually best to drain the water into a sump rather than to attempt to use the water from the flowing stream. In the case of a natural water source with a marshy bank or shore, it may be desirable to go out into the pond or stream to a point where water can be collected in a sump. From the sump in the pond or stream, a pipe is laid to drain to another sump, the latter located near a roadway or other point on which fire apparatus can stand.

In some sumps, and particularly in open water which freezes over in winter, there may be cases where covers are not feasible at the point where the sump is provided for pumper suction. At such locations, an anchored plug of wood can be floated where the pumper suction should be taken. Such a plug should have a minimum diameter larger than the pumper suction hose and be tapered so that, when frozen in ice, it can be driven down and out of position with a sledge hammer.

In some parts of the country, streams do not flow continuously. By providing a covered cistern of generous capacity, it may be filled when water flows. Thus, the water may be stored for a longer period than it would keep in an open reservoir.

Water from streams and ponds is of more importance in areas without public water systems than in a city. There are small groups of farm buildings and small communities where even a brook, if dammed, with a proper pumper approach and a suction basin, can provide a lot of fire protection at little cost.

For projects to develop static water which involve the damming of the flow of any stream of natural water, experienced local engineers should be consulted. Details of the dam construction and decisions as to the total amount of water to be impounded depend upon a great many factors and may require a comprehensive engineering survey in order not to encounter trouble. Its effect on users of the stream, and flood conditions, have to be considered.

Harbors and Rivers

Harbors and rivers as suction supplies pose problems additional to those encountered in developing supplies from ponds and small streams. These problems are principally due to the fact that the river and harbor water levels may change from time to time. In harbors, ocean tide levels vary throughout their entire range in 24 hrs. River water levels are seasonal but the problem is of the same general nature as encountered in tidal water.

Where there is little fluctuation in the level of a natural water source, a simple pier or platform may provide all that is needed to make the water available for pumper suction. If a pumper can be driven onto a pier, it can go to work when its suction line is dropped over the side. Where there are substantial fluctuations in water level, for example, due to tides, special arrangements are needed. At locations where the water is always deep enough for drafting, a hinged ramp leading down to a large float is feasible. But a common tide-water condition is a sloping beach down which the water recedes too far to be accessible at all times. Reservoirs which can be filled at high tide afford one solution to this problem.

Where a bridge passes over tidewater, water can be obtained by a permanent installation of a pump of the deep-well type with a discharge pipe to a point convenient for fire department pumper use. The most practical method of using tidewater supplies is to provide pumps on boats, supplementary to any fireboats the fire department may keep regularly in service. Relatively large quantities of water for fire fighting can be obtained from river and harbor sources because large capacity pumps are normally provided on fire-boats, and where there are no fireboats, large pumps can be installed on a boat or barge and pressed into use to supply water for fire protection. To make the water available for use on land, it is necessary to provide a place at which a fireboat, or a barge with pumps, can tie up and discharge into tanks, or a special pipe system with hydrants from which land-based pumping equipment can take the water.

Wells

Wells have become increasingly popular for both domestic use and fire supply for industrial sites, shopping centers, etc., that are located beyond the reach of a piped water supply. Before a well is constructed, a thorough examination of the ground water must be made. This examination generally includes an aquifer performance analysis and a review of the history of any nearby wells. The water in the ground must be of sufficient capacity and dependability, and of a reasonably good quality.

A vertical shaft turbine type pump is used to draw the water from wells into the fire system or into a storage tank. See Chapter 4 of this Section for information on the installation of vertical shaft fire pumps.

SI Units

The following conversion factors are given as a convenience in converting to SI units the English units used in this chapter.

1 Btu	=	1.055 kJ
1 in.	=	25.400 mm
1 ft	=	0.305 m
1 psi	=	6894.757 Pa
$\frac{5}{9}$ (°F − 32)	=	°C
1 gal	=	3.785 litres

Bibliography

References Cited

[1] Code for Welding in Building Construction, AWS D1.0-66, American Welding Society, Miami.

[2] AWWA Standard for Steel Tanks, Standpipes, Reservoirs, and Elevated Tanks for Water Storage, AWWA D100-73, AWS D5.2, American Water Works Association, New York.

[3] Building Code Requirements for Reinforced Concrete, ACI 318, 1963, American Concrete Institute, Detroit.

[4] AWPA Standards for Preservative Treatment by Pressure Processes: All Timber Processes, C1-65; Lumber, Timbers, Bridge Ties and Mine Ties, C2-66; and Tile, C3-66, American Wood Preservers Association, Washington, D.C.

[5] ASME Boiler and Pressure Vessel Code, Section VIII, 1974. Addenda: June 30, 1974, December 31, 1974, American Society of Mechanical Engineers, New York.

NFPA Codes, Standards, and Recommended Practices (see the latest *NFPA Publications and Visual Aids Catalog* for availability of current editions of the following document)

NFPA No. 22, Standard for Water Tanks for Private Fire Protection.

Chapter 4

FIRE PUMPS

Fire pumps are often used to supplement the supplies available from public mains, gravity tanks, reservoirs, pressure tanks, or other sources. They are not recommended as the only water supply to a private fire protection system.

A. General

The first modern fire pumps were the wheel-and-crank reciprocating type, belt-driven from mill machinery. If plant operations were stopped during a fire, the pump would be out of service. At best, this type of protection was inadequate.

The growth of automatic sprinkler protection required improved water supplies, and the mill pumps were replaced by rotary displacement pumps driven by friction drive from the horizontal water wheels supplying power to the plant. As steam supplanted water power, the reciprocating steam pump was adopted for fire protection service. For many years the "Underwriter" duplex, double acting, direct steam-driven unit was universally accepted as the "Standard" fire pump.

Today the centrifugal fire pump is standard. Its compactness, reliability, easy maintenance, hydraulic characteristics, and variety of available drivers (electric motors, steam turbines and internal combustion engines) have made the Underwriter pump obsolete, although not entirely extinct (see Part U of this chapter). An outstanding feature of a horizontal or vertical centrifugal pump is the relation of discharge to pressure at constant speed, insofar as when the pressure head is increased the discharge is reduced. With displacement pumps, however, the rated capacity can be maintained against any head if the power is adequate to operate the pump at rated speed and if the pump, fittings and piping can withstand the pressure.

Approved horizontal and vertical fire pumps are available with rated capacities up to 4,500 gpm. Pressure ratings range from 40 to 200 psi for horizontal pumps and 75 to 280 psi for vertical turbine pumps. Special fire service pumps are available in 150, 200, 300, and 450 gpm capacity ratings and pressure ratings of 40 to 100 psi; the overload capacity of these pumps is restricted to 130 percent.

The "size" of a horizontal centrifugal pump is generally the diameter of the discharge outlet; however, it is sometimes indicated by both suction and discharge pipe flange diameters. The "size" of a vertical turbine pump is the diameter of the pump column.

The NFPA standard on fire pumps is NFPA No. 20, Installation of Centrifugal Fire Pumps, referred to in this chapter as the NFPA Fire Pump Standard. Reference also should be made to other NFPA standards, including No. 21, Operation and Maintenance of Steam Fire Pumps; No. 13, Installation of Sprinkler Systems; No. 14, Standpipe and Hose Systems; No. 15, Water Spray Fixed Systems for Fire Protection; No. 16, Foam-Water Sprinkler and Spray Systems; No. 22, Water Tanks for Private Fire Protection; and No. 24, Outside Protection (Yard Piping).

B. Principles of Operation

The two major components of a centrifugal pump are a disc called the impeller, and the casing in which it rotates. The principle of operation is conversion of kinetic energy to velocity and pressure energy. Power from the driver (electric motor, internal combustion engine, or steam turbine) is transmitted directly to the pump through the shaft, rotating the impeller at high speed. The steps by which the energy conversion takes place vary with the class of pump. The three major classes are known as radial flow, mixed flow, and axial or propeller flow; these pumps are identified by the direction of flow through the impeller with reference to the axis of rotation (see Fig. 11-4B).

The horizontal shaft, one-stage, double suction volute pump, (Figs. 11-4C and 11-4E) is the type most commonly applied to fire protection service or to commercial use. In these pumps, water flow from the suction inlet in the casing divides and enters the impeller from each side through an opening called the "eye." Rotation of the impeller (see Fig. 11-4D) drives the water by centrifugal force from the eye to the rim, and through the casing volute to the pump discharge outlet. The kinetic energy acquired by the water in its passage through the impeller is converted to pressure energy by gradual reduction of velocity in the volute.

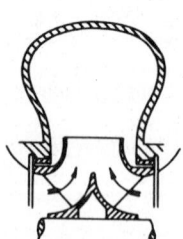 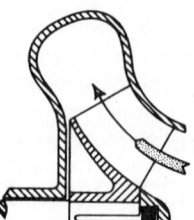 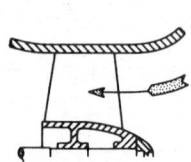

RADIAL FLOW
Pressure is developed principally by the action of centrifugal force. Liquid normally enters the impeller at the hub and flows radially to the periphery.

MIXED FLOW
Pressure is developed partly by centrifugal force and partly by the lift of the vanes on the liquid. The flow enters axially and discharges in an axial and radial direction.

AXIAL FLOW
Most of the pressure is developed by propelling or lifting action of the vanes on the liquid. The flow enters axially and discharges nearly axially.

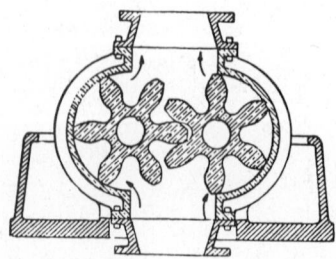

Fig. 11-4A. Sectional view of a rotary pump.

Fig. 11-4B. THE THREE MAJOR CLASSES OF FIRE PUMPS.

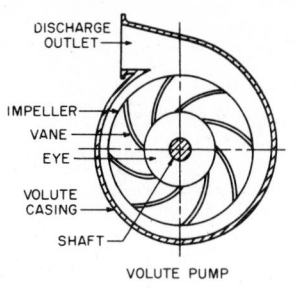

Fig. 11-4C. Sectional view of a volute casing.

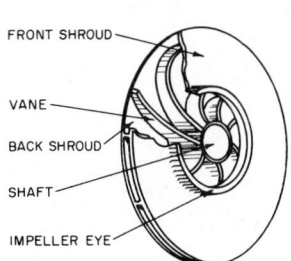

Fig. 11-4D. A typical pump impeller.

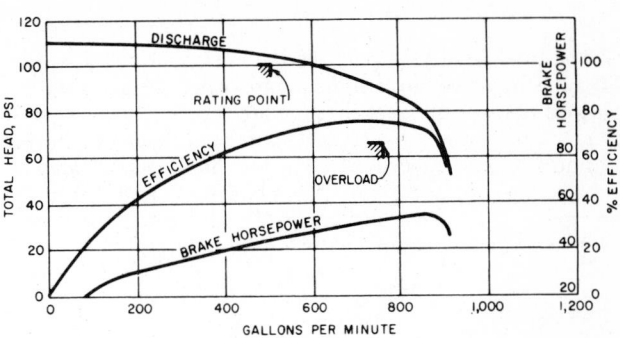

Fig. 11-4F. Typical fire pump characteristic curves. Illustrated curves are for a 500 gpm, 100 psi, 2,000 rpm, gasoline engine-driven pump with a 14-in. impeller and a maximum suction lift of 6.4 ft. Note that the shutoff point is 110 psi, maximum brake horsepower is 55, and the maximum efficiency is 75 percent of rated pressure and 150 percent of rated capacity at rated speed.

C. Characteristic Curves

The characteristic curves (see Fig. 11-4F) of a horizontal centrifugal, or a vertical turbine-type pump are:

1. Total head vs discharge (feet of head or pounds per square inch of pressure vs gallons per minute).

2. Brake horsepower vs discharge (water horsepower vs gallons per minute).

3. Efficiency vs discharge $\dfrac{\text{Water Hp}}{\text{Input Hp}}$ vs gpm.

These curves assume that the pump is operated at a constant speed equal to its rated rpm (revolutions per minute). In actual service, however, the speed of the driver may vary with changes in the load.

The flow and pressure ratings of commercial pumps are usually established on the basis of maximum efficiency and desired speed. Impellers can be designed for flat, medium, or steep head-discharge characteristics, as required for various uses. Fig. 11-4G illustrates how the head-discharge curve is affected by the diameter of the eye, width of the impeller, number of vanes, and the shape or angle of the vanes.

Multistage Pumps

To obtain a high pressure rating, two or more impellers and casings can be assembled on one shaft as a single unit, forming a multistage pump. The discharge from the first stage enters the suction of the second stage; discharge from the second stage enters the suction of the third, and so on. The pump capacity is the rating in gallons per minute of one stage; the pressure rating is the sum of the pressure ratings of the individual stages, minus a small head loss.

High Pressure Service Pumps

Single-stage pumps can be designed for high pressure service by increasing the impeller diameter or the rated speed. Both of these methods offer certain undesirable features. The large diameter pumps may be less efficient, and high speed pumps may not be readily matched to the driver.

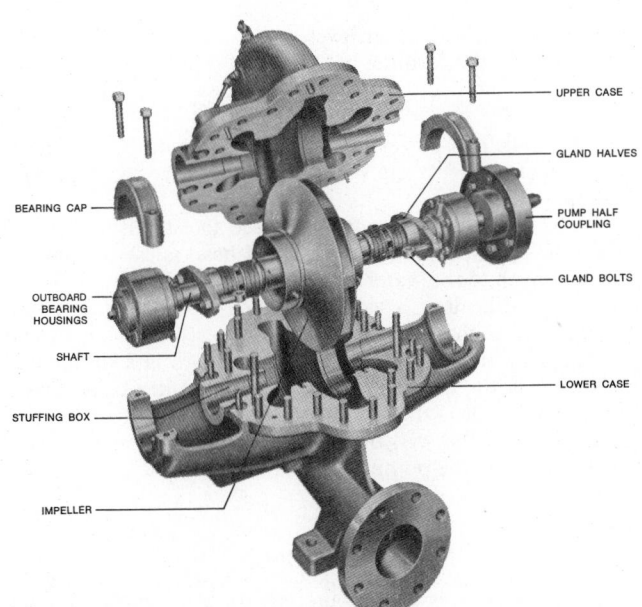

Fig. 11-4E. A horizontal shaft, single-stage centrifugal fire pump. (Peerless Pump Div., FMC Corp.)

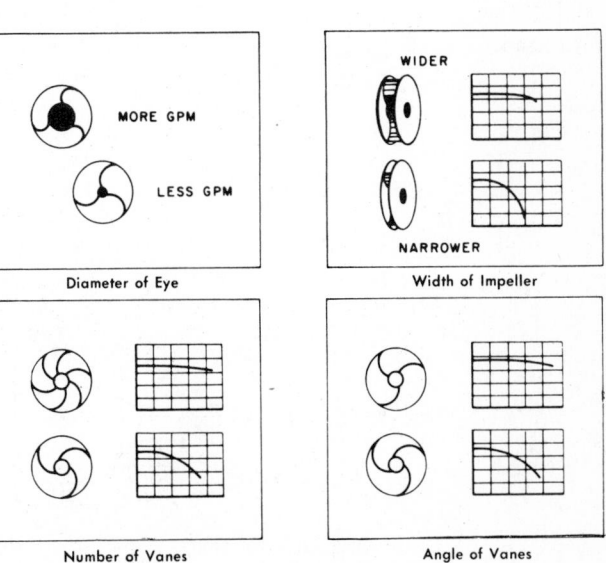

Fig. 11-4G. Effect of impeller design on head-discharge curves for fire pumps.

D. Total Head

The total head of a pump is the energy imparted to the liquid as it passes through the pump. It may be expressed in various units of pressure, but for fire protection purposes it is generally given in psi (pounds per square inch) or in feet of liquid measured vertically. The total head is calculated by subtracting the energy in the incoming liquid from the energy in the discharging liquid. Therefore the total head (H) of a pump is calculated by the formula:

$$H = h_d + h_{vd} - h_s - h_{vs}$$

in which

H = total head, feet

h_d = discharge head, feet

$h_{vd} = \dfrac{v_d^2}{2g}$ = discharge velocity head, feet

h_s = suction head, feet

$h_{vs} = \dfrac{v_s^2}{2g}$ = suction velocity head, feet

v = average velocity, feet per second

g = acceleration due to gravity, 32.2 ft/sec^2

For a horizontal split case pump, the individual heads are measured at the pump discharge nozzle flange and at the suction flange (see Fig. 11-4H). The heads are read from pressure gages attached to the pump flanges. The velocity head must be calculated for the volume of liquid passing through the flanges $\left(h_v = \dfrac{v^2}{2g} \right)$ (v = average velocity, g = gravitational acceleration). If the flanges have the same diameters, there will be no difference between the incoming and outgoing velocity and the calculation can be omitted.

For a vertical turbine pump, the discharge head is theoretically read at the discharge flange of the pump. Since this flange is usually inaccessible for gage readings, a gage is used at the discharge fitting at the top of the pump column

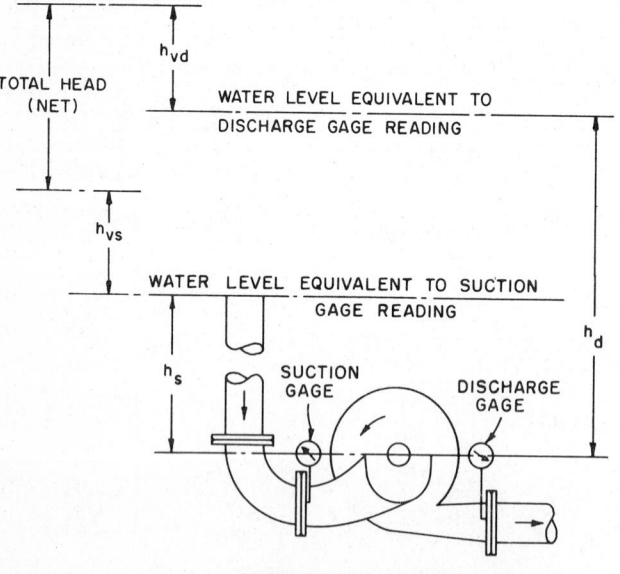

OPERATING UNDER HEAD

Fig. 11-4H. Typical head of horizontal shaft centrifugal fire pumps.

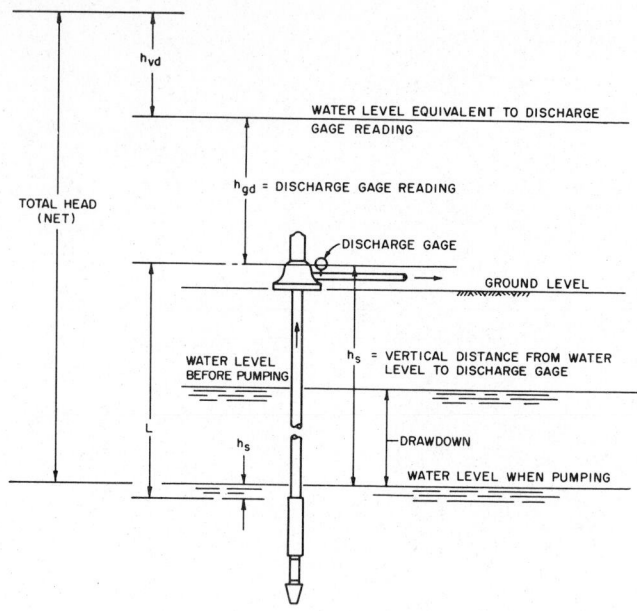

Fig. 11-4I. Total head of vertical turbine type fire pumps.

pipe (see Fig. 11-4I). The discharge pressure at the pump discharge flange therefore equals the pressure at the gage above plus the pressure effect of the vertical distance between the two points plus the friction loss between the two points. In most cases the friction loss is so small that it may be disregarded.

The suction head is the vertical distance from water level to the pump discharge flange. The velocity head of the incoming liquid is assumed to be zero. Hence the formula would now take the following form:

$$H = h_d + h_{vd} - h_s$$
$$= (h_{gd} + L) + h_{vd} - h_s$$

where h_{gd} = discharge gage reading, feet; L = gage to pump flange, feet; and H = gage to liquid level, feet.

However $L - h_s = h$ = the vertical distance between the discharge gage and water level.

Therefore the formula becomes:

$$H = h_{gd} + h_{vd} + h$$

Hydraulic and power losses within the pump (turbulence, disc friction, shock, etc.) are represented by the efficiency rating.

Total head at rated capacity is used to establish the rated head of a pump. Actually, the rated head is the amount of energy given to the water.

The total head of a vertical turbine-type pump also may be defined as the vertical water-to-water dimension of the system in which the pump operates. There is a difference, however, in the method of measuring total head. As shown in Fig. 11-4I, it is the sum of the vertical distance between water level in the well or pit; the discharge head indicated by the gage on the pump outlet; and the velocity head at the gage connection.

E. Specific Speed (N_s)

Specific speed is a number relating head, capacity, and speed of a centrifugal pump for design purposes. Actually, specific speed is the revolutions per minute of a geometrically similar impeller that will discharge one gallon per minute at one foot total head. The formula for calculating specific speed of a centrifugal pump is:

$$N_s = \frac{\text{rpm} \times \text{gpm}^{\frac{1}{2}}}{H^{\frac{3}{4}}}$$

where N_s is the specific speed number and H is the head in feet.

When values of head, speed, and capacity in the formula correspond to pump performance at optimum efficiency, the specific speed is an index to the type of pump. Impellers for high heads usually have low specific speeds, and impellers for low heads have high specific speeds.

A pump of low specific speed will operate satisfactorily with greater suction lift than a pump of same head and capacity with a higher specific speed. Experience shows that specific speed is a useful guide for determining maximum suction lift or minimum suction head.

When suction lift exceeds 15 ft, it may be necessary to provide a larger pump at less speed; with low lift or positive head on the suction, a smaller pump operating at greater speed may be used. Abnormally high suction lifts may seriously reduce pump capacity and efficiency or cause excessive vibration and cavitation.

F. Net Positive Suction Head

Net positive suction head (NPSH) is the pressure head that causes liquid to flow through the suction pipe and fittings into the eye of a pump impeller. The pump itself has no ability to "lift," and the suction pressure depends on the nature of the supply.

If a pump is supplied from a pond, stream, open well, or uncovered reservoir where the water level is below the pump, the suction head is atmospheric pressure minus the lift. If the water level is above the pump, as from a water main, penstock, aboveground tank, etc., the suction head is atmospheric pressure plus static pressure.

Pressure readings at the inlet flange of a pump operating under lift are negative with respect to the gage, but positive when referred to absolute pressure—hence the expression, "net positive suction head." (Absolute pressure is gage pressure plus barometric pressure.)

There are two kinds of NPSH to consider. Pump NPSH is a function of the pump design. It varies with capacity and speed of any one pump, and with the designs of different pumps. Curves of NPSH vs gallons per minute usually can be obtained from pump manufacturers (see Fig. 11-4J). Available NPSH is a function of the system in which the pump operates, and can be calculated readily.

When the water source is above the pump, available NPSH = atmospheric pressure (ft) + static head on suction (ft) − friction and fitting losses in suction piping (ft) − vapor pressure of liquid (ft). (Note: The vapor pressure of water at 90°F is 1.6 ft.)

When the water source is below the pump, available NPSH = atmospheric pressure (ft) − static lift (ft) − friction loss in piping and head loss in the fittings (ft) − vapor pressure of liquid (ft).

For any pump installation, the available system NPSH must be equal to or greater than the pump NPSH at the desired operating conditions. If the pump NPSH is greater than system NPSH, the suction layout should be altered, or a pump provided with more suitable characteristics. The NFPA Fire Pump Standard recommends that the total suction lift (friction and fittings loss plus static lift) should not exceed 15 ft at sea level, and that this figure should be reduced 1 ft for each 1,000 ft of altitude at the pump installation.

G. Cavitation

Cavitation is a complex phenomenon that may take place in pumps or other hydraulic equipment. In a centrifugal pump, as liquid flows through the suction line and enters the eye of the impeller, the velocity increases and pressure decreases. If the pressure falls below the vapor pressure corresponding to the temperature of the liquid, pockets of vapor will form. When the vapor pockets in the flowing liquid reach a region of higher pressure, the pockets collapse with a hammer effect causing noise and vibration. Tests have shown that extremely high instantaneous pressures may be developed in this manner, resulting in pitting various parts of the pump casing and impeller. Conditions may be mild or severe and mild cavitation may occur without much noise. Severe cavitation can result in reduced efficiency and ultimate failure of the pump if steps are not taken to eliminate the cause.

H. Affinity Laws

The mathematical relationships between head, capacity, brake horsepower, and impeller diameter are called affinity laws. Law 1 assumes constant impeller diameter with change of speed. Law 2 assumes constant speed with change in diameter of the impeller. These laws are expressed by proportion as follows:

Law 1.

$$\frac{Q_1}{Q_2} = \frac{N_1}{N_2} \qquad \frac{H_1}{H_2} = \frac{N_1{}^2}{N_2{}^2} \qquad \frac{\text{bhp}_1}{\text{bhp}_2} = \frac{N_1{}^3}{N_2{}^3}$$

Law 2.

$$\frac{Q_1}{Q_2} = \frac{D_1}{D_2} \qquad \frac{H_1}{H_2} = \frac{D_1{}^2}{D_2{}^2} \qquad \frac{\text{bhp}_1}{\text{bhp}_2} = \frac{D_1{}^3}{D_2{}^3}$$

The nomenclature for the relationships is: Q = capacity; H = head; N = speed; D = impeller diameter; and bhp = brake horsepower. Thus:

Q_1 = gpm at N_1 or D_1 $\qquad Q_2$ = gpm at N_2 or D_2
H_1 = head at N_1 or D_1 $\qquad H_2$ = head at N_2 or D_2
bhp_1 = brake horsepower at $\qquad \text{bhp}_2$ = brake horsepower at

$\qquad\qquad N_1$ or D_1 $\qquad\qquad\qquad\qquad N_2$ or D_2

Law 1 applies to common types of pumps, including horizontal centrifugal-type pumps and vertical turbine-type fire

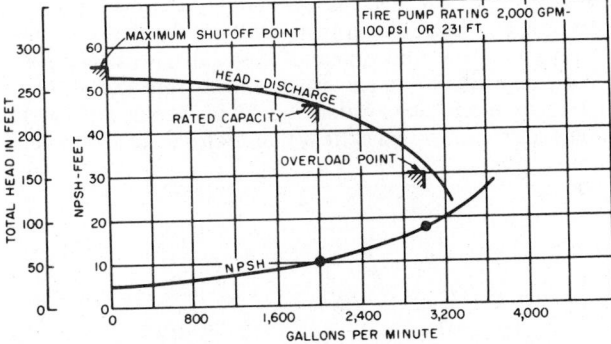

Fig. 11-4J. NPSH curve of a typical fire pump. Note that the required NPSH at 2,000 gpm is 10 ft and 18 ft at 3,000 gpm.

pumps. Law 2 applies to centrifugal pumps with reasonable close agreement between calculated and tested performance. Generally, pumps with low specific speeds show closer agreement than pumps with high specific speeds.

The affinity laws should be applied when proposed changes in a fire pump installation would increase the speed or significantly raise the pressure of the suction supply. Greater speed would increase the power demand, and high discharge pressure might be undesirable. In some instances, it is possible to trim the impeller or to install a speed-reducing gear between the pump and driver. This should not be done, however, without the approval of the pump manufacturer. For pumps operating under lift, possible changes in performance should be studied carefully, because greater velocity in the suction line could cause cavitation and substantially alter the characteristic curve.

I.   Fire Pump Approval and Listing

NFPA standards for design and installation of various fire protection systems recommend the use of approved and listed equipment, or both, including fire pumps for installations requiring them.

Under the approval system, the manufacturer is responsible for providing a listed or approved shop-tested pump that will perform satisfactorily when installed in conformance to the NFPA Fire Pump Standard. A contractor or others are responsible for installing the driver-pump combination in accordance with the provisions of the NFPA Fire Pump Standard, while it is the customer's obligation to provide adequate data about the pump driver, power supply, water supply, location, etc.

Fire pumps are designed to provide maximum reliability and specific net head-discharge characteristics. Except for periodic inspections and tests, fire pumps are idle most of the time. Pumps for commercial use, on the other hand, are chosen for maximum efficiency and economy of operation.

To obtain official listing of a new pump, the manufacturer submits plans and specifications to a recognized testing agency for review and comment. After any revisions or corrections have been agreed to, arrangements are made for representatives of the testing agencies involved to witness the required approval tests at the manufacturer's plant.

If the results are satisfactory, the new pumps are listed in the usual manner or with any restrictions considered desirable. It is the duty of the manufacturer to shop test every unit sold and to furnish certified curves of head, efficiency and brake horsepower vs discharge. Although not ordinarily shown, the NPSH curve of the pump, if available, should be provided upon request.

Many of the listed fire pumps used today are top quality commercial units. These pumps are upgraded when necessary, trimmed, and fitted to meet all the approval requirements for fire protection service.

J.   Standard Head-discharge Curves

The shape of the standard head-discharge curve of a fire pump is determined by three limiting points as follows:

Shutoff

With the pump operating at rated speed and the discharge valve closed, the total head of a horizontal centrifugal pump shall not exceed 120 percent of the rated head at 100 percent capacity. For a vertical pump, the total head at shutoff shall not exceed 140 percent of the rated head at 100 percent capacity.

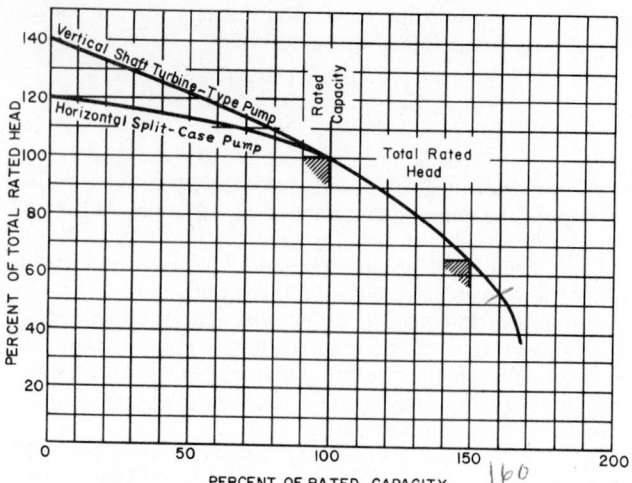

Fig. 11-4K.   Standard head-discharge curves for horizontal and vertical fire pumps.

The shutoff point represents the maximum allowable total head pressure; otherwise the pump would have a rising or convex characteristic curve. Such pumps are not listed. With a convex curve there could be two flow points for one pressure.

Rating

The curve should pass through or above the point of rated capacity and head (see Fig. 11-4K).

Overload

At 150 percent of rated capacity, the total head should not be less than 65 percent of rated total head. Here, also, the curve should pass through or above the overload point. Most modern fire pumps have curves with a significant margin above the theoretical overload. Some models have a cavitation or "break" point in the curve just beyond overload.

K.   Horizontal-shaft Centrifugal Fire Pumps

Horizontal-shaft fire pumps should be installed to operate under positive suction head, especially with automatic or remote-manual starting. If the water supply would be such that suction lift could not be avoided, consideration should be given to installation of vertical turbine-type fire pumps.

Suction Facilities

When streams, ponds, and other open bodies of water are used, properly screened intakes should be provided to prevent fish, eels and foreign material from entering the pump and the fire protection system. A foot valve of proper design should be provided on each suction inlet (see Fig. 11-4L).

Use of nonpotable water should be avoided when fire pumps discharge into a system that is also connected to pub-

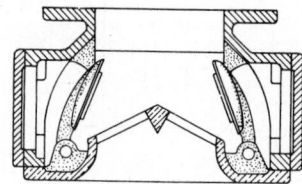

Fig. 11-4L.   A typical foot valve of good design shown in open position.

lic mains or other potable supplies. Otherwise, there would be cross-connections, which are prohibited, or in some locations restricted, by either health or water utilities authorities, or both, in most states and provinces. Above-ground covered tanks filled with potable water are recommended for supplying fire pumps.

The volume of suction storage should be sufficient to supply the pump at overload rate for the estimated duration of the water demand.

Fire pumps operating under lift should be provided with two independent and reliable methods of priming. They will not deliver water until air is removed and impellers, casings, and suction pipes are filled with water. For details of priming and other suction arrangements, see the NFPA Fire Pump Standard.

Types of Pumps

Booster Pumps: These are fire pumps taking suction from public water mains, industrial systems, or power penstocks. (In a mechanical sense all pumps are booster pumps.) As a prelude to installation, the available fire flow in the area is obtained by testing. Full overload capacity of the pump plus probable flow drawn from hydrants in the area by the fire department are calculated, and they should not drop the pressure in the water mains below 20 psi. Head rating of the pump should be sufficient to meet all pipe friction in the connection plus pressure demand.

Limited Service Fire Pumps: These small-capacity booster pumps are intended for use in small properties or for special fire protection systems requiring limited volume but good pressure. They are rated at 200, 300, and 450 gpm, limited to 130 percent of maximum capacity and for varying pressures with loads not greater than 30 hp rating; they are always arranged for automatic operation. They are especially useful to remedy a deficiency in pressure of other supplies for high areas of limited size, or as a means of making the full amount of water in a limited public supply available at adequate pressure. In the latter case, if there is a gravity tank on the property which cannot be filled by normal public water pressure, the special service pump can also serve as a tank filling pump.

Pump Accessories

Auxiliary devices have an important bearing on the complete functioning of a pump as a fire protection water supply, and their provision or omission should never be decided solely on the basis of costs. The NFPA Fire Pump Standard gives detailed information concerning their installation; the following are worthy of special consideration:

Relief Valves: These are necessary on the pump discharge if excess pressure results from operation of the pump. Pumps having adjustable speed drivers need relief valves, as do those where suction pressure plus shutoff pressure would exceed the pressure rating of the fire protection equipment.

Hose Valves: Approved $2\frac{1}{2}$-in. hose valves are used in testing the pump, and for hose stream fire protection. The valves should be attached to a header or manifold outside the pump room, or otherwise located to avoid water damage to the pump, driver, and controller. The number of valves needed depends on the pump capacity. For details see the NFPA Fire Pump Standard.

Automatic Air Release Valves: These are necessary on the top of the casing of pumps arranged for automatic or remote control operation. An umbrella cock may be adequate for a pump which can be started only by manual means by an operator in the pump room, but an automatic air release is

desirable on any pump with a casing that is normally full of water.

Circulation Relief Valves: These are necessary for pumps which may be started automatically or by remote control. Their function is to open at slightly above rated pressure, when there is little or no discharge, so that sufficient water is discharged to prevent overheating of the pump. These valves are not needed on engine-driven pumps where cooling water is taken from the pump discharge.

L. Vertical Turbine-type Fire Pumps

Vertical turbine-type pumps were originally designed to pump water from bored wells. As fire pumps, they are recommended in instances where horizontal pumps would operate with suction lift. An outstanding feature of vertical pumps is the ability to operate without priming. (See the NFPA Pump Standard for required submergence.) Vertical pumps may be used to pump from streams, ponds, wet pits, etc., as well as in booster service.

Suction from wells is not recommended for fire service, although it is acceptable if the adequacy and reliability of the well is established, and the entire installation made in conformance with the NFPA Fire Pump Standard. In many instances, the cost of a deep well fire pump installation would be prohibitive, especially if the pumping level at maximum rate would be more than 50 ft below ground level (200 ft is the limit).

If the yield from a reliable well is too small to supply a standard fire pump, low capacity well pumps could be used to fill conventional ground level tanks or reservoirs for the fire pump supply.

A typical vertical fire pump consists essentially of a motor head or right-angle gear drive, a column pipe and discharge fitting (see Figs. 11-4M and 11-4N), an open or enclosed drive shaft, a bowl assembly (containing the impellers), and a suction strainer. The principle of operation is comparable to that of a multistage horizontal centrifugal pump. Except for shutoff pressure, the characteristic curve is the same as for horizontal pumps (see Fig. 11-4K).

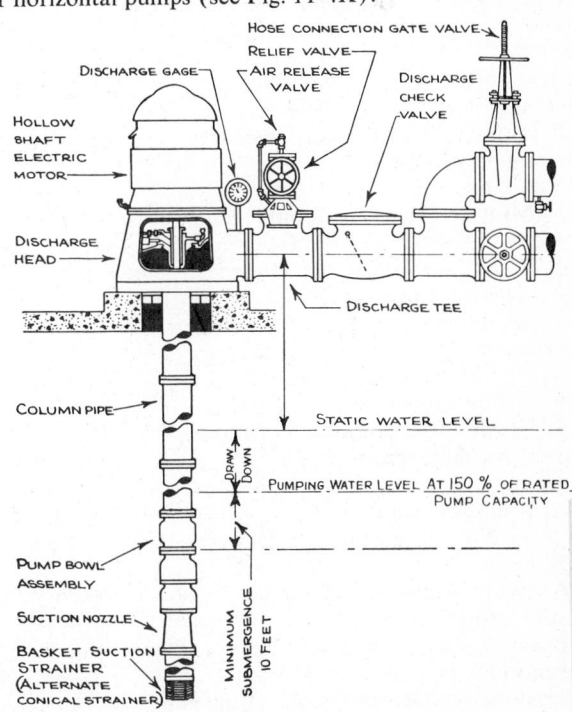

Fig. 11-4M. Vertical shaft turbine-type pump installation.

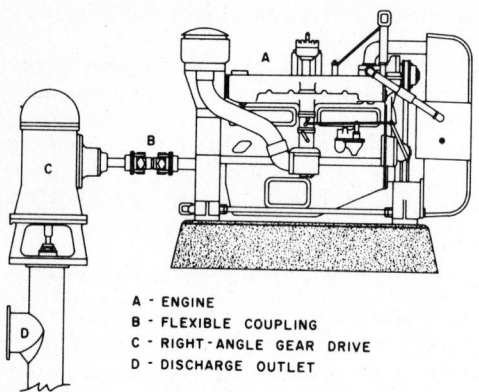

A - ENGINE
B - FLEXIBLE COUPLING
C - RIGHT-ANGLE GEAR DRIVE
D - DISCHARGE OUTLET

Fig. 11-4N. Engine-driven vertical fire pump.

Vertical pumps have the same standard capacity ratings as horizontal fire pumps. Pressure ratings are not standardized. By changing the number of stages and/or the impeller diameters, the pump manufacturer can provide a specific total head at rated speed.

For electrically driven pumps hollow shaft motors are used. Internal combustion engines or steam turbines can be used by means of right angle gear heads.

M.   Fire Pump Capacity and Head Rating

The capacity and pressure ratings of fire pumps should be adequate to meet flow and pressure demands consistent with water supply requirements for the property in question. Fire pumps are designed to provide their rated capacity with a safety factor built in (150 percent of rated capacity at at least 65 percent of rated pressure) to provide some protection in case of greater than expected demand at time of fire. The following examples show one method of how rated capacity and pressure can be determined by using the standard fire pump curve (see Fig. 11-4K).

Example No. 1: Horizontal Centrifugal Pump

The estimated water demand for sprinklers and hose streams is 1,400 gpm at 90 psi pump discharge pressure. The suction supply is a pond, and the estimated lift is 5 psi at maximum flow.

PROBLEM: Determine the required rated capacity and pressure of the pump.

SOLUTION:

1. Meet the demand (1,400 gpm) with the overload capacity of the pump (150 percent of rated capacity);

2. Thus, 1,400 ÷ 150 = 933 gpm. (The nearest standard pump rating is 1,000 gpm);

3. Therefore, 1,400 gpm demand would be 140 percent of capacity;

4. At 140 percent capacity, the total pressure is 73 percent rated pressure;

5. Under lift condition of operation, the total pressure equals discharge pressure (90 psi) plus suction pressure (5 psi);

6. Therefore, net pressure at 1,400 gpm equals 90 + 5 = 95 psi, and rated pressure at 1,000 gpm = 95 ÷ 73 percent = 130 psi.

ANSWER: Pump rating should be not less than 1,000 gpm at 130 psi.

Example No. 2: Vertical Turbine Pump (pump in a driven well)

The estimated water demand at the pump discharge gage is 1,100 gpm at 100 psi (ground level). Tests and weather records show that the aquifer (underground water source) is reliable and adequate at all seasons. The static level is 45 ft below the surface. The draw down, or vertical distance between the static and pumping water levels, is 40 ft at 1,100 gpm pumping rate.

PROBLEM: Determine rated capacity and pressure of the pump.

SOLUTION:

1. Meet the demand (1,100 gpm) with the overload capacity of the pump (150 percent of rated capacity);

2. Thus, 1,100 ÷ 150 percent = 733 gpm. (The nearest standard pump rating is 750 gpm);

3. Therefore, the 1,100 gpm demand would be 146 percent capacity;

4. At 146 percent capacity, the total pressure is 70 percent rated pressure;

5. At 1,100 gpm, pressure demand at the surface = 100 psi;

6. As the distance to water level at 1,100 gpm pumping rate is 45 + 40 = 85 ft × .434 = 37 psi; pumping pressure would be 100 + 37 = 137 psi which is 70 percent of rated pressure;

7. Therefore 137 ÷ 70 percent = 195 psi.

ANSWER: Pump rating should be not less than 750 gpm at 195 psi.

Example No. 3: Booster Pump on Public Water Connection

A sprinklered building in a city has an estimated sprinkler demand of 750 gpm at 60 psi pump discharge. Based on fire flow tests from nearby street hydrants, 750 gpm at 27 psi would be available for sprinklers at the inlet flange of the pump (allowance already made for hose streams).

PROBLEM: Determine the rated capacity and pressure of the pump.

SOLUTION:

1. Meet the demand (750 gpm) with the overload capacity of the pump (150 percent of rated capacity);

2. Thus, 750 ÷ 150 percent = 500 gpm, a standard pump rating;

3. The total pressure at 150 percent capacity is 65 percent rated net pressure;

4. With positive head suction supply, the net pressure equals discharge pressure minus suction pressure; thus, at 750 gpm flow, net pressure equals 60 − 27 = 33 psi;

5. Therefore, 33 ÷ 65 percent = 51 psi.

ANSWER: Pump rating should be greater than 500 gpm at 50 psi.

(Note that all three examples utilize the pump curve out to 150 percent. This leaves no reserve as pump curves drop off sharply after 150 percent. Generally a larger pump is recommended than these calculations indicate.)

N.   Horsepower of Fire Pumps

Before matching a driver to a pump, it is necessary to know the maximum brake horsepower demand of the pump at rated speed. This can be determined directly from the horsepower curve provided by the pump manufacturer. Typical fire pumps reach maximum brake horsepower between 140 and 170 percent of rated capacity (see Fig. 11-5F).

Horsepower can be calculated, if the curves are not available, by the formula

$$\text{bhp} = \frac{5.83 QP}{10,000} E \quad \text{or} \quad \text{bhp} = \frac{QP}{1,710} E$$

where

bhp = brake horsepower

Q = gallons per minute

P = total head (psi) or net pressure

E = efficiency = $\dfrac{\text{Water Horsepower}}{\text{Input Horsepower}}$

The efficiency at maximum brake horsepower is usually 60 to 75 percent.

EXAMPLE: Find by formula the minimum horsepower needed to drive a 1,000 gpm-100 psi-1,760 rpm horizontal centrifugal fire pump.

SOLUTION:

a. Assume 65 percent efficiency at 160 percent capacity;

b. From standard pump curve (Fig. 11-4K) the pressure is 55 percent at 160 percent capacity, or 55 psi at 1,600 rpm;

c. By formula, bhp = $\dfrac{5.83 \times 1,600 \times 55}{10,000 \times .65}$ = 79;

ANSWER: Not less than 79 usable brake horsepower.

O. Fire Pump Drivers

Power for driving fire pumps is selected on the basis of reliability, adequacy, economy, and safety. The reliability of utility electric power may be judged by the record of outages, and by review of the power sources and distribution layout of the system in question.

Gas utility systems may be subject to periods of restricted use because of high seasonal demand. To offset this, standby gas storage can be provided, or arrangements negotiated with utilities whereby the fire pump is supplied with gas even though the general use of gas is restricted.

There are many public utilities that operate steam distribution systems. When high pressure steam is available, it would be practical for large consumers to use turbine-driven fire pumps.

Many industrial plants generate their own steam-electric and hydro-electric power, or both. Utility power also may be used possibly on a standby basis.

Internal combustion engines have the advantage of not being dependent upon outside sources of power.

Electric Motors

Electric motors for driving fire pumps are not specifically approved or listed, but they are required to be made by reliable manufacturers in accordance with specifications of the National Electrical Manufacturers Association (NEMA) or the Canadian Electrical Manufacturers Association (CEMA). All electrical equipment and wiring in a fire pump installation should comply with the National Electrical Code except as modified by the NFPA Fire Pump Standard (see Fig. 11-4O).

The pump manufacturer, or the installing contractor, is responsible for providing a motor of sufficient capacity to avoid overloading beyond the limit of the service factor at maximum brake horsepower and rated speed. The service factor is a numerical value, and it depends on the type of motor (open, splashproof, or totally enclosed) and resistance of the insulation on the windings to heat and breakdown.

When the service factor exceeds 1.0, the excessive amount is stamped on the nameplate along with the voltage and the full load ampere rating. For example, a 75 hp motor, with

Fig. 11-4O. An electrically driven centrifugal fire pump. (Fairbanks Morse & Co.)

1.15 service factor, could safely meet a demand of 75 × 1.15 = 86.25 bhp.

Another use for the service factor is to estimate the maximum allowable ampere demand. For example, with a 40-amp full load rating and a 1.12 service factor, the maximum ammeter reading should not exceed 40 × 1.12 = 45 amps. Note also that for a given voltage, horsepower is proportional to amperes.

Only motors wound for 208 volts should be used on 208-volt services.

Direct-current motors for pumps are either of the stabilized shunt type, or cumulative compound-wound type. The speed of the motor with no load at operating temperature shall not exceed the speed of the motor under full load at operating temperature by more than 10 percent.

The most commonly used alternating-current motors are of the squirrel-cage induction type. They usually are equipped with across-the-line starting equipment, unless their starting characteristics would be objectionable to the company furnishing the power. In the latter case primary resistance starting may be employed, or a wound rotor type of motor with appropriate starting equipment may be substituted. When squirrel-cage motors are used, the voltage drop must not be so great as to prevent the motor from starting, i.e., not more than ten percent below normal voltage at moment of start. While the motor is running at rated pump capacity, pressure, and speed, the line voltage should not drop more than five percent below motor nameplate voltage.

This type of motor should have normal starting and breakdown torque. The locked rotor currents for motors of various horsepower ratings are specified in the NFPA Fire Pump Standard.

Electric Motor Controllers

Motor controllers are available for alternating current fire pump motors operating at standard voltages up to 600. A controller is a complete, assembled unit, wired and tested, and ready for service by connecting to the power supply and the proper motor terminals. Detailed specifications are described in the NFPA Fire Pump Standard. Higher voltages are not recommended, but acceptable controllers conforming to special requirements of the NFPA Fire Pump Standard can be provided.

Controllers are available for combined manual and automatic operation, or for manual operation only. They also are available for either squirrel-cage, wound-rotor, or partwinding motors, and for two-phase or three-phase power. Across-the-line starting is recommended and preferred, but

Fig. 11-4P. A steam turbine-driven centrifugal fire pump. (Peerless Pump Div., FMC Corp.)

controllers for primary-resistance, reduced-voltage starting are also available.

The circuit breaker of a fire pump controller permits normal starting without tripping, and provides stalled rotor and instantaneous short circuit protection. The interrupting capacity of the breaker should be adequate for the circuit in which it is located, but not less than 15,000 amps in any case.

Automatic controllers known as limited service controllers are available for across-the-line squirrel-cage motors of 30 hp or less driving special service booster fire pumps.

Steam Turbine

When adequate and reliable steam supplies are available, turbine driven fire pumps are acceptable (see Fig. 11-4P). Only well-built machines of good design with industrial records of proved reliability are used. Special arrangements are needed for automatic operation. Speed rating should not exceed 3,600 rpm, because this is the maximum speed of listed fire pumps. Detailed requirements for steam supply, speed governors, and controls are contained in the NFPA Fire Pump Standard.

Internal Combustion Engines

Engines powered by diesel fuel, gasoline, or natural gas are found in use for fire pump service. Engines powered by LP-Gas are not recognized by the NFPA Fire Pump Standard although they are approved by the Factory Mutual System. Only the vapor withdrawal method of supplying an engine with LP-Gas should be allowed.

Natural gas and LP-Gas engines differ from gasoline engines only in design of the carburetors, intake manifolds, and cylinder heads.

Large industrial consumers of natural or LP-Gas often prefer engine-driven fire pumps using these fuels.

In addition to the NFPA Fire Pump Standard, reference should be made to NFPA No. 37, Stationary Combustion Engines and Gas Turbines; No. 54, National Fuel Gas Code; No. 58, Storage and Handling of LP-Gas; No. 31, Installation of Oil Burning Equipment. Installations should be made in conformance to local codes.

The Standard for Combustion Engines and Gas Turbines specifically recognizes the need for special provisions covering engines driving fire pumps. In general, manual and automatic devices intended to limit or prevent the accidental discharge of flammable gases are needed, but the development of other unsatisfactory conditions, such as high cooling water temperature and low oil pressure, should be indicated by alarms, and not by shutting down of the engine. The intent is to keep the pump operating just as long as possible. The importance of supervision, especially for automatic pumps, is obvious.

Cooling Systems: An adequate cooling system is vital to reliable operation of an internal combustion engine. A closed pipe system with a heat exchanger is the only cooling arrangement for a fire pump unit recognized in the NFPA Fire Pump Standard. Only clean or potable water should be circulated through the engine block. Raw water is piped from the fire pump through the heat exchanger tubes to free discharge in a visible location such as the cone of the fire pump relief valve. On some engines, the manifolds, oil coolers, and other parts are equipped with water jackets, as recommended by the engine manufacturer (see Fig. 11-4R). Most engines require a raw water flow of 15 to 30 gpm or even more.

Fuel Tanks: The storage tank for liquid or gas fuel contains at least an 8-hr. supply; greater capacity is provided if facilities for prompt refilling are not available. Tank capacity may be estimated by allowing 1 pt of gasoline, diesel oil, or LP-Gas per hp per hr. (See diagrams of typical fuel systems in the NFPA Fire Pump Standard.)

Fig. 11-4Q. An engine-driven centrifugal fire pump. (Allis-Chalmers)

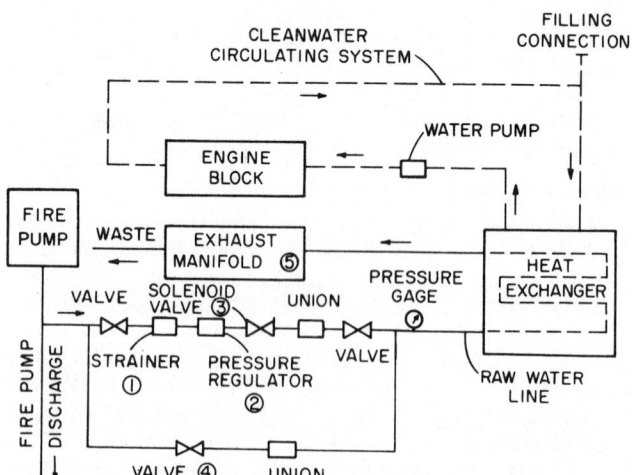

Fig. 11-4R. A typical heat-exchanger cooling system for an automatically controlled engine-driven fire pump. Raw water from the fire pump enters the system through the strainer (1), which prevents sediment from entering the system, and the pressure regulator (2), which protects the heat exchanger from excessive pressure. The solenoid valve (3) is required with automatic control of the engine. Valve (4), normally closed, may be used to bypass the regulator and solenoid valve. The exhaust manifold (5) may be cooled by the clean water circulating system.

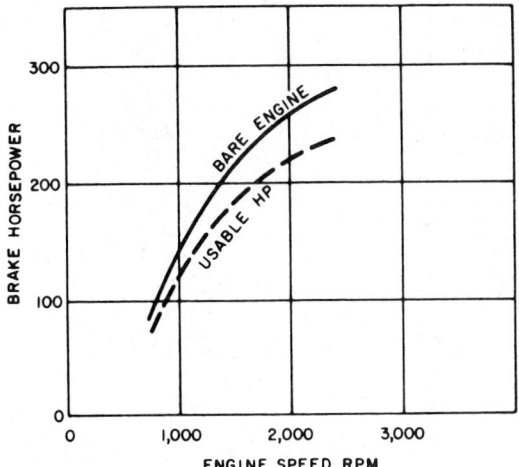

Fig. 11-4S. Typical engine horsepower curves.

Engine Horsepower

Engines specifically designed for use with fire pumps are rated by measuring the horsepower developed with all accessories in operation and then making some allowance for wear and tear. Other engines used with fire pumps are rated on the basis of "usable power," which is estimated by dividing bare engine horsepower by 1.20. Approximately 20 percent of bare engine outputs is allowed for operating the accessories, reserve power, wear and tear, and manufacturing tolerances. Typical bare engines and usable horsepower curves are shown in Figure 11-4S.

The engine manufacturer's test curves are based on standard barometric pressure at sea level and 60°F. The usable horsepower of a fire pump engine should be reduced for each 1,000 ft rise in altitude, by five percent for a gasoline engine, three percent for a diesel engine, and one percent for each 10°F rise above 60°F.

Engine Controllers

Controllers are used for automatic operation of engine-driven fire pumps. The specifications for construction, location, and methods of actuation of engine controllers are the same as for electric motor controllers. Automatic controllers are equipped with manual starting and stopping switches.

Alarm devices are provided to indicate low oil pressure in the lubrication systems, high engine jacket water temperature, failure of engine to start automatically, and shutdown from overspeed (diesel only).

There are optional features for controllers as given in the NFPA Fire Pump Standard. A weekly program timer can be provided. This device may be arranged to start the unit automatically once a week, and run for a predetermined number of minutes. A recording pressure gage records this performance.

Controllers are operated on low voltage direct current power from the engine's batteries. The program timer, battery charger, or other auxiliary devices not essential to pump control are powered by the regular alternating current power supply at the property.

P.   Automatic Pump Control

Most fire pump installations normally are arranged for automatic operation, preferably with automatic start and manual shutdown. The choice between manual and automatic shutdown depends on an evaluation of the specific conditions involved in a pump's installation and use. Horizontal centrifugal pumps under automatic control should always operate under a head to avoid the need of priming.

Each motor or engine controller is equipped with a pressure switch that actuates the pump unit when pressure in the water system piping drops to a preset level. Unless the normal water supply static pressure is higher than the pump starting pressure, an automatic jockey pump must be provided to maintain pressure in the system at the higher level.

Actuation of a pump by water flow instead of by pressure drop is desirable for certain installations, such as (1) where the opening of a moderate number of sprinklers would not drop the system pressure enough to move the pressure switch, (2) where fire in a high hazard occupancy would demand fire pump service without delay, (3) in a combined fire protection and plant service system where a pressure maintenance pump would be impractical, and (4) where pressure fluctuates so much that a stable cut-in pressure could not be obtained.

The wiring system of a pump controller includes terminals for connection of a relay to an external alarm circuit from a sprinkler, deluge, or special fire protection system. To secure reliable pump actuation, external circuits should be installed in conformance with one of the following NFPA standards, depending upon the nature of the signaling system:

No. 71, Central Station Signaling Systems
No. 72A, Local Protective Signaling Systems
No. 72B, Auxiliary Protective Signaling Systems
No. 72C, Remote Station Protective Signaling Systems
No. 72D, Proprietary Protective Signaling Systems

Circuits for remote automatic starting of fire pumps should be powered from the controller power.

Q.   Field Acceptance Tests

After a new fire pump has been installed, it is general practice for a performance test to be made. By this means, defects and faults can be discovered, and steps taken to remedy them. These tests enable the purchaser to determine that the contract has been properly concluded. They also demonstrate the need of future maintenance tests.

Details of the acceptance tests are given in the NFPA Fire Pump Standard. The test demonstrates the adequacy of the pump suction and the ability of the pump to deliver water in accordance with its head-capacity curve. The prime mover also is operated under various conditions and its performance noted. There are separate provisions for electric motors, steam turbines, and internal combustion engines. Repeated operations of the controlling equipment are required to insure that full operation of the unit will result from either manual or automatic operation of the controller. The total operating time of the pump during the testing period is at least for 1 hr.

Flow tests are made to develop the pressure-discharge characteristic curve of the pump. The procedure followed is to run the pump at five or six different flows, including "shutoff" with no water flowing. The rate in gallons per minute is determined with a pitot gage at the nozzles (preferably a standard 30-in. "Underwriter" playpipes) attached to hose lines from an outside hose-valve header. The discharge is varied by changing the number of lines and size of nozzle tips or both.

For every flow, pressure readings are taken at the suction gage and the discharge gage; the revolutions per minute are also measured, using a revolution counter or a tachometer, if available. (The tachometer on a fire pump engine is not sufficiently accurate.)

The net pressures are calculated from the pump gage readings, and the flows in gallons per minute corresponding to the pitot readings are obtained from discharge tables (Table 11-6B. for example).

The nozzles may be attached directly to outdoor headers, without hose lines, if water damage can be avoided. Disposal of test water is often a problem, and the length of hose lines would depend on the drainage facilities available, and exposure to property and people.

(With the growing problems of waste water disposal, many pump installations are equipped with water meters for the acceptance test and periodic service tests. The meters are installed in conformance with the NFPA Fire Pump Standard in order to function properly and not interfere with the operation of the pump.)

Vertical turbine fire pumps are tested in the same manner as horizontal pumps, except that there is no suction gage. Also, the pumping water level should be recorded at the several test points unless it is more or less constant.

Acceptance Test 1,500 gpm, 100 psi, 1,760 rpm Fire Pump

RPM	Discharge psi	Suction psi	*Net psi	No.	Size in.	Pitot Pressure psi	GPM*	Total*	GPM*	Net* psi
				Streams				corrected to 1,760 RPM		
1,700	125	+16	109	0	—	—	—	0	0	118
1,695	120	+18	102	1	1¾	70	742	742	772	110
1,690	110	+16	94	2	1¾	60, 60	687, 687	1,374	1,420	101
1,686	95	+17	79	3	1¾	55, 55, 55	657, 657 657	1,971	2,060	85
1,675	85	+16	69	4	1¾	35, 37, 48, 48	525, 540 614, 614	2,293	2,410	76

° Calculated from observed data.

Fig. 11-4T. An example of a log of a fire pump acceptance test.

Figure 11-4T is a tabulation of data obtained by a typical field acceptance test of a horizontal 1,500 gpm, 100 psi, 1,760 rpm engine-driven centrifugal pump. The net pressure and total flows are calculated from the observed data and plotted (see Fig. 11-4U). The curve best fitting the plotted points is then drawn (Curve A). In this installation the engine governor appeared to be out of adjustment, restricting the average speed to 1,689 rpm, whereas the rated speed was 1,760 rpm.

Since the pump was tested at less than rated speed, the observed net pressures and flows were converted to what they would have been at the rated speed of 1,760 rpm. Curve B is the characteristic curve at rated conditions. Although the rating point was barely reached, the overload point exceeded the minimum by a good margin. With the engine adjusted to operate at full speed, the pump performance would be acceptable. The following is the conversion calculation procedure that was followed:

Flow is directly proportional to revolutions per minute
Net pressure is proportional to (rpm)^2
EXAMPLE: Test flow 1,971 gpm at 1,686 rpm

$$\text{Flow at 1,760 rpm} = 1,971 \left(\frac{1,760}{1,686}\right) = 2,060 \text{ gpm}$$

Net pressure for 1,971 gpm at 1,686 rpm is 78 psi

$$\text{Net pressure for 2,060 gpm at 1,760 rpm is } 78 \left(\frac{1,760}{1,686}\right)^2 = 85 \text{ psi.}$$

In theory, the characteristic curve assumes operation at constant rated speed. Actually the speed of internal combustion engines and steam turbines is permitted to vary

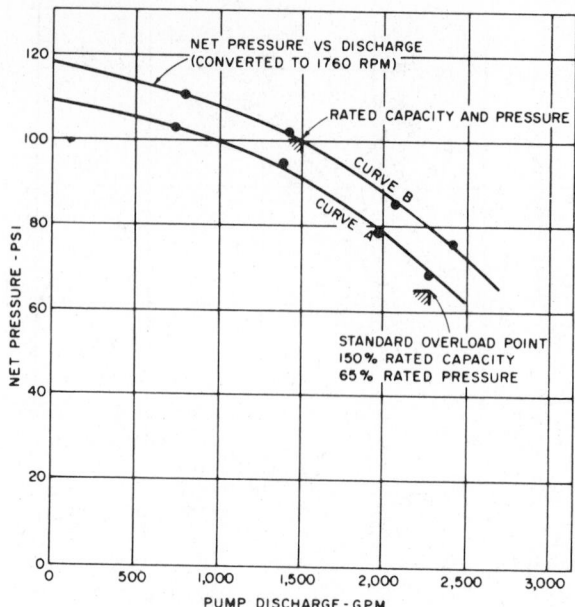

Fig. 11-4U. Head-capacity curves plotted from data compiled in a fire pump acceptance test (see Fig. 11-4T for the data used to plot these curves).

within range of 8 to 10 percent between shutoff and maximum load. Electric motor speed is more nearly constant. Speed reduction may occur if the power supply is overloaded.

R.   Location and Housing of Centrifugal Pumps

Fire pumps are housed in buildings of fire-resistive or noncombustible construction. Even when the climate is so mild that there is no danger of freezing, sufficient enclosure is needed to protect against dirt, corrosion, and tampering. Structural separation of the pump room from other parts of a property is desirable.

Pump rooms and power facilities are as free as possible from exposure to fire, explosion, flood, and windstorm damage.

Light, heat, ventilation, and floor drainage are provided for pump rooms. An abovegrade, dry location is preferred. For an internal combustion engine-drive unit, heat, ventilation, and abovegrade location are essential.

Fire pumps preferably are located as close as possible to those areas where protection is most important. In some large properties, it may be necessary to have water supplies at more than one point to obtain the most favorable distribution system. When this results in placing a pump in a somewhat isolated pump room, the requirements for housing and supervision are of special importance.

S.   Annual Pump Tests

A fire pump is tested annually to make certain that the pump, driver, suction, and power supply function properly, and to correct faults that may be disclosed. The hydraulic performance of the pump is measured by a flow test with hose and nozzles connected to the pump header or yard hydrants. Three points on the standard curve are checked: (1) shutoff, (2) overload (150 percent of rated capacity or more) and (3) a convenient rate of flow at or near capacity rating.

Automatic operation is tested by opening yard hydrants or sprinkler riser drains giving due consideration to the layout of the fire protection system (pressure drop or water flow actuation, jockey pump, etc.). It is not sufficient to initiate pressure drop by the test cock on the controller.

Water level of ponds and reservoirs, condition of suction screens and intakes, aboveground tanks, etc., are carefully examined.

The history of power outages, low water, and failure of any kind involving pump, driver or associated equipment, is investigated. Gage records from engine controllers (when so equipped) are examined.

T. Pump Operation and Maintenance

A fire pump can be depended upon to work in an emergency only if it is properly operated and maintained. It is desirable to have someone at the property at all times who has been designated and instructed in the operation of the pump and its driver. A short test by the regular pump operators is made each week by discharging water from some convenient outlet for a long enough time to indicate proper operation.

When a fire alarm is given or an alarm indicates an automatic fire pump is operating, the person responsible for the fire pump mans it immediately. The pump is preferably put in manual operation and allowed to run until the emergency is over, when it may be shut down manually. During this and every other operating period, the equipment should be carefully checked to see whether it is performing properly.

To prevent too frequent starting and stopping, an electric motor controller has a timer to keep the motor running for at least 1 min for each 10 hp motor rating (not more than 7 min required). It is preferable with all types of pump drivers to permit the unit to run until it is shut down manually. When there is more than one automatic fire pump, the control is arranged for operation of the pumps in a predetermined sequence. Control of the pump from one or more remote push buttons, which will start but not stop the pump, may be provided if desired. Also, if there is deluge valve control of an open discharge device system, the pump may be started by a drop-out relay in a closed circuit.

The cooling and lubrication of a centrifugal fire pump is so dependent upon water that the pump must never be run without the pump casing full of water. If it is a manual pump taking suction under lift, it must be fully primed; if it is an automatic pump, the casing must be kept full. In either case, it is wise to open the umbrella cock to check for water before operating. Close attention is given to the bearings and stuffing boxes during the first few minutes of running to see that there is no heating up and no need of adjustment. When water reaches the water seal, a small leak at stuffing box glands is desirable. The suction inlet and discharge outlet pressure gages are read occasionally to see that the inlet is not obstructed by a choked screen or foot valve.

With a vertical shaft turbine-type fire pump, the water level can be observed if suction is from a visible supply. If the pump takes suction from a well, water level testing equipment must be used. The ground water level at the pump should be checked at intervals during the year and the draw down should be determined during the annual 150 percent capacity test. These tests should indicate any important change in the ground water supply.

The direction of rotation of the pump and the speed of operation should always be checked.

Power Supply Maintenance

The source of power for the pump should also be checked. With an electric motor drive, this means current supply for the motor and its auxiliary equipment. For steam turbine drive, it means the steam supply up to the control valve and the absence of condensate from supply, turbine, and exhaust. If the pump is driven by an internal combustion engine, there must be adequate fuel for 8 hrs operation. The batteries must be fully charged.

The starting equipment must be test operated and its functioning carefully checked. Any evidence of drop in voltage to an electric motor or drop in steam pressure to a turbine must be investigated.

With an internal combustion engine drive, the crank case oil must be replenished or renewed as needed, the oil filter and air cleaner given necessary attention, the automatic battery charging equipment checked, and the specific gravity of battery electrolyte determined at least once a month. Spark plugs should be cleaned and reset once or twice a year, and replaced every four or five years. The use of "hot" plugs is usually in order. It is desirable to add degumming agents to the gasoline supply as gasoline deteriorates with age. In any event, the gasoline should be renewed once a year.

U. Reciprocating Steam Fire Pumps

Although few new reciprocating steam fire pumps have been installed in recent years, a number are still in service, and they should conform to NFPA No. 21, Operation and Maintenance of Steam Fire Pumps. (These fire pumps are commonly referred to as Underwriter Steam Fire Pumps.)

The general features of a direct-acting duplex steam pump are shown in Fig. 11-4V. The size of the steam and exhaust parts is larger than in the general purpose steam pump, thus permitting higher speeds. The steam supply pipe should be an independent line run from boiler to pump in such a way that it will not be damaged by fire or other hazards.

Automatic Control

Automatic control can be provided by a pressure governor to regulate steam supply to the pump in accordance with the water pressure on the pump discharge. For successful operation, it is nearly always necessary to provide a small, automatically controlled jockey pump to maintain system pressure and supply leakage and avoid continuous operation of the large pump.

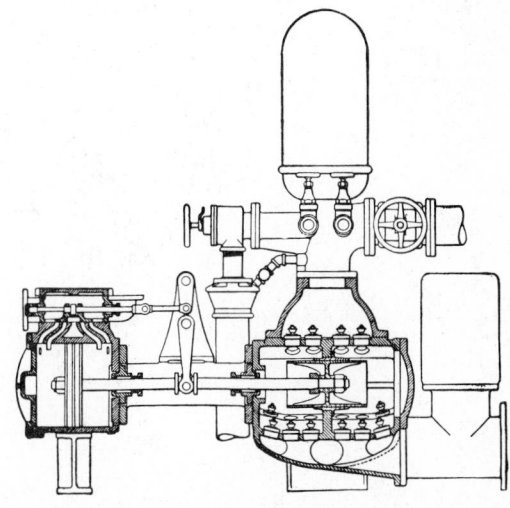

Fig. 11-4V. Sectional view of an approved duplex steam pump.

SI Units

The following conversion factors are given as a convenience in converting to SI units the English units used in this chapter.

1 in.	=	25.4 mm
1 ft	=	0.305 m
1 psi	=	6894.757 Pa
$\frac{5}{9}(°F - 32)$	=	°C
1 gal	=	3.785 litres
1 gpm	=	3.785 litres/min.

Bibliography

NFPA Codes, Standards, and Recommended Practices (see the latest _NFPA Publications and Visual Aids Catalog_ for availability of current editions of the following documents)

NFPA No. 13, Standard for the Installation of Sprinkler Systems.

NFPA No. 14, Standard for the Installation of Standpipe and Hose Systems.

NFPA No. 15, Standard for Water Spray Fixed Systems for Fire Protection.

NFPA No. 16, Standard for Foam-Water Sprinkler Systems and Foam-Water Spray Systems.

NFPA No. 20, Standard for the Installation of Centrifugal Fire Pumps.

NFPA No. 21, Standard for the Operation and Maintenance of National Standard Steam Fire Pumps.

NFPA No. 22, Standard for Water Tanks for Private Fire Protection.

NFPA No. 24, Standard for Outside Protection.

NFPA No. 37, Standard for the Installation and Use of Stationary Combustion Engines and Gas Turbines.

NFPA No. 58, Standard for the Storage and Handling of Liquefied Petroleum Gases.

NFPA No. 31, Standard for the Installation of Oil Burning Equipment.

NFPA No. 71, Standard for the Installation, Maintenance and Use of Central Station Signaling Systems for Guard, Fire Alarm and Supervisory Service.

NFPA No. 72A, Standard for the Installation, Maintenance and Use of Local Protective Signaling Systems for Watchmen, Fire Alarm and Supervisory Service.

NFPA No. 72B, Standard for the Installation, Maintenance and Use of Auxiliary Protective Signaling Systems for Fire Alarm Service.

NFPA No. 72C, Standard for the Installation, Maintenance and Use of Remote Station Protective Signaling Systems.

NFPA No. 72D, Standard for the Installation, Maintenance and Use of Proprietary Protective Signaling Systems for Watchmen, Fire Alarm and Supervisory Service.

Additional Readings

Cameron Hydraulic Data, 13th ed., New York, Ingersoll Rand Co.

FM Loss Prevention Data Sheets, Centrifugal Fire Pumps, DS 3-7N, 1974; Underwriter Steam Fire Pumps, DS 3-9, 1973; Factory Mutual System, Norwood, Mass.

Hydraulic Handbook, 2nd ed., Chicago, Fairbanks, Morse & Company, Chicago, 1956, pp. 16–33.

Hydraulic Institute, "Centrifugal Pump Section," _Standards of Hydraulic Institute,_ 12th ed., Hydraulic Institute, New York, 1969.

Karrasik, Igor and Carter, Roy, _Centrifugal Pumps, Selection, Operation and Maintenance,_ F. W. Dodge Corporation, New York, 1960.

Potts, J. E. and Harris, T. H., "Working Principles of the Centrifugal Pump," Chapter IV; "Construction of the Centrifugal Pump," Chapter V; _Fire Pumps and Hydraulics,_ Chemical Publishing Company, Inc., Brooklyn, 1943.

Chapter 5

TEST OF WATER SUPPLIES

One of the most important factors in public or private fire protection is the state of existing water supplies as indicated by available fire flow and reliability of water sources. This information is needed by fire departments, fire insurance engineers, and others responsible for the design and maintenance of public and private fire protection.

Flow tests of public water systems are made to determine the available fire flow in a specific area (business center, industrial park, shopping plaza, institutions, etc.), and to evaluate the performance of the system by comparison with recognized standards. Probably 80 percent or more of all industrial, commercial, and institutional property depends wholly or in part on water from public utility systems for fire protection.)

It is customary for insurance companies and inspection bureaus to have annual flow tests made of private fire systems. The operating performance of fire pumps, gravity tanks, utility connections, or other water sources is investigated, and the overall adequacy of the system determined. By careful testing, results accurate within 5 to 10 percent may be expected.

Flow testing of public water systems should not be conducted without the consent and cooperation of the water-works utility, and possibly the local police and fire departments. A progressive fire department will aid in the test work; the police may be needed to control vehicular and pedestrian traffic.

The hydraulic principles underlying water flow and pump testing procedures are presented in Chapter 4 and Chapter 6 of this Section; Chapters 1 and 2 cover water supply systems.

A. Test Equipment

A Pitot tube and gage combination are indispensable in conducting flow tests from hydrants and nozzles. Representative Pitot tubes are shown in Fig. 11-5A. The small opening at the end of the tube, not over $\frac{1}{16}$-in. in diameter, is inserted in the center of the stream with the opening in direct line with the flow and a distance in front of the opening of one-half the diameter of the opening. Velocity pressure is registered on the gage attached to the tube.

Test quality gages (Grade AA per ANSI Standard, B40.1-1968) graduated from 0 to 200 psi are recommended for general use; low-pressure gages graduated from 0 to 60 psi are best for Pitot readings.

For pump testing, a compound gage, graduated from 30 inches of mercury vacuum to 250 or 300 psi, is needed. Gages are tested and calibrated periodically, and it is advisable to stamp an identification number on each gage.

A $2\frac{1}{2}$-in. cap drilled and tapped for connecting a pressure gage to a hydrant is desirable (see Item 7, Fig. 11-5A). If a playpipe is available, a tapered nozzle plug may be used to connect a gage (see Item 2, Fig. 11-5A). Nozzle plugs readily fit $1\frac{1}{8}$-in. tips. A $\frac{3}{4}$-in. cap tapped for a gage connection having Standard pipe thread is a convenient means for attaching gages to sill cocks and outlets inside buildings (see Item 8, Fig. 11-5A). It is desirable to have a petcock on the line between the connection and gage so air can be bled off. This results in a more accurate reading.

B. Flow Tests of Water Systems

The usual procedure for conducting a flow test on a water system is to take Pitot readings on a sufficient number of hydrants to determine the capacity of the system in the area tested. Observed pressures without test hydrants flowing are called "static pressures"; those obtained with the test streams flowing are "residual pressures." One hydrant is chosen for observing the static and residual pressures, preferably located in the center of the group or where the best average pressure conditions might be expected (see Fig. 11-5B). Avoid using a flowing hydrant for this purpose.

Pitot readings should be taken on the test hydrants progressively, first with one open, then two open, etc. Residual pressure at the gaging hydrant should be recorded for each rate of flow. When the flowing hydrants have been shut off, the static pressure should be checked and averaged with the initial reading.

Pitot readings of less than 10 psi or over 30 psi at any open hydrant should be avoided. To keep within these pressure limits, the rate of flow can be controlled by throttling the hydrant and opening a second outlet, or both. Avoid using the larger pumper connection on a hydrant for

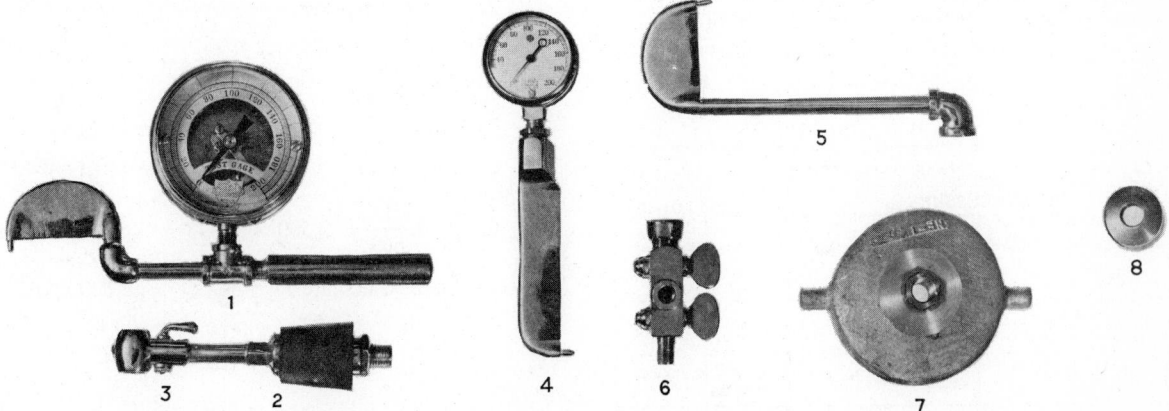

*Fig. 11-5A. Water-flow testing apparatus. **1**, Pitot tube with gage and air chambers. **2**, Rubber plug which may be inserted in nozzle for taking readings with a playpipe where hydrant threads are nonstandard. **3, 6**, Two types of double cocks. **4**, Pitot tube, knife-blade type, with gage for reading the flow from hydrant butts. **5**, Gooseneck-type Pitot for nozzle flow readings. **7**, Hydrant cap of light metal drilled and tapped for a gage. **8**, Cap for attaching gage to faucet.*

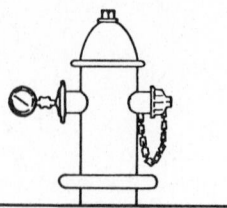

Fig. 11-5B.   *Gage on nonflowing hydrant to measure pressure.*

testing unless flow and pressure are strong enough to produce a good full stream, a condition rarely found.

Figure 11-5C is the record of a typical flow test. Hydrant No 1. was the gaging point and Hydrant No. 2, was the point where flow tests were actually made (see Chap. 6 of this Section for calculating flow dischargers.) Figure 11-5D is a graphical plot of the results of the tests.

Tests of this kind show the available flow over and above normal consumption, but only for the prevailing conditions. To properly evaluate the adequacy and reliability of a system, consideration is given to the sources of supply and the overall operating performance of the system. The hour of the day, the day of the week, the month of the year, the weather, a planned impairment made necessary by highway or other construction—all are factors that may adversely affect the sources of supply, the available yield, and the consumption demand. Fire flow found satisfactory when tested, might be hopelessly inadequate another time—not by accident, but because of deficiencies in the system or in its mode of operation.

A detailed study or analysis of a water utility may not be practical in conjunction with routine flow testing, but at least efforts should be made to learn whatever pumps, tanks, or other sources of supply were in actual use during the test period. Flow charts and pressure records when available provide useful data for studying the test results.

Unsuspected faults other than weak supplies are occasionally disclosed by fire flow tests of public systems. Valves are found partly or entirely shut; sometimes they are found broken or with bent valve stems. Valve boxes may be filled with muck or sand, or even paved over with concrete or asphalt cement. The presence of silt, stones, fish, or other foreign material may be confirmed visually by the hydrant streams. Too many faults of this nature would justify a more thorough survey of the systems.

It is customary to report the results of public fire flow tests in terms of gallons per minute at 20 psi residual pressure, which is the recommended minimum for fire engine use. The observed flow and pressures can be converted

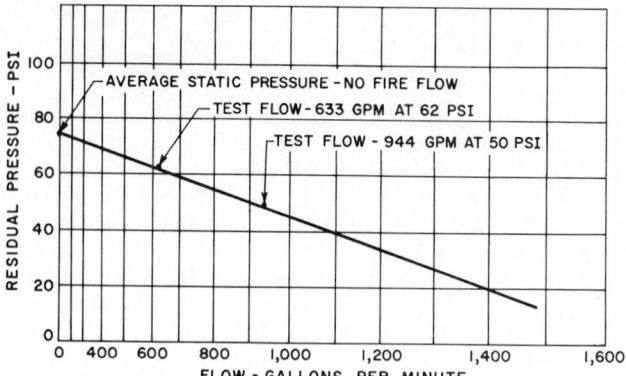

Fig. 11-5D.   *Curve plotted from flow test data given in Fig. 11-5C.*

readily to other values by a simple proportion derived from the Hazen-Williams pipe flow formula, which shows that the flow rate in gallons per minute is directly proportional to the 0.54 power of the head loss. (See Chap. 6 of this Section for a discussion of the Hazen-Williams formula.)

Head loss, which is mostly pipe friction, is the difference between the observed static pressure S and the residual pressure R. Gage value of S seldom indicates the true static (no flow) pressure; actually it is the residual pressure for the normal pipe flow. Observed residual pressure is a function of total flow or $Q + \Delta Q$, where Q is the normal rate of flow, and ΔQ is the measured discharge during the test.

For common fire flow tests, the difference between the true and observed values of S is not usually significant. When making loss-of-head tests to obtain the C value of a pipe (see Chap. 6 of this Section), the calculations should be based on total flow, not on fire flow only. When meter readings or other consumption data are not available, the normal flow should be estimated.

Example of Calculating Flow and Pressure Conversion

A 2,500-gpm test flow from a group of street hydrants dropped the pressure from 69 to 44 psi. (1) What flow would be available at 20 psi? (2) What would the residual pressure be if flow were increased to 3,000 gpm?

SOLUTION 1: Since the flow rate is directly proportional to the 0.54 power of the head (friction) loss, by proportion

$$\frac{Q_2}{Q_1} = \frac{(S - R_2)^{0.54}}{(S - R_1)^{0.54}} \quad \text{and} \quad Q_2 = Q_1 \frac{(S - R_2)^{0.54}}{(S - R_1)^{0.54}}$$

Substituting the known values:

$S - R_2 = 69 - 20 = 49$ psi From Table 11-6I $49^{0.54} = 8.18$

$S - R_1 = 69 - 44 = 25$ psi From Table 11-6I $25^{0.54} = 5.69$

$$Q_2 = 2,500 \frac{8.18}{5.69} = 2,500 \times 1.445 = 3,620 \text{ gpm (answer)}.$$

SOLUTION 2: Calculate R_2 when $Q_2 = 3,000$ gpm.

$$3,000 = 2,500 \frac{(69 - R_2)^{0.54}}{(69 - 44)^{0.54}}$$

or

$$(69 - R_2)^{0.54} = \frac{3,000}{2,500} (69 - 44)^{0.54} .$$

Since $(69 - 44)^{0.54} = 5.69$, then $(69 - R_2)^{0.54} = 1.20 \times 5.69 = 6.83$.

LOCATION: *Adams St. between Cox St. and Baker St.*						
HYDRANTS: *2½ In. Square Sharp Assumed C = 80*						
PRESSURE	PITOT PRESSURE				GPM	TOTAL GPM
HYD I	HYD 2	HYD 3	HYD 4			
72	—	—	—		0	0
62	18	—	—		633	633
50	10 / 10	—			472 / 472	944

GAGE 103 AT HYDRANT No.1 - GAGE 79 FOR PITOT READINGS

Fig. 11-5C.   *Log of a public water flow test.*

From Table 11-6I it is found by interpolation that 6.83 is $35.1^{0.54}$. Therefore $69 - R_2 = 35.1$ and $R_2 = 69 - 35.1 = 33.9$ psi, residual pressure at 3,000 gpm (answer).

For a graphical solution to the same two problems described above, see Figure 11-5G which is a hydraulic flow curve plotted on semiexponential paper.

Flow Test of Public Main at Plant Site

A common procedure using street hydrants to test the water supply for a connection to an industrial plant follows, using an example to describe the step-by-step testing procedures. The sprinkler system in the example is connected to the dead-ended Adams Street main (see Fig. 11-5E); therefore the entire supply comes from the 10-in. main in Baker Street. There are no yard hydrants. The test was conducted as follows:

Step No. 1: A gage was attached to No. 1 Hydrant with a cap. The hydrant was opened and the static pressure, 72 psi, was recorded (Fig. 11-5D). No. 1 Hydrant was chosen for the gaging point because it was upstream from the sprinkler system connection where the residual pressure would have been somewhat greater than noted at No. 1 Hydrant. The gage could have been located on the sprinkler riser in the building, but the hydrant location probably was more convenient.

Step No. 2: The caps were removed from Hydrant No. 2, and the outlets found to be square and sharp (see Fig. 11-5E). After replacing one cap, the hydrant was opened, and a Pitot reading made and recorded (18 psi). Before shutting off the flow, the residual pressure at No. 1 Hydrant was recorded (62 psi).

Step No. 3: The second butt at Hydrant No. 2 was opened, and 10 psi Pitot readings noted on both streams; at Hydrant No. 1 the residual pressure was now 50 psi. It is always desirable to obtain data for at least two rates of flow, one of which should be as heavy as facilities, conditions, and time will allow.

Step No. 4: Hydrant No. 2 was shut down slowly and carefully, and the caps replaced. The static pressure at No. 1 was read and found to be 72 psi, as before the test. The hydrant was then shut down, the gage cap removed, and the regular cap replaced.

Computing the flow: The rate of discharge is best determined by using the table of theoretical discharge (Table 11-6B) and by applying a suitable coefficient from Table 11-6E. In this instance the hydrant outlets justified use of $c = 0.80$ (square and sharp hydrant outlets in Fig. 12-1E). Table 11-6B shows that when the velocity pressure (Pitot gage reading) from a $2\frac{1}{2}$-in. orifice is 18 psi, the flow will be 791 gpm. The actual flow then would be 791×0.8 or 634 gpm at a residual pressure of 62 psi. With both outlets flowing, the Pitot reading on each was 10 psi, corresponding to 590 gpm. The total actual flow was $2 \times 590 \times 0.8 = 944$

gpm at a residual pressure of 50 psi. It is now possible to calculate a flow at any residual pressure. There may be times when an open outlet of a hydrant cannot be flowed because of the damage it will do. In that case a hose and nozzle can be attached to the outlet to direct the stream to a location where it will do no damage. This may be necessary also when water supplies are very weak and the available water does give a good Pitot reading with an open hydrant outlet flowing. Be sure to accurately measure the diameter of the nozzle when one is used.

Annual Tests

Annual tests of water supplies are recommended. Insurance companies usually require such tests of private supplies. Where there are multiple sources, each source should be tested separately and in combination to determine if the total supply is adequate to meet the maximum expected water demand.

Many faults are disclosed by flow tests. Among them are:
1. Valves partly or wholly closed, or inoperative.
2. Stones, silt, and other foreign material in the mains.
3. Tuberculated mains causing high friction loss.
4. Empty or partly filled gravity tanks.
5. Check valves leaking, or installed backward.
6. Mains smaller than indicated on plans.
7. Broken meters or clogged strainers.
8. Existence of meters and valves not previously known.
9. Inoperative hydrants.

Hydrants and gaging points are carefully chosen. Tests should be conducted in such a way that the available flow and pressure at high value or hazardous areas can be determined readily. Make sure that water from the test streams does not cause flooding or property damage. Do not use flowing hydrants for pressure readings; loss of head in hydrant and connection is unknown and difficult to estimate.

Care is taken while testing a water supply system that serves automatic sprinklers to restrict the flow to a rate that will maintain not less than 10 or 15 psi residual pressure on the top lines of sprinklers.

Because flow testing may involve valve operations, all control valves are carefully checked after the tests to insure that all are open and that the system is left in normal condition.

Faults are corrected as soon as possible, and recommendations made for desirable improvements.

Figure 11-5F illustrates how a private system supplied with public water would be tested.

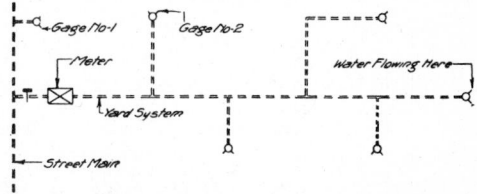

Fig. 11-5F. METHOD OF TESTING CITY WATER SUPPLY TO PRIVATE SYSTEM

Gage No. 1 shows street pressure and should, for gallons discharged, be consistent with data previously secured by street tests, if such tests have been made.

Gage No. 2 on branch line will show flowing pressures in main at the point where the branch takes off.

The difference in pressure between Gage No. 1 and No. 2 equals the loss in meter, pipe and fittings. Friction losses to be expected in fittings and pipes can be estimated from Tables 11-6A and 11-6B. Fire flow meter friction loss can be checked to see if it is unusually high by consulting Table 11-2H.

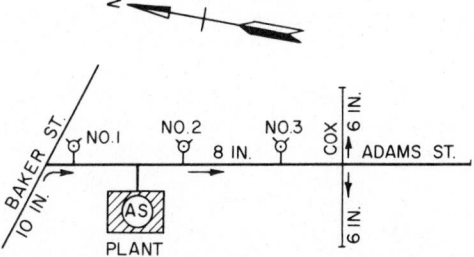

Fig. 11-5E. Data and sketch of a flow test of a public main at a plant site.

C. Hydraulic Flow Curves

Many problems involving water tests and flow in pipes can be solved readily by graphs plotted on semiexponential, semilogarithmic, or linear cross-section paper. Semiexponential paper, commonly called $N^{1.85}$ or "hydraulic" paper is recommended because a master sheet can be drawn easily and copies made by any modern duplicating process. Semilog paper, on the other hand, would be difficult to prepare and expensive to buy. The use of linear cross-section paper requires more test points and extra calculations.

The design of $N^{1.85}$ paper is based on the Hazen-Williams pressure-drop relation, i.e., head loss (static pressure less residual pressure) is proportional to the 1.85 power of flow. Table 11-6G gives values of unit flows from 1 to 20 gpm in $\frac{1}{2}$ gal increments raised to the 1.85 power, and the corresponding scale values when the distance from 0 to the 1 gpm point is 0.05 in. For plotting pressure, the vertical spacing is linear.

The unit values on either vertical or horizontal scales may be multiplied or divided by any constant that will best fit the problem.

See Figure 11-5G for an example of a flow curve plotted on $N^{1.85}$ semiexponential scale.

D. Flow in Loop Systems

It is sometimes necessary to estimate the friction loss and flow characteristics of loops or parallel pipe systems. Such problems are readily solved graphically by procedures based on the principle that pressure drop through a simple loop is the same in every leg; this is true regardless of size, condition, and length of pipe. The method described is not applicable to grid or network systems, although it is sometimes possible to treat a grid as a loop system by making certain assumptions. Grids can be solved by network analyzers or computers, or calculated by the Hardy Cross and other relaxation formulas. Because these matters are outside the scope of this HANDBOOK, the words of John R. Freeman might well be recalled: "A day of (flow) testing is worth a week of calculating."

Figure 11-5H illustrates a graphical solution of a simple loop having two legs, one 800 ft of 8-in. pipe, and the other 1,200 ft of 6-in. pipe. The Hazen-Williams coefficient is $C = 100$ (unlined cast-iron pipe about 15 to 20-years old and in good condition). Using Table 11-6C the calculations would be as follows:

Step No. 1: Friction loss in the 8-in. pipe was calculated

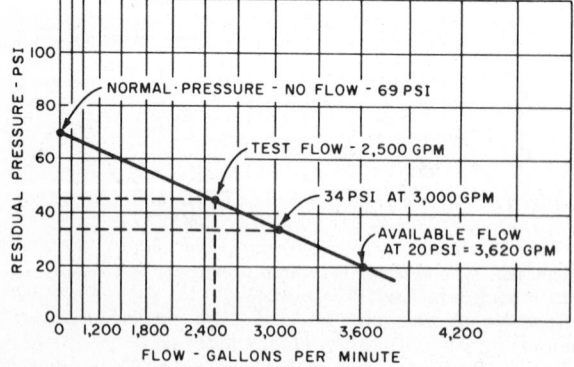

Fig. 11-5G. An example of a flow curve plotted on $N^{1.85}$ semiexponential paper. The illustration is a graphical plot of data involved in an example of a flow test of a public water system described in Part B of this chapter.

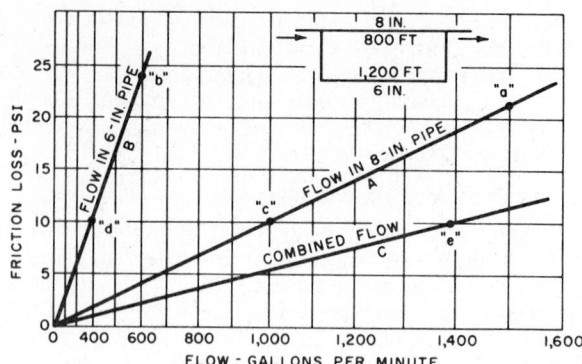

Fig. 11-5H. Graphic determination of flow in loop piping. The assumed friction coefficient is $C = 100$. Curve A represents flow in 800 ft of 8-in. pipe; Curve B flow in 1,200 ft of 6-in. pipe.

for an assumed flow of 1,500 gpm as follows: $1 \times 8 \times 2.71 = 21.6$ psi in 800 ft of 8-in. pipe (see Chap. 6 of this Section for friction loss calculations). Friction loss of 21.6 was plotted as Point "a" on the vertical 1,500 gpm line in Figure 11-5H. A straight line was drawn to connect Point "a" with 0/0, forming the Loss Curve "A" for the 8-in. leg.

Step No. 2: Assuming a flow of 600 gpm, follow the same procedure as followed in Step No. 1: $1 \times 12 \times 2.02 = 24.2$ psi loss in 1,200 ft of 6-in. pipe. Friction loss of 24.2 was plotted as Point "b" on the vertical 600 gpm line and connected to 0/0, thus forming Loss Curve "B" for the 6-in. pipe.

Step No. 3: The flows corresponding to 10 psi (a convenient pressure) on each curve (Points "c" and "d") were added together, and point "e" plotted at 1,400 gpm (400 gpm at Point "d" + 1,000 gpm at Point "c"). The straight line connecting Point "e" with 0/0 is the Curve C for the whole loop.

E. Graphical Determination of Yield from Combined Supplies

Determination of the yield from combined water supplies by actual testing is not always possible. One of the supplies may be impaired, such as a gravity tank emptied for repairs or painting, or it may be necessary to estimate the yield when a proposed supply is to be added to an existing one-source system.

Figure 11-5I shows how to develop the combined yield curve from a gravity tank and a public water connection. Each source had been tested separately, but a combined test was not possible. The test flows had been taken at the yard hydrant, and the pressures on the nearby sprinkler riser.

The curves were plotted from the test data as follows: tank: 1,260 gpm flowing from the tank (Curve "A") reduced pressure from 65 to 40 psi; 900 gpm flowing from the public supply (Curve "B") reduced pressure from 90 to 43 psi.

All the water would come from the public main until the residual pressure drops to the static pressure of the tank, in this case to 65 psi at approximately 600 gpm (Point "a"). From then on, water would come from both sources.

The curves cross at 750 gpm and 55 psi (Point "b"); with 750 gpm from each, the total flow at 55 psi would be 1,500 gpm (Point "c"). Connecting Points "a" and "c" with a straight line produces Curve C, which is the desired combined curve.

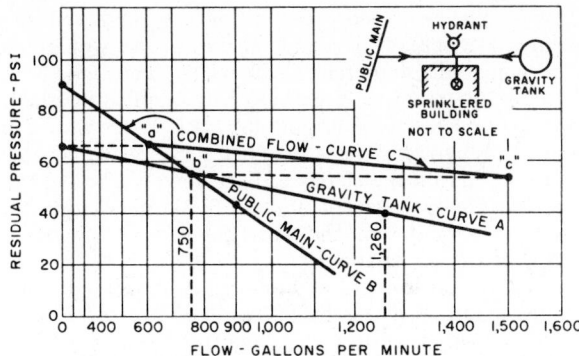

Fig. 11-5I. Graph of a combined water supply from a public system and a private gravity tank.

F.   Analyzing Test Data

A major purpose of flow testing is to determine whether or not the available water supply can meet the water demand required for acceptable protection of the property involved. Plotting test data on $N^{1.85}$ hydraulic paper offers a simple and convenient method of analyzing water supply and demand (see Part C, "Hydraulic Flow Curves" in this chapter).

As an example of analyzing data, assume that flow tests have been made on a water supply to a sprinklered building and the following data was developed: no flow at 72 psi; 633 gpm at 62 psi; and 944 gpm at 50 psi. Curve A in Figure 11-5J was drawn by fitting a straight line to the three points. By extending the curve, residual pressures at larger flows can be read off directly. For example, the residual pressure at 1,200 gpm would have been 40 psi. It is doubtful practice, however, to extrapolate much beyond the maximum flow point, because tests from networks often produce supply curves that flatten out as the rate of flow increases.

The fact that all three test points fix a practically straight line indicates that the observed static of 72 psi was close to a true figure and that the normal rate of flow was relatively small.

Curve B in Figure 11-5J represents the available supply at street level to the sprinkler system over and above a 500 gpm allowance for probable hose stream use by the fire department. Obviously, if more water were taken for hose streams, there would be less remaining for the sprinklers.

Curve B was developed by subtracting 500 gpm from Curve A at various pressures. The point at zero flow was

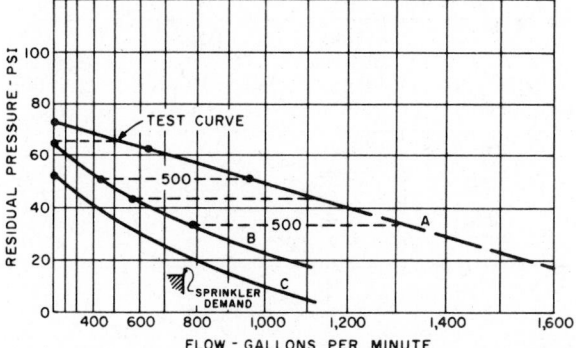

Fig. 11-5J. An example of a graphic water supply evaluation. Curve A is the test flow; Curve B the test flow less 500 gpm for hose streams; and Curve C is Curve B corrected for elevation (30-ft elevation in this example).

obtained by moving horizontally from the intersection of Curve A and the vertical 500 gpm line (see Fig. 11-5J). The next point was found by plotting 444 gpm (944 − 500) at 50 psi, which was the residual pressure for the 944 gpm test. Other points were plotted in the same way.

Curves developed by this method are approximations at best, the rate of flow being dependent on the 0.5 power of discharge pressure, and the 0.54 power of head loss. However, this manner of evaluating the water supply to sprinkler systems is practical and acceptable.

Curve C in Figure 11-5J is actually Curve B corrected for a 30-ft elevation difference between the residual pressure at street level and the top line of sprinklers. Therefore, every point of Curve C is 13 psi below the corresponding point of Curve B. Friction loss in pipe and fittings between the city main and the top of the sprinkler riser in the building were not considered; however, the losses could have been estimated with certain details assumed as follows (no meter and no fire department connection to sprinklers):

System Component	Equivalent Length (ft)*
Eighty feet of 6-in. pipe, $C = 120$ (riser and connection)	80.0
One 8- × 8- × 6-in. tee (connection to main)	21.5
Two 6-in. standard elbows (top and bottom of riser)	20.0
Two 6-in. gate valves (waterworks valve and sprinkler valve)	04.0
One 6-in. check valve	23.0
	Total 148.5 ft.

Friction loss at 750 gpm $= .714 \times \dfrac{148.5}{100} \times 3.05 =$ 3.24 psi ("Friction Loss Calculations" in Chap. 6 of this Section).

It is also assumed in the foregoing example that the sprinkler system in the building requires a flow of 750 gpm at the point of supply to the sprinklers while at the same time residual pressure at the top line of sprinklers does not drop below 15 psi. Curve C of Figure 11-5J shows that 750 gpm would be available at approximately 20 psi residual pressure.

G.   Hydraulic Gradient

An hydraulic gradient is a profile of residual pressure. Its function is to present graphically the flow characteristics of a pipe line. Gradient is an important factor in the design of water supply conduits and trunk mains. The hydraulic gradient is a useful procedure for investigating the condition of a public or private main when tests produce less than the expected flow.

The relations between pressure and elevation in a pipe having uniform flow are shown in Figure 11-5K. The axioms accompanying the diagram should be noted carefully.

Gradient tests of a private fire protection system usually involve shorter runs of pipe than tests of public mains. To reduce the number of tests, pipes should be chosen that are typical of the age and condition of the system. Relatively

---

* See Table 11-6A for head loss in valves and fittings expressed as equivalent feet of straight pipe.

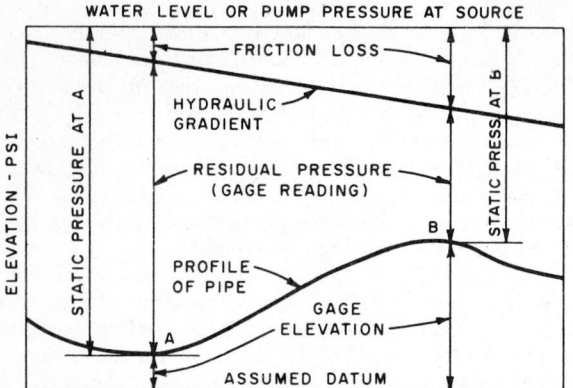

Fig. 11-5K. Principle of a hydraulic gradient. The following axioms apply:

1. Static-pressure readings measure distance below source. The higher the pipe elevation, the lower the static pressure.

2. Static pressure plus gage elevation (expressed in pounds per square inch) is constant for all points along pipe.

3. Static pressure minus residual pressure equals total friction loss from source to point of measurement.

4. Residual pressure plus gage elevation equals hydraulic-gradient elevation.

5. Friction loss is independent of elevation.

heavy flows should be induced through the test section to obtain a maximum pressure drop, thereby minimizing the effect of fluctuating pressure or inaccurate gage readings.

The data obtained from a hydraulic gradient are readily applied to calculating the *C* values (discharge coefficient) of the pipes tested. The head loss in valves and fittings, if any, should be deducted from the observed pressure drop before calculating *C*, otherwise the value obtained would be too low. Obviously, consideration of the *C* value is not part of gradient development; it is a convenient and widely used measure of determining the condition of pipe.

If there are more than two gaging points, an attempt should be made to take simultaneous readings, but satisfactory results can usually be obtained by moving the gage progressively from hydrant to hydrant while the test flow is maintained in the pipe. True static pressure obtained under no-flow conditions would plot as a horizontal line.

In a public main with normal flow, the observed static pressures are actually residual pressures, and would trace the normal gradient; therefore efforts should be made to find the true static pressure. If the system is supplied by gravity, it may be possible to determine the static by elevation differences, topographic maps or other survey data. If necessary to depend on the static readings it would be desirable to take readings between 1 am and 3.30 am when normal draft is at a minimum and observed static pressures are closer to the true elevations.

Static pressure on fire protection mains usually can be obtained readily because there would be little or no normal flow (except in properties with combined fire and industrial systems). With street mains it is often possible to close a valve below the downstream end of the section being tested, thereby reducing the normal flow temporarily.

It is usually desirable to plot the profile of the pipe being tested, along with the gradient. If a gradient should fall below the pipe line, it is an indication that pressure in the pipe is less than atmospheric. This condition could result in impairment to flow and initiation of dangerous pressure surges. The remedies are to restrict the rate of flow, to reduce the friction loss by cleaning and lining the pipe or to provide additional pipe capacity.

When *C* values less than 80 are found by gradient tests, the pipe should be cleaned and lined by standard methods.

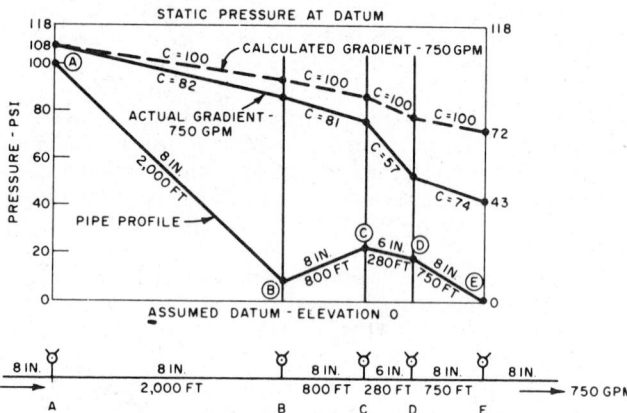

Fig. 11-5L. Hydraulic gradient and pipe profile.

Table 11-5A. Data for Hydraulic Gradient
(Rate of Flow — 750 Gpm)

(1)	(2)	(3)	(4)	(5)	(6)	(7)	(8)	(9)
			Gage Pressure			Loss Between Stations (Psi)	Gage Elevation Above Datum (Psi)	Gradient Elevation (Psi)
Gage Location	Actual Pipe Length (Ft)	Pipe Diameter (In.)	Static (Psi)	Residual (Psi)	Total Loss (Psi)			
A	—	—	18	8	10	—	100	108
B	A – B = 2,000	8	110	78	32	A – B = 22	8	86
C	B – C = 800	8	95	54	41	B – C = 9	23	77
D	C – D = 280	6	100	35	65	C – D = 24	18	53
E	D – E = 750	8	118	43	75	D – E = 10	0	43

Explanation:

Columns 1-5: Data from actual gradient test.

Column 6: Static pressure — residual pressure = total loss.

Column 7: Difference in total loss, station to station.

Column 8: Gage elevation above datum = static pressure at datum (118 psi in this example) minus observed static at each location. Thus **A** = 118 − 18 = 100; **B** = 118 − 110 = 8; **C** = 118 − 95 = 23; **D** = 118 − 100 = 18; and **E** = 118 − 118 = 0.

Column 9: Gradient elevation = gage elevation + residual pressure. Thus **A** = 100 + 8 = 108; **B** = 8 + 78 = 86; **C** = 23 + 54 = 77; **D** = 18 + 35 = 53; **E** = 0 + 43 = 43.

Table 11-5B.   Data for Calculated Hydraulic Gradient
(Rate of Flow — 750 Gpm — C = 100)

(1)	(2)	(3)	(4)	(5)	(6)	(7)	(8)	(9)
Gage Location	Actual Pipe Length (Ft)	Pipe Diameter (In.)	Gage Elevation Above Datum (Psi)	Static Pressure (Psi)	Calculated Loss Station to Station (Psi)	Total Loss (Psi)	Residual Pressure (Psi)	Gradient Elevation (Psi)
A	—	—	100	18	10	10	8	108
B	A − B = 2,000	8	8	110	15	25	85	93
C	B − C = 800	8	23	95	6	31	64	87
D	C − D = 280	6	18	100	9	40	60	78
E	D − E = 750	8	0	118	6	46	72	72

Explanation:

Columns 1-5: Data taken from Columns 1, 2, 3, 8, and 4 of Table 11-5A respectively.

Column 6: Calculated pressure loss from station to station (see Part L of Chapter 1 of this Handbook for friction loss calculations). The losses are:

$$\textbf{A to B} = 1 \times \frac{2,000}{100} \times .752 = 15$$

$$\textbf{B to C} = 1 \times \frac{800}{100} \times .752 = 6$$

$$\textbf{C to D} = 1 \times \frac{280}{100} \times 3.05 = 9$$

$$\textbf{D to E} = 1 \times \frac{750}{100} \times .752 = 6$$

Column 7: Total loss (accumulative loss at each location): Thus:

$$\textbf{A} = 10 \text{ psi}$$
$$\textbf{B} = \text{Loss A to B} + \text{Loss A} = 15 + 10 = 25$$
$$\textbf{C} = \text{Loss B to C} + \text{Loss B} = 6 + 25 = 31$$
$$\textbf{D} = \text{Loss C to D} + \text{Loss C} = 9 + 31 = 40$$
$$\textbf{F} = \text{Loss D to E} + \text{Loss D} = 6 + 40 = 46$$

Column 8: Residual pressure: equals the static pressure (Column 5) minus the total loss (Column 7) at each location.

Column 9: Gradient elevation is gage elevation (Column 4) plus the residual pressure (Column 8).

Table 11-5C.   Calculations for C Values
(Rate of Flow — 750 Gpm)

(1)	(2)	(3)	(4)	(5)	(6)	(7)
Gage Location	Actual Pipe Length (Ft)	Pipe Diameter (In.)	Loss Station to Station (Psi)	Loss per 100 ft (Psi)	C Factor	C
A	—	—	—	—	—	—
B	A − B = 2,000	8	A − B = 22	1.10	1.46	82
C	B − C = 800	8	B − C = 9	1.125	1.49	81
D	C − D = 280	6	C − D = 24	8.6	2.82	57
E	D − E = 750	8	D − E = 10	1.35	1.76	74

Explanation:

Columns 1-4: Data taken from Columns 1, 2, 3, and 7 in Table 11-5A respectively.

Column 5: Pressure loss from station to station (Column 4) divided by the actual pipe length (Column 2) multiplied by 100.

Column 6: The actual pressure loss by test for each 100 ft of pipe (Column 5) divided by friction loss for 100 ft of pipe with C = 100 (Table 11-6E).

Column 7: Values for C interpolated from Table 11-6F (Approximate linear interpolation is acceptable.) Example: For Station C the C factor is 1.49. Find C:

C	Factor	Factor	
85	1.35	1.35	$\frac{14}{16} \times 5 = 4.4$
?		1.49	
80	1.51		$85 - 4.4 = 80.6 = 81$ (answer).
5	14	16	

Regardless of C value, however, small-sized pipe causing a steep gradient slope should be replaced with pipe of adequate diameter. Iron or steel pipe, if used, should be lined; other types of pipe with near-constant C value are also available.

The choice of method depends on relative costs of cleaning and lining as opposed to replacement, and on other practical considerations.

When improvements and changes are in order, it is desirable to plot a calculated gradient for comparison with the one tested. Both gradients must be based on the same rate of flow.

Figure 11-5L is a graph of a gradient test together with pipe profile and a calculated gradient. A uniform flow of 750 gpm is assumed.

Table 11-5A shows the data for Fig. 11-5L, and explains the calculation.

Table 11-5B covers the calculated gradient.

Table 11-5C explains the calculation of C values.

SI Units

The following conversion factors are given as a convenience in converting to SI units the English units used in this chapter.

1 in. = 25.400 mm
1 psi = 6.895 kPa
1 gpm = 3.785 litres/min

Bibliography

Additional Readings

Gages, Pressure and Vacuum, Indicating Dial Type-Elastic Element, ANSI B40.1—1968, American National Standards Institute, Philadelphia.

Factory Mutual Engineering Corporation, "Testing Water Supplies," Chapter 21, *Handbook of Industrial Loss Prevention,* 2nd ed., McGraw Hill, New York, 1967, pp. 22–1, 22–13.

Ibid., "Hydraulic Flow Curves," Chapter 22, pp. 22–1, 22–6.

FM Loss Prevention Data Sheet, "Testing Water Supplies," DS3-34, 1971, Factory Mutual System, Norwood, Mass.

Chapter 6

HYDRAULICS

This chapter describes the physical properties of water that are pertinent to hydraulic calculations, and explains the formulas used to calculate flow and the effects of flow through orifices, nozzles, and pipes.

A. Hydraulic Properties of Water

The density of water varies with temperature. At maximum density, occurring at 39.2°F, fresh water weighs 62.425 pcf (pounds per cubic foot) in vacuo or 62.35 pcf in air. It weighs 62.400 pcf at 52.72°F in vacuo. For ordinary calculations, the approximate value of 62.4 pcf is generally used. The term "water" as used in this text refers to fresh water unless otherwise specified. Average sea water weighs 64.1 pcf.

The following units are based on water at 62.4 pcf. A gallon of water (U.S. Standard) is equivalent to 0.1337 cu ft or 231.03 cu in., and weighs 8.34 lbs. One cu ft equals 7.48 gal. All calculations in this text are in terms of U.S. gallons, unless otherwise indicated. An Imperial gallon equals 1.20 U.S. gallons.

Net Pressure or Normal Pressure: The pressure exerted against the side of a pipe or container by a liquid in the pipe or container with or without flow. Without flow this would be known as "static pressure" or "static head". Pressure (p) is customarily measured in pounds per square inch (psi) and head (h) in feet. The pressure produced by a column of water 1 ft high is $\frac{62.4}{144} = 0.433$ psi, represented by w in the formula $p = wh = 0.433h$. The head (h) corresponding to a pressure p (psi) will be $h = \frac{p}{w} = \frac{p}{0.433} = 2.31p$.

Pressure in an hydraulic system is measured in pounds per square inch by a pressure gage.

A 1-in. head of mercury gives a pressure of 0.491 psi or a 1.134-ft head of water.

Normal atmospheric pressure is taken as 14.70 psi, and is equivalent to a head of water of 33.96 ft and a head of mercury of 29.94 in.

Velocity Head or Velocity Pressure

The velocity (v) produced in a mass of water by pressure acting upon it is the same as if the mass was to fall freely, starting from rest, through a distance equivalent to the pressure head in feet. This relation is represented by $v = \sqrt{2gh}$, v being the velocity produced in feet per second, and h being the head in feet producing the velocity. This is a reversible relation because not only can a pressure head produce velocity, but velocity can be converted to an equivalent pressure head. This relation is h_v (velocity head) $= \frac{v^2}{2g}$ (ft). Because $p_v = 0.433h_v$, the velocity pressure $p_v = 0.433 \frac{v^2}{2g}$ (psi).

Values of velocity pressure for different rates of flow in various pipe sizes may be selected from Figure 11-6A. Velocity head or velocity pressure may be calculated by formulae involving velocity (rate of flow) and pipe diameter.

$$h_v = \frac{v^2}{64.4} \text{ or } p_v = \frac{.433v^2}{64.4} = \frac{v^2}{149}.$$

A convenient equation for calculating velocity in feet per second (fps) from the rate of flow can be developed from the relationship $Q = av$ as follows:

$$v = \frac{Q}{a}$$

in which v is velocity in feet per second; Q is expressed as flow in cubic feet per second $\frac{\text{(gallons per minute)}}{60 \text{ sec/min} \times 7.48 \text{ gal/ft}^3}$; and area in square feet for a pipe with a diameter (d) in inches is given as $\frac{\pi d^2}{4} \times \frac{1}{144}$.

Substituting as follows:

$$v = \frac{\text{gpm}}{60 \times 7.48} \div \frac{\pi d^2}{4 \times 144}$$

$$= \frac{\text{gpm} \times 4 \times 144}{60 \times 7.48 \times \pi d^2} = \frac{0.4085 \times \text{gpm}}{d^2}.$$

In terms of Q (flow in gallons per minute) h_v and p_v are respectively:

$$h_v = \frac{v^2}{2g} = \frac{(0.4085Q)^2}{(d^2)^2} \div 64.4 = \frac{Q^2}{d^4} \frac{(.4085)^2}{64.4} = \frac{Q^2}{386d^4}$$

$$p_v = \frac{Q^2}{d^4} \times \frac{.433}{384} = \frac{Q^2}{891d^4}.$$

As a liquid leaves a pipe, conduit or container through an orifice, all pressure is converted to velocity pressure. This velocity pressure is sometimes referred to as a Pitot pressure when it is being measured by a Pitot tube inserted into the stream at the point of maximum contraction.

EXAMPLE: Find the velocity pressure in 1-in. pipe with 36 gpm flowing. The actual inside diameter of 1-in. pipe is 1.05 in.

SOLUTION:

$$p_v = \frac{Q^2}{888(d)^4} = \frac{(36)^2}{888(1.05)^4} = 1.20 \text{ psi}.$$

Total Head

At any point within a piping system that contains water in motion, there is a pressure head h_p (normal pressure head) acting perpendicular to the pipe wall independent of velocity, and a velocity head h_v acting parallel to the pipe wall but exerting no pressure against the wall. Therefore, total head is $H = h_p + h_v$, and without flow (static condition) it is the static pressure head only. Total head expressed as pressure (psi) instead of feet is $p_t = 0.433h_p + 0.433 \frac{v^2}{2g}$.

When water discharges from an orifice or into a branch line from the side wall of a pipe through which water is flowing, the velocity pressure of the side discharge is equal to the *pressure* head in the pipe. When water is discharged through the open end of a pipe, the pressure of the jet is

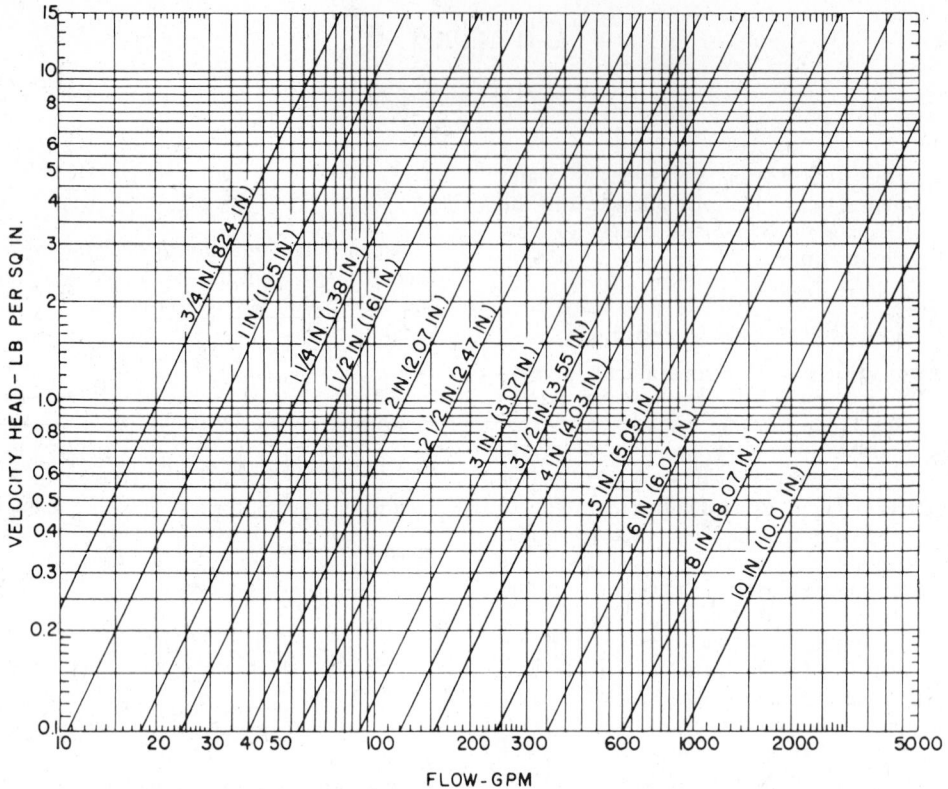

Fig. 11-6A. Graph for the determination of velocity pressure.

velocity pressure only, and is produced by the *total pressure* in the pipe at the *point of exit*.

Chapter 4 of Section 14 in this HANDBOOK describes a method of calculating the discharge of water from a sprinkler system by the use of normal pressure, velocity pressure, and total pressure.

Pressure Sources

The sources of pressure head at a specific location in a hydraulic system may be:

Gravity (elevated tanks, reservoirs, standpipes): Head is the elevation of the water supply surface above the point under consideration, measured directly in feet or converted from a pressure gage reading.

Pumping: Head is the combination of pump discharge pressure and any difference in elevation between the pump discharge gage and the point under consideration.

Pneumatic (pressure tanks): Head is the tank air pressure combined with any difference in elevation of the tank water surface and the point under consideration.

Combinations: Any combination of above pressure sources.

B. Bernoulli's Theorem

Bernoulli's Theorem expresses the physical law of the conservation of energy applicable to problems of incompressible fluid flow. The theorem may be defined as follows: "In steady flow without friction, the sum of velocity head, pressure head, and elevation head is constant for any incompressible fluid particle throughout its course." In other words, total head would be the same at all locations within the system.

In practice, pipe friction and other lost head is accounted for. Expressed mathematically, Bernoulli's Theorem when applied to locations "A" and "B," is

$$\frac{v_A{}^2}{2g} + \frac{p_A}{w} + z_A = \frac{v_B{}^2}{2g} + \frac{p_B}{w} + z_B + h_{AB}$$

in which

v = velocity in feet per second

g = acceleration of gravity 32.2 feet per second per second

p = pressure, pounds per square foot

z = elevation head (distance above assumed datum), feet

w = specific weight of fluid in pounds per cubic foot (62.4 pcf for water)

$\dfrac{v^2}{2g}$ = velocity head, feet

$\dfrac{p}{w}$ = pressure head, feet

h_{AB} = lost head between location A and location B in feet.

(Note that in Bernoulli's Theorem all the individual head terms, i.e., velocity head, pressure head, elevation head, and lost head are expressed in feet. When using velocities in feet per second (fps) and gage pressure in psi, they must be converted to feet.)

Application of Bernoulli's Theorem

Consider a reservoir and a pipe line discharging water to atmosphere at "B" (Fig. 11-6B). Assume datum through "B," and write Bernoulli's Theorem between the water level at "A" and the outlet at "B."

$$z_A + \frac{v_A{}^2}{2g} + \frac{p_A}{w} = z_B + \frac{v_B{}^2}{2g} + \frac{p_B}{w} + h_{AB}.$$

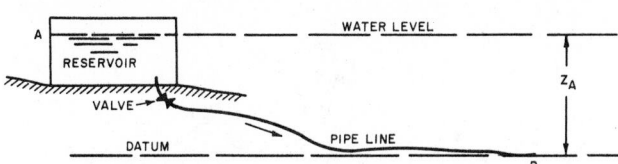

Fig. 11-6B. Graphic representation of the application of Bernoulli's Theorem to a reservoir and a pipe line.

The velocity at "A" is practically zero because the diameter of the tank is very large, and the gage pressure at "A" is zero because only atmospheric pressure works on the water surface. At "A" the elevation is z, measured in feet above the datum.

At "B," the elevation above the datum is zero; thus $z = 0$; likewise gage pressure p_B is zero and only velocity head is available as the water leaves the outlet. (A gage at right angles to the emerging stream would register zero pressure.)

Therefore,

$$z_A + 0 + 0 = 0 + \frac{v_B^2}{2g} + 0 + h_{AB}.$$

Therefore,

$$\frac{v_B^2}{2g} = z_A - h_{AB}.$$

Lost head is the sum of (1) hydraulic losses at the reservoir where water enters the pipeline, at the valve, and at the discharge outlet plus (2) the friction loss in the pipe line. The values of the components producing lost head can be estimated, as discussed subsequently in this chapter. The theoretical total head at "B" can be obtained readily by taking pressure gage readings with the flow shut off, and converting these gage readings to feet. Another method is to obtain the difference in elevation between "A" and "B" from a topographic map. The actual total head at "B" is the pressure head (h_n) plus the velocity head (h_v). The normal head in the example is zero, however, so the total head is the same as the velocity head in this example.

As a further example, determine what would be the head loss across 1,000 ft of 8-in. pipe with 750 gpm flowing from a $2\frac{1}{2}$-in. hydrant outlet at "B" and a residual pressure at hydrant "A" of 40 psi. With no flow, hydrant "A" has a 60 psi static pressure and hydrant "B" has an 80 psi static pressure. Assume datum through hydrant "B". Thus

$$\frac{v_A^2}{2g} + \frac{p_A}{w} + z_A = \frac{v_B^2}{2g} + \frac{p_B}{w} + z_B + h_{AB}.$$

Substituting

$$v_A = \frac{Q}{a} = \frac{Q}{\frac{\pi d^2}{4 \times 144}}$$

$$= \frac{\frac{750 \text{ gpm}}{7.48 \text{ gal/ft}^3 \times 60 \text{ sec/min}}}{\frac{3.1416 \times (8)^2}{4 \times 144 \text{ in.}^2/\text{ft}^2}} = 4.79 \text{ fps}$$

$$v_B = \frac{Q}{a} = \frac{\frac{750 \text{ gpm}}{7.48 \text{ gal/ft}^3 \times 60 \text{ sec/min}}}{\frac{3.1416 \times (2.5)^2}{4 \times 144 \text{ in.}^2/\text{ft}^2}} = 49.02 \text{ fps}$$

$$\frac{v_A^2}{2g} = \frac{(4.79 \text{ fps})^2}{64.4 \text{ fps/s}} = .36 \text{ ft} = 0.4 \text{ ft}$$

$$\frac{p_A}{w} = \frac{40 \text{ psi}}{62.4 \text{ pcf}} \times 144 \text{ in.}^2/\text{ft}^2 = 92.3 \text{ ft}$$

$$z_A = (80 \text{ psi} - 60 \text{ psi}) \times 2.31 \text{ ft/psi} = 46.2 \text{ ft}$$

$$\frac{v_B^2}{2g} = \frac{(49.02)^2}{64.4} = 37.3 \text{ ft}$$

$\frac{p_B}{w} = 0$ as there is no normal pressure because it is discharging to atmosphere.

$z_B = 0$ as datum is through Hydrant "B"

Thus $h_{AB} = 0.4 + 92.3 + 46.2 - 37.3 - 0 - 0 = 101.6$ ft.

C. Flow Through Orifices

The rate of flow from an orifice can be expressed in terms of velocity and cross-sectional area of the stream, the basic relations being $Q = av$ where Q = rate of flow in cubic feet per second; a = area of cross section in square feet; and v = velocity at the cross section in feet per second. From the discussion in Part A of this chapter on velocity head, it is known that $v = \sqrt{2gh}$. Therefore, substituting in the basic formula for rate of flow through orifices, $Q = a\sqrt{2gh}$. It follows that with the orifice diameter in inches, Q in gallons per minute would equal

$$60 \times 7.48 \times \frac{\pi d^2}{4 \times 144} \sqrt{64.4h}.$$

Because $h = 2.31p$ (see Part A for discussion of pressure equivalents for head values), the equation for Q in gallons per minutes becomes $Q = (448.8)(.00546d^2)(12.2)\sqrt{p_v}$.

Therefore, $Q = 29.83d^2\sqrt{p_v}$ (gallons per minute).

The above equation assumes that (1) the jet is a solid stream the full size of the discharge orifice, and (2) the available total head is converted to velocity head which is uniform over the cross section. This is a theoretical situation only, however, as these two conditions are not totally attainable as the following discussion will show.

Coefficients of Flow

In actual flow from nozzles or orifices, there are two departures from the theoretical values. The actual velocity, considered to be the average velocity over the entire cross section of the stream, is somewhat less than the velocity calculated from the head. The reduction is due to friction and turbulence and is expressed as the coefficient of velocity, designated c_v. Values of c_v are determined experimentally by laboratory tests. With well-designed nozzles, the coefficient of velocity is nearly constant and approximately equal to 0.98.

Some nozzles are so designed that the actual cross-sectional area of the stream is less than the calculated area of the orifice. This difference is usually considered a coefficient of contraction and designated as c_c. Coefficients of contraction vary greatly with the design and quality of the orifice or nozzle. For a sharp edge orifice, the value of c_c is about 0.62.

For practical use the coefficients of velocity and contraction can be combined as a single coefficient of discharge designated c_d; thus $c_d = c_v \times c_c$. If $Q = 29.83 (c_v \times c_c)d^2\sqrt{p_v}$, the expression may be written

$$Q = 29.83c_dd^2\sqrt{p_v}.$$

For any type of nozzle or orifice discharging in a solid stream to atmosphere, c_d may be defined as the ratio of the actual to the theoretical discharge. Approximate values of c_d are determined by standard test procedures, using carefully measured orifice or nozzle diameters. The rate of flow is measured by calibrated meters or "weigh tanks." The velocity pressure is measured by a Pitot gage. The theoretical flow assumes that $c_d = 1$, and is based on the measured diameter and the Pitot reading.

The drop in pressure produced by an orifice in a pipe or similar closed channel is used for the measurement of flow rate in some types of water meters, or as a measure for reducing objectionably high water pressure to fire hose lines from standpipes, or for other services. The coefficient applicable in this case differs from that of an orifice discharging into the open, and varies with several factors, including the ratio of diameters. Pressure reduction by orifices can be calculated only by making proper allowances for the specific conditions involved. Uncertainties in determining coefficients may make a solution by trial and error testing the most practical.

Such a method would involve the calculation of flow under theoretical conditions ($Q = 29.83d^2\sqrt{p_v}$) allowing unrestricted discharge from an open orifice directly into a measuring device. The actual flow divided by the theoretical flow is the coefficient of discharge. If this is not possible, then flow from a calibrated nozzle with accurate measurement of both velocity pressure and pressure head is used to establish conditions without any orifice restriction in the pipe. The same measurements are taken with the orifice in place. The flow with the orifice in place divided by the flow without the orifice is the coefficient for the orifice with the configuration as tested. Varying the discharge or flow rate will affect the coefficient for the orifice.

Standard Orifice

An orifice with a sharp entrance edge, shown as Form (1) in Figure 11-6C, is known as a standard orifice and is commonly used as a means of measuring water flow. In such orifices, the water as it leaves the orifice contracts to form a jet whose cross-sectional area is less than that of the orifice. The contraction is complete at the plane a' (see Figure 11-6D) which is located at a distance from the plane of the orifice equal to approximately half the diameter of the jet.

The quantity flowing is obviously the same at the orifice a as at the contracted section a', so the quantity flowing could be obtained by measurement of the velocity and area at either of these planes. Expressed in a formula, where Q is cubic feet per second, v is velocity in feet per second, and a' is area in square feet:

$$Q = va = v'a'$$

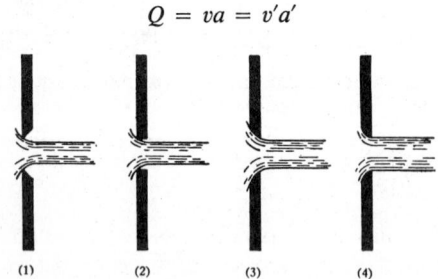

Fig. 11-6C.   ORIFICES OF VARIOUS SHAPES
If the shape of the orifice is changed so as to decrease the contraction, its capacity will be increased. Form (1) in the illustration is a standard orifice having a sharp edge on the approach side. Form (2), when in a thin plate, gives the same stream characteristics as Form (1). Form (3) is the reverse of (1). In Form (4), the edge is rounded to conform to the shape of the stream. The coefficients of discharge of (3) and (4) are greater than those of the standard orifices, approaching a value of 1.0 in the case of (4).

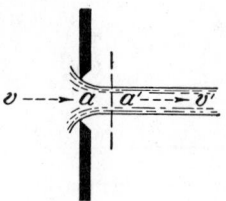

Fig. 11-6D.   Flow through a standard orifice.

The coefficient of discharge of a standard orifice would be the product of the coefficient of velocity and the coefficient of contraction, or $c = 0.98 \times 0.62 = 0.61$. Representative values for the coefficients of discharge are given in Table 11-6E.

D.   Flow in Short Tubes

A tube attached to an orifice is known as a standard short tube when its length is $2\frac{1}{2}$ or 3 times the diameter of the orifice and its diameter is the same as the orifice. A shorter tube will not flow full, and friction losses in a longer tube will affect results when used as a measuring device, hence the specified limit of length.

The characteristics of a standard short tube and a short conical converging tube are shown in Figures 11-6F and 11-6G. The principles of flow in orifices apply, but with different coefficients. With the conical tube the coefficients c_v and c_c vary with the angle β. When β is $0°$, the converging tube becomes a cylindrical tube with $c_c = 1$ and $c_v = 0.82$; c_d is then 0.82. As the angle β increases, the coefficient of contraction (c_c) develops and the coefficient of velocity (c_v) increases, approaching the 0.98 value for a sharp edge orifice. Relations are such that the coefficient of discharge attains a maximum value of 0.94 with a β angle of about 13°.

E.   Entrance Losses

Previous discussion in this chapter has shown that the actual velocity of the streams from orifices or short tubes is less than that which would be developed theoretically by the head producing the flow, the coefficient of velocity for a standard orifice being 0.98, and for a cylindrical short tube $c_v = 0.82$. The difference between the available head and the head equivalent to the actual velocity is the lost head. In terms of total head and coefficient of velocity, lost head equals

$$h(1 - c_v^2) \text{ or } \frac{v^2}{2g}(1 - c_v^2).$$

This is evidence of the energy lost by turbulence where the character of the flow changes, as from a large tank or reservoir through an orifice or into a pipe, or at a sharp change in pipe diameters. In many hydraulic calculations,

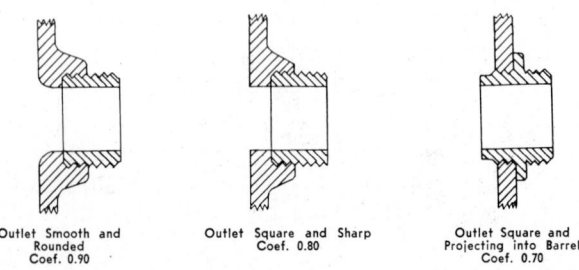

Outlet Smooth and
Rounded
Coef. 0.90

Outlet Square and Sharp
Coef. 0.80

Outlet Square and
Projecting into Barrel
Coef. 0.70

Fig. 11-6E.   Three general types of hydrant outlets and their coefficients of discharge.

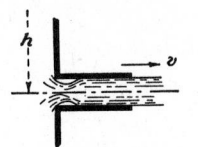

Fig. 11-6F. Flow in
cylindrical short tube.

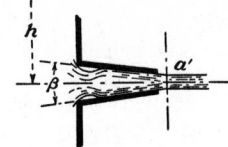

Fig. 11-6G. Flow in
conical converging tube.

desired accuracy makes it necessary to determine the lost head and/or the velocity head at different locations. This type of lost head is commonly designated as an "entrance loss."

When calculating the lost head at a sharp reduction in pipe size, it is necessary to consider that the head producing the flow in the smaller pipe is the total head (pressure head and velocity head) of the approaching stream.

Tapered fittings, such as at the entrance or discharge of centrifugal pumps, or at a valve with reduced water passageway inserted in a pipe line, greatly reduce the head lost where marked velocity changes occur in piping systems.

F. Venturi Tube

The Venturi principle has a number of applications in fire protection. The Venturi tube is essentially a tapered constriction in a pipe. In the constricted part, the velocity must be greater than in the straight tube, and the pressure is correspondingly less in accordance with Bernoulli's Theorem. If the increase in velocity through the constricted portion is sufficient, the pressure at that point will be less than atmospheric, and a suction will be created at any opening into the side of the tube. The Venturi tube is illustrated by Figure 11-6H. The diverging portion of a Venturi meter serves only to restore the system pressure with a minimum of friction loss.

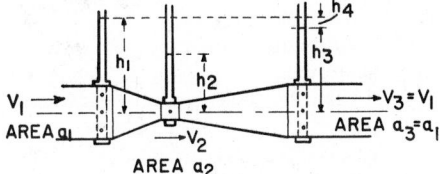

Fig. 11-6H. The Venturi tube.

Venturi Meter: The Venturi principle as applied in the Venturi meter for the measurement of flows in closed pipe lines under pressure is as follows:

With no elevation difference along the line of flow, Bernoulli's theorem becomes

$$\frac{v_1^2}{2g} + \frac{p_1}{w} + O = \frac{v_2^2}{2g} + \frac{p_2}{w} + O.$$

In Figure 11-6H, $\frac{p_1}{w}$ is represented by h_1, and $\frac{p_2}{w}$ by h_2, which are used in the following equations.

The quantity of liquid passing through all portions of the Venturi must be the same. Therefore,

$$Q = a_1 v_1 = a_2 v_2 \quad \text{or} \quad v_1 = \frac{Q}{a_1} \quad \text{or} \quad v_2 = \frac{Q}{a_2}.$$

Substituting in Bernoulli's Theorem,

$$\frac{\left(\frac{Q}{a_1}\right)^2}{2g} + h_1 = \frac{\left(\frac{Q}{a_2}\right)^2}{2g} + h_2$$

$$\frac{\left(\frac{Q}{a_2}\right)^2}{2g} - \frac{\left(\frac{Q}{a_1}\right)^2}{2g} = h_1 - h_2$$

$$Q^2\left(\frac{1}{a_2^2} - \frac{1}{a_1^2}\right) = 2g(h_1 - h_2)$$

$$Q^2\left(\frac{a_1^2 - a_2^2}{a_1^2 a_2^2}\right) = 2g(h_1 - h_2)$$

$$Q = \frac{a_1 a_2}{\sqrt{a_1^2 - a_2^2}}\sqrt{2g(h_1 - h_2)}.$$

For any specific Venturi, a_1 and a_2 are known constant values. There is also a friction loss coefficient which is usually determined by test and which does not remain constant with very low velocities. Combining the known constant values, the Venturi Meter Formula is generally expressed as:

$$Q = k\sqrt{h_1 - h_2}, \quad \text{or} \quad Q = k\sqrt{\frac{p_1}{w} - \frac{p_2}{w}}.$$

By test, a value of k for any specific meter can be established with reasonable accuracy.

When used as a device for inducting gas or liquid into the stream, as is made possible by the reduced pressure in the throat section, the hydraulic performance will not be in full accordance with the above theoretical calculations because energy is expended on the induced substance.

G. Pitot Tube Method of Measuring Flow

The most used method of measuring the flow in an open stream from an orifice, nozzle, or open pipe is by a direct measurement of the total head which produces the flow in accordance with the equation $v = \sqrt{2gh}$. This measurement makes use of the well known Pitot tube and pressure gage combination of which representative forms are shown in Figure 11-5A. When the small opening, usually not over $\frac{1}{16}$-in. diameter, is inserted in the center of a stream, with the opening directly in the line of flow, it will indicate, by water or mercury column, or by a pressure gage, the total head at that location. With the stream open to the atmosphere, there will be no pressure head so that the indicated reading will be velocity head alone, and the velocity of the stream can be calculated directly. Because the velocity at the surface of the stream is reduced slightly by friction against an orifice or nozzle, a coefficient of velocity of 0.97 is usually applied for nozzles of ordinary fire stream sizes. By knowing accurately the area of cross section of the stream at the location of the velocity measurement, the quantity flowing can be determined from the relation $Q = av = 29.83cd^2\sqrt{p}$.

When measuring flow from a nozzle, the use of the Pitot tube method only holds with reasonable accuracy for tip sizes up to $1\frac{3}{8}$ in. supplied by $2\frac{1}{2}$-in. hose. Above that the error rate increases beyond acceptable limits and the more accurate method described in section H of this chapter should be used.

A typical Pitot tube as used in measuring the flow from a free stream nozzle is shown in Figure 11-6I.

The gage is normally calibrated in pounds per square inches. This is measuring the velocity pressure at the point of maximum stream contraction. As the normal pressure is zero at this point, this is also measuring total head.

For the usual forms of orifices and nozzles, the coefficient of contraction (c_c) is accurately known, so that $a = c_c \times$ actual discharge opening. In the case of a sharp-edged orifice, the area of the stream may be determined from the

Fig. 11-6I.   Taking nozzle pressure with a Pitot tube.

actual diameter of the orifice opening and the use of the 0.62 coefficient of contraction. For a carefully made smooth nozzle the contraction is negligible, i.e., $c_c = 1.00$.

The rates of flow from various types and sizes of nozzles as given in Figure 11-6J are sufficiently accurate for most fire flow calculations.

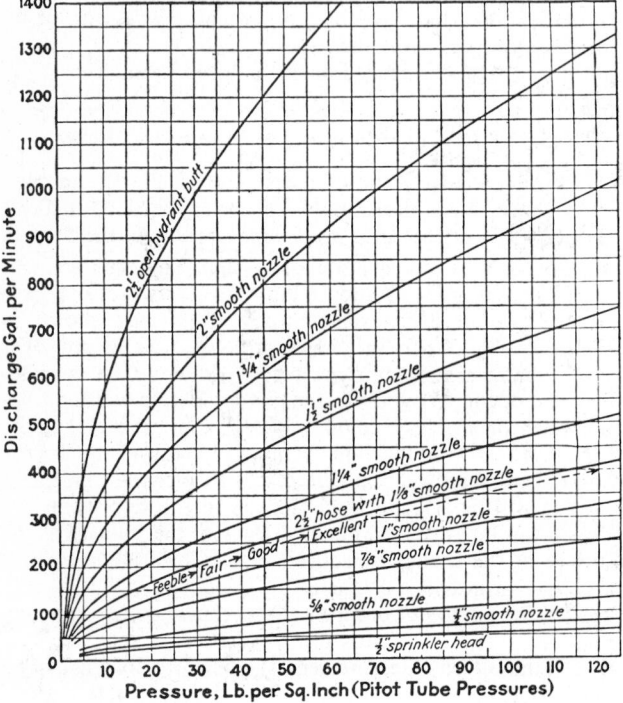

Fig. 11-6J.   Relative discharge curves. (Chemical Engineers' Handbook, McGraw-Hill Book Co.)

H.   The Nozzle Method of Measuring Flow

The hydraulic characteristics of good solid-stream nozzles are consistent within a wide range of flow conditions. The rate of discharge can be calculated from gas pressure at the base of the nozzle, or from Pitot pressure at the discharge outlet.

The flow formula for using base pressure is

$$Q = \frac{29.83cd^2\sqrt{p_1}}{\sqrt{1 - c^2\left(\frac{d}{D}\right)^4}}$$

in which

Q = flow in gallons per minute
c = coefficient of discharge
d = diameter of outlet, inches
p_1 = gage pressure at base of nozzle, psi
D = inside diameter of fitting to which gage is attached, inches.

This is the common formula for discharge from an orifice except that (1) gage pressure at the base of the nozzle is substituted for Pitot pressure, and (2) a factor is added which represents the ratio between gage pressure and total pressure at the nozzle base. (Total pressure is gage pressure plus velocity pressure.)

When base pressure is to be used, the gage is attached to a fitting close to the nozzle with a straight piece of approach pipe or hose to eliminate turbulence or unstable flow conditions. To obtain greater accuracy than provided by a simple fitting, a piezometer fitting may be used. With this device, the gage is connected to an annular tube or channel having a number of small holes drilled into the waterway around the circumference. The mean or resultant static pressure indicated by the gage is p_1 in the formula above.

EXAMPLE: The following is an example of using the formula to calculate flow. Assume a rate of discharge from a 2-in. nozzle with a pressure measured by a 2½-in. piezometer ring and gage at 80 psi at the base of the nozzle. Also assume a coefficient of discharge of .99. Thus:

$$Q = \frac{29.83 \times .99 \times (2)^2\sqrt{80}}{\sqrt{1 - (.99)^2\left(\frac{2}{2.5}\right)^2}}$$

$$Q = 1364.9.$$

Discharge coefficients for ordinary nozzles and orifices are given in Table 11-6E, or can be determined satisfactorily by careful testing procedures, using calibrated meters, nozzles, weigh tanks, etc.

Although accurate and convenient for fixed test arrangements, the measurement of pressure at the base of a nozzle is not practical for usual hose stream operations. Because a Pitot gage is useless with spray-type nozzles or other devices producing special types of discharge, the base pressure method is necessary.

I.   Discharge Calculations

The most common method of estimating nozzle or orifice discharge is to use the Table of Theoretical Flow (Table 11-6B). Knowing the diameter of the outlet; the flow corresponding to the Pitot pressure is multiplied by the applicable discharge coefficient (Table 11-6E).

EXAMPLE: Pitot reading was 20 psi at open 2½-in. hydrant butt; assumed coefficient was 0.90. Tabular flow for 20 psi is 834 gpm; 90 percent 834 = 751 gpm. (Or subtract 10 percent of 834 from 834 and get 751 gpm.)

Flow tables are available for certain nozzles, based on specific discharge coefficients.

Nozzle discharge also can be computed by the standard formulae previously discussed. (See Part C, "Flow Through Orifices," and Part H, "The Nozzle Method of Measuring Flow," in this chapter.)

To simplify calculations when it is desired to determine the flow in gallons per minute through an orifice or nozzle of a given diameter, and a known coefficient of discharge, the formula can be reduced to $Q = k\sqrt{p}$, where k combines the constants 29.83, c, and d^2. (See Table 11-6D) for k values of nozzles.)

Because $k = Q/\sqrt{p}$, the k values of spray nozzles can be calculated from data in testing laboratory listings of nozzles. Generally, the rate of flow at 50 and 100 psi base pressure, or both, is given in the listings for the various nozzles. Some nozzles are also listed at 25 and 125 psi base pressure.

EXAMPLE: A certain fire service spray nozzle is rated for 83 gpm at 50 psi. Therefore $k = 83/\sqrt{50} = 83/7.07 = 11.7$. At 25 psi base pressure the discharge would be $11.7\sqrt{25} = 11.7 \times 5 = 58.5$ gpm.

J. Flow of Water in Pipes

The theory of liquid flow in pipes involves (1) Bernouli's Theorem (taking into account friction losses), (2) the axiom that area multiplied by average velocity is the same at any cross section, assuming no significant discharge through branch lines or leaks, (3) lost head caused by friction and turbulence, (4) density of the liquid (fire protection hydraulics, with few exceptions, is based on a density of 62.4 pcf of ordinary fresh water), and (5) viscosity of the liquid. (Because ordinary water is used in fire protection systems, except for certain special applications, consideration of fluid viscosity is rarely needed.)

When water flows through a pipe there is almost always a drop in pressure. Theoretically, the lost head between two points is caused by (1) friction between the moving water and the pipe wall, and (2) friction between water particles, including that produced by turbulence when flow changes direction or when rapid increase or decrease of velocity takes place, such as at abrupt changes in pipe diameter. A change in velocity results in some conversion of velocity head to pressure head or vice versa.

At low velocity in a smooth pipe, very little turbulence is produced, and the flow is called "laminar." With this condition, all particles of water move along the pipe in essentially straight lines and in concentric layers; friction loss then occurs mainly in a thin layer at the pipe wall. The rate of loss is small compared to friction loss in turbulent flow.

In a pipe of specific diameter and roughness an increasing velocity changes laminar flow to unstable turbulent flow and then to complete turbulence. The range of flow condition from laminar to complete turbulence is called the transition zone.

Most fire protection systems and water distribution mains function under turbulent flow conditions, and friction losses within the pipe itself account for most of the lost head. Other losses are usually considered together and called the "loss in fittings."

Experimental data have established that frictional resistance is:
1. Independent of pressure in the pipe.
2. Proportional to the amount and character of frictional surface.
3. Variable with the velocity of flow (nearly proportional to the second power of the velocity for velocities above the critical; if velocity is below critical, resistance varies as the first power).

K. Friction Loss Flow Formulas

Perhaps the best known and oldest expression relating velocity to friction loss in pipe is known as the Chezy formula expressed as

$$v = c\sqrt{rs}$$

in which
 c is a factor depending on kind and roughness of pipe
 r (the hydraulic radius) = area/circumference = $d/4$ in which d = diameter of pipe
 s is a hydraulic slope = h/l = slope of hydraulic gradient in which h is the friction head in length of pipe l (see Chap. 3 of this Section for a discussion of hydraulic gradients).
 Therefore $v = c\sqrt{d/4 \times h/l}$ or $h = 4lv^2/c^2d$.

The classical formula for friction loss in long, straight pipes of uniform diameter and roughness is ascribed to Darcy, Manning, Fanning and others. In modern textbooks it is derived by analysis of forces acting on a flowing particle of water in a pipe. Actually, it is a variation of Chezy's formula with a friction factor f replacing c, and expressed as

$$h = \frac{flv^2}{d2g}$$

in which h = friction head; l = length of pipe; d = diameter of pipe; v = velocity; and g = acceleration of gravity.

The friction-flow formulas commonly used in the hydraulics of fire protection and water supply have been developed by experiment and experience. These formulas are exponential in the form $V = Cr^x s^y$, where V is velocity, C the coefficient of friction, r the hydraulic radius (area divided by circumference), and s the hydraulic slope (loss of head divided by length). The most popular exponential formula is the Hazen-Williams, its basic form being $V = 1.318Cr^{0.63}s^{0.54}$. The friction coefficients in formulas of this type are constant for a specific type or roughness of pipe, and are independent of velocity. Thus the accuracy of these formulas is variable. However, the fixed values generally asumed for viscosity and density are considered adequate.

Table 11-6A. Equivalent Pipe Length Chart

| Fittings and Valves | Fittings and Valves Expressed in Equivalent Feet of Pipe | | | | | | | | | | | | |
	$\frac{3}{4}$ in.	1 in.	$1\frac{1}{4}$ in.	$1\frac{1}{2}$ in.	2 in.	$2\frac{1}{2}$ in.	3 in.	$3\frac{1}{2}$ in.	4 in.	5 in.	6 in.	8 in.	10 in.	12 in.
45° Elbow	1	1	1	2	2	3	3	3	4	5	7	9	11	13
90° Standard Elbow	2	2	3	4	5	6	7	8	10	12	14	18	22	27
90° Long Turn Elbow	1	2	2	2	3	4	5	5	6	8	9	13	16	18
Tee or Cross (Flow Turned 90°)	4	5	6	8	10	12	15	17	20	25	30	35	50	60
Gate Valve	—	—	—	—	1	1	1	1	2	2	3	4	5	6
Butterfly Valve	—	—	—	—	6	7	10	—	12	9	10	12	19	21
Swing Check*	4	5	7	9	11	14	16	19	22	27	32	45	55	65

Use with Hazen and Williams $C = 120$ only. For other values of C, the figures in this table should be multiplied by the factors indicated:

Value of C	100	120	130	140
Multiplying factor	0.713	1.00	1.16	1.32

(This table is based upon the friction loss through the fitting being independent of the C factor applicable to the piping.)

* Due to the variations in design of swing check valves, the pipe equivalents indicated in the above chart to be considered average.

WATER SUPPLIES FOR FIRE PROTECTION

Table 11-6B. Theoretical Discharge
(United States Gallons

This table is computed from the formula $Q = 29.83cd^2\sqrt{p}$ with $c = 1.00$. The theoretical discharge of sea water, as from fireboat nozzles, may be found by subtracting 1 percent from the figures in the following table, or from the formula $Q = 29.47cd^2\sqrt{p}$.

When pressures are read with a Pitot gage at a nozzle, the nozzle discharge in most cases will correspond to the values in the tables within a range of 1 to 3 percent for nozzles up to $1\frac{3}{8}$ in. in diameter. For larger diameter nozzles, the principles discussed in Part G of

Velocity Head psi	Feet*	Velocity of Discharge fps	$\frac{1}{16}$	$\frac{1}{8}$	$\frac{3}{16}$	$\frac{1}{4}$	$\frac{3}{8}$	$\frac{1}{2}$	$\frac{5}{8}$	$\frac{3}{4}$	$\frac{7}{8}$	1	$1\frac{1}{8}$	$1\frac{1}{4}$
1	2.31	12.15	.12	.47	1.05	1.86	4.19	7.46	11.7	16.8	22.8	29.8	37.8	46.6
2	4.61	17.26	.16	.66	1.48	2.64	5.93	10.5	16.5	23.7	32.3	42.2	53.4	65.9
3	6.92	21.14	.20	.81	1.82	3.23	7.26	12.9	20.2	29.1	39.6	51.7	65.4	80.7
4	9.23	24.41	.23	.93	2.10	3.73	8.39	14.9	23.3	33.6	45.7	59.7	75.5	93.2
5	11.54	27.27	.26	1.04	2.35	4.17	9.38	16.7	26.1	37.5	51.1	66.7	84.4	104
6	13.84	29.82	.29	1.14	2.57	4.57	10.3	18.3	28.5	41.1	55.9	73.1	92.5	114
7	16.15	32.27	.31	1.23	2.78	4.93	11.1	19.7	30.8	44.4	60.4	78.9	99.9	123
8	18.46	34.42	.33	1.32	2.97	5.27	11.9	21.1	33.0	47.5	64.6	84.4	107	132
9	20.76	36.56	.35	1.40	3.15	5.59	12.6	22.4	35.0	50.3	68.5	89.5	113	140
10	23.07	38.50	.37	1.47	3.32	5.90	13.3	23.6	36.8	53.1	72.2	94.3	119	147
11	25.38	40.44	.39	1.55	3.48	6.18	13.9	24.7	38.6	55.7	75.7	99.0	125	155
12	27.68	42.18	.40	1.61	3.63	6.46	14.5	25.8	40.4	58.1	79.1	103	131	161
13	29.99	43.91	.42	1.68	3.78	6.72	15.1	26.9	42.0	60.5	82.3	108	136	168
14	32.30	45.55	.43	1.74	3.92	6.98	15.7	27.9	43.6	62.8	85.5	112	141	174
15	34.61	47.18	.45	1.81	4.06	7.22	16.2	28.7	45.1	65.0	88.4	116	146	181
16	36.91	48.71	.46	1.86	4.19	7.46	16.8	29.8	46.6	67.1	91.4	119	151	186
17	39.22	50.25	.48	1.92	4.32	7.69	17.3	30.7	48.0	69.3	94.2	123	156	192
18	41.53	51.68	.49	1.98	4.45	7.91	17.8	31.6	49.4	71.3	96.9	127	160	198
19	43.83	53.10	.51	2.03	4.57	8.13	18.3	32.5	50.8	73.3	99.5	130	165	203
20	46.14	54.53	.52	2.08	4.69	8.34	18.8	33.4	52.1	75.3	102	133	169	208
22	50.75	57.19	.55	2.19	4.92	8.74	19.7	35.0	54.7	78.9	107	140	177	219
24	55.37	59.74	.57	2.28	5.14	9.13	20.5	36.5	57.1	82.4	112	146	185	228
26	59.98	62.09	.59	2.38	5.35	9.51	21.4	38.0	59.4	85.8	116	152	193	238
28	64.60	64.44	.62	2.47	5.55	9.87	22.2	39.5	61.7	89.0	121	158	200	247
30	69.21	66.79	.64	2.55	5.74	10.2	23.0	40.8	63.8	92.2	125	163	207	255
32	73.82	68.93	.66	2.64	5.93	10.6	23.7	42.2	65.9	95.2	129	169	214	264
34	78.44	71.08	.68	2.72	6.11	10.9	24.5	43.5	67.9	98.2	133	174	220	272
36	83.05	73.12	.70	2.80	6.29	11.2	25.2	44.7	69.9	101	137	179	227	280
38	87.67	75.16	.72	2.87	6.46	11.5	25.9	46.0	71.8	104	141	184	233	287
40	92.28	77.10	.74	2.95	6.63	11.8	26.5	47.2	73.7	106	144	189	239	295
42	96.89	78.94	.76	3.02	6.80	12.1	27.2	48.3	75.5	109	148	193	245	302
44	101.51	80.78	.77	3.09	6.96	12.4	27.8	49.5	77.3	112	151	198	250	309
46	106.12	82.62	.79	3.16	7.11	12.6	28.4	50.6	79.0	114	155	202	256	316
48	110.74	84.46	.81	3.23	7.27	12.9	29.1	51.7	80.7	116	158	207	262	323
50	115.35	86.19	.82	3.30	7.42	13.2	29.7	52.7	82.4	119	161	211	267	330
52	119.96	87.83	.84	3.36	7.56	13.4	30.2	53.8	84.0	121	165	215	272	336
54	124.58	89.56	.86	3.43	7.71	13.7	30.8	54.8	85.6	123	168	219	277	343
56	129.19	91.20	.87	3.49	7.85	14.0	31.4	55.8	87.2	126	171	223	283	349
58	133.81	92.83	.89	3.55	7.99	14.2	31.9	56.8	88.7	128	174	227	288	355
60	138.42	94.36	.90	3.61	8.12	14.4	32.5	57.8	90.3	130	177	231	292	361
62	143.03	96.00	.92	3.67	8.26	14.7	33.0	58.7	91.7	132	180	235	297	367
64	147.65	97.53	.93	3.73	8.39	14.9	33.6	59.7	93.2	134	183	239	302	373
66	152.26	98.96	.95	3.79	8.52	15.1	34.1	60.6	94.7	136	186	242	307	379
68	156.88	100.49	.96	3.84	8.65	15.4	34.6	61.5	96.1	138	188	246	311	384
70	161.49	101.92	.97	3.90	8.77	15.6	35.1	62.4	97.5	140	191	250	316	390
72	166.10	103.35	.99	3.95	8.90	15.8	35.6	63.3	98.9	142	194	253	320	395
74	170.72	104.78	1.00	4.01	9.02	16.0	36.1	64.2	100	144	196	257	325	401
76	175.33	106.21	1.02	4.06	9.14	16.3	36.6	65.0	102	146	199	260	329	406
78	179.95	107.64	1.03	4.12	9.26	16.5	37.0	65.9	103	148	202	263	333	412
80	184.56	108.97	1.04	4.17	9.38	16.7	37.5	66.7	104	150	204	267	338	417
82	189.17	110.30	1.06	4.22	9.50	16.9	38.0	67.5	106	152	207	270	342	422
84	193.79	111.72	1.07	4.27	9.61	17.1	38.4	68.3	107	154	209	273	346	427
86	198.40	112.95	1.08	4.32	9.73	17.3	38.9	69.2	108	156	212	277	350	432
88	203.02	114.28	1.09	4.37	9.84	17.5	39.3	70.0	109	157	214	280	354	437
90	207.63	115.61	1.11	4.42	9.95	17.7	39.8	70.7	111	159	217	283	358	442
92	212.24	116.83	1.12	4.47	10.1	17.9	40.2	71.5	112	161	219	286	362	447
94	216.86	118.16	1.13	4.52	10.2	18.1	40.7	72.3	113	163	221	289	366	452
96	221.47	119.38	1.14	4.57	10.3	18.3	41.1	73.1	114	164	224	292	370	457
98	226.09	120.61	1.15	4.61	10.4	18.5	41.5	73.8	115	166	226	295	374	461
100	230.70	121.84	1.17	4.66	10.5	18.6	41.9	74.6	117	168	228	298	378	466
102	235.31	123.06	1.18	4.71	10.6	18.8	42.4	75.3	118	169	231	301	381	471
104	239.93	124.29	1.19	4.75	10.7	19.0	42.8	76.1	119	171	233	304	385	475
106	244.54	125.41	1.20	4.80	10.8	19.2	43.2	76.8	120	173	235	307	389	480
108	249.16	126.64	1.21	4.84	10.9	19.4	43.6	77.5	121	174	237	310	392	484
110	253.77	127.76	1.22	4.89	11.0	19.6	44.0	78.2	122	176	240	313	396	489
112	258.38	128.98	1.23	4.93	11.1	19.7	44.4	78.9	123	178	242	316	400	493
114	263.00	130.11	1.24	4.98	11.2	19.9	44.8	79.6	124	179	244	318	403	498
116	267.61	131.23	1.25	5.02	11.3	20.1	45.2	80.3	125	181	246	321	407	502
118	272.23	132.35	1.27	5.06	11.4	20.3	45.6	81.0	127	182	248	324	410	506
120	276.84	133.48	1.28	5.11	11.5	20.4	45.9	81.7	128	184	250	327	414	511
122	281.45	134.60	1.29	5.15	11.6	20.6	46.3	82.4	129	185	252	329	417	515
124	286.07	135.72	1.30	5.19	11.7	20.8	46.7	83.0	130	187	254	332	420	519
126	290.68	136.75	1.31	5.23	11.8	20.9	47.1	83.7	131	188	256	335	424	523
128	295.30	137.87	1.32	5.27	11.9	21.1	47.4	84.4	132	190	258	337	427	527
130	299.91	138.89	1.33	5.31	12.0	21.3	47.8	85.0	133	191	260	340	430	531
132	304.52	140.01	1.34	5.36	12.0	21.4	48.2	85.7	134	193	262	343	434	536
134	309.14	141.03	1.35	5.40	12.1	21.6	48.5	86.3	135	194	264	345	437	540
136	313.75	142.06	1.36	5.44	12.2	21.7	48.9	87.0	136	196	266	347	440	544

* 1 psi = 2.307 ft of water.

Through Circular Orifices
of Water per Minute)

this chapter of the HANDBOOK apply. Appropriate coefficients should be applied where it is read from a hydrant outlet. Where more accurate results are required, a coefficient appropriate to the particular nozzle must be selected and applied to the figures of the table.

The discharge from circular openings of sizes other than those in the table may readily be computed by applying the principle that quantity discharged under a given head varies as the square of the diameter of the opening.

Orifice in Inches														Velocity Head psi
1½	1¾	2	2¼	2½	2¾	3	3¼	3½	3¾	4	4½	5	6	
67.1	91.4	119	151	186	226	268	315	365	419	477	604	746	1074	1
94.9	129	169	214	264	319	380	446	517	593	675	854	1055	1519	2
116	158	207	262	323	391	465	546	633	727	827	1046	1292	1860	3
134	183	239	302	373	451	537	630	731	839	955	1208	1492	2148	4
150	204	267	338	417	504	600	705	817	938	1067	1351	1668	2401	5
164	224	292	370	457	553	658	772	895	1027	1169	1480	1827	2630	6
178	242	316	400	493	597	710	834	967	1110	1263	1598	1973	2841	7
190	258	337	427	527	638	759	891	1034	1186	1350	1709	2109	3037	8
201	274	358	453	559	677	805	945	1096	1258	1432	1812	2237	3222	9
212	289	377	478	590	713	849	996	1156	1326	1509	1910	2358	3396	10
223	303	396	501	618	748	890	1045	1212	1391	1583	2003	2473	3562	11
233	316	413	523	646	781	930	1091	1266	1453	1653	2093	2583	3720	12
242	329	430	544	672	813	968	1136	1318	1512	1721	2178	2689	3872	13
251	342	446	565	698	844	1005	1179	1367	1570	1786	2260	2790	4018	14
260	354	462	585	722	874	1040	1220	1415	1625	1848	2340	2888	4159	15
268	365	477	604	746	902	1074	1260	1462	1678	1909	2416	2983	4296	16
277	377	492	623	769	930	1107	1299	1507	1730	1968	2491	3075	4428	17
285	388	506	641	791	957	1139	1337	1550	1780	2025	2562	3164	4556	18
293	398	520	658	813	983	1170	1373	1593	1828	2080	2633	3251	4681	19
300	409	534	675	834	1009	1201	1409	1634	1876	2134	2701	3335	4803	20
315	428	560	708	874	1058	1259	1479	1714	1968	2239	2833	3497	5037	22
329	448	585	740	913	1105	1315	1544	1790	2055	2338	2959	3653	5261	24
342	466	608	770	951	1150	1369	1607	1863	2139	2434	3080	3802	5476	26
355	483	631	799	987	1194	1421	1667	1934	2220	2526	3196	3946	5682	28
368	500	654	827	1021	1236	1470	1726	2001	2298	2614	3309	4085	5882	30
380	517	675	854	1055	1276	1519	1782	2067	2373	2700	3417	4218	6075	32
391	533	696	882	1087	1315	1565	1837	2131	2446	2783	3522	4348	6262	34
403	548	716	906	1119	1354	1611	1890	2193	2517	2864	3624	4475	6443	36
414	563	736	931	1149	1391	1655	1942	2253	2586	2942	3724	4597	6620	38
424	578	755	955	1179	1427	1698	1993	2311	2653	3019	3820	4716	6792	40
435	592	773	979	1209	1462	1740	2042	2368	2719	3093	3915	4833	6960	42
445	606	791	1002	1237	1496	1781	2090	2424	2783	3166	4007	4947	7123	44
455	620	809	1024	1264	1530	1820	2137	2478	2845	3237	4097	5058	7283	46
465	633	827	1046	1292	1563	1860	2183	2532	2906	3307	4185	5167	7440	48
475	646	844	1068	1318	1595	1898	2228	2584	2966	3375	4271	5273	7593	50
484	659	860	1089	1344	1627	1936	2272	2635	3025	3442	4356	5378	7744	52
493	671	877	1110	1370	1658	1973	2315	2685	3083	3507	4439	5480	7891	54
502	684	893	1130	1395	1688	2009	2358	2735	3139	3572	4520	5581	8036	56
511	696	909	1150	1420	1718	2045	2400	2783	3195	3635	4600	5679	8178	58
520	708	924	1170	1444	1747	2080	2441	2831	3249	3697	4679	5776	8318	60
528	719	940	1189	1468	1776	2114	2481	2877	3303	3758	4756	5872	8456	62
537	731	955	1208	1491	1805	2148	2521	2923	3356	3818	4832	5966	8591	64
545	742	969	1227	1515	1833	2181	2560	2969	3408	3877	4907	6059	8724	66
553	753	984	1245	1537	1860	2214	2598	3013	3459	3936	4981	6150	8855	68
562	764	998	1263	1560	1887	2246	2636	3057	3510	3993	5054	6239	8985	70
570	775	1012	1281	1582	1914	2278	2674	3101	3559	4050	5126	6327	9112	72
577	786	1026	1299	1604	1941	2309	2710	3143	3608	4106	5196	6415	9238	74
585	796	1040	1317	1625	1967	2340	2747	3186	3657	4161	5266	6501	9362	76
593	807	1054	1334	1647	1992	2371	2783	3227	3705	4215	5335	6586	9484	78
600	817	1067	1351	1668	2018	2401	2818	3268	3752	4269	5403	6670	9605	80
608	827	1080	1367	1688	2043	2431	2853	3309	3799	4322	5470	6753	9724	82
615	837	1094	1384	1708	2068	2461	2888	3349	3845	4374	5536	6835	9842	84
622	847	1106	1400	1729	2092	2490	2922	3389	3890	4426	5602	6916	9959	86
630	857	1119	1417	1749	2116	2518	2956	3428	3935	4477	5667	6996	10074	88
637	867	1132	1433	1769	2140	2547	2989	3467	3980	4528	5731	7075	10188	90
644	876	1144	1448	1788	2164	2575	3022	3505	4024	4578	5794	7153	10300	92
651	886	1157	1464	1808	2187	2603	3055	3543	4067	4627	5856	7230	10411	94
658	895	1169	1480	1827	2210	2630	3087	3580	4110	4676	5919	7307	10521	96
664	904	1181	1495	1846	2233	2658	3119	3617	4153	4725	5980	7383	10630	98
671	914	1193	1510	1864	2256	2685	3151	3654	4195	4773	6041	7458	10739	100
678	923	1205	1525	1883	2278	2711	3182	3691	4237	4820	6101	7532	10846	102
684	932	1217	1540	1901	2301	2738	3213	3727	4278	4867	6160	7605	10951	104
691	941	1228	1555	1919	2323	2764	3244	3762	4319	4914	6219	7678	11056	106
698	949	1240	1569	1938	2344	2790	3274	3798	4359	4960	6278	7750	11160	108
704	958	1251	1584	1955	2366	2816	3305	3833	4400	5006	6335	7821	11263	110
710	967	1263	1598	1973	2387	2841	3334	3867	4439	5051	6393	7892	11365	112
717	975	1274	1612	1991	2409	2866	3364	3902	4479	5096	6450	7962	11466	114
723	984	1285	1626	2008	2430	2892	3394	3936	4518	5140	6506	8032	11566	116
729	992	1296	1640	2025	2451	2916	3423	3969	4557	5184	6562	8101	11665	118
735	1001	1307	1654	2042	2471	2941	3452	4003	4595	5228	6617	8169	11764	120
741	1009	1318	1668	2059	2492	2965	3480	4036	4633	5272	6672	8237	11861	122
747	1017	1329	1681	2076	2512	2990	3509	4069	4671	5315	6726	8304	11958	124
753	1025	1339	1695	2093	2532	3014	3537	4102	4709	5357	6781	8371	12054	126
759	1034	1350	1709	2109	2552	3037	3565	4134	4746	5400	6834	8437	12150	128
765	1042	1360	1722	2126	2572	3061	3592	4166	4783	5442	6887	8503	12244	130
771	1050	1371	1735	2142	2592	3084	3620	4198	4820	5484	6940	8568	12338	132
776	1058	1381	1748	2158	2611	3108	3647	4230	4856	5525	6992	8633	12431	134
783	1065	1391	1761	2174	2631	3131	3674	4261	4892	5565	7044	8697	12523	136

Table 11-6C.   Friction Loss in Pipe
Pounds per Square Inch per 100 Feet of Pipe
Hazen-Williams $C = 100$*

Actual Diameter of Pipe ½ through 3½ in.†
Nominal Diameter of Pipe for 4 through 30 in.

Gpm	½	¾	1	1¼	1½	2	2½	3	3½	4	Gpm
5	17.9	4.55	1.40	.369	.174	.052	—	—	—	—	5
10	64.5	16.4	5.06	1.33	.629	.186	.078	—	—	—	10
15		34.7	10.7	2.82	1.33	.394	.166	.064	.028	—	15
20	**5**	59.1	18.2	4.89	2.27	.671	.282	.109	.048	.027	20
30	.019	**6**	38.6	10.2	4.80	1.42	.598	.231	.102	.057	30
40	.033	—	65.8	17.3	8.17	2.42	1.02	.393	.174	.097	40
50	.050	.020	**8**	26.2	12.3	3.66	1.54	.593	.263	.147	50
60	.069	.029	—	36.6	17.3	5.12	2.16	.831	.369	.206	60
70	.092	.038	—	48.7	23.0	6.81	2.87	1.11	.490	.274	70
80	.118	.049	—	62.4	29.4	8.72	3.67	1.41	.628	.350	80
90	.147	.060	—	77.6	36.6	10.8	4.56	1.76	.781	.435	90
100	.178	.074	—	**10**	44.5	13.1	5.55	2.14	.949	.529	100
120	.250	.103	—	—	62.3	18.5	7.77	3.00	1.33	.741	120
140	.333	.137	.034	—	82.9	24.6	10.3	3.98	1.77	.986	140
160	.426	.175	.043	—	106.0	31.4	13.2	5.10	2.26	1.26	160
180	.529	.218	.054	.018	**12**	39.1	16.5	6.34	2.81	1.57	180
200	.643	.265	.065	.022	—	47.5	20.0	7.71	3.42	1.91	200
220	.768	.316	.078	.026	—	56.7	23.9	9.19	4.08	2.28	220
240	.902	.371	.091	.031	.013	**14**	28.0	10.8	4.79	2.67	240
260	1.05	.430	.106	.036	.015	—	32.5	12.5	5.56	3.10	260
280	1.20	.493	.122	.041	.017	—	37.3	14.4	6.37	3.55	280
300	1.36	.562	.138	.047	.019	—	42.3	16.3	7.24	4.04	300
350	1.81	.746	.184	.062	.026	.012	**16**	21.7	9.63	5.37	350
400	2.32	.955	.235	.079	.033	.015	—	27.8	12.3	6.88	400
450	2.88	1.19	.292	.099	.041	.019	—	34.6	15.3	8.55	450
500	3.51	1.44	.353	.120	.049	.023	.012	42.0	18.6	10.4	500
550	4.18	1.72	.424	.143	.059	.028	.015	50.1	22.2	12.4	550
600	4.91	2.02	.498	.168	.069	.033	.017	58.8	26.1	14.6	600
650	5.70	2.34	.577	.195	.080	.038	.020	68.2	30.3	16.9	650
700	6.53	2.69	.662	.223	.092	.043	.023	**18**	34.7	19.4	700
750	7.42	3.05	.752	.254	.104	.049	.026	—	39.4	22.0	750
800	8.36	3.44	.848	.286	.118	.056	.029	—	44.5	24.8	800
850	9.35	3.85	.948	.320	.132	.062	.032	—	49.7	27.7	850
900	10.4	4.28	1.05	.356	.146	.069	.036	—	**20**	30.8	900
950	11.5	4.73	1.17	.393	.162	.076	.040	—	—	34.1	950
1,000	12.6	5.20	1.28	.432	.178	.084	.044	—	—	37.5	1,000
1,250	19.1	7.85	1.94	.653	.269	.127	.066	—	—	**24**	1,250
1,500	**30**	11.0	2.71	.914	.376	.178	.093	—	—	—	1,500
1,750	—	—	3.61	1.22	.501	.236	.123	—	—	—	1,750
2,000	.007	—	4.62	1.56	.641	.303	.158	.089	.053	.022	2,000
2,250	.009	—	—	1.94	.797	.376	.196	.111	.066	.027	2,250
2,500	.011	—	—	2.35	.969	.457	.239	.134	.081	.033	2,500
2,750	.013	—	—	2.81	1.16	.545	.285	.160	.096	.040	2,750
3,000	.016	—	—	3.30	1.36	.641	.334	.188	.113	.046	3,000
4,000	.027	—	—	—	2.31	1.09	.569	.321	.192	.079	4,000
5,000	.040	—	—	—	3.49	1.65	.860	.485	.290	.119	5,000

* To convert friction loss at $C = 100$ or other values of C, see Table 11-6J.
† Schedule 40 pipe sizes ½- through 3½-in. steel pipe.

Note: Actual inside diameter for sizes ½ in. through 3½ in. is given for greater accuracy as these sizes include sprinkler branch lines and the smaller sizes of cross mains. For sizes 4 in. and greater, the nominal diameters were used as a fairly safe average for the diameters of various types of underground pipes as follows: cast iron unlined and Enameline, greater than nominal; cast iron cement lines and Class 200 asbestos cement, less than nominal; Class 150 asbestos-cement sizes 6 and 8 in. less than nominal, and other sizes even nominal. (A 0.10 variation is true for Class 150 cement lined only—see ASHD FT-9 through 45 for actual IDs.)

This table will be useful in approximating friction loss in flow through existing underground piping where the type, inside diameter, and condition are frequently unknown. However, in such cases, a flow test is recommended.

When the type, inside diameter, and condition are known, and in designing new systems for all sizes and types of pipes, the friction loss tables should be used. Friction tables based on Hazen-Williams formula are published in *Automatic Sprinkler Hydraulic Data* by "Automatic" Sprinkler Corporation of America, and tables based on Darcy-Weisbach formula are published in *Standards of the Hydraulic Institute.*

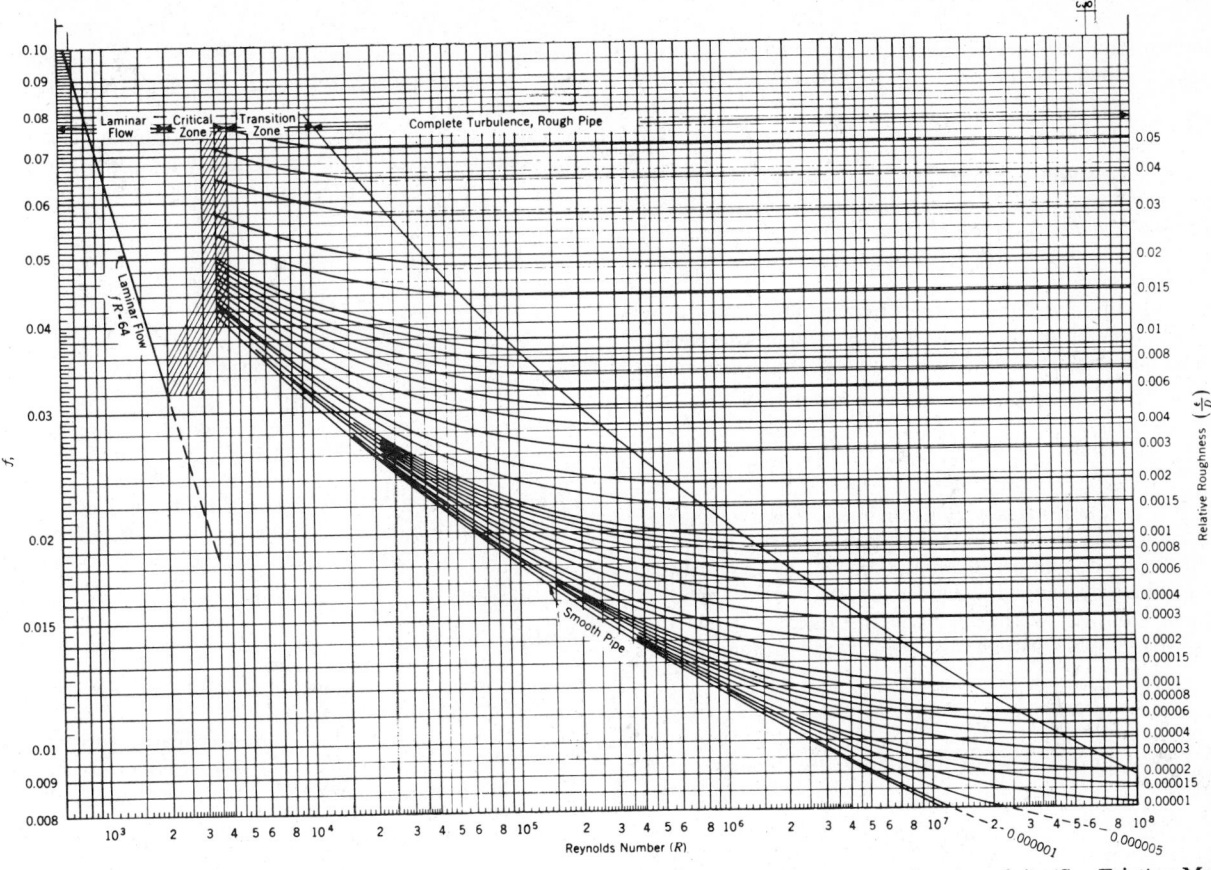

Fig. 11-6K. Moody Diagram for friction in pipe. The values for friction factor are on the vertical scale at left. (See Friction Manual © Hydraulic Institute.)

Table 11-6D. Values of *k* for Various Discharge Orifices

Type of Orifice	Nominal Diameter (Inches)	k
Sprinkler	$\frac{1}{4}$	1.3–1.5
Sprinkler	$\frac{5}{16}$	1.8–2.0
Sprinkler	$\frac{3}{8}$	2.6–2.9
Sprinkler	$\frac{7}{16}$	4.0–4.4
Sprinkler	$\frac{1}{2}$	5.3–5.8
Sprinkler	$\frac{17}{32}$	7.4–8.2
Nozzle	$\frac{1}{2}$	7.24
Nozzle	$\frac{7}{8}$	22.2
Nozzle	1	29.1
Nozzle	$1\frac{1}{16}$	32.8
Nozzle	$1\frac{1}{8}$	36.8
Nozzle	$1\frac{3}{16}$	41.0
Nozzle	$1\frac{1}{4}$	45.4
Nozzle	$1\frac{5}{16}$	50.1
Nozzle	$1\frac{3}{8}$	54.9
Nozzle (C = 0.97 for all nozzles)	$1\frac{7}{16}$	60.0
Nozzle	$1\frac{1}{2}$	65.4
Nozzle	$1\frac{9}{16}$	70.9
Nozzle	$1\frac{5}{8}$	76.8
Nozzle	$1\frac{11}{16}$	82.8
Nozzle	$1\frac{3}{4}$	89.0
Nozzle	$1\frac{13}{16}$	95.5
Nozzle	$1\frac{7}{8}$	102.0
Nozzle	$1\frac{15}{16}$	109.0
Nozzle	2	116.0
Hydrant butt (C = 0.90)	2	107.4
Hydrant butt (C = 0.90)	$2\frac{1}{4}$	135.9
Hydrant butt (C = 0.90)	$2\frac{1}{2}$	167.8

Fluid motion in a pipe may be either laminar or turbulent. In laminar or "streamline" motion the fluid particles follow definite paths, and the resistance to flow is due only to the shear stress of adjacent layers. Laminar flow is usually associated with low velocity.

In turbulent motion the fluid moves in an eddying mass, and at any point may vary in an irregular manner from instant to instant.

With low velocity and laminar flow in either a smooth pipe or a rough pipe the flow would remain laminar until the velocity reaches what is called the critical velocity. Beyond that and until turbulent flow is definitely established, the fluid motion is in a transition zone.

Ordinary fire protection and utility flow rates are in the turbulent range. When fluids other than water are involved,

Table 11-6E. Typical Discharge Coefficients of Solid Stream Nozzles

Standard sprinkler, average (nominal $\frac{1}{2}$ in. dia.)	0.75
Standard orifice (sharp edge)	0.62
Smooth bore nozzles, general	0.96–0.98
Underwriter playpipes or equal	0.97
Deluge or monitor nozzles	0.997
Open pipe, smooth, well rounded	0.90
Open pipe, burred opening	0.80
* Hydrant butt, smooth and well-rounded outlet, flowing full	0.90
* Hydrant butt, square and sharp at hydrant barrel	0.80
* Hydrant butt, outlet square, projecting into barrel	0.70

* See Figure 11-6*E*.

the conventional exponential formulas are not suitable, and a universal flow formula, such as the Darcy-Weisbach, is needed $\left(h = f\dfrac{l}{d}\dfrac{v^2}{2g} \right)$.

In the Darcy-Weisbach formula the friction factor f is dimensionless and variable, depending on (1) the roughness of the pipe and (2) on another dimensionless factor called the Reynolds number, which depends on the density, viscosity, and kinetic viscosity.

The value of f can be computed by a formula known as the Colebrook-White equation which is neither completely empirical nor rigidly theoretical. This equation is usually written as follows:

$$\frac{1}{\sqrt{f}} = -2\log_{10}\left[\frac{\varepsilon}{3.7D} + \frac{2.51}{R\sqrt{f}} \right]$$

where ε is a linear measure of roughness, f is the Darcy-Weisbach friction factor, D is the pipe diameter in feet, and R is the Reynolds number. Computation of f by the formula can be avoided by using tables and charts known as "Moody" diagrams, published by The Hydraulic Institute.[1]

Reynolds numbers can be calculated by the formula:

$$R = \frac{VD}{v}$$

where V = velocity, feet per second; D = diameter, feet; and v = kinetic viscosity, square feet per second (see Table 11-6A).

Values of R in terms of gallons per minute flow (Q) and pipe diameter (d) in inches at ordinary temperatures are:

$$R_{80°} = 3670\,\frac{Q}{d}$$

$$R_{74°} = 3410\,\frac{Q}{d}$$

$$R_{70°} = 3225\,\frac{Q}{d}$$

$$R_{60°} = 2810\,\frac{Q}{d}$$

Figure 11-6K is a Moody diagram by which f can be determined for any kind or size of pipe. Knowing R and the relative roughness ε, the value of f can be read directly off the chart. The dimension of $\dfrac{\varepsilon}{D}$ is difficult to obtain, and it may be necessary to assume a value for $\dfrac{\varepsilon}{D}$ based on experience and judgment. The roughness factor of new pipe usually can be provided by the manufacturer.

The basic form of the Hazen-Williams formula ($V = 1.318Cr^{0.63}s^{0.54}$) is not practical for ordinary fire protection flow calculations. In terms of pressure loss and gallons per minute the formula becomes

Table 11-6F.   Numbers to 1.85 Power

N	$N^{1.85}$	N	$N^{1.85}$	N	$N^{1.85}$
5	19.64	39	877.9	230	23,400
6	27.52	40	920.1	240	25,320
7	36.60	41	963	250	27,300
8	46.85	42	1,007	260	29,360
9	58.26	43	1,052	270	31,480
10	70.80	44	1,097	280	32,910
11	84.44	45	1,144	290	34,310
12	99.19	46	1,192	300	38,250
13	115.0	47	1,240	350	50,880
14	131.9	48	1,289	400	65,150
15	149.9	49	1,339	450	80,990
16	168.9	50	1,390	500	98,440
17	189.0	55	1,658	550	117,400
18	210.0	60	1,948	600	137,900
19	232.1	65	2,259	650	159,900
20	255.2	70	2,591	700	183,400
21	279.3	75	2,944	750	208,400
22	304.4	80	3,317	800	234,800
23	330.5	85	3,710	850	262,700
24	357.6	90	4,124	900	291,900
25	385.7	95	4,558	950	322,700
26	414.7	100	5,012	1,000	354,800
27	444.7	110	5,979	1,200	497,200
28	475.6	120	7,022	1,400	661,100
29	507.5	130	8,144	1,600	846,400
30	540.4	140	9,339	1,800	1,053,000
31	574.1	150	10,610	2,000	1,279,000
32	608.9	160	11,960	2,200	1,526,000
33	644.5	170	13,370	2,400	1,792,000
34	681.2	180	14,870	2,600	2,079,000
35	718.7	190	16,440	2,800	2,384,000
36	757.1	200	18,070	3,000	2,708,000
37	794.6	210	19,770	4,000	4,611,000
38	836.7	220	21,550	5,000	6,968,000

Figures in this table are for use with the Hazen-Williams formula. Determining the 1.85 power of numbers by proportional parts between the figures given (linear interpolation) will produce results with error of less than 2 percent.

Table 11-6G.   Data for Making $N^{1.85}$ Hydraulic Graph Paper

1	2	3	1	2	3
Gpm N	$N^{1.85}$	Scale value, inches from 0	Gpm N	$N^{1.85}$	Scale value, inches from 0
1	1.00	0.05	10.5	77.48	3.87
1.5	2.12	0.11	11	84.44	4.22
2	3.60	0.18	11.5	91.68	4.59
2.5	5.45	0.27	12	99.19	4.96
3	7.63	0.38	12.5	107.0	5.35
3.5	10.15	0.50	13	115.0	5.75
4	13.00	0.65	13.5	123.3	6.16
4.5	16.16	0.81	14	131.9	6.59
5	19.64	0.98	14.5	140.8	7.04
5.5	23.42	1.17	15	149.9	7.49
6	27.52	1.37	15.5	159.2	7.96
6.5	31.90	1.60	16	168.9	8.44
7	36.60	1.83	16.5	178.8	8.94
7.5	41.58	2.08	17	189.0	9.45
8	46.85	2.34	17.5	199.5	9.96
8.5	52.40	2.62	18	210.0	10.50
9	58.26	2.91	18.5	221.0	11.05
9.5	64.39	3.22	19	232.1	11.60
10	70.80	3.54	19.5	243.5	12.18
			20	255.2	12.76

Column 1. Gallons per minute or rate of flow in other units.
Column 2. $N^{1.85}$ from Table 11-6F or by interpolation from that table.
Column 3. Column 2 multiplied by distance in inches from $N = 0$ to $N = 1$ (0.05 in.).

Examples:
Scale value for $N = 7$ is $36.60 \times 0.05 = 1.83$ in.
Scale value for $N = 16$ is $168.9 \times 0.05 = 8.44$ in.
If scale value of $N = 1$ is 0.08, what is scale for $N = 9$?
Answer: $58.26 \times 0.08 = 4.66$ in.

$$p = \frac{452Q^{1.85}}{C^{1.85}d^{4.87}}$$

in which p is the pressure loss in pounds per square inch per 100 ft of pipe; Q is the rate of flow in gallons per minute; and d is the inside diameter of the pipe in inches.

The formula can be arranged in terms of Q instead of p

$$Q = \frac{Cd^{2.63}p^{0.54}}{27.19}$$

Thus Q is directly proportional to C or to $p^{0.54}$ and for a given pipe with p constant, the greater the value of C the greater the flow for the same friction loss. Similarly, when C is constant, Q is directly proportional to $p^{0.54}$ or approximately to $\sqrt{p}$.

L.   Friction Loss Calculations

The solution of fire protection problems involving pipe flow and friction seldom, if ever, requires direct calculation by the formula. Table 11-6C gives values of p when $C = 100$ for Standard pipe sizes from $\frac{1}{2}$ in. to 30 in. in diameter. For values of C other than 100, the tabular losses are multiplied by the corresponding factor in Table 11-6J.

EXAMPLE: Determine the friction loss with 700 gpm flowing in 700 ft of 8-in. cast iron pipe having a C value of 80.

SOLUTION: From Table 11-6C, the loss for 700 gpm per 100 ft of 8-in. pipe with $C = 100$ is .662 psi. From Table 11-6J, the factor for $C = 80$ is 1.51. Because friction loss is directly proportional to length of pipe, multiply .662 × 7 × 1.5 = 6.95 psi (answer).

Calculating C Values

The value of C for any rate of friction loss per 100 ft can be calculated by dividing the given loss per 100 ft by the loss from Table 11-6C, and finding the corresponding C value in Table 11-6J by interpolation.

EXAMPLE: Loss of head in 600 ft of 6-in. asbestos-cement pipe was found by test to be 24 psi, at 1,250 gpm. What is the C value of this pipe?

Table 11-6H.   Guide for Estimating Hazen-Williams C

Kind of Pipe	Value of C		
	1*	2†	3‡
Cast Iron, unlined:			
10 years old	110	90	75
15 years old	100	75	65
20 years old	90	65	55
30 years old	80	55	45
50 years old	70	50	40
Cast Iron, unlined, new	120		
Cast Iron, cement-lined	140		
Cast Iron, bitumastic enamel-lined	140		
Average steel, new	140		
Riveted steel, new	110		
Asbestos-cement	140		
Reinforced concrete	140		

* 1. Water mildly corrosive. Use same values for fire-protection mains having no mill-use or domestic draft.

† 2. Water moderately corrosive.

‡ 3. Water severely corrosive.

Note: C values chosen for design of piping systems should be based on applicable standards of NFPA or the authority having jurisdiction.

SOLUTION: Loss in 100 ft $= \frac{24}{6} = 4.00$ psi. From Table 11-6C loss in 100 ft $= 7.85$ psi. Thus $4.00/7.85 = 0.51$. Interpolating in Table 11-6J:

$C = 140$	.537		
$C = ?$		.510	
$C = 145$	.503	.503	
Differences	5	.034	.007

$\frac{.007}{.034} \times 5 = 1$ Therefore $C = 145 - 1 = 144$ (answer).

The procedure for using the friction loss table can be expressed by a simple formulation, $F = N \times L/100 \times T$, where $F =$ friction loss in given pipe length (see Table 11-6C); $N =$ conversion factor for C value; $L =$ pipe length; and $T =$ friction loss per 100 ft from Table 11-6J. With any three of the factors known, the fourth can be calculated. Solving for N: $N = F \times 100/L \times 1/T$. Applied to the example above, $N = 24 \times 100/600 \times 1/7.85 = 4/7.85 = 0.51$. Interpolating from Table 11-6C, as previously shown, $C = 144$.

Equivalent Pipes

Problems involving piped water supplies and fire protection systems occasionally require substitution of one pipe for another. The term "equivalent pipe" usually means a

Table 11-6I.   Numbers to 0.54 Power

h	$h^{0.54}$	h	$h^{0.54}$	h	$h^{0.54}$	h	$h^{0.54}$	h	$h^{0.54}$
1	1.00	36	6.93	71	9.99	106	12.41	141	14.47
2	1.45	37	7.03	72	10.07	107	12.47	142	14.53
3	1.81	38	7.13	73	10.14	108	12.53	143	14.58
4	2.11	39	7.23	74	10.22	109	12.60	144	14.64
5	2.39	40	7.33	75	10.29	110	12.66	145	14.69
6	2.63	41	7.43	76	10.37	111	12.72	146	14.75
7	2.86	42	7.53	77	10.44	112	12.78	147	14.80
8	3.07	43	7.62	78	10.51	113	12.84	148	14.86
9	3.28	44	7.72	79	10.59	114	12.90	149	14.91
10	3.47	45	7.81	80	10.66	115	12.96	150	14.97
11	3.65	46	7.91	81	10.73	116	13.03	151	15.02
12	3.83	47	8.00	82	10.80	117	13.09	152	15.07
13	4.00	48	8.09	83	10.87	118	13.15	153	15.13
14	4.16	49	8.18	84	10.94	119	13.21	154	15.18
15	4.32	50	8.27	85	11.01	120	13.27	155	15.23
16	4.48	51	8.36	86	11.08	121	13.33	156	15.29
17	4.62	52	8.44	87	11.15	122	13.39	157	15.34
18	4.76	53	8.53	88	11.22	123	13.44	158	15.39
19	4.90	54	8.62	89	11.29	124	13.50	159	15.44
20	5.04	55	8.71	90	11.36	125	13.56	160	15.50
21	5.18	56	8.79	91	11.43	126	13.62	161	15.55
22	5.31	57	8.88	92	11.49	127	13.68	162	15.60
23	5.44	58	8.96	93	11.56	128	13.74	163	15.65
24	5.56	59	9.04	94	11.63	129	13.80	164	15.70
25	5.69	60	9.12	95	11.69	130	13.85	165	15.76
26	5.81	61	9.21	96	11.76	131	13.91	166	15.81
27	5.93	62	9.29	97	11.83	132	13.97	167	15.86
28	6.05	63	9.37	98	11.89	133	14.02	168	15.91
29	6.16	64	9.45	99	11.96	134	14.08	169	15.96
30	6.28	65	9.53	100	12.02	135	14.14	170	16.01
31	6.39	66	9.61	101	12.09	136	14.19	171	16.06
32	6.50	67	9.69	102	12.15	137	14.25	172	16.11
33	6.61	68	9.76	103	12.22	138	14.31	173	16.16
34	6.71	69	9.84	104	12.28	139	14.36	174	16.21
35	6.82	70	9.92	105	12.34	140	14.42	175	16.26

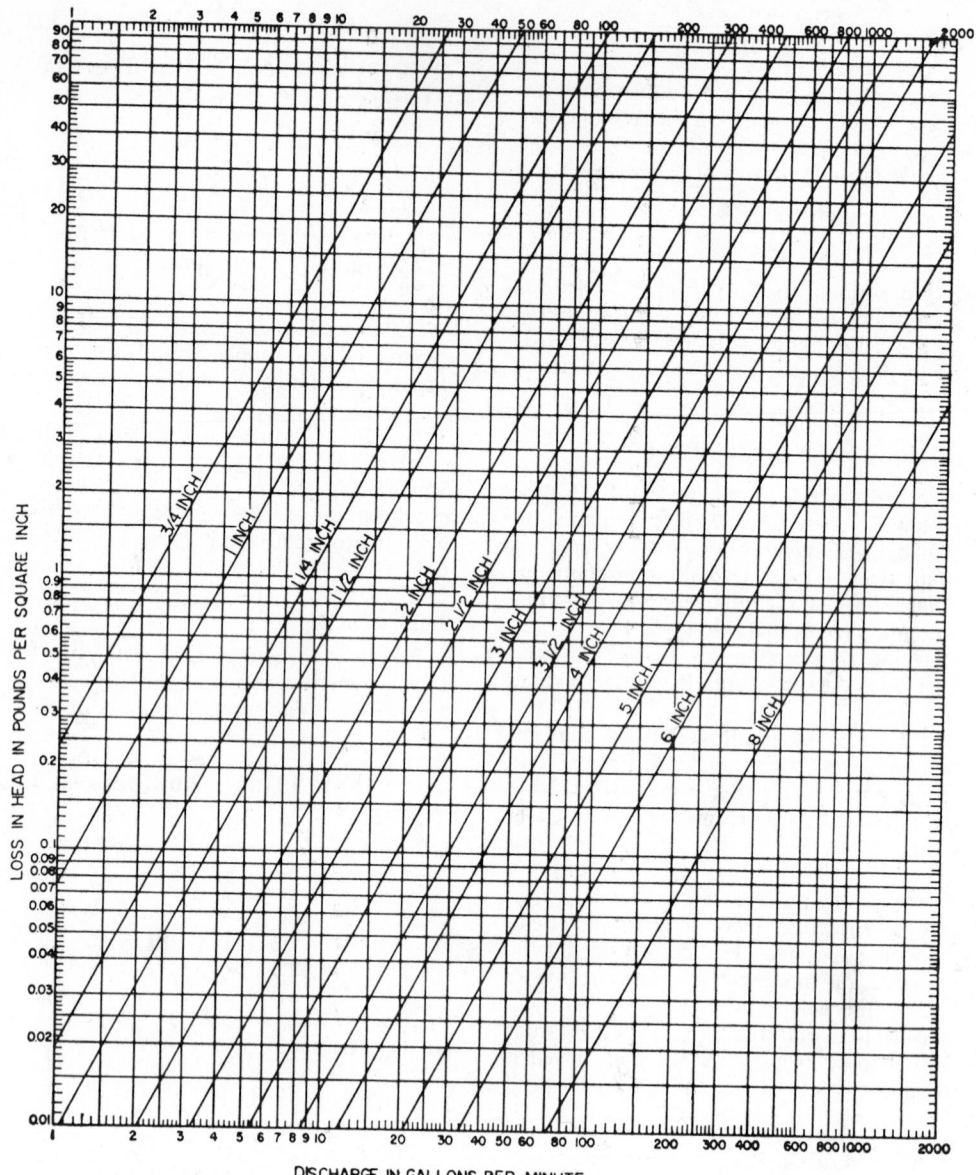

Fig. 11-6L. *Friction loss in pipe in sizes from $\frac{3}{4}$ in. through 8 in. per hundred feet based on Hazen-Williams formula with C = 100.*

Table 11-6J. Conversion Factors for Friction Loss in Pipe for Values of Coefficient Other Than 100

C	Factor	C	Factor	C	Factor
150	0.472	110	0.838	70	1.93
145	0.503	105	0.914	65	2.22
140	0.537	100	1.00	60	2.57
135	0.574	95	1.10	55	3.02
130	0.615	90	1.22	50	3.61
125	0.662	85	1.35	45	4.38
120	0.714	80	1.51	40	5.48
115	0.772	75	1.70	35	6.97

pipe having the same friction loss characteristic as the pipe for which it is being substituted. The formula for using the friction loss table is applicable here.

EXAMPLE: What length of 8-in. pipe $(C = 110)$ is equivalent to 700 ft of 6-in. pipe $(C = 85)$?

SOLUTION:

$$N_1 \times \frac{L_1}{100} \times T_1 = N_2 \times \frac{L_2}{100} \times T_2$$

Assume a rate of flow (say 1,000 gpm) and substitute known values:

$$1.35 \times \frac{700}{100} \times 5.20 = .838 \times \frac{L_2}{100} \times 1.28$$

Solving for L_2:

$$L_2 = \frac{1.35 \times 700 \times 5.20}{.838 \times 1.28} = 4,581 \text{ ft which can be rounded off to 4,600 ft.}$$

The Hazen-Williams Diagram

Figure 11-6L is a graphical presentation of Table 11-6C, but limited in scope to pipes not over 8 in. in diameter. Because of the reduced scale, the chart is less accurate than the table; otherwise there is no difference between the chart and the table.

EXAMPLE OF USE: What is the friction loss in 300 ft of 8-in. cement-lined, cast iron pipe, at 1,500 gpm?

SOLUTION: From the intersection of the 1,500 gpm vertical line with the sloping 8-in. pipe diameter line in Figure 12-1L, read left horizontally for loss of head value, which is found to be 2.7 psi per 100 ft. For 300 ft, the loss would be 3×2.7 or 8.1 psi. But the probable C value of cement-lined pipe is 140 (Table 11-6H), and the conversion factor .537 (Table 11-6J). Therefore, the friction loss is $8.1 \times .537 = 4.35$ psi.

M.   Water Hammer

Water hammer is the effect of pressure rise that may accompany a sudden change in the velocity of water flowing in a pipe. When deceleration of velocity is rapid or completely stopped, the kinetic energy of the moving water column is absorbed temporarily by elastic deformation of the pipe and by the compressibility of water. Consideration of water hammer and transient pressure surges is based on the elastic wave theories of Joukowski and Allievi. The force of water hammer is sometimes sufficient to rupture pipes, fittings, or hose lines. Theoretically, the resultant force could be infinite if the system were totally inelastic.

Pressure surges may be initiated by the closing of a valve, the stopping of a pump, or by the sudden development of an abnormal water demand when a water main breaks. Occasionally, the operation of automatic control valves in sprinkler systems may result in reversal of flow and a build-up of high pressure in the fire protection system.

The elasticity of hose tends to reduce the danger from water hammer, but the sudden closing of shutoff nozzles on long hose lines may cause a pressure rise sufficient to rupture the hose. Tests conducted by the New York City Fire Department indicated that pressure surges from closing of nozzles approximated twice the hydrant pressure. These tests point to the advantage of operating nozzle valves slowly.

Discharge lines from pumps are subject to water hammer caused by water column separation. This may occur when the pump suddenly stops (power failure, manual shutdown, etc.), or if the discharge valve is closed too quickly with the pump operating. Separation takes place somewhere downstream, especially at a summit, or where the downward slope of the pipe increases sharply. When forward movement becomes exhausted the flow reverses its direction and closes the gap.

When a pump is located at an elevation above the system outlet, a vacuum breaker in the line may provide effective control.

When there is static head on a pump at discharge, it is practically impossible to eliminate completely a water-column reversal. Surge suppressors may be effective, if used; likewise special type vacuum breakers designed to bypass a portion of the reverse flow water column around the check valve or control valve.

The restarting of a pump too quickly after a tripout may cause excessive surging, and installations subject to intermittment operation should be protected by time delay relays.

Simple relief valves are considered useless because their operation is too slow to counteract the speed of the pressure rise.

The principal factors contributing to water column separation are: (1) rate of flow-stoppage, either by rapid closing of a valve, or the fast deceleration of a pump; (2) length of pipe system (this determines the time that pressure continues to fall before positive pressure waves returning from the far end of the line counteracts the initial pressure drop); (3) the normal operating pressure at critical points, such as the crests of hills; and (4) the velocity of the water just before pump stoppage or valve closure occurs; (the greater the velocity, the larger the size of the void, reverse flow velocity, and the final pressure rise).

Elastic Wave Theory

The basic concepts are:

1. The magnitude of the pressure rise is proportional to the fluid velocity destroyed and to the velocity of the pressure wave.

2. The pressure rise is independent of the length and profile of the pipe.

3. The velocity of the pressure wave is the same as the velocity of sound through water.

The theoretical pressure rise when flow is stopped instantly may be calculated from the formula

$$\Delta p = \frac{0.433av}{g}$$

in which Δp = pressure rise in pounds per square inch; a = velocity of pressure wave in feet per second; v = water flow velocity in feet per second; and g = acceleration of gravity in feet per second per second.

In practice, the calculated Δp should be reduced to allow for valve closure characteristics, and friction loss in the pipe. Usually this is a matter of judgment and experience.

The pressure rise Δp is at maximum when the flow is stopped in a time equal to or less than the critical time of the pipe, which is the time required for the pressure wave to travel from the point of closure to the end of the pipe and return. The formula for critical time is:

$$t = \frac{2l}{a}$$

in which t = time in seconds; l = length of pipe in feet; and a = velocity of pressure wave in feet per second.

The value of a in the above formula can be calculated from the formula

$$a = \frac{12}{\sqrt{\frac{w}{g}\left(\frac{1}{k} + \frac{d}{Ee}\right)}}$$

in which

w = weight of water pounds per cubic foot

g = acceleration of gravity, feet per second per second

k = bulk modulus of compressibility of water, pounds per square inch

E = Young's modulus of elasticity of pipe wall material, pounds per square inch

e = thickness of pipe wall, inches

d = inside diameter of pipe, inches.

To avoid calculating a, use the chart in Figure 11-6M.

The calculated pressure rise in a 6-in. cast iron pipe is about 60 psi per foot of arrested velocity.

The water hammer potential of distribution systems, especially those with automatic pumps, should be examined,

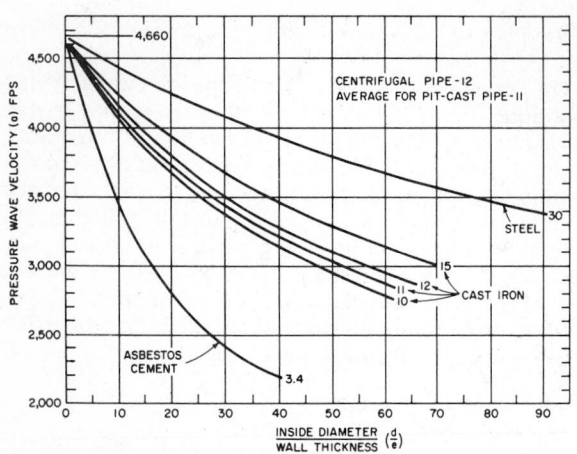

Fig. 11-6M. Surge wave velocity chart for water. The figures on the curves represent values of **E** *in millions of pounds per square inch (bulk modules of elasticity).*

and practical steps taken to reduce the probability of destructive pressure surges. Valves and hydrants should be maintained in good condition, and operated carefully. Public utility networks with inadequate pipe capacity might be subject to flow reversals and surging. Remote-controlled power-operated valves should be carefully timed to prevent too-fast closing (never less than 5 sec).

SI Units

The following conversion factors are given as a convenience in converting to SI units the English units used in this chapter.

1 in.	=	25.400 mm
1 ft.	=	0.305 m
1 lb	=	0.454 kg
1 psi	=	6894.757 Pa
$\frac{5}{9}(°F − 32)$	=	°C
1 gal.	=	3.785 litres

Bibliography

References Cited

[1] *Pipe Friction Manual,* Hydraulics Institute, New York, 1954.

Additional Readings

Albertson, Maurice L., Barton, James R., and Simons, Daryl B., *Fluid Mechanics for Engineers,* Prentice-Hall, Inc., Englewood Cliffs, N.J., 1960.

"Data Sections," *Standards of Hydraulic Institute,* 11th ed., Hydraulic Institute, New York, 1965.

Davis, Calvin V. and Sorensen, K. E., eds., *Handbook of Applied Hydraulics,* McGraw-Hill, New York, 1969.

Freeman, John R., "Experiments Relating to Hydraulics of Fire Streams," *Transactions of American Society of Civil Engineers,* 1889, pp. 303–482.

Freeman, John R., "The Nozzle as an Accurate Water-meter," *Transactions of American Society of Civil Engineers,* Vol. 24, 1891, pp. 492–527.

Howard, C. D. D., "Pipe Friction Coefficients from Measured Velocity Profiles," *American Water Works Association Journal,* Vol. 59, No. 5, May 1967, pp. 645–650.

King, Horace W., Wisler, Chester O., and Woodburn, James G., *Hydraulics,* 5th ed., John Wiley & Sons, New York, 1948.

King, H. W., and Brater, E. F., *Handbook of Hydraulics,* 5th ed., McGraw-Hill, New York, 1963.

Lescovich, J. E., "The Control of Water Hammer by Automatic Valves," *American Water Works Association Journal,* Vol. 59, No. 5, May 1967, pp. 632–644.

Richard, R. T., "Water Hammer," *Transactions of American Society of Mechanical Engineers,* Vol. 78, No. 6, August 1956.

Rouse, Hunter, ed., *Engineering Hydraulics,* John Wiley & Sons, New York, 1950.

Streeter, Victor L., ed., *Handbook of Fluid Dynamics,* McGraw-Hill, New York, 1961.

"Hydraulics of Pipelines," Chapter 5 in *AWWA M11 Steel Pipe Manual,* American Water Works Association, New York, 1964.

"Water Hammer and Surge," Chapter 7, *Ibid.*

Williams, G. S. and Hazen, A., *Hydraulic Tables,* John Wiley & Sons, New York, 1933.

Winn, W. P. "Techniques in Water Hammer Control and Surge Suppression," *American Water Works Association Journal,* Vol. 59, No. 5, May 1967, pp. 620–624.

Wood, Clyde, M., *"Automatic" Sprinkler Hydraulic Data,* 1961 ed., "Automatic" Sprinkler Corporation of America (reprinted 1974).

Wood, Don J., "Calculation of Water Hammer Pressure Due to Valve Closure," *American Water Works Association Journal,* Vol. 60, No. 11, Nov. 1968, pp. 1301–1306.

FIRE ALARM SYSTEMS, DETECTION DEVICES, AND GUARD SERVICES

Chapter 1

PUBLIC FIRE SERVICE COMMUNICATIONS

Good communications are an essential element in the fire defenses of any community. They include means by which a citizen can notify a fire department that a fire or related emergency has occurred, as well as means of communication within the fire department and to related municipal activities. This chapter covers the municipal fire alarm system, the public telephone system which can be used to call the fire department, the fire department radio system, and the departmental telephone system, all of which are components of public fire service communications.

A. Municipal Fire Alarm Systems

A complete municipal fire alarm system fulfills two functions, that of receiving alarms from the public through fire alarm boxes located on the street or private property, and that of transmitting the alarm to the fire companies and personnel who should respond to the emergency.

Municipal fire alarm systems, electrically operated, can be classified by their method of operation as either telegraph-type, telephone-type, radio-type or a combination of the three. The installation, maintenance, and use of all municipal fire alarm systems, regardless of the principles of operation, are covered in detail in NFPA No. 73, Standard for Public Fire Service Communications, hereinafter referred to in this chapter as the NFPA Public Fire Service Communications Standard. This Standard makes no distinction between a telegraph-type, a telephone-type, or a radio-type alarm system as they must perform the same function of providing a means by which an alarm can be transmitted from a street fire alarm box to the communication center, and from the communication center to the fire companies that are to respond to the alarm. Telegraph-type, series telephone-type, and radio-type systems are normally owned by the municipality, while parallel telephone-type systems are normally leased from a public utility.

A municipal fire alarm system may be used for the transmission of other signals or calls of a public emergency nature, provided such transmission does not interfere with the proper handling of fire alarms. For example, systems employing voice communication between the street fire alarm box and communication center can be used in transmitting alarms of a nonfire emergency nature. Fire alarm boxes in a radio-type system can be provided with push buttons for calling the police department, the ambulance service, or other emergency services, and signals can be transmitted directly to the service called. In parallel telephone-type systems (each box served by a separate circuit), the fire alarm operator can cross-connect to the proper emergency service, such as the police department, or systems can be arranged so that authorized persons, such as policemen, will be connected directly with their own department. In a series telephone-type system (a number of boxes connected to the same circuit), cross-connecting to other emergency services is usually not practical, but can be done. Use of the telephone-type box for other than fire alarm purposes should not be extended so as to corrupt the intended emergency use by extensive calls of a nonemergency nature, such as routine calls to various municipal departments. It should be noted that the parallel telephone-type system may be adapted by proper switching arrangements so street

boxes also may be used as a police-signaling system without interfering with their proper use in a fire alarm system and without involving the fire alarm dispatcher. Various arrangements are available whereby voice communication facilities may be added to a telegraph-type fire alarm system and still insure the integrity of the telegraph features even during the use of voice facilities.

Type A and Type B Systems

The NFPA Public Fire Service Communications Standard separates municipal fire alarm systems into two types based on whether alarms received at the communication center are retransmitted manually (Type A) or automatically (Type B) to the fire companies. The Type B system is designed for communities not desiring a Type A system and having less than 2,500 box alarms a year, or where the number of alarms retransmitted over the dispatch circuits is less than 2,500 alarms per year. A Type B system may be used in conjunction with a Type A system as a satellite operating automatically to provide protection in a given area of a community. Either Type A or Type B systems may have satellites connected to the communication center. When the number of alarms from municipal fire alarm boxes to a Type B satellite exceeds 2,500 per year, the Type B satellite should be converted to a Type A satellite or be divided into two or more Type B satellites. Automatic operation of required Type A systems is permitted if facilities are provided for the automatic receipt, storage, retrieval, and retransmission of alarms in the order received, and override capability is provided to the operators so that manual retransmission and dispatch are instantly available. (See Figs. 12-1A and 12-1B.)

B. Fire Alarm Boxes and Box Circuits

Fire alarm boxes are the visible portions of a municipal fire alarm system and are usually the only parts most persons ever see. The box circuit is the wire or radio channel

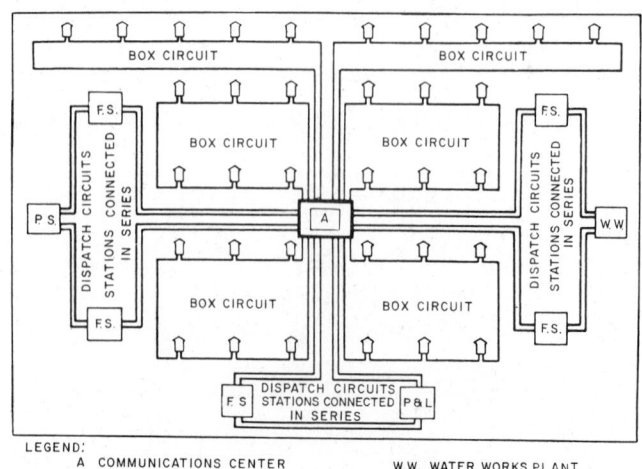

Fig. 12-1A. A schematic diagram of a Type A wired telegraph fire alarm system.

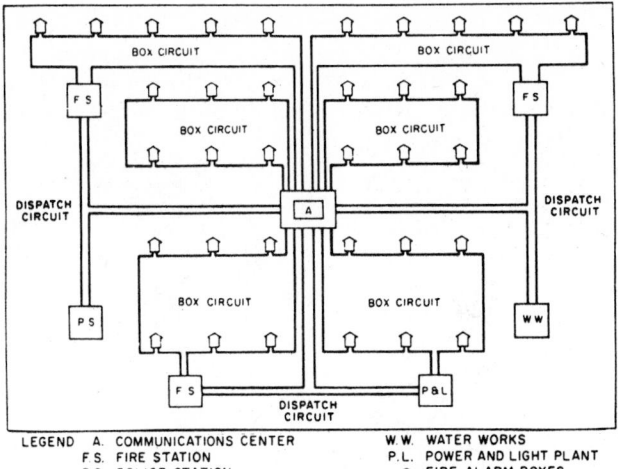

LEGEND A. COMMUNICATIONS CENTER   W.W. WATER WORKS
        F.S. FIRE STATION   P.L. POWER AND LIGHT PLANT
        P.S. POLICE STATION   ⬆ FIRE ALARM BOXES

Fig. 12-1B. A schematic diagram of a Type B wired telegraph fire alarm system.

over which an alarm is transmitted to an alarm communication center; it is the connection between the box and the communication center.

Telegraph-type

The wired telegraph-type fire alarm box was directly developed from the one invented by Dr. William F. Channing, a practicing physician in Boston, and Professor Moses G. Farmer, a professor of physics at the University of Maine, who developed the first municipal alarm system in 1847. The modern wired telegraph-type box is actuated by depressing a lever accessible through a small door. Depressing the lever starts a spring-wound clockwork mechanism which transmits a code number by the rotation of a code wheel causing the circuit to open and close. As the code number transmitted is different for each box, the location of the box transmitting the alarm is definitely known. Since coded wired alarm boxes are installed in series on the circuit, modern boxes are designed to transmit satisfactorily their codes even when up to four boxes are pulled at or about the same time. The first box pulled will transmit; the second box pulled will run but will not transmit (noninterference feature) over the box circuit until the first box is finished, at which time the second box will transmit its coded number (succession feature).

Modern boxes are often designed to transmit the coded signal through a ground connection when a circuit wire is broken. However, correspondingly modern communication center equipment is also necessary.

Older boxes of interfering design (i.e., code transmission will interfere with that from another box; two interfering boxes will result in a garbled signal) or of noninterfering, yet of the nonsuccession, design (i.e., will not transmit if another box is already operating), may result in no alarm being received from one or both of the boxes.

Wired telegraph-type boxes are installed in series on closed circuits which always carry a small current providing continuity supervision (i.e., a break in the wire will interrupt the current) as well as alarm indication (i.e., rhythmic interruption and restoration of the current by the box code wheel). Circuits should be laid out so that disruption of any one circuit will not remove box protection from more than a limited area in case of failure of a circuit. If a circuit utilizes aerial wire (sometimes called open wire) in whole or in part, the allowable area is that which would be protected by 20 properly spaced boxes. If the circuit is entirely in underground cable, or messenger-supported aerial cable, the allowable area is that which would be protected by 30 properly spaced boxes. If all boxes on a circuit and the associated communication center equipment are designed and installed to operate on an emergency ground-return basis, the allowable area may be doubled.

Telephone-type

The fire alarm box is essentially a telephone handset installed in a specially designed housing. (See Fig. 12-1D.)

Fig. 12-1C. A coded alarm box showing the actuating lever (arrow) that normally protrudes through the hole shown on the inner door at right. When depressed, the handle releases the springwound mechanism resulting in a coded signal from the code wheel shown at the center of the mechanism. (G. W. Gamewell Co.)

Fig. 12-1D. (Top left) A telephone-type fire alarm box. (Top right) A combination telegraph-telephone-type fire alarm box. Both doors are open (bottom left) to show the relative positions of the coding movement and telephone handset. (Bottom right) A telegraph-type fire alarm box.

Except in systems where a "concentrator identifier" is installed, each telephone handset is connected to a switchboard at the communication center. The location from which the alarm is transmitted is definitely established without dependence upon voice transmission and without interference from other boxes. Removing the handset from its cradle in the box causes a lamp to light on the switchboard and the number of the box to be visually recorded and the time printed. The circuit is supervised up to and including the handset.

There are two basic arrangements of telephone-type fire alarm systems, as follows:

Parallel: In this arrangement, each fire alarm box is served by an individual pair of wires. The circuits to telephone-type boxes are installed in the various cables of the telephone company; they are not segregated and should be distinctively identified at the points of attachment to the main frames in telephone central office buildings. Care must be exercised in the routing and installation of circuits to avoid conditions which may be accepted in a commercial telephone system, but which would be considered an unacceptable hazard to a fire alarm system. These include such conditions as circuits entering buildings not essential to fire alarm operation, attachment to buildings, particularly of combustible construction, and routing over roofs. While this type of system can be installed for ownership by a municipality, most have been leased from the local telephone company.

As each telephone-type box is on a separate circuit, the number of circuits terminating on the communication center switchboard becomes excessive in a large city. A combination of equipment known as a concentrator-identifier may be used to reduce the number of switchboard terminations needed for box circuits. Up to approximately 200 individual circuits from the street boxes can be terminated at concentrator equipment in a telephone building, from which up to 10 tie lines can extend to the alarm switchboard. In effect, the equipment concentrates the number of box circuits served by one switchboard termination in an approximate ratio of 40 to 1, with a minimum of two tie lines. The tie lines from concentrator equipment (and accompanying switchboard termination) do not serve any particular box, but are responsive only to the first 10 box alarms received. In addition, a holding arrangement stores up any additional calls until a tie line is free. While the concentrator process is going on, identifier equipment actuates both visual and recording equipment in the communication center identifying by number the boxes from which alarms are being received. Circuits from the concentrator to the boxes are under recurrent tests performed automatically every six minutes. Other box circuits and the tie lines between the concentrator and the alarm communication center switchboard are under continuous supervision.

Series: A circuit in a series system serves a number of boxes. The fire alarm box is essentially a telephone handset installed in a specially designed housing. Boxes which also contain a telegraph mechanism are called combination telephone-telegraph type, and both voice and coded signals can be transmitted to the communication center over the same circuit. (See Fig. 12-1D.) The series telephone-type box may also be intermixed with telegraph type street boxes and master boxes. Master boxes are connected to fire alarm systems installed in buildings.

Radio-type

The radio-type boxes may be powered by batteries or a prewound mechanism, or be "user-powered." Battery-

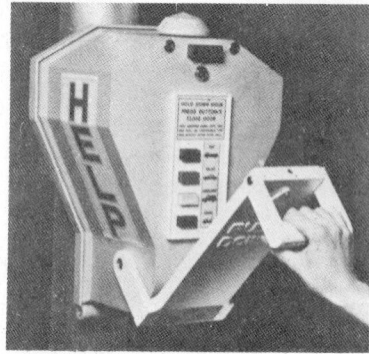

Fig. 12-1E. Radio-type fire alarm boxes. (Top left) Battery-powered box by G. W. Gamewell Co. (Top right) Battery-powered box by Eagle-Pitcher Industries, Inc. (Bottom) User-powered box by American District Telegraph Co.

powered boxes transmit supervisory or test signals every 24 hours, as well as a warning signal when battery power falls below a predetermined level. Batteries must be replaced periodically, but solar recharging is permitted. User-powered boxes contain a spring-wound alternator to provide power. The spring is wound when the operating handle is pulled down to uncover the push button or buttons. Radio-type boxes are interfering, but signal transmission is so fast that interference is less probable. Most boxes are designed with random spacing between the required three rounds of signals. When boxes having random spacing are operated at the same time, at least one correct round of the signal will be received from each box. Some battery-powered boxes have an electronic "memory," equivalent to the succession feature of modern telegraph-type boxes. Devices may be added to the box that would indicate to persons using it whether or not the signal had been received at the communication center. While present radio-type fire alarm boxes transmit coded signals, transmission of voice signals can be expected in the near future. (See Fig. 12-1E.)

C.　Distribution and Location of Boxes

The same principles of distribution and location of fire alarm boxes apply to all types. There should be a sufficient number of boxes so located as to protect all built-up areas of a municipality.

Distances Between Boxes

To provide proper distribution and protection to the community, a fire alarm box should be visible from the main entrance of any building in congested districts, and the travel distance to reach a fire alarm box should not be greater than one block or 500 ft in mercantile or manufacturing districts. In residential areas, the travel distance should not be greater than two blocks or 800 ft. There should be a fire alarm box at or near the entrance to every school, hospital, nursing home, and place of public assembly. A fire alarm box should be installed near the entrance to all fire stations since many persons are more aware of the location of the nearest fire station than of the nearest fire alarm box. Persons have often gone to the fire station to find the fire company away from the station on another alarm with no readily available means of transmitting an alarm to the communication center.

Boxes Inside Buildings

It is an undesirable practice to install fire alarm boxes inside buildings because of the lack of accessibility to the general public, and the potential hazard of mechanical damage to the circuits extended into the building. If boxes must be installed inside buildings, they should be located as near as possible to the point of entrance of the circuits, and the wiring should be protected against damage.

Identification Markings

The successful use of the fire alarm system by the general public depends more upon having an adequate number of properly placed, easily identified fire alarm boxes than on any other factor.

Fire alarm boxes, regardless of their location, should be readily visible. The visibility of a box depends upon various factors such as the color, the mounting, and the surroundings. Fire alarm boxes may be mounted on distinctive standards, or on utility poles. The boxes and the standards should be painted a distinctive color. When mounted on utility poles, the visibility of boxes may be further increased by painting a wide band of distinctive color around the pole. Such bands should extend sufficiently above the box itself in order to be visible over the tops of parked cars. Signs made of reflective paint or decals for the sides of a fire alarm box bearing the word "FIRE" enhance visibility. Fire alarm boxes should be located close to the curb line at street intersections, thus offering the greatest visibility from several directions.

Lights at Boxes: As the consequences of a delayed alarm can be much more serious at night and fire alarm boxes are less easily distinguished, it is important that all boxes in mercantile and manufacturing areas be made more visible by mounting, either on the box support or in the very close vicinity, a light of a distinctive color which can be plainly seen for at least 1,500 feet in all directions.

D.   Communication Center

A communication center is the location at which alarms are received and from which appropriate signals are transmitted to the fire department to initiate response of apparatus and personnel. The communication center houses the equipment and personnel to perform these two functions.

A communication center may serve a single municipality, several adjacent municipalities, an entire county, or other large political jurisdiction. The combining of municipal police and fire communications into one communication center is becoming more common.

Location of Communication Center

The communication center should be located, constructed, and laid out so the probability of interruption to operations due to fire or other causes will be minimized. A building in a park or other open space is most desirable; if so located, it can often be designed to be in harmony with the surroundings. When a separate building is not feasible and the communication center must be housed elsewhere, such as in city hall or in a fire station, then the center should be properly separated from the remainder of the building, preferably with entrance only from the outside. Protection should be provided against fire exposures and unauthorized entry. The Monroe County, N.Y., Communication Center is shown in Figure 12-1F.

Even the smallest fire department must have some means of receiving notice of a fire. In small communities, the communication center may consist of a telephone in a private residence(s) or business establishment(s) where someone is always available and where there is a switch to sound a siren or other device to call volunteers. Quite frequently, the police station serves as the communication center. As fire departments become larger, a room is often provided to house the fire alarm dispatcher and alarm facilities in a fire station.

Equipment for Receipt of Alarms

The performance requirements for facilities for receipt of box alarms at the communication center, as set forth in the NFPA Public Fire Service Communications Standard, may be met by a variety of methods and equipment. In general:

1. The alarm from the box should be automatically received and recorded.

2. The receipt of the alarm should be indicated both visually and audibly, and the visual means should indicate the exact location of the origin of the alarm.

3. The time of receipt and the exact location of the alarm should be automatically recorded.

A typical sequence of events in a communication center having a Type A (manual) telegraph-type alarm system may be similar to the description in the following paragraph.

A recording device receives the coded signal from a box

Fig. 12-1F. Communication center equipped with a status board (top center); controls for the status board to the left and right of the board; and radio controls near the base of the board. At lower left are city telegraph system recorders. A status board is a visual indication of the location of the various stations and the equipment housed in each station. Indicating lights at each location show the current disposition of apparatus, e.g., in service by radio, out of service, covering service, etc. Shown is the Monroe County, N.Y., Communication Center.

circuit and automatically punctures or prints on a tape the code received. It also automatically stamps the time of receipt of the alarm on the tape. A dispatcher reads the tape and removes a running card bearing the same code number from a file. This card cites the exact location of the alarm box and other pertinent information as to the location and the fire companies that should respond. The dispatcher then transmits the alarm to the fire companies that are to respond.

In a telephone-type system, when the handset is lifted from its cradle in the alarm box, a buzzer sounds, a light appears, and the box number and the time of alarm are printed on a tape at the communication center. A dispatcher answers the call (all voice transmissions should be recorded), obtains pertinent information, and then, knowing the number of the box, refers to the running card with the same number. The dispatcher then transmits the alarm to the fire companies that are to respond.

A typical base station for a radio-type system consists, essentially, of duplicate receivers and decoders, a printer, and audible warning devices. The dispatcher refers to the running card corresponding to the number of the fire alarm box, and then transmits the alarm to the fire companies that are to respond.

In a Type B (automatic) telegraph-type alarm system, box alarms are transmitted automatically to fire stations as well as to the communication center. Radio-type alarm systems can be arranged to transmit in a similar manner.

The communication center should also have facilities for receiving telephone calls for fires and related emergencies. Such calls should be automatically recorded.

Supervision and Testing Facilities

The communication center is also the location where trouble signals are received and testing facilities are generally provided. In a leased telephone-type system some test facilities are located in telephone buildings. In the event of trouble, both an audible and a visual signal should be provided. If the audible signal operates due to trouble in a circuit, it may be shut off; but it should be so arranged that it will operate in the event of trouble in any of the other circuits connected to the same supervisory device.

Power Supplies

Since municipal fire alarm systems must be in operating condition at all times, it is essential that box and dispatch circuits and related facilities have two power sources. These sources may be the public utility service, generators, batteries (storage type), and combinations of these. For example, the primary source may be from the line side of the main service of a commercial light or power circuit, and the secondary source from batteries or a generator driven by a continuously available prime mover. The secondary source should cut in automatically in the event of failure of the primary source. It should be kept in mind that wherever local power is used for facilities that are necessary for proper operation of the system, such as at fire stations, a secondary source should be provided.

Personnel

No matter how well designed, installed, and maintained, no system is any better than those who operate it. Therefore, proper personnel should be assigned to communication center duty. Systems should be supervised by responsible and competent persons whose duties include directing proper test and inspection programs. Fire alarm dispatchers should

have good health, should be free from disabling physical and mental defects that would affect their ability to efficiently handle the duties assigned, and should be temperamentally suited to the position. They should have the ability to remain calm and take decisive action during emergencies, to remain alert during periods of inactivity and when carrying out normal repetitive operations, to work harmoniously with other persons, and they should be familiar with general fire department operations.

E. Dispatch Circuits and Equipment

A dispatch circuit is the means used by the fire alarm dispatcher to notify fire companies to respond to an alarm. It must permit transmission of information on at least the location from which the alarm was received.

Facilities for Transmission of Alarms

The NFPA Public Fire Service Communications Standard has requirements which briefly state:

1. Two separate means should be provided at the communication center for transmitting alarms to fire stations, except that only one means is required when less than 600 alarms per year are received.

2. Each alarm transmitted and the date and time should be automatically recorded.

3. Devices for transmitting coded signals should be so arranged that they may be set manually and then operated automatically. The automatic dispatching of fire companies by the use of computers is under development.

4. Devices for recording all voice transmissions of an emergency nature should be provided.

5. Two dispatch circuits, including one supervised circuit, should extend to instruments in fire stations (except as permitted in the preceding No. 1) when only the supervised circuit need be provided.

6. A sounding device should be connected to each of the dispatch circuits in fire stations. When a coded signal is transmitted, the supervised circuit should also be connected to a device providing a permanent visual record.

Dispatch Circuits

Dispatch circuits are of various types, as follows:

Telegraph Circuits: These dispatch circuits are wired circuits, arranged for the transmitting and receiving of coded alarm signals. Signals are received at fire stations on a variety of instruments including large gongs, small bells or tappers, and punch or printing registers indicating the coded signal by holes in or marks on a tape. In a Type B fire alarm system of the telegraph type, box circuits may be used as an alarm circuit. This involves the installation of alarm receiving instruments in fire stations connected to box circuits; at the communication center, it involves installation of automatic repeating facilities which transmit an alarm received on one box circuit to fire stations having alarm receiving instruments connected to other box circuits.

Teletype Circuits: Another form of dispatch circuit is the teletypewriter circuit (either wired or microwave), whereby a fire alarm dispatcher transmits information on the alarm to the various fire stations by means of a teletypewriter. The alarms are received at the fire stations on the teletypewriter equipment which reproduces the typed information on a roll of paper. Teletypewriter facilities may be purchased, but are normally leased from a telephone company. They have the advantage that more information, if available, can be transmitted to the fire station, but have the disadvantage that their circuitry is more complex and more difficult to supervise. In addition, both normal and emergency sources of power must be provided at the stations where the alarm receiving equipment is located, as well as at the point of transmission.

Facsimile Circuits: Wired circuits using the telewriter, a device formerly in common usage by hotels and railroads, is still another form of dispatch circuit. The alarm dispatcher writes out dispatching instructions with a stylus on pressure sensitive paper tape, and the instructions are reproduced at the fire stations on a roll of paper tape. This type circuit can be supervised. Two sources of power must be provided at fire stations.

Another device in use is the teleprinter which reproduces written information, including drawings. Receiving units are generally installed in fire stations. When radio is used as a dispatch circuit, receivers may also be installed in fire department vehicles.

Voice Amplification Circuits: Voice amplification dispatch circuits are wired circuits. As the name implies, this is an arrangement whereby the fire alarm dispatcher talks into a microphone at the communication center and the information is amplified and received on loudspeakers located in the fire stations. This type of circuit can be supervised, and two sources of power must be provided at fire stations.

Radio Channel: A radio channel is another form of dispatch circuit for the transmission of signals. Transmitting equipment is located at the communication center and receivers at each fire station. In addition, transmitter-receivers on fire apparatus provide for communication with companies away from their stations. Dual base transmitters are considered to meet the intent of supervision, where such is required. A radio system has the advantage of not being connected to or dependent upon wires, unless the transmitter is located at a remote point from the fire alarm dispatcher, in which case the lines connecting the base transmitter with the remote control unit should be supervised. Two sources of power should be provided for the transmitter and at fire stations. Radio facilities are flexible and can be arranged for the selective calling of companies, individually or by groups.

Telephone Alerting Systems: Various arrangements of telephone alerting systems are available from telephone companies. Telephone systems are flexible and can be zoned as to persons being called. The advantage of these systems is that the general public is not alerted. However, many telephones must be involved in such systems, and volunteer fire fighters may not be available to receive calls.

Other Alerting Facilities: Many communities have organized fire departments where there is no one on duty at a fire station to receive an alarm, the fire companies being manned entirely by volunteer fire fighters. In these instances bells, air horns, whistles, or sirens are commonly used to alert the volunteers when an alarm has been received. A satisfactory arrangement is the sounding of coded signals which give the volunteer fire fighter a definite code for the location of the fire. The coding of siren signals is usually not satisfactory.

Radio receivers in volunteer fire fighters' residences or places of business and pages (portable receivers carried on the person) are frequently used for receiving alarms, either in addition to or in place of the previously mentioned outside alerting devices. Some receivers are normally muted and are activated by a special preliminary signal only for the receipt of emergency messages.

F. Commercial Telephone Facilities

The public telephone system, widely used for reporting fires, performs a very valuable function. Telephones are often the only means of communication readily available in outlying suburban and rural areas. The installation of outdoor telephone booths increases their availability for use in reporting fires.

Accessibility of Public Telephones

Telephones, however, are not always accessible for reporting fires. In business districts of cities where stores and offices are closed at night, on Sundays, and holidays, and in resort communities where most buildings are closed in off seasons, telephones might not be accessible. A coin-operated telephone, regardless of location, is also not "accessible" to a person lacking the proper coin necessary to contact the telephone operator, although in a few cities the telephone operator can be reached from coin operated telephones without the use of a coin. A public fire alarm system provides the fire department and the community with a dependable communication facility when telephone circuits may be "swamped" during an extreme emergency or when the public telephone system may be inoperative because of strikes or storm conditions.

From the standpoint of the dispatcher responsible for receiving the alarm, the use of a municipal fire alarm box eliminates the difficulty in determining the location from which the alarm is being transmitted. However, when a person transmitting the alarm by telephone is excited or speaks a foreign language, it is essential that recording facilities be provided at the communication center so that such alarms can be played back in the event that the person should hang up before the dispatcher has gathered all the pertinent information.

Telephoning the alarm may appear to be the quickest method of getting a call to the fire department, but where there is a municipal fire alarm system it is always prudent to send another person, if available, to sound the alarm from a street fire alarm box. It is important to realize that telephone service, unlike a municipal fire alarm system which has only one specific use, cannot be preempted for emergency calls when circuits are busy. If a telephone is out of order, the person trying to use it may not discover this fact immediately, and a delay may ensue. There have been many instances of a fire having destroyed the telephone circuit to the telephone instrument, thereby preventing the telephone from being used to transmit an alarm.

In some areas, the telephone directory states that the operator should be dialed or called whenever it is desired to transmit an alarm of fire to the fire department. Certainly, if the telephone number of the fire department is not known or if it is dark and no light is available to see the dial, the operator should be called rather than delay the transmission of the alarm. It is absolutely essential to give the correct address and name of the community in which the fire is occurring since one telephone central office building may serve many different communities, some of them quite distant from each other, and, quite often having the same or similar street names. Being able to dial directly from one community to another poses the danger of giving the information to the wrong department. There have been instances where the wrong fire department received the alarm or was sent to an address where there was no fire while a building was burning at the same street address in an adjacent community. A telephone company operator cannot be expected to be familiar with local conditions, such as duplicate street names or the arrangement of fire department service. For this reason, local fire department numbers should be posted on telephones and fire departments should, whenever possible, be called by their specific telephone number. In addition, that number should be listed in the telephone directory under "Fire Department" as well as under emergency numbers in the front of the directory and under the name of the community.

The nationwide emergency telephone number 9-1-1, sponsored by the Federal Government, has been placed in use by numerous municipalities, both large and small. A 3-digit number is easier to remember than a 7-digit number which also is different for each fire department. A serious disadvantage is that, with few exceptions, telephone company service boundaries do not coincide with municipal boundaries, thereby resulting in some of the 9-1-1 calls being received by the communication center in another municipality. It is important that operators who receive 9-1-1 alarms of fire be able to dispatch fire companies immediately. The transferring of such calls to other persons for handling, say from a police dispatcher to a fire alarm dispatcher, results in a delay and the possibility of losing the alarm.

The public telephone system should be connected to the communication center, preferably through a switchboard where there are facilities for receiving more than one call at a time. A public telephone may be installed in fire stations for the convenience of the fire fighters working in the station,

but such telephones should never be listed in the telephone directory as a person may try to call a specific fire company rather than the fire department dispatcher only to find that there is no answer because the company is not in the station at the time the call is placed. The trunk lines connecting the telephone switchboard to the public telephone system should be so arranged that at least one trunk (preferably more) are reserved for the transmission of emergency signals, and other trunks are to be used for the transaction of departmental business. Provisions should be made that, when the emergency number is dialed, there is automatic selection of reserve lines first, then progression to the general business lines when more emergency calls are being received than there are emergency trunk lines.

It should be noted that the telephone companies have available various special devices designed to simplify and assist in the operation of receiving calls in outlying areas and notifying the fire department. These include special designs of telephone instruments to be used in multiple as well as special switching arrangements. The local telephone utility should be contacted for information on these devices and their use in specific locations.

Bibliography

NFPA Codes, Standards, and Recommended Practices (see the latest *NFPA Publications and Visual Aids Catalog* for availability of current editions of the following document)

NFPA No. 73, Standard for Public Fire Service Communications.

Chapter 2

AUTOMATIC AND MANUAL PROTECTIVE SIGNALING SYSTEMS

Protective signaling systems installed for fire protection purposes involve automatic and manual systems, and systems for the supervision and actuation of fire extinguishing systems.

Signaling systems for fire prevention involve the supervision of industrial processes. This chapter discusses the principles of protective signaling, functions and classification of protective signaling systems, and sprinkler systems as fire detection systems.

A. Principles of Protective Signaling

Protective signaling, as an art, has a history of at least one hundred years in the United States. During that time there have developed certain principles which are the basis for, and find expression in, the established standards for the industry. However, because of their importance, they warrant more explicit expression.

Electrical Power Supplies

Experience has demonstrated quite conclusively the prime importance of power supplies of the first quality and with a high reputation for reliability. Distinction is made between primary supplies and secondary supplies. The primary supply furnishes power for transmission and reception or sounding of the alarm or supervisory signal. The secondary supply either provides energy to the system for fire alarm signaling in the event of failure of the main supply or provides for trouble signals and other functions which are not essential for alarm transmission, but which are associated with the reliability of the system or can provide both emergency signaling as well as trouble signals.

The selection of a primary power source stresses the importance of continual reliability under most of the conditions which are likely to be encountered in the property. In recent years, commercial light and power have been found sufficiently reliable, in most areas, to permit their use for primary system powering, provided they are used simultaneously to keep fully charged storage batteries which are automatically thrown into service when the commercial power fails. Such batteries are expected to have the capacity to operate the system for at least 60 hours. Other arrangements acceptable under NFPA Standards will be found by reference to the Standards themselves. Several of them have utility only where an attendant is continuously available for their employment and supervision.

A number of acceptable secondary supplies are suggested by the NFPA Standards, including a second phase of commercial power the first phase of which is used to supply the primary source. Under certain conditions, dry-cell batteries are acceptable.

Complete and Partial Systems

The established standards and the experience of most reputable operators in the field argue that there must be complete coverage by a signaling system in order to obtain maximum protection. Scanting on detector spacings, coverage of only selected areas in a plant, or a combination of such expense savers not only detract from the value of the system and make its nonoperability in an emergency entirely possible, but create a false sense of security which is likely to be a positive danger to the property involved.

Supervision of Signaling Systems

Distinction is necessary between supervision—the evidence that elements of a system are operable—and operability of system elements despite the presence of one or more faults. The following principles are generally recognized:

1. The occurrence of a simple outage in a system power supply (an open circuit or a grounded circuit of the wiring, or similarly noncomplex troubles) should not initiate an alarm of fire. It is expected, however, that such occurrence will signal itself distinctively, in such manner, and at such place, that correction of the trouble will be prompted.

2. A system which is self-correcting at the time it signals the occurrence of a simple fault of the kind described above is preferable to one which merely signals the presence of the fault and is then inoperative until the fault is corrected.

3. System layouts must be styled to the environment of the protected property and to the availability of outside assistance. Alarms should be sounded, of course, wherever they are needed, and should, as a matter of course, be omitted where they are not needed. Similar consideration should be given to the location and type of trouble signals provided, recognizing that in some instances the failure to attend to the situation which a trouble signal evidences means a complete loss of the protection which the system is intended to provide.

Testing and Maintenance Procedures

The protective signaling system that requires no maintenance is still to be developed. Just a bit closer to realization is the system which the user can maintain himself. But until these systems are developed and commercially available, the user should make sure that the system he selects is installed, regularly inspected, and periodically tested by an agency whose major activity is installing and servicing the type of equipment selected. Of equal importance should be the guarantee he receives that when trouble occurs, whether a fault in the system or following an alarm, the equipment will be restored quickly to full operating condition. The availability of replacement parts is important and a knowledge of the conditions of operation is best available from the manufacturer of the equipment, operating through local agents who have a responsibility both to the manufacturer and the user.

Signaling System Standards

Standards for the six types of generally recognized protective signaling systems described in Part C of this Chapter have been established by the National Fire Protection Association, and are as follows:

Central Station Systems: NFPA No. 71, Standard for Central Station Signaling Systems.

Local Systems: NFPA No. 72A, Standard for Local Protective Signaling Systems.

Auxiliary Systems: NFPA No. 72B, Standard for Auxiliary Protective Signaling Systems.

Remote Station Systems: NFPA No. 72C, Standard for Remote Station Protective Signaling Systems.

Proprietary Systems: NFPA No. 72D, Standard for Proprietary Protective Signaling Systems.

Household Fire Warning Systems: NFPA No. 74, Standard for Household Fire Warning Systems.

Basic minimum requirements for performance of automatic fire detectors are contained in NFPA No. 72E, Standard on Automatic Fire Detectors. Specific requirements for simple, local alarm units for use with automatic sprinkler systems are contained in NFPA No. 13, Standard for the Installation of Sprinkler Systems. NFPA No. 101, Life Safety Code, suggests provisions for alarm and fire detection systems having particular application to the hazard of life. Fire detectors and the components of fire detection systems should be tested and listed by nationally recognized testing laboratories.

B. Functions of Protective Signaling Systems

Protective signaling systems, in fire protection practice can be used to:

1. Notify occupants so they can evacuate the area when there is a fire.
2. Summon organized assistance to undertake, or assist in, fighting the fire.
3. Supervise extinguishing systems to assure their operability when needed.
4. Supervise industrial processes to warn of abnormalities that may contribute to the fire hazard.
5. Supervise personnel to assure performance of assigned duties.
6. Actuate fire control equipment.

The first two functions are thought of as pertaining to alarm systems; the next three are considered objects of supervisory systems; the last is inclusive of many fire control functions. Quite often an alarm system may be combined with a supervisory system to utilize equipment common to both.

Notification for Evacuation

Evacuation alarms range from simple electrically operated bells to intricate devices which not infrequently appear in electrical systems intended to warn occupants of large hotels, institutions, or multi-occupancy office buildings. Certain basic principles common to all systems are recognized as follows:

1. Local protective signaling systems are permitted to allow voice paging, musical programs, and coded alarm signals on common wiring. The alarm signal must be distinctive so that it cannot be confused with other signals produced in the same area. This possibility of confusion is the reason for requiring fire alarm signals to be distinctive in tone and that this tone be used for no other purpose. Also supervisory signals must be distinctive in their tone and this tone also must not be used for any other purpose.

It is equally important that the type of signal be suitable to the circumstances in which it is used. Audible signals, for example, cannot warn the deaf, nor can visual signals effectively warn the blind. A further consideration is whether or not occupants can respond immediately to alarm warnings. For example, in jails and many other institutions where occupants cannot take advantage of the warning, alarms may induce panic and make more difficult the task of attendants who are responsible for effective handling of the emergency. Where such a responsibility is confined to selected personnel only, it is important that they alone receive the warning.

2. The alarm must be heard or seen by all occupants for whom the warning is intended. If general alarm signals are to be sounded in a noisy machine shop, for example, their level of sound intensity must be sufficiently high to override the noise of the machines and to reach all occupants whose attention is desired. This consideration will frequently involve careful planning of alarm outlet locations and may dictate the use of special signals in some or all locations.

Developments are underway to establish a standardized fire warning signal to be utilized nationally. Once this signal is established, a public education program will be needed to implement it.

3. The system must be arranged so that it can be tested periodically. Such tests are best conducted in connection with evacuation drills, and the alarms sounded in the tests should be the same as those produced under anticipated emergency conditions.

4. Equipment should be designed and installed so that malicious operation or malicious interference with operation (tampering) would be, at least, difficult. In general, the operation of a noncoding station should establish evidence that the station has been operated.

5. Consideration must be given to the probable reaction of people in protected premises when deciding whether or not a general (public) alarm shall be given, or whether or not the alarm produced will be recognized only by selected personnel who can prompt and monitor the evacuation.

Summoning Organized Assistance

While an important purpose of alarm systems is to signal the need for evacuation, they are used even more frequently to call the fire department or other organized assistance. It is faulty planning to provide for evacuation without simultaneously furnishing means by which assistance can be called, and vice versa. Dependence on local signals to alert an employee whose duty it is to summon the fire department very often fails because that employee misjudges the extent of the fire and overestimates his ability to deal with the situation. In auxiliary and remote station types of systems, the fire department is called automatically.

There are two basic principles involved in setting up a notification system for calling outside assistance:

1. The alarm signal should be transmitted to the fire department or assistance agency as promptly as possible. Although many reasons have been advanced for delaying the initial alarm, or withholding its transmission until the cause has been "investigated" locally, authorities agree on and statistics show quite clearly the danger of such delays. Then too, fire department personnel resent such practice not only because of the greater possibility of loss of life and property, but because their work in extinguishing a fire is materially increased. Some cities make it illegal, by ordinance, to withhold the transmission of an alarm to the fire department, the individual being subject to prosecution.

2. The signal received at the fire department or assistance agency should locate specifically the site of the fire, or, as a minimum, localize the source of the signal as to building or area so that the fire is found quickly. In general, an alarm reaching a municipal department directly from protected premises will produce a coded signal agreeing with the department's assignment number for the building, or a noncoded signal coupled with a visual identification of the protected premises so that a minimum of translation is required to identify it. Where an alarm, such as a coded signal, is relayed through a central station or a proprietary central station, the transmission is usually further authenticated by telephone from the central station to the department. Deviation from this principle is permissible, as a rule, only where there is no outside agency to call on for assistance. In such cases dependence is usually placed upon a

brigade recruited from plant employees who are customarily engaged in other work. In the latter case it is not unusual to sound the evacuation alarm as a coded signal so that when it is sounded most of the employees are alerted to leave the premises, while those engaged in brigade service are cued by the code to go to the point of fire and there assume their brigade duties.

Supervision of Extinguishing Systems

Supervision of fire extinguishing systems, such as automatic sprinkler systems, carbon dioxide systems, etc., is a common application of protective signaling systems. Supervision implies that something can and will be done about an abnormality which the system signals. Such supervision assures that the system is continuously operable, in all essential respects, and that it can perform its intended function. The signaling system warns when such operability is lost or impaired, and announces when it is restored to normal. Since any physical state—position, pressure, volume, level, temperature, etc.—which can be measured or which is subject to change can initiate a signal, a wide variety of supervisory functions is possible in more complex systems. In general, the following principles are of importance:

1. Supervision can be applied to make evident (by nonoperation) the presence of the extinguishment agent in sufficient quantity and in a usable state, so that it can be used without being restricted or misdirected by closed valves or open valves which should be closed.

2. The devices or appliances used for supervision should, for the sake of dependability, measure only a single variable and should not be counted upon individually to perform a double function as, for example, the simultaneous signaling of a change in temperature and a change in pressure. They should be simple, rugged, and not subject to easy maladjustment or adjustment outside their limits of operability.

3. Device settings should be such that the supervisory signal is transmitted when the defect occurs. There is no value beyond the historic in knowing at the time a fire starts that the water supply is cut off by a closed valve, or to receive a low temperature signal from a supply tank only when the water has started to freeze.

4. Supervision should not be applied to monitor conditions which normally show frequent variations. Where such conditions exist they should be designed out of the extinguishment system since supervision of them merely destroys the value of the supervision through too much repetition of signals.

Typical of the elements supervised in connection with automatic sprinkler systems are air pressure in dry-pipe systems and pressure tanks, water levels and temperatures in tanks and reservoirs, valves controlling the operation of a system and the water supply for it, power to pumps necessary for the operation of the system, and in some instances supervision of the actual operation of pumps. In addition, special elements requiring supervision are frequently encountered as, for example, the supervision against leakage in pipes supplying the sprinkler system.

Supervision of Processes

A manufacturing process is supervised to assure that if interruption does occur, or if it approaches a hazardous condition, notification will be given so that corrective action can be taken. Supervision may also be extended to conditions in a plant, such as temperature and humidity, to assure their remaining reasonably constant. The same principles which apply to the supervision of extinguishing systems apply in these applications, of which the following are

typical: supervision of heating systems involving as a rule the supervision of room temperature, but extending to supply sources, pressures, flame failure, and the passage of the system to an unsafe condition in the case of failure of one or more elements; supervision of flow continuity; supervision of air conditioning systems; supervision of transformer temperatures and pressures; and supervision of electrical network characteristics.

Supervision of Personnel

The supervision of personnel in fire protection practice is concerned chiefly with the monitoring of guards, or fixed point supervisory personnel, charged with observing and maintaining the safe condition of the plant. Because such safety implies freedom from fire, guard service supervision is generally associated with a manual method for summoning organized extinguishment assistance. Thus, guard service report stations are often combined with manual fire alarm stations, or are located close to them. The principles and common methods of patrol supervision are discussed in Chapter 5 of this Section.

C. Classification of Protective Signaling Systems

Manual Systems

Manual systems employ the familiar fire alarm boxes which, for noncoded operation, may be simple electric switches. For coded operation, they contain mechanically or electrically driven motors which turn a code wheel to open and close successively an electric circuit. Noncoded types are usually constructed in such a manner that alarms cannot be caused accidentally, and so that operation leaves an indication that the device has been operated. It is customary to mark the station plainly to show its function, and where false alarms are quite probable, to require the destruction of a glass plate or rod to obtain access to the operating lever or to release the switch.

Automatic Systems

Automatic systems can employ any of the following types of detecting elements:

Heat Detectors: Sensitivity to abnormally high temperature, rate-of-temperature rise, and rate compensation.

Smoke Detectors: Sensitivity to visible or invisible particles of combustion.

Flame Detectors: Sensitivity to the infrared, ultraviolet, or visible radiation produced by a fire.

More detailed information on detection devices appears in Chapter 3 of this Section.

Properly included as automatic systems would be waterflow alarm systems, since they also provide automatic fire detection and an alarm signal.

Beyond the elementary classification of systems by method of operation (manual or automatic), systems are classified according to the location where the signal registers. The six classifications generally recognized are: (1) central station systems, (2) local systems, (3) auxiliary systems, (4) remote station systems, (5) proprietary systems, and (6) household fire warning systems.

Central Station System

In this system signals register in the office of an independent agency, usually located at a distance from the protected property. The agency has trained and experienced personnel continually on duty to receive signals, retransmit fire alarms to the fire department, and to take whatever action supervisory signals indicate is necessary.

Central station systems customarily serve a number of properties of different ownership, and are usually operated under contract by an agency which has no direct monetary interest in the protected properties. The ordinary central station furnishes service within a limited geographical area (about 200 square miles), is located centrally within that area, and is connected to the plants of its various subscribers by wire facilities which are usually leased telephone lines. To reduce expense, it is customary to connect the plants of several subscribers to a single transmission circuit; each such circuit terminates in a recording instrument, and each subscriber is distinguished by one or more coded signal numbers which are not otherwise repeated on that particular circuit. Limitations as to circuit loadings are prescribed in NFPA No. 71, Standard for Central Station Signaling Systems.

As a rule, direct transmission equipment is provided between the central station and the one or more fire departments serving the area, so that an alarm signal, upon receipt and following verification, may be transmitted to the appropriate fire department. This mechanical transmission is confirmed by voice over private tie lines between the central station and the fire department.

Supervisory signals are generally transmitted on individual supervisory circuits, or if placed on alarm circuits, take second place to the alarm transmission. Supervisory signals are handled by the central station operators directly with representatives of the subscriber or through the medium of its own runner service. Most central stations furnish, in addition to fire alarm and supervisory service, burglar alarm and holdup alarm service, either on a coded or noncoded basis.

Each central station is expected to time the receipt of signals, to record its routine operations, and to report details of special occurrences to its subscribers, and others who are interested. Such records are retained for reasonable lengths of time, according to their importance, and frequently are of value in placing an emergency occurrence in proper perspective.

There are systems in which signals are electronically transmitted over a signaling line. To transmit many different signals over a signaling line simultaneously or in an apparently simultaneous fashion, multiplexing principles are employed. The NFPA Central Station Signaling Systems Standard has devoted a complete chapter to "Multiplex

Alarm Systems". The requirements contained therein recognize the high speed in which different signals can be received and recorded. For this reason, those requirements are far more stringent than the requirements for conventional central station systems.

The advantage of a central station system is that its service is given on a commonly recognized standard basis in accordance with established rules and customs. (See Fig. 12-2A for a diagram of a typical central station system.)

Local System

In this system the alarm or supervisory signal registers in the protected premises. A local system is primarily for the notification of occupants.

From the relatively uncomplicated arrangement of gongs and bells on sprinkler systems have developed local signaling systems which embody a number of more sophisticated techniques directed to assure operability of equipment and to initiate alarm devices.

A first essential of a satisfactory local system is a reliable power supply, which should be one of the following: (1) a dependable commercial power service, (2) an engine-driven generator (where an operator is on duty at all times), (3) storage batteries, or (4) a rectifier.

In practice, the customary arrangement is the commercial light and power service. Conductors for the signaling system should be connected on the line side of the main service (if the supply is commercial) or to the main bus bars (if the supply is from an isolated power plant located on the premises). Circuit disconnecting means accessible only to authorized personnel, and devices for fusing each underground conductor should be provided.

The second essential of a satisfactory local system is the employment of wiring materials and methods suitable for the purpose. The requirements for protective signaling systems contained in NFPA No. 70, National Electrical Code, are applicable.

The third essential of a satisfactory local system is that the equipment shall signal distinctively the presence of trouble, such as a broken or grounded circuit or the failure of a main power source, where such trouble prevents the intended operation of the system. The extent to which a system must operate even in the presence of trouble is set forth in NFPA No. 72A, Standard for Local Protective Signaling Systems. Distinction is made between critical and noncritical circuits. It may be stated generally, however, that the system is expected to operate over troubles commonly encountered, or to signal its inability to operate where such inability exists. Trouble signals for this purpose are distinctive from alarm or supervisory signals and, as a rule, cannot be easily disabled or made inoperative.

Where panic resulting from a public alarm is anticipated, a presignal type of system can be employed which, at the first initiation of an alarm, operates a selected number of signals located where they will not be heard by all the occupants of the property, but will alert selected personnel whose responsibility will then be to sound a general alarm.

A variation from the standard method of operation is the so-called "common code" system in which a limited number of rounds (repetitions) of a location code is sounded following which all signals operate continuously, without coding, to alert occupants who have not heard or recognized the initial code.

In practice, local system alarm signals are of the coded or continuous vibrating sound type. The coded types may be of the selective code type indicating the exact station, area, or zone from which the alarm has been transmitted.

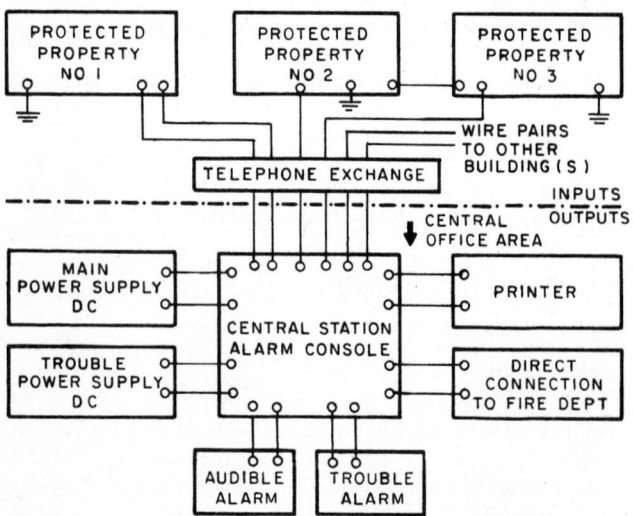

Fig. 12-2A. Diagram of typical central station system.

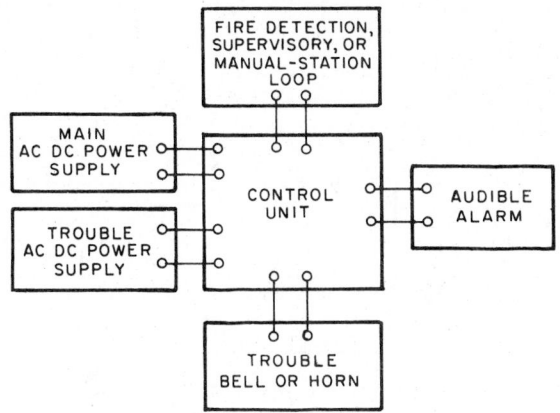

Fig. 12-2B. *Diagram of typical local system.*

Coded alarm signals may also come from a "master" code panel in which one common code is used for all stations. (See Fig. 12-2B for a diagram of a typical local system.)

Auxiliary System

In this system signals are recorded at a municipal fire department. The connecting facilities between the protected property and the fire department are part of the municipal fire alarm system. The devices in the protected plant are customarily owned and maintained by the property owner. Other equipment, including the means of connecting the devices to the city's circuits, are owned and maintained by the municipality or leased by the municipality as part of the municipal alarm system. Auxiliary systems are limited to alarm service only. (See Fig. 12-2C for a diagram of a typical auxiliary [local energy] system.)

There are three types of auxiliary systems in use: (1) local energy type; (2) shunt type; and (3) direct circuit type. The local energy and the shunt type auxiliary systems make use of the receiving equipment and the interconnecting wires of an established municipal fire alarm telegraph system. The direct circuit auxiliary system is one in which the alarms are transmitted over a circuit, usually leased lines, directly connected to the annunciating switchboard at an alarm communication center and terminated at the protected property by an end-of-line resistor or equivalent.

The Local Energy Type: This auxiliary alarm system is electrically isolated from the municipal alarm system and has its own power supply. The tripping of the transmitting device does not depend on the current in the municipal circuit. It is in effect a local system, which when actuated supplies local power to trip the transmitter.

The Shunt Type: This auxiliary alarm system is the simpler auxiliary system. It has no local control, but is an integral part of the municipal alarm system. It utilizes the municipal system's power supply for its operation. It is so arranged that the alarm initiating devices (manual stations, water-flow switches, and thermostats) are electrically part of the municipal system's circuit and are connected in series in a shunt around the transmitter trip coil. When the shunt circuit is broken, the power from the municipal system is applied to the trip coil and the transmitter is released to transmit the alarm signal.

The Direct Circuit Type: This auxiliary system is for connection to a municipal fire alarm system of the type in which each municipal alarm box has an individual circuit to the fire alarm switchboard.

Remote Station System

In this system the alarm or supervisory signal registers in the office of an agency usually located at a distance from the protected property. Signals are transmitted and received on privately owned equipment, and the agency receiving the signals may be a municipal fire department or a communications agency competent of receiving the signals and acting upon them. Systems of this type are generally leased by the occupant of the protected premises and maintained under contract by the leasing company.

If, in place of one or more of the alarm signals of a local system, a connection is made to sound alarms at a constantly attended agency at some distance from the protected plant, the elementary requirements for a remote station system are properly met. The ordinary connection to a remote station system, however, often replaces all local alarm signals and is used generally for protection of premises where there is frequently no one present. The equipment essentials are similar to those for local systems, and, as with local systems, are of two types of operation, coded and noncoded. The coded type system is used where several protected properties share common connecting facilities to the remote station. The noncoded type system is used where the alarm element at the remote station, whether a light, annunciator drop, or meter, applies only to a single protected location.

Of prime importance is the choice of the remote station.

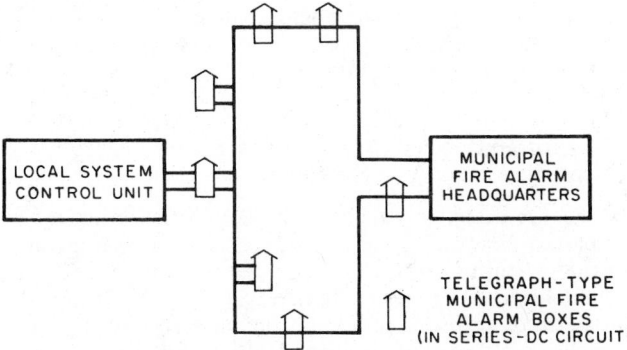

Fig. 12-2C. *Diagram of typical auxiliary (local energy) system.*

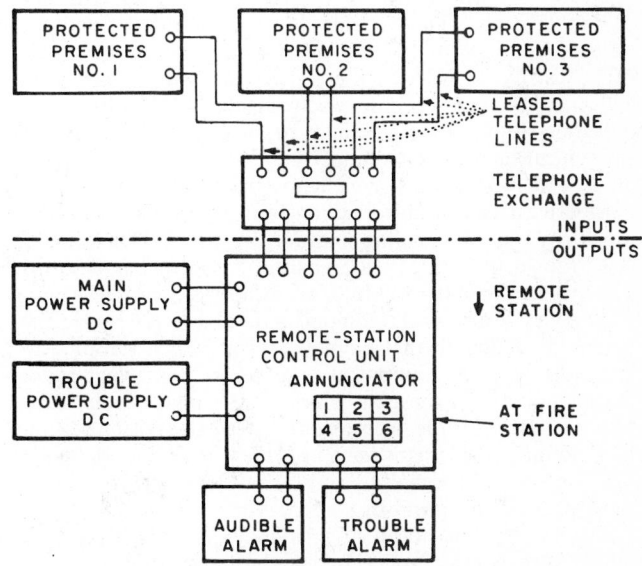

Fig. 12-2D. *Diagram of typical remote station system.*

For the purpose of registering alarms, the desirable agency is the municipal fire alarm headquarters, if it has personnel constantly in attendance. Supervisory signals, however, require different action than the dispatching of fire department equipment, and for these the preferred location for the remote station is in the quarters of a commercial agency open continuously and having personnel in attendance trained to provide proper response to the signals received. Such an agency may also serve in areas where fire department quarters are not continuously manned for the reception of fire alarm signals, it then being the function of the agency personnel to do whatever is needed to ensure prompt dispatching of fire department equipment. (See Fig. 12-2D for a diagram of a typical remote station system.)

Proprietary System

In this system signals are received at a central supervisory station, where trained and experienced operators are on duty at all times to take whatever action the signals call for. The central supervisory station is under the control of the owner or occupant of the protected property and is usually in or near that property. The operation of the central supervisory station and the signaling systems connected to it is a function of the personnel employed for this purpose by the owner of the property. The equipment is usually purchased by the user and subject to no outside control.

A proprietary system may be considered to be an elaborate local system to which recording devices at an inplant central supervising station have been added. The operations of the system are under the supervision of operators trained to investigate the situations which the system reports and to take whatever steps are necessary, such as the summoning of the fire department or the calling of inplant assistance to adjust abnormalities encountered. The distinguishing features of a proprietary system are its ownership by the occupant of the protected plant and the presence of a central supervising station within the confines of that plant.

Proprietary systems are generally used in large industrial establishments, basically for the supervision of patrolling guards and the reception of emergency signals from them when a fire or other unusual occurrence is discovered. In addition, alarm signals should have precedence over all other signals.

Where electromechanical devices are used to transmit signals over a signaling line to the central supervisory station, the number of different signals that can be transmitted is limited because fire alarm signals must have precedence. Further, because electromechanical transmission is rather slow, only one printer or recorder is required in the central supervisory station.

As with central station systems, the multiplex principle can be used to transmit electronically many signals simultaneously over a signaling line. NFPA No. 72D, Standard for Proprietary Protective Signaling Systems, has devoted a complete chapter to "Multiplex Alarm Systems."

In most respects the equipment used for a proprietary system is similar to that employed in a central station service, although the equipment tends to be somewhat more automatic than is the case with central station units. Provision is made for the proprietary central supervising station to summon outside assistance in the event of fire or, in the absence of such organized assistance in the area, to alert the organization's own brigades.

Proprietary and local systems may be auxiliarized, in which case NFPA No. 72B, Standard for Auxiliary Protective Signaling Systems, would apply to the circuitry be-

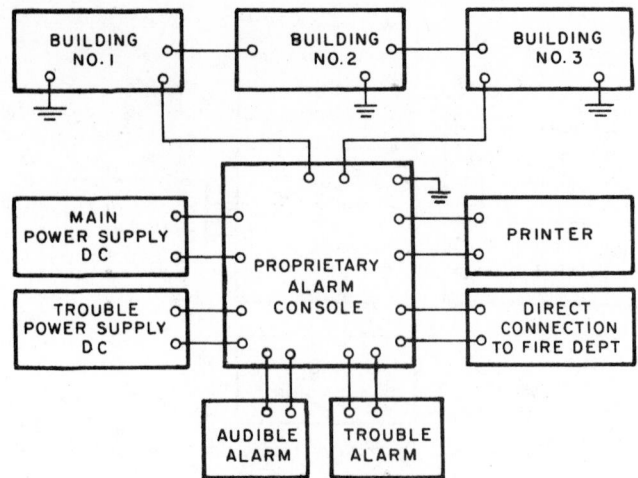

Fig. 12-2E. *Diagram of typical proprietary system.*

tween the proprietary or local system and the transmitting device. (See Fig. 12-2E for a diagram of a typical proprietary system.)

Household Fire Warning System

This class of system helps to provide reasonable fire safety for persons in family living units, and covers the requirements of a fire warning system for the home. Reasonable fire safety can be produced through a three-point program: (1) minimizing fire hazards, (2) providing a fire warning system, and (3) having and practicing an escape plan.

There are two extremes of fire to which household fire warning equipment must respond. One is the rapidly developing high heat fire. The other is the slow smoldering fire. Either can produce smoke and toxic gases.

Household fires are especially dangerous at night when the occupants are asleep. Fires produce smoke and deadly gases which can overcome occupants while they are asleep. Further dense smoke reduces visibility. Most fire casualties are the victims of smoke and gas rather than burns. To warn against a fire, NFPA No. 74, Standard for Household Fire Warning Equipment, requires at least one smoke detector located between a sleeping family and the rest of their residence, and recommends heat or smoke detectors in all other major areas.

The detection or alarm systems included in this category are for the sole use of the protected household. If the alarm is to be extended to any other location, such as a fire department, the system then should be considered to be one of the aforementioned systems (as applicable), except that the requirements of detector location and spacing, as they apply to home warning systems, would continue to be followed. These home fire warning systems are primarily concerned with life protection, not with protection of property.

D. Fire Extinguishing Systems as Fire Detection Systems

The fire-detecting capability of automatic sprinklers is employed to advantage in protective signaling by using any of the several forms of electrical water-flow alarm switches commonly used in automatic sprinkler systems to provide an alarm of sprinkler system operation. (Water-flow alarm switches are described in Sec. 14, Chap. 5.) To overcome the likelihood of false alarms as a result of fluctuations in the water supply system, it is customary to provide an electrical, thermo-electric, hydraulic, or pneumatic retarding device with the switch. This prevents the actual transmission of an alarm signal until the flow has persisted sufficiently long to provide reasonable assurance that the cause is an actual flow of water, and not a surge or water hammer.

Sprinkler supervisory switches (see Sec. 14, Chap. 5), designed for mounting at sprinkler system components (tanks, valves, etc.) which they are to supervise, are combined with appropriate transmitters and usually a local power supply. This assures the transmission of a supervisory signal when the supervised element passes into an abnormal condition, and a distinctive restoration signal when the abnormality disappears. In many instances, the switch and transmitter are integral. Operation of the switch trips the prewound transmitter mechanically. A coded supervisory or supervisory restoration signal is usually a single-round transmission, while the alarm signal upon a waterflow is a multiround signal.

Other types of automatic fire extinguishing systems can also serve as fire detection systems, such as those employing foam, foam-water high expansion foam, halogenated agent, carbon dioxide, dry chemical, water spray, etc. The same

sensing device which activated the extinguishing system also causes an alarm to be sounded.

Bibliography

NFPA Codes, Standards, and Recommended Practices (see the latest *NFPA Publications and Visual Aids Catalog* **for availability of current editions of the following documents)**

NFPA No. 13, Standard for the Installation of Sprinkler Systems.

NFPA No. 70, National Electrical Code.

NFPA No. 71, Standard for the Installation, Maintenance, and Use of Central Station Signaling Systems.

NFPA No. 72A, Standard for the Installation, Maintenance, and Use of Local Protective Signaling Systems.

NFPA No. 72B, Standard for the Installation, Maintenance, and Use of Auxiliary Protective Signaling Systems.

NFPA No. 72C, Standard for the Installation, Maintenance, and Use of Remote Station Protective Signaling Systems.

NFPA No. 72D, Standard for the Installation, Maintenance, and Use of Proprietary Protective Signaling Systems.

NFPA No. 72E, Standard on Automatic Fire Detectors.

NFPA No. 74, Standard for the Installation, Maintenance, and Use of Household Fire Warning Equipment.

NFPA No. 101, Life Safety Code.

Additional Reading

Phillips, Patrick E., "A Guide to Better Fire Detection Systems, Part 2," *Actual Specifying Engineer*, Jan. 1970, pp. 86-92.

Chapter 3

FIRE DETECTION MECHANISMS AND DEVICES

This chapter discusses the operating principles of fire detectors, the spacing of detection devices, fusible links and releases, and the actuation of fire controlling equipment.

A. Operating Principles and Types of Heat Detectors

Heat detecting devices fall into two general categories: (1) those that respond when the detection element reaches a predetermined temperature (fixed-temperature types), and (2) those that respond to an increase in heat at a rate greater than some predetermined value (rate-of-rise types). Some devices combine both the fixed-temperature and rate-of-rise principles. The same principles apply whether the devices are of the spot-pattern type, in which the thermally sensitive element is a compact unit of small area, or the line-pattern type, in which the element is continuous along a line or a circuit.

Fixed-temperature Detectors

Thermostats are the most widely used fixed-temperature heat detectors in signaling systems, and the common form of thermostat is the bimetallic type which utilizes the different coefficients of expansion of two metals under heat to cause a movement resulting in closing of electrical contacts.

Bimetallic Strip Thermostats: In its simplest form, the bimetallic strip operates against a fixed contact, and the distance the strip must travel to close against the contact determines the operating point, or temperature rating, of the thermostat. Some foreign thermostats take advantage of this property, and by fitting the unit with movable stops it is made usable across a fairly wide range of temperatures. In the United States, however, such variability is not designed into thermostats used in fire protection, and the usual form encountered is the nonadjustable, prerated unit, responsive to heat at its rated temperature.

Snap-action Disc Thermostats: The principle of unequal expansion in a bimetallic assembly is also used in snap-action disc thermostats (see Fig. 12-3A). The center of the disc is designed to toggle from concave to convex when the temperature at which the device is rated is reached. Disc-type devices develop a greater mechanical force at the point of operation than do ordinary bimetallic-strip-types, and

the force is used to close a pair of electrical contacts which are not part of the disc itself. The snap-action disc design eliminates one disadvantageous feature of the bimetallic strip, the relatively low pressure at which the contact of electrically live members is made. As the contacts in a bimetallic-strip-type approach each other, the pressure is so light that false alarms may occur below the rated temperature as the result of jarring or poor contact.

A major advantage of bimetallic thermostats of both the strip and snap-action disc types is their ability, after operation, to restore to their original condition with decrease of temperature. They are not destroyed or permanently damaged by operation. However, good practice dictates temperature checking of thermostats in close proximity to fire incidences.

Thermostatic Cable: While the bimetallic thermostat is used for fixed-temperature detection in spot locations, its operating characteristics, i.e., operation at a predetermined or rated temperature, is paralleled in line pattern use by fixed-temperature thermostatic cable. Such cable is an assembly, suitably covered for protection against mechanical injury of two tensioned metal cables held separated from each other by a heat-sensitive covering applied directly to the wires. At the rated temperature, the covering melts and the two wires come into contact with each other, initiating an alarm. The section of wire affected by heat must be replaced following operation. It is available in temperature ratings higher than ratings suitable for installation in areas subject to normal ambient temperatures. (See Fig. 12-3B.)

Fusible Links and Quartzoid Bulbs: Other forms of fixed-temperature heat detectors are the fusible link, occasionally employed to restrain operation of an electrical switch until the point of fusion is reached, and the quartzoid bulb thermostat, which serves the same function in a slightly different way in that operation in this case depends on removal

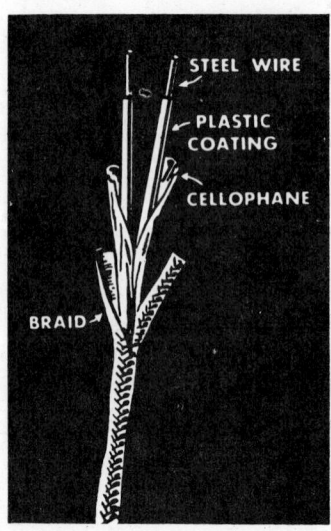

Fig. 12-3B. *View of the assembly of thermostatic cable $\frac{3}{16}$ in. in diameter, showing the two plastic coated conductors (stripped to show steel wire), wrapping of cellophane, and protective braid. (Protectowire)*

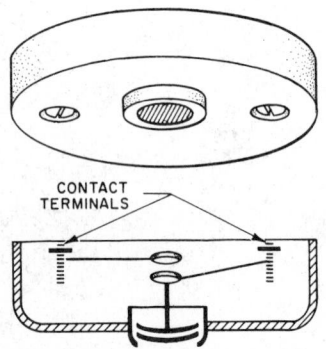

Fig. 12-3A. *A bimetallic, snap-action disc, fixed-temperature device. Snap disc is in the raised center portion of the device.*

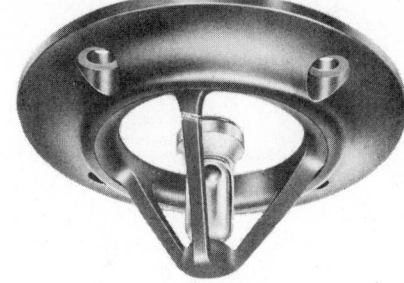

Fig 12-3C. Solder-type fusible link.

Fig. 12-3D. Grinnell quartzoid bulb-type fixed temperature device.

of the restriction by breaking the bulb. Both of these units require replacement after operation.

Rate-of-rise Detectors

Fire detectors that operate on the rate-of-rise principle function when the rate of temperature increase at the detector exceeds a stated rate (in number of degrees a minute). Detectors of this type invariably combine two functioning elements, one of which initiates an alarm on a rapid rise of temperature, while the other acts to delay or prevent an alarm on a slow rise in temperature.

The advantages of rate-of-rise devices are several: They can be set to operate more rapidly, under most conditions of combustion propagation, than can fixed-point devices; they are effective across a wide range of ambient temperatures, as, of course, fixed-point devices are not, making them equally useful in low-temperature and high-temperature areas; they recycle rapidly and are usually more speedily available for continued service than are fixed-point devices; and they tolerate slow increases in ambient temperature without giving an alarm. Their disadvantages for some applications are their susceptibility to false alarms where there is a rapidly increasing ambient temperature that is not the result of hostile combustion, and the possibility that they may fail to respond to a fire which propagates very slowly.

Pneumatic Tube Detectors: In a typical rate-of-rise pneumatic tubing detector, pressure is built up in the detector diaphragm chamber as heat reaches the tubing and causes contained air to expand. The expansion is in rough agreement with the expression

$$P = \frac{KT}{V}$$

where P is the pressure, T the temperature, V the volume of the pneumatic system, and K a constant fixed by the arrangement of the system elements. V is, for all practical purposes, also a constant within the limits of operation. If there were no other element involved (if the pneumatic system were closed), operation for an alarm would occur when P reached a point, as a result of an increase in T, where the diaphragm was moved to close an alarm circuit.

The rate-of-rise system is not closed, however, because a vent is provided which leaks off a portion of the heated air. If the vent were too large, pressure building up within the tubing and diaphragm chamber would be leaked off before it could move the diaphragm and thus actuate an alarm. Proper adjustment of the vent size permits retention of enough pressure to operate the diaphragm, although somewhat later than would be the case if the system were completely closed. Figure 12-3E shows the operating parts of a typical pneumatic tube detector.

A pneumatic tubing system for line operation consists of

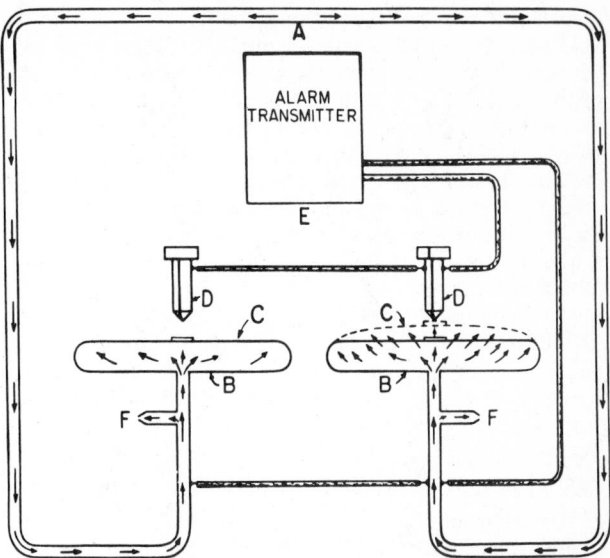

*Fig. 12-3E. A pneumatic tubing system operating on the rate-of-rise principle. The copper tubing (**A**) is fastened to ceilings or walls in a continuous loop and terminates at both ends in chambers (**B**) having flexible diaphragms (**C**) which control electrical contacts (**D**). When air in the tubing expands under the influence of heat, pressure builds within the chambers causing the diaphragms to move and close a circuit to alarm transmitter (**E**). Vents (**F**) compensate for small changes in pressure in the tubing brought about by small changes in temperature in the protected spaces. (American District Telegraph Co., and Its Associated Companies)*

a circuit of small-diameter copper tubing in the protected area with the circuit terminated in one or two chambers depending on the type of system. The chambers are topped with flexible diaphragms controlling electrical contacts, and are equipped with vents to permit the circuit to breathe. Small changes in air temperature surrounding the tubing result in small changes in pressure within the tubing and these pressure changes are handled by the vents without movement of the diaphragms. When the ambient air change is rapid, however, the contained air expands so rapidly the vents are incapable of relieving the pressure in the chambers. The diaphragms move and the contacts are closed to initiate an alarm.

Thermoelectric Detectors: A second form of rate-of-rise detector operates on the thermoelectric principle (see Fig. 12-3F). Two sets of thermocouples are commonly mounted in a single housing, so arranged that one set is exposed to

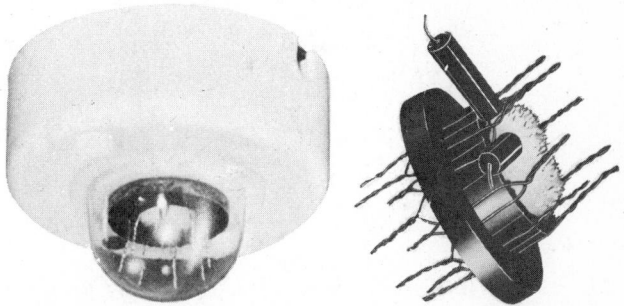

Fig. 12-3F. A rate-of-rise spot detection device operating on the thermoelectric effect. At left is the unit as it appears in a ceiling installation. At right is a closeup showing the heat sensing thermocouples. (American District Telegraph Co., and Its Associated Companies)

convection and radiation while the other is shielded. A voltage is produced when a temperature difference exists between the exposed and unexposed thermocouple junctions of the detector. This voltage produces a current increase in an electrically supervised circuit, operating a galvanometer relay, the contacts of which initiate an alarm signal.

A means of extending the thermoelectric principle to line operation is by running a cable assembly of four wires through the exposure area. Two wires are of a metal having a high coefficient of thermal resistivity, and two having a low coefficient. One of each pair is more fully exposed to heat variations than is its mate, and by suitable disposition in a bridge circuit, the variations between the two resistor pairs are translated into an alarm. Where the increase in temperature is slow both the exposed pair and the shielded pair vary resistance at approximately an equal rate, and the bridge stays in balance.

Combined Rate-of-rise and Fixed-temperature Detectors

While the bimetallic fixed-temperature thermostat finds considerable application by itself, it has become increasingly common, in recent years, to use it in combination with the rate-of-rise detection principle in the so-called rate-of-rise spot thermostat. Rate-of-rise thermostats were developed, presumably, to take advantage of the capability of the rate-of-rise feature to sense and respond rapidly to a fast fire and the fixed temperature operating limit to take care of a situation where the growth of a fire was slow—so slow that the rate-of-rise capability might never come into play. The typical form which the rate-of-rise thermostat takes is a vented air chamber which heats up in a flexible diaphragm carrying electrical contacts. Heat on the outside of the chamber causes air in the chamber to expand, and when that expansion exceeds the capacity of the vent to relieve pressure, the diaphragm is flexed to close the electrical contacts it controls. Slow changes in ambient temperature near the chamber allow it to "breathe" through its vent, and the diaphragm is not moved sufficiently to cause an alarm. Devices of this type have two ratings, one the speed of operation and the other the temperature at which the unit operates. The latter becomes operative only where the former has not functioned. (See Fig. 12-3G.)

Rate Compensation (Anticipation and Differentiation) Devices

Rate compensation devices provide an assured actuation at some predetermined maximum temperature and compensate for changes in rates of temperature rise.

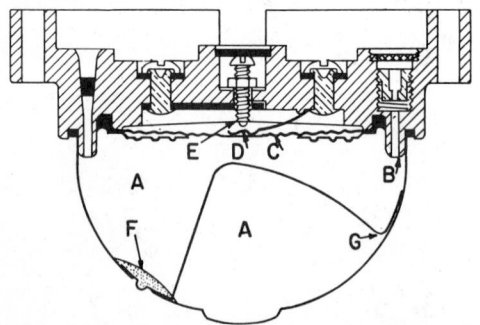

Fig. 12-3G. A spot-type combination rate-of-rise, fixed-temperature device. The air in chamber **A** *expands more rapidly than it can escape from vent* **B***. This causes pressure to close electrical contact* **D** *between diaphragm* **C** *and insulated screw* **E***. Fixed temperature operation occurs when fusible alloy* **F** *melts releasing spring* **G** *which depresses the diaphragm closing the contact points.*

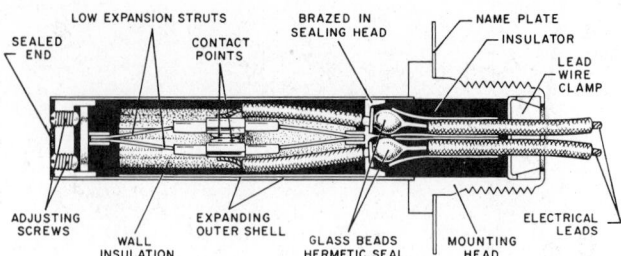

Fig. 12-3H. Section of a rate compensation-type fire detector. (Fenwal, Inc.)

A typical rate compensation device (see Fig. 12-3H) employs a cylindrical outer shell, housing struts in compression on which contacts are mounted. The metal of the shell has a higher coefficient of expansion than the metal of the struts. When the temperature rises, the shell elongates, relieving the compression on the struts and causing the contacts to close. If the rate of temperature rise is low (0 to 5°F per min), both the struts and the shell expand; but, because of the difference in coefficients of expansion, the compression on the struts is relieved and the contacts close.

B. Operating Principles and Types of Smoke Detectors

Photoelectric Detectors

Photoelectric detection of smoke, in varying degrees of density, has been employed for several years, particularly where the type of fire anticipated is expected to generate a substantial amount of smoke before temperature changes are sufficient to actuate a heat detection system. This type of detector operates on a light principle where smoke entering a light beam either obscures the beam's path or reflects light into a photocell.

Spot Type: One type of spot detector employs a short beam carried between source and receiver in a ceiling-mounted unit. The change in current resulting from partial obscuring of a photoelectric beam by smoke between a receiving element and a light source is measured and an alarm is tripped when this obscuration reaches a critical value.

Another type of spot photoelectric detector is the re-

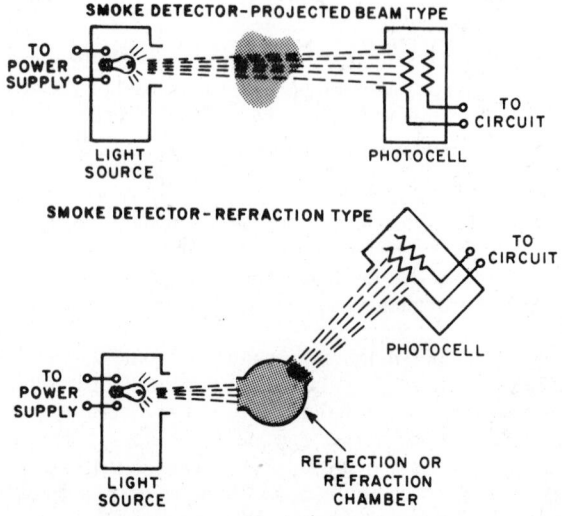

Fig. 12-3I. Simple illustrations of projected beam type and refraction type photoelectric principles.

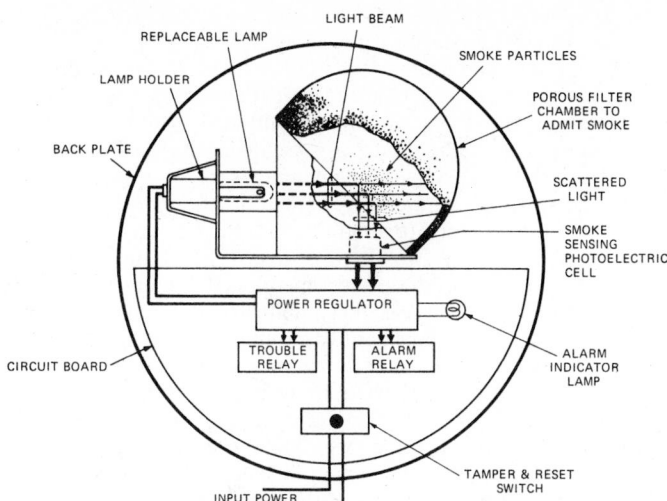

Fig. 12-3J. Refraction type photoelectric spot detector. (Electro Signal Lab, Inc.)

fraction-type which operates on the principle of the reflection of a light source into a photoconductive cell by means of smoke particles. (See Fig. 12-3J.) A small chamber, open to the atmosphere, contains a light source and a photoconductive cell so arranged that the beam of light from the light source does not impinge upon the photoconductive cell. When a sufficient quantity of smoke particles from fire enters the chamber, the light is reflected by the smoke particles into the photoconductive cell. This changes the resistance of the cell and a signal is obtained.

Beam Type: The beam-type detector employs a beam

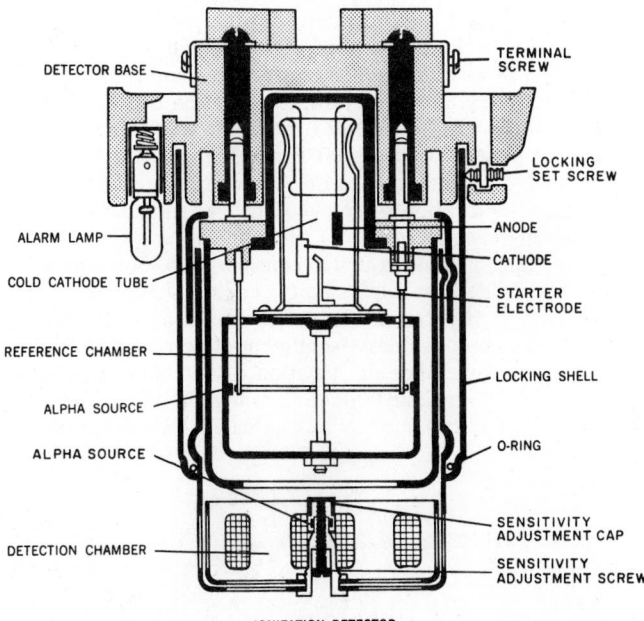

IONIZATION DETECTOR

*Fig. 12-3K. Ionization smoke detector, cross-sectional view. Air is ionized and made electrically conductive in outer **detection chamber** and inner **reference chamber** by **alpha source.** A DC voltage applied across the ionization chambers causes minute current flow through the ionized air. Combustion particles entering **detection chamber** impede current flow, increasing voltage on **starter electrode** of **cold cathode tube.** When sufficient combustion particles enter chamber, voltage is sufficient to fire tube which passes required current to operate alarm relay.* (Pyrotronics, Inc.)

carried between elements at extreme ends or sides of the protected area. Smoke between the light source and the receiving photocell reduces the light reaching the cell, causing actuation.

Ionization Detectors

Ionization-type detectors consist of one or two ionization chambers and the necessary related amplification circuits. The ionization detector has as a sensing element the ionization chamber which utilizes a principle wherein air is made electrically conductive (ionized) by bombardment of the nitrogen and oxygen molecules with alpha particles emitted by a minute source of radioactive material. A voltage applied across the ionization chamber causes a very small electrical current to flow as the ions travel to the electrode of opposite polarity. When invisible or visible combustion particles enter the chamber they attach themselves to the ions and cause a reduction in mobility and thus a reduction in current flow. The reduced current flow increases the voltage on the electrodes which, when reaching a predetermined level, results in an alarm. (See Fig. 12-3K.)

Resistance-bridge Detectors

Resistance-bridge type detectors (see Fig. 12-3L) employ an electron grid-bridge circuit. Atmospheric changes due to normal environmental conditions are accepted by the grid-bridge circuit and the bridge is kept in balance. However, increases of smoke particles and moisture, present in products of combustion, bring about fast impedance changes which upset the balance of the grid-bridge circuit causing an electronic triggering device to function and to initiate an alarm signal.

C.   Sampling Detectors

The sampling-type detector consists of tubing distributed from the detector unit to the area(s) to be protected. An air pump draws air from the protected area back to the detector through the air sampling ports and piping. At the detector, the air is analyzed for smoke particles.

A cloud chamber smoke detector is a form of sampling detector. The air pump draws a sample of air into a high humidity chamber within the detector. After the air is in

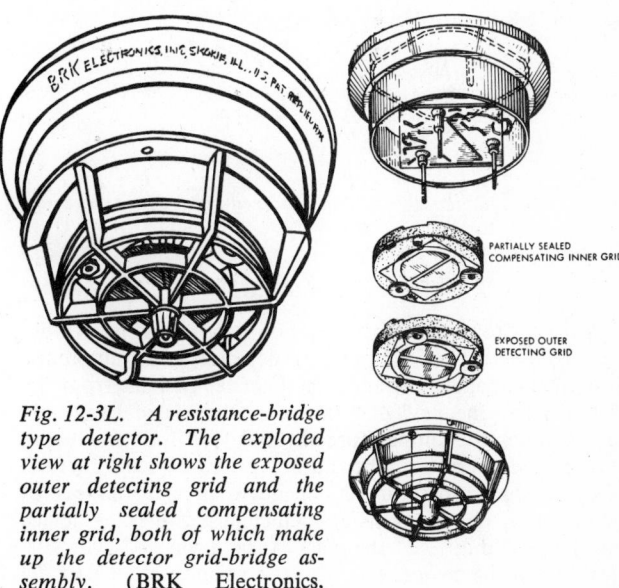

Fig. 12-3L. A resistance-bridge type detector. The exploded view at right shows the exposed outer detecting grid and the partially sealed compensating inner grid, both of which make up the detector grid-bridge assembly. (BRK Electronics, Inc.)

the humidity chamber, the pressure is lowered slightly. If smoke particles are present, the moisture in the air condenses on them forming a cloud in the chamber. The density of this cloud is then measured by the photoelectric principle. When the density is greater than a predetermined level, the detector responds to the smoke.

D. Flame Detectors

A flame detector responds to the appearance of radiant energy visible to the human eye (approximately 4,000 to 7,700 angstroms) or to radiant energy outside the range of human vision. These detectors are sensitive to glowing embers, coals, or actual flames which radiate energy of sufficient intensity and spectral quality to initiate response of the detector.

Types of Flame Detectors

There are four basic types of flame detectors.

Infrared: This device has a sensing element responsive to radiant energy outside the range of human vision (above approximately 7,700 angstroms). (See Fig. 12-3M.)

Ultraviolet: This device has a sensing element responsive to radiant energy outside the range of human vision (below approximately 4,000 angstroms).

Photoelectric: This device employs a photocell which either changes its electrical conductivity, or produces an electrical potential when exposed to radiant energy.

Flame Flicker: This device is a photoelectric type which includes means to prevent response to visible light unless the observed light is modulated at a frequency characteristic of the flicker of a flame.

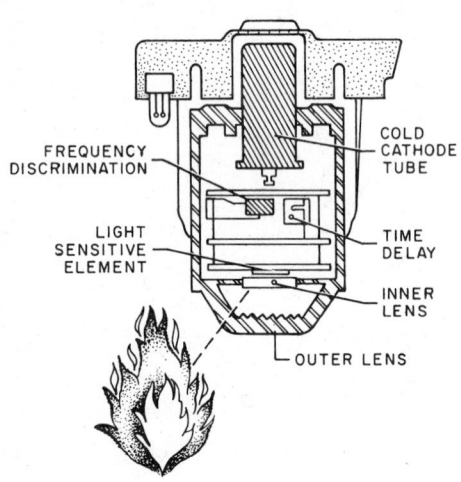

Fig. 12-3M. Schematic of an infrared-type flame detector. (Pyrotronics, Inc.)

E. Thermal Lag

When a fire occurs, the operation of a heat-sensitive device, such as a fixed-temperature detector or an automatic sprinkler, is dependent upon the transfer of heat from the heated air to the device. A heat-sensitive device will only operate when the temperature of the device itself reaches its operating temperature. The rate at which a device will reach its operating temperature is dependent upon a number of factors: (1) the heat transfer coefficient between the device and the heated air, (2) the mass of the device, (3) the surface area of the device, (4) the mass velocity of air past the device, (5) the temperature difference between the air and

the device, and (6) the rate at which the air itself is being heated during the heat transfer process.

From a consideration of the above factors, it is readily apparent that when a heat-sensitive device operates, the temperature of the surrounding air will generally be higher than the operating temperature of the device itself. This difference between the operating temperature of the device and the actual air temperature is commonly spoken of as "thermal lag." Under fire conditions, the difference in thermal lag between any two given devices is more dependent upon the first five of the above-mentioned factors than it is upon the sixth, whereas the amount of thermal lag for any given device is dependent more upon the sixth factor, the rate at which the temperature of the air is increasing. Testing laboratories, therefore, commonly prescribe a maximum of thermal lag. For example, when Underwriters Laboratories, Inc. tests a fixed-temperature thermostat proposed for a 15×15-ft maximum spacing, the maximum air temperature for operation of the device must not exceed 206°F. This is for thermostats having operating temperatures of 135° to 140°F.

F. Spacing of Detection Devices

Detailed spacing requirements, including regular spacing, may be found in NFPA No. 72E, Standard on Automatic Fire Detectors.

Spot-type heat detectors should be located upon the ceiling not less than six inches from the side wall, or on the side walls between six and twelve inches from the ceiling (see Fig. 12-3N). When complete coverage is required, detection devices should be installed throughout all parts of the building.

Factors to consider when spacing detection devices include ceiling construction, ceiling height, room volume, space subdivisions, the normal room temperature, possible abnormal room temperature conditions due to heat producing appliances or manufacturing processes, and draft conditions which may affect the normal operation of the device. Devices are available that are rated for use with normal ceiling temperatures up to 300°F and higher.

NFPA No. 72E, Standard on Automatic Fire Detectors, states that the location of smoke detectors should be based upon an engineering survey of the application of this form of protection to the area under consideration. Some conditions to consider are air velocity, ceiling shape, surfaces and height, configuration of contents, burning characteristics of stored combustibles, the number of detectors required for complete coverage, and location of detectors with respect to ventilating and air conditioning facilities. Typical conditions of occupancy to be evaluated include possible

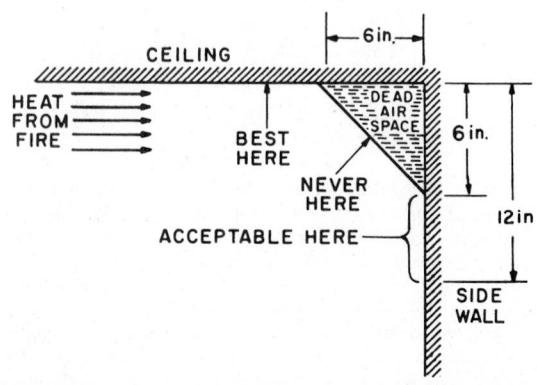

Fig. 12-3N. Spot-type heat detectors—location in corner areas.

obstruction of photoelectric light beams by the storage and movement of stock and the presence of dust or vapors which could result in the operation of the smoke detecting devices.

G.   Single Station Units

A single station unit is a self-contained device incorporating the detector, control equipment, and the alarm-sending device in one unit. It is operated from a power supply either in the unit, or obtained at the point of installation. Following are some examples of single station units.

Ionization Smoke Detection Type: This type is electrically operated and may use a cord connection provided the installation is connected to a receptacle not subject to loss of power by a wall switch. A restraining means must be used on the plug to prevent it from being accidentally disconnected. This type may also be powered by monitored batteries. A distinctive warning signal is automatically given when the batteries need replacing.

Photoelectric Smoke Detection Type: This type is electrically operated and, when used in home fire warning systems, may use a cord connection provided the installation is connected to a receptacle not subject to loss of power by a wall switch. A restraining means must be used on the plug to prevent it from being accidentally disconnected.

Mechanical-powered Heat Detection Type: This type of unit is actuated by a heat-sensitive element, and its alarm is powered by a mechanical switch which sounds a bell through a clocklike mechanism. A flag indicator is used to show when the device has been operated and needs rewinding.

Gas-powered Heat Detection Type: This type is actuated by a heat-sensitive element, and its alarm mechanism is a gas-operated horn. The presence of gas in the storage cylinder may be determined by visual observation through a sight glass in the side of the cylinder.

NFPA No. 74, Standard for the Installation, Maintenance, and Use of Household Fire Warning Equipment should be consulted for further requirements on single station units.

H.   Releases

Releasing systems use heat or smoke detecting devices which usually actuate electromechanical elements to perform the desired work. They may be used to shut fire doors and dampers, open valves to release water supplies to sprinkler systems, operate other extinguishing systems, open automatic drains, release covers on dip tanks, and to perform other operations. The detecting elements may be of fixed temperature, rate-of-rise, photoelectric, or ionization type. The power for operation is generally an electrical solenoid or a weight tripped by the system.

Fusible links are also used as release elements in a releasing system. An example of a fusible link can be seen in Figure 12-3C.

I.   Actuation of Fire Control Equipment

Operation of any of the types of fire detection devices may be used to actuate fire control systems. In addition, the systems may be actuated by any of several monitoring or detection devices operating in response to conditions other than fire, as, for example, vapor concentration.

Fire detection devices and accessory equipment used primarily in conjunction with fire control equipment and not as a separate fire detection system are discussed and illustrated in the remainder of this chapter.

Pneumatic Rate-of-rise Actuating Devices

The pneumatic rate-of-rise operating principle can be used to actuate fire control equipment.

The pneumatic detecting system consists of one or more thin-walled, bulb-shaped chambers, known as heat actuated devices (HADs), connected to a releasing mechanism by a small-diameter tubing system (see Fig. 12-3O), or it may be just a tubing system connected to the releasing mechanism. When heat expands air in the chamber or in the tubing system, the increasing air pressure is transmitted through the tubing to a diaphragm that actuates a mechanical or electrical release. Slow, normal changes in temperature do not produce a tripping pressure due to the provision of small equalizing air vents of predetermined capacity.

Location and Spacing: Location and spacing of heat actuated devices in rate-of-rise systems follow detailed practices prepared by the manufacturer and which are based on standards established by approving laboratories. Factors governing spacing include shape of ceiling, construction of ceiling, number of HADs likely to be affected by a fire, and occupancy and other specific conditions. The distance of HADs from walls and partitions is usually about one-half the distance allowed between lines of HADs.

For areas where temperatures are within a normal range, up to six HADs may be connected by three-way or four-way fittings to a single tubing line leading to the release. This gives the shortest total length of air tubing from the HADs to the release. If there are two or more such groups of HADs, each group and its line of tubing are connected to the release through a mercury check.

Mercury Checks: These checks are used to prevent pressure produced in the HADs in one group, by the heat of a fire, from being absorbed by HADs in another group. They also present a desirable moderate resistance to the passage of pressure from the HADs to the release diaphragm. When the increased pressure caused by a fire enters a mercury check, as at "D" in Figure 12-3P, it forces the small amount of mercury in the connecting passage into the chamber connected to the release diaphragm with little change in mercury level, and with little pressure difference. The air passing at "D" increases the pressure in the manifold which is connected to the other checks, and in connection to the release diaphragm. Due to the relative sizes

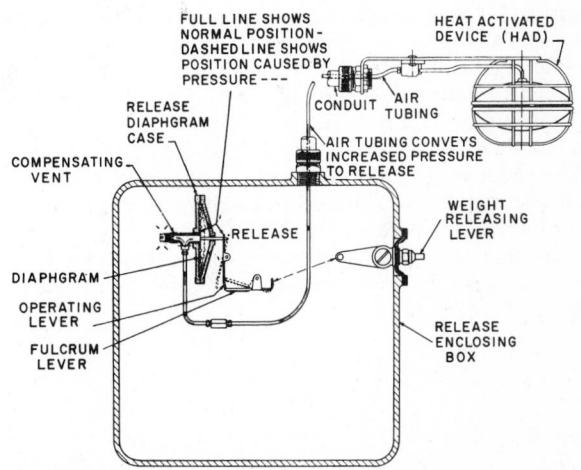

Fig. 12-3O. "Automatic" Sprinkler Corp. of America rate-of-rise fire detection system operating arrangement (unsupervised). The movement of the diaphragm, through a series of levers releases a weight. The dropping of the weight operates the fire protection device to which the release is attached.

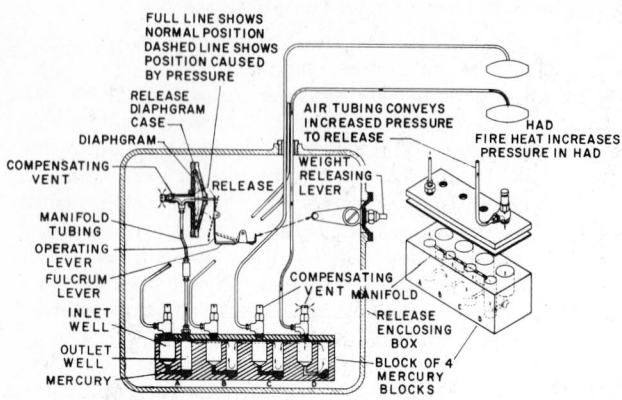

Fig. 12-3P.   Rate-of-rise detection system using mercury checks with multiple HADs (unsupervised system). (Automatic Sprinkler Corp. of America)

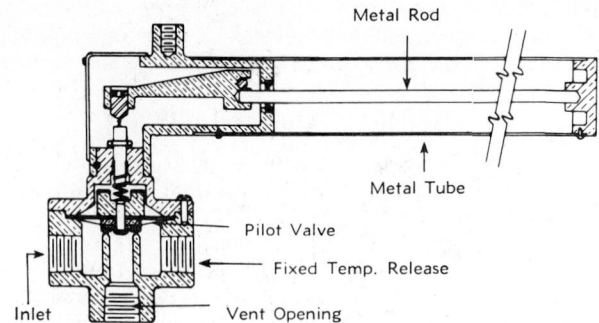

Fig. 12-3Q.   A rate-of-rise and fixed temperature release. (Viking Corporation)

and arrangement of the mercury check passages, the mercury columns do not allow any back flow to the inactive tubing systems. If two or more groups of HADs are affected by heat from a fire, one or more may contribute to the pressure on the release diaphragm. Compensating vents on the tubing system for each group of HADs and on the Release Diaphragm Case (Fig. 12-3P) keep all system pressures equal under normal conditions.

Metal-expansion Rate-of-rise Actuating Devices

The metal-expansion type of rate-of-rise detector involves a rate-of-rise action dependent upon the unequal expansion rates of two different sizes of metal rods to trigger a small valve at each detector which releases pilot air or water pressure to any connected pressure-operated mechanism. With slow rates of change in the exposing temperature, the two rods expand by approximately equal amounts. With a high rate of temperature change the smaller rod heats more quickly and expands faster than the larger rod. The difference in the length of the two rods is magnified by a mechanical leverage system to open the pilot air or water valve.

An example of a device operating on the metal expansion principle is shown in Figure 12-3Q. The difference in the heat expansion of the metal rod and metal tube brought on by rapid increase in temperature opens the pilot valve which exhausts the top chamber of the body and allows pressure in the release line to vent through a full $\frac{1}{2}$-in. opening, thereby operating the extinguishing system. The device will operate either on a pneumatic or hydraulic release line. An automatic sprinkler is used for a fixed temperature release. This release is generally used with a wet pilot line and automatic sprinklers to trip a control valve in deluge and pre-action sprinkler systems.

Location and spacing of rate-of-rise releases are in accordance with the standards established by approving testing laboratories.

Early Warning Detection Systems

Since smoke- and ionization-type detectors are generally considered early warning detectors, one suggested method of installation calls for two detectors to operate before the extinguishing medium is released. This is called "cross-zoning" and utilizes two zones on a control panel. One-half of the required number of detectors is connected to one zone, and the second half to a second zone. If only one detector alarms to a small fire, an alarm sounds but no agent is released. This permits a person to use a hand extinguisher. If no one responds to the alarm and the fire begins to progress, the second zone comes in and the agent is released.

Fixed Temperature Detection Systems

These systems, other than automatic sprinklers, may use the various kinds of electric thermostats connected to electrically operated extinguishing system valves, or they may use fusible element devices or "pilot" sprinklers to release pressure from a pilot air or water line controlling the valves. Such pilot sprinklers are not usually a part of the designed extinguishing agent distribution system.

SI Units

The following conversion factors are given as a convenience in converting to SI units the English units used in this chapter.

1 in.   = 25.400 mm
1 ft   = 0.305 m
$\frac{5}{9}$(°F − 32) = °C

Bibliography

NFPA Codes, Standards, and Recommended Practices (see the latest NFPA Publications and Visual Aids Catalog for availability of current editions of the following documents)

NFPA No. 72E, Standard on Automatic Fire Detectors.
NFPA No. 74, Standard for the Installation, Maintenance, and Use of Household Fire Warning Equipment Systems.

Additional Reading

Phillips, Patrick E., "A Guide to Better Fire Detection Systems, Part 2," *Actual Specifying Engineer*, Jan. 1970, pp 111-116.

Chapter 4

GAS AND VAPOR TESTING

Prevention of accidental fire requires an accurate knowledge of where and when a mixture within the flammable range can occur in order that extra precaution can be exercised to prevent ignition. Measurement of the oxygen concentration is important as a means of evaluating the effectiveness of inerting processes (Section 15, Chapter 7) and as a means of protecting personnel from the effects of oxygen deficiency.

Enclosed areas where flammable or combustible gases or vapors can be present may be found in public utility operations, in petroleum production, refining, and marketing; in chemical and petrochemical plants; in metallurgical industries; in distilleries; in paint and varnish making; in marine operations; and in many other industrial activities.

Flammable gases or flammable liquid vapors may be detected by instruments designed for that purpose. Such instruments are known as combustible gas indicators, flammable vapor detectors, combustible gas analyzers, and by many proprietary names. All operate by sensing some characteristics of a sample drawn into the instrument, and translating these characteristics into appropriate data.

A. Operating Principles

Most instruments in current use utilize the principle of "catalytic combustion." Mixtures of flammable gas or vapor and air cannot be ignited to cause self-sustaining flame unless the concentration of gas or vapor exceeds a minimum value called the lower flammable limit (LFL). Mixtures containing much lower concentrations, approaching zero, can "burn" on the surface of heated platinum, yielding heat in direct proportion to the gas or vapor concentration. This is called "surface" or "catalytic" combustion.

If the heated surface is an electrically heated platinum wire connected in an appropriate circuit (the Wheatstone bridge circuit, see Fig. 12-4A), the heat released by catalytic combustion can further increase the temperature of the wire, resulting in a change in electrical resistance, and a

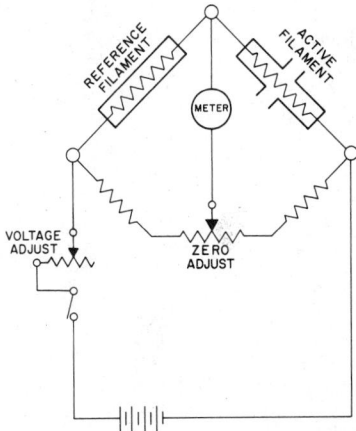

Fig. 12-4A. The Wheatstone bridge circuit in which the "Active Filament" is a platinum wire on which catalytic combustion takes place when a sample of the atmosphere being tested is passed across it. The resultant change in resistance in that arm of the circuit is translated into a corresponding deflection of an electric meter.

corresponding deflection of the hand of an electric meter. This is the operating principle of the usual combustible gas indicator of the hot-wire type. Other somewhat similar devices may employ a solid or porous catalytic mass instead of a wire, and may sense the temperature by means other than the increase in electrical resistance.

B. Calibration

The combustible gas indicator must be set to read "zero" when uncontaminated air is drawn into it. When making tests, the amount of gas present in the sample is read on a scale that shows the amount in terms of the fraction or percent of the lower flammable limit concentration. This is practical, since the heat of combustion at the lower flammable limit concentration of most flammable and combustible gases is approximately the same. Some vapors, e.g., carbon disulfide, give somewhat low readings in terms of true explosibility; others, such as natural gas, may give readings a little on the high side. Where exact readings at the upper part of the scale are required, special calibrations are used. For most purposes, where the sought-after condition is a "gas-free" atmosphere, these differences disappear as the reading approaches the previously set "zero."

The fact that the hot-wire type of instrument responds to all combustible gases or mixture of combustible gases, irrespective of chemical composition, is usually an advantage in that it is not necessary to know the exact identity of a gas to evaluate the risk of fire and explosion. Where it is desired to selectively measure the presence of some specific combustible gas in the possible presence of other combustibles, special or more refined techniques are necessary.

Other instruments, some generally similar in appearance to the ordinary combustible gas indicator, depend for their operation on properties of a gas or vapor other than combustibility, such as refractive index, density, diffusion or thermal conductivity. Calibrated on a specific gas or vapor, these instruments can be designed to give readings on higher concentrations up to pure gas or vapor. These instruments are not selective, however, and they will respond to almost any gas or vapor, combustible or not.

In some instruments, the catalytic combustion principle and the thermal conductivity principle are combined in a single device to permit extending the useful range into and beyond the flammable range. However, each section of the instrument retains the limitations of the method employed.

C. Operation and Limitations

As actual ignition of flammable mixtures may occur within the indicator, flame arresters are provided in the inlet and outlet connections to the chamber housing the catalytic filament to prevent combustion within the chamber from traveling outside to ignite the atmosphere being sampled. Flame arresters are suitable for conventional gas- or vapor-air mixtures. If the atmosphere is enriched in oxygen, i.e., the atmosphere contains more than 21 percent oxygen by volume or the partial pressure of oxygen exceeds 160 mm of mercury, special arresters may be necessary.

Tests may be made remotely by drawing a sample from a suspected location through a hose to an indicator, or on the spot by carrying the instrument (previously set to zero) into the suspected area. The former is preferred as a preliminary test because the operator is not exposed to possible flammable or toxic gas concentrations.

Instruments of the hot platinum filament type are designed specifically for measuring combustibles in air. They depend on an oxidation reaction for their operation, and the oxygen of the air is necessary for proper functioning. They will give a reasonably accurate indication of the presence of combustible gas even when the oxygen concentration has been substantially reduced by "inerting"; however, without special adaptation they cannot be relied upon to demonstrate whether or not the objective of inerting, i.e., the elimination of an explosive mixture, has actually been achieved.

Sampling steamy atmospheres will result in readings slightly on the high side, and condensation of water within the instrument is likely to cause trouble.

Sampling from ovens or driers at substantially elevated temperatures should be avoided unless it is known that the vapor is so dilute that condensation will not occur at the temperature of the instruments. However, if the solvent involved has a flash point below atmospheric temperature, explosibility readings can be relied upon irrespective of the oven temperature.

The catalytic filament can sometimes lose its catalytic

property if exposed to substances such as silicones, dust, and the vapors of tetraethyl lead. The listings of nationally recognized testing laboratories specify which instruments utilize filament temperatures sufficiently high to make them suitable for use on the vapors of gasoline containing tetraethyl lead.

All instruments need to be checked frequently enough to give the operator positive assurance that they are responsive to the particular gas or vapor in question. Manufacturers will supply information on testing methods for the service condition involved.

If an instrument responds to methane with reasonable accuracy, the operator is assured that it will also respond to the presence of any other gas which may be encountered. Several instrument manufacturers offer calibration kits containing known methane-air mixtures suitable for checking the response of combustible gas indicators. (Calibration curves for one particular make of combustible gas indicator are shown in Fig. 12-4B.)

D.   Types of Instruments

Portable Indicators

Portable indicators are generally lightweight, dry-cell-powered devices intended for field use, such as for testing sewers, manholes, basements, ducts, containers, or tanks where the presence of a combustible mixture is suspected. Samples are drawn through a hose or tube, frequently equipped with a rigid extension or "probe" for ease in reaching inaccessible points. Suction is provided by a hand-operated rubber aspirator bulb, or by a battery powered built-in motor driven pump.

There are portable indicators equipped with audible and visual alarms. Usually powered by rechargeable batteries, they are designed to run continuously for 8 to 10 hours on a full charge. The alarm circuits are energized when a preset concentration of combustible gas or vapor (usually $\frac{1}{5}$ of the LFL) is reached. These instruments usually depend upon diffusion and convection to bring the sample to the filament chamber.

A number of portable indicators are available for use in hazardous locations. The electrical circuits have been designed to meet the requirements of Article 500 of NFPA No. 70, National Electrical Code, and have been tested and listed by nationally recognized testing agencies. The manufacturers label and instructions indicate the type of approval granted for the particular instrument.

Continuous Analyzers

Continuous analyzers are permanently installed line-powered devices for continuously analyzing air samples from one to as many as 20 or more points. They may be either of the remote detection (diffusion) type or may draw samples through tubing to a central location by means of a suction pump or equivalent. The functions may include audible or visible alarms in addition to continuous recording of data, two-level alarms, e.g., a warning light at 40 percent of LFL and an audible alarm at 50 percent of LFL, automatic shutdown or startup of equipment, and similar features as required by the individual application.

The central equipment is available either for installation in nonhazardous locations, such as control rooms, or in listed explosion-proof enclosures for hazardous areas.

Continuous analyzers are frequently tailor-made to meet the exact requirements of the particular installation, and may also employ operating principles other than catalytic combustion.

CALIBRATION CURVES FOR FIELD REFERENCE					
GAS or VAPOR	L.E.L. %BY VOL	CURVE NO.	GAS or VAPOR	L.E.L. %BY VOL	CURVE NO.
ACETONE	2.5	5	HYDROGEN	4.0	1
ACETYLENE	2.3	3	METHYL ALCOHOL	6.7	2
BENZENE	1.4	5	METHYL ETHYL KETONE	1.8	6
CARBON DISULFIDE	1.0	10	NATURAL GAS	4.8	3
CARBON MONOXIDE	12.5	1	OCTANE	1.0	9
ETHYL ACETATE	2.2	7	PENTANE	1.4	5
ETHYL ETHER	1.7	7	PROPANE	2.2	4
GASOLINE	1.3	8	TOLUENE	1.3	4
HEXANE	1.2	7	XYLENE	1.0	7

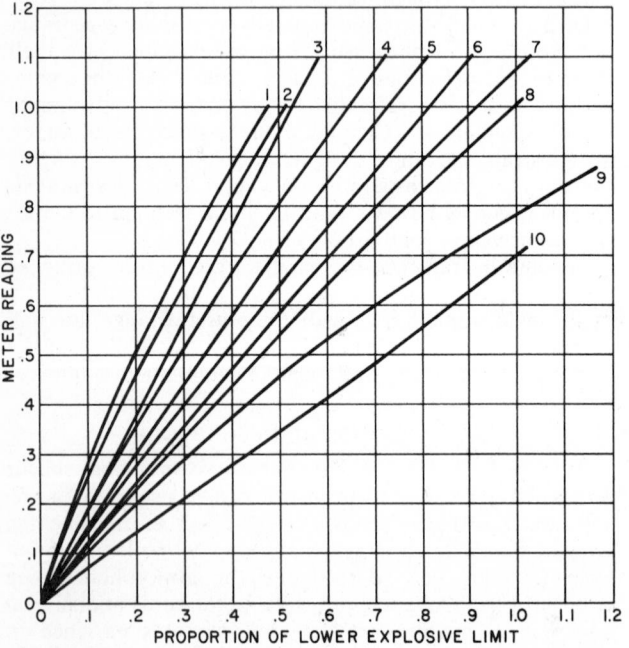

Fig. 12-4B. Calibration curves for one particular make of combustible gas indicator. Calibration curves for indicators of different manufacture may differ because of differences in the physical arrangement of the catalytic unit. Note that in spite of wide variations at higher concentrations, the error becomes negligible as the zero concentration is approached.

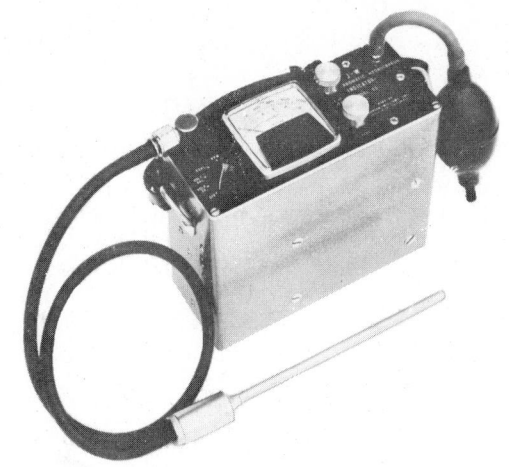

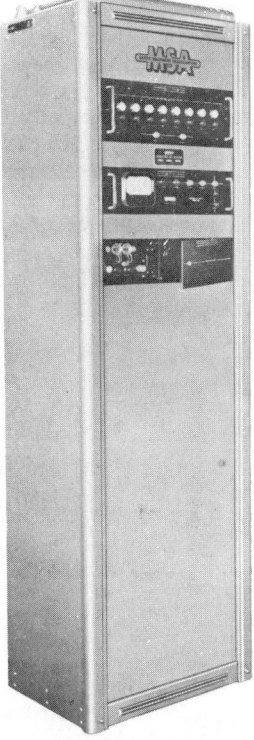

Fig. 12-4D. Combination combustible gas and oxygen detector. (Gas Tech, Inc.)

Fig. 12-4C. (Above) A typical portable flammable and combustible gas detector. Note the bulb-type aspirator for drawing the gas-air sample into the instrument's filament chamber for analyzing, and the hose tipped with a probe for taking the sample. (Johnson-Williams, Inc.) (Left) A continuous-type analyzer for sampling from one or more locations. Tubing carries the gas-air samples to the cabinet. One analyzer may be equipped with a valve mechanism to test alternately a number of locations. (Mine Safety Appliances Co.)

tent of the atmosphere in a closed space, either as an individual unit or as a combination unit incorporating also a combustible gas indicator.

The portable oxygen indicator operates on an electrochemical principle, the partial pressure of the oxygen in the atmosphere controlling the rate of diffusion through a porous membrane and into an electrochemical cell having suitable electrolyte and electrodes. The oxygen enters into an electrochemical reaction, generating a current which in turn produces a deflection of the meter hand. The meter reads oxygen percentage directly on a scale graduated 0 percent to 25 percent.

Except for setting the meter hand to read 21 percent while aspirating fresh air at the elevation (atmospheric pressure) where tests are to be made, no other calibration is necessary for accurate reading in the range of oxygen concentrations in which it is permissible for men to work (17.5 percent to 19.5 percent, depending on the authority having jurisdiction). Where readings are intended to be significant in the low range, as in connection with inerting systems, the zero setting can be confirmed by sampling some oxygen-free gas, such as propane or nitrogen.

Some models use an aspirator bulb or pump to draw the sample into the instrument, and have an appearance and configuration very similar to the standard combustible gas indicator. Other models utilize diffusion sampling, with the oxygen cell suspended at the end of a flexible cable. In either case, the electrical energy levels available from the cell are far below those which could constitute a source of ignition. Figure 12-4D shows a combination combustible gas and oxygen detector.

Other Types of Indicators

Numerous other devices are available, some reasonably portable, that are suitable for determining the presence of contaminating gaseous substances in air. Previously mentioned are those depending on refractive index, density, diffusion, or thermal conductivity of gases or vapors. Other operating principles include: chemical absorption in fluids (Orsat); tubes filled with granular material, where a color change indicates the presence of some specific substance; slow combustion (modified Orsat); direct trial in an explosion pipette, with or without dilution; infrared absorption; flame ionization (specific for hydrogen-containing compounds) and others. Generally these indicators are not specifically designed for combustible gases or vapors, but serve as special purpose instruments in process control applications not necessarily associated with fire protection.

Oxygen Indicators

Devices similar in appearance to the ordinary combustible gas indicator are available for measuring the oxygen con-

Bibliography

M. L. Bowser and W. E. Thomas, "Bureau of Mines Portable Recording Methanometer," Report of Investigations 7270, U.S. Department of the Interior, Bureau of Mines, July, 1969.

R. A. Bradburn and M. L. Bowser, "Miniature Bilevel Alarm for Oxygen-Deficient Atmospheres," Report of Investigations 7165, U.S. Department of the Interior, Bureau of Mines, August, 1968.

"Detection and Analysis of Binary Gas Phase Mixtures," J. F. Riley, *Fire Technology*, Vol. 9, No. 1, Feb. 1973, pp. 15-23.

Nelson W. Hartz, "Use of Combustible Gas Indicators," NFPA *Quarterly*, Vol. 52, No. 4, April, 1959, pp. 357-365.

J. E. Zatek, "Instruments for Measuring Hazardous Atmospheres," *Fire Journal*, Vol. 64, No. 5, September 1970, pp. 76-80.

Chapter 5

FIRE GUARD SERVICES AND WATCHCLOCK SYSTEMS

Guard services to protect a property against fire loss generally fall into three categories: (1) to facilitate and control the movement of persons within the property; (2) to carry out procedures for the orderly conduct of some operations on the property; and (3) to protect the property at times when the management is not present. Guards may be employees of management or employees of outside firms established to provide these services on a contract basis. The duties of these individuals may be supplemented, or in some cases replaced in part, by various approved protective signaling systems.

A. Guard Service Direction

The property manager should supervise guard service, or designate a responsible person to handle it for him (such as the fire loss prevention manager). The fire loss prevention manager should be consulted in setting up procedures of guard service affecting fire loss prevention. Procedures and specific instructions to guards should be geared to specific actions required. General instructions or superficial training are of little value. Meaningful, specific instructions cannot be prepared without the investment of time and thought by the management of the property.

Management should establish a clear line of succession in event of absences. Even when there are only two guards employed, one should be designated leader.

Supervision of guards from outside firms should be through the designated representatives of the company providing the guard service. That company should be given, in its contract or supplementary documents, as specific and complete details as possible regarding the services expected.

Management procedures should be established for the maintenance of equipment provided for supervision of guards. Even where equipment used in supervision or guard service is obtained under contract, management should assure itself that the necessary maintenance procedures for each type of equipment are being satisfactorily performed.

When a guard is asked to patrol a plant or warehouse during hours when the property is closed and otherwise unattended, management has the responsibility to provide adequate equipment and information to the guard in order to safeguard his health and safety. Situations which must be considered include:

1. Sudden illness or injury of the guard when he is alone at the property.

2. The possibility of a guard being abducted or attacked by an intruder.

3. Situations requiring management decisions.

The first situation might be cared for by providing each guard with a portable radio or radio paging system which would allow the guard to summon aid should he become ill or injured. In the second situation an intruder might prevent the use of any equipment carried by the guard, and it then becomes necessary to provide a system or procedure whereby his failure to transmit a signal or his failure to meet a predetermined schedule will be investigated promptly.

Situations may arise during hours that the property is attended by guards only, when management decisions are necessary and the guard must be instructed or have facilities for contacting management personnel. Such decisions— which usually require prompt action by management— ranging from unscheduled arrival of merchandise to anonymous bomb threats or even "wildcat" strikes, and may occur at hours when top level managers are not present.

B. Communication Equipment

Guards should be provided with facilities for communication within and outside the property. Local protective signaling systems should be designed to give signals for supervision of guard service at the property protected. With proprietary protective signaling systems, the property management should provide a control center at the property protected and the necessary qualified operators and runners.

Management should provide competent and experienced personnel to provide general supervision of the system, to do the necessary maintenance, and to test and inspect the system for proper operation. Where the management does not itself provide these facilities and their maintenance, it should provide them by contract.

Where patrolmen's clocks or time recording systems are used to assure the performance of patrols, the property management should adopt a practice of promptly reviewing the time records of patrolmen, dating and filing them for review by representatives of any authority having jurisdiction. Management should investigate irregularities thoroughly.

A control center should provide a point with which guards may communicate. The center should have communication facilities to points outside the property. Such a center is needed even when there is very limited guard service. For example, in a plant with only one or two guards, this center might be simply a room with a telephone. Even with central station service a control center on the property is necessary.

Where the equipment for guard communications, including guards on watch patrol, requires that signals from guards be monitored, the control center should be provided with an operator. Additional operators and around-the-clock operator service should be provided at the control center according to the character of guard service provided. For some services, runners or guards who can be dispatched to investigate signals should also be provided.

A directory of names, telephone numbers (including any other information to assist in making emergency calls to outside) in visible index or other form should be kept at the control center. This directory should give information about the public fire department, key management personnel, and other outside agencies it might be necessary to reach in an emergency.

C. Supervisory Systems

Guard supervisory services designed to report continuously the performance of a guard are found in connection with central station service, remote station service, and proprietary signaling systems. These services usually provide for supervised tours or compulsory tours.

Supervised Tours

In the first case, a series of patrol stations along the guard's intended route are successively operated by the guard with each station sounding a distinctive signal at a central headquarters. Customarily, the guard is expected to reach each of these stations at a definite time, and his failure to do so within a reasonable grace period thereafter prompts the central station to investigate his failure to signal. Frequently, manual fire alarm boxes that ordinarily transmit four or five rounds of signals for fire also can be actuated by a special watch key carried by the guard to transmit only a single round to the central station, thus signaling that he has visited that box.

By proper location of the stations, a fire or security guard can be compelled to take a definite route through the premises, and variations from that route would appear as misplaced signals on the recording tape. A further advantage is that the order of station operation can be varied from time to time in the interests of security or to meet special conditions within the plant.

Compulsory Tours

In the second case, only one station is wired to the central station, and as many as nine preliminary mechanical stations condition the guard's key to operate the wired station after, and only after, the preliminary stations have been operated in a prearranged order. This second arrangement is somewhat less flexible than the first, but has the advantages of the absence of interconnected wires between the preliminary stations and the reduction of signal traffic. The usual arrangement is to have the guard transmit only a starting and a finishing signal which must be received at the central point at times programmed for reception.

Delinquency Indicators

Delinquency indicator systems are a variation, from the unwired arrangement, in which a series of wired stations will transmit a signal if the guard does not reach the particular station within the preset anticipated period.

Telephone System

Use is sometimes made of extension telephones that terminate in a central supervisory office. The guard reports successively from each of the extensions, and his route is timed and checked off by the operating supervisor.

D.   Guard Clock Systems

A portable watch clock is widely used, where immediate supervision of the guard is not imperative, to record the performance of a guard on his tours. A number of stations, each consisting of a key, are located throughout the premises, and the guard, upon reaching a station, operates the key in his portable clock. This records the station number on a paper dial or tape in the clock, indicating the time of visit. Each time a clock is opened or closed for any purpose, a mark is punched on the dial, or tape, so that unauthorized tampering is readily detected. A representative portable watch clock is shown in Figure 12-5A.

A stationary guard clock system utilizes a clock installed at a central location with electric wiring extending to stations throughout the property. The guard carries a small crank-type key which he inserts at each station box. Turning the key operates a small magneto which generates sufficient current to actuate a recording mechanism in the central clock and indicates the time each station is visited.

Fig. 12-5A. Front view (top) and interior view (bottom) of a portable watch clock. This clock provides an embossed record in the tape, made directly from type on the recording key. The tape is divided into 24 ruled segments and is synchronized with the clock mechanism. If a watchman fails to punch in, the omission is indicated by a prominent white space on the tape. This clock has a "detector" showing when the clock was opened. (Detex Corp.)

E.   Guard Service Functions

A sufficient number of guards should be provided to accomplish the needed services. If a guard is assigned to part-time duties in addition to his regular guard services, these duties should be chosen so as not to interfere with his regular guard service.

Guard service can facilitate and control the movement of persons within a property when the number of persons in the property requires such service. Duties in this category include:

1. Prevent entry of unauthorized persons who might set a fire or do damage.

2. Control the activities of people authorized to be on the property, but who may not be aware of procedures established for the prevention of fire.

3. Control of pedestrian and vehicular traffic during exit drills, and evacuation of the property or parts of it during emergencies.

4. Control of gates and vehicular traffic to facilitate access to the property by the public fire department, members of any private fire brigade, and of off-duty management personnel in case of fire or emergency.

Guard service should be established to carry out certain procedures for the orderly conduct of the operations in the property, including procedures for fire loss prevention both by personnel associated with the property and outside contractors. Duties in this category include:

1. Checking permits for hot work including cutting, welding, and standing by where necessary to operate fire extinguishing equipment on such work.

2. Detecting conditions likely to cause a fire, such as leaks, spills and faulty equipment.

3. Detecting conditions likely to reduce the effectiveness with which a fire may be controlled, such as portable fire extinguishers not in place, sprinkler valves not open, and water supplies impaired.

4. Performing operations to assure that fire equipment will function effectively. These may include: testing automatic sprinkler and other fixed fire protection systems, fire

pumps and other equipment related to these systems and assisting in maintenance of this equipment; checking portable fire extinguishers and fire hose and assisting in pressure tests and maintenance service on these items; testing fire alarm equipment by actuating transmitting devices as required, and checking equipment provided on any motorized fire apparatus and making the periodic tests and maintenance operations required for it.

5. Promptly discovering a fire and calling the public fire department (also the fire brigade of the property, where there is such a brigade).

6. Operating equipment provided for fire control and extinguishment after giving the alarm and before the response of other persons to the alarm.

7. Monitoring signals due to the operation of protective signaling systems provided, such as alarms from manual fire alarm boxes on a system private to the property, signals for water flow in sprinkler systems, signals from systems for detecting fires and abnormal conditions, including trouble signals.

8. Making patrols over routes chosen to assure surveillance of all the property at appropriate intervals.

9. Starting up and shutting down certain equipment when there is no other personnel provided for the purpose.

F.   Patrol Routes and Rounds

Each route to be covered by a patrolman should be laid out by the responsible manager. The patrolman responsible for each route should be provided with instructions as to all details of the route, and what is expected of him in covering it. The route should be laid out so that the patrolman is required to pass through the entire area the patrol is to cover. It should be laid out to prevent shortcuts such as use of stairways, elevators, or bridges. A rest period between rounds is reasonable.

Patrolmen should make rounds at intervals determined by the management for the particular situation. When operations in the property are normally suspended, patrolmen should make rounds hourly unless management is willing to accept rounds at less frequent intervals. When there are special conditions, such as the presence of exceptional hazards or when protection is impaired, management should institute additional rounds as may be necessary to meet the fire safety requirements of such conditions.

The first round of a patrol should begin usually as soon as possible after the end of activities of the preceding work shift. The patrolman should have instructions requiring him to make a thorough inspection of all buildings or spaces on his routes during the first round. His instructions should cover such matters as the following:

1. Outside doors and gates should be closed and locked; windows, skylights, fire doors, and fire shutters should be closed.

2. All oily waste, rags, paint residue, rubbish, and similar items should be removed from buildings or placed in approved containers.

3. All fire apparatus should be in place and not obstructed.

4. Aisles should be clear.

5. Motors or machines carelessly left running should be shut off and reported.

6. All offices, conference rooms, and smoking areas should be checked for carelessly discarded smoking materials.

7. All gas and electric heaters, coal and oil stoves, and other heating devices on the premises should be checked.

8. All hazardous manufacturing processes should be left in a safe condition. The temperature of dryers, annealing furnaces, and similar equipment which continue to operate during the night, holidays, and weekends should be noted on all rounds.

9. Hazardous materials, such as gasoline, rubber cement, and other flammable and highly volatile combustibles should be kept in proper containers or removed from buildings.

10. All sprinkler valves should be open with gages indicating proper pressures. If not open, the fact should be reported immediately.

11. All rooms should be checked during cold weather to determine if they are heated properly.

12. All water faucets and air valves found leaking should be closed. If unable to stop leaks, the condition should be reported.

13. Particular attention should be given to new construction or alterations which may be under way.

G.   Selection of Guards

Management should require individuals considered for guard service to satisfactorily pass a character investigation. This investigation should attempt to evaluate the individual's reliability, self-control, and potential loyalty to his employer. Applicants for a position as a guard should be required to be fingerprinted and to give particulars of any police records. The local police should be furnished with this information, should corroborate the information, and should ask for checks by other police agencies. The fingerprint data should be cleared with state, national, or appropriate international agencies that maintain clearing facilities for police records. All applicants for a position as a fire or security guard or patrolman should be required to state any military service record and to submit evidence of such service, such as discharge papers, which may assist in an evaluation of the individual's suitabiilty for guard service.

Contracts for guard service should include a provision that the company furnishing guard service will replace any of its employees who, in the judgment of the company purchasing the service, are not qualified.

Management should be satisfied that individuals considered for guard service are mentally alert and have good powers of observation, intelligence, and judgment. Investigation should attempt to evaluate the individual's personality and temperament. Such an evaluation is more realistic than arbitrary tests of education or intelligence, or an age limit. Very young men may not qualify because they have not acquired a sense of responsibility or judgment. A very old man may have impaired alertness. Individuals should be sought who are known to be not easily confused by an emergency.

Annually, guards should be required to pass a written examination dealing with information about the property protected and procedures for fire loss prevention with which they are expected to be familiar.

Management should require that individuals considered for guard service pass an examination to determine whether they are physically able to perform the guard duties to which they will be assigned. Guards should also be required to pass an annual physical examination. The guard does not need to be an athlete, but neither should he have a heart condition or other physical ailment which might work to his disadvantage in moments of stress.

H. Training

Management should establish a continuing training program for its guards. Its scope should be established by the manager or by a fire loss prevention manager, acting for the manager. Advantage may be taken of courses for guards and fire fighters made available through training programs of vocational training agencies, schools, universities, and other training and educational-type agencies.

Management should require guards to have completed at least elementary courses of instruction in the use of portable fire equipment and emergency first aid to injured persons. The time spent in such preliminary training should be not less than two working days in each subject. During service, a guard should be given not less than the equivalent of two full working days per year of training to increase his knowledge and experience in the use of portable fire extinguishers, first aid to the injured, and other training likely to increase his usefulness in guard service work. Guards should be required, as a part of their training, to participate in appropriate meetings of operating personnel devoted to pre-fire planning. Guards can help accomplish this by working together with the public fire department when they establish their plan for the premises.

Management should require guards to know the location of portable fire extinguishers, hand hose, standpipes and hydrants, valves controlling sprinkler systems, inside riser valves, post indicator valves and sectional valves in the property's own water system, and how to start fire pumps. Guards may also need to know the location and purpose of valves controlling water other than for fire protection, and valves controlling steam, gas, and other services. Management should require guards to know the locations of dangerous machinery or materials and identify for them hazardous manufacturing processes, especially those continuing during the night, holidays, or weekends.

Bibliography

Reference Cited

[1] Bond, Horatio, ed., *Inspection Manual*, 3rd ed. National Fire Protection Association, Boston, 1970.

NFPA Codes, Standards, and Recommended Practices (see the latest *NFPA Publications and Visual Aids Catalog* for availability of current editions of the following documents)

NFPA No. 601, Recommendations for Guard Service in Fire Loss Prevention.

NFPA No. 601A, Standard for Guard Operations in Fire Loss Prevention.

SECTION 13

EXTINGUISHING AGENTS

Chapter 1

WATER AND WATER ADDITIVES FOR FIRE FIGHTING

Water is, and has long been, the most commonly used extinguishing agent. The physical characteristics of water that are pertinent to its extinguishing ability and its limitations as an extinguishing agent are discussed in this chapter. Also discussed in this chapter are the extinguishing actions of water's cooling, smothering, emulsifying, and diluting properties.

The basic principles of extinguishment of fire are contained in Section 2, Chapter 1, Chemistry and Physics of Fire, and Section 2, Chapter 4, Theory of Fire and Explosion Control. The systems and devices employed for the transportation and application of water as an extinguishing agent are contained in applicable chapters in Section 9, Public Fire Protection; Section 11, Water Supplies for Fire Protection; Section 14, Water Sprinkler Systems; Section 15, Special Fire Protection Systems; and Section 16, Portable Fire Extinguishers.

A. Physical Properties

The physical properties that contribute to the extinguishing capacity of water are as follows (other than water, there is no material normally practical to use which has the cooling capacity indicated by these characteristics):

1. At ordinary temperature water is a heavy, relatively stable liquid.

2. The melting of 1 lb of ice into water at 32°F absorbs 143.4 Btu, which is the heat fusion of ice.

3. One Btu is required to raise the temperature of 1 lb of water 1°F, which is the specific heat of water. Therefore, raising the temperature of 1 lb of water from 32°F to 212°F requires 180 Btu.

4. The heat of vaporization of water (converting 1 lb of water to steam at a constant temperature) is 970.3 Btu per lb at atmospheric pressure.

Another factor which affects the extinguishing action of water is that when water is converted from liquid to vapor, its volume at ordinary pressures increases about 1,700 times. This large volume of water (steam) displaces an equal volume of air surrounding a fire, thus reducing the volume of air (oxygen) available to sustain combustion in the fire zone. Applying water in the form of ice or snow to a fire would, obviously, utilize to the maximum water's most effective cooling action. However, practical equipment for such use is not available.

B. Extinguishing Properties

Extinguishment occurs only when the effect of the extinguishing agent is felt at the point where combustion is occurring. For hundreds of years the principal method used to extinguish fires was to direct a solid stream of water (from a safe distance) into the base of the fire. This same method of fire extinguishment, the application of streams of water through nozzles, continues today as the most conventional method of fire extinguishment.

A more efficient method is the application of water in spray form, and combination nozzles and sprinklers. Other similar devices for this type of application are now coming into general use.

Extinguishment by Cooling

In most cases, if the surface of the burning material is cooled below the temperature at which it will give off sufficient vapor to support combustion, the fire will be extinguished. Surface cooling is not usually effective on gaseous products or on flammable liquids that have flash points below the temperature of the applied water, and it is generally not recommended for flammable liquids having a flash point below 100°F.

The amount of water required for extinguishment will depend on the amount of heat which must be absorbed. The speed of extinguishment will depend on the rate of application in relation to the heat generated, the degree of coverage possible, and the form and character of the water applied. It is best to discharge water on a fire in a manner that exerts maximum cooling effect through heat absorption. To do this involves heating the water to 212°F and converting it to steam (a procedure more readily accomplished when the water is applied in droplets rather than as a solid stream).

Much theoretical information is available on the factors that affect the rates of heat absorption and vaporization of water droplets. Because these factors cannot be closely controlled under most actual fire conditions, it is not feasible to use such theoretical data for accurate fire ground calculations.

The principles affecting the cooling action of water in spray form are as follows:

1. The rate of heat transfer is proportional to the exposed surface of the liquid. For a given quantity of water, the surface is greatly increased by conversion to droplets.

2. The rate of heat transfer depends on the temperature difference between the water and the surrounding air or burning material.

3. The rate of heat transfer also depends on the vapor content of the air, particularly in regard to fire spread.

4. The heat-absorbing capacity depends upon the distance traveled and the velocity of the water in the combustion zone. (This factor must take into consideration the necessity for projecting a suitable volume of water to the needed location.)

Calculations indicate that the optimum diameter of a water droplet for extinguishing purposes is in the range of 0.3 to 1.0 mm. The best results are accomplished when the droplets are fairly uniform in size. Presently there is no discharge device capable of producing complete uniformity of size, although many discharge devices have been developed which achieve acceptable degrees of uniformity over a fairly wide range of pressures. The droplet must be large enough to have sufficient energy to reach the point of combustion despite air resistance, the opposing force of gravity, or the diverting movement of air caused by thermal updraft and other air currents.

Certain materials decompose chemically when their temperatures are raised. Water can normally be used to cool these materials below the temperature at which decomposition will be self-sustaining, unless the burning material reacts chemically with the water. In a limited number of cases the application of water accelerates combustion; this may be desirable to reduce the period of burning.

Wetting of combustible materials is a method frequently employed to prevent ignition of unburned materials. Moisture absorption by combustible materials frequently retards ignition since the moisture in the material must be "evaporated" before the temperature of the unburned material can be raised to its ignition temperature.

Extinguishment by Smothering

If steam is generated in sufficient amounts, air can be displaced or excluded. Fires in certain types of materials can be extinguished by this smothering action. Smothering action is aided by confinement of the steam generated in the combustion zone. The process of heat absorption by steam ends when the steam starts to condense, a change of state which requires heat release from the steam. This condition is made evident by the formation of visible clouds of water vapor. Such condensation occurring above the combustion zone has no cooling effect on the burning material. However, the steam may act to carry heat away from the fire zone where it can harmlessly dissipate itself into clouds of water vapor above the fire.

Fires in ordinary combustibles are normally extinguished by the cooling effect of water—not by the smothering effect created by the generation of steam. Although the latter might have the tendency to suppress flaming, it does not have the tendency to completely extinguish such fires.

Water may be used to smother a burning flammable or combustible liquid when the liquid has a flash point above 100°F, a specific gravity of 1.1 or heavier, and when the liquid is not water soluble. To achieve this result most effectively, a foaming agent is normally added to the water (see Chapter 2 of this Section). The water must then be applied gently to the surface of the liquid.

In cases where oxygen is liberated in decomposition of a burning material, smothering by any agent cannot be achieved effectively.

Extinguishment by Emulsification

An emulsion is formed when immiscible liquids are agitated together and one of the liquids is dispersed throughout the other in the form of minute droplets. Extinguishment by this process can be achieved by applying water to certain viscous flammable liquids, since the effect of cooling the surfaces of such liquids prevents the release of flammable vapors. With some viscous liquids (such as No. 6 fuel oil) the emulsification appears in the form of a "froth" which retards the release of flammable vapors. Care must be exercised in utilizing this emulsification process on liquids of appreciable depth, as the frothing may be violent enough to spread the burning liquids over the sides of the container. A relatively strong, coarse water spray is usually employed to obtain the emulsifying effect. However, a solid stream of water must be avoided or violent frothing will result.

Extinguishment by Dilution

Fires in flammable materials that are soluble in water may, in some instances, be extinguished by dilution. The percentage of dilution necessary for extinguishment varies greatly, and the volume of water and the time necessary for extinguishment will likewise vary. For example this dilution technique can be used successfully in a fire involving an ethyl or methyl alcohol spill where it is possible to get an adequate mixture of water and alcohol. The addition of water to achieve dilution, however, is not a common practice when tanks are involved. The danger of overflow because of the large amount of water required, and the danger of frothing should the mixture become heated to the boiling point of water, make this form of extinguishment seldom practical.

C. Electrical Conductivity of Water

Water in its natural state contains impurities that make it conductive. Applying water to fires involving live electrical equipment requires consideration of the shock hazard to the user, especially if high voltages or potentials are involved. The amount of current rather than the voltage determines the extent of the shock hazard. Principal variables, assuming contact with a live electrical charge, are:

1. The voltage and amount of current flowing.

2. The "break-up" of the stream as a result of the nozzle design, the pressures used, and the wind conditions. This break-up influences the conductivity of the stream as the air spaces formed between the droplets interrupt the electrical path to ground. Modern water spray nozzles and combination straight stream spray nozzles, the latter in the spray position, provide for effective dispersion of the water droplets. This dispersion decreases the conductivity hazard as compared with solid streams of water.

3. The purity of the water and the relative resistivity of the water.

4. The length and cross-sectional area of the water stream.

5. The resistance to ground through a person's body as influenced by his location (whether on wet ground or not), his skin moisture, the amount of current his body can endure, the length of exposure to the current, and other factors such as protective clothing.

6. The resistance to ground through the hose.

Conductivity and Hazard of Shock

There is usually little danger to fire fighters directing streams of water onto wires of less than 600 v to ground from any distance likely to be met under ordinary fire fighting conditions. However, it is dangerous when fire fighters, standing either in puddles of water or on moist surfaces, come into physical contact with live electrical equipment. In such cases the fire fighters' bodies complete an electrical circuit, and the current from the electrical equipment relayed through their bodies is more readily grounded than if it were conveyed through dry, nonconductive surfaces. Therefore, because rubber boots often contain enough carbon black to permit the passage of current through the body, rubber boots should not be relied upon as being resistant enough to prevent the completion of an electrical circuit through the body.

The results of research conducted by UL (Underwriters Laboratories, Inc.), presented in Bulletin of Research No. 14[1], covering electric fences, indicate that there are differences in the electric current to which individuals may be safely subjected, and that the maximum continuous (uninterrupted) current to which an individual may be safely subjected is 5 ma (milliamperes). The research also indicates that there is a definite relationship between the length of exposure to electric shock and the effect of the shock, in that momentary exposure has less-serious effects than more continuous exposure. Research work aimed at determining the shock hazard that might be transmitted to fire fighters using nozzles and hoses through which water is applied to live electrical equipment is based on an assumed maximum current ranging from 1 to 3 ma as being hazardous, and a maximum of 1 ma used in most of the work.

Impurities in water (mostly the mineral content) affect its conductivity. Tests of the resistivity of public water supplies in Indiana showed results ranging from 710 to 5,400 ohms per cc (cubic centimeters), the lowest values being found in supplies from deep wells. The deep-well supplies that were tested showed a resistivity ranging between 1,000 and 2,000 ohms per cc, and the river waters that were tested showed a resistivity in the range of 4,000 ohms per cc. In tests conducted by the Commonwealth Edison Company in cooperation with the Chicago Fire Department,[2] the results of the tests showed that the resistivity of Chicago river water ranged from 1,671 to 2,393 ohms per cc. At the time the tests were made, the normal hydrant water in the Chicago area had a resistivity of about 3,800 ohms per cc.

Safe Distances from Live Equipment

Criteria for recommending specific distances between nozzles dispensing water and live electrical equipment have been sporadically researched by many different authorities. The bibliography at the end of this chapter cites some of the more important reference papers pertaining to this type of research.

The conductivity of water streams should be considered in relation to the types of extinguishing equipment that use them. Among them are: (1) hand-held or manually supported solid stream nozzles, (2) hand-held water spray (water fog) nozzles, (3) fixed water spray systems for fire protection services, and (4) plain water and water solution portable fire extinguishers.

Available data on the minimum safe distances required between manually supported solid stream hose lines and live electrical equipment carrying voltages higher than 600 v are not wholly consistent because of the variances in the results of tests that have been made. The reasons for these variances are the different testing methods used, the variances in the purposes of the tests, the limitations of the tests (necessitated by the physical circumstances and available equipment, and the fact that the same voltages were not used in all of the tests).

The AIA (American Insurance Association), in "Fire Streams and Electrical Circuits," Special Interest Bulletin No. 91[3], suggests the distances given in Table 13-1A between solid stream nozzles (dispensing fresh water) and electrical conductors or equipment carrying voltages higher than 600 v to be the minimum for safety. The AIA data are based on tests run in the 1930's; thus the voltages given do not correspond to present-day, commonly encountered ranges, nor does the data extend to the higher ranges now

Table 13-1A. Distances Between Solid Stream Nozzles (Fresh Water) and Electrical Conductors
American Insurance Association

Voltage to Ground	Voltages Between Conductors	Minimum Safe Distance	
		1¼ in. Tip Nozzle (Feet)	1½ in. Tip Nozzle (Feet)
635	1,100	6	9
1,270	2,200	11	16
1,905	3,300	15	22
3,175	5,500	18	27
4,215	6,600	19	29
6,350	11,000	20	30
12,700	22.000	25	33
19,050	33,000	30	40

Table 13-1B. Limit of Safe Approach to Live Electrical Equipment
Hydroelectric Power Commission of Ontario

Voltage to Ground	Voltage Between Conductors	Minimum Safe Distance (Feet)
		⅝-in. Solid-Stream Nozzle*
2,400	4,160	15
4,800	8,320	20
7,200	12,500	20
8,000	13,800	20
14,400	24,900	25
16,000	27,600	25
25,000	44,000	30
66,500	115,000	30
130,000	230,000	30

* Nozzle pressure 100 psi; water resistance 600 ohms per cubic inch.

widely used. The Bulletin cautions that for streams from contaminated or salt water, or where additives have been introduced into the water, it is not possible to give simple rules due to the variances in the conductivity of the water.

Some limited tests made in 1958 by the Hydroelectric Power Commission of Ontario in cooperation with the Office of the Fire Marshal of Ontario, Canada[4], resulted in recommendations for minimum safe distances from live electrical equipment for a ⅝-in. solid stream nozzle (see Table 13-1B). The report recommends that solid streams greater than ⅝ in. should not be used near live electrical equipment, but the tests were limited to a maximum stream distance of 30 ft. It is possible that larger nozzles might produce sufficient stream dispersion over longer distances which would permit their use.

The results of tests made in 1934 for the Fire Brigade of Paris, France, present what is perhaps the most comprehensive guidance (see Table 13-1C).[5] The distances given in Table 13-1C are based on preventing the transmission of a 1 ma (milliampere) current to a fire fighter in contact with a nozzle or hose. The tests covered only voltages to ground ranging from 115 to 150,000 v, and the groupings of the voltages do not correspond to current standard U.S. voltages. The maximum size of the nozzle used in the tests is nonstandard in the United States.

The preceding information on the use of solid streams indicates that definite shock hazards exist unless adequate distances are kept, and that these distances can only be estimated from the available research data. It is difficult for fire fighters in the field to have specific knowledge of what electrical potentials might exist in any given situation. For this reason, as well as for those given in the following paragraphs, it is preferable, whenever possible, to use water spray streams rather than solid streams.

As previously noted, water spray nozzles or adjustable nozzles, when providing a spray pattern, reduce the conductivity hazard by virtue of stream break-up. The design of the nozzle and the resultant character of the spray determines the actual amount of leakage current that can flow in the stream at specified distances with a given electrical charge. Basically, each nozzle should be tested to determine precisely the characteristics it possesses. Tests which have been made utilizing various commercially available water spray nozzles indicate that a minimum distance of 4 ft should be maintained for voltages to ground up to about 10 kv. This distance is actually no greater than is desirable to prevent an operator from getting dangerously close to

Table 13-1C. Minimum Safe Distances Between Hose Nozzles and Live Electrical Equipment Recommended for the Paris, France, Fire Brigade

Voltage to Ground	Voltage Between Conductors	Safe Distance (Feet)		
		Diameter of Nozzle Orifice		
		¼ in.†	¾ in.†	1¼ in.†
115	230	1.6	3.3	6.6
460	480	2.5	9.8	16.4
3,000	5,195	6.6	16.4	32.8
6,000	10,395	8.2	19.7	39.4
12,000	20,785	9.8	21.4	49.2
60,000	103,820	14.8	39.4	72.2
150,000	259,800	19.7	49.2	82.0

† Figures rounded off from metric scale.

live electrical equipment. Distances should be increased when attacking fires involving live electrical equipment operating above this voltage. Figure 13-1A shows the test results of four researchers, as analyzed in Fire Research Technical Paper No. 13 by M. J. O'Dogherty.[6]

Tests made by the Toledo Edison Company in which water was discharged onto a screen at a potential to ground of 80,500 v (equivalent to a system or line voltage of 138 kv phase-to-phase), as reported to the Edison Electric Institute in January, 1967, have led to the adoption of the following safety rules by the utilities (the distance in these rules will limit leakage currents to less than 1 ma):

1. Using all hand-held water spray nozzles, the minimum approach distance is 10 ft.

2. Using hand-held, 1½-in. straight (solid) stream nozzles, the minimum approach distance is 20 ft.

3. Using hand-held, 2½-in. straight (solid) stream nozzles, the minimum approach distance is 30 ft.

It is preferable not to use combination nozzles for fighting fires in live electrical equipment because of the possibility of the accidental use of a solid stream discharge instead of a spray during the fire fighting evolution. When such hand-held nozzles must be utilized on live electrical equipment, fire fighters should be sure they have the desired spray pattern before applying the stream directly onto the equipment. The use of spray nozzles on "applicators" increases the possibility of accidental contact between the nozzle and live electrical equipment; therefore, most authorities recommend that such applicators not be used.

Clearance from Fixed Water Spray Systems

Fixed water spray systems are extensively used to protect high-value and/or critical electrical equipment such as

transformers, oil switches, and motors. These systems are designed to provide for effective fire control, extinguishment, prevention, or for exposure protection. NFPA No. 15, Water Spray Fixed Systems, hereinafter referred to in this chapter as the NFPA Water Spray Standard, gives installation recommendations for such systems, and includes a table of recommended clearances between water spray equipment and any unenclosed or uninsulated live electrical components at other than ground potential. (The NFPA Water Spray Standard should be consulted for more complete details.) Modern practice is to coordinate the required clearance with the electrical design. The BIL (Basic Impulse Insulation Level) values of the equipment being protected are used as the basis, although the clearance between uninsulated live parts of the electrical system equipment and any portion of the water spray system should be not less than the minimum clearances provided elsewhere for electrical system insulation on any individual component (the minimum unshielded straight-line distance from the exposed electrical parts to nearby grounded objects). The BIL (expressed in kilovolts) is the crest value of the full wave impulse test.

Portable Extinguishers and Hazard of Shock

Water-based or water-solution portable fire extinguishers are not recommended for use on fires involving live electrical equipment (Class C). NFPA No. 10, Installation of Portable Fire Extinguishers, recommends that extinguishers for the protection of Class C hazards be selected from those rated for such fires. When electrical equipment is de-energized, extinguishers for Class A or B fires may be used safely. Tests on the conductivity of portable fire extinguishers containing water indicate that soda-acid, loaded-stream, foam, and antifreeze solution extinguishers which produce solid streams and have a short range, are hazardous to use. One test involving an antifreeze-solution extinguisher showed a current of 157 ma for a potential of 1 kv with a $\frac{3}{32}$-in. stream at a distance of 1 ft. To reduce the current to below 1 ma, it would be necessary to use the device from a distance at which the stream is dispersed; it is generally agreed that for such extinguishers a minimum distance of approach should not be less than 4 ft for voltages up to 1 kv. Extinguishers containing plain water (without additives) might be used at shorter distances from the shock hazard point of view, but from general safety considerations near live electrical apparatus, a 4-ft distance should be maintained if it is necessary to use this type of extinguisher.

Water on Electrical and Electronic Equipment

In using water on electrical and electronic equipment, recognition must be given to the value of automatic sprinkler protection and water spray fixed systems as means of reducing fire damage, even where such electrical or electronic equipment may be exposed. There should be little concern relative to the shock hazard, or that the water will cause excessive damage to equipment in installations of this type. Experience has proved that if a fire develops sufficiently enough to operate sprinklers, the sprinklers, if properly installed and maintained, provide for effective fire control and extinguishment with virtually no hazard to personnel and with no measurable increase in damage to the electrical or electronic equipment (as comparable to damage traceable to heat, flame, smoke, and the possible need to use manual hose streams).

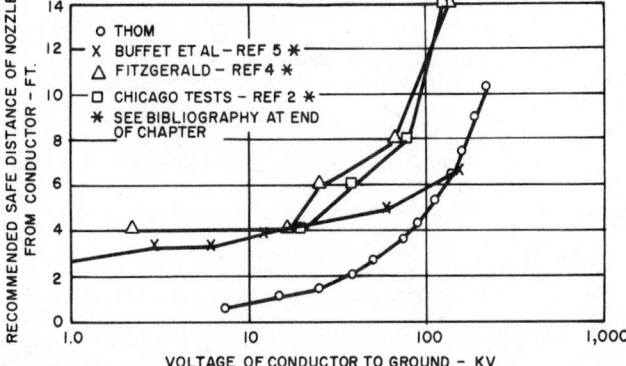

Fig. 13-1A. Variation of safe distance with conductor voltage for spray nozzles.

D. Freezing Temperatures and Antifreeze Additives

Because water freezes at 32°F, its use as an extinguishing agent is limited in climates or situations where such low temperature conditions exist. Freezing of a tank of water does not take place instantaneously, and the duration of the exposure prior to complete freeze-up depends on such factors as the amount of water, its temperature, and the air temperature and velocity.

There are several methods of reducing the problem of using water as a fire fighting tool under low temperature conditions. These methods vary from using dry-pipe sprinkler systems in lieu of wet-pipe systems (see Sec. 14, Chap. 2), circulating or heating of tank water supplies held for fire protection purposes (see Sec. 11, Chap. 3), the addition of freezing point depressants to the water, or a combination of any of these techniques.

The most widely used water soluble freezing point depressant in fire equipment is calcium chloride with a corrosion inhibitor additive (see Table 13-1D). This material is available commercially and comes in two forms. Type 1 (regular) is in flake form and contains a minimum of 77 percent calcium chloride; Type 2 (concentrated) is in pellet form and contains a minimum of 94 percent calcium chloride. Table 13-1D gives the various weights in pounds of calcium chloride required to achieve protection against freezing for various temperatures down to −59.8°F (note that after this point, added amounts of calcium chloride do not depress the freezing point further: they raise it).

Sodium chloride (common salt) is unsatisfactory for fire protection use due to its limited ability to depress the freezing point of water, and because sodium chloride solutions are highly corrosive.

Sprinkler Systems: Chemically pure glycerine (U.S. Pharmacopoeia 96.5 percent grade) or pure propylene glycol can be used to depress the freezing point of water in portions of wet-pipe systems connected to public water supplies if authorized by local health authorities. Diethylene glycol, ethylene glycol or calcium chloride, as well as glycerine or propylene glycol, can be used for the same purposes where public water is not connected. Both ethylene and diethylene glycol are poisonous when swallowed, and

Table 13-1D. Calcium Chloride Solutions to Depress Freezing Point of Water

Freezing Point	Lbs Calcium Chloride Type 1 (77% Min CaCl$_2$) per Gal Water at 60°F	per Gal Solution at 60°F	Lbs Calcium Chloride Type 2 (94% Min CaCl$_2$) per Gal Water at 60°F	per Gal Solution at 60°F	Hydrometer Readings Using Hydrometer Calibrated at 60/60° at 0°F	at 30°F	at 60°F	at 90°F
30	0.26	0.26	0.21	0.2	—	—	1.021	1.017
25	0.91	0.87	0.73	0.72	—	1.070	1.066	1.062
20	1.46	1.36	1.11	1.08	—	1.107	1.102	1.097
15	1.88	1.73	1.46	1.41	—	1.133	1.128	1.123
10	2.24	2.03	1.74	1.67	—	1.156	1.150	1.144
5	2.55	2.28	1.97	1.87	—	1.174	1.168	1.162
0	2.83	2.50	2.17	2.06	—	1.190	1.183	1.177
− 5	3.14	2.73	2.38	2.24	1.210	1.205	1.198	1.191
−10	3.38	2.92	2.55	2.40	1.224	1.219	1.212	1.205
−15	3.64	3.10	2.74	2.55	1.238	1.232	1.225	1.218
−20	3.89	3.28	2.90	2.69	1.250	1.245	1.237	1.229
−25	4.13	3.45	3.06	2.83	1.262	1.256	1.248	1.240
−30	4.37	3.61	3.21	2.95	1.272	1.266	1.258	1.250
−35	4.58	3.75	3.34	3.06	1.282	1.275	1.267	1.259
−40	4.73	3.85	3.44	3.15	1.289	1.282	1.274	1.266
−45	4.86	3.93	3.53	3.22	1.295	1.288	1.280	1.272
−50	4.94	3.98	3.59	3.27	1.298	1.291	1.283	1.275
−55	5.02	4.03	3.64	3.30	1.302	1.295	1.287	1.279
−59.8	5.10	4.08	3.69	3.35	1.306	1.298	1.290	1.282
−50	5.23	4.16	3.78	3.42	1.311	1.303	1.295	1.287
−40	5.39	4.26	3.87	3.50	1.318	1.310	1.302	1.293
−30	5.56	4.36	4.00	3.60	1.324	1.317	1.308	1.299

This Table is based on commercial calcium chloride meeting ASTM Specification D-98-68. This specification contains both Type 1—regular flake calcium chloride, 77 percent minimum CaCl$_2$, and Type 2—concentrated flake, pellet, or other granular calcium chloride, 94 percent minimum CaCl$_2$.

The concentration of the solution may be checked by a hydrometer. The temperature of the solution must be known since it affects the hydrometer reading.

The lowest freezing point obtainable with a calcium chloride solution is −59.8°F, obtained by using approximately 5 lbs of Type 1 or 3.7 lbs of Type 2 calcium chloride per gal of water.

Solutions of less than 29.6 percent CaCl$_2$ do not freeze solid at temperatures lower than shown in the first column of the Table; ice crystals are "frozen out" and a gradually thickening slush is produced which eventually becomes apparently solid. Calcium chloride solutions are not harmed if frozen and only require stirring after melting of the ice crystals.

Solutions should be prepared by measuring the water and adding the required amount of calcium chloride while stirring. The final volume of the solution will be somewhat greater than the original volume of water.

Calcium chloride solutions resist evaporation. Loss of water by evaporation even in open barrels is slow in ordinary climates. Any loss by evaporation can be replaced by adding water and stirring.

Calcium chloride solutions may result in corrosion of metals, particularly if they become acid. Corrosion due to electrolysis may occur when dissimilar metals are used in piping systems. Corrosion inhibitors are sometimes added to calcium chloride antifreeze solutions. If an inhibitor is deemed desirable, the addition of 0.5 percent sodium chromate to calcium chloride (e.g., ½-lb sodium chromate to a 100 lb bag of Type 1 or an 80-lb bag of Type 2 CaCl$_2$) is recommended. Where large quantities of antifreeze solution are required it is more economical to buy sodium dichromate and convert to sodium chromate by the addition of caustic soda. Add 27 lbs of caustic soda for each 100 lbs of dichromate. For 1,000 cu ft of calcium chloride solution, 125 lbs of sodium dichromate is required.

Table 13-1E. Solutions to Depress the Freezing Point of Water in Wet-pipe Sprinkler Systems Connected to Public Water Supply Sources if Authorized by Health Laws

Material	Solution (By Volume)	Sp Gr at 60°F	Freezing Point °F
Glycerine C.P. or U.S.P. Grade*	50% Water	1.133	−15
	40% Water	1.151	−22
	30% Water	1.165	−40
Hydrometer Scale 1.000 to 1.200			
Propylene Glycol	70% Water	1.027	+ 9
	60% Water	1.034	− 6
	50% Water	1.041	−26
	40% Water	1.045	−60
Hydrometer Scale 1.000 to 1.120 (Subdivisions 0.002)			

* C.P.—Chemically Pure.
U.S.P.—United States Pharmacopoeia 96.5 percent.

Table 13-1F. Solutions to Depress the Freezing Point of Water in Wet-pipe Sprinkler Systems Not Connected to Public Water Supply Sources

Material	Solution (By Volume)	Sp Gr at 60°F	Freezing Point °F
Glycerine	If glycerine is used, see Table 13-1E		
Diethylene Glycol	50% Water	1.078	−13
	45% Water	1.081	−27
	40% Water	1.086	−42
Hydrometer Scale 1.000 to 1.120 (Subdivisions 0.002)			
Ethylene Glycol	61% Water	1.056	−10
	56% Water	1.063	−20
	51% Water	1.069	−30
	47% Water	1.073	−40
Hydrometer Scale 1.000 to 1.120 (Subdivisions 0.002)			
Propylene Glycol	If propylene glycol is used, see Table 13-1E		
Calcium Chloride 80% Flake Fire Protection Grade*	Lbs CaCl₂ per Gal of Water		
Add corrosion inhibitor of sodium dichromate ¼ oz per gal water	2.83	1.183	0
	3.38	1.212	−10
	3.89	1.237	−20
	4.37	1.258	−30
	4.73	1.274	−40
	4.93	1.283	−50

* Free from magnesium chloride and other impurities.

must never be permitted to get into drinking water. Tables 13-1E and 13-1F give data on the amounts needed for the various low-temperature conditions which might be encountered. (For further information on antifreeze solutions in sprinkler systems see Sec. 14, Chap. 2.)

Fire Pails or Casks: Calcium chloride-water solutions are used where continuous temperatures below 40°F are encountered. Table 16-5A gives the amount of calcium chloride which should be mixed thoroughly with water to make 10 gals of antifreeze solution.

Water Type Extinguishers: Alkali-metal salt solutions provide protection against low temperature conditions. Only the solutions specified by the manufacturers of these types of extinguishers should be used, as the extinguishers are tested and listed by the testing laboratories using the particular solutions recommended for them, and assurance of their reliability cannot be guaranteed with other formulas. Glycol solutions should not be used in extinguishers since the amount required to achieve significant temperature reduction would be high (i.e., a 52.5 percent solution of ethylene glycol would be needed to achieve −40°F freezing point). The substitution of glycol solutions would significantly alter the extinguishing efficiency of the extinguisher and could also lead to complications in the event the water should "boil off" and leave a strong concentration of the glycol which, under certain conditions, could be ignited.

Efforts have been made to develop other additives which could be mixed with fresh or sea water to lower the freezing point to −65°F. This work has been largely stimulated by increased human activity in extremely low-temperature areas, with most of the research being done under the auspices of the U.S. military services. To date lithium chloride, lithium chloride-calcium chloride, and lithium chloride-anhydrous sodium chromate have produced satisfactory formulations in various proportions to accomplish this objective without causing corrosion or toxicity problems. No commercial use of these solutions is known, although the U.S. Naval Research Laboratory has developed a lithium chloride solution for fire extinguishers exposed to low temperatures (−65°F).

E. Surface Tension and Wetting Agent Additives

The relatively high surface tension of plain water slows its ability to penetrate burning combustibles and impedes its spread throughout any closely packed, baled, or stacked materials. Immersion of burning combustibles in water is rarely practical. When a fire originates or burrows in a mass of combustibles it is frequently necessary either to dismantle the mass and apply water to the interior portions, or to employ a wetting agent additive to lower the surface tension of the water and thus facilitate extinguishment. Numerous chemicals can fulfill the function of a wetting agent. Few chemicals, however, are suited to fire control work because of conditions such as toxicity, corrosive action on equipment, and stability when mixed with plain water. Minimum requirements for wetting agents for fire protection purposes are contained in NFPA No. 18, Wetting Agents. The purpose of the NFPA Wetting Agent Standard is to set forth recommendations for wetting agent additives that will improve the fire fighting properties of plain water while not producing wetting agent solutions that might be harmful to personnel, property, or equipment.

By decreasing the surface tension of the water, a wetting agent tends to increase the amount of free surface of the water available for absorption of heat while decreasing runoff, thus increasing the efficiency of the extinguishing properties of the water by increasing the rate of heat absorption for a given volume. In the United States, UL (Underwriters Laboratories, Inc.) lists wetting agents which are liquid concentrates that materially reduce the surface tension of plain water, thus increasing its penetrating and spreading qualities when added to plain water. They are investigated in order to evaluate these qualities and their extinguishing abilities on Class A or Class B fires, or both. Wetting agents used in fire fighting and fire protection are no more corrosive than plain water to brass, bronze, and copper, although limitations are placed on containers for continuous storage of wetting agents because they exhibit a tendency to accelerate corrosion due to the cleaning and penetrating action of the concentrates. The use of materials such as cast iron, aluminum, zinc, galvanized steel, lead or lead-coated iron, die cast alloys (such as white metal, zinc, etc.), or where "air-dried" types of coatings (which may include plastics, oil paint, lacquers, or asphalt) should be avoided. The use of wetting agent solutions should be limited to equipment for which the suitability of the wetting agent has been determined.

The greatest use of "wet water" (formed by the addition of a wetting agent to plain water) is to penetrate porous surfaces and allow the solution to reach hidden areas of burning combustibles, such as may be present in a "fire-packed" bale of cotton or in stacked hay, and to penetrate the subsurface of layers of ordinary combustible materials to prevent rekindling. Wet water has some application on outdoor fires such as grass, brush, or forest fires. Generally, these latter types of fires are more properly and easily handled by "thickened" water (see Part F of this Chapter).

Wet water has the same limitations as plain water on fires involving chemicals which react with water, such as sodium, calcium carbide, etc. The use of wetting agent solutions on flammable and combustible liquid fires is not common since bromotrifluoromethane, bromochlorodifluoromethane, carbon dioxide, dry chemicals, or foam are normally used on these types of fires. Wet water should not be used on flammable or combustible liquid fires where the liquids are water soluble (such as the alcohols, glycols, and some ketones).

In general, wet water solutions should not be used on live electrical equipment because of the conductivity of the wet water solution. A spray or fog application could, however, be employed with caution. Wet water, due to its penetrating characteristics, may have more increased harmful effects on motors, transformers, and similar equipment than plain water. Any electrical equipment that has been subjected to applications of wet water should be thoroughly flushed and cleaned before being returned to service.

Wetting agents may be either premixed with water, as in a tank on a fire truck, or added to the water through suitable proportioning equipment at the time the water is being used. Mixing of wetting agents of different manufacturers, or mixing a wetting agent with mechanical- or chemical-foam concentrates, is not recommended because such mixing can have adverse effects. Distinction must be made between wetting agents and wetting agent foams (see Chap. 2 of this Section) and other detergent-type foams (high expansion foam) and aqueous film-forming agents.

Methods of measuring the effect of the addition of a wetting agent to water to lower the surface tension are given in the appendix of the NFPA Wetting Agent Standard.

F.   Viscosity and Additives to Thicken Water

The relatively low viscosity of plain water limits its ability to penetrate a burning mass, makes it tend to run off surfaces quickly, and limits the ability of water to blanket a fire by forming a barrier on the surface of combustible materials. Additives to make water more viscous ("thickened" water) have been developed to make the use of water more efficient on certain types of fires.

Viscous water is water to which one of several viscosity agents has been added. In proper proportions, viscous water seems to have the following advantages over plain water in certain fire fighting operations:

1. Sticks and clings more readily to the burning fuel.
2. Spreads itself out in a continuous coating over the fuel surface.
3. Develops in a layer several times the thickness of plain water.
4. Absorbs heat proportional to the amount of water present.

5. Projects somewhat further and higher from straight-stream nozzles.
6. Forms a tough, dry film after drying which helps seal the fuel from oxygen.
7. Resists wind drift in some applications (as from aircraft in forest fire fighting).

Disadvantages of viscous water may be:
1. Does not penetrate the fuel as well as plain or wet water (see Part E of this chapter).
2. Increases friction loss in hose or pipe.
3. Increases water droplet size (where fine sprays are needed, they cannot be secured as readily).
4. Increases the slipperiness on coated surfaces making it more difficult to walk with safety in areas where it has been applied, and increases handling problems and logistics of fire control operations because of the need to handle and mix viscosity agents in water. (Under some conditions, stored solutions can lose viscosity, principally through water-temperature changes and possible bacterial or chemical contamination.)

A limited amount of research has been conducted on the application of these agents in fixed systems. Preliminary studies indicate that less water is required and fires are controlled sooner when these agents are used. The area of damage is also much smaller than with plain water systems. Several system design changes were made to accommodate the additives during the tests.

To date, most of the research on the use of viscous water has been directed at fighting forest fires. A detailed report on this application is contained in the NFPA publication "Chemicals for Forest Fire Fighting"[7], a report prepared by the NFPA Forest Committee with the cooperation of the U.S. Forest Service and other forest fire control specialists. Plain water is often capable of handling ordinary brush, grass, and forest fire situations; in some situations, such as burrowing fires in a mass of combustibles, "wet" water (see Part E of this chapter) is preferred. The advantage of viscous water is most evident on fires with high rates of heat energy output, whether forest or structural fuels, and where radiation is responsible for the advantage of the fire.

The two viscosity agents presently used in forest fire control are CMC (sodium carboxymethylcellulose) and Gelgard (a trade name product of the Dow Chemical Company). They are desirable for the following reasons:
1. Only a small quantity of dry powder is necessary for a batch mix.
2. It takes only a few minutes to mix an adequate batch.
3. Near maximum viscosity is reached within the batch mix period, and the viscosity is retained indefinitely (assuming no contamination or spoilage).
4. They are reasonable in cost.
5. They are nontoxic and noncorrosive.
6. They pump easily.
7. They provide for a good stream pattern.
8. They provide good coverage over the fuels.

Although other viscosity agents are available, they have not been used as extensively as CMC and Gelgard.

Forest fire control uses: short-term and long-term flame inhibiting chemicals, which are also thickening agents. Bentonite clay (montmorillonite) has been used as a short-term fire retardant and a slurry in water and produces a heavy coat of water. Longer-term retardants are ammonium phosphates and ammonium sulfates. The phosphates are about 1.5 times as effective as ammonium sulfate since the former seem effective against both flaming and glowing ignition, while the sulfates seem to be most effective only in flaming ignition. In addition, only about two-thirds as much ammonium phosphate as ammonium sulfate is required to perform the same level of work. Two solid ammonium phosphate chemicals notable for their fire retardant and fire extinguishing capabilities are diammonium phosphate (DAP) and monoammonium phosphate (MAP). Viscous retardant solutions employing DAP and CMC are available commercially, as are a liquid ammonium phosphate concentrate and an ammonium sulfate fire retardant.

The NFPA Forest Committee has prepared a special publication, "Air Operation for Forest, Brush, and Grass Fires[8]," covering the use of aircraft for reconnaissance, fire attack, and control of these types of fires.

G. Flow Characteristics Modifying Additives

Friction loss in fire hose is an ever-present problem for fire fighters. The longer the hose and the more water pumped through it, the greater the pressure loss. With good-quality fire hose, almost all of the pressure loss is the result of friction between particles of water generated by the turbulence in the flowing stream. Flow is either smooth or laminar and the friction loss tends to be very low with a slow stream of water; however, the amount of water delivered under laminar flow is generally too low to be beneficial for fire fighting. Fire fighting requires high velocity streams that generate turbulence which, in turn, results in friction between water particles. This friction accounts for about 90 percent of the pressure loss in good fire hose. The friction between the flowing water and the interior hose wall accounts for only 5 to 10 percent of the loss.

Until 1948 it was generally believed that not much could be done to reduce friction loss. At that time trace quantities of certain polymers were found to have an effect on reducing friction loss of turbulent streams. Most research people report that linear polymers (polymers that form a single straight line chain with no branches) are the most effective in reducing turbulent frictional losses and, of these, poly (ethylene oxide) is the most effective.

Poly is nontoxic, has no effects on plants or marine life, and will degrade in sunlight. Friction-reducing efficiency is a direct function of polymer linearity. Poly is a long linear chain, high-molecular weight polymer, and is 2 to 3 times more effective as a friction-reduction agent than other materials tested to date. This additive is an opaque, white slurry that has no odor and weighs 9.1 ppg (pounds per gallon). It must be kept within a temperature range of 0°F to 120°F. When it is injected into the hose stream, it dissolves completely and does not separate. It is compatible with all fire fighting equipment and is useful in fresh water as well as in brackish or sea water. One gallon of additive is sufficient to treat 6,000 gallons of water in order to achieve at least a 40 percent greater water delivery.

Tests run by the New York City Fire Department in conjunction with Union Carbide Corporation[9] developed the following information concerning the use of this water additive. In present systems without the additive, a 1-in. booster hose will deliver approximately 20 gpm. However, with this water additive and a change in nozzle design, 75 gpm were delivered during the test. A 1½-in. hose delivered 250 gpm, or as much as a 2½-in hose. With the additive, a 2½-in. hose was able to deliver more water than a 3-in. hose, and nearly as much water as a 3½-in hose.

From experience, fire fighters know that a heavy, charged 2½-in. hose can be difficult to move. Although a smaller, lighter, more mobile hose can be less difficult to manipulate when attacking fires, it can also deliver 250 gpm when this additive is used and should, therefore, be handled with the same respect as a 2½-in. hose.

Of equal significance, these tests showed that the additive nearly doubled the nozzle pressure and benefitted the effect of the water stream. The stream's reach was increased by nearly 30 percent, and the stream was more coherent. Little effect was found on the fog nozzle sprays other than that the water spray seemed to be more dense.

H. Reactivity of Water with Certain Materials

As a general rule, water should not be used on materials such as carbides, peroxides, metallic sodium, magnesium dusts, etc., which result in release of flammable gases and the evolution of heat (see Sec. 3, Chap. 5, and Sec. 13, Chap. 6, for further details on fire control with these and other reactive materials).

When wet, certain materials (such as unslaked lime) will heat spontaneously over a period of time where heat dissipation is not possible due to storage conditions.

I. Opacity and Reflectivity

Tests conducted at UL using water spray to provide exposure protection to a sheet metal surface from an exposing gasoline fire indicated that when the spray was applied as a thin film of water over the sheet metal, the temperature of the metal was contained within limits adequate enough to protect the metal from significant damage. This was not true, however, when the water spray was adjusted so that it did not contact the scheet metal, but did provide a water curtain between the metal and the exposing fire. In this latter case, temperatures on the metal were as much as 3 to 4 times greater than when the water flowed over the metal. These tests may indicate that because of its lack of opacity, water possesses little ability to prevent the passage of radiant heat. A principal value of water in protecting exposures is from the cooling obtained by evaporation of a water film on the exposed surfaces.

NFPA No. 13, Installation of Sprinkler Systems (including outside sprinklers for protection against exposure fire), calls for sprinklers to be so positioned that the water discharge will thoroughly wet exposed glass windows and run down over the window sash and the glass, wetting the entire window to the greatest possible extent. Similar recommendations are given to assure that as much of the cornice as possible be wetted when cornice sprinklers are installed. These rules reflect the experimental evidence.

In England, tests have been run to measure the transmission of radiation through water sprays from two types of nozzles.[10] The tests proved that the transmission of radation depends markedly on nozzle design, and that with certain nozzles a water curtain of low transmission could be produced for water flows comparable to those of sprinkler installations. The laboratory experiments are preliminary, and further experiments are recommended. Fire fighters have, of course, long made effective use of water curtains in situations where it was too hot or dangerous for them to remain exposed to flame and heat attack.

J. Water on Combustible and Flammable Liquid Fires

Heavy fuel oil, lubricating oil, asphalt, and other high flash point liquids do not produce flammable vapors unless heated. Once ignited, the heat of the fire will cause enough vaporization for continued burning. If water in spray form is applied effectively to the surface of such high flash point burning liquids, cooling will slow down the rate of vaporization—possibly adequate by enough to extinguish the fire.

The ability of water to effect extinguishment is limited on low flash point flammable liquids such as Class I flammable liquids (flash points below 100°F), as defined in NFPA No. 30, Flammable and Combustible Liquids. Any water that reaches the surface of a burning low flash point flammable liquid in a tank will probably sink and may cause the tank to overflow. In the case of a spill fire involving low flash point flammable liquids, the water will probably cause the fire to spread. Professional handling of certain types of water spray nozzles can result in extinguishment of fires in these liquids or, at a minimum, effective fire control. The use of water in fighting fires involving flammable liquid bulk storage tanks and tank vehicles is demonstrated in two NFPA training films (also available in slides) entitled "Fighting Tank Fires with Water," and "Tank Vehicle Fire Fighting." Another similar NFPA training film (also available in slides) entitled "Handling LP-Gas Emergencies," demonstrates the handling of both fires and unignited leaks of liquefied petroleum gas.

Oliver W. Johnson, in "Water on Oil Fires[11]," summarizes the uses of water on petroleum product fires as follows:

1. As a cooling agent, water may be used to:
   (a) Cut off the release of vapor from the surface of a high flash point oil, thus extinguishing the fire.
   (b) Protect fire fighters from flame and radiant heat when closing a valve or doing other work requiring close approach to the fire.
   (c) Protect flame-exposed surfaces; most effective when the surface is above 212°F.
2. As a mechanical tool, a water stream can do work at a distance to:
   (a) Control leaks.
   (b) Direct the flow of petroleum product to prevent its ignition, or to move the fire to an area where it will do less damage.
3. As a displacing medium, water may be used to:
   (a) Float oil above a leak in a tank either before or during a fire.
   (b) Cut off fuel escape by pumping it into a leaking pipe ahead of a leak.

SI Units

The following conversion factors are given as a convenience in converting to SI Units the English Units given in this chapter.

1 lb (mass)	=	0.454 kg
1 Btu	=	1.055 kJ
1 in.	=	25.400 mm
1 ft	=	0.305 m
$\frac{5}{9}$ (°F − 32)	=	°C
1 (U.S.) gal	=	3.785 litres
1 lb/gal	=	119.827 kg/m³

Bibliography

References Cited

[1] "Electric Shock as It Pertains to the Electric Fence," Bulletin of Research No. 14, Dec. 1939, Underwriters Laboratories, Inc., Chicago, Ill.
[2] "Conductivity of Electricity through Various Sizes and Types of Fire Streams" (An Engineering Report of Tests Conducted in Co-operation with the Chicago Fire Department, 1947, Commonwealth Edison Company).
[3] "Fire Streams and Electrical Circuits," Special Interest Bulletin No. 91, Dec. 1963, American Insurance Association, New York.
[4] Fitzgerald, G. W. N., Supervising Engineer, Electrical Testing Section, Research Division, Hydro-Electric Power Commission of Ontario, "Fire Fighting Near Live Electrical Apparatus," May 1958, Research Division Report No. 58–160.
[5] Buffet, le Commandant, Chef du Service Technique du Regiment de S-P. de Paris, *et al.*, "Peut-on Employer les Lances d'Incendie sur des Conducteurs Electriques?" 1934.
[6] O'Dogherty, M. J., "The Shock Hazard Associated with the Extinction of Fires Involving Electrical Equipment," Fire Research Technical Paper No. 13, 1965, Ministry of Technology and Fire Offices' Committee, Joint Fire Research Organization, (Published by Her Majesty's Stationery Office).
[7] "Chemicals for Forest Fire Fighting," a Report of the NFPA Forest Committee, 2nd ed., 1967, National Fire Protection Association, Boston.
[8] "Air Operations for Forest, Brush and Grass Fires." A Report of the NFPA Forest Committee, 1965, National Fire Protection Association, Boston.
[9] Clough, T. C., "Research on Friction Reducing Agents," *Fire Technology*, Vol. 9, No. 1, Feb. 1973, pp. 32–45.
[10] Heselden, A. J. M., and Hinkley, P. L., "Measurement of the Transmission of Radiation Through Water Sprays," Fire Research Note No. 520, April 1963, Dept. of Scientific and Industrial Research and Fire Offices' Committee, Joint Fire Research Organization, Boreham Wood, Herts, England.
[11] Johnson, Oliver W., "Water on Oil Fires," NFPA *Quarterly*, Vol. 55, No. 2, Oct. 1961, pp. 141–146.

NFPA Codes, Standards, and Recommended Practices (see the latest *NFPA Publications and Visual Aids Catalog* for availability of current editions of the following documents)

NFPA No. 10, Standard for the Installation, Maintenance, and Use of Portable Fire Extinguishers.
NFPA No. 13, Standard for the Installation of Sprinkler Systems.
NFPA No. 15, Standard for Water Spray Fixed Systems for Fire Protection.
NFPA No. 18, Standard on Wetting Agents.
NFPA No. 30, Flammable and Combustible Liquids Code.
NFPA No. 75, Standard for the Protection of Electronic Computer Data Processing Equipment.

Additional Readings

Aidun, A. R., and Grove, C. S., Jr., "Additives to Improve the Fire Fighting Characteristics of Water," Report No. Ch. E 504–6112F, 1961, Syracuse University Research Institute (sponsored by U.S. Dept. of the Navy).
Brown, H. F., "Report of Conductivity of Fire Streams Near 11,000 Volt Wires," 1945, New York, New Haven & Hartford Railroad Company.
Davis, J. B., Dibble, D. L., Richards, S. S., and Steck, L. V., "Gelgard—A New Fire Retardant for Air and Ground Attack, *Fire Technology*, Vol. 1, No. 3, Aug. 1965, pp. 216–224.
"Evaluation of Halogenated Hydrocarbon and Alkali-Earth-Metal Salt Fire Extinguishing Agents for Low Temperatures," Technical Memorandum M-108, 1 November 1955, U.S. Naval Civil Engineering Research and Evaluation Laboratory, Port Hueneme, Calif.
Fryburg, George, "Review of Literature Pertinent to Fire-Extinguishing Agents and to Basic Mechanisms Involved in their Action," NACA TN 2102, May 1950, National Advisory Committee for Aeronautics, Washington, D.C.
"High Voltage Electrical Conductivity Tests with Nu-Swift Dry Powder and Water Type Extinguishers," conducted at Institute of High Voltage and Measuring Technique, 1962, Technical High School, Darmstadt, Germany.
Hopping, R., and Knox, C., "Tests of Fire Fighting Streams," The Electricity Commission of New South Wales, Fire Protection Organization, File No. 8610, 1960.
"Mechanism of Extinguishment of Fire by Finely Divided Water," NBFU Research Report No. 10, 1955, American Insurance Association, New York.
Sprague, C. S., and Harding, C. F., "Electrical Conductivity of Fire Streams," Engineering Bulletin, Purdue University, Vol. XX, No. 1, January 1936 (Research Series No. 53).
Stratta, J. J., "Ablative Fluids in the Fire Environment," *Fire Technology*, Vol. 1, No. 3, Aug. 1969, pp. 181–192.
"Use of Water on Electronic Equipment Fires," NASA *Safety Journal*, 68–9, Sept. 6, 1968.
Walker, H. S., "High Tension Wires and Hose Streams," NFPA *Quarterly*, October 1930.

Chapter 2

FIRE FIGHTING FOAMS

Fire fighting foam is a mass of gas-filled bubbles formed by various methods from aqueous solutions of especially formulated foaming agents. Since foam is lighter than the aqueous solutions from which it is formed and lighter than flammable liquids, it floats on all flammable or combustible liquids, producing an air-excluding, cooling, continuous layer of vapor-sealing, water-bearing material for purposes of halting or preventing combustion.

Fire fighting foams are formulated in several ways for fire extinguishing action. Some foams are thick and viscous, forming tough heat-resistant blankets over burning liquid surfaces and vertical areas. Some foams are thinner and more rapidly spreading. Some are capable of producing a vapor-sealing film of surface-active water solution on a liquid surface. Some are meant to be used as large volumes of wet gas cells for inundating surfaces and filling cavities.

There are various methods of generating and applying foams. This chapter covers the basic characteristics of various foaming agents and the methods for producing fire fighting foams. Specific applications of equipment and systems useful for different types of hazards will be found in Section 15, Chapter 3.

The use of foam for fire protection requires attention to its general characteristics. Foam breaks down and vaporizes its water content under attack by heat and flame. It, therefore, must be applied to a burning surface in sufficient volume and rate to compensate for this loss, and to provide an additional amount to guarantee a residual foam layer over the extinguished portion of the burning liquid. Foam is an unstable "air-water emulsion" and may be easily broken down by physical or mechanical forces. Certain chemical vapors or fluids may also quickly destroy foam. When certain other extinguishing agents are used in conjunction with foam, severe breakdown of the foam may occur. Turbulent air or violently uprising combustion gases from fires may divert light foam from the burning area.

In general, foam is especially useful wherever a very light, cohesive, blanketing and cooling, fire controlling or extinguishing agent is needed. Certain special types of foam are required for special situations such as cavity filling and water-miscible solvent fire protection. Very definite engineering design requirements and application methods are needed for successful use of foams.

A.   Types and Characteristics of Fire Fighting Foams

The various types of fire fighting foams that are available and the characteristics of each are covered in this part of the chapter.

Protein Foaming Agents

Protein type air foams utilize aqueous liquid concentrates proportioned with water for their generation. These concentrates contain high molecular weight natural proteinaceous polymers derived from a chemical digestion and hydrolysis of natural protein solids. The polymers give elasticity, mechanical strength, and water retention capability to foams generated from them. The concentrates also contain dissolved polyvalent metallic salts, which aid the pro-

tein polymers in their bubble strengthening capability when the foam is exposed to heat and flame. Organic solvents are added to the concentrates to improve their foamability and foam uniformity as well as to control their viscosity at lowered temperatures. Protein type concentrates are available for proportioning to a final concentration of either 3 percent or 6 percent by volume using either fresh water or sea water. In general, these concentrates produce dense, viscous foams of high stability, high heat resistance, and better resistance to burnback than many other foaming agents. They are nontoxic and biodegradable after dilution. Normal use ambient temperature range for these concentrates is 20°F (−6.7°C) to 120°F (48.9°C).

Fluoroprotein Foaming Agents

The concentrates utilized for generating fluoroprotein foams are similar in composition to protein foam concentrates, but, in addition to protein polymers, they contain fluorinated surface active agents that confer a "fuel shedding" property to the foam generated. This makes them particularly effective for fire fighting conditions where the foam becomes coated with fuel, such as in the method of subsurface injection of foam for tank fire fighting, and nozzle or monitor foam applications where the foam may often be plunged into the fuel. Fluoroprotein foams are more effective for in-depth petroleum or hydrocarbon fuel fires than other agents because of this property of "fuel shedding." In addition, these foams demonstrate better compatibility with dry chemical agents than do the protein type foams. They also possess superior vapor securing and burnback resistance characteristics. Fluoroprotein type concentrates are available for proportioning to a final concentration of either 3 percent or 6 percent by volume using either fresh water or sea water. They are nontoxic and biodegradable after dilution. The normal use temperature range for these agents is 20°F (−6.7°C) to 120°F (48.9°C).

Low Temperature (Cold) Foaming Agents

This type of foam concentrate is similar to the protein type foaming agents, but it is protected for storage and use at low temperature by the inclusion of non-flammable freezing point depressants. Fluoroprotein foaming agents for use at low temperatures are also available. Low temperature foaming agents may be used at ambient temperatures as low as −20°F (−28.7°C). They are available for use at either 3 percent or 6 percent by volume concentration in either fresh or sea water.

Aqueous Film-forming Foaming Agents (AFFF)

Aqueous film-forming foam agents are composed of synthetically produced materials that form air foams similar to those produced by the protein-based materials. In addition, these foaming agents are capable of forming water solution films on the surface of flammable liquids; hence the term "aqueous film-forming foam" (AFFF). AFFF concentrates are available for proportioning to a final concentration of either 3 percent or 6 percent by volume with either fresh or sea water.

The air foams generated from AFFF solutions possess low viscosity, have fast spreading and leveling characteristics, and act as surface barriers to exclude air and halt fuel vaporization just as other foams do. These foams also develop a continuous aqueous layer of solution under the foam with surface activity which maintains a floating film on hydrocarbon fuel surfaces to help suppress combustible vapors and cool the fuel substrate. This film, which can also spread over fuel surfaces not fully covered with foam, is self-healing following mechanical disruption and continues as long as there remains a reservoir of nearby foam for its production. However, to insure fire extinction, an AFFF blanket, as with other types of foam, should entirely cover the fuel surface.

The result of the double action of aqueous film-forming foams is to yield a highly efficient foam extinguishing agent, in terms of water and concentrate needed and the rapidity with which it acts on fuel spills.

AFFF concentrates contain fluorinated, long-chain hydrocarbons with particular surface-active properties. Various water soluble high molecular polymers are added to aid in strengthening the bubble wall and to retard breakdown. They are nontoxic and biodegradable after dilution. The shelf life of AFFF concentrate compares favorably with other synthetic foam concentrates containing no naturally occurring substances that might change with time.

AFFF can be used as a foam cover and protecting material for flammable liquids which have not become ignited. It may be used under certain circumstances for extinguishment of certain water soluble polar solvents. Because of the extremely low surface tension of the solutions draining from AFFF, these foams may be useful under mixed class fire situations (Class A and Class B) where deep penetration of water is needed in addition to the surface spreading action of foam itself.

Foam generating devices yielding stable, homogeneous foams are not necessarily needed in the employment of AFFF. Less sophisticated foaming devices may be used because of the inherent rapid and easy foaming capability of AFFF solutions. Water spray devices may be used in some situations. AFFF also may be used in conjunction with dry chemical agents without compatibility problems. Although AFFF concentrates must not be mixed with other types of foam concentrates, foams made from them do not break down other foams in fire fighting operations.

Synthetic Hydrocarbon Surfactant Foaming Agents

There are many synthetically produced surface active compounds which foam copiously in water solution. When these are properly formulated, they may be used as fire fighting foams and employed in much the same manner as other types of foam.

Hydrocarbon surfactant foam liquid concentrates are employed in 1 to 6 percent proportions in water. When these solutions are used in conventional foam making devices, the resulting air foam possesses low viscosity and fast spreading qualities over liquid surfaces. Its fire fighting characteristics depend on the volume of the foam layer on the burning surface, which halts access to air and controls combustible vapor production, and the minor cooling effect of the water in the foam, which becomes available due to a relatively rapid breakdown of the foam mass. This water solution does not possess film forming characteristics on the flammable liquid surface, although under some conditions it may produce a temporary water emulsion due to its wetting agent or "detergent type" properties. Because of the low surface tension and wetting properties of the water solutions of these foams, they may also be used as extinguishing agents for Class A fires.

Synthetic hydrocarbon surfactant foams are generally less stable than other types of fire fighting foams. Their water solution content drains away rapidly to leave a bubble mass which is highly vulnerable to heat or mechanical disruption. Usually they must be applied at higher rates than other fire fighting foams to achieve extinction. Many formulations of this type of foam concentrate break down other foams if used simultaneously or sequentially.

"Alcohol-type" Foaming Agents

Air foams generated from ordinary agents are subject to rapid breakdown and loss of effectiveness when they are used on fires that involve fuels which are water soluble, water miscible, or of a "polar solvent" type. Examples of this type of liquid are the alcohols, enamel and lacquer thinners, methyl ethyl ketone, acetone, isopropyl ether, acrylonitrile, ethyl and butyl acetate, and the amines and anhydrides. Even small amounts of these substances mixed with the common hydrocarbon fuels will cause the rapid breakdown of ordinary fire fighting foams.

Certain special foaming agents have, therefore, been developed, called "alcohol-type" concentrates. Some of these concentrates must be foamed and applied to the burning surface almost immediately after they are proportioned into water. Solutions of this type cannot be pumped long distances because their "transit times" (the time required for foam solutions to travel from the eductor or foam generator to the discharge outlet) before foam production are short. They would be ineffective if this time was to be exceeded.

"Alcohol-type" foaming agents fall into three general categories:

1. Protein-base concentrates containing heavy metal soaps made soluble by ammoniacal or solvent solutions. Foams produced from these agents require gentle application to the burning surface and may have solution transit time limitations.

2. Two component concentrates consisting of a polymeric system in one part which is further polymerized by a catalyst solution in the second part to render solvent stability to the produced alcohol-resistant foam. This type may be used in devices which may not apply the foam gently to the surface and it has no transit time limitations.

3. Synthetic base concentrates in a single-component system to produce foams for application to either ordinary flammable liquids or polar type solvents by any device. Agents of this type have no transit time limitations.

Normal use temperatures for any of the "Alcohol-type" agents are 35°F (1.7°C) to 120°F (48.9°C).

High Expansion Foaming Agents

"High expansion" foam is an agent for control and extinguishment of Class A and Class B fires and is particularly suited as a flooding agent for use in confined spaces. The foam is an aggregation of bubbles mechanically generated by the passage of air or other gases through a net, screen, or other porous medium that is wetted by an aqueous solution of surface active foaming agents. Under proper conditions, fire fighting foams of expansions from 100 to 1 (100X) up to 1,000 to 1 (1,000X) can be generated.

High expansion foam is a unique vehicle for transporting wet foam masses to inaccessible places, for total flooding of confined spaces, and for volumetric displacement of vapor, heat, and smoke. Tests have shown that under certain circumstances high expansion foam when used in conjunction with water from automatic sprinklers will provide more positive control and extinguishment than either extinguishing agent by itself. (High-piled storage of rolled paper stock is an example.) Optimum efficiency in any one type of hazard is dependent on the rate of application and the foam expansion and stability.

Liquid concentrates for producing high expansion foams consist of synthetic hydrocarbon surfactants of a type that will foam copiously with a small input of turbulent action. They are used in about 2 percent proportion in water solution.

High expansion foam is particularly suited for indoor fires in confined spaces. Its use outdoors may be limited because of the effects of weather. High expansion foam has several effects on fires:

1. When generated in sufficient volume, it can prevent air, necessary for continued combustion, from reaching the fire.

2. When forced into the heat of a fire, the water in the foam is converted to steam, reducing the oxygen concentration by dilution of the air.

3. The conversion of the water to steam absorbs heat from the burning fuel. Any hot object exposed to the foam will continue the process of breaking down the foam, converting the water to steam, and of being cooled.

4. Because of its relatively low surface tension, solution from the foam, which is not converted to steam, will tend to penetrate Class A materials. However, deep-seated fires may require overhaul.

5. When accumulated in depth, high expansion foam can provide an insulating barrier for protection of exposed materials or structures not involved in a fire, thereby preventing fire spread.

Research has shown that using air from inside a burning building for generating high expansion foam has an adverse effect on the volume and stability of the foam produced. Combustion and pyrolysis products can reduce the volume of foam produced and increase the drainage rate when they react chemically with the foaming agent. The high temperature of the air breaks down the foam as it is being generated. Physical disruption also takes place apparently caused by vapor and solid particles from the combustion process. These factors which cause foam breakdown may be compensated for by higher rates of foam generation.

When foam is generated from the gases of combustion it becomes toxic, and entry to a foam-filled passage must not be attempted without self-contained breathing apparatus. The foam mass also obscures vision, and life lines must be used if entering into it.

Chemical Foam Agents and Powders

These foam producing materials have become obsolete because of the superior economics and ease of handling of the liquid foam-forming concentrates previously discussed. Chemical foam is formed from the temperature sensitive chemical reaction in aqueous solution between aluminum sulfate ("A") (acidic) and sodium bicarbonate ("B") (basic) which also contains proteinaceous foam stabilizers. In "wet systems," these chemicals are stored in solution in large separate tanks. In powder systems, and in all portable methods for its use, the chemicals are added through "hoppers," into flowing water streams. The foam is formed by the generation of carbon dioxide gas from the chemical reaction of the two solutions of compounds. Chemical foam is quite stable and heat resistant, but generally it is very stiff and slow-moving. It "bakes" under flame attack and will form open fissures in the foam layer which expose the underlying fuel.

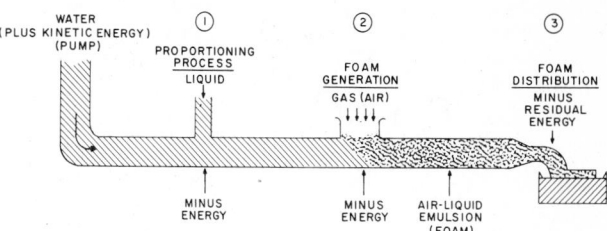

Fig. 13-2A. A generalized flow diagram of air foam generation.

Chemical foam "fixed" systems require constant maintenance, and portable devices for its use are very difficult to operate at a fire.

B. Air Foam Generating Methods

The process of producing and applying fire fighting air foams to hazards requires three separate operations, each of which consumes energy. They are the proportioning process, the foam generation phase, and the method of distribution. A flow diagram illustrating the relationship of the three operations is given in Figure 13-2A.

In general practice, the functions of air foam generation and distribution take place nearly simultaneously within the same device. There are also many types of proportioning and foam generating equipment.

In certain portable devices all three functions are combined into one device. The design and performance requirements of foam systems dictate the choice of types of proportioning, generating, and distributing equipment for the protection of specific hazards.

Foam Concentrate Proportioners

In order that a predetermined volume of liquid foam concentrate may be taken from its source and placed into a water stream to form a foam solution of fixed concentration, the following two general method classifications are made:

1. Methods which utilize the pressure energy of the water stream by venturi action and orifices to induct concentrate. (In general, such devices impose a 35 percent pressure drop on the water stream.)

2. Methods which utilize external pumps or pressure heads to inject concentrate into the water stream at a fixed ratio to flow.

Figures 13-2B and 13-2C illustrate the general principles of the two different methods of proportioning. Specific sys-

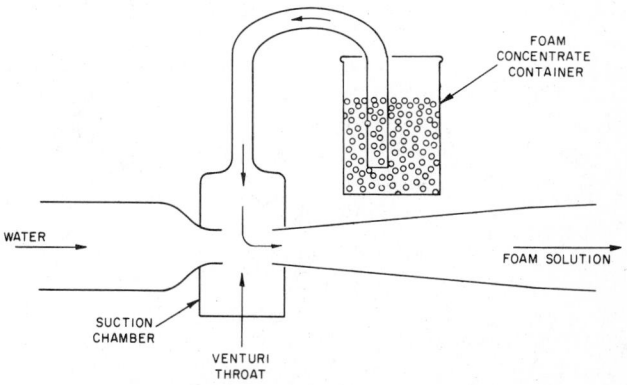

Fig. 13-2B. Venturi induction (in-line) proportioner.

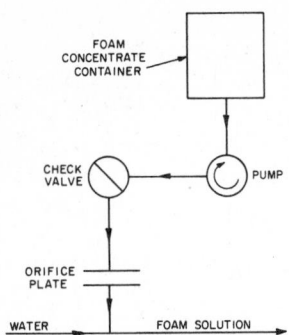

Fig. 13-2C. Concentrate pump proportioner.

tem designs of proportioning equipment are given in Section 15, Chapter 3 of this HANDBOOK.

These (and other) foam concentrate proportioning methods may be easily arranged to produce foam solutions in concentrations of 3 percent or 6 percent by volume of the liquid foam concentrate in the water stream.

Air Foam Generating Methods

Air foam nozzles, foam tubes, and foam makers are the devices that mix air with proportioned foam solution to form finished air foam for application to a hazard. The most widely used type of foam makers are those in which the foam is generated by inspiration of air into the device using a venturi nozzle. Specific design details of foam generating equipment are given in Section 15, Chapter 3.

Air foam generators can be put into five general categories depending on the amount of energy that is used in the foam-making process. They are:

Nonaspirating Methods: Devices such as water sprinklers or water spray nozzles produce a watery foam-froth. Use of such devices for foam production is confined to special applications because of the poor quality, sloppy foam that results. They do not actually inspirate air for foam production but rely on droplet collision and air turbulence for foam-froth production. The resulting froth is relatively unstable. Very little energy is required for this method of foam making. AFFF foams may be produced in these devices.

Air Aspirating Foam Nozzles, Foam Tubes, and Ordinary Foam Makers: These constitute the majority of commercial foam-making devices for portable use or fixed installation. They generate foam by venturi action and aspiration of air into a turbulent foam solution stream.

Figure 13-2D illustrates the basic principles of the air aspirating method of foam production.

Approximately 90 percent of the kinetic energy of the incoming foam solution is exhausted in this type of device

and the air foam issuing from it may be distributed only in ways which do not require large pressure differentials.

"High Back-Pressure" Foam Makers: These modified venturi devices are especially designed to conserve foam pressure energy. They operate at relatively high back-pressures for purposes of discharging foam through extended lengths of pipe or hose and for subsurface injection of foam for fuel tank fire fighting. They are also useful for converting old chemical foam systems to air foam systems. They operate at higher pressures than ordinary venturi devices but the foam produced retains some (25 percent) residual pressure. (See Fig. 13-2E.)

Pumped Foam Devices: In these systems compressed air is injected or pumped into the foam solution under pressure. They are inherently more expensive and find rather limited commercial or industrial application. They require additional increments of power to inject air but the resulting homogeneous foam retains some kinetic energy.

High Expansion Foam Generating Devices: There are two principal methods used for the generation of this type of fire fighting foam. One of these utilizes a modified venturi action with very turbulent flow and the other requires input of energy to form the finished foam. The latter system results in high expansion foam containing enough residual kinetic energy to enable it to be forced through large tubes and passageways.

Figures 13-2F and 13-2G illustrate the operating principles of high expansion foam generating devices.

C. Chemical Foam Generating Methods

Except for the generation of chemical foam from "wet systems" where the simple mixing of the two solutions ("A" and "B" solutions) will produce foam, it is necessary to pour two chemical powders into a water stream in a fixed ratio to produce the foam. The "A" and "B" chemicals may be mixed previously and stored together in tightly sealed containers. Figure 13-2H illustrates the equipment used to generate foam using previously mixed "A" and "B" powders.

The admixture of solids into water must be very carefully done so that clogging of the mixing throat does not occur. Back-up of water into the cone prevents free flow of the powders into the apex of the cone. If this should occur, which has often happened during fire fighting, the operation must be stopped and all moisture removed from the walls of the device.

D. Some Requirements Governing Fire Protection with Foams

Foams are primarily used for control and extinguishment of fires involving flammable or combustible liquids. In general, the following criteria for the hazardous liquid must be met for a foam to be effective:

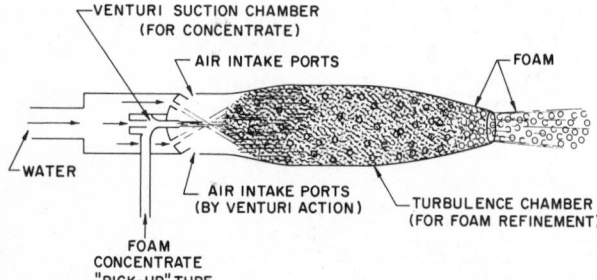

Fig. 13-2D. Cross section of an aspirating type foam maker with a concentrate "pick-up" tube.

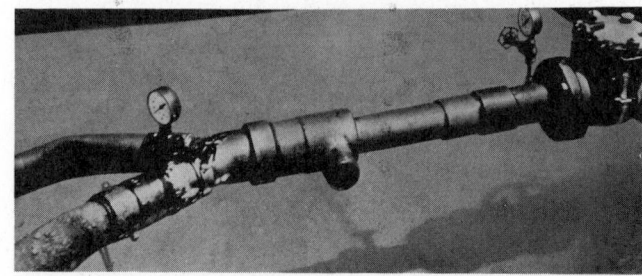

Fig. 13-2E. A "high back pressure" (or "forcing") foam maker.

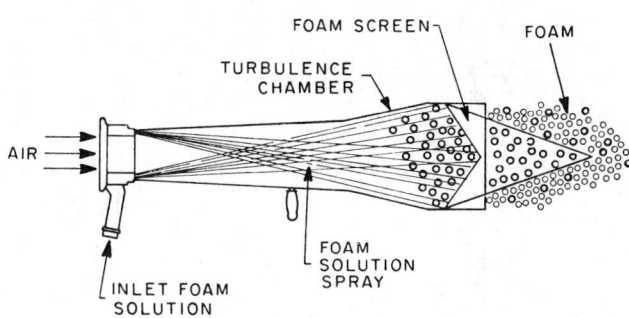

Fig. 13-2F. Aspirating type high expansion foam generator.

1. The liquid must be below its boiling point at the ambient conditions of temperature and pressure.

2. Care must be taken in application of foam to liquids with a bulk temperature higher than 212°F (100°C). At these fuel temperatures and above, foam forms an emulsion of steam, air, and fuel. This may produce a fourfold increase in volume.

3. The liquid must not be unduly destructive to the foam used, or the foam must not be highly soluble in the hazard to be protected.

4. The liquid must not be water-reactive.

5. The fire must be a horizontal surface fire. Three-dimensional (falling fuel) fires cannot be extinguished by foam unless the hazard has a relatively high flashpoint and can be cooled to extinguishment by the water in the foam. However, some foams are capable of "following" a flowing fuel fire.

The following general rules apply to the application and use of ordinary air foams.

1. The more gently the foam is applied, the more rapid the extinguishment and the lower the total amount of agent required.

2. Successful use of foam is also dependent on the rate at which it is applied. Application rates are described in terms of the amount (in gallons or litres) of foam solution reaching the fuel surface (in terms of total square footage or square meters) every minute. An application rate of 0.1 gpm/sq ft (4.17 litres/min.m²) means one-tenth of a gallon of foam solution is being applied every minute for each square foot of fuel surface. (If the foam has a 10 expansion, that means a gallon (3.8 litres) of finished foam is being applied every minute per square foot (0.09 m²).) Increasing foam application rate over the minimum recommended will generally reduce the time required for extinguishment. However, little time advantage is gained if application rates are increased more than three times the

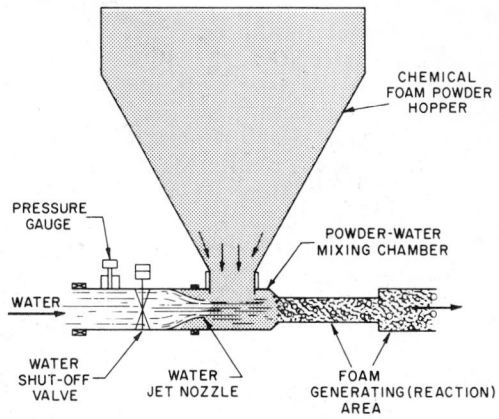

Fig. 13-2H. A chemical foam hopper generator for a single (previously mixed "A" and "B") powder system. When dual powders are used, two hoppers are piped in parallel to a single water source. Dual piping is used from their outlets.

minimum recommended. If application rates are less than the minimum recommended, extinguishment time will be prolonged or may not be accomplished at all. If application rates are so low that the rate of foam loss by heat or fuel attack equals or exceeds the rate at which foam is being applied, the fire will not be controlled or extinguished.

3. The critical application rate is the lowest rate at which a foam will extinguish a given fire under a particular set of conditions.

4. The minimum recommended application rate is the rate found by test to be the most practical in terms of speed of control and amount of agent required. The general curve in Figure 13-2I illustrates the rate-time relationship for foam application to a hazard. The curve may be displaced right or left depending on fuel and method of application; hence the need for carefully engineered systems based on actual test information.

5. In general, air foams will be more stable when they are generated with lower temperature water. Preferred water temperatures range from 35°F (1.7°C) to 80°F (26.7°C). Either fresh or sea water may be used. Water containing known foam contaminants such as detergents, oil residues, or certain corrosion inhibitors may adversely affect foam quality.

6. Foams are adversely affected by air containing certain combustion products. While the effect is minor with ordinary air foam and ordinary hydrocarbon fuels, it is desirable to locate fixed foam makers on the sides of, rather than directly over, the hazard.

7. Recommended pressure ranges should be observed for

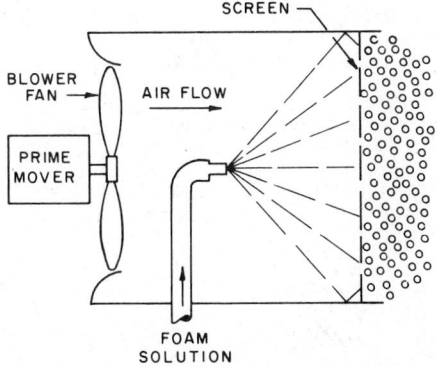

Fig. 13-2G. Fan-blower type high expansion foam generator.

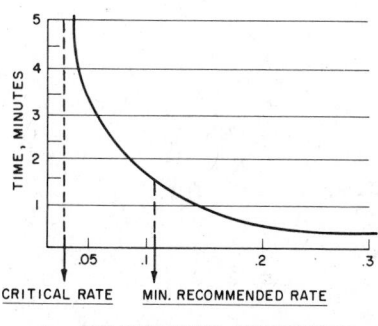

Fig. 13-2I. General relationship of foam application rate to time of application necessary for extinction.

all devices. Foam quality will deteriorate if these limits, both high and low, are exceeded.

8. Most air foams are adversely affected by contact with vaporizing liquid extinguishing agents or their vapors and by many dry chemical agents. Unless information to the contrary is available, these materials should not be used simultaneously with air foams. Gases from decomposing plastic materials have a similar breakdown effect on foams.

9. Foam solutions are conductive and, therefore, are not recommended for use on electrical fires. If foam is used, a spray is less conductive than a straight stream. However, because foam is cohesive, and contains materials that allow water to conduct electricity, a spray foam stream is more conductive than a water fog.

E. Important Uses for Fire Fighting Foams

Fire fighting foams are useful on surfaces wherever the cooling effect of water is needed and wherever continuous film-coating characteristics of a light, opaque form of water, capable of sealing vapors, are needed.

The most important use of foams is in fighting fires in flammable or combustible liquids. Foam is the only permanent extinguishing agent used for fires of this type. Its application allows fire fighters to extinguish fires progressively. A foam blanket covering a liquid surface is capable of preventing vapor transmission for some time, depending on its stability and depth. Fuel spills are quickly rendered safe by foam blanketing. The blanket may be removed after a suitable period of time; often it has no detrimental effect on the product with which it comes into contact.

Foams may be used to diminish or halt the generation of flammable vapors from nonburning liquids or solids. They may be used to fill cavities or enclosures where toxic or flammable gases may collect.

Foam is of great importance where aircraft are fueled and in operation. Sudden large fuel spills resulting from aircraft accidents or malfunction require rapid foam application. Hangar fire protection is best accomplished by foam-water sprinkler systems and portable foam equipment.

Foams of the high expansion type (100X to 1,000X) may be used to inundate or fill enclosures such as basement room areas or holds of ships where fires are difficult or impossible to reach. Here foams act to halt convection and access to air for combustion. Their water content also cools and diminishes oxygen by steam displacement.

Many foams are generated from solutions with very low surface tension and penetrating characteristics. Foams of this type are useful where Class A combustible materials are present. The water solution draining from the foam cools and wets the solid combustible in such instances.

SI Units

The following conversion factors are given as a convenience in converting to SI units the English units used in this chapter.

$$1 \text{ sq ft} = 0.0929 \text{ m}^2$$
$$\tfrac{5}{9}(°F - 32) = °C$$
$$1 \text{ gpm/ft}^2 = 40.746 \text{ litres/min m}^2$$

Bibliography

NFPA Codes, Standards, and Recommended Practices (see the latest *NFPA Publications and Visual Aids Catalog* for availability of current editions of the following documents)

NFPA No. 11, Standard for Foam Extinguisher Systems.
NFPA No. 11A, Standard for High Expansion Foam Systems.

Additional Readings

Alvares, N. J., and Lipska, A. E., "The Effect of Smoke on the Production and Stability of High-Expansion Foam," *Journal of Fire and Flammability*, Vol. 3, April 1972, pp. 88–114.

American Chemical Society, "Aqueous Foams—Their Characteristics and Applications," *Industrial and Engineering Chemistry*, Vol. 48, Nov. 1956.

Ballas, Thomas, "Electric Shock Hazard Studies of High Expansion Foam," *Fire Technology*, Vol. 5, No. 1, Feb. 1969, pp. 38–42.

Beers, R. J., "High Expansion Foam Fire Control for Records Storage," *Fire Technology*, Vol. 2, No. 2, May 1966, pp. 108–117.

Butlin, R. N., "High-Expansion Air Foam, A Survey of its Properties and Uses," Fire Research Note No. 669, May 1967, Fire Research Station, Boreham Wood, Herts, England.

Casey, James F., ed., Part 4, "Foam," *Fire Service Hydraulics*, 2nd ed., R. H. Donnelley Corporation, New York, 1970.

Cray, E. W., "High-Expansion Foam," NFPA *Quarterly*, Vol. 58, No. 1, July 1964, pp. 57–63.

"French Firm's 'Light Water' Tested for Aircraft Fires, Tunbridge Wells, Kent, England," *Fire International*, Vol. 3, No. 31, Jan. 1971, pp. 93–94.

Fittes, D. W., Griffiths, D. J., and Nash, P., "The Use of Light Water for Major Aircraft Fires," *Fire Technology*, Vol. 5, No. 4, Nov. 1969, pp. 284–298.

Fittes, D. W., and Nash, P., "Light Water," Fires, London, England, Sept. 1968.

Geyer, G. B., "Foam and Dry Chemical Application Experiments," Dec. 1968, Department of Transportation, Federal Aviation Administration, National Aviation Facilities Experimental Center, Atlantic City, N.J.

Hammack, James M., "Talking Extinguishing Equipment: Effects of Low Temperatures and Combustion Products on High Expansion Foam," *Fire Journal*, Vol. 64, No. 1, Jan. 1970, pp. 84, 86.

Hammack, James M., "Talking Extinguishing Equipment: Fluoroprotein Foams," *Fire Journal*, Vol. 64, No. 5, Sept. 1970, pp. 93–94.

Hird, D., Rodrigues, A., and Smith, D., "Foam—Its Efficiency in Tank Fires," *Fire Technology*, Vol. 6, No. 1, Feb. 1970, pp. 5–12.

Jamison, W. B., "Stability—The Key to Effective High Expansion Foam—Part II," *Fire Technology*, Vol. 6, No. 2, May 1970, pp. 140–147.

Meldrum, D. N., "Aqueous Film-Forming Foam—Facts and Fallacies," *Fire Journal*, Vol. 66, No. 1, Jan. 1972, pp. 57–64.

Meldrum, Donald N., and Williams, J. R., "Dry Chemical-Compatible Foam," *Fire Journal*, Vol. 59, No. 6, Nov. 1965, pp. 18–22.

———, "Foam Fire Protection for Liquid Propellants," *Fire Technology*, Vol. 2, No. 3, August 1966, pp. 234–238.

Meldrum, D. N., Williams, J. R., and Conway, C. J., "Storage Life and Utility of Mechanical Fire Fighting Foam Liquids," *Fire Technology*, Vol. 1, No. 2, May 1965, pp. 112–121.

Military Specification, "Fire Extinguishing Agent, Aqueous Film-Forming Foam (AFFF) Liquid Concentrate, Six Percent for Fresh and Sea Water," Amendment 5, 17 Feb. 1972, MIL-F-24385 (NAVY), Naval Ship Engineering Center, Department of the Navy, Hyattsville, Md.

Rasbash, D. J., "Notes for Specification of High Expansion Foam Liquid," Fire Research Note No. 706, April 1968, Fire Research Station, Boreham Wood, Herts, England.

"Suffocation in High Expansion Foam," *Fire International*, Vol. 18, Oct. 1967, pp. 27–30.

Tuve, R. L., Peterson, H. B., Jablonski, E. J., and Neill, R. R., "A New Vapor-Securing Agent for Flammable-Liquid Fire Extinguishment," March 13, 1964, U.S. Naval Research Laboratory, Washington, D.C.

Underwriters Laboratories, "Air Foam Equipment and Liquid Concentrates," UL-162, Northbrook, Ill., 1969.

Chapter 3

CARBON DIOXIDE

Carbon dioxide has been used for many years for the extinguishment of flammable liquid fires, gas fires, fires involving electrically energized equipment and, to a lesser extent, fires in ordinary combustibles such as paper, cloth, and other cellulosic materials. The properties that make carbon dioxide suitable for use on certain types of fires and the properties which limit its usefulness elsewhere are discussed in this chapter. Carbon dioxide extinguishers are discussed in Section 16, Chapter 3; carbon dioxide extinguishing systems in Section 15, Chapter 4; and use of carbon dioxide for inerting is described in Section 15, Chapter 7.

A. Properties Affecting Fire Extinguishment

Carbon dioxide has a number of properties that make it a desirable fire extinguishing agent. It is noncombustible and does not react with most substances, and it provides its own pressure for discharge from an extinguisher or storage cylinder. Since carbon dioxide is a gas, it can penetrate and spread to all parts of a fire area. It does not, however, form a homogenous mixture with air, and after a period of time it stratifies. As a gas or finely divided solid (snow), it will not conduct electricity and can therefore be used on energized electrical equipment.

Effect of Temperature and Pressure on Physical State

Under normal conditions, carbon dioxide is a gas. It is easily liquefied by compression and cooling and, by further compression and cooling, it can be converted to a solid. The effect of changes of temperature and pressure on carbon dioxide in a closed container is shown in Figure 13-3A.

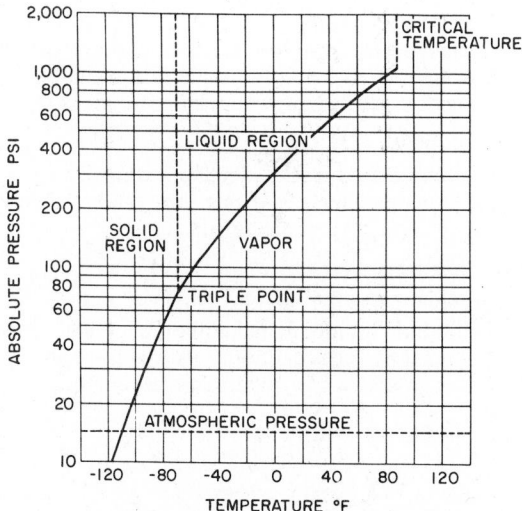

Fig. 13-3A. *Effect of pressure and temperature change on the physical state of carbon dioxide at constant volume. Above the critical temperature (87.8°F) it is entirely gas, irrespective of pressure. Between 87.8°F and −69.9°F (temperature of the triple point), in a closed container it is part liquid and part gas. Below the triple point it is either a solid or gas, depending on the pressure and temperature.*

For example, on that part of the curve between the "triple point" (75 psia [pounds per square inch absolute] and −69.9°F) and the "critical temperature" (87.8°F), carbon dioxide in a closed container is both a liquid and a gas. As the pressure increases, the density of the vapor increases: as the temperature increases, the liquid expands and its density decreases. At 87.8°F (the critical temperature) the density of the liquid and the vapor or gas are the same, and the liquid phase disappears. At temperatures above the critical temperature carbon dioxide is present entirely as a gas, irrespective of pressure.

Again, considering a liquid-vapor mixture in a closed container, reduction of the pressure by bleeding off some of the vapor will cause some of the liquid to vaporize and the remaining liquid to become colder. Figure 13–3A indicates that as the pressure and temperature are reduced, a point is reached at which carbon dioxide exists as a liquid, as a solid, and as a gas. As previously stated, this point is called the triple point and occurs at 75 psia and −69.9°F. Below a pressure of 75 psia, carbon dioxide must exist as a solid, vapor (gas), or as a mixture of both depending on the temperature and pressure. Reduction of the pressure to atmospheric results in further cooling. Solid carbon dioxide (dry ice) is obtained at a temperature of −110°F.

The following material explains the changes in physical state that take place when carbon dioxide is released into the atmosphere from a storage container. Assuming the carbon dioxide is to be stored as a liquid (with vapor above it), discharge of liquid to atmosphere results in a large part of the liquid expanding to a gas. Heat absorbed during this vaporization cools the remaining liquid to −110°F, at which temperature it becomes finely divided particles of dry ice. It is this dry ice (or snow) that gives the discharge its typical white, cloudy appearance.

Density

The relative density of carbon dioxide gas, when compared with dry air at 32°F and 1 atmosphere pressure, is 1.529. In other words, carbon dioxide is about 1½ times as heavy as air, a property that accounts for its ability to replace air above burning surfaces and maintain a smothering atmosphere.

The liquid density at 2°F is 63.4 pcf (pounds per cubic foot). At 80°F, the liquid density is 42.2 pcf.

Toxicity

Although carbon dioxide is only mildly toxic, it can produce unconsciousness and death when present in fire extinguishing concentrations. The action in this case is more related to suffocation than it is to any toxic effect of the carbon dioxide itself.

A concentration of 9 percent is about all most persons can withstand without losing consciousness within a few minutes. Breathing a higher concentration could render a person helpless almost immediately.

In most small enclosures protected by carbon dioxide, any person present when the discharge starts would probably have no difficulty escaping before a critical concentration is reached (providing the escape route is familiar, as a cloud condition will occur during the discharge). The hazard will be greater where the enclosure is large, egress for any reason is difficult, or if carbon dioxide has unexpectedly entered the area (e.g., a pit or a basement).

Low Temperature Behavior

No protection against freezing is normally required since carbon dioxide (as stored in cylinders and tanks) does not freeze at the lowest climatic temperature. Low temperature will, however, reduce the rate of discharge for high pressure cylinders. Extremely low storage temperatures must be taken into consideration when designing carbon dioxide extinguishing systems. High pressure systems are designed to operate effectively with storage cylinder temperatures as low as 32°F. (The upper temperature is 120°F.) If cylinder temperatures can fall below 32°F, heating or some other condition such as supercharging to compensate for the cold will be needed; e.g., a suitable expellant such as nitrogen may be necessary to assure a proper rate of discharge. Low pressure systems operate effectively with the storage container at 0°F. (See Sec. 15, Chap. 4 for further information on high and low pressure carbon dioxide systems.)

B. Extinguishing Properties

Carbon dioxide is effective as an extinguishing agent primarily because it reduces the oxygen content of the air to a point where it will no longer support combustion. Under suitable conditions of control and application, some cooling effect is also realized.

Extinguishment by Smothering

Carbon dioxide is stored under pressure as a liquid, and, when released, it is discharged into the fire area principally as a gas. In general, 1 lb of carbon dioxide in its liquid state may be considered as producing about 8 cu ft of free gas at atmospheric pressure. When released onto burning materials, it envelops them and dilutes the oxygen to a concentration which cannot support combustion. The theoretical minimum carbon dioxide concentration for extinguishment of various materials is given in Table 13-3A.

Extinguishment by Cooling

The rapid expansion of liquid to gas when carbon dioxide is released from a storage cylinder produces a refrigerating effect that converts part of the carbon dioxide into snow. This snow, which has a temperature of $-110°F$, soon sublimes into gas, absorbing heat from both the burning material and the surrounding atmosphere. Carbon dioxide snow has a latent heat of 246.4 Btu per lb, but since only part of the liquid carbon dioxide is converted to snow the total cooling effect of the gas and the snow is considerably less than might otherwise be expected. When the liquid is stored at 80°F, approximately 25 percent is converted to snow upon discharge, giving a total cooling effect of about 120 Btu per lb. When the liquid is stored at 0°F, approximately 45 percent is converted to snow upon discharge, giving a total cooling effect of about 170 Btu per lb. Water at 32°F has a theoretical cooling effect of about 1,150 Btu per lb, assuming that the water is completely evaporated into steam which, of course, is seldom the case.

C. Limitations as an Extinguishing Agent

Hot Surfaces and Embers

Fires apparently extinguished by carbon dioxide may reignite after the smothering atmosphere has been dissipated

Table 13-3A. Minimum Carbon Dioxide Concentrations for Extinguishment

Material	Theoretical Min. CO_2 Concentration (%)
Acetylene	55
Acetone	26*
Benzol, Benzene	31
Butadiene	34
Butane	28
Carbon Disulfide	55
Carbon Monoxide	53
Coal Gas or Natural Gas	31*
Cyclopropane	31
Dowtherm	38*
Ethane	33
Ethyl Ether	38*
Ethyl Alcohol	36
Ethylene	41
Ethylene Dichloride	21
Ethylene Oxide	44
Gasoline	28
Hexane	29
Hydrogen	62
Isobutane	30*
Kerosene	28
Methane	25
Methyl Alcohol	26
Pentane	29
Propane	30
Propylene	30
Quench, Lubricating Oils	28

Note: The theoretical minimum extinguishing concentrations in air for the above materials were obtained from Bureau of Mines, Bulletin 503.[1] Those marked * were calculated from accepted residual oxygen values.

if smoldering embers or hot surfaces remain. In such cases, it may be necessary to reduce the oxygen content to about 6 percent and to maintain this concentration long enough for the embers and hot surfaces to cool to below the ignition temperature of the fuel. Often, long periods of time are required for sufficient cooling in order to prevent reignition of freshly charred, hot, carbonaceous materials. To cool a deep-seated fire (such as a cotton bale fire in the hold of a ship), a period of several days may be required.

Oxygen-Containing Materials

Carbon dioxide is not an effective extinguishing agent for use on fires involving chemicals that contain their own oxygen supply (such as cellulose nitrate).

Reactive Chemicals

Fires involving reactive metals (such as sodium, potassium, magnesium, titanium, and zirconium) and fires involving the metal hydrides cannot be extinguished by carbon dioxide. The metals and hydrides decompose carbon dioxide.

SI Units

The following conversion factors are given as a convenience in converting to SI Units the English Units used in this chapter:

1 lb (mass)	= 0.454 kg
1 Btu/lb	= 2.326 kJ/kg
1 psi	= 6.895 kPa
$\frac{5}{9}$ (°F − 32)	= °C
1 ft³	= 0.0283 m³

Bibliography

References Cited

[1] Coward, H. W., and Jones, G. W., "Limits of Flammability of Gases and Vapors," Bulletin 503, 1952, USDI Bureau of Mines, Pittsburgh.

NFPA Codes, Standards, and Recommended Practices (see the latest *NFPA Publications and Visual Aids Catalog* for availability of current editions of the following document)

NFPA No. 12, Standard on Carbon Dioxide Extinguishing Systems.

Additional Readings

Goetz, C. A., "Carbon Dioxide Fire Protection," NFPA *Quarterly*, Vol. 49, No. 2, Oct. 1955, pp. 179–185.

Haessler, W. M., "Fire and Its Extinguishment," NFPA *Quarterly*, Vol. 56, No. 1, July 1962, pp. 89–96.

Irish, D. D., and Fassett, D. W., eds., *Patty: Industrial Hygiene and Toxicology*, 2nd revised ed., Vol. II, Interscience Publishers, New York, 1963, pp. 936–938.

Zabetakis, Michael G., *Flammability Characteristics of Combustible Gases and Vapors*, Bulletin 627, Washington, D.C., USDI Bureau of Mines.

Section 13

Chapter 4

THE HALOGENATED EXTINGUISHING AGENTS

Halogenated extinguishing agents are hydrocarbons in which one or more hydrogen atoms have been replaced by halogen atoms. The common halogen elements from the halogen series are fluorine, chlorine, bromine, and iodine. The hydrocarbons from which halogenated extinguishing agents are derived are highly flammable gases and, in many cases, the substitution of halogen atoms confers not only nonflammability but flame extinguishment properties to the resulting compounds.

A. Chemical Composition, Classification, and Properties

The halogen agents which have found use as extinguishing agents have been derived from methane (CH_4) and ethane (CH_3CH_3) and, depending on the degree and nature of halogen substitution, range from gases to liquids at room temperature. Carbon tetrafluoride (CF_4) is a gas which is chemically inert, nonflammable, and of low toxicity. It is believed to extinguish flame primarily by acting as a heat sink. Carbon tetrachloride (CCl_4) is a liquid which is chemically more reactive and nonflammable. It has increased chemical flame extinguishment properties and, despite its higher toxicity, it has been widely used as an extinguishant.

The halogenated extinguishing agents are currently known as Halons, and the "Halon System" for naming the halogenated hydrocarbons was devised by the U.S. Army Corps of Engineers. This simplified system of nomenclature describes the chemical composition of the materials without the use of chemical names or possibly confusing abbreviations (i.e., "BT" for bromotrifluoromethane and "DDM" for dibromodifluoromethane). Examples of this system are shown in Table 13-4A. The first digit of the number represents the number of carbon atoms in the compound molecule; the second digit, the number of fluorine atoms; the third digit, the number of chlorine atoms; the fourth digit, the number of bromine atoms; and the fifth digit, the number of iodine atoms (if any). In this system terminal digits are not expressed: bromotrifluoromethane ($BrCF_3$), for example, is referred to as Halon 1301 because its chemical formula shows one carbon atom, three fluorine atoms, one bromine atom, and no iodine atoms.

The three halogen elements commonly found in extinguishing agents are fluorine, chlorine, and bromine. Substitution of a hydrogen atom in a hydrocarbon with these three influences the relevant properties in the following manner: fluorine bestows stability, nonflammability, and low toxicity on a compound, but has little effect on boiling point and gives only limited extinguishment properties; compared to fluorinated materials those with chlorine have increased reactivity, increased flame extinguishment properties, increased boiling points, and increased toxicity. Substitution of bromine for chlorine again increases reactivity, flame extinguishment, boiling point, and toxicity. Thus, it would seem that effective extinguishment can be accomplished only with toxic materials such as methyl bromide (Halon 1001). This, however, is not the case, as several compounds which contain both fluorine and one or more atoms of chlorine or bromine—such as bromotrifluoromethane (Halon 1301) and bromochlorodifluoromethane (Halon 1211)—have acceptable levels of toxicity combined with excellent flame extinguishment properties. Currently, these compounds are widely used as fire extinguishants. The iodo compounds have not been used as they are too toxic and unstable.

Chloro compounds and (even more so) bromo compounds show increased chemical reactivity when compared to fluorine compounds. This refers to relative reactivity, and all the compounds used as fire extinguishants are relatively stable except under attack by strong chemicals. The halogen is linked to the carbon atom by a "covalent chemical bond," which means that unlike ionic halogen compounds such as common salt (sodium chloride), there is no tendency to ionize or become electrically conductive in the presence of water. The presence of a fluorine atom in the molecule increases the C-Cl and C-Br strength. For this reason, halogenated agents are very suitable for use on electrical fires from the standpoint of low electrical conductivity.

The term "halogenated agent" applies to both partially and totally substituted hydrocarbons. Not all partically halogenated compounds are nonflammable. Methyl chloride (Halon 101) is flammable, whereas methyl bromide (Halon 1001) is nonflammable under normal conditions and is an efficient, although toxic, extinguishant.

Although many halogenated hydrocarbons are possible fire extinguishants and have been tested as such, this chapter refers mainly to those which have been, or are currently being, widely used as fire extinguishants.

General Applications

Because they are either gases or liquids which rapidly vaporize in fire, halons leave little corrosive or abrasive residue after use. They are nonconductors of electricity and have high liquid densities which permit compact storage containers. The areas of major use are protection of electrical equipment, air and ground vehicle engines, areas where visibility after use is important, or where clean-up after use should be minimized. Protection may be either by use of a fixed system or by use of hand portables and wheeled units. Generally, the type of protection required determines which halons are used. In fixed systems, gaseous materials, such as methyl bromide (Halon 1001), bromotrifluoromethane (Halon 1301), and bromochlorodifluoromethane (Halon 1211), have been widely used. In portable applications, where liquid range is desirable, the higher-

Table 13-4A. Sample Halon Numbers for Various Halogenated Fire Extinguishing Agents

Chemical Name	Formula	Halon No.
Methyl bromide	CH_3Br	1001
Methyl iodide	CH_3I	10001
Bromochloromethane	$BrCH_2Cl$	1011
Dibromodifluoromethane	Br_2CF_2	1202
Bromochlorodifluoromethane	$BrCClF_2$	1211
Bromotrifluoromethane	$BrCF_3$	1301
Carbon tetrachloride	CCl_4	104
Dibromotetrafluoroethane	BrF_2CCBrF_2	2402

boiling liquefied gas Halon 1211 and vaporizing liquids, such as carbon tetrachloride (Halon 104), chlorobromomethane (Halon 1011), and dibromotetrafluoroethane (Halon 2402), have been widely used.

Worldwide concern over potential toxic hazards associated with halogenated agents has resulted in the withdrawal of materials such as carbon tetrachloride and chlorobromomethane, and their replacement by the significantly lower toxicity fluorocarbons such as bromotrifluoromethane (Halon 1301), bromochlorodifluoromethane (Halon 1211), and dibromotetrafluoroethane (Halon 2402). In the United States in 1974 the only two materials recognized in the NFPA Standards were bromotrifluoromethane (Halon 1301) and bromochlorodifluoromethane (Halon 1211).

B.   History of Halogenated Agents

The extinguishing effectiveness of carbon tetrachloride (Halon 104) was recognized in the late nineteenth century. However, it was not until the development of the electrolytic process for the production of chlorine from brine (which made that material available at low cost) that the use of carbon tetrachloride in extinguishers became economically viable.

Many carbon tetrachloride extinguishers available in the early part of the century were operated by hand pumps. With the advent of flying it became apparent that aircraft engines represented a significant fire hazard. A compact and efficient automatic system of fire protection was required, and in the 1920s the use of carbon tetrachloride was developed for this application. Carbon tetrachloride subsequently found use in automatic glass bulb devices, hand grenade type units, and aerosol cans as well as in portable extinguishers. However, for toxicological reasons, concern about its use gained significant momentum during the early 1960s, and in 1968 reference to this type of extinguisher (as well as bromochloromethane based extinguishers) was withdrawn from NFPA Standard No. 10, Installation of Portable Fire Extinguishers. Listings of extinguishers with carbon tetrachloride were withdrawn by ULC (Underwriters Laboratories of Canada) in 1967, and by UL (Underwriters Laboratories, Inc.) in 1970.

The potential of methyl bromide (Halon 1001) for aircraft applications was recognized during the late 1920s when it was found to be more effective than carbon tetrachloride.

In England in 1938 it was decided to utilize methyl bromide for fixed aircraft engine protection. In the early 1960s it was replaced on civilian aircraft by chlorobromodifluoromethane (Halon 1211), although it is still used on a few British military aircraft.

In Germany a 50:50 mixture of methyl bromide and ethylene dibromide was used on both military aircraft and ships. The mixture was highly toxic, and the use of methyl bromide was discontinued in Germany in 1941 in favor of bromochloromethane (Halon 1011). The use of methyl bromide in portable extinguishers never gained wide use because of its toxicity.

The third halogenated agent to gain widespread use was chlorobromomethane (Halon 1011). Halon 1011 has a relatively high boiling point (151°F), which makes it more appropriate for use in portable applications than in fixed systems. It was developed in Germany in 1939 and 1940 as a replacement for the highly toxic methyl bromide. In 1954 virtually all U.S. Air Force aircraft power plant extinguishing systems had been transformed from carbon dioxide and methyl bromide to chlorobromomethane.

Chlorobromomethane was used in portable and wheeled units by the USAF until late in 1973, when it began to replace chlorobromomethane 40-gal units with similar units using bromochlorodifluoromethane.

Following World War II, the field of potential extinguishants grew significantly with the development of fluorine technology to the point where halogenated agents containing fluorine could be efficiently and inexpensively produced. The widespread use of these materials as refrigerants, aerosol propellants, and industrial solvents presented a relatively inexpensive means for producing bromofluorocarbons having excellent fire extinguishant properties and relatively low toxicities.

In 1947 the Purdue Research Foundation performed a systematic evaluation for the U.S. Army of more than 60 candidate fire extinguishing agents to replace carbon tetrachloride and methyl bromide. From these tests four halogenated agents, bromotrifluoromethane (Halon 1301), bromochlorodifluoromethane (Halon 1211), dibromodifluoromethane (Halon 1202), and dibromotetrafluoroethane (Halon 2402), were selected for further evaluations in specific applications.

Bromotrifluoromethane, $BrCF_3$ (Halon 1301)

In 1954 Halon 1301, the least toxic and second most effective of the four agents, was selected by the U.S. Army for use in portable extinguishers, and by the CAA (Civil Aeronautics Administration) and the U.S. Navy for protection of aircraft engine nacelles. Commercial development of Halon 1301 began with the installation of systems for aircraft engine protection on the Lockheed Constellation and Douglas DC-7. Subsequently, it has been used on every commercial aircraft built in the United States. By contrast, Halon 1301 received little attention in Europe until the early 1970s.

Although a $2\frac{1}{2}$-lb portable extinguisher has been available since 1962, high cost has inhibited its development despite its significant technical advantages over carbon dioxide. The most recent work has been in the development of systems for which this agent is ideally suited. Systems range from small $\frac{1}{2}$-lb units for protection of outboard marine engines to $3\frac{1}{2}$-ton systems protecting 300,000 cu ft oil-processing buildings, the major use being the protection of computer room facilities. The low toxicity of Halon 1301 allows it to be discharged safely from total flood systems in occupied spaces, an advantage which no other gaseous agent has.

Bromochlorodifluoromethane, $BrCClF_2$ (Halon 1211)

Halon 1211 became established in Europe for use in aircraft engine protection systems and, subsequently, during the 1960s in both military and civilian use in a wide range of portable and systems applications. Despite its widespread use in Europe and other parts of the world, significant use of Halon 1211 in the United States did not start until 1973 when the first laboratory tested portable extinguishers became available and the U.S. Air Force began to use Halon 1211 to replace chlorobromomethane (Halon 1011) extinguishers on ramp patrol trucks.

The later development of Halon 1211 differs from that of Halon 1301 in that Halon 1211's major areas of use have been established for portable and wheeled units. Although significant use in total flooding systems has been developed in Europe, Halon 1211's toxicity level precludes its use in the total flooding of occupied spaces. However, its toxicity level is low enough for safe use in local application systems and in portable systems in occupied spaces. Small "thermatic" devices using Halon 1211 are available from several European manufacturers, and similar devices are now being developed in the U.S. To satisfy authorities of its safety, the development of Halon 1211 in the U.S. was not started until sufficient data on its toxicity had been collected.

Dibromotetrafluoroethane, BRF_2CCBrF_2 (Halon 2402)

Halon 2402 has found limited use, particularly in Italy and Russia, for aircraft engine protection systems and in portable extinguisher and fixed systems application. Other than being used in a few specialized explosion suppression systems, the general use of Halon 2402 has not been established in the United States.

Dibromodifluoromethane, Br_2CF_2 (Halon 1202)

Halon 1202, somewhat more effective than Halon 1301 on a weight-of-agent basis (but the most toxic of the four final candidates in the Purdue study), was selected by the U.S. Air Force for use in aircraft engine protection systems.[1] Currently its use is declining in this application, and other uses have not been developed.

C. Properties of Halogenated Agents

Some of the physical properties of the common halogenated fire extinguishing agents referred to in this chapter are shown in Table 13-4B. More details on bromotrifluoromethane and bromochlorodifluoromethane are given in the following paragraphs.

Physical Properties

Bromotrifluoromethane (Halon 1301) is a gas at 70°F with a vapor pressure of 199 psig (lbs per sq in. gage). Although this pressure would adequately expel the material, it decreases rapidly with a temperature fall to 56 psig at 0°F and 17.2 psig at −40°F. It is, therefore, usual to super pressure portable extinguishers or systems with nitrogen to a minimum of 350 psig which ensures adequate performance at all temperatures.

Bromochlorodifluoromethane (Halon 1211) has high effectiveness, and its low toxicity is comparable to that of carbon dioxide. It is a gas at 70°F, with a vapor pressure of 22 psig and a boiling point of 25°F. Its relatively high boiling point allows it to be projected as a liquid stream, thus enabling portable extinguishers to have a much greater range than other gaseous materials. The normal over-pressurization

with nitrogen is from 70 psig at 70°F which permits the use of inexpensive hardware.

Corrosion and Other Effects on Materials

The early nonfluorinated halogenated agents had significant corrosion problems: i.e., methyl bromide (Halon 1001) and chlorobromomethane (Halon 1011) would corrode aluminum and aluminum alloys, and carbon tetrachloride had to be stabilized with carbon disulphide. The fluorinated agents currently in use are chemically more stable, and neither of the two most generally used in the U.S.—bromotrifluoromethane (Halon 1301) and bromochlorodifluoromethane (Halon 1211)—has any significant corrosive action on the commonly used construction metals unless free water is present. (Free water is defined as the presence of a separate water phase in the liquid halon. When present in a small quantity, free water can provide a site for concentrating acid impurities into a corrosive liquid. It has been determined that dissolved water is not a problem.)

The effect of these two agents on plastics and elastomers has been studied and, because their effectiveness depends on the precise grade or composition of the plastics and elastomers, only broad, summary guidelines for their use are presented in this chapter: more precise guidelines should be obtained from the manufacturers of the materials. The rigid plastics which are normally satisfactory are polyvinyl chloride, nylon, and acetal copolymers. Elastomers of particular suitability are high nitrile and "Viton" fluoroelastomer rubbers. In general, Halon 1301 has considerably less effect on plastic materials than Halon 1211.

D. Extinguishing Characteristics

Section 16, Chapter 3, presents more specific details and information on procedures for determining concentrations for inerting, flame extinguishment, and explosion suppression where halogenated agent systems are concerned.

The extinguishing mechanism of the halogenated agents is not clearly understood. However, there is undoubtedly a chemical reaction as the agents are considerably more effective than heat removal or smothering can account for.

The chemical extinguishants are much more effective because of their ability to interfere with the combustion processes. They act by removing the active chemical species involved in the flame chain reactions (a process known as "chain breaking"). While all the halogens are active in this

---

Table 13-4B.   Some Physical Properties of the Common Halogenated Fire Extinguishing Agents

Agent	Chemical Formula	Halon No.	Type of Agent	Approx. Boiling Point °F	Approx. Freezing Point °F	Specific Gravity of Liquid at 68°F (Water = 1)	Approx. Critical Temp. °F	Estimated Pressure psig At 130°F	At Critical Temp.	Latent Heat of Vaporization cal/g Water = 540 cal/g CO_2 = 138 cal/g
Carbon tetrachloride	CCl_4	104	Liquid	170	−8	1.595	—	—	—	46
Methyl bromide	CH_3Br	1001	Liquid	40	−135	1.73	—	—	—	62
Bromochloromethane	$BrCH_2Cl$	1011	Liquid	151	−124	1.93	—	—	—	—
Dibromodifluoromethane	Br_2CF_2	1202	Liquid	76	−223	2.28	389	23	585	29
Bromochlorodifluoromethane	$BrCClF_2$	1211	Liquefied Gas*	25	−257	1.83	309	75	580	32
Bromotrifluoromethane	$BrCF_3$	1301	Liquefied Gas	−72	−270	1.57	153	435	560	28
Dibromotetrafluoroethane	BrF_2CCBrF_2	2402	Liquid	117	−167	2.17	—	3.8	—	25

* May be kept as a liquid at reduced temperatures.

way, bromine is much more effective than chlorine or fluorine.

The mechanism by which bromine inhibits combustion is not completely understood, nor indeed are the combustion processes themselves. However, a number of possible reactions have been proposed. The most active species in hydrocarbon combustion are oxygen and hydrogen atoms, and hydroxyl radicals (O, H, and OH). Under fire conditions, the halogenated agent—for example, bromotrifluoromethane (Halon 1301)—will break down to give up a bromine atom:

$$CBrF_3 \rightarrow CF_3{}^{\bullet} + Br^{\bullet}$$

The Br atom can react with some organic molecule:

$$R\text{-}H + Br^{\bullet} \rightarrow R^{\bullet} + HBr$$

One possible mechanism assumes the removal of H atoms and the formulation of H_2 molecules (this cannot happen by direct combination of two atoms since the energy released is sufficient to cause disassociation of the newly formed molecule):

$$H^{\bullet} + HBr \rightarrow H_2 + Br^{\bullet}$$

Another proposed system involves a reaction with OH radicals:

$$OH^{\bullet} + HBr \rightarrow H_2O + Br^{\bullet}$$

In this way, chain carriers are removed from the system while the inhibiting HBr is continuously regenerated. In hydrocarbon combustion, the removal of H or OH would be equally effective, as they are involved in an equilibrium reaction.

$$OH^{\bullet} + CO \rightleftharpoons H^{\bullet} + CO_2$$

Another "ionic" theory supposes that the uninhibited combustion process includes a step in which oxygen ions are formed by the capture of electrons which come from ionization of hydrocarbon molecules. Since bromine atoms have a much higher cross section for the capture of slow electrons than has oxygen, the bromine inhibits the reaction by removing the electrons that are needed for activation of the oxygen.

Fire Extinguishing Effectiveness

The effectiveness of the different halons as extinguishing agents has been the subject of many studies. The initial results of some of the early studies are contained in the October 1954 issue of the NFPA *Quarterly*.[1] It is now recognized that comparison of effectiveness of agents depends on whether portable extinguishers or fixed systems are being considered and, particularly in tests on portable units, whether the agents were being used at optimum overpressurization with nitrogen. Therefore, the following information should be used only as a general guide as other considerations, such as range of the unit (which varies on the gas or liquid characteristic of the individual halon and the total weight and volume of the equipment), may be of equal importance, depending upon use.

Table 13-4C gives the approximate pounds of agent required per unit of Class B rating obtained with small portable extinguishers listed with UL within the last ten years (see Sec. 16, Chap. 1 for information on UL testing criteria for Class B ratings). The performance of carbon tetrachloride was inferior to any of the halogenated agents shown.

The B ratings obtained for the halogenated agents should not be rigorously compared with those of dry chemicals, as pressure variations with temperature affect performance of gaseous halons to a more marked degree than dry chemical

Table 13-4C. Relative Effectiveness of Halogenated Agents on Small UL Class B Fires

Agent	Halon No.	Weight of Unit	UL B:C	Pounds Per Unit B Rating
Chlorobromomethane	1011	4*	2	2.0
Bromotrifluoromethane	1301	2.75	4†	0.6
Bromochlorodifluoromethane	1211	3.0	5	0.6
Carbon Dioxide	—	5	5	1.0

* One quart = 4 lbs.
† Originally rated 4 B:C by UL until this rating was dropped.

as evidenced in tests at low temperatures. Halons, however, do have the ability to penetrate obscured hazards in a way that dry chemicals cannot.

In a very general sense the performance of bromotrifluoromethane (Halon 1301) and bromochlorodifluoromethane (Halon 1211) is equivalent to that of sodium bicarbonate dry chemical. The relative performance of the halogenated agents in fire extinguishing systems is discussed in further detail in Section 15, Chapter 5. On a world-wide basis the development of systems using Halon 1301 and Halon 1211 together with the development of realistic test methods which have been applied to both these agents which are recognized by the NFPA have shown that in total flooding application for flame extinguishment or inerting, Halon 1301 requires an average of 10 percent less material on a gas volume basis than does Halon 1211 for any given fuel. Table 13-4D shows a comparison of flame extinguishment values submitted to the NFPA for inclusion in NFPA Standard Nos. 12A and 12B. It is generally recognized that on a weight-of-agent basis, Halon 1301 is approximately $2\frac{1}{2}$ times more effective than carbon dioxide. It is also generally recognized that halons have a significant effect on Class A fires when used in both portable units and fixed systems, mainly because of their cooling effect.

E. Toxic and Irritant Effects

In fire fighting the most important effects are the resultant toxic and irritant effects of short-term exposure to the vapors of the halogenated agents and their decomposition

Table 13-4D. Comparison of Flame Extinguishment Values for Bromotrifluoromethane (Halon 1301) and Bromochlorodifluoromethane (Halon 1211)

Fuel	Percent by Volume of Agent Required for Flame Extinguishment	
	Halon 1301	Halon 1211
Methane	5	5
Propane	5	5
n-Heptane	5	6
Ethylene	6	7
Benzene	5	5
Diethyl Ether	5	6
Methanol	10	11
Ethanol	6	6
Acetone	5	5
Ethyl Acetate	5	5

Note: At this writing, the above values have not been formally adopted by the NFPA Committee on Halogenated Fire Extinguishing Agent Systems for inclusion in NFPA Standards 12A and 12B, and therefore may be subject to change before appearing in future editions of the respective Standards.

products. Thus, industrially allowed concentrations for an 8-hr daily continuous exposure, as contained in "Guide to OSHA Fire Protection Regulations[2]," cannot be taken as an exact guide for the evaluation of the toxic effect of fire exposure for two reasons: (1) the effect may vary with respect to exposure concentration and time (that is, exposure time multiplied by exposure concentration does not yield a constant effect), and (2) except for carbon dioxide the maximum concentration ever accepted for manufacturing purposes is 1,000 ppm (parts per million) in air.

The first studies on the toxicity of the halogenated agents were carried out on small animals and rodents. Although these studies present a useful guide to the relative toxicity of the agents, more recent studies on human subjects with bromotrifluoromethane (Halon 1301) and bromochlorodifluoromethane (Halon 1211) show that the results of the first studies cannot be translated directly into toxicity levels appropriate to human exposure.

Table 13-4E, developed by the U.S. Army Chemical Center, presents a classification system suitable for short-term exposures, and Table 13-4F presents the UL system for classifying the life hazard of various vaporizing liquids and gases. Both the comparative tables are based on animal exposures.

The human exposure tests with halogenated agents are well documented, and much information was presented at a National Academy of Sciences symposium on "An Appraisal of Halogenated Fire Extinguishing Agents" given in Washington, D.C., in 1972.[3]

Neither Halon 1301 nor Halon 1211 has shown any residual poisoning effects, the effect of high concentration being of a temporary nature. Experiments on animals have shown that the toxic effects of the Halons is twofold: (1) they can either stimulate or depress the central nervous system to produce effects ranging from tremors and convulsions to lethargy and unconsciousness, and (2) they can sensitize the heart to adrenalin by causing disorders that range from a few isolated abnormal beats to the complete disorganization of normal rhythm. The human tests have shown that high concentrations of both agents lead to dizziness, impaired coordination, and reduced mental acuity. It is possible that prolonged exposure at high concentrations could lead to unconsciousness and even death. However, it is necessary to consider this possibility in relationship to the concentrations of each agent as required to extinguish fire. When this is done, the safety of these two agents for their appropriate applications is established.

Halon 1301 is the least toxic gaseous extinguishant, and for most total flooding applications can be discharged into occupied spaces. Most applications call for extinguishing concentrations ranging from 4 to 6 percent volume, and it has been established that there is minimal, if any, effect on the central nervous system with concentrations up to 7 percent volume. Between 7 and 10 percent volume concentration, light-headedness and reduced dexterity have been noted. However, it is only above a 10 percent volume that toxic effects can be considered as being potentially serious enough to be avoided.

Halon 1211 has a lower threshold safety limit than Halon 1301 and all evidence seems to indicate that the hazard for concentrations of equivalent fire extinguishment capability is comparable to that of carbon dioxide. This would indicate safe application from portable extinguishers but restricted use in fixed systems. Concentrations up to 4 percent volume have been shown to be tolerable for a time period up to one minute (compared to 10 percent for Halon 1301).

In view of its relatively wide use in portable extinguishers, a series of experiments were performed to determine the concentration which might occur from total discharge in confined spaces. A portable extinguisher containing 3 lbs of Halon 1211 was discharged into a 945 cu ft room. The calculated mean concentration was 0.73 percent, itself a safe figure. However, analysis of the atmosphere at 5 ft 6 in. above the floor (i.e., nose height) showed that the concentration never exceeded 0.5 percent, and rapidly fell to lower concentrations. In even more severe experiments, 3 lbs of Halon 1211 was discharged into a truck cab under various conditions (in no case did the concentration at nose height exceed 2 percent).

F. Decomposition Products of Halons

Consideration of the life safety of halogenated agents does not stop with the effects of the agents themselves, but must also be given to the effects of breakdown products which have a relatively higher toxicity. Decomposition of halogenated agents takes place on exposure to flame, or to surface temperatures above approximately 900°F. In the presence of available hydrogen (from water vapor or the combustion process itself) the main decomposition products of bromofluoromethane (Halon 1301) are the halogen acids hydrogen fluoride (HF) and hydrogen bromide

Table 13-4E.   Approximate Lethal Concentrations for 15-min Exposure to Vapors of Various Fire Extinguishing Agents*

Agent	Formula	Halon No.	Approximate Lethal Concentration in Parts Per Million	
			Natural Vapor	Decomposed Vapor
Bromotrifluoromethane	$BrCF_3$	1301	832,000	14,000†
Bromochlorodifluoromethane	$BrCClF_2$	1211	324,000	7,650
Carbon Dioxide	CO_2	—	658,000	658,000
Dibromodifluoromethane	$BrCF_2$	1202	54,000	1,850
Bromochloromethane	$BrCH_2Cl$	1011	65,000	4,000
Dibromotetrafluoroethane	BrF_2CCBrF_2	2402	126,000	1,600‡
Carbon tetrachloride	CCl_4	104	28,000	300
Methyl bromide	CH_3Br	1001	5,900	9,600

* Based on tests with white rats by the Medical Laboratories, U.S. Army Chemical Center.

† Subsequent tests by Kettering Laboratory of the University of Cincinnati (unpublished data) with a commercial Halon 1301 of improved quality indicated that the lethal concentration of decomposed vapor is at least 20,000 ppm. Other tests have given the ALC (Approximate Lethal Concentration) value of Halon 1301 decomposition products as low as 2,500 ppm. The variance is based on differing analytical procedures.

‡ This figure does not agree with manufacturer's data on their product.

Table 13-4F. Underwriters Laboratories Classification of Comparative Life Hazard of Various Chemicals (Based Upon Exposure of Test Animals)

Group	Definition	Examples
6 (least toxic)	Gases or vapors which in concentrations up to at least 20 percent by volume for durations of exposure of the order of 2 hrs do not appear to produce injury.	Bromotrifluoromethane (Halon 1301) Dichlorodifluoromethane (Halon 122 or R-12)
5a	Gases or vapors much less toxic than Group 4 but more toxic than Group 6.	Bromochlorodifluoromethane (Halon 1211) Carbon Dioxide
4	Gases or vapors which in concentrations of the order of 2 to 2½ percent for durations of exposure of the order of 2 hrs are lethal or produce serious injury.	Methyl Chloride (Halon 101) Dibromodifluoromethane (Halon 1202) Ethyl Bromide (Halon 2001)
3	Gases or vapors which in concentrations of the order of 2 to 2½ percent for durations of exposure of the order of 1 hr are lethal or produce serious injury.	Chlorobromomethane (Halon 1011) Carbon tetrachloride (Halon 114) Chloroform (Halon 103)
2	Gases or vapors which in concentrations of the order of ½ to 1 percent for durations of exposure of the order of ½ hr are lethal or produce serious injury.	Methyl bromide (Halon 1001) Ammonia
1	Gases or vapors which in concentrations of the order of ½ to 1 percent for durations of exposure of the order of 5 min are lethal or produce serious injury.	Sulfur Dioxide

(HBr), and free halogens (Br_2) with small amounts of carbonyl halides (CoF_2, $CoBr_2$). The decomposition products of bromochlorodifluoromethane (Halon 1211) are similar.

The approximate lethal concentrations for 15-min exposures to some of these compounds are given in Column 1 of Table 13-4G. Column 2 gives the concentrations of these materials that have been quoted by Sax as "dangerous for short exposures."[4]

It is necessary to establish the concentrations likely to be encountered when extinguishing fires with halogenated agents and to relate them not only to the absolute toxicity, but also to the toxic effects of the normal products of combustion.

Even in minute concentrations of only a few ppm, the decomposition products of the halogenated agents have characteristically sharp, acrid odors. This characteristic provides a built-in warning system for the agent, and at the same time creates a noxious, irritating atmosphere for those who must enter the hazard area following a fire. It also serves as a warning that other potentially toxic products of combustion (such as carbon monoxide) will be present.

The concentrations of decomposition products which may be expected depend upon many factors (i.e., size of room, intensity of fire, presence of large quantities of hot surfaces, and time of extinguishment). Test results which may help to put the situation into perspective have been made for both Halon 1301 and Halon 1211 in total flooding and portable applications. As an example of total flooding, Halon 1301 was used to extinguish a 25 sq ft, n-Heptane fire in a 10,000 cu ft enclosure. In one test, with extinguishment within 0.5 sec, the HF concentration was 12 ppm. In another test with extinguishment within 10 sec, an average HF level of 250 ppm over a 9 min period was obtained. For a similar example in portable extinguishers, bromochlorodifluoromethane (Halon 1211) was used in 3-lb portable units to extinguish a 2.5 sq ft, n-Heptane fire on a 2,500 cu ft room. The results of two tests, one normal extinction in 1 sec, and the second deliberately extended extinction in 10 sec, are given in Table 13-4H. In the case of normal extinction the levels of breakdown products are below those allowed by OSHA regulations for 8 hr continuous exposure.

The extensive studies on the toxicological effects of halogenated agents clearly indicate that authorities around the world were correct when they banned early agents such as carbon tetrachloride (Halon 104), chlorobromomethane (Halon 1011), and methyl bromide (Halon 1001). Equally indicated is that little, if any, risk is attached to the use of Halon 1211 when used in accordance with provisions of NFPA Standards which recognize the use of these agents.

Table 13-4G. Approximate Lethal Concentrations for Predominant Halon 1301 Decomposition Products

Compound	ALC for 15-min Exposure ppm by Volume in Air	Dangerous Concentrations ppm by Volume in Air*
Hydrogen Fluoride, HF	2500	50–350
Hydrogen Bromide, HBr	4750	—
Bromine, Br_2	550	50‡
Carbonyl Fluoride, COF_2	1500	—
Carbonyl Bromide, $COBr_2$	100–150†	—

* Source: Sax, N. Irving; Dangerous Properties of Industrial Materials.[4]

† Value is for carbonyl chloride, $COCl_2$ (phosgene); value for carbonyl bromide is not available.

‡ Value is for chlorine, Cl_2; value for bromine is not available.

Table 13-4H. Concentrations of Breakdown Products Obtained from Extinguishing 2.5 sq ft n-Heptane Fires with Halon 1211

Concentration of Breakdown Products—ppm V/A

Compounds	Test I Normal Extinction In One Second	Test II Prolonged Extinction In Ten Seconds
HCl + HBr	2	50
HF	0.5	10
Cl_2 + Br_2	Not detected[1]	2.5
$COCl_2$	Not detected[2]	Not detected[2]

[1] Limit of detection 0.1 ppm.

[2] Limit of detection 0.25 ppm.

SI Units

The following conversion factors are given as a convenience in converting to SI units the English units used in this chapter.

1 sq ft	$= 0.0929 \text{ m}^2$
1 in.	$= 25.400 \text{ mm}$
1 ft	$= 0.305 \text{ m}$
1 lb (mass)	$= 0.454 \text{ kg}$
1 psi	$= 6.895 \text{ kPa}$
$\frac{5}{9}(°F - 32)$	$= °C$
1 (U.S.) gal	$= 3.785 \text{ litres}$

Bibliography

References Cited

[1] Hansberry, H. L., et al., "Halogenated Extinguishing Agents," NFPA *Quarterly,* Vol. 48, No. 2, Oct. 1954, pp. 143–165.

[2] "Guide to OSHA Fire Protection Regulations," Vol. 1, 2nd ed., 1972, National Fire Protection Association, Boston, Mass., pp. 22140–22142.

[3] "An Appraisal of Halogenated Fire Extinguishing Agents," *Proceedings of a Symposium,* National Academy of Sciences, 1972.

[4] Sax, N. Irving, Section 12, *Dangerous Properties of Industrial Materials,* 2nd ed., Reinhold Publishing Co., New York, 1963.

NFPA Codes, Standards, and Recommended Practices (see the latest *NFPA Publications and Visual Aids Catalog* for availability of current editions of the following documents)

NFPA No. 10, Standard for the Installation, Maintenance, and Use of Portable Fire Extinguishers.

NFPA No. 12A, Standard for the Halogenated Fire Extinguishing Agent Systems—Halon 1301.

NFPA No. 12B, Standard for the Halogenated Fire Extinguishing Agent Systems—Halon 1211.

Additional Readings

Atallah, S., and Buccigross, H. L., "Development of Halogenated Hydrocarbon Foam (Halofoam) Extinguishants," *Fire Technology,* Vol. 7, No. 4, Nov. 1971, pp. 307–320.

———, "Extinction of Fire by Halogenated Compounds—A Suggested Mechanism," *Fire Technology,* Vol. 8, No. 2, May 1972, pp. 131–141.

Creitz, E. C., "Inhibition of Diffusion Flames by Methyl Bromide and Trifluoromethyl Bromide Applied to the Fuel and Oxygen Sides of the Reaction Zones," *Journal of Research of National Business Standards,* Vol. 65, No. 4, 1961.

Ford, C. L., "Where and Why to Use Halon 1301 Systems," *Actual Specifying Engineer,* Jan. 1972, pp. 74–83.

Hammack, James M., "Talking Extinguishing Equipment: Carbon Tetrachloride," *Fire Journal,* Vol. 65, No. 3, May 1971, p. 19.

Hough, R. L., "Determination of a Standard Extinguishing Agent for Airborne Fixed Systems," Wright Air Development Division Technical Report No. 60–552, 1960, Wright-Patterson Air Force Base, Ohio.

Wharry, David, and Hirst, Ronald, "Fire Technology: Chemistry & Combustion," Institution of Fire Engineers, 1974, Leicester, England.

Chapter 5

DRY CHEMICAL

Dry chemical is a powder mixture which is used as a fire extinguishing agent: it is intended for application by means of portable extinguishers, hand hose line systems, or fixed systems. Borax and sodium bicarbonate base dry chemical were the first such agents developed. Sodium bicarbonate became the "standard" because of its greater effectiveness as a fire extinguishing agent. In 1959, sodium bicarbonate base dry chemical was modified to render it compatible with protein based low expansion foams in order to permit a "dual agent" attack. In 1960, multipurpose (monoammonium phosphate base) and "Purple-K" (potassium bicarbonate base) dry chemicals were developed for fire extinguishing use. Shortly thereafter, "Super-K" (potassium chloride base) was developed to equal "Purple-K" in effectiveness. In 1967, the British developed urea-potassium bicarbonate base dry chemical. Presently, there are five basic varieties of dry chemical extinguishing agents and, as ongoing research is completed, more will become available.

The terms "regular dry chemical" and "ordinary dry chemical" generally refer to powders that are listed for use on Class B and Class C fires.[1] "Multipurpose dry chemical" refers to powders that are listed for use on Class A, Class B, and Class C fires. The terms "regular dry chemical," "ordinary dry chemical," and "multipurpose dry chemical" should not be confused with "dry powder" or "dry compound,"[2] which are the terms used to identify powdered extinguishing agents developed primarily for use on combustible metal fires.

Dry chemical is recognized for its unusual efficiency in extinguishing fires in flammable liquids. It can also be used on fires involving some types of electrical equipment. Regular dry chemical has certain limited applications in extinguishment of flash surface fires in ordinary combustibles, but requires water to put out deep seated smoldering fires. Multipurpose dry chemical can be used on fires in flammable liquids, fires involving energized electrical equipment, and fires in ordinary combustible materials. Multipurpose dry chemical seldom needs the help of water to completely extinguish fires in Class A materials.

This chapter contains information on the properties of dry chemicals affecting their use as extinguishing agents, and describes their uses and limitations, methods of storage and handling, and quality control. Dry chemical extinguishing systems are discussed in Section 15, Chapter 6, and portable dry chemical extinguishers are discussed in Section 16, Chapter 3 of this HANDBOOK. Dry powder extinguishing agents for combustible metal fires are discussed in Chapter 6 of this Section.

A. Chemical and Physical Properties

The principal base chemicals used in the production of currently available dry chemical extinguishing agents are sodium bicarbonate, potassium bicarbonate, potassium chloride, urea-potassium bicarbonate, and monoammonium phosphate. Various additives are mixed with these base materials to improve their storage, flow, and water repellency characteristics. The most commonly used additives are metallic stearates, tricalcium phosphate, or silicones which coat the particles of dry chemical to make them free-flowing and resistant to the caking effects of moisture and vibration.

Stability

Dry chemical is stable both at low and at normal temperatures. However, since some of the additives may melt and cause sticking at higher temperatures, an upper storage temperature limit of 140°F is usually recommended for dry chemical. At fire temperatures, the active ingredients either disassociate or decompose while performing their function in fire extinguishment.

Toxicity

The ingredients presently used in dry chemical are non-toxic. However, the discharge of large quantities may cause temporary breathing difficulty during and immediately after discharge, and may seriously interfere with visibility.

Particle Size

Particles of dry chemical range in size from less than 10 microns up to 75 microns. Particle size has a definite effect on extinguishing efficiency, and careful control is necessary in order to prevent particles from exceeding the upper and lower limits of this performance range. The best results are obtained by a heterogeneous mixture with a "median" particle in the order of 20-25 microns.

B. Extinguishing Properties

Fire tests on flammable liquids have shown potassium bicarbonate base dry chemical to be more effective than sodium bicarbonate base dry chemical. Similarly, the monoammonium phosphate base has been found equal to or better than the sodium bicarbonate base.[3] The effectiveness of potassium chloride is about equivalent to potassium bicarbonate, and urea-potassium bicarbonate exhibits the greatest effectiveness of all the dry chemicals tested.

When introduced directly to the fire area, dry chemical causes the flame to go out almost at once. The exact mechanism and chemistry of the extinguishing action are not definitely known. Smothering, cooling, and radiation shielding contribute to the extinguishing efficiency of dry chemical, but studies suggest that a chain-breaking reaction[4] in the flame may be the principal cause of extinguishment.

Smothering Action

For many years it was a widely held belief that regular dry chemical extinguishing properties relied primarily on the smothering action of the carbon dioxide released when sodium bicarbonate was heated by fire. The carbon dioxide does, undoubtedly, contribute to the effectiveness of dry chemical, as does the like volume of water vapor released when dry chemical is heated. However, tests have generally disproved the belief that these gases are a major factor. For example, 5 lbs of dry chemical is as effective as 10 lbs of carbon dioxide. Even if all the dry chemical were decomposed, it would produce only about 26 percent by weight carbon dioxide. It would appear, therefore, that dry chemical does not extinguish primarily because of smothering effects. As further evidence to disprove the smothering action theory, it has been shown that certain powdered salts that do not release carbon dioxide, water vapor, or other gases when heated (e.g., sodium carbonate) are effective extinguishing agents.

When multipurpose dry chemical is discharged into burning ordinary combustibles, the monoammonium phosphate, decomposed by the heat, leaves a sticky residue on the burning material. This residue seals the glowing material from oxygen, thus extinguishing the fire and preventing reignition.

Cooling Action

The cooling action of dry chemical cannot be substantiated as an important reason for its ability to extinguish fires promptly. A paper by C. S. McCamy, H. Shoub, and T. C. Lee[5] based on studies of the heat capacities of various powders tested for extinguishing effectiveness contains estimates of the amount of heat required to raise equal weights of various materials from 18°C to 300°C (64.4°F to 572.0°F). The authors found two extinguishing agents to be equal in extinguishing efficiency. These two agents are dry chemical containing 95 percent or more sodium bicarbonate (which absorbed 259 calories per gram), and borax with 2 percent zinc stearate (which absorbed 463 calories per gram). Sodium carbonate, which was only slightly lower in extinguishing efficiency, absorbed an estimated 79 calories per gram.

Radiation Shielding

Discharge of dry chemical produces a cloud of powder between the flame and the fuel. This cloud shields the fuel from some of the heat radiated by the flame. In reporting their tests to evaluate this factor, McCamy, Shoub, and Lee[5] concluded that the shielding factor is of some significance.

Chain-breaking Reaction

The preceding extinguishing actions, each to a certain degree, contribute to the extinguishing action of dry chemical. However, studies reveal that still another factor, which makes an even greater contribution than that of the other factors combined, is present.

The chain-reaction theory of combustion has been advanced by some investigators, such as A. B. Guise[6] and W. M. Haessler,[7] to provide the clue to what this unknown extinguishing factor may be. This theory assumes that free radicals are present in the combustion zone, and that the reactions of these particles with each other are necessary for continued burning. The discharge of dry chemical into the flames prevents reactive particles from coming together and continuing the combustion chain reaction. The explanation is referred to as the chain-breaking mechanism of extinguishment.

C.   Uses and Limitations

Dry chemical is primarily used to extinguish flammable liquid fires. Being electrically nonconductive, it can also be used on flammable liquid fires involving live electrical equipment. Regular dry chemical extinguishers have been tested and found suitable for use on flammable liquid and electrical fires (Class B and Class C fires) by nationally recognized fire equipment testing laboratories.

Due to the rapidity with which dry chemical extinguishes flame, dry chemical is used on surface fires involving ordinary combustible materials (Class A fires). There are several areas in the textile industry, notably opener-picker rooms and carding rooms in cotton mills, where regular dry chemical has been used effectively. However, wherever regular dry chemical is provided for use on surface type

Class A fires, it should be supplemented by water spray for extinguishing smoldering embers, or in case the fire gets beneath the surface. In some baled cotton storage areas, it is the practice to cover the tops of bales with regular dry chemical to prevent surface spread should fire break out. This preventive measure does not eliminate the need for automatic sprinkler protection in such areas. Since multipurpose dry chemical becomes sticky when heated, it is not recommended for textile card rooms or other locations where removal of the residue from fine machine parts may be difficult.

Dry chemical does not produce a lasting inert atmosphere above the surface of a flammable liquid; consequently, its use will not result in permanent extinguishment if reignition sources such as hot metal surfaces are present.

Dry chemical should not be used in installations where relays and delicate electrical contacts are located (e.g., in telephone exchanges), for in such installations the insulating properties of dry chemical might render the equipment inoperative. Because some dry chemicals are slightly corrosive, they should be removed from all undamaged surfaces as soon as possible after fire extinction.

Regular dry chemical will not extinguish fires that penetrate beneath the surface. Dry chemical will not extinguish fires in materials that supply their own oxygen for combustion.

Dry chemical may be incompatible with mechanical (air) foam unless the dry chemical has been specially prepared to be reasonably "foam compatible."

D.   Storage and Handling

Dry chemical is commercially available in various sized packages of 10 lbs or more in weight, or in metal drums, plastic-lined paperboard containers, or plastic bags. Whatever the container, it should be kept tightly closed and stored in a dry location in order to prevent absorption of moisture. Storage in a dry location is also essential for extinguisher recharging.

Low temperature storage does not adversely affect dry chemical, but storage temperatures should not be permitted to exceed 140°F. Above this temperature, additives may melt and cause the powder to cake. Once the powder has lost its free flowing characteristic, it should be discarded.

E.   Quality Control

Specifications have been established by nationally recognized fire equipment testing laboratories to assure the positive and consistent performance of dry chemical as an extinguishing agent. The characteristics controlled by these specifications are moisture content, water repellency, electrical resistivity, storage at elevated temperatures, flow capability, caking resistivity, and abrasive action. The discharge characteristics of the device in which the dry chemical is to be used are also evaluated. Extinguishing effectiveness is determined by performance tests of its application to standard fires under conditions recommended by the manufacturer.

SI Units

The following conversion factors are given as a convenience in converting to SI units the English units used in this chapter.

1 cal	= 4.184 J
1 ounce (mass)	= 28.350 g
1 lb (mass)	= 0.454 kg

Bibliography

References Cited

[1] *Fire Protection Equipment List,* Underwriters Laboratories, Inc., Chicago, published annually with bimonthly supplement.

[2] *Factory Mutual Approval Guide,* Factory Mutual Engineering Corporation, Norwood, Mass., published annually.

[3] Guise, A. B., "Potassium Bicarbonate-Base Dry Chemical," NFPA *Quarterly,* Vol. 56, No. 1, July 1962, pp. 21–27.

[4] Haessler, W. M., "The Extinguishment of Fire," revised ed., National Fire Protection Association, Boston, 1974.

[5] McCamy, C. S., Shoub, H., and Lee, T. G., "Fire Extinguishment by Means of Dry Powder," *Sixth Symposium on Combustion,* The Combustion Institute, Reinhold, N.Y., 1956, pp. 795–801.

[6] Guise, A. B., "The Chemical Aspects of Fire Extinguishment," NFPA *Quarterly,* Vol. 53, No. 4, April 1960, pp. 330–336.

[7] Haessler, W. M., "Fire and Its Extinguishment," NFPA *Quarterly,* Vol. 56, No. 1, July 1962, pp. 89–96.

NFPA Codes, Standards, and Recommended Practices (see the latest *NFPA Publications and Visual Aids Catalog* for availability of current editions of the following documents)

NFPA No. 10, Standard for the Installation of Portable Fire Extinguishers.

NFPA No. 17, Standard for Dry Chemical Extinguishing Systems.

Additional Readings

Dry Chemical Fire Extinguishing Characteristics, expanded 2nd ed., Fire Control Engineering Co., Ft. Worth, Texas.

Guise, A. B., "Dry Chemical Extinguishment Development," *Proceedings, Symposium on Fire Extinguishment Research and Engineering,* U.S. Naval Civil Engineering Research and Evaluation Laboratory, Port Hueneme, Calif., 1954, pp. 363–370.

Hird, D., and Fippes, D. W., "The Effect of Various Powdered Materials on the Stability of Protein Foams," British Joint Fire Research Organization, Jan. 1960.

Jablonski, E. J., and Gipe, R. L., "A New Method for Determining the Degree of Compatibility of Dry Chemical Powders with Mechanical Foams," NRL Report No. 5329, June 1959, U.S. Naval Research Laboratory, Washington, D.C.

Jensen, R. H., "Compatibility of Mechanical Foam and Dry Chemical," NFPA *Quarterly,* Vol. 57, No. 3, Jan. 1964, pp. 296–303.

Lee, T. G., and Robertson, A. F., "Extinguishing Effectiveness of Some Powdered Materials on Hydrocarbon Fires," *Fire Research Abstracts and Reviews,* Vol. 2, No. 1, Jan. 1960.

Meldrum, D. N., "Combined Use of Foam and Dry Chemical," NFPA *Quarterly,* Vol. 56, No. 1, July 1962, pp. 28–34.

Neil, R. R., "The Hydrocarbon Flame Extinguishing Efficiencies of Sodium and Potassium Bicarbonate Powders," NRL Report No. 5183, Aug. 1958, U.S. Naval Research Laboratory, Washington, D.C.

Peterson, H. B., et al., "The Development of New Foam Compatible Dry Chemical Extinguishing Powders," NRL Report No. 4986, Sept. 1957, U.S. Naval Research Laboratory, Washington, D.C.

"The Compatibility Relationship Between Mechanical Foam and Dry Chemical Fire Extinguishing Agents," UL Bulletin of Research No. 54, July 1963, Underwriters Laboratories, Inc., Chicago.

Tuve, R. L., "Light Water and Potassium Bicarbonate Dry Chemical—A New Two Agent Extinguishing System," NFPA *Quarterly,* Vol. 58, No. 1, July 1964, pp. 64–69.

———, "Recent Navy Research on Dry Chemicals," NFPA *Quarterly,* Vol. 54, No. 2, Oct. 1960, pp. 158–163.

Woolhouse, Dr. R. A., and Sayers, Dr. D. R., "Monnex Compared with Other Potassium-Based Dry Chemicals," *Fire Journal,* Vol. 61, No. 1, Jan. 1973, pp. 85–88.

Chapter 6

COMBUSTIBLE METAL EXTINGUISHING AGENTS

A variety of metals burn. Some metals burn when heated to high temperatures by friction or exposure to external heat: others burn from contact with moisture or in reaction with other materials. Because accidental fires may occur during the transportation of these materials, it is important to understand the nature of the various fires and hazards involved.

The hazards involved in the control or complete extinguishment of metal fires include extremely high temperatures, steam explosions, toxic products of combustion, explosive reaction with some common extinguishing agents, breakdown of some extinguishing agents with the liberation of combustible gases or toxic products of combustion, and dangerous radiation in the case of certain nuclear materials. Therefore, extinguishing agents and methods for their specific application must be selected with care. Some metal fires should not be approached without suitable self-contained breathing apparatus and protective clothing, even if the fire is small: other metal fires may be readily approached with minimum protection; still others may have to be fought with unmanned, fixed equipment.

During the years these metals have been used, a great many agents have been developed as extinguishants for combustible metal (Class D) fires. A given agent does not necessarily control or extinguish all metal fires: although some agents are valuable in working with several metals, other agents are useful in combating only one type of metal fire. Despite their use in industry, some of these agents provide only a degree of control and cannot be classed as actual extinguishing agents. Certain agents that are suitable for other classes of fires should be avoided in the case of metal fires, as violent reactions may result (e.g., water on sodium; vaporizing liquids on magnesium fires).

Certain of the combustible metal extinguishing agents have been in use for years, and their success in handling metal fires has led to the terms "approved extinguishing powder" and "dry powder." These designations have appeared in codes and other publications where it was not possible to employ the proprietary names of the powders. These terms have been accepted in describing extinguishing agents for metal fires, and should not be confused with the name "dry chemical" which normally applies to an agent suitable for use on flammable liquid and live electrical equipment fires. For more detailed information, see Chapter 5 of this Section. Other extinguishing agents discussed herein have been used only experimentally, in limited areas or at specific installations requiring a good deal of judgment in application.

The successful control or extinguishment of metal fires depends to a considerable extent upon the method of application, and the training and experience of the fire fighter. Practice drills should be held on the particular combustible metals on which the agent is expected to be used. Prior knowledge of the capabilities and limitations of agents and associated equipment is useful in emergency situations. Fire control or extinguishment will be difficult if the burning metal is in a place or position where the extinguishing agent cannot be applied in the most effective manner.

In locations where industrial plants work with combustible metals, public fire departments and industrial fire brigades have the advantage of fire control drills conducted under the guidance of knowledgeable individuals. The transportation of combustible metals creates unique problems in that a fire could occur in a location where knowledge and suitable extinguishing agents are not readily available. The Hazardous Materials Board of the U.S. Department of Transportation has anticipated such situations and specifies cargo limitations, labeling, and placarding for the various means of transportation.

Storage and handling of metals are discussed in Section 3, Chapter 9, which describes methods of fighting metal fires based on the types of metals.

A. Commercially Available Approved Combustible Metal Extinguishing Agents

A number of proprietary combustible extinguishing agents have been submitted to testing agencies for approval or listing. Others have not, particularly those agents developed for special metals in rather limited commercial use. Those described as follows have been approved or listed for use on fires in magnesium, aluminum, sodium, potassium, and sodium-potassium alloy.

G-1 Powder

G-1 Powder is stored in cardboard tubes or metal pails, coke to which an organic phosphate has been added. A combination of particle sizes is used to provide good packing characteristics when applied to the metal fire. The graphite acts as a heat conductor and absorbs heat from the fire to lower the metal temperature below the ignition point, with resultant extinguishment. The closely packed graphite also smothers the fire, and the organic material in the agent breaks down with heat to yield a slightly smoky gas that penetrates the spaces between the graphite particles, excluding air. The powder is nontoxic and noncombustible.

G-1 Powder is stored in cardboard tubes or metal pails, and can be stored for long periods of time without deterioration or caking. It is applied to the metal fire with a hand scoop or a shovel. The packing characteristics of the powder prevent its discharge from a fire extinguisher.

The powder is applied by spreading it evenly over the surface of the fire to a depth sufficient to smother the fire. A layer at least $\frac{1}{2}$-in. deep is recommended for fires involving fines (finely divided particles) of magnesium and magnesium alloys. Larger chunks of metal require additional powder to cover the burning areas.

Where burning metal is on a combustible surface, the fire should be extinguished by: (1) first covering it with powder, (2) then shoveling the burning metal onto another 1- or 2-in. layer of powder that has been spread out nearby, and (3) adding more powder as needed.

G-1 Powder is effective for fires in magnesium, sodium, potassium, titanium, lithium, calcium, zirconium, hafnium, thorium, uranium, and plutonium, and has been recommended for special applications on powder fires in aluminum, zinc, and iron. It is listed by the UL (Underwriters Laboratories, Inc.) for use only on magnesium and magnesium alloys (dry fines and moist fines that are not moistened or wetted with water or water soluble cutting oils) and is approved by the Factory Mutual System for use on fires in magnesium, aluminum, sodium, potassium, and sodium-potassium alloy. When it is planned to use G-1 Powder on those metals mentioned in this paragraph, practice fire drills should be held in advance. The products of combustion of thorium, uranium, beryllium, and plutonium can be a health hazard, and precautions should be observed consistent with the usual procedures in combating fires in radioactive material.

MetalGuard Powder

MetalGuard Powder is identical to G-1 Powder in composition, and is simply a trade name variation.

Met-L-X Powder

This dry powder, with its particle size controlled for optimum extinguishing effectiveness, is composed of a sodium chloride base with additives. The additives include tricalcium phosphate to improve flow characteristics, and metal stearates for water repellency. A thermoplastic material is added to bind the sodium chloride particles into a solid mass under fire conditions.

Met-L-X powder is noncombustible, and secondary fires do not result from its application to burning metal. No known health hazard results from the use of this agent. It is nonabrasive and nonconductive.

Stored in sealed containers or extinguishers, Met-L-X powder is not subject to decomposition or change in properties and periodic replacement of extinguisher charges is unnecessary. Extinguishers range from 30-lb portable hand units (carbon dioxide cartridge propellant) through 150- and 350-lb wheeled units to 2,000 lbs for stationary or piped systems. The wheeled units and piped systems employ nitrogen as the propellant.

The powder is suitable for fires in solid chunks (such as castings) because of its ability to cling to hot vertical surfaces. The technique used to control and then extinguish a metal fire is to fully open the nozzle of the extinguisher and, from a safe distance (in order to prevent blowing the burning metal into other areas), cautiously apply a thin layer of agent over the burning mass. Once control is established, the nozzle valve is used to throttle the stream to produce a soft, heavy flow. The metal can then be completely and safely covered from close range with a heavy layer. The heat of the fire causes the powder to cake, forming a crust which excludes air and results in extinguishment.

Met-L-X extinguishers are available for fires involving magnesium, sodium (spills or in depth), potassium, and sodium-potassium alloy (NaK). In addition, Met-L-X has been successfully used where zirconium, uranium, titanium, and powdered aluminum present serious hazards.

Comparison of G-1 and Met-L-X Powders

Based on their past usage and known value as extinguishing agents for metal fires, the two agents previously discussed (G-1 and Met-L-X powders) are the most notable. Continuous experience with these agents has provided sufficient information to list in Table 13-6A the capabilities and limitations of each when applied to certain metal fires.[1]

Na-X Powder

This powder was developed to satisfy the need for a low chloride content agent that could be used on sodium metal fires. Na-X has a sodium carbonate base with various additives incorporated to render the agent nonhygroscopic and easily fluidized for use in pressurized extinguishers. It also incorporates an additive which softens and crusts over an exposed surface of burning sodium metal.

Na-X is noncombustible, and secondary fires do not result from its application to burning sodium metal above temperatures ranging from 1,200° to 1,500°F. No known health hazard results from the use of this agent on sodium fires, and it is nonabrasive and nonconductive.

Stored in 50-lb pails, 30-lb hand portables, and 150- and 350-lb wheeled and stationary extinguishers, Na-X is listed

Table 13-6A.   Comparison of G-1 and Met-L-X Powders

Type of Fire	G-1 Powder Capable of Complete Extinguishment	Capable of Control Only	Unsatisfactory	Met-L-X Capable of Complete Extinguishment	Capable of Control Only	Unsatisfactory
Dry or oily magnesium chips or turnings	X			X		
Magnesium castings and wrought forms	X (1)			X (2)		
Dry or oily titanium turnings	X (3)			X		
Uranium turnings and solids	X			X		
Zirconium chips and turnings coated with water soluble oil	X			X		
Moist zirconium chips and turnings		X			X	
Sodium spills or in depth	X			X		
Sodium sprayed or spilled on vertical surfaces			X	X (4)		
Potassium or sodium-potassium alloy spill	X			X		
Potassium or sodium-potassium alloy fire in depth			X (5)			X (5)
Lithium spill	X			X		
Lithium fire in depth	X					X (6)
Aluminum powder	X			X		

Notes:

1. Requires sufficient powder to cover the burning pieces. More agent required than with Met-L-X.

2. Powder clings to vertical surfaces. Unnecessary to bury burning parts.

3. More effective pound for pound than Met-L-X.

4. Adheres to molten sodium on vertical surfaces.

5. Extinguished with difficulty.

6. Powder sinks into molten metal, the sodium chloride reacting with lithium to form lithium chloride and sodium. If continued until sodium is in excess, the fire can then be extinguished.

by UL for fires involving sodium metal (spills and in depth) at a fuel temperature of 1,200°F. Na-X has been tested on sodium metal (spills and in depth) at fuel temperatures as high as 1,500°F. Stored in the supplier's metal pails and extinguishers, Na-X is not subject to decomposition and periodic replacement of the agent is unnecessary.

B. Other Commercially Available Combustible Metal Extinguishing Agents

Foundry Flux

In magnesium foundry operations, molten magnesium is protected from contact with air by layers of either molten or crust type fluxes. These fluxes, which are also used as molten metal cleaning agents, consist of various amounts of potassium chloride, barium chloride, magnesium chloride, sodium chloride, and calcium fluoride. The fluxes are stored in covered steel drums. When applied to burning magnesium, these fluxes melt on the surface of the solid or molten metal, excluding air. The thin layer of protection can be provided by properly applying relatively small amounts of flux.

Fluxes are valuable in extinguishing magnesium spill fires from broken molds or leaking pots, and in controlling and extinguishing fires in heat-treating furnaces. In open fires, the flux is applied with a hand scoop or a shovel. Areas of furnaces that are difficult to reach can be coated by means of a flux-throwing device similar to those used to throw concrete onto building forms.

While fluxes would rapidly extinguish chip fires in machine shops, such use is not recommended: the fluxes are hygroscopic and the water picked up from the air, combined with the salts, causes severe rusting of equipment.

Lith-X Powder

This dry powder is composed of a special graphite base with additives. The additives render it free-flowing so that it can be discharged from an extinguisher. The technique used to extinguish a metal fire with this agent is the same as that used with Met-L-X. Lith-X does not cake or crust over when applied to the burning metal. It excludes air and conducts heat away from the burning mass to affect extinguishment. It does not cling to hot metal surfaces, so it is necessary to completely cover the burning metal.

Lith-X will successfully extinguish lithium fires. It is suitable for the control and extinguishment of magnesium and zirconium chip fires. It will extinguish sodium spill and sodium in depth fires: sodium-potassium alloy spill fires are extinguished, and fires in depth are controlled.

TMB Liquid

TMB represents the chemical term for trimethoxyboroxine.[2] The agent contains an excess of methanol to render it free-flowing, and for shipping purposes it is classed as a flammable liquid. The liquid is colorless and hydrolyzes readily to form boric acid and methanol. Contact with moist air or other sources of water must be avoided to prevent hydrolysis.

This agent is applied with a specially adapted 2½-gal stored pressure extinguisher which delivers either spray or straight stream. Typical application of TMB to a metal fire yields a heat flash due to the breakdown of the chemical compound and ignition of the methanol. The white metal fire is rapidly extinguished, and the secondary greenish flame is of short duration. A molten boric oxide coating on the hot metal prevents contact with air. A stream of water may be used to cool the mass as soon as metal flames are no longer visible. This should be done cautiously to avoid rupture of the coating. The fumes from the application of TMB are nontoxic. Indoor application (such as in machine shops) is not recommended due to the large volume of boric oxide smoke produced.

While TMB has been used primarily on magnesium fires, it has shown value in application to fires in zirconium and titanium. Although TMB applied as a spray has been used to control small sodium and sodium-potassium alloy fires, it is not recommended for fires in sodium, sodium-potassium alloy, and lithium. TMB reacts violently with lithium and sodium-potassium alloy. It will extinguish sodium in depth, but the protective coating formed by the TMB picks up moisture very rapidly and in time may penetrate through to the sodium, resulting in a violent reaction. Field experience has been limited to aircraft fires.

Pyromet Powder

Pyromet Powder is composed of specially processed sodium chloride, diammonium phosphate, protein, and a waterproofing and flow promoting agent.

The powder is discharged under pressure provided by a carbon dioxide gas cartridge. The unit contains 25 lbs of powder. The applicator consists of a tubular extension from the control valve, terminating in a cone-shaped nozzle. This cyclone-type nozzle is designed to absorb the discharge pressure and enable the operator to let the powder fall gently on the burning metal rather than scatter burning material under the blast of a jet of powder.

Pyromet has proven effective in handling fires involving sodium, calcium, zirconium, and titanium, as well as magnesium and aluminum in the form of powder or chips.

T.E.C. Powder

T.E.C. (Ternary Eutectic Chloride) Powder is a mixture of potassium chloride, sodium chloride, and barium chloride that is effective in extinguishing fires in certain combustible metals. The powder tends to seal the metal, excluding air. On a hot magnesium chip fire it is similar to foundry flux in its action. In tests reported by Rodgers and Everson[3], T.E.C. powder was the most effective salt for sodium, potassium, and NaK fires.

Small uranium and plutonium fires within glove boxes have been extinguished with T.E.C. A small plastic bag filled with the powder is simply placed directly on the metal fire.

The barium chloride in the mixture is poisonous, but this is of no practical concern when used within glove boxes. In other locations, the operator should avoid inhalation of the airborne powder.

C. Nonproprietary Combustible Metal Extinguishing Agents

Talc (Powder)

Talc, which has been used industrially on magnesium fires, acts to control rather than extinguish. It reacts with burning magnesium to provide a source of oxygen. The addition of organic matter (such as protein) to talc assists in the controlling action, but does not prevent the reaction which releases oxygen to the fire. Talc acts as an insulator to retain the heat of the fire, rather than as a coolant.

Graphite Powder

Graphite powder (plumbago) has been used as an extinguishing agent for metal fires. The action is similar to that of G-1 powder in that the graphite acts as a coolant. Unless the powder is finely divided and closely packed over the burning metal, some air does get through to the metal and extinguishment is not as rapid as with G-1 powder.

Sand

Dry sand has often been recommended as an agent for controlling and extinguishing metal fires. At times it seems to be satisfactory, but usually hot metal (such as magnesium) obtains oxygen from the silicon dioxide in the sand and continues to burn under the pile. Sand is seldom completely dry. Burning metal reacting with the moisture in the sand produces steam, and, under certain conditions, may produce an explosive metal-water reaction.

Fine, dry sand can be used to isolate incipient fires of aluminum dust by laying the sand around the perimeter of the fire.

Cast Iron Borings

Cast iron borings or turnings are frequently available in the same machine shops that work with the various combustible metals. Clean iron borings applied over a magnesium chip fire act to cool the hot metal and help extinguish the fire. This agent is used by some shops for handling small fires where, with normal good housekeeping, only a few combustible metal chips are involved. Contamination of the metal chips with iron may be an economic problem. Oxidized iron chips must be avoided to prevent possible thermite reaction with the hot metal. The iron chips must be free from moisture.

Sodium Chloride

Alkali metal fires can be extinguished by sodium chloride which forms a protective blanket that excludes air over the metal so that the metal cools below its burning temperature. Sodium chloride is an agent which is used for extinguishing sodium and potassium fires. It can also be used to extinguish magnesium fires.

Soda Ash

Sodium carbonate or soda ash (not dry chemical) is recommended for extinguishing sodium and potassium fires. Its action is similar to that of sodium chloride.

Lithium Chloride

Lithium chloride is an effective extinguishing agent for lithium metal fires. However, its use should be limited to specialized applications as the chemical is hygroscopic to a degree, and may present problems because of the reaction between the moisture and the lithium.

Zirconium Silicate

This agent has been used successfully for extinguishing lithium fires.

Dolomite

If zirconium or titanium in the form of dry powder becomes ignited, neither can be extinguished. Control can be effected by spreading dolomite (a carbonate of calcium and magnesium) around the burning area, and then adding more powder until the burning pile is completely covered.

Boron Trifluoride and Boron Trichloride

Boron trifluoride and boron trichloride have both been used to effect control of fires in heat-treating furnaces containing magnesium. The fluoride is considerably more effective. In the case of small fires, the gases provide complete extinguishment. In the case of large fires, the gases effect control over the flames and rapid burning, but reignition of the hot metal takes place on exposure to air. A combined attack of boron trifluoride gas followed by application of foundry flux completely extinguishes the fire. For details of gas application, see NFPA No. 48, Storage, Handling, and Processing of Magnesium.

Inert Gases

In some cases, inert gases (such as argon and helium) will control zirconium fires if they can be used under conditions that will exclude air. Gas blanketing with argon has been effective in controlling lithium, sodium, and potassium fires.[3]

Water

If a fire in a shop where magnesium or other combustible metals (except the alkali metals and fissionable materials) are being machined or fabricated gets out of control to the point where automatic sprinklers open, the large volume of water from the sprinklers normally will extinguish both the Class A and magnesium fires. Where automatic sprinkler protection is provided, a deflecting shield or hood is provided over furnaces, reactors, or other places where hot or molten metal may be present. Additional information on the use of sprinkler protection in shops handling magnesium or titanium can be found in the NFPA Magnesium Standard, and in NFPA No. 481, Titanium, Handling and Storage.

When burning metals are spattered with limited amounts of water, the hot metal extracts oxygen from the water and promotes combustion. At the same time, hydrogen is released in a free state and ignites readily. Since small amounts of water do accelerate combustible metal fires (particularly where chips or other fines are involved), common portable extinguishers containing water are not recommended except to control fires in adjacent Class A materials.

Water, however, is a good coolant and can be used on some combustible metals under proper conditions and application in order to reduce the temperature of the burning metals to below the ignition point. The following paragraphs discuss the advantages and limitations of using water on fires involving various combustible metals.

Water on Sodium, Potassium, Lithium, NaK, Barium, Calcium, and Strontium: Water applied to sodium, potassium, lithium, sodium-potassium alloys (NaK), barium, and probably calcium and strontium will induce chemical reactions that will lead to fire or explosion even at room temperature. Therefore, water must not be used on fires involving these metals.

Water on Zirconium: Powdered zirconium wet with water is more difficult to ignite than the dry powder. However, once ignition takes place, wet powder burns more violently than dry powder. Powder containing about 5 to 10 percent water is considered to be the most dangerous. Small volumes of water should not be applied to burning zirconium, but large volumes of water can be successfully used to cover completely solid chunks or large chips of burning zirconium (e.g., by drowning the metal in a tank or barrel of water). Hose streams applied directly to burning zirconium chips may yield violent reactions.

Water on Plutonium, Uranium, and Thorium: Limited amounts of water add to the intensity of a fire in natural uranium or thorium, and greatly increase the contamination cleanup required after the fire. A natural uranium scrap fire can be fought with water by personnel (wearing face shields and gloves and using long-handled shovels), shoveling the burning scrap into a drum of water in the open. Hydrogen formed may ignite and burn off above the top of the drum.

The radioactivity hazard of natural uranium is extremely low (uranium is in reality a metal poison, although considerably less toxic than lead). The use of water on enriched uranium or plutonium (fissionable materials) is generally prohibited. If ingested, plutonium is considerably more hazardous than uranium.

Water on Magnesium: Although water in small quantities accelerates magnesium fires, rapid application of large amounts of water is effective in extinguishing magnesium fires because of the cooling effect of water. Automatic sprinklers will extinguish a typical shop fire where the quantity of magnesium is limited. However, water should not be used on any fire involving a large number of magnesium chips when it is doubtful that there is enough water to handle the large area. (A few burning chips can be extinguished by dropping them into a bucket of water.) Small streams from portable extinguishers will violently accelerate a magnesium chip fire.

Burning magnesium parts, such as castings and fabricated structures, can be cooled and extinguished with coarse streams of water applied with standard fire hoses. A straight stream scatters the fire, but coarse drops (produced by a fixed nozzle operating at a distance or by use of an adjustable nozzle) flow over and cool the unburned metal. Then the hose streams are worked into the fire. Some temporary acceleration normally takes place using this procedure, but rapid extinguishment follows if the technique is pursued. Well-advanced fires in several hundred pounds of magnesium scrap have been extinguished in less than 1 min with two $1\frac{1}{2}$-in. fire hoses. Water fog, on the other hand, tends to accelerate such a fire rather than cool it.

Application of water to magnesium fires where quantities of molten metal are likely to be present must be avoided. The steam formation and possible metal-water reactions may be explosive.

Water on Titanium Fires: Water must not be used on fires in titanium fines and should be used with caution on other titanium fires. Small amounts of burning titanium (other than fines) can be extinguished, and considerable salvage realized by quickly dumping the burning material into a large volume of water in order to completely submerge it. Hose streams have been used effectively on fires in outside piles of scrap, but violent reactions have been reported in other cases where water was applied to hot or burning titanium.

Miscellaneous Agents

Agents which have been tested for cooling capacity and ability to extinguish magnesium fires, but which have not been developed beyond the laboratory state, include the following: (1) boric acid dissolved in triethylene glycol followed by foam to extinguish the secondary fire[4]; (2) diisodecyl phthalate combined with chlorobromomethane,[5] and (3) tricresyl phosphate followed by foam to handle the secondary fire. The Joint Fire Research Organization has developed a suitable powder for extinguishing burning magnesium, which consists essentially of powdered polyvinyl chloride and sodium borate.[6] The powder forms a coating on the molten metal and enables a fine water spray to be used to cool the metal to extinction. Research has been conducted at two U.S. laboratories on optimum methods of controlling zirconium and uranium fires with mixed halogen organic derivatives.

SI Units

The following conversion factors are given as a convenience in converting to SI units the English units used in this chapter:

1 in. $\quad= 25.400$ mm
1 lb (mass) $= 0.454$ kg
$\frac{5}{9}$ (°F − 32) $= $ °C
1 (U.S.) gal $= 3.785$ litres

Bibliography

References Cited

[1] Zeratsky, E. D., "Extinguishing Agents for Combustible Metals and Special Chemicals," *Safety Maintenance,* Vol. 120, No. 2, Aug. 1960, pp. 28–32.

[2] Tuve, R. I.; Gipe, R. L.; Peterson, H. B.; and Neil, R. R., "The Use of Trimethoxyboroxine for the Extinguishment of Metal Fires." NRL Report No. 4933, July 1957, Naval Research Laboratory, Washington, D.C.

[3] Rodgers, S. J., and Everson, W. A., "Extinguishments of Alkali Metal Fires." *Fire Technology,* Vol. 1, No. 2 (May 1965), pp. 103–111.

[4] McCutchan, R. T. "Investigation of Magnesium Fire Extinguishing Agents," WADC Technical Report No. 55-5, Jan. 1954, Wright Air Development Center (by Southwest Research Institute), Wright-Patterson Air Force Base, Ohio.

[5] Greenstein, L. M., and Richman, S. I., "A Study of Magnesium Fire Extinguishing Agents," WADC Technical Report No. 55-170, May 1955, Wright Air Development Center (by Francis Earle Laboratories, Inc.), Wright-Patterson Air Force Base, Ohio.

[6] Nash, P., "A Dry Powder Extinguishing Agent for Magnesium Fires," *Institution of Fire Engineers Quarterly,* Vol. 23, No. 51, Sept. 1963, pp. 275–276.

NFPA Codes, Standards, and Recommended Practices (see the latest *NFPA Publications and Visual Aids Catalog* for availability of current editions of the following documents)

NFPA No. 48, Standard for the Storage, Handling, and Processing of Magnesium.

NFPA No. 481, Standard for the Production, Processing, Handling, and Storage of Titanium.

NFPA No. 482M, Guide for Fire and Explosion Prevention in Plants Producing and Handling Zirconium.

Additional Readings

"Magnesium Data Sheet." No. 426, 1956, National Safety Council, Chicago.

"Methods Used by an AEC Contractor for Handling Sodium, NaK, and Lithium." *Accident and Prevention Information,* Feb. 1960, U.S. Atomic Energy Commission, Washington, D.C.

Petersen, M. E., "Dry Powder for Combustible Metals," *National Safety News,* Vol. 92, No. 1, Jan. 1963.

Riley, John F., "NaX, a New Fire Extinguishing Agent for Metal Fires." *Fire Technology,* Vol. 10, No. 3, Nov. 1974.

Stout, E. L., "Safety Considerations for Handling Plutonium, Uranium, Thorium, the Alkali Metals, Zirconium, Titanium, Magnesium, and Calcium," Report No. LA-2147, 1957, Los Alamos Scientific Laboratory, Los Alamos, N.M.

"Sodium-Sodium Metal, Metallic Sodium, Chemical Safety Data Sheet," SD-47, 1952, Manufacturing Chemists' Association, Washington, D.C.

"Titanium Data Sheet." No. D-382, 1957, National Safety Council, Chicago.

"Zirconium and Hafnium Powder, Chemical Safety Data Sheet," SD-92, 1966, Manufacturing Chemists' Association, Washington, D.C.

"Zirconium Powder Data Sheet," No. D-382, 1957, National Safety Council, Chicago.

SECTION 14

WATER SPRINKLER SYSTEMS

Chapter 1

FUNDAMENTALS OF SPRINKLER PROTECTION

Automatic fixed extinguishing systems are the most effective means of controlling fires in buildings. In order to understand the capabilities of these systems, a thorough understanding of their use is essential. This Section deals with one such extinguishing system; sprinklers.

A. Development of Sprinkler Protection

The rapid growth of business and industry and the resultant increase in fire hazards and property values brought about the need for more adequate protection against fire. The difficulty of reaching a fire with hose streams has often been demonstrated, and such simple fire protection as water pails, standpipes, and hose equipment has proved inadequate unless the fire was discovered in its early stages. Although

fire control has been made easier by improved building construction, comparatively little headway was made in reducing fire loss involving delayed detection until the advent of the automatic sprinkler.

The Automatic Sprinkler

Automatic sprinklers are devices for automatically distributing water upon a fire in sufficient quantity either to extinguish it entirely or to prevent its spread in the event that the initial fire is out of range of, or is of a type that cannot be extinguished by, water discharged from sprinklers. The water is fed to the sprinklers through a system of piping, ordinarily suspended from the ceiling, with the sprinklers placed at intervals along the pipes. The orifice of the fusible link automatic sprinkler is normally closed by a disk or cap held in place by a temperature-sensitive releasing element. Figure 14-1A shows in stop-action photo sequence the operation of a typical fusible link, upright automatic sprinkler.

Perforated Pipe and Open Sprinkler Systems

The forerunners of the automatic sprinkler were the perforated pipe and the open sprinkler. These were installed in a number of mill properties from 1850 to 1880 (see Fig. 14-1B). The systems were not automatic, the discharge openings in the pipes often clogged with rust and foreign materials, and water distribution was poor.

Open sprinklers, an improvement over perforated pipes, consisted of metal bulbs with numerous perforations attached to piping and intended to give improved water distribution. This system was only slightly better than the perforated pipe.

Early Automatic Sprinklers

The idea of automatic sprinkler protection, whereby heat from a fire opens one or more sprinklers and allows the

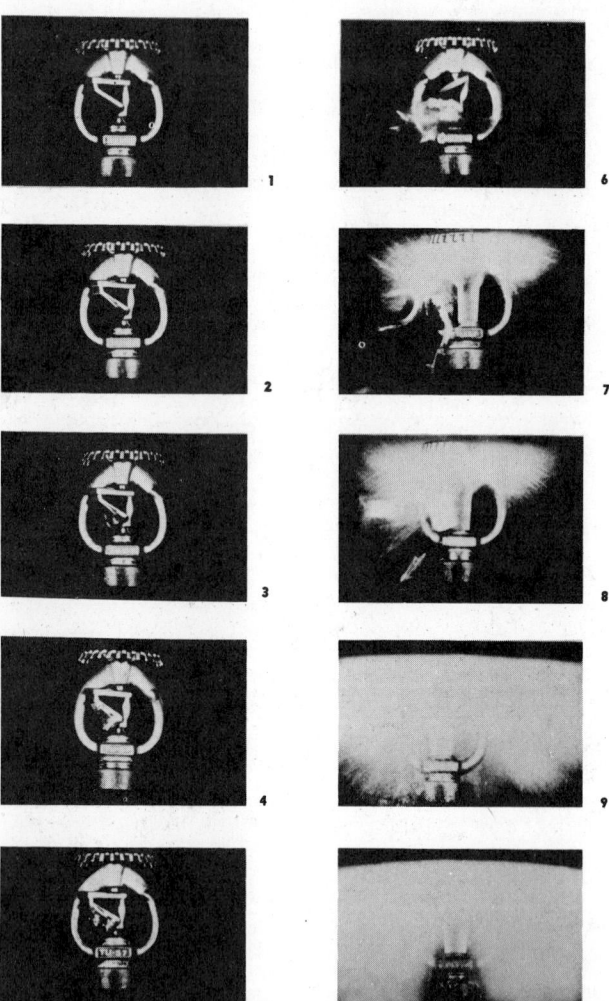

Fig. 14-1A. Operation of a typical fusible link automatic sprinkler is shown in this sequence of photos. As heat melts the solder, separation of members of the soldered link (the sloping side of the triangle in photos 1 to 5) is followed by complete separation of the link and lever arrangement (photo 6) which releases the cap over the sprinkler orifice allowing water to escape and strike the deflector (photos 7 to 10).

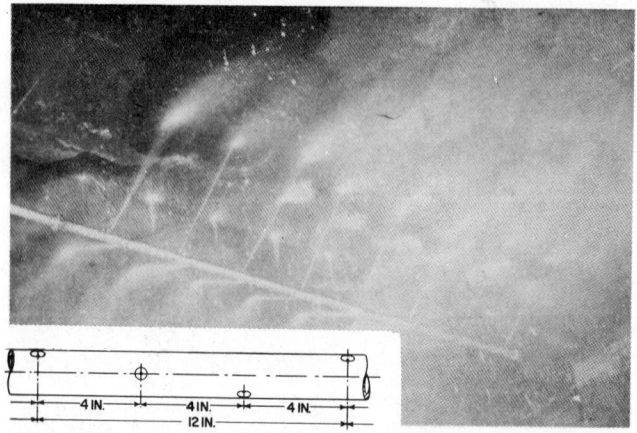

Fig. 14-1B. Early Perforated Pipe Sprinkler System: Water is shown discharging from a length of pipe representing what was the type of sprinkler protection in use from 1850 to about 1880. The inset shows the locations of perforations and the distances between them on a typical length of perforated pipe as was installed by the Providence Steam and Gas Pipe Co. (Grinnell Corp.)

Fig. 14-1C. An Early Automatic Sprinkler: Water is shown discharging from a Parmalee No. 3 upright sprinkler which was first used in 1875. It consisted of a brass cap soldered over a perforated distributor and was designed to screw onto a nipple. The inset shows a cross-sectional view of the sprinkler.

water to flow, dates back to about 1860. Its practical application in the United States, however, began about 1878 when the Parmelee sprinkler was first installed. This sprinkler, while very crude when compared with modern devices, gave generally good results and proved conclusively that automatic sprinkler protection was both practical and valuable. (See Fig. 14-1C.)

B. Value of Automatic Sprinkler Protection

Automatic sprinkler protection helped develop modern industrial, commercial, and mercantile practices. Large areas, high buildings, hazardous occupancies, large values, or many people in one fire area, all tend to develop conditions which cannot be tolerated without automatic fixed fire protection. Part C of this chapter contains material on the performance of automatic sprinkler systems.

Safety to Life

Automatic sprinklers, properly installed and maintained, provide effective safeguards against loss of life by fire. Their value is psychological as well as physical: they give a sense of security to the occupants of buildings, and minimize the possibility of panic.

NFPA records of loss of life by fire show that in completely sprinklered buildings fire fatalities have been minimal.* They are limited to situations where sprinklers cannot

_____

* The only fatalities in fully sprinklered properties reported to the NFPA were caused by explosions or flash fires; by ignition of the bedding or clothing of a person who was too young, too old, too intoxicated, or too handicapped in some other way to protect himself properly; by closure of water supply valves to the sprinkler system; or by hazards too severe for effective sprinkler performance in the protected property. Explosions in sprinklered properties have caused fatal injuries to occupants or have so damaged sprinkler piping as to render the systems virtually useless, with resultant loss of life. Severe flash fires have under unusual conditions traveled in advance of sprinkler operation, trapping victims before they had time to reach safety.

In those isolated instances of fatalities to sleeping, handicapped, or intoxicated persons, ignition of clothing or bedding caused fatal burns or asphyxiation either because the small fire did not generate sufficient heat to fuse a sprinkler, or because the victim had suffered fatal injuries before the sprinkler operated. In these latter instances, however, the sprinklers protected the lives of persons in adjoining areas.

be expected to be effective, such as in cases where the water is shut off, or where suffocation occurs before a fire is large enough to cause sprinklers to operate. Loss of life can also be caused by explosions where sprinklers have no opportunity to be effective.

Automatic sprinklers are particularly effective for life safety because they give warning of the existence of fire, and at the same time apply water to the burning area. With sprinklers there are seldom problems of access to the seat of the fire, or of interference with visibility for fire fighting due to smoke. While the downward force of the water discharged from sprinklers may lower the smoke level in a room where a fire is burning, the sprinklers also serve to cool the smoke and make it possible for persons to remain in the area much longer than they would if the room were without sprinklers.

Objections sometimes advanced against automatic sprinkler installation in the interest of life safety are generally based on misconceptions of the basic characteristics of sprinkler protection. The opinion is sometimes expressed that sprinkler discharge might drench people and cause panic or illness. This objection ignores the fact that without sprinklers the same people in the fire area would perhaps be burned to death. There is no case in the NFPA records of over 100,000 fires in sprinklered buildings where water from automatic sprinklers has in any way contributed to panic or caused any other hazard to occupants.

Another common misconception is that *all* sprinklers discharge water at the time of fire. This is not the case, as most fires are controlled by only a few sprinklers in the immediate vicinity of the fire.

Other objections to automatic sprinkler protection are based upon cost, and occasionally upon appearance. These objections are unsound where conditions are such that sprinklers are needed for life safety. Sprinklers are generally no more expensive than some decorative floor coverings, and aesthetic designs are available in sprinklers.

Contrary to popular opinion, automatic sprinklers are practicable for dwellings and other small properties. In country areas where water supplies are limited, a pressure tank can be provided with sufficient capacity to control the fire during evacuation.

NFPA 101, Life Safety Code, recognizes sprinklers in numerous ways, particularly to offset deficiencies in existing buildings. For example, longer travel distances to exits and interior finish of a higher combustibility are permitted with sprinklers.

Recent developments in the sprinkler industry have resulted in systems and discharge devices that will cycle on and off. When a fire occurs, this system reacts to the increase in temperature and discharges water. When the temperature decreases to a predetermined level because the fire has been controlled or extinguished, the system automatically stops the flow of water. Should the fire flare up again, the system will repeat this cycle. This cycling continues until the fire is either out or the system is shut off.

Protection of Property

Figures available on the fire loss in manufacturing and mercantile properties where sprinklers are installed show a much better loss/value ratio than those properties not so equipped. Insurance may largely compensate for property loss, but a severe fire loss goes much further.

Prevention of Business Interruption

In addition to the saving in direct fire losses due to sprinkler protection, there is a saving represented by the freedom from business interruption. There also is an undetermined but possibly even greater reduction in conflagration and exposure losses, which reasonably may be attributed to automatic sprinkler protection. The destruction of property and its adverse association and sometimes permanent effect upon business may be, and often is, a great hardship, not only to the owner, tenants, and employees, but also to the community as a whole. Safeguarding a business from serious interruption by fire is often a determining factor in a decision to install sprinkler protection.

In many situations, sprinkler protection is required by law for specific parts of the building only. Where partial systems are required, complete systems should be installed. Partial systems are not cost effective. Should the fire start remote to the system, it will have no effect on the growing fire. Should the fire burn into the protected area, it will generally have developed sufficient intensity to overpower the sprinklers, thereby wasting water needed by the fire service to fight the fire.

Minimizing of Water Damage

Standard sprinkler systems have devices which automatically give an alarm in case of sprinkler operation; thus, they not only apply water at the point most needed, but also give an audible signal. This permits immediate check of fire conditions and minimizes water damage.

A properly installed sprinkler system will generate less water damage than the application of hose streams by the fire service. Sprinklers are not hampered in their operation by smoke or heat as is the fire service. Sprinklers can apply water efficiently and promptly to the seat of the fire. For this reason, they are one of the greatest life-saving tools of the fire service.

Fear of water damage is sometimes offered as an objection to the installation of automatic sprinkler protection. This comes in part from the thoughtless emphasis placed upon water damage in news reports of fires. Statements that a fire was of insignificant size, but that water damage was severe have been frequent. The probability of very severe destruction by fire in the absence of automatic sprinkler protection is seldom mentioned in these news accounts.

Accidental discharge of water from an automatic sprinkler system or other parts of a fire service water system due to defects in sprinklers, water control devices, piping, or associated equipment, is very rare. Precautions to prevent unnecessary discharge of water as a result of mechanical injury, freezing or overheating, or corrosion are covered in Chapter 6 of this Section.

Economics of Sprinkler Protection

In addition to the protection against destruction of property values and interruption to business, the saving in insurance costs often makes the expenditure for automatic sprinkler protection a sound business investment.

Many buildings do not have automatic sprinkler protection because the per dollar cost of the protection has appeared unjustifiably high to the building owners in relation to the value of the building.

Savings in insurance premiums alone could in numerous cases be adequate to finance, over a few years time, the installation of automatic sprinkler protection. Of equal importance are the many building code "trade-offs" that are allowed when sprinklers are installed. These "trade-offs" permit an increase in undivided area and often less fire resistance for the building construction, and therefore less erection cost. No value can be placed on the life safety aspects of total sprinkler protection or the security occupants feel when such systems are installed.

C. Record of Automatic Sprinkler Performance

Periodically the NFPA prepares summaries of sprinkler performance from the fire data reported to its Fire Analysis Department. The information is published in the NFPA *Fire Journal* as the Automatic Sprinkler Performance Tables, and is also available in pamphlet form.[1]

Effectiveness of Automatic Sprinklers

Only in rare instances do automatic sprinkler systems fail to control fires. The failures are very seldom due to the sprinklers themselves, but rather to the lack of water. Even with older types of sprinklers which are no longer approved, the failure of the sprinkler itself has been very infrequent. Failure of the modern types under normal conditions is practically unknown. Some 117,770 fires in sprinklered buildings have been reported to the NFPA since 1897. Of these, 95 percent of the sprinklers showed satisfactory performance.

Because numerous fires extinguished by one or two sprinklers (with only a slight loss) are not reported to NFPA, the NFPA records do not represent the total number of fires in sprinklered properties. If it were possible to include a complete record, the efficiency of sprinkler performance would probably approach 100 percent.

It should be noted that recorded data reflect only the efficiency of operation, and are but indirectly related to the amount of fire losses. For example, where sprinklers do not operate because the water is shut off, unsatisfactory performance is recorded even though the fire may have been promptly discovered and extinguished by other means. Figure 14-1D shows graphically cumulative data from 1970 to 1974 on the number of sprinklers operating.

In recent years, the apparent percentage of satisfactory sprinkler operations has declined. From 1970 to 1974 it was 81 percent. This may be the result of the NFPA's data-gathering system which concentrates on those fires causing larger losses. Other studies (N.Y. Board of Fire Underwriters, Factory Mutual, etc.) that are based on approximately 100 percent reporting show considerably higher rates. The same is true of Australian records where all sprinkler actuations are reported.

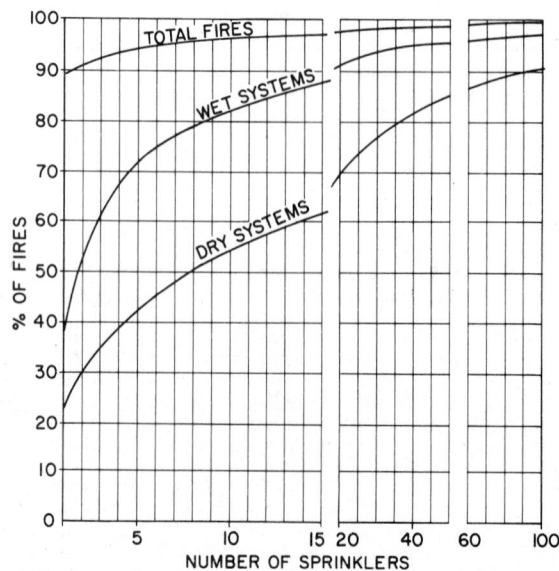

Fig. 14-1D. Number of sprinklers operating, cumulative data, 1970–74.

Effectiveness of Sprinklers by Occupancy Groups

Table 14-1A shows characteristic differences in sprinkler effectiveness for 22 major occupancy groups. As would be expected, some situations present a more difficult extinguishing problem than do others. This record of effectiveness is useful in evaluating the need for specially designed systems or auxilliary fire fighting facilities.

Unsatisfactory Sprinkler Performance by Occupancy Groups

Table 14-1A also lists by occupancy the reasons for unsatisfactory sprinkler performance for the same 22 occupancy groups. Closed sprinkler control valves are the most frequent cause, being responsible for 36 percent of the unsatisfactory performance reported. A study of the fires not controlled by sprinklers is of great importance, as it shows how to guard against such occurrences. It will be noted from Table 14-1A and from Figure 14-1E that in most cases there is a definite explanation for unsatisfactory performance. A more detailed analysis of unsatisfactory sprinkler performance will be found in the 1970 edition of the NFPA Automatic Sprinkler Performance Tables.[1]

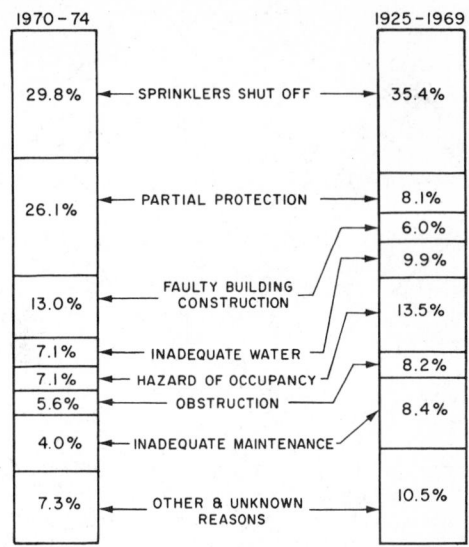

Fig. 14-1E. *Reasons for unsatisfactory sprinkler performance.*

D.   Standard Sprinkler Installations

The terms "sprinkler protection," "sprinkler installations," and "sprinkler systems" usually signify a combination of water discharge devices (sprinklers); one or more sources of water under pressure; water-flow controlling devices (valves); distribution piping to supply the water to the discharge devices; and auxiliary equipment, such as alarms and supervisory devices. Outdoor hydrants, indoor hose standpipes, and hand hose connections are also frequently a part of the system that provides protection. Figure 14-1F is an illustration of a typical sprinkler installation with all common water supplies, outdoor hydrants, and underground piping.

When considering water supply problems, the performance of sprinklers, dry-pipe or wet systems, or special arrangements of sprinkler protection, the designation "sprinkler system" applies to the sprinklers controlled by a single water supply valve. Under this definition large buildings require several sprinkler systems, and a single water system may supply a number of sprinkler systems.

The fundamentals of sprinkler protection evolve around the principle of the automatic discharge of water, in sufficient density, to control or extinguish a fire in its incipiency. In planning for a system that fulfills this objective, many factors must be considered. They can, however, be broadly grouped into four categories: the sprinkler system itself, features of building construction, hazards of occupancy, and water supplies.

Table 14-1A.   Sprinkler Performance Summary and Classification of Unsatisfactory Performance*

	Performance Summary				Classification of Unsatisfactory Performance												
Occupancies	Total No. of Fires	Total Unsatis-factory	Total Satis-factory	Total Satis-factory Per Cent	Water Shut Off	Partial Protection	Inadequate Water Supplies	System Frozen	Slow Operation	Defective Dry-Pipe Valve	Faulty Building Construction	Obstruction to Distribution	Hazard of Occupancy	Exposure Fire	Inadequate Maintenance	Antiquated System	Miscellaneous and Unknown
Residential	1,073	48	1,025	95.5	13	9	5	1	—	—	11	3	1	—	2	2	1
Assembly	1,551	52	1,499	96.6	23	10	3	—	1	—	9	1	—	1	4	—	—
Educational	241	20	221	91.7	4	8	1	—	—	—	5	—	—	—	1	1	—
Institutional	305	12	293	96.1	3	3	2	—	—	—	1	—	1	—	—	—	2
Office	494	13	481	97.4	4	2	1	—	—	1	2	—	1	—	1	1	—
Mercantile	6,237	176	6,061	97.2	83	11	4	4	4	5	35	11	12	1	4	1	1
Industrial																	
Beverages, essential oils	543	64	479	88.2	17	4	9	—	—	1	2	1	18	3	3	5	1
Chemicals	4,147	198	3,949	95.2	33	11	19	—	3	3	1	13	95	2	12	1	5
Fiber products	539	25	514	95.3	6	—	4	1	—	2	—	5	4	—	2	1	—
Food products	2,484	133	2,351	94.6	43	11	8	1	2	1	7	9	29	4	12	1	5
Glass products	519	23	496	95.6	8	—	3	1	—	—	2	1	5	—	3	—	—
Leather, leather products	2,864	114	2,750	96.0	43	8	7	3	2	4	9	7	9	4	9	6	3
Metal, metal products	9,807	305	9,502	96.9	91	36	22	3	6	6	15	35	43	6	29	7	6
Mineral products	394	19	375	95.2	10	4	2	—	—	—	1	—	—	—	1	1	—
Paper, paper products	7,147	234	6,913	96.7	75	16	34	3	2	2	16	32	21	2	23	4	4
Rubber, rubber products	1,489	61	1,428	95.9	21	4	3	—	1	1	1	10	14	1	5	—	—
Textiles—Manufacturing	16,119	291	15,828	98.2	109	15	32	3	5	3	11	27	18	1	50	9	8
Textiles—processing	6,527	127	6,400	98.1	52	6	11	—	5	1	8	13	15	2	7	1	6
Wood products	5,353	492	4,861	90.8	137	57	84	9	16	14	27	19	77	8	24	12	8
Miscellaneous industries	9,013	265	8,748	97.1	146	15	14	8	3	—	12	11	18	3	27	8	—
Total (Industrial)	66,945	2,351	64,594	96.5	791	187	252	32	45	38	112	183	366	36	207	56	46
Storage Occupancies	4,160	375	3,785	91.0	122	24	48	5	6	9	10	57	38	11	40	3	7
Other Occupancies	419	87	332	79.2	67	—	—	2	—	—	2	1	5	3	3	1	3
Total (All Occupancies)	81,425	3,134	78,291	96.2	1,110	254	311	44	56	53	187	256	424	52	262	65	60

* From the 1970 edition of the NFPA Automatic Sprinkler Performance Tables.

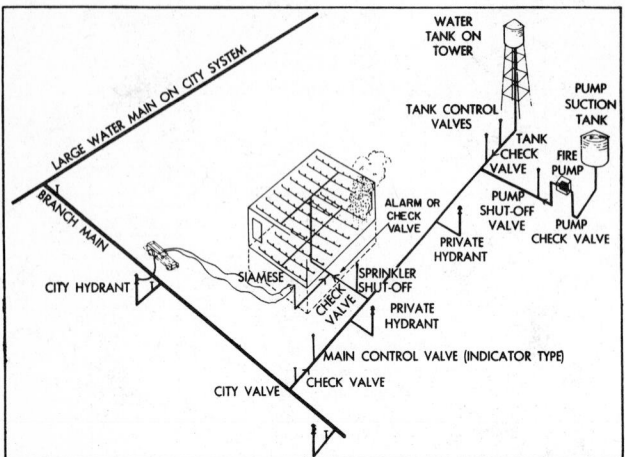

Fig. 14-1F. Illustration of a typical sprinkler installation showing all common water supplies, outdoor hydrants, and underground piping.

Automatic sprinkler systems of one type or another have been designed to extinguish or control practically every known type of fire in practically all materials in use today. It is essential, though, that for a given hazard the proper system be used. A sprinkler system designed to control and extinguish fire in an office occupancy with a relatively light amount of combustibles cannot be expected to have the same effectiveness in protecting a hazardous process involving considerable combustible materials, or a storage area where the fire loading is severe. On the other hand, it is not economical to "over protect" by installing sprinkler equipment capable of controlling and extinguishing fire of a magnitude beyond any conceivable situation that could arise in the lifetime of a building.

The NFPA Sprinkler Standard

NFPA No. 13, Standard for the Installation of Sprinkler Systems, hereinafter referred to in this chapter as the NFPA Sprinkler Standard, covers the planning and design of sprinkler protection, the type of materials and components used in systems, and the operations carried on in making the installation. The NFPA Sprinkler Standard has had a long and interesting history. When first printed in 1896 it concerned itself principally with sprinkler pipe sizes, sprinkler spacing, and water supplies. Since 1900, the NFPA Sprinkler Standard has been subject to considerable amplification and refinement, reflecting changes in building construction, materials and techniques, equipment, and occupancy conditions that have often posed serious threats to good sprinkler protection. In recent years the Standard has been revised to reflect improved efficiency in sprinkler design, and to incorporate modern design and protection methods.

Compliance with the nationally recognized NFPA Sprinkler Standard is often required by enforcement agencies, and the Standard is used by insurance companies and insurance inspection and rating bureaus. Property owners themselves often specify compliance with the Sprinkler Standard in order that the protection provided will be in accordance with the best known practices.

Approval or listing of sprinkler system devices by a recognized testing laboratory is a separate procedure. The uses of devices and equipment approved by such a laboratory may be required by an authority having jurisdiction, or the authority itself may approve equipment.

Other NFPA Standards

While the NFPA Sprinkler Standard is the primary standard for guidance on installation of sprinklers, other NFPA standards, recommended practices, and guides also have a direct bearing on certain phases of sprinkler protection. They should be referred to during design and construction of sprinkler systems.

E. Consideration of Building Features

When sprinkler protection is being planned, it is necessary to evaluate construction, design, and certain features of location of a building in order to ensure effective operation of the sprinkler equipment. In older buildings some typical modifications often needed are the following: (1) enclose vertical openings to divide multistoried structures into separate fire areas; (2) remove unnecessary partitions which could interfere with sprinkler discharge; (3) remove needless sheathing and shelving; (4) check concealed areas for the need for sprinkler protection or for the need for heat if such areas are to be sprinklered with wet-pipe systems; (5) pinpoint areas requiring high temperature sprinklers.

Older buildings often require some renovations to prepare them for sprinkler protection. On the other hand, designs for new buildings can incorporate features of construction and finish that are compatible to good sprinkler protection. Adding sprinklers as an afterthought is more expensive.

Further details concerning features of building design and construction as they relate to fire protection will be found in Section 6 of this HANDBOOK. The following paragraphs of this Section give information on some of the more prominent building features that deserve special mention.

Floor Cutoffs—Multistory Buildings

Sprinkler systems in multistory buildings are designed to extinguish fire in any one story, but not to extinguish simultaneous fires in several stories. Therefore, the cutoffs for vertical openings should be complete to prevent the spread of heat to upper stories. Unprotected vertical openings can lead to upward spread of fire and to the opening of excessive numbers of sprinklers which, in turn, can overtax the water supply.

Substantial fire resistive enclosures around stairways, elevator shafts, utility shafts, etc., with fire doors at all interior openings into the enclosures are the preferred protection. Nevertheless, there may be instances where less substantial barriers to the passage of products of combustion may be acceptable. An example is the "water curtain" method of protecting escalator or conveyor openings. The NFPA Sprinkler Standard suggests close spaced sprinklers for water curtains for this purpose. Chapter 8 of Section 6 of this HANDBOOK gives more complete details on the proper protection of vertical openings.

High Ceilings

Sprinkler action may be delayed by excessive distance between sprinklers and combustible materials at the floor level. As the hot products of combustion from a flaming fire rise, air from the surrounding atmosphere mixes with the gases so that the temperature of the mixture decreases. When fire occurs in a room with an excessively high ceiling, the temperature at the ceiling directly over the fire is less than when under a low ceiling.

Large clearances between sprinklers and combustibles below can also magnify the problem of obtaining the correct density and breakup of water discharge from sprinklers for maximum effect on fires, particularly in large masses of combustibles. The upward travel of combustion products creates temperature and draft conditions through which water droplets may have difficulty penetrating if the distance between a relatively intense flaming fire and the sprinklers is too great.

Fire tests conducted at the Factory Mutual Engineering Division Laboratories[2] have shown the relationship between varying clearances and varying water pressures, the latter governing the density and degree of atomization of the water droplets. The tests showed that high water pressures for sprinklers are of somewhat dubious advantage in compensating for extremes of height. Finely atomized water that must travel down through a strong fire draft is slowed by the upward velocity of the fire gases, and simultaneously the size of the droplets is being continually reduced by evaporation.

Fire tests conducted at Underwriters Laboratories, Inc., following the McCormack Place exhibition hall fire in January 1967[3] showed that a relatively coarse discharge density of 0.20 gpm per sq ft from sprinklers at ceiling heights of 30 ft and 50 ft was sufficient to control a fire under conditions similar to those that existed when the McCormack Place fire started. The test conditions simulated display booths representing a fire loading of 15 to 20 lb per sq ft. These tests indicate that the ratio of sprinklers opening during a fire will increase proportionately with ceiling height, assuming a constant discharge density. Higher fire loadings would require correspondingly higher discharge densities.

Concealed Spaces

Sprinklers should be installed in combustible spaces above ceilings because fire may spread into these spaces shielded by construction from sprinklers in the main area. It is important to eliminate ignition sources in such spaces, and it is desirable to provide firestopping to prevent entrance and spread of fire. Before sprinklers are installed in an older building, it is well to closely examine the interior finish; maybe some of the ceiling sheathing or hollow siding could be removed. Particularly objectionable are light flammable materials, such as paper, used for decorative effects.

Sprinklers may be omitted from concealed spaces where construction is noncombustible and contain no ignition sources, where the ceiling it attached directly to the beams or joist, or if the space is entirely filled with a noncombustible insulation. For detailed requirements, the NFPA Sprinkler Standard should be consulted.

Shielded Fires

Wide shelves or tables, partitions, conveyors, ducts, and other equipment that shield fire from sprinkler discharge may cause an excessively large number of sprinklers to operate. In some cases, these conditions require additional sprinklers.

Building Location

Exposure: A frequently unanticipated or neglected handicap to automatic sprinkler protection comes from exposure fires occurring outside the sprinkler protected building. Heat entering the building through improperly protected openings in the walls can easily open many sprinklers and tax the sprinkler water supply to the extent that fire can enter the building, particularly at upper stories. Interior sprinklers cannot be expected to be effective in protecting exterior combustible walls or roofs. When a nearby building offers a serious exposure to a sprinklered building, particularly if the latter has combustible walls or cornices and many unprotected exterior openings facing the exposure, the best

protection is a complete installation of outside sprinklers (see Part G of Chapter 2 of this Section).

Sprinkler Systems in Buildings Subject to Flood: These systems require special attention to the following: (1) the location and arrangement of piping so that it will not be washed out, nor its supports weakened; (2) location of valves so that they will be accessible during high water; (3) location of alarm devices so that they will remain operable during high water; (4) location and arrangement of fire pumps and their power supply and controls, secondary water supplies, and other auxiliary equipment, to provide reasonable safeguards against interference with operation.

Sprinkler Systems in Buildings Subject to Earthquake: These systems require measures to prevent breakage of piping. Excessive movement is prevented by sway bracing. Unavoidable movement is met by providing flexible couplings between the major parts of the system such as the top and bottom of risers, and the joints between sections of buildings, and pipe clearances at critical points such as foundations, walls, and floors.

F. Hazards of Occupancy

The use made of a building is an essential consideration in designing a sprinkler system that is adequate to protect against the hazards inherent in the type of occupancy. For the purposes of evaluating hazards, three main classes of occupancy are recognized in the NFPA Sprinkler Standard. Schedules of pipe sizes, spacing of sprinklers, sprinkler discharge densities, and water supply requirements differ for each in order to provide protection appropriate for the hazard while avoiding unnecessary expense.

Classification of Occupancies

The three main classifications are: light hazard, ordinary hazard, and extra hazard.

Light Hazard Class: Includes occupancies where the quantity and combustibility, or both, of materials is low, and fires with relatively low rates of heat release are expected. Examples are apartments, churches, dwellings, hotels, public buildings, office buildings, and schools.

Ordinary Hazard Class: This class is divided into three groups, mainly because each requires a somewhat different water supply for sprinklers. In general, this class includes the ordinary mercantile, manufacturing, and industrial properties. *Group 1* covers properties where combustibility is low, the quantity of combustibles is moderate, stock piles of combustibles do not exceed 8 ft, and fires with moderate rates of heat release are expected. Some examples are: canneries, laundries, and electronic plants. *Group 2* includes properties where the quantity and combustibility of contents is moderate, stock piles do not exceed 12 ft, and fires with moderate rates of heat release are expected. Examples are: cereal mills, textile plants, printing and publishing plants, and shoe factories. *Group 3* lists a small number of occupancies where the quantity and/or combustibility of the contents is high and fires of high rates of heat release are expected. Examples are: flour mills, piers and wharves, paper manufacturing and processing plants, rubber tire maufacturing, and storage warehouses (paper, household furniture, paint, etc.).

Extra Hazard Class: This class includes buildings or portions of buildings where the fire hazard is considered severe, such as cotton preparatory processes, explosives plants, oil refineries, varnish factories and similar occupancies, and others involving the processing, mixing, storing, and dispensing of flammable liquids.

While classification of occupancies into three broad categories serves as a good basic guide, it does not rule out the necessity of evaluating separately certain portions of an occupancy that may contain hazards more severe than in the remainder of the building. For example, a hotel is listed in the NFPA Sprinkler Standard as a light hazard occupancy. But certain areas in a hotel, such as kitchens and laundries, obviously are more hazardous than guest rooms. Consequently, the sprinkler protection for these more hazardous areas must be increased, and in this particular example, the design in the kitchen and laundry areas would conform to that required for ordinary hazard occupancies.

In each of the three broad groups the system may either follow an appropriate piping schedule and spacing rules, or the system may be hydraulically designed. Hydraulically designed systems are preferable from a protection standpoint in extra hazard occupancies, and are desirable in all classifications.

G.   Special Occupancy Conditions

Some conditions require more than ordinary sprinkler protection in order to provide dependable fire extinguishment and control. Sprinkler experience shows that occupancies which involve high-piled combustible stocks, flammable and combustible liquids, combustible dusts and fibers, large quantities of light, loose combustible materials, and chemicals and explosives, can permit rapid spread of fire and often cause the opening of excessive numbers of sprinklers with disastrous results. Complete automatic sprinkler protection with strong water supplies will usually control fires in occupancies containing these hazardous conditions, provided the severity of the hazards is plainly recognized and the sprinklers are appropriately designed for the hazards.

High-piled Combustible Material

Modern practices in storage and warehousing lead to high piling for many combustible solid or packaged commodities.[4] It is a matter of record that disastrous fires have occurred in sprinklered warehouses where combustible materials have been stored to heights approaching 50 ft. One of the principal factors contributing to the difficulty for sprinklers in controlling or extinguishing fires in high-piled stock is that water discharged from the sprinklers cannot penetrate to the interior or lower portions of high piles, the most frequent areas where fires originate. High, closely packed piles, particularly over 15 ft in height, have the inherent characteristics of shedding water; the bottom parts of the piles may not be adequately wetted to control fire spread.

Laboratory tests have shown that the method of piling, as well as the type of material in the piles, has a direct bearing on the degree of control or extinguishment that can be expected from sprinklers. A stable high pile, such as cartoned or crated "hard goods" (appliances, canned goods, etc.,) stubbornly resists fire control by sprinklers, but as soon as the pile collapses and opens up, control is more probable. Unstable piles of "soft goods" (foamed rubber pillows in cartons, packaged cereals, etc.,) collapse quicker under fire attack, lending themselves to faster fire control by sprinklers. Unbanded rolls of paper stored on end are particularly hazardous. Once ignited, the rolls peel and the loose paper continues to feed the fire.

The distance or spacing between individual piles also has an effect on fire intensity and spread of fire from pile to pile.

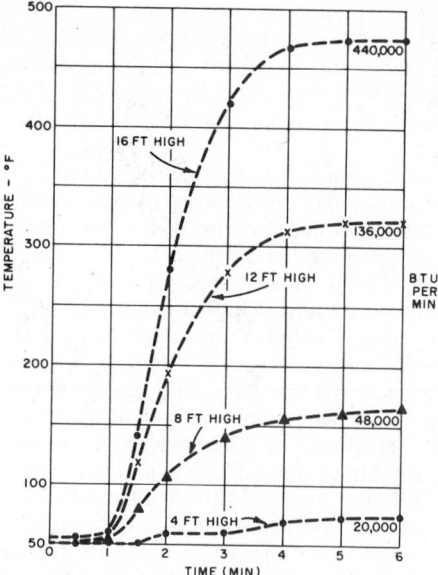

Fig. 14-1G.   Comparison of heat release values for test fires involving pairs of wooden panels of various heights spaced 8 in. apart. Temperatures given are average ceiling temperatures.

Closely spaced piles involving narrow clearances create vertical flues that serve to increase fire intensities in terms of heat produced. Figure 14-1G shows the results of a series of tests[3] involving 4-ft wide parallel vertical panels of spruce boards spaced 8 in. apart. The panels varied in height from 4 ft to 16 ft to simulate short sections of space which might occur between piles of heavy packing cases. The test fires were started at the floor and spread rapidly up through the spaces between the panels. Note from Figure 14-1G that the heat release in the 16-ft high panel was nine times as much as for the 8-ft panels.

Thermal updraft velocities in the narrow spaces also create pressure that can spread fire laterally into the voids between cartons and into the horizontal channels of pallets that are not firestopped. All these factors only tend to complicate the fire control problem by creating fire intensities beyond the cooling capacity of the relatively small amount of water that can penetrate the narrow spaces between closely stacked piles of combustibles.

The NFPA Sprinkler Standard specifies a minimum clearance of 18 in. below sprinkler deflectors to permit good water distribution in storage areas. These clearance requirements should not be used as an excuse for not installing sprinklers on the theory that more material could be stored if there were no sprinklers. If there are no sprinklers, a clearance of at least 36 in. is essential to allow room for effective use of hose streams.

Flammable and Combustible Liquids

The effectiveness of automatic sprinklers over flammable and combustible liquid tank and spill fires depends on the flash point, physical and combustion characteristics, temperature, areas of burning surface, and quantity of liquid involved. Sprinklers are usually effective in extinguishing fires in combustible liquids with flash points of 200°F and higher at normal room temperatures, in heavy flammable liquids (specific gravity greater than water), and in water-soluble liquids. Control of fire in low flash point (under 200°F) flammable liquids, but not extinguishment, can be expected from automatic sprinklers.

Combustible Liquids: The basic action of water spray from sprinklers in extinguishing fire in high flash point liquids is considered to be cooling of the liquid surface to a point where an insufficient quantity of vapors are produced for combustion. Most of the cooling is obtained by the absorption of about 8,000 Btu of heat through conversion of each gallon of water to steam. The vaporization of the spray should occur near the burning liquid surface; consequently, size of water droplets and the velocity of the droplets are critical factors in ensuring that the water does penetrate upward fire drafts and reaches the combustion zone at the right size for maximum cooling effect (see Sec. 13, Chap. 1). Some of the many combustible liquids in this category are medium and heavy fuel oils, quench oils, asphalts and lubricating oils.

"Heavy" Flammable Liquids: A few flammable liquids (i.e., carbon disulfide) are heavier than water and not soluble with water. As a consequence, spill and tank fires in such liquids are extinguished by vapor-air separation by a layer of water from sprinkler discharge floating on the liquid.

Water-soluble Liquids: Certain flammable liquids, i.e., methyl aclohol and acetone, are soluble in water and may be extinguished by dilution with water from sprinklers. The resulting liquid-water solution is less volatile than the liquid alone, depending on the degree of dilution with water. This has the effect of eventually raising the flash and fire point temperatures higher than the actual solution temperatures. Combustion will cease because there is an insufficient quantity of flammable vapors. Extinguishment by dilution, however, is not commonly relied upon due to the amount of water required to make most liquids nonflammable, and there may be the danger of frothing if the burning liquid is heated to over 212°F. Alcohol, for example, may require as much as 4 gal of water for each gallon of alcohol.

Low Flash-point Liquids: Fires in low flash-point flammable liquids that are not water soluble, and which have a specific gravity greater than water, cannot, as a rule, be extinguished with water, as the relationship between flash point and water temperature precludes adequate cooling. Water spray from sprinklers can, however, exert a degree of control short of extinguishment on fires involving low flash-point flammable liquids. Control is principally due to absorption of heat by water on conversion to steam. For example, a burning gasoline fire 100 sq ft in area will liberate about one million Btu per minute. Theoretically, it would take only 120 gpm of sprinkler water to absorb that amount of heat. Although 100 percent efficiency in converting water to steam in a combustion zone is rarely achieved, a substantial amount of water can be vaporized with absorption of considerable heat, provided the discharge from sprinklers is finely dispersed for maximum cooling effect. Thus, in this example, a good portion of the million Btu per minute released in the fire is present in the form of steam at 212°F, instead of hot gases at much higher temperatures.

Other factors contributing to the controlling effect of sprinkler discharge are the depositing of a protective film of water on exposed materials, and the slowing down of the rate of combustion. The net result is a limiting of the zone of high temperature to a relatively small area in the immediate vicinity of the burning liquid.

Normally, all equipment containing flammable liquids or vapors is closed. Accidents or mistakes in operating procedures, however, may release vapors which, on ignition, may result in an explosion that can cripple a sprinkler system, or a flash fire that may open an excessively large number of sprinklers. Efficient and reliable ventilation (see Sec. 6, Chap. 8, and Sec. 7, Chap. 4) and explosion protection equipment (see Sec. 15, Chap. 7) are important methods useful in reducing explosion hazards and consequent damage to sprinkler systems. Strong water supplies capable of supplying all the sprinklers in a single hazardous area, at higher than usual discharge densities, are essential. Densities ranging from 0.2 to 0.5 gpm per sq ft per minute are common. Excessively high discharge pressures, although yielding high discharge rates, may produce too fine a spray for effective extinguishment or control.

Combustible Dusts

Sprinkler systems may be crippled by severe dust explosions. A local dust explosion within equipment or a building can dislodge and ignite additional dust as the disturbance progresses to other areas. The explosion and flame may extend throughout a large area almost instantaneously, causing many sprinklers to operate.

Ordinary automatic sprinkler protection at properties where dust explosion hazards exist can be effective for fire control, provided it has been installed in a manner to reduce the probability that piping will be broken by an explosion. Also, to obtain full benefit from sprinkler protection, efficient dust removal systems and good housekeeping, combined with explosion venting construction, are essential. NFPA standards for the prevention of dust explosions cover essential precautions (see also Sec. 3, Chap. 8).

Chemicals and Explosives

The production and handling of hazardous chemicals and explosives frequently involve the use of materials that are unusually sensitive to shock or elevated temperatures. Ordinarily, to keep the hazards moderate, such materials are handled in small amounts and in closed or covered containers.

Fire in cellulose nitrate film, pyroxylin plastic, rocket propellants, and other chemicals subject to decomposition may generate much heat and also produce flammable or explosive vapors. Proper handling, process, and storage arrangements are thus primary operating principles to prevent excessive release of these vapors.

Conventional automatic sprinkler protection is not likely to arrest an explosion reaction once it starts. However, strong water supplies and closely spaced sprinklers (90 sq ft or less) on piping designed and installed to resist damage, insofar as possible, are helpful in preventing extension of damage. Water from sprinklers can protect combustible construction and equipment in the vicinity of an explosion and can cool the atmosphere, reducing the spread of an initial fire or other heat producing disturbance. It is essential that good explosion venting practices are followed to minimize explosion damage not only to the building and process equipment that may be involved, but to the sprinkler system itself (see Sec. 15, Chap. 7 for information on explosion venting techniques).

Rocket propellants used in the aerospace industry and in defense systems are examples of chemical hazards requiring more than ordinary sprinkler protection to guard against the explosive potential of high energy fuels. High speed water deluge systems employing special discharge devices and fast-acting water control valves that respond to rate-of-pressure increase or visual detection (infrared or ultraviolet) are used in locations where rocket propellants are manufactured, and on missile launching pads and in missile silos (see Part E of Chapter 2, this Section, for deluge systems).

H. Location and Spacing of Sprinklers

The fundamental idea in locating and spacing sprinklers in a building is to make sure there is no unprotected place, however unexpected, where a fire can start. In other words, no matter where a fire starts, there must be one or more sprinklers located in relation to that particular point that will operate promptly and discharge water when heat from the fire reaches them. Furthermore, there should be no direction that fire can spread in which it will not encounter other sprinklers to stop its progress.

Complete Protection

It is obvious, in theory at least, that complete installation of sprinklers throughout a building is necessary for complete protection of life and property. No areas should be left unprotected. The NFPA Sprinkler Standard treats specifically a number of locations where the need for sprinklers is sometimes questioned. These include locations such as stairways and vertical shafts; deep, blind, and concealed spaces; ducts; basements or subfloor spaces; attics and lofts; and under decks, tables, exhaust hoods, canopies, and outdoor platforms. It is risky to omit sprinklers from any single area because it is judged that the hazard is not sufficient to warrant them.

Partial Installations

Frequently, building codes and ordinances require partial sprinkler protection for specific areas with the intent of providing limited protection for certain hazardous areas, and as a life safety measure. But the limitations of partial protection often outweigh the supposed advantages they offer. The sprinkler performance record, compiled by the NFPA Fire Record Department (see Table 14-1A), shows that "partial installation" is second only to "water to sprinklers shut off" as a major cause of unsatisfactory sprinkler performance. (See Part H of Chapter 2 of this section for further information on partial installation.)

Area and Spacing Limitations

The location of sprinklers on a line, and the location of the lines in relation to each other determine the size of area protected by each sprinkler. The NFPA Sprinkler Standard gives a definite maximum area of coverage for each sprinkler, depending principally upon the severity of the occupancy hazard and, to a lesser degree, on the type of ceiling or roof construction above the sprinklers. The three classes of hazard are: light, ordinary, and extra (see Part F of this chapter); the four types of ceiling or roof construction and variations found in each type are: smooth ceiling, beam and girder, bar joist, and open wood joist.

The NFPA Sprinkler Standard also stipulates maximum permissible distances between sprinkler lines that can be used in allowing the maximum area of protection for each sprinkler on designing a system with a conventional piping arrangement. Exact distances are not specified; leeway is allowed for different building and ceiling configurations encountered. But the maximum area of coverage permitted for each sprinkler must not be exceeded. The Sprinkler Standard allows, however, for use of special sprinklers with greater areas of coverage when they have been tested for this greater coverage.

On the other hand, sprinklers and lines should not be spaced too close together. If sprinklers are less than 6 ft apart, baffles are required in order to prevent an operating sprinkler from wetting and thereby delaying operation of adjacent sprinklers.

Obstruction to Distribution

In addition to limits on the maximum distance between sprinklers on lines and between lines, certain limits of clearance have been established between sprinklers and structural members, such as beams, girders, and trusses, to avoid obstructing water being discharged from sprinklers. If a sprinkler is placed too closely to a beam that deflects the normal discharge pattern of the water, the area of protection for that sprinkler is considerably reduced and fire has a chance for additional growth, thus causing more sprinklers to operate than is necessary. The NFPA Sprinkler Standard is explicit in the limitations it places on distances between sprinklers and structural members to avoid obstruction to lateral distribution of water.

Clearance Between Sprinklers and Ceilings

The distance between sprinklers and the ceiling is important. The closer sprinklers are placed to the ceiling the faster they will operate (see Fig. 14-1H). However, except for continuous smooth ceilings, locating them too close to the ceiling is more likely to result in serious interference to lateral distribution of water from sprinklers by structural members. Then too, when a combustible ceiling is broken up into bays by beams framed into girders or into narrow channels by beams, purlins, or joists, it is quite possible for a fire of moderate to severe intensity to ignite the ceiling and spread for considerable distances if the sprinklers are not located at the correct distance below the ceiling. The NFPA Sprinkler Standard gives maximum distances below ceilings for a variety of construction types. The latest edition of the Standard should be consulted.

I. Sprinkler Piping

Sprinkler piping must be carefully planned and installed in accordance with the NFPA Sprinkler Standard. Lines of pipe in which the sprinklers are directly placed are designated "branch lines." The pipe directly supplying branch lines is designated as a "cross main." The pipe supplying a cross main is designated as a "feed main" (see Fig. 14-1I).

The size of piping supplying automatic sprinklers is determined either from the piping schedule discussed in detail later in this chapter, or on the basis of hydraulic calculations.

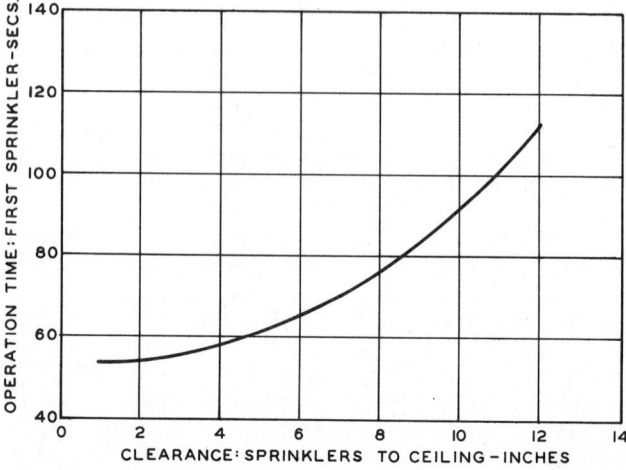

Fig. 14-1H. *Effect of clearance between ceiling and sprinklers on operating time of sprinklers.*

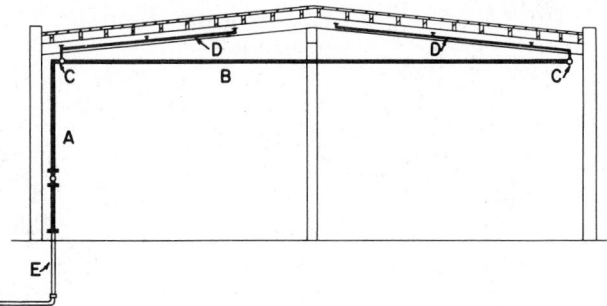

Fig. 14-1I. Building elevation showing parts of sprinkler piping system. (A) riser; (B) feed main; (C) cross main; (D) branch line; and (D) underground supply.

History of Pipe Schedules

In 1878 the Providence Steam and Gas Pipe Company, which for some years had been installing perforated pipes for fire protection, adopted a schedule of sizes for pipe. This schedule was the beginning from which all automatic sprinkler pipe schedules have developed.

In time, local changes resulted in different standards. In 1896, a conference, out of which grew the National Fire Protection Association, formulated a pipe schedule for automatic sprinklers. It was the generally accepted standard until 1905 when a schedule that reduced the number of sprinklers supplied by pipe sizes of 1½-in. and larger was adopted in the Sprinkler Standard which, with revisions, remained in force until 1940.

In that year the Sprinkler Standard made a radical departure in eliminating ¾-in. pipe for branch lines in order to improve water discharge at end sprinklers and to reduce danger of clogging. Also, the number of sprinklers permitted on branch lines for each occupancy classification was changed. For 3-in. and larger pipe for ordinary hazard occupancies, and for 2½-in. and larger pipe for light hazard occupancies, the number of sprinklers permitted was increased over the 1905 schedule.

Early pipe schedules have been commonly referred to as the 1-3-6 schedule (prior to 1896), the 1-2-4 schedule (1896), and the 1-2-3 schedule (1905), from the number of sprinklers allowed on the ¾-in., 1-in., and 1¼-in. pipe sizes, respectively.

The 1953 edition of the NFPA Sprinkler Standard, which first included the "spray" sprinkler (now the standard sprinkler) and which allowed increased sprinkler spacings, established the present schedule. The number of sprinklers on 2½-in. and larger pipe for light hazard occupancies was reduced, and for 6-in. and 8-in. pipe for ordinary hazard occupancies the number was increased.

In the 1955 Sprinkler Standard a reduction was made in the number of sprinklers for branch lines exceeding 12 ft in length, and for branch lines more than 12 ft apart.

The 1972 Sprinkler Standard was expanded to include density (gallons per minute per square foot) and water supply requirements for light and ordinary hazard occupancy.

General Pipe Schedule Requirements

No practical sprinkler piping arrangement can produce a completely uniform protective water discharge from sprinklers in different locations, or with various numbers of sprinklers simultaneously discharging water. The piping schedules listed in the NFPA Sprinkler Standard are based upon extensive and carefully controlled tests, and will provide consistently dependable sprinkler protection with

practical economy in installation costs and water supply. Hydraulically designed systems will usually provide a more uniform water distribution with additional economy.

If conditions call for either unusually long runs of pipe or many bends, an increase in the size of risers or feed mains may be required in order to compensate for friction loss.

Wet-pipe and dry-pipe installations follow the same schedule of piping, except that the longer average time between the operation of sprinklers and the discharge of water required in dry-pipe over wet-pipe systems calls for specific restrictions on the air capacity of dry-pipe system piping (see Chap. 2, this Sec.).

Sprinklers on Branch Line Piping

In pipe schedule systems branch lines for light hazard and ordinary hazard occupancies should not have more than eight sprinklers on either side of a cross main, and for extra hazard occupancies not more than six. This number may be increased or decreased in some special cases, such as where floors are slatted, where there are large unprotected openings, or where sprinklers are installed in blind attics. The NFPA Sprinkler Standard should be consulted for these modifications.

Arrangement of Sprinkler Supply Piping

Figure 14-1J illustrates various configurations for sprinkler system piping. Although it is permissible to supply water to sprinklers in one fire area by an overhead feed main which also supplies adjoining areas, this is not generally done except for small areas. The adjacent horizontal fire areas should usually have individual risers, each riser having its own control valve.

Risers

The proper location, arrangement, and size of risers at any given property are problems that require skilled judg-

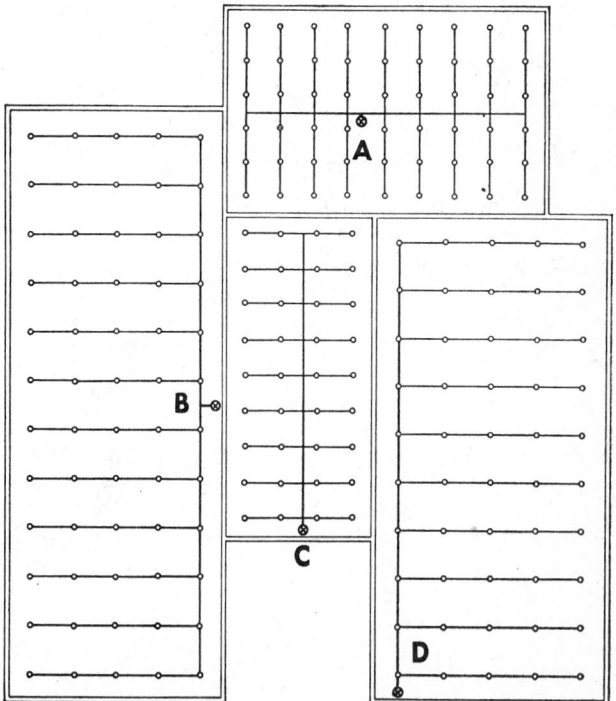

Fig. 14-1J. Location of risers. (A) central feed; (B) side central feed; (C) central end feed; and (D) side end feed.

ment. Construction, height, area, occupancy, and fire hazards must be carefully considered.

In a multistoried building having standard fire cutoffs between floors, the size of a riser supplying sprinklers on more than one floor is determined by the maximum number of sprinklers on any floor supplied by that riser or by hydraulic calculation.

The NFPA Sprinkler Standard covers methods of making riser connections to underground mains, the permissible location of connections to domestic supplies, and special piping arrangements needed when pressure tank supplies are used.

Water Supply Connections

Piping from the water supply to sprinkler risers should be at least as large as the riser. In private underground piping for buildings having other than light hazard occupancies, any dead-end pipe which supplies both sprinklers and hydrants should not be less than 8 in. in size. Underground pipe should be cast iron or asbestos-cement conforming to specifications and to rules for laying pipe as given in NFPA No. 24, Standard for Outside Protection. Steel pipes used underground may corrode and develop leaks in a short time unless special protection against corrosion is provided. Copper pipe may be used, but only if it has been tested and listed by a recognized testing laboratory as suitable for underground use.

Each sprinkler system should have an accessibly located control valve, to control flow of water to the system from all sources other than from fire department connections.

If there is more than one source of water supply, a check valve is needed in the connection from each source.

A common arrangement is to locate water supply gate and check valves in a covered valve pit. An indicator post above ground is used with gate valves buried in the ground. An indicator post is also sometimes used even though the control valve is located in a pit. It is considered the best practice to have sprinkler shutoff valves equipped with devices that will give an alarm on closing of the valve.

In large plants, fire main systems have sectional control valves to improve flexibility in the use of water supplies. It is important that such valves be plainly marked to show the location of the system controlled.

Information regarding the construction and operation of valves for controlling water supplies and other devices used in water supply connections is given in Section 11, Chapter 2.

Installation Standards for Sprinkler System Piping

Piping used in sprinkler systems should be of a type to withstand a working pressure of not less than 175 psi.[5] Piping should conform to Table 14-1B. Other types of pipe or tube may be used, but only if they have been tested and listed by a recognized testing laboratory as suitable for use as sprinkler piping.[6]

Pipe Fittings: If of cast iron, pipe fittings should be of extra heavy pattern for sizes larger than 2 in. if the normal pressure in the piping system exceeds 175 psi. If fittings are of malleable iron, standard weight pattern is acceptable in sizes up to and including 6 in. if the normal pressure in the pipe system does not exceed 300 psi.

Fittings should be of types designed for use in sprinkler systems. Reduction in pipe size should not be made by the use of bushings.

Cast iron screwed fittings (125 and 250 lb) and malleable-iron screwed fittings (150 and 300 lb) are covered in USAS B16.4–1963[7] and USAS B16.3–1963[8] respectively.

Table 14-1B. Sprinkler System Pipe or Tube Materials

Material and Dimensions	Standard
Ferrous Piping (Welded and Seamless) Welded and Seamless Steel Pipe For Ordinary Uses, Spec. For Black and Hot-Dipped Zinc Coated (Galvanized)	ASTM A 120–72a
Spec. for Welded Seamless Steel Pipe	ASTM A 53–72a
Wrought-Steel and Wrought-Iron Pipe	ANSI B36.10–70
Copper Tube (Drawn, Seamless) Spec. For Seamless Copper Tube Spec. For Seamless Copper Water Tube	ASTM B 75–72 or ASTM B 88–72
Spec. For General Requirements for Wrought Seamless Copper and Copper-Alloy Tube	ASTM 5 251–71
Brazing Filler Metal (Classification BCuP-3 or BCuP-4)	AWS A 5.8–69
Solder Metal, 95–5 (Tin-Antimony-Grade 95TA)	ASTM B32–70

All inside piping is installed by means of screwed, flanged, mechanical joint, or brazed fittings or, with specific approval, by welding or flexible couplings. Specifications for such welding are given in the USAS Code for Pressure Piping, B31.1.[9] Where welding of joints is allowed, or where fittings are brazed, the fire hazard of indoor welding must be suitably safeguarded.

Approved flexible couplings are used for earthquake resistance. Couplings, bends and tees of this type are sometimes employed in risers and feed mains if their use is of particular advantage.

Pipe Hangers and Clamps: These are used to attach sprinkler system piping to substantial structural elements of the building. The support offered by many forms of ceiling construction is inadequate to carry the load of sprinkler piping.

The types of hangers necessary to meet various conditions of construction have been tested and listed by testing laboratories. Representative types are shown in Figure 14-1K. For the larger pipe, trapeze bars of steel angle or pipe supported by double hanger rods are frequently used. Expansion shields for attaching hangers to concrete are preferably installed horizontally, although vertical installation may be used in some instances. The adequate support of sprinkler piping is an important consideration. The Sprinkler Standard provides detailed information.

Corrosive Conditions: Corrosive conditions call for the use of pipe, fittings, and hangers designed to resist the particular corrosive agent, or the application of protective coating over susceptible components. The choice depends on the kind and severity of the corrosive condition. Care must be taken that paint is not applied to the sprinklers when piping or other adjacent installations are being painted as protection against corrosion.

If it is necessary to use steel pipe underground as a connection from a system to sprinklers in a detached building, the pipe should be protected against corrosion before it is buried.

Test Equipment

Water Supply Test Pipes and Pressure Gages: These are supplied for each sprinkler system installation. Test pipes, which may also serve as drain pipes, must be provided to permit flow tests. Test connections are not less than 2 in. in size, and are equipped with a shutoff valve. The arrangement

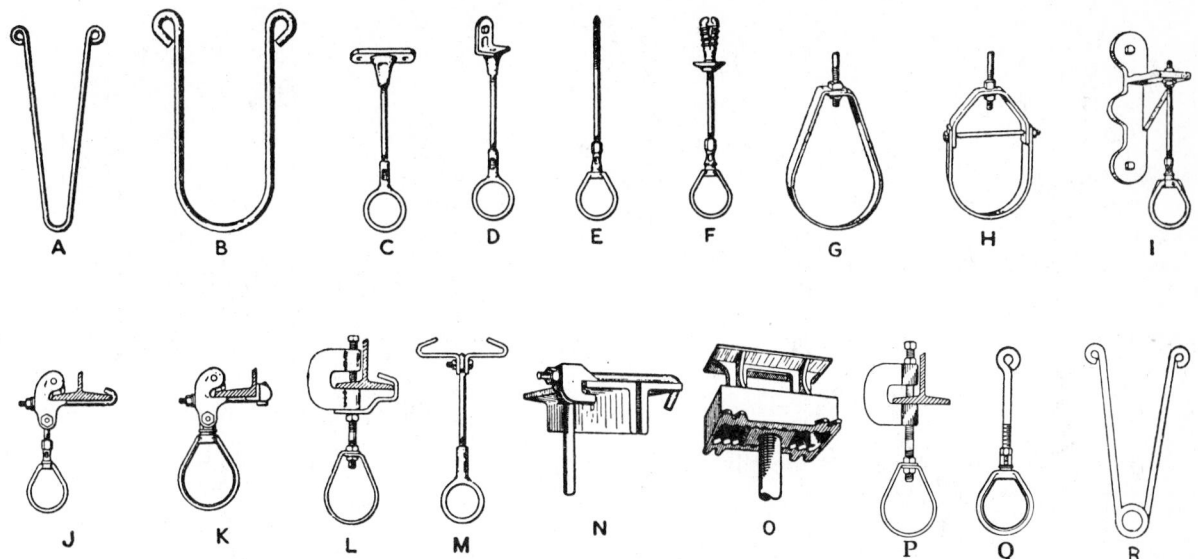

Fig. 14-1K.   Common types of acceptable hangers. (A) U-type hanger for branch lines; (B) U-type hanger for cross mains and feed mains; (C) adjustable clip for branch lines; (D) side beam adjustable hanger; (E) adjustable coach screw clip for branch lines; (F) adjustable swivel ring hanger with expansion shield; (G) adjustable flat iron hanger; (H) adjustable clevis hanger; (I) cantilever bracket; (J) "universal" I-beam clamp; (K) "universal" channel clamp; (L) C-type clamp with retaining strap; (M) center I-beam clamp for branch lines; (N) top beam clamp; (O) "CL-Universal" concrete insert; (P) C-type clamp without retaining strap; (Q) eye rod and ring hanger; (R) wrap-around U hook.

permits a test with the system's main water control valve wide open without its discharge causing damage. An approved gage must be installed to show the pressure in the rise at or near the test connection. A typical arrangement of a test and drain connection with pressure gage for a riser is shown in Figure 14-1L.

Sprinkler System Test Pipe: A test pipe, not less than 1-in. in size and terminating in a corrosion-resistant outlet which will give a flow equivalent to that from one sprinkler, is installed in the top story. This provides a proper method of testing alarm devices, and of tripping dry-pipe valves, and also shows that water can flow through the system. Typical arrangements are shown in Figure 14-1M.

Other Connections

Other connections to the sprinkler system piping should be limited to hand hose reserved exclusively for fire use. Circulation of water in sprinkler pipes is objectionable because of increased corrosion, which may impair the efficiency of the system. Sprinkler system piping must not be used in any way for domestic or utility water service.

Domestic or utility water service demands at peak periods could deplete the water supply required for fire service during a fire. Where hand hose is attached to sprinkler pipes within a room, it is done with the following restrictions: (1) hand hose should never be attached to a dry-pipe sprinkler system; (2) piping and hose valve are at least 1 in., hose not larger than $1\frac{1}{2}$ in., and nozzle not larger than $\frac{1}{2}$-in. nominal discharge capacity; (3) hose is not connected to any sprinkler pipe smaller than $2\frac{1}{2}$ in. (For details, see NFPA No. 14, Standard for the Installation of Standpipe and Hose Systems.)

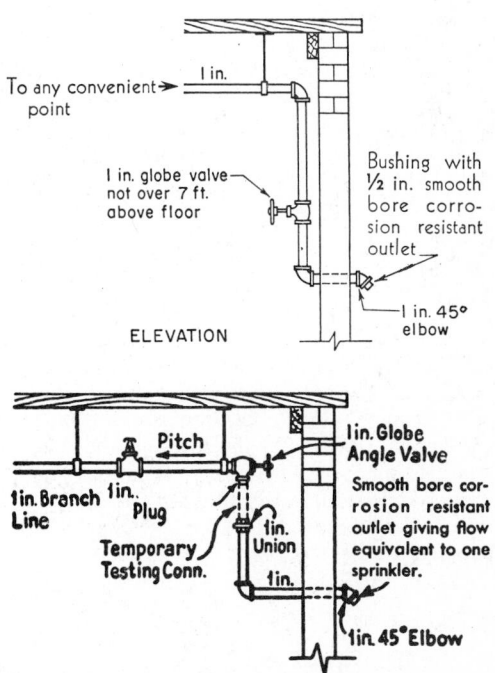

Fig. 14-1L.   Test and drain connection for wet-pipe sprinkler system riser.

Fig. 14-1M.   (Top) Wet-pipe sprinkler system test pipes. (Bottom) One-inch system test pipes on dry pipe system.

J. Valves and Other Features

Water-flow alarm valves, dry-pipe valves, and other special features are covered separately in subsequent chapters of this Section.

Identification Signs

Signs should be provided on all control, drain, test, and alarm valves to identify their purpose and function. Fire department connections should be properly identified to show whether they supply sprinkler systems, outside sprinklers, or hose standpipes. Manufacturers' instruction charts describing the operation and maintenance of equipment should be located near major sprinkler devices. Identification signs are shown in Figure 14-1N.

K. Approval of Sprinkler System Installations

Sprinkler system design and installation should be entrusted to only fully qualified and responsible parties. The installation of sprinkler systems is a trade by itself. Some large industrial properties, however, may have engineering and construction staffs to design and install automatic sprinkler systems and their water supplies.

Preparation of Plans

Before a sprinkler system is installed or remodeled, in order to avoid misunderstandings and errors a preliminary layout is prepared and submitted for approval to the agency responsible for its acceptance.

Preliminary Layout: The preliminary layout should identify property location and ownership; indicate if subject to earthquake or flood; provide other information pertinent to the installation, including the following: (1) construction and occupancy of the buildings; (2) water supply, including the size and location of supply mains and the results of tests made of the supply; (3) the approximate location and spacing of sprinklers in each fire area; (4) the number of sprinklers on each riser and on each floor and the total number on the system, and (5) the area covered by each riser on each floor.

If the installation is an addition to a present system, the combined number of new and old sprinklers on each riser per floor should be given as well as the combined area covered. In the case of a dry-pipe system, the air capacity of the piping of the system or systems, and the total existing number of sprinklers need to be indicated.

Working Plans: Working plans are required after the preliminary layout has been approved. These also are to be submitted for approval before the installation is made. In addition to the data on the preliminary layouts, working plans show the following: (1) false ceilings, partitions, areas requiring special consideration such as blind spaces, closets, wide benches, or tables in fixed locations, storage racks, etc.; (2) the make, size and model of all sprinkler devices to be used; (3) the location of alarm bells; (4) the cutting lengths of pipe; (5) the location and size of risers, mains, and fittings; (6) types of hangers, inserts, and sleeves; (7) control and check valves, fire department connections, drain pipes, test pipes; (8) hose connections; (9) provisions for flushing; and (10) all other details for procuring materials and installing the system (see Fig. 14-1O).

Final Approval

After the sprinkler system has been installed, it is then inspected and approved. Before asking for final approval, the installing company states in writing that the work

Style "A"
Sprinkler Control Valves

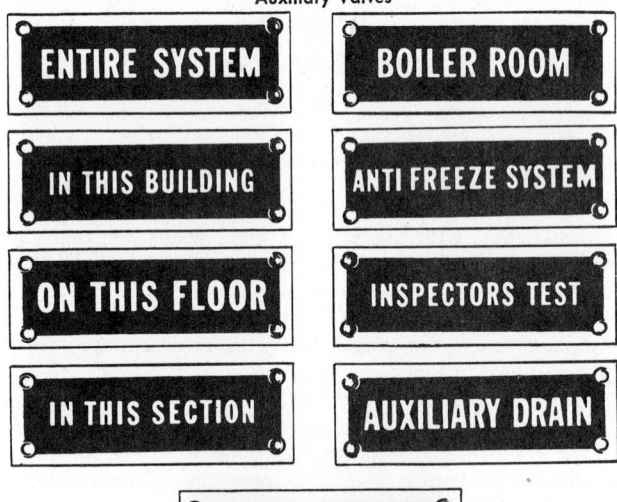

Style "B"
Auxiliary Valves

Style "C"
Outside Sprinklers

Fig. 14-1N. Identification signs.

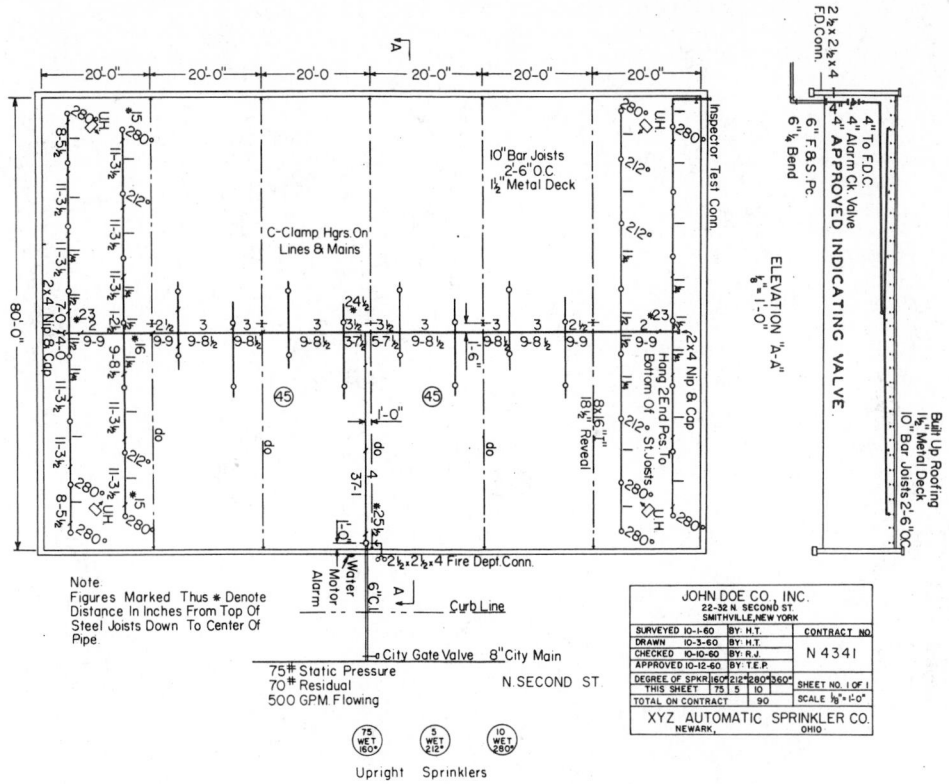

Fig. 14-10.   Typical sprinkler system working plan.

covered by its contract has been completed in accordance with the approved specifications and plans, and tested as called for by the Sprinkler Standard. A reporting form, known as "Sprinkler Contractor's Certificate Covering Materials and Tests," is used for this purpose.

All tests are made by the installer in the presence of an inspector or inspectors of the appropriate authority or authorities. In some cases, however, it may be satisfactory to have the tests witnessed by the owner or his representative.

Flushing and Tests

Before connecting sprinkler risers for testing, underground connections to sprinkler installations must be flushed thoroughly (see Sec. 11, Chap. 2 for flushing techniques). Obstructing materials in underground pipes can seriously impair sprinkler protection.

All piping and devices under pressure (including yard piping and fire department connections) are tested hydrostatically for strength and leakage at not less than 200 psi pressure for two hours, or at 50 psi pressure in excess of the maximum static pressure when that pressure is in excess of 150 psi (see Sec. 13, Chap. 5 for hydrostatic test methods). To prevent serious water damage in case of a break, a small test pump is used, the main controlling gate being kept shut.

Any blank gasket used in testing should be of a special self-indicating type having red lugs protruding out beyond the flange in such a way as to clearly mark its presence. These should be numbered so as to assure their return after the work is completed.

Tests of drainage facilities are made by opening the main drain valve while the control valve is wide open, to provide assurance that main control valves are open and that the water will be disposed of safely.

When the weather is too cold for testing with water, tests of dry-pipe systems are made by maintaining at least 50 psi air pressure for two hours. During such a test the clappers of differential-type dry-pipe valves should be held off their seats whenever a pressure in excess of 50 psi is used, in order to prevent injury to the valves.

Dry-pipe valves, quick-opening devices, and water-flow alarms should be given a working test before final acceptance of the system.

SI Units

The following conversion factors are given as a convenience in converting to SI units the English units used in this chapter.

1 ft^2	= .0929 m^2
1 Btu	= 1.055 kg
1 in.	= 25.400 mm
1 ft	= .305 m
1 lb (mass)	= .454 kg
1 psi	= 6.895 kPa
$\frac{5}{9}$(°F − 32)	= °C
1 gal (U.S.)	= 3.785 litres
1 gpm	= 3.785 litres/min

Bibliography

References Cited

[1] "Automatic Sprinkler Performance Tables," 1970 Ed., *Fire Journal*, Vol. 64, No. 4, July, 1970, pp. 35-39.

[2] Thompson, N. J., *Fire Behavior and Sprinklers*, National Fire Protection Association, Boston, 1964, pp. 104-110.

[3] Welb, W. A., "Automatic Sprinklers in Exhibition Halls," *Fire Technology*, Vol. 4, No. 2, May 1968, pp. 115-125.

[4] Thompson, N. J., "Hazard of High Piled Combustible Stock," NFPA *Quarterly*, Vol. 43, No. 1, July 1949, pp. 38-46.

[5] "Wrought Steel and Wrought Iron Pipe," USAS B-36.10-1959, United States of America Standards Institute, New York.

[6] "Black and Hot-Dipped Zinc-Coated (Galvanized) Welded and Seamless Steel Pipe for Ordinary Uses," ASTM A.120-62T, American Society for Testing and Materials, Philadelphia.

[7] "Cast Iron Screwed Fittings, (125 and 250 lbs)," USAS B16.4-1963, United States of America Standard Institute, New York.

[8] "Malleable-Iron Screwed Fittings (150 and 300 lbs)," USAS B.16-1963, United States of America Standards Institue, New York.

[9] "Code for Pressure Piping," USAS B31.1-1955, United States of America Standards Institute, New York.

NFPA Codes, Standards, and Recommended Practices (see the latest *NFPA Publications and Visual Aids Catalog* for availability of current editions of the following documents)

NFPA No. 13, Standard for the Installation of Sprinkler Systems.

NFPA No. 13A, Recommended Practice for the Care and Maintenance of Sprinkler Systems.

NFPA No. 14, Standard for the Installation of Standpipe and Hose Systems.

NFPA No. 20, Standard for the Installation of Centrifugal Fire Pumps.

NFPA No. 22, Standard for Water Tanks for Private Fire Protection.

NFPA No. 24, Standard for Outside Protection.

NFPA No. 71, Standard for the Installation, Maintenance, and Use of Central Station Signaling Systems.

NFPA No. 72A, Standard for the Installation, Maintenance, and Use of Local Protective Signaling Systems for Watchman, Fire Alarm, and Supervisory Service.

NFPA No. 72B, Standard for the Installation, Maintenance, and Use of Auxiliary Protective Signaling Systems for Fire Alarm Service.

NFPA No. 72C, Standard for the Installation, Maintenance, and Use of Remote Station Protective Signaling Systems.

NFPA No. 72D, Standard for the Installation, Maintenance, and Use of Proprietary Protective Signaling Systems for Guard, Fire Alarm, and Supervisory Service.

NFPA No. 80, Standard for Fire Doors and Windows.

NFPA No. 204, Guide for Smoke and Heat Venting.

Additional Readings

"Cast Iron Flanges and Flanged Fittings, (25, 125, 250 and 800 lbs)," USAS B16.1-1967, United States of America Standards Institute, New York.

Troutman, J. E., "Fire Protection for High-Piled Combustible Stock in Warehouses," NFPA *Quarterly*, Vol. 57, No. 1, July 1963, pp. 15–24.

Chapter 2

TYPES OF SPRINKLER SYSTEMS

There are six major classifications of automatic sprinkler systems. Each type of system includes piping for carrying water from a source of supply to sprinklers on the piping in the area under protection. In addition to the six major types of systems, there is one category of sprinkler equipment arrangement which, in a sense, constitutes sprinkler systems, but is not described as such by NFPA No. 13, Standard for the Installation of Sprinkler Systems, hereinafter referred to in this chapter as the NFPA Sprinkler Standard. It includes special types or so-called "nonstandard" systems designed for special applications. This chapter describes the six major classification systems as well as the special types of systems. It also gives information on installation of outside sprinklers for protection against exposure fires.

The six major classifications of systems are:

Wet-pipe Systems: These systems employ automatic sprinklers attached to a piping system containing water under pressure at all times. When a fire occurs, individual sprinklers are actuated by the heat, and water flows through the sprinklers immediately.

Regular Dry-pipe Systems: Regular dry-pipe systems have automatic sprinklers attached to piping which contains air or nitrogen under pressure. When a sprinkler is opened by heat from a fire, the pressure is reduced, a "dry-pipe valve" is opened by water pressure, and water flows out any opened sprinklers.

Pre-action Systems: Pre-action systems are dry-pipe systems in which the air in the piping may or may not be under pressure. When a fire occurs, a supplementary fire detecting device in the protected area is actuated; this opens a valve which permits water to flow into the piping system and be discharged by any automatic sprinklers that have been opened by the heat of the fire.

Deluge Systems: These systems are similar to pre-action systems, except that all sprinklers are open at all times. When heat from a fire actuates the fire detecting device, water flows to and is discharged from all sprinklers on the piping system, thus "deluging" the protected areas.

Combined Dry-pipe and Pre-action Systems: These include the essential features of both types of systems. The piping system contains air under pressure. A supplementary heat detecting device opens the water valve and an air exhauster at the end of the feed main. The system then fills with water and operates as a wet-pipe system. If the supplementary heat detecting system should fail, the system will operate as a conventional dry-pipe system.

Limited Water Supply Systems: Limited water supply systems use automatic sprinklers and follow the standard piping and spacing arrangements, but are supplied by a limited amount of water.

A.   Wet-pipe Sprinkler Systems

The essential features of wet-pipe sprinkler systems, which represent about 75 percent of sprinkler installations, are covered in Chapter 1 of this Section. They include provisions for water supplies, piping, location and spacing of sprinklers, and other pertinent details. This type of system is generally used wherever there is no danger of the water

in the pipes freezing, and wherever there are no special conditions requiring one of the other types of systems.

Where subject to temperatures below freezing, even for short periods, the ordinary wet-pipe system cannot be used as the system contains water under pressure at all times (see Fig. 14-2A). There are two recognized methods of maintaining automatic sprinkler protection in such locations. One is the use of systems where water enters the sprinkler piping only after operation of a control valve (dry-pipe, pre-action, etc.), and the other by use of antifreeze solution in a portion of the wet-pipe system.

Antifreeze Solutions

When a recommended antifreeze solution is maintained in the piping from the riser, the normal water supply does not flow except when the solution is discharged from an opened sprinkler. Because antifreeze solutions are costly and may be difficult to maintain, their use is limited to small,

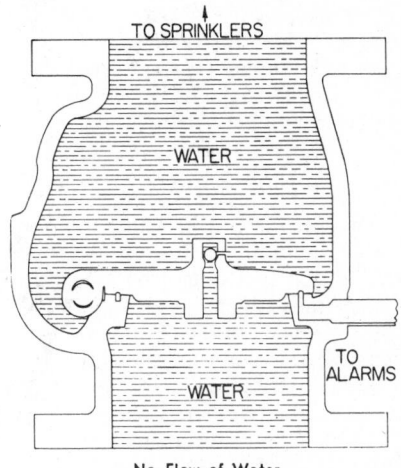

No Flow of Water

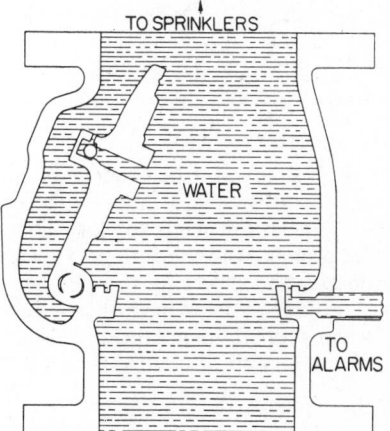

Water Flowing to Sprinklers and to Alarms

Fig. 14-2A.   A wet-pipe sprinkler system is under water pressure at all times so that water will be discharged immediately when an automatic sprinkler operates. The automatic alarm valve shown causes a warning signal when water flows from the sprinkler piping.

unheated areas served by a wet-pipe system where not more than 20 sprinklers are involved and where the piping would otherwise have to be shut off and drained during cold weather. Where more than 20 need to be supplied, the cost of refilling the system or even of replenishing losses from small leaks makes it advisable to use small dry-pipe valves. In any event, antifreeze solutions should be used only in accordance with applicable local health regulations.

The antifreeze solution generally consists of water and a water-soluble liquid, such as glycerine or certain glycols; the proportions specified in the NFPA Sprinkler Standard give the desired reduction in freezing temperature without producing a combustible mixture. Where the system is supplied from public water connections, the use of anti-freeze solutions other than chemically pure glycerine (U.S. Pharmacopoeia 96.5 percent grade) or propylene glycol must not be permitted. In other systems, diethylene glycol, glycerine, propylene glycol, ethylene glycol, or a calcium chloride solution containing a corrosion inhibitor (such as sodium chromate) may be used.

Details of supply piping and valves, and of testing, are given in the NFPA Sprinkler Standard.

Cold Weather Valves

Automatic sprinkler piping should not be shut off and drained as a regular practice to avoid freezing during cold weather. However, where the fire hazard is not severe, permission may be given to shut off not more than 10 sprinklers on a wet-pipe system. Such shutoff valves are commonly referred to as "cold weather valves."

B.   Dry-pipe Sprinkler Systems

Dry-pipe sprinkler systems in which the piping contains air under pressure until the dry-pipe valve operates are used only in locations that cannot be properly heated. The principle of a dry-pipe system is illustrated in Figure 14-2B.

A dry-pipe system is installed only where a wet-pipe system is impractical, as in rooms or buildings which are not properly heated. Dry-pipe systems are converted to wet-pipe systems when they become unnecessary because adequate heat is provided. No sprinklers should be shut off in cold weather.

When two or more dry-pipe valves are used, systems preferably are divided horizontally to prevent simultaneous operation of more than one system, resultant increased time delay in filling systems and discharging water, and receipt of more than one water flow alarm signal.

Efficiency of Dry-pipe Systems

According to fire records (see Chap. 1 of this Section), more sprinklers open on the average with dry-pipe than with wet-pipe systems; this tends to show that the control of fire is not as prompt with the former. However, in most classes of property, and especially those of light and moderate hazard, dry-pipe systems have shown generally good results and, when properly maintained, can be relied upon to satisfactorily extinguish or control fires.

Size of Dry-pipe Systems

The capacity of a dry-pipe system, determines the time before water is discharged. A system of not more than 750 gal capacity should be controlled by one dry-pipe valve. If the piping volume exceeds 750 gal, the system should deliver water to the far end of the system (inspector's test pipe) in not more than 60 sec, unless otherwise specified by the authority having jurisdiction.

Where two or more dry-pipe valves are used for a multi-storied building, the systems may be divided by floors or by vertical sections of the building. The area controlled should be identified by a standardized sign at each riser control valve and dry-pipe valve.

Dry-pipe Valve Designs

Most dry-pipe valves are designed so that a moderate air pressure in a dry-pipe system will hold back a much greater water pressure. The difference between the air pressure and the water pressure, expressed as the ratio of these pressures when the air pressure is reduced to the value at which the valve opens, is called the "differential."

If the differential is obtained by having a large diameter air clapper in a valve bear directly upon a smaller water clapper, the valve is often referred to as a "differential-type" dry-pipe valve.

If the air pressure in the sprinkler system acts upon a small disc, diaphragm, or clapper which is arranged with levers, links, and latches to provide the necessary closing force upon the water clapper, the valve may be designated as a "mechanical-type" or a "latched-clapper type."

To keep the size of a dry-pipe valve small, many approved valves make use of considerable mechanical leverage in securing the desired value for the differential. Modern dry-pipe valves combine, in varying degrees, the principles of differential and mechanical or latched-clapper valves. The NFPA Sprinkler Standard makes no distinction between these types of valves.

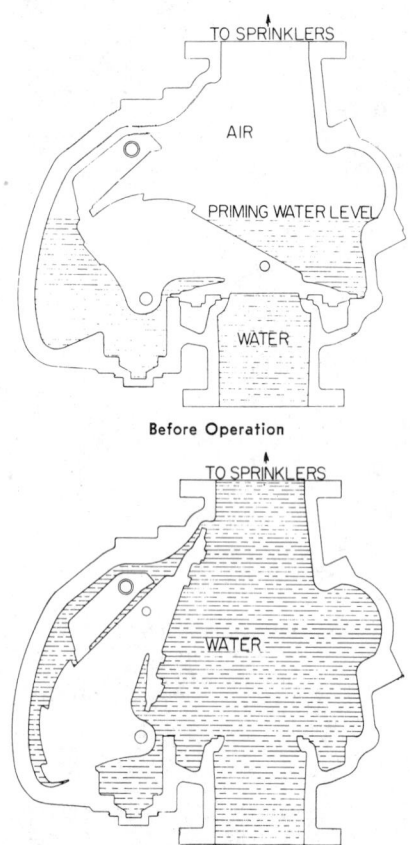

Fig. 14-2B.   The principle of a dry-pipe system is illustrated by these simplified drawings of a dry-pipe valve. Compressed air in the sprinkler system holds the dry valve closed, preventing water from entering the sprinkler piping until the air pressure has dropped below a predetermined point.

With a strictly differential-type dry-valve, the air pressure at the trip point depends upon the water pressure. With a strictly mechanical-type valve, the air pressure at the trip point is affected only slightly, or not at all, by the water pressure, and the air pressure at the trip point is predetermined by the design.

Originally, a differential of 5 or 6 to 1 (water pressure to air pressure) was accepted practice; this has been increased with some designs so that lower air pressures may be used.

Another type is the "low-differential" dry-pipe valve. The differential is usually 1.0 and 1.2 to 1 rather than the 5 or 6 to 1 common with ordinary differential dry-pipe valves. The low-differential valve, which resembles a check valve or alarm valve, is kept closed by air pressure on the sprinkler system side of the valve clapper that exceeds the pressure on the water supply side of the clapper. The valve operates when the air pressure is reduced to only about 10 percent less than the water pressure at the point of operation.

All approved dry-pipe valves give an unobstructed water flow when the valve is in the open or "tripped" position.

A rubber valve facing or ring is commonly used on air clappers, and to some extent on water clappers, to facilitate tightness in the closed position, and to compensate for small dimensional variations.

To reduce the danger of accidental tripping of ordinary dry-pipe valves subjected to higher than normal water pressure or to water hammer, it is usual practice to maintain an air pressure well above the normal trip point pressure. For example, with a valve having a 6 to 1 differential and used with a normal maximum water supply pressure of 100 psi, the air pressure of the trip point would be approximately 100/6 or 17 psi, but an air pressure of 30 psi to 35 psi would be maintained. Unless a valve has been designed for especially low pressures (in which case the manufacturer's instructions regarding pressures should be followed), it is customary to maintain the dry system air pressure 15 psi to 20 psi above the value at which the dry-pipe valve would trip. About the same amount of excess pressure is carried in low-differential systems.

Since the air pressure in the system must be reduced to the tripping point of the valve before water enters the piping, it is undesirable to carry excessive air pressure because a greater time must elapse before water reaches the sprinklers. Quick-opening devices described in this chapter may be used to reduce the tripping time. Automatic air pressure maintaining devices are sometimes used. The rate of air supply is restricted so that it will not delay operation of the sprinkler system, and a low air pressure alarm is provided to warn of a failure in the automatic supply. Low-differential systems require larger air compressor systems than ordinary differential systems because of the higher air pressure and the need to accommodate the "pump-up time" of currently recognized standards.

A small amount of priming water is maintained above the air clapper to aid in sealing against air leaks. Priming water may also help to keep rubber facings in pliable condition.

Valve Latches: After a dry-pipe valve has tripped and the piping has filled with water, the air and water clappers of ordinary differential valves must be prevented from returning to the set position should the water flow be interrupted, because this would water column the valve. Reseating under temporary back flow can produce water hammer sufficient to break the valve or its fittings. An automatic mechanical latch is provided to prevent a clapper from returning to its seat after it has opened appreciably. Details of a latch may be seen in Figure 14-2C.

Types of Dry-pipe Valves

Differential-type: Figures 14-2C, 14-2D, and 14-2E show the arrangement of parts, and the relative sizes of air and water clappers, in ordinary differential-type dry-pipe valves of recent and early manufacture. Large valve bodies are needed to accommodate the relatively large air clappers.

Low-differential Type: A low-differential type dry-pipe valve is shown in Figure 14-2F. This type of valve is useful in controlling dry systems where there would be a problem of debris entering the system because of the carrying force of water at the higher velocities associated with operation of dry valves having the usual differential of 5 or 6 to 1. An alarm of water flow signal is obtained through the same feature as would be found in an alarm valve, i.e., a split ring or a separate pilot valve.

Mechanical-type: These dry-pipe valves of early design are shown in Figures 14-2G and 14-2H. Such valves were mechanically complicated and difficult to keep in good operating condition.

A Latched-clapper Type: This dry-pipe valve of current manufacture is shown in Figure 14-2I.

Small Dry-pipe Valves: Small dry-pipe valves are used to provide protection for small portions of wet-pipe systems in locations subject to freezing, thereby avoiding the un-

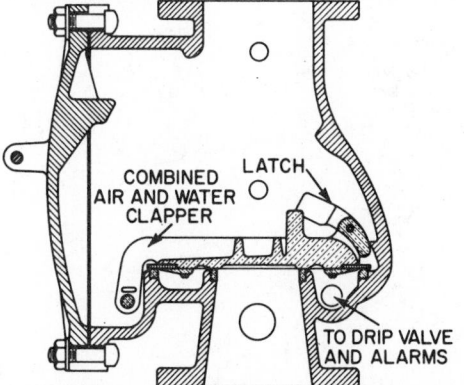

*Fig. 14-2C. Differential-type dry-pipe valve. When the downward force exerted on the **combined air and water clapper** by the system air pressure is reduced to the value of the upward force exerted by the water supply upon the clapper, the valve will open to permit the flow of water into the sprinkler system. The **latch** prohibits the valve from returning to the closed position. Shown is the Hodgman Manufacturing Co., Inc., Model C dry-pipe valve.*

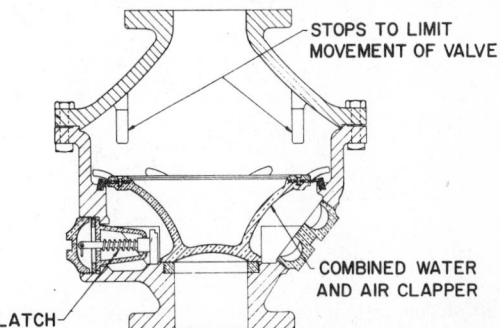

*Fig. 14-2D. Early-type differential dry-pipe valve (manufactured 1890 to 1916). When the valve trips, the **combined water and air clapper** lifts against the **stops**. Water flows annularly around the clapper. The valve is prevented from reseating by the **latch**. This valve was difficult to inspect, clean, and maintain. (Grinnell Company, Inc., Model 12)*

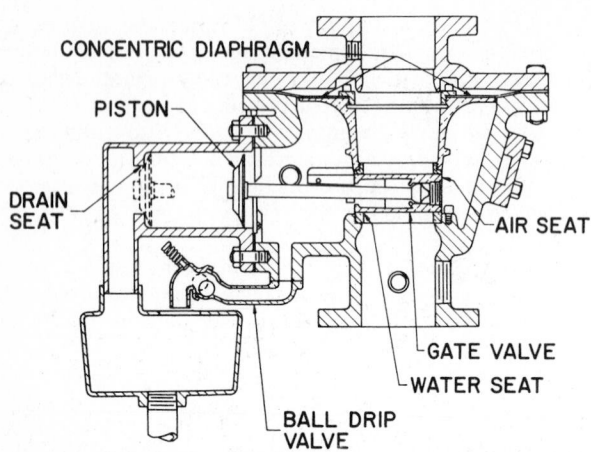

*Fig. 14-2E. Early-type Differential Dry-pipe Valve (manufactured 1905 to 1920). Air pressure on the **concentric diaphragm** and on the **air seat** of the **gate valve** holds the gate on the **water seat**. The **ball drip valve** prevents water leakage by the **water seat** from accumulating in the intermediate chamber. Release of air pressure allows the **gate valve** to lift slightly from the **water seat**. Pressure of water acts on the loosely fitting **piston** to withdraw the **gate valve** from the **air seat** and **water seat**. The **piston** against the **drain seat** prevents escape of water. (Grinnell Company, Inc., Models A and B)*

desirable practice of shutting off and draining sprinkler piping in winter. They are mostly 2-in. to 3½-in. models of approved 6-in. dry-pipe valves. For some installations, omitting priming arrangements, mechanical alarms, and possibly the water pressure gage is permitted. The chief difficulty with small dry-pipe systems is maintaining air pressure. The pipe volume is small and the entire system must be unusually tight. With a very small system, say less than 15 to 20 sprinklers, it may be necessary to provide an auxiliary air chamber to increase the capacity.

Quick-opening Devices

One characteristic of a dry-pipe system is a delay in time between the opening of a sprinkler and the discharge of

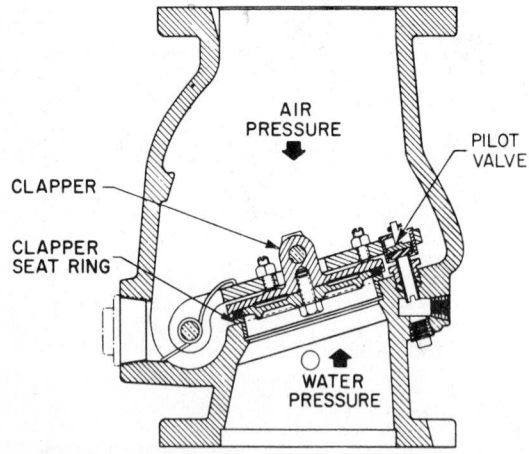

Fig. 14-2F. A low-differential dry-pipe valve. Air pressure 15 to 20 psi higher than the water pressure supplying the sprinkler system holds the clapper shut on the clapper seat ring. When the air pressure is reduced to about 10 percent below the water pressure, the clapper is lifted off its seat and water enters the sprinkler system, and flows out through the pilot valve to operate alarm devices. Low-differential valves are similar to alarm check valves used in wet-pipe sprinkler systems. Shown is the "Automatic" Sprinkler Corp. of America Model 15 valve.

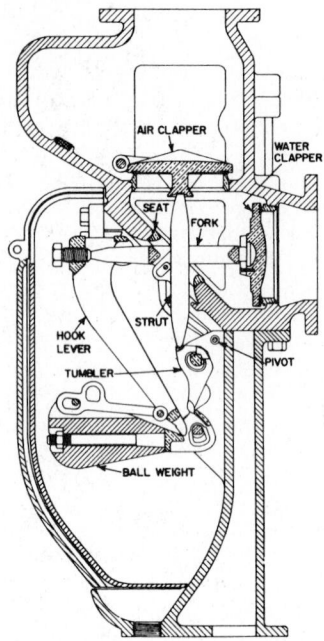

*Fig. 14-2G. Mechanical-type Dry-pipe Valve (manufactured 1909 to 1924). Water supply pressure on the **water clapper** is resisted by the **fork, hook lever, ball weight, tumbler,** and **strut,** and by air pressure on the **air clapper**. When the valve trips, the **strut** and the **fork** hinge on the **pivot** carrying the **water clapper** back to rest on the **seat** and thus prevent leakage into that portion of the valve containing the mechanical linkage assembly. ("Automatic" Sprinkler Corp. of America, International Models 4 and 5)*

water; a delay which may allow the fire to spread and more sprinklers to open. The difficulty may be partly overcome by installation of quick-opening devices which either increase the rate of discharge of air from the sprinkler piping or accelerate opening of the dry valve when one or more sprinklers operate, depending upon the type of device used.

Dry-pipe valves controlling systems having a capacity of more than 500 gal must have quick-opening devices. They are generally designated as "accelerators" or "exhausters" and operate, as described later in more detail, as a result of a prompt but not large drop in system air pressure produced by the opening of one or more sprinklers.

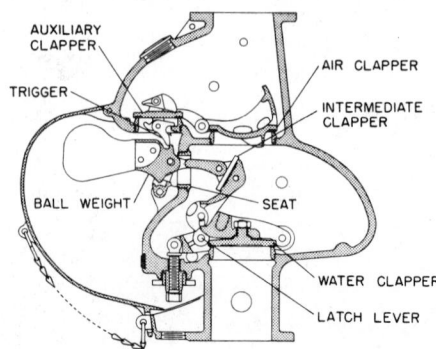

*Fig. 14-2H. Mechanical-type dry-pipe valve (manufactured 1917 to 1921). Water supply pressure on the **water clapper** is resisted by the **latch lever**, the **ball weight**, and the **trigger**, and by air pressure on the **auxiliary clapper**. The **air clapper** acts as a check valve to hold air pressure in the sprinkler system. The **intermediate clapper** against the **seat** prevents leakage after tripping. The Globe Model B, of similar design, was manufactured from 1921 to 1934. (Globe Automatic Sprinkler Co., Globe Models 5 and 6)*

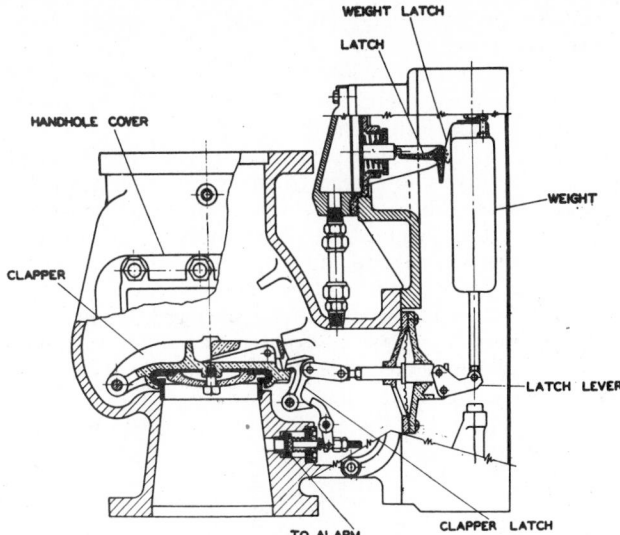

Fig. 14-2I. Latched clapper-type mechanical dry-pipe valve. The pressure of the water supply is resisted by a positive **clapper latch** *which is released by the falling* **weight** *when a reduced system air pressure releases the diaphragm actuated* **weight latch.** *An automatic float drain may be provided to prevent water columning by possible leakage at the water valve seat or condensate drainage in the sprinkler piping (See Fig. 14-2N). Shown is the "Automatic" Sprinkler Corp. of America Model 141 dry-pipe valve which is no longer manufactured.*

Quick-opening devices as a class do not include methods of tripping dry-pipe or other water control valves by fire detecting systems that are independent of automatic sprinklers. Quick-opening devices are necessarily somewhat more complicated, and proper care and maintenance in accordance with instructions of the manufacturer are essential to produce satisfactory results.

The failure of an approved accelerator or exhauster to operate does not prevent normal tripping of a dry-pipe valve.

In operating principle both accelerators and exhausters employ two air chambers. One chamber (often designated the "inlet" or "lower" chamber) has a connection always open to the dry-pipe system, while the second chamber (usually called the "upper" or "pressure" chamber) is closed except for a small orifice which allows its internal pressure to equalize slowly with that in the inlet chamber which is the normal dry-pipe system air pressure. The two chambers are separated by a diaphragm which is deflected whenever the pressure in the system becomes less than that in the upper chamber due to the escape of system air pressure through an opened sprinkler. Movement of the diaphragm actuates valves and mechanisms that produce prompt tripping of the dry-pipe valve.

Accelerators: Accelerators operate by using the movement of the diaphragm to open an auxiliary valve to admit sprinkler system air pressure to the intermediate chamber beneath the air clapper of the dry-pipe valve. This balances the closing force and allows the water valve to be opened by the water pressure. The automatic drain from the intermediate chamber must close automatically.

Latched-clapper or mechanical-type dry-pipe valves which do not have an intermediate chamber cannot be tripped by the use of accelerators.

Figure 14-2J shows an accelerator and gives an explanation of how it trips a dry-pipe valve. See Figure 14-2K for a view of the same accelerator attached to a dry-pipe valve as one of the latter's "trimmings."

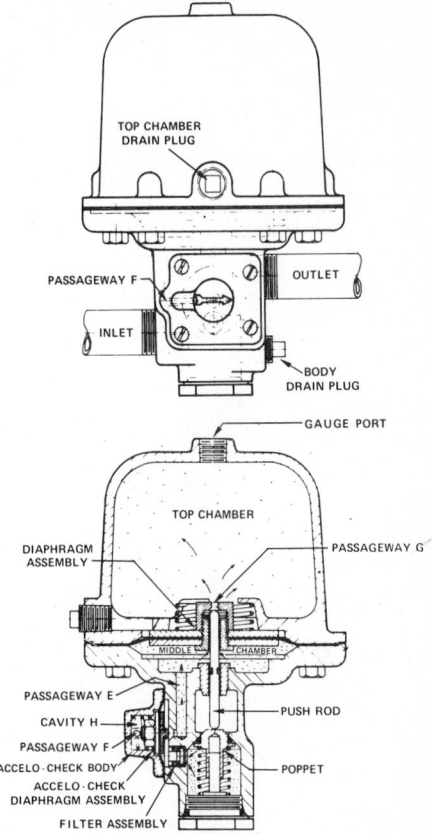

Fig. 14-2J. A dry pipe system accelerator with integral anti-flooding device. System air pressure enters the **top chamber** *from the* **inlet** *through* **passageways E** *and* **G.** *Once pressurized the* **diaphragm assembly** *closes on the* **push rod** *restricting air flow from the* **top chamber.** *The opening of an automatic sprinkler reduces the air pressure in the sprinkler system and the* **middle chamber.** *The* **top chamber** *being restricted from losing air instead moves the* **diaphragm assembly** *and* **push rod.** *This movement opens the* **poppet** *which admits system air pressure to the* **outlet** *and dry pipe valve intermediate chamber. The buildup in pressure in the* **outlet** *backs up through* **passageway F** *to close the* **accelo-check diaphragm assembly** *against* **passageway E** *preventing any water or contamination from flowing upward to the* **middle** *and* **top chamber.** *(Reliable Automatic Sprinkler Co., Inc.)*

Exhausters: Exhausters use the movement of the diaphragm to open an auxiliary valve which discharges system air pressure to the atmosphere. The auxiliary valve is of such size that the air pressure quickly falls to the normal trip point of the valve. After the dry-pipe valve trips, the exhauster valve closes automatically to prevent the discharge of water.

The reduction in operating time of a dry-pipe valve due to the use of a quick-opening device is recognized in the NFPA Sprinkler Standard by allowing an increase in the allowable size and capacity of a dry-pipe sprinkler system over that allowed if no accelerating device is used.

Most of the manufacturers of approved dry-pipe valves have accelerating devices of their own design with trimmings that make them readily adaptable to their dry-pipe valves. For simplicity in procurement and maintenance, it is advantageous to use dry-pipe valves and accelerating devices of the same manufacturer, although in many cases this is not necessary for proper functioning of the devices. An exhauster is shown in Figure 14-2L.

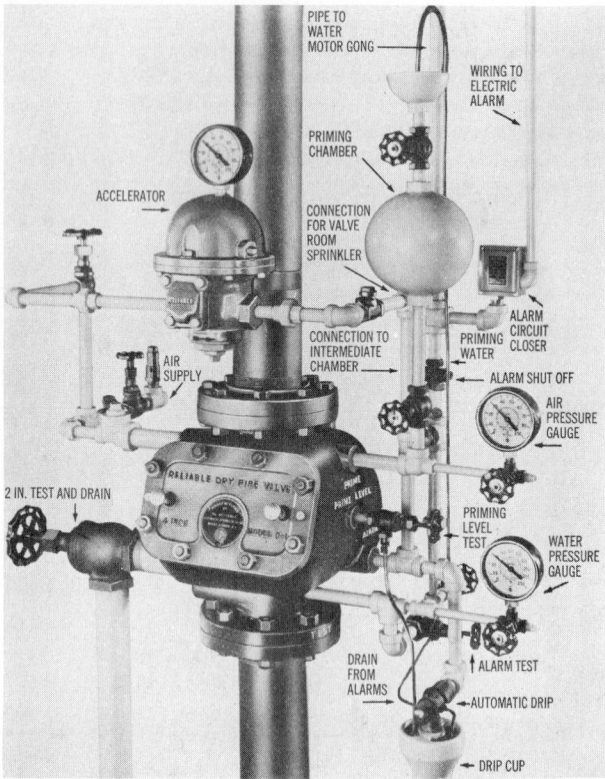

Fig. 14-2K. A representative dry-pipe valve and trimmings. The arrangement shown includes some recent simplification in the use of copper tubing and fittings in place of standard steel pipe and fittings still commonly furnished by most manufacturers. The functions of the various components have not been changed, and the arrangement is approved by the recognized testing laboratories. Shown is Reliable Automatic Sprinkler Co., Inc., Model C-2 dry-pipe valve.

Compressed Air Supplies

The compressed air supply should be from a reliable source available at all times, have a capacity of restoring normal air pressure in the system within a period of 30 min (except for low differential dry-pipe systems where the time may be 60 min), and be located preferably near the dry-pipe valve. One or more approved relief valves should be provided between the compressor and the controlling valve, and should be set to relieve at a pressure 5 psi in excess of maximum air pressure which should be carried in the system.

Automatic air control is sometimes provided (always with low differential systems) as by means of an electrically driven air compressor which cuts in and out at minimum and maximum pressures desired. Automatic air supply is through an orifice which is so small that in case of the fusing of a sprinkler, the air supply will not interfere with operation of the dry-pipe valve.

Special types of air pressure controls have been devised which, when combined with a high and low pressure trouble alarm, should be acceptable if properly maintained. Automatic control, even with trouble alarms, may need frequent regular inspection to make sure that air is properly maintained to prevent tripping of the dry valve under freezing conditions, or the building up of excessive air pressure.

Water Columning

Any leakage of water past the water valve of an ordinary dry-pipe valve, or water accumulating from slow drainage

or condensation, must not be allowed in dry-system piping above the valve.

Should water accumulate in a riser outside of the heated dry-pipe valve enclosure, freezing would make the system inoperative and possibly break the piping.

Due to the differential characteristics of most dry-pipe valves, a relatively low head of water accumulated in the riser will exceed the normal trip point of the valve so that when the system air pressure is released by sprinkler operation the valve will not open due to the head of water on the air clapper. The valve is then "water columned." (Because of the reduction of the differential to a very small value, low-differential dry-pipe valves are not subject to failure due to water columning although there is danger of excessive water above the valve clapper freezing. To prevent the latter possibility, low differential valves are usually equipped

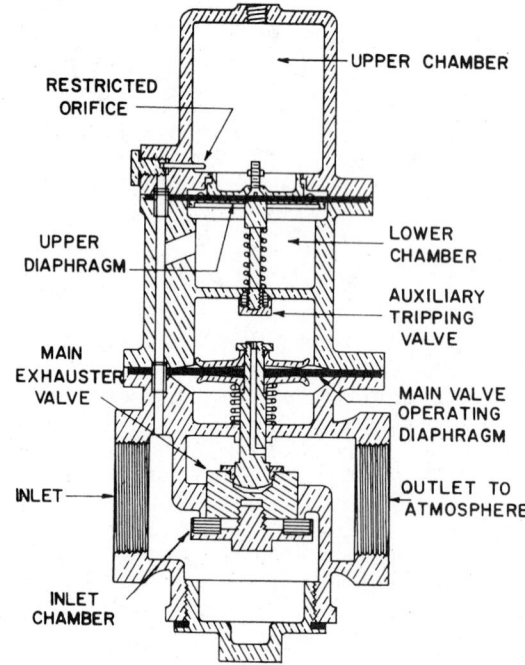

*Fig. 14-2L. A dry-pipe system exhauster. The **inlet** is connected to the sprinkler system side of the dry-pipe valve. System air pressure enters the **lower chamber** by way of an open passage from the **inlet chamber**. Pressure can also build up in the **upper chamber** slowly through **restricted orifice** between the **upper chamber** and **lower chamber**, so that normally their pressures are equal. The opening of an automatic sprinkler starts a reduction in the air pressure in the **lower chamber**. The higher pressure remaining in the **upper chamber** moves the **upper diaphragm** in the direction to open the **auxiliary tripping valve** which allows the pressure in the **lower chamber** and sprinkler system to enter the chamber above the **main valve operating diaphragm** where the pressure has been previously kept at atmospheric pressure by a small passage to the **outlet to atmosphere**. The pressure below the **main valve operating diaphragm** is kept at atmospheric pressure through a piped connection to the intermediate chamber of the dry-pipe valve. Because the area of the **main valve operating diaphragm** is much greater than that of the **main exhauster valve** the latter opens and allows the system air pressure to escape rapidly down to the pressure at which the dry-pipe valve trips. Water pressure through the connection to the intermediate chamber of the dry-pipe valve then enters the chamber below the **main valve operating diaphragm,** balancing the pressure above it, so that the **main exhauster valve** is closed by the spring aided by the flow which has been passing through the valve. Shown is Central Automatic Sprinkler Company Model A exhauster.*

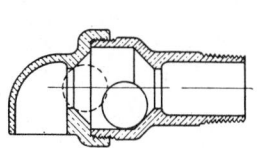

Fig. 14-2M. Automatic ball drip.

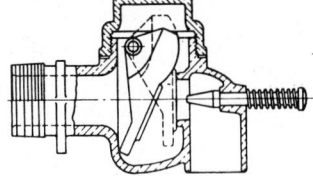

Fig. 14-2N. Clapper-type automatic drip.

with an automatic high water level signaling device or an automatic drain device.)

One common method of avoiding water columing of a dry-pipe valve due to leakage at the water seat is to make use of the intermediate chamber between the water and air clappers. When the valve is set, the intermediate chamber is open to the atmosphere through an auxiliary drip valve. Thus, water entering the chamber through a leaky water clapper will escape from the chamber through the open auxiliary valve. When the valve trips and the clappers take the open position, the auxiliary valve closes automatically to prevent the escape of water.

Some dry-pipe valves use an auxiliary valve normally held open by gravity but closed by a flow of water. On others, the auxiliary valve is held open by a lever arrangement between it and the clapper of the main valve. An auxiliary valve also may be called an "automatic drip" or "drain valve," a "ball drip valve," or a "velocity check valve." Two designs of auxiliary valves not using lever arrangements are shown in Figures 14-2M and 14-2N. These valves reopen by gravity when the dry-pipe valve is reset.

The latched-clapper-type dry-pipe valve does not have the usual intermediate chamber. Consequently, a float-type drain valve may be required to prevent water columning.

Location of Dry-pipe Valves

The dry-pipe valve should be located in an accessible place as near as practicable to the sprinkler system it supplies. It should be protected from mechanical injury. When exposed to cold, it should be housed in a well-constructed, lighted, and heated enclosure which will allow ready access to the valve. The water supply pipe below the dry-pipe valve contains water at all times, and must be properly protected from freezing.

A possible construction for a dry-pipe valve enclosure inside a sprinklered building is shown in Figure 14-2O. If the water control valve is located at the dry-pipe valve, the dry valve enclosure should be of fire-resistive construction and located outdoors, or accessible from outdoors.

Pipes and Drainage

A 2-in. water supply test pipe is connected below the water seat of the dry-pipe valve, and a 1-in. test pipe is installed at the end of the most distant sprinkler line in the highest story.

In some classes of property it may be necessary or desirable to have sprinklers placed pendent, in which case a special type of pendent sprinkler may be used.

The NFPA Sprinkler Standard requires that all pipes and fittings be so installed that they can be thoroughly drained. Where a few sprinklers do not drain back to the dry-pipe valve, provision should be made for special drains at these low points.

If any of the piping system under air pressure is underground, it is necessary to bury it below the frost line. Such piping is of wrought iron or steel properly coated to prevent corrosion. Under corrosive conditions it is advisable

to wrap the pipe in addition to painting or other coating. The piping may also be boxed for additional protection.

Special Locations

In cold storage rooms with temperatures maintained at 32°F or lower, special arrangements of piping and devices are needed to prevent accumulation of frost and ice inside the sprinkler piping, and to permit ready inspection for these conditions. Dry compressed nitrogen in cylinders in place of air will reduce the accumulation of moisture in the system, or propylene glycol or other suitable material may be substituted for the priming water. A small amount of mineral oil added to the surface of the priming water will prevent evaporation. Details are given in the NFPA Sprinkler Standard.

A nonvolatile priming liquid, such as propyleneglycol, may be used for the same purpose.

C. Pre-action Sprinkler Systems

Pre-action systems are designed primarily to protect properties where there is danger of serious water damage as a result of damaged automatic sprinklers or broken piping.

The principal difference between a pre-action system and a standard dry-pipe system is that in the pre-action system the water supply valve is actuated independently of the opening of sprinklers; that is, the water supply valve is opened by the operation of an automatic fire detection system, and not by the fusing of a sprinkler. The valve can also be operated manually.

The pre-action system has several advantages over a dry-pipe system. The valve is opened sooner because the fire detectors have less thermal lag than sprinklers. The detection

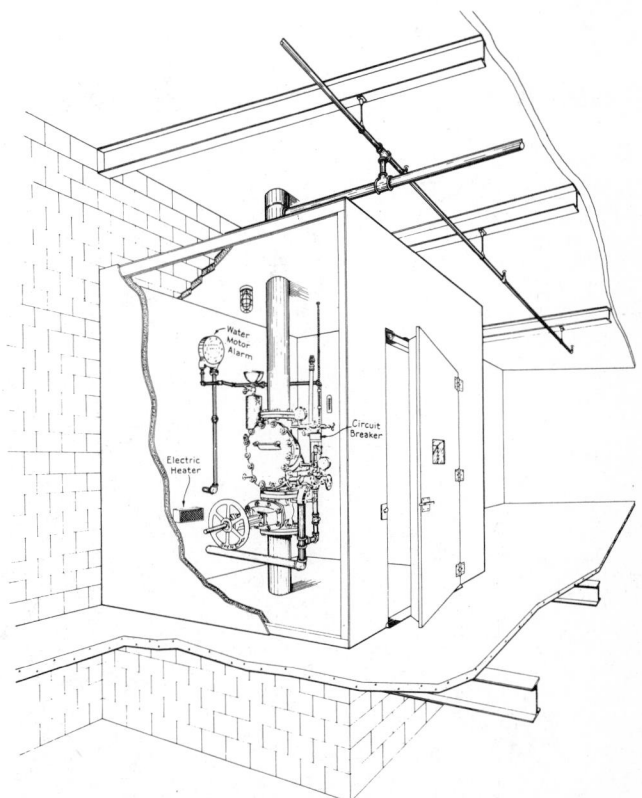

Fig. 14-2O. A permissible type of indoor dry-pipe valve enclosure. (Factory Mutual System)

system also automatically rings an alarm. Fire and water damage is decreased because water is on the fire more quickly, and the alarm is given when the valve is opened. Because the sprinkler piping is normally dry, preaction systems are nonfreezing and, therefore, applicable to dry-pipe service.

The same heat responsive devices and release mechanisms used in pre-action systems can also be used to operate water spray and foam extinguishing systems as well as to actuate alarm and supervisory systems (protective signaling systems) which are described in Section 12, Chapter 2.

The detection feature of a pre-action system can also be added to a conventional dry-pipe system in an arrangement that affords an acceptable means of supplying water through two dry-pipe valves to a system of larger size than is permitted by the NFPA Sprinkler Standard for a single valve. The arrangements of devices used in combined dry-pipe and pre-action systems are described later in this chapter.

Supervision

Piping on early pre-action systems contained air at atmospheric pressure, and water was admitted to the system when the pre-action valve was actuated by the fire detection system. Sprinklers or sections of piping could be removed without causing the system to operate. Subsequently supervision of the system was added by maintaining automatically a very low air pressure in the sprinkler piping. The rate of air supply is made low so that in case of air leakage, the supervisory air pressure will drop and cause a trouble signal without tripping the water control valve.

When a pneumatic fire detection system is used, supervisory air pressure can be maintained in the detection system through a separate flow and pressure control valve. A rapid reduction in this pressure due to air leakage will result in tripping the sprinkler control valve and, in effect, converting the pre-action system into a wet system while at the same time giving the normal tripping signal. Systems using an electrically actuated detection system may be provided with electric supervisory circuits on the detection system which give an audible local alarm in case of circuit failure.

Pipe Schedules and Sprinkler Spacing

The pipe schedules and the rules for sprinkler spacing, as given in the NFPA Sprinkler Standard and summarized in Chapter 1 of this Section, are generally followed for pre-action systems. However, not more than 1,000 closed sprinklers can be controlled by one pre-action valve.

Devices and Equipment

Water-control Valves: These valves control the supply of water in the pre-action system. Manufacturers use a wide variety of mechanical, pneumatic, hydraulic, and electrical devices for this purpose. In general, each manufacturer provides his particular complete combination of water-control valve release, heat detection system, and supervisory equipment. A control valve for a pre-action system is shown in Figure 14-2P.

Heat Responsive Devices: These devices are the most common means of actuating pre-action valves, and the three prevalent methods of heat detection are: (1) devices actuated by a predetermined fixed temperature, (2) devices actuated by a predetermined rate of temperature increase (rate-of-rise), and (3) devices combining fixed temperature and rate-of-rise devices. All of these devices are commonly designated "heat responsive devices," and their operating principles are explained in Section 12, Chapter 2. Illustrations and descriptions of representative approved heat responsive devices as well as flame and smoke detectors are found in that chapter. The same devices also can be used to actuate deluge sprinkler systems (see Part E of this chapter).

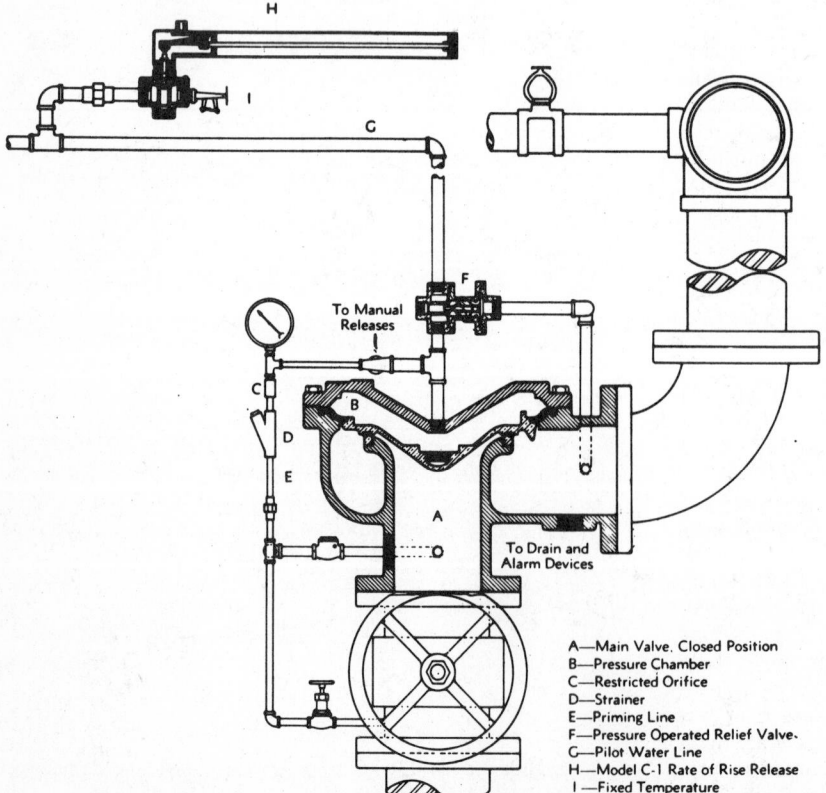

A—Main Valve, Closed Position
B—Pressure Chamber
C—Restricted Orifice
D—Strainer
E—Priming Line
F—Pressure Operated Relief Valve.
G—Pilot Water Line
H—Model C-1 Rate of Rise Release
I —Fixed Temperature

Fig. 14-2P. A special water control valve used in pre-action and deluge systems. The main valve (A) is held closed by the pressure of water in pressure chamber (B) admitted through restricted bypass (C) from the water supply side of the manual control valve. When either rate-of-rise release (H), the fixed temperature release (I) or manual releases on pilot water-line (G) operate, the pressure in chamber (B) is released, permitting main valve (A) to open. Water pressure in the output side of the main valve holds pressure operated relief valve (F) open which in turn continually vents the pressure chamber (B). Shown is the Viking Model D-4 Deluge Valve. Other manufacturers have similar arrangements of proprietary equipment for operation of pre-action and deluge valves.

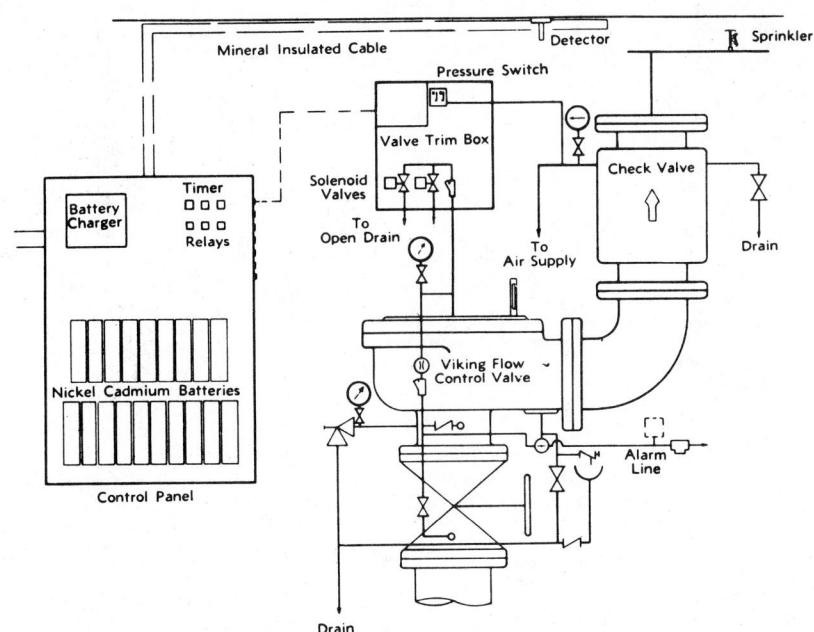

Fig. 14-2Q. The principal components of the Viking Corp. "Firecycle" system, a pre-action system with a recycling feature for controlling water to sprinklers.

Other means of actuating deluge and pre-action valves are smoke detectors, combustible gas detecting systems and automatic signals from process or other safety systems.

Alarms: Alarms are standard accessory equipment on control valves to provide an audible signal on the premises if the valve operates from any cause. Supervised preaction systems also give an audible alarm in case of loss of the supervisory means, or of an accident that would make the detection system inoperative. Alarm systems giving signals at a central station office or which are connected to public fire alarm systems are advantageous and often required.

Tests

One detection device on each circuit must be accessible for test purposes and connected at a point that will assure a proper test of that circuit. Additional information is given in the NFPA Sprinkler and Water Spray Fixed Systems Standards.

Pre-action System with a Recycling Feature

A further refinement of the pre-action principle is a recycling system for controlling sprinklers (Viking Corp. "Firecycle" system). It shuts off the water when the fire has been extinguished, reactivates itself if the fire rekindles, and continues cycling as long as fire persists—all automatically.

Automatic sprinklers are used in the conventional manner. Supply water is held back by a flow control valve that is kept closed by water pressure. Operation of the flow control valve is controlled by an electrical panel which is activated by a system of heat detectors located in much the same way as sprinklers, but with a specific ratio of detectors to sprinklers, depending on the type and use of building and the degree of hazard.

Operation of the Recycling System: Heat from a fire activates the detectors at 140°F which, through closed circuitry, activates two solenoid valves. These valves, upon opening, exhaust water from the top chamber of the flow control valve causing that valve to open and water to flow into the system piping. As sprinklers normally fuse at 160°F, there is a delay during which time water can reach the sprinklers in the fire area before the sprinklers fuse and begin

discharging water on the fire. As the sprinklers bring the fire under control, the temperature decreases until at 140°F the detectors again close the detector circuit. At this point a safety timer is activated, permitting the water to supply the system for a predetermined time. On completion of the timer cycle, the dual solenoid valves close, pressure builds up in the top chamber of the flow control valve and this valve closes. In case of a rekindle or of fire breaking out in another area, the detectors again turn on water when the temperature reaches 140°F and continue to repeat the cycle as long as a temperature of 140°F or higher persists. The system can be reset when the fire has been completely extinguished. Any damage to the closed detector circuit will automatically cause water to be supplied to the sprinklers which will then operate as a conventional wet-pipe system. To insure uninterrupted detector-circuit service, Type MI cable is used for the detector circuit. This cable consists of a copper wire surrounded by magnesium oxide insulating material and enclosed in a special copper sheath.

The "Firecycle" system is shown in Figure 14-2Q.

D. Combined Dry-pipe and Pre-action Systems

The intended purpose of a combined dry-pipe and pre-action system is to provide an acceptable means of supplying water through two dry-pipe valves connected in parallel to a sprinkler system of larger size that is permitted for a single dry-pipe valve by the NFPA Sprinkler Standard.

Although the NFPA Sprinkler Standard does not restrict the use of combined systems to any particular classes of property, such systems were originally developed for protection of piers where long lines of supply piping could have been subject to freezing if a number of conventional dry-pipe systems had been installed along the length of the pier. Due to the complications of combined dry-pipe and preaction systems and the increased possibility of delayed water discharge, it is general practice to install them only in situations where it is difficult to protect a long supply main from freezing.

The Main Features of a Combined System

The main features of a combined system are as follows:

1. A dry-pipe automatic sprinkler system usually with more than 600 sprinklers and supplied by a long feed main in an unheated area.

2. Two approved dry-pipe valves connected in parallel can be used to supply water to a single large sprinkler system. Two 6-in. dry-pipe valves, interconnected with the tripping means for simultaneous operation, are required if a system has more than 600 sprinklers or more than 275 in one fire area. A combination system must have a quick-opening device at the dry-pipe valves.

3. A supplemental heat detection system of generally more sensitive characteristics than the automatic sprinklers themselves is installed in the same areas as the sprinklers. Operation of the heat detection system, as from fire, actuates tripping devices which open the dry-pipe valves simultaneously without loss of air pressure in the system. The heat detection system is also used to give an automatic fire alarm.

4. Approved air exhaust valves, installed at the end of the feed main, are opened by the heat detection system to hasten the filling of the system with water, usually in advance of the opening of sprinklers.

5. Systems with more than 275 sprinklers in one fire area are divided into sections of 275 sprinklers or less by check valves at connections to the feed main. However, not more than 600 sprinklers can be supplied through a single check valve.

6. A means is provided for manual actuation of the heat detection system.

Advantages of a Combined System

Some of the advantages of a combined system include the following:

1. Elimination of the wrapping and heating required for long runs of exposed supply piping carrying water to dry-pipe valves.

2. A substantial reduction in the number of dry-pipe valves required for adequate protection for a given area, and a corresponding reduction in the number of dry-pipe valve enclosures required.

3. Elimination of extensive air-line piping from the compressor to dry-pipe valves.

4. Quick action of the rate-of-rise heat detection system enables water to enter the system piping by the time sprinklers operate.

5. Failure of the heat detection system does not prevent the system from operating properly as a conventional dry-pipe system, while failure of the dry-pipe system does not prevent the heat detection system from giving an automatic fire alarm.

Standard of Performance

To assure the expected action of the system, the NFPA Sprinkler Standard requires that after the action of the independent detection device, water must reach the farthest sprinklers within 1 min for each 400 ft of common feed main, with the total time for the system not exceeding 3 min.

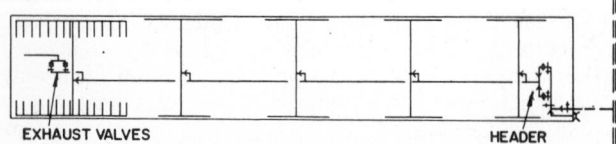

Fig. 14-2R. Typical piping layout for combined dry-pipe and pre-action sprinkler system. See Figure 14-2S for details of the exhaust valves and Figure 14-2T for details of the header.

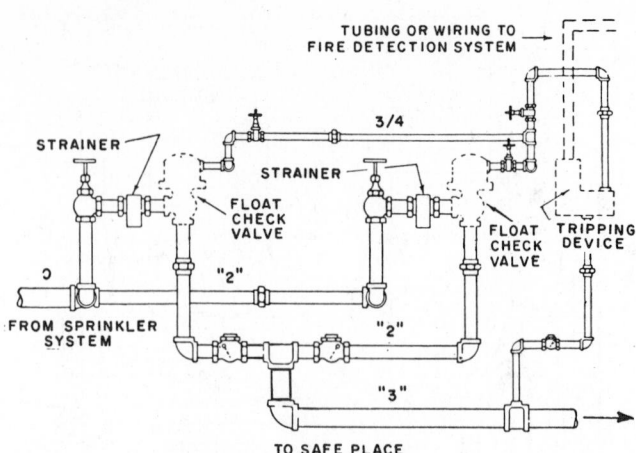

Fig. 14-2S. Arrangement of air exhaust valves for combined dry-pipe and pre-action sprinkler system.

Devices and Equipment

Combined dry-pipe and pre-action systems are not listed as single complete units by testing laboratories, but are assembled from individually tested and approved components. Details of a typical installation supplying more than a total of 600 sprinklers or more than 275 in one fire area are shown in Figures 14-2R, 14-2S, and 14-2T.

Figures 14-2U and 14-2V show an arrangement of devices which make up the basic combination of a single conventional dry-pipe valve and an auxiliary heat responsive system for a sprinkler system of not more than 275 sprinklers.

E. Deluge Sprinkler Systems

The purpose of a deluge system is to wet down an entire fire area by admitting water to sprinklers that are open at

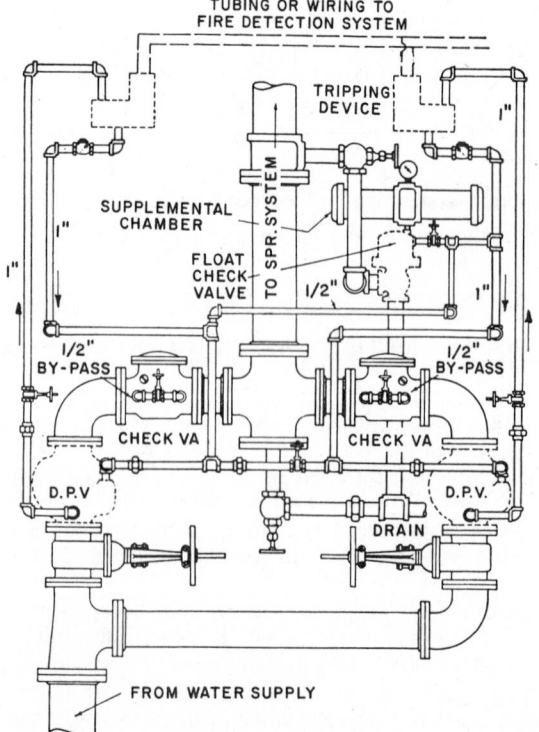

Fig. 14-2T. Header for combined dry-pipe and pre-action sprinkler system. Standard trimmings for dry-pipe valves are not shown.

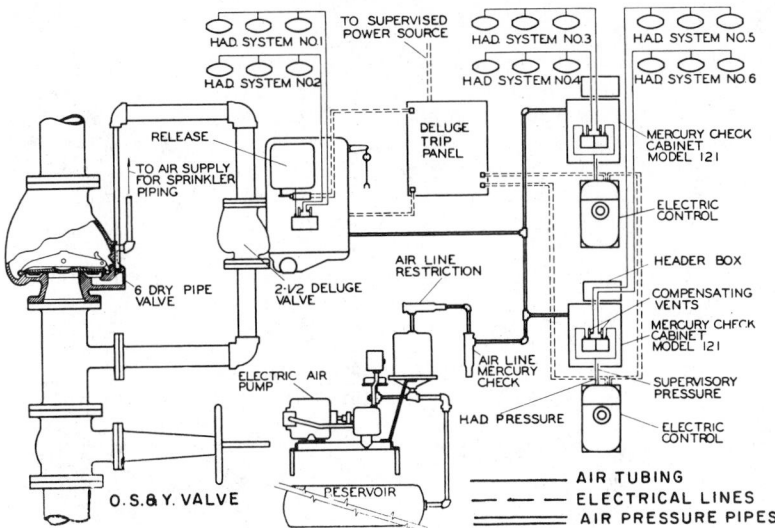

Fig. 14-2U. Components of a combined dry-pipe and pre-action sprinkler system of less than 275 sprinklers. Shown is an "Automatic" Sprinkler Corp. of America system. Other manufacturers have similar arrangements of proprietary equipment for operation of combined dry-pipe and pre-action systems.

all times. By using sensitive thermostatic controls operating on the rate-of-rise or fixed temperature principle, or controls designed for individual hazards, it is possible to apply water to a fire more quickly than with systems in which operation depends on opening of sprinklers only as the fire spreads.

Applications

Deluge systems are suitable for various extra hazard

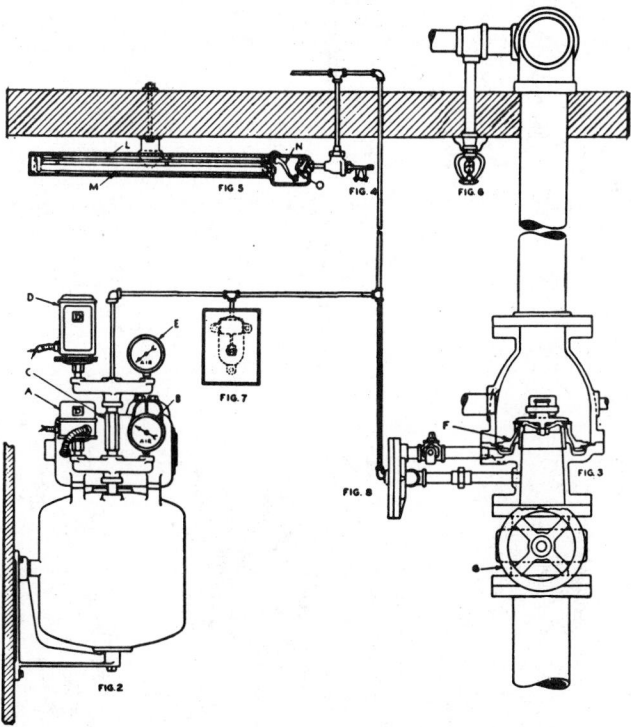

Fig. 14-2V. A combined dry-pipe and pre-action sprinkler system. The dry-pipe valve (Fig. 3) is tripped by either the rate-of-rise release (Fig. 5), fixed temperature air release (Fig. 4), hand release (Fig. 7), or an automatic sprinkler (Fig. 6). The diaphragm bypass valve (Fig. 8) operates when air pressure in the air pilot line drops due to operation of one of the releasing devices. An automatic air compressor unit (Fig. 2) supplies the operating pressure. Shown is The Viking Corp. Model C dry-pipe valve with special accessories for the pre-action feature. Other manufacturers have similar arrangements of proprietary equipment for operation of combined dry-pipe pre-action systems.

occupancies in which flammable liquids or rocket propellants are handled or stored, and where there is a possibility that fire may flash ahead of the operation of ordinary automatic sprinklers. They are also often used in aircraft hangars and assembly plants where ceilings are unusually high and where there is a likelihood that drafts, as from hangar doors, may deflect the direct rise of heat from an incipient fire so that ordinary sprinklers directly over the fire would not open promptly; however, others at some distance would open without effect on the fire.

Deluge systems may also be used to automatically control the water supply to outside open sprinklers for protection against exposure fires.

Open sprinklers and closed sprinklers may be combined in a single system where deluge protection is not needed over the entire area.

The use of deluge or other special types of water control valves as part of a water spray system for the extinguishment of flammable liquid and other intense fires is covered in Section 15, Chapter 2.

Design and Installation

Where deluge systems are used to protect large areas, the water supply requirements may be heavy as compared with those for ordinary sprinkler systems. Also, the design of piping systems and the hydraulic problems involved, particularly where sprinklers are on different levels, as in an arched roof hangar, call for careful engineering.

Pipe Schedule and Sprinkler Spacing

Because all the sprinklers on a deluge system must be simultaneously supplied with water at effective pressure, the NFPA Sprinkler Standard recommends that such systems be hydraulically designed. Systems with fewer than 20 sprinklers may use the extra hazard pipe schedule. Other special requirements given in the NFPA Sprinkler Standard must also be followed.

Spacing of sprinklers closer than usual may be needed to give the desired density of discharge. The sprinkler piping and the water supply should be designed and coordinated to be appropriate for the specific requirements.

Devices and Equipment

Valves: Valves controlling the water supply to deluge systems include a wide variety of mechanical pneumatic, hydraulic, electrical, and explosive squib devices. In general, each manufacturer provides his particular combination of water-control valve, releasing mechanism, heat detection system, and supervisory equipment. A deluge system and its components are shown in Figure 14-2W.

Heat Responsive Devices: These devices should be located and spaced in accordance with their listing by nationally recognized laboratories unless conditions call for closer spacing or special location. For unusual fire hazards, special arrangements are often needed.

Alarms: Alarms are required accessory equipment on control valves, their purpose being to give an audible alarm on the premise if the valve operates for any reason. Alarm systems to give signals at a central station office are often advantageous. Additional information is provided in Chapter 5 of this Section.

Because of the use of heat-responsive actuating devices, special testing facilities and procedures are necessary.

F.   Limited Water Supply Systems

Limited water supply systems are used where a public water supply or other conventional type of supply, such as a gravity tank or fire pump, is not available for sprinklers with sufficient volume or pressure to satisfy the water supply requirements in the NFPA Sprinkler Standard.

A pressure tank of limited capacity is one source of supply in this type of system which, in other respects, is the same as a conventional system because standard sprinklers and standard sprinkler system piping are used. The minimum sizes of pressure tanks recognized by the NFPA Sprinkler Standard for supplemental supply for limited supply systems contain 2,000 gal of water for light hazard occupancies, and 3,000 gal for ordinary hazard occupancies. Approval of plans for all proposed limited supply systems, including the amount of water available for pressure tanks, should be obtained from the appropriate regulating agency. See Part H of this chapter for special sprinkler systems which can, in some instances, qualify as limited water supply systems. See chapters 2 and 3 for a discussion of water distribution systems and water supply facilities.

G.   Outside Sprinkler Systems

The use of a water curtain on the outside wall of a building probably antedates automatic sprinklers. In the early years of sprinkler protection, ordinary sprinklers with the struts removed were used at the peaks of combustible roofs and at the eaves of buildings, particularly wooden buildings. Special types of open sprinklers have since been designed to protect window openings in brick walls. Others have been designed to protect combustible cornices. These sprinklers are placed near the top of the window or under the cornice. The water is discharged against the glass and frame or cornice, thus providing the desired protection.

Theory and Purpose

To be effective, outside sprinklers must wet the entire surface being protected. A water curtain not in contact with the window, the wall, or cornice is of little value, as the water is broken up into drops through which radiated heat can pass. The water discharge patterns from open sprinklers are fan-shaped or quarter spherical, rather than hemispherical as with standard sprinklers.

Because of the large volume of water required to supply an open sprinkler system, this form of protection is ordinarily recommended only when sufficient water is available to supply both open and automatic sprinklers, and any other needs for which there may be a demand at the same time. Where water supplies are limited, other methods of protection are preferable.

Outside sprinklers are usually needed at each floor level, except in the lower stories of multistory buildings where such a large volume of water is discharged from the open sprinklers on the upper stories that it is customary to assume that there will be ample water flowing down to protect the lower windows. Because window sills and other building structural details are commonly designed to deflect rain water away from the wall of the building, a larger quantity of water is required than might otherwise be necessary to wet the surface being protected. The NFPA Sprinkler Standard's provisions on outside sprinkler installations are based on building construction of conventional type with recessed windows.

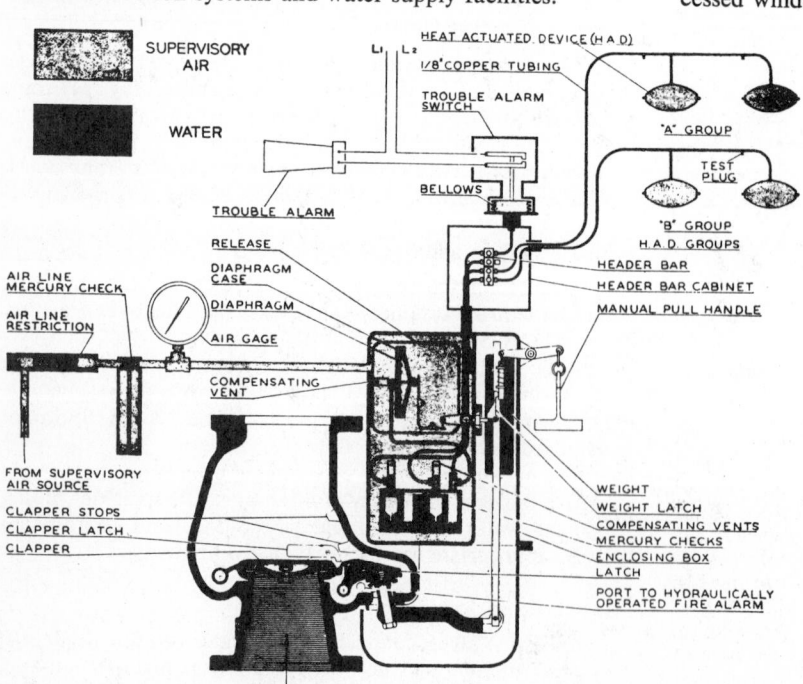

Fig. 14-2W. A deluge system showing the water control valve, weight latch releasing mechanism, and supervisory equipment for maintaining supervision of the heat actuated detection devices which trigger the system in a fire. Shown is the "Automatic" Sprinkler Corp. Suprotex system. Other manufacturers have similar arrangements of proprietary equipment for operation of deluge systems.

Water Demand and Control

The water supply for outside sprinklers should be of sufficient capacity to feed all the sprinklers designed to operate at one time and to maintain not less than 7 psi at any sprinkler with all sprinklers facing the exposure operating, for not less than 60 minutes. Where water supplies feed other fire protection appliances, such as inside sprinklers or hydrants, the system is so arranged that there is no danger of impairing the efficiency of such other appliances. In other words, the water supply should be of sufficient capacity to feed adequately such other appliances when the outside sprinklers are in operation.

Open sprinklers are operated manually by means of valves only where the protected area is constantly supervised. Where automatic control of the water supply to open outside sprinklers is used, the controlling valve is a deluge valve operated by a heat responsive system having thermostats spaced at specific intervals along the wall of a building depending on its height. Where more than one valve is required, the division between the sprinklers on each valve is vertical and not horizontal, and no one valve supplies open sprinklers on more than one side of a building.

Automatic protection against exposure fires also may be secured in some cases by means of automatic sprinklers connected to the sprinkler systems in buildings. Automatic sprinklers so used are equipped with baffles to direct water against the building. In locations where freezing weather is experienced, a dry-pipe valve is used to control the outside sprinklers if the sprinklers in the building are on a wet-pipe system.

Types of Outside Sprinklers

There are two common listed and approved window and cornice types of outside sprinklers. The small-orifice type has orifices $\frac{1}{4}$-in., $\frac{5}{16}$-in., $\frac{3}{8}$-in., and $\frac{7}{16}$-in.; the large-orifice type has $\frac{1}{2}$-in., $\frac{5}{8}$-in., or $\frac{3}{4}$-in. outlets. For good distribution, the small-orifice sprinklers require at least 8 to 12 gpm for each sprinkler, depending on the pressure and the arrangement of the pipes. Similarly, the large-orifice sprinklers require 13 to 30 gpm for each sprinkler. For efficient service, the flowing pressure should be not less than 5 psi at any sprinkler while water is running.

The relative discharge from open sprinklers of various sizes may be obtained from Table 11-6B, Theoretical Discharge Through Circular Orifices (Sec. 11, Chap. 6), applying a suitable coefficient of discharge. The coefficients vary considerably for sprinklers of different types. The coefficient for modern sprinklers of smooth cone pattern is 0.9 or higher; for sprinklers of the ring-orifice type, the average coefficient is about 0.8.

Location and Size of Sprinklers

Small-orifice Sprinklers: Small-orifice sprinklers are commonly used where windows are small or recessed into the wall, particularly when the water supply is limited, or when the buildings are low and not too severely exposed. Where but one horizontal line of window sprinklers is required, the sprinklers should have $\frac{3}{8}$-in. orifices.

Where there are over six horizontal rows of windows, it may be preferable to omit sprinklers over the first story or possibly even the second story windows, but if over six lines are used, the system should be divided horizontally with independent risers, and in some cases this may be desirable even where six lines or less are used. Representative small-orifice outside sprinklers for horizontal installation are shown in Figure 14-2X.

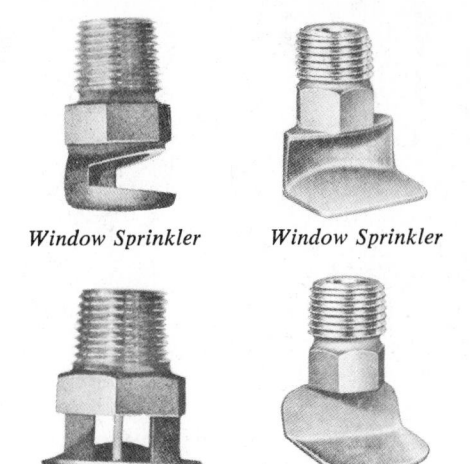

Window Sprinkler   *Window Sprinkler*

Window and Cornice Sprinkler   *Cornice Sprinkler*

Fig. 14-2X. Representative small-orifice outside sprinklers for horizontal installation.

Large-orifice Sprinklers: These sprinklers are used for the upper floors of multistoried buildings. They have deflectors designed to give a wide angle of distribution. The chief advantages of this type are: (1) the discharge of a large amount of water at low velocities with less waste by the splashing of water away from the building; (2) the comparative freedom from clogging; and (3) the possibility of protecting windows of two or more stories with one line of sprinklers.

Large-orifice sprinklers may be used for wide windows, windows in pairs, or for protecting windows in two stories from one line of sprinklers. For buildings not over three stories in height, one line of sprinklers located at the top story windows will often be sufficient.

For buildings more than three stories in height, a line of sprinklers can be used in every other story beginning at the top. With an odd number of stories, the lowest line can protect the first three stories.

See the NFPA Sprinkler Standard for information on the size of orifices for large outside sprinklers used on systems with multiple lines of piping and at windows of various size. Representative large-orifice outside sprinklers are shown in Figure 14-2Y. Areas of orifice, size of pipe threads on nipples, and approximate discharge capacities of large-orifice sprinklers are contained in Table 14-2M.

Sprinklers at Cornices

The same general rules apply to both window and cornice sprinklers, including the size of pipes. The minimum size discharge orifice used for cornice sprinklers is $\frac{3}{8}$ in., and

Window Sprinkler   *Cornice Sprinkler*
for Horizontal Installation   *for Horizonal Installation*

Fig. 14-2Y. Representative large-orifice outside sprinklers.

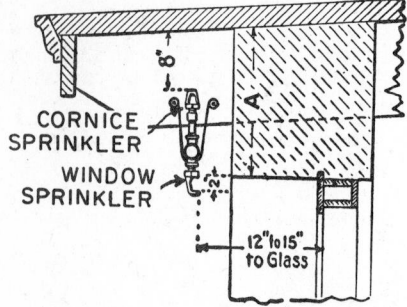

Fig. 14-2Z. Location of window and cornice sprinklers where "A" is less than 30 in.

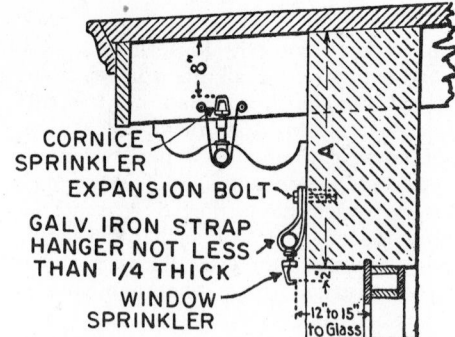

Fig. 14-2AA. Location of window and cornice sprinklers where "A" is more than 30 in.

sprinklers should not be more than 8 ft apart, except severe exposures may require a somewhat closer spacing. Typical arrangements of sprinklers at cornices are shown in Figures 14-2Z and 14-2AA. Special conditions may make modifications necessary. Sprinklers should be placed so that water will wet as much of the cornice as possible. With certain designs of cornices, extra sprinklers may be needed to protect the outside of the fascia.

Wooden cornices which are only a short distance above the windows can be protected by cornice sprinklers supplied by the same pipe used for the window sprinklers. Where the overhang of the cornice is too great to bring the pipe supplying the cornice sprinklers within 15 in. of the wooden wall, a separate line of pipe should be provided for the window sprinklers protecting the wall. A representative arrangement is shown in Figure 14-2AA.

Wooden Walls

For protection of the side of a wooden building, one row of window sprinklers at the extreme top should be used. They should be so arranged that both the cornice and the side of the building will be wet. Protection can usually be provided without the introduction of additional sprinklers for the cornice.

Where the overhang of the cornice is not much over 1 ft, window sprinklers are used and are spaced as follows:

$\frac{1}{2}$-in. sprinklers .... not over 5 ft apart
$\frac{5}{8}$-in. sprinklers .... not over 7 ft apart
$\frac{3}{4}$-in. sprinklers .... not over $9\frac{1}{2}$ ft apart

The window sprinklers are placed above the pipe near the outer edge of the cornice with the deflectors not over 3 in., down from the cornice and at such an angle as to throw the water upward and inward. With an overhang of more than about 1 ft, cornice sprinklers are used to protect the cornice, and window sprinklers to protect the wall.

Sprinkler Pipe Sizes

Risers for exposure sprinklers vary in size, as shown in Table 14-2B. Branch line pipe sizes for exposure sprinklers

are given in Table 14-2C. The NFPA Sprinkler Standard gives specific advice on the application of these rules for pipe sizes to meet the variety of conditions encountered in installing outside sprinkler systems. Problems that must be considered are the arrangement and length of the feed risers, the number of sprinklers on each line, the distance between sprinklers on lines, and the water supply.

Pipe, Fittings, and Strainers

Galvanized pipe or other approved corrosion-resistant pipe is used for the equipment as far back as the control valve on the water supply. Fittings need not be galvanized. Piping should be securely supported in a manner fully equal to that required for inside sprinklers. It is important that all pipes and fittings be carefully arranged and pitched so as to thoroughly drain the entire system as far back as the inside-riser-controlling valve. As an aid to flushing out scale and dirt which may accumulate inside the piping after installation, all branch lines should be extended horizontally 6 in., beyond the end sprinklers, and capped.

Strainers: Acceptable strainers are provided in risers or feed mains which supply sprinklers having orifices smaller than $\frac{3}{8}$ in. Systems having only $\frac{3}{8}$-in. sprinklers shall require a strainer. An acceptable strainer is one having $\frac{1}{4}$-in. screen openings and a ratio of free screen area to pipe cross-sectional area not less than 4 to 1.

H. Special Types of Systems

There are many situations where the installation of sprinklers is advisable, especially for life safety, even though it is economically or otherwise impractical to meet all the requirements of the NFPA Sprinkler Standard.

These types of installations, commonly called "nonstand-dard," involve features that depart from generally accepted

Table 14-2A. Areas of Orifices, Size of Pipe Threads on Nipples, and Approximate Discharge Capacities of Large-orifice Sprinklers

Size of Sprinklers or Orifices	Size of Pipe Thread on Nipple	Area of Orifices or Outlets	Discharge of Ring Nozzles (Coef. of discharge .8) Pressure at Sprinklers		
			5 lbs	10 lbs	15 lbs
$\frac{1}{2}$ in.	$\frac{1}{2}$ in.	.20 sq in.	13 gpm	19 gpm	23 gpm
$\frac{5}{8}$ in.	$\frac{3}{4}$ in.	.31 sq in.	21 gpm	29 gpm	36 gpm
$\frac{3}{4}$ in.	$\frac{3}{4}$ in.	.44 sq in.	30 gpm	43 gpm	52 gpm

Table 14-2B. Risers and Feed Main Sizes on Pipe Schedule Systems

Pipe Size	Number of Sprinklers		
	$\frac{3}{8}$" or smaller orifice	$\frac{1}{2}$" orifice	$\frac{3}{4}$" orifice
$1\frac{1}{2}$	6	3	2
2	10	5	4
$2\frac{1}{2}$	18	9	7
3	32	16	12
$3\frac{1}{2}$	48	24	17
4	65	33	24
5	120	60	43
6		100	70

Table 14-2C. Maximum Number of Sprinklers Supplied on Line

Size of Pipe Inches	Orifice Size—Inches						
	$\frac{1}{4}$	$\frac{5}{16}$	$\frac{3}{8}$	$\frac{7}{16}$	$\frac{1}{2}$	$\frac{5}{8}$	$\frac{3}{4}$
1	4	3	2	2	1	1	1
$1\frac{1}{4}$	8	6	4	3	2	2	1
$1\frac{1}{2}$		9	6	4	3	3	2
2				5	4	4	3

practices. This does not, however, necessarily imply questionable reliability or capacity to handle the specific fire problems for which they are intended. Their use does, of course, require evaluation by one qualified to determine their suitability.

Nonstandard sprinkler installations may involve water supplies of limited capacity, reduced pipe sizes, partial protection, sprinklers with orifice sizes different from those generally used, and other features not typical of standard installations.

Small Capacity Pressure Tanks

A sprinkler system may have a single water supply from a pressurized tank that is of less capacity (2,000 gals) than is recognized by the NFPA Sprinkler Standard for limited water supply systems, and may also depart from the Standard by having reduced pipe sizes, small-orifice sprinklers, or increased sprinkler spacing. These special systems may employ a water supply tank pressurized by air or by compressed inert gas, such as nitrogen or carbon dioxide, from cylinders. Manufacturers of fire protection equipment have supplied, and laboratories have tested, systems of the latter type which have the advantage of using the full water capacity of a tank, with the water being discharged at a preselected, nearly constant pressure.

Chemical Type Systems

Although no longer available for new installations, systems in which the tank pressure is produced by a soda-acid reaction have been approved or listed by the testing laboratories and are still in use. They were suitable for installation in light hazard occupancies where two or three sprinklers and a limited amount of extinguishing liquid (200 gal) could be expected to extinguish or hold a fire in check.

Substandard Water Supplies

Automatic sprinklers having water supplies from public mains, domestic or industrial systems, or other sources not meeting NFPA Sprinkler Standard requirements are sometimes installed to advantage. Such water supplies having pressure and capacity to effectively supply a few automatic sprinklers can provide valuable protection for light fire hazards in limited areas, provided the supply is continuously available. Public water supplies of limited capacity are likely not to be dependable due to varying supply-and-demand relations, small sizes of mains, and frequently long pipe lines. Occasionally, an automatic limited service fire pump can strengthen the supply pressure if sufficient volume is available.

Partial Installations

Installation of sprinklers throughout the premises is necessary for complete protection to life and property. However, in some cases partial sprinkler installations covering hazardous sections and other areas are specified in codes or standards for limited protection in the belief that they provide opportunity for safe exit from the building, to help reduce fire spread, and to improve access for manual fire control.

Partial systems are sometimes used in apartment houses; hotels; dormitories; stores; mercantile buildings with dwellings, offices, or similar occupancies above the first floor; homes for the aged; hospitals and other institutions; some public buildings; etc.

Just what portions of such buildings should be equipped depends on construction features as well as occupancy and fire hazards. For example, in multiple occupancy mercantile and apartment buildings, all portions occupied for stores or similar occupancies, as well as all basement areas, are frequently sprinklered to meet local codes. Many cities have passed special ordinances, some retroactive, calling for sprinklers in the basements of all mercantile buildings. These ordinances are predicated on the following: (1) the life hazard of fires originating in such areas, (2) the heavy concentration of storage frequently found, (3) the inaccessibility of many basement areas for manual fire fighting, and (4) the frequency of fires as shown by the fire records.

In apartment houses, tenements, dormitories, and similar properties of ordinary construction, partial sprinkler protection is frequently called for to cover basements, kitchens, laundries, storerooms, halls, stairways, elevators, and other floor openings.

Attics or spaces between roofs and ceilings of top floors present a special problem, as these portions may not be heated and a dry system may be required if sprinklers are installed.

When installing partial sprinkler protection, reliance cannot be placed on such partial sprinklers to prevent the spread of fire when the fire originates in an unsprinklered area, except in unusual cases. NFPA fire records contain many case histories where such partial systems have been overtaxed by fires originating in such unsprinklered portions.

Self-contained Systems

So-called "package-type" systems, all supplied by pressure tanks, can in some instances meet NFPA Sprinkler Standard requirements for a standard limited water supply sprinkler system. Other systems, because of the smaller capacity of pressure tanks supplying them and other features that depart from the NFPA Sprinkler Standard requirements, are limited to use only in situations where it is impractical to meet all provisions of the Standard.

Special systems with pressure tank water capacities below the minimum requirements of the NFPA Sprinkler Standard may be listed by testing laboratories and recognized by regulating agencies for the limited service for which they were designed. Some of the systems may employ a pressure source from separate compressed gas storage cylinders controlled by regulating valves for expelling water from the tank, while others have the gas supply approved and listed as a complete unit. In still other cases the individual devices making up the system are listed.

The following descriptions and illustrations cover the more generally used special-type sprinkler equipments.

The Aptan System: This system, manufactured by the "Automatic" Sprinkler Corp. of America (see Fig. 14-2BB) is a conventional hydro-pneumatic or pressure tank system of a wet-pipe or dry-pipe arrangement. The water storage capacity to be provided, the size of the tank, and the air pressure to be maintained are selected by the user. The water

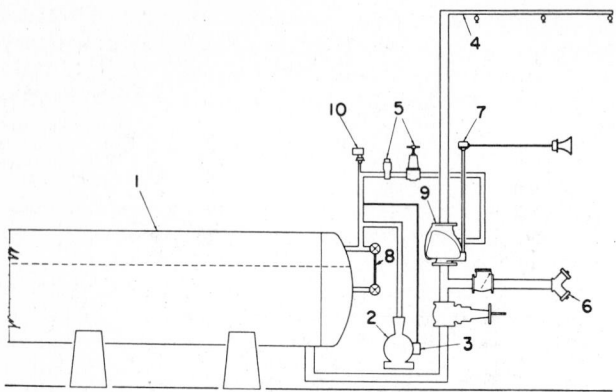

Fig. 14-2BB. *"Automatic" Aptan Sprinkler System.* (**1**) *water supply tank,* (**2**) *air compressor,* (**3**) *compressor motor control,* (**4**) *sprinkler piping,* (**5**) *pressure regulator and solenoid air valve,* (**6**) *fire department connection,* (**7**) *alarm switch,* (**8**) *water level gage,* (**9**) *dry-pipe valve, and* (**10**) *low pressure switch. The arrangement shown is for a dry-pipe system.*

capacity of the tank can be such that the system can meet requirements for a standard limited water supply automatic sprinkler system.

In the wet-pipe arrangement an alarm valve, to give an electric alarm if water flows into the sprinkler system piping, is located in the sprinkler riser slightly below the tank water level so that the valve clapper will be water sealed.

In the dry-pipe arrangement the discharge from the air compressor is piped to a line connecting the pressure tank and the system piping above the alarm valve. This line equalizes the air pressure in the sprinkler piping with that in the pressure tanks, and is arranged to prevent discharge of air from the tank into the riser when water is flowing from the system.

The air compressor is controlled by a pressure switch to maintain the required amount of air pressure in the pressure tank and sprinkler piping automatically.

A low air pressure alarm is provided in the sprinkler piping to indicate air pressure below a selected value.

The Trojan System: Manufactured by the Automatic Sprinkler Corp. of America (see Fig. 14-2CC), the Trojan System has a 500-gal pressure tank filled with water or a nonfreezing solution. Pressure to discharge the water is

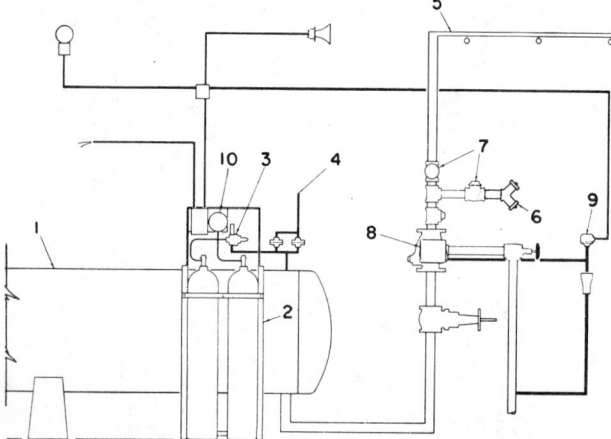

Fig. 14-2CC. *"Automatic" Trojan Sprinkler System.* (**1**) *water supply tank,* (**2**) *nitrogen cylinders stand assembly,* (**3**) *pressure regulator,* (**4**) *discharge vent,* (**5**) *distribution system,* (**6**) *fire department connection,* (**7**) *check valves,* (**8**) *alarm valve,* (**9**) *alarm switch, and* (**10**) *low pressure alarm.*

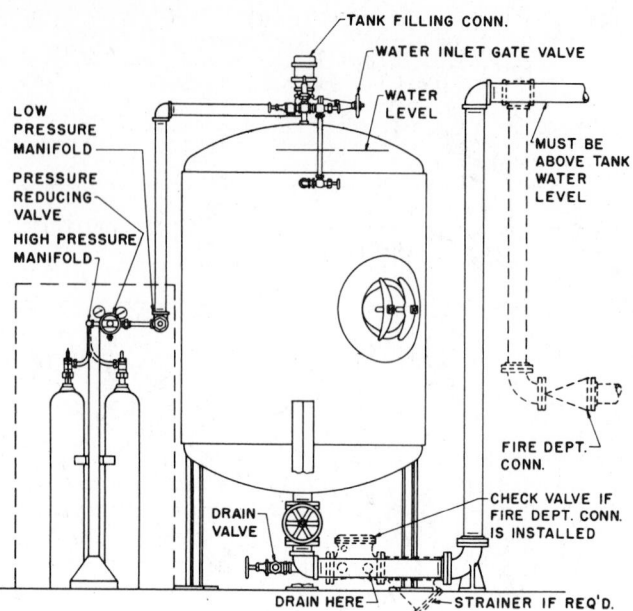

Fig. 14-2DD. *Grinnell Selfcon Limited Water Supply Sprinkler System.*

supplied by nitrogen gas in pressure cylinders with a regulating valve to maintain the desired discharge pressure. The water tank and sprinkler piping are under constant nitrogen pressure. The flow of nitrogen into the piping is restricted so that when sprinklers operate, water is expelled from the storage tank through the sprinklers.

The Selfcon Limited Supply System: This system, manufactured by the Grinnell Company, Inc. (see Fig. 14-2DD), consists of a pressure tank which supplies water to a specially designed piping system with sprinklers or spray nozzles. The tank is not continuously pressurized. When the system operates, the water is expelled by nitrogen gas from DOT specification cylinders at a predetermined constant pressure maintained by pressure regulating valves.

The pressurized gas supply is actuated by any approved automatic method such as one or more of the following: (a) fusible links in the protected area connected to a weight release at the cylinder location, (b) fixed type or rate-of-rise thermostats wired to an electric weight release at the cylinder location, (c) a thermopneumatic fire detecting system with a pneumatic weight release, (d) fixed or rate-of-rise electric thermostats wired to electrically fired discharge plugs at the compressed gas cylinder discharge heads, (e) a thermopneumatic fire detecting system with a pneumatically actuated switch controlling a circuit to electrically fired discharge plugs, or (f) a manual release at the nitrogen cylinder location.

The manufacturer's usual practice is to furnish a water storage tank with a capacity sufficient to supply water over a period of approximately three times that expected to be necessary for extinguishing a fire in the area protected. The relation of the amount of gas and size of regulators to the amount of water is such that all of the water will be expelled at effective pressure.

Simplex System: This system, manufactured by the Grinnell Co., Inc., consists of a standard dry-pipe sprinkler system (without a dry-pipe valve) with a water supply from a pressure tank. The devices used in a Simplex system and their arrangement are shown in Figure 14-2EE.

The air pressure in the tank is equalized with the pressure in the system through restricted bypass "Q" (Fig. 14-2EE).

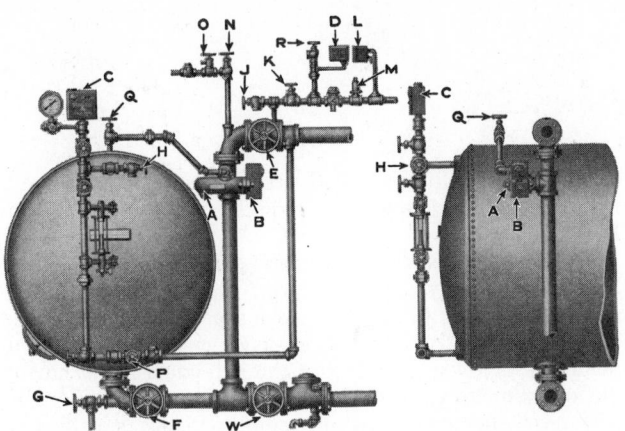

Fig. 14-2EE. Grinnell Simplex System. (**A**) *Simplex special waterflow fitting,* (**B**) *waterflow alarm switch,* (**C**) *low-pressure alarm switch,* (**D**) *air pressure regulator switch to air compressor,* (**E**) *sprinkler system shutoff valve,* (**F**) *tank shutoff valve,* (**G**) *drain valve,* (**H and J**) *blowoff and test valves,* (**K**) *air supply valve,* (**N**) *water supply valve,* (**Q**) *equalizing bypass, and* (**W**) *fire department connection.*

When a sprinkler opens, the pressure drop in the system is much greater than can be equalized through the restricted bypass to the tank. This causes the pressure in the tank to force water from the tank into the system through the discharge pipe.

As the water rises in the discharge pipe, it fills the lower chamber of Simplex fitting "A," and causes the equalizing bypass to be shut off. The bottled-up pressure in the tank continues to force the water from the tank into the system. At the same time the equalizing bypass is being closed, the alarm switch "B" is closed and the air compressor circuit through pressure regulator "D" is opened.

Other Special Systems

Small-orifice: Sprinklers with rates of discharge approximately one-half (⅜-in. orifice) and one-quarter (¼-in. orifice) of that of the ½-in. sprinkler are listed for special service. They are used in small enclosures or for other special conditions for which a reduced density of discharge is effective. They use water economically, and offer a saving in installation costs. A special schedule of piping is usually calculated in order to afford the most effective water distribution with the reduced pipe sizes.

Large-orifice: The established discharge rate of approved large-orifice (17/32-in.) sprinklers is 140 percent that of the ½-in. sprinkler (see Chap. 4 of this Section). They are intended for use where high density of water discharge is needed. They require a special engineering study of spacing and pipe size.

SI Units

The following conversion factors are given as a convenience in converting to SI units the English units used in this chapter.

1 in.	= 25.400 mm
1 ft	= .305 m
1 psi	= 6.895 kPa
$\frac{5}{9}$(°F − 32)	= °C
1 gal (U.S.)	= 3.785 litres
1 gpm	= 3.785 litres/min

Bibliography

NFPA Codes, Standards, and Recommended Practices (see the latest *NFPA Publications and Visual Aids Catalog* **for availability of current editions of the following documents)**

NFPA No. 13, Standard for the Installation of Sprinkler Systems.
NFPA No. 15, Standard for Water Spray Fixed Systems.

Additional Readings

Factory Mutual Approval Guide, published annually, Factory Mutual Engineering Corporation, Norwood, Massachusetts.

Factory Mutual Engineering Corporation, "Automatic Sprinkler Installation" and "Window Sprinklers," *Handbook of Industrial Loss Prevention,* 2nd ed., McGraw-Hill, 1967, pp. 12-1–13-3.

Fire Protection Equipment List, published annually with bi-monthly supplements, Underwriters Laboratories, Inc., Chicago.

Chapter 3

AUTOMATIC SPRINKLERS

As stated in Chapter 1 of this Section, automatic sprinklers are devices for automatically distributing water upon a fire in sufficient quantity either to extinguish it entirely, or to prevent its spread in the event that the initial fire is out of range of the sprinklers or is of a type that cannot be extinguished by water discharged from sprinklers. The water is fed to the sprinklers through a system of piping, ordinarily overhead, with the sprinklers placed at intervals along the pipes.

Since its early use, the performance and the reliability of the automatic sprinkler have been continually improved through experience and the efforts of manufacturers and testing laboratories.

In 1952 and 1953 a radical change was made in the pattern of the sprinkler's water discharge which considerably improved its effectiveness. Originally, this improved sprinkler was called the "spray sprinkler." In 1958 it became the "standard sprinkler," and sprinklers of the older design became known as "old-type" sprinklers. Redesign of the deflector was the principal feature of the new standard improvement.

There are now many types of approved sprinklers which have undergone rigid tests by leading testing laboratories.

A. Operating Principles of Automatic Sprinklers

In order to appreciate the ruggedness, mechanical simplicity, reliability in operation, and freedom from premature operation of an automatic sprinkler, a familiarity with the basic principles of its design, construction, and operation is necessary.

Operating Elements

Under normal conditions, the discharge of water from an automatic sprinkler is restrained by a cap or valve held tightly against the orifice by a system of levers and links pressing down on the cap and anchored firmly by struts on the sprinkler.

Fusible-link Sprinklers: The common fusible-link automatic sprinkler operates upon the fusing of a metal alloy of predetermined melting point. Various combinations of levers, struts, and links or other soldered members are used to reduce the force acting upon the solder so that the sprinkler will be held closed with the smallest safe amount of metal and solder in the soldered parts. This minimizes

the time of operation as it reduces the mass of fusible metal to be heated. A fusible-link sprinkler is shown in Figure 14-3A.

The solders used with automatic sprinklers are alloys of optimum fusibility composed principally of tin, lead, cadmium, and bismuth, and they have sharply defined melting points. Alloys of two or more metals may have a melting point that is lower than that of the individual metal having the lowest melting point. The mixture of two or more metals that gives the lowest melting point possible is called an "eutectic" alloy.

Frangible-bulb Sprinklers: A second type of automatic sprinkler has a frangible bulb operating element (Fig. 14-3B). The small bulb of special glass contains a liquid which does not completely fill the bulb, as there is a small air bubble entrapped in it. As the liquid is expanded by heat, the bubble is compressed and finally absorbed by the liquid. As soon as the bubble disappears, the pressure rises rapidly and the bulb shatters, releasing the valve cap. The exact operating temperature is regulated by adjusting the amount of liquid and the size of the bubble when the bulb is sealed.

Frangible-pellet Sprinklers: Another type has either a pellet of solder (Fig. 14-3C) or other eutectic metal (Fig. 14-3D) under compression which melts at a predetermined temperature and allows movement of the releasing elements. With this type, the fusible pellet is in a small cylinder having a sliding piston or plunger. In a fire, the melted solder or eutectic escapes around the plunger which then can move and release the mechanical parts holding the valve cap closed.

Sprinkler Dynamics

Figure 14-3E shows how the closing force exists in the link- and lever-type automatic sprinkler. The construction shown is diagrammatic and does not exactly represent any particular sprinkler.

The mechanical pressure normally exerted on the top of the cap or valve is many times that developed by the water pressure below, so that the possibility of leakage, even from "water hammer" or exceptionally high water pressure, is practically eliminated. The mechanical pressure is produced in three stages: first by the toggle effect of the two levers, second by the mechanism of the link parts, and third by the load in the solder between the link parts. The last force,

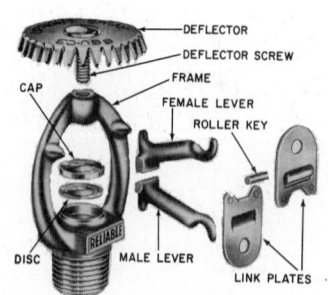

Fig. 14-3A. A fusible-link type automatic sprinkler.

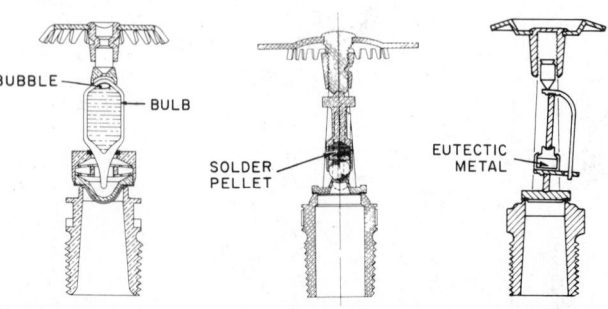

Fig. 14-3B. Grinnell "Quartzoid," Issue D.   *Fig. 14-3C. Star "Stargard," Issue D.*   *Fig. 14-3D. Globe "Saveall," Issue G.*

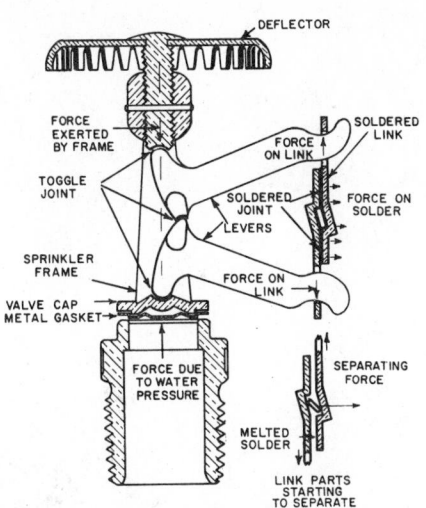

Fig. 14-3E. *Representative arrangement of the operating parts of a soldered-link automatic sprinkler.*

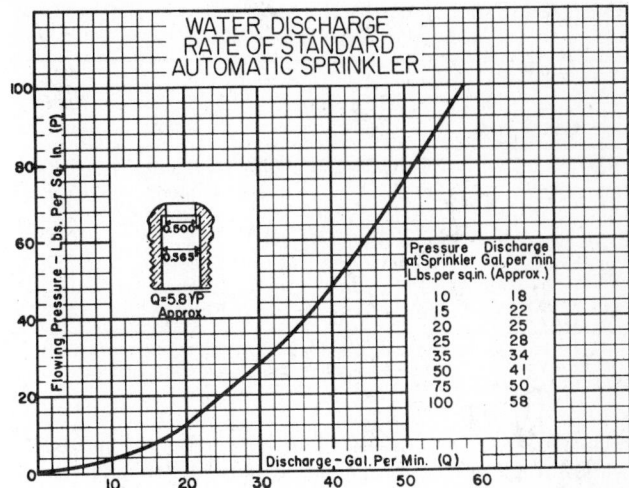

Fig. 14-3G. *Water discharge rate of standard automatic sprinkler.*

resisted by the solder, is made relatively low because solder of the composition needed to give the desired operating temperatures is subject to cold flow under high stress. The sprinkler frame or other parts possess a degree of elasticity to provide energy for producing a positive, sharp release of the operating parts.

Sprinklers illustrated in Figure 14-3F use modifications of the common link and lever construction.

Deflector Design

Attached to the frame of the sprinkler is a deflector or distributor against which the water is thrown with force and converted into a coarse spray designed to cover or protect a certain area. When the sprinkler is activated by the heating of the air around it, the operating parts are released and the water is discharged through the sprinkler orifice and against the deflector. The amount of water discharged depends upon the flowing water pressure and the size of the sprinkler orifice. Seven psi flowing pressure is generally considered a minimum for proper action. At this pressure, a sprinkler having a nominal ½-in. orifice will discharge 15 gpm and cover a floor area of more than 100 sq ft (see Fig. 14-3G for the quantity of water discharged at various water pressures).

In order to have even the minimum flowing pressure at sprinklers that are remote from the point of water supply, especially when a number of sprinklers are operating simultaneously, water supply pressures in the range of 50 to

100 psi are customarily provided. Hydraulically calculated systems are designed around the normally available water supply volume and pressure.

B. Temperature Ratings of Automatic Sprinklers

Automatic sprinklers have various temperature ratings that are based on standardized tests in which a sprinkler is immersed in a liquid and the temperature of the liquid raised very slowly until the sprinkler operates.

The temperature rating of all solder-type automatic sprinklers is stamped upon the soldered link. For other heat-sensitive modes of operation, the temperature rating is stamped upon some one of the releasing parts.

The maximum safe room temperature is closer to the operating temperature for bulb and fusible pellet sprinklers than for sprinklers having soldered fusible elements. This is because solder begins to lose its strength somewhat below its actual melting point.

Any premature operation of a solder sprinkler depends on the extent to which the normal room temperature is exceeded, the duration of the excessive temperature, and the load on the operation parts of the sprinkler.

The general rule of not using sprinklers of "Ordinary" temperature rating where temperatures exceed 100°F is necessary in order to provide a proper margin of safety. General practices regarding the use of automatic sprinklers of higher than the ordinary rating are outlined in NFPA No. 13, Standard for the Installation of Sprinkler Systems, hereinafter in this chapter referred to as the NFPA Sprinkler Standard. Sprinklers of ordinary temperature rating can be used safely throughout the United States inside buildings and other places where they are not subject to direct sun rays, except in monitors and in blind attics without ventilation, under metal or tile roofs, near or above heat sources, or in confined spaces where normal temperatures may be exceeded. (See Table 14-3A.)

When there is doubt as to maximum temperatures at sprinkler locations, maximum reading thermometers should be used and the temperature determined under conditions which would show the highest readings to be expected.

Sprinklers with Intermediate or High Temperature ratings may be used in place of ordinary-rated sprinklers in situations where fast-developing fire or a rapid rate of heat release can be anticipated. The higher-rated sprinklers may

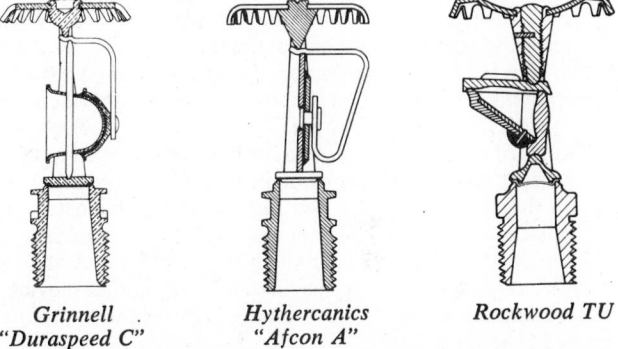

Grinnell "Duraspeed C"   Hythercanics "Afcon A"   Rockwood TU

Fig. 14-3F. *Modification of the common link and lever construction.*

Table 14-3A.   Standard Temperature Ratings of Automatic Sprinklers

Rating	Operating Temp. °F	Color*	Max. Ceiling Temp. °F
Ordinary	135°-150°-160°-165°	Uncolored†	100°
Intermediate	175°-212°	White	150°
High	250°-280°-286°	Blue	225°
Extra High	325°-340°-350°-360°	Red	300°
Very Extra High	400°-415°	Green	375°
" " "	450°	Orange	425°
" " "	500°	Orange	475°

* The frame arms only are colored to show the temperature rating.
† The 135° sprinklers of some manufactureres are half black and half uncolored.

have the advantage of reducing the number of sprinklers which would otherwise operate outside the fire area.

Automatic sprinklers take a minute or two before they operate over an ordinary fire, and may take a longer period where fires develop slowly. The point is that they are designed to operate quickly enough to control fire and prevent its spread. Actually, some delay in operation may be an advantage as it gives time to use hand extinguishers where fires are discovered in their incipient stage. In many cases, fires in sprinklered properties are put out with hand extinguishers before the sprinklers operate. In all cases, however, the fire department should be notified before any fire fighting action is attempted.

The speed of operation depends on the heat-absorbing capacity of the metal parts of the sprinkler. The time involved to operate depends, among other factors, upon the temperature differential between the surrounding atmosphere and the operating temperature of the sprinkler. Where fires develop rapidly, the time until operation of sprinklers is substantially less than with slowly developing fires. The actual temperature rating of sprinklers may be less important than is popularly supposed, and where ceiling temperatures rise rapidly the difference between a 165°F and a 212°F sprinkler may be unimportant.

In the testing of sprinklers, there is no distinction made between makes of sprinklers as to their speed of operation so long as the speed comes within limits that are generally accepted as necessary for proper fire control (usually less than two minutes). Where for any reason it is desired to secure faster operation, sprinklers can be selected accordingly. For example, the Grinnell Duraspeed sprinkler is designed for quicker operation than other Grinnell sprinklers. In cases where extreme speed of operation is necessary owing to the likelihood of a rapidly developing and spreading fire as, for example, in explosives manufacturing, the practice is to use deluge systems (see Chapter 2, this Section) in which the sprinklers are open and there is consequently no time delay in their operation, the water being admitted to the system as a result of the operation of quick-operating fire detecting devices.

C.   Standard Automatic Sprinklers

Standard sprinklers are generally similar in appearance to old-type sprinklers utilizing the same type of frame and linkage or other release mechanism. The essential difference is in the deflector; seemingly minor differences in the deflector design make major differences in discharge characteristics.

Several representative standard sprinklers are illustrated in Figure 14-3H.

Previous research on automatic sprinklers had been

Fig. 14-3H.   Standard sprinklers showing the various arrangements of releasing mechanisms. Clockwise from upper left are a fusible link and lever type (Reliable Automatic Sprinkler Co., Issue C); a perforated heat collector type, which is a variation of the link and lever type (Grinnell Company, Inc., Duraspeed, Issue C); a frangible pellet type (Star Sprinkler Corp., "Stargard," Issue D); and a frangible bulb type (Grinnell "Quartzoid," Issue D).

largely concerned with securing reasonably uniform distribution of water over the area protected by one sprinkler, and with wetting the ceiling, on the assumption that discharge of water against the ceiling was essential to fire extinguishment. Later research showed that more effective extinguishment and a larger area of coverage could be secured by directing all the water downward and horizontally. Research further showed that with this pattern, discharge is effective even in controlling fires on the ceiling above the sprinklers, owing to the improved cooling effect of the spray, better high-level water distribution, and decreased exposure to the ceiling because of more effective direct discharge of water on burning materials below.

Due to the design of the deflector, the solid stream of water issuing from the orifice of a standard sprinkler is broken up to form an umbrella-shaped spray. The pattern is roughly that of a half sphere filled with spray. Relatively uniform distribution of the water at all levels below the sprinklers is characteristic of a standard sprinkler. At a distance of 4 ft below the deflector, the spray covers a circular area having a diameter of approximately 16 ft when the sprinkler is discharging 15 gpm.

Standard sprinklers are made for installation in an upright or pendent position and must be installed in the position for which they are designed. (See Fig. 14-3I.) It is customary to replace old-type sprinklers with standard sprinklers in existing installations although the NFPA Sprinkler Standard permits replacing old-type sprinklers with similar devices. Most manufacturers, however, have discontinued producing old-type sprinklers.

The general patterns of water discharge from the old-type and the standard sprinklers are shown diagrammatically in Figures 14-3J and 14-3K.

Pendent   *Upright*

Fig. 14-3I. An approved and listed standard sprinkler showing the pendent and upright models of the same issue. Note the difference in the design of the deflectors on the two models. Shown is the C.S.B., Issue A.V., manufactured by the C.S.B. Sprinkler Division of the Vogel Fire Protection Co., Inc. Other manufacturers have both upright and pendent models of their currently approved and listed automatic sprinklers.

The water distribution characteristics of sidewall automatic sprinklers and picker trunk sprinklers are described in Part D of this chapter. The water distribution characteristics of window and cornice sprinklers are described in Part G of Chapter 2 of this Section.

Experimentation, engineering judgment, and experience determined that for pipe schedule systems a favorable rate of water discharge from an automatic sprinkler would be that of a $\frac{1}{2}$-in. diameter orifice. This is often not the case with hydraulically designed systems. Therefore, sprinklers of various orifice sizes are utilized. Standard automatic sprinklers have a nominal $\frac{1}{2}$-in. discharge orifice or a $\frac{7}{16}$-in. tapered nozzle orifice of the general forms shown in Figure 14-3L. Both types have about the same discharge rate.

The rate of water discharge from a sprinkler follows hydraulic laws and depends upon the size of the orifice or

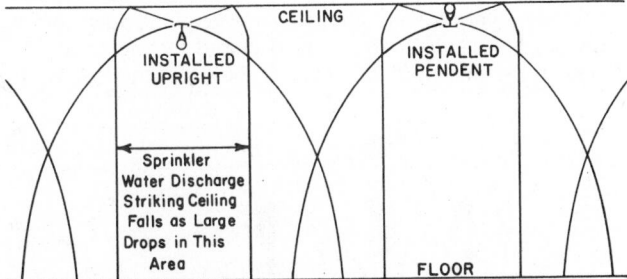

Fig. 14-3J. Principal distribution pattern of water from old-type sprinklers (previous to 1953).

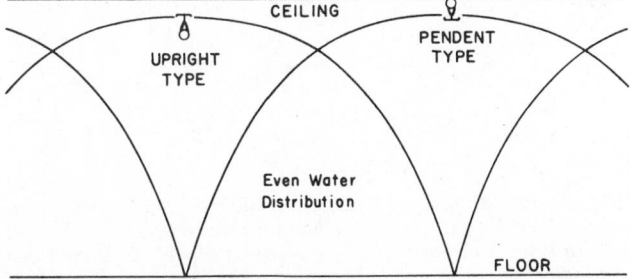

Fig. 14-3K. Principal distribution pattern of water from standard sprinklers (in use since 1953).

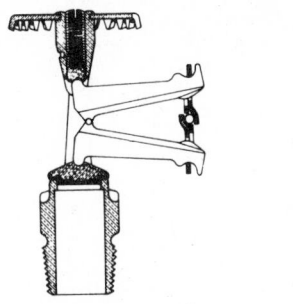 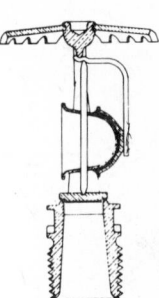

Fig. 14-3L. Typical sprinklers showing a straight $\frac{1}{2}$-in. diameter discharge orifice (ring type) at left and a $\frac{7}{16}$-in. tapered nozzle orifice at right.

nozzle and the water pressure. Approximate rates of discharge at different pressures may be obtained from the plotted curve or the table given in Figure 14-3G.

Sprinklers discharging water through smaller or larger orifices are discussed in Part D of this Chapter. With similar forms of sprinkler nozzles and at the same water pressure, the discharge from these types of sprinklers is approximately proportional to the area of the water opening.

Listed Automatic Sprinklers

In order to obtain acceptance or "approval" of their sprinklers, manufacturers submit them to recognized fire testing laboratories. After extensive tests, sprinklers found satisfactory are listed. Their acceptance by inspection departments or other regulatory agencies is based on such a listing.

Standard sprinklers are installed in their proper position, i.e., upright or pendent, as indicated by a stamping upon the deflector bearing the appropriate word or the letters "SSU" (Standard Sprinkler Upright) or "SSP" (Standard Sprinkler Pendent).

Double Deflectors: Several manufacturers developed a double deflector as their first design for use with upright sprinklers. A typical double deflector is shown in Figure 14-3M. Such sprinklers are as acceptable as the presently approved upright standard sprinklers having a one piece deflector.

Flush-type Sprinklers

Approved sprinklers of special designs but with the same water discharge pattern as standard pendent sprinklers are available for use with wet-system piping concealed above ceilings in areas where appearance is important. A typical sprinkler of this type is shown in Figure 14-3N. Testing laboratories customarily list these special sprinklers as ceiling-type or flush-type sprinklers. The special design allows a minimum projection of the working parts of the

Fig. 14-3M. Standard upright automatic sprinkler with typical double deflector.

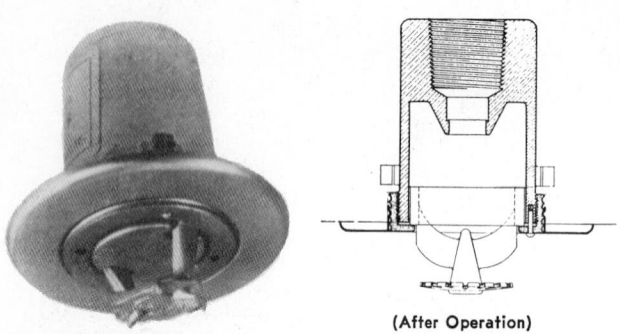

(After Operation)

Fig. 14-3N. A flush-type ceiling sprinkler. This type of sprinkler is used where appearance is considered of prime importance. The model shown is an "Automatic" Sprinkler Corp. of America Issue 38-400.

sprinkler below the ceiling in which it is installed without adversely affecting the heat sensitivity or the pattern of water distribution.

In an effort to render sprinkler protection, more aesthetic sprinklers have been designed that attractively blend into the ceiling material. Only a small round disc is visible from the floor when these sprinklers are installed.

When a fire occurs, the decorative cover (small round disc) drops away (at a temperature of 117°F) exposing the standard operating elements of these concealed sprinklers. When the operating elements reach 165°F, the sprinklers operate normally.

Dry Pendent Sprinklers

When, for appearance or other reasons, pendent sprinklers are needed with a dry-pipe system, water must not be allowed in the drop pipe supplying each sprinkler. Sprinklers designated and listed by approving laboratories as "dry pendent" automatic sprinklers may be used. The valve on each sprinkler which controls the flow of water is at, or slightly above, the bottom of the sprinkler supply piping so that there is no pocket or depression within which ice can form. The heat-sensitive operating mechanisms are adaptations of those used with automatic standard sprinklers. See Figure 14-3O for examples of dry pendent automatic sprinklers.

Ornamental Sprinklers

Ornamental sprinklers are automatic sprinklers that have been decorated by attachments or by plating or enameling to give desired surface finishes. Ornamentation or special decorative design must not unfavorably affect the operation or the water distribution. Approved types of ornamental sprinklers are for pendent installation in accordance with the NFPA Sprinkler Standard (see Fig. 14-3P).

D.   Sprinklers for Special Service Conditions

The standard sprinkler system using approved upright or pendent sprinklers is adaptable to a wide variety of conditions. However, there are situations for which special types of sprinklers and special sprinkler arrangements are suited. Under all conditions of service, it is important to have the distribution of water equivalent in effectiveness to that of a standard sprinkler system. In some cases, such as with sidewall sprinklers, special patterns of water distribution are necessary; in others, unusual temperatures or corrosive atmospheres call for special design or construction features.

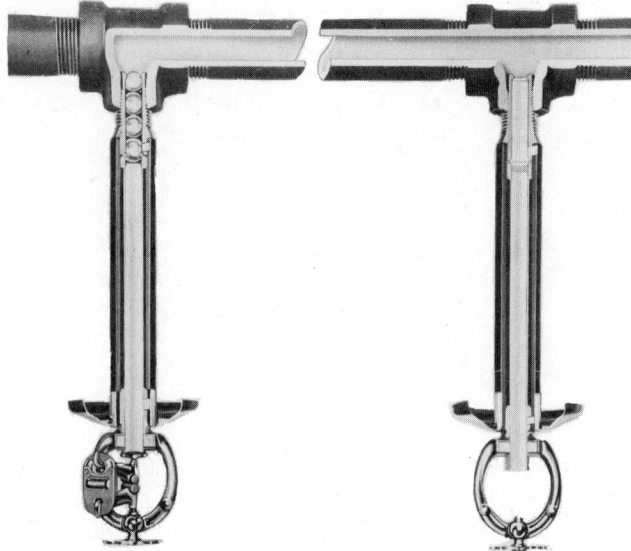

Fig. 14-3O.   Representative Dry Pendent Automatic Sprinkler. When the ambient temperature rises beyond the operating temperature of the soldered link, solder melts and link plates separate on roller key. Levers held in place by deflector screw are released and the fixed tension of the frame, acting as a spring, ejects the levers and link parts clear of the sprinkler. Inner tube, which also serves as a discharge orifice, being no longer held in place by the levers, moves to a predetermined position. With the support of the inner tube eliminated, the elements forming the watertight seal at the piping inlet pass through the inner tube and away from the sprinkler allowing water to flow through the unobstructed waterway striking the deflector which distributes it in a spray pattern comparable to that of a $\frac{1}{2}$ in. standard sprinkler. Shown is Reliable's Model C Dry Pendent. Other manufacturers have similar arrangements of proprietary equipment for dry pendent automatic systems.

Cycling Sprinklers

A recent development by the sprinkler industry is a sprinkler that cycles "on" and "off" as needed. The model shown in Figure 14-3Q, manufactured by the Grinnell Company, operates on a pilot valve principle. Under normal conditions, the pilot valve is held closed by the snap disc. Water in the piston chamber holds the piston closed. When

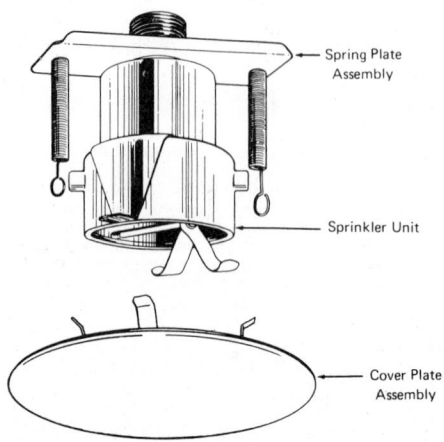

Spring Plate
Assembly

Sprinkler Unit

Cover Plate
Assembly

Fig. 14-3P.   Concealed ceiling sprinkler. Cover plate drops away when heat is applied to bottom side of plate. The model shown is the Star Sprinkler Corporation's Model "G" Concealed Sprinkler. Other manufacturers have similar concealed ceiling sprinklers.

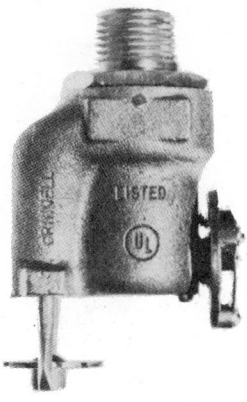

Fig. 14-3Q. An "on-off" pendent sprinkler. This particular sprinkler is used when piping is close to the ceiling or concealed in the ceiling. (Grinnell Company, Inc.)

the snap disc is heated to 165°F, it opens the pilot valve and releases the water from the piston chamber. This allows the piston to open and water to flow from the sprinkler. When the snap disc cools to 100°F, it closes the pilot valve. Water enters the piston chamber through a restricted orifice in the piston, and the difference in pressure forces closes the valve. The sprinkler is ready for repeated operation should the snap disc be again heated to 165°F. Both a pendent and a recessed model are available.

Sprinklers for Corrosive Conditions

Measures have been developed to protect automatic sprinklers from corrosive conditions, and studies have been made by testing laboratories of the value of each method. A complete covering of wax having a melting point slightly below the temperature at which the sprinkler operates is the most commonly used protective coating. A lead coating for the body of the sprinkler and the levers in combination with wax for protecting fusible elements is also common. Wax only, wax over lacquer, wax over lead, wax over lead or chrome, and wax over lacquer over lead or chrome are coatings used on listed sprinklers with temperature ratings from 135°F to 212°F. Lead coatings are used on listed sprinklers for corrosive atmospheres for all ratings of from 135°F to 500°F. Wax-rosin coatings are likewise offered by manufacturers for certain sprinkler ratings in the high temperature range. Enamel coatings of selected softening temperatures and unaffected by age are used for protection against corrosion in two cases for listed devices with ratings of 286°F and 360°F. Glass covers have been used over sprinklers to a limited extent, but the practice is now obsolete, and such sprinklers should be replaced.

Whatever the protective measures taken, they must not delay the fusing of the solder or the action of any other heat-responsive element, to interfere with the free release of operating parts, or alter the pattern of water distribution.

Occasionally automatic sprinkler systems are filled with a calcium chloride solution as a method of preventing freezing. Such systems, however, are usually troublesome to maintain and are seldom recommended. If a sprinkler system is to contain calcium chloride, the sprinklers on it must be made of carefully selected metals to avoid internal corrosion damage to the sprinklers. A number of sprinklers approved for this service are listed by approving laboratories.

Sidewall Sprinklers

Sidewall sprinklers have the components of standard sprinklers except for a special deflector which discharges most of the water toward one side in a pattern somewhat resembling one-quarter of a sphere. A small proportion of the discharge wets the wall behind the sprinkler. The forward horizontal range of about 15 ft is greater than that of a standard sprinkler. Located along the junction between a ceiling and sidewall, sidewall sprinklers provide protection adequate for light hazard occupancies, such as hotel lobbies, dining rooms, executive offices, and others, where the usual sprinkler pipes would be objectionable in appearance. Some sidewall sprinklers have been tested and listed for use in ordinary hazard occupancies. Sidewall sprinklers are not used, however, in situations where a standard sprinkler system can be installed without detracting from decorative schemes. They have been used extensively in light hazard occupancies where special appearance and protection were desired.

The directional character of the discharge from sidewall sprinklers makes them applicable to occasional special protection problems. They may be installed to give discharge in any desired direction.

Figure 14-3R shows five typical sidewall sprinklers. Selection has been made to show the different shapes of a variety of deflectors.

Sprinklers Without Operating Elements

Standard automatic sprinklers, or sidewall automatic sprinklers with the valve cap and heat-responsive elements omitted, are used in deluge sprinkler systems where the water supply is controlled by an automatic water control valve actuated independently of automatic sprinklers. The water distribution pattern and the density of the discharge of the open-head system are designed to be appropriate for the hazard to be protected.

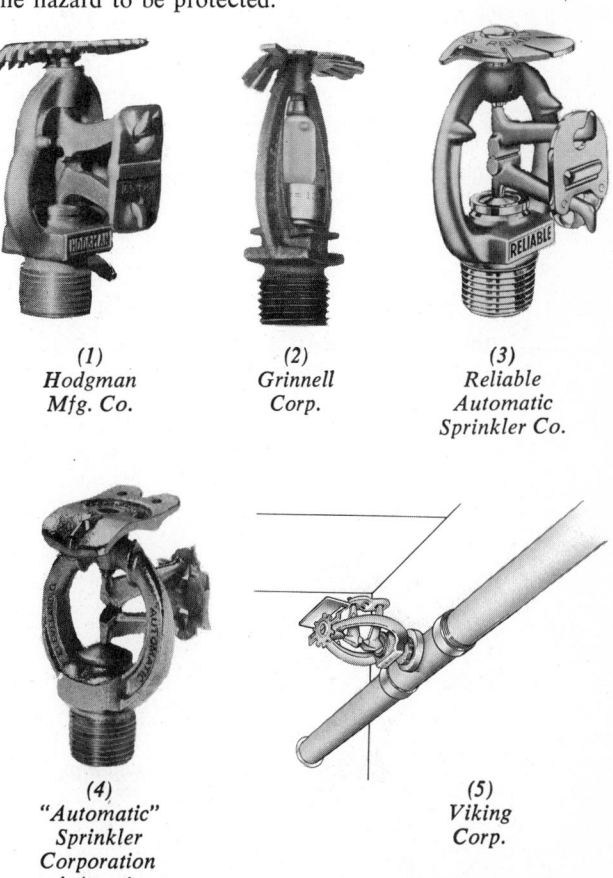

(1) Hodgman Mfg. Co.

(2) Grinnell Corp.

(3) Reliable Automatic Sprinkler Co.

(4) "Automatic" Sprinkler Corporation of America

(5) Viking Corp.

Fig. 14-3R. A representative selection of approved sidewall automatic sprinklers showing various shapes of deflectors.

Small- and Large-orifice Sprinklers

Automatic sprinklers having a water discharge rate greater or less than that of the standard ½-in. orifice sprinkler have a limited use in situations where the density of discharge can be obtained more readily by using sprinklers of different flow capacities than by adopting a sprinkler head spacing that might be impractical under specific conditions of water supply, size of area, and hazards to be protected. The pattern of the water discharge from small- and large-orifice sprinklers is similar to that of the standard ½-in. sprinkler.

The NFPA Sprinkler Standard, while recognizing large- and small-orifice automatic sprinklers, does not give pipe schedules or rules for spacing. Each installation calls for special study.

Whenever sprinklers are replaced, care must be taken to replace them with the proper types. Replacement of correct orifice size is critical in hydraulically calculated systems.

Small-orifice Automatic Sprinklers: These sprinklers have been approved with ¼-in. and ⅜-in. orifices. They have discharge capacities about one-quarter and one-half that of the standard ½-in. sprinkler respectively. Small-orifice sprinklers are identified by a pintle extending above the deflector and by the size stamped on the base of the sprinkler (see Fig. 14-3S).

Large-orifice Automatic Sprinklers: These sprinklers have a discharge rate of 140 percent of that of the standard ½-in. sprinkler and are identified by a ¾-in. pipe connection.

Pull-type Sprinklers

A pull-type sprinkler is a special-purpose sprinkler combining in one unit a frangible bulb automatic sprinkler with a supplementary pull-type mechanical release which can be operated remotely by either manual or automatic means by connection through a pull chain or stranded wire cord (see Fig. 14-3T). This sprinkler may be mounted at any angle required for the protection of the interior of duct work, air filters, or other small enclosed spaces. It may be fitted with either standard or special deflectors which must be selected in advance considering the pattern of water distribution that is desired.

Picker Trunk Sprinklers

Picker trunk automatic sprinklers (see Fig. 14-3U) are sprinklers with a small, smooth deflector which aids in reducing collections of lint and fiber on the sprinklers when automatic sprinkler protection is needed inside ducts or enclosures where moving air carries such foreign materials in suspension. Freedom from obstruction and a general breakup of the water stream are of more importance than any specific pattern of distribution.

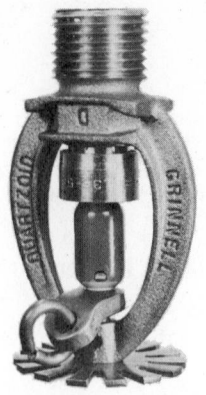

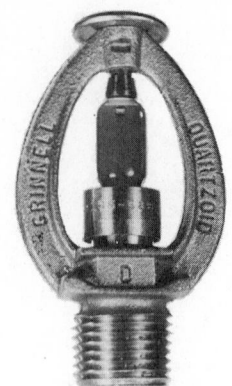

Fig. 14-3T.   A pull-type sprinkler which can be made with pendent or upright deflectors (note mechanical release between the deflector and frangible bulb). (Grinnell Company, Inc.)

Fig. 14-3U.   A picker trunk automatic sprinkler (Grinnell Company, Inc.)

Baffle Sprinklers

To improve the operation of sprinklers suspended at several different levels, sprinklers with large discs (baffles) above the deflectors have been developed. The baffles' primary purpose is to deflect water discharging from sprinklers operating above and away from the fusible element of the sprinklers below. This way sprinklers on several different levels can be actuated during a fire for better protection.

E.   Old-type Automatic Sprinklers

Until the 1955 NFPA Sprinkler Standard was adopted, the present old-type automatic sprinklers were designated as "standard" or "regular-type" sprinklers. These sprinklers were approved for use in either the upright or pendent position. Since 1955 under the designation of "old-type," their use has been restricted to the replacement of sprinklers of the same (old) type. Most sprinkler manufacturers can supply old-type sprinklers of the last models they manufactured before the standard sprinkler was adopted. It is generally considered good practice to replace sprinklers over 50 years old. If not replaced, a representative sample must be tested.

With few exceptions, all parts of the old-type sprinkler, other than the deflector, were retained for the then new standard sprinkler. The model or issue designations also were usually continued. Some representative old-type sprinklers are shown in Figure 14-3W.

Fig. 14-3S.   A small-orifice sprinkler (note pintle on top of deflector).

Fig. 14-3V.   An upright solder-type sprinkler with a 3-in. baffle. (Grinnell Company, Inc.)

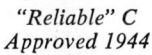

"Reliable" C
Approved 1944   Rockwood D
Approved 1911

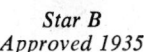

Star B
Approved 1935   "Automatic" A
Approved 1921

Fig. 14-3W. Four old-type sprinklers. Note, for example, the similarity between the "Reliable" C 1944 sprinkler illustrated above and the currently approved "Reliable" C sprinkler shown in Fig. 14-3H. The principal difference is in the design of the deflector.

F.   Automatic Sprinklers of Early Manufacture

Sprinklers of earlier manufacture than the old-type sprinklers are still found in service, although as a general rule they have been replaced with standard sprinklers. In no case should they be allowed to remain in service unless representative samples have been removed and tested in a sprinkler testing laboratory. The remaining sprinklers should be considered dependable only if all of the tested samples operate within time limits considered satisfactory by the laboratory.

Many early types of sprinklers have been produced and installed, and information concerning them is quite complete in the files of testing laboratories. Arrangements can usually be made with these laboratories for obtaining historical information and for testing representative sprinklers removed from systems still in service. A list of the more common types of sprinklers of early manufacture that may be found in service today is given in Table 14-3B.

SI Units

The following conversion factors are given as a convenience in converting to SI units the English units used in this chapter.

1 ft^2	= 0.0929 m^2
1 in.	= 25.400 mm
1 ft	= 0.305 m
1 psi	= 6.895 kPa
$\frac{5}{9}$(°F − 32)	= °C
1 gpm	= 3.785 litre/min

Bibliography

NFPA Codes, Standards, and Recommended Practices (see the latest *NFPA Publications and Visual Aids Catalog* for availability of current editions of the following documents)

NFPA No. 13, Standard for the Installation of Sprinkler Systems.
NFPA No. 13A, Care and Maintenance of Sprinkler Systems.

Additional Readings

Fire Protection Equipment List, published annually bi-monthly supplements, Underwriters Laboratories, Inc., Chicago.
Factory Mutual Approval Guide, published annually, Factory Mutual Engineering Corporation, Norwood, Mass.

Table 14-3B.   Automatic Sprinklers of Early Manufacture
Key: O = Obsolete; Q = Questionable; R = Considered Reliable

Name	Year	Rating	Name	Year	Rating
Associated B	1914	(R.)	J. Kane 4	1902	(Q.)
Cataract A	1906	(O.)	J. Kane 4½	1902	(Q.)
Cataract B	1907	(Q.)	Lapham B	1911	(Q.)
Clayton	1906	(O.)	Manufacturers B	1903	(Q.)
Esty 6	1903	(Q.)	Manufacturers C	1907	(Q.)
Evans B	1914	(R.)	Nacey A	1922	(R.)
Garrett	1906	(Q.)	Neracher 5	1902	(Q.)
Garth (Canadian)	1905	(O.)	Neracher 6	1902	(Q.)
Garth A (Canadian)	1914	(O.)	New York	1911	(O.)
Globe Garrett A	1911	(Q.)	Niagara-Hibbard A	1902	(Q.)
Globe B	1914	(R.)	Niagara-Hibbard B	1904	(Q.)
Grimes C	1925	(R.)	Niagara B	1912	(R.)
Grinnell A.B.C.D. (Metal Disc)	1882–1900	(O.)	Phoenix A	1905	(O.)
			"Reliable" A	1921	(R.)
Grinnell A (Glass Disc— Improved)	1903	(R.)	Rockwood A	1906	(O.)
			Rockwood B	1906	(R.)
			Rockwood C	1910	(R.)
Grinnell Silica Bulb	1923	(R.)	Rockwood E	1934	(R.)
Hibbard 4	1901	(O.)	Rundell Spence A	1913	(O.)
Hibbard H & I	1911	(R.)	Simplex	1902	(O.)
Hodgman A	1920	(R.)	Standard	1902	(O.)
Ideal A	1914	(O.)	Star A	1925	(R.)
Independent A	1916	(R.)	U.S.B.	1923	(R.)
International I	1900	(O.)	Viking A	1921	(R.)
International B	1906	(Q.)	Viking B	1935	(R.)
International C	1927	(R.)	Vogel (Laconia)	1904—English	(Q.)
J. Kane 3	1900	(O.)	Witter E	1906—English	(Q.)

NOTE: NFPA No. 13A, Care and Maintenance of Sprinkler Systems, and the American Insurance Association in its "Suggested Procedure for Testing Field Samples of Automatic Sprinklers" (AIA 13D) suggest that all sprinklers that have been in service for 50 years should be replaced without testing.

Chapter 4

WATER SUPPLIES FOR SPRINKLER SYSTEMS

It is vital that every automatic sprinkler system have a water supply of adequate pressure, capacity, and reliability. Both the rate of flow and the total volume that may be needed must be considered.

A. Types of Supplies

Sprinkler systems may be supplied with water from one or a combination of sources, such as street mains, gravity tanks, reservoirs, fire pumps, pressure tanks, rivers, lakes, wells, etc. (see Fig. 14-1F).

In theory, a single water supply would seem to be all that is necessary for satisfactory protection. However, that single supply may at times be temporarily out of service; it may be disabled at the time of a fire or before a fire is completely extinguished; or the pressure or the capacity may be below normal during an emergency. Therefore, a secondary supply may be necessary, depending on the strength and reliability of the primary supply, the value and importance of the property, the area, height and construction of the building, the occupancy, and the outside exposures. Occasionally, three supplies are needed, especially where neither the primary nor a single secondary supply is judged wholly satisfactory or reliable.

Connections to Public Water Works Systems

A connection from a reliable public water works system of adequate capacity and pressure is the preferred single or primary supply for automatic sprinkler systems. In determining its adequacy, consideration has to be given not only to the normal capacity and pressure of the system, but also to the probable minimum pressures and flows available at unfavorable times such as during summer months, during heavy demand on the system, or during impairment caused by flood or by winter conditions.

The size and arrangement of street mains and feeders from public water supplies are also important. Connections from large mains fed two ways or from two mains on a gridiron system may provide an excellent supply. Street mains less than 6 in. in diameter are usually inadequate and unreliable. Feeds from dead-end mains are also undesirable.

Water meters, if required by the water supply authority, should be of types approved for fire service (see Sec. 11, Chap. 2).

Flow and pressure tests under varying conditions of demand are generally necessary to determine the amount of public water available for fire protection. The proper method of making such tests is described in Section 13, Chapter 5.

Cross-connections Between Public and Private Supplies

Where a secondary supply is needed to supplement the public water supply, public and private supplies can be connected so as to feed into a single fire protection system. These systems are commonly referred to as being "cross-connected."

In some localities, cross-connections may be prohibited by health authorities.

Where they are not prohibited, regulations and sound practices must be complied with in order to avoid the possibility of public health being endangered by water of questionable potability entering the public system.

In general, cross-connections are permitted if carefully supervised precautions, such as a special double check valve, or other accepted devices for preventing backflow, are provided. In cases where one sprinkler supply is from public mains, health authorities usually permit, as a secondary source, either well constructed and well maintained covered steel tanks or concrete reservoirs that are filled with public water only.

Gravity Tanks

Gravity tanks of adequate capacity and elevation make a good primary supply and may be acceptable as a single supply. Details of the construction, heating, and maintenance of gravity tanks are given in NFPA No. 22, Standard for Water Tanks for Private Fire Protection, hereinafter in this chapter referred to as the NFPA Water Tank Standard (see also Sec. 11, Chap. 3 of this HANDBOOK). In determining tank size and elevation, consideration should also be given to the number of sprinklers expected to operate, duration of operation, the arrangement of underground supply piping, and the provision of hose standpipes, hydrants, and fire department connections.

Fire Pumps

A fire pump having both a reliable source of power and a reliable suction water supply provides a good secondary supply and in some instances is acceptable as a primary supply. With ample water a fire pump is capable of maintaining a high pressure over a long period of time, and may be a necessary part of some installations requiring greater water pressure than would otherwise be available.

For details of power sources, pump construction, installation, and methods of control and operation, NFPA No. 20, Standard for Centrifugal Fire Pumps, should be consulted (see also Sec. 11, Chap. 3 of this HANDBOOK).

Manually controlled pumps may be used if the primary water supply will last long enough to allow dependable starting of the fire pump, and if there is an automatic waterflow signal to make known the need for fire pump operation.

Automatic control of fire pumps is usually needed where a high water demand may occur immediately, as with a deluge system; or where a competent pump operator is not continuously present. Automatic fire pumps should have their suction under a positive head to avoid the delays and uncertainties of priming.

Under favorable circumstances of moderate property values and hazards, dependable power, and a dependable suction supply under a head, an electrically driven, automatically controlled fire pump supervised from a central station may be accepted as the primary supply for automatic sprinklers.

The automatic control of electrically driven centrifugal pumps must be arranged to prevent frequent repeated starting of the motor, either by initiating continuous running until stopped manually, or by a timing device that will stop the motor automatically only after a predetermined period of operation.

Pressure Tanks

Pressure tanks have several possible uses in automatic sprinkler protection. An important limitation is the small volume of water which can be stored in such tanks. Where a small pressure tank is accepted as the water supply, the system is classed as a Limited Supply System.

In situations where an adequate volume of water can be supplied by a public or private source but where the pressure is not sufficient to serve a sprinkler system directly, the pressure tank gives a good starting pressure for the first sprinklers that operate; the flow from it may be used while the fire pumps start automatically to increase the supply pressure.

In tall buildings where the public water pressure is too low for effective water distribution from the highest sprinklers, pressure tanks may be used to supply such sprinklers during the time required for a public fire department to begin supplying water through fire department connections.

Each proposed use of pressure tanks calls for special consideration and analysis of water capacity, location, and arrangement of the connection to the sprinkler system. Each installation is usually required to have specific approval. Details on the construction, installation, and maintenance of pressure tanks are given in the NFPA Water Tank Standard (see also Sec. 11, Chap. 3 of this HANDBOOK).

Fire Department Connections

Under fire conditions which result in a considerable number of sprinklers operating, public water or tank supplies may not provide water at sufficient pressure for effective discharge and distribution. Also, the pressure in many public water supplies to sprinkler systems may be materially reduced by hose streams from hydrants. In such cases, a connection through which the public fire department can pump water into the sprinkler system provides an important auxiliary supply. Fire department connections are therefore a standard part of sprinkler systems.

Fire department connections should be of approved type, readily accessible, and properly marked. Each connection should be fitted with a check valve, but not with a gate valve. There should be a proper drain, and an approved drip

Fig. 14-4A. Fire fighters attaching hose lines to a fire department (siamese) connection supplying a sprinkler system. The inset shows typical siamese connections for sprinkler systems and standpipes. A check valve allows the use of a single hose line.

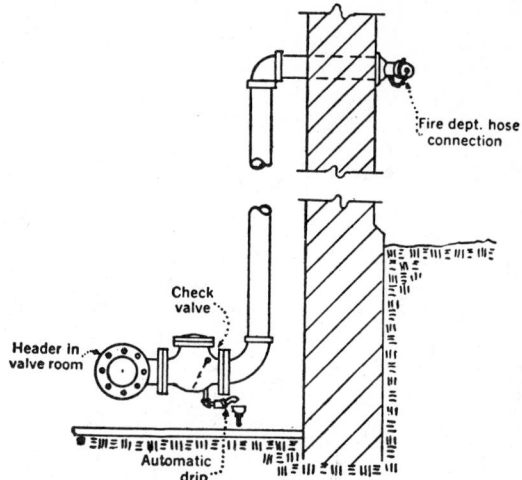

Fig. 14-4B. Typical fire department connection.

device between the check valve and the outside hose coupling. Figures 14-4A and 14-4B show the main features of a fire department connection. Other details of installation and pipe size are given in NFPA No. 13, Standard for the Installation of Sprinkler Systems, hereinafter referred to in this chapter as the NFPA Sprinkler Standard.

Where a sprinkler system has a single riser, the fire department connection should be attached to the system side of the controlling gate valve for a wet system, and between the dry-pipe valve and the gate valve for a dry system. This makes it possible to pump water into the system even if the gate valve is closed.

If there are two or more sprinkler system risers connected to a public main, each system must have its own fire department connection. If more than one riser is connected to a yard system, the fire department connection should feed into the yard system on the supply side of all riser shutoff valves, and there must be a check valve in all other water supply connections into the yard system to prevent backflow and loss of water supplied through the fire department connection. If one riser is shut off, the fire department connection can still supply all other risers.

In an emergency, a fire department can pump water from public hydrants or other sources of water into a sprinkler system through its hose and a yard hydrant or other hose connection using a double female hose coupling, if other supply connections have a check valve or a gate valve that can be closed.

B. Water Supply Requirements

The water supply needed for sprinkler systems raises questions that defy specific answers except with sprinkler systems where it is planned that all sprinklers in the fire area will discharge water. Such systems include deluge and water spray systems utilizing open sprinklers where the design must provide water supply for all the sprinklers in any fire area, systems employing closed automatic sprinklers in hazardous areas where the simultaneous operation of all sprinklers is usually assumed, and multiple open sprinkler systems in a single fire area where one or more systems can be expected to operate. With such sprinkler systems (largely used for special hazard situations) the water supply requirement resolves itself mainly into a matter of hydraulic and mathematical calculations. The answer to the water supply requirement with the majority of sprinkler systems, however, is not so definite. If a water source that could supply all the sprinklers is available, there would be no problem, but such a water supply is seldom practical except in the case of small systems. The water supply requirement for any sprinkler system is directly related to the number of sprinklers expected to operate, but this depends on so many variables and uncertain factors that no exact mathematical solution is possible.

The NFPA Sprinkler Tables show that in 93 percent of all fires in sprinklered buildings, twenty or less sprinklers opened. Experience shows that with adequate water supply the percentage of unsatisfactory sprinkler performance is extremely small. Thus, water supply is a significant problem, particularly with large sprinkler systems and with systems protecting greater than ordinary hazards.

The answer to the water supply requirement for any particular sprinkler system lies mainly in experienced engineering judgment, based on consideration of the factors for or against sprinkler control. Where the cooling effect from the water discharged by sprinklers is greater than the heat liberated by the fire, the sprinklers can gain control. When the reverse situation occurs, as from an overtaxed water supply, the sprinklers cannot control the fire and the sprinkler system may fail. Where all conditions are favorable, the control of fire should be accomplished by the operation of only a small number of sprinklers. As conditions vary, however, with different classes of occupancy, areas, and types of buildings, the number of sprinklers expected to operate in order to control a fire may range up to possibly the total number in the area, and the water supply should be provided accordingly. (See Fig. 14-1D for cumulative data for the various numbers of sprinklers operating in fires.)

C. Influence of Various Factors on Water Supply Need

The primary factors affecting the number of sprinklers which might open in a fire, and therefore to be considered in determination of the water supply requirement, include the following:

Hazard of Occupancy, Including Flash Fire Hazard and Potential Rate of Heat Liberation: This is the most important factor, and one involving experienced judgment to evaluate. Where the flash fire hazard is present, it is usually necessary to provide water sufficient for the operation of all the sprinklers in any individual fire area.

Initial Water Pressure: At a pressure of 15 psi, a standard sprinkler will discharge about 22 gpm, or an average of 0.17 gal per sq ft per min on an area of 130 sq ft. At 30 psi, the discharge is 33 gpm; at 50 psi, 41 gpm; and at higher pressures the discharge is correspondingly greater, also with a greater area of coverage. With a greater discharge and greater area of coverage, there is a better chance of fire control with a small number of sprinklers, and less need for large volumes of water to supply a large number of sprinklers.

Obstructions to Distribution of Water from Sprinklers, such as High-piled Stocks, Bale Tiering, Pallets, Racks, and Shelving: With obstruction, there is less likelihood that fire will be controlled in its initial stages, and a greater chance of opening a large number of sprinklers needing large water supplies.

High Ceilings and Draft Conditions: With ceilings of unusual height, there is greater chance that drafts will carry heat away from the sprinklers immediately over a fire, resulting not only in delay in the application of water but also in the opening of sprinklers remote from the place of origin of the fire. More water is usually needed under such

conditions. The same situation exists wherever there are drafts, such as in areas open to the weather on the sides, where winds can divert heat from sprinklers over the fire.

Unprotected Vertical Openings: Sprinkler systems in multistory buildings are usually designed on the assumption that fire will be controlled on the floor of origin. Where there are unprotected openings up which heat and fire may spread, it may be expected that more sprinklers will open, particularly in the case of a fire originating near the vertical opening. In case of high combustibility, the interconnected floors may need to be considered as one fire area. This means more water and larger pipe sizes in risers and supply main.

Wet or Dry System: Owing to the delay due to exhausting air from dry-pipe systems, more sprinklers open on dry-pipe systems than on wet systems. This may call for greater water supplies.

Size of Undivided Areas: A large undivided area has a greater number of sprinklers, with a possibility of a greater maximum number of sprinklers operating, and a consequently greater water demand than with a small area.

Configuration and Type of Ceiling Construction: These influence water demand, including such factors as curtain boards, or beams affording curtain board effects to retard fire spread, and the possibility that fire may spread under a combustible ceiling out of reach of sprinklers or burn through.

Extent of Coverage and Exposures: Any fire in an unsprinklered space extending to an area with automatic sprinklers places an abnormal demand on the sprinkler system, and requires increased water supplies for effective functioning of the system.

The preceding factors must be considered individually and collectively, and it is not feasible to derive any general formula or simple method of arriving at water supply requirements.

There are, however, certain general statements on this subject that may be made. One is that any situation may be effectively protected with much less water where the water is applied automatically rather than manually. Another is that it is good practice to provide more water, at higher pressure, than will probably be needed to extinguish any fire. Hose streams may be used to supplement sprinklers, even when not necessary, and an ample supply of water provides a margin of safety.

With a very large fire area of low to moderate hazard it is not reasonable to expect to supply all sprinklers simultaneously. Actually, the pipe sizes are not large enough to do so, except where very high supply pressures can produce a high discharge rate from sprinklers near the source of supply as well as effective discharge from the most remote sprinkler. This situation is aggravated where sprinkler supply is from an end or side of the system. The most effective piping pattern calls for sprinkler risers at the center.

The managers of large properties under sprinkler protection may, by "shopping," secure insurance coverage predicated on water supplies that are "shaded" for economy. Obtaining the desired coverage does not mean that, measured in terms of true fire safety, the property is sufficiently protected. Property owners who realize that any fire may cause indirect losses far beyond any insurance indemnity will consider full protection essential.

D. Water Supply Requirements for Pipe Schedule Sprinkler Systems

Notwithstanding the general problems involved in arriving at water supply requirements, the hazard of occupancy, being the factor of major importance, has made it possible to establish "Guides to Water Supply Requirements for Sprinkler Systems" using this factor as the primary consideration with latitude allowed for the contributing factors.

The established "Guide" tables contained in the NFPA Sprinkler Standard divide hazards of occupancy, for the purpose of determining water supplies, into several groups with specified minimum water supplies for each group (see Table 14-4A).

Where fire pumps contribute to the water supply, standard sizes of pumps should be used with adequate rate of discharge, as outlined in Section 11, Chapter 4. A suction supply for the pump should preferably be large enough for continuous operation, as outlined in Section 11, Chapter 4.

Where pressure tanks furnish the water supply, the provisions for pressure tanks in Section 11, Chapter 3, should be followed.

Where a combination of different water supplies is provided in the interest of reliability, it is good practice to have the rate of supply from each source at least equal to the minimum requirement for the system.

The "Guide" should be used only with experienced judgment, but it can serve for all cases qualifying in the Light Hazard and Ordinary Hazard, Groups 1 and 2, occupancy classifications which constitute the larger percentage of sprinkler installations. The other occupancy classifications usually involve more complex factors, and therefore require special consideration.

Light Hazard Occupancies

Examples of Light Hazard Occupancies are apartment buildings, dormitories, office buildings, seating areas of restaurants, and hospitals. In these occupancies the potential rate of heat liberation is low, areas are usually subdivided, and a small number of sprinklers should normally control any fire. Under these conditions, 500 gpm should generally be sufficient, with an upward range to 750 gpm where conditions are less favorable.

Ordinary Hazard, Group 1, Occupancies

The Ordinary Hazard, Group 1 classification includes occupancies where the combustibility of contents is generally low, such as in garages, bakeries, laundries, and canneries, but is greater than for the Light Hazard classification. In this group the water supply requirement may be as low as 700 gpm where small areas, noncombustible construction, and very limited hazards are encountered; it can range up to 1,000 gpm as these conditions become more adverse.

Ordinary Hazard, Group 2, Occupancies

Ordinary Hazard, Group 2 classification includes occupancies such as clothing factories, mercantiles, pharmaceutical manufacturing, and shoe factories. With this group the features of combustibility of contents, ceiling heights, and obstruction are generally unfavorable, separately or jointly, and as indicated the water supply requirements may range as high as 1,500 gpm. It will be noted, however, that an 850 gpm minimum is retained for this group and this, of course, would be applicable only under very favorable conditions.

Water supply requirements for the three classes mentioned, as in all cases, call for a careful consideration of all factors concerned, but the figures given in Table 14-4A are of value in placing lower and upper limits for the classes concerned. While it is never advisable to provide less than the lower limit indicated, the upper limit will usually be sufficient for all situations within the group classification.

Ordinary Hazard, Group 3, Occupancies

Ordinary Hazard, Group 3, consists of occupancies where standard sprinkler spacing and pipe schedules are considered satisfactory, but where more than ordinary water supplies are advisable. This group includes certain woodworkers and other occupancies such as flour and feed mills, paper mills, piers and wharves, and tire storage.

Table 14-4A. Guide to Water Supply Requirements for Pipe Schedule Sprinkler Systems

Occupancy Classification	Residual Pressure Required (See Note 1)	Acceptable Flow at Base of Riser (See Note 2)	Duration in Minutes (See Note 4)
Light Hazard	15 psi	500–750 gpm (See Note 3)	30–60
Ordinary Hazard (Group 1)	15 psi or higher	700–1000 gpm	60–90
Ordinary Hazard (Group 2)	15 psi or higher	850–1500 gpm	60–90
Ordinary Hazard (Group 3)	Pressure and flow requirements for sprinklers and hose streams to be determined by authority having jurisdiction.		60–120
Warehouses	Pressure and flow requirements for sprinklers and hose streams to be determined by authority having jurisdiction. Also see Chapter 7 of NFPA 13, NFPA 231, and NFPA 231 C.		
High-Rise Buildings	Pressure and flow requirements for sprinklers and hose streams to be determined by authority having jurisdiction. Also see Chapter 8 of NFPA 13.		
Extra Hazard	Pressure and flow requirements for sprinklers and hose streams to be determined by authority having jurisdiction.		

NOTES:

1. The pressure required at the base of the sprinkler riser(s) is defined as the residual pressure required at the elevation of the highest sprinkler plus the pressure required to reach this elevation.

2. The lower figure is the minimum flow including hose streams ordinarily acceptable for pipe schedule sprinkler systems. The higher flow should normally suffice for all cases under each group.

3. The requirement may be reduced to 250 gpm if building area is limited by size or compartmentation or if building (including roof) is noncombustible construction.

4. The lower duration figure is ordinarily acceptable where remote station water-flow alarm service or equivalent is provided. The higher duration figure should normally suffice for all cases under each group.

Extra Hazard Occupancies

Extra Hazard occupancies consist of properties where flash fires opening all the sprinklers in a fire area are probable, and call for close sprinkler spacing and larger pipe sizes. Such occupancies include explosives manufacturing, extra hazard chemical works, pyroxylin plastic manufacturing, cotton picking and opening operations, and other occupancies with a flash fire hazard.

It is not possible to lay down any general rules for these last two groups, and their water supply needs can be evaluated only on an individual basis by engineers with broad background experience. For this reason, the NFPA Sprinkler Standard refers to determination by the authority having jurisdiction as the only possible answer to the problem. It is in such occupancies that hydraulic calculations are most often needed to determine water supplies.

In any treatment of hazards by general groups of occupancy, it must be noted that individual properties differ markedly, and that buildings of the same nominal occupancy classification may show widely different individual hazards which should be considered in any determination of water supply.

E. Water Supply Requirements for Hose Stream Protection

The values given in Table 14-4A include hose stream requirements. In considering water requirements for hose streams, it should be realized that if sprinklers perform effectively little hose stream assistance is required. Although this is generally the case, a realistic viewpoint must be taken of possible contingencies and the amount of water that might be needed for hose stream protection under adverse conditions.

In evaluating hose stream requirements, possibilities should be considered such as the amount of water necessary for final extinguishment or clean-up operations, or in the event that sprinklers are retarding fire spread but are not fully effective in gaining control and extinguishment.

F. Water Supply Requirements for Hydraulically Designed Sprinkler Systems

A fire protection engineer planning new water supplies or evaluating existing supplies for sprinkler systems must have some information regarding the hydraulic behavior of sprinkler piping systems.

Hydraulic Calculations

A hydraulically designed sprinkler system is one in which pipe sizes are selected on a pressure loss basis to provide a prescribed density (gallons per minute per square foot) distributed with a reasonable degree of uniformity over a specified area. This permits the selection of pipe sizes in accordance with the characteristics of the water supply available. The stipulated design density and area of application will vary with occupancy hazard.

Table 14-4B is used to determine density, area of sprinkler operation, and water supply requirements for hydraulically designed sprinkler systems. Systems must be calculated to satisfy a single point on the appropriate design curve, and interior piping must be based on this design point. It is not necessary to meet all points on the selected curve. Total water supply available to the system at the base of the riser at the residual pressure required by the design must be not less than shown in Table 14-4B; this total water supply need not be calculated through the overhead piping.

Table 14-4B. Density, Area of Sprinkler Operation, and Water Supply Requirements for Hydraulically Designed Sprinkler Systems
Minimum Water Supplies

Hazard Classification	Sprinklers GPM	Combined Inside & Outside Hose—GPM	Duration in Minutes
Light	150	100	30
Ord.—Gp. 1	400	250	*60–90
Ord.—Gp. 2	600	250	*60–90
Ord.—Gp. 3	750	500	*60–120

NOTES: The lower duration figure is ordinarily acceptable where remote station water-flow alarm service or equivalent is provided.

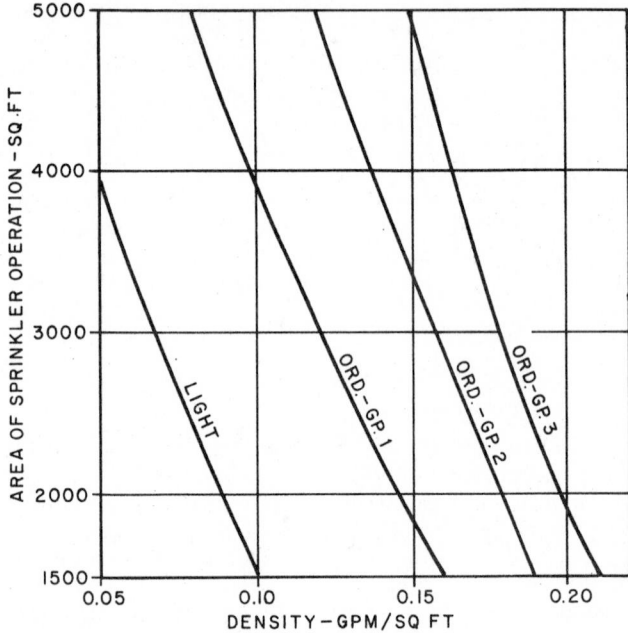

NOTES:
For dry systems increase area of sprinkler operation by 30 percent.
For combustible construction with wet or dry systems the minimum area of application is 3,000 sq ft.
For hazard classifications other than those indicated see appropriate NFPA Standards for design criteria.
Calculations shall be based upon the area of sprinkler operation selected from Table 14-4B, or upon the area of the largest room being considered, whichever is smaller. Such rooms must be enclosed by construction having a fire resistance rating at least equal to the water supply duration indicated in Table 14-4B, and wall openings must be protected in an approved manner. For areas of sprinkler operation less than 1,500 sq ft, the density for 1,500 sq ft is used.

The same hazard occupancy classifications apply to hydraulically designed sprinkler systems as apply to pipe schedule sprinkler systems as mentioned in Part D of this Chapter. The recommended water supply figures are, however, somewhat lower due to the greater efficiency of a calculated system.

The water allowances for inside hose and for outside hydrants may be combined and added to the system requirement at the system connection to the underground main. The total water requirement must be calculated through the underground main to the point of supply.

With deluge systems and water spray systems having open orifices, calculations are essential. (See NFPA No. 15, Standard for Water Spray Fixed Systems.) Automatic sprinkler systems protecting high piled storage situations require a specific water density for fire control. (See NFPA No. 231, Standard for Indoor Storage, and NFPA No. 231C, Standard for Rack Storage of Materials.) Hydraulically calculated systems can, however, be used for all types of occupancies.

Methods of making flow calculations for sprinkler systems are given in the following: (1) the NFPA Sprinkler Standard, (2) NFPA No. 15, Standard for Water Spray Systems for Fire Protection, (3) *"Automatic" Sprinkler Hydraulic Data* published by "Automatic" Sprinkler Corp. of America,[1] (4) Factory Mutual Corporation's *Handbook of Industrial Loss Prevention*,[2] and (5) an address "Water Flow Characteristics of Sprinkler Systems" reported in the Proceedings of the 58th Annual Meeting of the NFPA.[3]

The design area for the system is the hydraulically most remote area, and usually includes sprinklers on both sides of the cross main. Each sprinkler in the design area must discharge at a flow rate at least equal to the stipulated minimum water application rate (density). Begin calculations at the sprinkler hydraulically farthest from the supply connection. With common system configurations this will be the end sprinkler on the end branch line. The minimum operating pressure for any sprinkler must not be less than 7 psi.

The Most Remote Sprinkler

Assuming a minimum pressure of 10 psi at the most remote sprinkler and a discharge coefficient of 0.75 for a standard $\frac{1}{2}$-in. orifice sprinkler (the coefficient varies—0.78 is used elsewhere in this HANDBOOK), we will have a discharge of 17.7 gpm calculated from the formula $Q = 29.8\ cd^2\sqrt{P}$ (see Sec. 11, Chap. 6), used in calculating flows through orifices and short tubes. The value for $29.83\ cd^2$ in this instance is 5.6, a figure commonly used as the sprinkler discharge constant K in the simplified formula $Q = K\sqrt{P}$. Velocity pressure is not a factor at the more remote sprinkler, but it is considered at all the other sprinklers in the example that follows. Some organizations ignore velocity pressure in their calculations. The error introduced is on the safe side. NFPA No. 15, Standard for Water Spray Fixed Systems, recommends considering velocity only when it is more than 5 percent of the total pressure.

Assuming sprinklers 10 ft apart on branch lines, with the end section of pipe 1 in. nominal diameter, the friction loss at 17.7 gpm flow, with a Hazen and Williams formula coefficient of 120 (value for black steel pipe) will be 1.0 psi (see Fig. 11-6L in Sec. 11, Chap. 6 and change friction loss values in that graph, which are based on $C = 100$, to values based on $C = 120$ by multiplying by 0.714).

Second Sprinkler from the End

The total pressure at the second sprinkler will be 10.0 + 1.0 = 11.0 psi. Of this, velocity pressure based on a flow of 17.7 gpm will be 0.3 psi (see Fig. 11-6A, Sec. 11, Chap. 6). The normal pressure (pressure acting perpendicular to the pipe wall) acting on the second sprinkler is the total pressure of 11.0 psi less the velocity pressure of 0.3 or 10.7 psi. On all sprinklers except the end sprinkler, only normal pressure is considered as acting on the sprinklers.

The discharge from the second sprinkler, at a pressure of 10.7 psi, will be 18.3 gpm.

The pipe between the second and third sprinkler, also 1 in. diameter, 10 ft long, and with a flow of 17.7 + 18.3 = 36.0 gpm, will have a friction loss of 3.8 psi, and a velocity pressure of 1.2 psi. Total pressure at the third sprinkler equals 10.7 + 3.8 + 1.2 or 15.7 psi.

Other Sprinklers on a Branch Line

Up to this point, velocity pressure has been based on flow downstream from the sprinkler being considered; this has been confirmed by tests.[3] It has also been shown by those tests that beyond the second sprinkler velocity pressure should be figured from the flow on the upstream side of the sprinkler being considered. This is done by trial and error, assuming a flow from the sprinkler, calculating the velocity pressure from the total flow, determining a normal pressure, and calculating a flow from the normal pressure. If the calculated flow is not reasonably close to the assumed flow, assume a different flow and repeat the procedure until the two are close.

Assume a flow from the third sprinkler of 19.0 gpm, and also assume that the pipe between the third and fourth sprinkler is $1\frac{1}{4}$ in. Total flow is 36.0 + 19.0 = 55.0 gpm. Velocity pressure is 0.9 psi and normal pressure at the third sprinkler is therefore 15.7 − 0.9 or 14.8 psi. Corrected flow then becomes 21.6 gpm, which is not close enough to the 19 gpm assumed. Try an assumed flow of 21.4 gpm. Velocity pressure at 57.4 gpm is 1.0; normal pressure is 14.7 psi and the new corrected flow is 21.5 gpm. Total flow at the third head then becomes 36.0 + 21.5 = 57.5 gpm. The calculating procedure for the other sprinklers on the branch line is the same as for the third sprinkler.

At this point it will be seen that we have exceeded the 15 psi minimum riser pressure, unless, as is quite probable, the pressure with 57.5 gpm flow is substantially higher than that with 500 gpm flow. Whether or not the pressure with 57.5 gpm flow is higher than 15 psi depends on the characteristics of the water supply. However, in any case it appears that with not many more sprinklers open the pressure at the most remote sprinkler will be less than the 10 psi selected in this example.

Branch Lines, Cross Mains, Risers, and Fittings

Cross Main Pressure at the Branch Line Connection: This is the normal pressure at the nearest open sprinkler increased by the friction loss and the velocity pressure in the intervening pipe. If the branch line is fed through a tee and nipple, additional friction loss allowances must be made except that the friction loss in nipples less than 6 in. long is customarily neglected.

Two Branches in One Line of Sprinklers: These may have the same or different numbers of sprinklers. The pressure at the entrance to the two branches will always be the same. The computations starting at the end sprinklers will be duplicated for the number of open sprinklers.

After the discharge from any number of sprinklers on a branch line has been computed and the pressure to produce the flow has been determined, the entire branch line can be considered to have the discharge characteristics of a single orifice and the discharge constant K in the formula $Q = K\sqrt{P}$ can be determined, P being the net pressure where flows are taken from tees in the cross main.

Branches on Opposite Sides of a Cross Main: These branches may have different numbers of sprinklers open, in which case the cross main pressure must be the higher of the two computed values. This increases the discharge from the branch giving the lower computed pressure, and the actual discharge must be calculated for the higher pressure using the equation:

$$\frac{Q_1}{Q_2} = \sqrt{\frac{P_1}{P_2}}$$

in which P_2 is taken as the higher pressure, Q_2 the corresponding increased discharge to be determined, and P_1 and Q_1 the pressure and corresponding discharge from the branch requiring only the lower pressure.

After the appropriate increased discharge has been deter-

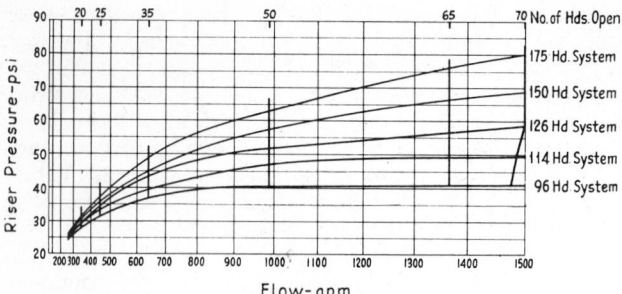

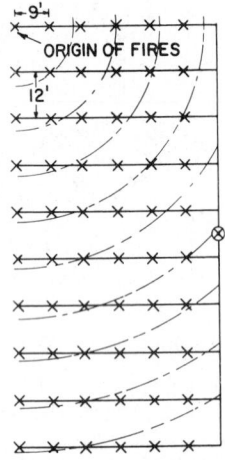

Fig. 14-4C. A flow curve for a side-central feed to sprinklers on a system having six sprinklers on each branch line is shown on the above graph. Below is the pattern of sprinklers opening on a side-central feed system. (Factory Mutual System)

mined, the two rates of flow can be combined and *K* for the combined branches calculated.

When sprinklers on the second branch line are assumed to have opened, starting at the cross main sprinkler, the opened sprinkler most remote from the cross main is considered as the end head in the branch line computation, the next opened is the second, etc., regardless of nonoperating sprinklers on the outer end of the branch.

Cross Main Pressures: Cross main pressures are calculated by the same procedure as used for sprinklers on a single branch line, except that it is not necessary to use the trial and error procedure for the third and additional branch lines since the effect of change in velocity pressure with flows passing through tees in the cross main is usually negligible. The net head producing the flow in successive branch lines is taken as the normal pressure at the end branch line increased by the friction loss in the pipe between the branches.

Riser Pressure: Riser pressure is taken as the normal pressure at the nearest flowing branch increased by the total friction loss between this branch and the riser and by the velocity pressure in the cross main at the riser connection.

Friction Loss in Fittings: This is generally included in calculations only when the fitting involves a change in direction of flow. An exception to this is the fitting immediately preceding the sprinkler.

Friction loss in control, gate and check valves, strainers, meters, and similar devices is always included.

The friction loss in piping between the source of supply and the opened sprinklers must obviously be included in all calculations.

Where there are differences in elevation, these must be allowed for on the basis that each foot of height represents 0.434 psi. In multistory buildings, this may be a substantial factor.

Feed mains, cross mains, and branch lines within the same system may be looped or gridded to divide the total water flowing to the design area.

Sprinkler System Water-flow Curves

To avoid repetition of laborious computation of water flows and pressures when such information is needed in cases involving standard sprinkler, spray, or open head systems, it is possible to prepare diagrams or "water-flow curves" from which riser pressures and corresponding total sprinkler flows may be determined for different numbers of opened sprinklers. One such series of curves, as developed by the Factory Mutual Engineering Corporation, and the piping arrangement and assumed pattern of opened sprinklers is shown in Figure 14-4C.

SI Units

The following conversion factors are given as a convenience in converting to SI units the English units used in this chapter.

1 ft^2	=	0.0929 m^2
1 in.	=	25.400 mm
1 ft	=	0.305 m
1 psi	=	6.895 kPa
1 gpm	=	3.785 litre/min

Bibliography

References Cited

[1] Wood, C. M., Automatic Sprinkler Hydraulic Data, 1961 ed., "Automatic" Sprinkler Corporation of America, Cleveland, Ohio, (reprinted 1964).

[2] Factory Mutual Engineering Corporation, "Hydraulics of Sprinkler Systems," *Handbook of Industrial Loss Prevention*, 2nd ed., McGraw-Hill, New York, pp. 23-1–23-13.

[3] Nickerson, Malcolm H., "Water Flow Characteristics of Sprinkler Systems," *Proceedings* of The Fifty-Eighth Annual Meeting, National Fire Protection Association, May 17-21, 1954, Washington, D.C., pp. 140-152.

NFPA Codes, Standards, and Recommended Practices (see the latest *NFPA Publications and Visual Aids Catalog* for availability of current editions of the following documents)

NFPA 13, Standard for the Installation of Sprinkler Systems.
NFPA 15, Standard for Water Spray Fixed Systems.
NFPA 20, Standard for Centrifugal Fire Pumps.
NFPA 22, Standard for Water Tanks for Private Protection.
NFPA 231, Standard for Indoor General Storage.
NFPA 231C, Standard for Rack Storage of Materials.

Additional Readings

Gomberg, Alan, and Cote, A. E., "The Computer Approach to Fire Protection Problems," *Fire Technology*, published by the National Fire Protection Association, Vol. 3, No. 3, Aug. 1967, pp. 202-212.

Merry, J. T., and Schiffhauser, "Hydraulic Sprinkler Systems Design—A Computer Approach," *Fire Technology*, published by the National Fire Protection Association, Vol. 2, No. 2, May 1966, pp. 95-107.

Patton, R. M., "Engineered Sprinkler Protection," *Fire Journal*, National Fire Protection Association, Vol. 60, No. 1, Jan. 1966, pp. 5-8, 18.

Wood, C. M., *Study Guide for Automatic Sprinkler Hydraulic Data*, "Automatic" Sprinkler Corp. of America, Ceveland, Ohio, 1964, 64 pp.

Chapter 5

WATER-FLOW ALARMS AND SPRINKLER SYSTEM SUPERVISION

Sprinkler systems should have devices and equipment for giving an alarm notification when water flows through risers or mains supplying the systems. The flow may be due to fire, leakage, or accidental rupture of the piping.

A sprinkler system with a water-flow alarm serves two functions: that of an effective fire extinguishing system, and that of an automatic fire alarm. Immediate notification by an alarm of the operation of sprinklers is important to complete extinguishment of the fire and place the system back in service. Under some conditions the sprinklers do not immediately or completely extinguish the fire, and it is vital to have someone notified to complete extinguishment, either by portable extinguishing devices, private hose streams, or fire department equipment.

The amount of loss or damage by water after fire has been extinguished may be held to a minimum by closing the control valve immediately after the need for sprinkler discharge has passed. One or two sprinklers may extinguish the fire, but water damage may be considerable unless the water is shut off as soon as it is safe to do so.

In addition to water-flow alarms, sprinkler systems frequently are equipped with additional devices to signal abnormal conditions which could make the protection inoperative or ineffective. In general, these devices, known as "supervisory" devices, give warning of troubles with equipment (shut valves, etc.), and require action by plant maintenance or security personnel, whereas water-flow alarms and fire alarms give warning of the actual occurrence of a fire or other conditions (broken pipes, etc.) causing water to flow through the system which alerts occupants and requires fire department response. Any signal, whether water-flow or supervisory, may be used to give only an audible local sprinkler alarm, or it may be the initiating signal for any of the protective signaling systems described in Section 12, Chapter 2 of this HANDBOOK.

A. Water-flow Sprinkler Alarms

Every sprinkler system needs a water-flow alarm. The established practices in providing sprinkler system water-flow alarms are given in NFPA No. 13, Standard for the Installation of Sprinkler Systems, hereinafter referred to in this chapter as the NFPA Sprinkler Standard.

The various types of sprinkler alarms include: (a) those which operate with an actual flow of water, (b) those which activate a hydraulic or an electric alarm when a water control device, such as a dry-pipe valve, trips to admit water to the alarm device or mechanically operates an electric switch whether or not water actually flows from sprinklers, and (c) those which not only signal the tripping of the control valve but which may also give supplementary warning signals in case of damage that might impair the operation of the system, or if maintenance features need attention.

Sprinkler systems are usually required to have an approved water-motor gong or an electric bell, horn, or siren on the outside of the building. An electric bell or other audible signal device may also be located inside the building. Water-operated devices must be located near the alarm valve, dry-pipe valve, or other water control valves in order to avoid long runs of connecting pipe. A sign worded as

follows is usually located as close as possible to the outdoor alarm: "Sprinkler Fire Alarm—When Alarm Sounds, Call Fire or Police Department."

All electric alarm devices, wiring, and power supplies should comply with NFPA No. 70, the National Electric Code, and with NFPA Signaling Systems Standards Nos. 71, 72A, 72B, 72C, and 72D.

Location of Alarm Signals

Because the purpose of a water-flow alarm is to give notification of conditions which might not otherwise be discovered promptly and to hasten remedial measures, it is important that audible or visual signals be located for greatest effectiveness. Outdoor alarm gongs, either electrically or water-motor operated, are needed especially if there is no dependable watch service or continuous supervision by central station or other protective signaling system services. However, outside alarms on buildings in remote areas or in urban areas which are sparsely populated at some times (as when residents are away or at work) may be of little value, making central station or other protective signaling system connections very desirable.

Water-flow Alarm Devices

The types of water-flow alarm devices and equipment described in this chapter are mostly those ordinarily furnished and installed by sprinkler manufacturers or contractors as part of a sprinkler system conforming to the NFPA Sprinkler Standard. They provide a complete local water-flow alarm system, and in many cases are basic units of more complete alarm and supervisory signaling systems.

B. Water-flow Alarm and Sprinkler System Supervisory Systems

There are several recognized signaling systems for transmitting alarms when water actually flows in an automatic sprinkler system and supervisory signals announcing abnormal conditions which could make the sprinkler protection inoperative or ineffective. The principal functions of each of these systems are described briefly in the following paragraphs. More detailed descriptions of these protective systems themselves are given in Section 12, Chapter 2.

Local Water-flow Alarm Systems: These systems give signals only at one or more places on the premises protected.

Proprietary Signaling Systems: These systems are frequently provided at large properties to transmit both water-flow alarms and supervisory signals to a constantly attended central alarm headquarters at the property protected. The devices and equipment for proprietary systems are usually supplied and installed by a signaling equipment manufacturer, a central station service organization, or an electrical contractor. Some central station service companies furnish these systems with a maintenance or inspection contract, or both, for these systems.

Central Station Signaling Systems: These systems transmit both water-flow alarm signals and supervisory signals to a constantly attended headquarters of a central station signaling service organization. The central station in turn notifies the fire department of all alarms, and the property owner of supervisory signals.

Auxiliary Signaling Systems: Auxiliary signaling systems send signals directly to a municipal fire department over the municipal fire alarm system through master boxes which may be of the telegraph, telephone, or radio-operated type.

Because municipal alarm systems can usually transmit only alarm signals, water flow signals only are transmitted to the fire department, and supervisory signals are transmitted over private circuits to some other location. Devices and equipment connected to the master box are generally installed by a supplier of signaling equipment or an electrical contractor.

Remote Station Signaling Service: This type of signaling service sends signals directly over private circuits to a fire department or other continually attended location where action will be taken immediately.

Because public fire departments are not established to assume supervisory responsibility, only water flow alarms are usually transmitted directly to fire departments, and supervisory signals are usually transmitted to some other continuously attended location. The devices and equipment are generally installed by a supplier of signaling equipment or an electrical contractor.

Sprinkler System Supervisory Devices

The sprinkler system supervisory devices and equipment described in this chapter are considered to be a part of sprinkler installations, even though manufactured, installed, and maintained by a central station or other supervisory service organization.

Sprinkler system supervision is commonly provided for: (1) water supply control valves, (2) low water level in water supply tanks, (3) low temperature in water supply tanks or ground level reservoirs, (4) high or low water level in pressure tanks, (5) high or low air pressure in pressure tanks, (6) high or low air pressure in dry-pipe sprinkler systems, (7) failure of electric power supply to fire pumps, and (8) automatic operation of electric fire pumps.

Sprinkler system devices that give water-flow alarms or supervise the condition of the installation are shown schematically in Figure 14-5A.

C. Wet-pipe Sprinkler System Alarm Devices

Water-flow alarm devices have been used to some extent ever since automatic sprinklers were first installed. They are generally located at or near the base of sprinkler risers but may be used as floor or branch alarms. They are designed and adjusted to give an alarm if a water flow equal to the discharge of one or more automatic sprinklers occurs in the sprinkler system. The alarm signal may be given electrically, or by water-motor driven gongs, or both. By far the most common types are the water flow alarm valve and the water flow indicator. The other types are rarely seen.

Water-flow Alarm Valves

The basic design of most water-flow alarm valves is that of a check valve which lifts from its seat when water flows into a sprinkler system. The movement of the valve clapper is used in one of the following ways:

1. The valve seat ring can have a concentric groove with a pipe connection from the groove to the alarm devices. Such valves are commonly called differential type or divided-seat ring-type valves. When the clapper of the alarm valve rises to allow water to flow to sprinklers, water also enters the groove in the divided-seat ring and flows through the pipe connection to an alarm-giving device. An alarm check valve of this type is shown in Figure 14-5B.

2. The clapper of the alarm check may have an extension arm connected to a small auxiliary (pilot) valve having its own seat and a pipe connection to alarms. When the auxiliary valve is lifted by movement of the main valve clapper, water is admitted to alarm devices. An alarm check valve of this type is shown in Figure 14-5C.

3. Movement of the main clapper by a flow of water can

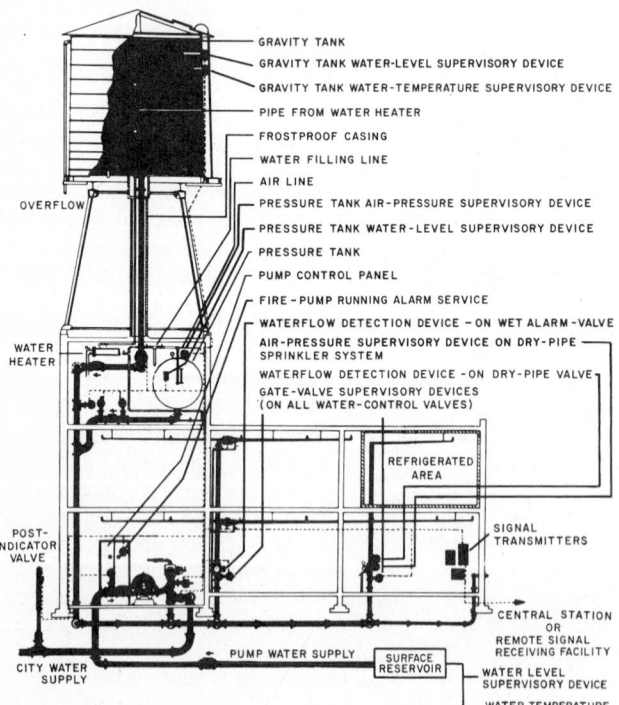

Fig. 14-5A.   Sprinkler system water-flow alarm and supervisory devices.

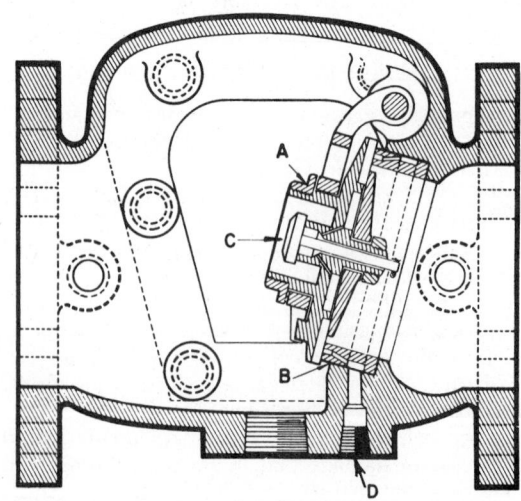

Fig. 14-5B. A water-flow alarm valve of the differential type. Water flowing through the valve lifts the main clapper (A) allowing water to enter the divided seat ring (B) and from there to the outlet to alarm devices (D). Bypass valve (C) permits small flows of water, such as from slow increases in water pressure, to enter the sprinkler system without lifting the main clapper and possibly causing a false alarm. Shown is the Grimes Model B valve for installation in a horizontal position.

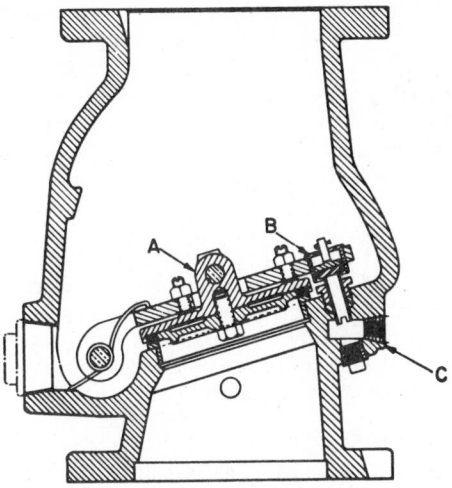

*Fig. 14-5C. A water-flow alarm valve of the pilot valve type. When the main clapper (**A**) is lifted by flow of water through the main valve, pilot valve (**B**) also is lifted off its seat to permit water to flow through the outlet to alarm devices (**C**). Shown is the "Automatic" Sprinkler Corp. of America Model 153 valve.*

operate mechanically an electric switch so located and arranged that it is not affected by the water pressure in the system. This method is limited to giving electric alarms and cannot supply water under pressure for the operation of water-motor gongs. It is being supplanted by other types of water-flow alarms, but a number of installations are still in service, mainly in central station signaling systems.

An alarm check valve installation with "trimmings" is shown in Figure 14-5D.

Water-flow Indicators

A water-flow indicator of the paddle or vane type consists of a movable flexible vane of thin metal or plastic which is inserted through a circular opening cut in the wall of a sprinkler supply pipe and which extends into the waterway sufficiently to be deflected by any movement of water flowing to opened sprinklers. Motion of the vane operates an alarm actuating electric switch or trips mechanically a signaling system transmitter. A mechanical, pneumatic, or electrical time delay feature in the detector or in the electric circuit or made a part of the signaling system transmitter prevents false alarms being given by transient flows caused by fluctuating water pressures. The retard feature must be of the instantly recycling type or otherwise arranged so that the effect of a sequence of flows, each of less duration than the predetermined retard period, will not have a cumulative effect. Electrically heated thermal retards have not performed satisfactorily. Water-flow indicators have no provision for supplying water to water-motor alarm gongs.

It is important that the flexible vane of a water-flow indicator be of a design and material not subject to mechanical injury or corrosion so that it cannot become detached and possibly obstruct the sprinkler piping.

Use of Water-flow Indicators

Water-flow indicators are commonly used, particularly on new systems. Situations where their use is most prevalent are: (1) where ease of installation and economy are important in installing a water-flow alarm, (2) where subdivision into several alarm areas is desired on a large sprinkler system, or (3) where a central station proprietary system or other remote signal station service is available which can receive only electric alarm signals from the protected property.

Water-flow indicators of the vane type cannot be used in dry-pipe systems, deluge systems, or pre-action systems because the vane and mechanism are likely to be damaged by the sudden rush of water when the control valve opens.

Water-flow indicators are supplied by manufacturers of both sprinkler equipment and signaling system equipment. Vane type indicators are shown in Figures 14-5E and 14-5F.

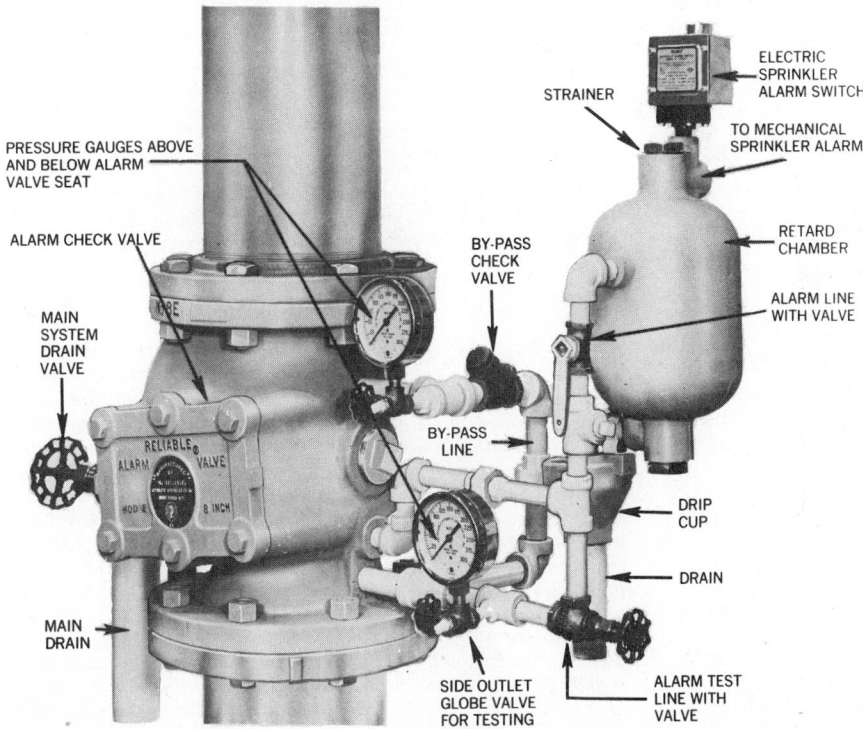

Fig. 14-5D. An alarm check valve installation with "trimmings." Shown is the Reliable Automatic Sprinkler Co., Inc. Model E valve. Other manufacturers have similar arrangements of proprietary equipment for alarm check valve installations.

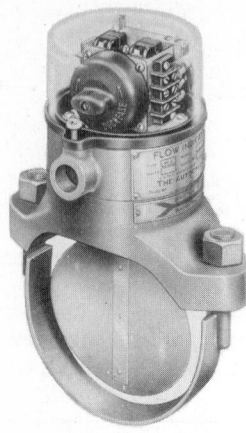

Fig. 14-5E. A water-flow indicator of the vane type with an adjustable, pneumatic, instantly recycling retard feature. Shown is the Autocall Co. Type WF-4.

Excess Pressure Pumps

Where great fluctuations in water pressures are encountered that exceed the normal adjustments of alarm valves, an excess pressure pump may be installed. An excess pressure pump is a small water pump of limited capacity which maintains pressure in the sprinkler system somewhat above the highest water supply pressure. Operation of an automatic sprinkler reduces the system pressure to the supply pressure. An electric pressure switch with its pressure setting slightly above the water supply pressure gives the water-flow alarm. A supervisory pressure switch with a setting slightly below the automatically maintained pressure but above that of the flow alarm switch, is provided to give a trouble signal in case of failure of the automatic pressure pump. An excess pressure pump installation is shown in Figure 14-5G.

System Alarm Attachments (Water Pressure Type)

These alarm attachments are designed to initiate an alarm by a drop in water pressure in the sprinkler piping and not by a flow of water through an alarm check valve although these devices are used with conventional alarm check valves. Figure 14-5H shows auxiliary attachment actuated by a drop in sprinkler system pressure.

Water-flow Detectors (Excess Pressure Type)

Another water-flow alarm principle depends upon the use

Fig. 14-5F. A vane type water-flow indicator having a mechanically tripped, adjustable, pneumatic, instantly recycling retard. It also has a one- or two-circuit electric switch. Shown is the Central Station Signals, Inc. (Wells Fargo Protective Services Model PRS-1.)

of an ordinary-type check valve to hold the pressure in the sprinkler system at the highest water supply pressure. A restricted bypass, also having a check valve, around the main clapper helps to produce and maintain the high pressure condition. The main clapper is weighted, or has a small differential provided by a divided-seat ring, so that there must be a positive drop in sprinkler system pressure before water can flow through the main check. This drop in pressure operates a sensitive diaphragm valve which admits pressure to the alarm circuit closer or opener. Flow of water into the sprinkler piping does not give an alarm, so that this alarm arrangement is free from false alarms caused by variations in the supply pressure. This alarm arrangement is adapted only to pressure actuated electric switches and not the operation of water-motor alarm gongs.

Alarm Retarding Devices

An alarm check valve that is subjected to fluctuating water supply pressures needs an alarm retarding device in order to prevent false alarms when the check-valve clapper is lifted from its seat by a transient surge of increasing pressure.

Retarding Chambers: One type of device, usually designated as a retarding chamber, is essentially a chamber

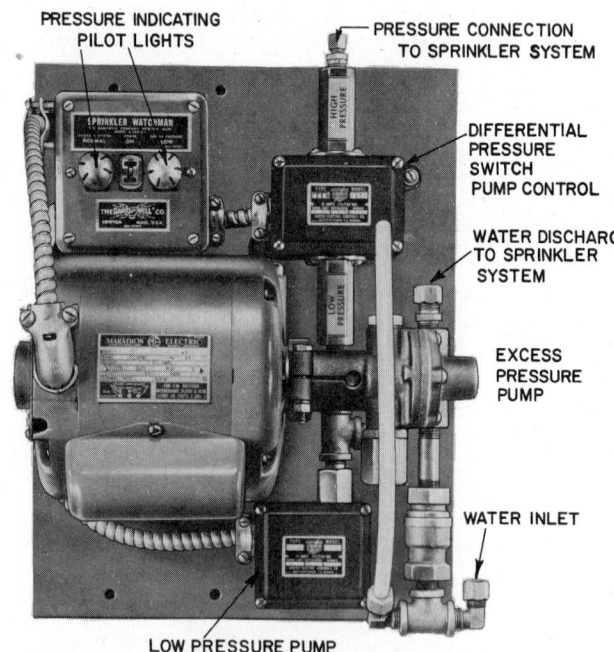

PRESSURE INDICATING PILOT LIGHTS

PRESSURE CONNECTION TO SPRINKLER SYSTEM

DIFFERENTIAL PRESSURE SWITCH PUMP CONTROL

WATER DISCHARGE TO SPRINKLER SYSTEM

EXCESS PRESSURE PUMP

WATER INLET

LOW PRESSURE PUMP SHUT-OFF SWITCH

Fig. 14-5G. An excess pressure pump for installation on a wet-pipe sprinkler system. The automatic excess pressure pump maintains a pressure 29 psi to 47 psi in excess of the water supply pressure above an alarm check valve. A continuous white pilot light, controlled by a differential switch, indicates when the pressure in the sprinkler system is more than 29 psi above the supply pressure. Should the water supply fail, a low pressure switch shuts off the current to the pump so that it will not run without water. This switch also controls a red pilot light to show when the supply pressure drops below 29 psi. A second pressure switch on the sprinkler system (not a part of the pump unit) is connected into the sprinkler system alarm circuit and gives an alarm if system pressure fails completely (e.g., a closed water control valve) when a sprinkler operates. A third pressure switch gives a warning by a local bell or other means in the event the pressure pump fails to maintain system pressure within the established excess pressure range. (G & W Gamewell/Alarmtronics)

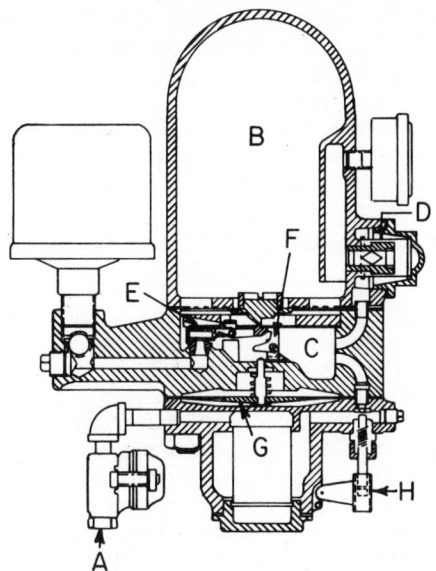

*Fig. 14-5H. An alarm device actuated by a drop in sprinkler system water pressure. Inlet chamber (**C**) is connected to the sprinkler system above the alarm check valve through inlet (**A**). Pressure chamber (**B**) connects to chamber (**C**) through restricted passage (**D**) so that system pressure and pressure in chambers (**B**) and (**C**), separated by flexible metal diaphragm (**G**), are normally equal. A pressure difference above and below the alarm valve clapper, caused when a sprinkler is opened, is adequate to deflect the diaphragm and open water valve (**E**), leading to alarm devices, before water flows into the sprinkler system. Latch (**F**) prevents the flow valve from closing and is released by a plunger acted upon by diaphragm (**G**). The valve is reset by pushing up resetting valve (**H**), thus closing the passage into intermediate chamber (**C**). A target on the resetting valve shows "Normal Operating Position" or "Shut-Danger" as the case may be. Shown is the Firematic Sprinklarm, Model A.*

inserted in the water line from the alarm check valve to the water-motor gong and electric circuit closer. Flows of short duration from the alarm check valve to the alarm device first accumulate in the retarding chamber which must become filled before water passes to the alarm device. The size of the chamber and of the water inlet are predetermined by the manufacturer to give a delay needed to make sure that the water flow is continuous before an alarm is given. The air displaced from the alarm piping in advance of water escapes at low pressure and does not operate the alarm devices. The retarding chamber is self-draining so that unless surges follow in close succession the full retard interval is restored between surges. A retarding chamber is shown and described in Figure 14-5I.

Check Valve Bypass: To assist in avoiding false alarms in case of slow increases in water supply pressure, an alarm check valve is sometimes arranged with a small bypass opening through the main clapper, or piped through an exterior bypass. The bypass is restricted so that possible flow through it is small in comparison with the flow through a single automatic sprinkler, and it has a check valve intended to hold the pressure in the sprinkler piping at the highest value that occurs in the water supply system. An external bypass is shown in Figure 14-5J and a bypass valve in the main clapper of an alarm valve is shown in Figure 14-5B.

Early Types of Water-flow Alarm Valves

Early types of alarm check valves with outside levers, weights, or movable pins operated by movements of a clapper are obsolete. Many features made these early check

valves unreliable. For example, the free movement of the clapper was easily retarded. Also, such valves were not responsive to small flows of water.

Improvement has been largely in mechanical and electrical design rather than operating principle. Some of the earliest devices made previous to 1890 used the movement of a water clapper to actuate an electric switch. Grooved (divided) check valve seats and pilot valves to admit water to water-motor gongs were early developments.

The following descriptions are representative of early types of alarm valves. These valves are obsolete and few, if any, will be found in service. Many other designs were developed and used.

The "English" Sprinkler Alarm Valve: This valve (see Fig. 14-5K) was manufactured and installed by the Providence Steam and Gas Pipe Co., and the General Fire Extinguisher Co. (predecessor of the Grinnell Company, Inc.) from 1888 to 1908. This was a vertical check with a

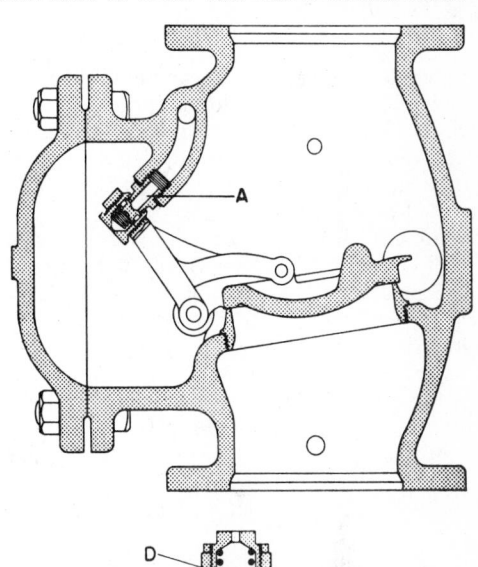

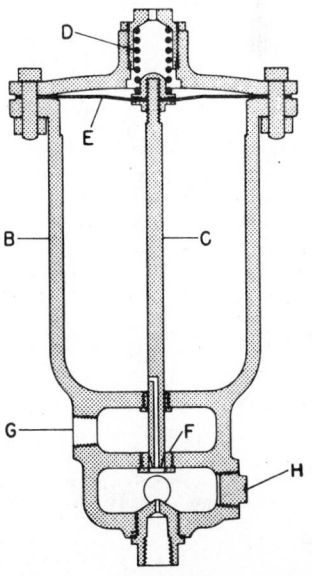

*Fig. 14-5I. Water-flow alarm valve and retarding chamber. Water from the pilot valve (**A**) of the water-flow alarm valve slowly enters the upper chamber (**B**) of the retarding chamber through space between the guide bushing and loosely fitting valve stem (**C**). After the upper chamber pressure has reached a value determined by the setting of the adjusting spring (**D**), the diaphragm (**E**) is moved upward opening the valve (**F**) from the inlet (**G**) from the alarm valve to the outlet (**H**) leading to alarm devices. Illustrated are a Globe Model E alarm valve and Model E retarding chamber.*

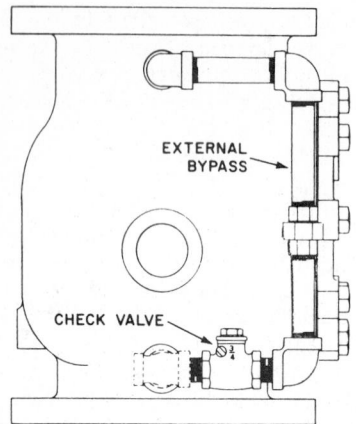

Fig. 14-5J. An alarm check valve with an external bypass. Shown is the Star Sprinkler Corp. Model C Alarm Valve in vertical position.

central valve stem and a divided-seat ring. When the clapper was lifted by a flow of water into the sprinkler system, water was also discharged through the groove in the valve seat to a water-motor gong and to an electric circuit closer. This type of alarm check performed satisfactorily but had an obstructed waterway.

International Alarm Valve, Auxiliary Valve Type (Models C, D, and E): These valves were manufactured from 1903 to 1928 by the "Automatic" Sprinkler Corp. of America. It was designed so that a flow of water into the sprinkler system raised the main valve clapper and opened a pilot valve which admitted water to a retard chamber.

Increasing pressure in the retard chamber depressed a diaphragm and opened an auxiliary valve which admitted water supply pressure to an electric alarm switch and to a pipe leading to a water-motor gong. This valve is similar to the later "Automatic" Model 153 alarm valve (see Fig. 14-5C).

The Venturi Alarm Valve: This valve, manufactured from 1907 to 1927 by the "Automatic" Sprinkler Corp. of America, had a weighted water clapper which when lifted by a flow into the sprinkler system caused a small flow to pass through a venturi tube producing a pressure differential which was applied to a mercury chamber arranged

as a large tube with a floating iron weight. A time delay was provided by a restriction in the passage to the mercury chamber. The floating weight actuated a small valve which admitted service water pressure to a water-motor gong and an electric alarm pressure switch. The valve, being mechanically complicated, required careful maintenance and testing.

D. Water-flow Alarms for Dry-pipe Sprinkler Systems

It is relatively simple to arrange a connection from the intermediate chamber of a dry-pipe valve to a pressure operated alarm device. The intermediate chamber of the dry-pipe valve normally contains air only at atmospheric pressure. When the valve trips, the intermediate chamber immediately fills with water at supply pressure which is available to operate the alarm devices that are the same as those used with alarm check valves except that a retarding device is not needed. Both an outdoor water-motor gong and a pressure operated electric switch are usually provided.

E. Alarm Devices for Deluge and Pre-action Sprinkler Systems

The alarm devices used with deluge and pre-action systems usually are of the same type as those used for dry-pipe systems. They are connected to the sprinkler system side of the valve. It is also a common practice to have an electric alarm switch arranged so that an electric alarm will be given whether or not water flows through the valve after operation of the fire detecting system.

Pre-action system piping is also often supervised with a low air pressure along with the actuating device circuits.

F. Water-motor Gongs

All manufacturers of water-flow alarm check valves and dry-pipe valves can supply approved water-motor driven alarm gongs for local outdoor alarms near dry-pipe valves or alarm check valves.

Approved water-motor gongs are similar in operating principle and mechanical construction, and are designed for mounting on the outside of building walls. Waste water may be discharged outdoors or drained off through a connection to the sprinkler system drain. A representative water-motor gong is shown in Figure 14-5L.

G. Water-flow Alarm and Supervisory Pressure Actuated Switches

Electric switches, frequently called circuit closers, with contacts arranged to open or to close an electric circuit when subjected to increased or reduced pressure, are used in combination with dry-pipe valves, alarm check valves, and some other types of water control valves to initiate an electric water-flow alarm signal when a flow of water to sprinklers occurs or to give a supervisory signal if pressures increase or decrease beyond established limits.

Manufacturers of dry-pipe valves, alarm check valves, and special types of water control valves regularly furnish approved pressure-operated switches to operate local electric water-flow alarms. In most cases, the motion to actuate a switch is obtained from a diaphragm exposed to the pressure on one side and opposed by a fixed adjustable spring on the other side. A typical water-flow alarm switch is shown in Figure 14-5M.

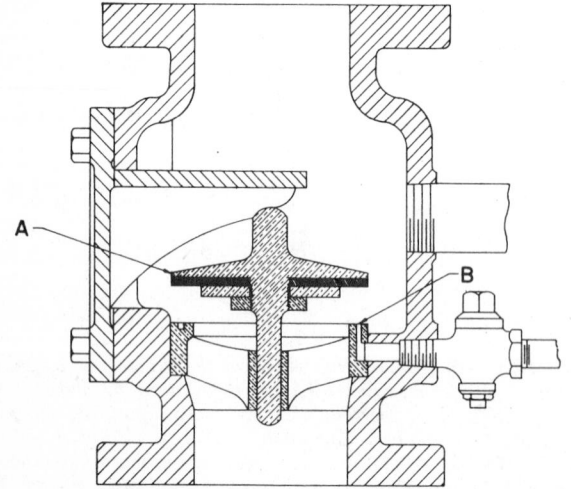

Fig. 14-5K. "English" alarm valve, divided-seat ring type (manufactured 1888 to 1908). (A) vertical check valve in open position, and (B) divided-seat ring leading to alarm attachments.

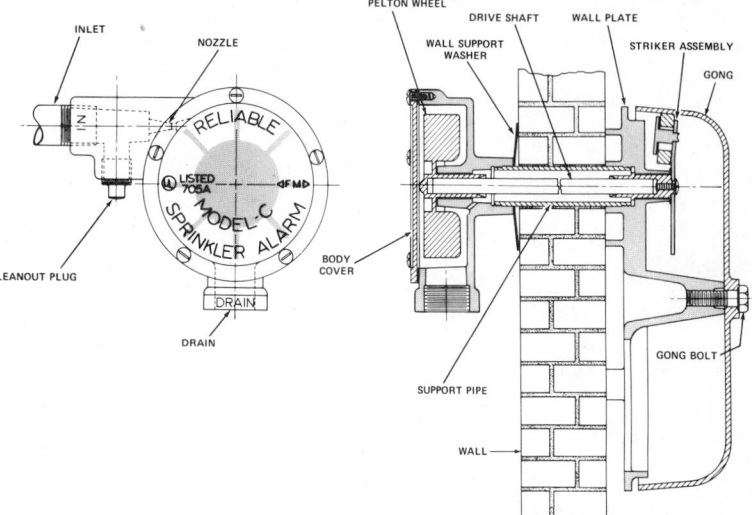

Fig. 14-5L. A representative water-motor gong. Shown is the Reliable Automatic Sprinkler Co., Inc. model. Other manufacturers have similar arrangements of proprietary equipment for water-motor gong installations.

Mercury switches and other types of electric contacts may be used. Commercial pressure-actuated switches, of which a representative design is shown in Figure 14-5N, may be adapted to water-flow alarm service.

H.   Sprinkler System Supervisory Devices

Gate Valve Supervisory Switches

Electric switches for sprinkler system water supply control valve supervision are of different mechanical designs for the different types of control valves.

General requirements for supervisory signaling systems include electrical supervision of circuits to indicate conditions that could prevent the required operation of the sprinkler system.

Electric switches can be for open or closed circuit supervisory systems. Supervision may also be by means of signaling transmitters mechanically tripped by operation of the gate valve.

The signal to indicate valve operation is given within two turns of the valve wheel from the wide open position. The restoration signal is given when the valve is restored to its fully open position.

Figures 14-5O, 14-5P, and 14-5Q are of representative approved devices for supervision of sprinkler valves.

Temperature Supervision for Water Tanks

The temperature of the water in fire service tanks exposed to cold weather is usually shown by a thermometer in the cold water return to a circulating-type heater or near the bottom of a large riser.

Supervisory equipment is available for detecting dangerously low temperature near the surface of the water at the tank shell where freezing is most likely to start, as well as for checking manual supervision or automatic heat control.

Water Level Supervision

Devices for supervising the water level in pressure tanks differ from those used in water supply tanks in that level sensing elements are continuously subject to high pressure. The supervisory signal is given if the water level reaches

Fig. 14-5M. A water-flow alarm switch that can be used in combination with a conventional dry-pipe valve or alarm check valve to actuate a fire alarm transmitter for water-flow signals in a central station, proprietary, or remote station signaling system. Shown is the Type C 68 switch of American District Telegraph Company (N.J.) and Its Associated Companies.

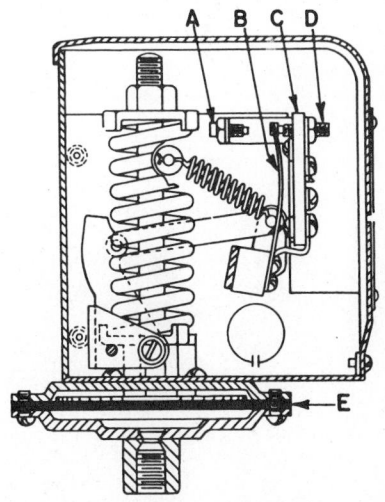

Fig. 14-5N. A pressure switch of the commercial type adaptable for fire protection purposes. Shown is The Viking Corporation Pressure Switch, Class 9018. (A), stationary contact; (B), movable contact; (C), stationary contact; (D), stationary block assembly, and (E), rubber diaphragm.

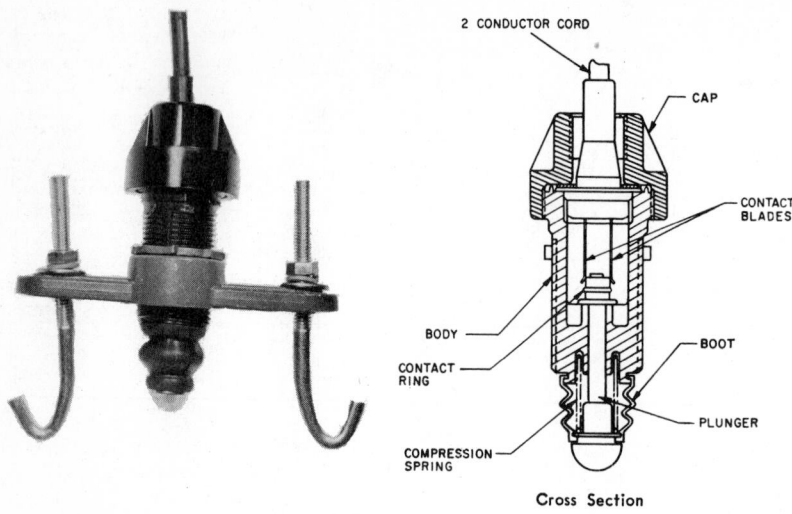

Cross Section

*Fig. 14-5O. A gate valve supervisory switch. The switch is attached to the two sides of the valve yoke by the hook bolts shown in the photo at left. When the valve is wide open, the tip of the **plunger** enters a $\frac{1}{8}$-in. deep depression drilled in the valve stem. The switch is adjusted so that in the open valve position the **contact ring** closes the electric circuit between the **contact blades**. When the valve is closed not over two turns, the tip of the **plunger** rides out of the depression in the valve stem and opens the electric circuit. Should the switch be tampered with or removed, the **plunger** takes the position shown in the sectional view and opens the electric circuit. Shown is the Model B-613 switch of American District Telegraph Company (N.J.) and Its Associated Companies.*

*Fig. 14-5P. An indicator post valve supervisory switch. The operating stem of the **switch** is held against the movable **target assembly** by springs within the switch housing. The switch end of the operating stem carries an insulator which separates contact springs and opens the electric circuit when the **target assembly** is moved in the valve closing direction by about two turns of the valve stem. Shown is the Model B611 switch of American District Telegraph Company (N.J.) and Its Associated Companies.*

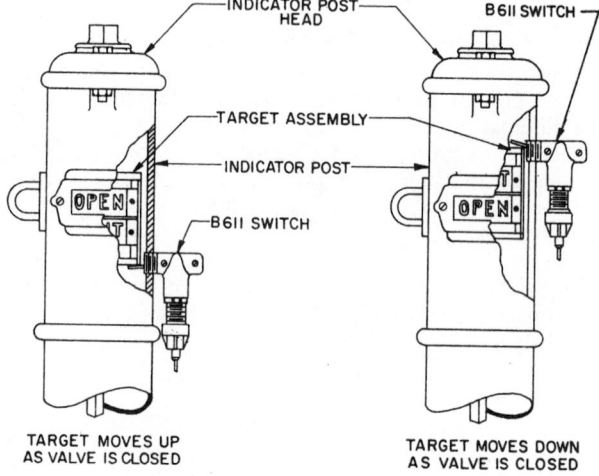

TARGET MOVES UP
AS VALVE IS CLOSED

TARGET MOVES DOWN
AS VALVE IS CLOSED

Fig. 14-5Q. Water supply valve position indicator switch. The pivoted external control arm actuates the internal electric signal switch. When an outside-screw-and-yoke gate valve is in the wide open position, the control arm engages a shallow vee notch in the valve stem. If the stem is moved to close the valve, the arm slides out of this notch and opens the electric signal circuit. If the switch is loosened or removed, the switch arm is moved by a spring and actuates the alarm switch. On indicator post valves the arm extends into the indicator post and is adjusted to be operated by movement of the indicating target. Shown is the Notifier Company Model NGV/NIP switch.

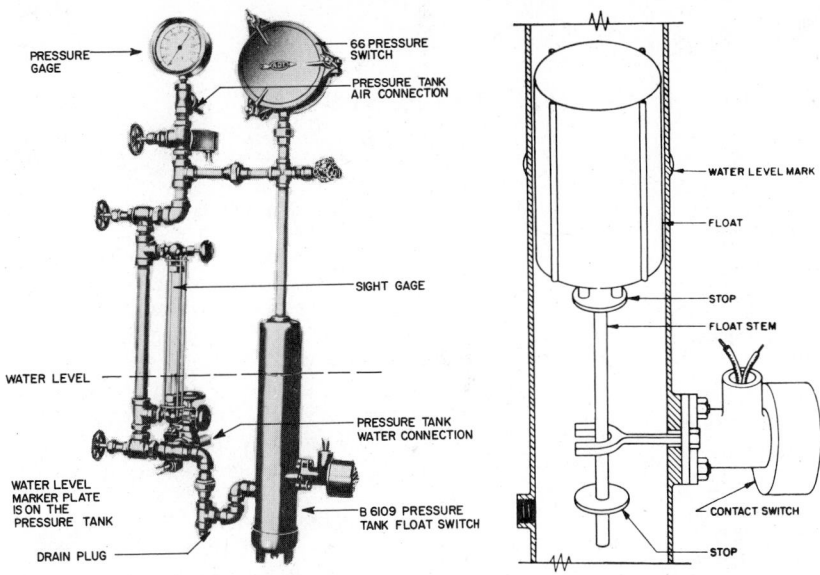

Installation Arrangement

*Tank Float Switch
Sectional View*

*Fig. 14-5R. A supervisory switch for pressure water tanks. If the water level rises or falls about 3 in., one of the **stops** on the **float stem** in the tank float switch comes in contact with the **forked lever** which operates the **contact switch**. The switch is usually connected into the circuit of a supervisory signal transmitter. Shown is the Type B6109 switch of American District Telegraph Company (N.J.) and Its Associated Companies.*

3 in. above or below the proper point, usually by means of an electrical connection to a separate signal transmitter.

Figure 14-5R shows a water level supervisory switch for gravity tanks.

Bibliography

NFPA Codes, Standards, and Recommended Practices (see the latest *NFPA Publications and Visual Aids Catalog* for availability of current editions of the following documents)

NFPA No. 13, Standard for the Installation of Sprinkler Systems.
NFPA No. 70, National Electric Code.

NFPA No. 72A, Standard for Local Protective Signaling Systems.
NFPA No. 72B, Standard for Auxiliary Protective Signaling Systems.
NFPA No. 72C, Standard for Remote Station Protective Signaling Systems.
NFPA No. 72D, Standard for Proprietary Protective Signaling Systems.

Additional Readings

Fire Protection Equipment List, published annually with bi-monthly supplements, Underwriters Laboratories, Inc., Chicago.
Factory Mutual Approval Guide, published annually, Factory Mutual Engineering Corporation, Norwood, Mass.

Chapter 6

CARE AND MAINTENANCE OF SPRINKLER SYSTEMS

This chapter deals with the care and maintenance of the devices and equipment upon which reliable mechanical performance of sprinkler systems depends. A guide for sprinkler system maintenance, including inspection, is given in NFPA No. 13A, Care and Maintenance of Sprinkler Systems, hereinafter referred to in this chapter as the NFPA Sprinkler Care and Maintenance Standard.

Care and maintenance include more than just the inspection and testing of sprinkler devices and equipment. If sprinkler protection is to be fully effective, the proper relation between hazard and protection must be maintained. This calls for careful consideration of the fire hazards to be protected, and requires a decision regarding the adequacy of the protection to cope with conditions which vary and which may have increased the fire hazard beyond that for which the protection had originally been designed and installed.

The supply of water which actually extinguishes or controls the fire may be treated as a part of a sprinkler system, or, more commonly, considered separately as the supply portion of a general fire protection system. Either way, equal degrees of care and maintenance are required for sprinkler system devices and equipment, and the water supply elements of a fire protection system.

The maintenance of water supply equipment such as tanks, fire pumps, etc., is treated in the chapters relating to those items of equipment.

Chapters 1 through 5 in this Section give information relating to the design, construction, and operation of the major devices used in sprinkler systems. Section 11 contains detailed information about the major elements of water supply systems.

A. Importance of Automatic Sprinkler System Maintenance

Diligent, careful, and thorough attention to the care and maintenance of sprinkler systems is necessary to assure dependable fire protection. The primary purpose of an automatic sprinkler system is to protect life and property. Serious fires very rarely occur in properties completely protected with properly maintained automatic sprinkler systems.

Automatic sprinkler systems employing standard devices and installed in accordance with the established rules are sturdy and durable, and require a minimum of expenditure for maintenance. However, like other types of equipment, they may suffer deterioration or impairment through neglect or from certain conditions of service. Definite provision for regular and competent attention to maintenance is a prime requirement if the system is to serve its purpose effectively. If not correctly installed and then properly maintained, any protective system may be worse than useless due to a false sense of security.

Deterioration, freezing, or mechanical damage to sprinkler system devices and equipment may result in accidental escape of water without the occurrence of fire. Such cases are classed as "sprinkler leakage," and are discussed later in this chapter.

B. Responsibility for Maintenance

It is the obligation of the owners or managers of property where automatic sprinkler systems are installed to so care for that equipment at all times that the lives of those who are housed or employed on that property may not be in danger, and that there may be continuity of revenue, production, and employment essential to any going business. In order to obtain this desired result, proper attention must be given to the system itself, and to other features that may affect the correct and satisfactory control of fire by the sprinkler system.

A large part of the troubles that have been experienced with sprinkler systems has been due to lack of responsibility rather than lack of knowledge. Regardless of fire inspections that may be made by others (e.g., insurance organizations, public fire departments, sprinkler contractors), it is management alone that can act to keep the fire protection adequate in extent and in good operative condition at all times, and to have properly informed, trained personnel to handle any fire situation effectively. For this, a carefully developed self-inspection procedure must be adopted.

The type of organizations required to perform the various inspection, testing, and maintenance functions varies greatly. Size and value of the property are major considerations. The establishment of an appropriate organization is the responsibility of management, as treated in Section 11, Chapter 3.

Inspection procedures have some seasonal differences, most of which are indicated later in this chapter under the various items of sprinkler equipment being considered. The following are examples of inspections governed by seasonal effects:

Spring Inspection: As soon as danger of freezing is past, the spring inspection will give attention to the opening of cold weather valves, testing, cleaning, and resetting dry-pipe valves, testing water-motor gongs, and conducting water-flow tests.

Fall Inspection: At the approach of freezing weather, the fall inspection will give special attention to such items as closing cold weather valves and draining pipes exposed to freezing temperatures (drain valves on the exposed piping are left slightly open), testing the specific gravity of the solution in antifreeze sprinkler systems, checking dry-pipe valves to make sure that the systems are holding air properly and that the electric and water-motor alarms are in order, checking drains at low points of the dry piping to make sure they are properly clear of water, checking heating provisions for the dry valves, examining gravity tanks to determine if adequate protection against freezing is assured and that any heating system employed is in operative condition, checking the condition of fire pump reservoirs and the suction intakes from other water sources, and looking over buildings to make sure that cold air will not enter, nor unduly expose, sprinkler piping to freezing.

C. Types of Sprinkler System Inspections

In addition to the indispensable self-inspection procedures followed by the property owner, other inspection services are available.

Insurance Inspections

In insured properties, sprinkler systems are frequently given special attention by the insurance carrier. Routine testing of sprinkler systems and devices at regular intervals by insurance inspection organizations is a service extended by some insurance companies in the common interest of both the owner and the company. By these routine tests, the equipment can be shown to be in good operating condition, or any defects or impairments revealed. Since such tests are made at the owner's responsibility and risk, intelligent co-operation in conducting the tests serves the best interest of the owner.

Fire Department Inspections

Inspections are made of sprinkler equipments by many fire departments at varying intervals. The inspection is principally to make sure that valves are open and to ensure familiarity with the use of the system by the fire department. Inspections are customarily made by the fire company in whose district the installation is located.

Sprinkler Contractors' Services

Standardized sprinkler equipment inspection and maintenance services offered by sprinkler manufacturers and competent sprinkler contractors are particularly advantageous to a property owner who must rely on an outside inspection service because no one in his employ is competent to look after his system. This service provides periodic examinations and reports, and is of value to the property owner not only for the regular checkup of the condition of his sprinkler equipment, but also because of valuable instruction that can be given to employees in the process. In addition to sprinkler devices and equipment, it also covers other items (such as tanks and fire pumps) that are important in the fire protection of the property.

Inspection and maintenance services offered by sprinkler contractors normally follow a form that is acceptable to most insurance interests. A copy of this form is shown in Figures 14-6A and 14-6B.

Central Station Supervisory Service

Central station supervision of sprinkler alarm and control devices provided under contract is a specially valuable aid to maintenance. The outside agency reporting to the owner or manager each incident involving water flow or gate closure or other supervised action keeps a constant check on the condition of the equipment and stimulates care on the part of the plant fire organization.

D. General Maintenance of Sprinklers and Sprinkler Piping

Life of Automatic Sprinklers

Automatic sprinklers installed where they are not subjected to abnormal conditions such as corrosion, loading, abnormally high temperatures, or mechanical abuse, will give continued satisfaction over a great many years. Some sprinklers accepted by insurance organizations when first installed proved unreliable after years of service. Those falling into this category are so identified in Table 14-3B. Sprinklers listed by leading testing laboratories since 1900 have generally given satisfactory service even though superseded by new or improved sprinklers. The NFPA Sprinkler Care and Maintenance Standard, however, recommends replacement of all sprinklers that are 50 years old.

Reliability Tests of Automatic Sprinklers

Where sprinklers are subject to loading or corrosion, even to only a moderate or slight extent, they should be carefully and frequently examined. If the condition of the sprinklers appears to be doubtful, a representative sample (six or more) should be removed, carefully packed to avoid injury in transit, and sent for testing to testing laboratories or to the sprinkler manufacturer. During these tests the sprinklers are destroyed. The results of their testing will indicate the condition of similar sprinklers remaining in the property. (NOTE: Removal of sprinklers for cleaning or for replacement involves the necessity of closing valves and having the system temporarily out of service. Care should be taken to minimize the period of interruption of protection and to make sure that all valves are left open after sprinklers are replaced. Precautions to be taken when sprinkler valves are closed are given later in this chapter.)

To prevent mechanical injury and distortion when installing or removing sprinklers that are to be cleaned and reinstalled, the special wrenches provided by manufacturers for their own size and shape of sprinklers should be used.

Accumulation of Foreign Material on Sprinklers

In many classes of properties, conditions exist which cause an accumulation of foreign material on automatic sprinklers so that operation of the sprinkler may be retarded or prevented. This condition is commonly called "loading" (see Fig. 14-6C).

Any accumulation of foreign material on sprinklers tends to retard their operation, owing to the heat-insulating effect of the loading material. If the deposit is hard, it may retard or prevent the sprinkler from operating. The best practice is to replace such loaded sprinklers with new sprinklers, rather than to attempt to clean them. Attempts at cleaning, particularly in instances where deposits are hard, are likely to injure the sprinkler, rendering it inoperative or causing possible leakage.

Deposits of light dust, such as may be found on sprinklers in woodworking plants and grain elevators, are less serious than hard deposits. Dust may be expected to delay the operation of sprinklers, but ordinarily will not prevent the eventual discharge of water. Dust deposits can be blown or brushed off, but blowing by compressed air should not be undertaken where it can create a dust explosion or ignition hazard. If a brush is used, it should be soft to avoid possible injury to sprinkler parts.

Water-solution cleaning liquids of caustic or acid type are likely to be injurious to sprinklers and should not be used for cleaning. No hot solution of any kind should be used for cleaning.

Sprinklers are sometimes protected when ceilings or sprinkler piping are being painted by temporarily placing small, lightweight paper or plastic bags over them, and securing the bags with a rubber band. Bags, however, are likely to delay the operation of the sprinklers, and should be removed immediately after the painting is completed.

There is no known method whereby paint under the water cap or on the fusible link can be adequately removed. Sprinklers that have been painted other than by the manufacturer must be replaced with new units.

Sprinklers in spray booths present a special problem for which there is no wholly satisfactory solution except to conduct the spraying process in such a manner that no spray will reach the sprinklers. If so located as to minimize deposits, and if cleaning is done very frequently, conveniently accessible sprinklers may be cleaned without removing. Using a coating of grease, motor oil, or soft neutral soap

REPORT OF INSPECTION

Inspection Report
No. ....

Conferred With
....

Inspection Contract
No. ....

Bureau File
No. ....

REPORT TO ....   BUILDING OR LOCATION..

STREET ....   INSPECTOR ....

CITY & STATE ....   DATE..

	Yes	N.A.‡	No*
1. GENERAL			
a. Is the building occupied?..		●●●●●	
b. Is occupancy same as previous inspection?.................................		●●●●●	
c. Are all systems in service?..		●●●●●	
d. Are all fire protection systems same as last inspection?..................			
e. Is building completely sprinklered?..		●●●●●	
f. Are all new additions and building changes properly protected?.......			
g. Is all stock or storage properly below sprinkler piping?.................			
h. Was property free of fires since last inspection? (Explain any fire on separate sheet)......			
i. In areas protected by wet system, does the building appear to be properly heated in all areas, including blind attics, perimeter areas and are all exterior openings protected against entrance of cold air?			
2. CONTROL VALVES (See Section 16)			
a. Are all sprinkler system main control valves open?......................		●●●●●	
b. Are all other valves in proper position?...................................		●●●●●	
c. Are all control valves in good condition and sealed or supervised?....		●●●●●	
3. WATER SUPPLIES (See Section 17)			
a. Was a water flow test made and results satisfactory?....................		●●●●●	
4. TANKS, PUMPS, FIRE DEPT. CONNECTIONS	Yes	N.A.†	No*
a. Are fire pumps, gravity tanks, reservoirs and pressure tanks in good condition and properly maintained?..........			
b. Are fire dept. connections in satisfactory condition, couplings free, caps in place and check valves tight?......			
5. WET SYSTEMS (See Section 13)			
a. Are cold weather valves open or closed as necessary?...................			
b. Have anti-freeze systems been tested and left in satisfactory condition?....			
c. Are alarm valves, water flow indicators and retards in satisfactory condition?....			
6. DRY SYSTEMS (See Section 14)			
a. Is dry valve in service and in good condition?...........................			
b. Is air pressure and priming water level normal?........................			
c. Is air compressor in good condition?......................................			
d. Were low points drained during fall and winter inspections?..........			
e. Are Quick Opening Devices in service?...................................			
f. Has piping been checked for stoppage within past 10 years?...........			
g. Has piping been checked for proper pitch within past 5 years?........			
h. Have dry valves been trip tested satisfactorily as required?...........			
i. Are dry valves adequately protected from freezing?....................			
j. Valve house and heater condition satisfactory?.........................			
7. SPECIAL SYSTEMS (See Section 18)			
a. Were valves tested as required?..			
b. Were all heat responsive systems tested and results satisfactory?.....			
c. Were supervisory features tested and results satisfactory?.............			
8. ALARMS			
a. Water motor and gong test satisfactory?.................................			
b. Electric alarm test satisfactory?...			
c. Supervisory alarm service test satisfactory?.............................			

Fig. 14-6A. Sheet No. 1, of a sample Report of Inspection (Sprinkler System Equipment) form as recommended in NFPA No. 13A, Recommended Practice for the Care and Maintenance of SprinklerSystems.

facilitates washing or wiping off deposits. If grease is used, it should be a grease with a low melting point (vaseline, etc.). Unless cleaning is done very carefully, deposits are likely to accumulate to such an extent as to interfere seriously with sprinkler operation. The use of paper bags to protect sprinklers in spray booths is a fairly common, but not a recommended, practice.

Corrosion of Automatic Sprinklers

Corrosive conditions are likely to make automatic sprinklers inoperative or retard the speed of their operation. Corrosive vapors may seriously affect not only the heat-actuated element and the valve-retaining members of an automatic sprinkler, but also may be severe enough to weaken or destroy other portions of the sprinkler. In most

		Yes	N.A.‡	No*

9. SPRINKLERS — PIPING
   a. Are all sprinklers in good condition, not obstructed, and free of corrosion or loading?.... ●●●●●
   b. Are all sprinklers less than 50 years old?......................... ●●●●●
   c. Are extra sprinklers readily available?............................ ●●●●●
   d. Is condition of piping, drain valves, check valves, hangers, pressure gauges, open sprinklers, strainers satisfactory?................. ●●●●●
   e. Are all sprinklers of proper temperature rating?................. ●●●●●
   f. Are portable fire extinguishers in good condition?...............
   g. Is hand hose on sprinkler systems satisfactory?..................

*Explain "No" answers in Item #19   ‡Not Applicable

10. Date Dry System Piping last checked for stoppage. ....

11. Date Dry System Piping last checked for proper pitch. ....

12. Date Dry Pipe Valve last trip tested. ....

13. Wet Systems: No?   Make and Model?......................................

14. Dry Systems: No?   Make and Model?......................................

15. Special System: No?   Type ....
    Make and Model?......................................Condition?......................................

			Open		Secured		Closed		Signs		Condition
16. CONTROL VALVES	No?	Type?	Yes	No	Yes	No	Yes	No	Yes	No	
City Connection Control Valve........											
Tank Control Valves...................											
Pump Control Valves..................											
Sectional Control Valves..............											
System Control Valves................											

17.   WATER FLOW TEST

Water Pressure?................CITY................PSI   TANK................PSI   FIRE PUMP................PSI

Water Flow Test?.. (If none made, Why?)................................

Test Pipe Located	Size Test Pipe	Pressure Before	Flow Pressure	Pressure After	Test Pipe Located	Size Test Pipe	Pressure Before	Flow Pressure	Pressure After

18. Heat Responsive Devices: Type?   Type of test?
    Valve No................A......B......C......D......E......F......   Valve No................A......B......C......D......E......F......
    Valve No................A......B......C......D......E......F......   Valve No................A......B......C......D......E......F......
    Valve No................A......B......C......D......E......F......   Valve No................A......B......C......D......E......F......
    Valve No................A......B......C......D......E......F......   Valve No................A......B......C......D......E......F......
    Auxiliary equipment: No?............. Type?................Location?................ Test Results?..........

19. Explanation of any "No" answers.

20. Recent changes in building occupancy or fire protection equipment.

21. Adjustments or corrections made.

22. Desirable Improvements.

DUPLICATE TO: ....

STREET ....CITY & STATE ....

*Explain "No" answers in Item #19

Fig. 14-6B.   Sheet No. 2 of a sample Report of Inspection (Sprinkler System Equipment) as recommended in NFPA No. 13A, Recommended Practice for the Care and Maintenance of Sprinkler Systems.

instances, such corrosive action is slow but sure, and thus must be vigilantly watched. Illustrations of some typical corroded sprinklers are shown in Figure 14-6D.

Some types of sprinklers are less susceptible than others to corrosive conditions. Nonferrous metal is used for sprinkler parts, but special protective coatings are necessary for all types when exposed to extreme corrosive conditions. Approved corrosion-resistant or special coated sprinklers are needed in locations where chemicals, moisture, or corrosive vapors exist. Representative occupancies having corrosive conditions likely to affect sprinklers adversely are given in the NFPA Sprinkler Standard.

Protection of Pipe Against External Corrosion

Under some conditions, corrosive vapors may cause rapid deterioration of steel pipe and hangers, necessitating

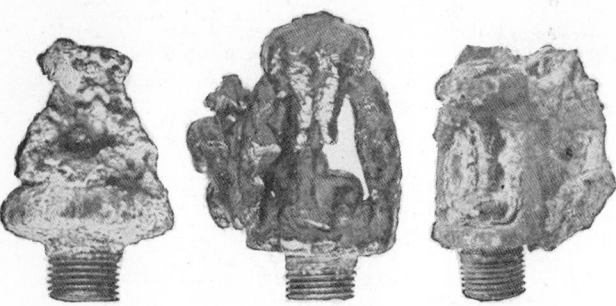

Fig. 14-6C. Examples of loaded automatic sprinklers.

frequent replacement unless the proper protection is provided. However, under most conditions cast-iron fittings will not be seriously affected.

There are two methods available for avoiding pipe corrosion: first, protective coatings, and second, the use of other than steel pipe. Under severe corrosive conditions, protective methods are not wholly satisfactory. Genuine wrought iron pipe, copper, or special alloy noncorrosive pipe will give the best results.

Galvanized steel, under some conditions, may be the best and most economical method of obtaining reasonably long life for the piping system. This might apply to chemical plants, salt works, or similar properties where corrosion may be severe. Stainless steel and copper piping have also been used in some cases.

When corrosion of existing equipment becomes a maintenance problem, replacement or the application of a recognized type of protective coating are remedial measures.

Emergency Measures for Maintaining Sprinkler Protection During Repairs or Alterations

The NFPA Automatic Sprinkler Performance Tables and the large loss building fire records show the seriousness of having sprinklers shut off when a fire starts. Such a situation arises if the sprinkler system water supply is shut off for (1) extensions or alterations to the sprinkler piping, (2) repairs due to accidental damage to piping or sprinklers, (3) replacement of sprinklers after a fire, or (4) maintenance or replacement of sprinklers and other sprinkler system devices. When, of necessity, sprinkler protection is interrupted, every effort must be made to limit the extent and duration of the interruption. A cardinal rule is to notify the fire department whenever such sprinkler impairment exists so that, in the event of a fire, they will not place false reliance on the systems. Most insurance companies also request that owners advise them when there is interruption of sprinkler protection so that alternate means of protection can be arranged if judged necessary or desirable.

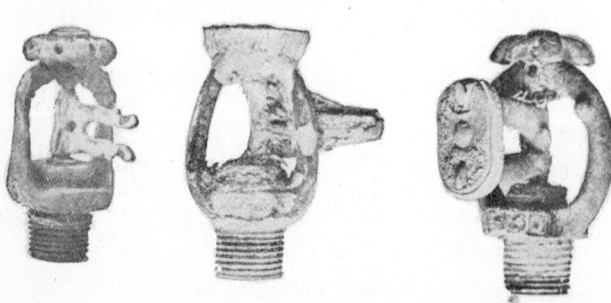

Fig. 14-6D. Examples of corroded automatic sprinklers.

Advance Preparations

When sprinklers must be shut off, the work should be planned for a time when the least hazard exists. In industrial plants, about three times as many fires occur during operations as during idle periods. It is thus advisable that the work be done on a weekend or other idle period. Special watchman service may be required, however, to attempt to assure prompt detection of any fire which might develop while the sprinklers are shut off.

Sectional valves, rather than main valves, should be used where possible to reduce to a minimum the number of shutoff sprinklers and to take all possible advantage of multiple water supplies.

All personnel, materials, and tools should be made ready before the sprinkler protection is impaired.

If underground mains are involved, use a tapping machine when possible to avoid shutting off the water. If mains are to be opened, prepare wooden or other plugs or caps, and clamps to close the end of pipes quickly. Take emergency measures to maintain the maximum possible water supply to sprinklers. One possibility is to make a temporary hose connection from a hydrant still in service or from a domestic or industrial supply to the sprinkler riser or risers. These connections are normally made to the 2-in. drain with the drain valve and hydrant valve left open. Such arrangements are shown in Figure 14-6E. Adapters for connecting 2½-in. hose to sprinkler systems should be kept on hand.

Definite procedures for supervising closed valves (see Sec. 10, Chap. 1), for notifying the fire department and insurance companies, and for making water-flow tests after the work is completed should be followed.

E. Basic Principles of Maintenance and Inspection

The purpose of the care and maintenance of any piece of fire protection equipment is to assure its optimum condition to operate as intended whenever called upon to extinguish fire. As far as sprinklers are concerned, the major considerations are: (1) that the sprinkler protection is complete in the areas protected, (2) that there are no obstructions (high-piled stock, partitions, etc.) to the effective distribution of water discharge from the sprinklers, (3) that the water supply is constantly available, (4) that there is no danger that any portion of the sprinkler system can freeze, and (5) that all devices forming a part of a sprinkler system, alarm, supervisory systems, or water supply are in dependable operating condition.

Inspection is merely an organized, methodical procedure for determining the operating condition of devices, equipment, and, in some cases, the qualifications of personnel, for the detection of conditions calling for maintenance, repair, or remedy.

Maintenance of protection involves making the inspections as well as performing any special investigations or tests bearing on the performance of the devices and equipment, taking action to repair or keep devices and equipment in dependable operating condition, and assuring correct procedures by personnel responsible for the performance or use of the equipment.

Inspection and maintenance functions are closely related and may overlap in some features. Management is responsible for their correlation. Inspections frequently involve matters which may be classed as maintenance, and maintenance sometimes requires its own inspections and tests beyond those made routinely during so-called fire inspections.

Fig. 14-6E. When it is necessary to shut off the water supply to a sprinkler system when repairs or extensions are to be made, a temporary supply can be provided by a hose line, keeping all or part of the system in service.

F. Care and Maintenance of Specific Components of Sprinkler Systems

The following specific items of sprinkler care and maintenance are treated in relation to routine inspection, test, and maintenance procedures, and are independent of the organization performing the inspection and maintenance functions, whether watchman, fire inspector, maintenance man, supervisor, others making up the fire organization at any particular propery, or outside contractors.

Public and Private Water Supply Equipment

Information relating to the inspection and test of public water supplies and of private water supply equipment, such as tanks and fire pumps, is given in Section 11, Chapters 3, 4, and 5.

Water Control Valves and Meters

The inspection and supervision of valves which affect the flow of water in fire protection systems, including sprinkler systems, is covered in Section 11, Chapter 2, and also in NFPA No. 26, Standard for the Supervision of Water Supply Valves.

Service Valves: Service valves at private fire system connections to public systems are usually under the control of the water department and are seldom operated. Their condition is usually indicated adequately by water-flow tests made from the private protection system as covered later in this chapter.

Meters: Meters in public water system connections are also generally under the control of the water utility but are sometimes located in pits on the protected property.

Check Valves: Check valves in public water connections, where needed to prevent back flow from private systems into public systems, are usually a part of the protection system for which the property owner is responsible. Testing and maintenance procedures are covered in Section 11, Chapter 2.

Sprinklers and Sprinkler Piping

Observe whether there is any building or room from which sprinklers have been omitted, including such places as basements, lofts, show windows, concealed spaces, towers, under stairs, under skylights, and inside elevator wells, vertical shafts, small enclosures (such as drying and heating enclosures), and closets (unless open at the top). Observe also whether there are sprinklers under large air ducts, shelves, benches and tables, overhead storage racks, platforms, and similar surfaces which might obstruct distribution of water from sprinklers above.

Additional branches and sprinklers installed after the original installation was made should be examined to make sure that the system, particularly the smaller distributing pipes, has not become overloaded by supplying too many sprinklers for the size of the supply piping and water pressure available. Where the system is hydraulically designed, calculations should be kept available on additions to the system to help in checking on the effect of these additions.

Sprinklers must not be obstructed by highly piled stock or other material, nor by partitions or walls which might prevent free and proper water distribution. A clear space of not less than 18 in. below the deflectors of sprinklers is normally required.

Observe whether proper schedule of spacing is followed by referring to the NFPA Sprinkler Standard for spacing recommendations given for the various occupancy classes.

Note whether all pipes in dry systems have the proper pitch. This feature is of special importance, for water remaining in pockets or low places is likely to freeze and cripple the system.

Are any hangers loose or piping not properly supported? Observe whether sprinkler piping is used for the support of stock, clothing, etc. Sprinkler piping should not be used for such purposes.

Note whether the sprinklers are placed in an upright or pendent position. Sprinklers must be installed in the position for which they are designed and marked.

The distance of the deflectors from the ceiling or bottom of beams or joists should conform to the sprinkler installation standard.

Note the type and design of the sprinkler, the year of its manufacture, and date of installation (sometimes old sprinklers are used in a new installation).

Are all sprinklers of the proper temperature rating? Ordinary-degree sprinklers should be substituted for high-degree sprinklers when the latter are unnecessary. Wherever temperature around sprinklers may exceed 100° F to 110° F, high-degree sprinklers should be used (see Chap. 5 of this Section).

Are any sprinklers corroded or loaded? Are sprinklers of a proper type, or properly protected against corrosion? If any sprinklers are in doubtful condition, samples should be removed and tested.

Sprinklers having coatings of paint, excessive deposits or

incrustations, whitewash, bronzing, or other coating should be replaced by new sprinklers.

A supply of extra sprinklers should be kept in a sprinkler cabinet, so that any sprinklers that have operated or have been injured in any way may be replaced promptly. These sprinklers should correspond in type and in temperature ratings to the sprinklers in the property. The cabinet should be situated in a cool location. The number of sprinklers stocked for replacement purposes is governed by the size and number of systems, the location of the protected property relative to the source of supply for replacement sprinklers, and the number of sprinklers likely to be opened by extraordinary conditions such as a flash fire.

Ordinarily, under average conditions, the stock of emergency sprinklers should be as follows:

For systems having not over 300 sprinklers– 6 sprinklers
For systems having 300 to 1,000 sprinklers–12 sprinklers
For systems having above 1,000 sprinklers–24 sprinklers

For systems aboard vessels or in isolated locations, a greater number of sprinklers should be carried to permit restoring equipment to service promptly after a fire.

A special sprinkler wrench should be kept in the cabinet to be used in the removal and installation of sprinklers. This wrench should always be used for installing new sprinklers.

Sprinkler System Water Supply Control Valves

Gate and check valves should be properly arranged and located in accordance with the Sprinkler Standard.

All control valves should be readily accessible and unobstructed so that they can be closed promptly.

Valves should be examined to see that they are open and in good operative condition, turn easily, and do not leak.

Wrenches should be kept at the indicator post valve or at a location where they are readily accessible.

Pits for gate or check valves should be kept reasonably dry and clean so that valves can be tested, examined, and maintained in good condition. Manhole covers should be kept clear of snow and ice.

Tightness of check valves should be determined periodically by proper tests, depending on water supplies.

Each control valve should be numbered at the valve and listed (giving location, use, or portions of the system controlled) on a plant fire inspection report form as explained in Section 10, Chapter 2. There should be a plan posted at a central point known to plant and public fire officials showing valve locations.

There should be a sign at each valve showing what it controls, with the sign bearing the legend "Must Be Open at All Times" or other proper wording. See Figure 14-1N for available standardized signs. Underground valve locations should be shown by distance markings on nearby buildings, and on accurate plans of the property.

All control valves should be sealed or locked open (see Sec. 10, Chap. 2 for information on valve sealing) unless there is central station supervisory service.

There should be someone on the premises at all times who knows the use and location of all of the control and drain valves. This includes the watchman or any others who may be on duty at night.

Sprinkler System Water-flow Tests

The NFPA Sprinkler Standard calls for a water supply test pipe and pressure gages to be provided at locations that will permit flowing tests to be made to determine whether water supplies and connections are in order. A 2-in. drain at the sprinkler riser may suffice as a water supply test pipe if so installed that the valve may be opened wide for a sufficient time to assure a proper test without causing water damage.

There should be provision for checking the gage and pressure with an inspector's gage.

The pressure on the sprinkler system side of alarm or check valves may be higher than that of the water supply, as any momentary high pressure on the supply will be transmitted to the system and retained by the check valves. This excess pressure is relieved when a water-flow test is made.

The drop in pressure below the normal static pressure with the 2-in., water supply test pipe (drain) wide open can be noted, and general flow conditions evaluated. For instance, if the normal static pressure is 50 psi, and if previous tests have shown a pressure drop to 45 psi when the drain valve is opened, it will be apparent that if at inspection the pressure drops to, say, 35 psi or under, there is some obstruction to the flow which should be removed, or some other defect which should be located and remedied.

At each inspection, a flow test should be made separately for each water supply and each connection from a supply. This can be accomplished by closing the water supplies temporarily, except the one under test. Too much emphasis cannot be placed on the value of flow tests to determine whether there is any obstruction to full flow. It is mandatory that all water supplies be returned to service immediately after testing.

If there is water-flow supervisory service, tests should not be made without first notifying the central station or other alarm headquarters.

There should be a 1-in. test pipe (¾-in. prior to 1940) having a standard brass ½-in. outlet at a remote point of each system. This should be operated at each inspection of a wet system to make sure that there is free flow at good pressure and to test the water-flow alarm. In dry systems, this test pipe is used to trip the dry-pipe valve as referred to later.

Dry-pipe Sprinkler Systems

The generally accepted best practice is to keep dry-pipe systems in the dry condition throughout the year. When water flows into sprinkler piping, rust and foreign material tend to be carried into the smaller pipes, where accumulation and obstruction to flow can occur. Annual tripping of the dry-pipe valve to make the system wet accelerates this behavior.

When systems are wet, with the dry-pipe valve tripped, the water-flow alarm feature of the dry valve is out of service.

Old, obsolete, unapproved, and any dry-pipe valves in poor mechanical condition are likely to be unreliable and should be replaced with currently approved or acceptable types.

Instruction charts are provided for the maintenance of dry-pipe valves by the sprinkler installing company and should be posted at or near these valves.

All dry-pipe valves should be numbered and listed on inspection report forms.

Check the air pressure on each dry-pipe system at least once a week and pump up the systems when necessary. A daily check is recommended for the first week after dry-pipe valve resetting. If pressure is lost rapidly, requiring frequent pumping, the piping system should be gone over and made tight. Avoid air pressure higher than that called for by the valve manufacturer's instructions.

Make sure that the priming water is maintained at the proper level above the dry-pipe valve.

Slight freezing of a dry-pipe valve may cause it to be inoperative. It is extremely important to make sure both that adequate provision is made for the heating of the valve enclosure or the room in which it is located, and that the heating equipment is safe and in order.

Dry system piping should be thoroughly drained before freezing weather and kept clear of water during the winter. The freezing of a small amount of water in the piping may cause rupture of the piping or sprinklers and the operation of the valve. Make sure that all low point drains of the system are kept free of water.

Dry-pipe valves should be examined externally at frequent intervals to detect evidences of deterioration.

It should be made certain that the automatic drip or drain is clear and free to operate.

Thoroughly clean and reset each dry-pipe valve once yearly during the warm weather. On such occasions, the valve body should be thoroughly washed out, preferably with warm water, care being taken to make sure that the small ports and piping leading to the alarm connections are free from obstructions.

Operating tests of dry-pipe valves, including quick opening devices, if any, should be made from time to time. Such a test may be combined with the annual cleaning and resetting, and with any necessary service with respect to renewal of rubber parts or the adjustment of gages, alarm devices and connecting piping, and quick opening devices.

When dry valves are tripped for testing purposes, the procedure should be such that only the minimum flow of water needed to trip the valve is admitted to the sprinkler riser. This can usually be done by having the control valve only one or two turns open and by closing it immediately after the dry valve trips.

Operating tests and servicing of dry-pipe valves, including quick opening devices, should be conducted either by a sprinkler installing company, or other fully qualified personnel.

No grease or other sealing material should be used on seats of dry-pipe valves in an effort to stop leaks. Force should not be used in an attempt to make dry-pipe valves tight.

Dry-pipe valves should carry a tag or card showing the date on which the valve was last tripped and the name of the organization making the test. Such tags are usually available from the installing company or the insurance authorities.

Quick Opening Devices

The operation of quick opening devices usually can be tested either with or without operating the dry-pipe valve itself. The manufacturer's instructions for testing and resetting the device should be carefully followed.

If the device does not operate properly on test, it can, if necessary, be removed and the sprinkler system kept in operative condition. Repair parts can be ordered from the manufacturer, or the device sent to the manufacturer for repair or adjustment.

Pressure Gages

Water pressure and air pressure gages should be tested for accuracy whenever the dry valve is cleaned and reset and at other times if the pressure indication is questionable.

Water-flow Alarm Devices

Test water-flow alarm devices at regularly scheduled inspections of fire protection equipment. Electric alarms should be tested by the bypass test valve at dry-pipe valves and alarm valves, or by test switches. Actual water-flow alarm tests should be made when cold weather does not make the outdoor discharge of water from test or drain valves objectionable. Water-motor gongs should not be tested in freezing weather.

Keep the small valve or cocks controlling the water supply to alarm devices sealed open.

Deluge and Pre-action Systems

Complete charts are furnished by installing companies showing in detail the proper method of operating and testing thermostatically controlled systems. Only competent men fully instructed with respect to the details and operation of such systems should be employed in their repair and adjustment. It is highly advisable for the owner to arrange with the installing company for regular periodic inspection and testing of the equipment.

The automatic valves controlling the flow of water into these systems operate through the effect of fire temperatures on actuating devices. Ordinarily, when it is necessary to repair the actuating system, as distinguished from the piping system itself, the piping system is run "wet" and automatic sprinkler protection is thus maintained on a pre-action system, provided there is no danger of freezing.

Sprinkler System Supervisory Services

Central station, proprietary, remote station, fire alarm, and supervisory services for sprinkler systems interpret sprinkler system water-flow signals as fire alarms and immediately initiate fire department response. Signals of other types, such as valve supervision, pressure, or temperature supervision, etc., do not serve as fire alarms, but initiate appropriate courses of action as prearranged between the supervisory service and the property owner. It is extremely important that the headquarters of any of these services be notified and any special arrangements be made in advance of any inspection or tests of equipment that will cause a signal to be transmitted.

Brief information covering sprinkler system alarm and supervisory devices is given in Chapter 5 of this Section. Detailed information regarding system operation is given in Section 12, Chapter 2.

Gravity Water Tanks (see Sec. 11, Chap. 3)

Pressure Tanks (see Sec. 11, Chap. 3)

Fire Pumps (see Sec. 11, Chap. 4)

Fire Department Connections

Inspect each fire department connection regularly to make sure that caps are in place, threads are in good condition, the ball drip or drain is in order, and that the check valve is not leaking. A hydrostatic test should be conducted periodically on old fire department connection piping to assure that it will withstand the required pressure.

Open Sprinkler Equipment

Test outside or open sprinkler equipment once each year during warm weather. These tests should preferably be made in conjunction with the inspection department having jurisdiction and, if desired, with representatives of the fire department.

Before making operating tests, care should be exercised to make sure that all windows and doors through which water might enter are tightly closed. Proper precautions must be taken to prevent damage from discharge or accumulation of water to sidewalks, streets, areaways, or adjoining buildings.

Determine by test whether the sprinklers and the system piping are in good condition and free from plugging. Any piping or sprinklers that are found clogged should be removed, cleaned, and replaced at once.

G.　Obstructions in Sprinkler System Piping

Obstructions in sprinkler piping or yard mains will reduce or cut off the flow of water from a part or all of the sprinklers, and the system will not give the protection intended. Obstructed piping is one of the well recognized causes of unsatisfactory sprinkler performance. One source of obstruction is foreign material in the water supply system, and a second is foreign material originating within the sprinkler system piping itself.

Foreign material, such as sand, gravel, stones, pieces of wood, etc., may enter underground mains as a result of carelessness of workmen when laying or repairing the mains. Sand, silt, or wood chips may also enter the mains through inadequately protected fire pump suction inlets. Sometimes when gravity tanks are cleaned, foreign material enters the drop pipes unless care is taken to prevent it.

Scale, corrosion, and incrustations can also form in the piping. In dry-pipe systems, the condensation of moisture in the air supply may result in hard scale forming along the bottom of piping. Deep-well water and water containing natural salts tend to corrode pipe interiors, and the piping of wet systems may be found obstructed by rust and corrosion. Obstructing material is carried into the sprinkler piping when wet-pipe systems are refilled after draining, when a dry-pipe valve trips, or when sprinklers operate during a fire. It may plug one or more fittings or obstruct a number of sprinklers at the end of the system.

Pipe capacities may be reduced by incrustation in localities where water contains lime or magnesia.

If the water is badly discolored during flow tests, or if gravel or stones are discharged with the water, it indicates the probable presence of foreign material in the piping. Foreign material found in a fire pump suggests that there may also be similar material in the sprinkler piping. Foreign material found in resetting dry-pipe valves or examining check valves indicates a possible serious impairment of the entire fire protective system.

Obstructions to the flow of water from the sprinklers usually comprise concentrations of the lighter materials such as silt, sand, small pebbles, etc., piling up in the ends of the cross mains and in the nearby branch lines, with the heaviest solids collecting nearer the system risers. There are some cases where the foreign material deposits extend so far back into the system from the ends of the cross mains that complete cleaning of the entire system is necessary. More often, however, a preliminary investigation will disclose that while foreign material may cause complete stoppage of water flow from sprinklers on branch lines connected to the ends of the cross mains, there may be no stoppage at any point on branch lines farther back in the system.

Conditions Indicating Possible Obstruction in Piping

Evidence of possible obstruction in piping is given by any one of the following:

1. Plugging of test connections, or discharge of dirty or colored water.
2. Discharge of foreign material during routine water tests.

3. Foreign material in dry-pipe valves, check valves, or fire pumps.
4. Obstructing material found in sprinkler piping dismantled for building or piping alterations.
5. Defects found in fire pump suction screens when source is from open bodies of water.
6. Repairs made in public water mains in vicinity.
7. Underground piping not flushed before connecting sprinkler systems.
8. Plugged sprinklers at time of fire.
9. Old equipment, especially dry-pipe systems.

Investigation of Severity and Extent of Obstruction

An investigation of conditions must be made when evidence of foreign materials in sprinkler systems is found or obstruction is suspected. Where needed, cleaning or flushing procedures must subsequently be carried out to remove obstructing materials. Inspection and flushing methods outlined in this chapter are treated more completely in the AIA pamphlet, *Internal Cleaning of Sprinkler Piping*,[1] and in the FM *Loss Prevention Data Sheets*.[2]

Flushing Feed Main

The flushing of newly installed underground mains is covered in Section 11, Chapter 2 of this HANDBOOK.

Existing yard piping suspected of containing obstructing material should be thoroughly flushed through hydrants at dead ends of the system, blowoff valves, or groups of riser drains, by opening simultaneously as many outlets as possible and allowing the water to run until clean. If the water is supplied from more than one direction or through a looped system, divisional valves should be closed to produce a high-velocity flow through each single line.

It is usually desirable to learn the nature and extent of foreign material that may be in the piping and this can best be done by fastening burlap bags securely to the flowing outlets.

The connections to sprinkler risers should next be flushed through drain valves. If the foreign material is too large to pass through a riser drain valve, some ingenuity must be used to procure a larger opening. Fire department connections can be used by removing the clappers. Flanged check valves or check valve covers, or flanged fittings can be removed and a siamese fitting substituted.

Flushing Sprinkler System Piping

In choosing the critical points for examination, consideration should be given to the arrangement of the piping and the probable pattern of the flow of water when the system is rapidly filled (as in a dry-pipe system), or when a large flow of water from the system occurs due to the operation of many sprinklers on a wet-pipe system.

After selection of the area in which ordinarily the heaviest deposit of foreign material would be expected, the investigation should take into consideration how much of the equipment in that area might be made ineffective by the obstructing material at a time of fire. It is important that the preliminary investigation should indicate the extent of cleaning that may be necessary.

Flow Tests

Flow tests at critical points in a sprinkler system provide a positive means of determining whether there is foreign material in the system that may cause stoppage of water flow from any of the sprinklers, and also of indicating how much of the equipment is affected. Valved hose connections are made to sprinkler fittings at the ends of two, three, or four branch lines, on one side of and at the end of the cross main in the selected area, and flows are taken simultaneously from these points.

If stoppage occurs at all of the two, three, or four branch lines tested simultaneously, additional similar tests may be necessary at points farther back on the system toward the system riser. These tests, if desired, may next be extended to other floors for a reasonably adequate determination of the extent of cleaning operations that may be necessary for complete removal of all foreign material that might cause stoppage.

Foreign deposits in sprinkler systems tend to be crowded toward the ends of the cross mains and in the end branch lines. Of course there will be exceptions to this general statement, such as, for example, where highly corrosive material has been introduced into the system and has caused severe corrosion and scaling of the interior surfaces of the piping uniformly throughout the system.

Visual Examination

Visual inspection of the interior of piping is not a safe substitute for flow tests because it is difficult to judge the behavior of a deposit within the piping from its appearance in place. However, after obstructing material has been found by flow tests, inspection of the interior may assist in determining the extent and type of flushing needed.

To examine the interior of a cross main, back out several upright branch-line nipples, remove the end elbow of the cross main, and inspect the interior of the pipe by means of a flashlight at the openings.

A further check is to take down some of the suspected piping and clean the interior, carefully noting the character of the material removed.

H. Extent of Cleaning Required

When preliminary tests show evidence of obstruction in sprinkler system piping, the next step is to undertake a cleaning program to remove the obstructing material. There are three degrees of cleaning: (1) complete cleaning, (2) limited cleaning, and (3) flushing extremities only. The selection of the degree required is dictated by the character, extent, and location of the obstruction.

It can be said generally that when stoppage occurs only in the branch lines at extremities of the system, the flushing extremities only procedure can be used to clean the system. If stoppage occurs at several test points, but indications are that free flows are available on the other lines back toward the riser, a limited cleaning procedure may be followed. If the stoppage is more extensive, then a complete cleaning procedure should be undertaken.

Before any cleaning is undertaken, however, written specifications or procedure plans covering the entire proposed operations should be understood by all concerned. After completion of the work, the sprinkler contractor or other party performing the cleaning operation should furnish a written statement to those concerned to the effect that all operations have been completed in accordance with the approved procedure, that the specified examinations and tests have been made, and that the system has been left in normal condition.

Complete Cleaning

There are some cases where the foreign material is of such character and extends so far back into the system from the ends of the cross mains that complete cleaning of the entire system will be necessary. In such cases, it is of prime importance that a plan of the piping system be prepared and be marked numerically to show the proper sequence of the cleaning operations, the size and length of hose to be used, the points where the hose is to be attached, and the number of flows to be made at each point.

Limited Cleaning

Where points of impairment of protection can be identified as occurring within restricted areas rather than throughout the system, and if these points exist in any appreciable amount only in the ends of cross mains and in the branch lines connected at or near those points, not all branch lines need to be cleaned. The cleaning procedure may be limited to the branch lines at or near these points and to the cross mains on each floor.

Limited cleaning operations serve to minimize the time during which sprinkler protection is impaired; they lessen the disturbance to normal activities within the premises where the cleaning operations are under way; and they materially lower the cost of the work as compared with the costs of more extensive cleaning.

Since only a fraction of the total number of branch lines are being cleaned directly under the limited procedure, periodic flow tests should be made as the cleaning progresses in order to determine the effectiveness of the work. The limited procedure takes into account the purging effect in branch lines not actually flushed, caused by high-velocity water and air flow along the cross main.

Cleaning System Extremities Only

This cleaning method should be used only in cases in which impairment of dry-pipe sprinkler protection has been found to occur solely at the system extremities, and it relates to every floor protected, regardless of the number of floors.

Extreme care should be exercised before this cleaning method is employed. Adequate examinations and flow tests are made to make certain that only the sprinklers located at the extremities of the system are subject to plugging. It should not be used where the deposits extend back into the cross main beyond the second branch line from the end of the cross main.

I. Cleaning Methods

There are two methods in general use for cleaning sprinkler systems: water flushing and hydro-pneumatic. Experience has indicated that either of these two methods may be employed by competent workmen with reasonable anticipation of a successful conclusion. In both methods, the cleaning is accomplished by a stream of water which passes through the pipes with sufficient velocity to loosen and raise foreign material and carry it out of the system. Effectiveness, economy, and convenience are the three factors which usually govern the selection of the method to be used.

Flushing should be effective if water in adequate volume and pressure is available, and if the discharge of water can be made without excessive choking through long lengths of hose that may be required to reach points where the water can be safely discharged.

The comparative economy of the two methods usually depends upon a number of factors. Among them are the number of flushing connections to be made, availability of electric power service and special equipment required, and labor costs.

Convenience is a factor that may make the hydro-pneumatic method preferable to the water flushing method. With the former, there is no open discharge of water outside the building; there is less disturbance of plant operations; frequent fillings and drainings of the sprinkler system are unnecessary; there is considerably less pipe work; and a complete operation is performed at a given flush point.

Both the water flushing and hydro-pneumatic methods are appropriate for complete cleaning and limited cleaning procedures. Good practice is first to flush the underground piping and then to clean all private sources of water supply that might cause silting in the underground main.

Water Flushing Method

The water flushing method employs a direct discharge of water from the system through hose attached to the end of each cross main and to the end of each branch line. The size and length of hose, points of hose attachment, and other engineered features are designated for each cleaning job.

Bulk or Feed Mains: Each such main should be flushed from its extremity at a rate of flow of not less than 1,000 gpm for 8-in. mains and 500 gpm for 6-in. mains (see Table 14-6A). To accomplish this usually requires the attachment of one or more 2½-in. hose lines with suitable connections and with discharge of water to a safe place. If necessary, the flow may be established through connected cross mains.

Cross Mains: Beginning at the lowest floor, each cross main should be flushed through a 2½-in. hose. With cross mains that terminate in piping smaller than 2 in., the smaller pipe should be removed and hose attached to the 2-in. end of the main. The smaller piping should be cleaned separately before replacing. Where it is difficult to obtain a 2-in. connection, a simultaneous flow should be taken from two connecting outlets of 1½-in. size.

Branch Lines: After all of the cross mains on one floor or section of the building have been flushed, each branch line, beginning nearest the riser or supply pipe, should be flushed through hose not less than 1¼ in. in diameter, connected to a gate or angle valve which is attached to the 1-in. pipe at or near the end of the branch line by removing the end fitting or by removing the ¾-in. pipe if any pipe of this size is encountered. If the branch lines are long, it may be found advisable to remove the end sections of pipe to permit flushing through the end of the 1¼-in. pipe. Any end pipe sections removed should be separately cleaned before they are replaced.

To expedite the work of flushing branch lines, gate or angle valves may be installed on the ends of a number of branch lines at one time, and several lengths of hose may be attached for flushing several lines simultaneously. Two or three crews of men, with each crew equipped with a dozen valves and one or more lengths of hose, can work together on a system and greatly speed up the work.

Table 14-6A. Water-flow Recommended for Flushing Piping

Size of Pipe Inches	Flow Gpm	Size of Pipe Inches	Flow Gpm
¾	10	3½	180
1	16	4	240
1¼	28	5	360
1½	38	6	500
2	60	8	1,000
2½	90	10	1,500
3	130	12	2,000

Branch Line Testers

If it is anticipated that a sprinkler system may need periodic testing for obstruction or repeated flushing, a branch line tester may be installed permanently as a nippled fitting at the end of branch lines or between the last sprinkler and the end fitting on branch lines. The tester has a normally closed and capped outlet connection for hose. Turning a wrench head opens a passage to the outlet which has a 1-in. hose coupling thread. It is not necessary to remove the sprinkler.

Water Flushing Dry-pipe Systems

When the water flushing method is used in cleaning the extremities of dry-pipe systems, the following procedure should be followed:

The lowest floor should be flushed first, followed successively by the floor above, with the top floor flushed last.

Attach the valved hose connections to 1-in. pipe at Points 1 and 2, shown in Figure 14-6F. Set system dry-pipe, and trip the system by release of air through both hose connections at one time. Repeat the same process for Points 3 and 4 and Points 5 and 6, resetting the system dry-pipe for each pair of hose attachments.

With Points 1 and 2 wide open and serving as air vents when the dry-pipe valve trips, the heavy rush of water through the cross main will create sufficient velocity of flow to carry the accumulation of foreign material to the small ends at 1 and 2, where it should readily wash out through the hose. The same results could not be obtained, however, if the system should be filled with water before the valves at Points 1 and 2 are opened.

In following this procedure there will be a temptation to open the main system shutoff valve without resetting the dry-pipe valve in order to save considerable labor cost. This may prove satisfactory in some cases, but it is not considered good practice.

In order to avoid repeatedly resetting the dry-pipe valve, there may be a tendency to flush from all points simultaneously. This also is considered poor practice, since the water entering the cross mains will flow in several different directions. It is better to concentrate the flow of water through one cross main.

Hydro-pneumatic Method

Hydro-pneumatic cleaning employs a stream of water flowing in the opposite direction to that used in the water flushing method: i.e., a short column of water is driven by compressed air through the pipe lines from the small extremities, through the cross main, and is discharged at the base of the system riser.

When the hydro-pneumatic method is used in the limited

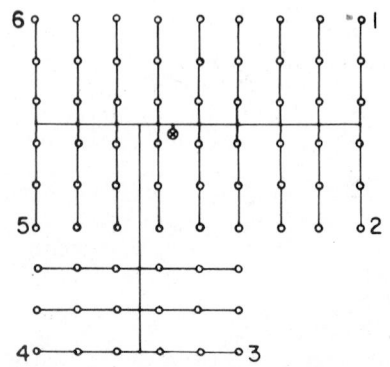

Fig. 14-6F. Valved hose connection attachments.

cleaning procedure, branch lines next adjoining those in which obstructing material was found are also blown out as an added safety measure.

A complete description of the hydro-pneumatic method and the equipment used will be found in the pamphlet, *Internal Cleaning of Sprinkler Piping*.[1]

Hydro-pneumatic Equipment Needed

The hydro-pneumatic apparatus most commonly used at the present time is a relatively simple arrangement of water and air tanks mounted on wheels called the hydro-pneumatic cleaning machine, or tank truck (see Fig. 14-6G). A machine of this type, if constructed as illustrated, and if properly used, will adequately clean any system regardless of its size or the arrangement of the piping.

The air supply should have sufficient capacity to charge the air tank on the machine to at least 100 psi pressure without an excessive loss of labor time. A 30 cu ft per min air compressor, with a 5 hp electric motor mounted on a small receiver tank on wheels, provides a compact mobile unit of sufficient air supply and a motor that is not too large for convenient electrical service.

The equipment recommended for general use is as follows: hydro-pneumatic machine, one 100-ft length of 1-in. pneumatic hose, two 50-ft lengths of 1-in. pneumatic hose, one 30-ft length of 1-in. pneumatic hose, one 30-ft length of 2½-in. hose, and a supply of gate or angle valves (not less than 12) for attachment of hose to branch lines.

J.   Sprinkler Leakage

The term "sprinkler leakage" is ordinarily intended to cover all leakage or discharge of water from the sprinkler system except in case of fire. The system includes sprinklers, piping, tanks, and any other water supplies used for fire protection.

The danger of accidental water discharge is often exaggerated, because a sprinkler system is very rugged, and the pipe, sprinklers, and fittings are made to stand far greater water pressures than are met with in practice. The supports are strong also, and the system is so installed that it should remain intact, even under severe mechanical strain, including any anticipated earthquake shock or movement.

There is no reasonable ground for omission of sprinklers from areas in hospitals and other institutions occupied by patients. While it is true that accidental discharge of cold water from sprinklers might, for example, have an adverse effect upon certain patients in a hospital, the probability of loss of life in event of fire is infinitely more serious than any slight danger of an accidental cold shower from the sprinklers. Conditions which might result in accidental discharge of water from sprinklers are highly unlikely where ordinary hospital care would preclude the existence of either freezing temperatures or temperatures so high as to cause the opening of sprinklers except in the case of fire.

A 5-yr (1954 to 1959, inclusive) record of sprinkler leakages reported to insurance companies from properties protected by automatic sprinklers provides the following major loss causes based upon the amount of loss:

	percent
Freezing of sprinklers and piping	26
Mechanical breakage of piping or sprinklers	23
Breakage of underground mains due to settlement and corrosion	20
Overheating of automatic sprinklers	16
Miscellaneous—unclassified	15
Total	100

It also has been estimated, based on sprinkler leakage loss reports, that the chance that a sprinkler may open accidentally because it is defective is less than one in a million each year.

Automatic sprinkler protection for property particularly susceptible to water damage, such as computers, finely made complicated mechanical equipment, works of art, valuable books, etc., should not be omitted due to fear of premature

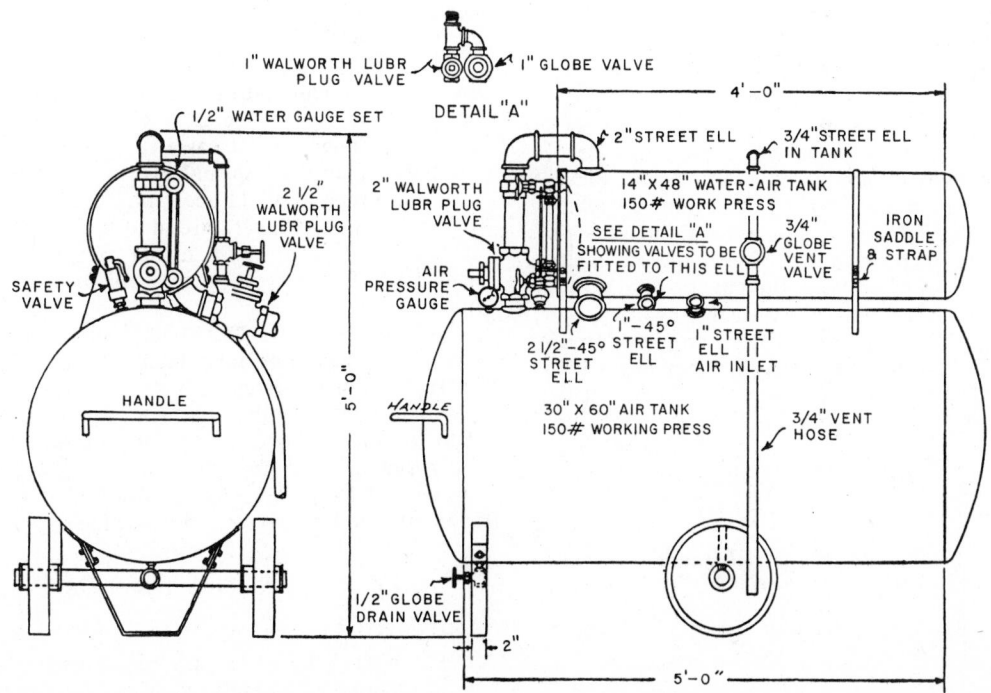

Fig. 14-6G.   Hydro-pneumatic tank truck.

operation of sprinklers if reasonable precautions against freezing, overheating, and mechanical injury are taken.

Some of the more important conditions responsible for sprinkler leakage and water loss are explained in the remaining paragraphs of this part of this chapter.

Mechanical Injury

Automatic sprinklers are designed to withstand at least 500 psi pressure without injury or leakage. If properly installed there is little danger of the sprinkler breaking apart unless it is injured in some way. All of the listed sprinklers are rugged and will stand considerable abuse. The frames can be bent somewhat without opening the sprinkler.

Where the sprinkler is so located as to be easily subject to mechanical injury, it is desirable to provide metal guards to protect it. Such guards can be secured from the sprinkler companies (see Fig.14-6H).

The use of lift trucks or tractors in handling materials indoors must be carefully planned and supervised to avoid contact with sprinklers and sprinkler piping. This is a major hazard which has developed recently with changes in materials handling methods.

Improper Installation and Maintenance

Improper installation includes lack of proper supports for risers and feed mains, lack of proper tie rods where inside piping is connected to cast-iron fittings, and defective pipe hangers or supports.

Breaks or leaks sometimes occur in underground work due to improper laying of underground mains or poor workmanship in making joints. Sometimes breaks occur in properly installed systems due to undue stresses on the piping system, such as those caused by settling of the building or foundations, or lack of clearance around pipes where they pass through foundations.

Every piping system should be frequently inspected and properly maintained. The condition of hangers and supports should be watched to determine whether they are in good order, or loose, or with screws or fastenings pulled out.

Sprinkler piping should never be used as a support for ladders, stock, or other material. Any system of piping under constant internal pressure should receive proper care and not be subject to mechanical abuse.

Freezing

The freezing of water in pipes is a common cause of trouble and the remedy in most cases is self-evident. Where this is a local condition and not unduly severe, ice in the sprinkler head or fittings may rupture the sprinkler without damage to the pipe or fittings. When the ice melts, water is discharged. In other cases, the pipe or fittings may burst, causing serious damage and expensive repairs.

In some types of sprinklers a moderate amount of freezing may not break the sprinkler open, but may cause it to leak at the seat after ice melts.

Fig. 14-6H. Metal guard protection against mechanical injury.

Some of the conditions which cause trouble from freezing are:

1. Insufficient heat in certain portions for severe weather conditions, such as concealed spaces under roofs or blind attics, large open doorways for trucks or railway cars, entryways, and space under buildings.
2. Windows left open during severely cold weather.
3. Insufficient heat because of shortage of fuel supply.
4. Branch lines of dry-pipe systems not correctly pitched to drain.
5. Feed mains or piping in unheated areas, or not properly protected to prevent freezing.
6. Freezing of tank risers due to lack of heat or lack of adequate protection; obstructed circulating pipes of heating systems.
7. Freezing of water in underground mains not buried deep enough in the ground.

Overheating

Overheating is the most common cause of accidental water damage from sprinklers and is the term used when an automatic sprinkler operates as a result of abnormally high temperatures, but without the presence of fire. This condition is usually caused by hot manufacturing processes, artificial heating, or lack of ventilation. It may result from a sudden increase in temperature which operates the heat-responsive element, or from longer exposure to temperature sufficiently high to cause gradual weakening. In the solder type of sprinkler the latter condition, sometimes termed "cold flow," is indicated by partial separation of the soldered members.

In practice there are a number of conditions which cause unsafe temperatures, such as:

1. Climatic condition causing temperatures well above normal (110°F or above).
2. Ordinary low-temperature sprinklers located too near steam mains, unit heaters, heating ducts, etc. Temperatures higher than anticipated may occur after installation of sprinklers. Changes in heating methods, installation of unit heaters, changes in manufacturing processes or equipment, etc., after sprinklers are installed, are of frequent occurrence.

The NFPA Sprinkler Standard gives some information on sprinkler temperature ratings near unit heaters. Unit heaters should never be used without a careful study of conditions, and in most cases sprinklers near unit heaters must be replaced by sprinklers with a higher temperature rating in order to avoid accidental operation.

3. Changes in temperatures due to changes in occupancy, or processes which cause higher temperatures than contemplated. This may be general, or local in portions of a building.
4. In some cases a fire which opens a number of sprinklers may weaken other sprinklers in that vicinity. This is not a common occurrence.

When conditions occur which require sprinklers higher than "ordinary" degree rating, the maximum temperature at the sprinkler level must be determined and sprinklers of the correct temperature rating installed if trouble is to be avoided (see Chapter 3 of this Section).

K.   Reducing Water Damage

Alarm Service

It is evident that if leakage occurs when there is no one in the building and no proper means of alarm notification to outsiders, the leakage may continue for a considerable length of time and serious loss occur, even if the rate of water discharge is relatively small, as with one sprinkler operating.

While good or "standard" watchman service is of value, it may not be adequate unless there is a sprinkler alarm gong which will notify the watchman if water is flowing.

Every sprinkler system should have a water-flow alarm device and properly located alarm gong, not only to give alarm in case sprinklers operate because of fire but also to minimize loss from sprinkler leakage.

Most large losses from sprinkler leakage are due to lack or failure of local sprinkler alarm devices or gongs, or failure to notify promptly some authorized person who will investigate immediately and shut off the water if there is no fire. In some cases water runs for many hours without anyone knowing about it, and the operation of even one sprinkler on an upper floor of a building containing expensive merchandise may cause a very heavy loss.

Sprinkler supervisory service, as described in Chapter 5 of this Section, is of great value in the prompt discovery of any leakage from the system, and in securing appropriate action to minimize the water loss.

Other Safeguards

Various provisions or safeguards may be taken to lessen the damage to stock from water used to extinguish fire (see Sec. 6 of this HANDBOOK). Similar provisions are of value in case of sprinkler leakage.

SI Units

The following conversion factors are given as a convenience in converting to SI units the English units used in this chapter.

1 in.	$= 25.4/mm$
1 ft	$= 0.305\ m$
1 hp	$= 0.746\ kW$
1 psi	$= 6.895\ kPa$
$\frac{5}{9}(°F - 32)$	$= °C$
1 ft³	$= 0.0283\ m^3$
1 gpm	$= 3.785\ litre/min$

Bibliography

References Cited

[1] *Internal Cleaning of Sprinkler Piping*, American Insurance Association, New York, 1959.
[2] Factory Mutual Engineering Corporation, "Sprinkler System Maintenance," *Loss Prevention Data Sheets*, 2nd ed., McGraw-Hill, New York, 1967, pp. 14-1, 2.

NFPA Codes, Standards, and Recommended Practices (see the latest *NFPA Publications and Visual Aids Catalog* for availability of current editions of the following documents)

NFPA No. 13, Standard for the Installation of Sprinkler Systems.
NFPA No. 13A, Standard for the Care and Maintenance of Sprinkler Systems.
NFPA No. 26, Standard for the Supervision of Water Supply Valves.

SECTION 15

SPECIAL FIRE PROTECTION SYSTEMS

Chapter 1

STANDPIPES AND HOSE SYSTEMS

Standpipe and hose systems provide a means for manual application of water to fires in buildings. They do not take the place of automatic extinguishing systems which are generally the preferred form of protection. They are always needed where automatic protection is not provided, and in areas of buildings not readily accessible to hose lines from outside hydrants.

Standpipe systems are designed for fire department use to provide quick and convenient means for obtaining effective fire streams on the upper stories of high buildings or large low buildings. NFPA 14, Standard for Standpipe and Hose Systems, hereinafter referred to in this chapter as the NFPA Standpipe and Hose Systems Standard, should be consulted for installation details.

Many jurisdictions have discontinued the requirement for occupant-use hose systems in buildings that are completely protected by automatic sprinklers. The most effective use of standpipe systems is when they are used by fire departments or personnel who are trained in the use of 2½-in. hose streams at high pressures.

A. System Classification

Class I systems (2½-in. hose connections) are provided for use by fire departments and those trained in handling heavy fire streams. In nonsprinklered high-rise buildings beyond the reach of fire department ladders, Class I systems can provide water supply for the primary means of fire fighting, i.e., manual attack on the fire.

Class II systems (1½-in. hose lines) are provided for use by the building occupants until the fire department arrives. The hose is connected to ⅜- or ½-in. open nozzles or combination spray/straight stream nozzle with shutoff valves. Shutoff or spray nozzles are seldom provided unless the occupancy is one where hand hose would be used frequently. Normally, the hose is kept attached to the shutoff valves at the outlets. Where the occupant-use hose streams can be properly supplied by connections to the risers of wet-pipe automatic sprinkler systems, separate standpipes for these smaller streams are not required.

Class III systems are provided for use by either fire departments and those trained in handling heavy hose streams, or by the building occupants. Because of the multiple use, this type of system is provided with both 2½-in. hose connections (for use by fire departments or those trained in handling heavy hose streams) and 1½-in. hose connections (for use by the building occupants). One method for accommodating this multiple use is by means of a 2½-in. hose valve with an easily removable 2½ × 1½-in. adapter, permanently attached to the standpipe.

B. Water Supplies

The water supply for standpipe systems depends on the size and number of required streams and the length of time they may have to be operated, as well as consideration for automatic sprinklers using the same riser. The probable number of streams required should be ascertained before the water supply is decided upon. Water supplies for standpipes should be over and above those required for the simultaneous operation of automatic sprinklers except for calculated sprinkler systems in high-rise buildings. For further details see Chapter 8 of NFPA No. 13, Installation of Sprinkler Systems, hereinafter referred to in this chapter as the NFPA Sprinkler System Standard. Standpipe and hose systems should have water pressure maintained at all times. Where this is impractical, as in unheated buildings, the system should be arranged to admit water automatically by means of a dry pipe valve or other approved device.

Acceptable water supplies include the following:

1. City waterworks systems where pressure is adequate.
2. Automatic fire pumps.
3. Manually controlled fire pumps with pressure tanks.
4. Pressure tanks.
5. Gravity tanks.
6. Manually controlled fire pumps operated by remote control devices at each hose station.

Two independent sources of water supply are desirable. The primary water supply should be capable of supplying the streams first operated until the secondary sources can be brought into action. The secondary supply should be adequate for long periods.

Minimum city water and fire pump supplies for standpipes supplying 2½-in. hose that will be used by fire departments or specially trained men (Class I and II systems) are given as 500 gpm for a period of at least 30 min where only one standpipe is required. Where more than one standpipe is required, the minimum supply is 500 gpm for the first standpipe and 250 gpm for each additional standpipe, with the total supply not exceeding 2,500 gpm for at least 30 min. In addition, the supply is required to be strong enough to maintain a residual pressure of 65 psi at the topmost outlet of each standpipe (including outlets on the roof) with 500 gpm flowing.

The water supply for Class II service (1½-in.) is 100 gpm for a period of at least 30 min. It is also required to be strong enough to maintain a residual pressure of 65 psi at the topmost outlet of all standpipes (including roof outlets) with 100 gpm flowing.

Connections for a public fire department to pump water into a standpipe system makes a desirable auxiliary supply. One or more fire department connections is required for Class I and Class III systems (see Fig. 15-1A). However, it is essential that fire department connections be on the street side of buildings near fire hydrants, and installed in a manner that permits hose lines to be attached to them easily and conveniently. Obstructions, such as adjacent buildings, fences, posts, shrubbery, etc., must be avoided.

C. Types of Systems

The four generally recognized standpipe system concepts are:

1. A wet standpipe system, having supply valve open and water pressure maintained at all times. This is the most desirable type of system.

2. A dry standpipe system arranged to admit water to the system through manual operation of approved remote con-

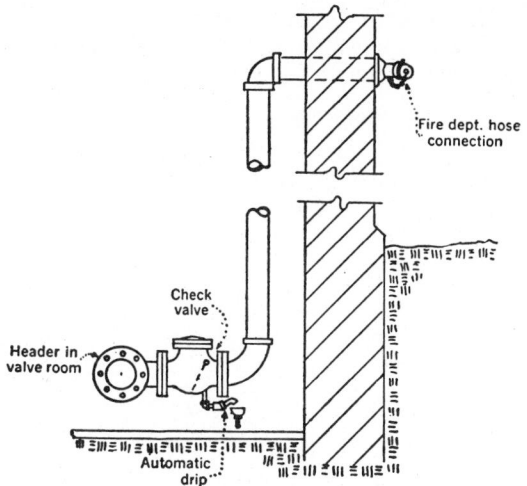

Fig. 15-1A. Typical fire department connection.

trol devices located at each hose station. The water supply control mechanism introduces an inherent reliability factor which must be considered.

3. A dry standpipe system in an unheated building. The system should be arranged to admit water automatically by means of a dry pipe valve or other approved device. The depletion of system air at the time of use introduces a delay in the application of water to the fire and increases the level of competency required to control the pressurized hose and nozzle assembly during the charging period.

4. A dry standpipe system having no permanent water supply. This type would be used for reducing the time required for fire departments to put hose lines into action on upper floors of tall buildings. This type of system might also be used in buildings during construction, where allowed in lieu of the wet standpipe in unheated areas.

D. System Components

Pipe and Tubing

Steel pipe assembled with welded joints, with screwed fittings, with flanged fittings, with rubber gasketed fittings, or with a combination of the above, is the most common material used for standpipes. Copper tubing assembled with brazed joints is also used. For brazing or welding refer to the NFPA Standpipe and Hose Systems Standard.

For Class I and III systems, standpipes not exceeding 100 ft in height are a minimum of 4 in.; standpipes over 100 ft in height, a minimum of 6 in. Where $2\frac{1}{2}$-in. hose outlets are provided on combined automatic sprinkler and standpipe risers, the minimum size is 6 in., except if the building is completely sprinklered, when the risers may be hydraulically calculated in accordance with provisions of the NFPA Sprinkler Systems Standard. When pumps supplying two or more zones are located at the same level, each zone has a separate and direct supply—a minimum of 8 in. Zones with two or more standpipes have at least two direct supply pipes—a minimum of 8 in.

For Class II systems, standpipes less than 50 ft in height are to be a minimum of 2 in. and above 50 ft a minimum of $2\frac{1}{2}$ in.

In designing a Class I and III system, the top 100 ft of a standpipe in excess of 100 ft could be constructed of 4-in. pipe, and the lower part of the vertical standpipe constructed of 6-in. pipe.

Fittings

The fittings should be rated for a minimum of 175 psi. On parts of the standpipe system where the pressure would exceed 175 psi, extra heavy pattern fittings should be used.

Nozzles, Hose and Hose Cabinets

Each hose outlet for a building occupant-use may have up to 100 ft of small hose attached with a $\frac{3}{8}$- or $\frac{1}{2}$-in. open nozzle at the end ready for use. Excessive hose length may result in excessive kinking and other trouble during use. Lightweight woven-jacket, rubber-lined hose is preferred for standpipe or other inside service because of the lower friction loss, although unlined linen hose has been used extensively in the past since it takes up less space than the lined hose. Recent developments using synthetic materials for the jacket and lining have resulted in hose that takes up little more space than the unlined linen hose. When stored dry in heated atmospheres, unlined linen hose will last almost indefinitely; but, under moist or wet conditions it is subject to rapid deterioration. Hose should be kept on a standard rack, i.e., rack designed for use with the type of hose. For typical hose and valve connections, see Figure 15-1B.

Hose for occupant-use should always be in a readily accessible location within convenient reach of a man standing

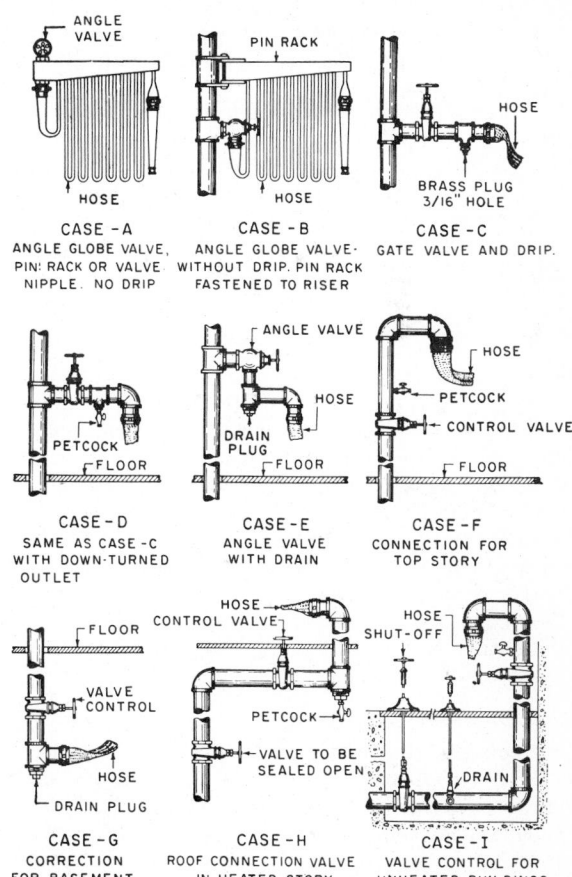

Fig. 15-1B. Hose valves and drip connections used to prevent leakage from entering hose. Racks of "semiautomatic" type, similar to that illustrated in Case A, are commonly used for $1\frac{1}{2}$-in. hose. Hose, hung on pins, is released as nozzle is pulled away from rack. Valve may be opened wide before hose is pulled from racks; folds in hose will stop flow of water until hose is pulled from rack.

on the floor. It should be clearly visible and in a place not likely to be obstructed. Where hose is in cabinets or closets, doors should open readily and have glass panel or other form of easily recognized identification. Signs, such as over aisles in front of the hose station, indicating the location of hose stations are valuable when the stations are not directly visible from all directions.

The general practice is not to provide 2½-in. hose, but to depend upon hose brought in by the fire department at the time of fire. Nevertheless, some city codes require that 2½-in. hose be attached to standpipes. The latter presents the possibility of use of hose by untrained occupants of buildings, which introduces personal injury hazards and the probability of unnecessary water damage.

Where hydrostatic pressure at any outlet for small hose exceeds 100 psi, a device should be installed at the outlet to reduce the pressure to such a value that the nozzle pressure will be limited to approximately 80 psi. One method of obtaining the pressure reduction under flow conditions is by use of an orifice disc. Another method is by the use of pressure reducing devices providing positive pressure control under both static and flow conditions. These devices are available for installation with 1½- and 2½-in. hose connections. They may be factory set for a specific inlet pressure to insure a specific pressure from the discharge of the device, regardless of flow condition. These devices can be a combination pressure reducer and shutoff valve.

Pressure-reducing devices, hose valves, racks, and reels of suitable types for use on standpipes are listed by recognized testing laboratories.

Fire hose should be maintained in proper position on the racks and in good condition. At intervals, new gaskets should be installed in the couplings, at hose valves, and at nozzles. Unlined linen hose should not routinely be tested, as it will rot or mildew if left even slightly damp, and thorough drying after it has been wet is extremely difficult. It should be carefully examined for cuts, loose couplings, and deterioration. Nozzles should be removed and examined for foreign objects.

Valves

A hose valve is provided at each outlet for attachment of hose. These valves are either straightway gate valves or globe valves with soft removable discs.

Indicating valves should be provided at the main riser for controlling branch lines to hose outlets so that in the event that the branch is broken during a fire, the fire department may shut off the branch, thereby conserving water for their use.

Drip connections, however, should be provided on either type of valve to protect hose against possible wetting and resultant deterioration.

Fire Department Connections

An approved fire department connection is to be provided for each Class I or Class III standpipe system. For high-rise buildings having two or more zones, at least one fire department connection is needed for each zone. Fire department connections are on the street side of buildings near fire hydrants for easy connection to fire department pumpers, and are to be marked either "STANDPIPE" or "STANDPIPE AND AUTO. SPKR.," depending on the service.

Gages

An approved 3½-in. dial spring pressure gage is connected to each discharge pipe from fire pumps, to each supply connection from the public waterworks, at each pressure tank as well as at the air pump supplying the pressure tank, and at the top of each standpipe.

Alarm and Supervisory Equipment

Water flow devices and tamper switches that give a signal, either locally or at a central station, are desirable additions to a standpipe system. The equipment used is the same as that used for a sprinkler system.

E. System Design

The standard most widely used for standpipe system design is the NFPA Standpipe and Hose Systems Standard. Some large cities, notably New York and Chicago, have their own applicable codes. Federal building criteria usually supplements the NFPA Standard.

Number and Location of Outlets

The number of standpipes and the arrangement or distribution of equipment for proper protection are governed by local conditions such as occupancy, type and construction of building, exterior exposures, and accessibility. Standpipes supplying both 1½- and 2½-in. hose are located so that all portions of each story are within 30 ft of a nozzle attached to 100 ft of hose. Standpipes should be protected against mechanical and fire damage, with outlets for large hose in stairway enclosures and for small hose in corridors or adjacent to stairway enclosures. Location of occupant-use hose lines within an exit stair enclosure should be avoided, as use of the hose could lead to infiltration of the stairway by smoke or heat, thus jeopardizing use of the exit and endangering those attempting to escape via these stairs.

Standpipes for large hose may furnish valuable protection against exposure fires. In addition to the use of hose streams from windows, roof connections are often employed, and these may be equipped with hose houses or monitor nozzles. Care should be exercised in the choice of location to ensure that the window, door, or roof hatch can be opened under conditions experienced during a fire.

Where a standpipe system is supplied by a fire pump, one 2½-in. hose outlet for each 250 gpm pump capacity may be provided at ground level for fire department use on exposing fires.

Where buildings are within 60 ft of exposing buildings, standpipes for large streams should be located to afford protection against exterior exposures as well as interior protection.

Zoning

The NFPA Standpipe and Hose Systems Standard limits zone height to 275 ft, except the height may be increased to 400 ft when a pressure-reducing device which controls nozzle pressure at both flow and no-flow conditions is installed at each outlet. When pressure regulating devices are used, they are set to give 100 psi maximum at the hose valve outlet.

The best practice is to divide the tall building into pressure zones. About twelve stories in a zone results in water pressures being about normal. This simplifies fire protection measures, as excessive pressure for hose lines does not have to be compensated for by pressure reducing devices and other complications. Water storage for fire protection should be calculated for each pressure zone much as one calculates storage for areas of buildings on hills or other elevations supplied by municipal systems. Tanks providing storage in each pressure zone may be filled from the piping supplying

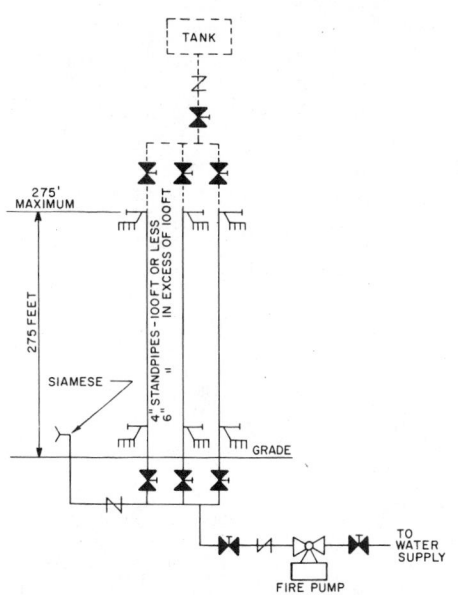

Fig. 15-1C. Typical single zone system.

water for other purposes in the building. Each pressure zone should have a gravity tank and a fire pump, the latter taking suction from the gravity tank in the next lower zone. Each zone should have its own fire department connection.

For a typical single-zone system see Figure 15-1C. In this system a 1,000 gpm fire pump would be required. For a typical two-zone system where the zones are independent (see Fig. 15-1D), two 1,000 gpm fire pumps would be required. The first fire pump, connected to the city water system, supplies the low-level zone including standpipe and

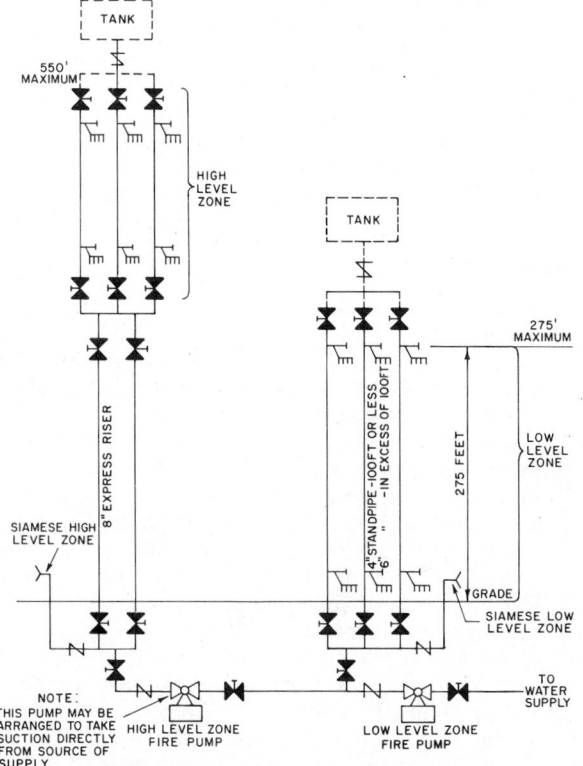

Fig. 15-1D. Typical two-zone system.

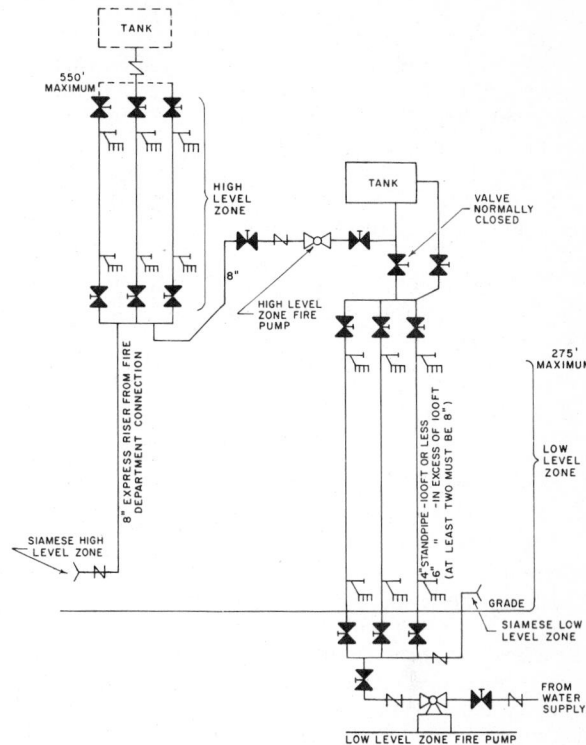

Fig. 15-1E. Alternate typical two-zone system.

storage, and furnishes high-pressure suction to the second fire pump, which serves the high-level zone.

For an alternate two-zone system, see Figure 15-1E. The first fire pump serves the low-level standpipe and the tank that serves as a source for the suction of the high-level fire pump. Both fire pumps would be 1,000 gpm rating to provide enough water for the three standpipes shown.

Standpipes in buildings with more than two zones would be designed as in Figure 15-1E, except there would be additional piping and pumps for the additional zones.

The choice of the location of the fire pumps would depend partially on the economics of the situation. Fire pumps at higher levels would require a lower pressure rating, but more protected wiring and less piping.

F. Combined Sprinkler and Standpipe System

In a combined sprinkler and standpipe system, the sprinkler risers can be used for feeding both the sprinkler system and the hose outlets. The outlets are $2\frac{1}{2}$ in. If the building is completely sprinklered, $1\frac{1}{2}$-in hose for occupant-use should be omitted.

The piping should comply with the requirements of the NFPA Sprinkler Systems Standard for the automatic sprinkler portions of the system, and with the NFPA Standpipe and Hose Systems Standard in regard to sizing of vertical risers and water supplies.

Completely Sprinklered High-Rise Buildings

The minimum water supply for a combined system for a light hazard high-rise occupancy building is 500 gpm. The minimum water supply for other types of high-rise buildings is 1,000 gpm.

G. Inspections

Periodic inspection of all portions of standpipe systems is essential. The tanks should be kept properly filled, and where pressure tanks are employed at least 75 psi pressure should be maintained (see Sec. 11, Chap. 3).

Valves in the automatic sources of water supply should be open at all times. Where the system depends on such valves, they must be electromechanically supervised (see Sec. 12, Chap. 2). Valves at the hose stations should be examined frequently for tightness. Leakage at the hose valves may be detected by inspection of the drips at the valves. Care should be taken to see that the connections and the drips are not clogged with dirt or sediment. Dry standpipes are not desirable and should be avoided to minimize maintenance difficulties.

H. Outside Hose Systems

Hose and Hydrant Houses and Equipment

Where hose is kept connected to hydrants in hose houses, fire lines can be laid and water turned on in about half a minute, as compared with two or three minutes required where a hose cart must be run up, hose coupled to hydrants, run out, and nozzle attached before water is turned on. In addition to the advantage of accessibility, hose kept in dry hose houses lasts longer than hose kept in heated buildings. In large plants having a fire department with trained fire fighters and hose-carrying vehicles, hose houses may not be needed, but for most plants they provide the best means for storing hose.

NFPA No. 24, Standard for Outside Protection, gives requirements for construction and equipment for outside hose and hydrant houses. The principal features considered are ventilation and protection against weather. The ventilation, being secured through slatted floor and shelves and through vent spaces under overhanging roof, is so arranged that rain cannot drive into the building.

Hose is generally attached to one of the hydrant outlets, leaving one or more available for additional lines which can be laid from a hose cart or from reserve hose in the house. Sometimes, equipment for two hose lines is connected to one hydrant. One shelf in a standard hose house will carry 150 ft to 200 ft of woven-jacket, rubber-lined hose folded forward

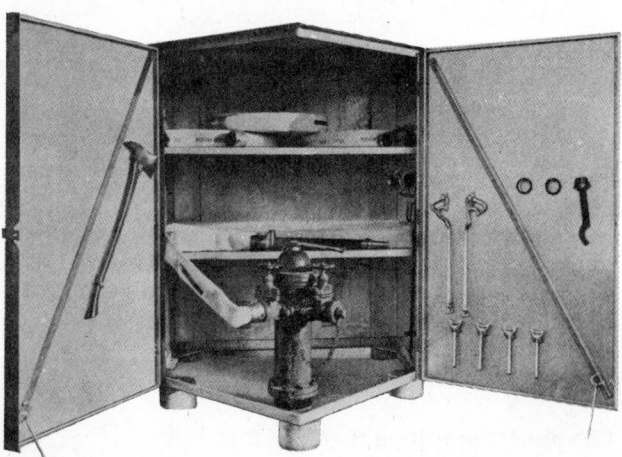

Fig. 15-1F. Hose house of the five-sided design for installation over a yard hydrant. Such houses may be of wood or steel with a tight floor installed after erection. (Grinnell Co. and W. D. Allen Mfg. Co.)

Fig. 15-1G. Steel hose house of compact dimensions for installation over a yard hydrant. House is shown closed. Top lifts up and doors on front side open for complete accessibility. (Seco Mfg. Co.)

and back. So placed, it will be ventilated and can be readily inspected.

With double outlet hydrants, it is desirable to have the hose attached to one outlet and a closed hose valve attached to the other. Hydrants having three and four outlets should have independent gates for each outlet.

Where the conditions are such that it is necessary to lock hose houses, this can be accomplished by using a special lock with a brittle shackle, or by having a latch placed behind a glass plate to be broken at the time of fire.

Figures 15-1F and 15-1G are examples of hose houses of suitable design which can be supplied by nearly all fire equipment dealers.

Amount of Hose

At least 100 ft and preferably 150 ft of 2½-in. woven-jacket rubber-lined hose should always be attached to the hydrant so that a fire stream can be put into action with minimum delay. The total amount of hose that should be maintained will depend on local conditions. If longer hose lays are anticipated, hose carts or other means of conveyance should be utilized.

In order to determine the hose required, a line should be laid in easy curves from the hydrant to the building, through the door, up the stairs to the top story. Also, a line should be taken up an exterior fire ladder to the roof, allowing sufficient hose to have about one spare length on the roof. When necessary to afford the ability to hoist hose to the roof, a checkup should be made as to the necessity of any required hoisting ropes and hose straps by applying them at the required points.

Sufficient hose must be provided to play a fire stream on all sides of the structure, allowing enough hose to hold the nozzle at a safe and effective distance from the building.

Accessories

The usual accessory equipment for a hydrant house includes nozzles, holders, spanners, fire axe, and other tools.

Hose Carriers

Hose carriers or carts are useful where there are no hydrant houses with hose normally coupled up, where supply is needed to supplement hydrant houses, where long interior travel distances are anticipated (such as in large factories or warehouses), or where there are outlying buildings or yard storage areas to be reached. A carrier should have a capacity usually not exceeding 500 ft of 2½-in. woven-jacket rubber-lined hose, and it should be equipped with hydrant wrenches, spanners, extra gaskets, and other tools and equipment. One or two nozzles should be included. The carrier can be a cart pulled by manpower or a motor driven cart for in-plant service. It may be a compartment that is stored for pickup and transportation by a lift truck.

Carriers or carts should be stored in a separate building, similar to a ventilated hose house, provided with a sloping approach to facilitate removal when needed. This incline can ordinarily be in position or it can be swung up into the building before the doors are closed. Electric lights outside or inside such a cart house should be available.

Power driven carriers have the advantage of better loading and greater carrying capacity for hose and appliances. Such carriers are occasionally provided with special appliances, water tanks, and some form of pumping equipment. Hose reels built on a roller platform to enable rapid transfer to pickup trucks or other automatic equipment can be used.

Monitor nozzles

Where large amounts of combustible materials such as log piles, lumber piles, or railway car or bus storage are located in yards, it is necessary to provide a means of delivering large quantities of water at effective pressures.

This can best be accomplished by installing permanent monitor nozzles around the piles, and occasionally where necessary on special trestles or roofs of buildings (see Fig. 15-1H). Portable deluge sets for use with siamesed hose lines are also valuable in many cases.

The location of this apparatus should be chosen so that the available water supplies are used efficiently. Hard to reach locations should be covered by the monitor nozzles. The piping and control valves usually require special consideration.

SI Units

The following conversion factors are given as a convenience in converting to SI units the English units used in this chapter.

1 in.	= 25.400 mm
1 ft	= .305 m
1 psi	= 6.895 kPa
1 gal (U.S.)	= 3.785 litres
1 gpm	= 3.785 litres/min

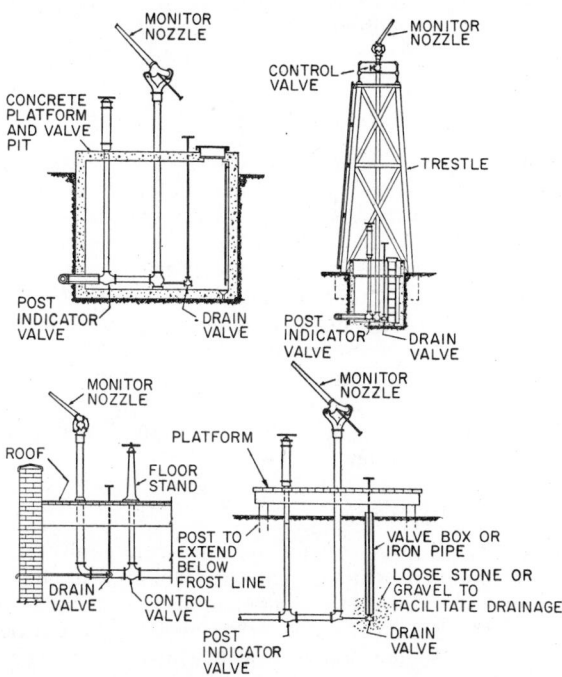

Fig. 15-1H. Four standard monitor nozzle installations. To keep the illustration simple, the monitors shown have levers for changing the position of nozzles and thus the direction of the stream. Geared wheels facilitate changing of the position of the monitor without shutting down the stream.

Bibliography

NFPA Codes, Standards, and Recommended Practices (see the latest *NFPA Publications and Visual Aids Catalog* **for availability of current editions of the following documents)**

NFPA No. 13, Standard for the Installation of Sprinkler Systems.
NFPA No. 14, Standard for Standpipe and Hose Systems.
NFPA No. 24, Standard for Outside Protection.
NFPA No. 194, Standard for Screw Threads and Gaskets for Fire Hose Connections.

Additional Readings

Fire Protection Equipment List, Underwriters Laboratories, Inc., Chicago, published annually with bimonthly supplements.
Factory Mutual Approval Guide, Factory Mutual Engineering Corporation, Norwood, Mass., published annually.
Nolan, J. W., "How to Approach Standpipe Design," *Actual Specifying Engineer*, Vol. 24, No. 7, July 1970, pp. 85–89.

Chapter 2

WATER SPRAY PROTECTION

This chapter deals with water spray from fixed nozzle systems. The term "water spray" refers to the use of water that has a predetermined pattern, particle size, velocity, and density, and that is discharged from specially designed nozzles or devices.

Water spray for fire protection has been called "water fog," "fog," or by trade name designations applied by equipment manufacturers. The use of such designations cannot be taken as indicative of any specific discharge pattern or spray characteristics of the nozzles so marketed, and has been discouraged.

NFPA No. 15, Standard for Water Spray Fixed Systems, hereinafter referred to in this chapter as the NFPA Water Spray Standard, gives design and installation details for fixed water spray systems for special applications not covered in NFPA No. 13, Standard for the Installation of Sprinkler Systems, hereinafter referred to in this chapter as the NFPA Sprinkler Standard.

There is no sharp line of demarcation between water spray protection and sprinkler protection. The discharge from nozzles or sprinklers producing a spray pattern differs only in the particular form of the spray and the other variables indicated in the introductory paragraph of this chapter. In some cases, the same device may serve both purposes.

A. Purpose of Water Spray Protection

Generally, water spray can be used effectively for any one or a combination of the following purposes: (1) extinguishment of fire, (2) control of fire, (3) exposure protection, and (4) prevention of fire.

Extinguishment: Extinguishment of fire by water spray is accomplished by cooling, smothering from the steam produced, emulsification of some liquids, dilution in some cases, or a combination of these factors. The action by which fire is extinguished by plain water is described more completely in Section 13, Chapter 1.

Controlled Burning: With its consequent limitation of fire spread controlled burning may be applied if the burning combustible materials are not susceptible to extinguishment by water spray, or if extinguishment is not desirable.

Exposure Protection: Exposure protection is accomplished by application of water spray directly to the exposed structures or equipment to remove or reduce the heat transferred to them from the exposing fire. Water spray curtains mounted at a distance from the exposed surface are less effective than direct application (see Sec. 14, Chap. 2, for information on outside sprinkler protection against exposures).

Prevention of Fire: Prevention of fire is sometimes possible by the use of water sprays to dissolve, dilute, disperse, or cool flammable materials.

B. Application of Water Spray Protection

Water spray protection is used for one or more of the purposes outlined in the preceding material and is usually applied to the following types of materials or equipment:

1. Ordinary combustible materials such as paper, wood, and textiles, particularly to extinguish fires in such materials.

2. Electrical equipment installations such as transformers, oil switches, and rotating electrical machinery.

3. Flammable gases and liquids, particularly to control fires in these materials and to extinguish certain types of fires involving combustible liquids.

4. Flammable liquid and gas tanks, processing equipment, and structures, as protection for those installations against exposure fires.

Fixed water spray systems are specifically designed to provide optimum control, extinguishment, or exposure protection for special fire protection problems. Fixed spray systems are not intended to replace automatic sprinkler systems. They may be independent of, or supplementary to, other forms of protection. There are limitations to the use of water spray which should be recognized. Such limitations involve the nature of the equipment to be protected, the physical and chemical properties of the materials involved, and the environment of the hazard.

C. Fixed Water Spray Systems

A water spray system is a special fixed pipe system connected to a reliable supply of fire protection water, and equipped with water spray nozzles for specific water discharge and distribution over the surface or area to be protected. The piping system is connected to the water supply through an automatically or manually actuated valve which initiates the flow of water. An automatic valve is actuated by operation of automatic detection equipment, usually installed in the same area as the water spray nozzles. Typical fire detection devices are described in this HANDBOOK in Section 12, Chapter 3, and water control valves are described in Section 14, Chapter 5.

Application of Systems

Fixed water spray systems are most commonly used to protect flammable liquid and gas tankage, piping and equipment, and electrical equipment such as transformers, oil switches, and rotating electrical machinery; and openings in firewalls and floors through which conveyors pass. The type of water spray required for any particular hazard will depend on the nature of the hazard and the purpose for which the protection is provided.

A water spray installation operating under test at a group of liquefied petroleum gas tanks is shown in Figure 15-2A. The spray system shown is designed to give complete surface wetting with a preselected water density, taking into consideration nozzle types, sizes and spacing, and the water supply. Ordinarily, it is neither expected nor desired that escaping liquefied petroleum gas be extinguished by the water spray. However, the rate of burning may be reduced by the cooling effect of the water on the tanks, and the severity of the exposure reduced until the gas supply to the fire is exhausted or can be shut off.

Water spray protection for a group of oil-filled electric transformers is shown under test in Figure 15-2B. Due to the relatively high flash point and boiling point of trans-

Fig. 15-2A. Water spray protection for LP-Gas tanks. The spray keeps the tanks cool in case of fire, prevents boiling away of the liquid contents, and protects the tank shells against rupture due to localized high temperature flame impingement.

Fig. 15-2B. A water spray system for oil-filled electric power transformers. A thick layer of crushed stone and subsurface drainage is provided around the base of the transformer installation to avoid the possibility that burning oil might flow beyond the ground area protected by the spray.

former oil, transformer fires can be expected to be extinguished quickly by properly designed water spray systems.

Design of Systems

The practical location of the piping and nozzles with respect to the surface to which the spray is to be applied, or to the zone in which the spray is to be effective, is determined largely by the physical arrangement and protection needs of the installation requiring protection. Once the criteria are established, the size (rate of discharge) of nozzles to be used, the angle of the nozzle discharge cone, and the water pressure needed can be determined.

The first thing to determine is the water density required to extinguish the fire or to absorb the expected heat from exposure or heat of combustion. When this is determined, a nozzle may be selected which will provide that density at a velocity adequate to overcome air currents and to carry the spray to the equipment to be protected. Each nozzle selected must also have the proper angle of discharge to cover the area to be protected by the nozzle.

Once the type of nozzle has been selected and the location and spacing to give the desired area coverage has been determined, hydraulic calculations are made to establish the appropriate pipe sizes and water supply requirements.

When water spray is to be used for the fire protection of oil-filled electrical equipment such as transformers and large switch gear, special care must be taken to provide safe electrical clearances (see Sec. 13, Chap. 1 for information on water and water additives for fire fighting). To give the high spray density needed, combined with good range, subject to minimum interference by wind, and a simplified piping arrangement that does not need to be located close to live electrical parts, special fixed spray nozzles have been developed.

Size of Water Spray Systems

Many factors govern the size of a water spray system, including the nature of hazard or combustibles involved, amount and type of equipment to be protected, adequacy of other protection, and the size of the area which could be involved in a single fire. The size of the system needed may be minimized by taking advantage of possible subdivision by fire walls, by limiting the potential spread of flammable liquids by dikes, curbs, or special drainage; and

by water curtains or heat curtains; or by combinations of these features.

Because most water spray systems must perform as deluge type systems with all nozzles or devices open, and because a high density of water discharge is often needed, there is a heavy water demand. Each hazard should be protected by its own single system which should be adequate for dependable protection.

The NFPA Water Spray Standard advises that the size of a single water spray system be limited so that the designed discharge rate, calculated at the minimum pressures for which the nozzles are effective, will not exceed 3,000 gpm. Separate fire areas should be protected by separate systems.

In cases where two or more systems are required for protection of a single fire area, the discharge capacity of each system is to be kept within the 3,000 gpm limit.

Water Supplies

Fixed spray systems are usually supplied from one or more of the following:

1. Connections from a reliable waterworks system of adequate capacity and pressure.

2. Automatic fire pumps having reliable power and a water supply of adequate capacity and reliability.

3. An elevated (gravity) tank of adequate capacity and elevation.

The capacity of pressure tanks generally is inadequate to supply water spray systems. Such tanks, however, may be acceptable as water supplies to small systems whose water and pressure requirements do not exceed the capabilities of the pressure tanks.

In some situations where the water supply is extremely limited, a cycle system, which collects and reuses water, may be acceptable. It is imperative, however, that foreign material and fuel be separated from the water before it is returned to the water spray system.

Water Demand Rate

The water supply must be adequate to supply, at effective pressure, all of the spray nozzles that may be expected to be in operation as a result of fire at any point in the protected area. Additional water may be required for hose streams and should be considered when the system is designed. The duration of the discharge required will vary with the nature of the hazard, the purpose for which the system is designed, and other factors which can only be evaluated for each installation.

Water demand is specified in terms of the density of a uniformly distributed spray measured in gallons per minute per square foot of area protected. The discharge rate per unit of area depends on whether the spray system is installed for extinguishment of fire, control of fire, exposure protection, or prevention of fire, and upon the characteristics of the materials involved.

Pipe Sizes

Pipe sizes must be calculated for each system in order that the water at the spray nozzles will have adequate pressure. A procedure for making the hydraulic calculations for a fixed pipe water spray system is given in Section 11, Chapter 6, and in the Appendix to the NFPA Water Spray Standard.

Selection and Use of Spray Nozzles

The selection of spray nozzles takes into consideration such factors as the character of the hazard to be protected, the purpose of the system, and possible severe wind or draft conditions.

High velocity spray nozzles, generally used in piped installations, discharge in the form of a spray-filled cone, while low velocity spray nozzles usually deliver a much finer spray in the form of either a spray-filled spheroid or cone. Due to differences in size of orifices in the various nozzles and the range of water particle sizes produced by each type, nozzles of one type cannot ordinarily be substituted for those of another type in an individual installation without the possibility of seriously affecting fire extinguishment. In general, the higher the velocity and the coarser the size of water droplets, the greater the effective "reach" or range of the spray.

A problem in the maintenance of water spray protection systems using special spray nozzles or sprinklers is keeping small water passages clear. This may require special attention in the case of systems subject to paint vapors and similar conditions. Nozzles with blowoff caps are available for protection against accumulation of foreign matter and attack from corrosive gases on nozzle orifices and the interior of the piping system (see Fig. 15-2C).

Strainers

Strainers are ordinarily required in the supply lines of fixed piping spray systems to prevent clogging of the nozzles (see Fig. 15-2D). They should be selected with baskets having holes small enough to protect the smallest water passages in the nozzles used.

Fig. 15-2C. A Grinnell Mulsifyre nozzle with blowoff cap.

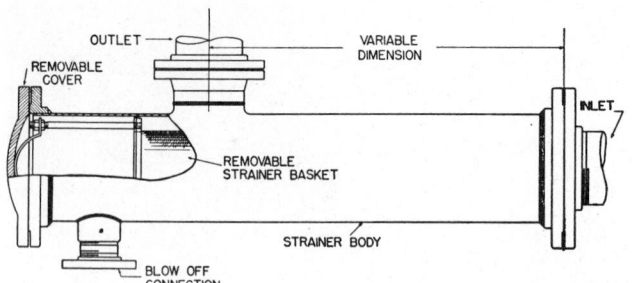

Fig. 15-2D. A Grinnell Model A strainer having a basket-type screen of corrosion resistant metal. It is available in 3-in., 4-in., 6-in., 8-in. and 10-in. sizes.

Water spray nozzles having very small water passages may have their own internal strainer as well as a supply line strainer to remove the larger foreign material.

Drainage

Fixed pipe, open nozzle, water spray systems discharge large quantities of water. To limit the spread of flammable liquids, special drainage and disposal facilities may be important. Pitched floors, curbs or dikes, and sumps or trenches designed for safe disposal may be used alone or in combination as best adapted to specific situations.

Maintenance

It is important that fixed water spray systems be inspected and maintained on a regularly scheduled program. Included in the program for checking are such items as strainers, piping, control valves, heat actuated devices, and the spray nozzles, particularly those equipped with strainers. Flow tests are frequently conducted to assure satisfactory operation, following which it is necessary to clean all strainers and to check all valves to be sure the system is in normal operating condition.

D.   Fixed Spray System Nozzles

Some open (nonautomatic) spray nozzles produce spray by giving the water high rotary motion in spiral passages inside the nozzle body. Sectional views of spray nozzles having internal spiral water passages are shown in Figure 15-2E.

Another type of water spray nozzle of current manufacture uses the deflector principle of the standard sprinkler (usually pendant type). The water discharge nozzle is unobstructed. The angle of the spray discharge cones is

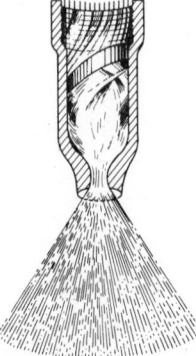
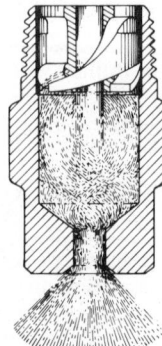

Fig. 15-2E. Water spray nozzles having internal spiral water passages. (Spraying Systems Co., Type H, and "Automatic" Sprinkler Corp. of America, Type MA)

Open   Automatic

Fig. 15-2F. Water spray nozzles using the deflector principle of the standard automatic sprinkler. The nozzle at right has fusible elements for automatic operation. (Star Model D Spray Nozzles)

governed by the design of the deflector. Some manufacturers make spray nozzles of this type individually automatic by constructing them with heat responsive elements as used in standard automatic sprinklers. An open spray nozzle and an automatic nozzle of this type are shown in Figure 15-2F.

One characteristically different type of water spray nozzle discharges water from its nozzle along the axis of a spiral of diminishing inside diameter. This spiral continuously peels off a thin layer of water from the surface of the cone. This thin layer of water breaks into spray as it leaves the spiral (see Fig. 15-2G).

E. Specialized Systems Utilizing Water

Specialized systems utilizing water spray have been developed to fill particular fire control needs.

Ultra-high-speed Water Spray Systems

These systems are designed to handle extremely rapid fires of the type that can occur in the handling of solid propellants, sensitive chemicals, and any industrial process or oxygen-enriched environment possessing this type of fire potential. The essential features of ultra-high-speed water spray systems which differ from conventional water spray systems are the use of high speed detectors (normally photosensitive [infra-red] or ultra-violet), the use of solid state devices (including an amplifier) to speed the signal from the detectors to the control panel, the employment of an explosively actuated valve, and the use of pre-primed piping

Fig. 15-2G. A spiral-type water-spray nozzle. (Bete Fog Nozzles, Inc. N Series)

which speeds the water to the source of the fire upon the signal from the transistorized amplifier. Since the supply water and the priming water fill all cavities of the valve and all piping to the nozzle orifices (no air pockets anywhere in the system), the first movement of the valve results in water delivery within milliseconds from time of initial detection. These systems use water spray nozzles which are fitted with caps to hold the priming water under a gravity head. These caps blow off as pressure is released into the system by the high-speed valve. The number of milliseconds allowed for operation varies with the installation. In a group of hyperbaric test chambers where such ultra-high-speed water spray systems are installed, the time from fire ignition to delivery of water at design nozzle pressure was 96 milliseconds. Another installed system in a solid propellant installation operates in about 240 milliseconds. Such installations must be carefully engineered for each special hazard to be protected and must be maintained by qualified experts. A number of fire protection equipment manufacturers can furnish and maintain this type of equipment.

SI Units

The following conversion factor is given as a convenience in converting to SI units the English units used in this chapter.

1 gpm = 3.785 litres/min

Bibliography

NFPA Codes, Standards, and Recommended Practices (see the latest *NFPA Publications and Visual Aids Catalog* for availability of current editions of the following documents)

NFPA 13, Standard for the Installation of Sprinkler Systems.
NFPA 15, Standard for Water Spray Fixed Systems.

Chapter 3

FOAM EXTINGUISHING EQUIPMENT AND SYSTEMS

The employment of fire fighting foams for the control and extinguishment of fire requires proportioning equipment to enable the mixing of a definite volume of foam concentrate with water, and provision for mixing this solution with air to form foam. There are many different devices to accomplish these functions, the designs for which depend on the many factors affecting the hazard to be protected. This chapter describes foam proportioners and generators for all types of foam, and the application methods of various equipment types for various hazards are dealt with from viewpoints of portable and fixed equipment recommendations. The modern concept of "combined agent" fire fighting equipment is fully treated with respect to fuel fire control. Some procedures for the test and surveillance of foam materials and equipment are also described. The use of foams in aviation fire protection is covered in Section 17, Chapter 1, and the basic characteristics of foam concentrates and foam equipment are given in Section 13, Chapter 2. Other special uses of foams are dealt with in various sections of this HANDBOOK and are classified under hazards or broad fields of application.

A. Types of Air Foam Equipment and Systems

There is a wide variance in the types of equipment and systems for generating and applying fire fighting air foam (also called mechanical foam, ordinary foam, conventional foam, low expansion foam—vs. the 100X to 1000X type, which is "high expansion" foam) to the hazard requiring protection. Consideration of the following factors must be taken into account: the type of foam concentrate chosen for the hazard, the type of flammable liquid protected, the availability of manpower, water and materials at the site, and the geometry of the areas being protected. The alignment of these variables with equipment designs is dealt with in the following descriptions of equipment and systems, and also in Section 13, Chapter 2. The Appendices of NFPA No. 11, Foam Extinguishing Systems, and NFPA No. 16, Foam Water and Spray Systems, contain additional information and illustration on the various devices and equipment used in air foam making systems.

Foam Concentrate Proportioning Devices

The first step required for the ultimate generation of air foam is the mixing, metering, or proportioning of the correct volume amount of liquid foam concentrate from its container or storage tank into water, or into a water stream, so that a foam solution (or, more correctly, a "foam-forming" solution) is produced. The following methods may be used.

In-line Inductor: This type of proportioner educts or drafts foam concentrate from a container or tank by venturi action, utilizing the operating pressure of the hose line water stream on which it is installed. It then injects foam concentrate into that flow of water. Its correct operation is very sensitive to throughput water rates and pressures. Changes in either of these factors from those for which the inductor was designed will result in incorrect proportioning. Distances of more than 6 ft (183 cm) elevation of the inductor to the lowest liquid level of the foam concentrate container will also result in incorrect proportioning. Foam

generation devices and maximum downstream lengths of hose recommended for each inductor must be carefully adhered to. This proportioning device may be used at a point in the hose line leading to the foam generation device. An inductor of this type may also be installed at the foam concentrate tank in a fixed system or at the pump discharge of a mobile pumper.

Some designs of this proportioning device incorporate metering valves in the foam concentrate intake line so that various volume percentages of concentrate in the water stream may be obtained. A check valve is usually placed in this intake so that water cannot flow back into the foam concentrate container if a blockage occurs or a valve is closed in the downstream hose. The use of this inductor requires an allowance for a pressure loss of about 33 percent in the system or layout.

Around-the-pump Proportioner: This type of proportioner also operates on the venturi principle, except that it must be situated at the pump and connected to both its suction and pressure sides. Its advantage is that pressure recovery of the venturi action is attained, and pump delivery pressures to the foam making device or devices downstream require no compensation for pressure loss except for that in the layout hose length. The net delivery volume of the pump will be decreased by about 10 percent in this method of proportioning (see Fig. 15-3A).

A small portion of the pump discharge flows through a bypass line to the suction side of the pump. A venturi eductor in this line produces a negative pressure on the foam concentrate pickup line from the foam concentrate container. Foam concentrate is led to the eductor where it mixes with water and is delivered to the suction side of the pump.

This method requires that the pressure on the suction side of the pump must always be zero gage pressure, or on the negative pressure (vacuum) side. As is always the case with venturi eductor devices, the maximum lift for drafting of concentrate from a container must not exceed 6 ft (183 cm) at any time.

Multiple foam makers may be supplied with foam solution by this type of proportioner when it is supplied with a multiported metering valve designed for the required flows.

Pressure Proportioning Tank: This type of proportioner may consist of: one tank or pressure container with or

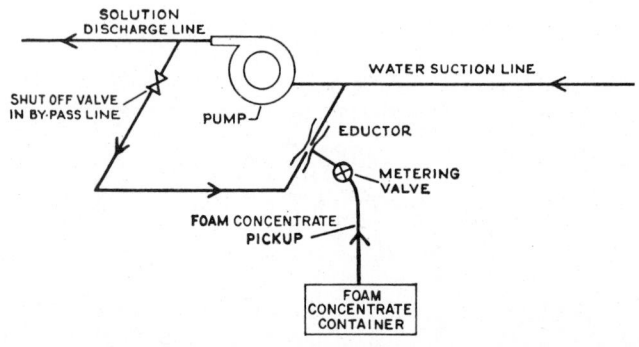

Fig. 15-3A. An around-the-pump proportioner.

without a watertight divider so that it operates as two tanks; two tanks separately connected to the water and foam solution lines; or, the tanks in the system may each be fitted with flexible diaphragms to separate the "driving" water from foam concentrate, or they may rely simply on differences in density of the two liquids to retard mixing during operation. ·

The principle of operation of this device is simple. A small amount of the flowing water volumetrically displaces foam concentrate into the main water stream. The working pressure of the vessel must, of course, be above the maximum static water pressure encountered in the system.

Water is allowed to enter the foam tank from the main stream with as little friction loss as possible, while pressure in the main stream is dropped about 10 percent by means of an orifice. Liquid in the tank is metered into the low-pressure area by a second orifice. Advantages of this system are its low pressure drop, automatic proportioning over a range of flows and pressures, and its freedom from external power. Its disadvantages are a long refill time (since it is a "batch" method, the tank must be drained of its "driving" water and refilled with concentrate), and an economic limit on size.

Coupled Water Motor-Pump Proportioner: This proportioner, which is a volume flow-metering device deriving its pumping energy from the water stream traversing it, meters foam concentrate flow in proportion to water flow within the tolerable limits of the "slip" of its rotors. It consists of two positive displacement rotary pumps mounted on a common shaft. Water delivered to the larger pump (motor) causes it to drive the smaller pump which is used to draft concentrate from a container and deliver it (at line pressure) to the water discharge line from the larger pump. By proportioning the sizes of the two pumps, the correct volume of concentrate is delivered to the water stream.

This proportioner is manufactured in only two sizes for water throughputs of 60 to 180 gpm (227 litres to 680 litres) and 200 to 1,000 gpm (756 litres to 3,780 litres). Both sizes are presently designed for proportioning foam concentrates recommended for use at 6 percent concentration. A pressure drop of 25 to 30 percent in the water stream supplied to the device is required for its operation.

Balanced Pressure Proportioners: The use of a separate pump for transporting and pressurizing foam concentrate to be delivered in the correct proportions to a flowing water stream offers the greatest advantage for reliable and accurate operation of a foam concentrate proportioning system which must function at varying rates of volume or pressure during its use.

There are several ways a pump can be used. Many pumps require manual attention to flow meters, duplex gages, or other measuring devices during operation of the system. Generally, such designs have been replaced by automatically operated proportioning systems which do not require manual attention.

The balanced pressure type system is simple in principle, and reliable during an emergency. It relies on: (1) a hydraulically monitored pressure control valve in a bypass foam concentrate line from a pump, and (2) a correctly sized venturi type proportioning controller in the water line for correct and automatic proportioning over wide ranges of flow.

This system is more applicable to fixed installations protecting various occupancies requiring foam protection, or in large fuel storage areas where central foam concentrate tank systems are piped to hazards. It must be carefully designed for the hydraulic requirements of the installation.

Variable Orifice, Variable Flow Demand Proportioners: This type of balanced-pressure system utilizes a specially designed flow-sensitive moveable piston section in the water supply which controls a variable orifice in the foam concentrate line. A pump supplies concentrate at monitored pressures to the metering orifice which changes in size in proportion to the demand for foam solution of the system. The device is especially designed for large capacity systems, and is not yet in wide use. Its present design provides accurate proportioning over ranges of flow of water of approximately 2.3 to 1.

Premixed Foam Solution: This method of proportioning is a "batch" type of mixing of concentrated liquid with water, usually in a container or open tank of some sort. The measured volume of concentrate is poured into a measured volume of water to yield a foam solution of the recommended strength: i.e., for a 6 percent solution in a container which holds 100 gallons (378 litres) of liquid, 94 gallons (355.3 litres) of water are poured into it and 6 gallons (22.6 litres) of foam concentrate are mixed with it to give a solution of 6 percent volume. The final solution mixture is then inducted to a pump, or placed in a pressurizing vessel. Premixing is no longer used except in an emergency when dynamic (flowing) proportioning methods are not available. In the case of small portable foam extinguisher units, it becomes necessary to use such premixed solutions; however, the manufacturers' recommendations concerning storage life and effectiveness of the solutions must be carefully followed. In most cases a time-degradation of effectiveness of stored premix solutions of foam concentrates will be experienced. Most foam concentrates which are specifically designed for use on alcohol or polar solvent flammable liquids cannot be used as a premix.

The Nozzle Eductor: This type of foam concentrate proportioner is of simple design and is widely used in portable foam making nozzles. Incorporating a modified venturi within the foam making nozzle section, it drafts concentrate from a portable container. Using a properly sized orifice or pipe section at the low pressure cavity, the concentrate is mixed in proper proportion to the fixed flow and operating pressure of the nozzle, and foam generation proceeds.

Foam Making Equipment and Systems

The classification of the many different types of foam generating and distribution equipment and systems in a logical or compartmented manner under such headings as their "application modes" or "the hazard requiring protection"—such as fuel storage tanks or aircraft hangars—becomes very difficult and repetitive because of the many different uses to which this equipment may be put.

In the following descriptions of "ordinary" foam generating equipment, they will be listed under broad headings as to their use as portable or fixed equipment. Under these listings will be found a categorization as to their principles of operation. Information will also be given concerning the general areas of utility of each type of device and system. The latter aspect is dealt with further in the various NFPA Codes and Standards listed at the end of this chapter.

1. Portable Foam Generating Equipment

(a) Aspirating Type Devices

Because of the difficulties associated with pumping or transporting foam in pipes or hoses and the age-old familiarity of fire fighters with nozzles at the end of a hose, the earliest designs of air foam generators were devised to be used in much the same manner as water nozzles. They incorporated a crude venturi design whereby a jet or jets of foam solution enter an open contracted portion of a large diameter "foam tube". This action lowers the atmospheric pressure surrounding the jets, and air is drawn or "aspirated" into the throat of the tube. Downstream of the contracted portion of the tube there occurs a high turbulence and mixing of air and foam solution. This turbulence may be increased by internal turbulence-accelerating devices such as screens or baffles. The kinetic energy of the fluid contributes to this mixing action so that a usefully stable foam issues from the tube at a relatively low pressure.

The basic design principles of this method of making air foam have been changed in many ways to yield, for many purposes, foams with greatly differing characteristics. However, all types of nozzles incorporating foam solution jets leading into free air mixing cavities followed by discharge apertures of one kind or another utilize the aspirating action for making foam.

The Hoseline Foam Nozzle: This is the most universally used portable, air aspirating, foam fire fighting device for flammable liquid fire operations. It is manufactured in a variety of operating capacities for one-man handling. Supplied with foam solution from a proportioner or by means of a pickup tube, it successfully combats fires resulting from spills or leaks of flammable liquid or not too large fires in tanks or fuel pits. In order to provide for a variety of foam stream patterns which may be needed for the extinguishment operation, these nozzles usually contain built-in devices which allow continuous foam pattern variation from a solid straight stream to an inverted filled umbrella shape. (Note: As with water streams, foam is employed in a solid straight stream for range or reach; a flat, wide, bushy shape for gentle "snowstorm" application on the burning fuel surface; and a very wide, circular bushy shape for radiance shielding of the operator during fire extinguishment or penetration into the fire area.)

Larger capacity hose foam nozzles [250 gpm (946 litres per min) and more] are designed for one or two man operation at a solid stream foam pattern only.

Another type of hoseline foam nozzle is especially designed for quick, portable, one-man use during emergency operations from mobile crash-rescue vehicles at airports. It is customarily called a "handline foam nozzle". It is equipped with a foam pattern changing device, and some types are supplied with a valve control for diverting the water or solution stream into a water spray for cooling purposes.

The "Fog-foam" Nozzle: Many situations in fuel fire extinguishment do not require foams of particular physical characteristics such as high stability or homogeneous bubble size. Where easy nozzle handling and simple foam pattern requirements are important, the discharge from the "fog-foam" type nozzle offers superior portability and high foam rate discharge (see Fig. 15-3C). The open ports in the back side of this nozzle induct air due to a crude venturi action which occurs in the short cavity, followed by turbulence at the front face screen which forms foam that is issued in a

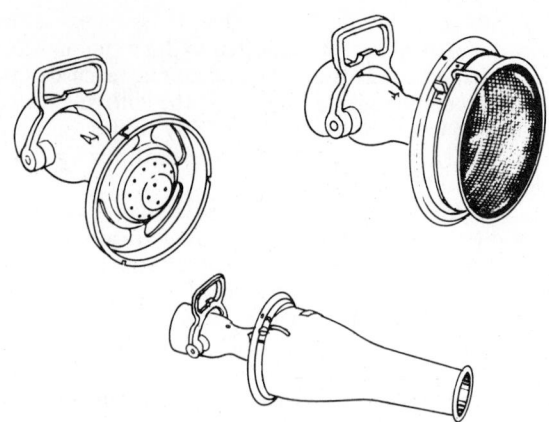

Fig. 15-3C. Fog-foam type nozzles with foam-spray pattern screen and stream shaper attachments.

wide, bushy pattern. By removal of all attachments from the internally impinging jet head of the nozzle, it may be used as a high velocity water fog nozzle with a wide water spray pattern.

With the screen in place, a wide fully filled foam pattern is obtained for gentle "snowstorm" application to a burning surface. The "stream-shaper" attachment affords a consolidated foam stream of greater reach.

Foam and Foam-water Monitors: In large-scale fuel fire fighting operations it may become necessary to position a foam-making nozzle with a high discharge rate at an advantageous position for continuous application of foam over an area, or at one point. Devices for this purpose are available in a variety of types, with wheels for towing to the fire ground or with hinged extender legs. Many foam monitors of this type are provided with two nozzles: one for the discharge of water if cooling water is needed, and (by a simple nozzle lever change) the other for the discharge of foam. The foam pattern change is accomplished by opening or closing the "jaws" at the exit end of the large tube.

The High Back Pressure Foam Maker: There are certain circumstances where it is necessary that foam be generated and supplied under pressure for transmission in pipes, or under a definite pressure head. The subsurface foam injection method for fuel tank fire extinguishment requires this type of foam maker. The "high back pressure foam maker" or "forcing foam maker" is a venturi device which is carefully designed to make foam by aspiration, and to supply it at pressures of 25 to 50 psig (1.72 to 3.44 bars) at a carefully selected ratio of air to foam solution, usually 4 to 1 (4X). This type of foam maker operates at higher foam solution input pressures [100 psig minimum (6.9 bars)]. In use, this foam device is brought to the fixed piping foam inlet, installed, and then supplied with foam solution by a portable or mobile pumper.

(b) Non-aspirating Type Portable Foam Making Devices

There are two devices which do not use venturi type aspiration for making fire fighting foam: they are foam pumps and ordinary water fog or spray nozzles, neither of which is widely used other than for certain special applications.

Foam pumps: These consist of rotary positive displacement pumps of the "flying vane" type in which an off-center rotor is supplied with foam solution at a fraction of the volume of each cavity formed by the vanes. As the vanes

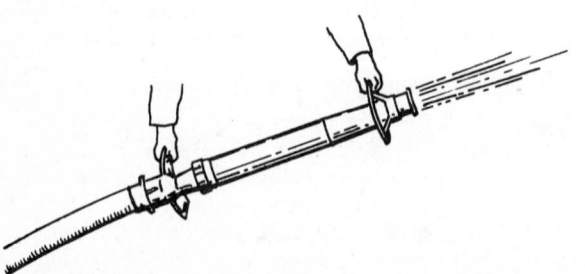

Fig. 15-3B. Large capacity air foam hose nozzle.

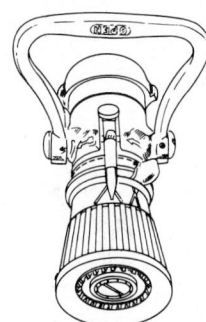

Fig. 15-3D. Variable pattern water fog nozzle for use with AFFF.

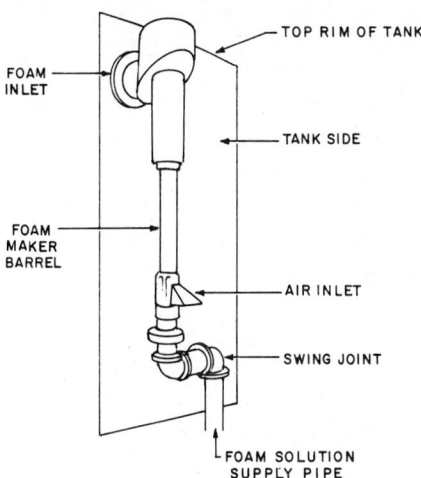

Fig. 15-3E. Air foam maker at top of storage tank.

rotate, the air taken in by each cavity is swept to the discharge outlet with the solution in diminishing cavity volume, thus pressurizing the air and forcing the mixture through a foam refining section to piping. The resulting homogeneous foam is distributed under pressure to nozzles for application to the hazard.

As long as the pump's revolutions per minute remain constant with a constant rate of foam solution input, the composition and characteristics of the foam will not change. In the case of mobile fire fighting vehicles for combatting fuel fires resulting from aircraft accidents or crashes, foam characteristics are critical if maximum efficiency of extinguishment is to be maintained. It is here that the foam pump has found its principal use, although it is being replaced with aspirating type monitor nozzles in present-day vehicles.

Water Fog or Spray Nozzles: There are several types of water fog or spray nozzles for portable use which provide an acceptable fire fighting foam of adequate characteristics when supplied with certain foam concentrates, the most universal design of which is shown in Figure 15-3D.

These portable water fog nozzles can be used with aqueous film forming foam solutions (AFFF) for combatting fuel spill fires in shallow depth, and are sometimes used in this manner on crash-rescue mobile vehicles. The foam product resulting from the discharge of AFFF solution devices which do not aspirate air is generally fast draining and does not impart the same degree of burnback resistance as the foam produced from AFFF agents from foam generating devices.

2. Fixed Foam Generating Equipment

(a) Devices for the Protection of Flammable Liquids in Bulk Tanks

Where flammable liquid fire protection is required for permanently installed hazards such as fuel storage tanks or dip tanks containing flammable or combustible liquids, air foam generating and distributing devices are installed integrally with the hazard. These devices which are piped to a source of water, foam concentrate, or foam solution, may be arranged for automatic activation by fire detectors in the event of fire, or may be manually controlled.

The Open Dip or Quench Tank Fixed Foam Extinguisher: This consists of a small aspirating type foam maker supplied by a water line and foam concentrate educted to the foam maker. Foam discharges into a mixing box which also acts as a surface distributor for gentle foam application.

Large Fuel Storage Tank Fixed Foam Makers: The fire protection of exterior fuel storage tanks requires that several foam makers be installed at equally spaced positions on the

top periphery of the tank. These are connected to a line or lines on the ground which supply foam solution to each foam maker simultaneously in case of ignition of the flammable contents of the tank. Frangible seals at the discharge outlet of the foam maker prevent vapor loss from the tank. These seals are designed to burst when foam pressure is applied. The air inlet to the aspirating foam maker is provided with a screen to prevent clogging from foreign matter, such as bird nesting material. A universal or swing pipe joint is installed (see Fig. 15-3E) in the foam solution inlet pipe to prevent tank top distortion from fracturing the supply piping during the fire.

Internal Tank Foam Distributing Devices: A prime requirement for efficient fuel tank extinguishment by topside foam making devices has always been that the foam must be applied to the burning surface without undue plunging into the fuel, or allowing the foam to become coated with burning fuel. This gentle application of foam must be accomplished at any level of the contents of the tank. Many devices have been developed to gently apply foam from one point, regardless of burning fuel level. These devices are listed as "Type I" foam discharge outlets for tanks and are required by most alcohol type foams.

When foam discharge into a tank is allowed to fall unimpeded to the burning fuel surface or is deflected, it is called a "Type II" outlet or foam application.

(b) Devices for the Protection of Hazardous Open Areas

Spray Foam Nozzles: There are many situations in commercial plants handling flammable or combustible liquids where accidental spillage or flow of fuels may occur at floor or ground levels. The utility of a fixed foam making device situated above the hazardous area and capable of instantaneously and completely covering that area can readily be seen. The spray deflector shown in Figure 15-3F accomplishes this action when installed from an overhead piping grid with nozzle outlets arranged so that their foam pattern overlaps each nearest nozzle pattern. The nozzle is supplied with foam solution, and foam is produced by air aspiration at the head just prior to the deflector construction. These devices are not designed for water-only discharge. In operation the foam discharge pattern of these nozzles provides complete simultaneous coverage.

3. Systems for Fixed Equipment Using Foam

Fixed air foam systems which include a supply of foam concentrate and a foam solution proportioning system piped

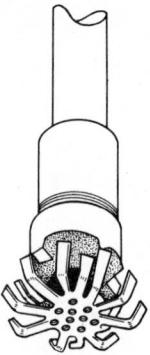

Fig. 15-3F.   Spray foam nozzle (pendant).

to foam makers discharging onto the protected area are used in both large and small installations for extinguishment of flammable liquid fires. The systems may be designed for automatic activation by fire detectors in the event of fire, or may be manually activated and controlled.

Because of its securing action in establishing a foam blanket to extinguish by vapor securing action and cooling, foam is especially well suited and reliable for protection of large flammable liquid installations: however, although extinguishment is assured when foam is used in a fixed system to protect a large area, the action may be relatively slow when compared to some other type agents. Large fixed systems are often installed for protection of petroleum fuel storage tanks, aircraft hangars and warehouses, or manufacturing buildings where special hazard protection is needed.

(a) Petroleum Fuel Storage Tank Fixed Foam Systems

There are many different types or designs of fuel storage tanks, and there are several types of fixed or semi-fixed foam system designs that may be used for fire protection in these cases. The following systems are generally employed for the protection of "fixed room" or integrally constructed fuel storage tanks.

Central "Foam House" Distributing Systems: These systems consist of an enclosure housing a foam concentrate supply tank and a proportioning device of an automatic or balanced pressure type. Foam solution is supplied under adequate pressure from this "foam house" to the piping system controlled by appropriate valves so that the foam makers on the burning tank receive foam solution.

The foam chambers or foam makers are installed on the tank shell slightly below the curb angle, and are designed as shown in Fig. 15-3E. Systems of this and of the following intermediate back pressure system type are frequently employed for the protection of fixed roof vertical tanks where the seam attaching the roof to the side shell is intentionally designed to fail in the event of an explosion or over pressure.

Intermediate Back Pressure System: Although this system of tank protection is similar to the preceding central "foam house" distributing systems, it utilizes strong and well braced *foam* delivery pipes on the side of the tank which act as supports for preventing buckling of the tank from heat. This system requires that a mobile foam concentrate supply and proportioner must pump foam solution to the piping outside the dike or firewall of the burning tank.

These systems require careful design. The minimum requirements for their installation are found in NFPA No. 11, Standard for Foam Extinguishing Systems, hereinafter referred to in this chapter as the NFPA Foam Extinguishing System Standard.

Subsurface Foam Injection Systems: The problems inherent with the application of foam from above the burning surface (topside) are sometimes difficult to combat. They may consist of: explosion or fire damage to the foam makers or tank-side piping; forceful upward fire drafted air currents which prevent the falling foam from reaching the burning surface; hazard to workers attempting to erect portable foam distributing devices near the burning tank; inability of foam applied from the periphery of a large (greater than about 200 ft [61 meters] in diameter) tank to flow and form a complete center seal during fire attack.

The obvious solution to these problems is to apply foam from the under side of the fire by causing it to come up through the contents of the tank. The subsurface foam injection system accomplishes this by injecting foam under the pressure of the head of fuel in the tank, using the high back pressure foam maker referred to earlier.

Entry of foam may be provided at several points at the base of the tank (base injection), or it may be accomplished by means of the product line. Where large tanks are involved, a branched pipe foam distributor may be installed on or slightly above the floor of the tank, connected to a central foam injection point outside the tank.

Mobile foam concentrate proportioning equipment is used with these systems, pumping from a protected position outside the dike or berm around the tank.

Design requirements for subsurface injection systems are contained in the NFPA Foam Extinguishing Systems Standard and in NFPA No. 11B, Standard for Synthetic Foam and Combined Agent Systems.

Portable Foam Devices for Tank Protection: The employment of special foam making and distributing devices for use during fires in fuel storage tanks is extremely hazardous because of the need for personnel to approach the tank. The extensible aluminum pipe foam tower shown in Figure 15-3G is first assembled on the ground and then raised to the top edge of the burning tank by four to six men. It must be supplied with foam solution from a mobile pumping truck.

Under certain conditions, a mobile foam monitor of high capacity discharge (foam cannon) may be used to direct a

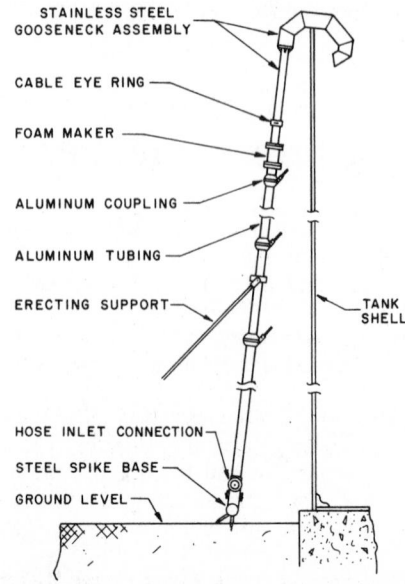

STAINLESS STEEL
GOOSENECK ASSEMBLY

CABLE EYE RING

FOAM MAKER

ALUMINUM COUPLING

ALUMINUM TUBING

ERECTING SUPPORT

TANK SHELL

HOSE INLET CONNECTION

STEEL SPIKE BASE

GROUND LEVEL

Fig. 15-3G.   Portable foam tower pourer.

Fig. 15-3H.   Portable (trailer) foam monitor (cannon). (Angus, Fire Armour, Inc.)

stream of foam over the open top rim of a burning tank so that foam will fall into the burning area. Nozzles of this type are also used to extinguish fires in the overflow space inside the dike surrounding the tank. Skill is needed in directing the foam stream from such devices, as shown in Figure 15-3H.

Temporarily rigged foam devices of the latter type may be very wasteful of foam because of cross-winds, fire updrafts, and inability to place the equipment in an advantageous position. Requirements of at least a 60 percent additional foam application rate must be included in the design of this type of protection. Additional design details for portable foam devices for this use are contained in the NFPA Foam Extinguishing Systems Standard.

The Fire Protection of "Open Top-floating Roof" and "Covered-floating Roof" Fuel Storage Tanks: The floating roof type storage tank has an excellent record of freedom from fire. Consequently, fixed foam systems are usually not required for their protection. Under certain circumstances, however, there may be a need for a foam flooding system for the open top type of tank.

As indicated by its name, the "covered" floating roof tank is totally enclosed above the floating roof with a properly vented steel roof.

Usually Class IB flammable liquids such as gasolines and crudes are stored in "open top" or "covered" floating roof tanks. During storage operation there is no vapor space between the bottom of the floating roof and the stored product surface. However, during periods of initial fill, a flammable vapor space may exist until the floating roof is buoyant. In the case of "covered" floating roof tanks, the space between the fixed and the floating roof may be within the flammable range during periods of initial fill, and up to 24 hours later depending on atmospheric temperatures, wind, and vapor pressure of the stored product. Class II and III combustible liquids are usually stored in fixed roof tanks of ordinary integral design. When the flash point of the product stored exceeds 140°F (60°C), foam protection is not usually deemed necessary unless the tank is heated.

In an "open top" floating roof tank, all that can be expected is a rim fire. Rim fires can be caused by atmospheric disturbances such as lightning, but usually do not occur if the floating roof is properly bonded to the shell as specified in NFPA 78, Lightning Protection Code. "Covered" float-

ing roof tanks are proof against rim fires due to atmospheric disturbances because of the "Faraday Effect" of the fixed roof.

Fixed foam fire protection for the "open top" floating roof consists of an ordinary aspirating type foam maker installed so that when it is supplied with foam solution, its foam discharge floods the annular area formed by the seal around the tank periphery. A metal foam dam restricts the foam to this area. Further details of such construction are contained in the NFPA Foam Extinguishing Systems Standard and its Appendix.

When foam protection is desired for "covered" floating roof tanks, a foam system is provided similar to those described for fixed roof tanks. Subsurface injection systems are not recommended for floating roof tanks because of the possibility of tilted roofs resulting in improper foam distribution.

(b) Fixed Foam Systems for the Protection of Aircraft Hangars, Petrochemical Areas, and Various Hazardous Occupancies.

Foam-water Sprinkler and Spray Systems: The advantages of permanently installed water sprinkler systems for the protection of many types of occupancies in terms of the saving of lives and property is well known. In areas where flammable and combustible liquids are processed, stored, or handled, a water discharge is often ineffective for controlling or extinguishing fires in these hazards. The evolution of aspirating type foam-making sprinklers and spray nozzles has been successful in replacing water sprinkler nozzles for such systems so that fires in these occupancies may be controlled and property safeguarded.

Sprinkler system piping "grids" provided with foam-water nozzles generate air foam when supplied with foam solution in essentially the same "water-sprinkler" pattern as when water is discharged from the same nozzle. This dual capability affords the system with a Class A and a Class B hazard extinguishment ability.

Foam-water spray nozzles also discharge water or foam, and are used in exactly similar sprinkler system designs where a special directional discharge pattern of foam or water is desired. These are used in fewer instances than the foam-water nozzle.

Obviously, fixed systems using these nozzles require that foam concentrate tanks, proportioners, and suitable pumps be provided in order to supply the system with foam solution or water. Detection devices may also be used to activate the system, or it may be manually activated.

It has been found that ordinary water sprinkler nozzles may be employed with effectiveness in such fixed systems if they are provided with specific AFFF concentrates.

Detailed design requirements of these systems are contained in NFPA No. 13, Standard for the Installation of Sprinkler Systems, NFPA No. 16, Standard for Foam-Water Sprinkler and Spray Systems, and NFPA No. 409, Standard for Aircraft Hangars.

Certain hazardous areas such as aircraft hangars require additional foam making and distributing devices such as foam monitors mounted at near-floor level. Often, these devices are provided with an automatic oscillator so that foam is continually distributed over the floor for extinguishing burning spilled fuel under obstacles such as aircraft wings, etc.

Other Fixed System Uses: Fixed foam systems employing foam sprinklers or monitors are used to protect large oil-water separators, pump pits, and oil piping manifolds. In most countries fixed foam systems are not used to protect tank diked areas; large wheeled monitors or trailer-mounted foam cannons are used for this purpose. In Germany many large tank diked enclosures are protected by fixed foam systems designed in accordance with German DIN Standard 14493. Other countries, including France and Great Britain, permit the use of large foam cannons for extinguishment of tank fires, regardless of tank size.

Fixed foam systems are used to protect petroleum piers and wharves where products and crude are handled. In many European countries, foam monitors of 1,000 to 1,500 gpm (3,785 to 5,676 litres per min) capacity are mounted on towers and remotely operated to cover both the pier and the tanker deck in the pipe manifold area. Below deck, foam spray or oscillating monitors are installed to keep the pier tenable in the event of a spill fire floating on the water surface under the pier.

Fixed systems consisting of automatically operated combinations of foam sprinklers and foam monitors are often installed to protect chemical processing plants. Special foams, some of which require gentle application, are frequently used. In these designs, process vessels, pumps, and piping are often all included within the foam distribution pattern for overall protection where there may be a high risk. The system can be automatic, being activated by heat or fire detectors.

4. Mobile Fire Protection Vehicles Using Foam

Crash-rescue trucks used at airports, and industrial foam trucks generally used at oil refineries and petrochemical plants make up the majority of the mobile fire protection vehicles using foam. Many of these vehicles are also equipped to discharge dry chemical in combination with foam. These are combined or "twinned" agent equipment, and are described in Part D of this Chapter.

(a) Crash-rescue Trucks

These mobile foam trucks, developed by the U.S. Air Force, the U.S. Navy, and municipal authorities in the United States and other countries, are large, custom designed vehicles, with oversize running gear which allows them to travel over all types of airport terrain. The trucks carry their own water supply as well as foam concentrate, usually for 6 percent proportioning. Automatic "balanced pressure" type proportioning is usually provided, although in some designs an "around-the-pump" proportioning system is used. The trucks are equipped with separate engine-driven water pumps and foam concentrate pumps so that their turret monitor nozzles and roadway foam nozzles can be discharged while in motion. Recent designs accomplish this using only one engine for all power requirements needed. Crash-rescue trucks are equipped with large capacity, adjustable foam monitors of 500 to 1,500 gpm discharge, depending on truck size. The foam monitors are usually installed on top of the cab with remote-operated controls. The trucks are also equipped with portable handlines. Although their supply of foam concentrate and water is limited, it is sufficient to enable fire fighters to form a passageway for access to a burning aircraft for rescue. Their primary purpose is rescue of people, and not necessarily a total extinguishment of fire. Aircraft crash-rescue foam vehicles are of special design and require special attention to detail in their fabrication and performance requirements. NFPA No. 414, Standard for Aircraft Rescue and Fire Fighting Vehicles, provides standards for such vehicles.

(b) Industrial Foam Truck Design

Foam trucks are manufactured by vendors who make a speciality of this design, and by some vendors of fire department pumpers. Generally, using as a design basis NFPA No. 19, Standard for Automotive Fire Apparatus, these trucks are fabricated on a suitable commercial truck chassis adapted for the purpose. In the United States they are available with booster pumps in sizes from 750 to 1,500 gpm (NFPA rating) using gasoline engine drives. Designs have been projected to 2,000 gpm at 150 psig discharge pressure when operating with suction lift, using a diesel engine drive. Most European foam trucks use diesel engine drives, but are of smaller capacities in the neighborhood of 900 gpm.

Automatic pressure differential or "balanced" proportioning is provided for maximum flexibility and simplification. A rotary type foam concentrate pump taking suction from a 900- to 1,000-gal foam liquid storage tank is employed. The foam concentrate pump is driven by a power takeoff, while the water booster pump is driven by a transfer gear from the main drive shaft behind the transmission. A metering valve at each truck outlet can vary foam proportioning from 3 to 6 percent. When the truck is equipped with an articulated boom, a second power takeoff is used to power the boom hydraulic system.

As well as the maximum of 1,000 gal of foam concentrate, each foam truck usually carries $1\frac{1}{2}$-in., $2\frac{1}{2}$-in., and 3-in. fire hose, foam nozzles and adjustable water fog nozzles, hose holders, hose adapter, and other accessories. The GVW is kept below 40,000 lb, and the maximum turning radius allowed is 36 ft so that the trucks are reasonably maneuverable on plant roads. The maximum height is limited to 10 ft to permit passage beneath most pipeways and similar obstructions. In this way, the truck can be maneuvered to fight process equipment fires as well as tank fires.

Foam trucks for special hazard application have become increasingly popular for refinery and petrochemical plant use, instead of installing fixed foam systems. Their advantages are:

1. Capability of discharging their maximum capacity at any hazard in the plant, rather than only to the limited areas covered by a fixed system.

2. Improved reliability, because their equipment is easily maintained; thus, operating procedures can be simplified and fire fighters more easily trained.

As well as fighting tank fires, industrial foam trucks are used to extinguish spill fires in process areas, piping runs, and tank diked areas. They are equipped with 500 to 1,000 gpm foam-water monitors for fighting major spill fires, and also $1\frac{1}{2}$-in. and $2\frac{1}{2}$-in. hand lines. Usually 3-in. hose is carried for large capacity flow requirements. Some designs are equipped with monitor nozzles on articulated or telescopic

Fig. 15-31. Typical industrial foam truck. (National Foam System, Inc.)

booms. This enables the operator to discharge foam at various elevations in and around process equipment. In some cases, a tank fire or a floating roof rim fire can be extinguished with this equipment. Figure 15-3I illustrates a typical industrial foam truck.

B. Chemical Foam Systems

Chemical foam systems have been almost completely replaced by air foam systems. While no new chemical foam systems are being installed, a number are still in use. The types of equipment for producing chemical foam include self-contained equipment, closed-type generators, hopper-type generators, and stored solution systems.

Types of Chemical Foam Generators

Self-contained Units: These are used for local or "spot" protection. They have the foam-producing chemicals stored in solution in equipment which may be automatic or manually operable. Generally, the foam is discharged through fixed distribution outlets. The discharge time, hence fire extinguishing capacity, is limited to the quantity of foam-producing materials in the device. These have been used primarily for localized protection of relatively small indoor hazards. Periodic replacement of the stored solutions is necessary.

Closed-type Generators: These devices utilize foam-producing chemicals stored in dry form. Upon automatic or manual operation, the generator meters the chemicals into a water stream where they dissolve and react with each other to form the foam which is discharged through piping and chemical foam outlets. Used for moderate-sized hazards, these systems are limited to the capacity of the generators. The powders must be kept dry and free-flowing.

Hopper-type Generators: This type of system utilizes either single powder or dual "A" and "B" powders. They are used for portable nozzle applications or large fixed systems. The chemicals are poured into the hoppers from pails or bins and are drawn into a water stream by suction. The foam is delivered by hose streams or fixed piping connections.

Stored Solution Systems: These are systems wherein the "A" and "B" chemicals are stored in solution in large tanks. They are largely obsolete. In these, the chemical solutions are pumped through duplex piping to discharge outlets where the solutions are mixed to cause the foam-producing reaction.

Maintenance and test procedures relating to chemical foam systems are contained in the NFPA Foam Extinguishing Systems Standard.

C. High Expansion Foam Generating Equipment and Systems

High expansion foam is an aggregation of bubbles resulting from the mechanical expansion of a foam solution by air (or by other gases) with expansion ratios in the range of from 100:1 (100X) to approximately 1,000:1 (1,000X). There are three types of high expansion foam systems: total flooding systems, local application systems, and portable foam generating devices.

High Expansion Foam Generators

The foam generators for such high expansion systems are of two types: aspirator and blower. In either case, a properly proportioned water-foam solution at appropriate velocity is impinged on a porous screen (or series of screens) in a moving air stream. The aspirator-type device utilizes jet streams of water-foam solution, entraining suitable amounts of air, which is then impinged on the screens to produce foam. The aspirator type produces foam of expansion 100X to 250X.

With blower-type devices the water-foam solution is discharged onto the screens through which an air stream, developed by a fan or blower, is passing; as the air passes through the screens, wetted with the foam solution, large masses of bubbles or foam are formed. The blower may be powered by compressed air or gas, by an electric motor, by an internal combustion engine, or by a hydraulic or water motor. This type produces foam of expansion up to 1,000X.

System Design and Employment

High expansion foam systems are basically used to control or extinguish fires involving surface fires in flammable and combustible liquids and solids, and deep-seated fires involving solid materials subject to smoldering. Three-dimensional fires in flammable liquids (falling or flowing under pressure) having flash points below 100°F generally cannot be extinguished with this technique, although such fires may be kept under control by application of high expansion foam. Key factors to consider in determining the design adequacy of a high expansion foam system are:

1. The quality and adequacy of water supply, the adequacy of supply of foam liquid concentrate, and the source of the air supply.

2. Suitability of the generator and foam delivery system (piping, fittings, valves, ducts).

3. Needed submergence volume and time as influenced by the space being protected, the nature of the hazards involved, leakage of the foam, and similar factors.

In actual practice the preceding design factors are assigned numerical values which have been determined by test or experience. They are then used in the following relationship to determine minimum foam discharge rates or total generator capacity for a given hazard volume:

$$R = \left(\frac{V}{T} + Rs\right) \times C_N \times C_L$$

where

R = rate of discharge (cfm) (cubic meters per minute)

V = submergence volume (cf) (cubic meters) (volume of space to be protected)

T = submergence time (min) (predetermined for different hazards and enclosure construction, varies from 2 to 8)

R_S = rate of foam breakdown by sprinklers (cfm) (cubic meters per minute) (predetermined or determined by test; see NOTE)

C_N = compensation for normal foam shrinkage (this factor has been found by experience to be 1.15)

C_L = compensation for leakage (this is estimated by the design engineer through evaluation of possible leakage around door openings, etc.; varies from 1.0 to 1.2)

(NOTE: In the absence of test data for rate of foam breakdown, R_S may be determined by the result of multiplying the estimated total discharge in gpm (litres per minute) from the maximum number of sprinklers expected to operate by 10.)

For detailed information on high expansion foam systems, reference should be made to NFPA No. 11A, Standard for High Expansion Foam Systems (Expansion Ratios over 100X).

Recent tests have shown that high expansion foam may

be useful in controlling liquid natural gas fires by forming an ice layer on the liquid.

Total Flooding Systems: A total flooding system may be used where there is an enclosure surrounding the hazard being protected which will permit the required amount of high expansion foam to be built up to extinguish or control the fire. Examples of such enclosures are rooms, vaults, and basement areas. Even an entire building may be so protected where the foam generators are of sufficient capacity and steps are taken to assure effective distribution of the foam and its retention. Since the efficiency of the high expansion foam system depends upon the development and mainte- nance of a suitable quantity of foam within the particular enclosure, leakage of the foam from the enclosure must be avoided. It is thus important that doorways or windows be designed to close automatically with consideration being given to the evacuation of personnel. High level venting is required for the air which is displaced by the foam.

For adequate protection, sufficient high expansion foam must be discharged at a rate to fill the space to an effective depth above the hazard before an unacceptable degree of damage occurs. The depth of the foam above the hazard will vary depending upon the type of materials creating the hazard. Generally, the minimum depth above the hazard should be two feet. The time allowed to cover the hazard will likewise vary depending upon the type of material in- volved, construction features, and whether the enclosure also has an automatic sprinkler system or similar protection. Consideration has to be given to the disintegration of the foam by the heat of the fire; by normal foam shrinkage; by leakage around doors, windows, and through unclosable openings; and by the effects of sprinkler discharge where sprinkler protection is provided.

Local Application Systems: Local application systems can be used where total flooding systems may be impractical or unnecessary and only a specified hazard is to be pro- tected. Such hazards may be indoors or outdoors (where air currents are not likely to be severe). These systems are best adapted to the protection of flammable or combustible liquids in dip tanks and associated drainboards, and for pits and trenches; high expansion foam may be used for extin- guishing spill fires where it is feasible to apply the foam from fixed or portable nozzles at adequate rates of discharge to develop a foam blanket for purposes of achieving com- plete extinguishment.

Portable Foam Generating Devices: Portable foam gen- erating devices consist of a high expansion foam generator, manually operable and transportable, which is connected by means of a hose, or piping and hose, to a supply of water and foam concentrate. The proportioning equipment may be integral with, or separate from, the foam generator. A separate foam concentrate supply may be provided for each unit, or the solution may be piped from central proportion- ing equipment. Only lined hose should be used to connect the generator to the water or solution supplies.

The rate and duration of the discharge is determined by the type and potential size of the hazard. Successful ex- tinguishment of a fire with portable foam generating devices will also depend upon the individual ability and technique of the operator. Therefore, training is essential in the operation of the equipment and in the necessary fire fighting tech- niques. When using these devices in the open, the effect of wind should be considered since some of the foam may be dissipated by air currents.

Precautions To Be Observed with High Expansion Foam

A space filled with high expansion foam is normally not toxic to persons who may be trapped in the space, since the air entrained in the foam is generally not contaminated; however, because of the foam bubbles, some difficulty may be experienced in breathing. Air for high expansion foam is usually taken from a source of clean air: where products of combustion are introduced, the foam quality may be substandard because of the contaminates present and the temperatures of the heated air. Because loss of vision and disorientation in an atmosphere of high expansion foam introduces life and injury hazards, entering a foam-filled space should be avoided unless adequate precautions are taken. A coarse water spray may be used to "cut" a path in the foam. Personnel should wear self-contained breathing apparatus and employ a lifeline when entering an area filled with high expansion foam.

D.   Combined Agent or "Twinned" Equipment

The superior capability of dry chemical agent (especially potassium salt types) for very fast flame control and three- dimensional flowing fuel extinguishment is well-docu- mented. Its fire fighting deficiency of reflash protection over fuel surfaces that have been extinguished is also well known. With the advent of dry chemical compatible aque- ous film forming foam (AFFF) concentrates, it became possible to almost simultaneously apply a coating of vapor- securing foam to a burning fuel surface which has been freshly extinguished by the chemical action of dry chemical discharges.

The logical extension of these facts has been incorporated into portable and mobile devices for one-man operation of dual trigger-valve controlled nozzles and monitor nozzles discharging AFFF and dry chemical, but linked together (twinned) for coordinated action and control. Figure 15-3J illustrates the twinned pistol-grip trigger-valve dual nozzle device for portable dual hoseline use. The use of this combined agent attack allows flammable liquid fire extin- guishment with both speed and freedom from reignition.

Fig. 15-3J. Twinned nozzle applicator for combined agent use—AFFF nozzle in operator's left hand and dry chemical nozzle in right hand.

Combined Agent Equipment Design and Usage

The earliest (1964) application of the combined agent concept was associated with the control and extinguishment of accidental aircraft fuel fire emergencies where a mobile system was designed for quick response. The fire fighting vehicle shown in Figure 15-3K is the modern unit for aircraft crash-rescue purposes and for other extinguishment purposes on freeways or in plant protection using combined agents.

In use, the twinned hose from the hose reel supplies dry chemical and AFFF to a dual portable nozzle for one-man operation. Similarly, the turret nozzles above the cab discharge dry chemical on one side and AFFF on the other. With a sweeping motion the flames are controlled with the dry chemical, quickly followed by a vapor-securing, cooling layer of foam to prevent reflash. This rapid action halts flame radiation and makes advancement over the fire area safe and cool.

A newer design, especially for petroleum refinery plant protection, involves the combined agent concept in a triple use arrangement consisting of a 2,000 lb dry chemical tank, a 200 gallon AFFF premixed solution tank, nitrogen bottles for pressurization of both tanks, a 250 gallon fluoroprotein foam concentrate tank, a 1,500 gpm water booster pump, and pressure differential "balanced" foam solution proportioning up to 1,800 gpm. Three monitors are mounted behind the truck cab. Two of the monitors, "twinned" for operation as a unit, consist of a 50 lb per sec dry chemical turret nozzle and a 180 gpm AFFF nozzle. The third monitor, mounted in an adjacent position, is a 500 gpm AFFF adjustable foam monitor. In addition, the truck carries two twinned hose reels—each with 100 ft of twinned hose, and with hose nozzles for dry chemical and AFFF arranged for twinned operation. The hose reels are equipped with electric motor rewind. Foam nozzles, adjustable water fog nozzles, 1½-in., 2½-in. and 3-in. hose as well as other accessories are also carried on the truck. The truck GVW is kept at less than 40,000 lbs, and the turning radius is limited to no more than 36 ft.

The dry chemical turret nozzle will extinguish three-dimensional or pressure fires at a distance of 100 ft, at grade or overhead. It will also extinguish spill fires at a distance of about 150 ft. Both pressure and spill fires can be knocked down, controlled, and extinguished in less than 20 seconds, and immediately secured using AFFF agent. In addition, for long-range operation with lengthy duration, the 500 gpm foam-water monitor has a range of about 200 ft. The foam concentrate tank normally carries 250 gal of 3 percent fluoroprotein air foam liquid concentrate.

Fig. 15-3K. Combined agent vehicle. (Ansul Company)

With foam solution proportioning up to 1,800 gpm and with the engine sized to provide necessary power, the truck is capable of fighting fires in fixed roof oil storage tanks up to 150 ft in diameter. The foam solution proportioning system is designed to permit an external tank such as a tank trailer to be used for foam concentrate supply. Transfer to the second source of foam concentrate can be accomplished without stopping foam solution proportioning.

E. Foam Equipment Testing and Surveillance

The continued effective emergency performance of foam equipment depends entirely on fully adequate maintenance procedures, with periodic testing where possible. The many variations in system design and equipment applications for hazards requiring foam make it impossible to establish anything other than general procedures for periodic inspection. Although it is realized that air foam concentrates and foam equipment and systems for fire protection are subject to change, variation, and even malfunction over long unattended spans of time, it must be assumed that they are adequate for the purpose for which they are designed.

Foam Concentrate Surveillance

Because all air foam concentrates are water solutions of organic and inorganic chemicals of one sort or another, they must be carefully observed for changes in constitution and characteristics. Their storage in shipping containers and in storage tanks must be carried out according to the manufacturer's recommendations. Exposure to extreme heat, cold, contamination, or mixing with other materials must be avoided. Sedimentation or precipitate formation in containers or tanks of concentrate should be carefully checked periodically. The manufacturer or his representative is best qualified to test and determine the extent of reliability of foam concentrates under questionable conditions of deterioration of these liquids.

Foam Equipment Testing and Surveillance

The performance of all foam equipment under emergency conditions is best guaranteed by periodic test activation of the equipment, if possible. Original design specifications of fixed installations should include provision for periodic testing of proportioners, pumps, and other ancillary equipment without the trial distribution of foam to the hazard being protected.

Problems of corrosion, clogging of orifices, sticking of valves, and malfunction of electric circuitry may be detected by suitable means without full system activation.

In the absence of actual fire, and without full system activation, the complete testing of foam equipment performance for fire protection adequacy may be accomplished by various suitable means. In the absence of actual fire, complete testing may be accomplished by several physical test methods. However, because these tests are similar in nature to "fingerprint" tests, their results can only be interpreted on the basis of comparison with similar tests conducted at the installation acceptance of the equipment, or as provided for under the performance guarantee of the manufacturer.

Foam equipment performance can be tested for the following physical characteristics of foam:

1. The dimensions of the discharge pattern or patterns of the device or system.

2. The percent concentration of foam concentrate in the finished foam solution.

3. The degree of expansion of the finished foam.

4. The rate at which water drains from the foam (i.e., 25 percent drainage time. This correlates with its viscosity or rate of spreading over fuel surfaces.)

5. Film forming capacity of the foam concentrate.

The preceding tests require specially designed test equipment and standardized techniques. With the exception of test No. 2, they require qualified operators and cannot be easily carried out in the field. Detailed information concerning the equipment required, methods used, and some interpretations of the test results will be found in the Appendices of NFPA No. 11, Standard for Foam Extinguishing Systems (Tests for Protein Base Foams and Chemical Foams), NFPA No. 11B, Standard for Synthetic Foam and Combined Agent Systems (Tests for AFFF Type Foams), and NFPA No. 412, Standard for Evaluating Foam Fire Fighting Equipment on Aircraft Rescue and Fire Fighting Vehicles (Tests for Foam Discharge Patterns, AFFF Type Foams, and Protein Base Foams).

The test for the concentration of the foam concentrate is very important because it indicates the efficiency of operation of the concentrate proportioning device in the system. It is easily performed in the field with a hand refractometer and volume measuring device.

SI Units

The following conversion factors are given as a convenience in converting to SI units the English units used in this chapter.

1 in.	= 25.400 mm
1 ft	= .305 m
1 lb (mass)	= .454 kg
1 psi	= 6.895 kPa
$\frac{5}{9}(°F - 32)$	= °C
1 gal (U.S.)	= 3.785 litres
1 gpm	= 3.785 litres/min

Bibliography

NFPA Codes, Standards, and Recommended Practices (see the latest *NFPA Publications and Visual Aids Catalog* for availability of current editions of the following documents)

NFPA No. 11, Standard for Foam Extinguishing Systems.
NFPA No. 11A, Standard for High Expansion Foam Systems.
NFPA No. 11B, Standard for Synthetic Foam and Combined Agent Systems.
NFPA No. 13, Standard for the Installation of Sprinkler Systems.
NFPA No. 16, Standard for Foam Water Sprinkler and Spray Systems.
NFPA No. 402, Standard for Aircraft Rescue Procedures.
NFPA No. 403, Standard for Aircraft Rescue and Fire Fighting Services at Airports.
NFPA No. 409, Standard for Aircraft Hangars.
NFPA No. 412, Standard for Evaluating Foam Fire Fighting Equipment.
NFPA No. 414, Standard for Aircraft Rescue and Fire Fighting Vehicles.
NFPA No. 418, Standard for Roof-top Heliport Construction and Protection.

Additional Readings

"Air Foam Equipment and Liquid Concentrates," UL-162, 1969, Underwriters Laboratories, Northbrook, Ill.
American Chemical Society, "Aqueous Foams—Their Characteristics and Applications," *Industrial and Engineering Chemistry*, Vol. 48, Nov. 1956.
Beers, R. J., "High Expansion Foam Fire Control for Records Storage," *Fire Technology*, Vol. 2, No. 2, May 1966, pp. 108–117.
Breen, D. E., "Hangar Fire Protection with Automatic AFFF Systems," *Fire Technology*, Vol. 9, No. 2, May 1973, pp. 119–131.

Butlin, R. N., "High-Expansion Air Foam, A Survey of Its Properties and Uses," Fire Research Note No. 669, May 1967, Fire Research Station, Boreham Wood, Herts, England.
Casey, James F., ed., *Fire Service Hydraulics*, 2nd ed., Part 4, "Foam," R. H. Donnelley Corporation, New York, 1970.
Cray, E. W., "High-Expansion Foam," NFPA *Quarterly*, Vol. 58, No. 1, July 1964, pp. 57–63.
Eriksson, Lars, "Semi-Subsurface Foam System," NFPA *Quarterly*, Vol. 58, No. 1, July 1964, pp. 54–56.
"Fire Extinguishing Agent, Aqueous Film Forming Foam (AFFF) Liquid Concentrate, Six Percent for Fresh and Sea Water," Military Specification MIL-F-24385(NAVY), Amendment 8, Naval Ship Engineering Center, Department of the Navy, Hyattsville, Md.
"Fighting Fuel Storage Fires with Subsurface Foam," *Fire International*, Vol. 3, No. 26, Oct. 1969.
Fittes, D. W., Griffiths, D. J., and Nash, P., "Extinction of Experimental Aircraft Fires with Light Water," *Fire*, Vol. 62, No. 773, Nov. 1969, pp. 315–317.
———, "The Use of Light Water for Major Aircraft Fires," *Fire Technology*, Vol. 5, No. 4, Nov. 1969, pp. 284–298.
"French Firm's 'Light Water' Tested for Aircraft Fires," *Fire International*, Vol. 3, No. 31, Jan. 1971, pp. 93–94.
Geyer, G. B., "Extinguishing Agents for Hydrocarbon Fuel Fires," *Fire Technology*, Vol. 5, No. 2, May 1969, pp. 151–159.
———, "Foam and Dry Chemical Application Experiments," National Aviation Facilities Experimental Center, Federal Aviation Administration, Atlantic City, N.J., Dec. 1968.
Hird, D., "The Use of Foaming Agents for Aircraft Crash Fires," *Fire*, Sept. 1974, pp. 179–180.
Hird, D., Rodrigues, A., and Smith, D., "Foam—Its Efficiency in Tank Fires," *Fire Technology*, Vol. 6, No. 1, Feb. 1970, pp. 5–12.
International Fire Service Training Association, Aircraft Fire Protection and Rescue Procedures, Oklahoma State University, Stillwater, Okla., 1973.
Jamison, Will B., "High-Expansion Foam in the Fire Departments," *Fire Journal*, Vol. 61, No. 6, Nov. 1967, pp. 43–47.
"Large Scale Tests on Light Water," *Fire International*, Vol. 25, Oct. 1968, pp. 60–65.
Martin, G. T. O., "Fire Fighting Foam," *The Institution of Fire Engineers Quarterly*, Vol. 32, No. 86, June 1972, pp. 165–176.
Meldrum, D. N., Williams, J. R., and Conway, C. J., "Storage Life and Utility of Mechanical Fire-Fighting Foam Liquids," *Fire Technology*, Vol. 1, No. 2, May 1965, pp. 112–121.
Meldrum, D. N., Williams, J. R., and Gilroy, D., "Foam Fire Protection of Liquid Propellants," *Fire Technology*, Vol. 2, No. 3, Aug. 1966, pp. 234–238.
"Navy Tests 'Light Water' Airborne Fire Fighting System," *Aviation Week and Space Technology*, Aug. 23, 1965, pp. 90–91.
Peterson, H. B., "Suppression Capability of Foam on Runways," NFPA Aviation Bulletin No. 250.
———, "Research Tests with Foam-Water Sprinklers," U.S. Naval Research Laboratory, Vol. 52, No. 1, July 1958, pp. 17–27.
Peterson, H. B., et al., "Full-Scale Fire Modeling Test Studies of 'Light Water' and Protein Type Foams," NRL Report 6573, 1967, U.S. Naval Research Laboratory, Washington, D.C.
Rasbash, D. J., and Langford, B., "The Use of Nets as Barriers for Retaining High Expansion Foam," *Fire Technology*, Vol. 2, No. 4, Nov. 1966, pp. 298–302.
Rivkind, L. E., and Myerson, I., "Foams for Industrial Fire Protection," *Industrial and Engineering Chemistry*, American Chemical Society, Nov. 1956.
Rivkind, L. E., "Testing of Fire Fighting Foams," NFPA *Quarterly*, Vol. 54, No. 1, July 1960, pp. 139–150.
"Subsurface Foam Application for Tank Fires," NFPA *Quarterly*, Vol. 39, No. 4, April 1946, pp. 306–317.
"Subsurface Foam for Tank Fires," *National Safety News*, July 1965.
"Suffocation in High Expansion Foam," *Fire International*, Vol. 18, Oct. 1967, pp. 27–30.
Sumi, K., "Compatibility Tests for Dry Powders and Protein Foams," DBR Research Paper No. 304, Feb. 1967, Division of Building Research, National Research Council, Ottawa.
Tuve, R. L., "Light Water and Potassium Bicarbonate—A New Two-Agent Extinguishing System," NFPA *Quarterly*, Vol. 58, No. 1, July 1964, pp. 64–69.
———, "New Methods of Protecting American Aircraft Carriers," *Fire International*, Vol. 3, No. 25, July 30, 1969.
———, "Twinned Agent Extinguishing System Uses," *Fire Engineering*, Vol. 117, No. 5, May 1964, pp. 358–360.
Wesson, H. R., Walker, J. R., and Brown, L. E., "Control LNG Spill Fires," *Hydrocarbon Processing*, Dec. 1972.
Wilder, Ira, "High Expansion Foam for Shipboard Fire Protection," *Fire Technology*, Vol. 5, No. 1, Feb. 1969, pp. 25–37.

Chapter 4

CARBON DIOXIDE EXTINGUISHING SYSTEMS

Carbon dioxide has many applications in the field of fire protection. One of these uses, carbon dioxide extinguishing systems, is the subject of this chapter. Carbon dioxide extinguishers are discussed in Section 16, Chapter 3, and the use of carbon dioxide to inert fire hazardous areas in Chapter 7 of this Section. Properties of carbon dioxide affecting its usefulness in the field of fire prevention and protection are covered in Section 13, Chapter 3.

NFPA No. 12, Standard for Carbon Dioxide Extinguishing Systems, hereinafter referred to in this chapter as the NFPA Carbon Dioxide Extinguishing Systems Standard, was prepared for the guidance of those responsible in any way for the proper installation and operation of carbon dioxide systems.

A. Application of Carbon Dioxide Systems

Carbon dioxide can be used to extinguish fires in practically all combustible materials except for a few active metals and metal hydrides, and in materials (such as cellulose nitrate) that contain available oxygen. However, its most widespread use is in extinguishing flammable liquid fires because it can rapidly form a temporary inert atmosphere above the surface of the liquid. As carbon dioxide is electrically nonconductive, it also is used extensively for the protection of electrical equipment. The nondamaging characteristics of carbon dioxide make it attractive as protection for rooms containing high value contents such as fur and record vaults, computer rooms, and computer tape storage rooms. Where prompt resumption of operations after a fire is important, carbon dioxide is often used to protect production equipment and processes. Carbon dioxide does little or no damage to equipment or materials in process, and, as there are no liquid or solid residues to clean up, damage and downtime after a fire is held to a minimum. Carbon dioxide has the advantage of providing its own pressure for discharge through pipes and nozzles, and being a gas it can penetrate and spread to all parts of the hazard.

Methods of Application

There are two general methods of applying carbon dioxide to extinguish fire. One method is to create an inert atmosphere in the enclosure or room in which the hazard is located. In some cases it is necessary to maintain this inert atmosphere in the enclosure for some time until extinguishment is complete. This method is known as total flooding.

The other method is to discharge carbon dioxide at the surface of liquids or noncombustible surfaces coated with flammable liquids or light deposits of combustible residues. This method is known as local application. No enclosure is needed around the hazard, but it is essential in local application that all fire be completely extinguished without any possibility of reignition during the period of carbon dioxide discharge. The various types of carbon dioxide systems employing these two general application techniques are discussed in Part C of this chapter.

Hazards to Personnel

Discharging large quantities of carbon dioxide to extinguish fires may create hazards to personnel. Carbon dioxide "snow" in the discharge may seriously interfere with visibility during and immediately after the discharge period. In addition, the noise of discharge may frighten people who have not experienced it previously or been prepared as to what to expect. Oxygen deficient atmospheres will be produced where extinguishment depends on creating such an atmosphere in an enclosed space or room. They also may be produced by any large volume of carbon dioxide drifting and settling in adjacent low spaces, such as cellars, tunnels, or pits.

Hazards of oxygen deficient atmospheres can be controlled by the installation of warning systems and devices, by establishing specific emergency procedures, by delayed discharge of the carbon dioxide, and by other similar steps.

Limiting Factors

The principal property limiting the use of carbon dioxide is its low cooling capacity compared with water. The problem of providing enough carbon dioxide to extinguish some types of fire completely without danger of reignition may rule out using a carbon dioxide system despite other factors that may make its use desirable.

Extinguishing Surface Fires

Where a surface fire exists, such as in a flammable liquid fire, cooling takes place very rapidly after the flame is extinguished, assuming that no masses of metal have been heated by the fire. In most cases where actuation of the carbon dioxide is automatic, there will be little time to heat metal before the fire is extinguished. Where metal has been heated, additional carbon dioxide can be applied by extended discharge until the metal is cooled to a point where reignition will not take place.

Extinguishing Deep-seated Fires

Deep-seated fires that smolder beneath the surface may be produced in carbonaceous materials such as paper, wood, and cotton. Fires in such materials are classified as "Class A" fires, and the most effective way to extinguish them is by cooling. Because of the low cooling capacity of carbon dioxide, the deep-seated fire may be difficult to extinguish by this medium. Carbon dioxide can quickly extinguish the flaming fire and control its rapid spread, but complete extinguishment of the remaining smoldering fire may require the maintenance of an inert atmosphere within the enclosure or room in which the hazard is located for a considerable period of time. Many variables determine the carbon dioxide concentration needed and the length of time the inert atmosphere must be maintained. In many cases, an atmosphere containing 30 to 50 percent of carbon dioxide and maintained for one-half hour to one hour may be adequate for complete extinguishment. In extreme cases an atmosphere of practically 100 percent carbon dioxide maintained for days or weeks may be needed. Where the period of time needed for complete extinguishment is comparatively short, the required carbon dioxide concentration can often be satisfactorily maintained by a continuous or intermittent automatic discharge of carbon dioxide into the room or enclosure about the hazard. Where this period is comparatively long, the required carbon dioxide concentration may be maintained by sampling and measuring the oxygen concentration within the enclosure or room and then manually operating the carbon dioxide system to supply the additional carbon dioxide needed.

Although the low capacity for cooling inherent in carbon dioxide makes it difficult to obtain complete and permanent extinguishment of some deep-seated fires, carbon dioxide systems are successfully used for this purpose rather extensively where other characteristics of carbon dioxide make the use of this medium desirable or imperative.

Selecting the Proper System

In planning for protection by a carbon dioxide system, the situation may be such that, although the principal hazard is one that will produce a surface fire, there also may be present within the fire area materials that can produce a deep-seated fire. In this situation a decision has to be made whether or not to design a system having the capability of extinguishing both types of fires. The answers to such questions as the following will aid in making the decision:

1. Considering the speed of fire detection and fire extinguishment of the contemplated system, will there be time for a deep-seated fire to develop?

2. If a deep-seated fire does develop, will circumstances be such that there will not be reignition of an active fire with additional loss?

3. If such additional losses are a possibility, can they be satisfactorily minimized by the back-up of automatic sprinkler protection, or by arrangement for manual extinguishment after the carbon dioxide discharge?

4. Must a system designed to extinguish a deep-seated fire be provided because of the high values involved or the importance of equipment to continuous production?

If there is only a remote possibility that additional losses may be suffered due to deep-seated fires, a system designed to extinguish surface fires only may be selected in many instances. As an example, oil-filled transformers are usually protected by systems designed to extinguish surface fires, although there is a chance that a heated core will cause a deep-seated fire in the electrical insulation. However, the importance of some electrical equipment to continuous production often justifies a system designed to extinguish a possible deep-seated fire, even though such a possibility is remote.

Design of Carbon Dioxide Systems

Research and development carried on by manufacturers of carbon dioxide systems and testing laboratories have provided the specific knowledge that permits accurate engineering in many areas of design. Until the results of further research and development are available, there remain other areas of design where only general statements developed by experience can be made. Such statements have to be interpreted by the skill and experience of the designer to meet the specific requirements of each situation. Experienced engineers can design efficient and effective systems and can see that such systems are properly installed. Others may not be able to do so.

B.   Carbon Dioxide Systems Components

The ability of a carbon dioxide system to put out a fire depends upon the way in which the carbon dioxide is discharged into the fire area, the rate of application, and the total quantity discharged. Design features that affect these two variables include the method and location of carbon dioxide storage, piping, fittings, and nozzles.

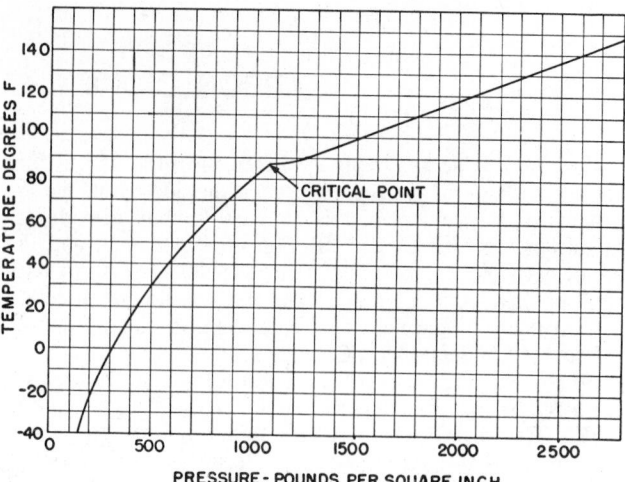

Fig. 15-4A.   Variation of absolute pressure of carbon dioxide with change in temperature (at constant volume and at equilibrium). Critical point is at 87.8°F and 1,072.1 psia. Above 87.8°F, carbon dioxide is entirely gas, irrespective of pressure. Below 87.8°F and above—69.9°F (triple point temperature, see Fig. 13-2A), carbon dioxide is part liquid and part gas.

Carbon Dioxide Storage

The carbon dioxide supply may be stored in "high pressure" or "low pressure" containers. Because of the differences of the pressures maintained in these two types of containers, the design of a system is influenced by the method of storage.

High Pressure: High pressure storage containers (usually cylinders) are designed to store liquid carbon dioxide at atmospheric temperature. Since the maximum pressure in the cylinder or other container is affected by the ambient temperature, it is important that the container be designed to withstand the maximum expected pressure. Figure 15-4A shows the change in absolute pressure with temperature. It will be noted that if the temperature of the storage container is 70°F, the pressure in the container is about 850 psia. It will also be noted that there is a rapid rise in pressure with increase in temperature. For this reason 130°F has been chosen as the maximum permissible temperature for storage containers. This maximum provides a margin of safety below the 3,000 psi bursting pressure of the frangible disc in the container.

Another safeguard to prevent excessive container pressure is the maximum filling density (percent filling) limitation. Although carbon dioxide liquid expands with increase in temperature, the expansion does not increase the pressure in the container as long as there is a vapor space. If the container becomes liquid full, however, the pressure will increase rapidly with slight increase in temperature. It is for this reason that DOT specifications limit the weight of carbon dioxide in a container to 68 percent of the weight of water that the container can hold at 60°F. (42.5 pcf of cylinder volume with CO_2.)

Abnormally low ambient storage temperatures adversely affect the rate of discharge from high pressure storage containers. Storage temperatures below 32°F are not permitted by the NFPA Carbon Dioxide Extinguishing Systems Standard unless some method of compensating for pressure decrease, such as external heating or special design, is used.

Low Pressure Systems: Low pressure storage containers are pressure vessels with a design working pressure of at least 325 psi. They are maintained at a temperature of

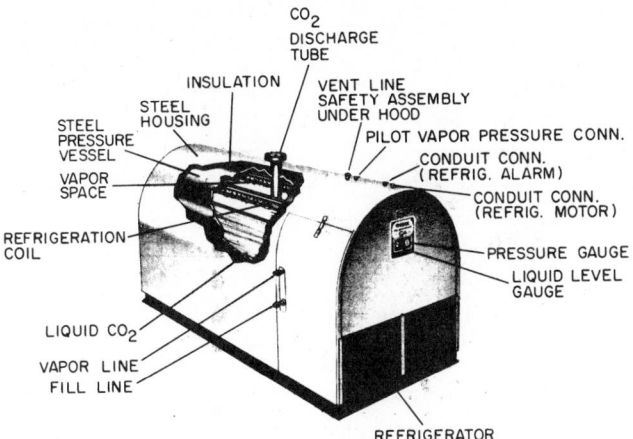

Fig. 15-4B.   Low pressure storage unit. Carbon dioxide is maintained at 0°F by refrigeration. The pressure is 300 psi. (Cardox Division of Chemetron Corporation)

approximately 0°F by means of insulation and mechanical refrigeration. At this temperature the pressure is approximately 300 psi. A compressor controlled by a pressure switch in the tank circulates refrigerant through coils near the top of the tank. Condensation of carbon dioxide vapor by the coils controls the tank pressure. Figure 15-4B shows a typical low pressure storage container.

The use of low storage pressures makes it economically practical to store carbon dioxide in quantities from 500 lbs to several hundred tons. Liquid carbon dioxide is delivered through pipelines from low pressure storage units to open nozzles having discharged capacities as high as 2,500 lbs per min. Multiple hazards are usually protected by one storage unit.

Filling density is not as important a consideration with low pressure containers as it is with high pressure containers. With temperatures controlled by refrigeration and with properly set pressure relief valves to cause vaporization and resultant liquid cooling, the low pressure storage container will not become liquid full. Consequently, low pressure containers are not subject to the same filling density limitations as are high pressure containers. It is only necessary to provide sufficient vapor space to provide for expansion of the liquid under the maximum storage temperatures that can be obtained with the settings of the pressure relief valves. Filling densities of low pressure containers usually range from 90 to 95 percent.

Relief valves on a container to prevent the pressure from exceeding safe limits, as from a refrigeration failure, include a diaphragm valve set to bleed off vapor if the pressure exceeds 341 psi, and a pop valve set to operate at 357 psi for more rapid release if the pressure should continue to rise. Further safeguard is furnished by a frangible disc designed to burst at 600 psi and which is vented to the outside of the building. For a 4-ton storage unit, no carbon dioxide is lost until about 24 hrs after refrigeration failure. With air temperature at 80°F, the release is approximately 100 pounds per day for a storage unit of this size.

Piping and Fittings

Piping systems, normally empty, are used to convey carbon dioxide from the storage container to open nozzles at the fire. By means of a dip tube in the container, carbon dioxide enters the piping as a liquid. Friction causes loss in pressure, and as pressure drops, the liquid boils, resulting in a mixture of liquid and vapor in the piping. The vapor in-

creases in volume as the mixture passes through the piping with a continuing drop in pressure.

It is essential to design the piping so that the pressure will not drop to 75 psia (the triple point, see Sec. 13, Chap. 3) since below this pressure the remaining liquid will flash to vapor and solid carbon dioxide snow. The snow will tend to clog the nozzle orifices. Another reason, of course, why pressure drop is an important consideration in piping systems design is the effect of pressure drop on weight-rate of discharge of carbon dioxide from nozzles. The minimum design pressures are 150 psia and 300 psia respectively for systems with low and high pressure storage containers (see NFPA Carbon Dioxide Extinguishing Systems Standard).

Work conducted at the Factory Mutual Laboratories for the carbon dioxide industry and reported in the NFPA *Quarterly*,[1] showed the effect of rate of discharge on extinguishment. The pressure drop may be such that the rate of discharge is reduced below that required for fire extinguishment. Recommended rates of discharge for different types of fires are contained in the NFPA Carbon Dioxide Extinguishing Systems Standard.

To resist maximum pressures that could be expected, piping and fittings in high pressure systems are required to have a minimum bursting pressure of 5,000 psi except valves which are constantly under pressure must have a minimum bursting pressure of 6,000 psi. The minimum bursting pressure of low pressure system piping and fittings is 1,800 psi. Corrosion resistance, noncombustibility, and ability to withstand the temperature extremes that may be encountered are other characteristics of carbon dioxide system piping and fittings to be considered.

Nozzles

The discharge characteristics and locations of nozzles are of primary importance. Nozzles are usually of the shielded (low velocity) type or jet (high velocity) type, and each nozzle has an optimum discharge rate. Either type can be used where an enclosure is to be flooded, but low velocity nozzles are generally used for those systems designed to discharge carbon dioxide directly on a flammable liquid fire.

Where an area is to be flooded, the number and total orifice area of nozzles should be sufficient to achieve the required carbon dioxide concentration within specified periods that vary with the type of fire. Nozzles on systems discharging directly on a fire are selected and located so that all areas are covered and all liquid carbon dioxide is discharged within 30 seconds except for the amount required for an additional cooling period.

In all applications the type of nozzles and their locations should be such that the discharge will not splash flammable liquids, create dust clouds, or draw air into the fire area.

C.   Types of Systems

Total Flooding

Total flooding with carbon dioxide is a method of fire extinguishment whereby the air in the room or other enclosure in which a fire is burning is diluted with carbon dioxide to a point where burning cannot continue.

Extinguishment of surface fires involving flammable liquids and solids is the most common application of total flooding, but deep-seated fires involving solids subject to smoldering can also be extinguished by this method.

Where carbonaceous materials, such as paper, wood, cotton, etc., are involved in fire, smoldering combustion takes place which can readily cause reignition even after a considerable period of time. The concentration of carbon dioxide to stop active flaming in bulk paper, for example, is 0.125 pcf. While active flaming oxidation is stopped at this concentration, even though there is no visible combustion, oxidation can continue as long as oxygen is present and temperatures in the neighborhood of 700°F to 1,000°F remain. The cooling process thus may take much longer, and extinguishment may require maintaining the carbon dioxide concentration for a long period of time. It may be desirable to measure the oxygen concentration with a gas sampling device and to operate the carbon dioxide system manually as needed to maintain the oxygen concentration at a low level. Fire fighting forces, seeing that visible combustion has stopped, are prone to open a burning area where carbon dioxide has been used before extinguishment is complete, sometimes with disastrous consequences.

Furthermore, freshly formed charcoal or char from the partial burning of paper is chemically active, is subject to spontaneous ignition, and at temperatures in the range of 200°F to 300°F will continue to oxidize in very low oxygen concentrations.

A total flooding method of extinguishing fires in rotating electrical equipment by a continuous extended discharge is described under "Extended Discharge" in Part D of this Chapter. Flammable liquid storage rooms and fur storage vaults are examples of enclosures where surface and deep-seated fire hazards, respectively, can be protected by total flooding types of carbon dioxide systems. Figures 15-4C and 15-4D are examples of how total flooding systems can be used.

Total flooding extinguishment depends upon filling an enclosure with a predetermined concentration of carbon dioxide and maintaining it until everything in the enclosure is cooled to below the ignition temperature of the fuel. It is therefore important that leakage of carbon dioxide from the enclosure be kept to a minimum. This does not mean that an airtight enclosure is necessary or in fact desirable. There are limits, however, to the amount of unenclosed area above

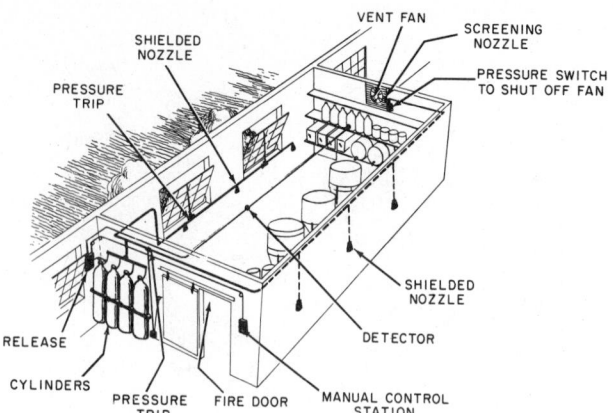

Fig. 15-4D. *Diagram of high pressure carbon dioxide system for total flooding.*

which total flooding becomes impractical. In the case of surface fire hazards, total flooding can be effective with up to 10 percent of the total enclosure (walls, floor, ceiling) unenclosed. For deep-seated fires requiring retention of carbon dioxide in the enclosure for relatively long periods the only openings that usually can be tolerated are small ones at or near the ceiling. Because carbon dioxide is heavier than air, gas escaping through openings near the top during carbon dioxide discharge into the enclosure is mostly air and products of combustion.

Too little vent area must also be avoided in areas protected by total flooding systems. In theory, the pressure generated against the walls and roof of some tight enclosures is more than they can withstand. In practice, however, it has been found that leakage at doors, windows, and dampers is usually sufficient to relieve the pressure buildup. Record rooms, for example, have been found to need no additional venting under average conditions. For very tight enclosures, however, vent areas determined by calculation to be adequate must be provided. When special vents are used, they should be located near the ceiling so that venting of the enclosure will not result in loss of large quantities of the incoming carbon dioxide.

Operation of a total flooding system will result in flammable vapors, gases, and products of combustion being forced from the enclosure. In many cases these displaced vapors and gases could be the means of spreading fire beyond the protected enclosure. For this reason, vents discharging to the outdoors are desirable. Openings are frequently protected by screening nozzles. These project carbon dioxide across the openings to prevent egress of flames.

Local Application

Local application systems extinguish fires by discharging carbon dioxide directly onto the surface of the burning material. In this method, air necessary for combustion is removed from the immediate vicinity of the fire and replaced by an inert atmosphere until the fire is extinguished. A fundamental principle of local application system design is prompt discharge of the carbon dioxide so that the fire can be extinguished before excessive amounts of heat can be absorbed by materials within the protected area. This method of extinguishment is suitable for surface fires involving flammable liquids and combustible deposits (paint, etc.) where there is no enclosure or the enclosure is not

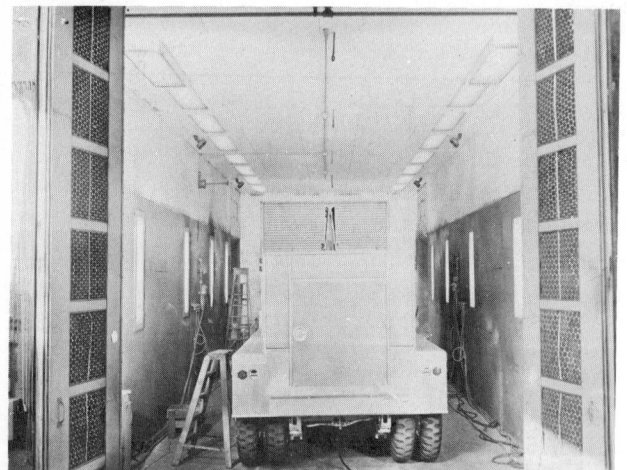

Fig. 15-4C. *A carbon dioxide total flooding system protects this vehicle paint spraying room. Carbon dioxide discharge nozzles are located on the ceiling near each side wall and also above the doorway (not visible). A row of heat detectors midway between the side walls and beneath the ceiling extends from the front to the rear of the room. Doors are normally closed during paint spraying. In installations such as this, the detector operates an alarm, shuts down exhaust systems, and after a delay long enough to allow occupants of the room to get out, actuates the carbon dioxide system. (Cardox Division of Chemetron Corporation)*

Fig. 15-4E. A carbon dioxide fire extinguishing system for a restaurant kitchen range and exhaust system. Outlets are so arranged that discharge of carbon dioxide under the hood floods the surfaces of the cooking equipment and enters the exhaust system to extinguish grease fires in the duct system. (Norris Industries, Fire & Safety Equipment Division)

adequate for total flooding. The most common applications are flammable liquid hazards such as dip tanks, spray booths, and oil-filled transformers, and for grease fires in restaurant kitchens. An example of a local application system is shown in Figure 15-4E.

The gas discharge outlets must be carefully located to cover the entire surface that may become involved. For example, it is not enough to cover the surface of the liquid in a dip tank. Drainboards, hoods, ducts, and other areas to which a fire might spread immediately must also be protected if the system is to be effective.

Nozzles should also be located to avoid agitation of burning liquids with resulting increase in fire intensity, and to avoid creation of dust clouds that could cause a dust explosion. Another important consideration in nozzle installation is their location so as not to aspirate air unduly into the fire area.

Extended Discharge

Extended discharge applies carbon dioxide at a high initial rate, followed by the release of additional carbon dioxide to cool heated metal or to maintain the desired concentration in an enclosure until extinguishment is complete. The secondary discharge may be continuous or intermittent. Extended discharge may be used on total flooding or local application systems. It can be used in those situations where glowing and smoldering material requires maintaining an atmosphere of carbon dioxide for a considerable period.

Extended discharge is particularly applicable to enclosed rotating electrical equipment, such as generators, motors, and convertors, where the carbon dioxide might otherwise be dispersed before extinguishment could be effected. An alternate method for extinguishing fires in rotating equipment provides for the release of larger quantities of carbon dioxide over a prolonged period of time by one continuous extended discharge.

In either method, oxygen concentration is held for a prolonged period below a point at which fire can rekindle, until

glowing embers are extinguished and all of the combustible materials are cooled to below their ignition temperatures.

Hand Hose Lines

Carbon dioxide systems consisting of hand hose permanently connected to a fixed supply of carbon dioxide by means of fixed piping can be used for total flooding or local application. Although not a substitute for a fixed system, a hose line may be used to supplement fixed systems when the hazard is accessible for manual fire fighting. They can also be used to supplement portable equipment.

The carbon dioxide supply for hand hose line systems may be separate or it may be a central storage unit supplying several carbon dioxide systems. In either case, the supply should be large enough to permit use of the handline for at least a minute.

Hand hose lines are required to have a minimum bursting pressure of 5,000 psi if connected to a high pressure supply, or 1,800 psi if the supply is low pressure. The hoses are equipped with quick-opening shutoff nozzles. They are not under pressure until the valve actuating the systems is opened.

In some systems the carbon dioxide supply is remotely located from the hose line; in these cases a remote pull box is located near the hose outlet. Otherwise, the valve is located near the hose reel. Figure 15-4F shows a hand hose line system.

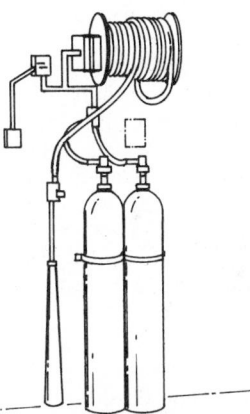

Fig. 15-4F. Carbon dioxide hand hose extinguishing system with hose mounted on a reel. This system offers flexibility for attacking fires. (Walter Kidde & Company, Inc.)

Standpipe Systems and Mobile Supply

Total flooding, local application, and hand hose line systems without a permanently connected carbon dioxide supply are known as standpipe systems. They are supplied by containers of carbon dioxide mounted on mobile units that can be brought to a standpipe system and quickly coupled to it in case of fire.

These systems can be used to supplement complete fixed fire protection systems, or they may be used alone for the protection of hazards where extinguishment will not be adversely affected by the delay in attack necessitated by the time required to bring the mobile supply to the scene and attach it to the standpipe. Mobile supplies may be equipped with hand hose lines for the protection of scattered hazards.

The vehicle on which the carbon dioxide supply is mounted may be one that can be pulled to the fire manually or by a motor vehicle, or it may be self-propelled.

D. Operation of Systems

Method of Actuation

Total flooding and local application carbon dioxide systems are designed to operate automatically or manually. Automatically operated systems are required to have an independent means of manual actuation.

For automatic operation, a reliable means of detecting the fire or dangerous condition is provided which in turn actuates a device to set in motion those operations necessary for successful performance of the system. The detection device may be any of the listed or approved devices that are actuated by heat, smoke, flame, flammable vapors, or other abnormal process conditions that could lead to a fire or explosion. Actuation of the system may be by an automatic electric switch to open a cylinder valve, or it may be a more complicated electrical timing device consisting of a series of motor-driven cams designed to operate switches in proper sequence and at the proper time to give the alarm, shut down equipment, close fire doors, start and stop the carbon dioxide flow, and to do other things necessary to extinguish the fire safely and quickly or to correct dangerous conditions. The latter method is used in low pressure systems.

Whether supplemental to automatic actuation or the sole means of placing a system in operation, manual controls must of necessity be easy to operate, accessible in case of fire, and located close to the valves they control. Other remote manual controls are usually located near an exit for a total flooding installation or near a hazardous area for a local application installation. The control valve for manual charging of hand hose line systems, for example, should be located in the immediate vicinity of the hose reel, and nozzles should be designed for simple and quick hand opening and closing. Hand hose line systems can be charged automatically by an electric switch actuated by raising the nozzle from its holder. Since the success of any manual operation connected with a carbon dioxide system will depend on the availability of skilled operators at the time of the emergency, attention to training personnel is as important as the system itself.

Carbon Dioxide Requirements

The quantity of carbon dioxide required for extinguishment depends on the type of fire, type of extinguishing systems, and conditions in the fire area that would adversely affect the successful performance of the system. Where continuous protection is required the quantity of carbon dioxide on hand will have to be at least twice that needed for extinguishment.

Total Flooding—Surface Fires: To extinguish surface fires, such as flammable liquid fires, by total flooding, enough carbon dioxide is required to reach a minimum design concentration in the enclosure. The minimum design concentration consists of the theoretical minimum concentration of carbon dioxide for extinguishment plus a 20 percent increment as a safety factor. Theoretical minimum concentrations have been determined for many flammable liquids and gases (see Table 13-3A). The amount of carbon dioxide theoretically needed to reach a minimum design concentration in an enclosure of known volume will have to be increased to compensate for carbon dioxide escaping through small openings in the enclosure during injection of the carbon dioxide or lost through large openings such as ventilating systems. Quantities of carbon dioxide, including an amount to compensate for leakage through small openings, have been determined for spaces of different volumes. The

amount of carbon dioxide necessary to compensate for leakage decreases with increase in volume of the enclosure on the assumption that the ratio of boundary area to volume decreases with increase in volume. Specific information on leakage considerations is contained in the NFPA Carbon Dioxide Extinguishing Systems Standard. To compensate for larger openings that cannot be closed at time of fire, an additional quantity of carbon dioxide is required. Losses through openings will depend on several factors which must be evaluated. One pound of carbon dioxide per square foot of opening may be considered to be a representative loss.

Since surface fires normally are extinguished during the period of carbon dioxide discharge into the enclosure, it is not usually necessary to provide additional carbon dioxide to maintain the concentration.

Total Flooding—Deep-seated Fires: Deep-seated fires in combustible material can be extinguished by total flooding if the required carbon dioxide concentration can be maintained until all of the material is cooled to below its ignition temperature. This method of extinguishing deep-seated fires is only practical with fairly tight enclosures. Based on practical test conditions, the pounds of carbon dioxide per cubic foot of enclosure for certain materials subject to deep-seated fires have been determined. For electrical machines of under 2,000 cu ft volume, the recommended quantity of carbon dioxide is 0.1 lb per cu ft. The quantity for fur vaults is 0.166 lb per cu ft. These basic quantities may require adjustment to compensate for openings that cannot be closed. In those situations where the leakage may be considerable and where there is no suitable alternate extinguishing method not affected by leakage, an additional extended discharge of carbon dioxide may be a solution.

Local Application—Rate by Area Method: Nozzles used in local application systems are rated for their ability to extinguish flammable liquid fires. For any given height of nozzle over a liquid surface, the area which can be extinguished and the carbon dioxide flow rate are known. This information is published by fire testing laboratories on nozzles that have been submitted for test.

To protect a dip tank, first the height of the nozzle above the surface of the liquid is measured; second, from the testing laboratory data, the area that this nozzle will protect at the particular height in question is determined (see Fig. 15-4G); third, the number of nozzles is calculated by dividing the area of the tank by the area per nozzle. Also from

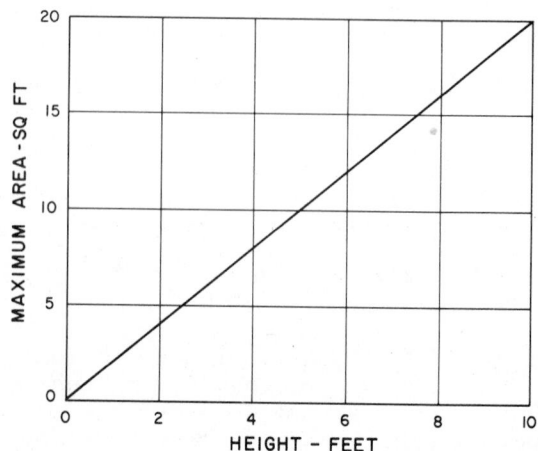

Fig. 15-4G. A listing or approval curve of a typical carbon dioxide nozzle showing maximum area versus height or distance from liquid surface.

the published information, the flow rate in pounds per minute is determined for this particular nozzle. The total flow rate for the system will then be the flow rate per nozzle multiplied by the number of nozzles. The normal duration of discharge is 30 sec. This must be liquid carbon dioxide discharge from the storage means.

The flow rate in pounds per minute multiplied by 30 sec will give the quantity of liquid discharge required. In high pressure cylinders, it has been found that about 70 to 75 percent of the total contents is discharged as liquid, the balance as gas. For this reason 40 percent additional cylinder capacity is required. Therefore, the amount of carbon dioxide as determined by the preceding method must be multiplied by 1.4 to obtain the total cylinder capacity.

While the height of overhead-type nozzles above the surface of a hazard is the criterion for determining their flow rates, the rates for tankside and linear nozzles are calculated on a different basis. Flow rates for tankside nozzles are based on the area of coverage for each nozzle with certain limitations on spacings along the edge of a tank and on maximum distances at right angles to the sides of a tank.

Flow rates for linear nozzles are based on the "throw" or maximum distance to be protected by a nozzle measured at right angles to the nozzle.

Information on area coverages and maximum distances across hazards versus minimum and maximum flow rates for various nozzles can be found in fire laboratory listings and approval curves. Figure 15-4H is a typical listing or approval curve of a tankside nozzle showing flow rate versus area coverage. Figure 15-4I is a typical listing or approval curve of a linear nozzle showing flow rate versus the hazard width or limits of "throw" of the nozzle.

Drainboards are calculated in a similar manner except that areas may be increased by 40 percent per nozzle.

The above carbon dioxide requirements include protection for objects, the tops of which are not more than two feet above the liquid or drainboard surface. Higher objects require additional carbon dioxide projected at them.

Local Application—Rate by Volume Method: Where the hazard consists of three dimensional, irregular objects that cannot be easily reduced to equivalent surface areas, the rate by volume method is used. The discharge rate of the system is based on the volume of an assumed enclosure entirely surrounding the hazard. The assumed walls and ceiling are calculated to be two feet from the hazard unless there are one or more actual walls nearby.

The total discharge rate is equal to 1 lb/min/cu ft of assumed volume. Certain reductions can be made if actual walls exist. As an example, should actual walls completely surround the enclosure, the rate can be reduced to .25lb/min/cu ft.

Extended Discharge: When it is necessary to maintain an inert atmosphere after extinguishment long enough for hot metals and other reignition sources to cool, the initial carbon dioxide requirement is supplemented by a quantity sufficient to maintain the desired concentration to the end of the extinguishing period. The extended discharge quantity is based on an estimate of the leakage rate from the enclosure and on the concentration that is to be present at the end of the extended extinguishing period.

Protection of rotating electrical equipment is the primary application of extended discharge. Where there is a reasonably tight enclosure around the equipment, the recommended quantity of carbon dioxide for the initial discharge is at least 1 lb for each 10 cu ft of space up to 2,000 cu ft and 1 lb for each 12 cu ft for larger spaces. The quantity of a subsequent extended discharge should be sufficient to assure a 30 percent concentration at the end of the deceleration period. For large equipment this may be a matter of hours. Amounts of carbon dioxide to produce a 30 percent concentration at the end of various deceleration times for equipment with different internal volume are published in the NFPA Carbon Dioxide Extinguishing Systems Standard.

Hand Hose Line Systems: The carbon dioxide supply depends in theory on the type and size of the hazard to be protected, but as a practical matter, as much more carbon dioxide as can be conveniently provided should be available to counteract possible waste by inexperienced users. In any case, there should be enough carbon dioxide to permit operation of the system for at least a minute.

Mobile Supplies: The mobile carbon dioxide supply for fixed systems should be the same as if the supply were a fixed part of the system, with an extra quantity to compensate for the delay in getting the supply to the system standpipe.

Supervision of Carbon Dioxide Systems

Carbon dioxide systems require different degrees of supervision depending on the complexity of the system. As a minimum requirement, every system should be supervised to the extent that an audible or visual signal will indicate that the system has operated and should be placed back in service. An audible alarm is necessary to warn occupants of any area where the discharge of carbon dioxide will

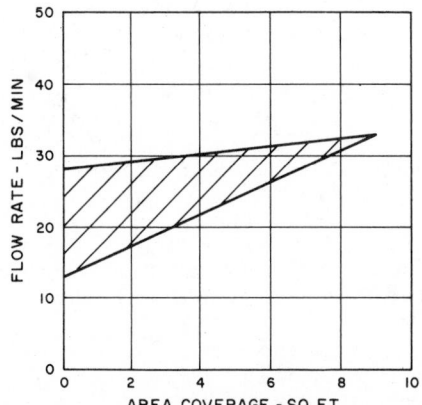

Fig. 15-4H. A typical listing or approval curve of a tankside carbon dioxide nozzle showing the flow rate versus area coverage.

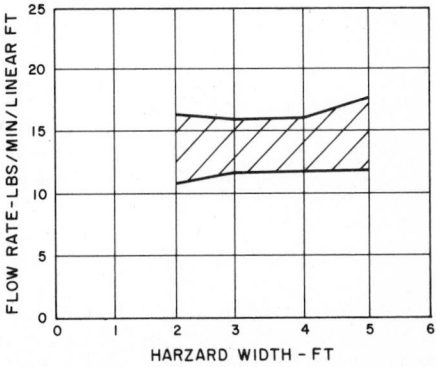

Fig. 15-4I. A typical listing or approval curve of a linear carbon dioxide nozzle showing flow rate versus hazard width.

Fig. 15-4J.   Two examples of carbon dioxide local application protection for strip mills. The three photos at left, from top to bottom, show the beginning of discharge, full protection, and the start of sublimation of the carbon dioxide. At right is another installation, and the three photos, from top to bottom, were taken at intervals of 13, 20, and 35 sec after the system was tripped. At 45 sec, the carbon dioxide concentration on the work surface was 65 percent. (Cardox Division of Chemetron Corporation)

create an oxygen deficient atmosphere. They should have time to escape before the carbon dioxide is released. This may mean delaying the discharge of the carbon dioxide for a time after the alarm sounds.

Where the detection and control systems are so extensive and complex that they cannot be visually checked, a supervisory system should be arranged to give prompt and positive indication of any failure.

E.   Maintenance, Inspection, and Test Procedures

Maintenance of carbon dioxide systems in operating condition requires frequent scheduled visual checks and tests at least annually to be sure all parts of the system are in proper operating condition. In order to run a satisfactory test, it may be necessary to discharge enough carbon dioxide to operate all pressure-actuated parts of the system.

Cylinders should be weighed at least semiannually to detect loss by leakage. Cylinders which show loss of weight of 10 percent or more should be replaced. In remote locations where prompt replacement after a fire is not possible, additional carbon dioxide cylinders should be kept on hand.

High pressure cylinders can be refilled at manufacturers' filling stations located near most large cities, or by transfer from commercial cylinders at the site.

The liquid level gage on a low pressure storage container should be checked frequently. Refilling is usually called for if the loss is more than 10 percent. If the container still contains more than enough to satisfy the requirements of the system, immediate refilling is not necessary. Low pressure units can be refilled by either tank trucks or tank cars carrying liquid carbon dioxide at low temperature.

SI Units

The following conversion factors are given as a convenience in converting to SI units the English units used in this chapter.

1 pcf	= 16.018 kg/m³
1 lb (mass)	= .454 kg
1 lb (force)	= 4.448 n
1 psi	= 6.895 kPa
$\frac{5}{9}$(°F − 32)	= °C
1 cu ft	= .0283 m³

Fig. 15-4K. The four hand lines being used in this demonstration of fighting an aircraft fire are discharging carbon dioxide at the rate of 450 lbs per min. (Boeing Airplane Co.)

Bibliography

References Cited

[1] Cousins, E. W., "Carbon Dioxide Extinguishment Tests," NFPA *Quarterly*, Vol. 54, No. 2, Oct. 1960, pp. 164–172.

NFPA Codes, Standards, and Recommended Practices (see the latest *NFPA Publications and Visual Aids Catalog* for availability of current editions of the following document)

NFPA No. 12, Standard for Carbon Dioxide Extinguishing Systems.

Additional Readings

Barker, R. K., and Sprado, C. G., "Carbon Dioxide System Design Analysis by Computer," *Fire Technology*, NFPA, Vol. 3, No. 4, Nov. 1967, pp. 306–313.

Factory Mutual Approval Guide, Factory Mutual Engineering Corporation, Norwood, Mass., published annually.

Fire Protection Equipment List, Underwriters Laboratories, Inc., Chicago, Ill., published annually with bimonthly supplements.

Haessler, W. M., "Static Electricity Generation by Carbon Dioxide Extinguishers," NFPA *Quarterly*, Vol. 56, No. 3, Jan. 1963, pp. 221–226.

Jensen, R. H., and Bellman, R. F., "Testing Carbon Dioxide Equipment," NFPA *Quarterly*, Vol. 55, No. 3, Jan. 1962, pp. 304–309.

Williamson, H. V., "A New Standard for CO Systems," NFPA *Quarterly*, Vol. 58, No. 1, July 1964, pp. 70–77.

—— "Carbon Dioxide Flows in Pipes and Nozzles," NFPA *Quarterly*, Vol. 53, No. 1, July 1959, pp. 70–82.

—— "New Protection for Electronic Equipment," *Fire Technology*, NFPA, Vol. 2, No. 4, Nov. 1966, pp. 279–286.

Chapter 5

HALOGENATED EXTINGUISHING AGENT SYSTEMS

This chapter includes the following aspects of fire extinguishing systems which use halogenated agents: (1) history, (2) definition and types of systems and typical applications, (3) design considerations, and (4) testing and maintenance of systems.

The properties of halogenated fire extinguishing agents are discussed in Section 13, Chapter 4. The use of halogenated agents in portable fire extinguishers is included in Section 16.

A. History of Halogenated Extinguishing Agent Systems

Until development of the fluorinated agents (Halon 1301, Halon 1211, Halon 1202, and Halon 2402)* following World War II, the application of halogenated agents to fire extinguishing systems was limited. Halon 104 (carbon tetrachloride, CCl_4) was used primarily in portable fire, extinguishers, although some systems and small "thermatic" units were introduced in the 1920s and 1930s. In the early 1920s Halon 104 systems were used experimentally in aircraft engines, but unreliability associated with corrosiveness of Halon 104 resulted in these systems being discontinued in favor of carbon dioxide systems by the U.S. Army Air Corps in 1931.[1]

Systems containing Halon 1001 (methyl bromide, CH_3Br) and Halon 1011 (bromochloromethane CH_2BrCl) were developed for a variety of applications during World War II by British and German military forces.[2] Systems using the halogenated agents were attractive because they were smaller and lighter than similar ones using carbon dioxide. Their chief disadvantage was their relatively high inhalation toxicity. Systems using both Halons 104 and 1001 were evaluated for use in aircraft in 1939-1941, resulting in recommendations for the adoption of Halon 1011 on-board extinguishing systems for military aircraft. These systems were later adopted by the U.S. Air Force, and some are still in service today.[3,4]

In England about 1950, the concept of explosion suppression was invented at the Royal Aircraft Establishment in Farnborough[5]. During the period 1950-1960, explosion suppression systems using Halons 1001 and 1011 were installed on British aircraft and later in industry.

Halons 104 and 1011 also found their way into commercial systems. A number of thermatic units were developed, most of which were small glass bulbs containing a pound or two of agent, designed to break in the heat of a fire. Only a few were listed by the laboratories. One such unit, the Stop-Fire Model SP-30 containing one gallon of

Halon 1011 pressurized with carbon dioxide, continued on the market until the late 1960s when Underwriters Laboratories and Factory Mutual began to withdraw listings of equipment containing Halon 104 or Halon 1011. In the period 1950-1960 in England, fixed fire extinguishing systems using Halon 1001 and Halon 1011 were designed for fighting vehicles, diesel rail cars, etc. These systems, plus Halon 1001 systems on aircraft used in World War II which were later converted to civilian service, were converted to Halon 1211 about 1962. Except for a few Halon 1001 and 1011 systems still in service on several older models of European and U.S. military aircraft, and for certain explosion-suppression applications, systems containing these three early halogenated agents have been removed from service.

Following their development, aircraft and military vehicles represented the first uses of the modern halogenated agents (Halon 1301, 1211, 1202, and 2402) in systems.[6,7] These systems were rather quickly adopted to protect engine compartments on military land, air, and water craft, such as battle tanks[8,9,10], personnel carriers, trucks, aircraft hydrofoils, and hovercraft.

Also in 1966, the Boeing Company conducted a series of tests with water fog and Halon 1301 to protect airplane passenger cabins. The Douglas Company in 1968 evaluated high-expansion foam blown with a 5 percent Halon 1301/ 95 percent air mixture for the same purpose. Both studies were performed as a part of an Aircraft Industries' Association crashworthiness program. A further study was initiated by the Federal Aviation Administration in 1972, which currently (1975) is still in progress. In 1970, a self-contained automatic extinguishing unit utilizing Halon 1301 was introduced to protect aircraft interiors during construction and maintenance[11]. About this same time, a study was concluded by the FAA[12,13] which led to the introduction of a Halon 1301 system to protect the cargo compartment and lower galley of the Boeing 747 aircraft. Similar systems were later installed in the McDonnell-Douglas DC-10 and the Lockheed L-1011.

The concept of utilizing halogenated agents in commercial total flooding systems seems to have originated between 1962 and 1964. By the latter date, experimental work toward this method of application was in progress by both E. I. du Pont de Nemours & Company and Fyr-Fyter Company (now Norris Industries), using both flammable liquid and cellulosic fuels. Between 1964 and 1968, a number of Halon 1301 total flooding systems were installed in the United States, utilizing carbon dioxide equipment and technology. Such a system installed in Winterthur Museum was described in the November 1969 issue of *Fire Journal*[14].

In 1966 the NFPA organized a Technical Committee on Halogenated Fire Extinguishing Agent Systems to develop standards on "fire extinguishing systems utilizing bromotrifluoromethane (Halon 1301) and other similar halogenated extinguishing agents, covering the installation, maintenance, and use of such systems." The Committee developed a Standard, NFPA No. 12A, Standard for Halogenated Extinguishing Agent Systems—Halon 1301 (hereinafter referred to in this chapter as the NFPA Halon 1301 Standard), which was adopted in 1970. In 1971 this same

---

* The Halon nomenclature system is described in detail in Section 13, Chapter 4. For reference, the Halon number and chemical names of the common halogenated fire extinguishing agents are as follows:

Halon 104—carbon tetrachloride, CCl_4
Halon 1001—methyl bromide, CH_3Br
Halon 1011—bromochloromethane (also known as chlorobromomethane, CH_2ClBr),CH_2BrCl
Halon 1202—dibromodifluoromethane, CBr_2F_2
Halon 1211—bromochlorodifluoromethane, $CBrClF_2$
Halon 1301—bromotrifluoromethane, $CBrF_3$
Halon 2402—dibromotetrafluoroethane, $CBrF_2CBrF_2$

Technical Committee developed NFPA No. 12B, Standard for Halogenated Fire Extinguishing Agent Systems—Halon 1211 (hereinafter referred to in this chapter as the NFPA Halon 1211 Standard), which was approved as a permanent Standard in 1972.[15,16] At the present time, systems utilizing only these two halogenated agents, Halon 1301 and 1211, are recognized in NFPA Standards.

About 1966, attention began to focus on the use of Halon 1301 to protect computer rooms and EDP equipment. In 1972, following extensive testing by several major companies on the effects of Halon 1301 decomposition products on electronic equipment[17], the NFPA Committee on Electronic Computer/Data Processing Equipment recognized Halon 1301 total flooding systems in NFPA No. 75, Standard for Electronic Computer/Data Processing Equipment. With suitable precautions, such as time delays*, Halon 1211 systems are in use in Europe to protect computer rooms and EDP equipment.

In 1967 the first operational halogenated agent system was installed in a car that won the Indianapolis 500 race. Later that same year seven Ford cars in the 24-hour endurance race at Le Mans were equipped with Halon 1301 on-board systems. In Europe similar systems utilizing Halon 1211 were introduced, and in 1969 the Federation International de l'Automobile recognized both Halon 1301 and Halon 1211 on-board fire extinguishing systems. In 1970 such systems were made mandatory by the National Hot Rod Association, and in 1971 by the United States Automobile Club and by the American Hot Rod Association. Although a series of tests was conducted on this application in 1971[18], there are no recognized standards for on-board race car systems.

Systems using the fourth "modern" halogenated agent, Halon 2402, have found only limited use. Halon 2402 explosion-suppression systems were applied to protect fuel vent tanks in Boeing 707 and C-135 aircraft in 1967, but these systems were discontinued in 1968 for economic reasons. Except for a few specialized explosion-suppression applications, Halon 2402 systems are not used to a significant degree in the United States. In Europe, however, particularly in Italy[19] and in the USSR, Halon 2402 systems are seeing somewhat wider use. Virtually none of this equipment has appeared in the United States, and consequently Halon 2402 systems are not currently recognized by any NFPA standards.

B. Definition of Systems; Types of Systems; Typical Applications

A *system* differs from a portable or mobile appliance primarily in that the agent discharge stream is not directed by a person. The discharge stream or pattern is usually determined in advance, as is either the quantity of agent or the discharge rate or both, and the number and types of nozzles provided. A system consists of a supply of agent, a means for releasing or propelling the agent from its container, and one or more discharge nozzles to apply the agent into the hazard or directly onto the burning object. A system may also contain other elements, such as one or more detectors, remote and local alarms, a piping network, mechanical and electrical interlocks to shut down ventilation, close fire doors, etc., directional control valves, installed reserve agent supplies, etc. The extent of the auxiliary functions of a system is usually dependent upon the nature of the hazard, in keeping with the desires and resources of the end-user.

A system is generally considered to be a fixed or stationary apparatus, but some portable or mobile systems have been designed. A portable or mobile system may be moved from one hazard to another similar one, but it is placed in a stationary position while it is in service. In this regard all systems may be considered to be "fixed," but not necessarily permanently so.

Systems may also be distinguished by their method of design. An engineered system is custom designed for a particular hazard, using components which are approved or listed only for their broad performance characteristics. Components may be arranged into an almost unlimited variety of configurations.

In pre-engineered systems the number of components and configurations are determined in advance and included in the description of the system's approval or listing. While the degree of "pre-engineering" can differ from one system to another, the following limits of components and configurations are typical:

1. Maximum number of cylinders per manifold.
2. Maximum and minimum size and length of piping.
3. Maximum and minimum size and number of elbows, tees, and discharge nozzles.
4. Container volume, fill density, and level of nitrogen superpressurization.

Systems may also be distinguished by their primary or intended mode of operation. Automatic systems include one or more fire detectors which are arranged to actuate the system without the intervention of a person. A strictly manual system requires a person to perform some operation, such as pulling a cable or pushing a button, to actuate the system. A manual system may include some automatic features, such as detecting the fire, sounding remote alarms, operating interlocks, etc. Both types of systems, in accordance with the NFPA Halon 1301 and Halon 1211 Standards, must have an independent means of operating the system manually.

Finally, systems may be classified by their methods of applying agent to the hazard. The two main types recognized in the NFPA Halon 1301 and Halon 1211 Standards are "total flooding" and "local application" systems. Another category, termed *specialized systems* here, includes those which are designed to protect special or unique hazards, and which have been tested and approved under these specific conditions.

Total Flooding Systems: These systems protect enclosed, or at least partially enclosed, hazards. A sufficient quantity of extinguishing agent is discharged into the enclosure to provide a uniform fire-extinguishing concentration of agent throughout the entire enclosure. Examples of total flooding systems using halogenated agents are computer rooms, magnetic tape-storage vaults, and electronic controls rooms; storage areas for art work, books, and stamps; aerosol filling rooms; machinery spaces in ships; cargo areas in large transport aircraft; processing and storage areas for paints, solvents, and other flammable liquids, etc. Halon 1301, by virtue of its lower toxicity, higher volatility, and lower molecular weight, offers particular advantages for total flooding systems. Halon 1211 total flooding systems, with suitable safeguards† are in use outside the United States.

Local Application Systems: These systems, as the name implies, discharge extinguishing agent in such a manner that

* The use of time delays in halogenated agent systems is not recognized in the NFPA Halon 1301 and Halon 1211 Standards.
† See footnote on page 15–32.

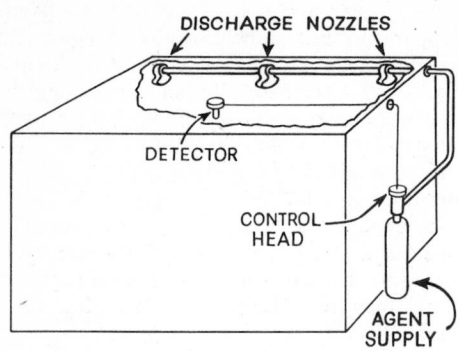

Fig 15-5A. A total flooding system.

the burning object is surrounded locally by a high concentration of agent to extinguish the fire. In local application systems, neither the quantity of agent nor the type or arrangement of discharge nozzles is sufficient to achieve total flooding of the enclosure containing the object. Often, too, a local application system is required because the enclosure itself may not be suitable to provide total flooding. Examples of areas protected by local application systems are printing presses, dip and quench tanks, spray booths, oil-filled electric transformers, vapor vents, etc.

Because of its lower volatility, Halon 1211 is well-suited for local application systems.

The lower volatility, plus a high liquid density, permit the agent to be "sprayed" as a liquid and thus propelled into the fire zone to a greater extent than is possible with other gaseous agents. Halon 1301 has been used to a limited extent in local application systems in the United States. At the present time, there is no listed equipment for local application systems using halogenated agents.

Specialized Systems: These systems, using both Halon 1301 and Halon 1211, are in wide use throughout the world. Systems to protect aircraft engine nacelles, racing cars, military vehicles, emergency generator motors, etc., all fall into this category. The distinguishing characteristic of a *specialized system* is that it can be applied only to the specific hazard for which it was designed and tested. For example, a system designed to protect the jet engines of a Boeing 707 aircraft cannot be applied *per se* to an M-60 battle tank. For each such application, the system is developed by a comprehensive test program.

Systems protecting racing cars are somewhat less specialized, although they properly fit into this category. Sanctioning bodies such as the Federation International de l'Automobile, the United States Automobile Club, and the National Hot Rod Association have formulated general rules governing these systems. One study showed a wide variety of sizes and performance characteristics of commercially available Halon 1301 systems available in the United States. Virtually none of these systems are listed or approved by nationally recognized testing laboratories. In spite of this, they have been credited with saving a large number of lives in the racing field.

Another type of "specialized" system is what has been termed a "thermatic" unit. This unit consists of a small container connected to a thermally actuated release device similar to a water sprinkler head. When heat from the fire activates the valve, the extinguishing agent is released to attack the fire. One unit that has been tested contains $3\frac{1}{2}$ lbs Halon 1301 and is listed for use on Class B and Class C hazards in enclosures not to exceed 7×7 ft floor area, or a gross volume of 441 cu ft. The present list-

ing does not permit the use of multiple units in larger enclosures. A smaller Halon 1301 thermatic unit is produced in Israel. Similar units containing Halon 1211 are available in the United Kingdom, in South Africa, in Australia, and in the United States, although as yet none have received testing laboratory listings.

A final example of a "specialized" system is one designed to protect a specific hazard, such as a kitchen ventilating system and associated cooking appliances: such a system has been tested and listed for this application.

C. Design Considerations

This section covers many of the aspects contained in the NFPA Halon 1301 and Halon 1211 Standards and follows their general organization. Rather than reiterate the material contained in these standards, however, this section highlights those requirements which are unique to halogenated agent systems and provides some background information for those requirements.

Uses and Limitations

Halogenated agent systems are generally considered useful for the following types of hazards:

1. Where a clean agent is required.
2. Where live electrical or electronic circuits exist.
3. For flammable liquids or flammable gases.
4. For surface-burning flammable solids, such as thermoplastics.
5. Where the hazard contains a process or objects of high value.
6. Where the area is normally, or frequently, occupied by personnel.
7. Where availability of water, or space for systems using other agents, is limited.

Whereas water sprinkler systems generally protect the structure of a hazard, halogenated agent systems are generally considered to protect the contents of a hazard.

There are several types of flammable materials on which halogenated agents are ineffective. These are:

1. Fuels which contain their own oxidizing agent, such as gunpowder, rocket propellants, cellulose nitrate, organic peroxides, etc.
2. Reactive metals, such as sodium, potassium NaK eutectic alloy, magnesium, titanium, and zirconium.
3. Metal hydrides, such as lithium hydride.

In the first category—in which the compound contains its own oxygen supply, often built into the fuel molecule—the halogenated agent is unable to penetrate into the reaction zone quickly enough to put out the fire. The oxidizer is physically in too close proximity to the fuel to permit interaction by the extinguishing agent. Often the only effective agent for such fuels is a water deluge to dilute the fuel and attempt to remove heat ahead of the combustion front. In the second category, the reactive metals and metal hydrides are too reactive at flame temperatures for the halogenated agent to operate effectively. In fact, if the extinguishing agent is highly concentrated, particularly in liquid form, a reaction between the halogenated agent and the fuel is possible. (In dilute mixtures of either Halon 1301 or Halon 1211 with air, say below 20 percent by volume, reactions between fuel and agent have not been observed.) Also, the flame chemistry of metal fires is quite different from those of hydrocarbon fires.[5]

Although halogenated agents will not extinguish these types of fires, systems using them may still find application to hazards containing these materials, with two benefits. First, the presence of the extinguishing agent may extinguish fires in adjacent common combustibles to prevent the problem fuels from becoming ignited. Second, if the problem fuel is already involved, the halogenated agent can prevent adjacent common combustibles from becoming ignited, thus isolating and limiting the problem fuel fire so that it can be dealt with by other means. If the problem fuel occupies a large portion of the hazard, a large amount of agent decomposition may occur due to continued combustion in contact with the halogenated agent. As in all other circumstances, an element of judgment must be applied by the system designer.

A more commonly encountered limitation of the capabilities of a halogenated agent is its limited effectiveness on Class A fires at concentrations below 10 percent by volume. A Class A fire may consist of two types of combustion: a surface fire, which exhibits flames and glowing embers on the surface of the material; and a deep-seated fire, which implies glowing combustion within the mass of burning fuel.

Both Halon 1301 and Halon 1211 at concentrations of $3\frac{1}{2}$ to 4 percent have been shown capable of extinguishing surface fires in Class A combustibles. The flaming combustion of such fires is extinguished almost immediately upon application of the agent. Surface embers are extinguished within a 5 to 10 min soaking period.

If the fire has become deep-seated, however, or has begun as a deep-seated fire, then it will not likely be extinguished by concentrations of halogenated agents below 10 percent. In fact, some types of deep-seated fires require concentrations above 20 percent to ensure complete extinguishment. In the presence of low concentrations of Halon 1301 or Halon 1211, deep-seated fires will burn at a much reduced rate of combustion. They will also be prevented from spreading to adjacent fuel arrays, and from again breaking out into flames. This element of control has been found to be a useful technique in applying halogenated agent systems to Class A hazards. In such cases, rapid response of outside help is a necessity. Otherwise, products of partial combustion from the fire and from decomposition of the extinguishing agent will eventually accumulate to undesirable levels.

Safety

The safety properties of halogenated agents are covered in detail in Section 13, Chapter 4. While both Halon 1301 and Halon 1211 have a low order of vapor toxicity, there are hazards in exposing personnel to high concentrations of either agent (above 10 percent Halon 1301 or above 4 percent Halon 1211). Further, the inhalation hazard produced by the fire itself may be substantial, as may decomposition of halogenated agents in contacting flames and hot surfaces during extinguishment. Several general safety precautions are listed in the Appendices of the NFPA Halon 1301 and Halon 1211 Standards.

Detection and Actuation

Halogenated agent systems generally have requirements for operation similar to systems using other types of agents. However, there are strong recommendations in the NFPA Halon 1301 and Halon 1211 Standards for the use of automatically actuated systems. The primary reason behind this recommendation is to limit the size and severity of fire with which the system must deal, and thus minimize decomposition of the agent during extinguishment. In the case of a

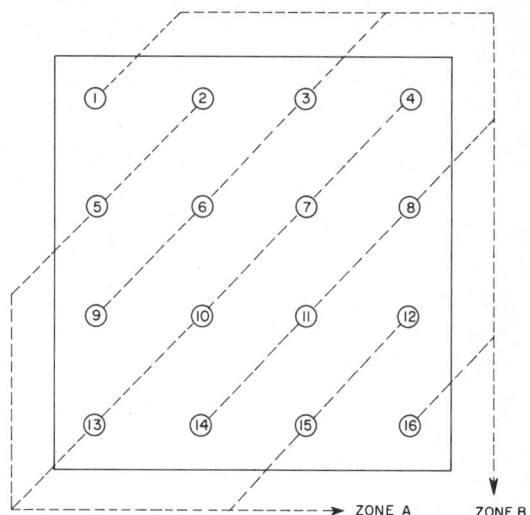

SIXTEEN DETECTORS IN A 4 x 4 ARRAY ARE CONNECTED SO THAT ADJACENT DETECTORS ARE ON DIFFERENT CIRCUITS, OR "ZONES". FOR EXAMPLE, CONSIDER DETECTOR NO. 7, CONNECTED TO ZONE A. ADJACENT DETECTORS, NOS. 3,6,8, AND 11 ARE CONNECTED TO ZONE B.

Fig. 15-5B. A cross-zoned detector circuit.

Class A hazard, automatic actuation coupled with sensitive detectors can prevent the fire from becoming deep-seated, thereby ensuring complete extinguishment.

The detector portion of the system is therefore extraordinarily important in the design of a system. The detector must be sensitive enough to the fuel in question to give rapid response to the fire at an early stage. But too great a sensitivity may produce false actuations, thus imposing an economic burden on the owner, causing unnecessary outage of fire protection, and degrading confidence in the system. Designers have successfully combined sensitivity and reliability by utilizing multiple detectors connected in a double circuit, or a "cross-zoned", mode of operation. Each zone consists of one or more detectors installed in the hazard so that actuation of any one detector in the zone causes that zone to alarm. Actuation of either zone alone activates local and remote alarms, but does not discharge the extinguishing agent. Actuation of both zones simultaneously causes the agent to discharge. This arrangement prevents a false signal by an individual detector in a large system from discharging the entire system. "Cross-zoning" refers to the practice of connecting a matrix of detectors so that adjacent detectors are on separate zones, or circuits. Figure 15-5A illustrates the principle of cross-zoned detectors. Ionization detectors are popularly used in cross-zoned systems. Different types of detectors have also been utilized, with one zone of ionization detection providing early warning, and one zone of rate-compensated thermal detectors to release the extinguishing agent.[20]

Particular attention must be given to locating detectors within a hazard. The amount and location of combustibles, the listed sensitivity-spacing relationship of the detectors considered, and ventilation characteristics of the hazard are all important factors.

Agent Supply

The relatively high cost of halogenated agents and the specialized nature of systems using them dictates that a finite supply of agent be provided to protect a given hazard or set of hazards. Conventionally, the agent is contained in one or more pressurized vessels which are installed near to or within the protected area. Steel pressure cylinders or spheres containing from a few pounds to several hundred pounds are commonly used. Larger "bulk" tanks containing several tons of agent are in use in Europe and have been proposed in the United States as well. In the United Kingdom, "dry pipe" systems, consisting of plumbing only, have been designed; they are fed by a mobile one-ton tank of Halon 1211 which is connected onto the piping system in the event of a fire.

Superpressurization of storage containers with nitrogen is required by the NFPA Halon 1301 and Halon 1211 Standards. For Halon 1211, this extra pressurization is necessary to expel the contents of the storage container at temperatures below the atmospheric boiling of 26°F (−3.4°C) and at a practical rate at higher temperatures. Two levels of superpressurization are recognized in the NFPA Halon 1211 Standard, 150 psig and 360 psig at total pressure at 70°F. Although the vapor pressure of Halon 1301 at all reasonable temperatures (above −30°F) is sufficient to expel the contents of the container completely, superpressurization is used to flatten the pressure vs. temperature characteristics during storage, to provide a higher average pressure in the storage container during discharge, and to permit the use of smaller piping. Two levels of superpressurization of Halon 1301 are permitted by the NFPA Halon 1301 Standard: 360 psig, and 600 psig total pressure at 70°F.

For both agents, the 360 psig level was selected as being the maximum level which could be used in welded steel cylinders by DOT (Department of Transportation) regulations. These regulations permit a maximum service pressure of 500 psig for welded cylinders of the 4B or 4BA specification. The regulations state that the contents of the container at 120°F shall not exceed five-fourths times the service pressure of the container, or 625 psig maximum at 120°F. Halon 1301 superpressurized with nitrogen to 625 psig or 120°F relates to 360 psig at 70°F, including a maximum permissible error of 5 percent at 70°F. Applying the same criterion to Halon 1211 would permit a somewhat higher maximum superpressure level to be used with 500 psi service pressure containers, but the 360 psi level was adopted by the NFPA Committee for sake of uniformity between the two standards. Higher levels of superpressurization (e.g., the 600 psi level for Halon 1301) require the use of seamless steel cylinders of 3A or 3AA specification, whereas the lower level of 150 psig permitted for Halon 1211 allows containers even lighter than 500 psi service pressure to be used. In the United States, each manufacturer of Halon 1301 equipment has standardized on one level of superpressurization for his equipment. Only one manufacturer currently offers equipment for the 600 psig pressurization level. Thus, the level of superpressurization is not a variable which the system designer can select freely.

The fill density of a container is defined as the weight of agent divided by the internal volume of the container. The NFPA Halon 1301 and Halon 1211 Standards permit maximum fill densities of 70 pcf for Halon 1301, and 102 pcf for Halon 1211. These limits are set by DOT regulations for shipping containers, which require that the container not become liquid full at temperatures below 130°F. The maximum fill densities permitted in the standards coincide with the liquid densities of the two agents at 130°F in the presence of nitrogen at the highest level of superpressurization, again allowing for a 5 percent maximum error in filling the container. Most manufacturers utilize a variable fill density in their design to obtain maximum economy in

the system. There is no lower limit on permissible fill densities in the NFPA Halon 1301 and Halon 1211 Standards.

Flow Characteristics

The flow of Halon 1301 and Halon 1211 through pipe and tubing has been determined experimentally. For Halon 1301, the flow is two-phase liquid-vapor. Although the agent exists as a single-phase liquid in the storage container, it begins to vaporize as soon as it begins to undergo pressure drop during flow. By the time the agent reaches the discharge nozzle, a substantial reduction in density has resulted from this vaporization. Therefore, classical single-phase flow equations of the Moody or Fanning type cannot be used to predict the frictional pressure losses during flow of Halon 1301. The flow charts in the NFPA Halon 1301 Standard take the two-phase flow characteristics into account, but in a simplified way. Perhaps the greatest weakness of these simplified charts is their assumption of a constant pressure drop per unit length of pipe along the entire length of pipe. Recent experimentation has shown this assumption to be incorrect. Actually, the unit pressure drop is smaller than average during early stages of flow, and much greater than average during the later stages. This characteristic is especially significant when the system is "unbalanced"; that is, if the flow paths to all discharge nozzles in a multiple-nozzle system are unequal. Manufacturers of Halon 1301 equipment for installing unbalanced systems have accounted for the nonlinear pressure drop in two ways. One has taken a conservative approach by multiplying the pressure drop from the flow chart by 2.5. Another has developed a set of two-phase flow equations for Halon 1301 similar to the ones used for carbon dioxide. Thus, it appears that each manufacturer is using a different method to calculate the flow properties of Halon 1301.

To achieve some uniformity throughout the industry, the Fire Equipment Manufacturers Association has established a subcommittee to reconcile the various methods. Although the subcommittee has not yet issued a final report, it appears likely that the following treatment will be adopted:

1. Use the existing NFPA flow calculation method for balanced systems only, perhaps with some additional limitations on maximum flow rates or minimum nozzle pressures which can be used with this simplified system.

2. For unbalanced systems, use a method of calculation which accounts rigorously for the two-phase condition. The basic principles of applying this method must still be distributed to the industry.

Because the solubility of nitrogen in the liquid phase of Halon 1211 is only half as great as for Halon 1301, the flow properties of Halon 1211 are treated as single-phase liquid flow in the NFPA Halon 1211 Standard. Field experience with Halon 1211 systems in Europe has apparently borne this out. Presently there is only limited experience with Halon 1211 systems in the United States.

Total Flooding Systems

The great majority of Halon 1301 systems in the United States and of Halon 1211 systems throughout the rest of the world are of the total flooding type. Not only does this type of system receive the most extensive treatment in the NFPA Halon 1301 and Halon 1211 Standards, but the design methods outlined for them have been proven by wide experience.

As described earlier, a total flooding system is one which develops a uniform extinguishing concentration of agent throughout an enclosure, such as a room. It is capable of extinguishing a fire within the enclosure regardless of the location of the fire. Wickham[21] outlines the main design elements of a total flooding system as follows:

1. Hazard definition, which includes the dimensions and configuration of the enclosure, the maximum and minimum net volumes, the fuels involved, the expected temperature range in the hazard area, ventilation and unclosable openings, and occupancy status.

2. Establish a minimum design concentration based upon the fuels involved.

3. Calculate the minimum agent quantity based upon the minimum design concentration, the maximum net volume, the minimum expected temperature of the enclosure, and compensation for losses from ventilation and unclosable openings.

4. Calculate the maximum possible concentration which could occur if the hazard is at the conditions of minimum net volume and maximum temperature. This concentration must not be greater than that permitted by the NFPA Halon 1301 and Halon 1211 Standards for the occupancy status of the hazard.

5. Agent storage container selection, based upon the design quantity of agent and the sizes of standard containers available from the equipment manufacturers.

6. Determine the minimum agent flow rate by dividing the design agent quantity by the maximum permissible discharge time. This time is currently set by the NFPA Halon 1301 and Halon 1211 Standards at 10 sec, subject to some discretion.

7. Determine the size of piping, considering the location of the agent storage containers and locations of the discharge nozzles. This step must be performed concurrently with the following step 8.

8. Determine the number, size, and locations of discharge nozzles. Discharge rate and nozzle area coverage data must be obtained from laboratory listings or from design manuals of the equipment manufacturers.

Jensen[22] regards the first of the preceding elements as the single most important one. Certainly it is the most important one in which the end user can usually participate. The remainder of the system design is generally performed by the equipment manufacturer.

In establishing the minimum design concentration (Step 2 above) one must consider the conditions under which the fuels are used. For flammable liquids or vapors where an explosion is not likely, a "flame extinguishment" concentration may be used. This concentration will be adequate to extinguish flames of the given fuel, such as from a spill fire, where the fuel has not been premixed with air. If an explosion potential is considered likely, then an "inerting" concentration must be used which is higher than the "flame extinguishment" concentration for any particular fuel. The inerting concentration is sufficient to prevent combustion of a fuel to air ratio which might occur in the enclosure. It must therefore be applied upon development of a dangerous condition, and not after ignition has occurred. Minimum design concentrations for both flame extinguishment and inerting for a variety of flammable liquids and gases are included in the NFPA Halon 1301 and Halon 1211 Standards. Guidelines for determining which level should be used are also given in the Standards.

For flammable solids or Class A hazards, the possibility and consequences of developing a deep-seated fire must be considered. Here, a "deep-seated" fire is one in which continued smoldering combustion of the fuel will occur in the presence of a 5 percent agent concentration following a 10-min soaking time. Recent studies have shown that most Class A combustibles do not develop deep-seated fires. They have also shown that the combustion rate and agent decomposition rate are greatly reduced by the presence of the halogenated agent at 5 percent. Rapid detection and prompt application of agent can also help to prevent a Class A fire from becoming deep-seated. Remote alarms to summon outside assistance should be an integral part of a fire protection system.

Methods of compensating for agent losses through ventilation or unclosable openings is also given in the NFPA Halon 1301 and Halon 1211 Standards. In ventilated enclosures, it is not necessary to shut down closed-loop ventilation systems in which all the exhaust air is returned to the room. In fact, continued operation of such systems will improve agent distribution and reduce the rate at which agent is lost through unclosable openings. Fresh air makeup ducts and exhaust ducts to the outside must, of course, be closed off at the time of agent discharge. Losses through unclosable openings are more insidious in that they often are undetected in a casual inspection of a plan of the enclosure. Because of the high density of the vapors of halogenated agents, there is a definite tendency of agent/air mixtures to find their way out of openings, particularly ones in the lower portion of the enclosure. As this mixture leaves the enclosure, it is replaced by fresh air which enters and collects near the top of the enclosure. This often gives the impression that the agent is separating itself from the air, which it is not. Also, the tendency often is to compensate for such losses by providing a higher concentration initially. This, of course, simply aggravates the situation by increasing the rate at which the loss occurs. An extended agent discharge or providing for mechanical mixing during the soaking period are the only effective ways to overcome a serious loss of agent through unclosable openings. Fortunately, since the fire hazard in most applications is located in the lower half of the room, some agent losses in this manner can be tolerated. Most authorities will permit the mixture interface to descend a maximum of halfway down within the specified soaking period.

Local Application System

While a number of local application systems have been installed for both Halon 1301 and Halon 1211, design methods for these systems have not yet become as well established as for total flooding. The information currently appearing in the NFPA Halon Standards on local application systems is useful only as a guide to the equipment manufacturer or testing laboratory. Existing local application installations have had to be proven by extensive (and expensive) testing.

The principle of local application is greatly different than total flooding. Local application is similar to a portable fire extinguisher in that the discharge nozzle is directed at the surface or object on which the fire is anticipated. However, the nozzles in a local application system are generally fixed, rather than movable, and are often connected to a remote storage container by piping. Detectors may be employed to operate the system automatically, to sound alarms, to shut down the process, etc., and in this regard it possesses many of the aspects of a total flooding system.

The most important single element in a local application system is the discharge nozzle. The discharge velocity and rate must be sufficient to penetrate the flames and produce extinguishment, but not be so great as to cause splashing of fuel and thus increase the fire hazard. The performance of the discharge nozzle must be determined in advance by laboratory testing; the location, position, and orientation of nozzles in the installation must be in strict accordance with these listings. To date, there is no listed equipment for local application systems for either Halon 1301 or Halon 1211 in the United States. A test program is now in progress in England to provide basic data for Halon 1211 local application systems. As this program develops, more definite information will be provided in the NFPA Halon 1211 Standard for local application system design.

D.　Testing and Maintenance of Systems

Following installation, a system must first be tested to ensure that it will perform in accordance with the design, and thereafter it must be maintained to ensure its continued performance at some later time. Although minimum requirements for testing and maintenance of halogenated agent systems are given in the NFPA Halon Standards, some elaboration on both topics seems in order.

Testing of Halogenated Agent Systems

While the performance of individual components comprising the system has been determined by laboratory testing and listings, certain tests must be made on the complete installation to ensure that it has been installed properly, and that the system as a whole performs according to design. The extent to which tests are conducted on a completed system depend in part upon the complexity of the system, the novelty of the application, the number of unknown variables which might be present in the hazard, and the experience of individual personnel involved. The testing required may range from a checkout of the detection and actuation circuit to a full-scale discharge test.

The first stage of a system test is a thorough visual inspection of the system and the hazard. Nameplate data on the storage containers should be compared to the design. The piping, operational equipment, and discharge nozzles are inspected for proper size and location. The locations of alarms and manual emergency releases should be confirmed. The configuration of the hazard should be compared to the original hazard specification. Also, the hazard should be inspected closely for unclosable openings and sources of agent loss which may have been overlooked in the original specification. Any serious deviation of these factors from design must be corrected before conducting any actual test.

The second stage of testing a system is to check the operation of the detection and actuation circuits with the agent release mechanism disconnected. The performance of detectors, local and remote alarms, and interlocks to shut down processes or ventilating equipment, is determined to be suitable. Manual emergency releases are also checked in this stage. Interlock switches which are operated from agent pressure in the piping system may be checked at this stage by tripping them manually. Compressed air may be connected to the piping system and the piping blown out to be sure it is free from obstructions. In fact, everything is tested short of discharging agent. Often, these two stages of testing are sufficient.

The third stage of testing a system is to conduct a full-scale discharge test, if required. Because it is a somewhat special test, it should be conducted only after careful planning. In the first place, a full-scale test is expensive, even if a substitute agent is used. Secondly, the time and manpower necessary to perform a full-scale discharge test justify sufficient planning to make sure that all objectives of the test are accomplished.

A full-scale discharge test is usually required when conditions in the hazard are such that the agent discharge time, design concentration, distribution of concentration, or maintenance of concentration during a required soaking time are in doubt. Further, these are the only items that should be tested in a discharge test. Other items, as described above, should be tested separately and in advance of the discharge test. Placing a tape recorder near a discharge nozzle is helpful in accurately determining the discharge time. Monitoring agent concentrations at several locations within the hazard (three sampling points are sufficient for most enclosures) with continuous recording analyzers provides a satisfactory means of measuring initial agent concentrations, distribution, and maintenance of concentration. Full-scale discharge tests have been described by Brenneman and Charney,[23] and outlined in a recent publication by Cardox, Div. of Chemetron Corporation.[24]

Maintenance of Halogenated Agent Systems

The NFPA Halon 1301 and Halon 1211 Standards specify certain items that must be checked at semiannual and annual intervals. Semiannually, the system should be given a visual inspection for evidence of corrosion or other damage, and the storage containers checked for loss of agent. This latter item involves a two-fold check. First, the pressure corrected for temperature should be measured to insure no loss of pressurizing gas. Second, each container must be weighed to determine loss of agent. Neither check alone is sufficient; both are required. In large bulk systems, liquid level indicators are often provided to indicate the quantity of agent, rather than weighing the entire tank. There is currently some effort to develop a liquid level indicator for smaller containers to replace weighing, which is often cumbersome and time consuming.

At least annually, the operational characteristics of the system should be retested. This generally involves repeating Stages 1 and 2 as previously outlined. A full-scale discharge test is rarely required as a part of an annual inspection.

Both the semiannual and annual inspections should be performed by knowledgable and qualified personnel. The NFPA Halon 1301 and Halon 1211 Standards recommend that they be performed under contract by the equipment manufacturer or installer. Reports of the inspection should be filed with the authority having jurisdiction and with the owner of the system. Needless to say, all impediments found in these inspections must be corrected promptly.

SI Units

The following conversion factors are given as a convenience in converting to SI units the English units used in this chapter.

1 ft	= .305 m
1 lb (mass)	= .454 kg
1 psi	= 6.895 kPa
$\frac{5}{9}$(°F − 32)	= °C
1 cu ft	= .0283 m³

Bibliography

References Cited

[1] Hough, Ralph L., *Determination of a Standard Extinguishing Agent for Airborne Fixed Systems,* WADD Technical Report 60–552, Oct. 1960, Wright Air Development Division, Wright-Patterson Air Force Base, Ohio.

[2] Strasiak, Raymond R., *The Development History of Bromochloromethane (CB),* WADC Technical Report 53-279, Jan. 1954, Wright Air Development Center, Ohio.

[3] "Aircraft Engine Fire Extinguishing Tests—B-17 Airplane" Final Report No. R-662, March 18, 1946, Walter Kidde & Company, Belleville, N.J.

[4] "Aircraft Power Plant Fire Protection," Final Report on A.A.F. Contract No. W-33-038-ac-8489, February 1948, C-O-Two Fire Equipment Company, Newark.

[5] Wharry, David and Hirst, Ronald, *Fire Technology: Chemistry and Combustion,* Institution of Fire Engineers, Leicester, England, 1974.

[6] Tarbell, Lyle E., *Determination of Means to Safeguard Aircraft from Power Plant Fires in Flight—Part V, The Lockheed Constellation,* Technical Development Report No. 198, April 1953, Civil Aeronautics Administration, Technical Development and Evaluation Center, Indianapolis.

[7] The Halogenated Extinguishing Agents, NFPA *Quarterly,* Vol. 48, No. 8, Part 3, NFPA, Boston, 1954.

[8] *Fire Extinguisher Comparisons,* Military Vehicles Organization, Allison Division of General Motors Corporation, Cleveland Army Tank-Automotive Plant, Cleveland, Oct. 28, 1968.

[9] *Final Report LVT-P5A1 Vehicle Fire Suppression System,* Technical Report No. 1666, 1967, FMC Corporation, San Jose, Ca.

[10] Steinberg, Marshall, "Toxic Hazards from Extinguishing Gasoline Fires Using Halon 1301 Extinguishers in Armored Personnel Carriers," *An Appraisal of Halogenated Fire Extinguishing Agents,* National Academy of Sciences, Washington, D.C., 1972.

[11] Wilson, Rexford, "That Extinguishing Thing (Firepac)," *Fire Journal,* Vol. 64, No. 1, Jan. 1970.

[12] Gassman, Julius J. and March, John F., "Application of Halon 1301 to Aircraft Cabin and Cargo Fires," *An Appraisal of Halogenated Fire Extinguishing Agents,* National Academy of Sciences, Washington, D.C., 1972.

[13] Gassman, Julius J. and Hill, Richard G., *Fire Extinguishing Methods for New Passenger-Cargo Aircraft,* National Aviation Facilities Experimental Center, Atlantic City, 1971.

[14] Dowling, John H. and Ford, C. B., "Halon 1301 Total Flooding System for Winterthur Museum," *Fire Journal,* Vol. 63, No. 6, Nov. 1969.

[15] *NFPA No. 12A, Standard for Halogenated Extinguishing Agent Systems—Halon 1301,* 1973, NFPA, Boston.

[16] *NFPA No. 12B, Standard for Halogenated Fire Extinguishing Agent Systems—Halon 1211,* 1973, NFPA, Boston.

[17] Ford, Charles L., "Halon 1301 Computer Fire Test Program—Interim Report," Jan. 10, 1972, E. I. du Pont de Nemours & Co., Inc., Wilmington, Del.

[18] Curry, Thomas H., "Halon 1301 Protects Racing Cars," *Fire Journal,* Vol. 67, No. 2, March 1973.

[19] Rainaldi, Nicola, "Advance Report on Halon 2402," *Fire Technology,* Vol. 6, No. 1, Feb. 1970.

[20] Grabowski, George J., "Fire Detection and Actuation Devices for Halon Extinguishing Systems," *An Appraisal of Halogenated Fire Extinguishing Agents,* National Academy of Sciences, Washington, D.C., 1972.

[21] Wickham, Robert T., "Engineering and Economic Aspects of Halon Extinguishing Equipment," *An Appraisal of Halogenated Fire Extinguishing Agents,* National Academy of Sciences, Washington, D.C., 1972.

[22] Jensen, Rolf, "Halogenated Extinguishing Agent Systems," *Fire Journal,* Vol. 66, No. 3, May 1972, pp. 37–39.

[23] Brenneman, James J. and Charney, Marvin, "Testing a Total Flooding Halon 1301 System in a Computer Installation," *Fire Journal,* Vol. 68, No. 6, Nov. 1974.

[24] "Halon System Testing," *Hot Spots,* Cardox Products, Chemetron Corp., Chicago, 1974.

NFPA Codes, Standards, and Recommended Practices (see the latest *NFPA Publications and Visual Aids Catalog* for availability of current editions of the following documents)

NFPA No. 12A, Standard for Halogenated Extinguishing Agent Systems—Halon 1301.

NFPA No. 12B, Standard for Halogenated Fire Extinguishing Agent Systems—Halon 1211.

NFPA No. 75, Standard for Electronic Computer/Data Processing Equipment.

Additional Readings

Bonawitz, George W., "Halon 1301 Protection for a Computer Facility," *Fire Journal,* Vol. 67, No. 5, Sept. 1973, pp. 134–135.

Botteri, B. P.; Cretchner, R. E.; and Kane, W. R., "Aircraft Applications of Halogenated Hydrocarbon Fire Extinguishing Agents," *An Appraisal of Halogenated Fire Extinguishing Agents,* National Academy of Sciences, Washington, D.C., 1972.

Cholin, Roger R., "How Deep is Deep? (Use of Halon 1301 on Deep-Seated Fires)," *Fire Journal,* Vol. 66, No. 2, Jan. 1972.

———, "Testing the Performance of Halon 1301 on Real Computer Installations," *Fire Journal,* Vol. 66, No. 5, Sept. 1972, pp. 105–108.

Echternacht, John E., "Halon Extinguishing Systems Design Criteria," *Fire Journal,* Vol. 65, No. 6, Nov. 1971, pp. 51–55, 66.

Edmonds, Albert, "Use of Halon 1211 in Hand Extinguishers and Local Application Systems," *An Appraisal of Halogenated Fire Extinguishing Agents,* National Academy of Sciences, Washington, D.C., 1972.

Ford, Charles L., "Extinguishment of Surface and Deep-Seated Fires with Halon 1301," *An Appraisal of Halogenated Fire Extinguishing Agents,* National Academy of Sciences, Washington, D.C., 1972.

———, "Halon 1301 Fire Extinguishing Agent: Properties and Applications," *Fire Journal,* Vol. 64, No. 6, Nov. 1970.

———, "Where and Why to Use Halon 1301 Systems," *Actual Specifying Engineer,* Jan. 1972.

Franck, Thomas E., "Clean Room Protection Using Halon 1301," *Fire Journal,* Vol. 65, No. 2, March 1971, pp. 77–79.

Gaskill, J. R.; Leonhart, E. C.; and Sanborn, E. N., *A Halon 1301 Fire Extinguishing System for Trailers,* Lawrence Radiation Laboratory, University of California, Livermore, Calif., Aug. 19, 1969.

Hammack, James M., "More About Halon 1301," *Fire Journal,* Vol. 66, No. 4, July 1972, pp. 43–44.

Languille, E., "Applications of Halon 1211 Fixed Systems in Normally Occupied Areas," *An Appraisal of Halogenated Fire Extinguishing Agents,* National Academy of Sciences, Washington, D.C., 1972.

McDaniel, Dale E., "Evaluation of Halon 1301 for Shipboard Use," *An Appraisal of Halogenated Fire Extinguishing Agents,* National Academy of Sciences, Washington, D.C., 1972.

Peterson, Parker E., "A Systems Approach to Optimum Damage Control," *Fire Journal,* Vol. 67, No. 2, March 1973, pp. 70–73.

Poeschl, Paul M., "Large-Scale Halon 1301 Fire Test Program," *Fire Journal,* Vol. 67, No. 6, Nov. 1973, pp. 35–38.

Sayers, David R., "Halon 122-Areas of Particular Effectiveness," *Fire Journal,* Vol. 67, No. 6, Nov. 1973, pp. 14–15.

Sheehan, Daniel F., *An Investigation into the Effectiveness of Halon 1301 (Bromotrifluoromethane, $CBrF_3$) as an Extinguishing Agent for Shipboard Machinery Space Fires,* U.S. Coast Guard, Washington, D.C., 1972.

Williamson, H. V., "Halon 1301—Minimum Concentrations for Extinguishing Deep-Seated Fires," *Fire Technology,* Vol. 8, No. 4, Nov. 1972.

Section 15

Chapter 6

DRY CHEMICAL EXTINGUISHING SYSTEMS

Dry chemical has been found to be an effective extinguishing agent for fires in flammable liquids and in certain types of ordinary combustibles and electrical equipment, depending upon the type of dry chemical used. Properties of dry chemical and its uses and limitations are discussed in Section 13, Chapter 5. Portable dry chemical extinguishers are discussed in Section 16.

Dry chemical has been used for many years in fire extinguishers, but dry chemical extinguishing systems are of comparatively recent origin. In 1952 the NFPA Committee on Dry Chemical Extinguishing Systems was established, and in 1957 the first edition of NFPA No. 17, Standard for Dry Chemical Extinguishing Systems was adopted. In 1954 the first dry chemical extinguishing system was tested and listed by a nationally recognized testing laboratory.

A.   Application of Dry Chemical Systems

Dry chemical extinguishing systems can be used in those situations where quick extinguishment is desired and where reignition sources are not present. Dry chemical systems are used primarily for flammable liquid fire hazards such as dip tanks, flammable liquid storage rooms, and areas where flammable liquid spills may occur. Systems have been designed for kitchen range hoods, ducts, and associated range-top hazards such as deep fat fryers. Where it is necessary to extinguish a flammable liquid or gas fire being fed by fuel under pressure, dry chemical hand hose line systems can be used.

Since dry chemical is electrically nonconductive, extinguishing systems using this agent can be used on electrical equipment that is subject to flammable liquid fires, such as oil-filled transformers and oil-filled circuit breakers. Dry chemical system protection is not recommended, however, for delicate electrical equipment such as telephone switchboards and electronic computers: such equipment is subject to damage by dry chemical deposit and, because of the insulating properties of the dry chemical, may require excessive cleaning to restore operation.

Hand hose line systems containing regular or ordinary dry chemical have been used to a limited extent for quick-spreading surface fires on ordinary combustible material such as baled cotton. In such applications the dry chemical system is only for the purpose of stopping or preventing a rapid surface spread, and must be supplemented by a water-type extinguishing device to put out deep-seated smoldering fire. Fixed systems containing multipurpose dry chemical (ammonium phosphate base) are now available and have the added ability of being suitable for the protection of ordinary combustibles provided the dry chemical can reach all burning surfaces.

B.   Methods of Application

The two basic types of dry chemical systems are referred to as fixed systems and hand hose line systems. Other methods of applying dry chemical are by portable and wheeled type extinguishers (see Sec. 16, Chap. 5).

Fixed Systems

Fixed dry chemical systems consist of a supply of dry chemical, an expellant gas, an actuating method, fixed piping, and nozzles through which the dry chemical can be discharged into the hazard area. Fixed dry chemical systems are of two types: total flooding and local application.

In total flooding, a predetermined amount of dry chemical is discharged through fixed piping and nozzles into an enclosed space or enclosure around the hazard (see Fig. 15-6A). Total flooding is applicable only when the hazard is totally enclosed or when all openings about a hazard can be closed automatically when the system is discharged. Only where no reignition is anticipated can total flooding be used, as the extinguishing action is transient.

Local application differs from total flooding in that the nozzles are arranged to discharge directly into the fire. Local application is practical in those situations where the hazard can be isolated from other hazards so that fire will not spread beyond the area protected and where the entire hazard can be protected. The principal use of local application systems is to protect open tanks of flammable liquids. As in the case of total flooding systems, local application is ineffective unless extinguishment can be immediate and there are no reignition sources.

Hand Hose Line Systems

Hand hose line systems consist of a supply of dry chemical and expellant gas, with one or more hand hose lines to deliver the dry chemical to the fire (see Fig. 15-6B). The hose stations are connected to the dry chemical container either directly or by means of intermediate piping. They can provide a large quantity of extinguishing agent for quick knockdown and extinguishment of relatively large fires such as might be experienced at gasoline loading racks, flammable liquid storage areas, diesel and gas turbine locomotives, and aircraft hangars.

Fig. 15-6A.   This 16-ft by 24-ft flammable liquids storage building is protected by a total flooding type dry chemical system. On actuation of the system by a heat-sensitive device, nitrogen is discharged into the 150-lb storage container and dry chemical is thereby expelled to eight nozzles beneath the roof.

Fig. 15-6B. Dry chemical hand hose line system of expellant gas assembly, dry chemical storage tank assembly, and discharge assembly. Dry chemical capacities of hand hose line systems range from 125 lbs to 2,000 lbs. The 2,000-lb system shown contains four nitrogen cylinders and two $\frac{3}{4}$-in. hoses equipped with shutoff nozzles. (The Ansul Company)

C. Design of Dry Chemical Systems

Usually, dry chemical systems consist of dry chemical and expellant gas storage tanks, piping and/or hose to carry the agent to the fire area, nozzles to assure proper distribution of the agent into the fire or area to be protected, and automatic and/or manual actuating mechanisms.

Dry chemical systems are called either "engineered" or "pre-engineered" depending upon how the quantity of dry chemical, rate of flow, size and length of piping, and number and size of fittings are determined. An "engineered" system is one in which individual calculation and design is needed to determine the flow rate, nozzle pressures, pipe sizes, quantity of dry chemical, and the number, types, and placement of nozzles for the hazard being protected. A "pre-engineered" system, sometimes called a "package" system, is one in which the size of system (i.e., the quantity of dry chemical), pipe sizes, maximum and minimum pipe lengths, number of fittings, and number and type of nozzles are all predetermined by fire tests for specific sizes and types of hazards. Installation within these limits of hazard and system design assures adequate flow rate, nozzle pressure, and pattern coverage without individual calculation.

Pre-engineered systems are very frequently used for kitchen range and hood fire protection, including deep fat fryers. Alkaline dry chemicals only can be used in these cases (sodium bicarbonate, potassium bicarbonate, etc.) in order to saponify fats and oils. Never use multipurpose dry chemical (monoammonium phosphate).

Storage of Dry Chemical and Expellant

The dry chemical is stored in a pressure container, usually of welded steel construction, either under atmospheric pressure until the system is actuated, or under the pressure of the integrally stored expellant gas.

Containers in which dry chemical is stored separately under atmospheric pressure are equipped with an expellant gas inlet, a moisture-sealed fill opening, and a dry chemical outlet. The gas inlet leads to an internal gas tube arrangement constructed so that when the gas flows into the tank

it agitates and permeates the powder, making it fluidized. The dry chemical outlet is provided with a rupture disc or valve to permit buildup of proper operating pressure in the tank before the dry chemical can start to flow. The expellant gas assembly consists of a pressure storage vessel together with necessary valves, pressure regulators, and piping to deliver the expellant gas to the dry chemical storage tank at the correct pressure and rate of flow, (see Fig. 15-6A). The expellant gas is usually nitrogen, but carbon dioxide is used in some of the smaller systems. The volume and storage pressure of the expellant are dictated by the gas used and the requirements of the system. Containers in which dry chemical and the expellant gas are stored together are equipped with a moisture-sealed fill opening, a valve with integral discharge outlet and expellant gas charging inlet, and a pressure gage (see Fig. 15-6C). The expellant gas is usually nitrogen, but dry air can be used.

It is desirable to locate the dry chemical-expellant gas assemblies as near as practicable to the hazard to be protected. An area in which temperatures will not exceed 140°F is necessary to maintain the quality of the dry chemical. Low temperatures will not affect dry chemical, but if the expellant is carbon dioxide, temperatures below 32°F may adversely affect the discharge rate. The use of nitrogen permits successful operation to as low as −65°F, which is a most valuable characteristic for certain hazards.

System Actuation

Actuation in the case of fixed systems is by automatic mechanisms that incorporate sensing devices located in the hazard area, and automatic mechanical or electrical releases which initiate the flow of dry chemical, actuate alarms, and shut down process equipment. In systems having separate dry chemical and expellant gas containers, the flow of dry chemical is started by releasing the expellant gas to pressurize the dry chemical chamber to the point where the rupture disc in the dry chemical outlet operates. The dry chemical is then carried by the expellant gas through the distribution system to the hazard. In stored pressure systems, however, the flow of dry chemical is started by merely opening the valve on the dry chemical chamber. An easily accessible device for manual operation is required for all automatically operated systems.

When automatically actuated systems are used, considera-

Fig. 15-6C. A double 30-lb stored pressure dry chemical system with pneumatic release for automatic actuation. Each cylinder contains 30 lb of dry chemical pressurized with nitrogen to 350 psi. (Safety First Products Corp.)

tion should be given to the reduced visibility and temporary breathing difficulty sometimes caused by quick discharge of large amounts of dry chemical in a restricted space. In all cases where there is a possibility that personnel may be stationed in such locations, suitable alarms and safeguards are incorporated in the system to assure adequate warning and prompt evacuation.

Operation of a hand hose line system requires two or, at the most, three steps. The first: pressurizing the dry chemical chamber by opening the expellant gas valve if the dry chemical and expellant gas containers are separate, or opening the main discharge valve if dry chemical is under stored pressure. The second: operating the nozzle at the end of the hose line. If multiple hose stations are supplied by the same dry chemical supply, a distribution valve must be opened to direct the flow to the particular hose station to be used.

Fixed piping systems normally blow themselves clear. However, in hand hose line systems where the operator exercises control over the amount of dry chemical discharged, it is vital that all pipes and hose be independently blown clear before recharging to prevent blockage.

Distribution System

The provisions for conveying the dry chemical to the hazard area and discharging it properly consist of piping, in the case of fixed systems, or piping and hose lines or hose lines alone, in the case of hand hose line systems. Nozzles designed to emit jets or wide, flat, or round streams in desired patterns are available to meet the requirements of specific hazards. Adjustable nozzles permitting an operator to vary the range and shape of the discharge are also available for use with hand hose line systems.

The piping and valving for dry chemical systems are of special design because dry chemical, while tending to behave as a fluid, has distinct flow characteristics.

Control of the flow of dry chemical starts at the dry chemical storage tank. In systems of separate dry chemical and expellant gas containers, expellant gas must be admitted to the tank in such a way as to fluidize properly the dry chemical while the pressure builds up equally throughout the entire volume of the tank before the dry chemical is released from the tank. Should the pressure increase too rapidly above the dry chemical, the powder will not be properly fluidized and, upon release, the pressure drop in the piping or hose line will be excessive and result in a rate of dry chemical flow too low for proper extinguishing effectiveness.

If the expellant gas is permitted to channel to the outlet before the top of the dry chemical storage tank is properly pressurized, insufficient dry chemical will be carried by the flowing stream of gas, and again the fire extinguishing effectiveness of the system will be greatly reduced.

After release from the storage tank, dry chemical is carried by the expellant gas at high velocities through the piping and is thrown to the wall of the piping by centrifugal force whenever the direction of flow is sharply altered, as by an elbow. Should an elbow be directly connected to a tee and lie in the same plane as the tee, it is obvious that the two branches of the tee will carry appreciably different proportions of gas and dry chemical. This condition is overcome by installing all tees in planes perpendicular to the planes of adjacent elbows, by allowing sufficient length of straight pipe between tees and elbows, or by inserting special venturi devices between tees and elbows to insure proper redistribution of dry chemical in the stream of gas before the mixture enters the tee.

Another critical factor in dry chemical distribution system design is the pressure drop through various lengths of pipe, hose, or fittings. Consequently, the length and size of piping and hose, and the number and size of fittings must be selected in order to provide the required rate of discharge and nozzle distribution. In "pre-engineered" systems this is already assured by virtue of the limitations established for piping and fittings. In "engineered" systems this selection must be made on the basis of actual calculation of pressure drop and subsequent flow rate.

For "engineered" systems pressure drop data have been obtained at various rates of flow for various sizes of pipe and fittings. In one manufacturer's system, the pressure drop through a standard elbow is equivalent to the pressure drop through 20 ft of straight pipe of the same size.[1] Pressure drop through a tee is equivalent to that of 45 ft of straight pipe of the same size.

Nozzles

The selection of the proper types and sizes of nozzles for fixed systems is necessary in order to obtain proper coverage of the hazard.

Nozzles for hand hose line systems may be of either a one-position or two-position type. One-position nozzles provide a modified straight stream, while two-position nozzles provide a straight stream or a fan. Since the straight stream has a longer reach than the fan discharge, it is considered the better for initial attack; the shorter, wider fan-shaped stream is usually preferred for the closer range attack to complete the extinguishment.

Quantity and Rate of Application of Dry Chemical

The quantity of dry chemical and rate of flow must be sufficient to create a fire extinguishing concentration throughout all parts of the enclosure protected by a total flooding system or over the specific fire area protected by a local application system. Minimum rate of flow is a critical factor, as dry chemical will not put out a fire if applied too slowly. In local application systems application at too high a rate may result in uneven discharge, or discharge of all dry chemical before extinguishment is accomplished.

Optimum quantities of dry chemical and rates of application have been determined by experiment for "engineered" total flooding and local application systems. For "pre-engineered" systems the maximum sizes of hazards that can be protected by the various sizes of systems within specific piping limitations have been determined.

From tests with one manufacturer's "engineered" total flooding system, it has been determined that the weight in pounds of dry chemical required is obtained by multiplying the number of cubic feet in the net volume of the open space to be flooded by 0.0385. Net volume is the gross volume less the volume of machinery or other permanently located bulky objects.

The minimum flow rate in pounds per second is determined by multiplying the net volume in cubic feet by 0.00125. These volume factors apply only to this manufacturer's equipment and are cited merely to illustrate the procedure currently used.[1] Quantities and flow rates determined in this manner are contingent on a nozzle arrangement that gives even distribution throughout the volume. They also assume that devices will be installed to close automatically all doors, windows, ventilators, or other openings through which dry chemical could escape from the enclosure.

In one manufacturer's "pre-engineered" total flooding system, a 1,000 cu ft space not longer than 20 ft can be protected by a 30-lb system with 4 nozzles and no more than 90 ft of ¾-in. pipe, 13 elbows, 3 tees, and 3 venturi devices.[2] As with "engineered" systems, successful extinguishment is contingent upon proper nozzle location, shutdown of ventilation, and the closing of all openings such as doors and windows.

Although shutdown of ventilation simultaneously with the actuation of a total flooding system is the normal procedure, one exception exists. This exception is the special case of kitchen range hood and duct protection wherein "pre-engineered" systems are specifically designed to provide extinguishment, regardless of whether the ventilation is operating or not.

Quantities of dry chemical and rates of flow for "engineered" local application systems are obtained from graphs plotted from tests using different flammable liquid surface areas, weights of dry chemical, and rates of application. These graphs are available from the manufacturer. For "pre-engineered" local application systems, the limitations of hazard size, system size, and piping arrangement are established by test and used in the same manner as for total flooding systems.

The minimum recommended quantity of dry chemical for hand hose line systems is enough to permit use of the system for 30 sec. Capacities of hand hose line systems range from 125 lbs to 2,000 lbs, and as many as four hose lines can be operated from a single system. As with fixed systems, a minimum rate of flow must be maintained to prevent surging or interruption of flow. Minimum rates depend on the equipment used, and are determined by the equipment manufacturer.

D. Maintenance, Inspection, and Test Procedures

In general, all dry chemical systems, including alarms and shutdown devices, should be thoroughly inspected and checked for proper operation at least annually. The frequency of inspection depends on the type of hazard being protected. Systems subjected to process deposits (such as paint and dust) and corrosive conditions will require more frequent inspection of components.

The amount of expellant gas should be checked semiannually to ensure that there is enough to provide an effective discharge, and to automatically clean out the piping after the dry chemical has dissipated. In systems with separate expellant gas containers, this is accomplished by checking the pressure (if nitrogen) or weight (if carbon dioxide) against the manufacturer's recommended minimums. In stored pressure systems, the pressure gage is checked to see that it is in the operable range.

At least semiannually the quantity of dry chemical should also be checked either by visual inspection of the powder level in the separate dry chemical chamber, or by weighing the stored pressure chamber. Except in stored pressure systems, the dry chemical should be checked annually for any evidence of caking which could subsequently prevent proper flow.

Most dry chemicals are alkaline (sodium and potassium bicarbonate and potassium carbonate). One is neutral (potassium chloride) and the multipurpose type (monoammonium phosphate) is acidic. Inadvertent mixing of different base dry chemicals can initiate undesirable reactions, generating carbon dioxide gas and/or double-decomposition resulting in equipment failure or loss of discharge capability.

During the periodic inspections, the nozzles should be examined to see that they are properly aimed, are free of obstruction, and are in good operating condition. The system actuating devices, such as fusible links, pneumatic heat detectors, or electric thermostats, should also be checked to see that they are not loaded with residues or otherwise impaired.

The inspection and maintenance of hand hose line systems will vary with the location and climate conditions. Equipment located in extremely hot or humid areas will require more frequent checking because the heat can cause cylinder pressure to increase and possibly cause leakage.

Inspection of hand hose line systems consists primarily of checking the pressure of the expellant gas container, or the pressure of the unit itself if it is of the pressurized type. It is also advisable to inspect all hose lines and nozzles to be sure that they are unobstructed and in good operating condition.

SI Units

The following conversion factors are given as a convenience in converting to SI units the English units used in this chapter.

$$1 \text{ in.} = 25.400 \text{ mm}$$
$$1 \text{ ft} = .305 \text{ m}$$
$$1 \text{ psi} = 6.895 \text{ kPa}$$
$$\tfrac{5}{9}(°F - 32) = °C$$
$$1 \text{ cu ft} = .0283 \text{ m}^3$$

Bibliography

References Cited

[1] Guise, A. B., Lindlof, J. A., "A Dry Chemical Extinguishing System," NFPA *Quarterly,* Vol. 49, No. 1, July 1955, pp. 52–60.
[2] "Safe-T-Meter Automatic Dry Chemical Fixed Systems," Bulletin UP-30M, Safety First Products Corporation, Elmsford, N.Y.

NFPA Codes, Standards, and Recommended Practices (see the latest *NFPA Publications and Visual Aids Catalog* for availability of current editions of the following document)

NFPA No. 17, Dry Chemical Extinguishing Systems.

Additional Readings

Dry Chemical Fire Extinguishing Characteristics, Expanded Second Edition, Fire Control Engineering Co., Fort Worth, Texas.
Factory Mutual Approval Guide, Factory Mutual Engineering Corporation, Norwood, Mass., published annually.
Fire Protection Equipment List, Underwriters Laboratories, Inc., Chicago, published annually with bimonthly supplements.
Guise, A. B., "Extinguishment of Natural Gas Pressure Fires," *Fire Technology,* Vol. 3, No. 3, Aug. 1967, pp. 175–193.
Guise, A. B., and Paulsen, W. P., U.S. Patent 2,709,605 (May 17, 1955).
McGarry, J. E., "Improved Fire Safety for the Indianapolis 500," *Fire Journal,* Vol. 60, No. 2, March 1966, pp. 32–36.
"Natural Gas Fire Tests," Technical Bulletin No. 32, September 1953, The Ansul Co., Marinette, Wis.
Stevens, R. E., "Dealing with the Grease Duct Fire Problem," NFPA *Quarterly,* Vol. 56, No. 3, Jan. 1963, pp. 216–220.
Tuve, R. L., "Light Water nad Potassium Bicarbonate Dry Chemical—A New Two Agent Extinguishing System," NFPA *Quarterly,* Vol. 58, No. 1, July 1964, pp. 64–69.
Weaver, E. F., "Dry Chemical," *Electrical World,* Aug. 26, 1957, pp. 60–62.
Woolhouse, R. A., and Sayers, D. R., "Monnex Compared with other Potassium-Based Dry Chemicals," *Fire Journal,* Vol. 67, No. 1, Jan. 1973, pp. 85–88.
Wesson, H. R., "Studies of the Effects of Particle Size on the Flow Characteristics of Dry Chemical," *Fire Technology,* Vol. 8, No. 3, Aug. 1972, pp. 173–180.

Chapter 7

EXPLOSION PREVENTION AND SUPPRESSION SYSTEMS, AND EXPLOSION VENTING

Despite the adequacy of explosion prevention recommendations, explosions do occur from time to time—usually because one of the explosion prevention measures in the various NFPA Standards has been violated. Explosion prevention measures should, therefore, be supplemented by protection systems that prevent the development of destructive pressures within the enclosure containing the combustible material. These protection systems require equipment for combating or eliminating one or more of the principal factors that contribute to the destructive nature of an explosion. Three different principles are used in these systems. They are: (1) venting to relieve the pressure, (2) suppression to extinguish or inhibit the deflagration, and (3) purging to eliminate the combustible combination.

This chapter discusses the fundamentals of venting, suppression, and purging practices, and describes the methods and equipment used to implement them.

Any flammable dust, vapor, mist, or gas mixed with air or other supporter of combustion will, under certain conditions, burn with sufficient speed to generate high pressures in a confined volume. Consequently, explosion protection systems, in addition to explosion prevention measures, should be considered for equipment, housings, rooms, and buildings associated with the manufacture, handling, processing, and storage of any flammable liquids, dust, vapor, mist, or gas. Flammable or explosive limits of gases or vapors are discussed in Section 2, Chapter 1 of this HANDBOOK, while the various types of explosions are discussed in detail in Chapter 2 of the same Section. Other pertinent references are found in Section 3 of this HANDBOOK, with Chapter 3 covering Flammable Liquids, Chapter 4, Gases, and Chapter 8, Dusts. In each of these references in Section 3, information is given on the combustibility of these materials, as well as the factors influencing the development of combustible mixtures.

The principal factors influencing the generation of pressure from a confined deflagration are: (1) the nature of the material, i.e., chemical structure, (2) the concentration of the material in air or other supporter of combustion, (3) the particle size in case of dusts, (4) the oxygen or oxidizer concentration, (5) the turbulence of the mixture, (6) the temperature of the flammable mixture, (7) the pressure of the flammable mixture, (8) the effect of moisture and diluting substances, such as inert materials, and (9) the pressure relief openings in the enclosure. The violence of the explosion which may result from this confined deflagration is dependent upon the extent and rate of pressure development and the physical construction of the enclosure.

A. Fundamentals of Explosion Venting

The following five fundamentals of good explosion venting practice should be taken into account whenever means of minimizing explosion damage are being considered:

1. Explosion damage may be minimized by locating hazardous operations or equipment outdoors, by segregating them in small detached buildings, or by locating them in vented units separated from other portions of a building by pressure-resisting walls.

2. Where it is impractical to locate an operation outdoors, the equipment should be placed above grade in a one-story building, or in the top story of a multistory building.

3. Vents which are properly designed and located will relieve explosion pressures sufficiently in most instances to minimize property damage and prevent injuries.

4. The necessary area of the explosion vents depends primarily upon the expected intensity of an explosion, the strength of the equipment or building, and the type of vent closure.

5. The vent should be located so that vented pressures will not cause injuries or structural damage.

Basic Considerations for Venting Explosions

The following principles established by test and experience should be considered when applying the fundamentals of explosion venting:

1. Many substances not ordinarily considered combustible will burn and explode under certain conditions of particle size, increased temperature, or increased oxygen concentration.

2. Most ordinary building walls will not withstand a sustained internal pressure as great as 1 psi (144 lbs psf). Hence, explosion vents for buildings must be designed to operate at pressures well below those at which the building walls will fail.

3. There is a rise in pressure during an explosion within an enclosure even with open, unrestricted vents, and any delay in opening venting devices increases that pressure. Delay in opening vents may be due to the pressure required to open the vent, or to the inertia of the vent closure. Therefore, it is essential that various relieving devices, including devices actuated by detonators, should start to open at as low a pressure as possible, and also that the devices are of light construction so that full opening can be quickly attained.

4. The present knowledge of the mechanism of large-scale explosions and the resistance of buildings to internal forces does not permit precise recommendations for explosion venting. However, from experience and testing, it is known that it may not be practical to provide sufficient vent area to prevent serious damage from an optimum-mixture explosion involving a large volume of the building. Experience has shown that most explosions of dusts, vapors, and gases do not involve a large part of the total volume of the enclosure, and frequently occur near the limits of the explosive range. Consequently, such explosions are relatively weak compared with the optimum, and venting as recommended in NFPA No. 68, Guide for Explosion Venting, hereinafter referred to in this chapter as the NFPA Explosion Venting Guide, will prevent major damage in nearly all incidents. Since explosion venting is a complex subject about which much essential information is lacking, only certain generalizations can be made.

5. Explosion pressures developed in test galleries with vent openings have been determined for a number of combustible dusts. These data, obtained by the Bureau of Mines,

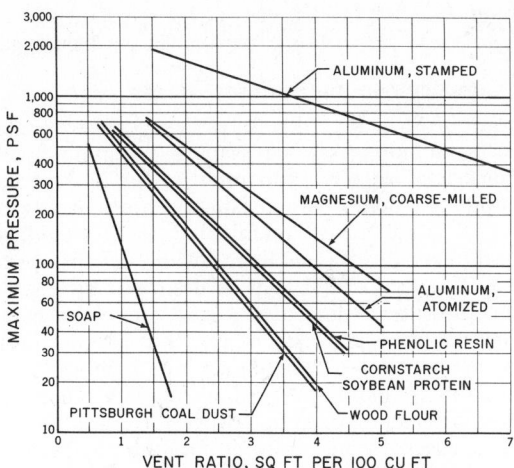

Fig. 15-7A. Effect of unrestricted vents on pressures developed by mild dust explosions. These explosions were produced in a 64 cu ft gallery. (Bureau of Mines, U.S. Department of Interior)

are shown graphically in Figure 15-7A for mild dust explosions, and in Figure 15-7B for strong dust explosions. The mild explosions were produced in the 64 cu ft gallery by dispersing the dust with compressed air; the effective dust concentration was below optimum. The strong explosions were produced in a 1 cu ft gallery when the dust was dispersed more uniformly and during a shorter time interval. The data for the twelve dusts illustrated plot as straight lines on semilog paper as the mathematical relation between the pressure and vent ratio in the range shown is $P = Ae^{kr}$ where P is the maximum explosion pressure, A and k are constants, e is the base of natural logarithm, and r is the vent ratio expressed in sq ft of opening per cu ft of gallery volume.

B.   Vent Closures

The most effective vent for the release of explosion pressures is an unobstructed vent opening. However, the fact that very few operations can be conducted in open equip-

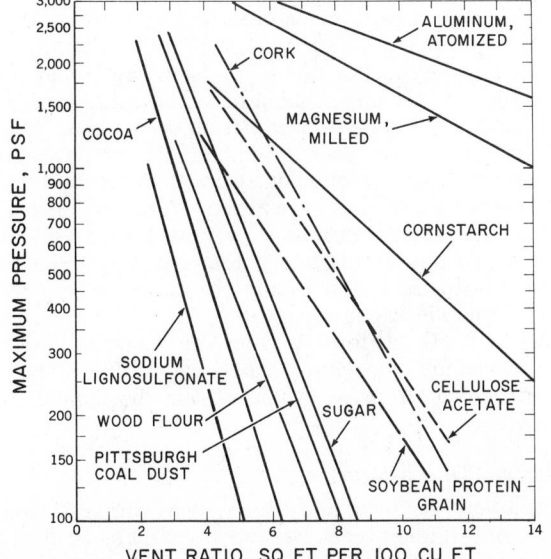

Fig. 15-7B. Effect of unrestricted vents on pressures developed by strong dust explosions. These explosions were produced in a 1 cu ft gallery. (Bureau of Mines, U.S. Department of Interior)

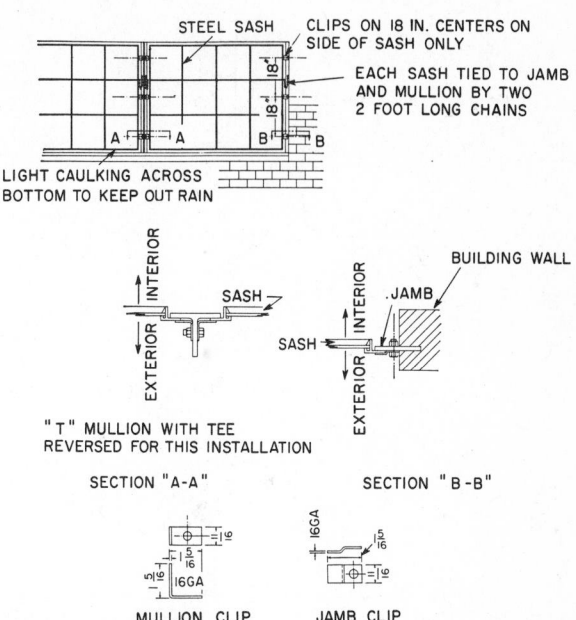

Fig. 15-7C. Method of converting standard steel sash to explosion venting type.

ment installed in buildings without walls necessitates the use of various types of vent closures designed to open quickly and automatically under increased pressure from within. Some types of vent closures are shown in Figures 15-7C, 15-7D, and 15-7E, while further illustrations are given in the NFPA Explosion Venting Guide. Important fundamental principles of explosion vent design and installation are:

1. In most instances, several small vents will relieve explosion pressures as effectively as one large vent that is equal in area to the combined areas of the small vents. This principle may not hold true in a large structure where the position of the vents in relation to the origin of the explosion is important.

2. Closed vents must be larger in area than unenclosed vents in order to provide equivalent explosion pressure relief.

3. Rupture of paper, plastic, and metal diaphragms is facilitated by sawtoothed cutters at the periphery, or by piercing cutters at the center (see Fig. 15-7D).

4. Rectangular unrestricted vents are as effective as square vents of equal area.

5. Pressure required to rupture diaphragms of the same

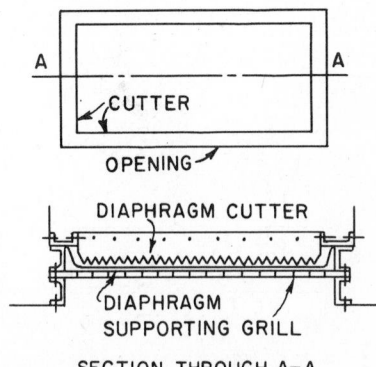

Fig. 15-7D. Explosion vent with diaphragm cutter and supporting grill.

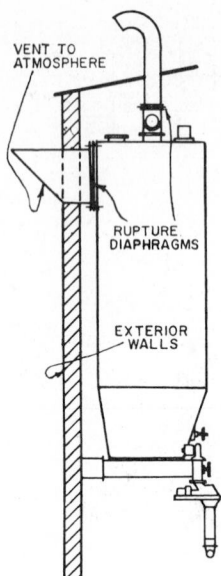

Fig. 15-7E. Dust explosion venting for bulk storage bins or silos, showing explosion vents for tanks.

material and thickness but of different areas decreases with increase in areas.

6. Pressure required to rupture diaphragms of the same area and material but of different thickness increases with increase in thickness.

7. Limited tests indicate that the rupturing pressure of a diaphragm appears to be independent of the maximum rate of pressure rise.

8. Lightweight, hinged panels are nearly as effective as unrestricted vents for the release of relatively slow explosions (e.g., coal dust).

9. Unless a swinging-type vent closure is designed to remain open after the initial positive pressure, a destructive negative pressure may develop in the explosion area.

10. The nearer a vent is located to the point of origin of an explosion, the greater is its effectiveness.

11. Vent closures can be designed to prevent their being accidentally opened by moderate wind pressure. Experimental data showing the relative effectiveness of circular, square, and rectangular openings with and without an em-

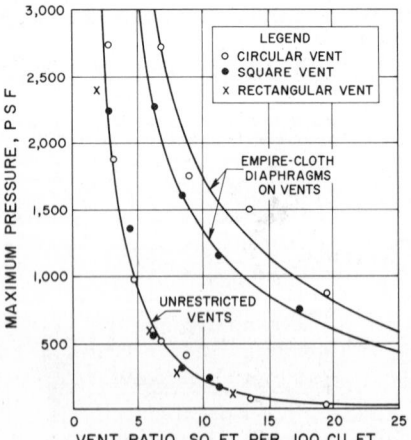

Fig. 15-7F. Relative effectiveness of various types of vent configurations for relieving cellulose acetate dust explosions in a 1 cu ft gallery. (Bureau of Mines, U.S. Department of Interior)

pire cloth diaphragm as a vent cover are shown in Figure 15-7F for cellulose acetate explosions in the 1 cu ft gallery.

Basic Considerations for Enclosure Design

Design of Structures: Pressures developed by explosions of most common gases and vapors excepting hydrogen, acetylenic and olefinic compounds, in air in experimental laboratory test bombs at atmospheric pressure, are of the order of 120 psi for optimum mixtures. It would be impractical to construct a building to withstand such pressures when a 12-in. brick wall may be destroyed by a sustained internal pressure of less than 1 psi. Therefore, explosion venting should be provided to vent the internal pressures before they reach destructive pressures. Such vents may be in the form of louvers, explosion venting windows, wall panels, roof hatches, or even lightweight wall sections. The effects of external wind pressure or suction on these devices should be considered in designing such vents since wind pressures may reach over 30 lbs per sq ft in severe wind storms. However, it is often necessary to compromise between building safety and frequent wind pressure operation of the explosion vents. Counterweights will slow down the action of the vents due to their inertia.

The rate of pressure rise of explosions is an important factor in explosion venting since it determines the time interval available for some of the combustion products to escape. The slower the rate of pressure rise, the more easily an explosion can be vented. Table 15-7A classifies materials according to the explosion hazard and ease of venting. The degree of venting required increases as the explosion hazard increases from weak to severe.

Empirical formulas for computing the size of vent openings for a specific vessel have been developed. However, the state of technology for combustion (explosion) venting is still only partially developed. Combustion venting involves many variables, only some of which have been investigated. Even the investigation of any particular variable has been limited in scope. The investigations which have been done do allow certain generalizations to be made. From these, recommended calculation bases have been developed; however, they must be recognized as approximations only.

Vent Ratio Recommendations

Larger vent areas are required for the more hazardous materials having a rapid rate of pressure rise than for materials having a slow rate of pressure rise. Small enclosures, such as machines, should be vented more generously than buildings because if an explosion occurs in a machine, its entire volume may be involved; in buildings, only a small portion of a room or building space might contain an explosive mixture and thus be involved. Weak structures, such as sheet metal enclosures, must be vented more generously than the enclosures for heavy equipment, and the vents should be of such size and design as to prevent rupture of the protected device or apparatus.

The NFPA Guide for Explosion Venting contains recommended methods for approximately calculating vent areas, and numerous references which explain the limitations of the methods.

Piping and Duct Systems

Explosions in piping and duct systems can be vented by the use of explosion vents. Ductwork should be as short and straight as possible. Since the explosion wave tends to travel in a straight line, any bends in such ductwork should be vented in the direction of travel of the explosion.

Table 15-7A. Classification of Hazard of Materials According to the Pressure and Rate of Pressure Development

Class A—Weak

Dusts

Antimony	Phenylarsonic acid, 4-nitro
Citrus	Polyvinyl chloride
Coffee	Thiourea
Cotton linters	Tin
Cottonseed hulls	Trioxane
Hydrazine tartrate	Urea formaldehyde
Kelp	Vanadium
Manganese	Zinc
Moss	
Onion	*Vapors*
	Ethylene Dichloride

Class B—Moderate

Dusts

Alfalfa	Sodium meta-nitro benzoate
Amino acid	Tantulum
Cocoa	Uranium
Hydrogen reduced iron	
Coals (low volatile)	*Vapors*
Rice	Propylene Dichloride
Skimmed milk	

Class C—Strong

Dusts

Adipic acid	Polyethylene
Chromium	Salicylanilide
Coals (high volatile)	Silicon
Crude rubber	Sodium benzoate
Iron carbonyl	Soy protein
Methyl methacrylate	Styrene maleic anhydride
Peanut hulls	Sugar
Phenol formaldehyde	Torula yeast
Phthalic anhydride	Walnut shell

Class D—Severe

Dusts

Aluminum	Sodium sorbate
Anthranilic acid	Sorbic acid
Asphalt	Stearic acid
Benzotriazole	Sugar
Bisphenyl A	Titanium
Cellulose acetate	Zirconium
Cork	
Cornstarch	*Vapors and Gases*
Diallyl phthalate	Acetone
Epoxy resin	Acetylene
Ethyl cellulose	Alcohols (methyl, ethyl,
Flour	isopropyl and butyl)
Hexamethylene tetramine	Carbon disulfide
Magnesium	Ethers
Nitrosamine	Ethylene
Pea flour	Gasoline
Penta aerythritol	Hydrocarbons
Phthalimide	Hydrogen
Pitch	Methyl-ethyl ketone

There should preferably be no duct in the venting system. If a duct must be employed, it should have just as short an effective length (including effective length of bends in producing pressure drop) as possible. For any appreciable duct length, the duct cross sectional area should be at least twice that of the vent device. It should be noted that combustion

Fig. 15-7G. Venting an explosion of starch dust through hinged windows and hinged doors in a building of light construction.

can take place in the vent duct itself; i.e., unburned gases may be the first to exit from the vent. This has two implications. The first is that the duct should be capable of withstanding a pressure at least as high as that expected to develop in the vessel during venting. The second is that high turbulence can develop in a duct. In the case of gas burning within the duct, that turbulence could possibly lead to transition of the deflagration to detonation. In that case, far higher pressure could develop in the duct.

Rupture Diaphragms

The pressures at which diaphragms (3 in. in diameter or larger) will rupture are almost independent of the rate of pressure rise. Since the rupture pressure for a specific thickness of a diaphragm is dependent upon the area of the vent, specific materials can be tested with air pressure for different areas and can be plotted as shown in Figure 15-5I to determine the required vent size which will rupture at a particular pressure.

Venting can also be by metal or glass discs which are fractured by explosive charges detonated electrically by a suitable detector (see Part E of this chapter). Complete opening is accomplished within a few milliseconds after detection, thus virtually providing an open vent. These vents are designed to withstand high pressure while still providing maximum effectiveness in the vent area.

Fig. 15-7H. Almost 100 percent of the wall area of this building is explosion vent area. Each of the lightweight aluminum wall panels is secured by shear pins designed to release the panel at 30 psi. A chain at the top of each panel prevents it from being blown any distance if blown out by an explosion. (Kodak Park Industrial Photo)

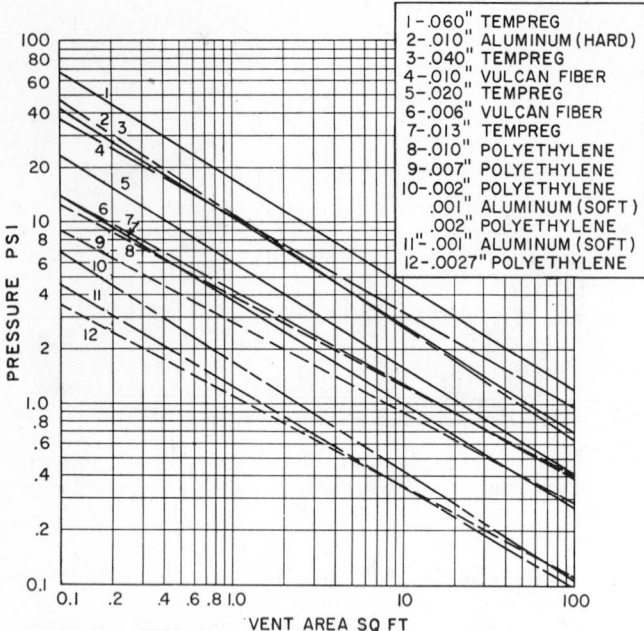

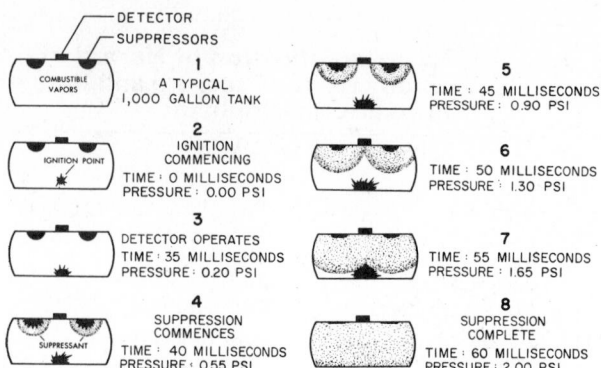

Fig. 15-7J. *Schematic diagram of suppression of an explosion in a typical 1,000-gal tank.*

Fig. 15-7I. Rupture pressure vs. vent area of various venting materials. The graph shows that the bursting pressure of venting materials is a function of the vent area.

C.   Maintenance of Vent Closures

Vent closures should be inspected periodically to detect damage, obstructions, corrosion to the working parts, or other conditions which can affect the operation of the vents in time of necessity. Ice crystals have been known to form between the vents and frames due to high humidity when exposed to freezing temperatures. The ice crystals act as a cement on the vent allowing greater pressures to build up before the vent functions. A coating of grease on the adjacent surfaces may prevent the bridging of ice crystals between the members of the vent. Corrosion and paint may also increase the friction in opening vents.

D.   Fundamentals of Explosion Suppression Systems

The suppression of explosions is possible under certain conditions because a short but significant period of time elapses before destructive pressures are developed. If the conditions are right, it is possible to utilize the time available to operate a suppression system. A typical example of the operation of a suppression system is shown in Figure 15-7J where it can be seen that the explosion pressure is kept to a relatively small value by the actuation of the suppression system during the explosion's incipient growth.

Effective use of the rate of pressure rise to suppress an explosion requires three major considerations in the design of suppression systems. They are:

1. **Detection:** The explosion must be detected in its incipient stage to allow sufficient time for the operation of the suppression equipment. Due to the relatively short period of time that is available, detection must be automatic, with provisions to discriminate between the explosion and ambient variables that normally exist.

2. **Suppression:** The mechanism for dispersal of the agent must operate at extremely high speed to fill the enclosure completely within milliseconds after detection of the explosion. Actuation of this equipment must be automatically initiated by the detector to assure no time lag. The extinguishing agent must be dispersed in a very fine mist or dust form at a rapid speed, normally through the use of an explosive force.

3. **Suppressing Agent:** The agent is normally a liquid compatible with the combustion process to be encountered; however, some specific dusts are also being used. Factors involved in the suppression mechanism are the same as those of fire extinguishing, such as cooling, inerting, blanketing, and combustion inhibiting. In certain cases, overenrichment of the mixture has been successfully used.

E.   Suppression Equipment

Equipment for use in an explosion suppression system that fulfills the three preceding requirements has been designed as follows:

Detectors

The most commonly used type of detector is a very sensitive and stable type of pressure switch, designed to close electrical contacts very early in the pressure growth. This may be set to sense as low as 0.1 psig, depending on plant conditions.

One type of explosion detector is designed to sense the rate of pressure rise acting in an explosion. This detector is a simple diaphragm assembly utilizing a bleed hole across the diaphragm to obtain the proper rate of operation. On slow rates of rise experienced in a process, the pressure on both sides of the diaphragm is allowed to equalize by means of the bleed hole, while under fast explosion rates a differential is built up which moves the diaphragm to close the electrical contacts. In order to prevent blockage, protection is provided for the bleed hole by a secondary diaphragm. Normal settings of a detector of this type are from 5 to 10 psi per sec, a range in which it has been found most incipient explosions can be detected.

Another type of detector is the surveillance detector designed to sense either the radiation or visible light from the incipient explosion. This device utilizes a photocell of the greatest spectral response for the combustion process, and through electronic circuits, provides a signal for actuation of the suppression system. Such a device is normally faster than the rate of pressure rise detector, but is more complicated and requires greater maintenance. Its use is generally confined to special applications where the flame propagation rates are very rapid and a greater stress is placed on the detection time.

Suppressors

Suppressors provide the automatic dispersal of the agent upon detection of the explosion. Two types are used, with the selection dependent upon the explosion characteristics and the process variables encountered.

Frangible suppressors consist of thin-walled reservoirs filled with the suppressing agent into which a small explosive charge such as a blasting detonator is inserted. Since the device is not pressurized, the force to disperse the agent is supplied by the explosive charge which also ruptures the wall of the reservoir. The charge is detonated electrically when contacts on the detector diaphragm are closed. The shape of the reservoir and the position of the detonator establish the pattern of dispersal. Normal shapes for suppressors are hemispherical and tubular.

Pressurized suppressors, known as "high rate discharge extinguishers," contain the agent under nitrogen pressure. While the dispersal force is supplied by the nitrogen pressure, the opening of the container is accomplished with an explosive charge. A very large bore is used in order to allow dispersal of the agent in a minimum period of time. While these suppressors are slower than the frangible type, they are sufficiently fast for combustibles having slow or medium rates of pressure rise.

F.   Application of Suppression Systems

For the application of an explosion suppression system to a hazardous area, the following must be known:

Explosion Characteristics

The rate of explosion pressure rise of the mixtures that will be contained in the hazardous area must be known in order to determine the type of detection system necessary. In cases where surveillance detectors are expected to be used, the spectral characteristics of the combustion must also be known in order to assure that the best combination of photocell and filter is provided. In addition, it is necessary to have information regarding the chemical nature of the mixture in order to assure compatibility with the suppressing agent used.

Ignition

Since the explosion characteristics can be affected by ignition energy, it is necessary to determine the possible sources of ignition that would exist in the area. If these are of sufficient energy to affect the explosion, this must be taken into consideration in the system design. The location of the ignition source is also important, since positioning of the equipment in the area will be dependent upon this information. If ignition sources exist in only one small area, it is possible to provide complete protection with considerably less equipment than if ignition sources were randomly located.

Process Variables

Since the temperature and pressure of a mixture prior to an explosion involving it will affect the characteristics of the explosion, it is necessary to have this information in order to determine accurately the factors necessary for system design. These variables will also affect the operation of the equipment, and in cases where exceedingly high temperatures and pressures are encountered, special techniques must be used in order to assure adequate life service for the equipment.

Structural Integrity

Since an explosion is allowed to start and build up to a small pressure before the suppression system operates, it is necessary that the enclosure be able to withstand this pressure. Under normal sea level pressures and room temperatures, the maximum pressure that can be expected to be encountered is 3 psi before the explosion is controlled. Therefore, the enclosure must have sufficient strength to withstand this pressure.

To illustrate the application of an explosion suppression system, a typical installation for a grinding plant is shown in Figure 15-7K. In plants such as this, while ignition normally starts due to malfunction in the grinder, the explosion reaches dangerous proportions in the cyclone. Therefore, the cyclone becomes the prime area in this process for protection, and is the starting point of all applications of suppression equipment. A detector and two suppressors are located on the cyclone, and suppressors are affixed beneath the rotary gate valve at the bottom of the cyclone and also in the exit to the bag filter to prevent propagation of the explosion flame into those areas. An isolation valve is placed at the entrance to the bag filter to stop the flame front, and a suppressor is located directly after the valve to extinguish any burning particles that may get past the seal. A suppressor is also located at the entrance to the grinder, the suppressing agent discharged from it inerting the grinder and the duct entering into the cyclone. The complete system would be operated by the detector located on the cyclone through a power supply which would provide the current necessary for actuation of all the equipment and supervision of the electrical circuit.

Figure 15-7K illustrates the method of applying an explosion suppression system to a process. In general, the system is applied by determining the most hazardous area in the process and working from this area to other possible hazards in order to assure that all of these would be successfully suppressed by the equipment. This method has been applied to many other areas in industry such as the following:

Storage Tanks: The storage of flammable liquids in many cases presents a severe explosion hazard, and suppression systems have been applied to these tanks to prevent explosions from rupturing and spreading the fire to other tanks in the area.

Coal Pulverizing: Ball mills and other grinding means have been protected by this system in order to prevent explosions resulting from the entrance of tramp metal into

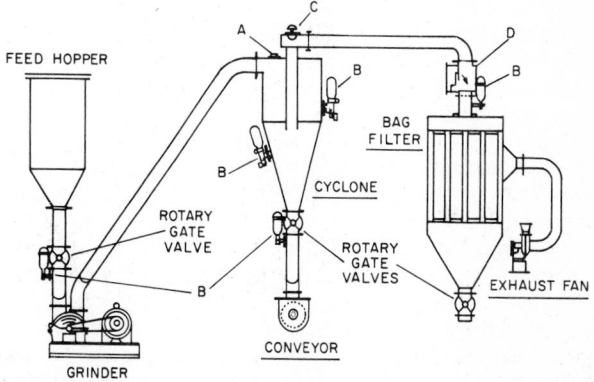

Fig. 15-7K. Explosion protection for a typical grinding plant. The explosion detector at (A) actuates the high-rate discharge bottles (B), hemispherical unit (C), and the isolation valve (D).

the grinder, or flashback from the combustion chambers. The application is quite similar to that shown in Figure 15-7K.

Feed and Grain Processing: Suppression systems have been applied to milling operations encountered in the feed and grain industry where extreme explosion hazards exist due to the dust that is created. In these cases, it has also been applied in storage areas where several explosions have been recorded.

Chemical Reactors: Explosion hazards exist in reactors due to many conditions that can be encountered, and suppression systems have been applied to prevent serious damage. In reactors, it is necessary to assure compatibility of the suppressing agent with the mixture encountered in order not to add further to the explosion hazard.

Plastic Grinding: The equipment for grinding plastics is quite similar to that shown in Figure 15-7K and represents an extreme hazard. Several of the suppression installations that are made have operated successfully and have shown the value of this form of protection.

Transportation: Explosion suppression has been provided for various types of vehicles where explosion hazards have been encountered. These involve both the transportation of hazardous materials and the inherent hazards that are normally encountered in the forms of transportation themselves.

G. Fundamentals of Inerting Systems

The fire and explosion hazard of many materials can be safeguarded during storage and processing operations by the use of a suitable inert gas, since combustion of most materials will not occur if there is an absence of atmospheric oxygen or if its concentration is reduced below a certain specific limit.

The principal function of inert gas, when used as a means of controlling fires and explosions, is to prevent the formation of explosive vapor-air mixtures, generally in enclosed spaces. Typical examples are its use to inert tanks prior to repair, to empty flammable liquid storage tanks by pressure, to prevent the formation of explosive mixtures in drying ovens, and to blanket flammable products in storage tanks or reaction equipment.

In many cases, dust explosions can be prevented by inert gas. Industries that are faced with the explosion hazard of flour, starch, sugar, coal, metal, and other combustible dusts have found it practical to install inert gas protection. Equipment such as grinders, pulverizers, mixers, conveying systems, dust collectors, sacking machines, and the like can be protected in this manner.

Other applications of inert gas include use in chemical processes where there is a continuous explosion hazard if oxygen is present for protection of operations which must be conducted above the ignition temperature of the materials involved, to arrest spontaneous heating of products in storage, and as a means of achieving explosion suppression. The use of carbon dioxide and halons as fire extinguishing agents are discussed in Section 13, Chapter 4.

The limitations of inerting methods should be recognized. These include reliability and adequacy of supply, freedom from moisture or any other constituents which could cause contamination or degradation of product, dependability of instrumentation and excess pressure relieving devices, and the suitability of the supply system to insure sufficient quantity under peak demand.

Personnel must be protected by proper respiratory equipment before entering any enclosure in which inert gas has been used and which might have created an atmosphere deficient in oxygen. Air-supplied or oxygen-supplied masks should be used. Self-contained breathing apparatus of short duration has been recognized by the U.S. Bureau of Mines for self-rescue. Filter-canister-type masks are inadequate for work involving inert gas because they do not supply any oxygen. The toxicity of certain gases used for inerting must also be recognized.

H. Basic Installation Criteria

NFPA No. 69, Standard for Explosion Prevention Systems, provides a considerable amount of information on systems for suppressing explosions, inerting materials and methods for installing inerting systems, and oxidant and combustible concentration reduction, including basic design data for the guidance of engineers.

Hazard Evaluation: First consideration should be given to the evaluation of all hazards which are to be protected, to the operating equipment involved, and to any abnormal conditions which might be encountered. Such an overall study is essential in order to properly plan the most practical and reliable installation and distribution system.

The need for inert gas protection and its provision can influence basic plant layout design: for example, it may be desirable to locate the gas supply near the operation with the largest demand. Likewise, the type, size, and location of process vessels, and the storage facilities might be quite different if inert gas protection is to be provided.

Type of Gas: There are a number of inert gases which are readily available, the two most common being carbon dioxide and nitrogen. Others, such as argon, helium, and the chlorinated or fluorinated hydrocarbons (Halons), may satisfy special needs.

The gas which is most suitable for specific application will depend on a number of factors. In addition to being inert from a fire and explosion standpoint, it must be chemically unreactive with the materials to be protected, and it must be free from contaminants. If there is a corrosion problem, or if it will come in contact with water-reactive chemicals, control of moisture must be possible and practical.

There will have to be a sufficient volume of gas available at an adequate pressure to satisfy requirements at periods of peak demand. A completely oxygen-free gas may be necessary for process reasons or in order to maintain product quality, though not essential for fire protection. However, it is always advisable to maintain as low an oxygen concentration as practicable. The maximum permissible oxygen percentage below which ignition will not occur varies with the flammable materials involved and the inerting medium, as shown in Tables 15-7B, 15-7C, and 15-7D.

Quantity Requirements: The amount of inert gas required and the rate of application will depend upon the oxygen concentration that is permissible, the amount of oxygen in the inert gas—if any, the "factor of safety" to be observed, the amount of loss through leakage, atmospheric conditions, operating conditions, size and shape of the equipment to be protected, and the method of application.

I. Methods of Application

There are two ways of applying inert gas to insure the formation of a noncombustible atmosphere within an enclosed tank or space. These may be designated as: (1) the batch or the fixed volume requirement method, and (2) the

Table 15-7B. Maximum Permissible Oxygen Percentage to Prevent Ignition of Flammable Gases and Vapors Using Nitrogen and Carbon Dioxide for Inerting

	N₂-Air		CO₂-Air	
	O_2 Percent Above Which Ignition Can Take Place	Maximum Recommended O_2 Percent	O_2 Percent Above Which Ignition Can Take Place	Maximum Recommended O_2 Percent
Acetone	13.5	11	15.5	12.5
Benzene (Benzol)	11	9	14	11
Butadiene	10	8	13	10.5
Butane	12	9.5	14.5	11.5
Butene-1	11.5	9	14	11
Carbon Disulfide	5	4	8	6.5
Carbon Monoxide	5.5	4.5	6	5
Cyclopropane	11.5	9	14	11
Dimethylbutane	12	9.5	14.5	11.5
Ethane	11	9	13.5	11.0
Ether	—	—	13	10.5
Ether (Diethyl)	10.5	8.5	13	10.5
Ethyl Alcohol	10.5	8.5	13	10.5
Ethylene	10	8	11.5	9
Gasoline	11.5	9	14	11
Gasoline				
73–100 Octane	12	9.5	15	12
100–130 Octane	12	9.5	15	12
115–145 Octane	12	9.5	14.5	11.5
Hexane	12	9.5	14.5	11.5
Hydrogen	5	4	6	5
Hydrogen Sulfide	7.5	6	11.5	9
Isobutane	12	9.5	15	12
Isopentane	12	9.5	14.5	11.5
JP-1 Fuel	10.5	8.5	14	11
JP-3 Fuel	12	9.5	14	11
JP-4 Fuel	11.5	9	14	11
Kerosine	11	9	14	11
Methane	12	9.5	14.5	11.5
Methyl Alcohol	10	8	13.5	11
Natural Gas				
(Pittsburgh)	12	9.5	14	11
Neopentane	12.5	10	15	12
n-Heptane	11.5	9	14	11
Pentane	11.5	9	14.5	11.5
Propane	11.5	9	14	11
Propylene	11.5	9	14	11

Note:

Data in this Table were obtained from publication of the U.S. Bureau of Mines.

Data were determined by laboratory experiments conducted at atmospheric temperature and pressure. Vapor-air inert-gas samples were placed in explosion tubes and exposed to a small electric spark or open flame.

In the absence of reliable data, the U.S. Bureau of Mines or other recognized authority should be consulted.

continuous method. Each have several modes of application which are described in NFPA No. 69, Standard for Explosion Prevention Systems.

Fixed Volume Method: In one mode of this method, the system to be protected is purged and the atmosphere rendered inert by first reducing the pressure and then introducing inert gas. Equipment which normally operates under a vacuum may be inerted for periods of shutdown

Table 15-7C. Maximum Permissible Oxygen Concentration to Prevent Ignition of Combustible Dusts Using Carbon Dioxide and Nitrogen for Inerting

	Oxygen Percent by Volume Above Which Ignition Can Occur	
	Carbon Dioxide-Air	Nitrogen-Air
Aluminum (atomized)	2	7
Antimony	16	—
Dowmetal	0	—
Ferrosilicon	16	17
Ferrotitanium	13	—
Iron, Carbonyl	10	—
Iron, Hydrogen reduced	11	—
Magnesium	0	2
Magnesium-Aluminum	0	5
Manganese	14	—
Silicon	12	11
Thorium	0	2
Thorium Hydride	6	5
Tin	15	—
Titanium	0	4
Titanium Hydride	13	10
Uranium	0	1
Uranium Hydride	0	2
Vanadium	13	—
Zinc	9	9
Zirconium	0	0
Zirconium Hydride	8	8

Notes:

Data in this Table were obtained principally from publications of the Bureau of Mines.

In the furnace test dust clouds of Zr, Th, U, and UH₃ also ignited in CO_2. During heating for several minutes, undispersed layers of samples of the following metal powders ignited (glowed) in CO_2: Stamped Al, Mg, ZnMg-Al, Dowmetal, Ti, TiH₂, Zr, ZrH₂, Th, ThH₂, U, and UH₃. Visible burning of dust layers was also observed in N₂ with powders of Mg, Sn, Mg-Al, Dowmetal, Ti, TiH₂, Zr, Th, ThH₂, U and UH₃.

In the absence of reliable data for combustible dusts, the U.S. Bureau of Mines or other recognized authority should be consulted.

Data were obtained by laboratory experiments conducted at atmospheric temperature and pressure. An electric spark was the ignition source.

in this manner. Conversely, inert gas under pressure can be introduced into an enclosure and, after mixing has taken place, the pressure can be reduced to normal by venting to atmosphere. Several pressurizing cycles may be necessary to sufficiently reduce the oxygen content.

This method is useful when containers that are filled with a flammable material are to be emptied and an inert atmosphere provided. In all cases the design limitations of the equipment must be observed. Enclosures may be purged by displacing or diluting the flammable vapors at substantially atmospheric pressure. One or more vents discharging to a safe location are opened and the inert gas added until the oxygen content, as shown by test, has been reduced to the desired limit.

Continuous Methods

Fixed Rate Mode: In this method the inert gas is added continuously in an amount sufficient to supply peak requirements. The quantity required is based on the maximum in-breathing rate under conditions of sudden cooling, such as that caused by rain, plus the maximum product withdrawal.

This is a relatively simple method and has the advantage

Table 15-7D.   Maximum Permissible Oxygen Content to Prevent Ignition by Spark of Combustible Dusts Using Carbon Dioxide as the Atmospheric Diluent

Dust	Maximum allowable oxygen concentration, percent	Dust	Maximum allowable oxygen concentration, percent
Agricultural		**Plastics Ingredients**	
Clover seed	15	Azelaic acid	14
Coffee	17	Bisphenol A	12
Cornstarch	11	Casein, rennet	17
Dextrin	14	Hexamethylenetetramine	14
Lycopodium	13	Isophthalic acid	14
Soy flour	15	Paraformaldehyde	12
Starch	12	Pentaerythritol	14
Sucrose	14	Phthalic anhydride	14
		Polymer glyoxyl hydrate	12
Chemicals		Terephthalic acid	15
Ethylene diamine tetra acetic acid	13		
Isatoic anhydride	13	**Plastics—Special Resins and Molding Compounds**	
Methionine	15	Coumarone-indene resin	14
Ortazol	19	Lignin	17
Phenothiazine	17	Phenol, chlorinated	16
Phosphorous pentasulfide	12	Pinewood residue	13
Salicylic acid	17	Rosin, DK	14
Sodium ligno sulfonate	17	Rubber, hard	15
Steric acid and metal stearates	13	Shellac	14
		Sodium resinate	14
Carbonaceous			
Charcoal	17	**Plastics—Thermoplastic Resins and Molding Compounds**	
Coal, bituminous	17	Acetal resin	11
Coal, subbituminous	15	Acrylonitrile polymer	13
Lignite	15	Butadiene-styrene	13
		Carboxymethyl cellulose	16
Metals		Cellulose acetate	11
Aluminum	2	Cellulose triacetate	12
Antimony	16	Cellulose acetate butyrate	14
Chromium	14	Ethyl cellulose	11
Iron	10	Methyl cellulose	13
Magnesium	0	Methyl methacrylate	11
Manganese	14	Nylon polymer	13
Silicon	12	Polycarbonate	15
Thorium	0	Polyethylene	12
Titanium	0	Polystyrene	14
Uranium	0	Polyvinyl acetate	17
Vanadium	14	Polyvinyl butyral	14
Zinc	10		
Zirconium	0	**Plastics—Thermosetting Resins and Molding Compounds**	
		Allyl alcohol	13
Miscellaneous		Dimethyl isophthalate	13
Cellulose	13	Dimethyl terephthalate	12
Lactalbumin	13	Epoxy	12
Paper	13	Melamine formaldehyde	17
Pitch	11	Polyethylene terephthalate	13
Sewage sludge	14	Urea formaldehyde	16
Sulfur	12		
Wood flour	16		

Notes:

Data in this table are from U.S. Bureau of Mines Rept. of Inv. 6543. The data were obtained by laboratory experiments conducted at room temperature and pressure, using a 24-watt continuous spark as the ignition source.

For moderately strong igniting sources, such as a low-current electrical arc or a heated motor bearing, the maximum permissible oxygen concentration is 2 percentage points less than the corresponding value for ignition by spark.

For strong igniting sources, such as an open fire, flame or glowing furnace wall, the maximum permissible oxygen concentration is 6 percentage points less than the corresponding value for ignition by spark.

The maximum permissible oxygen concentration for ignition by spark, when nitrogen is used as the atmospheric diluent, can be calculated by a "rule of thumb" formula:

$$O_n = 1.30_c - 6.3$$

where "O_n" = the maximum permissible oxygen concentration using nitrogen as the atmospheric diluent.

"O_c" = the maximum permissible oxygen concentration using carbon dioxide as the atmospheric diluent.

Research data on the use of dry powders or water as inerting materials and on the effects of inerting on pressure development in a closed vessel are given in BuMines Repts. of Inv. 6543, 6561 and 6811.

of requiring no mechanical devices such as regulators or motor valves. The principal disadvantage consists of the waste of inert gas. Since the peak rate is applied continuously, there are vapor losses due to the "sweeping" action of the inert gas passing through the vapor space. An additional objection is the possible plugging by rust, scale, or ice of the orifice plates controlling the flow of inert gas. A

personnel hazard also may exist in the immediate area of the vents because of oxygen deficiency. However, where large volumes of inexpensive gas are available, this method may be found most suitable.

Variable Rate Mode: In this method the inert gas is admitted to the system being protected on a demand basis. As shown in Figure 15-7L, a low volume bleed provides for

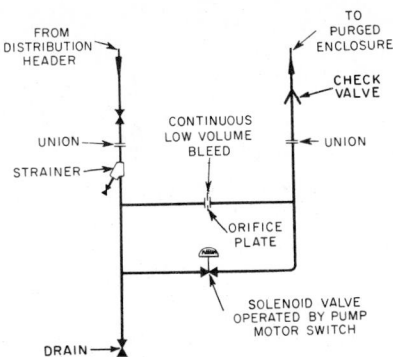

Fig. 15-7L. Schematic sketch showing a method of flow control that can be used with variable rate application.

minor pressure changes in the enclosure while the solenoid valve, which is operated by the pump motor switch, immediately supplies the inert gas flow needed when enclosure contents are being removed. This method has the advantage of reducing vapor losses by maintaining a slight positive pressure, it is the most efficient procedure, since the gas is introduced primarily as needed.

The variable rate method is recommended for maintaining an inert atmosphere in systems that are subject to a wide variation in inert gas demand.

J.   Inert Gases

The inerting media for fire and explosion prevention purposes must be obtained from a dependable source that is capable of continuously supplying the amount required to maintain an atmosphere which will not support combustion. Distribution should be in conformance with accepted piping standards, with protection provided against physical damage, and with main distribution lines so located that exposure to fire is minimized.

Carbon dioxide or nitrogen in cylinders is probably the best source of inert gas for small plants, or where the systems to be protected are of small cubical content and loss through leakage is relatively small. Under some conditions, commercially available carbon dioxide or nitrogen may be the most practical supply—even for large installations. Carbon dioxide fire extinguishers should not be used since they are designed to discharge liquid rather than vapor.

Where no oxygen can be tolerated, carbon dioxide gas or nitrogen as a source of supply has many advantages. Bonding and grounding to prevent any static discharge during inerting are important.

A common method of obtaining inert gas is by the combustion of hydrocarbons as from flame-type producers which operate on liquid or gaseous fuels, natural gas, or manufactured gas. The products of combustion generally contain 9 to 12 percent carbon dioxide, some carbon monoxide, and about 85 percent nitrogen. Oxygen will also be present in inert gas, 2 to 8 percent with fuel oil and usually less than 1 percent with gas as the fuel. The composition of the gas produced by combustion of hydrocarbons varies depending upon the operation of the combustion equipment. If purified inert gas is necessary, the oxygen and traces of carbon monoxide can be removed in one operation, and the carbon dioxide, if it is also undesirable, can be removed in a second operation. Coolers and scrubbers are needed with flame-type producers to remove any particles of glowing soot that might be present, and to make certain the combustion products are not hot enough to ignite any vapor

mixtures in the equipment being purged. Inert gas produced in this manner may be stored, or piped directly to the point of use. Provision for adequate reserves is important so that continuation of protection can be assured in case of producer failure.

The products of combustion from process furnaces or boiler furnaces find considerable use where large volumes are needed. The flue gas from power plant stacks will contain from less than 9 percent to about 14 percent carbon dioxide, and usually only a fraction of a percent carbon monoxide though the latter may reach several percent depending upon the efficiency of the combustion process. Likewise, it is not unusual for the oxygen content to reach 15 or 16 percent if dampers are not properly adjusted. So-called "blow-off gas" from certain chemical oxidation processes may also be suitable for use in inerting. Purification equipment for these waste gases will vary depending upon composition and specific needs. A means for removing solid particles from the gas stream must be provided, and there will generally be a scrubber, dryer, some means for removing excess oxygen, and a compressor. The exact order of the units will vary with individual installations.

Inert gas can also be obtained by the catalytic oxidation of ammonia with air. This method produces a high purity nitrogen with only traces of carbon dioxide, hydrogen, oxygen, and residual ammonia.

Another means of obtaining inerting media is by the liquefaction of air with subsequent fractionation to produce nitrogen. Package units of various capacities using this method are now commercially available.

Distribution piping must be properly sized to deliver the required volume of inert gas at adequate pressure, and it must be constructed of suitable material. Moisture traps and strainers may be necessary. Back pressure valves are recommended for each branch from the main distribution line to prevent reduction of the pressure in the main below a predetermined set pressure if there is excessive demand in a branch line. Contamination of the entire inert gas system, due to reversal of flow either through loss of inert gas pressure or by excessive pressure in an inerted unit, may be prevented by installation of check valves. The entire distribution facility should be installed, inspected, and maintained with the same care and attention as given automatic sprinkler systems.

For the special problems of safeguarding aircraft fuel tank atmospheres by the use of inert gas, reference should be made to NFPA No. 410C, Standard for Aircraft Fuel System Maintenance.

K.   Purged Enclosures for Electrical Equipment

In 1967 the first edition of NFPA No. 496, Standard for Purged and Pressurized Enclosures for Electrical Equipment in Hazardous Locations, hereinafter referred to in this Chapter as the NFPA Purged Enclosures for Electrical Equipment Standard, was officially adopted. This standard filled the need for a nationally recognized method of using air (or inert gas) to purge and pressurize electrical equipment enclosures in Class I locations so that the atmosphere in the enclosure is nonflammable. In such enclosures, the electrical equipment need not be explosionproof. For example, in chemical plants it is common practice to install as much of the electrical equipment as possible in an air-pressurized control room. As long as a positive pressure is maintained in the control room with clean air, flammable vapors and gases cannot enter from adjoining Class I areas of the plant. Motors, instruments, and control equipment can be located in hazardous locations if the enclosure or case is purged and pressurized, and if the enclosure is designed so that external surface temperatures cannot approach the ignition temperature of the gas or vapor in the Class I location in which the enclosed equipment is installed.

Several factors have to be considered when designing a purging and pressurizing system, including a source of clean air, safe discharge of air from the enclosure, purging procedures to be followed before equipment in the enclosure is turned on, and construction of the enclosure. Recommendations on these and other considerations are given in the NFPA Purged Enclosures for Electrical Equipment Standard. This Standard defines three types of purging with different safeguards for each type. They are:

Type X Purging: Type X purging reduces the classification within an enclosure from Division 1 (normally hazardous) to nonhazardous. Because the probability of a hazardous concentration of gas or vapor external to the enclosure is high and the enclosure normally contains a source of ignition, an essential safeguard in Type X purging is the automatic deenergizing of all equipment in the enclosure if purging is interrupted.

Type Y Purging: Type Y purging reduces the classification within an enclosure from Division 1 to Division 2 (hazardous only under abnormal conditions). Electrical equipment in the enclosure must be suitable for use in Division 2 locations (equipment that does not normally contain a source of ignition). Thus, a hazardous condition will exist in the enclosure only if an electrical equipment failure creates an ignition source within the enclosure at the same time that the purging system fails. In Type Y purging an automatic warning is given when purging fails, but the electrical equipment within the enclosure is not automatically deenergized.

Type Z Purging: Type Z purging reduces the classification within an enclosure from Division 2 to nonhazardous. Since the area surrounding the enclosure is Division 2, a hazardous condition will exist within the enclosure only if purging failure occurs simultaneously with some other occurrence that changes the area surrounding the enclosure from Division 2 to Division 1. As in Type Y purging, an automatic warning is required if purging fails so that steps can be taken to reestablish purging, but automatic shutdown of power in the enclosure is not required.

SI Units

The following conversion factors are given as a convenience in converting to SI units the English units used in this chapter.

1 in. = 25.400 mm
1 ft   = .305 m
1 psi = 6.895 kPa
1 cu ft = .0283 m³

Bibliography

NFPA Codes, Standards, and Recommended Practices (see the latest *NFPA Publications and Visual Aids Catalog* for availability of current editions of the following documents)

NFPA No. 68, Guide for Explosion Venting.
NFPA No. 69, Standard for Explosion Prevention Systems.
NFPA No. 410C, Standard for Aircraft Fuel System Maintenance.
NFPA No. 496, Standard for Purged and Pressurized Enclosures for Electrical Equipment.

Additional Readings

Bartknecht, W. and Kühnen, G., *Forschungsbericht F45*, Bundesinstitute für Arbeitsschutz, 1971.

Bonyun, M. E., "Protecting Pressure Vessels with Rupture Discs," *Chemical and Metallurgical Engineering*, Vol. 42, May 1945, pp. 260–263.

Bourgoyne, J. H. and Wilson, M. J. G., "The Relief of Pentane Vapor-Air Explosions in Vessels," Symposium Chemical Process Hazards, S. 25/29, Institute of Chemical Engineering, 1960.

Brown, Hylton, "Design of Explosion Pressure Vents," *Engineering News-Record*, Oct. 3, 1946.

Brown, K. C., et al., *Transactions of the Institution of Mining Engineers*, Vol. 74, No. 8, 1962, pp. 261–76.

Brown, K. C. and Curzon, G. E., "Dust Explosions in Factories: Explosion Vents in Pulverized Fuel Plants," Research Report 212, 1962, Safety in Mines Research Establishment, Sheffield, England.

Coffee, R. D., "Dust Explosions: An Approach to Protection Design," *Fire Technology*, Vol. 4, No. 2, May 1968, pp. 81–87.

Coffee, R. D., Raymond, C. L., and Crouch, H. W., "A Linear Variable Differential Transformer as a Transducer," Eastman Kodak Company, Rochester, N.Y., 1950.

———, "The Testing of Materials for Pressure Relief Vents," Eastman Kodak Company, Rochester, N.Y., 1950.

Consion, J., "How to Design a Pressure Relief System," *Chemical Engineering*, Vol. 67, No. 15, July 25, 1960, p. 109.

Cotton, P. E. and Cousins, E. W., "The Protection of Closed Vessels Against Internal Explosions," Paper No. 51-PRI-2, April 1951, The American Society of Mechanical Engineers, New York.

Cousins, E. W., and Cotton, P. E., "The Protection of Closed Vessels Against Internal Explosions," Paper No. 51-PRI-2, 1951, American Society of Mechanical Engineers, New York.

———, "Design Closed Vessels to Withstand Internal Explosions," *Chemical Engineering*, Vol. 58, No. 8, Aug. 1951, pp. 133–137.

Coward, H. F. and Hersey, M. D., "Accuracy of Manometry of Explosions," RI 3274, 1935, USDI Bureau of Mines, Pittsburgh.

Coward, H. F. and Jones, G. W., "Limits of Flammability of Gases and Vapors," Bulletin 503, 1952, USDI Bureau of Mines, Washington, D.C.

Creech, M. D., "Combustion Explosions in Pressure Vessels Protected with Rupture Discs," *Transactions of the American Society of Mechanical Engineers*, Vol. 63, No. 7, 1941.

Creech, M. D., "Study of Combustion Explosion in Pressure Vessels," Black, Syvalls and Bryson, Inc., Kansas City, Mo., Feb. 1940.

Crouch, H. W., et al., "Maximum Pressures and Rates of Pressure Rise Due to Explosions of Various Solvents," Eastman Kodak Company, Rochester, N.Y., 1952.

Cubbage, P. A., "Flame Traps for Use with Town Gas/Air Mixtures," Gas Council Research Communication GC63, 1959, London.

Donat, C., "Release of the Pressure of an Explosion with Rupture Discs and Explosion Valves," paper presented at Achema 73, Frankfurt, West Germany.

———, *Staub-Reinhaltung der Luft*, Vol. 31, No. 4, April 1971, pp. 154–160.

"Dust Explosions in Factories," Her Majesty's Factory Inspectorate, Safety, Health and Welfare Booklets New Series 22, S.38, Her Majesty's Stationery Office, London, 1963.

Evans, C. H., "Designing Safe Installations for Inert Gas Machines," presented at the ASTM 12th Annual Petroleum Mechanical Engineering Conference, Tulsa, Okla., Sept. 1957.

Fiock, E. F., "Measurement of Burning Velocity," *High Speed Aerodynamics and Jet Propulsion*, Vol. 9, University Press, Oxford, 1955, pp. 409–38.

Fishkin, C. I. and Smith, R. L., "Handling Flammable Dusts," *Chemical Engineering Progress*, April 1964.

Freeston, H. G., Roberts, J. P., and Thomas, A., *Proceedings of the Institution of Mechanical Engineers* (London), Vol. 170, No. 24, 1956, pp. 811–62.

Grabowski, G. J., "Progress in Industrial Explosion Protection Systems," *Fire Journal*, Vol. 62, No. 1, Jan. 1968, pp. 21–24.

———, "Explosion Protection Operating Experience," NFPA *Quarterly*, Vol. 52, No. 2, Oct. 1958, pp. 109–19.

———, "Theoretical and Practical Aspects of Explosion Protection," *Fire Protection Manual for Hydrocarbon Processing Plants*, Gulf Publishing Co., Houston, Tx., 1964.

Hammond, C. B., "Explosion Suppression—New Safety Tool," *Chemical Engineering*, Dec. 1961, pp. 85–88.

Harris, G. F. P. and Briscoe, P. G., *Combustion and Flame*, Vol. 2, No. 4, Aug. 1967, pp. 329–338.

Hartmann, I. and Nagy, J., "Effect of Relief Vents on Reduction of Pressures Developed by Dust Explosions," RI 3924, 1946, USDI Bureau of Mines, Pittsburgh.

Hartmann, I., "Bureau of Mines Optical Pressure Manometer," RI 3751, 1935, USDI Bureau of Mines, Pittsburgh.

———, "Dust Explosions," *Marks Mechanical Engineers' Handbook*, 5th ed., McGraw-Hill, 1950, pp. 795–800.

————, "Explosion and Fire Hazards of Combustible Dusts," *Industrial Hygiene and Toxicology*, Vol. 1, Chap. 13, Sec. 2, Interscience Publishers, Inc., New York, 1948, pp. 439–454.

————, "Pressure Release for Dust Explosions," NFPA *Quarterly*, Vol. 40, No. 1, July 1946, pp. 47–53.

————, "Recent Research on the Explosibility of Dust Dispersions," *Industrial and Engineering Chemistry*, Vol. 40, No. 4, April 1948, pp. 752–758.

————, "The Explosion Hazard of Metal Powders and Preventive Measures," *Metals Handbook*, American Society of Metals, Metals Park, Ohio, 1948, pp. 52–54.

Hartmann, I., Cooper, A. R., and Jacobson, M., "Recent Studies of the Explosibility of Corn Starch," RI 4725, 1950, USDI Bureau of Mines, Pittsburgh.

Hartmann, I. and Greenwald, "The Explosibility of Metal Powder Dust Clouds," *Mining and Metallurgy*, Vol. 26, 1945, pp. 331–335.

Hartmann, I. and Nagy, J., "Effect of Relief Vents on Reduction of Pressures Developed by Dust Explosions," RI 3924, 1946, USDI Bureau of Mines, Pittsburgh.

————, "Inflammability and Explosibility of Powder Used in the Plastics Industry," RI 3751, 1944, USDI Bureau of Mines, Pittsburgh.

————, "The Explosibility of Starch Dust," *Chemical Engineering News*, Vol. 27, July 18, 1949, p. 2071.

Hartmann, I., Nagy, J., and Brown, H. R., "Inflammability and Explosibility of Metal Powders," RI 3722, 1943, USDI Bureau of Mines, Pittsburgh.

Hartmann, I., Nagy, J., and Jacobson, M., "Explosive Characteristics of Titanium, Zirconium, Thorium, Uranium and Their Hydrides," RI 4835, 1951, USDI Bureau of Mines, Pittsburgh.

Heinrich, H. J., "Dimensions of Pressure-Release Openings for the Protection of Plants in the Chemical Industry Which Are Endangered by Explosions," *Chemie, Ingenieu, Tecknik*, Vol. 38, No. 11, Nov. 1966, pp. 1125–33.

Howard, W. B., *Loss Prevention*, Vol. 6 (a CEP Technical Manual) American Institute of Chemical Engineers, 1972, pp. 68–73.

"An Investigation of Large Electric Motors and Generators of the Explosion Proof Type for Hazardous Locations, Class I, Group D," Bulletin of Research No. 46, 1951, Underwriters Laboratories, Inc., Chicago.

Jacobson, M.; Cooper, A. R.; Nagy, J., "Explosibility of Metal Powders," RI 6516, 1964, USDI Bureau of Mines, Pittsburgh.

Jenett, E., "Design Considerations for Pressure Relieving Systems," Part I, *Chemical Engineering*, July 1963, p. 125; Part II, *Chemical Engineering*, Aug. 1963, p. 151; and Part III, *Chemical Engineering*, Sept. 1963, p. 83.

Jones, W. M., "Determination of Dust Explosion Possibilities," Special Hazard Study No. 4, 1940, Factory Insurance Association, Hartford, Conn.

————, "Prevention and Minimizing the Effects of Dust Explosions in Manufacturing Plants," Special Hazard Study No. 5, 1940, Factory Insurance Association, Hartford, Conn.

Jones, G. W., Harris, E. S., and Beattie, B. B., "Protection of Equipment Containing Explosive Acetone-Air Mixtures by the Use of Diaphragms," Bureau of Mines Technical Paper 553, 1933, USDI Bureau of Mines, Washington, D.C.

Le Vine, R. Y., "Electrical Equipment in Outside Chemical and Petroleum Plants," *Fire Journal*, Vol. 59, No. 3, May 1965, pp. 30–31.

Loison, R.; Chaineaux, L.; and Delclaux, J., "Study of Some Safety Problems in Fire Damp Drainage," Eighth International Conference of Directors of Safety in Mines Research, Paper No. 37, Dortmund-Derne, 1954.

"The Lower Limit of Flammability and the Autogeneous Ignition Temperatures of Certain Common Solvent Vapors Encountered in Ovens," Bulletin of Research No. 43, 1950, Underwriters Laboratories, Inc., Chicago.

Mainstone, R. J., Current Paper 26/71, Building Research Station, Garston, Watford, England, 1971.

Maisey, H. R., "Gaseous and Dust Explosion Venting," Part I, *Chemical and Process Engineering*, Oct. 1965, pp. 526–535; Part II, *Chemical and Process Engineering*, Dec. 1965, pp. 662–672.

Murphy, T. S., "Rupture Diaphragms, Calculations, Characteristics and Uses," *Chemical and Metallurgical Engineering*, Nov. 1944.

Nagy, J., Zeilinger, J. E., and Hartmann, I., "Pressure Relieving Capacities of Diaphragms and Other Devices for Venting Dust Explosions," RI 4636, 1950, USDI Bureau of Mines, Pittsburgh.

Nagy, J., Dorsett, H. G., and Jacobson, M., "Preventing Ignition of Dust Dispersions by Inerting," RI 6543, 1964, USDI Bureau of Mines, Pittsburgh.

"A New Type of Bomb for Investigation of Pressures Developed by Dust Explosions," Bulletin of Research No. 30, March 1944, Underwriters Laboratories, Inc., Chicago.

Palmer, K. N., "Dust Explosion Venting—a Reassessment of the Data," Fire Research Note No. 830, Aug. 1970, Fire Research Station, Boreham Wood, Herts., England.

Philpott, J. E., *Engineering Materials and Design*, Vol. 6, No. 1, 1963, pp. 24–29.

Potter, A. E., "Flame Quenching," *Progress in Combustion Science and Technology*, Vol. 1, Pergamon Press, Oxford, 1960, pp. 145–81.

Rasbash, D. J., *The Structural Engineer*, Vol. 47, No. 10, Oct. 1969, pp. 404–407.

Rasbash, D. J., and Rogowski, Z. W., "Relief of Explosions in Dust Systems," *Symposium on Chemical Process Hazards with Special Reference to Plant Design*, Institution of Chemical Engineers, 1961, pp. 58–69.

————, "Relief of Explosions in Propane/Air Mixtures Moving in a Straight Unobstructed Dust," *Second Symposium on Chemical Process Hazards with Special Reference to Plant Design*, Institution of Chemical Engineers, 1964.

Runes, E., *Loss Prevention*, Vol. 6 (a CEP Technical Manual), American Institute of Chemical Engineers, 1972, pp. 63–67.

Salter, R. L., Fike, L. L., and Hansen, F. A., "How to Size Rupture Discs," *Hydrocarbon Processing and Petroleum Refiner*, Vol. 42, May 1963, pp. 159–160.

Schmidt, H., Haberl, K., and Reckling Hausen, M. K., *Technische Ueberwachurg*, Vol. 7, No. 12, 1955, pp. 423–29.

Schwab, R. F. and Othmer, D. F., "Dust Explosions," *Chemical and Processing Engineering*, April 1964.

Sestak, E. J., "Venting of Chemical Plant Equipment," Engineering Bulletin No. N-53, April 1965, Factory Insurance Association, Hartford, Conn.

Simmonds, W. A. and Cubbage, P. A., "The Design of Explosion Reliefs for Industrial Drying Ovens," *Symposium on Chemical Process Hazards with Special Reference to Plant Design*, Institution of Chemical Engineers, 1961, pp. 69–77.

Smith, J. B., "Explosion Pressures in Industrial Piping System," Factory Mutual Insurance Association, Hartford, Conn., 1949.

"The Spontaneous Ignition and Dust Explosion Hazards of Certain Soybean Products," Bulletin of Research No. 47, 1953, Underwriters Laboratories, Inc., Chicago.

Stretch, K. L., "Part I—The Relief of Gas and Vapor Explosions in Domestic Structures," *The Structural Engineer*, Vol. 47, No. 10, Oct. 1969, pp. 408–411.

"Symposium on Bursting Discs," *Transactions of the Institution of Chemical Engineers*, Vol. 31, No. 2, 1953.

Thompson, N. J. and Cousins, E., "Explosion Tests on Glass Windows; Effect on Glass Breakage of Varying the Rate of Pressure Application," *Journal of the American Ceramic Society*, Vol. 32, No. 10, Oct. 1949.

————, "Measuring Pressures of Industrial Explosions," *Electronics*, Nov. 1947.

Tonkin, P. S. and Berlemont, C. F. J., "Dust Explosions in a Large Scale Cyclone Plant," Fire Research Note No. 942, July 1972, Fire Research Station, Boreham Wood, Herts., England.

Valentine and Merrill, "Dust Control in the Plastics Industry," *Transactions of the American Institute of Chemical Engineers*, Vol. 38, No. 4, Aug. 1942.

Wood, L. E., "Rupture Discs," *Chemical Engineering Progress*, Vol. 61, Feb. 1965, p. 93.

Zebatikis, M. G., "Flammability Characteristics of Combustible Gases and Vapors," Bulletin 627, 1965, USDI Bureau of Mines, Pittsburgh.

Chapter 8

LIGHTNING PROTECTION SYSTEMS

Lightning is a frequent fire cause, and in some areas it is a leading cause. It is also feared as a cause of loss of life and personal injury because it is instantaneous and seemingly unpredictable. Unlike many other causes of death and injury that one can run away from, lightning comes before the warning thunder. The principles of protection and personal safety are well known and are spelled out in NFPA No. 78, Lightning Protection Code (ANSI C5.1), hereinafter referred to in this chapter as the NFPA Lightning Protection Code: however, it must be remembered that lightning involves many uncertainties, and, while a given pattern of behavior may be probable, there is no guarantee that a lightning discharge will not deviate from that pattern.

Frequency and Severity of Thunderstorms: The frequency of thunderstorms varies throughout the world. The *severity* of thunderstorms, as distinguished from their *frequency* of occurrence, is much greater in some locations than in others. Hence, the need for protection varies geographically, although not necessarily in direct proportion to thunderstorm frequency. A few severe thunderstorms a season may make the need for protection greater than a relatively large number of storms of lighter intensity (see Figs. 15-8B and 15-8C for statistical data on the frequency of thunderstorms in Canada and the United States, and Fig. 15-8D for world data).

Value and Nature of Building and Contents: Buildings often have an historical or sentimental value which is uninsurable. The construction of a building will also have a large influence upon the extent of protection to be considered. Some buildings do not require supplemental lightning protection due to their construction. The real or intangible value of the contents of the building must also be considered, and, in some cases, attention must be given to the nature of the contents and the susceptibility of the contents to damage by induced lightning currents, e.g., stores of explosives.

Personal Hazards: The lightning hazard to human beings in a building is a major consideration. In buildings of any type (other than those constructed of grounded metal framing) a stroke of lightning may lead to a considerable degree of discomfort, if not injury or death. Hence, lightning pro-

tection may be deemed desirable to eliminate possible personal hazards, even though it might otherwise not be considered for strictly economic reasons. In places of public assembly the potential of panic should be considered because a lightning discharge over a structure, even if not accompanied by fire, can have visual and audible effects which may induce panic.

Relative Exposure: In closely built-up towns and cities, the hazard is not as great as in the open country. In the latter, farm barns are most frequently hit. In hilly or mountainous districts, a building upon high ground is usually subject to greater hazard than one in a valley or otherwise sheltered area.

Indirect Losses: In addition to direct loss due to damage of buildings or their contents by lightning, fire resulting from lightning, killing of livestock, etc., there may be indirect losses. An interruption to business or to farming operations, especially at certain times of the year, may involve losses quite distinct from and in addition to the losses arising from the direct property damage. There are also cases where whole communities depend for safety and comfort in some respects on the integrity of a single structure, as, for instance, on the brick chimney of a water-pumping plant. A stroke of lightning to the unprotected chimney of a plant of that sort might have serious consequences resulting in lack of sanitary drinking water, irrigating water, water for fire protection, or similar effect.

A.   Theory of Lightning Protection

The theory of lightning protection is simple: provide means by which a lightning discharge may enter or leave the earth without damaging the property protected. There is no evidence that any form of protection can prevent the occurrence of a lightning discharge. A lightning protection system has only one function—to intercept a lightning discharge before it can strike the object protected, and then to discharge the lightning current harmlessly to earth. The normal lightning leader discharge is a self-propagating discharge that progresses toward the ground, but is not affected by any features on the ground until the critical breakdown strength of the remaining distance from the ground is reached. At that point, an upward streamer discharge is initiated and the leader discharge is diverted toward it. The "attractive" range from a lightning conductor is a statistical quantity, depending primarily on the severity of the lightning discharge. The maximum range of "attraction" of a lightning discharge of average intensity would be a distance of only about twice the height of the conductor; the distance might be reduced if any unprotected part of a building were of such a shape and in such a position as to be capable of initiating an upward streamer discharge. The down conductors to ground must be substantial and must provide a reasonably direct path. The blocking effect of electrical induction must be avoided. For example, a lightning conductor run through a piece of iron pipe for protection, unless connected with the pipe at the top and bottom, largely nullifies the value of the conductor.

Fig. 15-8A.   Triple lightning bolt lighting up Milwaukee's Water Tower Park during a thunderstorm. (Associated Press)

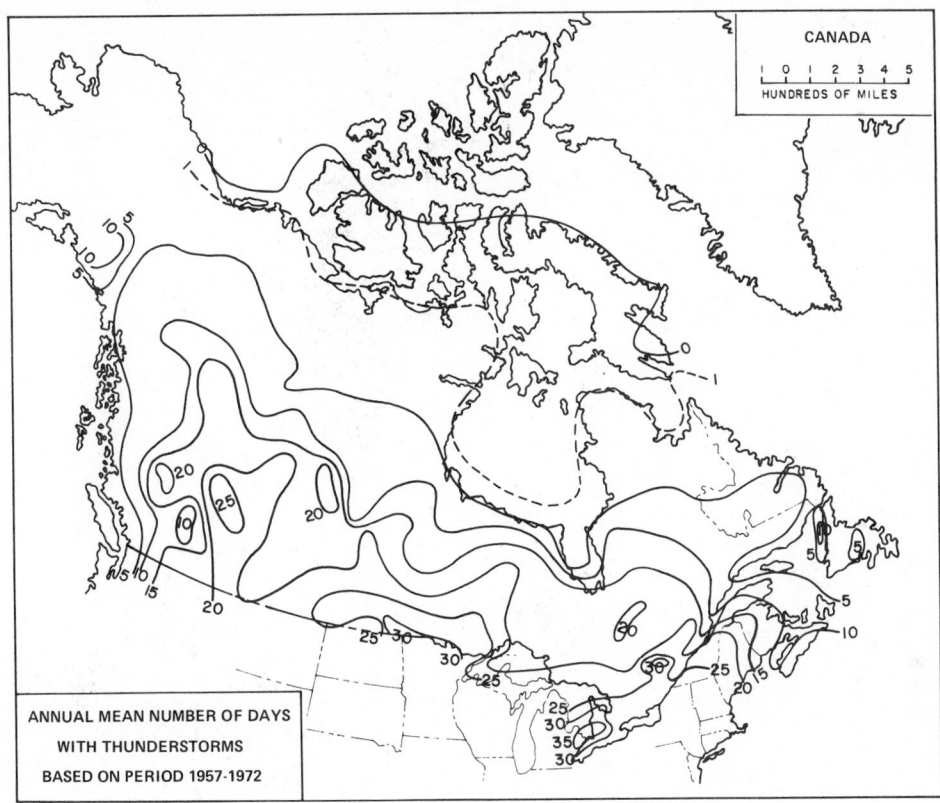

Fig 15-8B.   Canadian statistics showing annual average of days with thunderstorms. Data based on the period 1957–1972. (Meteorological Division, Department of Transportation, Canada)

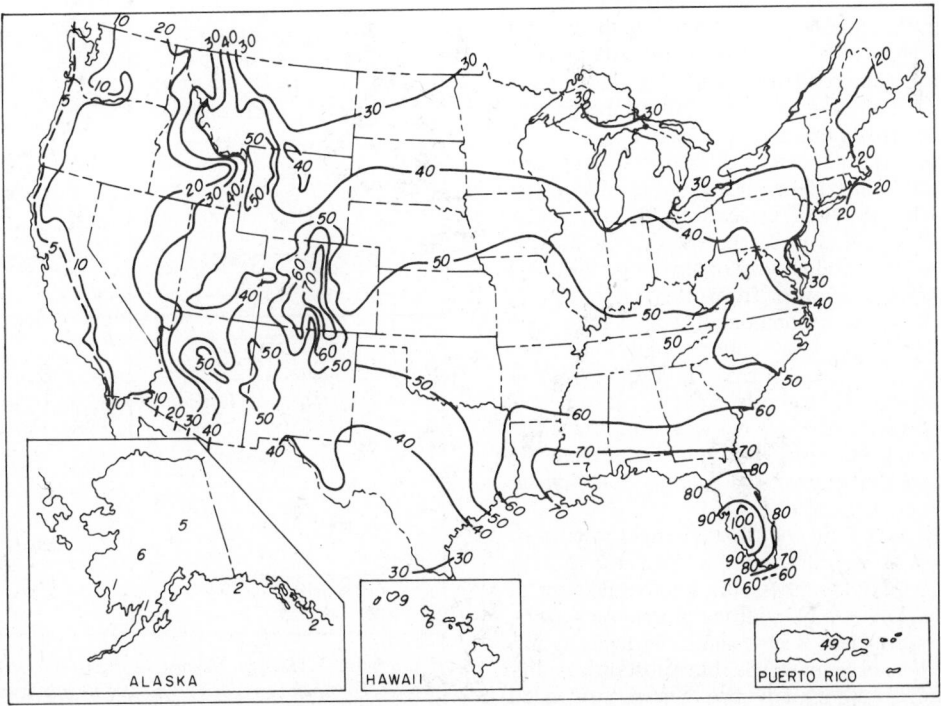

Fig. 15-8C.   Statistics for Continental United States showed mean annual number of days with thunderstorms. The highest frequency is encountered in south-central Florida. Since 1894, the recording of thunderstorms has been defined as the local calendar day during which thunder was heard. A day with thunderstorms is so recorded regardless of the number occurring on that day. The occurrence of lightning without thunder is not recorded as a thunderstorm. (Data supplied by Environmental Science Service Administration, U.S. Department of Commerce)

Fig. 15-8D. Annual frequency of thunderstorm days as compiled by the World Meteorological Organization, 1956. (World Meteorological Organization).

B. Nature of Lightning

There are four types of lightning strokes: (1) the negative downward stroke; (2) the positive downward stroke; (3) the positive upward stroke; and (4) the negative upward stroke. These are illustrated in Figure 15-8E.

Lightning strokes may occur between clouds or between clouds and the earth. In the latter, charges of opposite polarity are generated in the cloud while the charge in the ground below the cloud is induced by the lower cloud charge. The result is, in effect, a giant condenser, and when the charge builds up sufficiently a discharge occurs. This discharge may take place in an extremely short period of time.

A lightning stroke is made up of a number of separate discharges. First, a "pilot leader stroke" of only a few amperes, followed by others of increasing intensity, propagates downward from cloud to earth, ionizing the air and increasing the electrical conductivity of the path; the main stroke then propagates upward from the earth. Other strokes follow. As many as 40 component strokes have been observed in a single flash. Speeds range from 100 miles per second for the first pilot leader stroke to 20,000 miles per second for the main stroke. Currents range up to two hundred thousand amperes in extreme cases, lasting for a few millionths of a second, but lesser currents are present for a longer period. Potentials have been estimated as high as tens or hundreds of millions of volts.

Because of the high voltage and rapid changes in current flow, induced charges are important. Thus, the NFPA Lightning Protection Code requires the interconnection of metallic masses as a part of any lightning protection system.

Lightning causes fire only where sufficient heat is produced to ignite combustible materials, but substantial damage can be produced without any fire. Often, dry wood beams in houses struck by lightning are severely splintered, and windows are blown outward; such damage primarily results from pressure generated by the expanding lightning channel. Some of the effects of lightning are indirect—it is not necessary that lightning strike the building to damage it.

For example, lightning striking overhead wires may be conducted to buildings over the wires—lightning arresters are often provided to minimize such damage. Lightning arresters are of several types; all have the function of permitting the free flow of lightning charges to ground, but of preventing the flow of ordinary electric current over the same path.

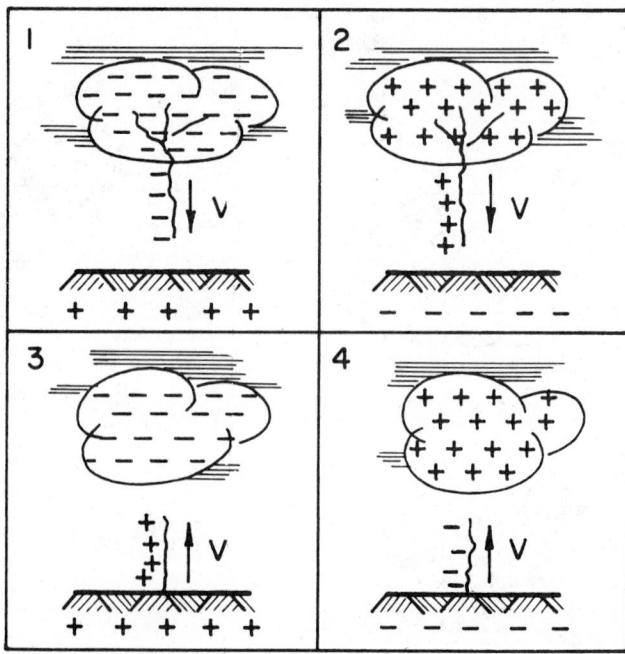

Fig. 15-8E. The four types of lightning strokes: (1) negative downward stroke (negative charge) negative current—this is the normal case over open country and most residential areas; (2) positive downward stroke (positive charge) positive current; (3) positive upward stroke (positive charge) negative current—this is the normal case with exceptionally tall structures; and (4) negative upward stroke (negative charge) positive current. V is the direction of stroke propagation.

C.   Property Protection

In current United States practice, as indicated in the NFPA Lightning Protection Code and ANSI C5.1, required conditions of protection for ordinary buildings are met by placing metal air terminals on the uppermost parts of the building or its projections, with conductors connecting the air terminals with each other and to the ground. By this means a relatively small amount of metal, properly proportioned and distributed, affords a satisfactory degree of protection, and, if desired, the material may be so placed as to give minimum interference with the contour and appearance of the building. In the current British Standard Code of Practice for "Protection Against Lightning" (CP 326:1965) the use of pointed air terminal (vertical finials) is not regarded essential except where dictated by practical considerations.

Conductors

The NFPA Lightning Protection Code specifies the use of corrosion resistant metals for use as lightning conductors, or specifies that they shall be protected against corrosion. Where two different metals, such as copper and aluminum, are used together, special precautions must be taken against electrolytic corrosion. Conductors are coursed along ridges of sloping roofs, around the edges of flat roofs, and vertically from these and from the air terminals to ground. Vertical runs are designated as "down conductors" and are never less than two on any kind of structure, except for flagpoles, masts, spires, and similar structures. The down conductors are normally placed at diagonally opposite corners of square or rectangular structures, but other factors such as direct coursing, security against displacement, location of metallic elements in the structure, location of water pipes, and where ground conditions are most favorable, need to be considered in determining optimum placement. For detailed instruction as to installation of conductors, their form and size, and on the installation of air terminals, refer to the NFPA Lightning Protection Code.

Grounding

Properly made ground connections are essential to the effective functioning of a lightning protection system, and every effort should be made to provide ample contact with the earth. This does not necessarily mean that the resistance of the ground connection must be low, but rather that the distribution of metal in the earth, or upon its surface in ex-treme cases, shall be such as to permit the dissipation of a stroke of lightning without damage.

Low resistance is, of course, desirable, but not essential, as may be shown by the extreme comparison of a building resting on moist clay soil, and another building resting on bare solid rock. In the first example, if the soil is of normal resistivity of from 200 to 5,000 ohm-centimeters, the resistance of a ground connection made by extending the conductor 10 ft into the ground will be from 20 to 50 ohms, and two such ground connections on a small rectangular building have been found by experience to be sufficient. Under these favorable conditions, providing adequate means for collecting and dissipating the energy of a flash without serious chance of damage is a simple and comparatively inexpensive matter.

In the second example, it would be impossible to make a ground connection in the ordinary sense of the term because most kinds of rock are insulating, or at least of high resistivity, and in order to obtain effective grounding, other and more elaborate means are necessary. One effective means is to use an extensive wire network laid on the surface of the rock surrounding the building, after the manner of counterpoise to a radio antenna, to which the down conductors could be connected. Another is to use "ring" conductors. One ring should be installed at the bottom of the foundation to which the down conductors or structural steelwork are connected, with a second ring conductor provided by blasting a circular trench around the periphery and placing in it a strip conductor: the blasted area should be thoroughly compacted with backfill, and the two ring conductors electrically interconnected. Using one of these methods would make the distribution of the electrical potential around the protected building substantially the same as if it were resting on conducting soil, and the resulting protective effect would be equal.

In general, the extent of the grounding arrangements will depend upon the character of the soil, ranging from simple

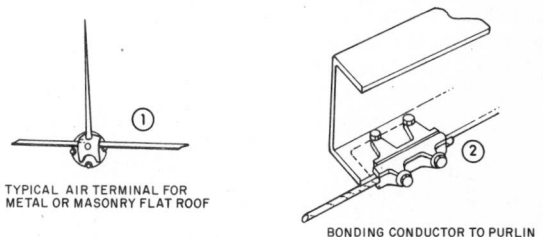

TYPICAL AIR TERMINAL FOR
METAL OR MASONRY FLAT ROOF

BONDING CONDUCTOR TO PURLIN

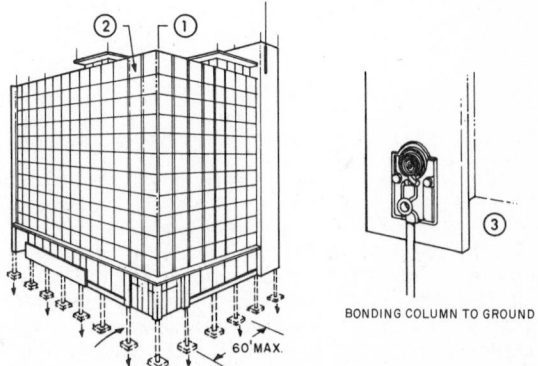

BONDING COLUMN TO GROUND

Fig. 15-8F.   Schematic of a typical lightning protection system on a low-level, large area structure (installation hardware enlarged to illustrate principles).

Fig. 15-8G.   A type of lightning protection system installation in a modern steel-frame high-rise building.

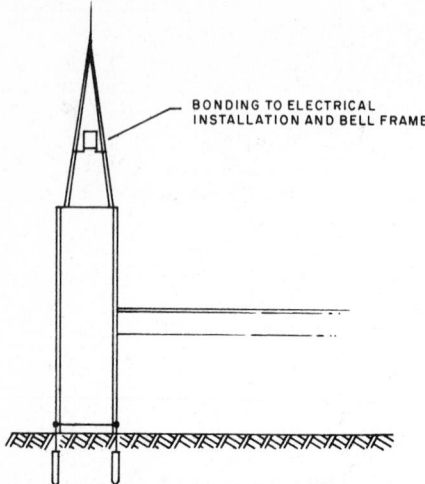

Fig. 15-8H.   An installation of a lightning protection system in a church steeple according to British Code requirements. (Note absence of air terminals on lower-level portion.)

extension of the conductor into the ground where the soil is deep and of high conductivity, to an elaborate buried network where the soil is very dry or of very poor conductivity. Where a network is required, it should be buried if there is soil enough to permit it as this adds to its effectiveness. Its extent will be determined largely by the judgment of the person planning the installation, with due regard to the minimum requirements of the NFPA Lightning Protection Code and keeping in mind that as a rule the more extensive the underground metal available, the more effective the protection.

Structural Steel Buildings

Buildings with structural metal framing may be protected by the installation of air terminals at the high parts of the building, connecting such air terminals to the metal framing, and grounding the framing at the bottom end. This assumes that the structural steel framework is electrically continuous, or is made electrically continuous by bonding.

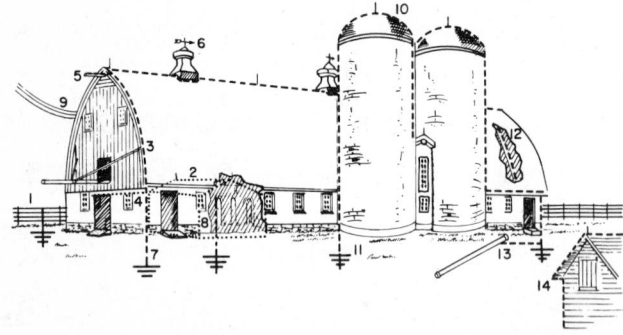

Fig. 15-8I.   Lightning protection system on a typical large barn. The numbers indicate the following features: (1) ground attached wire fence; (2) extend protection to any addition; (3), (4), and (5) show branch conductors to litter, metal-door, and hay tracks; (6) shows air terminal on cupolas, ventilators, etc; (7) indicates ground connection (there should be at least two grounds); (8) illustrates tie-in of metal stanchions; (9) power lines to building need lightning arresters; (10) at least one air terminal should be on each domed silo (at least two on each flat roof or unroofed silo); (11) shows special ground for silo, if required; (12) illustrates connections to vents; and (13) connections to water pipes, and (14) illustrates desirability of protecting adjacent buildings.

Grounding is required from approximately every other steel column around the perimeter, and is arranged so that grounds average not more than 60 ft apart.

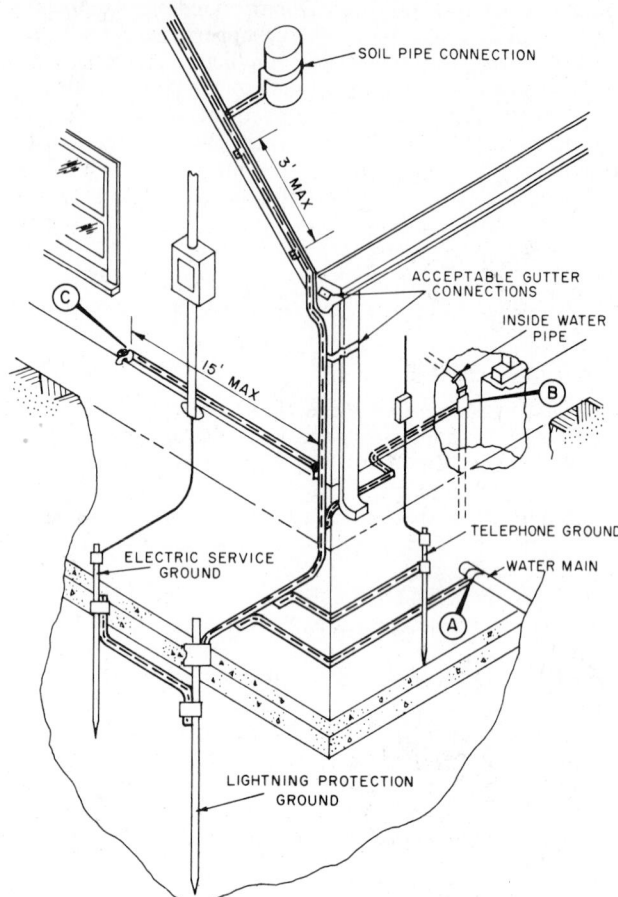

Fig. 15-8J.   Grounding and bonding of lightning down conductors. Water pipe grounds (if pipes are metallic) can be made at A, B, or C.

Reinforced Concrete Structures

Reinforced concrete buildings, in which the reinforcing rods are adequately electrically bonded together and grounded, are of the nature of metal-frame buildings in regard to lightning protection. In usual building practice, as successive reinforcing bars are fitted, they are made to overlap lengthwise with bars already installed, and then are tied together by metal binding wire. With thousands of such connections in a completed framework, the electrical resistance is fully acceptable for the purpose of lightning protection. However, if the reinforcing rods are electrically discontinuous, the building should be treated the same as a building of nonconducting materials. Lightning strokes to reinforced concrete buildings where there are insulating gaps between reinforcing rods are likely to be very destructive by causing cracks at places where beams and floor slabs are connected to their supports. Prestressed concrete buildings are a particular problem. If the wires in precast units are not interconnected (as they frequently are not), individual units are isolated and in event of a lightning charge being induced, serious damage can result.

Metal-roofed and Metal Clad Buildings

Metal-roofed buildings and buildings with both metal roofing and siding are self-protecting in varying degrees, depending upon the continuity (electrically) of the metallic components and their resistance (impedance to the flow of electricity). Buildings which are roofed, or roofed and clad, with metal in the form of sections insulated from one another, or so applied that they are not in electrical contact, are not considered self-protecting against lightning damage. When all metal sheets are made electrically continuous by approved means of interlocking contact or by bonding, the NFPA Lightning Protection Code permits some modification of the standard protection required for ordinary buildings. The Code emphasizes, however, that buildings having metal sidings only—not equipped with standard lightning protection or metal roofs (electrically continuous) of adequate thickness ($\frac{3}{16}$ in.)—shall not be considered protected against lightning, even though such siding is bonded and grounded.

Underwriters Laboratories, Inc., Lightning "Master Label Service"

Underwriters Laboratories, Inc. has had a "Master Label Service" for lightning protection systems since 1923. It provides for both factory inspection and labeling of lightning protection materials, as well as field inspections of a substantial number of installations for which Master Labels have been issued. The service covers the installation of labeled lightning protection materials on all types of structures, with the exception of those used for the production, handling, or storage of ammunition, explosives, flammable liquids or gases, and explosive ingredients. Protection of electrical transmission lines and equipment is also not within the scope of the Master Label Service.

Tanks Containing Flammable and Combustible Liquids and Gases

Tanks containing flammable and combustible liquids or flammable gases stored at atmospheric pressures have been set on fire by lightning. Fires may be started by direct hits which ignite vapors escaping from the tank, or may be started on the roofs of wood-roofed tanks. A lightning stroke in the vicinity may by induction produce sparks which may ignite such vapors. If there are openings in the roof, either intentional or accidental, such as leaving a gage cover open or from corrosion to the tank roof, externally ignited vapors may carry flame inside the tank, possibly resulting in an explosion or fire if there is a flammable or combustible vapor-air mixture inside.

Aboveground tanks storing flammable or combustible liquids or flammable gases at atmospheric pressures are considered to be reasonably well protected against lightning if constructed entirely of steel, and if: (1) all joints between steel plates are riveted, bolted, or welded; (2) all pipes entering the tanks are metallically connected to the tank at point of entrance; (3) all vapor openings are closed or are provided with flame arresters (Class I or II liquids as defined in NFPA No. 321, Standard for Basic Classification of Flammable and Combustible Liquids); (4) if the metal tank and roof have adequate thickness so holes will not be burned through by lightning strokes ($\frac{3}{16}$ in. roof sheets on tanks when built have proved adequate); and (5) the roof is continuously welded to the shell, or bolted, or riveted and caulked, to provide a vapor-tight seam and electrical continuity. Where additional protection is desired, the internal supporting members of the roof may be bonded to the roof at 10-ft intervals, or an overhead ground-wire system or mast protection may be installed (see Fig. 15-8K).

Steel tanks in direct contact with the ground or above-

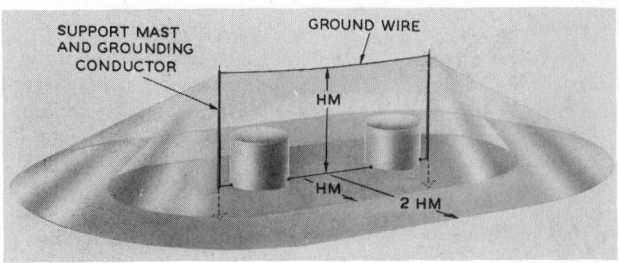

Fig. 15-8K. Zone of protection provided by a horizontal aerial ground wire. "HM" indicates the height of the mast.

ground steel tanks connected to extensive metallic piping systems, properly grounded, are considered to be inherently grounded.

Steel tanks with wooden or other nonmetallic roofs are not considered self-protecting, even if the roofs are essentially vapor-tight or sheathed with thin metal. Such tanks should be protected by air terminals above the roof in sufficient number to receive all discharges, an overhead ground-wire system, or mast protection (see Fig. 15-8K).

Floating roof tanks with hangers located within a vapor space may be protected by bonding the roof to the shoes of the seal at 10-ft intervals around the circumference of the tank and by providing insulated joints or installing jumper bonds around each pinned joint of the hanger mechanism. Based upon experience, floating roof tanks without vapor spaces would not appear to need lightning protective measures.

Aboveground storage tanks or containers of flammable liquids or liquefied petroleum gas under pressure are considered to be safe from lightning-caused explosions since the vapor-air mixture is "too rich" to burn, and the vapor is contained within the tank.

Tall Structures

Church steeples, spires, masts and flagpoles of materials other than metal, and similar tall structures need one or more air terminals extending 10 in. or more above the uppermost point according to the Lightning Protection Code. In Britain, brick-built chimneys are protected by using two down conductors connected at the top to an existing metal cap, or to a circular conductor with no air terminals. Slender structures, such as flagpoles, may be effectively protected by a single down conductor to ground. Where the tall structure is part of a building, as in the case of a church steeple, the down conductor is connected to the conductors protecting the remainder of the building and normally should have two down conductors on opposing sides (see Fig. 15-8J). Metal smokestacks need no protection against lightning other than that afforded by their construction if they are properly grounded.

Trees, Other Specialized Structures, and Facilities

Trees are sometimes provided with lightning protection where they are especially valuable, are of historical significance, overhang buildings, or provide a shelter for livestock. Guidance on the installation of lightning protection is given in the NFPA Lightning Protection Code. Other sections of the Code cover: (1) sailboats, power boats, small boats, and ships; (2) aircraft and aircraft hangars; (3) livestock in fields, and (4) picnic grounds, playgrounds, ball parks, and other open places.

Grounding Metal Masses

Extensive masses of metal which form part of a building or its appurtenances, such as metal ventilators and television or radio antennas, should be bonded to the lightning rod system, or if entirely inside and nowhere within 6 ft of a lightning conductor, they may be independently grounded. Details are given in the Lightning Protection Code. The 6-ft distance mentioned is not universally acceptable with some European codes having different minimum permissible clearances.

Maintenance

Proper maintenance of lightning rods is essential to effective protection. Particular attention should be given to ground connections, as rods may be broken or corroded at the ground level or just below, where the damage is not apparent.

Lightning Arresters on Electrical Apparatus and Circuits

The installation of lightning arresters on power and communication lines where they enter structures and at power utility plants is covered in National Electrical Code Article 280. More detail on the protection of electrical apparatus and circuits against damage due to lightning appears in the Factory Mutual Loss Prevention Data Sheets 5-11/14-19. The use of secondary service arresters on electric services is recommended for buildings equipped with Master Labeled Lightning Protection Systems. Such arresters may be installed at the yard pole, at the outside electric service entrance, or at the interior service entrance box, depending on local regulations. Home lightning protectors are available designed for installation at the dwelling weatherhead or indoors at the service entrance box. These protectors (arresters) drain lightning surge-induced charges harmlessly to ground, and then close to restore electrical service to normal. Before installing a secondary service arrester, it should be determined that the neutral wire is adequately grounded. For installing lightning arresters on television antennas, see Figure 15-8L.

In the United States, except on the Pacific Slope where lightning storms are infrequent, most electric utilities install lightning arresters on the primaries of important transformers on systems of 44,000 volts or less.

D.   Protection of Persons

The lightning hazard is greatest among persons whose occupations keep them outdoors. The probability of injury to the individual from lightning is in general very small,

except under certain circumstances of exposure out of doors. Within buildings of considerable size and dwelling houses of modern construction, cases of injury from lightning are relatively rare. They are more frequent within small unprotected buildings of the older type. Isolated small schoolhouses and small churches where people may congregate during thunderstorms present a considerable lightning hazard if unprotected.

Personal Conduct

Do not go out of doors or remain out during thunderstorms unless it is necessary. Seek shelter inside buildings, vehicles, or other structures or locations which offer protection from lightning.

Seek shelter in the following places which protect personnel from lightning:

1. Large metal or metal-frame buildings.
2. Dwellings or other buildings which are protected by standard lightning protection systems.
3. Large unprotected buildings.
4. Automobiles and buses with metal tops and bodies.
5. Trains and streetcars.
6. Mobile homes or travel trailers with metal bodies.
7. Enclosed metal boats or ships.
8. Boats which are protected against lightning.
9. City streets which are shielded by nearby tall buildings.

If possible, avoid the following places which offer little or no protection from lightning:

1. Small unprotected buildings, barns, sheds, etc.
2. Tents and temporary shelters (not lightning protected).
3. Automobiles (nonmetal-top or open).
4. Recreational vehicles (nonmetal).

Certain locations are extremely hazardous during thunderstorms and should be avoided if at all possible. Approaching thunderstorms should be anticipated, and the following locations avoided when storms are in the immediate vicinity:

1. Tractors and other farm machinery operated in open fields.
2. Golf carts, scooters, motorcycles, and bicycles.
3. Open boats.
4. Open fields (farms).
5. Athletic fields.
6. Golf courses.
7. Swimming pools, lakes, and seashores.
8. Near wire fences, clotheslines, overhead wires, and railroad tracks.
9. Isolated trees.
10. Hilltops and wide open spaces.

It may not always be possible to choose an outdoor location that offers good protection from lightning. Where possible, retreat to either dense woods or depressed areas, avoiding hilltops and high places. If shelter cannot be found, it is best to squat or sit down; if with a group of people, do not crowd together as this involves the risk of a large potential difference across a larger area.

SI Units

The following conversion factors are given as a convenience in converting to SI units the English units used in this chapter.

1 in.   = 25.400 mm
1 ft   =   .305 m
1 mile = 1.609 km

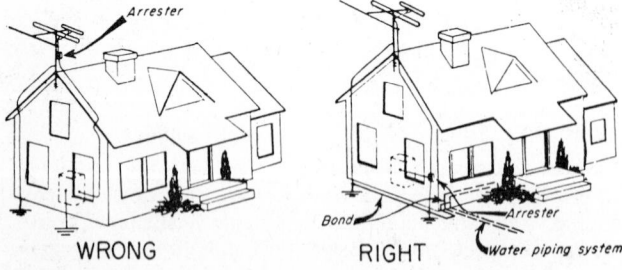

WRONG   RIGHT

Fig. 15-8L. The right and wrong way of installing a lightning arrester. Installation on the antenna mast leaves the receiver virtually unprotected. If, however, the arrester is mounted approximately as near to earth as the receiver, lightning induced charges may be carried to ground efficiently.

Bibliography

NFPA Codes, Standards, and Recommended Practices (see the latest *NFPA Publications and Visual Aids Catalog* for availability of current editions of the following documents)

NFPA No. 78, Lightning Protection Code (ANSI C5.1).

NFPA No. 302, Fire Protection Standard for Motor Craft (ANSI Z120.1).

NFPA No. 70, National Electrical Code (Article 280) (ANSI C1).

Additional Readings

"A Feasibility Study of Improved Lightning Protection Systems," Report No. 64PT146, Aug. 6, 1964, available from Clearinghouse for Federal Scientific and Technical Information, Cameron Station, Alexandria, Va.

"The Protection of Structures Against Lightning," British Standard Code of Practice, CP326, 1965, British Standards Institute.

Electrical Construction Materials List, published annually with bimonthly supplements, Underwriters Laboratories, Inc., Chicago.

FM Loss Prevention Data Sheets, Lightning Arresters and Grounds, 5-11/14-19.

Frydenlund, M. M., "Modern Lightning Protection," *Fire Journal,* Vol. 60, No. 4, July 1966.

Golde, R. H., "Lightning Protection," Edward Arnold (Publishers) Ltd., 25 Hill Street, London, WIX 8LL (ISBN 0 7131 3289 2).

Golde, R. H., "Protection of Structures Against Lightning," Proceedings, The Institution of Electrical Engineers, Vol. 115, No. 10, Oct. 1968.

Hedlund, C. F., "Lightning Protection for Buildings," IEEE *Transactions on Industry and General Applications,* Vol. IGA-3, No. 1, January/February 1967, Institute of Electrical and Electronics Engineers, New York.

Hooker, Dan, "Home Lightning Protection Reduces Fire Danger," *Fire Journal,* Vol. 63, No. 3, May 1969.

Journal of the Franklin Institute, Philadelphia, Vol. 253, No. 5, May 1952, (Special Issue on Lightning Protection).

Ibid., Vol. 274, No. 1, July 1962, "The Protection of Houses by Lightning Conductors—an Historical Review."

Ibid., Vol. 283, No. 6, June 1967, (Special Issue on Lightning Protection).

Lewis, W. W., "The Protection of Transmission Systems Against Lightning," Dover Publications, New York. 1965.

Malan, D. J., "Thunderstorms and Protection Against Lightning," The Institution of Certificated Mechanical and Electrical Engineers, South Africa.

Miller-Hillebrand, D., "Lightning Protection," *Proceedings* of the 3rd International Conference on Problems of Atmospheric and Space Electricity, May 1963.

Peterson, Alvin E., "Lightning Hazards to Mountaineers," The American Alpine Club, New York, 1962.

"The Philosophy of Lightning Protection," *Fire Journal,* Vol. 61, No. 6, Nov. 1967, Boston.

"Service Coles in High Flats; Protection Against Lightning," Design Bulletin No. 3, Part 7, Ministry of Housing and Local Government, Her Majesty's Stationery Office, London, 1967.

Towne, H. M., "Lightning—Its Behavior and What To Do About It," United Lightning Protection Association, Inc., Ithaca, N.Y.

Underwriters Laboratories, Inc., Installation Requirements Master Labeled Lightning Protection Systems, (UL 96A), 8th ed., June 1963, Chicago.

Chapter 9

SPECIAL SYSTEMS AND EXTINGUISHING TECHNIQUES

There are certain fire extinguishing and control systems, agents, devices, and techniques that are used with varying degrees of success which do not fit into the more commonly recognized categories of systems described in previous chapters of this Section. They include: (1) systems using water or water solutions for particular fire control needs, (2) combustion gases used for extinguishment, (3) air agitation for oil tank fire control, (4) agents and techniques for controlling fuel and chemical spills, (5) steam smothering systems, and (6) combined-agent systems. This chapter covers each of them briefly.

A. Specialized Systems Utilizing Water or Water Solutions

A number of specialized systems have been developed to fill particular fire control needs utilizing water or water solutions. These specialized systems divide themselves into three logical subdivisions: (1) ultra-high-speed water spray systems, (2) wetting-agent systems, and (3) viscous-water systems. Most of these systems are "tailor-made" to fill each demand or need.

Ultra-high-speed Water Spray Systems

These systems are designed to handle extremely rapid fires of the type that can occur in the handling of solid propellants, sensitive chemicals, and any industrial process or oxygen-enriched environment possessing this type of fire potential. For further details on ultra-high-speed systems see Chapter 2 of this Section.

Wetting-agent Systems

Most wetting-agent systems (as opposed to the use of wetting agents through manually operated hose lines from mobile tank supplies on through portable proportioners) are designed to dispense wetting agent foam. Each installation's design, volume, and purpose, depends on the hazard being protected. Normally, systems using wetting agents meeting the requirements of NFPA No. 18, Standard for Wetting Agents, can utilize standard water spray, sprinkler, or foam system equipment; however, this should be carefully checked to assure maximum efficiency. The detergent action of a wetting agent solution may introduce some special problems. Wet water foam is an admixture of wet water with air to form a cellular structure foam that breaks down into its original liquid state at temperatures below the boiling point of water. This breakdown is proportional to the heat exposure, and is intended to be sufficient to cool the surface on which the foam is applied. These properties improve the ability of plain water to protect exposed properties against heat transfer, and water requirements are thus appreciably reduced. Wet water systems can introduce the potential of increased water damage to exposed stocks due to the high absorption ability of wet water, and increase the load on any flooring affected because of the retention of large volumes of wet water in such stocks; these factors must be considered in the design phase of such installations.

Viscous ("Thickened") Water Systems

Systems for applying viscous water vary in detailed components, depending on whether the equipment is designed for application from the ground or from aircraft. Most ground applications are from conventional fire tankers with some modifications. The NFPA manual "Chemicals for Forest Fire Fighting[2]" lists the following four basic systems for ground applications:

Injector-recirculating Ground Tanker System: In this system water is drawn from the tank bottom through a centrifugal pump and bypassed through an added return line to the injector-disperser where the liquid and dry powder combine and flow into the tank. The centrifugal pump serves as a mixing device, recirculation continuing until the correct amount of powder is added.

Demand Viscous Water Tanker-mixer: This system consists of an auxiliary mixing tank, an auger feed mechanism, and a positive displacement rotary meter acting as a power unit for the feed system. This system uses the tank, centrifugal pump, and discharge lines of a conventional tanker.

Slip-on Chemical Tanker-mixer: This system is a skid-mounted, all metal unit for mounting onto a heavy duty tractor-trailer for off-road assignments. The major assemblies consist of a mixing tank, chemical hopper, hose reel, engine, pump, and pump priming tank.

Trailer-mounted Sprayer-mixer (Modified for Certain Long-term Retardants): This system has only been used experimentally utilizing a modified ordinary agricultural sprayer.

Nozzles used for viscous water or light gels are conventional fire nozzles. Fine-fog nozzles should be avoided, but those giving coarse droplets normally give satisfactory results. Screens are removed. Slurry-type fire-retardant chemicals need special nozzles because most conventional nozzles of brass and aluminum erode quickly; cast alumina inserts (a ceramic aluminum oxide) seem to be satisfactory, however, and can be made inexpensively.

The NFPA manual "Chemicals for Forest Fire Fighting" gives additional helpful information on equipment for mixing the chemicals, pumps for handling the chemicals, distribution systems, storage of mixed and unmixed chemicals, and means for judging the quality of the solutions in the field.

"Air Operations for Forest, Brush, and Grass Fires[3]," another NFPA manual, contains information on the use of aircraft for fire control operations. This manual covers: air operations plans; airports, heliports, and helistops; suitable aircraft; operating principles and procedures; and amphibious operations. Special equipment is needed to utilize aircraft for these purposes, and the manual should be reviewed for details.

B. Use of Combustion Gases for Fire Extinguishment

For many years carbon dioxide and, to a lesser extent, nitrogen and helium have been used as extinguishing agents (see Sec. 13, Chap. 3). Carbon dioxide extinguishes fires by reducing the concentrations of oxygen and/or the gaseous phase of the fuel in the air to the point where combustion stops. It has thus been long recognized that fires can be extinguished if a sufficient volume of an inert gas is introduced into an enclosed space where a fire is burning, and if this concentration can be retained for an adequate period of time to prevent reflash or rekindling of the burning material.

Experiments have been conducted on the use of the gases of combustion to achieve similar results. In this work, inert gas was generated by an experimental turbo-jet engine specially designed for the test work. The engine burned most of the oxygen in the air it used, and the hot combustion gases were cooled by vaporizing water introduced as a fine spray. The most efficient inert gas produced by this experimental appliance contained 46 percent nitrogen, 44 percent water vapor, 3 percent carbon dioxide, and 7 percent oxygen. The highest rate of delivery used was 45,000 cfm when the appliance consumed 70 imperial gallons per minute of water and 6.5 imperial gallons per minute of kerosine. The emergent gas was cooled to 90° to 120°C (194° to 248°F). In this experimental work either the inert gas alone was used, or a high-expansion foam was made with the inert gas. By spraying a solution of a suitable detergent on a screen, and blowing the inert gas through the wetted screen at a velocity not exceeding 5 fps, an inert gas high-expansion foam was generated with an expansion ratio of 1,000 to 1. Between 50 and 80 percent of the gas was made into foam. To convey the gas or foam to the fire site, a flexible ducting was used (made of Terylene with a neoprene coating to make it impermeable).

A Canadian proposal for a gas turbine to generate inert gas for fire fighting calls for air compression, followed by substantially stoichiometric combustion to reduce the oxygen content to nearly zero, and a massive pre-turbine injection of water which, on evaporation, would cool the gases to the lowest temperature at which the cycle would operate. After further cooling by passing the combustion products through a work turbine (which would drive the compressor), the inert gases could be ducted into a burning building or space.

C. Air Agitation for Oil Tank Fire Control

A fire in an oil storage tank may, under some conditions, be controlled or extinguished by introducing air under pressure near the bottom of the tank. The principle is founded upon the fact that flammable and combustible liquids require a temperature greater than their flash point temperature to sustain burning. If a tank of oil having a flash point above the actual temperature of the liquid itself becomes ignited when the temperature at the surface is raised above the flash point, or the oil itself has become contaminated with a low flash point liquid, the resulting fire may be controlled or extinguished by agitation of the oil mass. By agitating the oil mass, cool oil, circulated at a proper rate, decreases the temperature of the oil burning at the surface by displacement and mixing to a point below its flash point, thus slowing or inhibiting further combustion. The time element during which such control operations must be actively pursued is critical; if the oil mass heats too excessively, the cooling effect might not be adequate, and if the burning liquid is crude oil, the time before boiling occurs can be shortened considerably. This technique is not considered a standard method of combating oil tank fires. Under most circumstances, where fire protection is provided for such storage tanks, foam fire fighting equipment, meeting the recommendations contained in NFPA No. 11, Standard for Foam Extinguishing Systems, is employed.

D. Handling Spilled Fuels and Chemicals

Emulsifying Agents—Detergents

Various types of emulsifying agents or detergents have been used with varying degrees of success in extinguishing or controlling flammable liquid spill fires either on land or on water. These agents also have been used on unignited spills of such liquids to minimize the hazard of possible ignition. In general, these agents mix the oil and water to form an emulsion which is not combustible. A major problem with the use of emulsifying agents and detergents in lakes, rivers, harbors, etc., is that the resultant emulsions often have a more severe effect on aquatic forms of life than does oil alone; however, relatively nontoxic emulsifying agents may be developed.

Removal of Spills

Spills of hazardous liquids or chemicals, either on land or water, preferably should be confined and removed either by vacuum trucks or pumps. If spills on land enter sewer systems, the sewage disposal plant should be notified immediately. If the spills are on water, particularly on rivers from which municipalities derive their drinking water, all agencies concerned should be notified. Water soluble chemicals can be, of course, a particularly difficult problem from a health and safety viewpoint.

Booming of Spills on Water and Removal of Contaminants

Booming of spills has been proven effective in containing spills of liquids on relatively calm and current-free waters. Various makeshift designs of booms have been tried with relative ineffectiveness, but commercially available booms, which recognize the hydrodynamics and aerodynamics involved in the confinement of spills on water, have proven quite effective.

Following confinement of spills on water, various ways of removing the confined oil have been used, including skimming devices or absorbents. Absorbents such as straw, plastics, sawdust, and peat moss have been spread on the surface of the spill and then collected and burned on shore. Skimming devices operate on several principles, including pumps and separators, and power boats with skimmers on the bow which scoop up oil and water sending it through an oil separator and rollers to which oil adheres; the oil is then removed by scraping or compression.

Sinking agents to which oil may adhere and sink to the bottom have been utilized in the past. Several proprietary sinking agents have been developed, but such products as carbonized sand, brick dust, crushed clinkers, and cement also have been utilized. However, sinking agents are objectionable as they contribute to water pollution and are no longer recommended, except possibly for use in the ocean far from land.

Regardless of whether a spill occurs on land or on water, preplanning is imperative and should include prompt notification of all local, state, or federal agencies dealing with the problem of water pollution.

E. Steam Smothering Systems

The principle by which steam may smother a fire is similar to the manner inert gases may achieve the same result; e.g., reducing the concentrations of oxygen and/or the gaseous phase of the fuel in the air to the point where combustion stops. The use of steam systems for fire extinguishment precedes the use of such other modern smothering systems as carbon dioxide and foam extinguishing systems, and is rarely used today. It is clearly not a practical method to employ except where a large steam supply is continuously available, and where arrangements have been made so that this supply can be effectively and efficiently tapped when a fire emergency arises. The possible personal injury hazard of burns must be considered in any steam extinguishing installation.

Steam extinguishing systems are not recommended in any current NFPA Standards for fire protection purposes, although NFPA No. 86A, Standard for Industrial Furnaces, Design, Location, and Equipment, does offer in an appendix suggestions on steam systems which may be followed "where steam flooding is the only alternative" for fire protection after considering automatic sprinklers or water spray systems and approved types of supplementary fire protection (carbon dioxide, foam, or dry chemical systems). To protect ovens, the guidance given in this Standard calls for steam outlets to supply at least 8 lbs of steam per min for each 100 cu ft of oven volume. (One pound of saturated steam at 212°F and normal atmosphere pressure has a volume of 26.75 cu ft.) Steam outlets should be located near the bottom of the oven, but may be located at the top, pointing downward, if the oven is not over 20 ft high. Pipe sizes and the steam supply should be sufficient to deliver the required amount of steam and maintain a pressure of at least 15 psi at the outlet. Following is a formula for the discharge of steam:

$$W = 0.7A \ (P \text{ plus } 15)$$

where: W is pounds of steam per minute, 0.7 is the coefficient of discharge, A is the area of discharge opening in square inches, and P is the gage pressure of steam at outlet in pounds per square inch. One pound of steam per minute is equivalent to two boiler horsepower. The Standard recommends that release devices for such systems be manual, and that controls be arranged to close down oven outlets as far as practicable. Additional guidance offered includes arrangements to reduce hazards to personnel.

Steam smothering systems used to be employed for the protection of cargo spaces and the holds of steamships. This method is no longer recommended. Tests indicating the relative inefficiency of such systems to control cotton cargo fires were conducted by the U.S. Coast Guard during the period 1944–1946 ("Operation Phobos").[4]

F.   Combined-agent Systems

To take advantage of the best qualities of any two agents in the interest of achieving fast fire control and permanent extinguishment, it is common practice in fire fighting to use two or more agents simultaneously or in rapid sequence. Some common combinations used in manual fire control work include: (1) water (usually water spray) and foam; (2) carbon dioxide and foam; and (3) certain dry chemicals and foam. Aircraft rescue and fire fighting operations (see Sec. 17, Chap. 1) have long utilized such "combined agent" methods using water spray, carbon dioxide, or dry chemical to secure rapid flame "knock-down" plus the simultaneous or sequential use of foam as a permanent smothering agent. During World War II the combined use of bulk applications of carbon dioxide from mobile low-pressure carbon dioxide trucks with simultaneous applications of foam from specialized crash trucks achieved many significant personnel rescues in aircraft fire accidents, as well as achieving quick fire extinguishment or control. This technique is still being used, as is the combined use of foam-compatible dry chemicals and foam. While these techniques do involve simultaneous and/or sequential use of two agents, each agent system is independent of the other, most often on separate mobile vehicles.

Recent developments involving "dual-agent systems" combine (1) "light water" (see this Section, Chapter 3) with potassium salt based dry chemical, or (2) mechanical (air) foam with potassium salt based dry chemical, providing the foam is compatible with dry chemical. These systems are systems in the sense that they are designed to give a balanced discharge of the agents, although the agents themselves are not premixed. The two agents are discharged through independent but "twinned" nozzles (both nozzles independent but under the control of one fire fighter). Some experimental work has been done with encouraging results by "entraining" certain dry chemicals in the water-foam concentrate turret stream. Developments of such dual agent systems are continuing, and the bibliography contains references to some of the current technical papers on the subject.

SI Units

The following conversion factors are given as a convenience in converting to SI units the English units used in this chapter.

1 sq in.	=	645.160 mm²
1 sq ft	=	.929 m²
1 cu ft	=	16.018 kg/m³
1 in.	=	25.400 mm
1 ft	=	.305 m
1 lb (mass)	=	.454 kg
1 psi	=	6.895 kPa
$\frac{5}{9}$ (°F − 32)	=	°C
1 gal (U.S.)	=	3.785 litres
1 gpm	=	3.785 litre/min

Bibliography

References Cited

[1] *Fire Protection Equipment List,* published annually with bi-monthly supplements, Underwriters Laboratories, Inc., Chicago.

[2] "Chemicals for Forest Fire Fighting," 2nd ed., 1967, A Report of the NFPA Forest Committee, NFPA, Boston.

[3] "Air Operations for Forest, Brush, and Grass Fires," rev. ed., 1975, A Report of the NFPA Forest Committee, NFPA, Boston.

[4] *Proceedings* of the Fifty-First Annual Meeting of the National Fire Protection Association, May 26-29, 1947, pp. 119–123.

NFPA Codes, Standards, and Recommended Practices (see the latest *NFPA Publications and Visual Aids Catalog* for availability of current editions of the following documents)

NFPA No. 11, Standard for Foam Extinguishing Systems.

NFPA No. 18, Standard for Wetting Agents.

NFPA No. 12A, Standard for Halogenated Agent Extinguishing Systems, Halon 1301.

NFPA No. 86A, Standard for Industrial Furnaces, Design, Location, and Equipment.

NFPA No. 403, Standard for Aircraft Rescue and Fire Fighting Services at Airports and Heliports.

NFPA No. 414, Standard for Aircraft Rescue and Fire Fighting Vehicles.

Additional Readings

Ault, Wayne E., "Automatic Water Deluge Systems for Exotic Fire Protection Applications," NFPA *Quarterly,* Vol. 57, No. 4, April 1964, pp. 399–405.

Averill, Charles F., and Kazarian, Haik R., "Ultra High Speed Fire Protection System for Solid Propellants," Reprint of a presentation given by Mr. Averill at the Fourth Explosives Safety Seminar on High Energy Solid Propellants (Available from Grinnell Company, Inc., Providence, R.I. 02901).

Downing, A. G., and Fassuliotis, William, "Air Agitation Tests in Arabia," NFPA *Quarterly,* Vol. 48, No. 1, July 1954, pp. 61–68.

Eggleston, Lester A., "Evaluation of Fire Extinguishing Systems for Use in Oxygen Rich Atmospheres," Final Report, May 18, 1967, Southwest Research Institute, San Antonio, Texas (SWRI Project 3-2094, Prepared for Aerospace Medical Division, Brooks AFB, Texas).

Hutchinson, J. H., "Automation—Its Influence on Fire Protection," NFPA *Quarterly,* Vol. 50, No. 1, July 1956, pp. 23–26.

Jensen, Rolf H., "Compatibility of Mechanical Foam and Dry Chemical," NFPA *Quarterly,* Vol. 57, No. 3, Jan. 1964, pp. 296–303.

Meldrum, Donald N., "Research on Combined Use of Foam and Dry Chemical," NFPA *Quarterly,* Vol. 56, No. 1, July 1962, pp. 28–34.

Meldrum, Donald N., and Williams, J. R., "Dry Chemical Compatible Foam," *Fire Journal,* Vol. 59, No. 6, Nov. 1965, pp. 18–22.

Peterson, H. B., "New Light-Water Development," NFPA Meeting Paper 67–4, 1967, National Fire Protection Association, Boston, Mass.

Rasbash, Dr. D. J., "New Developments in Fire Fighting Equipment," Reprint from "The Official Papers and Discussions of the International Fire Conference" by *Fire Protection Review,* Benn Brothers, Ltd., London.

Risinger, J. L., "Extinguishing Oil Tank Fires by Agitation," NFPA *Quarterly,* Vol. 46, No. 1, July 1952, pp. 83–92.

Robertson, W. D., "Protection at Seattle Tacoma International Airport," NFPA Aviation Bulletin No. 314, NFPA, Boston, Mass.

Stark, G. W. V., "Use of Jet Engine for Fire Fighting," Reprint from *The Institute of Fire Engineers Quarterly,* 1966.

Tuve, Richard L., "Light Water and Potassium Bicarbonate Dry Chemical—a New Two-Agent Extinguishing System," NFPA *Quarterly,* Vol. 58, No. 1, July 1964, pp. 64–69.

Wilder, Ira, "A Dual-Agent Fire Extinguishing System," *Fire Journal,* Vol. 60, No. 6, Nov. 1966, pp. 10–12, 45.

Wilson, Rexford, and Ledoux, Edward F., "High-Speed Protection for Personnel in Oxygen-Enriched Atmospheres," *Fire Journal,* Vol. 62, No. 2, March 1968, pp. 23–26.

SECTION 16

PORTABLE FIRE EXTINGUISHERS

Chapter 1

THE ROLE OF EXTINGUISHERS IN FIRE PROTECTION

Virtually all fires are small at origin and could be easily extinguished provided the proper type and appropriate amount of extinguishing agent were readily available and promptly applied. Portable fire extinguishers are designed to fulfill this need.

Fire extinguishers are the first line of defense against unfriendly fires, and their need should be established irrespective of other fire control measures.

A. Historical Background

The first real portable fire extinguishers were developed in the late 1800s. They were soda-acid devices, originally constructed with glass bottles of acid which, when broken, dumped the acid into cylinders containing soda solution. The resulting chemical action produced sufficient gas pressure to expel the solution.

Cartridge-operated water extinguishers were introduced in the late 1920s. Because they contained a calcium chloride solution which enabled them to be installed in unheated areas, cartridge-operated extinguishers had the advantage over soda-acid extinguishers. In 1928 a nonfreeze alkali-metal salt solution called "loaded stream" was developed for use in cartridge-operated extinguishers. In 1959 stored-pressure water extinguishers were developed. Although greatly superior to soda-acid and cartridge-operated water extinguishers from both operational and maintenance standpoints, it took more than 10 years for stored-pressure extinguishers to gain wide recognition. Gradually, stored-pressure loaded stream extinguishers replaced cartridge-operated models.

During 1917 the foam extinguisher was developed (see Sec. 13, Chap. 2). By mixing in water an alkaline salt solution with an acid salt solution, it was possible to produce a cooling and smothering extinguishing agent for use on normal combustible solids and flammable liquid fires. Originally, to improve foam stability, powdered animal glue was added to the alkaline salt solution. Later, the animal glue was replaced with an extract of licorice.

The physical appearance and operating characteristics of the foam extinguisher closely resembled the soda-acid extinguisher. However, upon discharge, the foam solution was able to expand (by a ratio of approximately 8 to 1) into a thick, sudsy layer. The use of foam extinguishers steadily increased over the years until, during the 1950s, dry chemical extinguishers gained widespread acceptance.

In 1969 the manufacture of all inverting type extinguishers (soda-acid, foam, and cartridge-operated loaded stream) was discontinued in the United States. These extinguishers are no longer listed or approved by testing laboratories. Information on their use, operational characteristics, and maintenance is contained in Chapter 3 of this Section.

Vaporizing Liquids

One of the earliest (1908) chemicals to be employed in portable fire extinguishers was carbon tetrachloride (CCl_4). The vapors of CCl_4 proved to be quite toxic, and when used on a fire the more toxic decomposition products of hydrogen chloride and phosgene resulted. After World War II a similar but slightly less toxic agent, chlorobromomethane (CH_2ClBr), was introduced, and the term "vaporizing liquid" was used to designate extinguishers of this type. In the early 1950s a number of Federal agencies banned their use for toxological reasons. This action, coupled with the availability of more suitable extinguishing agents, resulted in their rapid decline. By the mid-1960s the Federal Government, many states, cities, and numerous industrial firms no longer permitted the use of any type of vaporizing liquid extinguisher. In the late 1960s listings by testing laboratories were discontinued.

Liquefied Gases

Although vaporizing liquids proved to be unacceptable as extinguishing agents, other less toxic halogenated hydrocarbon chemicals, in the form of liquefied gases, are being used increasingly (see Sec. 13, Chap. 4). Bromotrifluoromethane (Halon 1301) was first introduced in 1954 as a high pressure liquefied gas extinguisher for use on fires in flammable and combustible liquids and on live electrical equipment. Although it bears some resemblance to a small CO_2 extinguisher, it is lighter in weight and has a disposable shell which contains $2\frac{3}{4}$ lbs of agent. A low pressure liquefied gas extinguisher utilizing bromochlorodifluoromethane (Halon 1211) became available in 1973, and by 1974 was being manufactured in a full range of sizes. In 1974 it had an initial UL (Underwriters Laboratories, Inc.) listing for flammable liquid and electrical fires, and tests conducted at that time indicated considerable potential for use on fires in ordinary combustibles.

In 1974 extensive testing was being conducted on extinguishers containing dibromotetrafluoromethane (Halon 2402), which is a liquid at room temperature. The tests indicated a potential for using the extinguishers on all different types of fires (ordinary combustibles, flammable liquids and gases, and electrical equipment).

Carbon Dioxide

The first carbon dioxide extinguishers were produced during World War I (see Sec. 13, Chap. 3). During World War II they became the leading extinguisher for flammable liquid fires; however, by 1950 their lead was relinquished to the dry chemical agents.

Dry Chemicals

Although the fire extinguishing capabilities of sodium bicarbonate were first recognized in the late 1800s, it wasn't until 1928 that an effective cartridge-operated dry chemical extinguisher was developed (see Sec. 13, Chap. 5). Considerable developmental work took place during the early 1940s, and an improved, finely granulated agent was introduced in 1943. In 1947 the original extinguisher was replaced with an improved model that utilized the new agent to its best advantage.

The rapid increase in the use of flammable liquids and chemicals and their associated process hazards brought about the development of many new dry chemical agents with greater "fire killing" power. The first was a potassium bicarbonate base agent (in 1959) which was about twice as effective as the sodium bicarbonate ("ordinary") base agent.

Multipurpose Dry Chemical

Next (in 1961) came a new type of agent called "multipurpose" dry chemical. In addition to being about 50 percent more effective on flammable liquid and electrical fires, multipurpose dry chemical was also listed as an effective agent on fires in ordinary combustibles. Originally, the less expensive diammonium phosphate was used; however, preference soon shifted to monoammonium phosphate because it had the advantage of being considerably less hygroscopic.

An agent utilizing potassium chloride as a base was first marketed in 1968. Compared to ordinary dry chemical it was about 80 percent more effective, but more corrosive and more hygroscopic than potassium bicarbonate. A urea-potassium bicarbonate base agent was developed in Europe in 1967 and brought to America in 1970. Its comparable effectiveness is judged to be at least 2½ times better than "ordinary" dry chemical.

The first stored-pressure model (rechargeable type) was introduced in 1953; a disposable (nonrechargeable) model first appeared in 1959 and was rapidly adopted for use in dwellings, cars, boats, etc.

Dry Powder

The increased use of combustible metals (magnesium, sodium, lithium, etc.) brought about the need for a special agent to extinguish fires in these materials (see Sec. 13, Chap. 6). In 1950 the first dry powder extinguisher using a sodium chloride base agent was introduced. The designation "dry powder" was specifically adopted to indicate suitability for Class D (combustible metal) fires only, and to clearly establish the differentiation that "dry chemical" would only apply to Class B:C fires or Class A:B:C fires in ordinary combustibles, flammable liquids, and electrical equipment.

B. Reliability and Design Safety of Fire Extinguishers

Portable fire extinguishers may not be operated for many years. When they are used, reliability is essential and they must function with maximum efficiency and without hazard to users. It is also essential that extinguishers be selected with consideration being given to the type, size, and intensity of any fires that might be encountered. Since most extinguishers are designed as pressure vessels, they are subject to possible rupture if the shell is not properly designed, constructed, and maintained. Extinguisher design safety, basically the responsibility of the manufacturer, is determined by the standards, performance testing, inspection, and labeling procedures of the responsible fire testing laboratories. Once an extinguisher is placed into service, it is the owner's responsibility to maintain it during its life cycle: the owner may require the assistance of a qualified service company.

In North America, nationally recognized fire testing laboratories have developed construction standards for portable fire extinguishers. These laboratories evaluate extinguishers with reproducible test procedures. The National Fire Protection Association promulgates an installation standard for extinguishers, NFPA No. 10, Standard for the Installation, Maintenance, and Use of Portable Fire Extinguishers, hereinafter referred to in this chapter as the NFPA Extinguisher Standard. The standard is widely adopted by property owners and enforcing officials, partly based on the results of the tests.

To assist purchasers of extinguishers in the United States and Canada, UL (Underwriters Laboratories, Inc.) ULC (Underwriters Laboratories of Canada), and FM (Factory Mutual System) authorize manufacturers to affix a label to extinguishers which have been constructed in accordance with specific standards, and which have successfully passed the fire tests prescribed for each type of extinguisher. UL and ULC also require periodic examinations of, and tests on, samples of extinguishers taken from current production and/or stock to ensure continuing compliance with construction standards. FM requires periodic follow-up inspections of the manufacturer's facilities and quality control procedures to ensure that "approval" standards are maintained. NFPA standards call for the use of listed or approved extinguishers, and most responsible authorities and property owners rely on this requirement to determine the acceptability of the devices selected.

C. Relation of Extinguishers to Classes of Fires

To facilitate proper use of extinguishers on different types of fires, the NFPA Extinguisher Standard has classified fires into the following four types:

Class A: Fires involving ordinary combustible materials (such as wood, cloth, paper, rubber, and many plastics) requiring the heat-absorbing (cooling) effects of water, water solutions, or the coating effects of certain dry chemicals which retard combustion.

Class B: Fires involving flammable or combustible liquids, flammable gases, greases, and similar materials where extinguishment is most readily secured by excluding air (oxygen), inhibiting the release of combustible vapors, or interrupting the combustion chain reaction.

Class C: Fires involving live electrical equipment where safety to the operator requires the use of electrically nonconductive extinguishing agents. (Note: when electrical equipment is deenergized, the use of Class A or B extinguishers may be indicated.)

Class D: Fires involving certain combustible metals (such as magnesium, titanium, zirconium, sodium, potassium, etc.) requiring a heat-absorbing extinguishing medium not reactive with the burning metals.

Some portable fire extinguishers are of primary value on only one class of fire; some are suitable on two or three classes; none is suitable for all four classes of fire.

Most currently manufactured extinguishers are labeled with a classification system so that users may quickly identify the class of fire for which a particular extinguisher may be used. The classification system is contained in the NFPA Extinguisher Standard which gives the applicable class symbol (or symbols) with supplementary words to recall the meaning of the letters (see Fig. 16-1A). Color coding is also used. UL and ULC require the classification system on their labels.

Numerals are used with the identifying letters for extinguishers labeled for Class A and Class B fires. The

ORDINARY COMBUSTIBLES   FLAMMABLE LIQUIDS   ELECTRICAL EQUIPMENT   COMBUSTIBLE METALS

Fig. 16-1A. Markings for extinguishers indicating classes of fires on which they should be used. Color coding is part of the identification system, and the triangle (Class A) is colored green, the square (Class B) red, the circle (Class C) blue, and the five-pointed star (Class D) yellow.

"numeral" indicates the relative extinguishing effectiveness of the device. For example, on an extinguisher rated for Class A fires, the rating and numeral that precedes the letter "A" indicates the size of standard test fires the device is able to extinguish successfully under reproducible laboratory conditions. On an extinguisher rated for Class B fires, the rating numeral that precedes the "B" gives a proportionate indication of the maximum square foot area of a flammable liquid fire of appreciable depth ($\frac{1}{4}$ in.) which can be protected.

No rating numerals are used for extinguishers labeled for Class C fires. Since electrical equipment has either Class A or Class B combustibles, or both, as part of its construction, the type of Class C rated extinguisher selected should be based on the construction features of the electrical equipment protected and the nature and amount of the combustibles in the immediate vicinity.

Extinguishers rated for Class D fires likewise have no rating numeral. The effectiveness of each listed extinguisher on specific combustible metals is detailed on the nameplate of the device.

Extinguishers that are effective on more than one class of fire have multiple "letter" and "numeral-letter" classifications and ratings. These are shown on the labels applied by UL and ULC to each extinguisher, and in the published lists issued by these organizations. Fractional ratings are not recognized in the NFPA Extinguisher Standard and are not issued by UL.

Extinguishers produced by different manufacturers, or even by the same manufacturer, having the same quantity of the same extinguishing agent, sometimes get different ratings. All are tested on the same basis to determine their relative extinguishing capability, with the differences in performance influenced by extinguisher design characteristics (including rates of discharge, nozzle design, discharge patterns, etc.).

D. Extinguisher Testing by UL

UL and ULC use a series of reproducible fire tests for evaluating fire extinguisher performance. The classification system contained in the NFPA Extinguisher Standard is used to report test results. Full details of the tests are contained in UL Standard 711, Rating and Fire Testing of Fire Extinguishers.

Tests for Class A Ratings

In determining Class A ratings, three tests are used for extinguishers rated 1-A to 6-A. They are the wood-crib fire test, wood-panel fire test, and the excelsior fire test. For extinguishers having a Class 10-A and higher rating, only the wood-crib fire test is used.

The Wood-crib Fire Test: This test consists of layers of nominal 2 by 2-in. or 2 by 4-in. kiln-dried spruce or fir lumber of a specified moisture content arranged as shown in Figure 16-1B. The length, size, and number of individual wood members and their arrangement are varied to test the capability of the extinguishers. For example, a wood-crib test fire for a 1-A rating has 50 wood members, a 2-A has 78, a 4-A has 120, and a 40-A (the largest) has 224. The number of wood members and the nominal size and length of each increase as higher ratings are secured. The crib is ignited by burning n-Heptane in a pan placed symmetrically under the vertical axis of the crib. The size of the square pans and the amount of n-Heptane used increase with the size of the cribs (i.e., from $\frac{1}{4}$ gal for a 1-A test to 10 gal for a 40-A test). Freeburn times are standardized as well as

Fig. 16-1B. *A wood crib as used by UL for Class A fire tests.* (Underwriters Laboratories, Inc.)

methods of recording observations. The tests are conducted indoors in a draft-free room, or outdoors in essentially still air. (Fig. 16-1C)

The Wood-panel Fire Test: This test is conducted indoors and consists of a solid square wood-panel backing on which are applied two horizontal sections of furring strips spaced apart and away from the panel by vertical furring strips. This provides for a large vertical surface area of wood subject to combustion. A typical panel is illustrated in Figure 16-1D. The panel sizes vary from 64 sq ft for the 1-A test fire to 100 sq ft for a 2-A, 144 sq ft for a 3-A, 196 sq ft for a 4-A, and 289 sq ft for a 6-A. All lumber used is kiln dried to a specified moisture content. In front of the panels, four separate and equal windrows of excelsior (seasoned basswood, poplar, or aspen) are laid, with the first windrow directly at the base of the test panel and the other three held in reserve about 10 ft from the front of the panel. The amount of excelsior varies from 10 to 60 lbs for the 1-A to 6-A test fires. Fuel oil is used to soak the excelsior, and a small amount of n-Heptane is used as a fuse. The three windrows of excelsior are pushed up to the base of the panel at 45-sec intervals during the preburn period. At 3 min, 20 sec all the remaining excelsior is cleared away. The extinguishant is applied after the furring strips have fallen away from not less than 10 ft of the face of the test panel.

Fig. 16-1C. *A fire test with a wheeled extinguisher containing a multipurpose (ammonium-phosphate based) dry chemical on a Class A (wood crib) fire.* (The Ansul Company)

Fig. 16-1D. A typical wood panel used by UL to test extinguishers designed for use on Class A (ordinary combustibles) fires. (Underwriters Laboratories, Inc.)

The Excelsior Fire Test: This test utilizes new and seasoned materials in a dry state which are pulled apart and spread evenly and loosely over a prescribed test area, and then packed to a depth of 1 ft (see Fig. 16-1E). The area covered varies from 6 lbs of excelsior spread 2 ft, 10 in. by 5 ft, 8 in. for the 1-A test, to 36 lbs of excelsior spread 6 ft, 11 in. by 13 ft, 11 in. for the 6-A test. The material is ignited by a small fuse of n-Heptane, and the fire attack is begun from a distance of not less than 15 ft.

Tests for Class B Ratings

In determining Class B ratings, the flammable liquid test fires consist of burning n-Heptane in square steel pans not less than 8 in. in depth and varying in size. Figure 16-1F illustrates a typical test pan. Tests for portable extinguishers receiving ratings up to and including 20-B are conducted indoors in an essentially draft-free room. (There are five ratings: 1-B, 2-B, 5-B, 10-B, and 20-B.) Tests for higher rated devices are conducted outdoors under conditions of essentially still air and no precipitation. For an extinguisher to become eligible for a given classification and rating, the specified test fires must be extinguished repeatedly and each test conducted by starting with a fully charged extinguisher. The selected data given in Table 16-1A provide further insight into the UL's Class B fire test procedures.

Tests for Class C Ratings

In determining a Class C designation, the extinguishing agent is tested for electrical conductivity only, although no

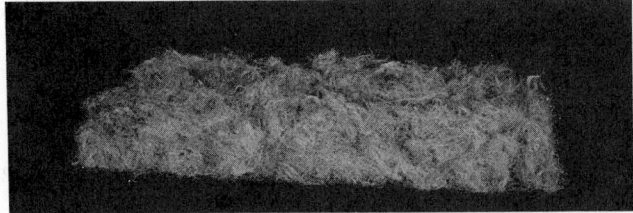

Fig. 16-1E. Excelsior prepared for the Class A fire extinguisher test as used by UL. (Underwriters Laboratories, Inc.)

Fig. 16-1F. A typical pan arrangement for UL testing of Class B extinguishers. (Underwriters Laboratories, Inc.)

Class C rating is provided unless the extinguisher has an established Class A or Class B, or both, rating. The discharge of the agent from the extinguisher under the test condition must not increase the electrical conductivity, as measured by a milliammeter, through a 10-in. air gap established between an electrically insulated extinguisher and a grounding plate, at a potential of 100,000 V, 60 cycle ac. Figure 16-1G shows the test setup used by UL. Each extinguisher is operated for 20 sec, discharging the agent against the target with the potential of 100,000 V impressed between the extinguisher and the target. The condition is then checked for an additional 15 sec discharge with each type of horn or nozzle utilized. In at least one test, the target plate is heated to an initial temperature of 700°F prior to the discharge of the extinguisher. All tests must show no meter readings.

Tests for Class D Ratings

In Class D tests, fire extinguishers must be capable of extinguishing combustible metal test fires as designated by the testing laboratory for a given metal. The burning metal must not be scattered beyond the test-bed area during the test. An extinguished test fire must not be subject to reignition after the test, and there must be sufficient unburned combustible metal remaining to show extinguishment by the agent prior to burnout. In addition, studies are made with respect to toxicity of the agent as well as of the liberated fumes and products of combustion when used on combustible metal fires. Possible reactions which might occur between the burning metals and the agents must be evaluated to assure safe usage.

Table 16-1A.   UL Class B Fire Test Procedures

Classification and Rating of Extinguishers	Minimum Effective Discharge Time (Seconds)	Inside Pan Size (Square Feet Inside)	n-Heptane U.S. Gallons (Approximate)
Indoor Tests			
1–B	8	2½	3¼
2–B	8	5	6¼
5–B	8	12½	15½
10–B	8	25	31
20–B	8	50	65
Outdoor Tests			
40–B	13	100	125
80–B	20	200	250
160–B	31	400	500
320–B	48	800	1,000
640–B	75	1,600	2,000

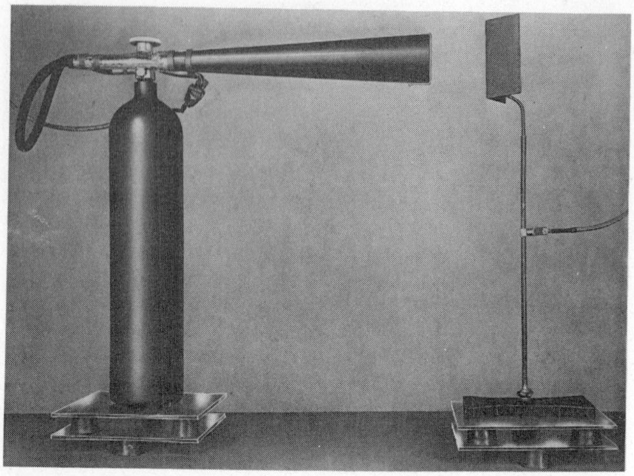

Fig. 16-1G. Test setup for evaluating electrical conductivity. (Underwriters Laboratories, Inc.)

Conversion of Old Extinguisher Ratings

In 1955 the NFPA Committee on Portable Fire Extinguishers revised the method of rating fire extinguishers to that described herein. Many extinguishers manufactured prior to 1955 are still in use and bear the classifications in effect prior to that year. To give present-day users of Class A extinguishers labeled under the old system an approximate classification under the existing present rating system, Table 16-1B can be used.

To give present-day users of Class B listed extinguishers labeled under the pre-1955 system and the system used between 1955 and June 1, 1969 an approximate classification, a conversion, using Tables 16-1B and 16-1C is necessary.

E. Extinguisher Testing by FM

FM approves and labels extinguishers submitted to it which have met its performance requirements. They conduct comprehensive tests of the same general type as those

Table 16-1B. Conversion of Extinguisher Classifications Pre-1955 to June 1, 1969

Extinguishing Agent	Extinguisher Type and Size	Pre-1955 UL Classification	Classification 1955 to June 1, 1969
Chemical Solution (Soda-Acid)	$1\frac{1}{4}$, $1\frac{1}{2}$ gallon	A-2	1-A
	$2\frac{1}{2}$ gallon	A-1	2-A
	17 gallon	A	10-A
	33 gallon	A	20-A
Water	$1\frac{1}{2}$, $1\frac{3}{4}$ gallon (pump or pressure)	A-2	1-A
	$2\frac{1}{2}$ gallon (pump or pressure)	A-1	2-A
	4 gallon (pump or pressure)	A-1	3-A
	5 gallon (pump or pressure)	A-1	4-A
	17 gallon (pressure)	A	10-A
	33 gallon (pressure)	A	20-A
	5 12-quart or 6 10-quart water-filled pails; 55-gallon water-filled drum with 3 fire pails; 25- to 55-gallon water-filled bucket tank with 5 or 6 fire pails	A-1	2-A
Loaded Stream	1 gallon	A-2, B-4	1-A
	$1\frac{3}{4}$ and $2\frac{1}{2}$ gallon	A-1, B-2	2-A, $\frac{1}{2}$-B†
	33 gallon	A	20-A
Foam	$1\frac{1}{4}$ and $1\frac{1}{2}$ gallon	A-2, B-2	1-A, 2-B
	$2\frac{1}{2}$ gallon	A-1, B-1	2-A, 4-B
	5 gallon	A-1, B-1	4-A, 6-B
	10 gallon	A, B	6-A, 8-B
	17 gallon	A, B	10-A, 10-B
	33 gallon	A, B	20-A, 20-B
Carbon Dioxide	6 or less pounds of carbon dioxide	B-2, C-2	1-B, C
	$7\frac{1}{2}$ pounds of carbon dioxide	B-2, C-1	2-B, C
	10 to 12 pounds of carbon dioxide	B-2, C-1	4-B, C
	15 to 20 pounds of carbon dioxide	B-1, C-1	4-B, C
	25 and 26 pounds of carbon dioxide	B-1, C-1	6-B, C
	50 pounds of carbon dioxide	B-1, C-1	10-B, C
	75 pounds of carbon dioxide	B-1, C-1	12-B, C
	100 pounds of carbon dioxide	B, C	12-B, C
Dry Chemical	4 to $6\frac{1}{4}$ pounds of dry chemical	B-2, C-2	4-B, C
	$7\frac{1}{2}$ pounds of dry chemical	B-2, C-1	6-B, C
	10 to 15 pounds of dry chemical	B-1, C-1	8-B, C
	20 pounds of dry chemical	B-1, C-1	16-B, C
	30 pounds of dry chemical	B-1, C-1	20-B, C
	75 to 350 pounds of dry chemical	B, C	40-B, C
Wetting Agent	10 gallons	A, B	6-A
	20 gallons	A, B	12-A
	50 gallons	A, B	30-A

Note: Carbon dioxide extinguishers with metallic horns do not carry any "C" classification.

† Note: Portable fire extinguishers with fractional ratings do not meet the requirements of the NFPA Extinguisher Standard.

Table 16-1C. Conversion of Discontinued Class B Ratings

Discontinued Rating	Approximate Present Classification
4–B	2–B
6–B	5–B
8–B	5–B
12–B	10–B
16–B	10–B

utilized by UL, but do not use the rating system set forth in the NFPA Extinguisher Standard. In the standard FM Class B fire test, for example, a 2 in. depth of n-Heptane is floated on 4 in. of water in a square steel test pan having a 6-in. freeboard above the fuel surface. A 1-min preburn is allowed before the fire is attacked. The minimum discharge time of a device is set at 10 sec. Complete extinguishment is required.

F.   Substandard Extinguishers

Extinguishers are designed for emergency use to control and extinguish fires, and should be thought of as vital tools to protect life and property. The nationally recognized testing laboratories have construction and performance standards for portable fire extinguishers and test methods to evaluate the capabilities and limitations of each extinguisher submitted to them for labeling or listing. The public should purchase only those extinguishers which are listed or labeled by a nationally recognized testing laboratory.

Purchase of extinguishers that are offered for sale without the label of one of the nationally recognized testing laboratories makes it very difficult for the purchaser to know whether he has secured a reliable and effective fire protection device. Procurement of such equipment may result in a false sense of security, and may not offer the desired and necessary protection. A number of small pressurized (aerosol) cans containing small amounts of vaporizing liquids or dry chemicals, various types of "glass bulb grenades," and dry chemical "shaker units" are available. Many of these devices have instructions that indicate they are useful on all types of fires, and that they may be used indoors or outdoors. Many of them do not indicate the exact composition of the extinguishing agent, and those operating on the aerosol principle may lose pressure without the knowledge of the owner. Although some of the extinguishers may contain recognized extinguishing agents, it cannot be assumed that they contain all of the necessary design safeguards built into the approved types of extinguishers.

G.   Fire Extinguishment in the Home

(While the following chapters in this Section of the HANDBOOK present detailed information on the selection, use, and maintenance of portable fire extinguishers, the salient points of each of those considerations as it applies to the role extinguishers play in home fire protection is summarized here as a convenience to HANDBOOK users who frequently are called upon to answer inquiries on fire protection for the home.)

The cardinal rules for life safety when fire occurs in the home are: (1) make sure that everyone gets out of the house before exitways become blocked by heat or smoke, (2) be certain that the fire department is called immediately, and (3) if the fire is small, try to control or extinguish it. To achieve the latter, every home should have readily available easy-to-use fire fighting equipment.

Listed or approved portable fire extinguishers are the most reliable "first aid" fire fighting equipment that can be used in the home. In addition, a garden hose may offer opportunities for fire control and extinguishment. (See Chapter 5 of this Section for information on using garden hose.)

Selection of Extinguishers

Since most dwelling fires occur in ordinary (Class A) combustible materials, the most practical and economical extinguishing agent is water. Although stored-pressure water extinguishers or pump tanks could be used, they are generally considered undesirable because they are large, unattractive, heavy, expensive, and require frequent maintenance. Ideally suited for use on any incipient fire that may occur in the home are the small, efficient dry chemical agent extinguishers which have been developed by fire equipment manufacturers. The most readily available are stored-pressure models with capacities ranging from 1 to 5 lbs, and filled with ammonium phosphate (multipurpose) agent. The most popular size contains about $2\frac{1}{2}$ lbs of agent and both refillable and disposable shell models are sold. Many home owners prefer the disposible shell type because they can keep a replacement shell on hand. The disposable shell type also requires less maintenance.

In general, an extinguisher of this type will provide adequate protection for small Class B fires which may involve greases or cooking oils in the kitchen, paints and solvents in the basement or utility area, and oils or gasoline in the garage or outdoors. When used on fires in ordinary combustible materials, the small sizes will be of limited value. The larger sizes, given Class A ratings by the testing laboratories, are more suitable. Even though a small extinguisher of this type may rapidly extinguish the flames in combustible materials, it is important that the deepseated burning embers (especially in furniture cushions, pillows, or bedding) be thoroughly wetted with water.

The 5 lb and larger sizes can be obtained in cartridge operated models. It is essential that once the extinguisher is used it must then be refilled or replaced *as soon as possible*. Even if only a short burst of agent is released the extinguisher will probably lose the rest of its pressure in a very short time.

Possibly the best approach to home fire extinguishment is to provide fire extinguishers for Class B:C protection, and rapid flame "knock-down" for Class A fires. A hose should be utilized as the principal protection for Class A fires. If the homeowner decides to install a fire hose, he may also decide to forego the Class A capability of the multipurpose agent and purchase an extinguisher with the more powerful potassium base agents. The small sized stored-pressure models are available with the other dry chemical agents described in Chapter 5, Section 13.

Home owners who have extensive home workshops, gasoline powered equipment, etc., should consider utilizing additional, conveniently located fire extinguishers in order to control any fire which might occur in such work areas. A logical choice would seem to be a dry chemical extinguisher having a capacity of 5 lbs or greater.

For private automobiles, a dry chemical extinguisher should be effective for dealing with engine fires and any electrical fires in the vehicle. For small trucks, NFPA committees have recommended extinguishers in the 5 to 20 B:C range, depending on the type of vehicle being considered (see Sec. 19, Chap. 2, Part F).

Location of Extinguishers

Fire experience in dwellings clearly indicates that the living room and kitchen are the starting points for most dwelling fires. Thus, at least one extinguisher should be located where it can be quickly reached from both these rooms. For safety, it is best to locate each extinguisher in the path of exit travel so that if the fire cannot be readily controlled with the device, there is a good escape route out of the house. In bedroom areas the extinguisher should be located in a handy closet or cabinet, again preferably along the route of exit travel. For use in basements, the head of the basement stairs is generally preferred except where a basement workshop may indicate the need for shifting the extinguisher location. It is important that each extinguisher location should be known to each member of the family who is able to use the device. A permanently mounted bracket on which to hang the extinguisher will help to assure that it remains in place, is not tucked away in a closet, or is difficult to obtain in case of emergency.

Utilization of Extinguishers

Mere provision for an extinguisher in the home is not worthwhile unless the home owner is willing to: (1) assume the responsibility of learning to properly use the device, (2) give instructions to family members who might be expected to handle the extinguisher, and (3) be responsible for having the extinguisher maintained in accordance with the maintenance and recharging instructions of the extinguisher.

It is important for home owners to realize that extinguishers of the sizes discussed herein have a discharge time of only 8 to 12 sec: thus, in actual use, no time can be wasted in determining the best way to use the device to extinguish a fire. Operating instructions are imprinted on each listed or approved extinguisher, and most of them are designed to facilitate understanding of their operating features. Wherever possible, families should practice the use of extinguishers in a safe outdoor location.

Maintenance of Extinguishers

Maintenance requirements for each extinguisher vary according to the extinguisher selected. Maintenance information is given on each device. Most of the small modern extinguishers designed for home use have a pressure gage to indicate operability. This gage should be checked on a regular basis. Also, to be sure that it can be readily removed from its bracket and that it is in good physical condition, the extinguisher should occasionally be lifted from its bracket and handled. The family should periodically review the operating instructions, the use of the extinguisher, and the information contained in the owner's manual.

SI Units

The following conversion factors are given as a convenience in converting to SI units the English units used in this chapter.

1 in.	$= 25.4$ mm
1 (U.S.) gal	$= 3.785$ litres
1 ft	$= 0.305$ m
1 sq ft	$= 0.0929$ m^2
1 cycle/sec	$= 1$ Hz
$\frac{5}{9}$ (°F $- 32$)	$= $ °C

Bibliography

(see Page 16-33)

Chapter 2

SELECTION, DISTRIBUTION, AND IDENTIFICATION OF FIRE EXTINGUISHERS

The selection and installation of extinguishers solely because of their nominal ratings, relative costs, or because of advertising claims, should be avoided. To secure maximum protection, the characteristics of the extinguisher and the special problems of the individual property should be carefully evaluated.

A.   Principles of Selecting Extinguishers

Selection of the best portable fire extinguisher for a given situation depends on: (1) the nature of the combustibles which might be ignited, (2) the potential severity (size, intensity, and speed of travel) of any resulting fire, (3) effectiveness of the extinguisher on that hazard, (4) the ease of use of the extinguisher, (5) the personnel available to operate the extinguisher and their physical abilities and emotional reactions as influenced by their training, (6) the ambient temperature conditions and other special atmospheric considerations (wind, draft, presence of fumes), (7) suitability of the extinguisher for its environment, (8) any anticipated adverse chemical reactions between the extinguishing agent and the burning materials, (9) any health and operational safety concerns (exposure of operators during the fire control efforts), and (10) the upkeep and maintenance requirements for the extinguisher.

Portable fire extinguishers are designed to cope with fires of limited size, and are necessary and desirable even though the property may be equipped with automatic sprinkler protection, standpipe and hose systems, or other fixed fire protective equipment.

The initial selection of the type and capacity of an extinguisher is based on the hazards of the area to be protected. NFPA No. 10, Standard for the Installation, Maintenance, and Use of Portable Fire Extinguishers, hereinafter referred to in this chapter as the NFPA Extinguisher Standard, has established three hazard levels in order to provide a simplified method of determining the probable size of a fire relative to the kind of incipient fire and its potential severity:

Light Hazard: Where the amount of combustibles or flammable liquids present is such that fires of small size may be expected. These may include offices, schoolrooms, churches, assembly halls, telephone exchanges, etc.

Ordinary Hazards: Where the amount of combustibles or flammable liquids present is such that fires of moderate size may be expected. These may include mercantile storage and display areas, auto showrooms, parking garages, light manufacturing areas, warehouses not classified as extra hazard, school shop areas, etc.

Extra Hazards: Where the amount of combustibles or flammable liquids present is such that fires of severe magnitude may be expected. These may include woodworking areas, auto repair shops, aircraft servicing areas, warehouses with high-piled combustibles (over 15 ft in solid piles, over 12 ft in piles that contain horizontal channels), and areas involved with processes such as flammable liquid handling, painting, dipping, etc.

The class of hazard can influence the type of extinguisher selected, as well as the size or fire extinguishing capability

(i.e., $2\frac{1}{2}$ gal capacity stored pressure or pump tank water extinguishers are rated 2-A and are only suitable for light or ordinary hazard protection. When extra hazard conditions exist, multipurpose dry chemical extinguishers having ratings of 3-A to 40-A will provide the degree of protection needed).

B.   Matching Extinguishers to the Hazard

The first step in evaluating the selection of an extinguisher for the protection of a property is to determine the nature of the materials which might be ignited. Some extinguishers are suitable for only one class of fire, others for two, and still others for three. For example, a plain water extinguisher is suitable for Class A fires only (see Chapter 1, of this Section).

The successful use of a Class A fire extinguisher on an incipient fire is directly related to the quantity of combustible material (contents and interior finish or both) involved. The amount of combustibles is sometimes referred to as the "fire loading" of a building, figured as the average pounds of combustibles per sq ft of area. The larger the amount of combustibles, the greater the fire loading and the greater the potential fire hazard that the extinguisher may be called upon to combat. Based on this concept, Class A fire extinguishers are allocated according to the average fire loading which may be encountered in the occupancy to be protected.

Virtually every structure, even if of fire resistive or noncombustible construction, has some combustible building components in the form of interior finish, partitions, etc. Thus, for building protection, extinguishers suitable for Class A fires are standard. Likewise, in virtually every situation, whether it be a building, a vehicle, or an outdoor exposure, ordinary combustible materials are found. It is also true that where ordinary combustibles are present, there may be the need for extinguishers suitable for use on Class B and C fires (i.e., in a restaurant the principal combustibles present are wood, paper, and fabrics; in the kitchen area the essential hazard involves cooking greases, and a Class B extinguisher should be installed). Since all Class B extinguishers currently being manufactured are also suitable for Class C hazards, there is no basic problem in connection with the application of such agents on any live electrical equipment that might also be present. As another example, although in hospitals, there is a general need for Class A extinguishers to cover spaces such as the patient's rooms, corridors, offices, etc., Class B:C extinguishers should be available in the laboratories, kitchens, areas where flammable anesthetics are stored or handled, or in electrical switchgear or generator rooms. Each area should be surveyed for its actual fire extinguisher requirements, keeping in mind the variety of conditions that exist in that particular area.

In connection with Class B (flammable liquid) fires, three basic conditions may exist: (1) flammable liquid fires of appreciable depth ($\frac{1}{4}$ in. or more) such as those found in dip tanks and quench tanks in industrial plants, (2) spill fires or running fires where the depth of the liquid does not accumulate appreciably, and (3) pressurized flammable liquid or gas fires from damaged vessels or product lines. Each of these fire conditions presents significantly different problems in extinguishment which can be further complicated by variations between indoor and outdoor conditions.

The Class B ratings given by testing laboratories are based on flammable liquid fires of appreciable depth with one numerical unit of extinguishing potential per square foot of flammable liquid surface. Built into this rating system is a safety factor. This safety factor compensates for the fact that tests are conducted under controlled conditions in the testing laboratories by people experienced in the handling of extinguishers and wearing protective clothing.

Portable fire extinguishers should not be relied upon when the surface area of an open tank located in a building is in excess of 20 sq ft. In such cases, serious consideration should be given to installing fixed fire protection equipment, unless it is established that portable devices can be effectively used by available personnel. The principal problems in the handling of deep-layer flammable liquid fires with surface areas greater than 20 sq ft indoors are heat radiation and smoke development (inherent in such fires), which place obvious limits on the manual application of the extinguishing agent.

The size and type of the Class C extinguisher selected should be based on the construction features of the electrical equipment, the degree of agent contamination that can be tolerated, the size and extent of Class A and Class B components, or both, that are a part of the equipment and the nature and amount of combustible materials in the immediate vicinity. For example, large motors and power panels will contain a considerable amount of Class A insulating materials as compared to the Class B material in an oil-filled transformer.

Once an analysis is made of the nature of the combustibles present and their potential fire severity, a study is made of the various candidate extinguishers which might be provided to meet fire protection needs. Although in most cases a number of choices are available, the object is to select the optimum device. For the Class A fire there are two basic types of extinguishers which can be used: water-base extinguishers, or multipurpose (ammonium-phosphate-base) dry chemical extinguishers. For Class B fires there are carbon dioxide, dry chemical, or halon extinguishers. Some small extinguishers are rated less than 4-B or 5-B and, as indicated by their omission from Table 16-2A, may not be permitted as a required extinguisher. For Class C fires there are carbon dioxide, dry chemical, or halon extinguishers. The various types of extinguishing agents for Class D fires are discussed in Section 13, Chapter 6.

C. Selecting the Right Extinguisher

Selecting the right extinguisher for the class of hazard depends upon a careful analysis of the advantages and disadvantages (under various conditions) of the various types available. The following paragraphs review some of the points that should be considered.

Water-base Extinguishers

When the manufacture of all inverting types of extinguishers (soda-acid, cartridge operated water, and foam) was discontinued, the remaining selection of water types for Class A fires diminished to stored-pressure and pump tanks.

Table 16-2A. Fire Extinguisher Size and Placement for Class B Hazard Excluding Protection of Deep Layer Flammable Liquid Tanks

A. For Extinguishers Labeled Between 1955 and June, 1969*		
Type of Hazard	Basic Minimum Extinguisher Rating	Maximum Travel Distance to Extinguishers
Light	4–B	50 ft
Ordinary	8–B	50 ft
Extra	12–B	50 ft

B. For Extinguishers Labeled After June 1, 1969		
Type of Hazard	Basic Minimum Extinguisher Rating	Maximum Travel Distance to Extinguishers
Light	5–B	30 ft
	10–B	50 ft
Ordinary	10–B	30 ft
	20–B	50 ft
Extra	20–B	30 ft
	40–B	50 ft

* For extinguishers listed prior to 1955. Table 16-1B should be used to find the approximate equivalent values.

The Table is divided into two parts, A and B, in order to accommodate the new UL rating system adopted June 1, 1969.

Since the pump tank extinguisher (hand carry type) cannot be operated while being carried, it is considered somewhat more difficult to use. However, it does possess some advantages over stored-pressure under certain applications. It is an excellent choice for use as a standby extinguisher on welding or cutting operations, protecting buildings in remote locations, and for use by the construction industry. It can easily be filled from any convenient, relatively clean water supply, can be used without the need for pressurization, and can be easily maintained. For freezing conditions, chemical additives containing corrosion inhibitors can be used; however, copper tank models are recommended because they will not corrode as easily. The back-pack style of pump tank, which can be carried and operated at the same time, is ideally suited for use in combating brush fires.

Carbon Dioxide Extinguishers

The principal advantage of CO_2 (carbon dioxide) extinguishers is that the agent does not leave a residue after use. This may be a significant factor where protection is needed for delicate and costly electronic equipment. Other typical applications are food preparation areas, laboratories, and printing or duplicating areas. Since the agent is discharged in the form of a gas/snow cloud, it has a relatively short range of 3 to 8 ft. This type of extinguisher is not recommended for outdoor use where windy conditions prevail, or for indoor use in locations which are subject to strong air currents because the agent may rapidly dissipate and prevent extinguishment.

Liquefied Gas Extinguishers

In general, liquefied gas extinguishers—bromotrifluoromethane (Halon 1301) and bromochlorodifluoromethane (Halon 1211)—have features and characteristics similar to CO_2 extinguishers. The bromotrifluoromethane (Halon 1301) extinguisher has never been available in a size larger than $2\frac{1}{2}$ lbs. It has a listed rating of 2-B:C, which is below the minimum requirements of Table 16-2A. This extinguisher does not appear to have significant advantages over other liquefied gas extinguishers.

The bromochlorodifluoromethane (Halon 1211) extinguisher is available in a wide range of sizes, with listed ratings of 2-B:C to 10-B:C. The agent is similar to CO_2 in that it is suitable for cold weather installation, is noncorrosive, and leaves no residue. It is considerably more effective on small Class A fires than CO_2; however, water may still be needed as a follow-up to extinguish glowing embers and deep-seated burning. Compared to CO_2 on a weight-of-agent basis, bromochlorodifluoromethane (Halon 1211) is at least twice as effective. When discharged, the agent is in the combined form of a gas/mist with about twice the range of CO_2. To some extent, windy conditions or strong air currents may make extinguishment difficult by causing the rapid dispersal of the agent. The shells for the bromochlorodifluoromethane (Halon 1211) extinguishers are light weight aluminium or mild-steel, and weigh considerably less than CO_2 cylinders.

Dry Chemical Extinguishers

Due to the different designs and the various types of dry chemical agents, choosing the most suitable dry chemical extinguisher requires careful evaluation. Hand portable models have a discharge stream which ranges from 10 to 30 ft depending on extinguisher size. Compared with carbon dioxide or liquefied gas extinguishers, they will also perform better under windy conditions. Dry chemical extinguishers are available in two basic styles: stored-pressure, and cartridge operated. The stored-pressure (rechargeable) type is the most widely used and is best suited where infrequent use is anticipated and where skilled personnel with professional recharge equipment are available. The cartridge-operated type has the advantage of being quickly refilled in remote locations without the need for special equipment. Some dry chemical models can be equipped with long-range (high velocity) nozzles or applicators which are beneficial in applying the agent under certain special fire fighting conditions.

There are five available types of dry chemical agent, and each has certain advantages and disadvantages. These advantages and disadvantages should be reviewed by potential users. The approximate fire extinguishing capabilities of each type using sodium bicarbonate base (circa 1960) for comparison and a uniform application rate is as follows: sodium bicarbonate base (1), ammonium phosphate base (1.5X), potassium chloride base (1.8X), potassium bicarbonate base (2X), and urea-potassium bicarbonate base (2.5X). (See Part A, Chapter 1, of this Section.) Although there may be considerable variation in cost between the different agents, initial selection should be based on choosing the type(s) most compatible with fire protection needs.

The potassium and urea-potassium base bicarbonate agents are selected in preference to sodium bicarbonate, principally because of their greater fire extinguishing capabilities. If corrosion that could be caused by agent residue is not a factor, potassium chloride can also be included in this group. However, the potassium chloride base agent is not widely used and does not have any specific extinguishing characteristics that are superior to the potassium bicarbonate base agents.

The monoammonium phosphate base agent (multipurpose) is the only one that is suitable for Class A protection. In some cases where there is a need for Class A:B:C protection, water type extinguishers can be omitted when multipurpose extinguishers are installed. However, the multipurpose extinguisher is not generally considered as a practical replacement for water extinguishers. Of principal importance in making this decision is the need for the capacity to extinguish deep-seated Class A fires.

Where dry chemical extinguishers are utilized for Class C protection, it is important to consider that the residue of potassium chloride is somewhat more corrosive than other dry chemicals, and that a multipurpose base agent will be more difficult to remove because it hardens when it cools. Any of the other dry chemical agents, depending upon protection requirements, may prove to be a more practical choice for Class C protection.

Wheeled Extinguishers

The selection of any type of wheeled extinguisher is generally associated with a recognized need to provide additional protection for special hazards or large, extra hazard areas. Where wheeled extinguishers are to be installed, consideration should be given to mobility within the area in which it will be used. For outdoor locations, models with rubber tires or wide-rim wheels will be easier to transport. For indoor locations, doorways, aisles, and corridors need to be wide enough to permit the ready passage of the extinguisher. Because of the magnitude of the fire it will generally be used on, this type of extinguisher should be reserved for use by operators who have either used the equipment, who have received special instructions on the use of the equipment, or who have used the equipment in live fire training.

D. Available Personnel—Ease of Use

Extinguisher selection must take into consideration potential users. Such consideration should include their physical abilities, their reactions under stress, and any prior training they may have had on how to use the equipment. Fire extinguisher manufacturers supply equipment in a number of designs, sizes, and types. Therefore, the operating principles and ease of use are important considerations.

There is no one "universal" fire extinguisher that is equally suitable and desirable for use on all classes of fire. Although it is important to carefully match the extinguisher to the kind of fire fighting job it can do best, it is also important to select types and styles that operate in a like manner. When confronted with an emergency, the more choices and decisions that the user must make the greater are his chances for error. Many firms have standardized the various types of extinguishers they use so that employees need only learn the method of operation for one model of each type. In cases where firms utilize trained fire brigades, a greater variation in extinguisher selection may be considered.

The emotional reaction of an individual in a fire emergency will be largely influenced by his familiarity with the equipment, his experience in using or observing the use of the equipment, and his training and self confidence. Training is, therefore, very important. Many establishments provide for the use of equipment by employees when the units are scheduled for recharging or hydrostatic testing.

In some applications the size and weight of an extinguisher are important factors which must be considered. Size and weight are particularly important when the physical abilities and limitations of potential users are considered (i.e., if the extinguisher needs to be carried up or down stairs or through an obstruction in order to reach a fire). In some cases, extinguisher shells add considerable weight. The weight problem can sometimes be overcome by the selection of similar models with lighter weight shells, or by the selection of agents with more extinguishing capacity per unit of weight.

The current "standard" water extinguisher is the $2\frac{1}{2}$ gal size weighing about 30 lbs. There is considerable flexibility, however, with carbon dioxide and dry chemical extinguishers. Where weight may be a problem for a certain Class B hazard, one manufacturer offers two sizes of dry chemical extinguishers—each with a 40-B:C rating. The sodium bicarbonate-base model with a 20-lb capacity weighs a total of 27 lbs, compared to the potassium bicarbonate-base model with a 9-lb capacity which weighs only 14 lbs.

E. Physical Environment

Another factor in the selection of an extinguisher concerns the physical environment in which the device is to be located. Perhaps the most obvious example is where the extinguisher might be subject to low or high temperature conditions.

Normal practice is for the testing laboratories to evaluate water type extinguishers within the range of 40°F to 120°F (4°C to 49°C) and all other types within the range of −40°F to 120°F (−4°C to 49°C). When extinguishers are installed in locations subject to temperatures outside this range, they should be of a type approved and listed for the temperature to which they are exposed, or they must be placed in an enclosure capable of maintaining the stipulated range of temperatures. Some Class B extinguishers of the stored-pressure type utilize nitrogen as the pressurizing medium, rather than air or carbon dioxide. When it is desired that these units perform effectively at temperatures as low as −65°F, UL separately lists units for use at low temperatures.

Other atmospheric conditions which must be considered are snow, rain, air-borne debris, and the presence of corrosive fumes. When extinguishers are located outdoors, installing them in cabinets, sheltered areas, or placing protective covers over them will help protect them from premature deterioration.

Corrosive materials can play havoc with extinguishers not specially designed to withstand such exposures. UL has separate classifications for corrosive conditions (e.g., extinguishers for use in salt-air atmospheres appear under the heading: "Marine Type, USCG"). Where corrosive fumes are developed in industrial establishments, a special analysis

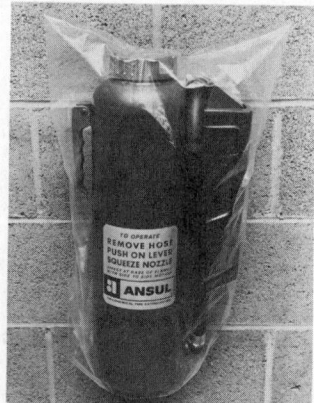

Fig. 16-2A. A plastic-covered outdoor extinguisher mounted on an outside wall.

should be made prior to the selection of portable extinguishers.

Extinguishers are sometimes installed in locations which are subject to vibration (such as shakers and hammer mills, trains, vehicles, and power boats). Under such conditions, it is essential that the type and model selected be of a rugged design, securely restrained in a bracket mounting, and inspected at frequent intervals.

F. Health and Operational Safety Considerations

Potential hazards associated with the use and maintenance of extinguishers (which may involve health and safety) are important considerations which involve extinguisher selection and employee training.

Manufacturers normally provide prominent precautionary labels on extinguishers when the agent contained therein might produce toxic vapors or toxic decomposition products. In other cases, it might be necessary to provide warning signs at entry points to confined areas in which extinguishers might be used with some hazard to the operator. Sometimes such problems are overcome by provision for remote operation of the extinguisher, by specially designed long-range extinguisher nozzles, by ventilation, or by the provision of self-contained breathing apparatus for employees who might use the equipment.

All water type extinguishers, rated only for Class A fires, can react adversely on a Class B fire by making it flare up, spread, and possibly cause danger to the operator. If any water extinguisher is used on a fire in or near live electrical equipment, the conductivity of the water stream has the potential of transmitting a fatal shock to the operator.

Carbon dioxide, while not considered toxic itself, will not support life when used in sufficient concentration to extinguish a fire. The use of this type of agent in an unventilated space also dilutes the oxygen supply. Prolonged occupancy of such spaces could result in loss of consciousness or loss of life due to oxygen deficiency. The opaqueness of a cloud of carbon dioxide gas may also cause persons in such spaces to become disoriented.

Older model carbon dioxide extinguishers have metal horns which conduct a shock to the user when contact with live electrical equipment is made. Such metal horns should be replaced with nonmetallic types. Occasionally, operators using carbon dioxide extinguishers may experience a shock even though they are not in contact with live electrical equipment. These "shocks" come from a buildup of static electricity when the extinguisher is being discharged, and are generally more of an annoyance than a hazard. The principal cause is a damaged or defective pick-up tube which can easily be replaced.

Dry chemical extinguishing agents are not regarded as toxic materials, but can be irritating if breathed in sufficiently high concentrations. If discharged in a small, enclosed area they can also cause disorientation by reducing visibility. Monoammonium phosphate dry chemical is the most irritating, followed by potassium base agents which are somewhat more irritating than sodium bicarbonate.

The initial discharge of agent from the extinguisher has considerable force and, if aimed at close range on a relatively small flammable liquid or grease fire, can cause extensive spreading before extinguishment or control is achieved.

Dry chemical deposits on electrical contacts can prevent or reduce the subsequent conductivity of the contacts, as these chemicals are nonconductors of electricity. These agents may also clog filters if discharged near intakes of air conditioning or air cleaning systems.

Multipurpose dry chemical (monoammonium phosphate base) is acidic, and in the presence of a small amount of moisture or dampness will corrode some metals unless promptly and thoroughly cleaned up.

Bromotrifluoromethane (Halon 1301) and bromochloro-difluoromethane (Halon 1211) extinguishers contain extinguishing agents having a low toxicity vapor under normal conditions. However, their decomposition products can be hazardous. When using these extinguishers in unventilated places (small rooms, closets, motor vehicles, or other confined spaces), operators and others should avoid breathing the vapors or the gases produced by thermal decomposition of the agent (see Sec. 13, Chap. 4).

Class D fires involving burning metal chips could be scattered if the full force of a dry powder extinguisher is used at close range. To avoid spreading the fire, the nozzle should be opened slowly at a safe distance.

In evaluating the health and safety considerations of portable fire extinguishers it should be emphasized that virtually every fire produces toxic decomposition products, and that some burning materials create highly toxic gases. Until the fire has been extinguished and the area well ventilated, it is important to avoid unnecessary breathing of air in the vicinity of the fire.

G. Distribution of Fire Extinguishers

Portable fire extinguishers are most effectively utilized when they are readily available in sufficient number and with adequate extinguishing capacity for use by persons familiar with their operation.

In fire emergencies where extinguishers are relied upon, someone usually has to "travel" from the fire in order to obtain the device, and then return to the fire before beginning extinguishing operations. This connotes "time," with the number of seconds or minutes governed mainly by the "travel distance" involved in securing the extinguisher and placing it in operation. Sometimes extinguishers are purposely kept nearby (as in welding operations): however, recognizing that a fire outbreak usually cannot be prejudged as to location, extinguishers are more often strategically positioned throughout areas. Travel distance is not merely a simple circle radius matter, but is the actual distance the user of the extinguisher will need to walk. Consequently, travel distance will be affected by partitions, location of doorways, aisles, piles of stored materials, machinery, etc.

Arrangement in a Building

The actual placement of fire extinguishers can best be accomplished through a physical survey of the area to be protected. In general, locations should be selected that will: (1) provide uniform distribution, (2) provide easy accessibility, (3) be relatively free from blocking by storage and equipment, or both, (4) be near normal paths of travel, (5) be near entrance and exit doors, (6) be free from the potential of physical damage, and (7) be readily visible.

When extinguishers are installed in locations subjected to temperatures outside the range of 40° to 120°F, they must be placed in a heated enclosure or be of a type that is suitable for the temperature to which they will be exposed.

Mounting Extinguishers

The majority of extinguishers are mounted to walls or columns by securely fastened hangers so that the weight of the extinguishers is adequately supported. Should an extinguisher fall, it could cause injury or be damaged to the extent that replacement would be necessary.

Where extinguishers may be dislodged, brackets specifically designed to cope with this problem are available. In cases where they are subject to physical damage (such as warehouse aisles), protection from impact is desirable. In large open areas (such as aircraft hangars), extinguishers can be mounted on moveable pedestals or wheeled carts. In order to maintain some pattern of distribution or to specify intended placement, locations should be marked on the floor.

Many extinguishers are mounted in cabinets or wall recesses. It is important, though, that the operating instructions face outward and that the extinguisher be placed so that it can easily be removed. Cabinets should be kept clean and dry.

The NFPA Extinguisher Standard specifies floor clearance and mounting heights, based on extinguisher weight, as follows:

1. Extinguishers having a gross weight not exceeding 40 lbs shall be installed so that the top of the extinguisher is not more than 5 ft above the floor.

2. Extinguishers having a gross weight greater than 40 lbs (except wheeled types) shall be so installed that the top of the extinguisher is not more than $3\frac{1}{2}$ ft above the floor.

3. In no case shall the clearance between the bottom of the extinguisher and the floor be less than 4 in.

When extinguishers are mounted on industrial trucks, vehicles, boats, aircraft, trains, etc., special mounting brackets (available from the manufacturer) should be used. Although cabinets or lockers are sometimes used, these locations frequently become cluttered with other items which can hamper quick retrieval. It is important that the extinguisher be located at a safe distance from the hazard so that it will not become involved in the fire.

Class A Extinguisher Distribution

Table 16-2B is a guideline for determining the minimum number and rating of extinguishers for Class A fire protection needs in accordance with the occupancy hazard consideration previously discussed. In certain instances, through a fire protection analysis of specific areas, process hazards, or building configurations, extinguishers with higher ratings may be required. This does not mean, however, that the recommended maximum travel distances can be exceeded.

Where the floor area of a building is less than 3,000 sq ft, at least one extinguisher of the minimum size recommended should be provided.

The first step in calculating Class A fire extinguisher needs is to determine the proper class of occupancy (light, ordinary, or extra hazard). Depending on the rating of the extinguisher (1-A to 40-A), the maximum area that it will protect can be determined. For example, each $2\frac{1}{2}$-gal stored pressure water extinguisher (rated 2 A) will protect an area of 3,000 sq ft in an ordinary hazard occupancy. The requirements in Table 16-2B also specify that the travel distance (actual walking distance) from any point to the nearest extinguisher shall not exceed 75 ft. It is necessary to select extinguishers which fulfill both the distribution and travel distance requirements for a particular occupancy classification.

The figure of 11,250 sq ft. in Table 16-2B is used instead of 12,000 sq ft (which would appear to be a normal progressive increment). However, if a circle with a 75 ft radius is drawn, the largest square inside that circle would be 106 ft by 106 ft, or 11,250 sq ft. As buildings are usually rectangular in shape, this is the largest open area one can

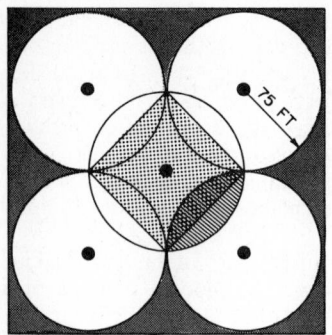

Fig. 16-2B. The dotted squares show the maximum area (11,250 sq ft) that an extinguisher can protect within the limits of the 75-ft radius.

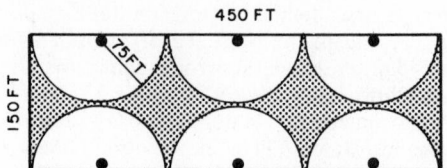

Fig. 16-2C. A diagrammatic representation of extinguishers located along the outside walls of a 450- by 150-ft building. (The dots represent extinguishers.) The shaded areas indicate "voids" which are farther than 75 ft to the nearest extinguisher.

have and still comply with the 75-ft travel distance rule. (See Figure 16-2B for an illustration of this concept.)

The NFPA Extinguisher Standard also provides that up to one-half of the complement of extinguishers, as specified in Table 16-2B, may be replaced by uniformly spaced small hose stations for use by the occupants of the building (see Sec. 15, Chap. 1). The hose stations and extinguishers, however, are located in such a manner that the hose stations do not replace more than every other extinguisher.

The following examples of distribution illustrate the number and placement of extinguishers according to occupancy type and rating. The sample building is 150 ft × 450 ft, giving a floor area of 67,500 sq ft. Although several different ways of placing extinguishers are given, a number of other locations could have been used with comparable results.

The first example demonstrates placement at the maximum protection area limits (11,250 sq ft) allowed per extinguisher in the NFPA Extinguisher Standard for each class of occupancy. Installing extinguishers with higher ratings will not affect distribution or placement.

EXAMPLE 1:

$$\frac{67,500}{11,250} = 6$$

- 4-A Extinguishers for Light Hazard Occupancy
- 10-A Extinguishers for Ordinary Hazard Occupancy
- 20-A Extinguishers for Extra Hazard Occupancy

This placement, along outside walls, would not be acceptable because the travel distance rule is clearly violated (see

Fig. 16-2C). Relocation and/or additional extinguishers are needed.

Examples 2 and 3 are for extinguishers having ratings which correspond to protection areas of 6,000 and 3,000 sq ft respectively. The examples show only one of many ways these extinguishers could be placed. As the number of lower rated extinguishers increases; meeting the travel distance requirement generally becomes less of a problem. Similar examples could be worked out for protection areas of 4,000 and 4,500 sq ft as required by Table 16-2B.

EXAMPLE 2:

$$\frac{67,500}{6,000} = 12$$

- 2-A Extinguishers for Light Hazard Occupancy
- 4-A Extinguishers for Ordinary Hazard Occupancy
- 6-A Extinguishers for Extra Hazard Occupancy

Extinguishers could be mounted on exterior walls or, as shown in Figure 16-2D, on building columns or interior walls, and conform to both distribution and travel distance rules.

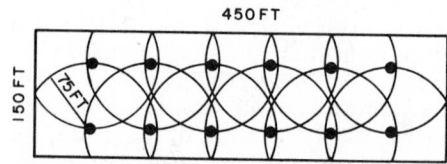

Fig. 16-2D. Requirements for both travel distance and extinguisher distribution are met in this configuration representing twelve extinguishers mounted on building columns or interior walls.

Table 16-2B. Fire Extinguisher Size and Placement for Class A Hazards

Basic Minimum Extinguisher Rating for Area Specified	Maximum Travel Distances to Extinguishers	Areas to be Protected per Extinguisher		
		Light Hazard Occupancy	Ordinary Hazard Occupancy	Extra Hazard Occupancy
1-A	75 ft	3,000 sq ft	†	†
2-A	75 ft	6,000 sq ft	3,000 sq ft	†
3-A	75 ft	9,000 sq ft	4,500 sq ft	3,000 sq ft
4-A	75 ft	11,250 sq ft	6,000 sq ft	4,000 sq ft
6-A	75 ft	11,250 sq ft	9,000 sq ft	6,000 sq ft
10-A	75 ft	11,250 sq ft*	11,250 sq ft*	9,000 sq ft
20-A	75 ft	11,250 sq ft*	11,250 sq ft*	11,250 sq ft*
40-A	75 ft	11,250 sq ft*	11,250 sq ft*	11,250 sq ft*

* 11,250 sq ft is considered a practical limit.
† Protection requirements may be fulfilled by several extinguishers of the minimum specified rating with the approval of the authority having jurisdiction.

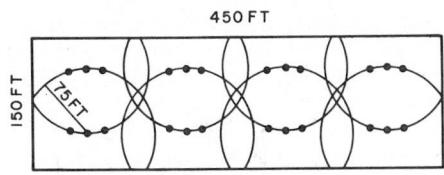

Fig. 16-2E. Extinguishers grouped together.

EXAMPLE 3:

$$\frac{67,500}{3,000} = 24$$

1-A Extinguishers for Light Hazard Occupancy

2-A Extinguishers for Ordinary Hazard Occupancy

3-A Extinguishers for Extra Hazard Occupancy

This arrangement, illustrated in Figure 16-2E, shows extinguishers grouped together on building columns or interior walls in a manner that still conforms to distribution and travel distance rules.

Class B Extinguisher Distribution

Normal Class B fire hazards fall into two quite different general categories regarding requirements for extinguishers. One condition is where the fire does not involve flammable liquids in appreciable depth, such as spilled fuel on an open surface, a fire involving vapors issuing from a container or piping system, or a running fire from a broken container. The other condition is where the fire involves flammable liquids in appreciable depth (defined as a depth of liquid greater than $\frac{1}{4}$ in.), such as fires involving open tanks of flammable liquids commonly found in industrial plants (dip tanks used for coating, finishing, treating, or similar processes).

In situations where flammable liquids are not in appreciable depth, extinguishers should be provided according to Table 16-2A. Once the type of hazard is determined, the selected Class B extinguisher must have a rating equal to or greater than specified, and be so located that the maximum travel distance is not exceeded.

The reason the basic maximum travel distance to Class B extinguishers is 50 ft as opposed to 75 ft for Class A extinguishers, is that flammable liquid fires reach their maximum intensity almost immediately. It is imperative that the extinguisher be brought to the fire in a much shorter period of time than allowed for a slower developing Class A fire. This is recognized in Part B of Table 16-2A which establishes dual maximum travel distances based on extinguisher ratings. Thus under a given hazard condition, if the smaller rated extinguisher is selected, is must be no more than 30 ft from the hazard (as compared to 50 ft for the higher rated extinguisher.)

Even though Table 16-2A specifies maximum travel distances for Class B extinguisher placement, judgment should be exercised in actually establishing them. The closer the extinguisher is to the Class B hazard the better—up to the point where the extinguisher itself might be involved in a fire, or access to it made difficult because of flame, heat, or the products of combustion.

Where an entire room or area is judged to be a Class B hazard (such as an automobile repair garage), extinguishers should be placed at regular intervals so that the maximum walking distance from any point to the nearest extinguisher does not exceed the travel distances specified in Table 16-2A.

For fires in flammable liquids of appreciable depth, a Class B fire extinguisher is provided on the basis of one numerical unit of Class B extinguishing potential per square foot of flammable liquid surface for the largest tank within the area. The travel distance requirements in Table 16-2A should also be used to locate extinguishers for spot hazard protection; however, the type of hazard and the availability of the extinguisher must be carefully evaluated. One extinguisher can be installed to provide protection against several hazards, provided travel distances are not exceeded. Where hazards are scattered or widely separated and travel distances are exceeded, then individual protection should be installed according to the square foot rule.

Where open process tanks containing flammable or combustible liquids are present, and liquid surfaces of the tanks are in excess of 20 sq ft, consideration must be given to providing fixed fire protection systems suitable for Class B fires rather than placing complete dependence on portable fire extinguishers. Fires involving large tanks can reach a size and intensity that prohibit extinguisher users from approaching close enough to guarantee effective use of portable extinguisher streams. When fixed Class B extinguishing systems are installed, the provision of portable fire extinguishers may be waived for that one hazard, but not for the structure, other special hazards, or the rest of the contents. Sometimes a burning tank can result in burning liquid spills outside the range of the fixed equipment, or the fire may originate adjacent to the tank rather than in its liquid content. Therefore, having portable extinguishers available is desirable, even though hazards of this type are protected with fixed extinguishing systems.

Fires involving pressurized flammable liquids and pressurized flammable gases deserve special attention. The method used to specify the amount of extinguishing potential for Class B fires in flammable liquids of appreciable depth is not applicable to these types of hazards.

The selection of the proper type and size of Class B extinguishers for fires in pressurized fuels is made on the basis of the recommendations of the manufacturers of this specialized equipment available for that type of hazard. Special nozzle design and rates of agent application are necessary in order to be able to cope with hazards of this magnitude. Also, it is generally undesirable to attempt to extinguish pressurized fuel fires unless there is reasonable assurance that the source of fuel can be promptly shut, thus avoiding a possible explosion. The travel distances for hand portable extinguishers should not exceed those specified in Table 16-2A.

In fighting a Class B fire, the flow rate of the extinguishing agent, and the duration of discharge are prominent factors that can spell success or failure. For these reasons, the NFPA Extinguisher Standard does not permit the substitution of two or more extinguishers of lower rating for the minimum values given in Table 16-2A, except in limited situations where foam extinguishers may still be in use. This exception recognizes the fact that foam progressively "secures" a fire, and the application from one unit remains effective during the time which is unavoidable in bringing successive units into operation. The larger capacity carbon dioxide and dry chemical extinguishers (the most common types used) have higher flow rates in pounds per second, and longer continuous discharge durations, than smaller devices. Thus, one 20-B rated extinguisher of these types has greater "fire-killing" power than four 5-B rated units. The basic reasons for this are: (1) the range of streams,

(2) the times of discharge, and (3) the rate of agent application. This philosophy may be modified where access is limited for fire control efforts, and trained fire brigade people with different extinguishers are on hand to simultaneously attack a fire from several positions.

Class B wheeled extinguishers having ratings from 40-B to as high as 480-B are available. Such devices are chiefly designed for outdoor fire fighting purposes. They should be used only by well-trained employees, and should be distributed according to the 50-ft travel distance rule in order to ensure that they can be brought into service as quickly as possible. Longer travel distances may be authorized by the proper authorities.

Class C Extinguisher Distribution

To protect extinguisher operators in situations where live electrical equipment may be encountered, extinguishers with Class C ratings are required. Extinguishers so rated utilize a nonconducting extinguishant—types of extinguishers possessing Class C ratings employ carbon dioxide, dry chemical, bromotrifluoromethane (Halon 1301), or bromochlorodifluoromethane (Halon 1211).

When the power of a piece of electrical equipment is cut off, the fire changes character to that of a Class A, Class B, or a combined Class A and B fire depending on the nature of the burning electrical components and any material burning in the immediate vicinity (see Chapter 1, this Section). Deenergizing electrical equipment eliminates the possibility of shock hazards to the extinguisher operator should the operator accidentally come into physical contact with the equipment, or should the operator bring any conductive part of an extinguisher within arcing distance. Deenergizing also eliminates fault currents from prolonging the fire or from being a source of reignition. Switches or circuit breakers that cut electric power to specific equipment can prevent hazardous side effects (e.g., plunging an entire multistory building into darkness or shutting down the essential electric power which supplies life support equipment, etc.). Often, fires involving an electrical component are relatively minor and, by a short application of a Class C extinguishant, can be effectively extinguished without disturbing electrical continuity.

The capacity of the extinguishers supplied for each major Class C hazard situation must be individually judged according to: (1) the size of the electrical equipment, (2) the configuration of the electrical equipment (particularly the enclosures of units) which influences agent distribution, and (3) the effective range of the extinguisher stream. Each of these factors influences the amount and type of agent needed, the desired rate of agent discharge, the associated duration of application, and the potential wastage factors. For large installations of electrical apparatus where the power continuity is critical, fixed fire protection is desirable. At locations where such fixed systems are installed, it is practical to also provide Class C portable fire extinguisher units to handle quickly discovered fires: obviously, the number and size of these units can be reduced under such conditions.

Class D Extinguisher Distribution

For Class D hazards the availability of special portable extinguishers (or equivalent equipment to contain or extinguish any fire developing in a combustible metal) is particularly important. Extinguishing equipment for such fires should be located no less than 75 ft from the hazard.

Use of the wrong extinguisher can instantly increase or spread the fire. Quantitatively, the amount of agent needed is normally measured by the surface area of combustible metals which might become involved, plus the potential severity of the fire (which could cause "bake-off" of the extinguishant) as influenced by the shape and form of the metal. Because fires in magnesium fines are more difficult to extinguish than fires involving magnesium scrap, the amount of agent needed to handle fires in magnesium fines is correspondingly greater. Extinguishers labeled for Class D fires are not necessarily equally effective on all combustible metal fires: often, extinguishers so labeled might be hazardous when used on some fires. (For further information, see Sec. 13, Chap. 6)

H.   Identification of Extinguishers

The ability to quickly identify the types and locations of extinguishers so that the right kind can be used on a fire is

1. WATER

2. CARBON DIOXIDE, DRY CHEMICAL, BROMOCHLORODIFLUOROMETHANE, AND BROMOTRIFLUOROMETHANE

3. MULTIPURPOSE DRY CHEMICAL

4. MULTIPURPOSE DRY CHEMICAL (INSUFFICIENT AGENT FOR "A" RATING)

5. DRY POWDER

Fig. 16-2F. Typical marking combinations for the various types of fire extinguishers.

a must. Successful schemes have been developed for marking various types of extinguishers and identifying their location throughout an area.

Marking of Extinguishers

To assist in the selection of the most appropriate fire extinguisher in an emergency, the NFPA has developed and recommends the use of markings which employ the Class letter (supplemented by words), a distinctive symbol, and a color code. Use of this marking system is valuable as a training aid, helps to make extinguishers more conspicuous, and helps to standardize international marking practices. The shape of the symbols is varied so that persons who are colorblind can select the correct extinguisher (see Fig. 16-1A, Chapter 1, this Section).

These markings may be obtained from the NFPA, from extinguisher manufacturers and distributors, from some property insurance companies, and from commercial sources in the form of decals or adhesive labels. Those placed on extinguishers should be readable at a distance of 3 ft; those placed on walls near extinguishers should be larger and readable at a distance of 25 ft. Extinguishers which are rated for more than one Class of fire (such as Class A:B or Class B:C) should carry each marking symbol. Some typical marking combinations for various types of extinguishers are shown in Fig. 16-2F.

Marking Locations

Clearly marked extinguisher locations are of utmost importance. In an emergency it is essential that the extinguisher is located quickly and put into use while the fire is in the incipient stage. The locations of wall or column mounted extinguishers can easily be designated by painting a red rectangle or band above the extinguishers at a height of approximately 8 to 10 ft. It is also good practice to paint red either the extinguisher or the background on which the extinguisher is mounted. Some firms, as an aid in checking extinguishers for location, maintenance, and inventory, stencil their extinguishers with corresponding numbers on the background.

If extinguishers for different classes of fire are mounted at the same location (such as a water extinguisher and a carbon dioxide extinguisher), then extra attention should be given to identifying the type of fire each can be used on.

Where extinguishers can easily be blocked by storage or equipment, barriers and floor markings can be employed. If this problem persists, it may be more practical to find an alternate location.

Extinguishers that are installed in recessed cabinets or wall recesses are generally more difficult to locate unless clearly marked. Where possible, the cabinet frame or wall recess should be painted red. However, when such installations are in long halls or corridors, it may still be very difficult to locate the extinguisher unless a sign is mounted perpendicular to the cabinet wall at a height of about 8 ft.

In many public and commercial buildings, extinguisher locations are camouflaged for aesthetic reasons or they are installed in hidden areas such as closets or stairwells. Unless one knows where to look or just happens to see a small sign on a door, extinguishers so camouflaged are of little value in time of emergency.

SI Units

The following conversion factors are given as a convenience in converting to SI units the English units used in this chapter.

1 cu ft	$= 0.0283 \text{ m}^3$
1 ft	$= 0.305 \text{ m}$
1 in.	$= 25.4 \text{ mm}$
1 lb (mass)	$= 0.054 \text{ kg}$
$\frac{5}{9}(°F - 32)$	$= °C$
1 (U.S.) gal	$= 3.785 \text{ litres}$

Bibliography

(see Page 16-33)

Chapter 3

OPERATION AND USE OF FIRE EXTINGUISHERS

The same extinguisher in the hands of different persons can produce widely different results depending on the operator's familiarity with it. To use extinguishers effectively requires a basic knowledge of their capabilities to extinguish different types of fires and how they should be used on fires. This chapter gives information on the operating characteristics of the different types of extinguishers that are available and summarizes the techniques that are used in discharging the contents of extinguishers effectively.

People who use fire extinguishers fall into one of four general groups. They are:

1. Fire departments—municipal and industrial (trained).
2. Employees—business and industrial (trained and untrained).
3. Private owners (generally trained).
4. The general public (untrained).

As part of their job training, employees who are expected to use extinguishers should be familiar with all the information contained on the manufacturer's nameplates and in the instruction manuals furnished with most extinguishers. When they have not been properly trained, the operation of extinguishers may be seriously delayed, or the operator may be injured.

When they are confronted with the need to use an extinguisher, private owners and the general public usually rely on the extinguisher's nameplate instructions. Often, the extinguisher's potential fire fighting capabilities are negated since the majority of persons have never operated, nor observed, an extinguisher in operation. The fact that many extinguishers discharge their entire contents within 8 to 15 sec means that during emergency conditions, operators do not have the time to experiment. Therefore, attempting to learn the operating procedures and techniques of application under the stress of emergency conditions can place operators at serious disadvantages in their attempts to extinguish fires that are within the capacities of the extinguishers being used.

Operational Characteristics

Fire extinguishers are classified into five major groupings, based on the general content of their extinguishing media. These groupings also serve to describe the operational characteristics of fire extinguishers. They are (1) water-type extinguishers, (2) compressed gas extinguishers, (3) liquefied gas extinguishers, (4) dry chemical extinguishers, and (5) dry powder extinguishers.

A.   Water-type Extinguishers

Stored-pressure Type

There are two basic types of extinguishers that use water. They are the stored-pressure type and the pump type. This is the most common water-type extinguisher in the 2½-gal size. It has a listed rating of 2-A. This same type of extinguisher can also be obtained in an anti-freeze model charged with an alkali-metal salt solution if the shell is stainless steel, or calcium chloride if the shell is cupro-nickel or brass.

The 2½-gal size weighs about 30 lbs and has a solid stream range of approximately 35 to 40 ft, horizontally. This ex-

tinguisher has the advantage of intermittent operation, but under continuous use it has a discharge time of about 55 sec. It consists of a single chamber or shell which contains the agent and the expellant gas. The extinguisher should only be filled to the "fill mark" which, on some models, is stamped into the shell about 6 in. from the top. Some manufacturers have installed an overfill tube in the shell opening in order to ensure filling to the proper level. The cap (head) assembly consists of a siphon tube, combination carrying handle/operating lever, discharge valve, air pressure valve and gage, discharge hose, and nozzle. Through an automobile tire-type air valve, the extinguisher is pressurized with air or inert gas. Charging pressures vary from 90 to 125 psi. The air pressure gage has a marking showing the normal pressure range.

The operating lever is held in a locked position to prevent accidental discharge while being carried. Most manufacturers use a ring pin which must be pulled out before the operating lever can be depressed. To do this, it is best to set the extinguisher on the ground and, while loosely holding the combination handle in one hand, pull out the ring pin (or release a small latch) with the other hand. Then, grasp the hose and nozzle in one hand and squeeze the discharge lever with the other. The stream should be directed at the base of the flames, working from side to side or around the fire. Application should begin as close to the fire as possible. As the flames diminish and it is possible to get closer to the fire, the solid stream can be changed to a spray by extending the tip of the index finger over the end of the nozzle. A spray stream will be more effective in extinguishing burning embers. In order to thoroughly wet deep-seated smoldering or glowing surfaces, it is best to kick or poke apart burning materials. This same technique can also be used when using other water type extinguishers.

Pump Tank

Pump tanks are the simplest types of water extinguishers. Sizes range from 2½ to 5 gal capacity, and listed ratings range from 2-A to 4-A. The extinguishers have cylindrical metal containers and carrying handles. In some models the carrying handle is combined with the pump handle, and in others it is attached to the container. A built-in, hand-oper-

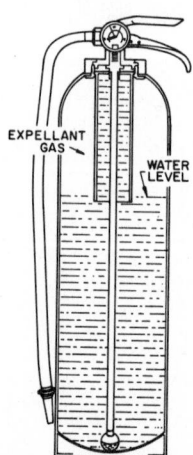

Fig. 16-3A. Stored pressure water extinguisher.

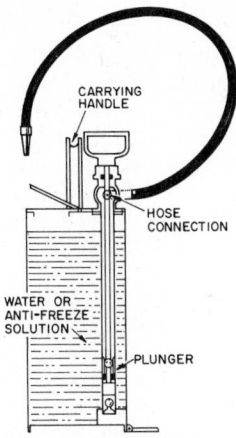

Fig. 16-3B. Pump tank fire extinguisher.

ated vertical piston pump, to which a short rubber hose and nozzle is attached, provides the means for discharging the water onto the fire. The pump is of the double acting type which discharges a stream of water on both the up and down strokes.

When brought to a fire, the pump tank water extinguisher is placed on the floor and, to steady the unit, the operator puts one foot on a small extension bracket attached to its base. To force the water through the hose, the operator then pumps the handle up and down. To work around the fire or to move closer to the fire as the flames subside, the operator must stop pumping and carry the extinguisher to a new location. The force, range, and duration of the stream are dependent, to a degree, upon the operator. Pump tank water extinguishers kept in unheated areas where freezing temperatures might occur should be filled with an antifreeze water solution containing a corrosion inhibitor. Only the antifreeze charge recommended by the extinguisher manufacturer should be used. Common salt or other freezing depressants may corrode the extinguisher, damage the pump assembly, or affect the fire extinguishing capability of the device.

Although somewhat more expensive, copper shell models do not corrode as easily as steel and should be used in conjunction with antifreeze agents.

Back Pack: This type of pump extinguisher is primarily used for fighting outdoor fires in brush and wildlands. The tank has a capacity of 5 gal and weighs approximately 50 lbs when full. Although it is listed by UL (Underwriters' Laboratories), it does not have a designated rating.

The tank may be constructed of fiberglass, stainless steel, galvanized steel, or brass. As its name implies, it is designed to be carried on the operator's back. The back pack extinguisher has a large opening for fast refilling, as well as a

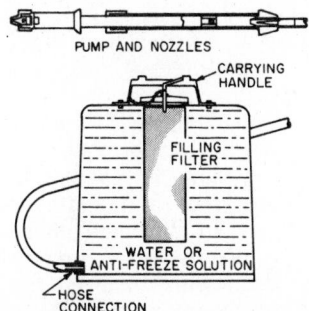

Fig. 16-3C. Pump tank back-pack fire extinguisher.

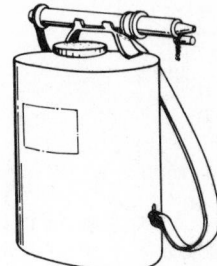

Fig. 16-3D. Pump tank back-pack fire extinguisher with 5-gal unit of fiberglass construction. Pump action is at nozzle (trombone-type action). (D. B. Smith & Company)

tight fitting filter to prevent foreign material from entering and clogging the pump. Generally, plain water is used as the extinguishant. However, antifreeze agents, wetting agents, or other special water base agents may be used. When used in rural areas, back pack extinguishers can be refilled from any nearby water sources such as ponds, lakes, or streams.

The most commonly used model has a trombone-type, double acting piston pump connected to the tank by a short length of rubber hose. Discharge occurs when the operator, holding the pump in both hands, moves the piston section back and forth.

Back pack extinguishers have also been manufactured with compression pumps mounted on the right side of the tanks. This model is operated by first pumping up the air pressure in the tank with about 10 strokes of the handle, and then maintaining sufficient expellant air pressure with slow, easy pumping strokes. Discharge is controlled by the left hand by means of a lever-operated shut off nozzle which is attached to the end of the hose.

This extinguisher can be transported by a carrying handle which is mounted on the top of the tank. The carrying handle is used when setting the extinguisher on the ground. More commonly, it is carried on the back by means of two shoulder straps. The straps allow both hands the freedom to operate the pump while the extinguisher is being carried. The firefighting techniques are the same as for other water type extinguishers.

B. Compressed Gas Extinguisher

Carbon dioxide (CO_2) is the most commonly utilized compressed gas in fire extinguishers. This type of extinguisher is primarily intended for use on Class B:C fires. If used on a Class A fire, some degree of control may be achieved until water or some other suitable Class A extinguishant can be used. Sizes range from 5 to 20 lbs for hand portable models, and from 50 to 100 lbs for wheeled models. The CO_2 is retained in a heavy metal shell in a liquid state at a pressure of 800 to 900 psi at temperatures below 88°F. The extinguisher consists of a pressure cylinder (shell), a siphon tube and valve for releasing the agent, and a discharge horn or horn/hose combination. The siphon tube extends from the valve to almost the bottom of the shell, so that normally only liquid CO_2 reaches the discharge horn until about 80 percent of the content is released. The remaining 20 percent of the content enters the siphon tube as a gas. The rapid expansion from a liquid to a gas, when the CO_2 leaves the discharge horn, produces a refrigerating effect that converts about 30 percent of the liquid to a solid "snow" or "dry ice" which soon sublimes into a gas.

Hand portable models are transported by a carrying handle which is attached to the valve assembly. To operate

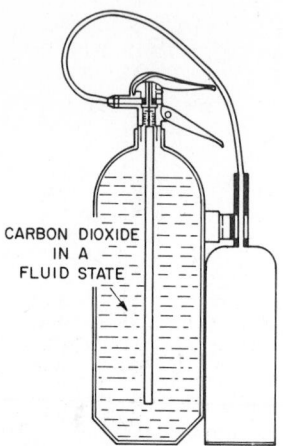

Fig. 16-3E. Carbon dioxide fire extinguisher.

the extinguisher it is held in an upright position, the locking ring pin is pulled, and the operating lever is squeezed. Older models have a valve wheel (instead of an operating lever) which is turned. On the smaller 2 to 5 lb models the discharge horn is attached to the valve assembly by a metal tube/swing-joint connector. The smaller models are designed to be operated with one hand. On the larger hand portables, the discharge horn is attached to several feet of flexible hose. The larger models require a "two-hand" operation. Wheeled models have a cylinder valve (with a locking ring pin), a long hose (15 to 40 ft), and a projector which consists of a horn, long handle, and control valve. Once the cylinder valve is opened, the operator controls the discharge with the valve on the projector handle.

The extinguishers have a limited range which varies from a maximum of 3 ft for the smaller sizes, to 8 ft for the larger sizes. The initial application must start relatively close to the fire (about 3 to 4 ft), but not so close as to "blast" burning liquids from an open vessel or across an open space. Minimum discharge time varies from 8 to 30 sec, depending on size. The most commonly used method of agent application is to start at the near edge and direct the discharge in a slow, side-to-side sweeping motion, gradually progressing toward the back of the fire. The other method is called overhead application. The horn handle is grasped in a downward thrust dagger position, and the discharge is directed at an angle of about 45° toward the center of the burning area. Generally, the horn is not moved, as in the other method, because the discharge stream enters the fire from above and spreads out in all directions over the burning surface. The side-to-side sweeping method may give better results on spill fires, and the overhead method may be best for confined fires. Agent application should be continued (even after the flames appear to be extinguished) to allow added time for cooling and, if possible, to prevent any reflash from adjacent hot surfaces or open fingers of flame.

On fires involving electrical equipment, discharge should be directed into the source of the flames. It is important to de-energize the equipment as soon as possible, to eliminate the potential source of reignition.

The discharge horn can become extremely cold during operation, and should not be touched. In using these extinguishers in subzero temperatures, the valve must remain open at all times as a blockage of the discharge may occur if the extinguisher is operated intermittently (unless, of course, a special low temperature charge is added).

C.   Liquefied Gas Extinguishers

Bromochlorodifluoromethane (Halon 1211) extinguishers are currently available in sizes having a capacity of 2 to 12 lbs. Larger sizes, including wheeled models, are currently under development. This type of extinguisher is primarily intended for use on Class B:C fires. When the smaller sizes are used on Class A fires, some degree of control may be achieved until water or other suitable Class A extinguishants can be employed. Listed ratings for the smaller sizes range from 2 to 10 B:C.

The Halon 1211 extinguisher consists of an agent chamber (shell), siphon tube and valve for releasing the agent, and a discharge nozzle or hose/nozzle combination. The agent is retained under pressure in a liquid state in a lightweight, mild steel or aluminum alloy shell. Although the agent has a medium vapor pressure of about 40 psia at 70°F, the shell is super-pressurized with nitrogen to improve operation. Upon actuation, the vapor pressure causes the agent to expand so that the discharge stream consists of a mixture of liquid and vapor droplets. The smaller sizes have a horizontal stream range of 9 to 15 ft which is not affected by wind as much as CO_2 or bromotrifluoromethane (Halon 1301). Halon 1211 does not have the cooling/refrigerating effect that is typical of CO_2.

On Class B fires, Halon 1211 extinguishers are used in the same manner as an operator would apply agent from a CO_2 or Halon 1301 (bromotrifluoromethane) extinguisher. Best results are achieved with a slow side-to-side sweeping technique. The initial discharge should not be directed at the burning surface at close range, or the force of the stream may cause the fire to spread. On Class C fires the agent should be directed at the source of the flames and, if possible, the equipment should be de-energized as the electricity presents a potential source of reignition. Halon 1211 leaves no residue to clean up, is virtually noncorrosive, is nonabrasive, and is more effective than CO_2; however, it is slightly more toxic than Halon 1301. Test data indicate that inhalation of 4-5 percent for 1 min is the maximum that can be safely tolerated. When used on a fire, the decomposition products consist of hydrogen chloride, hydrogen bromide, hydrogen fluoride, and traces of free halogens. Normally, only small quantities of these materials are formed and, as a warning of their presence, they give off sharp acrid odors. Breathing of vapors should be avoided, especially in confined and unventilated spaces or both.

When stored under pressure, bromotrifluoromethane (Halon 1301) is a liquefied gas extinguishant which is recommended for use on Class B:C fires. Only one extinguisher of this type is available, having a capacity of 2½ lbs and a rating of 2-B:C. Although the manufacturer has withdrawn this extinguisher from the commercial market, it is still being produced for the Federal government.

The design, operational characteristics, and fire fighting techniques are virtually the same as for the 2½-lb CO_2 extinguisher. The discharge time is 8 to 10 sec with a stream range of 4 to 6 ft. Although the agent has a high vapor pressure and is self-expelling, a booster charge of nitrogen is added to improve operation at low temperatures. On a weight-of-agent basis, bromotrifluoromethane (Halon 1301) has about the same fire extinguishing capacity as sodium bicarbonate dry chemical, and about twice that of CO_2. Both in its normal state and after decomposition, brought about by fire fighting, bromotrifluoromethane (Halon 1301) in the amounts contained in this extinguisher should not present a toxicity problem. However, breathing of vapors should be avoided, especially in unventilated

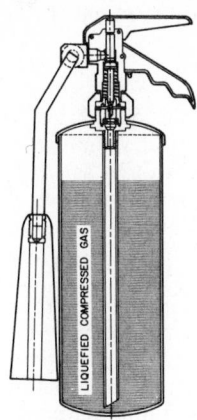

Fig. 16-3F. Liquefied-gas fire extinguisher.

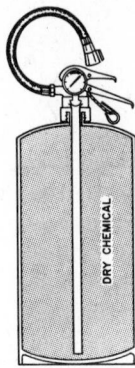

Fig. 16-3H. Dry-chemical fire extinguisher, stored pressure with disposable shell.

spaces such as small rooms, closets, motor vehicles, etc. To recharge, the spent cylinder is removed and replaced with a new self-pressurized container.

D. Dry Chemical Extinguishers

Cartridge-operated hand portable models range in size from 4 to 30 lbs, and stored pressure models from 1 to 30 lbs. For models filled with the same type of dry chemical agent, the listed rating for any particular size may vary somewhat between manufacturers. However, there is considerable variation in the extinguishing performance of the five general types of dry chemical agents currently in use (see Part A, Chap. 2, this Section). For example, one manufacturer has 20-lb stored pressure models listed at 40-B:C with sodium bicarbonate base agent, 60-B:C with multipurpose agent, and 80-B:C with Purple K. This does not imply that the best extinguisher is the one with the highest rating. End usage and operational features are of primary consideration.

Although all dry chemical agents are treated for water repellancy to minimize the likelihood of caking (hardening), it is essential to avoid moisture contamination during storage, handling, and recharging.

Expellant Methods

There are two methods whereby dry chemical agent can be discharged from an extinguisher shell depending on the

basic design of the extinguisher. They are the (1) cartridge-operated method and (2) the stored pressure method.

Cartridge Operated: This design consists of a chamber, with a large fill opening at the top, in which the agent is kept at atmospheric pressure. A small cylinder of propellant gas (CO_2 or nitrogen) is threaded into a puncture valve and gas tube assembly attached to the side of the shell. The agent is discharged through a hose attached to the bottom edge of the shell. Discharge of the agent is controlled by a squeeze grip nozzle on the end of the hose.

To activate, the extinguisher is generally placed on the ground in an upright position (although some operators choose to pressurize while carrying). The nozzle should first be removed from its holder and held in one hand while the puncture lever is pushed down. On some models, a locking ring pin must first be pulled to release the puncture lever. Pushing the puncture lever releases the propellant gas which, in turn, pressurizes the large chamber containing the dry chemical agent. Operation requires two hands: one hand is needed to carry the extinguisher, and the other hand is needed to release and direct agent discharge. It is important to note that several hours after the extinguisher is pressurized the propellant gas can leak away and result in a "dead" extinguisher, even though no agent has been discharged. Recharging should take place promptly after actuation or use.

Stored Pressure: There are two types of stored pressure dry chemical extinguishers: one type has a disposable shell, and the other type has a rechargeable shell. For most disposable models, the agent and pressurizing gas is in a factory-sealed cylinder which is threaded into a valve and nozzle assembly. Following use, the spent cylinder is discarded and a new one is attached to the assembly. Some small models are disposable, and are designed so that the entire extinguisher can be discarded.

Once the extinguisher has been used, even though only a small amount of agent has been discharged, particles may adhere to the valve seat and allow the propellant gas to leak away. Recharging or replacement should immediately take place.

For rechargeable models, the propellant gas (usually nitrogen) and the agent are intermixed in the extinguisher shell. Once the extinguisher is activated, the agent is forced up the siphon tube where its release can be controlled by the operator. From a mechanical standpoint, there are two distinct design types. Each type can be used either intermittently or continuously, depending on the nature of the fire. One type has a threaded valve assembly and a combination carrying handle/operating lever which screws into the fill

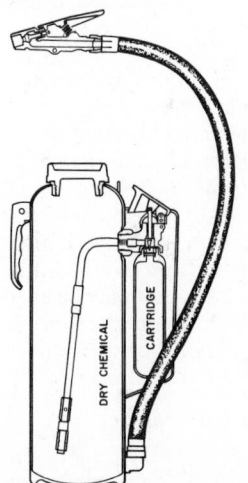

Fig. 16-3G. Dry-chemical fire extinguisher, cartridge operated.

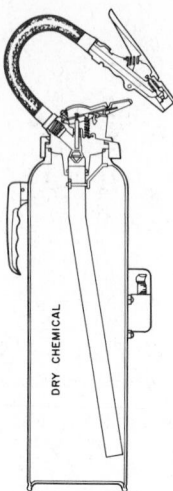

DRY CHEMICAL

Fig. 16-31. Dry-chemical fire extinguisher, stored pressure with rechargeable shell.

opening on the top of the shell. Once the locking device is released, the agent can be discharged by squeezing the operating lever. On small sizes, because the nozzle is part of the valve assembly, only one hand is needed for operation. Larger sizes, having a hose and nozzle, require two hands for operation. One hand is needed to squeeze the operating lever and carry the extinguisher, and the other hand is needed to direct the agent discharge from the hose.

The other rechargeable model has a release lever, and a hose, attached to the cap assembly, covers the fill opening. The other end of the hose has a squeeze grip nozzle for controlling the discharge. To activate, the ring pin is pulled and the release lever is pushed down. Upon activation, the agent travels up the hose to the nozzle where its discharge is controlled by the operator. This model requires a "two-hand" operation; one to carry the extinguisher, the other to release and direct the agent discharge. The manufacture of this model was discontinued in 1974.

Principles of Using Dry Chemical Extinguishers

All dry chemical extinguishers less than 10 lb in size will discharge their entire contents in 8 to 10 sec. Models weighing 10 lbs and larger may take as long as 30 sec. Therefore, since there is little time for experimentation, it is important that the operator be prepared to correctly apply the agent at the outset. All dry chemical extinguishers can be carried and operated simultaneously, and can be discharged intermittently. The discharge stream has a horizontal range of 5 to 30 ft depending on extinguisher size. The stream should be directed at the base of the flame. Best results are generally obtained by attacking the near edge of the fire and progressing forward, moving the nozzle rapidly with a side-to-side sweeping motion. Care must also be taken not to direct the initial discharge directly at the burning surface at close range (less than 5 to 8 ft) because the high-velocity of the stream may cause splashing and/or scattering of the burning material. When used on outdoor fires, maximum effectiveness can be achieved when the wind is in back of the operator. In this way the wind bends the flames away from him and helps to carry the agent into the area of the fire, thus extending the effective range. Special long-range nozzles are available where potential fire fighting conditions may require greater distance. These nozzles are also useful on pressurized gas or liquid fires, or where strong winds prevail. All dry chemical agents can be used at the same time that water (straight stream or fog) is being applied.

Dry Chemical on Class A Fires

For Class A fires, the only listed dry chemical agent is multipurpose dry chemical. Although this agent extinguishes the flames in the same manner as other dry chemical agents, when in contact with hot surfaces it has the additional characteristic of softening. In this way it can adhere to burning materials and form a coating which will smother and isolate the fuel from air. When applying the agent, it is important to try and coat all burning areas in order to eliminate or minimize the number of small embers which may be a potential source of reignition. The agent itself has little cooling effect and cannot penetrate below the burning surface. This means that multipurpose dry chemical cannot be relied upon for the extinguishment of deep-seated fires. It is usually desirable to watch carefully for any evidence of rekindling, and to subsequently apply water where more rapid cooling is desired.

Under certain conditions dry chemical agents other than the multipurpose type may be used with a limited degree of effectiveness on Class A fires. Once the flames are extinguished, the operator should kick or poke apart the fire debris. This will assist and hasten the natural cooling of burning embers. Hot spots or small areas that reignite can be controlled with short intermittent bursts of agent. If available, water can be used to extinguish burning embers or deep-seated hot spots. It is recommended that this method of extinguishment be attempted only if the operator has had training and previous experience in this technique.

Dry Chemical on Class B Fires

Although operational features may vary with different models, the techniques for fire fighting are basically the same as described in the previous paragraph. Correct application techniques for extinguishing Class B fires will vary depending on actual fire conditions. In general, there are six types of Class B fires, i.e., liquid spills, liquids in depth, three dimensional (running or falling) liquid leaks or spills, pressurized liquid leaks, and pressurized gas discharge. Where obstacles are present in the fire area, a more difficult extinguishing condition will be encountered. For example, in a spill fire in a flammable liquid storage room where 55-gal drums are standing on the floor the drums would present an obstacle by shielding the flames from a lone operator. This type of fire condition requires the combined attack of two operators.

The effect of dry chemical extinguishers on Class B fires is most commonly explained as a "chain-breaking reaction" wherein the chemicals used prevent the union of free radical particles in the combustion process so that combustion does not continue when the flame front is completely covered with the agent. Reflashing can occur if hot surfaces or another ignition source remains in the fire area, or if the dry chemical does not cover the entire flaming area. The intensity with which Class B fires burn, and the complex extinguishing conditions that may be encountered, are prime reasons for providing comprehensive training to potential operators. Proper application techniques are frequently of critical importance in achieving effective results.

Dry Chemical on Class C Fires

When Class A or Class B fires, or both, involve live electrical equipment, dry chemical can be effectively and safely used under dry conditions. If a moisture film is present due to dampness or water, dry chemical agents may combine to form a conductive path to ground. The initial discharge should first be directed at the base of the flames, and then rapidly sprayed over other burning areas. Because it presents a potential source of reignition, it is important to shut off electrical power as soon as possible. De-energizing will also prevent arcing and equipment damage or both that may be caused by the dry chemical. Once the power is off the fire is essentially a Class A or Class B fire, or both, and it may be more practical to utilize a different agent for final extinguishment. Before de-energized electrical equipment is returned to service, it is essential to clean off all agent residue to avoid damage that could be caused by abrasion, corrosion, current leakage, or reduced conductivity.

E. Dry Powder Extinguishers

Only one type of hand portable extinguisher is available for use on combustible metal fires: it is a 30-lb cartridge-operated model with a design similar to the cartridge-operated dry chemical extinguisher. With the nozzle fully open, it has a range of 6 to 8 ft. The extinguishing agent is composed of sodium chloride (NaCl), with additives to render it free flowing in order to cause it to form a crust over the fire. Particle size is controlled for optimum extinguishing effectiveness. A thermoplastic material is added to bind the NaCl particles into a solid mass when applied on burning metals.

The cartridge-operated dry powder extinguisher is also available with a sodium carbonate base agent. This dry powder agent was specifically developed to satisfy the need for a low chloride extinguishant for use on sodium metal fires only. It is nonabrasive, nonconductive, and has extinguishing characteristics which are similar to the sodium chloride base agent.

The method of agent application depends on the type of metal, the quantity which is burning, and its physical form. In the case of a very hot fire, initial discharge should be started at maximum range with the nozzle fully open. Once control is established, the nozzle valve should be partially closed to produce a soft heavy flow so that complete and safe coverage can be done at close range. The nozzle is designed so that the operator can throttle or reduce the rate and force of the agent discharge. This technique is extremely important when the metal is in the form of granules, chips, turnings, or a liquid, so that the burning material will not be scattered. For most small metal fires, the agent should be continuously applied until a thick layer covers the burning area. The heat given off by the metal fire will cause the agent to form a hard crust which should not be broken until the metal has cooled. When applying the agent to a casting fire, the operator should throttle the discharge so that it will adhere to vertical surfaces, thus making it unnecessary to completely bury the casting. Extinguishment is achieved by excluding air and containment until the burning metal cools below its ignition temperature. When dark brown spots form on the crust, it is an indication that more agent should be applied to form a thicker layer. Additional information on metal fires and other types of extinguishing materials is contained in Section 13, Chapter 6.

F. Wheeled Extinguishers

Where extra hazard conditions prevail, wheeled extinguishers containing either carbon dioxide, foam, dry chemical, or dry powder may be utilized. Although the operating characteristics and techniques of application may be somewhat similar to the respective hand portable models, it is advisable that only trained operators use this equipment. The size and intensity of the fire on which this equipment may be used requires the expertise of an operator who periodically receives practical experience in using wheeled extinguishers on live fires.

Wheeled carbon dioxide models with capacities of 50, 75, and 100 lbs have listed ratings ranging from 10-B:C to 40-B:C. Depending on size, they have an effective horizontal range of 8 to 10 ft and a discharge time ranging from 10 to 30 sec.

Dry chemical models for Class B:C fires range in capacity from 50 to 350 lbs, and are available with the same types of agents used in the hand portable models. Listed ratings vary from 40-B:C to 480-B:C, depending on the amount and type of agent. The effective horizontal range varies from 15 to 70 ft with an approximate discharge time ranging from 30 to 150 sec. Multipurpose dry chemical models are available in capacities of 50 to 300 lbs with listed ratings of 20-A to 40-A, and 60-B:C to 240-B:C. The horizontal discharge range is from 15 to 45 ft, and the discharge time is 30 to 60 sec.

Wheeled foam extinguishers for Class A:B fires, although no longer listed by UL, are still used to a limited extent and may be obtained on special order.

A dry powder extinguisher is available in a wheeled model having a capacity of 350 lbs.

G. Obsolete Extinguishers

In 1969 the manufacture of all inverting type extinguishers (soda-acid, foam, and cartridge-operated water and loaded stream) was discontinued in the United States. Subsequently, extinguishers of this type are no longer being tested and listed by UL. It was not only the difficult and unorthodox "upside-down" method of actuation that brought about the discontinuance of these extinguishers: of significantly greater importance was the fact that after being in service for 10 to 15 years, the inverting types tended to lose their reliability in meeting the minimum test pressure requirements of the NFPA Extinguisher Standard (original factory test pressure). When pressurized, the failure record, including hydrostatic test failures, was alarmingly high. Since the inverting types are not normally pressurized, potential failures are generally not evident until the time of operation or hydrostatic testing.

When inverted, normal operating pressures are about 100 psi: however, should the discharge elbow or hose become blocked, pressures in excess of 300 psi may occur. Numerous failures have occurred that have resulted in serious injury or death to the operator. From an operational standpoint, these extinguishers have many disadvantages compared to more modern types. Some of these disadvantages are:

1. They are extremely good conductors of electricity.
2. They cannot be turned off once actuated.
3. The agent is more corrosive than plain water.
4. Inspection, maintenance, and recharging is more costly.
5. They are more costly to service.
6. They are potentially dangerous to the operator during use.

There are still several million inverting type extinguishers in use, with soda-acid models accounting for about 85 percent. It is good practice to terminate the use of all inverting types and to use currently manufactured extinguishers of other types as replacements. As the availability of suitable replacement parts and recharge materials diminishes, it will become increasingly more difficult to maintain these types of extinguishers in a safe and reliable operating condition.

Vaporizing liquid extinguishers of the CCl_4 (carbon tetrachloride) and CBM (chlorobromomethane) type became obsolete in the late 1960s. The toxic properties of these agents exposed the operator to unwarranted health hazard conditions, and their use was supplanted by safer, more effective extinguishers. If any extinguishers of this type are found in use they should be promptly destroyed and replaced with currently available extinguishers. The information contained herein is for historical purposes.

Soda-acid Extinguishers

This extinguisher was most commonly manufactured in the 2½-gal size, weighing about 30 lbs fully charged, with a listed rating of 2A for use on Class A fires only. Some models were also manufactured in the hand portable size of 1¼ and 1½ gal, and in wheeled models with capacities of 17 and 33 gal.

As its name implies, this extinguisher contains two chemicals; sodium bicarbonate and sulfuric acid. Inside and near the top of the extinguisher shell is an acid bottle or container supported in an upright position by a wire cage. This container has a loose lead or ceramic stopple, and contains a quantity of 66° baume sulfuric acid (4 oz in the 2½-gal units). The extinguisher shell is filled to a prescribed level with water in which a specific quantity of sodium bicarbonate has been thoroughly dissolved. When the extinguisher is inverted, the loose stopple moves to allow the acid to slowly intermix with the soda solution to form carbon dioxide. At the time of mixing the extinguisher becomes a pressure vessel, and it is important that the extinguisher shell is not in a weakened condition due to corrosive action or physical damage. When these extinguishers are located in areas subject to low temperatures (below 40°F), they must be placed in heated enclosures to prevent freezeup. Antifreeze additives should never be put into the bicarbonate solution, as this would interfere with the needed chemical reaction and render the extinguisher inoperative and even unsafe.

Cartridge-operated Water Extinguishers

This type of extinguisher closely resembles the soda-acid extinguisher. In general, their operational and fire fighting characteristics are very similar. The most common model manufactured was the 2½-gal size which had a listed rating of 2-A. Some 1¼-gal models rated at 1-A were also manufactured.

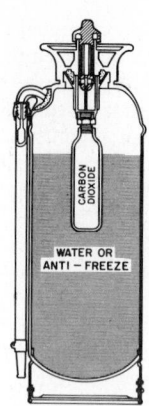

Fig. 16-3K. Cartridge operated water fire extinguisher.

The extinguisher shell contained water, and a small cylinder of carbon dioxide gas that provided the expellant force to discharge the water. Two basic designs were used to hold and puncture the CO_2 cylinder. One employed a sliding pin type plunger which was part of the cap. To operate, the extinguisher was inverted and bumped on the ground. This would cause the pin to break the seal of the CO_2 cylinder which was screwed into a fitting on the underside of the cap. In the other type, the CO_2 cylinder was placed in a cage located within the shell just below the cap. Upon inversion, the weight of the cylinder would cause it to strike a rupture pin. Sometimes this model also needed to be bumped on the ground to break the seal.

By filling it with an antifreeze agent, it was possible to install this extinguisher in areas which were subject to freezing temperatures. Potassium carbonate was used in stainless steel shells, and the less expensive calcium chloride was used in brass or copper shells.

Foam Extinguishers

Foam extinguishers are similar in external appearance to soda-acid extinguishers. They were most popular in the 2½-gal size and were useful on both Class A and Class B fires. A typical listed rating for a 2½-gal size was 2-A:4-B. Other sizes manufactured included 1¼ and 1½-gal hand portables, and 17 and 33-gal wheeled models. The 33-gal size is still available on special order.

The extinguisher has an inner chamber or cylinder, fitted with a loose stopple, which contains an aluminum sulphate "A" solution. The main extinguisher shell is filled to the prescribed level with the "B" solution which contains sodium bicarbonate and a foam-stabilizing agent. When the extinguisher is inverted, the stopple moves just enough to

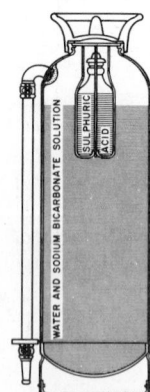

Fig. 16-3J. Soda-acid fire extinguisher.

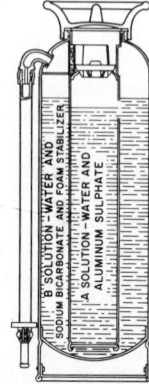

Fig. 16-3L. Foam type fire extinguisher.

Fig. 16-3M. Vaporizing liquid fire extinguisher.

allow the "A" solution to intermix with the "B" solution to produce carbon dioxide, the expellant gas evolved from the mixture, and a liquid foam that expands in a ratio of approximately 1 to 8; i.e., $2\frac{1}{2}$ gal of solution produces a minimum of 18 gal of foam (see Sec. 13, Chap. 2 for information on chemical foam).

When these extinguishers are located in areas subject to low temperatures (below 40°F), they must be placed in heated enclosures to prevent freezeup. Antifreeze additives should never be put into the bicarbonate solution, as they would interfere with the needed chemical reaction and render the extinguisher inoperative and even unsafe.

Although foam extinguishers were primarily designed for use on Class B fires, they could be used on Class A fires with about the same effectiveness as soda-acid. For fires in ordinary combustible materials, the foam is used to directly coat the burning surface. For liquid spill fires the foam can be flowed over the burning surface by bouncing it off the floor just ahead of the flame front, or by standing back and curving the foam stream upward so that it will fall lightly on the burning area. On flammable liquid fires of appreciable depth, best results are obtained when the discharge from the extinguisher is played against the inside of the back wall of the vat or tank just above the burning surface, so as to permit the natural spread of the foam back over the burning liquid. If this cannot be done, the operator should stand far enough away from the fire to allow the foam to fall lightly upon the burning surface. Discharging the foam stream directly into the burning liquid might cause the fire to spread to other areas. Where possible, walking around the fire while directing the stream will give maximum coverage during the discharge period.

Vaporizing Liquid Extinguishers

Historically, this type of extinguisher was produced in two basic designs: (1) where the agent was expelled by means of a manually operated pump, and (2) where the expellant force was a gas (carbon dioxide or nitrogen) or air, stored either within the agent chamber or from an attached cartridge. The extinguishing agent was listed for Class B:C fires and consisted of either specially treated CCl_4 or CBM. Although both are liquids, they vaporize too quickly to be effective on deep-seated fires in Class A materials.

The hand pump operated models came in sizes ranging from 1 qt to 2 gal, with the most common size being 1 qt. Pressure operated models came in sizes ranging from 1 qt to $3\frac{1}{2}$ gal. When the agent stream was directed at the base of a fire, it rapidly evaporated to form a smothering blanket of vapor that was heavier than air and would not support combustion.

SI Units

The following conversion factors are given as a convenience in converting to SI units the English units used in this chapter.

1 in.	$= 25.4$ mm
1 ft	$= 0.305$ m
1 lb (mass)	$= 0.454$ kg
1 oz (mass)	$= 28.350$ g
1 psi	$= 6.895$ kPa
$\frac{5}{9}$(°F − 32)	$= °C$
1 (U.S.) gal	$= 3.785$ litres

Bibliography

(see Page 16-33)

Chapter 4

INSPECTION AND MAINTENANCE OF FIRE EXTINGUISHERS

Once the purchaser of a fire extinguisher installs an extinguisher, it becomes the responsibility of that purchaser, or his assigned agent, to maintain the device so that it remains fully operable. To adequately fulfill this responsibility, there should be a program to provide for: (1) periodic inspection of each extinguisher, (2) an effective fire extinguisher maintenance program, (3) recharging each extinguisher following discharge, and (4) hydrostatic testing of each extinguisher requiring such checks. Frequently items (3) and (4) are part of item (2), the extinguisher maintenance program.

A fire equipment servicing agency is usually the most reliable means available to the general public for having maintenance and recharging performed. Large industries often find it desirable to establish their own maintenance and recharge facilities by training personnel to perform these functions.

A. Basic Principles

The principles of maintaining fire extinguishers in good working order evolve around a systematic approach to inspection and maintenance procedures and attention to precise and orderly records of the work that has been done on them.

Inspection

Inspection is defined as a "quick check" to visually determine that the fire extinguisher is available and will operate. The intent is to give reasonable assurance that the extinguisher is fully charged and will function effectively when fulfilling its intended purpose.

Inspection should determine that the extinguisher is: (1) in its designated place, (2) is conspicuous, (3) that access to it is not obstructed in any way, (4) that it has not been actuated and partially or fully emptied, (5) that it has not been tampered with, (6) that it has not sustained any obvious physical damage or been subjected to adverse environment conditions which could interfere with its operation (such as corrosive fumes), and (7) if the extinguisher is equipped with a sight gage to indicate operability and tamper indicators, or both, that each shows conditions to be satisfactory. Inspections are useful to check the maintenance record tag, which should be provided on each unit for the most recent maintenance date.

The effectiveness of inspections depends upon the frequency, regularity, and thoroughness with which they are done. If the premises are small and there are only a few extinguishers the manager, property owner, or some designated person can check these extinguishers at the beginning of each work day. If the premises are large enough to employ security guards or watchmen, extinguishers can be inspected at least once on each 8-hr shift. In industrial plants, the plant fire brigade or fire inspector is often charged with making extinguisher inspections on either a daily, weekly, or monthly basis. An individual evaluation must be made of each property and situation to determine the needed frequency of inspections.

Some of the items to consider are: (1) the nature of the hazards being protected (which would influence the potential use of the equipment), (2) the exposure of the extinguisher to tampering, vandalism, and malicious mischief, (3) any extraordinary atmospheric conditions, (4) the likelihood of the equipment being accidentally damaged, and (5) the possibility that visual or physical obstructions might interfere with the accessibility of extinguishers. Where a particular operation is potentially "fire prone" or is crucial to the use of the property, or both, more frequent inspections are made of all extinguishers. For example, if all the products manufactured in a particular industrial plant had to be painted before they could be sold, a fire in the painting room could be disastrous. Here inspections should be very frequent. Past experience showing high fire frequencies would clearly indicate the need for greater attention to the operating condition and the availability of the extinguishers in that particular location.

Maintenance

Maintenance, as distinguished from inspection, implies that if fire extinguishers undergo a thorough check to give maximum assurance, they will operate properly and safely. A maintenance check includes a complete examination of each extinguisher, the making of any necessary repairs, recharging, or replacement of parts. Maintenance checks sometimes reveal the need for special testing of extinguisher shells or other components. A maintenance check involves disassembly of the extinguisher, examination of all its parts, cleaning, replacement of any defective parts, reassembly, recharging, and, where appropriate, repressurization. Such a maintenance check may reveal that the extinguisher container should be hydrostatically tested or even scrapped and replaced.

Maintenance should be performed at periodic intervals; at least once a year, after each use, or when the need becomes obvious during an inspection. For example, if, during an inspection, there is evidence of serious damage by corrosion, the extinguisher should be subjected to a thorough maintenance check even though it may have recently undergone such a check. After such a condition is detected, steps should be taken to eliminate the source of the corrosive fumes before the extinguisher is returned to service. This same problem can also be solved by substituting a corrosion-resistant extinguisher, or by protecting the extinguisher by means of an enclosure. Similarly, if an inspection shows evidence of tampering, that the extinguisher has been physically damaged, or if there is evidence of agent leakage, a complete maintenance check should be initiated.

Tags, Seals, and Tamper Indicators

Extinguisher tags have been used for many years as a convenient means for recording periodic inspections. Some firms also use tags to record the dates that maintenance service is performed. Generally, for routine inspections, a tied-on tag or pressure-sensitive label is used to record the date and the inspector's initials. If inspection or maintenance is performed by an independent fire extinguisher servicing company, that company will have a tag attached to the extinguisher. Should the owner do his own inspections and maintenance, he will need to purchase record-keeping tags or labels.

Seals and tamper detectors should be utilied in conjunction with an extinguisher inspection program. The seal or tamper indicator may consist of a thread, band, plastic insert, or other device that conforms to the standards of the testing laboratories. Lead and wire seals were commonly used until plastic seals were introduced in 1972. As long as the device remains unbroken, there is reasonable assurance that the actuating mechanism of the extinguisher has not been used. (It is important, however, to note that a stored-pressure extinguisher can develop a leak and lose its pressure even though the tamper indicator has remained intact. A maintenance examination should be performed when extinguishers are found with broken or missing seals or tamper indicators.

B. Maintenance Operations

In any maintenance program for portable fire extinguishers there are three basic items that need to be checked:

1. The mechanical parts of the device (that is, the extinguisher shell and other component parts).

2. The amount and condition of the extinguishing agent.

3. The condition of the means for expelling.

Fire extinguisher maintenance programs include the keeping of a record of dates of purchase as well as maintenance dates. Although these dates may be logged on the extinguisher, a separate record is desirable that includes information such as:

1. The maintenance date and the name of the person or agency performing the maintenance.

2. The date when last recharged and the name of the person or agency performing the recharge.

3. The hydrostatic retest data and the name of the person or agency performing the hydrostatic test.

4. Description of dents remaining after passing a hydrostatic test.

5. The date of the 6-year maintenance for certain stored-pressure dry chemical types.

Persons responsible for performing maintenance may be trained industrial safety or maintenance personnel, extinguisher service agencies, or individual owners (e.g., self-employed, home owner, boat owner, car owner, etc.)

Individuals who own extinguishers often neglect them because there is no planned periodic follow-up program. It is recommended that such owners become familiar enough with their extinguishers so that they can detect telltale warnings which may suggest the need for maintenance. An alternative is to have the dealer from whom the extinguisher was purchased establish an annual follow-up maintenance program.

The purpose of a well-planned and well-executed maintenance program is to afford the probability that an extinguisher will:

1. Operate properly between the time intervals established for maintenance examinations in the environment to which it is exposed.

2. Not constitute a potential hazard to persons in its vicinity, or to operators or rechargers of extinguishers. Any parts needed for replacement should be obtained from the manufacturer or his representative.

On properties where extinguishers are maintained by the occupant, a supply of recharging materials should be kept on hand. When recharging other than plain water extinguishers, use only those recharging materials specified on the extinguisher nameplate. Other recharging materials may impair the efficiency of the extinguisher, or may cause a malfunction that could result in the rupture of the extinguisher and serious injury to the operator. Special precautions are necessary for certain specific types of extinguishers which are discussed separately in this chapter.

Extinguishers that are pressure vessels, have threaded connections, and they can be a weak point. Damaged or mismatched threaded connections cannot be tolerated in the interest of safety to the operator and the proper functioning of the extinguisher.

The NFPA Extinguisher Standard has an appendix which contains a checklist of items requiring maintenance examination. One section of the checklist is arranged to pinpoint the mechanical parts (containers and their compounds) common to most extinguishers. This lists such items as the extinguisher shell, nameplate, nozzle or horn, hose assembly, restraining or locking device, gage or pressure indicating device, shell or cylinder valve, nozzle shutoff valve, puncture mechanism, gas cartridge, gas cylinders, wheel cap or fill cap, disposable shell, carriage and wheels, carrying handle, seals or tamper indicator, hand pump, inner cage, chamber stopple, acid container or tube, pressurizing valve, gasket "O" ring and seals, brackets, gas tube and siphon or pickup tube, pressure regulator, and safety relief device.

The second part of the checklist is arranged by expelling means and extinguishing material. Extinguishers of the stored-pressure type involve a pressure vessel. Hence, it is mandatory to depressurize the unit before making a complete maintenance check of the device. After such depressurization, the extinguisher can be opened for detailed investigation and cleaning. As opposed to those using water, a loaded stream, or a liquefied gas, different checks are needed for stored pressure extinguishers utilizing dry chemicals.

Most of the stored-pressure types of extinguishers of modern design have a sight gage to indicate whether the extinguisher is pressurized. These sight gages have a low pressure marking, and as long as the arrow is pointed in the "normal" pressure zone, the units are generally assumed to be operable. During maintenance, it is important to verify that the sight gage gives an accurate indication of the operability of the unit (i.e., that the needle is not stuck or damaged).

Water Type Extinguishers

Inspection and maintenance for stored-pressure models is frequently regarded as quite simple. Other than routine inspection checks, or unless the extinguisher has been used or an inspection reveals a defective condition, maintenance is sometimes disregarded until the 5-year hydrostatic test is performed. This practice has resulted in many failures and malfunctions. Principal items that need to be checked during an inspection are: worn or damaged hose, loose hose, plugged nozzle, dented shell, damaged indicator gage, and a damaged or jammed ring pin. Normal maintenance service, as specified in the NFPA Extinguisher Standard, must be performed annually.

Mechanical pump extinguishers, such as pump tanks and back packs, are easy to inspect and maintain, although the tanks containing the water or antifreeze solution must be checked to ensure they are in good condition, have not been weakened by corrosive action, and do not contain sediment which would tend to block the stream during the pumping operation. For any 12-month period during which the extinguisher has not been used, it is advisable to remove the liquid from the tank, flush the tank, and then fill it with new liquid. Pumps may require lubrication from time to time.

They should be checked annually to be sure that the plungers are in proper condition, that seals and washers have not deteriorated, and that vents are not clogged. Antifreeze solutions may need to be checked to determine that they provide the proper protection against the ambient temperatures encountered, and that they have not been contaminated.

Dry Chemical Extinguishers

Dry chemical extinguishers should be inspected monthly. They should also undergo normal annual maintenance. The quantity of agent for cartridge-operated models can be checked by weighing, or by removing the fill cap and checking visually. The gas cartridge is also checked by weighing. For stored-pressure models the pressure gage will indicate if adequate pressure is maintained, and the agent quantity is checked by weighing. During annual maintenance all agent should be dumped or vacuumed from the shell.

Dry chemical extinguishers need to be promptly refilled after use, even when only partially discharged. Before refilling dry chemical extinguishers, extreme caution must be taken to see that no water or moisture is allowed to enter the cylinder. Even though dry chemical agents are treated for moisture repellency, they can eventually harden if moisture is present. When dry chemical extinguishers are hydrostatically tested they must be thoroughly dried so that no trace of water or moisture remains. Before dry chemical is added it is advisable to remove all of the unused agent by dumping or vacuuming, and to remove any dry chemical residue from the hose.

The type of dry chemical specified by the manufacturer is used in recharging. For example, if an extinguisher contains a Class B:C type dry chemical (bicarbonate base or potassium chloride) it should not be replaced with a Class A:B:C agent (monoammonium phosphate base). Intermixing types of dry chemical agent can result in malfunction or damage to the extinguisher or both. The bicarbonate base agent is chemically basic and will react with the acidic monoammonium phosphate. This reaction is aggravated by exposure to heat or the presence of moisture or both in amounts as small as 0.1 percent. One result is caking (hardening) of the agent; another result that is possible is the internal corrosion of the extinguisher. Under certain conditions the reaction will cause a significant pressure buildup within the shell to the point of damage or rupture of the extinguisher.

Substituting another manufacturer's dry chemical of the same type is *not* recommended unless it has the same chemical and physical characteristics, or has been tested and found to give equivalent performance. The problems involved in substituting other than the same type chemical as supplied by the manufacturer include:

1. The flow rate of the dry chemical which could influence extinguishing efficiency.

2. The amount of agent that could be placed in the extinguisher which could influence discharge time.

3. Incompatibility between dry chemicals including chemical reactions, caking, and jamming of hose or nozzles. The flow rate can change with the particle size and density of the agent. A discharge nozzle designed to dispense efficiently one dry chemical might well be less efficient for another. An extinguisher designed to hold a given weight of one formulation might not hold the same amount of another. Dip tubes, hoses, or valves could be plugged.

In essence, do not substitute another dry chemical unless its characteristics and performance are known to be equal or better. Converting an extinguisher to use a different type

Fig. 16-4A. *Disposable shell, factory sealed dry chemical extinguisher designed primarily for home, boat, or car use.* (The Ansul Company)

of dry chemical agent or the substitution of parts are items that should be referred directly to the equipment manufacturer.

Recharge operations for the cartridge-operated models are relatively easy. The rubber sleeves on the gas tube should be checked for cracks or over-stretched shape, the gasket and the gasket seats on the shell and cap wiped clean, and the cap screwed on hand tight. In replacing the cartridge care should be taken to see that the threads are not dirty, cross-threaded or otherwise damaged. For stored-pressure models the entire valve body, stem, and "O" ring should be thoroughly cleaned (carefully wiped clean and blown out with dry nitrogen) to ensure against agent residue which might cause a pressure leak.

Nitrogen gas used for pressurizing should be of the dry commercial type so that it is free from moisture. Once the extinguisher is pressurized, it should be given a leak test or allowed to stand for about 12 hours so that it can be checked for leaks before returning to service.

Some stored-pressure extinguishers are of the factory sealed, nonrechargeable types (see Fig. 16-4A). No effort should be made to recharge these units in the field. The shell of the extinguisher is thrown away following use; normally, only the valve and nozzle assembly are retained. Factory-sealed extinguishers require refill units from the manufacturer, and detailed instructions for replacement are included on the extinguisher nameplate.

The general inspection and maintenance procedures for dry powder (Class D) extinguishers are the same as for cartridge-operated dry chemical extinguishers.

Carbon Dioxide Extinguishers

Weighing is the only method of determining that carbon dioxide extinguishers are fully charged. They should be examined at least semiannually for loss of weight, deterioration, or physical damage. Any carbon dioxide extinguisher that has a weight loss of 10 percent or more should be recharged and leak tested. Recharging is generally done by an extinguisher servicing company. However, should on-site recharging be desirable, then the equipment manufacturer should be contacted for assistance in setting up an approved recharging station.

Recharging extinguishers with carbon dioxide from dry ice converters is not advisable unless stringent restrictions are enforced to prevent the introduction of moisture into the cylinder. The vapor phase of carbon dioxide shall not be less than 99.5 percent carbon dioxide. The water content of the liquid phase shall not be more than 0.01 percent by weight ($-30°F$ dew point). Oil content of the carbon dioxide shall not exceed 10 ppm by weight.

Specific recommendations are given for such recharging in the NFPA Extinguisher Standard. The preferable source of carbon dioxide for recharging extinguishers is a low pressure carbon dioxide supply (300 psi at 0°F), either directly from the source or through dry cylinders used as an intermediary means. It cannot be emphasized too strongly that internal moisture within an extinguisher can create a serious corrosive environment. The most likely time for moisture to be introduced into a cylinder is either during the recharging operation or following a hydrostatic test.

Liquefied Gas Extinguishers

The general inspection and maintenance procedures for rechargeable liquefied gas extinguishers are similar to the requirements for other extinguishers. Bromotrifluoromethane (Halon 1301) is comparable to carbon dioxide and bromochlorodifluoromethane (Halon 1211) to stored pressure dry chemical extinguishers. Those models which are of the nonrechargeable (disposable) type are inspected and maintained in the same manner as the nonrechargeable dry chemical extinguishers.

C. Hydrostatic Testing of Extinguishers

The purposes of hydrostatic testing of portable fire extinguishers that are subject to internal pressures are to safeguard against unexpected, in-service failures from: (1) undetected internal corrosion caused by moisture in the extinguisher, (2) external corrosion caused by atmospheric humidity or corrosive vapors, (3) damage caused by rough handling (which may or may not be obvious by external inspection), (4) repeated pressurizations, (5) manufacturing flaws in the construction of the extinguisher, (6) improper assembly of valves or safety relief discs, or (7) exposure of the extinguisher to abnormal heat, as after exposure in a fire.

NFPA recommendations for hydrostatic testing call for periodic hydrostatic pressure tests not exceeding the periods for the types of extinguishers listed in Table 16-4A. The first hydrostatic retest may be conducted between the 5th and 6th years for those with a designated test interval of 5 years. These test intervals, based on experience, have been established in an effort to present general guidance. Hydrostatic tests should also be conducted immediately after dis-

Table 16-4A. Hydrostatic Test Interval for Extinguishers

Extinguisher Type	Test Interval (years)
Soda acid	5
Cartridge operated water and/or antifreeze	5
Stored pressure water and/or antifreeze	5
Wetting agent	5
Foam	5
Loaded stream	5
Dry chemical with stainless steel shells or soldered brass shells	5
Carbon dioxide	5
Dry chemical, stored pressure, with mild steel shells, brazed brass shells, or aluminum shells	12
Dry chemical, cartridge operated, with mild steel shells	12
Bromotrifluoromethane—Halon 1301	12
Bromochlorodifluoromethane—Halon 1211	12
Dry powder, cartridge operated, with mild steel shells*	12

* Except for stainless steel and steel used for compressed gas cylinders, all other steel shells are defined as "mild steel" shells.

covering any indication of mechanical injury or corrosion to the extinguisher shell.

In the United States, various rules of the U.S. Department of Transportation apply to specific types of cylinders used for fire extinguishers. Title 49 of the Code of Federal Regulations calls, with some exceptions, for the hydrostatic retesting every 5 years of compressed gas cylinders offered for interstate transportation in a charged condition. Paragraph 173.34(e) calls for periodic retesting of DOT compressed gas cylinders whether or not the cylinders are shipped interstate. Paragraph 173.301(c) requires that these cylinders be retested before a shipment can be made should the retest have become due. Par. 173.306(c) (5) specifies that fire extinguishers containing compressed gas for expelling fire extinguishing contents and having an internal volume not exceeding 1,100 cu in. and an internal pressure not exceeding 200 psi at 70°F be tested before shipment to at least 3 times the pressure in the container at 70°F when charged, and to not less than 120 psi. Similar tests must, under these rules, be accomplished before each refilling or reshipment. The exceptions to the DOT 5-year hydrostatic requirement apply to 3E and 3HT cylinders which are used to a limited extent for carbon dioxide service.

A great many different DOT specification cylinders are used for dry chemical extinguishers, including Types DOT-4B and DOT-4BA. The requirements for these types are peculiar to them.

The U.S. Coast Guard Regulations (Title 46, Code of Federal Regulations, Part 147, Paragraph 147.04-1(a)(2) and (3) specify that compressed gas cylinders brought aboard a vessel shall have been tested hydrostatically within 5 years. After that, a cylinder continuously installed in place on board a vessel as part of the vessel's equipment for a period of time exceeding 5 years, shall, after 12 years have elapsed from the date of previous test and marking, be removed from the vessel, its contents discharged, and the cylinder retested and remarked. Any cylinder, the contents of which have been discharged, or which for any cause has been removed from a vessel subsequent to 5 years from the last test, shall be retested and remarked. The Board of Transport Commissioners of Canada has published rules covering these same subjects.

The preferred way of hydrostatic testing of compressed gas cylinders is the water-jacketed, volumetric-expansion method. (It is recommended in the NFPA Extinguisher Standard.) The guide to follow in conducting this type of test is Pamphlet C-1, "Methods for Hydrostatic Testing of Compressed Gas Cylinders," published by the Compressed Gas Association, Inc. (CGA). For visually evaluating the condition of cylinders made to DOT specifications, the CGA's Pamphlet C-6, "Standard Visual Inspection of Compressed Gas Cylinders," is helpful.

Procedures for testing *other* than compressed gas extinguishers (or affixed compressed gas cylinders) are detailed in the NFPA Extinguisher Standard. Table 16-4B gives the basic data on the hydrostatic test pressure requirements. Figures 16-4B and 16-4C illustrate equipment used in this hydrostatic testing work.

It is not necessary to hydrostatically test certain extinguishers such as pump tanks, back packs, and similar devices. The factory-sealed, nonrefillable, disposable types of fire extinguishers cannot be hydrostatically tested. (Where such extinguishers are damaged they should be replaced.)

Proper hydrostatic testing requires that competent personnel do the work, that suitable testing equipment and facilities be provided, and that testers have a practical

Table 16-4B. Hydrostatic Test Pressure Requirements

Soda-acid Foam Cartridge operated water	Original factory test pressure* as shown on nameplate
Carbon dioxide extinguishers Carbon dioxide and nitrogen cylinders (used with wheeled extinguishers)	5/3 service pressure† stamped on cylinder
Carbon dioxide extinguishers with cylinder specification ICC3	3,000 psi
All stored pressure and Bromochlorodifluoromethane (1211)	Factory test pressure not to exceed 2 times the service pressure
Carbon dioxide hose assemblies	1,250 psi
Dry chemical and dry powder hose assemblies	300 psi

* The factory test pressure is the pressure at which the shell was tested at time of manufacture. This pressure is shown on the nameplate.

† The service pressure is the normal operating pressure as indicated on the gage and nameplate.

knowledge of pressure testing procedures and safeguards. Usually, a fire equipment servicing agency is the most reliable means available to the public for having this type of testing performed. Large industries may find it desirable to establish their own test facilities, and to train men to operate such facilities.

The preparation for testing and the precautions to remove all traces of water and moisture by using special drying equipment after testing are very important, and rein-

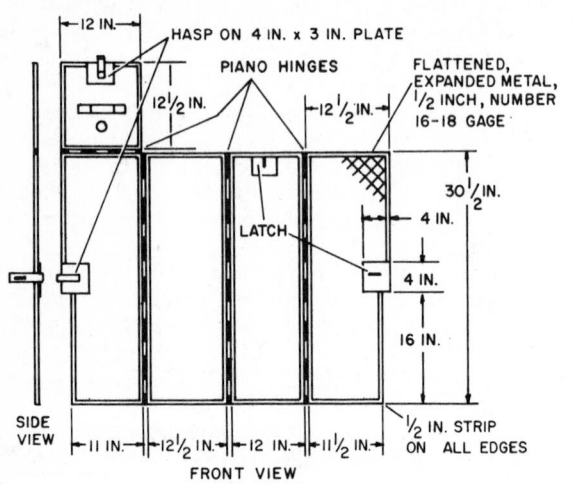

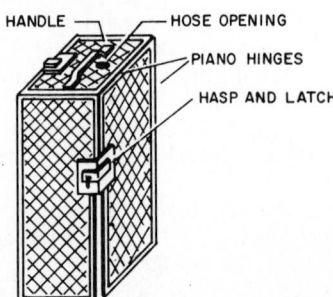

Fig. 16-4B. Low pressure portable hydrostatic test cage used for hydrostatic tests of noncompressed gas extinguishers. (Cage is not used for hydrostatic testing of compressed gas cylinders.) Cage should not be anchored to floor during testing operation. Such cages can be made by any metal fabricator.

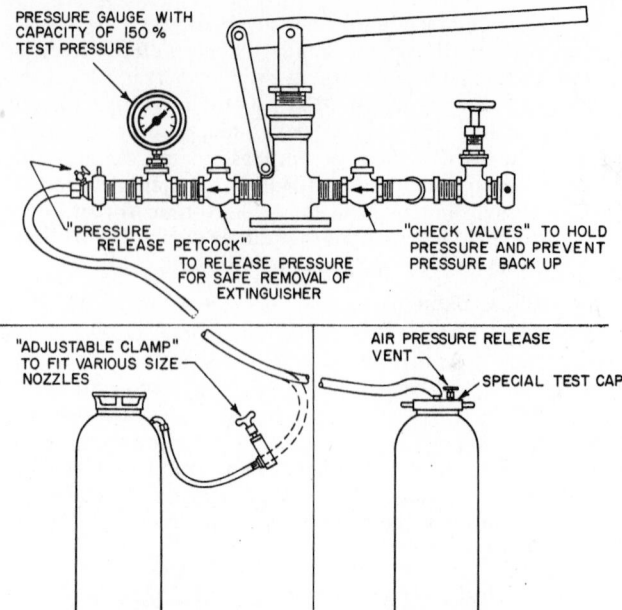

Fig. 16-4C. Hydrostatic testing equipment for use with other than compressed gas cylinders. The equipment consists of a hydrostatic test pump (top), a flexible connection for attachment to the extinguisher nozzle (lower left), or a test bonnet or fitting to attach to the extinguisher fill collar (lower right).

force the recommendation that only those experienced in this type of work should undertake such servicing.

Extinguisher hoses of certain types also need to be hydrostatically tested. Procedures for hydrostatic testing are detailed in the NFPA Extinguisher Standard.

Because hydrostatic test records are of major importance, they must be recorded on the extinguisher. For compressed gas cylinders and cartridges passing a hydrostatic test, the month and year is stamped into the cylinder in accordance with Pamphlet No. C-1, Compressed Gas Association, or the Canadian Transport Commission. It is important that the recording (stamping) be placed only on the shoulder, top head, neck, or footing (when so provided) of the cylinder. For noncompressed gas type extinguisher shells the test information should be recorded on a suitable metallic label, or on equally durable material. The label (Fig. 16-4D) should be affixed by a heatless process to the shell, and should be self-destructive if removal is attempted. The label must include the following information:

1. Month and year the test was performed, indicated by a perforation, such as by a hand punch.

2. Test pressure used.

3. Name or initials of person performing the test, or name of agency performing the test.

Emphasis is placed on the following points in connection with hydrostatic testing procedures. Allow only competent

HYDROSTATICALLY TESTED BY												
YEAR	1975				1976				1977			
MONTH	1	2	3	4	5	6	7	8	9	10	11	12
PRESSURE PSI	2 0 0		3 0 0		4 0 0		5 0 0		6 0 0		7 0 0	8 0 0

Fig. 16-4D. Typical metallic label used to record hydrostatic test data.

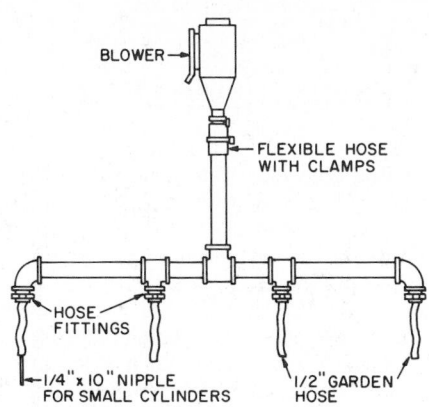

Fig. 16-4E. Drying equipment and piping arrangement for moisture removal from non-water type extinguishers.

personnel having the proper testing equipment and facilities to do the testing. Do not use air or gas for pressure testing because of the hazard of a violent rupture occurring in cases of failure. Place extinguishers undergoing test in a protective cage before applying the test pressures. Remove *all* traces of moisture from dry chemical, liquefied gas, and dry powder extinguishers after each test before refilling; a heated air stream (temperature not exceeding 150°F) is recommended for such drying (Fig. 16-4E). Destroy any extinguisher shell which fails a hydrostatic test—do not repair.

Destroy any extinguisher cylinder or shell that has one or more of the following conditions—do not hydrostatically test it:

1. When there exist repairs by soldering, welding, brazing, or use of patching compounds. (For welding or brazing on mild steel shells, consult the manufacturer of the extinguisher.)

2. When the cylinder or shell threads are damaged.

3. When there exists corrosion that has caused pitting, including corrosion under the removable nameplate band assemblies.

4. When the extinguisher has been burned in a fire.

5. When a calcium chloride type of extinguishing agent was used in a stainless steel extinguisher.

D.   Extinguisher Maintenance Services

Fire extinguisher maintenance (particularly hydrostatic testing) is a specialized activity and should be performed by competent, dependable people. Fire extinguishers are provided to protect life and property: this means that there should be no doubt as to their reliability or safe use in time of emergency. Extinguisher owners are thus urged to seek out and utilize the services of reliable fire extinguisher maintenance firms. Such firms should be able to show proof of their competence and the adequacy of their facilities.

SI Units

The following conversion factors are given as a convenience in converting to SI units used in this chapter.

1 psi $\quad = \quad 6.895$ kPa

$\frac{5}{9}$ (°F − 32) $= $ °C

1 cu in. $\quad = 16.3872$ cubic millilitres

Bibliography

(see Page 16-33)

Chapter 5

AUXILIARY PORTABLE FIRE EXTINGUISHING DEVICES

There are occasions where quantities of water or other agents are desirable for fire extinguishing or control purposes, but where commercial extinguishers are considered either not feasible or in need of replacement. The most common reasons given for supplying auxiliary portable fire extinguishing devices are that property owners have had trouble with theft or vandalism of standard extinguishers, that the property value does not justify the provision of standard extinguishers, that standard extinguishers cannot be effectively handled and used at a particular location, and (as far as fire blankets are concerned) that they are easier and safer to use should a person's clothes catch fire. Information about the following auxiliary portable fire extinguishing devices is presented in this chapter: (1) covered buckets of water, (2) barrels and pails—bucket tanks, (3) sand buckets, (4) fire blankets, and (5) garden hose.

A. Covered Buckets of Water

A standard fire bucket has a 10 or 12 qt capacity. It differs from an ordinary metal bucket in that it is made of heavy galvanized metal and has a rounded or pointed bottom that makes it unsuitable for general use because it cannot remain upright when set down. Fire buckets are intended to be carried to a fire and the contents thrown over the burning material. This, of course, limits their effective range to about 10 ft. Fire buckets are primarily for use inside buildings, and should be placed on racks which are located no more than 5 ft and no less than 2 ft above the floor.

Fire buckets should have lids or covers to exclude foreign matter such as used cigarette packages, cigarette and cigar butts, dust accumulations, trash, etc. They should be painted in bright red, and the word "Fire" should be stenciled on them in contrasting paint. Frequent inspection and refilling is required in order to take care of normal evaporation.

B. Barrels and Pails—Bucket Tanks

For outdoor locations some property owners provide a source of water in the form of 55-gal barrels or used oil drums. These should also have lids or covers to exclude foreign matter. Pails should be hung on hangers around the top edges of the barrels, either nested on racks above the barrels or immersed (but easily accessible) inside the barrels or bucket tanks.

Barrels and drums should be painted bright red, and the buckets, if not immersed, should have the word "Fire" stenciled on them in contrasting paint. The following combinations are considered as the equivalent of possessing two units of extinguishing potential for Class A fires (2-A):

1. Five 12 or six 10-qt water-filled standard fire pails.
2. Five 12 or six 10-qt standard fire pails immersed in a 25 to 55-gal capacity water-filled bucket tank.
3. Three standard fire pails hung on, or racked above, one 55-gal water-filled drum, cask, or barrel.

Because these extinguishing devices are plain water solution, they are subject to freezing. However, the plain water they contain can be readily converted to an antifreeze solution by the addition of dissolved calcium chloride (free

from magnesium chloride). Table 16-5A gives the amounts of calcium chloride required to prepare a proper antifreeze solution, based upon probable lowest temperatures.

Considerable heat is developed when calcium chloride is dissolved in water. Therefore, when planned for use in galvanized containers, such solutions are best mixed in separate tanks and allowed to cool before being placed in galvanized barrels or drums. When mixing such solutions, it is suggested that the following two steps be taken:

1. First, place approximately ¾ of the barrel or bucket tank's capacity into a separate container as plain water.
2. Next, slowly add the calcium chloride while stirring the solution with a paddle or mechanical agitator until the solution is uniform and cooled.

The specific gravity of the cooled final solution can be checked with a commercial hydrometer until it approximates the values shown in Table 16-5A.

C. Sand Buckets

Although their value as extinguishing agents is almost nil, buckets of sand are still used on a limited basis. They are not considered as being equivalent to any type of fire extinguisher. However, they may be useful in controlling flammable liquid spill fires by curtailing the flow of any spilled liquid by forming dams or channels. Dry sand is of limited use on certain combustible metal fires (see Sec. 13, Chap. 6), and is of some value on fires involving small low-voltage electrical equipment. Because of its abrasiveness, sand should not be used where there are moving parts.

A bucket or box of sand can be useful in extinguishing incipient fires caused by small pieces of burning metal or sparks from cutting or welding operations. Frequently, large efflux particles fall on or become lodged in combustible or flammable materials. Spreading sand on the hot spot and wetting it down with water provides a convenient means of extinguishment.

D. Fire Blankets

Fire blankets are made of high-grade woven asbestos, aluminized fabrics, or flameproof wool. They are available in various sizes (62 × 82 in. being the most common size)

Table 16-5A. Calcium Chloride Required to Make 10 Gallons of Antifreeze Solutions for Fire Pails, Drums, and Bucket Tanks

Probable Lowest Temp. (°F)	Water Quantity (gallons)	Calcium Chloride (pounds)	Specific Gravity of Solution	or	Degrees Baumé of Solution
+10	9	20	1.139		17.7
0	8½	25	1.175		21.6
−10	8	29½	1.205		24.7
−20	8	33½	1.228		26.9
−30	8	36½	1.246		28.6
−40	8	40	1.263		30.2

Note: Use only the manufacturer's recommended antifreeze solution for a water-type extinguisher that is to be located in an area having freezing temperatures.

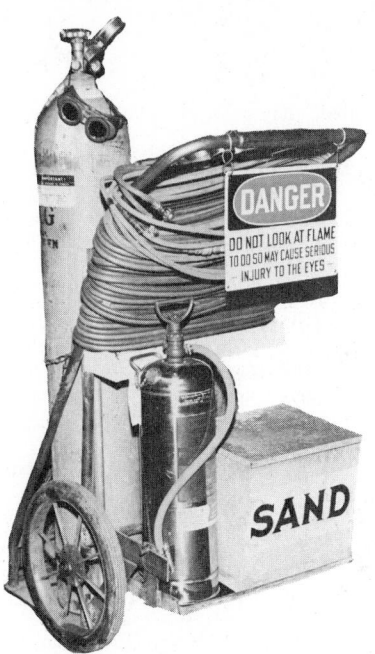

Fig. 16-5A. Water pump tank extinguisher and container of inert material, mounted on oxyacetylene cart, intended for control of "hot spot" fires. Larger Class B extinguishers are kept at full charge as standby protection for use when needed. (Automatic Electric Company)

and are customarily folded in metal wall cases or in portable canvas bags. While fire blankets are principally used for smothering fires in clothing, they can also be used in the absence of other extinguishing means to smother the fire or control the fire spread in other small Class A fires. Asbestos curtains are frequently used to prevent sparks from reaching combustibles around cutting and welding operations, and aluminized fabrics are sometimes provided as heat shields.

E.   Small Hose

Many industrial plants and construction firms have effectively used small diameter hose as a supplemental extinguishing means. Where convenient outlets are available in permanent or temporary water piping systems, small diameter $\frac{3}{4}$ to 1 in. commercial hose or $\frac{1}{2}$ to $\frac{3}{4}$ in. garden type hose can be installed. The water system supply and pressure should be sufficient to give a straight stream discharge, through a nozzle, of at least 30 ft.

Even though small in size, such a hand hose, when compared to a fire extinguisher having a rather limited discharge time, has the advantage of virtually unlimited discharge time. However, because of its length, the hose is limited in range, as compared to the extinguisher which can be carried directly to the fire.

Many types of hose nozzles are available. Some operate by twisting the nozzle from shutoff to spray to straight stream; others have a squeeze grip device that actuates them from a shutoff position. Several types have been approved by FM (Factory Mutual System) as combination water-spray nozzles for garden hose. They are designed for use on $\frac{5}{8}$, $\frac{3}{4}$, or 1-in. rubber hose, and may deliver a flat spray, a cone spray and solid stream, or a solid cone spray. Specifications for garden hose threads and couplings are included in ANSI Standard B2.4-1966, "Hose Coupling Screw Threads."

Garden Hose in the Home

An ordinary garden hose connected to the domestic water system is an effective and inexpensive means for combating fires in ordinary combustible materials. This connection can be made either in the cold water supply pipe to kitchen, bathroom, or utility sinks, or near the entry point to the hot water heater; because of its central location, the bathroom is generally an ideal place. In large multilevel homes it may be advantageous to have several hose installations. The hose can be coiled up and placed on a shelf under the sink, or the pipe connection can be extended through a wall into an adjoining closet or stairway where the hose can be hung on a bracket. The special hose reels available for garden use are also ideal for indoor installation. Any lightweight plastic hose, at least $\frac{1}{2}$ in. inside diameter, would be a good choice; however, it should be equipped with an adjustable squeeze-grip nozzle, and should be long enough to reach all intended areas. Such hand hose equipment, even though small in size, has the advantage of providing a good means of extinguishing incipient dwelling fires *provided* it remains connected, is periodically checked for deterioration, and is reserved for fire emergencies only.

SI Units

The following conversion factors are given as a convenience in converting to SI units the English units used in this chapter.

1 in.	= 25.4 mm
1 ft	= 0.305 m
1 lb (mass)	= 0.454 kg
$\frac{5}{9}$(°F − 32)	= °C
1 (U.S.) qt	= 0.946 litre
1 (U.S.) gal	= 3.785 litres

Bibliography

NFPA Codes, Standards, and Recommended Practices (see the latest *NFPA Publications and Visual Aids Catalog* for availability of current editions of the following documents)

NFPA 10, Standard for the Installation, Maintenance, and Use of Portable Fire Extinguishers.

NFPA 10L, Standard for the Model Enabling Act for the Sale or Leasing and Servicing of Portable Fire Extinguishers.

NFPA 13, Standard for the Installation of Sprinkler Systems.

NFPA 14, Standard for Standpipe and Hose Systems.

NFPA 34, Standard for Dip Tanks Containing Flammable or Combustible Liquids.

NFPA 182M, Standard for Hazards of Vaporizing Liquid Agents.

NFPA 407, Standard for Aircraft Fuel Servicing.

NFPA 408, Standard for Aircraft Hand Fire Extinguishers.

Additional Readings

"Beware of the Fire Extinguisher Servicing Racket," *Fire Journal*, Vol. 60, No. 3, May 1966, pp. 22–23.

"Carbon Tetrachloride," *Fire Journal*, Vol. 65, No. 3, May 1971, p. 19.

"Design Changes in Standards for Portable Fire Extinguishers," *Fire Journal*, Vol. 66, No. 6, Nov. 1972, pp. 95–98.

"Discontinued Extinguishers," National Association of Fire Equipment Distributors, Chicago.

Factory Mutual Engineering Corporation, "Portable Fire Extinguishers, *Handbook of Industrial Loss Prevention*," 2nd ed., McGraw-Hill, New York, 1967.

"Fire Extinguishers—Can They Be Dangerous?," National Association of Fire Equipment Distributors, Chicago.

Haessler, Walter M., "Truck Fire Extinguisher Tests," NFPA *Quarterly*, Vol. 58, No. 2, Oct. 1964, pp. 182–198.

"Hazards of Carbon Tetrachloride Fire Extinguishers," Recommended Practice No. 3, Jan. 1967, Federal Fire Council, Washington, D.C.

"Know Your A, B, C, and D's of Portable Fire Extinguishers," NFPA, Boston.

"Know Your Fire Extinguishers," TR LS-393; O.O.S.S.-66, U.S. Department of Labor, Bureau of Labor Standards, Washington, D.C.

"Methods of Testing Small Fire Extinguishers," BMS Report 150, 1957, U.S. Department of Commerce, National Bureau of Standards, Washington, D.C.

Peterson, H. B., and Gipe, R. L., "Discharge Characteristics of Potassium Bicarbonate Dry Chemical Fire Fighting Agents from Cartridge and Stored Pressure Extinguishers," NRL Report 5853, Dec. 13, 1962, U.S. Naval Research Laboratory, Washington, D.C.

"Portable Fire Extinguishing Appliances," Fire Protection Association (U.K.), Aldermary House, Queen St., London, E.C.4., England.

"Portable Fire Extinguisher Selection Guide," ibid.

Proven, J. A., "The Need for Legislation on Fire Extinguisher Servicing," *Fire Journal*, Vol. 61, No. 6, Nov. 1967, pp. 33–37.

"Revised Standards for the Distribution and Maintenance of Portable Fire Extinguishers," National Association of Fire Equipment Distributors, Chicago.

Sayers, David R., "Halon 1211, Areas of Particular Effectiveness," *Fire Journal*, Vol. 67, No. 6, Nov. 1973, pp. 14–15.

Thorne, P. S., "Why Extinguishers Burst," *Fire Journal*, 1968.

"Training Your Fire Brigade to Use First Aid Extinguishers," Walter Kidde & Company, Belleville, N.J.

Tryon, G. H., "Hydrostatic Testing of Fire Extinguishers," *Fire Journal*, Vol. 61, No. 1, Jan. 1967, pp. 32–35.

Tuve, Richard L., "Dry Chemical Fire Extinguishers," *Security World*, July-Aug. 1966.

"Your Guide for Home Fire Fighting," NFPA, Boston.

Underwriters Laboratories, Inc., Safety Standards

UL 7, Dec. 1965, Soda-Acid Fire Extinguishers.

UL 7(b), July 1950, Foam Extinguishers (2¼ Gallon).

UL 68, July 1950, Foam Extinguishers (33 Gallon).

UL 154, 3rd ed., 1971, Carbon Dioxide Fire Extinguishers.

UL 299, 5th ed., April 1971, Dry Chemical Fire Extinguishers.

UL 626, 3rd ed., April 1971, 2½-Gallon Stored-Pressure, Water-Type Fire Extinguishers.

UL 711, 2nd ed., April 1973, Rating and Fire Testing of Fire Extinguishers.

UL 715, 2nd ed., May 1973, 2½-Gallon Cartridge-Operated, Water-Type Fire Extinguishers.

Underwriters Laboratories, Inc., Bulletins of Research

No. 26, July 1942, Electrical Conductivity of Snow and Gas Discharged from First-Aid Carbon Dioxide Extinguishers.

No. 42, Aug. 1948, The Life Hazards and Nature of the Products Formed When Chlorobromomethane Extinguisher Liquid is Applied to Fires.

No. 50, Dec. 1957, A Study of the Corrosion of Vaporizing-Liquid Type Fire Extinguishers.

No. 54, July 1963, The Compatibility Relationship Between Mechanical Foam and Dry Chemical Fire Extinguishing Agents.

Federal Specifications

O-E-910D, June 14, 1972, Carbon Dioxide Fire Extinguishers (Hand and Wheeled Types).

O-E-915C, June 19, 1972, Dry Chemical Fire Extinguishers (Portable).

O-E-920A, Aug. 20, 1965, Foam Fire Extinguishers (on wheels).

O-E-925A, Apr. 21, 1965, Foam Fire Extinguishers (2¼ Gallon).

O-E-927, Nov. 26, 1966, Soda-Acid Fire Extinguishers (Hand).

O-E-930A, Apr. 7, 1965, Soda-Acid Fire Extinguishers (on wheels).

O-E-940A, Aug. 29, 1968, Water Fire Extinguisher (Hand-pump, tank, portable).

O-E-942B, June 15, 1972, Water Fire Extinguishers (2½-gallon, Stored-Pressure).

O-E-945A, March 15, 1967, Water Fire Extinguisher (2½-gallon, Cartridge Operated).

O-F-371A, Oct. 31, 1966, Sodium Bicarbonate Dry Chemical Fire Extinguishing Agent.

SECTION 17
TRANSPORTATION FIRE HAZARDS

Section 17

Chapter 1

AVIATION

Included in the factors that contribute to effective flight safety are the requirements that aircraft be both "airworthy" and "crashworthy"; that pilots and crew members possess the required skills and have the ability to fully utilize such skills; that airborne and ground navigational aids are adequate and functional; that control is maintained over the use of airway take-off and landing patterns; that airports are properly designed, adequately maintained, and possess the required safety equipment; that severe weather conditions do not adversely affect aircraft utilization; and that the problem of fires in-flight, at time of impact or on the ground, are nonexistent. The content of this chapter discusses only the problem of fire.

A.   Aircraft Operational Fire Safety

Fire safety in aircraft starts on the drawing board. Aeronautical engineers bear the brunt of the fire prevention responsibility when designing aircraft in which large quantities of aviation gasoline or turbine fuels are placed in close proximity to high thrust populsion systems. This is particularly true when additional hazards such as those associated with combustible lubricating and hydraulic fluids, electrical systems, heating systems, oxygen equipment, auxiliary power units, galleys, and cargo and passenger compartments are also present.

Prevention of fire in flight requires a skillful blending of reasonable fire safeguards that are consistent with weight limitations and which, at the same time, do not unduly interfere with the use and mission of the particular aircraft. Installed fire detection and extinguishing equipment are normally required to cover areas that possess inherent fire hazards and ignition potentials. In-flight protection from fire requires the separation of flammable fluid system components from ignition sources, compartmentation of fire hazardous areas from aircraft structural components and control systems essential to the airworthiness of the aircraft, and judicious use of fire resistant and noncombustible materials. Safety considerations should predominate because aircraft fires present tragic life hazard potentials.

Fire following impact accidents—the reason for the loss of many lives—is an aircraft design problem, the design objective being to reduce the severity of fire following impact when the impact forces are not so severe as to be totally responsible for the fatalities. Many methods have been and are being studied to reduce the post-crash fire hazard. Such methods include: (1) segregation of flammable fluid containers and systems with respect to ignition sources, (2) improved methods of fuel containment, (3) deenergizing electrical systems prior to impact, (4) inerting the air volumes around engines and cooling hot engine surfaces at time of impact, and (5) stopping engine rotation to prevent backfire flame emission (which requires that fuel flow to all engines be cut off before touchdown). Experimental work has been done to try to "thicken" fuel by gelling or emulsifying to reduce the probability of ignition by reduction of the combustible fuel "mists" produced because of air shearing of released fuel at time of impact, reduction in the rate of evaporation, and/or reduction in the rate of flame propagation over spilled fuel surfaces. The techniques for "thickening" fuels are well established; however, problems remain concerning the use of "thickened" fuel in aircraft fuel systems, particularly because of pumping demands.

Aircraft ground fire safety depends on careful control of hazardous fueling and maintenance procedures, proper storage of aircraft in the open and in hangars, safe practices in taxiing and maneuvering aircraft on the movement area of airports, and proper engine starting procedures.

B.   Aircraft Power Plants

U.S. civil aircraft are subject to extensive federal regulation through the U.S. Department of Transportation, Federal Aviation Administration. The Code of Federal Regulations, Title 14, "Aeronautics and Space," contains the Federal Aviation Regulations. The following paragraphs numbered 1 to 9 contain interpretations of the detailed provisions on aircraft power plants:

1. All reciprocating engines, auxiliary power units, fuel-burning heaters, and other combustion equipment intended for operation in flight, as well as the combustion, turbine, and tail pipe sections of turbine engines, are isolated from the remainder of the aircraft by "fire walls," shrouds, or equivalent means, so that no hazardous quantity of air, fluids, or flame can pass from these compartments to other portions of the aircraft. The "fire walls" and shrouds specified must be protected against corrosion, and must be made of a material that will withstand heat at least as well as steel in dimensions appropriate for intended use. When applied in power plants, the material must perform "under the most severe conditions of fire and duration likely to occur in such zones," and all openings in the "fire walls" and shrouds are to be sealed with close-fitting fire resistant grommets, bushings, or fittings. In reciprocating engine nacelles, a "fire wall" (often called a "fire seal" or "bulkhead" in this use) is used to isolate the engine power section and all portions of the exhaust system from the engine accessory compartment. The main power plant "fire wall" separates the engine accessory compartment from the rest of the nacelle which may be the wheel well space or rear nacelle skate. In gas turbine engine nacelles a transverse sealed "bulkhead" is furnished to isolate the combustion, turbine, and tailpipe sections from the compressor and accessory sections (see Fig. 17-1A).

2. The cowling and nacelle "skin" are designed and constructed so that fire originating in any fire zone cannot enter into any other zone of the nacelle, including the wheel well space (where applicable).

3. No tanks containing flammable fluids are located in a fire zone except when it is proved that tank construction, the shutoff means, connecting lines, and controls provide the same degree of safety as would segregation. A $\frac{1}{2}$-in. air space must be provided between any tank and "fire wall" or shroud, and no component of a flammable-fluid carrying system is located in close proximity to materials that can absorb such a fluid.

4. Shutoff means are provided for each engine, each auxiliary power unit, and each fuel-burning heater to prevent flammable liquids from flowing in any fire zone.

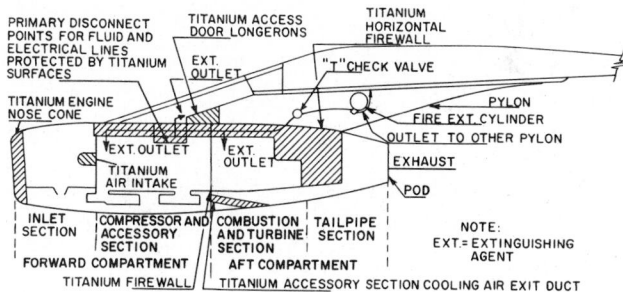

Fig. 17-1A. A typical turbine engine "pod" of a civil transport showing the main sections, the "fire wall" divisions, the extinguishing-agent supply cylinder, and high-rate discharge outlets.

These shutoffs must be fire resistant or must be located and protected so that any fire in a fire zone will not affect its operation. Operation of the shutoffs must not interfere with the subsequent emergency operation of other equipment (such as propeller feathering mechanisms), and closing a fuel shutoff for any engine must not make the fuel supply to other engines unavailable.

5. All flammable liquid lines in fire zones are fire resistant with fire resistant end fittings to prevent leakage or burnout. Where lines and fittings are attached to the engine or subject to relative motion between components, they must be flexible as well as fire resistant. Vent or drain lines, which constitute a hazard, are fire resistant in fire zones.

6. All controls for stopping reciprocating or turbo-prop engine rotation (propeller feathering system, ignition, etc.) in fire zones are fire resistant. Oil required for propeller feathering must remain available regardless of possible engine oil-supply failure or emergency shutoff.

7. Engine air intakes do not open within the cowling unless that portion of the cowling is isolated from the engine accessory section by a "fire wall," or provision is made to prevent emergence of back-fire flames. For turbine-engine-powered aircraft, provisions are made to prevent hazardous quantities of fuel leakage or overflow from drains, vents, or other components of flammable fluid systems from entering the engine intake system under normal operating conditions. Induction-system ducts, installed ahead of the supercharger, are provided with safely located drains to prevent hazardous accumulations of fuel and moisture in the ground attitude. Induction-system ducts within any protected fire zone are fire resistant.

8. Exhaust systems are designed to dispose of exhaust gases without introducing a fire hazard, and exhaust gases are discharged so as not to be a hazard to any flammable-fluid system. Precautions are required when any parts are located in hazardous proximity to flammable-liquid lines or vapor release sources, or when located under portions of systems that are subject to leakage. All components upon which hot exhaust gases impinge or are subject to high temperatures are fire resistant. Exhaust system components outside the engine compartments are segregated from adjacent aircraft surfaces by fire-resistant shields or shrouds.

9. Provisions are incorporated for the drainage and ventilation of all fire zones in the event of malfunction of components that contain flammable fluids; they are arranged so as not to cause an additional fire hazard (ventilation openings in one zone should not permit entrance of flammable fluids, vapors, or flame from any other zone). Except for engine power section in reciprocating engines, the inlet section of turbine engines, and the combustion-heater ventilating air ducts, provisions are made to permit the crew

to shut off sources of forced ventilation in any fire zone, unless enough extinguishing agent capacity is available and can be discharged at a sufficiently high rate to accomplish extinguishment despite the air flow.

Other basic fire prevention fundamentals for reciprocating engine power plants covered by Federal Aviation Regulations or considered good design practice are:

1. The entire nacelle and wing skin in the vicinity of the nacelle should be constructed of fire-resistant metals. Stainless steel, monel, inconel, or titanium are the principal metals used.

2. Exhaust systems should be located high in engine installations.

3. Electrical systems should be above other engine parts. Electrical equipment that might be an ignition source should be contained within an "explosion-proof" casing.

4. Fuel, oil, and hydraulic systems should be leakproof and in a low position. Nonflammable hydraulic fluids should be used.

5. Fire zone drainage and ventilation should prevent dangerous concentrations of flammable vapors.

6. Cowling interiors should be smooth and clean to prevent trapping flammable liquids and vapors.

7. Air inlets should be forward. Drains, vents, and air outlets should be piped to a common low-pressure area as far aft as possible so that the discharge cannot enter or impinge on any other part of the aircraft, and so that normal slip stream cannot result in either excessive vacuum or blowback through the drain lines.

8. The exhaust system should be separated from engine accessory compartment and the rest of the nacelle by a double steel (or equivalent) shroud carrying a ventilating air flow. Joints in the shrouds should be staggered so that fluids cannot reach the exhaust. Louvers should not be used for providing ventilation; smooth flows of air have proved safer than turbulent air introduced through louvers.

9. Vacuum pumps should incorporate fusible plugs. The outlet from the plug should drain free of any other part of the aircraft.

10. Direct fuel injection has some fire-safety advantages over the carburetor systems.

Turbine powered aircraft are now used by world-wide military and commercial interests. (See Fig. 17-1A for a typical turbine power plant.) The type of failures and hazards considered basic to gas turbine engines are:

1. Thermodynamic failure of the turbine blades if there is serious blockage of the required excess air (above that used for combustion). If blade melting begins, there is increased heat and a rapid loss of thrust. If the temperature increases suddenly (as by, perhaps, icing of the inlet air screen), blades (red hot) can be thrown outward tangential to the turbine, which could result in complete or partial severance of the tailcone and penetration of the aircraft wing or fuselage sections by the blades.

2. Mechanical failure of turbine blades, which can be serious, especially if the failure occurs in a forward stage of a multistage turbine. In this event, pieces of the broken blade can cause interference between the stator and rotor blades. Titanium blades used in some engine sections may ignite under these circumstances.

3. Mechanical disruption of the axial flow compressor, which could result in compressor case breakage and rupture of fuel or oil lines in the presence of hot engine parts.

4. Burn-through of engine cases due to a high flow of fuel through a maladjusted nozzle.

5. Tailpipe fires or explosions after shutdown because of residue fuel not properly drained.

6. Afterburner mechanical failure (usually a split seam or wall failure) or fires in the afterburner due to fuel line leaks.

Armor may be used for protection from turbine failures on primary structures or fuel tanks and lines. The thickness and materials used will vary with the potential kinetic energy that might be developed (taking into consideration the protection afforded by the engine housing), and the area to be covered.

The same fire prevention design features basically apply to both turbine engines and reciprocating engines, i.e.: (1) compartmentation to separate combustibles from sources of ignition; (2) proper drainage to prevent flammable fluids from collecting in fire zones and from being drawn into adjacent compartments by suction; (3) use of "fire walls" to isolate combustibles from hot engine parts that may be an ignition source; (4) adequate ventilation to reduce environmental temperatures and to minimize the possibility of flammable vapor concentrations, etc. There are some special problems of turbines associated with: (1) the need to keep inlets for the aft compartment separated from all outlet flows or drainage in the forward compartments, and (2) safe compressor bleed "plumbing," so that maximum integrity of all ducting and joints is assured.

C.   Aviation Fuels

To understand the fire hazard properties of aviation fuels in current use, they should first be evaluated as to their susceptibility or ease of ignition. This involves consideration of the flash point of the fuels, their flammability limits, their vapor pressure, their autoignition temperature, their distillation range (initial and end boiling points), and their electrostatic susceptibility. (NOTE: Octane rating, as such, has no relation to the degree of fire hazard of a fuel for a power plant.) See Table 17-1A for summary data, and Figure 17-1B for variations caused by altitude on the flammability limits of various fuels.

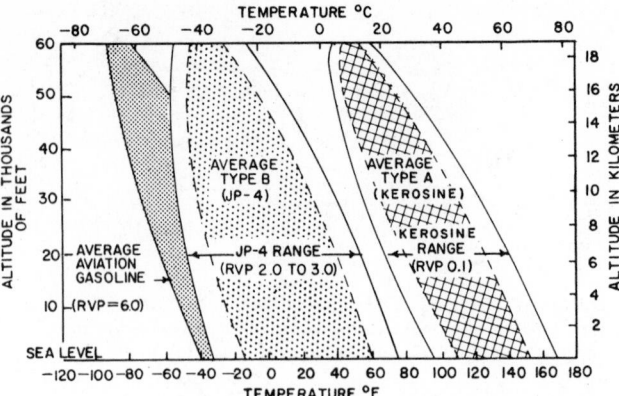

Fig. 17-1B. Flammable ranges of aviation gasoline and JET A (kerosine) and JET B (JP-4) turbine fuels showing variations with altitude. According to laboratory studies some of the sea level flammable limits shown on this chart for JET A and JET B turbine fuel do not agree exactly with Table 17-1A as the test data used to develop this chart were from a single source and the Table combines and averages data from all available sources.

Flash Point Data

The flash point data given in Table 17-1A uses, as indicated, the "Tag" closed-cup method of testing. From the information in the Table, it may be observed that AVGAS and JET B turbine fuels at normal temperatures and pressures will give off vapors that are capable of forming ignitible mixtures with the air near the surface of the liquid or within the vessel in which it is stored. The kerosine grades of turbine fuel will not form ignitible mixtures at normal temperatures and pressures.

Flammability Limits

There is relatively little significance in the variations between the lower and upper flammability limits of the three

Table 17-1A.   Summary Data on the Fire Hazard Properties of Aviation Fuels

Characteristics	Gasoline AVGAS	Kerosine Grades JET A JET A-1 JP-5, JP-6 JP-8	Blends of Gasoline and Kerosine JET B and JP-4
Freeze Point	−76°F	−40°F −58°F	−60°F
Vapor Pressure (Reid-ASTM D323-58)	5.5 to 7.0 lb/sq in.	0.1 lb/sq in.	2.0 to 3.0 lb/sq in.
Flash Point (By Closed-Cup Method at Sea Level)	−50°F	+95°F to +145°F	−10°F to +30°F
Flash Point (By Air Saturation Method)	−75°F to −85°F	None	−60°F
Flammability Limits Lower Limit Upper Limit Temp. Range for Flam. Mixtures	1.4% 7.6% −50°F to +30°F	0.74% 5.32% +95°F to +165°F	1.16% 7.63% −10°F to +100°F
Autoignition Temperature	+825°F to +960°F	+440°F to +475°F	+470°F to 480°F
Boiling Points Initial End	110°F 325°F	325°F 450°F	135°F 485°F
Pool Rate of Flame Spread*	700–800 ft per min	100 ft per min or less	700–800 ft per min

* In mist foam, rate of flame spread in all fuels is very rapid.
NOTE: Figures vary for some of these values in different data sources. Those shown herein are average figures based on the latest available information.

types of aviation fuels. More significant, is the temperature range during which it might be possible to have such flammable vapor-air mixtures. In discussing the flammability limits for these fuels, we are speaking only of what might be called "stable" conditions. An entirely different situation develops under aircraft crash impact conditions when "fuel mists" are created following tank failures. In this "mist" condition, almost all these fuels are readily ignitible. Unfortunately, in many aircraft accidents, these "mists" result when a major failure of the wing structure releases large quantities of fuel which are air sheared into a "mist."

The flammability loops shown in Figure 17-1B are based on laboratory tests in which only variations in temperature and pressure are considered. The flammability ranges of fuel vapors as they exist within the vapor spaces of aircraft fuel tanks in flight extend to the lean side to a significant degree; this difference results from fuel sloshing, splashing, foaming, and misting under varying temperature, pressure, and ventilation conditions during flight, maneuvers, and changes in the altitude of the aircraft.

Vapor Pressure

AVGAS gives off flammable vapors in ignitible amounts at normal temperatures and pressures, but, when these vapors are confined, the vapor-air mixture over the liquid surface most frequently is too rich to be ignited by sparks (being above the upper flammability limit). Kerosine grades of turbine fuels, on the other hand, do not give off flammable vapors in ignitible amounts unless the fuel temperature is above 95°F. This would not be anticipated except in conditions where an aircraft may sit for many hours under tropical conditions. With the JET B type of turbine fuel, due to the relatively low vapor pressure as compared to AVGAS, the vapor-air mixture above the liquid surface under normal temperature and pressure conditions frequently will be within the flammability range.

Autoignition Temperature

The test conditions under which autoignition temperatures are measured vary. Most of the figures available are derived from reproducible laboratory test procedures, whereas, in actual field conditions, these temperatures may be higher. It can be seen from the data in Table 17-1A that both the turbine fuels have ignition temperatures considerably lower than those of AVGAS. They are, in fact, among the lowest found among common hydrocarbons.

Boiling Points

This data, along with the flash point and vapor pressure criteria, indicates the relative volatility of the fuels; the initial and end boiling points show the overall volatility of the fuel through its entire distillation range, while the flash point and vapor pressure measure the initial tendency of the fuel to vaporize.

Electrostatic Susceptibility

The degree to which a static charge may be acquired and built up is difficult to measure because it depends on many factors: the amount and type of impurities, the linear velocity of the fuel in movement, the type and condition of the charge-separating surfaces, and the presence of extraneous materials (such as water, air, sludge, reagents, etc.). It is clear, however, that the turbine fuels, by their very nature, retain more impurities than does AVGAS; thus, both the JET A and the JET B grades are more prone to acquire static charges than is AVGAS. Antistatic additives have been developed to reduce this hazard, and these additives are becoming more widely used in aviation fuels.

Severity of Fire After Ignition

The severity of fire can be evaluated basically from two points of view: heat of combustion and rate of flame spread. There is actually very little difference in the heat of combustion between the three types of aviation fuels.

The more important factor is the rate of flame spread. This is quite difficult to measure, but where there are quiescent pools of spilled fuel, at say 65°F, there is a marked difference in the rate of flame spread over pools of JET A (kerosine) grades of turbine fuel as compared with either of the other two types. Under these conditions, a direct relationship exists between the rate of flame spread and the vapor pressures; for instance, AVGAS and JET B type turbine fuel have been calculated to have a rate of flame spread of between 700 to 800 fpm, whereas the rate of flame spread for the kerosine grades of turbine fuel under the same condition is substantially lower and is less than 100 fpm. This is a very important factor in evaluating the severity of the fire hazard, although when both JET A and JET B fuels are heated to above their flash points, flame spread rates are virtually equal.

It should be emphasized that the slower rate of flame propagation for the unheated kerosine grades of fuel does not hold where the fuel is released in a "mist" form. This agrees with the similar behavior of the fuels as regards their flash point discussed earlier. When a "mist" condition exists, the speed of flame spread will be essentially the same regardless of the liquid spilled. It is usually true that this fuel "mist" will, however, be consumed in seconds (rather than in minutes) after a serious crash, and once the "ball of flame" burns off, approach can be made to effect rescue. Rarely will fire departments arrive at the scene until after this phenomenon occurs. The main difficulty occurs when a "mist" explosion propagates flame over large spilled areas of fuel which can readily ignite any exposed combustible.

Relative Safety of Fuels

JET A (kerosine grades) of turbine fuel offer a safety advantage over other grades of aviation fuels, especially during fuel servicing operations and aircraft fuel system maintenance. JET A fuels do not, however, reduce measurably the seriousness or severity of fire situations in aircraft crashes to permit any relaxation of protection recommendations for aircraft rescue and fire fighting services at airports. Current world-wide fuel shortages and refining problems introduce the possibility of reducing what safety advantages exist with JET A fuels since "wide-cut" formulations are likely to be substituted as an energy conservation measure.

D. Aircraft Fuel Tanks and Distribution Systems

Wing structures that contain fuel can be extensively damaged in aircraft accidents, even when the fuselage and personnel may be unharmed. This damage can be caused by the impact or by the momentum of the contained fuel following rapid aircraft deceleration. Present-day fuel tanks and wing structures that serve as tanks (so-called "integral" tankage) do not offer much resistance to these forces. The result is a high frequency of "crash fires," since the released fuel or its vapors (in the form of a "fuel mist") can be readily ignited by multiple ignition sources in the area (e.g., hot engine surfaces, electrical components, etc.). See Figure 17-1C for a typical arrangement of a fuel tank system in a modern transport aircraft.

The most promising solution proposed (but not widely used) is the development of crash-resistant fuel tank constructions with breakaway fuel lines and an automatic fuel

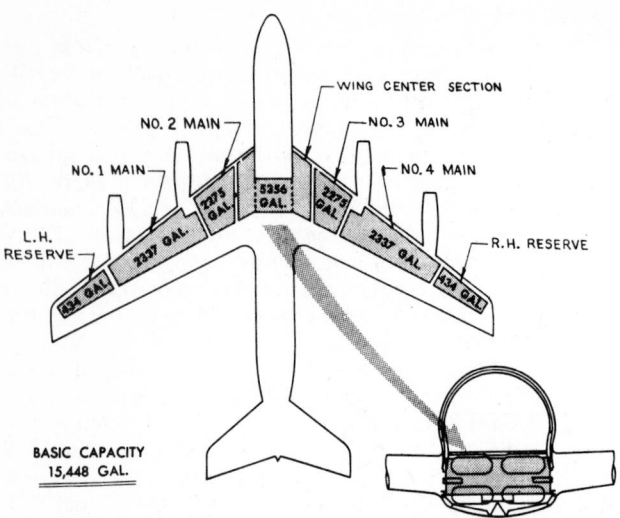

Fig. 17-1C. Arrangement of fuel tankage in a typical turbine-powered air-carrier aircraft. The reserve tanks and Nos. 1, 2, 3, and 4 are "integral" tanks in this particular plane, and the wing center section tank is of the "bladder" type.

shutoff valve system to take the loads imposed in "survivable" impacts. "Survivable" in this usage implies the ability of the occupants, or a portion thereof, to live through the impact forces within the environment of the aircraft: it assumes seat belts and shoulder harnesses, or both, and delethalizing of the aircraft interior components. Such a "crashworthy" fuel system has been developed and is in use in certain helicopters operated by the United States Army (the AH-1G, OH-58, UH-1D, and UH-1H). With these systems in use during the period 1970 to 1973 there were 776 accidents involving these models of helicopters equipped with the "crashworthy" fuel system without a single fatality or injury due to thermal trauma. In 960 other accidents involving the same helicopters without the "crashworthy" fuel system, there were 74 postcrash fires resulting in 101 thermal casualties and 86 thermal injuries.

"Integral-type" fuel tankage, in which the wing is the tank, is used, in whole or in part, on virtually all U.S., British, French and Russian-made civil transport aircraft. The Boeing 707 design, for instance, makes use of a type of bladder tank in the wing center section as it passes through the fuselage, but has "integral-type" tankage in the remaining wing cavities utilized for fuel storage. (Separate metal tanks are found only in some personal aircraft and such older transports as the C-46.) Weight limitation and increased range of aircraft (as influenced by maximum use of fuel carrying space) have been the major factors favoring "integral" tankage.

Fuel tank location in the wing is of utmost importance. Wherever possible, fuel tankage should be excluded from the wing center section, the fuselage, and the wing area between the inboard engines and the fuselage. It is of utmost importance, also, that landing loads not be applied directly to the fuel-containing structures; wing structural members that support the fuel tankage should not have to support the landing gears, too. (Shear pins on undercarriage supports are used by some when wing spars must support both the fuel-containing structures and landing gear.) The Boeing 707 design mounts the landing gear on rear wing spars to permit the gear to be "wiped off" in some ground impact situations without resulting in fuel tank rupture.

In aircraft equipped with "integral-type" tanks (often called "wet-wing" aircraft), proper sealing of the wing

structure is important; in bladder-type tanks, care is necessary to make sure the bladders and all connecting piping are leak proof. Wing-tip fuel tanks have been recommended to remove fuel storage as far as possible from occupied portions and ignition sources, but they have so far been used principally to augment the fuel storage capacity of the aircraft and this has not improved the crash-fire susceptibility of the aircraft. Wherever located, fuel tanks should be isolated from passenger and crew compartments by vapor-proof barriers. A "fire wall" at the wing root will reduce the chance of internal flame spread to the fuselage in event of a fire involving the wing tanks. (For ventilation of wing spaces see Part H of this Chapter.)

A tank expansion space (of not less than 2 percent capacity) and adequate venting facilities are required to take care of fuel expansion because of temperature changes (preventing overflow or self-siphoning) and to accommodate vapor release during fueling operations. Fuel tanks are generally required to withstand an internal pressure of at least 3.5 psi; 125 percent of the maximum air pressure developed in the tank from ram effects; fluid pressures developed during maximum accelerations and deflections with a full tank; and fluid pressures developed during the most adverse combination of aircraft roll and fuel load.

Other considerations of significance regarding fuel storage and safety are bonding of structural components to guard against the accumulation of electrostatic charges; padding (using nonabsorbent, noncombustible materials) to prevent chafing between any fabricated tank and supports; facilities to permit complete drainage; spill-proof filler connections (either over-wing or under-wing); a fuel-tight filler cap; vents to equalize pressure as tanks are emptied or filled; adequate provision to prevent structural damage to interconnected tanks resulting from common tank fuel-transfer systems or fuel tank venting systems; and a safely arranged method for fuel jettisoning which is sometimes a necessary or desirable in-flight operation to reduce gross aircraft weight prior to an emergency landing (e.g., with landing gear difficulty). Supersonic aircraft fuel systems have special design problems because of exposure to high temperatures and low ambient pressures, such as when cruising at Mach 2.0 at 60,000 ft.

Lightning as a source of ignition to flammable fuel vapors aboard aircraft has been a major concern for years. All-metal aircraft seemed to eliminate much of the earlier concern since the aircraft itself became a Faraday cage to "shield" all aircraft contents. The principal concerns from lightning during aircraft operational modes are: (1) ignition of vapors at fuel tank vents located at lightning-prone "strike" areas; (2) electrical discontinuities within fuel tanks; (3) the flammability hazard in tank vapor spaces (see Fig. 17-1B); (4) thickness of the "skin" of fuel tank containing structures; and (5) the proper location and installation of static discharges and lightning diverters.

The fuel distribution system must be adequate to absorb the loads which might be imposed on lines and fittings due to fuel pressures, flight conditions, and crash-impact forces. Items to consider are: fire resistance of the piping used; flexibility; security at connections; routing of lines (proximity to the electrical system, passage through personnel or cargo compartments); vulnerability to impact hazards—particularly lines to rear-mounted power plants running through the fuselage; feeds to auxiliary equipment; leakage in areas where absorption of fuel might produce a hazard; positive stops at fuel valves (permitting closure of sectional lines, relief of excessive pressures, etc.); and effective fuel system drains. Each fuel line within the fuselage must be designed and installed to allow a reasonable degree of deformation and stretching without leakage and/or be encased in a crash-resistant assembly.

Maintenance of aircraft fuel tankage has produced some special fire problems, and NFPA No. 410C, Recommendations on Safeguarding Aircraft Fuel System Maintenance, includes procedures for safeguarding fuel tank atmospheres during ground handling (air ventilation and inerting procedures).

E. Aircraft Lubricating and Hydraulic Systems

Ignition of lubricants on hot engine and exhaust surfaces is a hazard and security of lubricating-oil lines is thus vital. Flammable hydraulic fluids have been the cause of serious fires; in systems employing high pressures (about 3,000 psi), the fluid atomizes when released and most fires have resulted from electrical sparks or heated surfaces (e.g., brakes). Research has resulted in the development of a group of less flammable hydraulic fluids suitable for aircraft use (proper fluidity under a wide range of temperatures and adequate lubricity). When flammable fluids are used, the distribution system and tank supply should be similar (where pertinent) to the fuel system.

F. Aircraft Electrical Systems

The modern aircraft has a complex electrical system that requires skillful layout, installation, and maintenance. Starting with the battery and ending with tailcone warning lights, fire safety can only be realized by the closest attention to potential hazards from short circuits, overloads, sparking at contacts, and exposure to adjacent flammable liquid lines and vapors, oxygen systems, doped fabric surfaces, and high resistance contacts.

Automatic protective devices for electrical circuits are specified to minimize the hazards from wiring faults or electrical malfunctions. If the ability to reset a circuit breaker or replace a fuse is essential to safety in flight, that circuit breaker or fuse must be located and identified so that it can be readily reset or replaced in flight. If fuses are used, there must be spare fuses for use in flight equal to at least 50 percent of the number of fuses of each rating required for complete circuit protection.

U.S. Federal Aviation Regulations limit the components of the electrical systems from the fire safety and smoke development viewpoints, and restrict to fire resistant constructions electrical cables, terminals, and equipment in designated fire zones. Main power cables in the fuselage must be isolated from flammable fluid lines, and shrouded by means of electrical insulated flexible conduit in addition to the normal cable insulation; also, insulation on electrical wire and cable in the fuselage must be "self-extinguishing" when tested in a prescribed manner. (For emergency exit lighting see Part K or this Chapter.)

G. Other Inherent Aircraft Hazards

Other "built-in" fire problems in aircraft construction include the materials of construction in the personnel accommodations; the insulation and the sound-deadening materials (and the "binders" used to hold them in place); the ventilation, heating and deicing systems, the oxygen equipment; and the combustible metals sometimes utilized.

Magnesium castings of the type used in aircraft engines can be ignited under conditions of high air flow in a comparatively short time, and might be ignited before other structural failures occur. Ignition of magnesium parts by severe fires, as following a crash or fuel fire, complicates extinguishment with conventional fire control agents, although, in most cases, ignition of major magnesium components does not occur in such fires until after the time element for rescue has passed.

Titanium and titanium alloys in sheet and casting forms are used quite extensively in modern aircraft as a compromise metal that has desirable properties for such use without the weight penalty of steel. While titanium is difficult to ignite, under certain conditions, titanium rotor blades in turbine engines have caught fire. Once involved, they are very difficult to extinguish and normally have to be left to burn out with water cooling streams, if available, utilized to cool adjacent parts. For data on combustible metal extinguishing agents, see Section 13, Chapter 6.

When titanium, magnesium, and certain steels and steel alloys scrape along runways as the result of wheels-up landings or crashes, friction sparks capable of igniting flammable vapors have followed. Aluminum and its alloys do not have comparable friction spark hazards on either concrete or macadam.

Brake and tire fires have been a problem, particularly with high performance aircraft that land at high speeds and require "heavy" braking under some operational conditions. When flammable hydraulic fluids are used to raise and lower the landing gear, these fluids have increased the hazard. Tire and wheel explosions also have been a major concern to fire fighters since a number of such explosions occurred after or during fire control efforts. Tire blow-out plugs have been incorporated in the latest wheel designs to reduce this hazard.

H. Aircraft Fuselage Compartments

The behavior of aircraft cabin interior materials, once ignited from any source, can be crucial from a life safety viewpoint and can result in severe structural damage to the aircraft. Extra precautions are, therefore, justified to restrict both the amount of combustibles and the nature of these combustibles subject to ignition, and to provide the maximum feasible degree of fire protection within the cabin.

Flame-retardant materials are now specified for seat cushions and covers, passenger service units, wall and ceiling linings, floor coverings, and other similar elements. For transport category aircraft, the current U.S. regulations require that cabin materials be "self-extinguishing" when tested in a vertical position and subjected to a Bunsen burner flame. A notice of Proposed Rule Making has been issued by the Federal Aviation Administration to also limit smoke emission from cabin materials. Definitive smoke and toxic gas test procedures have not, however, as yet been developed to permit formalizing this rule. Various governmental and nongovernmental fire research groups are working on this subject, and in the meantime the requirement for flame-retardant materials remains in effect.

The two greatest aircraft cabin fire dangers are from:

1. Fires originating in the concealed spaces behind cabin liners.

2. Ignition of cabin interiors following a crash, or from a ground fire (as during a fueling operation). Cigarette ignitions can be a problem where detection is not prompt and the fire spreads beyond the control capability of portable extinguishers (assuming occupants are available to use same), or where the actual ignition occurs in an inaccessible area from the cabin interior (i.e., lighted cigarettes being put in towel disposal bins which recess behind cabin paneling in lavatories). Oxygen enrichment

due to the accidental release of this nonflammable gas inside the aircraft has been a factor in the intensity and severity of a number of aircraft cabin fires. Ignition of cabin materials during aircraft cleaning and refurbishing operations presents a special problem during aircraft construction and maintenance operations; most of these fires result from the improper use of flammable cleaning agents, the vapors of which are ignited from work lights or other sources of energy.

While cabin fires are not frequent, when they do occur their life loss potential while the aircraft is in flight can be most severe. Where a fire, originating on the exterior of the aircraft, penetrates the fuselage and ignites the cabin materials (as following an impact accident or a ground fire), the available time for evacuation of any occupants is drastically shortened.

With regard to smoking aboard aircraft and the attendant hazards, operators prohibit smoking normally during take-offs and landings, while flying in turbulent air, or on other occasions when the pilot decides that smoking may constitute a hazard to the safe operation of the aircraft. The principal fire-safety reasons for these restrictions are: (1) to forestall accidental contact of lighted cigarettes or matches with combustible materials in the cabin, the clothing of the individuals or their personal effects during accelerations, decelerations or turbulence; and (2) to eliminate this source of ignition in the event of release of flammable vapors under these critical flight conditions.

Fires which originate in or propagate to the wall or ceiling of concealed spaces (between the interior decorative cabin paneling and exterior fuselage "skin") are particularly dangerous and difficult to control. These concealed spaces contain insulation materials as well as critical electrical, mechanical, and structural components subject to severe damage under fire conditions. The "binders" or adhesives used with the insulation produce highly noxious or toxic fire gases which can spread rapidly throughout the aircraft. A number of severe ground fires originating in such spaces have occurred while aircraft are unattended and parked; since these concealed spaces have no fire barrier subdivisions, such fires spread virtually the length of the aircraft.

Hazardous Cargoes

Hazardous cargoes present another hazard to aircraft both in flight, on the ground, and during ground handling. This is an international problem because of the high frequency of shipments across national boundaries. Many agencies are therefore involved in the regulatory aspects of hazardous cargo carriage. The International Air Transport Association has issued IATA "Regulations Relating to the Carriage of Restricted Articles by Air." The Airline Tariff Publishers, Inc., publishes the "Official Air Transport Restrictive Articles Tariff" on behalf of U.S. air carriers. The U.S. Department of Transportation, Office of Hazardous Materials and its Hazardous Materials Regulations Board has overall responsibility for establishing definitions of hazardous materials, labeling requirements, and promulgating a list of hazardous materials and shipping limitations on behalf of the United States (see Code of Federal Regulations, Title 49—Transportation, Parts 170-189). Federal Aviation Regulations, Part 103, "Transportation of Dangerous Articles and Magnetized Materials," prescribes rules for loading and carrying such materials in any civil aircraft in the United States, and in civil aircraft of United States registry anywhere in air commerce. Different rules apply for passenger aircraft as opposed to "cargo-only"

aircraft. The United Nations has developed labels for hazardous materials which many member countries and international groups dealing with hazardous materials have or are preparing to utilize. The latest labels for use in the U.S. are consistent with the U.N. labeling methods (see Section 3, Chapter 10). The U.S. Departments of the Air Force, the Army, the Navy, and the Defense Supply Agency have published a manual on "Packaging and Handling of Dangerous Materials for Transportation by Military Aircraft" (AFM71-4).

There are many problems of increasingly serious magnitude in the policing of the air carriage of such hazardous materials. Several serious incidents and one serious accident in 1973 (Pan American 707 crash at Logan International Airport, Boston, Mass.) brought the issues into sharp focus. Radiation exposure as well as fire, corrosion hazards, and toxic or noxious gas release are issues being subjected to close international and national scrutiny. Airport authorities are as concerned as aircraft operators. The fire service has the need to know what types of hazardous cargoes they can expect to encounter in handling any aircraft emergency or air cargo storage situation. The biggest problem is in the enforcement of such regulations as are now in effect, and international agreement on just what these regulations should stipulate. Divided responsibility exists between: (1) producers, (2) shippers (land, sea, and air) and the intermodal shipping problems (in one trip a container or cargo travels on two or more modes of transportation), (3) regulatory supervision of labeling, packaging, and acceptability of the particular commodity in the quantity offered for shipment, (4) the awareness of the crew of the nature of the hazardous materials aboard an aircraft, and recognition of the degree of hazard involved under normal and abnormal flight conditions.

Air Flows

Air flows within the fuselage are generally from nose to tail when in flight to restrict the spread of a fire. Air flow seals normally provided include: (a) those between power and accessory sections of power plants, (b) between the wing and engine nacelle, (c) between the exhaust and accessory compartment and the wheel well, (d) between the wing and the fuselage, (e) between cargo spaces inaccessible in flight and occupied compartments, and (f) between the crew and passenger compartments. Separate ventilation controls should be furnished for the crew and passenger compartments, with provision for rapid ventilation of smoke or toxic fumes from the crew compartment starting with full pressurization (when applicable) and without depressurizing beyond safe limits.

I. Aircraft Fire Detection and Extinguishing Systems

Built-in aircraft fire detection and extinguishing systems are designed to provide protection for many of the previously mentioned fire hazards. Uncontrolled fire in flight can cause disastrous structural failure of aircraft supporting surfaces and control facilities in an exceedingly short period of time. The need for immediate fire detection and prompt application of effective extinguishing media thus assumes life-saving importance.

Installed Aircraft Fire Detection Systems

Most fire detectors installed in aircraft operate either at a fixed temperature, rate of temperature rise, a combination of fixed temperature and rate of rise, or by flame contact. A new development is the use of a continuous (line type) detector which makes use of excess heat to generate sufficient electrical power to provide a warning signal.

Requirements for aircraft detectors and associated components are severe. They must be arranged to permit the crew to check the integrity of the system in flight and on the ground. Visible and audible alarms to the flight crew are required; the visual warning, in particular, must indicate the fire zone involved. Wiring and other components in the fire zones must be fire resistant. Detector units or continuous-type (line type) equipment must not fail because of any extremes of temperature, vibration, inertia, corrosion, humidity, altitude, exposure to oil, water, or other fluids to which they might be subjected. Detectors must be automatically resetting and the warning light in the cockpit should go off when the fire is extinguished or the temperature drops below the set point. But, most important, abnormal temperature or the presence of flame must be detected within a very few seconds of exposure in order to prevent structural failure. This means a high degree of sensitivity; however, at the same time, a system that is too sensitive is subject to the bugbear of false alarms, which are particularly critical in aircraft operations. What is known in the trade as a "fault-free" detector is essential to avoid false alarms. This requirement calls for a design characteristic that will prevent accidental grounding or a broken detector circuit from producing an alarm. More than once, false fire alarms have resulted in emergency landings at considerable life hazards risk to the occupants; yet, if pilots lose confidence in the equipment, the danger is worse.

Detection systems sensing incipient fire by photoelectric principles or on other than heat-detection principles (e.g., carbon monoxide detectors, visual smoke detectors, and olfactory smoke detectors) may be required in some special situations.

Zones Requiring Detectors

Any area containing ignition sources (hot metals, hot gases, potential sparks, or arcing) and flammable fluid system components that are not deliberately inerted, can be considered as a potential fire zone. The need for detection in such zones should not be predicated on the availability of fire extinguishment equipment. The aircraft crew must know of fire anywhere in the aircraft at all times, whether or not fire extinguishing equipment is available.

Reciprocating Engines: Reciprocating engines need detection devices in the power section—from the front of the engine aft to the fire seal or diaphragm cowl; the accessory section—from the rear of the diaphragm to the fire wall; and in the nacelle section (wheel well)—the nacelle aft of the fire wall.

Turbine Engines: Turbine engines need detection devices in the compressor and accessory section—this is generally a forward zone of relatively low velocity airflow (aft of the inlet section), normally containing engine accessories (it is similar to the accessory section of a piston engine installation, generally extending from the inlet section to the fire wall); the combustion and turbine section—this section normally is subject to low air velocity but high temperatures, and in many respects is similar to the power section of the piston engine installation; the accessory bullet nose—when this compartment contains flammable fluid system components and electrical equipment, it becomes hazardous (it is normally a small space with very low air flows situated at the front of the engine); and the after-

burner section—located at the aft end of the engine installation, this section is generally subject to high temperatures.

Other Spaces that Might Require Fire Detectors: Other spaces that might require detection devices are: the fuel-fired aircraft heater area—depending upon the specific heater installation, hazardous areas containing flammable fluid system components and ignition sources need detection (generally, all installations should incorporate detectors in the ducts downstream of heaters), the area of auxiliary power units (APU)—fire zones for such combustion driven units should be established after the manner of the power plants and similar detection systems that have been provided; and the cargo or baggage compartments—including those where the presence of a fire would not be easily discovered by a crew member while at his or her station, and where access to each part of the compartment is not accessible in flight.

Location of Detectors

The most effective location for fire detectors is the path of airflow. The precise location of fire ignition and immediate path of flame from that point cannot always be predicted. However, the airflow through ventilated zones assures that the air outlets will become areas through which the flames must pass. The detector coverage necessary (number of unit detectors or lengths of continuous detector) depends on the area to be covered and on the velocity of airflow. The higher the airflow, the more the detector coverage needed due to the stratification of air and flame that occurs. In summary, detectors should be installed in any duct used as an air outlet from a fire zone, any duct leading between fire zones, any duct downstream of a heater installation, or in any other potential fire source.

It is important to distinguish between simple "overheat" conditions and "fire." Many alleged "false alarms" are actually "overheats" that do not result in a fire. Separate detection devices for the two conditions may be needed. Fire detectors should be set to operate at temperatures sufficiently above maximum operating ambient conditions so that there can be no confusion between overheat and fire, or at least 30 percent greater than the maximum rate of temperature rise during normal engine starting and operation. It should be noted that under flight conditions presently encountered there is no record of a fire burning at temperatures in the range from 400°F to 900°F which are the present range of fire detectors settings.

Installed Aircraft Fire Extinguishing Systems

Most built-in aircraft extinguishing systems are installed so that the extinguishing agent is distributed by specially designed piping to each "fire zone" from one or more fixed supply sources. One practice is to use a central cylinder supply from which the agent may be distributed to any one of a number of fire zones; another technique is to provide each fire zone with its own cylinder supply. This latter type of system is usually used to better advantage in an emergency landing because the piping is not so apt to be disrupted by the impact forces. Both systems have control facilities that are visible and accessible to the pilot or flight engineer.

Bromotrifluoromethane (Halon 1301), bromochlorodifluoromethane (Halon 1211), chlorobromomethane, methyl bromide, and carbon dioxide are the chief agents currently used in built-in aircraft extinguishing systems. All are effective on flammable liquid and electrical fires of the type liable to be encountered; however, quantity and weight requirements penalize the use of carbon dioxide, while toxicity and corrosion handicap the employment of methyl bromide or chlorobromomethane (methyl bromide has particularly serious toxicity problems). Most authorities agree, though, that toxicity is not an important factor in multiengine aircraft when the supply and area protected are outside the occupied portions and cabins are protected against vapor travel. Tests in both the United States and Great Britain show that smaller quantities of bromotrifluoromethane, bromochlorodifluoromethane, and methyl bromide are required to achieve fire extinguishment in aircraft power plants than with carbon dioxide or chlorobromomethane. The former agents are of about equal extinguishing ability while under optimum discharge and distribution conditions.

Of equal importance to the type of agent selected is the assurance that there will be an adequate quantity of the agent, that it will be properly distributed to the hazard zones, and that the rate of discharge will effectively extinguish the fire considering the air flows existing in the protected space. In most cases these factors must be individually analyzed. To achieve the desired rates of discharge, pyrotechnic capsules are sometimes used to expel the extinguishing agent from the container.

Structural design influences extinguishing agent effectiveness in aircraft nacelles and compartments. Structural ribs and irregularities, as well as joints or holes in the nacelle skin or fire walls, handicap efficiency. Agent efficiency is materially reduced by the use of long feed lines and tubing that are below size. Short, open-ended tubes have replaced perforated tubing, resulting in "high-rate discharge" systems which are more effective and lighter than the older complex distribution systems. "High-rate discharge" systems have proved very effective, particularly in zones of high air flow. Such systems tend to momentarily disrupt normal air flow and produce good extinguishing agent distribution by virtue of the turbulent action.

Extinguishment of engine fires during flight depends upon proper action by the pilot. There are numerous design refinements to aid the pilot and assure effective results. Those deserving mention include: simplified controls for activation of the propeller feathering system upon detector operation; effective cutoffs of fuel, oil, and ignition to the affected section; and the closing of air ducts to effect best results.

Other areas sometimes protected by built-in fire extinguishing systems include inaccessible baggage or cargo compartments, combustion heaters, and wheel wells. Baggage compartment fire protection has been the subject of tests which indicate that the sealing of compartments, ventilation shutoff, and the use of heat resistant noncombustible lining materials are effective measures in the control of cargo fires. Carbon dioxide or bromotrifluoromethane systems proved effective in rapid suppression of flames in these cargo compartment tests.

J. Aircraft Hand Fire Extinguishers

Hand fire extinguishers of the proper types are required in the cabins of all aircraft. The NFPA has issued NFPA No. 408, Standard on Aircraft Hand Fire Extinguishers, covering the type, capacity, location, and quantity of hand fire extinguishers and accessory equipment. Under this Standard, the crew compartment is to have one approved carbon dioxide hand extinguisher with a minimum rating of 2B:C. Passenger compartments, where the hazard is chiefly from ordinary combustible materials, require a minimum 1-qt (nominal) water extinguisher. Aircraft

accommodating no more than 30 passengers should have one such approved extinguisher easily accessible and clearly visible to the occupants. At least two extinguishers should be provided in aircraft accommodating from 31 to 60 passengers, one of which should be an approved water extinguisher; the second extinguisher may be an approved carbon-dioxide type with a minimum 2B:C rating. For larger aircraft, the Standard recommends at least two approved water extinguishers and one additional extinguisher which may be an approved carbon-dioxide type with a minimum 2B:C rating. Where passenger compartments are divided, each shall have at least one water extinguisher (division to include a door, curtained opening, stairwell, or other arrangement that obscures vision or impairs air circulation). Where cooking facilities are provided in a galley, one approved carbon dioxide extinguisher having a minimum rating should be provided. As noted previously, this may also be the second extinguisher recommended for passenger compartments.

The Federal Aviation Administration's Technical Standard Order C-19b describes a special loaded-stream water-solution extinguisher for aircraft use, and the FAA authorizes the use of extinguishers meeting this TSO in U.S. aircraft on certification by the manufacturer.

Extinguishers utilizing halogenated extinguishing agents classified by the Underwriters Laboratories, Inc., as falling in UL Toxicity Group 5 or 6 may be substituted for the carbon dioxide extinguishers if it can be shown that there is sufficient free-air volume within the aircraft cabin space to avoid producing serious irritating effects on the occupants. The irritating effects should be calculated by establishing the discharge of the total quantity of extinguishing agents (of all such extinguishers carried) within the smallest occupied space within the aircraft under full-load aircraft conditions and with no mechanical ventilation equipment in operation. In aircraft in which all occupants are provided with oxygen masks or respiratory equipment intended for continuous use, this factor may be taken into consideration. Halogenated extinguishing agents with lower numerical UL toxicity ratings should not be used because of the greater toxicity of the agents and the possibility of producing greater quantities of harmful or irritating decomposition products when the agents are applied to a fire.

Extinguishers containing dry chemicals are not recommended for use in aircraft cabins because of problems introduced by the nonconductivity of the agent on fine electrical contacts, the corrosive properties of some dry chemical formulations, the reduction of visibility which may be encountered when the agent is discharged in the confined space of an aircraft cabin, and the problem of removing powder residues following extinguishment.

K. Means of Egress from Aircraft

In aircraft, exit facilities are particularly important because impact forces might jam the normal means of egress, and, in the event of fire, evacuation must be extremely rapid in the interest of life safety. Federal Aviation Regulations on transport category aircraft have detailed requirements for emergency exits, their number to be determined by the seating capacity. For example, aircraft accommodating 40 to 79 passengers must have a minimum of two 24-in. by 48-in. floor-level exits located as far aft in the passenger area as is practicable (one on each side), and two (one on each side) 20-in. by 36-in. emergency hatches located over the wing (a step-up inside the aircraft to be not more than 20 in., and a step-down outside the aircraft to the wing to be not more than 27 in.). For aircraft accommodating 110 to 139 passengers, there must be four 24-in. by 48-in. floor-level exits (two on each side), and two 20-in. by 36-in. over-the-wing exits (one on each side). Crew exits are separately specified.

Exits must be operable from both inside and outside, except that sliding window emergency exits in the flight crew area need not be able to be opened from the outside if other approved exits are convenient and readily accessible to the flight crew area. They must be designed to resist jamming, and must be easily located and operable. Sections 25.803 to 25.817 of the Federal Aviation Regulations cover the emergency evacuation requirements, flight crew emergency exits, emergency exit arrangements and marking, emergency lighting, emergency exit access, width of aisles, and maximum allowable number of seats abreast for transport category airplanes holding FAA certification.

Under current U.S. air carrier aircraft regulations, each certificated holder must demonstrate that the emergency evacuation procedures for each type and model of aircraft with a seating capacity of more than 44 passengers will allow the evacuation of the full seating capacity, including crew members, in 90 sec or less, utilizing not more than 50 percent of the available exits. Procedures for carrying out the demonstration are detailed in the Federal Air Regulations (Appendix D to Part 121 of the Code of Federal Regulation, Title 14).

L. Special Military Aircraft Hazards

Military aircraft have a number of special hazards that rescue and fire fighting crews must appreciate in order to avoid unnecessary risk to themselves, to any bystanders at an accident site, or to exposed property. The United States Air Force has produced an Air Force Technical Manual, "Aircraft Emergency Rescue Information (Fire Protection)," identified as T.O. 00-105E-9, which is available to organized fire departments from MMSTD, Robins Air Force Base, GA 31093. It includes information on U.S. military aircraft essential to those concerned with crash/rescue emergencies, giving data on current U.S.A.F. bomber, cargo/transport, fighter, helicopter, observation, reconnaissance, trainer, utility, and STOL aircraft, plus U.S. Army aircraft in current service, and some common commercial aircraft. A special section covers entry and exit facilities; prevention of suffocation; removal of personnel from seats; types, safetying, and hazards of ejection seats; and forcible entry. NFPA No. 402 contains extracts of this information for the most common military aircraft in current service.

Ejection Seats and Canopy Ejectors: These are provided in many military aircraft to permit crew members to catapult themselves (and the canopy and seat) clear of the aircraft when forced to bail out at any speed due to in-flight difficulties (flame-out, fire, mid-air collosions, etc). Safety pins are used to prevent inadvertent firing of the ejection seat catapult while on the ground; one of these pins also "safeties" the canopy. The pins are removed prior to each flight so that the ejection equipment can be operated without delay. When making rescues, these safety pins must be inserted by rescue crews (if the pilot is incapacitated) to avoid the real danger of accidental operation. Canopy releases are prominently marked on the exterior of these aircraft.

Armament: Armament on military aircraft may consist of machine guns, cannons, or rockets. The guns may be fixed or movable, with the movable ones installed in turrets. Rescue crews are advised to stay away from the line of fire

of guns while approaching military aircraft on fire. If a gun is loaded, the round in the chamber may "cook off" and the projectile ejected if the gun barrel is hot. Another hazard arises if there is a short or other defect in an electrical firing circuit because the burned insulation or crash damage may cause the gun to fire. Magazines and stored ammunition should be removed, if possible, from their wing or fuselage positions following a crash; this is normally done by trained crews, assuming they know the location of the magazines in the particular aircraft. When 50-caliber ammunition is subject to heat from a fire, the hazard is not too great because, in most cases, the velocity of the segments discharged, as a result of cartridge rupture, blown caps, or bullets driven out of their cases, is moderate. Exploding 50-caliber ammunition is more nerve-shaking than it is hazardous, although powder charges and incendiary or tracer cores can project an awesome flame. Detonation of larger caliber ammunition is more hazardous because fragments are larger and projections normally travel at higher velocity.

Bombs: Bombs may explode due to fire exposure. Ordnance experiments prove that certain types that have been subject to intense heat will detonate within 2¼ to 5¼ min. It is well, therefore, to try to keep bomb bays or wing racks cool whenever possible. The hazard is related more to high-explosive detonation than to any other factors, and this applies to nuclear weapon components as well as conventional bombs. The usual procedure followed at USAF and USN air bases when a fire occurs aboard an aircraft known to be armed with bombs is to advance immediately to take what rescue measures may be expedient in the first few minutes (time decided on the basis of fire intensity) and then, if fire control has not been accomplished, to retire to a safe distance until the explosion hazard has passed.

Rockets: Rockets are extremely dangerous if in their launchers and subject to intense heat from a fire. Time is a factor in the exposure to heat, as it will take some minutes (maybe up to approximately 5 min) for a direct fire exposure to heat the propellant to its autoignition temperature (most approximately 570°F). The severity of a rocket explosion would depend on whether the warhead or the rocket propellant exploded. If the latter, the resulting blast would probably split the motor tube, issue exhaust gases which would be extremely hot (in the neighborhood of 4,000°F), but might not fire the rocket itself in a normal manner. If the rocket did fire, it is probable that it would follow its normal course; fire fighters should stand clear both fore and aft of rocket installations. If a rocket warhead ignited, the blast effect would probably not only result in the destruction of the aircraft structure, but also would detonate any other warheads aboard. Where it may be possible to cool rocket packages, the U.S. Navy recommends carbon dioxide, dry chemical, and foam in preference to the use of water spray because the latter agent adds to the intensity of burning rocket propellants.

Pyrotechnics: When used in military aircraft, pyrotechnics are for signaling, photographic lighting, and other special purposes. They usually consist of a rapid-burning powder, magnesium, or flammables, and will spread fire quickly if ignited, usually involving the cockpit or fuselage. Types of current pyrotechnics used include smoke grenades, parachute flares, drift signals, drift flares, etc.

Missile Propellants: Missile propellants found in armed military aircraft may be divided into two general classes: (1) liquid propellants, and (2) solid propellants. Liquid propellants can be divided into three classes: (1) fuels, (2) oxidizers, and (3) monopropellants. In the class of fuels are found: (1) liquid ammonia, (2) the alcohols, (3) aniline mixtures, (4) hydrazines, (5) hydrogen, and (6) various petroleum products and derivatives. In the class of oxidizers are: (1) liquid oxygen, (2) fuming nitric acids, (3) fluorine, (4) chlorine trifluoride, (5) ozone, (6) ozone-oxygen mixtures, and (7) concentrated hydrogen peroxide. Among monopropellants are: (1) ethylene oxide, (2) hydrazine, (3) hydrogen peroxide, and (4) nitromethane. (Note that hydrazine and hydrogen peroxide may be utilized as a fuel and oxidizer respectively, as well as a monopropellant.) The properties of most of these propellants are covered in Chapter 8 of the *Fire Officer's Guide to Dangerous Chemicals* by Charles W. Bahme (1972). That chapter contains a reference list to other technical reference documents on the subject.

Rockets and Space Vehicles: Those presently in operation utilize a complexity of liquid propellants, solid propellants, ordnance items, high pressure gases, and other materials that present particular fire and explosion hazards. Inadvertent mixing of some propellants, a static spark, stray R-F signals, human failure, component failure—any one of these and many other ignition sources—can cause a sudden holocaust. Fire control is virtually futile when large quantities of an oxidizer are involved in a fire because, to date, no effective reaction-stopping agent is available for all of the propellant combinations in use. Fire prevention needs are thus paramount, especially in handling some propellants that require no ignition source to combust (as, for instance, when nitrogen tetraoxide and unsymmetrical dimethyl hydrazine are combined to form what is called a hypergolic mixture).

Missile Launch Sites: These require strict attention to fire prevention measures and fire protection engineering for the security of these installations. Besides the fuels and propellants, there are the hazards of missile accessories, cryogenic storage of oxidizers, and the handling of pyrophoric materials (materials which ignite spontaneously when exposed to air, such as tri-methyl and tri-ethyl aluminum that are used as igniter materials).

The primary requirement for fire protection at missile sites is an adequate water supply. At some of the larger stands, cooling water flowing over the flame deflector buckets must be at a rate of 30,000 or more gpm, with additional water required for cooling exposed parts of the structure. Some fixed fire extinguishing systems have been installed at major missile launching sites and have proven to be effective in minimizing stand damage after accidental missile launch failures or missile fueling accidents. Water is, however, reactive with many propellants (such as liquid fluorine and liquid igniters of the alkyl aluminum variety), and thus has definite limitations. When there is a massive oxidizer spill it is usually preferable to allow evaporation than to apply water.

M. Aircraft Rescue and Fire Control

The inherent fire hazards of aircraft (see also Part L on Special Military Aircraft Hazards) possess severe implications in the event of ground accidents. There are two distinct types of accidents to consider. One type involves high impact force ("power-on" ground collisions) when major aircraft structural failure results and death is almost certain to be instantaneous to all occupants. The other type involves relatively low-impact forces when it can be expected that "walk-away" rates will be high and occupant injuries nonfatal, if fire does not block escape.

In the case of most "power-on" impacts, rescue is im-

probable and fire control is sought principally to protect exposed properties, permit identification of the victims, and to preserve evidence to aid investigators in determining the cause of the accident. In the low-impact crash, rescue comes first. This means that facilities must be available, wherever possible, to attack aircraft fires quickly and at least hold the fire in check until the occupants can be rescued.

In the U.S., the National Transportation Safety Board reports that during the years 1970 to 1973, of a total of 198 air carrier accident records in their files, 93 occurred on the airport or heliport while 21 others occurred within 5 miles of the airport. This means that about 58 percent of these accidents do occur on or in the immediate vicinity of airports. Sixty-two of these accidents occurred during the landing phase, 23 during takeoff, 17 while the aircraft was parked, and 16 during taxiing—or about 60 percent on airports, with the balance (40 percent) during the flight phase.

The seriousness of the crash fire problem results from aircraft design factors that place large quantities of fuel in relatively light containers (wing structures) in such a position that ground or accidental impacts release the fuel. The usual impact forces result in "atomization" of fuel due to the high rates of deceleration and bulk spillage of the liquid. In the presence of multiple ignition sources (e.g., hot engine exhaust surfaces and exhaust gases, aircraft electrical circuits, burning lubricating oils ignited by spillage on hot engine surfaces, electrostatic and friction sparks, etc.) this "atomized" fuel may ignite quickly and burn rapidly. From a limited series of tests it has been estimated that occupant survival time may range from 50 to 300 sec in a serious crash fire. The period may be as short as a half minute when flame travel is unimpeded within the cabin.

There are two methods to reduce the life hazard of crash fires: namely, improved design to make aircraft more "crash-fire-worthy," and adequate airport-based aircraft rescue and fire fighting equipment and personnel. The National Aeronautics and Space Administration and the Federal Aviation Administration (National Aviation Facilities Experimental Center) have pinpointed many of the design factors responsible for crash fires, and some "crash-fire-worthy" features have been incorporated into the latest aircraft designs (see Part D of this Chapter). Other efforts to reduce the fire hazards at time of crash impact include research on "thickened" fuel, emulsification of the fuel, and fuel tank inerting systems; however, to date none of these research efforts have found their way into operational aircraft (see Part A of this Chapter). While the kerosine grades of turbine fuel (JET A) have favorable features in reducing the speed of flame propagation under normal conditions, severe crash fires have occurred in aircraft utilizing this grade of fuel because of the atomization factor following impact and the release of large quantities of liquid fuel.

As of May 20, 1973, no person could operate a land airport serving any CAB-certificated air carrier operating aircraft into that airport in the United States without an airport operating certificate. Certification requires that the airport have fire fighting and rescue equipment as specified in Part 139 of Title 14 of the Code of Federal Regulations. Airports are "Indexed" by the longest large aircraft operated into the airport an average of at least 5 scheduled departures per day (with some exceptions based on frequency of such movements by the longest aircraft). FAA Advisory Circular 150/5210-6B gives the recommended levels as compared to the minimum levels in Part 139.

The International Civil Aviation Organization (1080 University Street, Montreal, Quebec, Canada) has recommendations in Annex 14 (Aerodromes) to the Convention on International Civil Aviation on rescue and fire fighting services at airports. ICAO Aerodrome Manual, Part 5, contains material on rescue and fire fighting, and Part 16 is a Training Manual for Aerodrome Fire Service Personnel. NFPA Publications that provide guidance on crash equipment, training, and procedures are: NFPA No. 402, Standard Operating Procedures, Aircraft Rescue and Fire Fighting; NFPA No. 403, Aircraft Rescue and Fire Fighting Services at Airports and Heliports; NFPA 406M, Aircraft Rescue and Fire Fighting Techniques for Fire Departments Using Structural Fire Apparatus; NFPA No. 412, Evaluating Foam Fire Fighting Equipment on Aircraft Rescue and Fire Fighting Vehicles; NFPA No. 414, Aircraft Rescue and Fire Fighting Vehicles; and NFPA No. 422M, Aircraft Fire Investigator's Manual.

Aircraft rescue and fire fighting vehicles must have superior off-highway capability plus high acceleration and speed. NFPA Standard No. 414 specifies the design and performance requirements for this specialized service.

Techniques of aircraft crash fire control found most successful to date involve the use of protein, fluoroprotein, or aqueous film-forming foaming concentrates with water, sometimes with either foam-compatible dry chemical or carbon dioxide (low pressure). High discharge rates of these agents are required to achieve rapid blanketing and effective cooling within the time element available for rescue. Often extinguishment is a requirement for successful rescues. Quantities of agents needed vary with the type of aircraft being protected. The FAA recommendations in the Advisory Circular, the guidance given in the material promulgated by the International Civil Aviation Organization, and the guidance in NFPA No. 403 follow the same principles but with some differences in applications and in the quantities of agents for airports served by various types and sizes of aircraft.

Heat radiation and the entry of fire gases into the occupied portions appear to be the most critical factors in occupant survival. Maintaining the integrity of the fuselage as a shield is essential if persons are trapped within an aircraft and fire is on the exterior. Since "burn-throughs" can be rapid, quick fire control is essential. When it is not possible to exclude flame or fire gases from the occupied portions of the aircraft, rescue opportunities are restricted, as suffocation or anoxia may cause death before entry can be made by rescue crews.

Ramp fires (not involving crashes) further justify the provision of aircraft rescue and fire fighting services at airports. Controlling fires that may be caused by fueling or maintenance accidents has proven to be a major responsibility and activity. The fire prevention services of airport fire fighters have paid handsome dividends in supervision over hazardous practices.

N. Airport and Heliport Design Safety

There are many factors involved in the safety of aircraft operations at airports and heliports: proper runway lengths and construction, navigational aids, clearances off operational runways below the navigable air space, terrain conditions between runways and taxiways, zoning regulations, and fire protection. Heliports have special problems because they frequently are found in congested areas of cities, on the roofs of buildings, on elevated platforms constructed over piers, or on the water's edge. Although this HANDBOOK deals solely with the fire protection problems, many of these other factors are closely related.

A number of serious accidents have occurred because of airport hazards, and their seriousness has been increased due to inadequate zoning regulations and clearances off the operational runways. Airports are frequently surrounded, in part or in whole, by water; thus, the provision of water-borne crash rescue facilities becomes a specialized problem for these airports unless Coast Guard, Naval, or municipal water-borne rescue and fire control equipment is immediately available to perform whatever rescue services may be needed in the event an aircraft ditches in the water.

The undershoot areas off runways have been the scene of a number of accidents, and create special problems where dikes or unimproved terrain conditions exist. In some cases, blast fences have been erected at the ends of runways to protect adjacent structures or highways, or to reduce the noise factor when take-off power is applied to aircraft power plants, particularly the turbine engine aircraft. Under poor visibility conditions, crashes have resulted when aircraft have struck these dikes and blast fences. During airport construction and repair, especially on the movement areas, the additional hazards of the construction and resurfacing equipment has been a factor in accidents. Another principal area where accidents frequently occur is in the overrun portions of runways; a number of the most serious accidents have occurred here when aircraft have not been able to brake effectively and have run off the runway, striking airport boundary fences, or have been damaged by bogging down while traversing unimproved ground surfaces. In the military, considerable use has been made of arresting gears of various designs to prevent overrun, but such equipment has not, as yet, been used extensively in commercial airports since, in most cases, the use of such arresting mechanisms requires corresponding design changes in the aircraft itself (installation of a "hook"). Unimproved ground surfaces between runways have frequently resulted in aircraft being inaccessible to fire and rescue equipment, especially equipment that is not specifically designed for off-highway use. Many airports are built on "filled" land, which is one of the principal reasons why aircraft rescue and fire fighting equipment must be especially designed to have off-pavement traction capability.

Aircraft Hangars: Hangars have special fire protection problems, one of which involves the number of aircraft they are frequently required to house; as aircraft have increased in size, so have, necessarily, the areas of these buildings. The height of the structures also presents special problems with regard to the installation of automatic fire protection equipment. Almost all hangars, except small unit-type hangars for personal use, are used for aircraft maintenance, and it is the rule rather than the exception that aircraft undergoing maintenance in these buildings are fueled. Analysis of hangar fire losses indicates that frequently the contents of a hangar are several times more valuable than the hangar itself, and with the modern jet transports valued in the millions, this fact can be readily appreciated.

NFPA No. 409, Standard on Aircraft Hangars, deals with the construction and protection of these facilities. Area limitations are recommended in this Standard for hangers of different construction types, with or without sprinkler protection. The Standard prohibits basements in hangars because of the hazard of large fuel spills on hangar floors, and it establishes rules for segregating adjoining and communicating areas, particularly those presenting special hazards, such as when there is paint spraying, or where stocks of tools or flammable liquids are stored. Recommendations are included in the Standard on design of doors to accommodate aircraft, landing gear pits and tunnels, drainage of apron and hangar floors, installation of draft stops in sprinklered hangars, installation of heating equipment, installation of electrical equipment, grounding facilities for the removal and control of static electrical accumulations on aircraft, and for exit and access facilities.

As far as fire protection for aircraft hangars is concerned, the NFPA Standard on Aircraft Hangars divides hangars into three "Types": (1) Type I, (2) Type II, and (3) Type III.

Type I: Type I is a hangar with a clear door height of over 28 ft or with a fire area in excess of 40,000 sq ft. (Hangars housing strategically important military aircraft are automatically considered Type I hangars.)

Type I aircraft hangar storage and servicing areas are required under the Standard to be equipped with an approved sprinkler system, hand hose systems, portable fire extinguishers, and, where the aircraft accommodated therein have a wing area in excess of 3,000 sq ft, by a supplemental system for external aircraft protection as specified in the Standard. The sprinkler protection required should preferably be an approved foam-water sprinkler system or can be approved water deluge system. The foam-water systems may use protein, fluoroprotein, or aqueous-film-forming-foam (AFFF) liquid concentrates. The supplemental system is designed to overcome the difficulties caused by the configuration and positioning of aircraft and hangar servicing platforms and equipment which could compromise the effectiveness of the high-level protection by "shielding" the areas beneath the wing and wing center sections of the aircraft. The Standard gives required discharge densities and water supply durations.

Type II: Type II is a hangar with a clear door height of 28 ft or less and with a fire area of 40,000 sq ft or less, but greater than those specified in the Standard as the maximum permissible area for hangars not protected by an approved fire protection system (areas vary with types of construction).

Type II aircraft hangar storage and servicing areas may use the same protection systems specified for Type I hangars, or may use a hydraulically calculated closed-wet-pipe sprinkler system or a preaction system in conjunction with an approved low- or high-expansion foam extinguishing system meeting the provisions of the Standard. Again, hose systems and portable extinguishers are part of the protection package, and the Standard specifies the required discharge densities and water supply criteria.

Type III: Type III is a hangar with a clear door height of 28 ft or less, and with a fire area up to the maximum permitted in the Standard for hangars not to be equipped with an approved fire protection system (areas vary with types of construction).

Type III aircraft hangars are required only to have portable fire extinguishers, although the systems specified for Type II or even Type I are recommended where practicable. It is recognized that Type III hangars can normally be adequately protected by a standard automatic sprinkler system following the rules for ordinary hazard occupancies.

Airport Terminal Buildings: Airport terminal buildings is the subject of NFPA Standard No. 416, Standard for Airport Terminal Buildings, which sets forth requirements developed for these structures due to their exposure to operations on adjacent airport ramps, and the large number of people who are normally within these buildings. As defined, an airport terminal building is used primarily for air passenger enplaning or deplaning and may include a number of convenience facilities such as ticket sales, baggage handling, restaurant facilities, etc. As used in the Standard, a terminal includes any fully enclosed extensions functioning as passenger concourses to aircraft loading gates, or "satellite" buildings used for passenger handling or aircraft flight service functions. There are special requirements outlined in the Standard for the construction of these buildings; they include rules for the sloping of ramps adjacent thereto, for protection of below grade areas, limitations on occupancy, heating, ventilating, and air-conditioning equipment, exits, covered plane-loading positions, and for windows facing the ramp. (See Fig. 17-1D for data on the intake and exhaust hazards of turbine engines.)

Roof-Top Heliport Construction and Protection: This is covered in NFPA Standard No. 418, Standard for Roof-Top Heliport Construction and Protection, which deals with the special fire problems existing for this type facility, covering landing deck construction, drainage, egress, and fire protection.

Aircraft Fueling Ramp Drainage: This is a special problem because of the area of the ramps and the need to accommodate water runoff and to minimize the danger inherent in fuel spills. A Standard on this subject has been developed (NFPA No. 415, Standard for Aircraft Fueling Ramp Drainage) which calls for aircraft fueling ramps to slope away from terminal buildings, passenger concourses, aircraft hangars, or other structures at a minimum grade of 1 percent for the first 50 ft. Beyond this distance, the sloped drainage inlets may be reduced to a minimum of 0.5 percent. When drainage inlets are provided, the Standard asks for them to be a minimum of 50 ft from any structure. Additional details are given in the Standard on various types

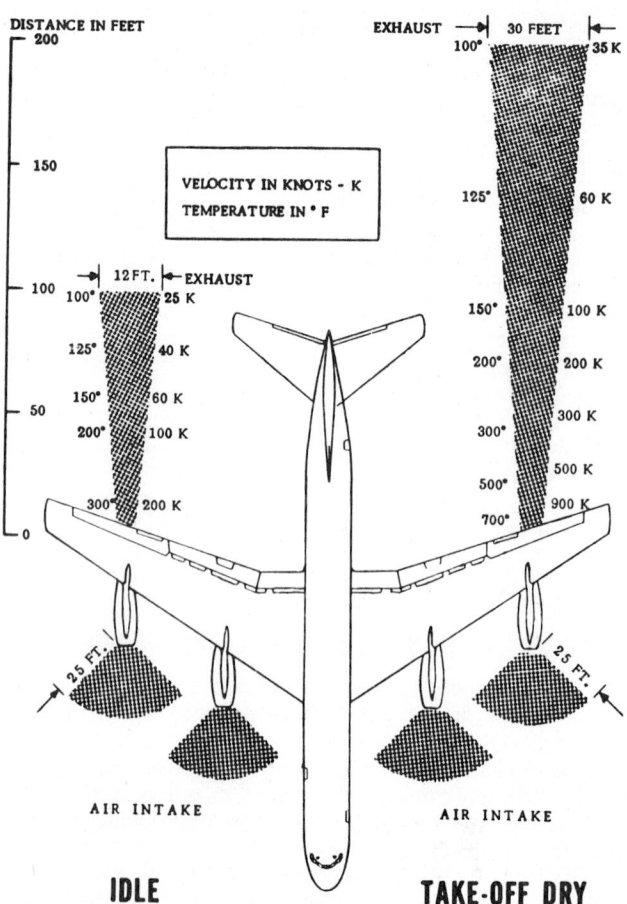

Fig. 17-1D. Engine intake and exhaust hazard areas of turbine transport aircraft when at idle and take-off power settings.

of drainage facilities, location of inlets, use of water-seal traps, and design of interceptors or separators.

Aircraft Loading Walkways: These walkways have come into considerable use at the larger airports in recent years. They are elevated devices designed to allow passengers to walk between a point in an airport terminal building (usually at the second floor level) and an aircraft without being exposed to the weather and without using stairs. NFPA Standard No. 417, Standard for Aircraft Loading Walkways, was developed to assure the integrity of walkways as a means of safe emergency egress from an aircraft positioned for walkway loading or unloading should a fire occur under or around it. While these walkways are primarily for convenience in handling passengers, they can offer distinct advantages from a fire safety viewpoint during normal aircraft ramp servicing operations and if their design includes provisions for safe use for evacuation of an aircraft connected thereto in the event of a ramp fire emergency. Different methods of accomplishing this latter objective are recommended in the Standard, based on maintaining the walkway as a means of egress from a connected aircraft for a period of at least 5 min under severe fire exposure conditions.

Aircraft Fuel Servicing: Fuel servicing on airport ramps requires precautions against the hazard of ignition of spills and vapor releases by static sparks, aircraft engines and heaters, automotive equipment, electrical arcing from sources such as ground power generators, open-flame devices, high-frequency radar equipment, and the carelessness of persons who may have access to the ramp, particularly in the careless disposal of smoking materials. NFPA No. 407, Standard for Aircraft Fuel Servicing, outlines the specific precautions to be followed to control the extent of this hazard and, in addition, gives recommendations on the design of aircraft fueling hose, inspection and hydrostatic test procedures for this hose, aircraft fuel servicing tank vehicle design, and recommendations on airport fixed-fueling systems.

Airport and Heliport Fire Safety Regulations: Every airport and heliport should have fire safety regulations designed to fit their own needs, with definite responsibilities assigned to the airport fire chief or the airport manager for enforcement of fire safety practices. Most of the airlines have their own fire prevention and protection regulations governing the maintenance and servicing of their equipment, but individual situations at airports vary, making it necessary and desirable for airport management to apply local regulations tailored to their particular needs.

O.   Other Organizations in the Field of Aviation Fire Safety

Private organizations working in various fields of aviation fire safety other than the NFPA include:

Aerospace Industries Association of America, Inc., 1725 DeSales St., N.W., Washington, DC 20036

Air Line Pilots Association, International, 1625 Massachusetts Avenue, N.W., Washington, DC 20036

Air Transport Association of America, 1709 New York Avenue, N.W., Washington, DC 20006

Air Transport Section and Aerospace Section of the National Safety Council, 425 North Michigan Avenue, Chicago, IL 60611

Airport Operators Council, International, 1700 K Street, N.W., Washington, DC 20006

American Association of Airport Executives, 2029 K St., N.W., Washington, DC 20006

Aviation Technical Service Committee of the American Petroleum Institute, 1801 K Street, N.W., Washington, DC 20006

Flight Safety Foundation, Inc., 1800 N. Kent Street, Arlington, VA 22209

Society of Automotive Engineers, Inc., 2 Pennsylvania Plaza, New York, NY 10001

U.S. Government organizations working in the various aviation fire safety fields include:

Department of the Air Force (U.S. Department of Defense): The work of the USAF is coordinated through the Headquarters USAF (PREE), Washington, DC 20230, for operational and administration work and through the Air Force Systems Command (Wright-Patterson Air Force Base, OH 45433) for research work in the field.

Department of the Army (U.S. Department of Defense): The work of the Army in aviation fire safety is primarily coordinated through the U.S. Army Agency for Aviation Safety (Fort Rucker, AL 36360) and the U.S. Army Mobile Equipment Research and Development Center (Fort Belvoir, VA 22060).

Department of the Navy (U.S. Department of Defense): The work of the Navy in aviation fire safety is primarily coordinated through the Naval Facilities Engineering Command, Washington, DC 20390 and the Naval Research Laboratory, Washington, DC 20390.

Department of Defense, Aircraft Ground Fire Suppression and Rescue Systems Program: This office is headquartered at Wright-Patterson Air Force Base, OH 45433, and coordinates the research programs of the U.S. Departments of the Air Force, Army and Navy in the field of ground fire suppression equipment and rescue programs.

Federal Aviation Administration (U.S. Department of Transportation): Several branches of the FAA are concerned directly with aviation fire safety, including Flight Standards Service and Airport Services, headquartered in Washington, DC 20590, and the National Aviation Facilities Experimental Center, Atlantic City, NJ 08405.

National Aeronautics and Space Administration, 600 Independence Ave., S.W., Washington, DC 20546, is primarily concerned with space vehicle safety problems but conducts research into conventional subsonic and supersonic aircraft fire problems as well.

National Transportation Safety Board (U.S. Department of Transportation): Washington, DC 20590. The NTSB has responsibilities for determining the cause of aircraft accidents (except for certain light-plane accidents) formerly handled by the Civil Aeronautics Board. The NTSB also promotes safety by studies in accident prevention, and makes safety recommendations to the Federal Aviation Administration.

In Canada, the civil aviation fire protection program is coordinated through the Air Services Fire Marshal of the Canadian Department of Transport (Ottawa 4, Ont.), and the military program through the Fire Marshal, Canadian Forces (Ottawa 4, Ont.).

International aviation organizations interesting themselves in aviation fire safety include:

International Air Transport Association (IATA), 1155 Mansfield Street, Montreal 3, P.Q., Canada (through the office of the Technical Director).

International Civil Aviation Organization (ICAO), 1080 University Street, Montreal 101, P.Q., Canada (the Chief of Aerodromes of the Aerodromes, Air Routes and Ground Aids Division coordinates their program).
International Federation of Airline Pilots Associations, 1 Hyde Park Place, London W2, England (through the office of the Executive Secretary).

Space does not permit listing organizations in other countries or a further breakdown of United States and Canadian organizations which work at the state or provincial level or within the various industries.

SI Units

The following conversion factors are given as a convenience in converting to SI units the English units used in this chapter.

1 sq ft	$= 0.0929$ m^2
1 in.	$= 25.400$ mm
1 ft	$= 0.305$ m
1 psi	$= 6.895$ kPa
$\frac{5}{9}(°F - 32)$	$= °C$
1 qt	$= 0.946$ litres
1 gpm	$= 3.785$ litres per min

Bibliography

NFPA Codes, Standards, and Recommended Practices (see the latest NFPA Publications and Visual Aids Catalog for availability of current editions of the following documents)

NFPA No. 402, Standard Operating Procedures, Aircraft Rescue and Fire Fighting.
NFPA No. 403, Recommended Practice for Aircraft Rescue and Fire Fighting Services at Airports and Heliports.
NFPA No. 406M, Manual on Aircraft Rescue and Fire Fighting Techniques for Fire Departments Using Structural Fire Apparatus and Equipment.
NFPA No. 407, Standard for Aircraft Fuel Servicing.
NFPA No. 408, Standard on Aircraft Hand Fire Extinguishers.
NFPA No. 409, Standard on Aircraft Hangars.
NFPA No. 410A, Safeguarding Aircraft Electrical System Maintenance Operations.
NFPA No. 410B, Safeguarding Aircraft Breathing Oxygen System Maintenance Operations.
NFPA No. 410C, Safeguarding Aircraft Fuel System Maintenance.
NFPA No. 410D, Safeguarding Aircraft Cleaning, Painting, and Paint Removal.
NFPA No. 410E, Safe Practices for Aircraft Welding Operations in Hangars.
NFPA No. 410F, Safeguarding Aircraft Cabin Cleaning and Refurbishing Operations.
NFPA No. 412, Standard for Evaluating Foam Fire Fighting Equipment on Aircraft Rescue and Fire Fighting Vehicles.
NFPA No. 414, Standard for Aircraft Rescue and Fire Fighting Vehicles.
NFPA No. 415, Standard on Aircraft Fueling Ramp Drainage.
NFPA No. 416, Standard on Construction and Protection of Airport Terminal Buildings.
NFPA No. 417, Standard on Construction and Protection of Aircraft Loading Walkways.
NFPA No. 418, Standard on Roof-Top Heliport Construction and Protection.
NFPA No. 419, Recommended Practice for Master Planning Airport Water Supply Systems for Fire Protection.
NFPA No. 421, Recommended Practice on Aircraft Interior Fire Protection Systems.
NFPA No. 422M, Aircraft Fire Investigators Manual.

Additional Readings

"Aircraft Fire Safety," Transportation Fire Hazards, National Fire Protection Association, Boston, 1973, pp. 16–29.

U.S. Government Publications

Code of Federal Regulations, Title 14, "Aeronautics and Space," Parts 1 to 59, revised Jan. 1, 1974, Washington, D.C.
Ibid., Parts 60 to 199, revised Jan. 1, 1974.

Federal Aviation Administration Advisory Circulars (U.S. Department of Transportation, Washington, D.C.) with the following designations and titles:

"Aircraft Data," 150/5325-5A, Jan. 12, 1968.
"Aircraft Fire and Rescue Communications," 150/5210-7A, Mar. 16, 1972.
"Aircraft Fire and Rescue Facilities and Extinguishing Agents," 150/5210-6B, Jan. 26, 1973.
"Airport Operations Manual," 150/5280-1, June 16, 1972.
"Fire and Rescue Service for Certificated Airports," 150/5210-12, Mar. 2, 1972.
"Fire Prevention During Aircraft Fueling Operations," 150/5230-3, Apr. 8, 1969.

Aircraft Rescue and Fire Fighting Evaluations and Test Reports:

Alger, R. S. and Capener, E. L., "Aircraft Ground Fire Suppression and Rescue Systems—Basic Relationships in Military Fires, Phases I and II," AGFSRS 72-1, Apr. 1972, Tri-Service System Program Office for Aircraft Ground Fire Suppression and Rescue, SMF, Wright-Patterson Air Force Base, Ohio.
Atallah, S.; Kalelkas, A. S., and Hagopian, J., "Evaluation of Auxiliary Agents and Systems for Aircraft Ground Fire Suppression, Phase I," ASD-TR-72-75, Aug. 1972, Tri-Service System Program Office for Aircraft Ground Fire Suppression and Rescue, ASD/SMF, Wright-Patterson Air Force Base, Ohio.
Campbell, J. and Salzberg, F., "Aircraft Ground Fire Suppression and Rescue Systems—Current Technology Review," AGFSRS 70-1, Oct. 1969, Tri-Service System Program Office for Aircraft Ground Fire Suppression and Rescue, ASWF, Wright-Patterson Air Force Base, Ohio.
Cohn, B. M. and Campbell, J. A., "Minimum Needs for Airport Fire Fighting and Rescue Service," AS-71-1, Jan. 1971, Airports Service of U.S. Department of Transportation, Washington, D.C.
Einhorn, I. N., "Physio-Chemical Study of Smoke Emission by Aircraft Interior Materials, Part I, Physiological and Toxicological Aspects of Smoke During Fire Exposure," FAA-RD-73-50 I, July 1973, Federal Aviation Administration, U.S. Department of Transportation, Washington, D.C.
Einhorn, I. N.; Kanakia, M. D.; and Seader, J. D., "Physio-Chemical Study of Smoke Emission by Aircraft Interior Materials, Part II, Rigid and Flexible Urethane Foams," FAA-RD-73-50, II, July 1973, Federal Aviation Administration, U.S. Department of Transportation, Washington, D.C.
"Fire Fighter's Exposure Study," AGFSRS 71-2, Dec. 1970, Tri-Service System Program Office for Aircraft Ground Fire Suppression and Rescue, SMF, Wright-Patterson Air Force Base, Ohio.
Fu, T. T., "Aviation Fuel Fire Behavior Study," AGFSRS 72-2, Feb. 1972, Aircraft (Ground) Fire Suppression and Rescue System Program Office (DOD AGFSRS), Wright-Patterson Air Force Base, Ohio.
Geyer, G. B., "Effect of Ground Crash Fire on Aircraft Fuselage Integrity," Interim Report NA-69-37, Dec. 1969, Federal Aviation Administration, U.S. Department of Transportation, National Aviation Facilities Experimental Center, Atlantic City, N.J.
———, "Evaluation of Aircraft Ground Firefighting Agents and Techniques," AGFSRS 71-1, Feb. 1972, Tri-Service System Program Office for Aircraft Ground Fire Suppression and Rescue, SMF, Wright-Patterson Air Force Base, Ohio.
Geyer, G. B.; Neri, L. M. and Urban, C. H., "Evaluation of the Structural Integrity of an Aircraft Loading Walkway Under Severe Fuel-Spill Fire Conditions," FAA-RD-73-144, Oct. 1973, Federal Aviation Administration, U.S. Department of Transportation, Washington, D.C.
———, "Evaluation of a High-Capacity Firefighting Foam-Dispensing System, Final Report, FAA-RD-74-204, Jan. 1975, Federal Aviation Administration, U.S. Department of Transportation, Washington, D.C.
Gross, D., et al., "Smoke and Gases Produced by Burning Aircraft Interior Materials," NA 68-36, 1968, Federal Aviation Administration, U.S. Department of Transportation, National Aviation Facilities Experimental Center, Atlantic City, N.J.
Hibbard, R. R., et al., "An Evaluation of the Relative Fire Hazards of JET A and JET B for Commercial Flight," NASA TM X-71437, Oct. 1973, National Aeronautics and Space Administration, Washington, D.C.
Kuchta, J. M., "Fire and Explosion Manual for Aircraft Accident Investigations," AFAPL-TR-73-74, Aug. 1973, U.S. Department of the Air Force, Air Force Aero Propulsion Laboratory, Wright-Patterson Air Force Base, Ohio.
Marcy, J. F. and Johnson, R., "Flaming and Self-Extinguishing Characteristics of Aircraft Cabin Interior Materials," NA-68-30, 1968, Federal Aviation Administration, U.S. Department of Transportation, National Aviation Facilities Experimental Center, Atlantic City, N.J.

Sarkos, C. P., "Titanium Fuselage Environmental Conditions in Post-Crash Fires," FAA-RD-71-3, Mar. 1971, Federal Aviation Administration, U.S. Department of Transportation, Washington, D.C.

Stucker, R. N.; Supkes, D. E.; and Price, L. J., "Full-Scale Aircraft Cabin Flammability Tests of Improved Fire-Resistant Materials," NASA TM X-58141, June 1974, National Aeronautics and Space Administration, LBJ Space Center, Houston, Texas.

International Civil Aviation Organization Publications, available from the ICAO, Montreal, Canada

Aerodrome Manual, Part 5, Vol. 1, "Equipment, Procedures, and Services," 4th ed., Doc. 7920-AN/865, 1969 (with amendments).

Aerodrome Manual, Part 6, "Heliports," 4th ed., Doc. 7920-AN/865, 1971.

International Standards and Recommended Practices: Aerodromes, Annex 14 to the Convention on International Civil Aviation, 6th ed., Sept. 1971 (with amendments).

Manual of Aircraft Accident Investigation, 4th ed., Doc. 6920-AN/855/4, 1970 (with amendments).

Training Manual, Part 16, "Aerodrome Fire Services Personnel," 2nd ed., Doc. 7192-AN/857, 1971.

Aircraft Rescue and Fire Fighting Manuals

"Aircraft Emergency Rescue Information, Technical Manual," T.O. 00-105E-9, July 1972, Hq. NRAMA-MMSTD, Robins Air Force Base, Ga.

Aircraft Fire Protection and Rescue Procedures, 1st. ed., International Fire Service Training Association, Oklahoma State University, Stillwater, Okla., 1970.

"Department of Trade and Industry Aerodrome Fire and Rescue Services," DORA Report 7201, Jan. 1972, Her Majesty's Stationery Office, London. (EASAMS Reference No. 5631-1-3.)

Hewes, Capt. B. V. and Robinson, Capt. P. R., "IFALPA—A Survey of Airport Fire and Rescue Facilities, Interim Report, 34 Countries (Excludes U.S.A.)," 1971, ALPA Fire and Rescue Committee, College Park, Ga.

Hewes, Capt. B. V.; Robinson, Capt. P. R.; and Couch, Capt. A. L., "ALPA—A Survey of Airport Fire and Rescue Facilities, North America, 1971," ALPA Fire and Rescue Committee, College Park, Ga.

"U.S. Navy Aircraft Firefighting and Rescue Manual," NAVAIR 00-80R-14, Jan. 1968, Naval Air Systems Command, Code 1416C, Washington, D.C.

Chapter 2

MOTOR VEHICLES

Many factors influence motor vehicle fire safety: (1) vehicle design and construction, (2) materials from which a vehicle is constructed or which are carried by a vehicle (particularly upholstery, plastic, wood, fuel and hazardous cargo materials), (3) vehicle maintenance including safeguards against fire during vehicle repair, (4) vehicle operation including avoidance of collisions and of other accidents such as with smoking materials, and (5) garaging or storage of vehicles. The degree of fire hazard depends on: (1) the type of vehicle (passenger car, motorcycle, motor home, tank truck, etc.), (2) the use of the vehicle (pleasure driving, commercial service, off road use, etc.), (3) the climate and environment in which it is used (hot weather, high humidity, polluted air, etc.), (4) the age of the vehicle, (5) the condition and maintenance of the vehicle (crash damage, leakage of lubricants, under-inflated tires, dragging brakes, etc.), (6) the material and construction standards to which it is built (particularly the fuel and electrical systems), and (7) the type of fuel used (gasoline, diesel fuel, propane, etc.) and the way the fuel is contained.

Research into the causes of motor vehicle fires has not yet yielded complete or reliable statistics or insights into fire hazards. However, individual crash investigations and collections of crash and other loss data indicate the magnitude of the motor vehicle fire problem and some specific causal factors in motor vehicle fires.

Motor vehicle fires represent between 12 and 20 percent of all reported fires, and most vehicle fires result from causes other than crashes. Yet serious injury from vehicle fires occurs overwhelmingly from crash related fires—fires that occur at a rate of around one per 1,000 crashes.

Property loss from motor vehicle fires probably averages from one to several hundred dollars per incident. However, estimates may be skewed by the nonreporting of minor fires and of fires in uninsured vehicles as well as ambiguous reporting on police and fire department forms.

A. The Nature of Vehicle Fires

As with other fires, motor vehicle fires require a flammable substance, an ignition source, and oxygen. Virtually all motor vehicles carry a flammable fuel: gasoline, diesel oil, or another hydrocarbon compound. Vehicle upholstery, insulating and sound deadening materials, electrical wiring insulation, and plastic body and trim parts also can fuel a motor vehicle fire. Materials carried as cargo and fare in or on motor vehicles, particularly trucks, may be flammable.

Ignition sources include: (1) electrical short circuits or other electrical malfunctions that cause excessive heating of conductors or components, (2) sparks from an engine ignition system (it is generally accepted that sparks from a six or twelve volt source are not sufficiently hot to ignite a gasoline or fuel oil fire), (3) hot exhaust system components, (4) backfiring of an engine, (5) overheating of tires, brakes, and bearings, (6) friction generated sparks from a collision or from metal components scraping against the pavement, and (7) careless use of cigarettes and other smoking materials. There is generally sufficient oxygen for a motor vehicle fire.

Table 17-2A summarizes data on a study of the frequency and area of origin of fires in passenger cars involved in noncollision and collision-related incidents.

Human injury in motor vehicle fires comes both from direct exposure to heat and from inhalation of toxic combustion products. In some cases, an injury results from or is exacerbated by the inability of a vehicle occupant to get out of a burning vehicle because the doors or seats are jammed by a crash or because the occupant is injured or stunned by the crash. For example, in a fire of record a 1972 two-door sedan was driven onto the third rail of an electrified railroad track. There were not significant crash forces to cause injury, but a fire was started by the electric current arcing across a short circuit caused by the car body. The front seat passengers escaped, but investigators concluded that the three rear seat passengers were trapped in the burning vehicle probably because of their difficulty in locating and operating the front seat back latch.

Hazardous cargoes in motor vehicles present a particular fire problem. The National Transportation Safety Board (NTSB), the Bureau of Motor Carrier Safety (BMCS), and the NFPA have all carried out a number of detailed accident investigations into such fires. These investigations have resulted in numerous standards for construction and maintenance of hazardous cargo vehicles and for the handling of hazardous cargos. Despite such precautions, hazardous cargo fires and explosions continue to occur, primarily when vehicles carrying hazardous cargoes are involved in collisions.

The NTSB has issued a series of reports on accidents in which hazardous cargoes exploded or burned following a crash. Among them are:

Hoppy's Oil Service, Inc., Truck Overturn and Fire, State Route 128, Braintree, Mass., October 18, 1973.

Multiple Vehicle Collision Followed by Propylene Cargo-Tank Explosion, New Jersey Turnpike, Exit 8, September 21, 1972.

Propane Tractor-Semitrailer Overturn and Fire, U.S. Route 501, Lynchburg, Virginia, March 9, 1972.

Table 17-2A. Passenger Car Fires by Type of Incident and Area of Fire Origin*

| Area of Fire Origin | Type of Incident | | | |
| | Noncollision | | Collision-related | |
	Number of Fires	Percent	Number of Fires	Percent
Engine	1,085	59	39	54
Passenger	647	35	3	4
Fuel tank	59	3	24	33
Trunk	31	2	3	4
Tire/brake	29	2	3	4
Total	1,851	100†	72	100†

* Source: "1973 National Survey of Motor Vehicle Fires" commissioned by the Insurance Institute for Highway Safety.

† Column does not add to total due to rounding.

Note: Figures do not include fires of unidentified origin. The 1,923 passenger car fires in which the area of origin was identified comprised 83 percent of the 2,325 passenger car fires surveyed, and 73 percent of the 2,637 total motor vehicle fires surveyed.

Tank-Truck Combination Overturn onto Volkswagen Microbus Followed by Fire: U.S. Route 611, Moscow, Pennsylvania, September 5, 1971.

Automobile-Truck Collision Followed by Fire and Explosion of Dynamite Cargo on U.S. Highway 78 near Waco, Georgia, June 4, 1971.

(These and other NTSB reports are available from NTSB, 800 Independence Ave., S.W., Washington, DC 20591).

As a result of these and other highway crash investigations, the NTSB makes numerous recommendations to the BMCS concerning modification and enforcement of the BMCS regulations, as well as to other agencies.

B.   Federal Motor Vehicle Fire Standards

Under the authority of the National Traffic and Motor Vehicle Safety Act of 1966, the National Highway Traffic Safety Administration (NHTSA) of the Department of Transportation is authorized to set minimum safety standards applicable to both new and used motor vehicles, trailers, and motor vehicle equipment. To date, only two fire related standards have been issued for new vehicles and none has been issued for vehicles in use. The NHTSA also has the authority to investigate motor vehicle defects (some of which may present a fire hazard) and order notification of owners and repair by the manufacturer.

Motor Vehicle Safety Standard (MVSS) 301 has applied to new passenger cars sold in the U.S. since January 1, 1968. MVSS 301 limits the allowed spillage of fuel from a vehicle during and after a frontal crash into a fixed barrier at 30 mph to 1 oz on impact and 1 oz per minute following the impact.

A revision of MVSS 301, which was to become effective beginning on September 1, 1975, will eventually apply to all passenger cars, multipurpose passenger vehicles (Jeep-type vehicles, truck-based station wagons, etc.), trucks, and buses with a gross vehicle weight rating (GVWR) of up to 10,000 lbs and using a fuel with a boiling point above 32°F.

Initially, revised MVSS 301 adds only a requirement that following the frontal barrier crash, the automobile be statically rolled over. Fuel spillage during the operation cannot exceed an average of 1 oz per min.

Beginning on September 1, 1976, passenger cars will have to undergo rear and side moving barrier impacts by a 4,000-lb barrier coasting at 20 mph before the impact. Following each crash, the vehicle must be statically rolled over to check for fuel spillage. At the same time, the other vehicles covered by the standard that are 6,000 lbs GVWR or under must meet the frontal barrier crash and rear moving barrier crash requirements. Vehicles with a gross vehicle weight rating between 6,000 and 10,000 lbs must meet only the frontal barrier crash requirements beginning on September 1, 1976.

On September 1, 1977, all passenger car requirements will apply to the other vehicles covered by the standard.

The second NHTSA fire standard, MVSS 302, applies to the flammability of the interior materials used in passenger cars, multipurpose passenger vehicles, trucks, and buses. A recent proposed amendment, issued at the request of the Recreational Vehicle Institute, extends the coverage of MVSS 302 to recreational campers and trailers. The standard applies a horizontal flame test to all materials used in the interior of the vehicles covered to determine their ability to resist ignition.

The complete federal motor vehicle safety standards are contained in Section 571 of Title 49 of the Code of Federal Regulations.

The other federal agency with responsibility for setting motor vehicle safety standards is the Bureau of Motor Carrier Safety (BMCS) in the Federal Highway Administration (also in the Department of Transportation). The BMCS has authority to set safety standards and regulations governing motor vehicles used as commercial carriers on public roads in interstate commerce. The agency's fire regulations include: electrical wiring requirements, fuel system requirements, heating system requirements and prohibitions, exhaust system requirements, a requirement for carrying a fire extinguisher on most powered units, certain prohibitions against carrying flammable materials, and special requirements for transporting hazardous materials. The complete BMCS regulations are contained in Chapter III of Title 49 of the *Code of Federal Regulations*.

A third federal agency with an interest in the fire safety of motor vehicles is the National Transportation Safety Board. This independent agency has authority to investigate the safety of all types of transportation systems. As a part of this responsibility, the Board regularly investigates motor vehicle accidents involving explosions and fires, and makes recommendations to other DOT agencies.

In the Congress, the Senate Committee on Commerce and the House Subcommittee on Commerce and Finance of the Committee on Interstate and Foreign Commerce have responsibility for legislation and oversight on transportation. These committees have taken an active interest in the activities of the federal government in the field of motor vehicle safety. They both regularly hold legislative and oversight hearings into the activities of the National Highway Traffic Safety Administration and occasionally into the activities of the BMCS and the NTSB. Reports of these hearings are available from the Superintendent of Documents or from the committees themselves.

C.   Design and Construction Safeguards

The extensive use of all-metal bodies in private passenger automobiles makes total losses in such vehicles quite remote from fires originating from any of the hazards in their design. Interior finishes, particularly upholstery, are susceptible to ignition from the careless disposal of cigarettes and other smoking materials or from electrical faults in wiring in contact with these fabrics.

Some trucks and trailers have wood framing, flooring, and bodies, or use canvas tarpaulins to protect cargo areas. Many of the latter lack fire retardant treatments.

Vehicle Fuel Tanks and Systems

The location, construction, and security of fuel tanks are important features of design for fire safety in motor vehicles. Liquid fuel tanks for general passenger car use are generally thin-gage steel of various shapes and dimensions, dependent on other body and chassis characteristics. The vast majority of U.S. built cars, trucks, and buses have liquid fuel tanks that are located at the rear of the vehicle, frequently in a position where they are not entirely enclosed in the body. The most severe losses both in terms of loss of life and property occur from fires following rear-end collisions.

The IIHS (Insurance Institute for Highway Safety) in 1973 commissioned two series of crash tests in which six cars were tested for fuel system integrity in rear-end collisions.[1] These tests showed that contemporary automobile fuel tanks are vulnerable in such crashes. In the first series of tests, the six cars (1973 models of AMC Ambassador, Chevrolet Vega, Ford Pinto, Opel 1900, Plymouth Fury III, and Toyota Corona) were each impacted by other vehicles at speeds ranging from 36 to 40 mph. The NHTSA proposed regulations for MVSS 301 (see Part A of this chapter) rear impacts were tested in the second series of tests. Six of the same models were struck in the rear by a 4,000-lb barrier moving at 20 mph. In all twelve crashes, the fuel tank was ruptured spilling gasoline and posing a threat of fire. In one of the crashes, a fire started instantaneously when a part of the struck car's jacking system hit the pavement generating sparks that ignited the leaking gasoline.

D.   NFPA and Related Standards on Motor Vehicles

Three NFPA standards contain requirements for transportation of specific hazardous materials by truck. Fire and explosion prevention as relates to transportation of explosive materials, which include driver qualifications, vehicle design, placarding, fire fighting equipment and vehicle operation, is treated in detail in NFPA No. 495, Code for Explosive Materials. The Code is widely used as the basis for state regulations.

The design and construction requirements for cargo tanks of tank vehicles, auxiliary equipment, and operation of tank vehicles are contained in NFPA No. 385, Tank Vehicles for Flammable and Combustible Liquids, and NFPA No. 407, Aircraft Fuel Servicing, with the latter limited to the special requirements for aircraft fuel servicing tank vehicles and aircraft fuel servicing hydrant vehicles.

Requirements for transportation of liquefied petroleum gases, including requirements for transporting portable containers, requirements for cargo tanks, and for parking and garaging vehicles used to carry LP-Gas cargo are all treated in detail in NFPA No. 58, Storage and Handling of Liquefied Petroleum Gases. NFPA No. 58 also contains requirements for installation of LP-Gas systems in vehicles fueled by LP-Gas. It has been adopted for regulatory purposes by 47 states, and for vehicles in interstate commerce, by the DOT.

NFPA No. 51L, Truck Fire Protection, is a general text on property-carrying motor vehicles.

Protection from fire of vehicle occupants on limited access highways, bridges, and in tunnels is the primary objective of NFPA No. 502-T, Fire Protection for Limited Access Highways, Tunnels, Bridges, and Elevated Structures. A standard on Fire Protection for Air Rights Structures, now in preparation (1975), will have as one of its objectives protection for the users of highways from fires in structures over or beneath the highway.

As noted, NFPA No. 58 covers parking and garaging of LP-Gas cargo vehicles. Two other NFPA standards also cover parking of trucks: NFPA No. 513, Motor Freight Terminals, although primarily concerned with fire protection of freight while in a terminal, contains recommendations for parking vehicles at terminals. Parking of vehicles hauling explosives is a particularly sensitive problem as is evidenced by the explosions of parked explosives trucks at Roseburg, Ore., in 1959 and Marshalls Creek, Pa., in 1964. This is the subject of a separate NFPA standard, No. 498, Explosives Motor Vehicle Terminals.

The dependence of the fire service on motor vehicles is well recognized and it is, of course, particularly important that motor fire apparatus be safely constructed. NFPA No. 19, Specifications for Automotive Fire Apparatus, and

NFPA No. 414, Standard for Aircraft Rescue and Fire Fighting Vehicles, are references which should be checked on the various types of apparatus indicated by the titles.

Mobile homes are sometimes classified as "vehicles," but modern practices tend to remove them from this category. NFPA No. 501B, Mobile Homes, covers: (1) body and frame design and construction, (2) plumbing systems, (3) heating systems, and (4) electrical systems.

Recreational vehicles can be divided into four rather distinct types: (1) travel trailers, (2) motor homes, (3) camp trailers, and (4) campers. NFPA No. 501C, Recreational Vehicles, covers details of plumbing, heating, and electrical systems for these over-the-road recreational units. NFPA No. 501C also covers life safety and exiting requirements for these vehicles when they are used for temporary living quarters.

Underwriters Laboratories, Inc.

Certain over-the-road motor vehicle components and signaling appliances which have special fire hazard significance are investigated by Underwriters Laboratories, Inc., and listed in its *Accident, Automotive, and Burglary Protection Equipment Lists*. The specific items include:

1. Electrical Equipment (automobile fuses, switches);
2. Fill and Vent Fittings;
3. Fuel Equipment (backfire deflectors, fuel feed systems, electric gasoline gages, automotive type LP-Gas accessories, automotive fuel tanks, tubing);
4. Automotive Heaters (combustion types);
5. LP-Gas Fueled Automotive Vehicles (farm and road tractors incorporating fuel systems designed for use of LP-Gas as engine fuel);
6. Mufflers for Automobiles;
7. Signals and Signaling Appliances (highway emergency signals).

UL also has its own Standard on Automotive Fuel Tanks (UL 395) for liquid fuel tanks mounted outside the frame or in other exposed locations on gasoline of diesel-powered trucks, tractors, or trailers. It also has issued a Standard on Liquid Fuel-Burning Heating Appliances for Mobile Homes and Travel Trailers UL 307(a) and a Standard for Gas-Heating Appliances for Mobile Homes and Travel Trailers UL 307(6).

Society of Automotive Engineers, Inc.

Society of Automotive Engineers, Inc. (SAE) is concerned with any vehicle that moves under its own power and has a standardization program covering passenger cars, trucks and buses, farm and earth-moving machinery, marine propulsion units, aircraft, and space vehicles, as well as the materials and components that go into them. The SAE Standards are limited to environmental and operating problems with these vehicles. The SAE Handbook contains all their surface vehicle documents.

E.   Other Cooperating Agencies Interested in Highway Safety

The American Petroleum Institute (1801 K St., N.W., Washington, DC 20006): This organization is active in the field of truck transportation of petroleum products and has a number of publications of interest and value from the fire safety viewpoint.

The American Trucking Associations, Inc. (1616 P St., N.W., Washington, DC 20036): This organization reproduces as a tariff the DOT Regulations Governing the Transportation of Explosives and Other Dangerous Articles by Motor, Rail and Water, including Specifications for Shipping Containers. This action (similar to the action taken by Association of American Railroads) makes available to the participating truck carriers the current DOT regulations.

Center for Auto Safety (1223 Dupont Circle Bldg., Washington, DC 20036): An organization dedicated to improving the safety and value of automobiles, other motor vehicles, highways, and mobile homes. The Center has no regular publications, but issues reports, books, comments on federal rule making, and other materials regularly.

The Compressed Gas Association, Inc. (500 Fifth Ave., New York, NY 10036): This organization provides technical services in a manner similar to the Manufacturing Chemists on products of interest and concern to their membership.

Consumers Union of U.S., Inc. (256 Washington St., Mount Vernon, NY 10550): A consumer information organization with a large technical staff. CU regularly tests automobiles (and occasionally trucks and other motor vehicles) and reports on them in *Consumer Reports*, its monthly publication.

The Insurance Institute for Highway Safety (600 New Hampshire Ave., N.W., Suite 300, Washington, DC 20037): An independent, nonprofit, scientific, and educational organization. It is dedicated to reducing the losses—deaths, injuries, and property damage—resulting from crashes on the nation's highways. The Institute is supported by the American Insurance Association, the National Association of Automotive Mutual Insurance Companies, the National Association of Independent Insurers, and several individual insurance companies.

The Manufacturing Chemists' Association (1825 Connecticut Ave., N.W., Washington, DC 20009): This organization has an active technical service on transportation and packaging. They have issued Chemical Safety Data Sheets (listing available on request) covering, in many cases, details on bulk transportation. The MCA "Chem-Card Manual" is a compilation of guides for the safe handling of chemicals involved in highway emergencies.

Mobile Homes Manufacturers Association (Box 201, Chantilly, VA 22021): This organization represents the manufacturers of mobile homes east of the Rocky Mountains.

National Safety Council (425 North Michigan Ave., Chicago, IL 60611): This nonprofit organization dedicated to accident prevention has an extensive program on highway safety geared principally to the motoring public. It produces a number of publications of value on transportation and highway safety.

The National Tank Truck Carriers, Inc. (1616 P St., N.W., Washington, DC 20036): This organization is a Conference of the American Trucking Associations, Inc., and assists their members (operators of tank fleets) in solving problems associated with the safe handling of flammable liquids, gases, and chemicals.

Physicians for Automotive Safety (50 Union Ave., Irvington, NJ 07111): This is an organization of medical doctors who are concerned with preventing death and injury in motor vehicle accidents. They have taken a particular interest in the safety of children in motor vehicles.

Professional Drivers Council for Safety and Health (Suite 700, 2000 P St., N.W., Washington, DC 20036): A membership group of truck and bus drivers with an interest in their occupational safety and health. PROD issues a monthly newsletter to its members.

Recreational Vehicle Institute, Inc. (2720 Des Plaines Ave., Des Plaines, IL 60018): This organization represents the recreational vehicle industry nationally. Their manufacturing members produce travel trailers, truck campers, camping trailers, and motor homes.

Trailer Coach Association (3855 East LaPalma Ave., Anaheim, CA 92807): This organization represents the manufacturers of mobile homes and recreational vehicles whose equipment is manufactured or distributed on the west coast.

The Truck Body and Equipment Association, Inc. (5530 Wisconsin Ave., Washington, DC 20015): This is a trade association of the manufacturers of truck bodies, suppliers of component parts, and distributors. It has a Fire Apparatus Manufacturers Division (formerly a separate Association known as Fire Apparatus Manufacturers Association). The TBEA represents their members in Washington in dealing with the DOT on safety legislation.

Truck Trailer Manufacturers Association (2430 Pennsylvania Ave., Washington, DC 20037): A trade association of manufacturers of truck trailers. Through its various committees and representatives, it cooperates with NFPA, other allied industry associations, and governmental agencies in matters affecting the design and fabrication of tank transports.

For large trucks and buses, more substantial tanks are normally used, and such vehicles, used in interstate commerce must comply with the DOT's Motor Carrier Safety Regulations. Fuel tanks built to pass the drop, rupture, vent, and spillage tests of the DOT or UL, provide acceptable protection to comply with DOT Regulations. Side-mounted gasoline fuel tanks ("saddle tanks") having a fuel capacity in excess of 25 gal, are provided with a fusible safety vent or vents, designed to limit pressure rise in the tank under any fire condition to a maximum of 50 psig. The vent area must be sufficient to prevent a rise in internal tank pressure of more than 10 percent of the release pressure of the safety vents. At least one fusible safety vent shall be in the top of the tank. Polyethylene fuel tanks are used in some instances for motor vehicles. Some of the advantages claimed are freedom from rusting, resistance to impact, and although the tanks will melt in a fire, they will not rupture explosively to spread a fire.

Vibration, dirty gasoline, corrosion, and improper maintenance are the chief factors responsible for failures at other points in a liquid fuel system, particularly at carburetors, fuel pump fittings, tubing, and filters. Glass filter bowls are subject to breakage from accidental causes as well as from vibration. A small particle of foreign material in gasoline which lodges between a float valve and its seat can cause carburetor flooding, particularly when the throttle is closed (as when driving downhill). This might result in spillage of gasoline on the exterior of the engine which, in turn, could ignite.

LP-Gas containers on vehicles are securely mounted on the exterior or interior (in a recess or cabinet vaportight to the inside of the vehicle) in locations reflecting the possibility of mechanical damage. On passenger carrying vehicles, the capacity of containers is limited to a maximum of 200 gal water capacity. On nonpassenger carrying vehicles, the water capacity is limited to 300 gal. On passenger carrying vehicles, the substitution of so-called "remote filling" arrangements is permissible in lieu of vaportight compartmentalization. In such cases, the point of connection of filling valves and the discharge from all relief valves and liquid level gages are located outside the container compartment.

Any radio equipment or other sources of ignition are isolated from this space.

Other provisions governing the safety features of LP-Gas fuel systems on vehicles are detailed in NFPA No. 58.

Vehicle Electrical Systems

Automotive lighting and accessory circuits are usually 6-v or 12-v circuits, but vehicle ignition systems have high voltage, though low amperage. Automobile electrical system fire safety is largely a matter of proper installation, fusing, and maintenance. Important points include: (1) the location and protection afforded the battery; (2) battery cable integrity and protection of exposed battery terminals; (3) adequate fire resistant insulation on all wiring; (4) proper fusing of normal lighting and accessory circuits; (5) proper support, location, and security of all wiring, with adequate protection afforded by rubber insulating bushings where wiring passes through metal; and (6) correct ignition system maintenance.

Fires of electrical origin are usually fed by oily deposits in and around the engine, or ignite combustible materials such as interior fabric linings and upholstery. In the event of collision or upset, electrical short circuits are very apt to occur which might cause ignition of fuel vapors. It is desirable, particularly on buses and trucks, to provide an approved type of battery-generator manual disconnect switch, preferably one incorporating short-circuit supervision.

Miscellaneous Vehicle Hazards

Proper exhaust system installation is important because the hot surfaces might ignite nearby combustible vehicle components. Hot carbon particles discharged from the exhaust can ignite flammable liquids, grease, or similar exposed materials.

Brakes, especially on trucks and buses, may be a fire hazard in the event of overheating with resulting ignition of grease, oil, or leaking flammable hydraulic brake fluid. Overheating of brakes is especially troublesome in descending long hills. Unless the engine (with transmission shifted into low gear) or a retarder is used, the brakes may overheat to the extent of starting a fire directly, or, they may lose their effectiveness and cause an accident, with or without fire involved.

Truck or bus tires may ignite during vehicle operation if overloaded, if underinflated, if run continually at high speed, or if dual tires chafe or rub when soft or flat.

Alcohol-type antifreeze vapors present an added hazard during the winter months, as do combustion-type heaters.

While the fire and explosion hazard of oil used for diesel truck fuel is less than that of gasoline, the prevention of ignition of oil on heated engine and exhaust system parts requires the same attention to the security of fuel lines.

Farm Tractors, Motorcycles, and Motorbikes

Fire dangers inherent in these vehicles arise from the exceptionally close spacing of such components as the fuel tank, carburetor, ignition system, and exhaust pipe; the lack of protection afforded operators by the vehicles' framings; and the more severe vibration forces to which the equipment is normally subjected. Air-cooled types are particularly vulnerable, while water-cooled engines have lower engine operating temperatures. Particular care is required to avoid fuel system leakage or spillage (especially during fueling) because of the high surface temperatures and the close proximity of exhaust piping. Each fuel system should have means, readily accessible to the operator, for quickly stopping the flow of fuel to the tank. Sparks from exposed electrical circuit points to ground are a major ignition

hazard. Oil and grease accumulations on such vehicles are also serious hazards.

F. Prevention of Motor Vehicle Fires

Responsibility for fire prevention in motor vehicles requires the attention of a number of parties. Vehicle designers should be aware of fire hazards in their vehicles. Sources of heat and ignition must be kept away from flammable materials as much as possible. Consideration should be given to the vulnerability of fuel system components: in their basic integrity, their location away from the perimeter of and from crash collapsible and intrusive parts of the vehicle, and their location away from potentially hot exhaust and electrical components.

An example of location hazards comes from the recall of some 1972 Chevrolet Vegas. In these cars, defective mufflers were located just ahead of the gasoline tank. When the mufflers failed, hot exhaust gases were directed at the fuel tank. If the tank was full, the heated gasoline expanded and overflowed down the sides of the tank. Then, a backfire through the exhaust system possibly could ignite the spilled fuel causing a fire that could render the car a total loss.

Since electrical system failures are often the cause of property damage fires, more attention needs to be paid to the routing of wiring, aging of insulation and components, and failure modes of components. (That is, do they short-circuit or open-circuit when they fail?)

To minimize the potential for leakage of fuel in both minor and major crashes, extraneous plumbing and openings in fuel and in hazardous liquid and gaseous cargo containers should be eliminated. Necessary plumbing should be properly designed so that it is protected from potential crash damage.

In the construction of vehicles, care must be taken to insure that the fuel and electrical lines are correctly routed and that connections are secure. In addition, care must be taken to insure that sharp or pointed components are not located near to fuel or hazardous cargo tanks.

The greatest fire hazard posed during the repair of vehicles comes from the use of torches, usually in the repair of exhaust systems and of crash damage. Some of the items used in vehicle repair are particularly flammable: paint, solvents, adhesives, and oily rags. Operating an engine with the carburetor air cleaner removed may result in a fire if the engine backfires through the carburetor.

Care must be taken in the maintenance and rebuilding of crashed vehicles to insure that their fuel and electrical systems do not pose hazards that are not present in the original vehicle.

There is no general requirement for a portable fire extinguisher on all types of motor vehicles. Private owners and operators of private motor vehicles will provide themselves with some protection against excessive fire damage if they carry a hand extinguisher, preferably one that as a minimum can be used on both Class B (flammable liquid) and Class C (electrical) fires. See Section 16 for information on the ratings and use of fire extinguishers.

Fire extinguishers are required on most commercial vehicles by BMCS regulations. NFPA standards concerned with motor vehicles (No. 58 [truck transportation of LP-Gas], No. 385 [tank vehicles for flammable liquids], No. 407 [aircraft fuel servicing vehicles] No. 495 [transportation of explosives materials], and No. 512, [general cargo truck]) contain specifications for the number, type, and size of portable extinguishers that must be carried as minimum protection.

The practice of carrying extra gasoline in loose cans or bottles is particularly dangerous. Gasoline or other fuels should only be carried in properly designed fuel tanks that are installed in a vehicle.

Smoking by vehicle occupants (particularly drivers) is not a good practice. Lit cigarettes, ashes, and matches are a common source of upholstery and dashboard fires. Also, the high levels of carbon monoxide that will build up from smoking in a closed vehicle interior (as on a cold day or when an air conditioner is operating) will cause drowsiness.

Vehicle operators should also be conscious of defects that might cause vehicle fires such as a leaking exhaust system, leaking fuel system, underinflated tire, or an overheated component.

Should a vehicle fire occur, the following steps should be taken:

1. Turn off the ignition and other electrical systems that can be quickly reached.

2. Get everyone out of and well away from the burning vehicle. Remember that protection of life and limb is much more important than reduction of property loss.

3. Call or send for help from the fire department.

4. If the fire is minor and well away from sources of flammable vapors, or if the fire threatens human life, the fire can be attacked from the windward side and from the outside of the vehicle. If the fire is in the engine, try to raise the hood and apply the extinguishing agent to the base of the fire. If the hood cannot be raised, aim the extinguisher up from underneath or through any openings into the engine compartment. If the fire originates from a fuel tank leak, put out any fire in spilled fuel and work toward the tank and upwards to the point of the leak using an extinguisher for Class B fires. If the fire is in the upholstery, saturate the area with water and make sure that no hidden smoldering remains. If a tire is burning, it is generally necessary to apply a large amount of water or to attack it with a dry chemical extinguisher. A burned or very hot tire (such as a flat) should be removed from a vehicle.

5. After a fire has been put out, do not operate the vehicle until the cause of the fire has been discovered and corrected.

Bibliography

References Cited

[1] *Fuel Tank Fires,* Insurance Institute for Highway Safety, Washington, D.C., 1973.

NFPA Codes, Standards, and Recommended Practices (see the latest *NFPA Publications and Visual Aids Catalog* for availability of current editions of the following documents)

NFPA No. 19, Standard for Automotive Fire Apparatus.

NFPA No. 58, Standard for the Storage and Handling of Liquefied Petroleum Gases.

NFPA No. 385, Recommended Regulatory Standard for Tank Vehicles for Flammable and Combustible Liquids.

NFPA No. 407, Standard for Aircraft Fuel Servicing Including Aircraft Fueling Hose, Aircraft Fuel Servicing Vehicles and Airport Fixed Fueling Systems.

NFPA No. 414, Standard for Aircraft Rescue and Fire Fighting Vehicles.

NFPA No. 495, Code for the Manufacture, Transportation, Storage, and Use of Explosive Materials.

NFPA No. 498, Standard for Explosives Motor Vehicle Terminals.

NFPA No. 502-T, Tentative Standard on Fire Protection for Limited Access Highways, Tunnels, Bridges, and Elevated Structures.

NFPA No. 512, Recommended Good Practices for Truck Fire Protection.

Additional Readings

Cooley, Peter, "Fires in Motor Vehicle Accidents: An HSRI Special Report," April 1974, Highway Safety Research Institute, The University of Michigan, Ann Arbor, Mich.

Johnson, E. F., "Fire Protection Developments in CNG-Fueled Vehicle Operations," *Fire Journal,* Vol. 66, No. 6, Nov. 1972, pp. 11–15.

Storrs, C. D. and Lindemann, O. H., "Federal Flammability Standards for Interiors of Motor Vehicles," *Fire Journal,* Vol. 66, No. 4, July 1972, pp. 24–27, 44.

The following reports were sponsored by the National Highway Traffic Safety Administration:

"An Assessment of Automotive Fuel System Fire Hazards," DOT HS-800 624, Dec. 1971, Dynamic Science, Phoenix, Ariz.

"Escape Worthiness of Vehicles and Occupant Survival," DOT HS-800 428, Dec. 1970, University of Oklahoma Research Institute, Norman, Okla.

"Flammability Characteristics of Vehicle Interior Materials," DOT HS-800 205, May 1969, Engineering Mechanics Division, IIT Research Institute, Chicago, Ill.

"Prevention of Electrical Systems Ignition of Automotive Crash Fire," DOT HS-800 392, Mar. 1970, Dynamic Science, Phoenix, Ariz.

Chapter 3

RAIL TRANSPORTATION SYSTEMS

Railroads, as common carriers, have the responsibility of safely transporting passengers and billions of dollars worth of merchandise of every description annually. With approximately 277,000 miles of main track lines in the country, the rail network is a vital link in our transportation system. A fire disaster that incapacitates even a portion of the rail system has an effect far beyond the actual scene of the disaster.

To operate this transportation system, railroads own or control a vast fleet of locomotives and rolling stock of all kinds as well as complex support facilities and systems, such as communications networks, computer centers, diesel shops, fueling facilities, classification yards, bridges and trestles, office buildings, warehouses, etc. The world of a railroad encompasses the fire hazard associated with many other industrial and commercial activities plus some that are peculiar to the nature of rail operations.

This chapter identifies the different types of rail rolling equipment that are encountered on North American railroads and discusses fire hazards associated with them. Fire problems involving rights-of-way and specialized railroad facilities are also discussed as are the fundamental considerations in identifying hazardous materials that will be found in transit on the rail network. The more "common" facilities associated with rail operations, such as building structures, computers and communication facilities, warehousing of materials etc., are discussed in other chapters of this HANDBOOK.

Rail rapid transit systems used in urban environments for movement of people in the mass transit mode are covered in Chapter 4 of this Section.

Rolling stock in railroad terminology includes locomotives, freight cars, cabooses, and track work equipment.

A. Locomotives

Diesel Electric Locomotives

What is generally referred to as a diesel locomotive is actually a diesel electric locomotive. (See Fig. 17-3A.) The power is developed by the diesel engine which, in turn, drives a main traction generator. The output of this main traction generator is transmitted to the traction motors mounted in the trucks and geared to the axles and wheels which actually drive the locomotive. The locomotive includes numerous supporting systems, including a battery which is used to provide power to start the diesel engine; an auxiliary direct current generator, which charges the battery and also supplies low voltage direct current for control and lighting circuits; and an auxiliary alternator mounted integrally with the main traction generator, which furnishes power for excitation, for the radiator cooling fan motors, as well as for a blower motor which cleans the inertial carbody filters.

Mainline locomotives have a normal service life exceeding 15 years, and thousands of units that are still in service have operated for 20 years or longer and average between 150,000 and 250,000 miles per year, thus attesting to their reliability and durability.

The diesel electric locomotive is an enclosed, self-contained piece of equipment. Fire prevention in the engine room area of the diesel electric locomotive is almost totally related to housekeeping and maintenance in assuring that any fuel oil, lubricant oil, or exhaust leaks which occur are repaired quickly, and that debris and products of any leakage are not allowed to accumulate. Improved carbody filtration through the development of self-cleaning inertial-type carbody filters and carbody pressurization help create a more stable engine room environment in modern diesel electric locomotives.

The development of fire retardant wire and cable insulation in recent years, and the practice of ventilating electrical cabinets with filtered air, thus preventing explosive gases from collecting and also keeping dirt out of the electrical cabinet, has resulted in a virtually "fireproof" electrical cabinet on EMD locomotives. Improvements in wiring insulation, wiring techniques including the increased use of circuit breakers and fuses, and the development of the pressurized and ventilated electrical cabinet have contributed greatly both in the areas of locomotive reliability and fire prevention. Design improvements in direct current traction motors and the advent of the ac/dc traction generator replacing the older dc generators have also had an impact in the area of fire prevention.

Fire Protection for Diesel Locomotives

Fire protection for a diesel locomotive revolves around the following:

Hot Engine Protection: High engine cooling system temperature and hot engine oil protective devices are provided to prevent a build-up of excessive heat in the engine and supporting systems and, generally, to prevent uncontrolled situations from developing.

Engine Crankcase Protection: This device detects a dangerous build-up of pressure in the engine and will shut the engine down when such a build-up is detected.

High Voltage Ground Protection: If a high voltage fault develops on the locomotive and goes to ground, the ground relay will detect the fault and drop the electrical load to the locomotive.

Emergency Fuel Cut-off Switches: In the event of an emergency, the fuel supply to the engine can be stopped by pressing any one of three emergency fuel cut-off push buttons. Two push buttons, one on either side of the locomotive, are located on the underframe in the vicinity of the fuel filler and the third is located on the engine control panel in the cab.

Main Battery Knife Switch: This large, single-throw knife switch is located in the cab of the engine and is found at the lower portion of the fuse panel. It is used to connect the battery to the locomotive low voltage system.

Fire Protection Equipment: Each diesel electrical locomotive is equipped with portable fire extinguisher protection (dry chemical or carbon dioxide, or both)—the quantity and type depending upon the size of the locomotive and its use (yard, local, or mainline service).

Preventative Maintenance and Inspections: Based on lifetime expectancy of component parts, empirical failure data, and FRA (Federal Railroad Administration) regulations, diesel electric locomotives are inspected, tested, and serviced on a scheduled basis.

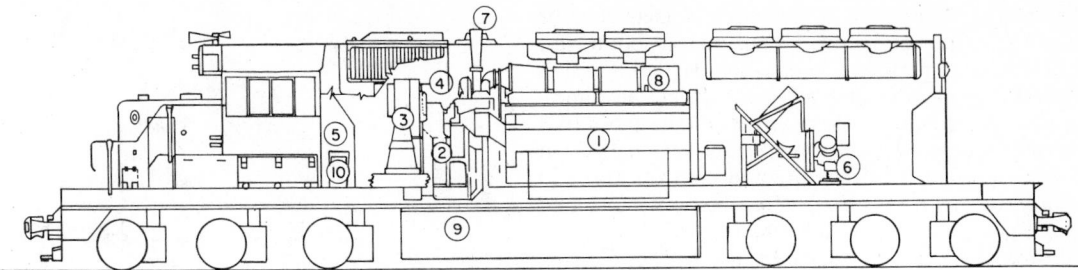

Fig. 17-3A. A diesel electric locomotive showing the location of principal components of the power system. 1, Engine; 2, generator-alternator; 3, traction motor-generator blower; 4, auxiliary generator; 5, electrical control cabinet; 6, air compressor; 7, engine exhaust stack; 8, exhaust manifold; 9, fuel tank; and 10, electrical cabinet air filter.

Electric Locomotives

Electric locomotives, by their very nature, operate with voltages considerably higher than those seen on diesel locomotives. Modern electric locomotives have vacuum breakers which trip in a matter of cycles; thereby short circuits, which on older motive power could cause fires, are considerably reduced.

Preventative Maintenance: Preventative maintenance is mandatory to preclude down time caused by fire or failure of the equipment. Electrical circuits are tested for grounds or other defects when at major shops or at intervals of no more than 3 months. All tests and scheduled maintenance are made in compliance with DOT (Department of Transportation) rules as a minimum.

Fire Protection Equipment: The majority of electric locomotives are equipped with portable fire extinguishing equipment (dry chemical and/or carbon dioxide) and, like the diesel locomotive, the quantity of extinguishers is based on the size of the locomotive and its use.

Operation of Electric Locomotives

Figure 17-3B illustrates the general arrangement of an electric locomotive. This particular unit can deliver 5,100 hp at the rail and operates on 25,000 or 50,000 V alternating current from an overhead wire.

Insofar as the electric locomotive derives its power from an electrical circuit, it is necessary to deenergize the circuit to safely extinguish any electrical fire.

Emergency Stop Buttons: These buttons, one on each side of the locomotive under the operator's cab, are accessible at ground level. Depressing either of the buttons will trip the vacuum circuit breaker on the roofs of all the locomotives in the consist and remove the power.

Manual Pantograph Grounding Switch: A manual pantograph grounding switch is located in the right rear of the locomotive. The switch is used to ground the pantograph before performing maintenance or before climbing to the roof through the rear hatch. Grounding of the pantograph (catenary) is covered by special instructions and will vary depending upon the type locomotive and type overhead system employed. With this in mind, fire department personnel are cautioned to contact railroad officials for this information and to include it in prefire plans.

Emergency Shutdown Switch: The red emergency shutdown switch is located on the master control housing. This switch is used in emergencies to remove power from the locomotive during single unit operation or to remove power from all units of the consist during multiple operation.

Safety Precautions

Certain precautions are observed in boarding electric locomotives in an emergency:

1. Never enter any high voltage compartment when the locomotive is energized.

2. Never touch motors, switches, protective barriers, or other electrical apparatus without being fully instructed as to their use.

3. Never climb on the roof of the locomotive unless the locomotive ground switch is secured and the catenary wire is deenergized.

4. To protect against fatal or serious personal injury, be sure the pantograph is actually latched down before opening the roof hatch.

B. Freight Cars and Equipment

The eight major causes of fires in freight equipment, including motive equipment, are:

1. Brake shoe sparks	5. Collision/
2. Incendiary or suspicious	derailments
origins	6. Exhaust sparks
3. Cotton—all causes	7. Electrical
4. Hot boxes	8. Internal
	combustion engines

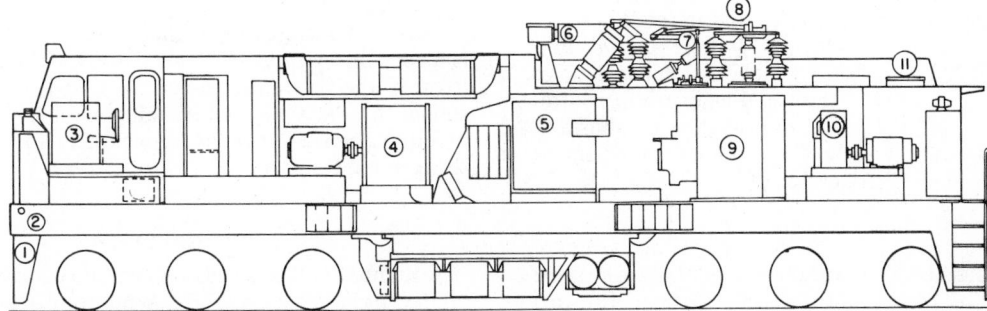

Fig. 17-3B. An electric locomotive showing location of some essential pieces of apparatus: 1, proximity switch; 2, emergency stop button; 3, operator's console; 4, equipment blower; 5, main rectifier compartment; 6, vacuum circuit breaker; 7, panto grounding hook; 8, pantograph (in folded position), 9, transformer; 10, air compressor; and 11, roof hatch.

The key to the elimination or reduction in frequency of fires caused by brake shoe sparks, exhaust sparks, hot boxes, electrical failures, and internal combustion engines is design and preventative maintenance. Recent design advances, such as spark retention exhaust manifolds, brake shoes that do not produce sparks, heat detectors, sensors and indication lamps supervising electrical circuits and components, and the increased use and efficiency of hot box detectors and roller bearings should reduce the frequency of fires.

The shrink film concept in packaging cotton bales is being used more frequently, eliminating the need for metal bale bands. A frequent cause of fires in banded cotton bales is friction heat originating in bale band movement which ignites loose cotton.

Fires resulting from collision/derailments are a major concern of the railroad industry, and operating rules and safety programs are undergoing major revisions. A program to inventory and reduce all grade crossings is underway. The inventory will be used as a planning tool with which individual states can develop priorities for crossing projects. Once implemented a systemized approach to reducing grade crossing accidents can be accomplished.

Refrigerator Cars

Three types of refrigerator cars are commonly used by the railroads in the transportation of perishable and semi-perishable commodities that require refrigeration, heater service, or protection from the extremes of heat or cold while in transit:

1. The standard ice car (RS) is gradually being phased out of service. Most railroads no longer furnish ice for shipment in such cars. However, such cars may be used to keep commodities from freezing, in which case portable liquid fuel heaters are installed in the end ice bunkers. These heaters burn a mixture of methanol and isopropanol.

2. The insulated bunkerless car (RB) is widely used to protect all types of semi-perishable commodities, such as canned goods, beer, grocery products, and drugs and medicines, from extremes of heat and cold. These cars provide no refrigeration but are equipped for application of portable liquid fuel heaters. The heaters are usually suspended by chains from hooks (four per heater) in the ceiling of the doorway areas. The ceiling is protected above each heater with asbestos covered with galvanized metal.

3. The mechanically refrigerated car (RP) is the most modern and versatile of the freight cars used for perishables. It can provide automatically controlled temperatures from zero to 70°F. Foamed-in-place polyurethane insulation helps to assure consistent and dependable car temperatures. A compressor-evaporator is powered which may be operated either directly from the alternator output of a diesel-electric unit or from any suitable 220 V standby power supply. The fuel tank is suspended below the car and normally carries 500 to 550 gal of either No. 1 or No. 2 diesel fuel oil. Fire fighting problems are sometimes complicated due to lack of knowledge of the location of the diesel engine stop control (which is clearly identified) and to insulation combustion. (Fig. 17-3C is a cutaway view of the engine compartment of a typical mechanical refrigerator car.)

Box Cars

The basic design of all box cars is essentially the same with the exception of the capacity and length of the car. Such additions as special racks, dunnage devices and nailable steel floors have permitted damage from movements without adding to the combustibility of the car.

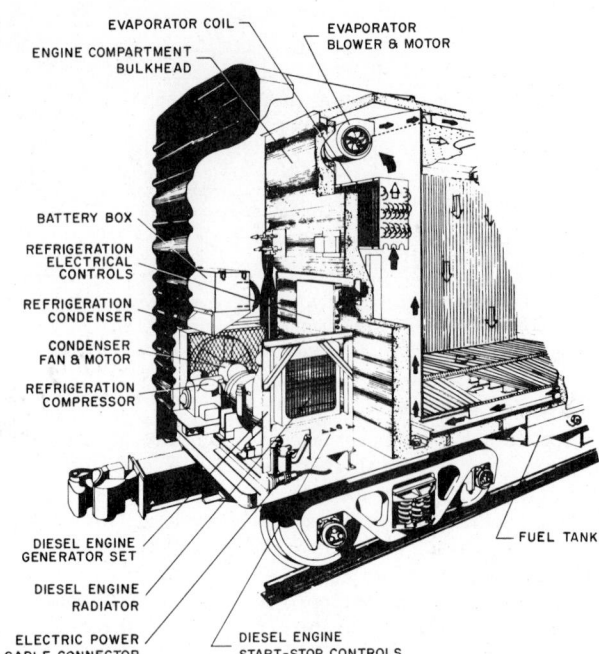

Fig. 17-3C. The engine compartment of a typical mechanical refrigerated car. Note that the start-stop control for the diesel engine is at the lower left mounted on the side of the car.

Specialized Equipment

Specialized equipment used to meet special shipping needs include articulated cars, multilevel and enclosed cars for automobiles; "high cube" (large capacity) box cars; 100-ton capacity covered hoppers; side loading "all door" box cars; aerated cars to handle bulk materials which require pneumatic loading and unloading mechanisms to "inhale" cargo at the loading point and "exhale" it at destination. Another innovative approach to packaging is the "snowy" freight car. The "snowed-on" look comes from 2 in. of foam insulation on the outside. These cars are capable of carrying four times as much freight as conventional refrigerator cars.

Cabooses: Fire hazards associated with cabooses are the combustible furnishings in the caboose and the method of heating them. The source of heat is usually coal or oil, and experience has indicated that the major cause of fires is the radiation of heat from the stoves or stove pipes because of inadequate clearances. Fire protection varies from water extinguishers to portable dry chemical extinguishers, and some carriers have discontinued providing this protection because of the theft problem.

Intermodal Equipment

This equipment can be either a trailer or a container and is loaded on specially designed flat cars. The only difference between the two is the trailer has wheels. Fire hazards are similar to those of the trucking industry and the commodities carried range from explosives to frozen foods in refrigerated trailers.

C. Tank Cars

A number of rail accidents have involved tank cars containing hazardous materials. While tank cars are built to operate safely under normal conditions, it is not yet feasible to build a car capable of withstanding the impact of a derailment under all conditions that may be encountered.

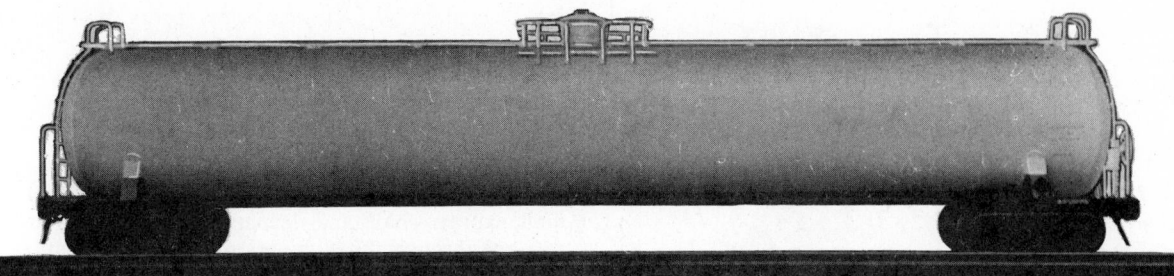

Fig. 17-3D. A standard tank car for the transportation of compressed gases. The car is not insulated, and the relief valve has a start-to-discharge setting of 255 psi.

Tank cars in service today are built to regulated specifications imposed by federal regulatory agencies. The Materials Transportation Board of the DOT (Department of Transportation) writes the specifications, and the FRA (Federal Railroad Administration) administers them. Finally, before a car can be placed in service, it must be approved by the Association of American Railroads.

In a rail accident involving tank cars, it is important to know what materials the tank cars contain. The following paragraphs give brief descriptions of the various types of tank cars that may be encountered. There are certain identifiable physical characteristics associated with the various cars that have been designed to carry specific types of commodities.

Design of Tank Cars

Tank cars are segregated into several classes by Part 179, "Specification for Tank Cars," of the DOT Hazardous Materials Regulations.[1] The most frequently used classes are the pressure tank car tanks and the nonpressure tank car tanks.

Figure 17-3D illustrates the details and general arrangement of a 100-ton, 33,600 water gallon capacity, DOT 112A340W tank car used for the transportation of compressed gases such as butane, propane, butadiene, and anhydrous ammonia. This class of tank car is not insulated, must be painted white, and is equipped with a safety valve having a start-to-discharge setting of 255 psi, and a dis-

charge capacity sufficient to prevent a pressure build-up in the tank in excess of 82.5 percent of the test pressure (340 psi). (The DOT has authorized a higher setting of 280.5 psi, and the majority of this class of tank cars are so equipped.) Safety relief valves on tank cars of this type have a rated discharge capacity on the order of 34,000 cfm when fully open.

Figure 17-3E illustrates the details and general arrangement of a typical general service, DOT 111A100W-1 tank car suitable for the transportation of commodities such as vegetable oil, diesel fuel oil, gasoline, and many chemical commodities. These cars come in a variety of sizes ranging from 20,800 up to 30,000 water gallon capacity. The safety relief valve is set to discharge at 75 psi.

Figure 17-3F shows a DOT 105A500W tank car having a payload of 90 tons of liquid chlorine. It is mounted on 100-ton trucks and insulated with 4 in. of foam insulation. The safety relief valve is set to discharge at 360 psi. A smaller version of this car has a chlorine capacity of 55 tons. Fig. 17-3G illustrates the fittings arrangement on either car. All chlorine tank cars have standard fittings so arranged as to accept a safety kit which can be used to seal a fitting leak.

Fig. 17-3H depicts a DOT 111A100W-1 tank car equipped with 4 in. of insulation, and may be equipped with interior heater coils or exterior heater coils. Tank cars of this type are used to carry commodities which must be melted in order to be unloaded, such as asphalts, heavy fuel oils, phenol, petroleum waxes, etc.

Fig. 17-3E. A typical general service tank for such commodities as food, petroleum, and chemical products. It is not insulated and the relief valve is set to discharge at 75 psi.

Fig. 17-3F. A standard tank car for the transportation of liquid chlorine. See Figure 17-3G for details of dome fittings.

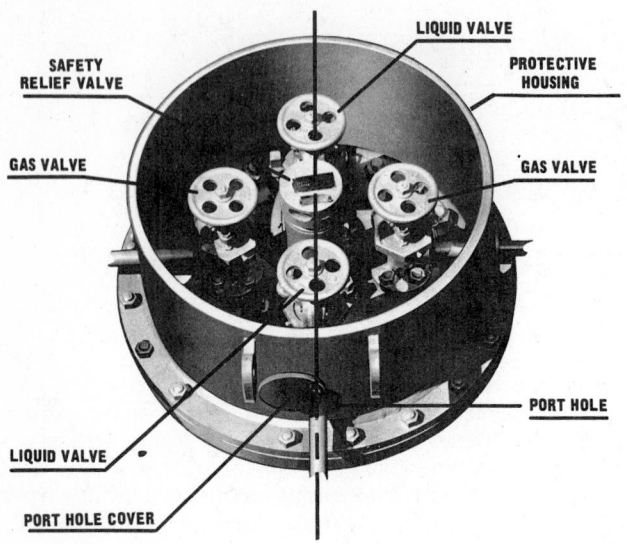

Fig. 17-3G. Details of the protective housing, or dome, on a liquid chlorine tank car.

Tank Car Safety Research

Current tank car safety research is directed toward containment of hazardous material in the tank under all normal operating conditions and in developing justifiable design improvements for containment under abnormal conditions. Cooperatively supporting the research are the FRA, the tank car builders, and owners through the Railway Progress Institute, and the railroads through the AAR.

Three important areas are being investigated:

1. Cause: Tank car head punctures from couplers on adjacent cars. Possible Solutions: (1) Interlocking couplers (top and bottom shelf design), and (2) head shields at the end of each car.
2. Cause: Product loss from damaged valves and fittings. Possible Solution: Protective "skids" or shields.
3. Cause: Shell failure from fire exposure. Possible Solution: Thermal shielding.

Tank Car Fire Hazards

Fire hazards associated with tank cars are minimal unless a car is damaged in an accident. Consequently, knowledge of the contents is essential prior to attempting to fight a fire. Caution should be exercised in approaching a tank car exposed to radiant energy from a fire and particularly direct flame impingement. The commodity in such a car, due to heat, may generate significant vapor pressures which present special hazards depending on the characteristics of the commodity which may be corrosive, toxic, or otherwise noxious.

Direct contact by personnel with vapors discharged from tank cars under emergency conditions is to be avoided unless personnel are garbed with suitable protective clothing.

D. Passenger Equipment

Modern steel and aluminum passenger coaches, diners, mail, express, chair, and sleeping cars represent a fire safety advance through the elimination of large amounts of combustible materials. The major causes of fire involving passenger equipment are careless smoking and electrical faults. With respect to diners, hazards are identical to those inherent with restaurants; namely, grease and exhaust system fires. Air conditioning and heating systems must be properly safeguarded and preventive maintenance is a must. The frequency of fires involving passenger equipment is relatively low.

Self-propelled electrical passenger equipment, such as used in Amtrak Metroliner service, have safety emergency cutoffs similar to electric locomotives. To deenergize the equipment it is necessary to lower and ground the pantograph. This can be accomplished either automatically by operating the pantograph control located in the engineer's compartment or by using the pantograph pole which is inside a tube mounted horizontally on the side of the car. If it is necessary to mount the car, a control on top, at the end of each car flagged, "Danger High Voltage—Ground Pantograph Before Going on Roof," must be activated. When cars are interconnected, it is necessary to deenergize all connected cars by lowering and grounding the pantograph on each connected car. As mentioned in the discussion on electric locomotives, it is essential to contact railroad officials as to the proper operation of the grounding system and this should be practiced prior to an emergency.

With the pantograph lowered, the battery operating the emergency lights and doors can be disconnected by using the battery cutoff switch inside the electrical cabinet.

E. Miscellaneous Railroad Facilities

Some facilities on a railroad are similar to that of the manufacturing industry and, therefore, hazards are common. However, there are some facilities that are peculiar to the railroad industry, such as diesel shops, heavy repair shops, paint shops, fueling facilities, etc. Such a facility as a diesel shop has hazards associated with cutting and welding, housekeeping, and leakage of fuel.

Fueling facilities are a particular area that need protection, not so much for the economic value of the systems themselves but for the value of the locomotives and possible interruption of service. Fuel pump houses preferably are

Fig. 17-3H. An insulated sloping bottom tank car that may be equipped with heaters (interior or exterior) for transportation of products requiring heat for ease of handling.

constructed of masonry and equipped with an automatic fire protection system as well as light fixtures and devices suitable for hazardous locations (see Sec. 7, Chap. 2). Leakage is the prime hazard and housekeeping and preventive maintenance is essential. In newer facilities the pumps are not enclosed, reducing the fire hazard. Portable fire extinguishers and high pressure water pumps spotted along the fueling rack are desirable.

Other facilities critical to the operation of the railroads could stop the movement of trains in a given territory if involved in fire. Such facilities include computer centers, microwave facilities, centralized train control facilities, classification yards, etc. These facilities are highly protected with private detection and protection systems. Typical suppression systems found in these facilities range from sprinkler to carbon dioxide and Halon 1301.

Bridges and Trestles

Prevention is the key to continued operation of these structures. Susceptibility to fire damage can be reduced by the application of fire retardant material, water barrels, fire detection systems, standby pipe and hose systems, and watchman service. At some particularly valuable and critical bridges, fireboats and the use of water buckets attached to helicopters have been provided.

Exposures to Freight Equipment

Exposure fires that destroy loaded and unloaded freight equipment reflect the need for close analysis of terminal fire hazards where there is a large concentration of cars. In designing large classification or switching yards, adequate fire protection is a prime consideration.

Recent loss experience involving large yards indicated that lack of accessible fire mains and hydrants were a contributing factor.[2] In the event of a disaster, fire fighting activities should be confined to containment and protection of exposed property. A fire plan should include knowledge of fire mains and hydrants in close proximity to the yard, as any existing protection in the yard may be rendered useless in a disaster.

Railroad sidings that service properties present a similar exposure hazard, particularly at such installations as grain elevators, lumber yards, flammable liquid or LP-Gas unloading facilities, and similar industrial properties.

Self-propelled Fire Fighting and Derrick Equipment

Most carriers have the capability of clearing derailments and rerailing derailed freight equipment. They utilize derrick outfits ranging from 150-ton steam or diesel derricks to 250-ton derricks. These derricks are included in the work train consist which also may include water cars and fire pumps that are designed to operate either by the train air line or independently by an internal combustion engine. Fire hose, nozzles, foam compound, play pipes and a quantity of extinguishers are also provided for fire fighting purposes.

Work train outfits have proved most valuable where an emergency occurs in a remote and inaccessible area. Often such emergencies have been handled by mounting a fire department pumper on a flat car which can be taken to an emergency site.

Some railroads even have self-propelled fire fighting cars that can be used independent of the work train. Knowledge of the availability of such fire fighting equipment is often overlooked in preplanning emergencies and should be considered in the overall prefire plan including mutual involvement of the fire service agencies and the railroads.

F. Rights-of-Way

Prevention of Fires

A common and most difficult fire is the right-of-way fire (land adjacent to the roadbed). While they still exist, the frequency and severity have been dramatically reduced by controlled burning, spraying of the vegetation with chemicals, and installing fire breaks.

Cooperation with the forestry service has led to technological advances in the development of spark arresters, spark arrester exhaust manifolds, and sparkless brake shoes. Planned vegetation is another potential solution.

Safety

Whenever in the vicinity of a railroad track, assume it is a "live" track and that a train may appear at any moment. A number of close calls have been recorded where fire fighting personnel have narrowly escaped injury due to passing trains that were unaware of their presence. Imagine the situation where hose lines have been laid across the track to fight a fire only to have the hoses cut by a passing train.

Communication is essential and railroad personnel should be contacted to alert train crews of the location of the fire so they can be on the alert for fire fighting personnel.

G. Transportation of Hazardous Commodities

Rail transportation of hazardous commodities, which annually represent less than 4 percent of the carloads of freight moving over the system, is strictly regulated by the DOT and the Bureau of Explosives of the AAR. The responsibility for regulating the transportation of hazardous materials being moved by the U.S. railroads is vested with the DOTs Federal Railroad Administration (FRA). The Bureau of Railroad Safety, a component of the FRA, inspects and enforces the regulations, and they are binding on the shippers and carriers. The Hazardous Materials branch of the FRA has as its main goal reasonable and adequate safety to the public by regulating the shipper preparation and carrier transportation of explosives and other dangerous articles. Canadian roads are regulated by the Canadian Transport Commission (CTC), and regulations are handled in similar fashion to the U.S.

When a rail accident occurs involving hazardous articles, the danger is increased. Release of the product, fire, and even explosions must be confronted by the fire, health, and safety people.

It is essential that fire safety personnel have knowledge about the presence, type, quantity, and nature of any hazardous articles in the accident. This information is available in two forms. The first is the "placard" which is affixed to both ends and both sides of the railroad car. The purpose of the placard is to alert personnel that the car contains a dangerous article. The name of the hazardous material is on the placard, and is also often stenciled on the shell of the tank car. Often, due to the nature of the accident, the placard cannot be read, or it is prudent not to approach the car so as to read the placard. (In some instances binoculars may be helpful.)

The second available means of identification of the hazardous article is the "waybill." Regulations state the conductor of the train must have in his possession a piece of paper, usually a waybill, but sometimes a switch ticket or other document, which shows the placard notation, the car number, the shipper, the prescribed name and hazardous commodity classification of the chemical and the amount of material. Often, the emergency telephone num-

Table 17-3A.   Major Causes of Railroad Fires*

Cause	$ Loss	1971 Freq.	$ Loss	1972 Freq.	$ Loss	1973 Freq.
Derailments/Collisions	2,159,415	(454)	2,708,497	(33)	3,498,776	(35)
Sparks from Brake Shoes	970,217	(339)	954,010	(547)	3,166,546	(957)
Unknown	2,468,681	(454)	1,149,039	(255)	1,422,244	(245)
Diesels—Electrical Equipment Fires	605,766	(115)	773,214	(126)	626,306	(112)
Trespassers	349,222	(205)	563,875	(214)	735,735	(257)

* Compiled by the NFPA Railroad Section from reports representing 56 percent of railroad main track.

ber of the shipper is included. In addition, the conductor will have a separate list identifying all the cars in the train that are dangerous.

In both Canada and the United States, violations in accidents, fires or explosions, and leaking broken containers occurring in connection with the transportation or storage on carrier's property of explosives or other dangerous articles, must be reported promptly to the Bureau of Explosives. The Bureau's telephone number, 202-293-4048, can be reached 24 hrs a day, 7 days per week and someone is always available who can advise as to the proper procedure to follow in an immediate emergency. Bureau representatives are also dispatched to the scene of major emergencies.

Technical assistance is also available by calling Chemtrec, toll free, at 800-424-9300; 202-483-7616 in Alaska and Hawaii; or 483-7616 in the District of Columbia.

Many carriers have prepared guides and recommendations for handling rail emergencies and have made them available to fire departments along their rights-of-way. In addition, they have assisted the fire service agencies by participating in fire-oriented seminars and providing instructors at fire schools.

Emergency Action Teams

Some carriers have developed Emergency Action Teams that are well trained and specialize in the handling of emergencies on their system lines. Such teams are equipped with special kits and tools to repair leaks and control pollution problems. This concept is rapidly spreading throughout the industry. See Section 3, Chapter 10 for further information on availability of hazard emergency teams.

Bibliography

References Cited

[1] DOT Hazardous Materials Regulations, "Specifications for Tank Cars," Part 179, Department of Transportation, Hazardous Materials Regulation Board, Washington, D.C.

[2] Sharry, John, "Coordinated Attack Limits, Post-Blast Damage," *Fire Command!*, Vol. 42, No. 7, July 1975, pp. 14–17.

NFPA Codes, Standards, and Recommended Practices (see the latest *NFPA Publications and Visual Aids Catalog* for availability of current editions of the following documents)

NFPA No. 10, Standard for the Installation, Maintenance, and Use of Portable Fire Extinguishers.

Additional Readings

"Recommended Good Practice for Handling Collisions and Derailments Involving Hazardous Materials in Transportation," Hazardous Material Emergency Guide, B.E. Pamphlet No. 1, June 1973, Bureau of Explosives, Association of American Railroads, Washington, D.C.

"Recommended Good Practice for Handling Fires or Spills Involving Explosives and Other Dangerous Articles in Transportation," Hazardous Material Emergency Guide, B.E. Pamphlet No. 2, June 1973, Bureau of Explosives, Association of American Railroads, Washington, D.C.

Chapter 4

RAIL RAPID TRANSIT SYSTEMS

The environment of a rail rapid transit system lends itself to some peculiar and difficult firesafety problems. Large numbers of people in subterranean enclosures compound the life safety problems. Fires occurring within subways have attracted national attention over the years due to the location of the fire and the resultant danger to passengers evacuating trains through smoke-filled trackways.

Among fire causes in a subway system are mechanical failure of undercar components, electrical short circuits, accumulation of combustible debris along the trackways and within vent shafts, accumulation of road film and oils on the underside of revenue vehicles, combustible materials within car components, combustible construction of the tunnel, including cross-ties and the ever-present hazard associated with the human factor involving so-called juvenile pranks or actual arson.

This chapter concerns itself with areas within a rapid transit system requiring special attention, and it includes subways, underground stations, and above-ground stations.

A.   Subways

Fires occurring within the confining areas of a subway system are among the most difficult to extinguish due to limited room for fire personnel to operate. Access points for fire personnel, emergency exit locations for passengers, availability of water supply, and ventilation capabilities are among the fundamentals that must be considered in providing adequate safeguards for passengers and facilities for fire fighting forces to adequately cope with emergencies.

A direct liaison between rapid transit authorities and fire officials is essential to keep emergency forces apprised of current conditions within the underground installations. Floor plans of stations and subways must be continually reviewed. Fire protection included in the original design of the system may have changed, thus requiring updating.

Ventilation

Ventilation of underground subways is of primary importance. Serious study must be given to the removal of smoke under fire conditions. Exiting schemes must also be developed which will allow passengers to exit into fresh air at all times. Some rapid transit systems have installed fully reversible fans within vent shafts. These are capable of moving large quantities of air, either by intake or exhaust, thus permitting smoke to be purged from the subway in a predetermined direction so that passengers can be evacuated to the closest station. Ventilation shafts and fans have been placed at each end of an underground station and, in some instances, are located between stations. When vertical shafts are included in the ventilation criteria, the possibility of flammable liquid entering the shaft at street level must be considered, and adequate sumps to retain such spills must be developed. Electrical equipment which may be installed within shafts and fan rooms should meet the requirements for the expected exposure as determined by the local authority having jurisdiction.

Access/Egress

Walkways: Primary consideration must be given to the evacuation of large numbers of passengers to a safe point of refuge, which could be a station platform or direct to the open air at grade by means of vertical exitways. Many existing systems evacuate passengers by having them climb from the train to the trackway where they then walk between the rails on cross-ties until a vertical exit or station platform is reached. Modern transit systems prefer to have passengers evacuate the train to a walkway which allows passengers to step directly from the train to the walkway which is constructed along the side of the trackway on the side opposite the third rail power source (see Fig. 17-4A). This method of evacuation keeps passengers off the trackway and allows specially equipped vehicles to respond to train problems. If trackways are separated by concrete walls and fire doors, the walkway system also provides easy access to a train on the opposite trackway and provides an acceptable horizontal exit path which remains relatively free of smoke and heat. Obviously, adequate lighting must be maintained to allow safe evacuation.

Tunnel or Bore: Many rapid transit systems presently are operating underground on trackways which are completely separated from each other by concrete walls and fire doors (see Fig. 17-4B). As previously mentioned, this concept provides a place of refuge for passengers provided adequate train control and planning is practiced. Separation walls should have no less than a 2-hr fire resistance rating with openings protected by 1½-hr fire doors. Hardware normally used in the installation of fire doors and frames have been found inadequate for the pressures generated by a train moving through the bore. Special study and consideration must be given to the type of door, frame, hinges, locking device, and method of securing the frame to the opening. Sliding fire doors with counter weights require special attention.

Emergency Exits: When determining exit requirements from an underground subway system, a number of factors must be considered:

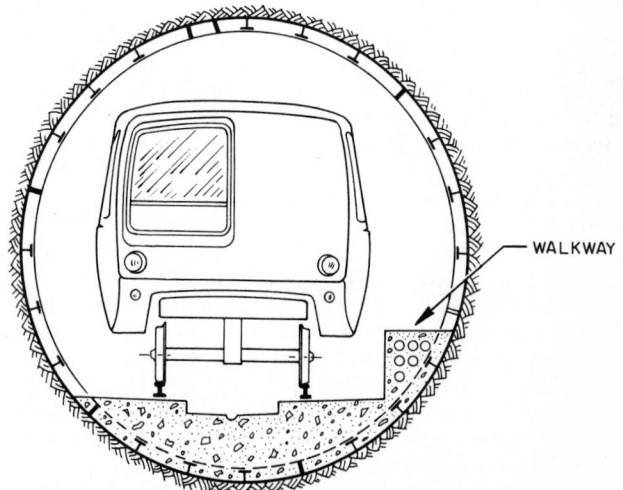

Fig. 17-4A.   A section view of a single-tube subway tunnel showing the location of the emergency passenger walkway to the floor of the car. The walkway is located on the opposite side of the tracks from the live third rail.

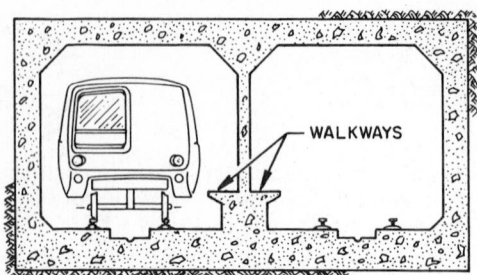

Fig. 17-4B. A section view of a subway tunnel having track-ways separated from each other by a concrete wall. Openings through the wall, protected by fire doors, can provide an acceptable horizontal exit path from the tunnel where an accident has occurred to the other which remains relatively free of smoke and heat.

1. Length of train.
2. Depth of trackway below grade.
3. Accessibility to exit at grade.
4. Accessibility to exit at trackway.
5. Time and distance to surface.
6. Available ventilation and controls.
7. Access to trackway for fire services.

Obviously, no transit system can operate safely with unlimited vertical shafts. Not only would it develop confusion underground, but it would play havoc with required transit security. NFPA 101, Life Safety Code, should be followed as closely as possible in considering emergency exiting requirements for subway tubes.

Many transit systems have utilized ventilation shafts as emergency exits by constructing conventional stairways in the shaft. Unless the stairway is completely separated from the vent shaft by 2-hr fire resistant construction and adequate control of air currents within the bore is maintained, this concept is extremely risky, since smoke and heat may contaminate the vertical exitway.

Under no circumstances should required exitways contain straight vertical ladders. Internally illuminated exit signs with two sources of supply should be installed at trackway level to direct passengers and emergency lighting should be provided within the exit enclosure.

Communication

Probably one of the most serious problems encountered during underground emergencies concerns communications. Emergency telephones are normally identified as to location throughout the subway system by a distinctive light. Most systems designate a blue color light for emergency phone locations. Communication from trackway direct to a central control room is accomplished by merely picking up the instrument. Some systems utilize the Centrex principle to complete their calls.

Blue light stations identifying the location of emergency telephones can also serve multiple purposes. For example, on the Bay Area Rapid Transit Systems (BART), headquartered in Oakland, Cal., the stations include a third rail or power trip button, a maintenance jack, a 110 V outlet and a 20-lb multipurpose dry chemical extinguisher. The stations are spotted at 1,000-ft intervals or in line of sight, whichever is shortest, throughout the underground system.

Communication through a subway system is sometimes very difficult. Fire department portable radios may not function as intended. Fire authorities should make every effort to test their communications systems under actual conditions throughout the subway system. Consideration

should be given to utilization of wired communication systems which may already exist. Relaying of information in line of sight by use of portable radios, or by establishing a command post at the central headquarters of the transit system and utilizing the emergency telephone or a train radio should be considered.

Traction Power

Traction power, or the electrical energy needed to run the trains, may be carried throughout the system by means of a third rail or overhead wiring. If traction power is provided by means of a third rail, modern transit systems have installed a fiberglass coverboard throughout the system which prevents accidental contact with the third rail by people. The coverboard ideally is strong enough to hold a 350-lb weight over a 10-ft span and is supported in such a manner as to allow a fire department ladder to safely rest against it. Warning signs, as required, should be affixed to the top of the coverboard in any area accessible to the public.

As previously mentioned herein, disconnect switches should be strategically located throughout the system in order to allow traction power to be cut as quickly as possible under emergency conditions.

Fire Protection in Subways

One of the principal fire protection devices in use in rapid transit systems is the standpipe hose system. Wet standpipe systems are generally not found throughout a subway system with the following exceptions.

1. Station locations (see Part B of this Chapter).
2. Tubes or tunnels running under large expanses of water or under large hills where the installation of a dry standpipe system is impractical.
3. In locations where a delay in getting water to the scene may result in death or destruction.

NFPA No. 14, Standpipe and Hose Systems, provides good guidance for installations.

Dry Standpipes: Dry standpipes may be located throughout the underground subway system. Generally speaking, the locations of standpipe outlets are determined by the local fire authorities with consideration being given to fire department access at tunnel level, available vertical access shafts for emergency forces, availability of street access to the fire department, siamese connection at grade, etc.

Some rapid transit systems require that dry standpipe outlets be placed no farther than 200 ft apart throughout the underground; others have determined that maximum separation distances of 300, 400 and 500 ft are acceptable.

Most rapid transit systems place bins or boxes containing 2½-in. hose in close proximity to dry standpipe outlets, with the inspection and testing of such hose being left up to the concerned rapid transit system. Fire authorities operating under this principle should seriously consider assigning personnel to witness hose inspections and required testing.

Special Apparatus: In lieu of the supply of fire hose required at standpipe stations, innovative measures have been taken by some systems to insure by other means that hose is available when needed. BART, for example, with the approval of fire authorities, has removed all fire hose from its subway system with the exception of 1½-in. hose located within stations. In turn, BART has agreed to furnish five fully equipped, specially designed fire engines capable of traveling either by street or rail to previously designated rendezvous points where the responding fire department would board the apparatus and go to the fire or emergency location within the underground. Each piece of apparatus includes as part of its inventory 1,200 ft of 2½ in. hose and

400 ft of 1½-in. hose, as well as nozzles, a portable emergency generator, a power saw, a cutting torch, extension cords, flood lights, demand breathing apparatus, life lines, miscellaneous tools, a high expansion foam unit and nozzle, a 300-gal water tank and a small pressure pump.

Fire Extinguishers: Fire extinguishers should be placed throughout the underground system generally at or in close proximity to the previously mentioned blue light or emergency station. The size and type of the extinguisher to be used is dictated by the size and type of exposure expected.

Drainage: Adequate drainage of water accumulated during a fire emergency requires careful consideration. Fire authorities should be made aware of the underground system's drainage capabilities and recognize that large amounts of water placed ineffectively could seriously impair other required rescue operations.

When fighting structural fires at street level in close proximity to station entrances or street ventilation grills, fire officers should alert the rapid transit officials that water intrusion into their system may be expected.

B. Stations (Below Ground)

Underground rapid transit stations preferably are constructed of noncombustible materials with all steel beams, girders, or columns protected by 2-hr fire resistant construction. Modern rapid transit systems use reinforced concrete construction for the station's outer shell and protected steel beams, girders and columns within the shell—a concept resulting in a relatively firesafe structure. Contrary to general opinion, very few fires of major proportions have occurred within stations themselves. Most station fires are attributed to poor housekeeping or electrical fires occurring in escalator machine rooms. The primary exposure to underground stations lies in two areas—concessions and trains. When referring to concessions, it must be understood that small concessions within a station selling newspapers and magazines normally would have a low-risk classification, while major concessions, which could include restaurants or theaters, would have a high risk classification as it refers to smoke and heat development.

Newspaper and magazine types of concessions must be placed in areas which do not block required exits and should be limited in size. Automatic fire protection should be installed to protect the entire concession area. Possible expansion of the area should be considered when designing the fire protection system.

Openings Into Underground Stations: Major concessions or openings into existing commercial structures from the concourse level of the rapid transit station need special attention. Fire authorities may invoke basic building code requirements applicable to property lines. This could require as a minimum 3-hr fire-rated doors at openings between the rapid transit system property and the commercial establishment or concessionnaire. Even if the commercial activity and the station are owned by the rapid transit system, good separation between the two areas is desirable. Fire barriers can be established by installation of fire doors or automatic fire extinguishing systems to prevent the spread of fire and smoke from the commercial occupancy into the station or from the station into the commercial occupancy. Before any openings into a rapid transit system are made, the existing conditions on both sides of the proposed opening must be reviewed carefully in an effort to develop an equitable fire protection plan.

Protection for Underground Stations

An underground rapid transit station may be compared to a multiple basement structure with the exception that a rapid transit station generally has a low fire loading factor when compared to a commercial basement structure. Strict application of building or fire code requirements may develop exceptionally high construction costs which are not necessarily justified. If minimal combustible storage or concession areas are involved, large open public areas may be left with little or no fire risk involvement. If such is the case, limiting automatic fire protection systems to those areas containing combustibles and designing the systems for possible expansion should the future so dictate may have some merit, although the limitations of partial protection must be clearly understood.

Fire Detection Systems: All nonpublic areas commonly classified as support or ancillary areas, if not protected by an automatic fire protection system, should be fully protected by a fire detection system. Ionization-type detectors, which can detect minute products of combustion, are preferable, although rate-of-rise-type detectors may be used if authorized by the concerned fire authority.

It is good practice to provide supervision for all fire detection and automatic fire protection systems. Supervisory signals should be received at the system's command center as well as being annunciated by zones at the station agent's booth or kiosk.

Wet Standpipes: Wet standpipes are supplied by a piping system separate and distinct from that used for automatic sprinkler systems. Separate fire department siamese connections, properly labeled, and installed at grade level, allow the fire department to service either system.

Fire hose cabinets, placed as recommended in the NFPA Standpipe and Hose Streams Standard, may contain 1½-in. and 2½-in. control valves. A maximum of 100 ft of attached 1½-in. hose with nozzle is included within the cabinet. Normally no 2½-in. hose is stored in cabinets as responding fire departments generally prefer to use their own larger hose. A suitable fire extinguisher may be placed in the cabinet together with a hose spanner. To reduce pilferage of fire equipment, cabinets are locked and a breakaway glass panel installed which will allow ready access under emergency conditions. Some rapid transit systems have installed intrusion alarms which send a signal to the station agent if a fire hose cabinet has been opened.

Access/Egress to Underground Stations

When determining required exit widths, consideration must be given to future occupancy needs. Once a station has been constructed, it becomes very difficult, if not impossible, to place additional stairs or escalators where they will best serve the public. While it is recognized that meeting required exit width may become a major difficulty to designers, a good source of guidance is NFPA No. 101, The Life Safety Code.

In order to establish required exit widths for any structure, it is first necessary to determine the occupancy classification. The State of California, for example, has determined that places where people await transportation be classified as an assembly occupancy. Although this classification may appear restrictive to the designer, it must be recognized that during heavy commute hours, large numbers of people will congregate at platform and concourse levels. Adequate exitways to grade are absolutely essential.

Since rapid transit systems are in business to move people rapidly, most new systems have installed escalators that operate at the rate of 120 feet per minute, with plans being formulated to considerably increase this speed. Escalators are now designed to be fully reversible, depending upon commute conditions. In many instances, escalators will penetrate two or more floor levels to gain access to the intended platform. This can pose special design problems since many designers prefer to maintain an open environment throughout a station complex. Vertical penetration of more than one floor without enclosures has been accomplished in some rapid transit systems by increasing automatic fire protection.

When escalators are designed and accepted as required exits, serious study must be given to the usability of such units in evacuating a station under emergency conditions. Consideration also must be given to methods of stopping escalators so as to prevent injury to patrons. One possibility is by notifying patrons via a taped public address announcement, which may be activated through the fire alarm system, stating the escalator will stop within a specified time period. This allows patrons to grasp the handrail and obtain a firm footing or may even alert patrons not to board escalators until they have stopped.

Exit Barriers

Rapid transit stations contain two basic areas to properly separate those individuals who have paid their fare from those who have not paid. These are commonly called paid areas and free areas. Patrons in the free area are able to move directly to the outside with no barrier problems. Patrons who are within the paid area must go through fare barriers to gain access to the free area. Under emergency evacuating conditions, consideration must be given to either automatically opening all fare barriers, allowing patrons to rapidly evacuate the station, or to installing specially designed access gates for the same purpose. With more and more emphasis being directed to handicapped patrons, the use of access gates becomes more useful in basic design.

Many stations are completely closed off by grills or steel doors when a station is secured after normal revenue hours. The installation of small doors in the grills can provide easy access for fire department personnel as well as serve as an acceptable means of exit for any employees who may be working in the station.

Emergency Procedures

Due to the variety of hazards involved in a rapid transit system, local fire authorities must establish a direct line of communication with the system's top management personnel. Good inspection techniques must be developed and coordinated emergency response procedures planned. Access points to all parts of the system must be pinpointed, and engine and truck company response patterns tailored to meet special access problems. Information from the system is needed on floor plans, electrification, revenue vehicle, structures, and communications to plan emergency procedures properly. A wise course for a fire department is to assign one command officer the responsibility of coordinating all the emergency activities required to protect against fires on rapid transit trains, on the right-of-way, and outside of the right-of-way.

C. Surface or Above Ground Trackway and Stations

Generally speaking, fires occurring in stations at grade or above are no more difficult to combat than any other at grade type of fire. Primary consideration must always be given to the traction power and even though assurance is given that the power is shut off, fire department personnel should operate under the assumption that the third rail or overhead wire is still hot.

Items which should be considered during a plan review of the trackway would include:

1. Designated mileage markers which would provide a response location for fire personnel.
2. Locations where the overhead tracks may intersect with known street locations.
3. Access gates which would allow patrons to exit the system under fire department direction.
4. Wayside communications availability which would allow the fire department to communicate directly to the system's command center.
5. Locations of substations, switching stations, gap breaker stations or other major electrical installations which would be of concern to local fire authorities.

Bibliography

NFPA Codes, Standards, and Recommended Practices (see the latest *NFPA Publications and Visual Aids Catalog* for availability of current editions of the following documents)

NFPA No. 14, Standard for the Installation of Standpipe and Hose Systems.

NFPA No. 101, Code for Safety to Life from Fire in Buildings and Structures.

Additional Readings

Bond, H., "Underground Buildings," *Fire Journal,* Vol. 59, No. 4, July 1965, p. 52–55.

Chapter 5

MARINE

Marine fire hazards, including those on small pleasure boats, small commercial boats, and commercial vessels, are discussed in this chapter. Parts A through D deal with pleasure and small commercial boats, and Parts E through J deal with commercial vessels.

A. Pleasure and Small Commercial Boats

According to U.S. Coast Guard statistics (1972), nearly six million pleasure and small commercial boats were registered in the United States. Of that number, 5,044 were involved in accidents that caused the deaths of more than 1,400 people, 20 of whom were killed by fire or explosion, making this the least frequent cause of death in marine accidents. The same 5,044 accidents caused almost 900 injuries, 127 being caused by fire or explosion. Property damage, however, is a different picture. The accidents tabulated in these same statistics reported property damage to the extent of slightly more than seven million dollars. Fire and explosion, which often destroy the boat or make it completely useless, accounted for almost 2.2 million dollars, the largest single cause of marine property damage.

B. Pleasure and Small Commercial Boat Hulls

The arrangement of the hulls on pleasure and small commercial boats must be such that all compartments are as accessible as practicable, and that escape hatches are unobstructed, readily accessible, and adequate for the designed purpose. Extreme congestion of engine compartments is unsafe: for example, it should not be necessary to crawl over engines or auxiliaries for servicing purposes. Also, ventilating requirements increase with the addition of auxiliary machinery.

Materials

Construction materials, in addition to wood, include a wide variety such as fiberglass reinforced plastic, steel, aluminum, and concrete. Each of these materials has certain advantages and disadvantages, with the final selection usually based on the individual's particular needs. Where flammability is one of the disadvantages, that hazard should be immediately recognized and increased protection provided. Such protection should include maximum use of fire resistive materials and coatings.

Ventilation

Ventilation is defined as the positive changing of air within a compartment by natural or mechanical means. Ventilation of a compartment may be by means of general dilution of contaminated air through the introduction of fresh air or by local exhaust method. Ventilation cannot be relied upon to remove all flammable vapors that are possible from fuel system failures (leakage). Accordingly, ventilation requirements can only be properly evaluated when it has been determined that the entire fuel system is in satisfactory operating condition.

Lightning Protection

Protection from lightning can be afforded boats by following certain procedures regarding grounding and bonding. Metallic fittings at extremities of wooden masts and yards should be effectively grounded, and all metallic structural parts or accessories of any appreciable size installed on spars should be connected to the grounding conductor. With proper bonding and grounding, a cone of protection is provided as shown in Figure 17-5A. This protective zone is largely immune to direct strokes of lightning. No part of the vessel to be protected should extend outside the cone. Thus, in the cabin cruiser illustrated in the lower part of Figure 17-4A, adequate lightning protection is afforded only by the grounded antenna equipped with a lightning arrester or gap on the loading coil.

C. Pleasure and Small Commercial Boat Equipment

Engines

The engines may be either water or air-cooled. If air-cooled, a visual or audible device must be installed to warn

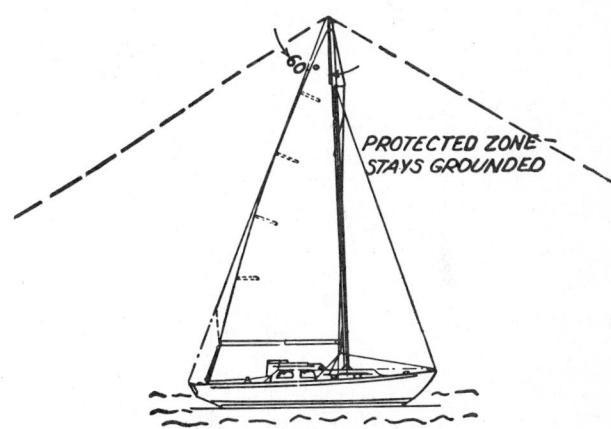

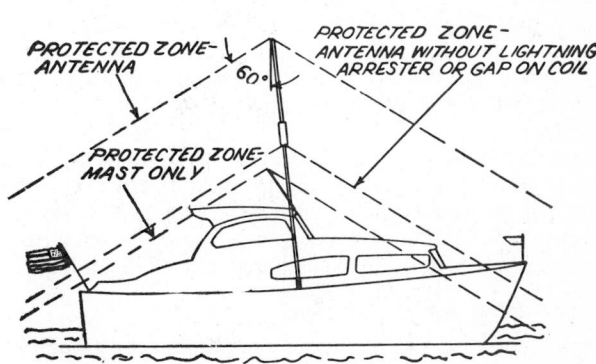

Fig. 17-5A. Diagrams illustrating the "cone of protection" provided by a grounded mast or antenna. This protective zone is largely immune to direct strokes of lightning. No part of the vessel to be protected should extend outside the cone of protection. Thus, in the cabin cruiser illustrated, adequate lightning protection is afforded only by the grounded antenna equipped with a lightning arrester or gap on the coil.

of excessive engine temperatures. If air-cooled engines are enclosed, the compartment ventilation must be adequate to meet the needs of the engine in addition to the normal ventilation requirements. Air that is used for engine cooling must be discharged outside the hull by means of a duct system. Water-cooled engines and auxiliaries are preferable for marine use. On water-cooled engines the head, block, and exhaust manifold must be water-jacketed and cooled by water from a pump that operates whenever the engine is operating. Gages that indicate cooling water discharge temperatures and lubricating oil pressures must be located at the helm position. It is recommended that an approved marine strainer be installed in the raw water intake line. Carburetors should be designed for marine use, must not leak fuel around the shafts or other connections, and must not be externally vented. Carburetors must be equipped with drip collectors of adequate capacity, and drip collectors must be capable of returning all drip and overflow to the engine intake manifold. The accumulated fuel in the drip collector must not be allowed to escape into the bilges or engine compartments.

Fuel Systems

The general requirements for fuel systems demand that they should be liquid and vaportight with respect to the interior of the hull. The individual components of any system must be designed and installed to meet the purposes of the system and to withstand the stresses and exposure of marine service such as pressure, vibration, shock, movement, lubricating grease and oil, bilge solvents, and corrosive environment. The system and all of its components as installed in the boat must be capable of withstanding an exposure fire free burning for at least $2\frac{1}{2}$ min without any failure that might result in leakage of liquid or vapor. The fuel system must be electrically bonded from the fill plate on the deck to the engine.

Appliances

Open flame devices are more liable to promiscuous unskilled or ignorant operation than any other boat equipment involving fire risk. It is therefore imperative that such items be selected and installed with the aim of minimizing personal and physical hazards.

Galley stoves must be manufactured, approved, and labeled for marine use. Printed instructions for proper installation, operation, and maintenance must be furnished by the manufacturer. A durable and permanently legible instruction sign covering safe operation and maintenance must also be provided by the manufacturer and installed on or adjacent to the consuming appliance where it may be readily read.

Installation of a coal, charcoal, or wood burning stove should preferably be on a hollow tile base. If not, it must be mounted on legs providing clearance of at least 5 in. between stove bottom and deck, and the deck effectively insulated with a noncombustible material or sheathing.

Liquefied Petroleum Gas Systems

In the interest of safety, it is important that the properties of liquefied petroleum gases be understood and that safe practices for their use be followed. Under moderate pressure the gases liquefy; upon relief of the pressure they are readily converted into the gaseous state. Advantage of this characteristic is taken in their usage, and for convenience they are shipped and stored under pressure as liquids. In their gaseous state, they present a hazard comparable to any flammable natural or manufactured gas, except that they

are heavier than air. Although the vapors tend to sink to the bottom of an enclosed compartment into which they are released, they will diffuse throughout and will not be readily dispelled by overhead ventilation.

Electrical Systems

An ungrounded electrical system means any two-wire electrical system in which all current-carrying conductors including the source of power and all accessories are completely insulated from ground throughout the system. An ungrounded system is recommended for any voltage. All wiring should be secured in position in order to prevent any motion or chafing. Batteries should not be located in or under living spaces.

A grounded electrical system means any two-wire system which utilizes the common ground point of the boat only as a means to maintain the return conductors of one side of the system at ground potential. Except for engine mounted accessories which may use the engine block as a common ground return, all electrical circuits should be of the two-wire type with insulated conductors to and from the power source. The grounded side of the system should be of the negative polarity.

All boats with fixed electrical systems should be equipped with a bonding ground system to: (1) prevent stray current corrosion by confining stray current leakage inside the hull, (2) provide a low resistance path to ground for voltages that may be considerably in excess of those for which the system is designed, such as lightning, and (3) minimize radio interference.

Fire Extinguishers

The fire extinguishment potential of portable fire extinguishers is normally evaluated by recognized testing laboratories. The U.S. Coast Guard also classifies portable fire extinguishers based upon the U.L. classification of fires, but using a different method of indicating extinguishment potentials. These designations are shown in Table 17-5A.

D. Pleasure and Small Commercial Boat Operations

General Maintenance

Operation and maintenance of pleasure and small commercial boats consist mainly of good housekeeping. The boat must be kept shipshape at all times. Clean waste and rags should be kept in covered metal containers; used waste and rags should be kept in separate covered metal containers. Dirty waste and rags should be properly disposed of each time the boat is docked. Flammable paint and varnish removers must be used with caution, and only in well-ventilated areas. When repainting interior areas, fire retardant paint should be used. Unprotected electric lights or open flames should not be taken into areas of possible vapor accumulation, and gasoline or other flammable liquid for cleaning purposes (including paint brushes) should not be used in such areas. Ventilation ducts and exhaust blowers must be maintained at top efficiency.

Good maintenance and sensible operation of fuel systems is probably the most important duty of a boat owner in the prevention of fire. Gasoline vapors are heavier than air and will not escape from low-lying cockpits such as bilges or tank bottoms unless drawn or forced out. Atmospheric concentrations of gasoline vapor as low as 1.4 percent and as high as 7.6 percent are flammable. The entire system, including tanks, piping, vent lines, and other accessories must be frequently checked for leaks or evidence of cor-

Table 17-4A. Number and Distribution of Fire Extinguishers

Type of Boat	Class of Extinguishers	Minimum Required	Recommended Locations
Open boats under 16 ft	1-B	1	Helmsman's position.
Open boats over 16 ft	1-B	2	Helmsman's position and passenger space.
Boats under 26 ft	1-B	2	Helmsman's position and cabin.
Boats 26 ft–40 ft	1-B	3	Engine compartment, helmsman's position and galley.**
Boats 40 ft–65 ft	1-B	4*	Engine compartment, helmsman's position, crew quarters and galley.**
Boats 65 ft–75 ft	1-B	5*	Engine compartment, helmsman's position, crew quarters and galley.**
Boats 75 ft–100 ft	1-B	6*	Engine compartment, helmsman's position, crew quarters and galley.**

* Where more than three 1-B units are recommended, the extinguishing capacity may be made up of a smaller number of larger units, provided each recommended location is protected with an extinguisher readily accessible; e.g., three 2-B units may be used in lieu of 4, 5, or 6 of the smaller 1-B units.

** Extinguishers recommended for "engine compartment" should not be located inside such compartment, but near an entrance to the compartment unless someone is normally present in the compartment.

rosion. Connections must be kept tight. Fuel carried on board outside of the fixed fuel system should be in approved containers or in portable tanks which should be safely stowed away.

Fueling

Utmost care must be exercised during fueling operations. Following are some general guidelines to be observed during fueling operations:

1. Fueling should never be undertaken at night except under well-lighted conditions.

2. Smoking must be forbidden on board and nearby.

3. Before opening tanks, the following precautions should be observed:

   (a) All engines, motors, and fans should be shut down.

   (b) All open flames should be extinguished.

   (c) All ports, windows, doors, and hatches should be closed.

   (d) The quantity of fuel to be taken aboard should be determined prior to the start of the fueling operation.

4. The fuel delivery nozzle should be put in contact with the fill pipe before delivery of the fuel is commenced; this contact should be continuously maintained until the flow has stopped. (There is a serious hazard from static discharge if this rule is not followed.)

5. Tanks should not be completely filled. A minimum of 2 percent of the tank space should be allowed for expansion and, if an outboard motor tank, at least 5 percent of the tank space should be allowed. This space allowance should be increased to 6 percent or more if the fuel being taken aboard is below 32°F. To simplify, do not fill tank full.

6. After fuel flow has stopped:

   a. The fill cap shall be tightly secured.

   b. Any spillage should be completely wiped up.

   c. Vent (open) the entire boat before starting engines.

Storage Between Voyages

Before a boat is stored, even for a short period of time, several precautionary actions should be taken. First, a thorough inspection of the entire vessel should be made. All combustible trash and rags should be removed, as well as painting materials and other nonessential flammable liquids.

Fuel lines, engine and appliance, should be secured at both ends. Bilges should be inspected and pumped dry. Shaft logs and rudder bearings should be checked and tightened if necessary. All through-hull fitting valves should be closed, except scuppers which permit drainage of rain water. Batteries should be checked and all electrical services except automatic bilge pumps secured. When maximum ventilation is necessary, locker doors, drawers, and bilge hatches should be secured in a partially opened position.

E. NFPA Boating Standards

Recommendations relating to pleasure and commercial craft, both inboard and outboard powered, using either gasoline or diesel fuel, are contained in NFPA No. 302, Fire Protection Standard for Motor Craft. These recommendations indicate what is considered good practice toward reducing the fire danger of motor craft to a reasonable and acceptable level. Among the subjects covered are: hull arrangement, finish and ventilation; lightning protection; engines (main and auxiliary) and exhaust systems; fuel tanks and systems; cooking, heating and refrigeration; electrical systems; fire extinguishing equipment; and operation and maintenance.

Recommendations suggesting safe practices for areas used for the construction, repair, storage, launching, berthing and fueling of small craft are contained in NFPA No. 303, Standard for Fire Protection of Marinas and Boatyards. Among the subjects covered are: location, design, and construction of berthing facilities; storage and handling of fuels, paints, spirits, and lumber; heating; electrical wiring and equipment; operational hazards (paint removing, welding and cutting, woodworking, battery service, LP-Gas Service, boat storage); fire extinguishment facilities; and fire detection and alarm facilities.

F. Other Organizations Contributing to Boating Safety

The American Boat and Yacht Council, Inc.

The American Boat and Yacht Council, Inc. was established in 1954 to bring to bear the knowledge, experience, and skills of technicians within the boating industry on the development of recommended practices and engineering standards for improving and advancing the design, construction, equipage, and maintenance of small craft with reference to their safety. A cooperative working relationship exists between the council and the NFPA insofar as fire protection of motor craft is concerned, and consistency of recommendations is sought by both.

The National Association of Marine Surveyors (NAMS)

The NAMS includes a group of professional marine surveyors who have associated themselves to assist in the exchange of information concerning the latest approved and recommended practices, new materials and their application in the marine field, and the control of new hazardous materials within the scope of surveyors' operations.

Underwriters Laboratories, Inc.

Underwriters Laboratories, Inc., founded in 1894, is chartered as a not-for-profit, independent organization testing for public safety. It maintains and operates laboratories for the examination and testing of devices, systems, and materials to determine their relation to life, fire casualty hazards, and crime prevention. In 1969 the UL acquired the Yacht Safety Bureau and established a Marine Testing Department.

The American Bureau of Shipping

The American Bureau of Shipping is the American classification society whose technical committees develop rules for the dimensions and use of materials in the construction and conversion of marine vessels. After completion according to the rules, under constant supervision of an ABS field inspector, a vessel is classified and listed by the Bureau as having met all design and structural safety requirements.

G.   Commercial Vessels

Almost any accident involving a vessel carries either a direct or secondary threat of fire. Collision or stranding can rupture tanks or containers of hazardous materials and provide enough frictional heat to ignite the contents. The same result can be achieved by the heavy pounding of a ship in bad weather. Even the leakage of water into a cargo hold can cause accelerated oxidation and eventual combustion of some organic substances. In considering marine fire hazards, we must therefore include both the transfer of cargo and the vessel's operation in addition to the traditional fire problems.

Steadily increasing world population and demand for foreign merchandise have resulted in an ever-increasing volume of waterborne tonnage. Americans have had to develop many new and innovative labor-saving practices to meet foreign competition. While most of the problems generated by these innovative practices have been solved, others have not; still others are being worked on.

Life Safety at Sea

A few years back several disastrous accidents occurred aboard foreign cruise ships operating out of U.S. ports. The rapid spread of fire on these vessels was at least partially due to the fact that they were built and maintained at a lower level of safety than permitted on U.S. flag vessels.

Because of its regulatory responsibility in the area of marine safety, the U.S. Coast Guard promptly took action on several fronts. A new international Safety of Life at Sea

(SOLAS '60) conference was called, which resulted in improved international safety standards for passenger vessels. The thoroughness of the few inspections the U.S. Coast Guard is permitted to make aboard foreign vessels was reinforced. Also, it was established that foreign cruise ships that could not meet the new safety standards of SOLAS would not be permitted to embark passengers in U.S. ports.

Hazards in Handling Cargo

Fire hazard problems in a ship's cargo start when the cargo first comes aboard the vessel, and sometimes even before. While a ship's officers are primarily concerned with matters such as the proper stowage of the cargo, proper weight distribution throughout the vessel, location of the cargo in accordance with the vessel's anticipated sequence of ports, and the proper separation of different consignments, it is very easy to overlook the fact that two adjacent containers may carry materials that are incompatible. Although the U.S. Coast Guard has developed a list of hazardous materials that will react with each other, and has designated certain areas of the vessel for stowage of particular hazardous materials, the labeling of some chemical products is quite ambiguous and enforcement of the labeling regulations for hazardous materials is often inadequate. NFPA publications covering marine fire hazards and hazardous materials should be in the reference library of every ship's cargo officer (see Bibliography at the end of this Chapter.)

The reactivity of fire hazard problems of bulk chemicals is an even greater problem. It is more critical in inland barge operations than aboard ocean-going tankers. In most cases, tankers are loaded at a refinery or similar facility where knowledgeable personnel can assist the ship's officers and offer their guidance. Skilled people generally are available at tanker discharge ports. While the same is true at loading ports for inland barges, frequently there is no one available at the discharge point other than the towboat's crew. A number of accidents and fires have been definitely traced to the handling of hazardous materials in bulk by crewmen having little or no knowledge of the necessary safety precautions.

Cargo Fires at Sea

Once the cargo is loaded and the vessel secured and underway, there is no assurance that the cargo fire problems have been solved. Most cargo fires occur (or are discovered) several days and many miles from the loading port. Aboard tank ships, overfilling can result in spillage if the vessels proceed into warm tropical waters. The warming of a bulk cargo can result in a heavy discharge of vapors from the vessel's vent system. On a heavy humid day with a slight following wind the vapors tend to settle from the masthead vents down to the deck level of the vessel. While there have been fires resulting from cargo expansion and spilling at sea, most vapor problems have developed during the loading of flammable products at a very high rate. The rapid filling of the cargo tank causes the heavy flammable vapors to be forced up and out of the vent system from where they can, under proper conditions, fall directly back down on deck and create a severe fire hazard.

Fires in dry cargo holds can come from many sources. Most, however, can be traced to the forbidden practice of smoking in the cargo hold. Such fires usually smolder for several days before they develop enough heat or smoke to trigger the alarm system. The procedures for extinguishing fires in dry cargo holds can vary quite widely according to the cargo and location of the fire center. Unfortunately, in too many cases improper use of a ship's installed fire protection equipment has resulted in substantial loss of life and total loss of the vessel and its cargo.

Hazards on Inland Waters

Commercial transportation on our inland waterways is growing. Pushing towboats with up to 10,000 hp move as many as 30 to 40 barges (each approximately 195 by 52 ft) lashed together with ratchet-tightened wire rope. Normal procedure is to load each of the barges to its marks in deep water and to within 6 in. of the controlling depth of shallower channels. The tows run approximately 1,150 ft in overall length and have obvious maneuvering problems depending on the contour of the channel and the speed of the current. The real miracle is that there are comparatively few collision and stranding casualties for the number of vessels operating on our inland waterways. As river transportation increases, the risk of accident increases. In some river areas, and with some of the hazardous commodities carried, an accident could turn into a disaster. For that reason, the U.S. Coast Guard changed its regulatory philosophy from the development of regulations to prevent a recurrence of a particular type of accident to the formation of regulations that would prevent the first accident from occurring.

Another problem area is in the vicinity of busy locks at dams operated by the U.S. Army Corps of Engineers. Such locks are usually 600 ft long by approximately 110 ft wide, and most tows must traverse them in two steps. The tow is broken in the middle with the first three 195 ft barges (either two or three abreast, depending upon the individual barge width) being sent through the locks first. Next, the tow boat with the other two rows of barges follows. The entire operation can take an hour or more from the time the tow first reaches the lock wall until it is finally made up again for departure from the other side of the dam. Since tows are accepted into the locks on a first-come first-served basis, there is sometimes a considerable waiting period. It is not unusual to see two or three tows being pulled diagonally into the riverbank to await their turn to go through the locks. In the event of an accident and fire in a lock, two or three full tows loaded with hazardous materials immediately downstream of the lock could present the potential for a holocaust.

Tank Cleaning and Gas Freeing

One of the most hazardous processes in the operation of either tank ships or tank barges is that of tank cleaning and gas freeing. This procedure is carried out in varying degrees for a change of cargo, on or off charter survey, periodic U.S. Coast Guard inspection, and for repairs. Although tank ships are usually cleaned and gas freed at sea while barges are cleaned in port, the procedure is very similar.

The big problem in tank cleaning and gas freeing is the necessity to reduce the flammable vapors in the atmosphere from a point above the upper explosive limit to a point below the lower explosive limit. In other words, the atmosphere of the space must be brought down through the full flammable range of the material of the previous contents. If there should be a spark or other source of ignition within the space during the time the atmosphere is within the explosive range, an explosion could occur.

The most common and most feared source of ignition during cleaning and gas freeing operation is a spark caused by static electricity discharge. During washing operations, water mist forms in a tank's atmosphere and it takes on an electrical charge from the cleaning water jet which penetrates the mist. Should any ungrounded object be lowered into the tank space, a static discharge, similar to a small lightning bolt, could travel from the mist cloud to the ungrounded object.

Another severe fire and explosion hazard arises while a vessel is being repaired. Even though the tanks may have been thoroughly cleaned and gas freed at sea, there is no guarantee that they will remain in the same condition throughout the duration of repairs. As required by both U.S. Coast Guard and U.S. Department of Labor regulations, each space is tested and certified to be safe for hot work by an NFPA certified marine chemist before any hot work can be commenced. The fact that a cargo tank has been found to be completely safe, and so certified by a marine chemist, does not necessarily mean that it will remain in that condition. The warm sun beating down on a tank with a rusty interior can release sufficient flammable vapors inside the tank to bring the atmosphere from a safe condition to well within the explosive range. Therefore, the marine chemist must not only evaluate the atmospheric condition that exists within the space at the time of the inspection, but, must also evaluate the weather conditions and vessel interior conditions that may cause a regeneration of the flammable vapors. Where there is any doubt, the marine chemist should recommend additional precautionary measures to be taken by the repairer, and should specify the circumstances under which a marine chemist should be recalled for further testing.

Timely and regular use of the services of NFPA certified marine chemists has helped to virtually eliminate some of the most severe fire and explosion hazards in the entire marine industry—the hazards associated with the tank cleaning and gas freeing operations of tank ships and tank barges.

H.   Government Marine Regulations

Fire protection aboard merchant vessels has been given detailed attention by both the United States and other major shipping countries throughout the world. As previously noted in this chapter basic to marine fire protection is the International Convention for the Safety of Life at Sea, 1960 (SOLAS '60). This international convention, which became effective on May 26, 1965, regulates construction and operation of merchant ships of all signatory countries.

Under terms of the International Convention, a certificate attesting to a ship's safety issued by a signatory country is accepted by all other countries as having the same force as a certificate issued by them. This arrangement insures a minimum level of safety and also permits ships to operate freely from one country to another without risk of discrimination due to their safety features. Many governments, such as the United States, use the Convention as a basis for the development of higher safety standards.

International fire protection regulations deal primarily with the construction of vessels, provision of fire fighting equipment, and, to a lesser extent, the transportation of dangerous goods. The most detailed provisions apply to construction of passenger ships. Following a number of disastrous passenger ship fires in the 1930s, individual countries developed different approaches to the problem of fire protection aboard passenger ships. The International Convention for the Safety of Life at Sea, 1948, predecessor to SOLAS '60, first reflected these differences of approach by allowing any one of three methods to be employed in the construction of passenger ships. SOLAS '60 retains these three methods with but little change. All three of the methods are based upon three basic principles: (1) separation of the passenger accommodation spaces from the remainder of the ship by thermal and structural boundaries, (2) containment, extinction, or detection of the fire in the space of origin, and (3) protection of the means of escape. Implementation of these principles takes a different form in each of the three methods. Following is a brief summary of each method:

Method I—The construction of internal divisional bulkheads using noncombustible, fire-resisting materials. Generally, a sprinkler system or fire detection system is not installed. The objective of this method is to contain a fire to the space of origin.

Method II—The fitting of a fire alarm system and an automatic sprinkler system for the detection and extinction of fire in all spaces in which a fire might be expected to originate, generally with no restriction on the type or combustibility of internal divisional bulkheads. The objective of this method is to extinguish any fire in the space of origin.

Method III—A system of fire subdivision, each of limited area, dependent upon the size and nature of various compartments, together with the fitting of an automatic detection system and some limit on the combustibility of construction materials, but generally without the installation of an automatic sprinkler system. The objective of this method is to detect a fire in the space of origin and to limit its possible growth.

Although SOLAS '60 recognizes three methods of construction, regulations governing the construction of United States flag vessels only permit Method I. Reasons for this are considered in subsequent paragraphs. At this point it is necessary only to note that a number of fires on non-U.S. flag passenger ships during the period of 1963–1966 found the Convention lacking on two counts. First, the International Conventions of 1948 and 1960 applied only to ships constructed after the effective date of the Convention. A "grandfather clause" permitted existing passenger ships to continue operation with little or no improvement of fire safety. Second, because of numerous technical advances, the three construction methods permitted by the 1960 Convention did not represent the highest practicable level of fire safety for new passenger ships.

Prompted by disastrous passenger ship fires, the Intergovernmental Maritime Consultative Organization (IMCO), which operates under the auspices of the Economic and Social Council of the United Nations, undertook an intensive study of passenger ship fire safety in 1966 and 1967. This resulted in advancing two comprehensive proposals for amendment of SOLAS '60. These amendments have been agreed to by the IMCO General Assembly and await only formal ratification by the required number of countries before coming into force.

The first amendment deals with existing passenger ships. It would require, in essence, that fire safety of existing passenger ships be improved so as to comply with one of the three construction methods required by the 1948 Convention for new ships. This may be likened to making a building construction code retroactive. When effective, it will necessitate rebuilding numerous passenger ships or removing them from service. In anticipation of the amendment, the fire safety of a number of ships has already been improved and several other ships have been withdrawn from service.

As important as the first amendment is, it is intended only as an interim measure until many of the older passenger ships become unprofitable to operate. Of greater importance in future years will be provisions of the second amendment. This amendment will eliminate the three construction methods recognized by SOLAS '60 and will replace them with a single system of construction with several design alternatives. The new method will permit only minimal quantities of combustible material to be used in construction of future passenger ships. Additionally, depending upon the design alternative chosen, an automatic sprinkler system or an automatic fire detection system will be fitted throughout the ship. Bulkheads and decks between various compartments will be required to have a specified fire resistance, determined by the nature of the adjoining spaces and whether or not an automatic sprinkler system is installed. The intended performance of this new construction method is perhaps best summarized by one of the basic principles underlying the system: containment and extinction of any fire in the space of origin.

International requirements for the construction of cargo and tank vessels are far less detailed than those for passenger ships. However, improved regulations will be forthcoming on these two types of vessels. The end result will be to upgrade the fire protection afforded these two types of vessels. On certain tank vessels, for example, deck foam systems and gas inerting systems will become mandatory.

Also, requirements to limit the combustible construction of these vessels will be put forth.

Current international marine fire protection efforts are being devoted to developing internationally acceptable fire testing methods and fire protection aboard newer types of craft such as hydrofoils and ground effect machines, and mobile offshore vessels.

U.S. Federal Regulations

In the United States, government fire safety requirements for merchant vessels have developed at a somewhat faster pace over a longer period than the international requirements. For U.S. flag ships, SOLAS '60 requirements are embodied in the Code of Federal Regulations (CFR), Chapter I, Title 46. These regulations are developed in cooperation with representatives of the marine industry, and are administered by the U.S. Coast Guard. In addition to implementing requirements of the International Convention, the Code of Federal Regulations contains additional fire safety measures necessary to assure an acceptable level of safety aboard United States flag vessels. These regulations, together with NFPA and other standards and a concern for fire safety by the U.S. maritime industry, ensure that United States flag vessels are among the safest in the world.

Since 1936, U.S. flag passenger ships have been constructed in accordance with general provisions of Method I of the International Convention, but under regulations which are much more detailed. The U.S. regulations are based upon the three principles underlying the present International Convention plus a very important fourth principle: minimum use of combustible materials in construction of the vessel. These construction provisions have proven extremely successful. No life has been lost due to fire aboard a U.S. flag passenger ship constructed in accordance with the requirements developed in 1936, a remarkable record. United States government regulations approximate very closely those recently agreed upon by the international community. Requirements for other types and sizes of vessels are based on the same principles, but are less detailed than those for large passenger ships. Regulations for the various types and sizes of ships are contained in the following publications:

1. Rules and Regulations for Passenger Vessels (CG-256).
2. Rules and Regulations for Cargo and Miscellaneous Vessels (CG-257).
3. Rules and Regulations for Tank Vessels (CG-123).
4. Rules and Regulations for Oceanographic Vessels (Subchapter U).
5. Rules and Regulations for Small Passenger Vessels (CG-323).
6. Rules and Regulations for Uninspected Vessels (CG-258).
7. Rules and Regulations for Nautical School Ships (CG-269).

Additional requirements for systems and equipment installed aboard U.S. flag merchant vessels are contained in the following publications:

1. Electrical Engineering Regulations (CG-259)
2. Marine Engineering Regulations and Material Specifications (CG-115)
3. Equipment Lists (Items Approved or Accepted Under Marine Inspection and Navigation Laws) (CG-190)
4. Rules and Regulations for Military Explosives and Hazardous Munitions (CG-108)
5. Regulations Covering "Explosives or Other Hazardous Articles on Board Vessels" (Title 46, Chapter I, Parts 146-147)

Besides containing detailed constructional fire protection provisions for various types of vessels, the preceding regulations specify types of fire extinguishing equipment required. Unlike the construction provisions which vary for different types, sizes, and operation of vessels, fire extinguishing system requirements are largely independent of these factors. Fire extinguishing systems required aboard large passenger ships are generally required on other types of vessels.

The Captain of the Port

The Port Safety/Security Program, a U.S. Coast Guard activity carried out under the authority of the Ports and Waterways Safety Act of 1972 (P.L. 92–340) and E. O. 10173 (as amended), is designed to safeguard and prevent damage to, or the destruction or loss of any vessel, bridge, harbor, port, waterfront facility, or other structure on or in the navigable waters of the United States. Destruction or damage may be due to a variety of causes including sabotage, subversive acts, fire, accidents, and environmental harm resulting from vessel or structure damage.

The Captain of the Port (a U.S. Coast Guard officer) may supervise and control the transportation, handling, loading, discharging, stowage of explosives, flammable or combustible liquids in bulk, or other dangerous articles or cargo covered by Part 146, "Explosives or Other Dangerous Articles on Board Vessels," of Title 46, CFR, and the regulations governing tank vessels (Parts 30 to 40 inclusive, of Title 46, CFR). The Captain of the Port may prescribe such conditions and restrictions relating to the safety of waterfront facilities and vessels in port as he finds necessary under existing circumstances. Such conditions and restrictions may extend to fire prevention and protection measures for such vessels and waterfront facilities.

U.S. Coast Guard fire fighting equipment is furnished primarily for the protection of U.S. Coast Guard property. However, whenever requested by local authorities, or whenever U.S. Coast Guard forces are in a position to respond before local fire fighting forces, U.S. Coast Guard equipment and personnel, as may be available, may be used to assist in fighting marine and waterfront fires; however, they are not to assume control of the overall fire fighting efforts when appropriate local authorities are present.

All Captains of the Port are encouraged to work closely with municipal fire departments, facility operators, mutual aid, and other interested organizations to exchange information, develop lines of communication, cooperative efforts, and, if desirable, to negotiate formal reciprocal fire protection agreement that would be beneficial to both the U.S. Coast Guard and the community.

I. Ship Construction

Basically a ship may be considered as a huge box girder consisting of the hull plating and the main deck. These parts are, in turn, strengthened by such members as the keel, frames, beams, keelsons, stringers, girders, pillars, lower decks, and transverse bulkheads. To appreciate a ship in its entirety, it is well to understand the functions of each of its parts.

The keel is primarily the backbone of the ship. It consists of a rigid fabrication of plates and structural shapes which run fore and aft along the center line of the ship. The stem is connected to the forward end, and at the after end is the stern frame which supports both the rudder and the propeller.

The frames are the ribs of the ship. Their lower ends are attached at intervals along the keel, and their upper ends are attached through brackets to the beams which support the deck. Internal bracing is provided by keelsons and stringers running fore and aft. The frames determine the form of the ship, and support and stiffen the shell plating.

The shell plating, although essentially necessary for watertightness, is one of the principal strength members of the ship. Running continuously from the stem to the stern frame, and from the keel to the weather deck, the shell plating forms three of the sides of the box girder. The plating, aided by the frames, must be able to withstand the pressure of water, stress from the buffeting of waves, and rubbing and bumping against docks.

The main deck of the ship forms the fourth side of the girder, and for this reason must be of strong construction. The plating is connected to beams which extend from side to side across the ship. The deck is strengthened by the doubling of plates in regions weakened by openings such as hatchways and companionways, and also under all deck machinery, chocks, and bits. The deck is supported from below by girders and pillars, as required.

The bottom, sides, and main deck of the ship, however, would not be strong enough to stand the stresses of an ocean voyage without some internal stiffening. This is provided by the lower decks and the main transverse bulkheads.

In addition to furnishing support for the shell and decks, the main transverse bulkheads are made watertight, thus subdividing the vessel into watertight compartments, so that in the event of damage water can be confined. All doors through these bulkheads must be fitted with gaskets so that they can be made watertight; also, they must be kept clear at all times so that they can be closed instantly.

The first bulkhead aft of the stem is known as the collision bulkhead, as its purpose is to limit the flooding that might occur after a collision. No doors or other openings are permitted in this bulkhead below the main deck.

Further protection against damage is provided by the double bottom tanks. These are formed by a second complete layer of watertight plating located a few feet above the outer bottom and extending from bilge to bilge. Any grounding or similar damage which merely pierces the bottom plating will flood one or more of these tanks, instead of allowing water to enter one of the main holds. Under ordinary service conditions, these tanks are used to carry fresh water, fuel oil, or salt water ballast.

The engine and boiler rooms are usually located amidships. In these, special foundations are necessary for the support of heavy engines and boilers. In order to provide sufficient headroom for the propelling machinery, it is usually necessary to omit one or more of the decks in this region. To maintain the vessel's strength in the absence of these decks, several extra heavy web frames and transverse hold beams are fitted.

The propeller shaft extends through the after holds from the engine to the stern gland. As this must be accessible at all times for inspection and lubrication, it is enclosed in a narrow tunnel known as the shaft alley. The entrance to the shaft alley from the engine room is closed by a watertight door, and the sides are of watertight construction so that a fracture of the tail shaft or similar accident will cause only the tunnel to be flooded.

The necessity for good drainage requires special attention in the design and construction of a ship. Free water on the decks, in a hold, or in the bilges is detrimental to the stability of the vessel. Therefore, the drainage system must be as efficient as is possible.

The decks are cambered to permit drainage to the scuppers which lead the water either overboard or to the bilges. Sufficient scuppers and suctions must be provided so that the drainage will be effective in any condition of list or trim of the ship. Solid bulwarks, where fitted around a deck, are pierced by large freeing ports to allow any water that is shipped to quickly escape. (For typical space allocations of cargo-passenger vessels, see Fig. 17-5B).

Tank Vessels

Tankers differ from most other vessels in both arrangement and construction. The engine space is almost invariably located in the after end of the vessel, separated by a cofferdam (two watertight transverse bulkheads enclosing a narrow space which can be filled with water to form an effective fire break) from the cargo-carrying portion of the vessel.

The medium-size modern tank vessels are subdivided from bow to stern into some nine or ten compartments which are identified as cargo tank No. 1, No. 2, etc. Each compartment is further subdivided by two longitudinal bulkheads which create two wing tanks and one center tank. These cargo-carrying compartments extend uninterrupted over the entire length of the vessel's middle body, with the possible exception of an amidships pump room. In construction, tankers also differ from dry cargo and passenger vessels in that they have fewer, but heavier transverse frames, reenforced by many light longitudinal frames running along both the skin of the vessel and the longitudinal bulkheads.

Ventilation

The type of ventilation used in a vessel depends upon the nature of the space and the service of the ship. It can be natural, mechanical, or a combination of the two, and may be extended to air heating, cooling, cleaning, humidifying, and dehumidifying. Air movement in natural ventilation systems is created by the difference in density of inside and outside air and depends on the relative air temperatures. Ventilators that are dependent upon wind direction and velocity for induction of air currents are used with these systems. Natural ventilation is generally limited to a few ships, lockers, and storerooms, depending upon their location, and some dry cargo holds, although it is sometimes used for engine and boiler rooms. In dry cargo holds it is generally accomplished with vents in the forward end for exhaust, and cowls at the after end for supply. Large ducts are required because of the low velocity necessary for air flow. In a mechanical system air is moved by various types of fans driven by electric motors, providing positive circulation of air at desired temperature and volume, functioning regardless of outside atmospheric conditions, and easily controlled to meet possible variations in requirements.

Stability

The stability of a ship, or the property of a floating body to remain at rest in a stable position is controlled by the interaction of two opposing forces. The center of gravity (point G in Figures 17-5C, 17-5D, and 17-5E) is a point at which the weight of the ship, and any other weight aboard, is concentrated. It remains in a constant position until the weight distribution aboard the vessel is changed, and acts with a downward force. The center of buoyancy may be defined as the center of gravity of the body of water displaced by a floating vessel. It is the center of the immersed part of the ship and acts with an upward force, perpendicular to the surface of the water.

When a ship is in a state of vertical equilibrium, as shown in Figure 17-5B, the downward force of gravity (G) and the upward force of buoyancy (B), lie in the same vertical line.

When the ship is inclined by some external force the center of gravity (G) remains in its original position. The center of buoyancy (B), since it is the center of the immersed part of the ship, shifts toward the lower side as shown in Figure 17-5C. In that situation, the central force of (G) downward, combined with the outer force of (B) upward from the low side, act together to return the vessel to an upright position.

The addition of water into the upper portion of the hull, as shown in Figure 17-5D, produces an entirely different situation. The addition of weight at a high point within the hull raises the center of gravity. The fact that water runs to, and stays at the lowest point, inclines the vessel and holds it in an inclined position. The center of buoyancy, of course, shifts to the lower side as it did before. If the addition of weight (water) is stopped while the downward

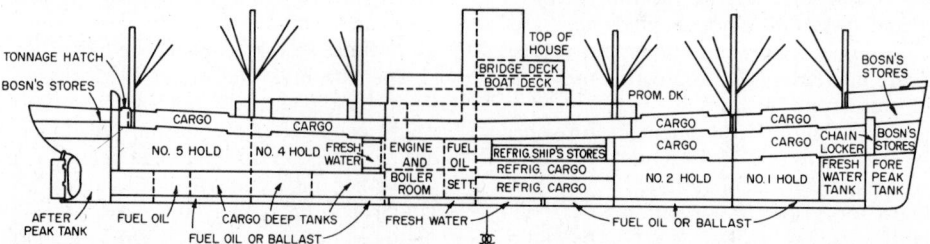

Fig. 17-5B. *A cargo passenger vessel showing location of the principal cargo and tank spaces.*

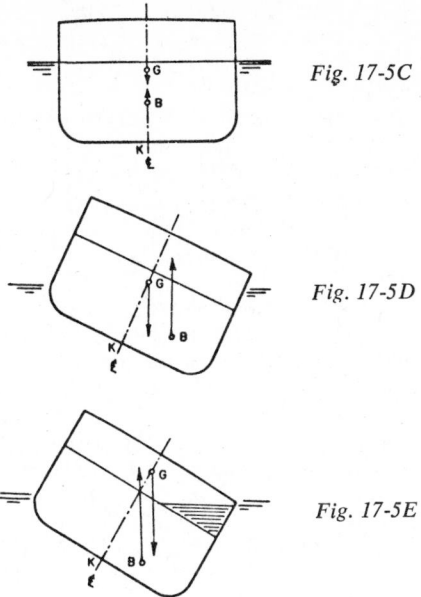

Fig. 17-5C

Fig. 17-5D

Fig. 17-5E

force of (G) is inboard (toward the center line) of the upward force of (B), the vessel will settle in a new stabilized position, inclined toward the side of the additional weight. If sufficient water is added to bring the downward force of (G) outside the upward force of (B), as shown in Figure D, the vessel will continue to roll over and capsize.

J. Shipboard Fire Extinguishing Equipment

Since every ship is different, it follows that fire protection systems will rarely be identical. Under U.S. Coast Guard Regulations governing U.S. merchant vessels, several alternative fire protection systems may be either permitted or required, depending upon their designed purpose. Foreign flag vessels are likely to have different systems or arrangements. Similar systems manufactured and installed by competing companies can vary widely. Most fire extinguishing and fire detection equipment for use aboard vessels is approved by the U.S. Coast Guard (see U.S. Coast Guard Equipment List [CG-190]). Most structural fire protection materials used on vessels are approved in a similar manner. Other fire extinguishing equipment, such as portable fire extinguishers, are listed and labeled by testing laboratories for marine use.

Firemain System

The firemain system is the backbone of all fire fighting systems aboard ships, and the quantity of water available for fire fighting is limited only by the capacity of the fire pumps supplying the system. Most vessels are required to have two fire pumps with all suction inlets, sources of power, etc., located in separate spaces so that one fire incident will not put both pumps out of operation. An alternate is installing both pumps in the same space and protecting the space with a carbon dioxide extinguishing system. This latter method is permitted only in unusual circumstances where separation of pumps will not increase safety—a course usually acceptable for small vessels only.

The size of the required pumps depends upon the vessel's size and service. It also depends upon the arrangements of the particular fire pumps and piping aboard the vessel.

Hydrants on the firemain system are located so that two effective hose streams may be directed into all portions of

the vessel accessible to passengers and crew as the vessel is being navigated. One of the streams must be from a single length of hose, so it is essential that the hose is long enough to direct water into all portions of the space and not just long enough to get the nozzle to the door.

International Shore Connection

One particular item of equipment required by SOLAS '60 deserves special mention. That is the international shore connection. Vessels are required to be fitted with a special bolted plate capable of being attached to the firemain. The purpose of this fitting is to eliminate the problem of hose threads aboard vessels not matching those of the port facilities. Provision of such connections is not mandatory for shore installations, but would prove invaluable to organizations having marine fire fighting responsibilities.

Carbon Dioxide Systems Aboard Vessels

Carbon dioxide as an extinguishing agent (see Sec. 13, Chap. 3) aboard ship has many desirable properties. It will not of itself damage cargo or machinery, and it leaves no residue to be cleaned up after a fire. Even if a ship is without power, a carbon dioxide system, because it is a pressurized system, can deliver the agent to all parts of a space. Basically, there are two different carbon dioxide systems for protecting compartments in a ship. They may be classified as "cargo" systems and "total flooding" systems.

Cargo Systems: Fires in Class A combustibles carried in cargo holds generally start with some smoldering and production of large quantities of smoke. Only when sufficient heat is developed to reach the temperature at which solid combustibles give off sufficient gases to support continued rapid combustion will rapid burning occur. Until that time, the rate of combustion is relatively slow. Time to flashover in a ship's hold after a smoldering fire is discovered would perhaps be at least 20 min, depending upon oxygen available and other circumstances. This would allow time to prepare fire fighting operations and techniques. Carefully sealing the hold prior to release of the carbon dioxide is extremely important.

Cargo Tank Systems: Cargo tanks aboard cargo and passenger vessels may be protected by a carbon dioxide system that is a modification of the cargo system, although they are not specifically required. A tank system is most commonly found aboard tank vessels in lieu of a steam smothering system or a deck foam system. This system calls for discharge of a specified amount of carbon dioxide within 5 min. The quantity of carbon dioxide required to protect a given space is based upon a volume factor of 30 (one pound of carbon dioxide for each 30 cu ft of space). Operating instructions should state the minimum number of carbon dioxide bottles to be released as related to the amount of cargo in the tank.

Total Flooding Systems: Fires in machinery and similar spaces are generally Class B (flammable liquids). In this type of fire the heat buildup is rapid. The safety of a ship depends to a great extent upon the equipment in the machinery space; thus, it is important to introduce the extinguishing gas quickly. Quick release also prevents heat from possibly causing failure of bulkheads, making it impossible to maintain a sufficient concentration of carbon dioxide, and prevents structural members from reaching high temperatures. It also prevents heat updraft from the fire from carrying away the carbon dioxide, as well as limiting damage to equipment. Discharge of 85 percent of the required quantity of carbon dioxide in these systems should be completed within two minutes; slow release might result in no extinguishment. Two separate and deliberate operations are required to avoid unintentional release of the gas. One control releases at least the required amount of carbon dioxide; another control is required to operate the stop valve or direction valve.

Mechanical Foam Systems Aboard Ship

Mechanical foam is produced by introducing foam concentrate in proper proportions into a flowing stream of water and aspirating with air (see Sec. 16, Chap. 2). Aboard ship the foam concentrate is normally introduced by means of proportioning equipment near the foam concentrate storage container at some central location on the vessel. The foam solution thus formed is pumped through fixed piping to foam nozzles, monitors, etc., in the area to be protected. Air is mixed with the foam solution at the discharge nozzle, and foam is produced.

Deck Systems: Deck foam systems are frequently installed aboard tank vessels in lieu of fixed-pipe, inert gas smothering systems for cargo tanks. An advantage of a deck foam system over a fixed-pipe inert gas system is that in the latter system an accidental rupture of a key gas line would make it impossible to maintain an effective inert gas concentration.

The deck foam system is intended to protect any deck area using a predetermined rate of flow from foam stations (monitors or hose stations) aft of the area to be protected. Piping and foam stations are so arranged that ruptured sections of piping in the way of a fire may be isolated. With this arrangement, wherever fire occurs it will be possible to effectively fight the fire by working forward from the after house assuming machinery, foam pumping, and proportioning equipment are aft.

The concentrate normally supplied for mechanical foam is suitable for use on most, but not all, flammable liquids carried aboard tankers. For example, it is impossible for foam made from ordinary concentrate to form a blanket on alcohols, esters, ketones, or ethers (commonly called water-soluble or polar liquids). An alcohol-type foam concentrate is available for shipboard fires involving water-soluble flammable liquids. An alternate method of combating alcohol-type fires is the use of water spray to dilute the flammable liquid and cool the surrounding areas.

Water Spray Systems

Although water spray systems may be designed to perform any of a number of functions, e.g., extinguishment of fire, control of fire, or exposure protection, the objective of shipboard installations is complete extinguishment of a fire. In special purpose spray systems, as may be installed aboard LPG carriers, the function may be to reduce the quantity of heat absorbed by the tank or surrounding structure.

Sprinkler Systems

Aboard U.S. vessels, manually operated sprinkler systems are employed in only very limited locations. In Method I (SOLAS) ship construction, primary dependence is placed upon structural fire protection rather than automatic sprinkler protection. This is in contrast to the British method (Method II) in which combustible construction is permitted in combination with a complete sprinkler system. (Method II employs automatic sprinkler systems in lieu of manual sprinkler systems.)

For installations on vehicular decks, such as aboard ferry vessels, the sprinkler system should be designed to protect the structural integrity of the vessel, confine the fire to the location of origin, and wash flammable liquid spills to safe location. Installation on vehicular decks is the primary marine use of sprinkler systems in the United States.

Bromotrifluoromethane System

Bromotrifluoromethane (Halon 1301) is one of the many halogenated "vaporizing liquid" and "liquefied gas" extinguishing agents introduced in recent years (see Sec. 13, Chap. 4). In general, the halogenated agents have a high extinguishing efficiency per unit weight. This makes them particularly suitable for installations which are weight critical, e.g., hydrofoils.

At present the only halogenated agent which has been found satisfactory for marine use is bromotrifluoromethane (Halon 1301). This agent is permitted to be used only in fixed systems installed in unmanned spaces. The size of spaces which may be protected is limited, as well as the maximum size of a single system. To date, hydrofoils are the only craft for which Halon 1301 has been specifically approved by the U.S. Coast Guard.

The U.S. Coast Guard has expanded its efforts in this area. U.S. Coast Guard requirements are divided into two areas: (1) machinery space protection of U.S. flag vessels, and (2) fixed systems for recreational pleasure craft.

In the first case, the Halon 1301 system has been conceptually approved. Approval is on a ship-by-ship basis, with review at U.S. Coast Guard Headquarters level.

In the second case, the U.S. Coast Guard is in the process of developing a standard for systems aboard pleasure craft. A test program has been jointly developed with Underwriters Laboratories.

Fire Fighting Plan

All United States vessels of 1,000 gross tons and over, and United States vessels of any tonnage on an international voyage, permanently display a fire fighting plan of the ship. Although the primary purpose of the plan is to serve as a guide to shipboard personnel, it contains the following information that can greatly assist port fire fighting groups:

1. Fire control stations for each deck.
2. Sections enclosed by fire-resistive bulkheads.
3. Sections enclosed by fire-retardant bulkheads.
4. Fire alarms, detecting systems, sprinkler systems.
5. Fire extinguishing appliances.
6. Access to different compartments, decks, etc.
7. Ventilating systems, including master fan controls, positions of dampers, location of remote controls, and the identification numbers of the ventilating fans serving each section.

In some instances, instead of being posted on a plan, the preceding information may be set forth in a fire fighting booklet. In that case, the booklet is required to be aboard at all times.

Whether posted as a fire fighting plan or presented as a separate booklet, information is also available on all watertight compartments, openings therein, means of closure, and controls. Additionally such information includes the arrangements for correcting any list due to flooding. (For illustration of a fire fighting plan for the aft end of a super tanker, see Fig. 17-5F.)

K.　Barges

Virtually any commodity can be shipped by water. The Inland Waterways Industry has implemented this theory by developing a variety of types and sizes of barges for the efficient handling of products ranging from coal in open hopper barges to chemicals and "thermos bottle" barges,

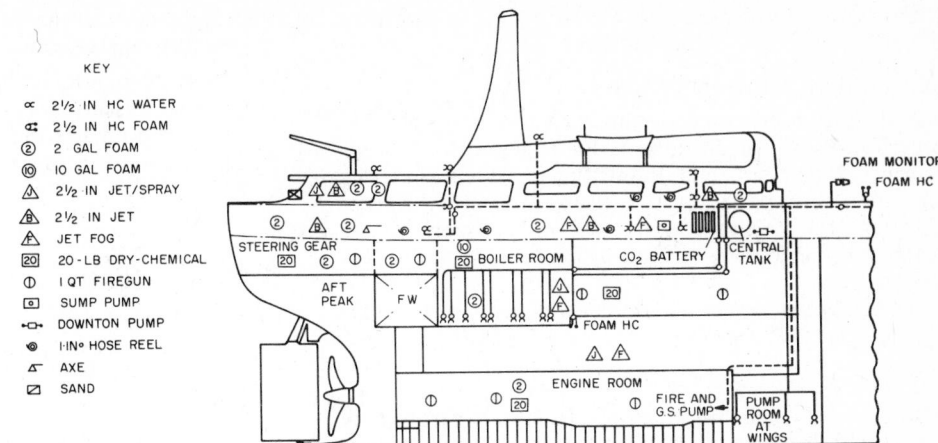

Fig. 17-5F. Fire fighting plan for the aft end of a super tanker.

and from dredged rock in dump scows to railroad cars on car floats. Barging is the only practical mode of marine transportation for long distance moving of outside machinery, tanks, kilns, and some of the space vehicles.

Three popular sizes of barges (with maximum capacities noted) are:

1. One thousand ton capacity (302,000 gal); length, 175 ft; breadth, 26 ft; draft, 9 ft.

2. Fifteen hundred ton capacity (454,000 gal); length, 195 ft; breadth, 35 ft; draft, 9 ft.

3. Three thousand ton capacity (907,200 gal); length, 290 ft; breadth, 50 ft; draft, 9 ft.

The most versatile, least costly, and most numerous type of barge in the U.S. inland fleet is the hopper barge. With minor modifications, it can be adapted to the transportation of literally any solid commodity in bulk or package. It is basically a single-skinned, open-top box, the inner shell forming a long hopper or cargo hole. The bottom, sides, and ends of the hole are free of appendages. They are generally of welded plate construction, usually with a double bottom for greater safety. They are braced to resist the heaviest of external blows, as well as to absorb the impact of loading and unloading buckets.

The covered dry cargo barge is used for bulk-loading commodities that need protection from the elements. Generally, the only difference between these vessels and the open hopper barge is that covered dry cargo barges are equipped with watertight covers over the entire cargo hold.

Three basic types of tank barges are used for the transportation of liquid commodities: (1) single-skinned tank barges, (2) double-skinned tank barges, and (3) cylindrical tank barges.

Single-skinned tank barges have bow and stern compartments separated from the midship by transverse collision bulkheads. The entire midship shell of the vessel constitutes the cargo tank. Hydrodynamic considerations require that this huge tank be divided by bulkheads. The usual compartmentation consists of a center line bulkhead with three transverse bulkheads forming four separate cargo compartments on either side. The entire framing structure is inside the cargo tanks.

Double-skinned tank barges have, as the term implies, an inner and outer shell. The inner shell forms cargo tanks that are free of appendages and are, therefore, easier to clean and to line. Poisons and other hazardous liquids require the protection of the void compartments between the outer and inner shell.

Barges having independent cylindrical tanks are used to transport liquids under pressure or in cases where pressure

is being used to discharge the cargo. Because of the high efficiency of linings and insulation, or both, which can be incorporated, cylindrical tank barges can be used to carry cargoes at or near atmospheric pressures. Cylindrical cargo tanks are generally mounted in the barge hopper and are thus free to expand or contract independent of the whole structure. For this reason, they are preferred for high temperature cargoes such as liquid sulphur at 280°F, or refrigerated cargoes such as anhydrous ammonia at −28°F.

All barges carrying hazardous materials are required to have a 2×3 ft warning sign facing outboard without obstruction, on which is printed "WARNING—DANGEROUS CARGO. NO VISITORS, NO SMOKING, NO OPEN LIGHTS." The sign also has to specify the names and locations of all cargoes aboard the vessel.

In addition to the warning sign, barges carrying hazardous materials must have an information placard giving information details about each of the hazardous cargoes aboard. These placards are required to be carried in some type of waterproof container as near to the warning sign as practicable.

Information placards for all hazardous materials in the entire tow are required to be maintained in the towboat wheelhouse where they are readily accessible to the oprator. In case of any problem, the towboat operator on watch should be able to furnish specific details over the radio on any hazardous cargo in his tow.

L. NFPA Marine Standards

NFPA recommendations relating to marine vessels are contained in the following:

1. NFPA No. 306, Control of Gas Hazards on Vessels to be Repaired. This Standard describes the conditions necessary for safety before making repairs on any vessel carrying or having carried as a fuel or as cargo combustible or flammable liquids, flammable compressed gases, and chemicals in bulk. It also applies to vessels being scrapped.

2. NFPA No. 311, Fire Signal for Vessels in Harbor. This Recommendation specifies that, in event of fire occurring on any vessel in harbor and not under way, the vessel will sound five prolonged blasts of its whistle or siren to indicate fire aboard or at dock to which vessel is moored.

3. NFPA No. 312, Fire Protection of Vessels During Construction, Repair, and Lay-Up. These recommendations cover reasonable measures for preventing and controlling fires on vessels while in the building yard, repair yard, or while laid up. Each of the foregoing circumstances is covered in a separate part.

M. Other Organizations Contributing to Marine Fire Safety

The American Petroleum Institute

In the area of marine fire fighting and fire protection, the American Petroleum Institute (API) is active in the development of domestic and international standards, codes, regulations, etc., pertaining to the subject. Under the policy direction of the Central Committee on Transportation by Water, most actions are directed by the Committee on Tank Vessels.

Ad hoc groups are sometimes utilized for special studies of a nonrepetitive nature.

The Marine Chemists' Association

This professional association of chemists is certified for marine work by the National Fire Protection Association in accordance with provisions of NFPA No. 306, Standard for the Control of Gas Hazards on Vessels to be Repaired. The association had its origin in May 1938 as the Marine Chemists' Subsection of the NFPA Marine Section. With the discontinuance of the Marine Section, the Marine Chemists organized their present association in 1948.

The National Cargo Bureau, Inc.

The National Cargo Bureau, Inc., is a nationwide nonprofit membership organization established in 1952 for the purpose of providing a private, nongovernmental agency to formulate recommendations to various governments as to regulations on the safe stowage of dangerous goods and other cargoes, and to supply recommendations on the cargo handling gear used with them.

The National Academy of Sciences-USCG Advisory Committee on Hazardous Materials

This is a committee of the National Academy of Sciences —National Research Council charged with advising the U.S. Coast Guard on scientific and technical questions relating to safe maritime transportation of hazardous materials.

SI Units

The following conversion factors are given as a convenience in converting to SI units the English units used in this chapter.

$$1 \text{ in.} = 25.400 \text{ mm}$$
$$1 \text{ ft} = 0.305 \text{ m}$$
$$\tfrac{5}{9}(°F - 32) = °C$$
$$1 \text{ gal} = 3.785 \text{ litres}$$

Bibliography

NFPA Codes, Standards, and Recommended Practices (see the latest *NFPA Publications and Visual Aids Catalog* for availability of current editions of the following documents)

NFPA No. 302, Fire Protection Standard for Motor Craft.

NFPA No. 303, Fire Protection Standard for Marinas and Boatyards.

NFPA No. 306, Standard for the Control of Gas Hazards on Vessels to be Repaired.

NFPA No. 307, Standard for the Operation of Marine Terminals.

NFPA No. 312, Standard for the Fire Protection of Vessels During Construction, Repair, and Lay-Up.

Additional Readings

Fire Protection Guide on Hazardous Materials, 5th ed., National Fire Protection Association, Boston, 1973.

SECTION 18

MISCELLANEOUS DATA

Chapter 1

INSPECTION, SURVEYING, AND MAPPING

The reasons for inspecting a property are: (1) to provide a basis for evaluating the danger to life from fire, and (2) to provide a basis for evaluating and determining ways for minimizing fire danger to buildings or contents. Inspections are made by fire protection engineers, building and fire officials, insurance representatives, and other similarly qualified or interested parties.

In order to properly evaluate the protection for a property or specific hazard, a tour or inspection of the premises must be made. Three essential results of the inspection should be:

1. A permanent, precise, and complete narrative report describing the fire protection features and fire hazards of the property.

2. A plan indicating the physical characteristics and layout of the premises.

3. Recommendations for improvement (if necessary).

A. Inspection

The functions performed during an inspection, and the compilation of the narrative report resulting from the inspection are discussed in detail in the *NFPA Inspection Manual*.[1] The following list is an outline of the key items that should appear in the written report:

1. Property identification, date of report, inspector's name, and building identification.
  (a) Name of company and address.
  (b) Date of report.
  (c) Name of inspector.
  (d) Building.
2. Occupancy.
  (a) Names of tenants in a building of multiple occupancy, but not necessarily including, for example, every tenant in an apartment house or office building.
  (b) Class of occupancy; e.g., garage, school, warehouse, or other. If mixed occupancy, state each principal occupancy and its location. In the case of industrial plants, the finished product; in warehouses, the products stored; etc.
  (c) Factors making fire spread possible inside buildings; i.e., lack of horizontal cutoffs, unprotected stairways, elevator shafts, and other vertical openings.
  (d) Analysis of fire hazards.
3. Construction.
  (a) Types of construction.
    (1) Table of buildings and/or construction reported by percentage.
  (b) Exposure.
    (1) Exterior.
    (2) Interior.
  (c) Fire areas, walls, and partitions.
  (d) Protection of openings.
    (1) Horizontal.
    (2) Vertical.
4. Life safety.
  (a) Exit facilities.
    (1) Adequacy.

    (2) Deficiencies.
  (b) Exit illumination and emergency lighting.
  (c) Interior finish.
  (d) Evacuation plan and drills.
5. Common hazards.
  (a) Heat, light, power, air conditioning.
  (b) Housekeeping, brush and grass.
  (c) Ordinary combustibles.
  (d) Electrical appliances.
  (e) Smoking.
6. Special hazards.
  (a) Finishing processes.
  (b) Flammable liquids.
  (c) Flammable gases.
  (d) Welding and cutting.
  (e) Cooking.
  (f) Chemicals and plastics, etc.
  (g) Electronic equipment.
  (h) Others.
7. Water supply.
  (a) General description including adequacy and reliability.
  (b) Fire flow requirements, availability determined by tests.
  (c) Storage requirements.
  (d) Sources of supply.
  (e) Storage facilities.
  (f) Pumps.
  (g) Distribution system and appurtenances.
  (h) Maintenance, inspections, and tests.
8. Extinguishing systems and devices.
  (a) Automatic sprinkler systems.
    (1) Types.
    (2) Coverage-temperature rate of sprinkler heads, pipe schedules, spacing of heads, and branchlines.
    (3) Adequacy.
    (4) Tests and maintenance.
  (b) Carbon dioxide, foam, dry chemical, and/or Halon systems.
    (1) Types.
    (2) Adequacy.
    (3) Tests and maintenance.
  (c) Portable extinguishers.
    (1) Type and coverage.
    (2) Tests and maintenance.
  (d) Standpipes and fire hose systems.
9. Alarm and detection systems.
  (a) Automatic fire alarm (detection systems).
    (1) Type, coverage, connected to fire alarm.
    (2) Power supply.
    (3) Maintenance and test.
  (b) Local evacuation alarm systems.
    (1) Type, coverage, connected to fire alarm.
    (2) Power supply.
    (3) Maintenance and test.
10. Fire prevention.
  (a) Building inspection program.
    (1) Frequency, scope, recording forms.
  (b) Fire protection system inspection program.

(1) Type, frequency, scope, recording forms.
  (c) Employee fire safety training.
    (1) Adequacy and frequency of training.
    (2) Reference material.
  (d) Fire brigade program.
11. Recommendations.

B. Surveying

When touring a property, there are many different routes to choose from. Therefore, the particular route to choose becomes a matter of personal preference and comfort. The inspector should choose a standard touring procedure with which he is comfortable, and should adopt that pattern for normal use. Ultimately, it is important for the inspector to pass through the building and the plant yard systematically without leaving any space uncovered.

A thorough understanding of the features depicted on a complete plan is absolutely necessary. The features of any property can be placed in one of four categories: Construction -C-; Occupancy -O-; Protection -P-; and Exposure -E- (COPE). These major classifications of important features are comprised of many components as shown in the following list:

1. CONSTRUCTION.
  (a) Buildings(s) identification.
  (b) Dimensions—to allow plan to be drawn moderately to scale.
    (1) Buildings.
    (2) Distances to exposures.
    (3) Width of streets.
  (c) Date of construction.
  (d) Height of building(s); i.e., number of floors, concealed spaces, etc.
  (e) Type of construction material of:
    (1) Walls.
    (2) Floors.
    (3) Roofs.
  (f) Location of fire doors and/or other horizontal protected/unprotected opening(s).
  (g) Location of stairways, elevators, and other vertical protected/unprotected openings.
  (h) Type of windows; i.e., plain glass, wire glass, etc.
  (i) Location and type of suspended ceilings.
  (j) Location of interior fire walls and type of material.
  (k) Location of roof parapets.
  (l) Chimney location, construction, and height.
  (m) Location of fire escape ladder.
2. OCCUPANCY.
  (a) Floor by floor listing or major occupancy process.
  (b) Location, size, content, and construction of tanks and/or cylinders.
  (c) Ratings for buildings, boilers, furnace. Locations of chimneys or smoke stacks.
  (d) Cooling towers, dust collector, silos, cranes, conveyors, or other unique equipment.
  (e) Electrical transformers.
    (1) Capacity.
    (2) Ownership.
    (3) Protection.
    (4) Cutoffs.
3. PROTECTION.
  (a) Automatic sprinklers.
    (1) Wet pipe.

(2) Dry pipe w/wo accelerator or exhauster.
    (3) Deluge-type.
    (4) Diameter.
    (5) Approximate location.
  (b) Control valves for water supplying sprinklers, fire pump.
    (1) Location.
    (2) Size.
    (3) Type of valve.
    (4) Label status of valve only if it is normally "shut."
  (c) Fire pumps — label symbol with following items.
    (1) Capacity rated — GPM, PSI.
    (2) Type-centifugal, vertical turbine rotary, or steam.
    (3) Manufacturer's name.
    (4) Type of motor drive — diesel, electric, gas, gasoline, or steam.
    (5) Suction pressure — head or lift (in feet).
    (6) Starting mechanism — automatic or manual.
  (d) Water tank, gravity tanks, suction tank for fire pumps.
    (1) Capacity — GPM, PSI.
    (2) Height.
    (3) Pipe arrangement to yard main or fire pump.
    (4) Percent of capacity for fire protection use.
  (e) Public water supplies.
    (1) Type of system — gravity, direct pumping.
    (2) Size of all water mains and locations in relation to plant.
    (3) Location, size, and type of control valves.
    (4) Type of water service — high and low pressure or fire service only.
  (f) Yard water mains by symbols only.
    (1) Location.
    (2) Size.
    (3) Connection arrangement to all supply sources available.
    (4) Type of pipe — cement line, cast iron, etc.
  (g) Fire alarm and detection systems.
    (1) Water flow detection on sprinkler risers.
    (2) Location of main control valve/panel (label type of detection units).
    (3) Products of combustion — rate of heat rise, fixed temperature.
    (4) Fire department alarm box.
  (h) Location and type of check valves and water meters.
  (i) Hydrants.
    (1) Public.
    (2) Private.
    (3) Frost proof.
    (4) Fire department pumper connections.
4. EXPOSURE.
  (a) Indicate proximity, construction, and occupancy of buildings or structures facing the four sides of the plant.
  (b) Location of rivers or other natural exposures (i.e., forests, etc.)
  (c) Railroad tracks.
  (d) Yard storage.
By formulating a short checklist similar to the preceding for each COPE feature, the inspector will be assured of having all the necessary information for preparing a good

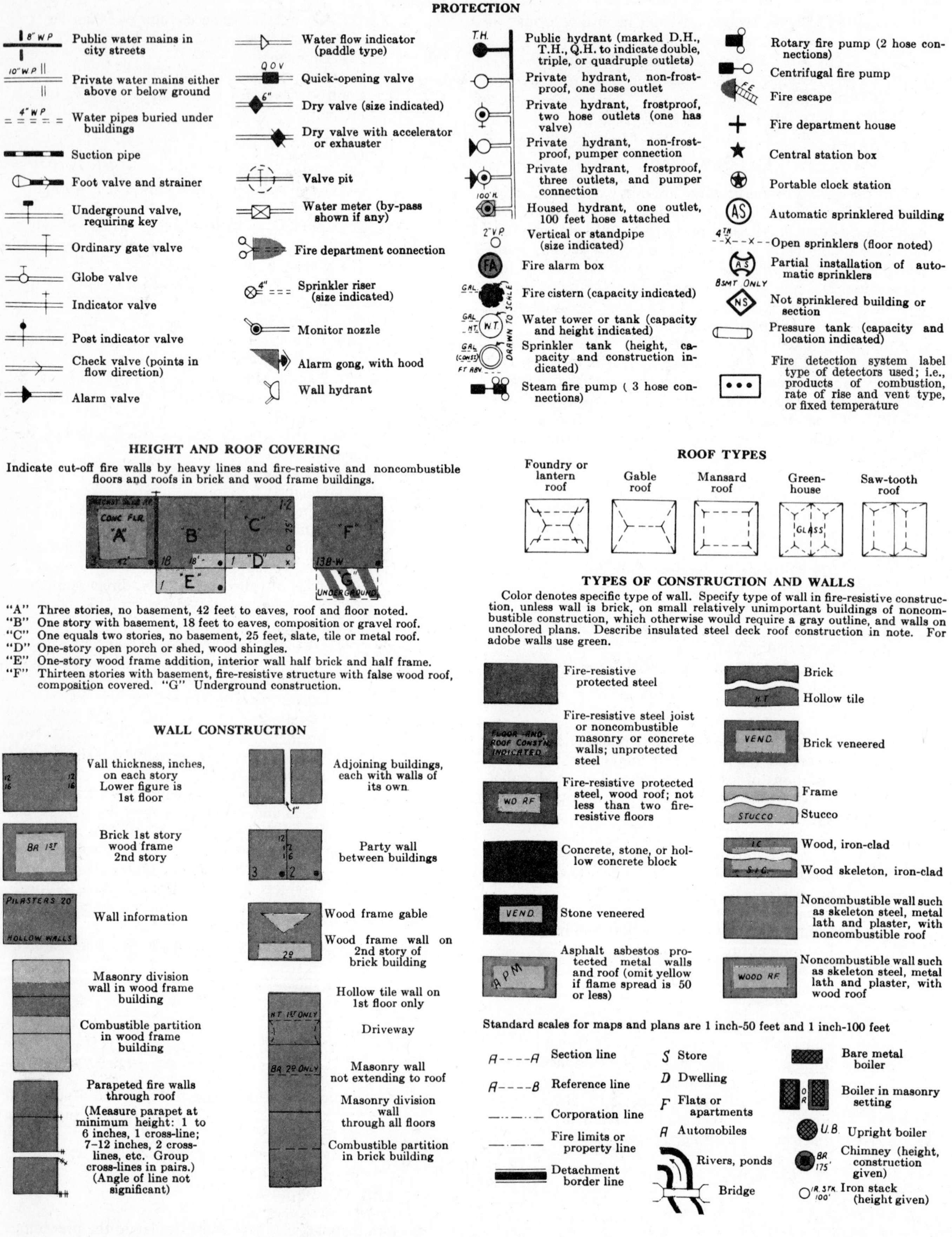

PROTECTION

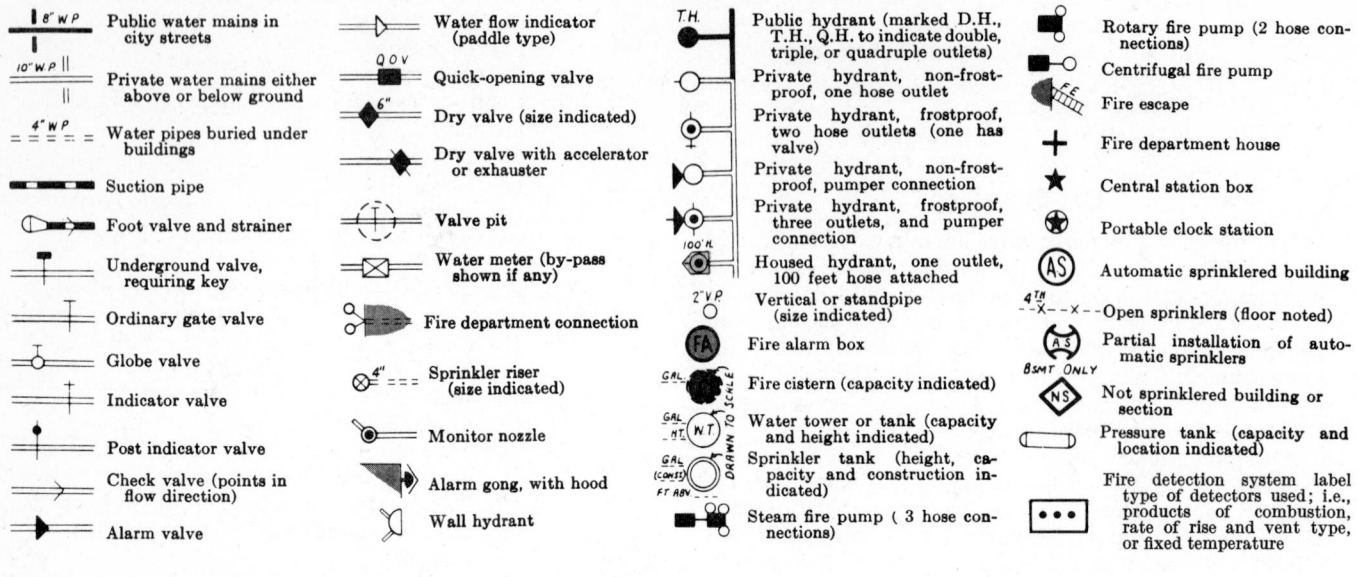

⊩ 8" W.P	Public water mains in city streets
10" W.P ‖	Private water mains either above or below ground
4" W.P	Water pipes buried under buildings
	Suction pipe
	Foot valve and strainer
	Underground valve, requiring key
	Ordinary gate valve
	Globe valve
	Indicator valve
	Post indicator valve
	Check valve (points in flow direction)
	Alarm valve

	Water flow indicator (paddle type)
Q.O.V	Quick-opening valve
6"	Dry valve (size indicated)
	Dry valve with accelerator or exhauster
	Valve pit
	Water meter (by-pass shown if any)
	Fire department connection
4"	Sprinkler riser (size indicated)
	Monitor nozzle
	Alarm gong, with hood
	Wall hydrant

T.H.	Public hydrant (marked D.H., T.H., Q.H. to indicate double, triple, or quadruple outlets)
	Private hydrant, non-frost-proof, one hose outlet
	Private hydrant, frostproof, two hose outlets (one has valve)
	Private hydrant, non-frost-proof, pumper connection
	Private hydrant, frostproof, three outlets, and pumper connection
100'H.	Housed hydrant, one outlet, 100 feet hose attached
2" V.P.	Vertical or standpipe (size indicated)
FA	Fire alarm box
GAL.	Fire cistern (capacity indicated)
GAL. HT. W.T.	Water tower or tank (capacity and height indicated)
GAL. (CONST) FT ABV	Sprinkler tank (height, capacity and construction indicated)
	Steam fire pump (3 hose connections)

	Rotary fire pump (2 hose connections)
F.E.	Centrifugal fire pump
	Fire escape
	Fire department house
★	Central station box
	Portable clock station
AS	Automatic sprinklered building
4TH --X--X--	Open sprinklers (floor noted)
AS BSMT ONLY	Partial installation of automatic sprinklers
NS	Not sprinklered building or section
	Pressure tank (capacity and location indicated)
• • •	Fire detection system label type of detectors used; i.e., products of combustion, rate of rise and vent type, or fixed temperature

HEIGHT AND ROOF COVERING

Indicate cut-off fire walls by heavy lines and fire-resistive and noncombustible floors and roofs in brick and wood frame buildings.

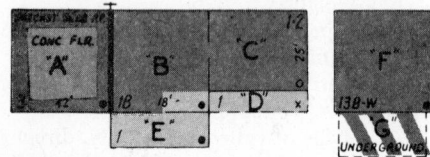

"A" Three stories, no basement, 42 feet to eaves, roof and floor noted.
"B" One story with basement, 18 feet to eaves, composition or gravel roof.
"C" One equals two stories, no basement, 25 feet, slate, tile or metal roof.
"D" One-story open porch or shed, wood shingles.
"E" One-story wood frame addition, interior wall half brick and half frame.
"F" Thirteen stories with basement, fire-resistive structure with false wood roof, composition covered. "G" Underground construction.

WALL CONSTRUCTION

	Wall thickness, inches, on each story Lower figure is 1st floor
BR 1ST	Brick 1st story wood frame 2nd story
PILASTERS 20' HOLLOW WALLS	Wall information
	Masonry division wall in wood frame building
	Combustible partition in wood frame building
	Parapeted fire walls through roof (Measure parapet at minimum height: 1 to 6 inches, 1 cross-line; 7–12 inches, 2 cross-lines, etc. Group cross-lines in pairs.) (Angle of line not significant)

	Adjoining buildings, each with walls of its own
	Party wall between buildings
	Wood frame gable
2°	Wood frame wall on 2nd story of brick building
	Hollow tile wall on 1st floor only
H.T. 1ST ONLY	Driveway
BR 2° ONLY	Masonry wall not extending to roof
	Masonry division wall through all floors
	Combustible partition in brick building

ROOF TYPES

| Foundry or lantern roof | Gable roof | Mansard roof | Green-house | Saw-tooth roof |
| | | | GLASS | |

TYPES OF CONSTRUCTION AND WALLS

Color denotes specific type of wall. Specify type of wall in fire-resistive construction, unless wall is brick, on small relatively unimportant buildings of noncombustible construction, which otherwise would require a gray outline, and walls on uncolored plans. Describe insulated steel deck roof construction in note. For adobe walls use green.

	Fire-resistive protected steel
FLOOR AND ROOF CONSTN. INDICATED	Fire-resistive steel joist or noncombustible masonry or concrete walls; unprotected steel
WD.RF.	Fire-resistive protected steel, wood roof; not less than two fire-resistive floors
	Concrete, stone, or hollow concrete block
VEN.D	Stone veneered
A P M	Asphalt asbestos protected metal walls and roof (omit yellow if flame spread is 50 or less)

	Brick
H.T	Hollow tile
VEN.C	Brick veneered
	Frame
STUCCO	Stucco
I.C.	Wood, iron-clad
S+I.C.	Wood skeleton, iron-clad
	Noncombustible wall such as skeleton steel, metal lath and plaster, with noncombustible roof
WOOD R.F.	Noncombustible wall such as skeleton steel, metal lath and plaster, with wood roof

Standard scales for maps and plans are 1 inch-50 feet and 1 inch-100 feet

A----A	Section line
A----B	Reference line
—·—·—	Corporation line
	Fire limits or property line
	Detachment border line

S	Store
D	Dwelling
F	Flats or apartments
A	Automobiles
	Rivers, ponds
	Bridge

	Bare metal boiler
O B O R	Boiler in masonry setting
U.B.	Upright boiler
BR 175'	Chimney (height, construction given)
IR.STK. 100'	Iron stack (height given)

Fig. 18-1A. Standard plan symbols used to represent the general location and type of COPE (Construction -C-; Occupancy -O-; Protection -P-; and Exposure -E-) features of a facility.

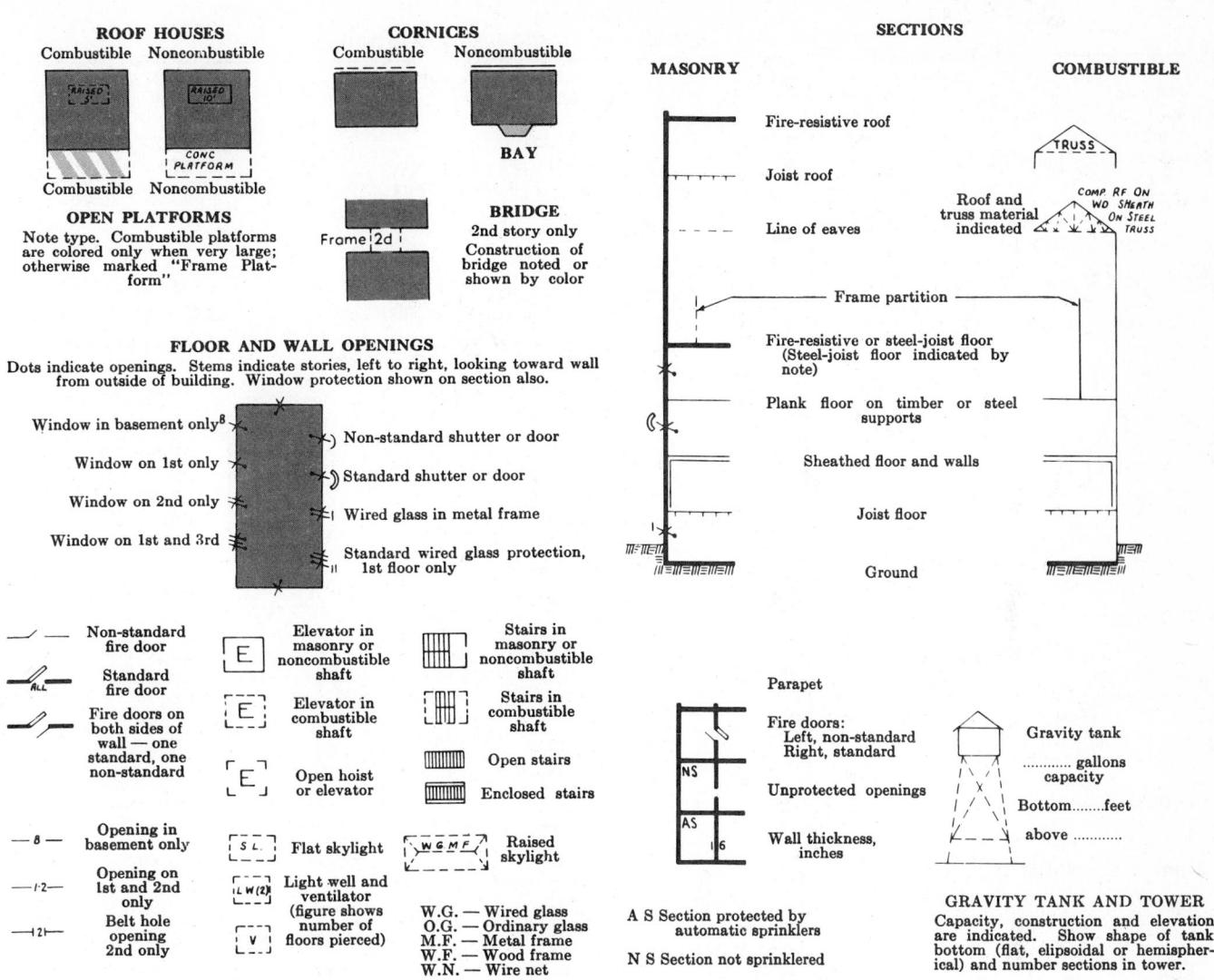

Fig. 18-1A.   (Cont.)

sketch after the tour. Utilizing such checklists to make rough, hand-drawn sketches of *every* individual section, floor, or building will reduce the difficulty of preparing the finished plan.

C.   Symbols

The symbols in Figure 18-1A are used to represent the general location and type of the COPE features of a facility. Occasionally, the use of a symbol will not sufficiently describe the situation alone. In that case, it will be necessary to also label that point on the plan. Table 18-1A gives a list of standard abbreviations that can be used. The list is brief but does provide all of the abbreviations that are commonly needed. "Abbreviations for Use on Drawings and in Text," [2] prepared by the National Standards Institute, provides a list of additional less commonly used abbreviations.

D.   Preparation of Plans

Once the necessary information has been collected, the

drawing of a site plan can be readily accomplished. A good, easy approach is to split the preparation into three parts:

1. Building sketch.
2. Addition of fire protection equipment.
3. Detailing occupancy and specific processes or hazards.

The initial step is to outline the shape of the building utilizing an appropriate architect/engineer scale on an adequately sized sheet of paper. Once the shell is complete, add the other important construction features referenced in the preceding section on surveying and label various construction material.

The inspector should draw enough sectional views of the plant to show all vertical areas of the plant. Figure 18-1B illustrates what a typical, simple, single "building sketch" would look like when completed.

The second step is to plot the "fire protection facilities and equipment" on the finished "building sketch." Figure 18-1C graphically represents this step. Two important points should be noted about Figure 18-1C. First, water supplies (public or private [yard] mains) are continuous from a point of origin to the individual automatic sprinkler risers.

Table 18-1A. Legend of Common Abbreviations*

Above	ABV	Maximum Capacity	MAX CAP
Acetylene	ACET	Mean Sea Leves	MSL
Aluminum	AL	Metal	MT
Asbestos	ASB	Mezzanine	MEZZ
Asphalt Protected Metal	APM	Mill Use	MU
Attic	A		
Automatic Fire Alarm	AFA	Normally Closed	NC
Automatic, Sprinklers	AS	Normally Open	NO
Avenue	AVE	North	N
		Number	No
Basement	B		
Beam	BM	Open Sprinklers	OS
Board on Joist	BDOJ	Outside Screw & Yoke Valve	OS & Y
Brick	BR	Partition (Label Composition)	PTN (ie WD PTN)
		Plaster	PLAS
Cast Iron	CI	Plaster Board	PLAS BD
Cement	CEM	Platform	PLATF
Cinder Block	CB	Pound (Unit of Force)	LB
Concrete	CONC	Pressure	PRESS
Corrugated Iron	COR IR	Unit of Pressure-pounds Per Square Inch	PSI
		Protected Steel	PROT ST
Domestic	DOM	Private	PRIVATE
Double Hydrant	DH	Public	PUB
Dry Pipe Valve	DPV		
		Railroad	RR
East	E	Reinforced Concrete	RC
Elevator	ELEV	Reinforcing Steel	RST
Engine	ENG	Reservoir	RES
		Revolutions per Minute	RPM
Feet	FT	Roof	RF
Fibre Board	FBR BD	Room	RM
Fire Escape	FE		
Fire Department Pumper Connection	FDC	Slate Shingle Roof	SSR
Fire Detection Units	FDPC	Space	SP
Products of Combustion	POC	South	S
Rate of Heat Rise	RHR	Stainless Steel	SST
Fixed Temperature	FTEP	Steel	ST
Floor	FL	Steel Deck	ST DK
Frame	FR	Stone	STONE
Fuel Oil (Label with Grade Number)	FO#_____	Story	STO
		Street	STREET
Gallon	GAL	Stucco	STUC
Gallons Per Day	GPD	Suspended Acoustical Plaster Ceiling	SAPL
Gallons Per Minute	GPM	Suspended Acoustical Tile Ceiling	SATL
Galvanized Iron	GALVI	Suspended Plaster Ceiling	SPC
Galvanized Steel	GALVS	Suspended Sprayed Acoustical Ceiling	SSAL
Gas, Natural	GAS		
Gasoline	GASOLINE	Tank (Label Capacity in Gallons)	TK
Generator	GEN	Tenant	TEN
Glass	GL	Tile Block	TB
Glass Block	GLB	Timber	TMBR
Gypsum	GYM	Tin Clad	TIN CL
Gypsum Board	GYM BD	Triple Hydrant	TH
		Truss	TR
High Voltage	HV		
Hollow Tile	HT	Under	UND
Hose Connection	HC		
Hydrant	HYD	Vault	VLT
		Veneer	VEN
Inch, Inches	IN	Volts (Indicate Number Of)	450v
Iron	IR		
Iron Clad	IR CL	Wall board	WLBD
Iron Pipe	IP	Wall Hydrant	WLH
		Water Pipe	WP
Joist, Joisted	J	West	W
		Wire Glass	WGL
Liquid	LIQ	Wire Net	WN
Liquid Oxygen	LOX	Wood	WD
		Wood Frame	WD FR
Manufacture	MFR	Yard	YD
Manufacturing	MFG		

* Some words that have a common abbreviation, e.g. "ST" for "street," are spelled out fully to avoid confusion with similar abbreviations used herein for other terms.

Conversely, the automatic sprinkler systems within the buildings are not entirely shown (NOTE: sprinkler scheduling and spacing is referred to in the body of the narrative Inspection Report). Secondly, when space limitations

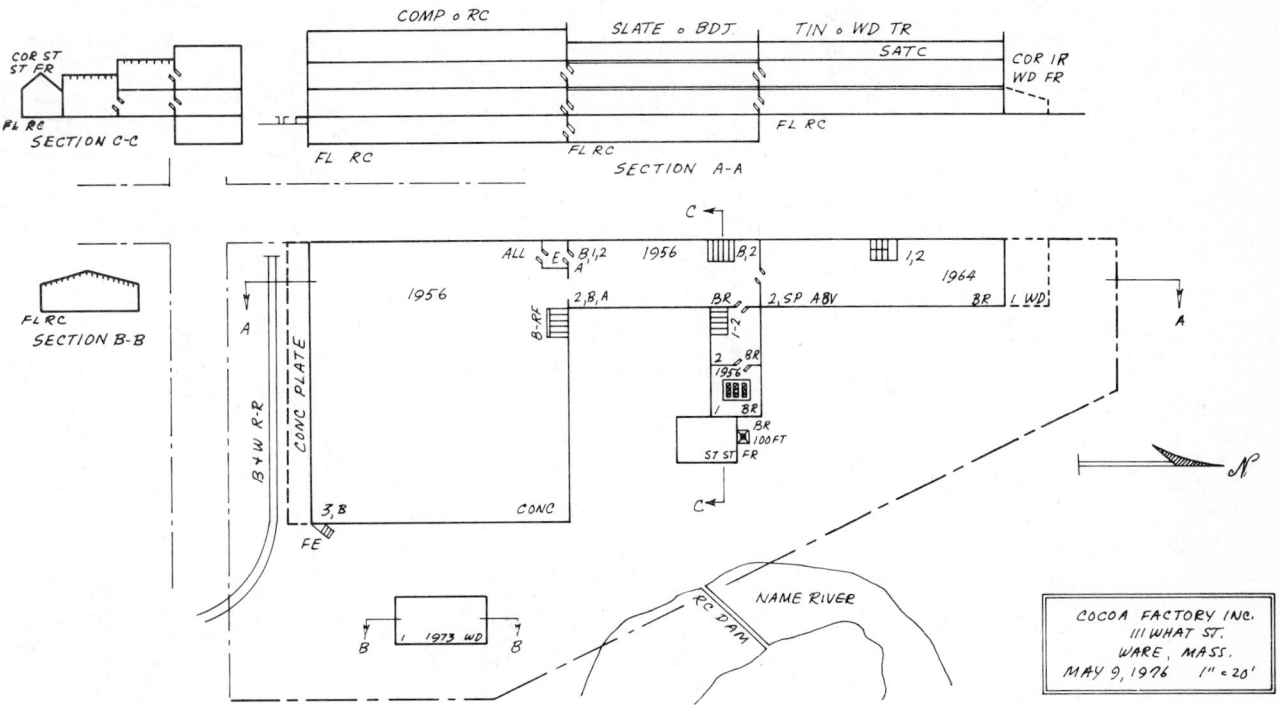

Fig. 18-1B. Typical building sketch similar to those prepared and presented in the inspector's report. The drawing shown here gives an overall view of the plant for which side sketches are shown in Figs. 18-1C and 18-1D.

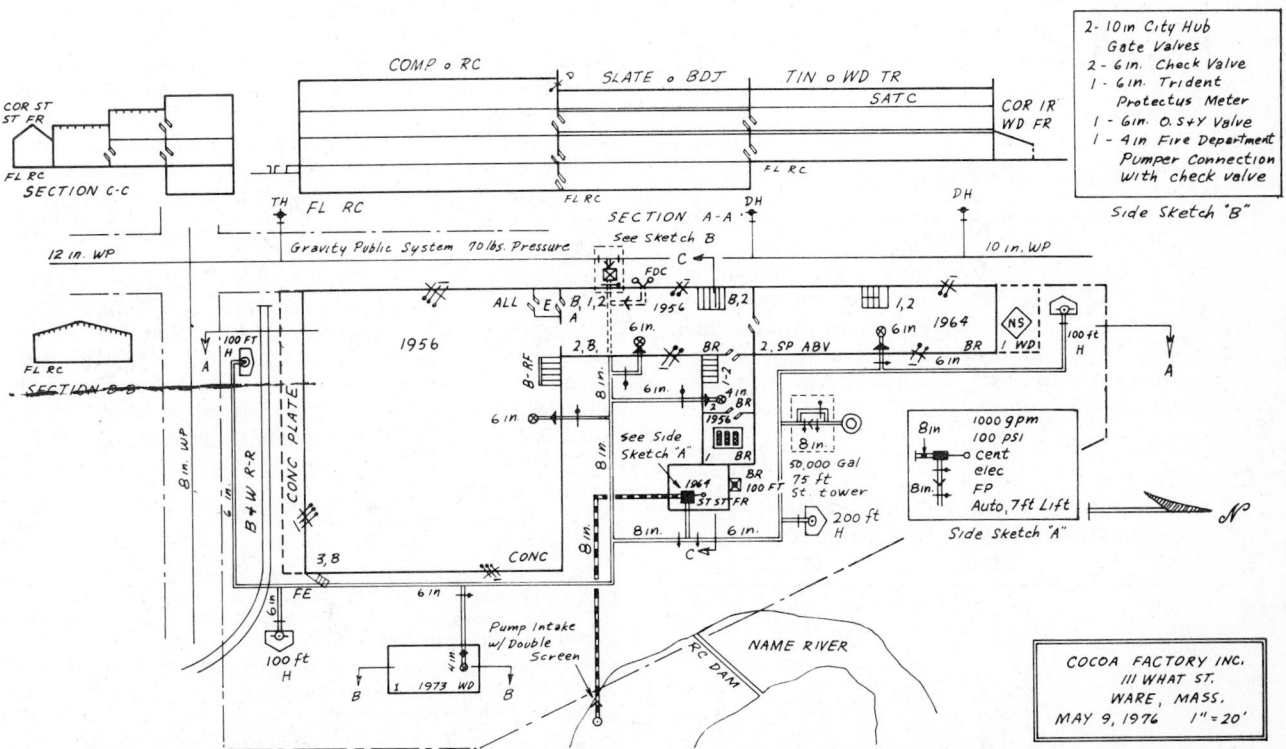

Fig. 18-1C. Building sketch showing the fire protection facilities and equipment of the plant illustrated in Fig. 18-1B.

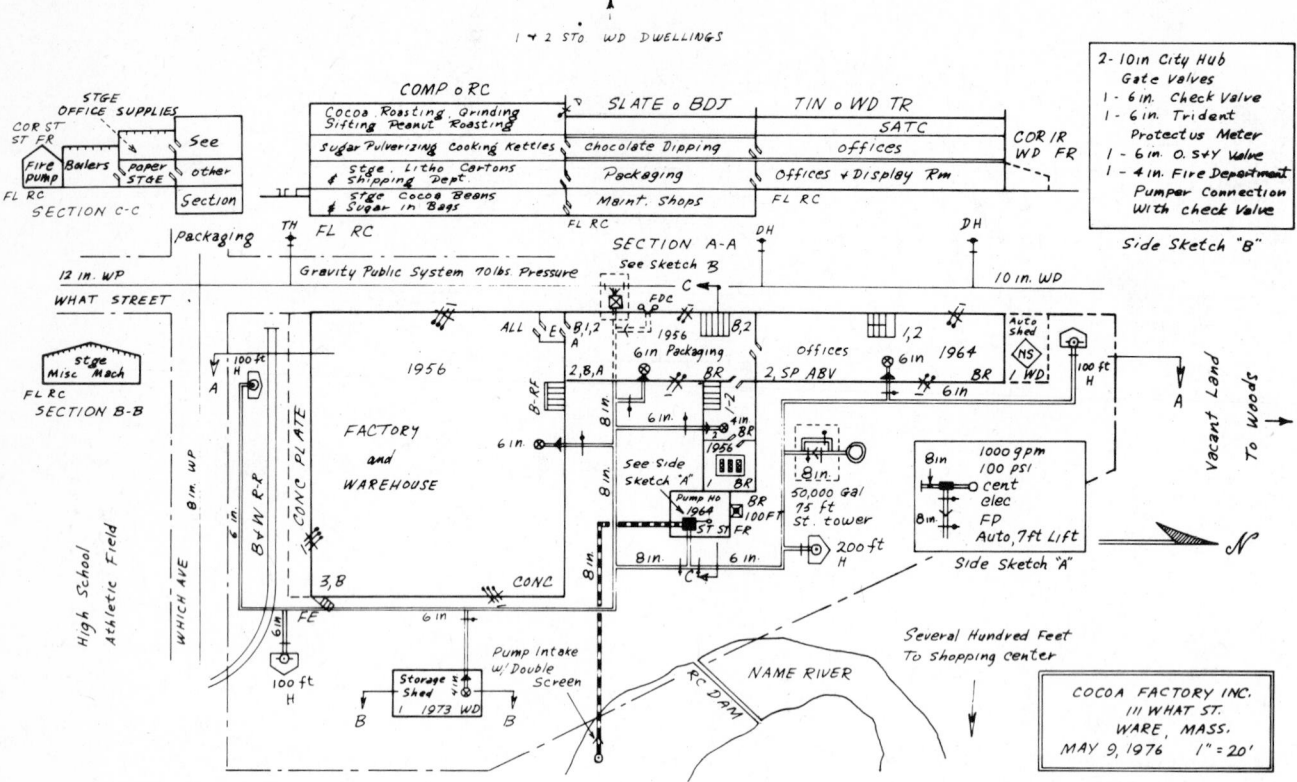

Fig. 18-1D.   Building sketch showing the internal processes of each area of the plant shown in Fig. 18-1B.

prohibit drawing all the equipment on the plan at approximate actual locations (due to size, quantity of symbols, or labeling requirements), a small side sketch (not drawn to scale) can be used effectively.

The last step in completing the plan is labeling the internal occupancy or processes of each area of the plant, and any yard storage or processes of interest. Figure 18-1D depicts this addition to the example.

E.   Other Building Plan Information Sources

The symbols and plans in this HANDBOOK will enable any inspector to develop a building plan in accordance with widespread convention. However, just as there are many different models of automobiles, there are also many organizations using a slightly different set of symbols and layouts. When trying to take information from a plan developed from another source, it will be necessary to refer to the legend of symbols used by that company to accurately interpret the information.

Table 18-1B.   Color Code for Denoting Construction Materials for Walls

Color	Interpretation
Brown	Fire resistive protected steel
Red	Brick, hollow tile
Yellow	Frame-wood, stucco
Blue	Concrete, stone, or hollow concrete block
Gray	Noncombustible (sheet metal or metal lath and plaster) unprotected steel

At one time, colors were used to describe the type of construction materials used for walls. Currently, color-coded plans are being replaced by black and white drawings for ease of preparation and economic reasons.

A narrative explanation of the color code used by the Western Actuarial Bureau and the Sanborn Map Company is contained in Table 18-1B. As can be seen from Table 18-1B, there are only five basic groups of construction materials coded. Since basic construction materials can be utilized in many different combinations, a convention was developed for using more than one color in combination also. Normally, the color in the center of the building represented the structural framing material and the building's border color represented the "facing or veneering material." For example, a building with a yellow center and a red border (note both colors totally within the building's sketched dimensions) would represent a wood-framed building with brick veneer. To avoid confusion on complicated plans, the construction materials were also labeled in accordance with the abbreviations in Table 18-1A.

Bibliography

References Cited

[1] Bond, Horatio, *NFPA Inspection Manual*, 3rd ed., National Fire Protection Association, Boston, 1970.

[2] "Abbreviations for Use on Drawings and in Text," ANSI Y1.1–1972, American National Standards Institute, New York.

NFPA Codes, Standards, and Recommended Practices (see the latest *NFPA Publications and Visual Aids Catalog* for availability of current editions of the following documents)

NFPA No. 206M, Guide on Building Areas and Heights.
NFPA No. 220, Standard Types of Building Construction.
NFPA No. 241, Standard for Safeguarding Building Construction and Demolition Operations.

Chapter 2

MATHEMATICAL TABLES AND GEOMETRIC FORMULAE

A. Logarithms

Logarithms provide a means for multiplying and dividing by the labor saving process of adding and subtracting logarithmic numbers as found in prepared tables of logarithms, and for raising numbers to powers or extracting roots by the multiplication or division of logarithms by the numerical power or root sought.

The power to which the number 10 must be raised to give any number is called the *common logarithm* of that number, or the logarithm to the base 10. In the mathematical sciences, bases other than 10 may be used, in which case the base is always specified.

Since the common logarithm of 10 is 1.0000, of 100 is 2.0000, and of 1,000 is 3.0000, it follows that the logarithms of numbers from 10 to 999.9+ are between 1 and 3. Table 18-2A in this HANDBOOK gives 5-place logarithms for numbers from 0 to 1,000.

Characteristics and Mantissas

The integral part of a logarithm for any number is called the *characteristic* and is 1 less than the number of figures on the left of the decimal point in the number for which the logarithm is sought. This part of the logarithm is not included in log tables. If the logarithm of a number such as 144 is sought, the characteristic will be 2, increased by the decimal part of the logarithm, called the *mantissa*, as determined from the log table. In finding the logarithm of the number 144, from the logarithm tables, the mantissa for 144 will be +.15836. The complete logarithm is, then, 2 + .15836.

The characteristic becomes negative when the number is less than 1. The negative value is one more than the number of zeros between the decimal point and the first figure of the number. For finding the logarithm of the number 0.0314, the characteristic is −2, and the mantissa (from the table) +.49693. The complete log is −2 + .49693.

For convenience in computation, it is desirable in most cases to change negative characteristics to an equivalent value of 10 minus the characteristic minus 10, 20 minus the characteristic minus 20, etc. For example, the logarithm −2 + .49693 is written simply 8.49693 −10.

Interpolation of Mantissas

In the last column of the table of logarithms headed "$\frac{1}{2}$ Avg Diff" ($\frac{1}{2}$ Average Difference) will be found numbers which represent one half the average differences between successive mantissas on the designated line. For instance, on line 54 the $\frac{1}{2}$ Average Difference is 40, and if we wished to obtain the mantissa for the number 5.455, we would take the mantissa shown in the table for the number 5.45 and add 40, thus:

Mantissa for 5.45	.73640
$\frac{1}{2}$ Average Difference	.00040
Mantissa for 5.455	.73680

Similarly, if we wished the mantissa for the number 5.451, we would add one-fifth of 40 to the mantissa for 5.45, obtaining .73648; and if we wished the mantissa for the number 5.459, we would subtract one-fifth of 40 from the mantissa for 5.46, obtaining .73711. It is important to remember to take the proper proportional part of $\frac{1}{2}$ Average Difference and, if the last digit in the required number is 5 or less, to add to the preceding mantissa; and if the last digit is over 5, to subtract from the following mantissa.

Interpolation depends on the number of significant figures required for a reasonable solution to a problem. In the example of the use of logarithms for multiplication, interpolation was not considered necessary for a reasonable solution. In the example of the use of logarithms for division, the answer without interpolating would not be a sufficiently accurate solution to satisfy the significance of the number of digits in the original problem.

Multiplication by Use of Logarithms

When two numbers are multiplied, the logarithm of the product is the sum of the logarithms of the two numbers. Using the values in the examples above, for multiplying 144 by 0.0314,

Log	144 =	2.15836
Log	0.0314 =	8.49693 − 10
Sum		10.65529 − 10 or .65529

From the table, the number corresponding to the mantissa of this logarithm, called the "antilogarithm," is, for the nearest figure given, 452 (nearest mantissa = 65513). In addition of these logarithms, the characteristic became zero. Therefore, the number sought is 4.52.

Division by Use of Logarithms

Division is carried out by subtracting the logarithm of the divisor from the logarithm of the dividend to give the logarithm of the quotient. For example, in dividing 144 by 0.0314,

Log of Dividend	2.15836
Log of Divisor	8.49693 − 10
Difference	?

Note that if the subtraction is done, the logarithm would be negative. Whenever it is necessary to subtract one logarithm from a smaller one, or a negative logarithm from a positive one, increase the characteristic of the dividend by 10 and then subtract 10 to compensate.

Log of Dividend	12.15836 − 10
Log of Divisor	8.49693 − 10
Difference	3.66143

The antilog of 66143 = 458. The characteristic is 3. Therefore, the quotient is 4586.

Exponential Procedures

Power of a Number: A number is raised to the desired exponential value by multiplying the log of the number by the exponent and finding the antilog of the product. For example, in finding the value of $(37.5)^4$,

Log 37.5 =	1.57403
	×4
	6.29612

Table 18-2A. Logarithms of Numbers From 0 to 1,000
(Verified by Clyde M. Wood)

No.	0	1	2	3	4	5	6	7	8	9	½ Avg. Diff.
10	00000	00432	00860	01284	01703	02119	02531	02938	03342	03743	
11	04139	04532	04922	05308	05690	06070	06446	06819	07188	07555	
12	07918	08279	08636	08991	09342	09691	10037	10380	10721	11059	
13	11394	11727	12057	12385	12710	13033	13354	13672	13988	14301	
14	14613	14922	15229	15534	15836	16137	16435	16732	17026	17319	
15	17609	17898	18184	18469	18752	19033	19312	19590	19866	20140	
16	20412	20683	20952	21219	21484	21748	22011	22272	22531	22789	
17	23045	23300	23553	23805	24055	24304	24551	24797	25042	25285	
18	25527	25768	26007	26245	26482	26717	26951	27184	27416	27646	
19	27875	28103	28330	28556	28780	29003	29226	29447	29667	29885	
20	30103	30320	30535	30750	30963	31175	31387	31597	31806	32015	
21	32222	32428	32634	32838	33041	33244	33445	33646	33846	34044	
22	34242	34439	34635	34830	35025	35218	35411	35603	35794	35984	
23	36173	36361	36549	36736	36922	37107	37291	37475	37658	37840	
24	38021	38202	38382	38561	38739	38917	39094	39270	39445	39620	
25	39794	39967	40140	40312	40483	40654	40824	40993	41162	41330	
26	41497	41664	41830	41996	42160	42325	42488	42651	42813	42975	
27	43136	43297	43457	43616	43775	43933	44091	44248	44404	44560	
28	44716	44871	45025	45179	45332	45484	45637	45788	45939	46090	
29	46240	46389	46538	46687	46835	46982	47129	47276	47422	47567	
30	47712	47857	48001	48144	48287	48430	48572	48714	48855	48996	72
31	49136	49276	49415	49554	49693	49831	49969	50106	50243	50379	69
32	50515	50651	50786	50920	51055	51188	51322	51455	51587	51720	67
33	51851	51983	52114	52244	52375	52504	52634	52763	52892	53020	65
34	53148	53275	53403	53529	53656	53782	53908	54033	54158	54283	63
35	54407	54531	54654	54777	54900	55023	55145	55267	55388	55509	62
36	55630	55751	55871	55991	56110	56229	56348	56467	56585	56703	60
37	56820	56937	57054	57171	57287	57403	57519	57634	57749	57864	58
38	57978	58092	58206	58320	58433	58546	58659	58771	58883	58995	57
39	59106	59218	59329	59439	59550	59660	59770	59879	59988	60097	55
40	60206	60314	60423	60531	60638	60746	60853	60959	61066	61172	54
41	61278	61384	61490	61595	61700	61805	61909	62014	62118	62221	53
42	62325	62428	62531	62634	62737	62839	62941	63043	63144	63246	51
43	63347	63448	63548	63649	63749	63849	63949	64048	64147	64246	50
44	64345	64444	64542	64640	64738	64836	64933	65031	65128	65225	49
45	65321	65418	65514	65610	65706	65801	65896	65992	66087	66181	48
46	66276	66370	66464	66558	66652	66745	66839	66932	67025	67117	47
47	67210	67302	67394	67486	67578	67669	67761	67852	67943	68034	46
48	68124	68215	68305	68395	68485	68574	68664	68753	68842	68931	45
49	69020	69108	69197	69285	69373	69461	69548	69636	69723	69810	44
50	69897	69984	70070	70157	70243	70329	70415	70501	70586	70672	43
51	70757	70842	70927	71012	71096	71181	71265	71349	71433	71517	43
52	71600	71684	71767	71850	71933	72016	72099	72181	72263	72346	42
53	72428	72509	72591	72673	72754	72835	72916	72997	73078	73159	41
54	73239	73320	73400	73480	73560	73640	73719	73799	73878	73957	40

The average difference variation for these mantissas is from 2 to 16. The following variations are from 0 to 2.

No.	0	1	2	3	4	5	6	7	8	9	½ Avg. Diff.
55	74036	74115	74194	74273	74351	74429	74507	74586	74663	74741	39
56	74819	74896	74974	75051	75128	75205	75282	75358	75435	75511	39
57	75587	75664	75740	75815	75891	75967	76042	76118	76193	76268	38
58	76343	76418	76492	76567	76641	76716	76790	76864	76938	77012	38
59	77085	77159	77232	77305	77379	77452	77525	77597	77670	77743	37
60	77815	77887	77960	78032	78104	78176	78247	78319	78390	78462	36
61	78533	78604	78675	78746	78817	78888	78958	79029	79099	79169	36
62	79239	79309	79379	79449	79518	79588	79657	79727	79796	79865	35
63	79934	80003	80072	80140	80209	80277	80346	80414	80482	80550	34
64	80618	80686	80754	80821	80889	80956	81023	81090	81158	81224	34
65	81291	81358	81425	81491	81558	81624	81690	81757	81823	81889	33
66	81954	82020	82086	82151	82217	82282	82347	82413	82478	82543	33
67	82607	82672	82737	82802	82866	82930	82995	83059	83123	83187	32
68	83251	83315	83378	83442	83506	83569	83632	83696	83759	83822	32
69	83885	83948	84011	84073	84136	84198	84261	84323	84386	84448	31
70	84510	84572	84634	84696	84757	84819	84880	84942	85003	85065	31
71	85126	85187	85248	85309	85370	85431	85491	85552	85612	85673	31
72	85733	85794	85854	85914	85974	86034	86094	86153	86213	86273	30
73	86332	86392	86451	86510	86570	86629	86688	86747	86806	86864	30
74	86923	86982	87040	87099	87157	87216	87274	87332	87390	87448	30
75	87506	87564	87622	87679	87737	87795	87852	87910	87967	88024	29
76	88081	88138	88195	88252	88309	88366	88423	88480	88536	88593	29
77	88649	88705	88762	88818	88874	88930	88986	89042	89098	89154	28
78	89209	89265	89321	89376	89432	89487	89542	89597	89653	89708	28
79	89763	89818	89873	89927	89982	90037	90091	90146	90200	90255	28
80	90309	90363	90417	90472	90526	90580	90634	90687	90741	90795	27
81	90849	90902	90956	91009	91062	91116	91169	91222	91275	91328	27
82	91381	91434	91487	91540	91593	91645	91698	91751	91803	91855	26
83	91908	91960	92012	92065	92117	92169	92221	92273	92324	92376	26
84	92428	92480	92531	92583	92634	92686	92737	92788	92840	92891	26
85	92942	92993	93044	93095	93146	93197	93247	93298	93349	93399	26
86	93450	93500	93551	93601	93651	93702	93752	93802	93852	93902	26
87	93952	94002	94052	94101	94151	94201	94250	94300	94349	94399	25
88	94448	94498	94547	94596	94645	94694	94743	94792	94841	94890	25
89	94939	94988	95036	95085	95134	95182	95231	95279	95328	95376	24
90	95424	95472	95521	95569	95617	95665	95713	95761	95809	95856	24
91	95904	95952	95999	96047	96095	96142	96190	96237	96284	96332	24
92	96379	96426	96473	96520	96567	96614	96661	96708	96755	96802	24
93	96848	96895	96942	96988	97035	97081	97128	97174	97220	97267	23
94	97313	97359	97405	97451	97497	97543	97589	97635	97681	97727	23
95	97772	97818	97864	97909	97955	98000	98046	98091	98137	98182	23
96	98227	98272	98318	98363	98408	98453	98498	98543	98588	98632	23
97	98677	98722	98767	98811	98856	98900	98945	98989	99034	99078	22
98	99123	99167	99211	99255	99300	99344	99388	99432	99476	99520	22
99	99564	99607	99651	99695	99739	99782	99826	99870	99913	99957	22

The antilog of 29612 = 198 (nearest mantissa, 296676). The characteristic is 6. Therefore, the desired power is 1,980,000.

Root of a Number: The desired root of a number is obtained by dividing the log of the number by the numerical value (index) of the root, and finding the antilog of the quotient. For example, find $\sqrt[5]{13200}$

$$\text{Log} \quad 13200 = 4.12057$$
$$\text{(divide by 5)} = 0.82411$$

Antilog of 0.82411 = 667. The characteristic is 0. Therefore, the 5th root is 6.67.

In extracting the root of a number having a negative characteristic such as the 6th root of a number whose log is −2. + 78542, it is desirable not to change the form to 8.78542 −10, but to make it 28.78542 −30. The log of the root is then 4.79757 −5 = −1. + 79757. The number is 0.627.

Powers and Roots That Are Not Integral: Powers and roots are not necessarily simple integers. The use of logarithms in such cases follows the general rule of multiplying the logarithm of the number by the value of the exponent, or dividing it by the index of the root. The antilog is then found and the characteristic used for the proper location of the decimal point.

Solution of Exponential Formulae

In engineering calculations, of which a good example relates to the determination of friction loss in a hydraulic piping system, the relation of the several factors to the final result is such that numerical values for powers and roots that are not simple integers must be used. For example, a common formula for determining the friction loss of water flowing in a pipe is:

$$F = \frac{4520\ G^{1.85}}{C^{1.85}\ d^{4.87}},$$

in which F = loss in pounds per square inch per 1,000-ft length of pipe, G = flow rate in gallons per minute, C = coefficient depending upon the roughness of the interior of the pipe, and d = internal diameter of the pipe in inches.

The arithmetical solution of such a problem without the use of logarithms is highly impractical. The use of logarithms makes the computation both simple and accurate.

To make a numerical procedure possible, an assumed set of values can be as follows: G = 1,500 gpm, C = 140, d = 5.20. The solution is as follows:

Log G (1,500)	= 3.17609	
(multiplied by 1.85)	=	5.87577
Log 4520	=	3.65514
Log of numerator in formula	=	9.53091
Log C (140)	= 2.14613	
(multiplied by 1.85)	=	3.97034
Log d (5.20)	= 0.71600	
(multiplied by 4.87)	=	3.48692
Log of denominator in formula =		7.45726
Log of numerator		9.53091
Log of denominator		7.45726
Difference		2.07365

Therefore, the antilog (mantissa, 07365) = 1185; the number = 118.5 psi per 1,000 ft.

B. How to Find Square Root

Point off the given number into periods of two places each, starting at the units place. Find the greatest number whose square is less than the first left-hand period and place it as the first figure in the quotient. Subtract its square from the lefthand period and to the remainder annex two figures of the second period for the new dividend. Double the first figure of the quotient for a partial divisor; find by trial that number which when added to 10 times the trial divisor gives a sum which when multiplied by the number itself gives a product most nearly approaching the dividend without exceeding it. This number is the second figure of the quotient; to get the third figure subtract from the new dividend the product obtained above and annex to the difference the next period, giving a new dividend. For the new trial divisor, double the first two figures of the quotient and proceed as before.

Example: Find the square root of 3.14159.

```
                   3.  14'  15'  90|1.772
                   1
        20 +7      2  14
                   1  89
        340 + 7       25  15
                      24  29
        3540 + 2          86  90
                          70  84
```

Answer is therefore 1.772.

Table 18-2B. Square Roots of Numbers

n	$\sqrt{n}$	n	$\sqrt{n}$	n	$\sqrt{n}$	n	$\sqrt{n}$	n	$\sqrt{n}$	n	$\sqrt{n}$	n	$\sqrt{n}$	n	$\sqrt{n}$	n	$\sqrt{n}$
1	1.000	57	7.5498	113	10.6301	169	13.0000	225	15.0000	281	16.7631	337	18.3576	393	19.8242	449	21.1896
2	1.414	58	7.6158	114	10.6771	170	13.0384	226	15.0333	282	16.7929	338	18.3848	394	19.8494	450	21.2132
3	1.732	59	7.6811	115	10.7238	171	13.0767	227	15.0665	283	16.8226	339	18.4120	395	19.8746	451	21.2368
4	2.000	60	7.7460	116	10.7703	172	13.1149	228	15.0997	284	16.8523	340	18.4391	396	19.8997	452	21.2603
5	2.236	61	7.8102	117	10.8167	173	13.1529	229	15.1327	285	16.8819	341	18.4662	397	19.9249	453	21.2838
6	2.449	62	7.8740	118	10.8628	174	13.1909	230	15.1658	286	16.9115	342	18.4932	398	19.9499	454	21.3073
7	2.646	63	7.9373	119	10.9087	175	13.2288	231	15.1987	287	16.9411	343	18.5203	399	19.9750	455	21.3307
8	2.828	64	8.0000	120	10.9545	176	13.2665	232	15.2315	288	16.9706	344	18.5472	400	20.0000	456	21.3542
9	3.000	65	8.0623	121	11.0000	177	13.3041	233	15.2643	289	17.0000	345	18.5742	401	20.0250	457	21.3776
10	3.162	66	8.1240	122	11.0454	178	13.3417	234	15.2971	290	17.0294	346	18.6011	402	20.0499	458	21.4009
11	3.3166	67	8.1854	123	11.0905	179	13.3791	235	15.3297	291	17.0587	347	18.6279	403	20.0749	459	21.4243
12	3.4641	68	8.2462	124	11.1355	180	13.4164	236	15.3623	292	17.0880	348	18.6548	404	20.0998	460	21.4476
13	3.6056	69	8.3066	125	11.1803	181	13.4536	237	15.3948	293	17.1172	349	18.6815	405	20.1246	461	21.4709
14	3.7417	70	8.3666	126	11.2250	182	13.4907	238	15.4272	294	17.1464	350	18.7083	406	20.1494	462	21.4942
15	3.8730	71	8.4261	127	11.2694	183	13.5277	239	15.4596	295	17.1756	351	18.7350	407	20.1742	463	21.5174
16	4.0000	72	8.4853	128	11.3137	184	13.5647	240	15.4919	296	17.2047	352	18.7617	408	20.1990	464	21.5407
17	4.1231	73	8.5440	129	11.3578	185	13.6015	241	15.5242	297	17.2337	353	18.7883	409	20.2237	465	21.5639
18	4.2426	74	8.6023	130	11.4018	186	13.6382	242	15.5563	298	17.2627	354	18.8149	410	20.2485	466	21.5870
19	4.3589	75	8.6603	131	11.4455	187	13.6748	243	15.5885	299	17.2916	355	18.8414	411	20.2731	467	21.6102
20	4.4721	76	8.7178	132	11.4891	188	13.7113	244	15.6205	300	17.3205	356	18.8680	412	20.2978	468	21.6333
21	4.5826	77	8.7750	133	11.5326	189	13.7477	245	15.6525	301	17.3494	357	18.8944	413	20.3224	469	21.6564
22	4.6904	78	8.8318	134	11.5758	190	13.7840	246	15.6844	302	17.3781	358	18.9209	414	20.3470	470	21.6795
23	4.7958	79	8.8882	135	11.6190	191	13.8203	247	15.7162	303	17.4069	359	18.9473	415	20.3715	471	21.7025
24	4.8990	80	8.9443	136	11.6619	192	13.8564	248	15.7480	304	17.4356	360	18.9737	416	20.3961	472	21.7256
25	5.0000	81	9.0000	137	11.7047	193	13.8924	249	15.7797	305	17.4642	361	19.0000	417	20.4206	473	21.7486
26	5.0990	82	9.0554	138	11.7473	194	13.9284	250	15.8114	306	17.4929	362	19.0263	418	20.4450	474	21.7715
27	5.1962	83	9.1104	139	11.7898	195	13.9642	251	15.8430	307	17.5214	363	19.0526	419	20.4695	475	21.7945
28	5.2915	84	9.1652	140	11.8322	196	14.0000	252	15.8745	308	17.5499	364	19.0788	420	20.4939	476	21.8174
29	5.3852	85	9.2195	141	11.8743	197	14.0357	253	15.9060	309	17.5784	365	19.1050	421	20.5183	477	21.8403
30	5.4772	86	9.2736	142	11.9164	198	14.0712	254	15.9374	310	17.6068	366	19.1311	422	20.5426	478	21.8632
31	5.5678	87	9.3274	143	11.9583	199	14.1067	255	15.9687	311	17.6352	367	19.1572	423	20.5670	479	21.8861
32	5.6569	88	9.3808	144	12.0000	200	14.1421	256	16.0000	312	17.6635	368	19.1833	424	20.5913	480	21.9089
33	5.7446	89	9.4340	145	12.0416	201	14.1774	257	16.0312	313	17.6918	369	19.2094	425	20.6155	481	21.9317
34	5.8310	90	9.4868	146	12.0830	202	14.2127	258	16.0624	314	17.7200	370	19.2354	426	20.6398	482	21.9545
35	5.9161	91	9.5394	147	12.1244	203	14.2478	259	16.0935	315	17.7482	371	19.2614	427	20.6640	483	21.9773
36	6.0000	92	9.5917	148	12.1655	204	14.2829	260	16.1245	316	17.7764	372	19.2873	428	20.6882	484	22.0000
37	6.0828	93	9.6437	149	12.2066	205	14.3178	261	16.1555	317	17.8045	373	19.3132	429	20.7123	485	22.0227
38	6.1644	94	9.6954	150	12.2474	206	14.3527	262	16.1864	318	17.8326	374	19.3391	430	20.7364	486	22.0454
39	6.2450	95	9.7468	151	12.2882	207	14.3875	263	16.2173	319	17.8606	375	19.3649	431	20.7605	487	22.0681
40	6.3246	96	9.7980	152	12.3288	208	14.4222	264	16.2481	320	17.8885	376	19.3907	432	20.7846	488	22.0907
41	6.4031	97	9.8489	153	12.3693	209	14.4568	265	16.2788	321	17.9165	377	19.4165	433	20.8087	489	22.1133
42	6.4807	98	9.8995	154	12.4097	210	14.4914	266	16.3095	322	17.9444	378	19.4422	434	20.8327	490	22.1359
43	6.5574	99	9.9499	155	12.4499	211	14.5258	267	16.3401	323	17.9722	379	19.4679	435	20.8567	491	22.1585
44	6.6332	100	10.0000	156	12.4900	212	14.5602	268	16.3707	324	18.0000	380	19.4936	436	20.8806	492	22.1811
45	6.7082	101	10.0499	157	12.5300	213	14.5945	269	16.4012	325	18.0287	381	19.5192	437	20.9045	493	22.2036
46	6.7823	102	10.0995	158	12.5698	214	14.6287	270	16.4317	326	18.0555	382	19.5448	438	20.9284	494	22.2261
47	6.8557	103	10.1489	159	12.6095	215	14.6629	271	16.4621	327	18.0831	383	19.5704	439	20.9523	495	22.2486
48	6.9282	104	10.1980	160	12.6491	216	14.6969	272	16.4924	328	18.1108	384	19.5959	440	20.9762	496	22.2711
49	7.0000	105	10.2470	161	12.6886	217	14.7309	273	16.5227	329	18.1384	385	19.6214	441	21.0000	497	22.2935
50	7.0711	106	10.2956	162	12.7279	218	14.7648	274	16.5529	330	18.1659	386	19.6469	442	21.0238	498	22.3159
51	7.1414	107	10.3441	163	12.7671	219	14.7986	275	16.5831	331	18.1934	387	19.6723	443	21.0476	499	22.3383
52	7.2111	108	10.3923	164	12.8062	220	14.8324	276	16.6132	332	18.2209	388	19.6977	444	21.0713	500	22.3607
53	7.2801	109	10.4403	165	12.8452	221	14.8661	277	16.6433	333	18.2483	389	19.7231	445	21.0950	501	22.3830
54	7.3485	110	10.4881	166	12.8841	222	14.8997	278	16.6733	334	18.2757	390	19.7484	446	21.1187	502	22.4054
55	7.4163	111	10.5357	167	12.9228	223	14.9332	279	16.7033	335	18.3030	391	19.7737	447	21.1424	503	22.4277
56	7.4833	112	10.5830	168	12.9615	224	14.9666	280	16.7332	336	18.3303	392	19.7990	448	21.1660	504	22.4499

Table 18-2B. Square Roots of Numbers (Cont.)

n	√n	n	√n	n	√n	n	√n	n	√n	n	√n	n	√n	n	√n	n	√n
505	22.4722	561	23.6854	617	24.8395	673	25.9422	729	27.0000	785	28.0179	841	29.0000	897	29.9500	953	30.8707
506	22.4944	562	23.7065	618	24.8596	674	25.9615	730	27.0185	786	28.0357	842	29.0172	898	29.9666	954	30.8869
507	22.5167	563	23.7276	619	24.8797	675	25.9808	731	27.0370	787	28.0535	843	29.0345	899	29.9833	955	30.9031
508	22.5389	564	23.7487	620	24.8998	676	26.0000	732	27.0555	788	28.0713	844	29.0517	900	30.0000	956	30.9192
509	22.5610	565	23.7697	621	24.9199	677	26.0192	733	27.0740	789	28.0891	845	29.0689	901	30.0167	957	30.9354
510	22.5832	566	23.7908	622	24.9399	678	26.0384	734	27.0924	790	28.1069	846	29.0861	902	30.0333	958	30.9516
511	22.6053	567	23.8118	623	24.9600	679	26.0576	735	27.1109	791	28.1247	847	29.1033	903	30.0500	959	30.9677
512	22.6274	568	23.8328	624	24.9800	680	26.0768	736	27.1293	792	28.1425	848	29.1204	904	30.0666	960	30.9839
513	22.6495	569	23.8537	625	25.0000	681	26.0960	737	27.1477	793	28.1603	849	29.1376	905	30.0832	961	31.0000
514	22.6716	570	23.8747	626	25.0200	682	26.1151	738	27.1662	794	28.1780	850	29.1548	906	30.0998	962	31.0161
515	22.6936	571	23.8956	627	25.0400	683	26.1343	739	27.1846	795	28.1957	851	29.1719	907	30.1164	963	31.0322
516	22.7156	572	23.9165	628	25.0599	684	26.1534	740	27.2029	796	28.2135	852	29.1890	908	30.1330	964	31.0483
517	22.7376	573	23.9374	629	25.0799	685	26.1725	741	27.2213	797	28.2312	853	29.2062	909	30.1496	965	31.0644
518	22.7596	574	23.9583	630	25.0998	686	26.1916	742	27.2397	798	28.2489	854	29.2233	910	30.1662	966	31.0805
519	22.7816	575	23.9792	631	25.1197	687	26.2107	743	27.2580	799	28.2666	855	29.2404	911	30.1828	967	31.0966
520	22.8035	576	24.0000	632	25.1396	688	26.2298	744	27.2764	800	28.2843	856	29.2575	912	30.1993	968	31.1127
521	22.8254	577	24.0208	633	25.1595	689	26.2488	745	27.2947	801	28.3019	857	29.2746	913	30.2159	969	31.1288
522	22.8473	578	24.0416	634	25.1794	690	26.2679	746	27.3130	802	28.3196	858	29.2916	914	30.2324	970	31.1448
523	22.8692	579	24.0624	635	25.1992	691	26.2869	747	27.3313	803	28.3373	859	29.3087	915	30.2490	971	31.1609
524	22.8910	580	24.0832	636	25.2190	692	26.3059	748	27.3496	804	28.3549	860	29.3258	916	30.2655	972	31.1769
525	22.9129	581	24.1039	637	25.2389	693	26.3249	749	27.3679	805	28.3725	861	29.3428	917	30.2820	973	31.1929
526	22.9347	582	24.1247	638	25.2587	694	26.3439	750	27.3861	806	28.3901	862	29.3598	918	30.2985	974	31.2090
527	22.9565	583	24.1454	639	25.2784	695	26.3629	751	27.4044	807	28.4077	863	29.3769	919	30.3150	975	31.2250
528	22.9783	584	24.1661	640	25.2982	696	26.3818	752	27.4226	808	28.4253	864	29.3939	920	30.3315	976	31.2410
529	23.0000	585	24.1868	641	25.3180	697	26.4008	753	27.4408	809	28.4429	865	29.4109	921	30.3480	977	31.2570
530	23.0217	586	24.2074	642	25.3377	698	26.4197	754	27.4591	810	28.4605	866	29.4279	922	30.3645	978	31.2730
531	23.0434	587	24.2281	643	25.3574	699	26.4386	755	27.4773	811	28.4781	867	29.4449	923	30.3809	979	31.2890
532	23.0651	588	24.2487	644	25.3772	700	26.4575	756	27.4955	812	28.4956	868	29.4618	924	30.3974	980	31.3050
533	23.0868	589	24.2693	645	25.3969	701	26.4764	757	27.5136	813	28.5132	869	29.4788	925	30.4138	981	31.3209
534	23.1084	590	24.2899	646	25.4165	702	26.4953	758	27.5318	814	28.5307	870	29.4958	926	30.4302	982	31.3369
535	23.1301	591	24.3105	647	25.4362	703	26.5141	759	27.5500	815	28.5482	871	29.5127	927	30.4467	983	31.3528
536	23.1517	592	24.3311	648	25.4558	704	26.5330	760	27.5681	816	28.5657	872	29.5296	928	30.4631	984	31.3688
537	23.1733	593	24.3516	649	25.4755	705	26.5518	761	27.5862	817	28.5832	873	29.5466	929	30.4795	985	31.3847
538	23.1948	594	24.3721	650	25.4951	706	26.5707	762	27.6043	818	28.6007	874	29.5635	930	30.4959	986	31.4006
539	23.2164	595	24.3926	651	25.5147	707	26.5895	763	27.6225	819	28.6182	875	29.5804	931	30.5123	987	31.4166
540	23.2379	596	24.4131	652	25.5343	708	26.6083	764	27.6405	820	28.6356	876	29.5973	932	30.5287	988	31.4325
541	23.2594	597	24.4336	653	25.5539	709	26.6271	765	27.6586	821	28.6531	877	29.6142	933	30.5450	989	31.4484
542	23.2809	598	24.4540	654	25.5734	710	26.6458	766	27.6767	822	28.6705	878	29.6311	934	30.5614	990	31.4643
543	23.3024	599	24.4745	655	25.5930	711	26.6646	767	27.6948	823	28.6880	879	29.6479	935	30.5778	991	31.4802
544	23.3238	600	24.4949	656	25.6125	712	26.6833	768	27.7128	824	28.7054	880	29.6648	936	30.5941	992	31.4960
545	23.3452	601	24.5153	657	25.6320	713	26.7021	769	27.7308	825	28.7228	881	29.6816	937	30.6105	993	31.5119
546	23.3666	602	24.5357	658	25.6515	714	26.7208	770	27.7489	826	28.7402	882	29.6985	938	30.6268	994	31.5278
547	23.3880	603	24.5561	659	25.6710	715	26.7395	771	27.7669	827	28.7576	883	29.7153	939	30.6431	995	31.5436
548	23.4094	604	24.5764	660	25.6905	716	26.7582	772	27.7849	828	28.7750	884	29.7321	940	30.6594	996	31.5595
549	23.4307	605	24.5967	661	25.7099	717	26.7769	773	27.8029	829	28.7924	885	29.7489	941	30.6757	997	31.5753
550	23.4521	606	24.6171	662	25.7294	718	26.7955	774	27.8209	830	28.8097	886	29.7658	942	30.6920	998	31.5911
551	23.4734	607	24.6374	663	25.7488	719	26.8142	775	27.8388	831	28.8271	887	29.7825	943	30.7083	999	31.6070
552	23.4947	608	24.6577	664	25.7682	720	26.8328	776	27.8568	832	28.8444	888	29.7993	944	30.7246		
553	23.5160	609	24.6779	665	25.7876	721	26.8514	777	27.8747	833	28.8617	889	29.8161	945	30.7409		
554	23.5372	610	24.6982	666	25.8070	722	26.8701	778	27.8927	834	28.8791	890	29.8329	946	30.7571		
555	23.5584	611	24.7184	667	25.8263	723	26.8887	779	27.9106	835	28.8964	891	29.8496	947	30.7734		
556	23.5797	612	24.7386	668	25.8457	724	26.9072	780	27.9285	836	28.9137	892	29.8664	948	30.7896		
557	23.6008	613	24.7588	669	25.8650	725	26.9258	781	27.9464	837	28.9310	893	29.8831	949	30.8058		
558	23.6220	614	24.7790	670	25.8844	726	26.9444	782	27.9643	838	28.9482	894	29.8998	950	30.8221		
559	23.6432	615	24.7992	671	25.9037	727	26.9629	783	27.9821	839	28.9655	895	29.9166	951	30.8383		
560	23.6643	616	24.8193	672	25.9230	728	26.9815	784	28.0000	840	28.9828	896	29.9333	952	30.8545		

MISCELLANEOUS DATA

Table 18-2C. Diameters, Squares of Diameters, Areas of Circles

Diameter	Square of Diameter	Area	Diameter	Square of Diameter	Area	Diameter	Square of Diameter	Area
$\frac{1}{16}$	.0625	.003906	.00307	3.5	12.25	9.6211	48	2304	1809.6
$\frac{1}{8}$	.1250	.01563	.01227	4.0	16.00	12.566	49	2401	1885.7
$\frac{3}{16}$	.1875	.03516	.02761	4.5	20.25	15.904	50	2500	1963.5
$\frac{1}{4}$	.2500	.0625	.04909	5.0	25.00	19.635	51	2601	2042.8
$\frac{5}{16}$	.3125	.09766	.07670	5.5	30.25	23.758	52	2704	2123.7
$\frac{3}{8}$	.3750	.1406	.11045	6.0	36.00	28.274	53	2809	2206.2
$\frac{7}{16}$	.4375	.1914	.15033	6.5	42.25	33.183	54	2916	2290.2
$\frac{1}{2}$	.5000	.2500	.19635	7.0	49.00	38.485	55	3025	2375.8
				7.5	56.25	44.179	56	3136	2463.0
$\frac{9}{16}$	.5625	.3164	.24850	8.0	64.00	50.265	57	3249	2551.8
$\frac{5}{8}$	.6250	.3906	.30680	8.5	72.25	56.745	58	3364	2642.1
$\frac{11}{16}$	.6875	.4727	.37122	9.0	81.00	63.617	59	3481	2734.0
$\frac{3}{4}$	.7500	.5625	.44179	9.5	90.25	70.882	60	3600	2827.4
$\frac{13}{16}$	.8125	.6601	.51849	10.0	100.00	78.540	61	3721	2922.5
$\frac{7}{8}$	.8750	.7656	.60132	10.5	110.25	86.590	62	3844	3019.1
$\frac{15}{16}$	.9375	.8789	.69029	11.0	121.00	95.033	63	3969	3117.2
1	1.0000	1.0000	.7854	11.5	132.25	103.87	64	4096	3217.0
				12.0	144.00	113.10	65	4225	3318.3
$1\frac{1}{16}$	1.0625	1.1289	.8866	13	169	132.73	66	4356	3421.2
$1\frac{1}{8}$	1.1250	1.2656	.9940	14	196	153.94	67	4489	3525.7
$1\frac{3}{16}$	1.1875	1.4102	1.1075	15	225	176.71	68	4624	3631.7
$1\frac{1}{4}$	1.2500	1.5625	1.2272	16	256	201.06	69	4761	3739.3
$1\frac{5}{16}$	1.3125	1.7227	1.3530	17	289	226.98	70	4900	3848.5
$1\frac{3}{8}$	1.3750	1.8906	1.4849	18	324	254.47	71	5041	3959.2
$1\frac{7}{16}$	1.4375	2.0664	1.6230	19	361	283.53	72	5184	4071.5
$1\frac{1}{2}$	1.5000	2.2500	1.7671	20	400	314.16	73	5329	4185.4
				21	441	346.36	74	5476	4300.8
$1\frac{9}{16}$	1.5625	2.4414	1.9175	22	484	380.13	75	5625	4417.9
$1\frac{5}{8}$	1.6250	2.6406	2.0739	23	529	415.48	76	5776	4536.5
$1\frac{11}{16}$	1.6875	2.8477	2.2365	24	576	452.39	77	5929	4656.6
$1\frac{3}{4}$	1.7500	3.0625	2.4053	25	625	490.87	78	6084	4778.4
$1\frac{13}{16}$	1.8125	3.2852	2.5802	26	676	530.93	79	6241	4901.7
$1\frac{7}{8}$	1.8750	3.5156	2.7612	27	729	572.56	80	6400	5026.5
$1\frac{15}{16}$	1.9375	3.7539	2.9483	28	784	615.25	81	6561	5153.0
2	2.0000	4.0000	3.1416	29	841	660.52	82	6724	5281.0
				30	900	706.86	83	6889	5410.6
$2\frac{1}{16}$	2.0625	4.2539	3.3410	31	961	754.77	84	7056	5541.8
$2\frac{1}{8}$	2.1250	4.5156	3.5466	32	1024	804.25	85	7225	5674.5
$2\frac{3}{16}$	2.1875	4.7852	3.7583	33	1089	855.30	86	7396	5808.8
$2\frac{1}{4}$	2.2500	5.0625	3.9761	34	1156	907.92	87	7569	5944.7
$2\frac{5}{16}$	2.3125	5.3477	4.2000	35	1225	962.11	88	7744	6082.1
$2\frac{3}{8}$	2.3750	5.6406	4.4301	36	1296	1017.9	89	7921	6221.1
$2\frac{7}{16}$	2.4375	5.9414	4.6664	37	1369	1075.2	90	8100	6361.7
$2\frac{1}{2}$	2.5000	6.2500	4.9087	38	1444	1134.1	91	8281	6503.9
				39	1521	1194.6	92	8464	6647.6
$2\frac{9}{16}$	2.5625	6.5664	5.1573	40	1600	1256.6	93	8649	6792.9
$2\frac{5}{8}$	2.6250	6.8906	5.4119	41	1681	1320.3	94	8836	6939.8
$2\frac{11}{16}$	2.6875	7.2227	5.6727	42	1764	1385.4	95	9025	7088.2
$2\frac{3}{4}$	2.7500	7.5625	5.9396	43	1849	1452.2	96	9216	7238.2
$2\frac{13}{16}$	2.8125	7.9102	6.2127	44	1936	1520.5	97	9409	7389.8
$2\frac{7}{8}$	2.8750	8.2656	6.4918	45	2025	1590.4	98	9604	7543.0
$2\frac{15}{16}$	2.9375	8.6289	6.7771	46	2116	1661.9	99	9801	7696.9
3	3.0000	9.0000	7.0686	47	2209	1734.9	100	10000	7854.0

RECTANGULAR BOX

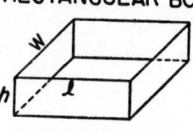

Volume = $l \times w \times h$

ROOF SPACE

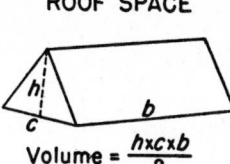

Volume = $\dfrac{h \times c \times b}{2}$

SPHERE

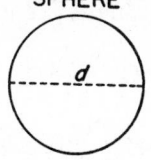

Surface Area = $\pi \times d^2$

Volume = $\dfrac{1}{6} \pi \times d^3$

TRIANGLE

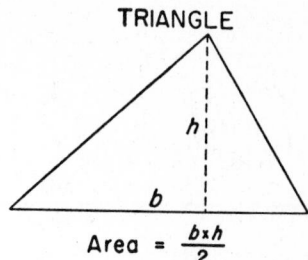

Area = $\dfrac{b \times h}{2}$

CIRCLE

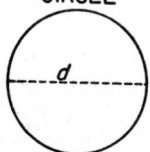

Circumference = $\pi \times d$

Area = $\dfrac{1}{4} \pi \times d^2$

$\pi = \dfrac{22}{7} = 3.1416$

CONE

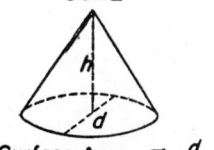

Curved Surface Area = $\pi \times \dfrac{d}{4} \times \sqrt{d^2 + 4h^2}$

Volume = $\dfrac{\pi \times d^2 \times h}{12}$

RECTANGLE

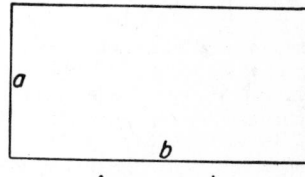

Area = $a \times b$

CYLINDER (RIGHT)

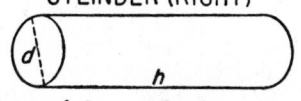

Area of Curved Surface = $2\pi r h$

Volume = $\dfrac{\pi \times d^2 \times h}{4}$

PARALLELOGRAM

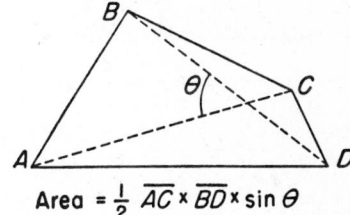

Area = $h \times b$

TENSION IN CYLINDER SHELL

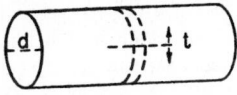

t, Tension in Shell (Tending to Open Lengthwise Split) Lbs. Per Inch of Length of Cylinder = $\dfrac{1}{2} d \times p$

d = Diameter in Inches

p = Pressure Inside Cylinder, psi

LADDERS

(Neglecting Friction and Weight of Ladder)

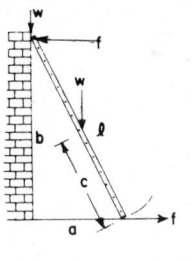

f = Horizontal Force to be Resisted at Bottom of Ladder (Also Same Force Against Wall at Top of Ladder)

w = Weight on Ladder

l = Length of Ladder

a = Distance of Foot of Ladder from Vertical Wall

b = $\sqrt{l^2 - a^2}$

c = Distance of w from Foot of Ladder

If Weight is at Bottom of Ladder: f = o

If Weight is at Top of Ladder:

$$w \times a = f \times b$$

or

$$f = \dfrac{w \times a}{b} = w \dfrac{a}{\sqrt{l^2 - a^2}} \qquad (1)$$

If Weight is at Intermediate Height: f = Maximum Force as Determined by (1) Multiplied by the Ratio $\dfrac{c}{l}$

QUADRILATERAL

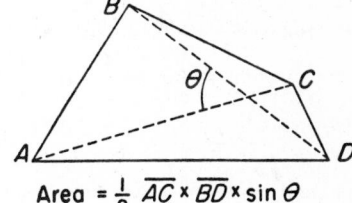

Area = $\dfrac{1}{2} \overline{AC} \times \overline{BD} \times \sin \theta$

PYRAMID (REGULAR)

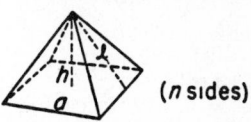

(n sides)

Lateral Area = $\dfrac{1}{2} n \times a \times l$

Volume = $\dfrac{1}{3} h \times$ Area of Base

RIGHT TRIANGLE

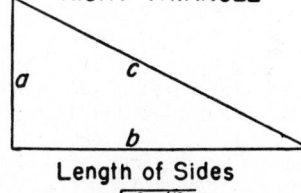

Length of Sides

$a = \sqrt{c^2 - b^2}$

$b = \sqrt{c^2 - a^2}$

$c = \sqrt{a^2 + b^2}$

TRAPEZOID

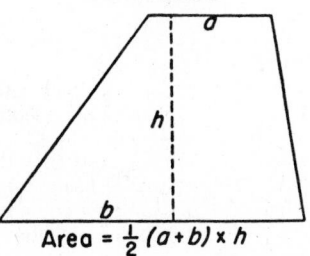

Area = $\dfrac{1}{2}(a + b) \times h$

FREE FALLING BODIES

$$S = \dfrac{g \times t^2}{2}$$

WHERE S = DISTANCE IN FEET

g = ACCELERATION OF GRAVITY (APPROXIMATELY 32 FT. PER SEC. PER SEC.)

t = TIME IN SECONDS

Fig. 18-2A. Geometric and miscellaneous formulae. (Any units of measurement can be used in these formulae provided they are consistent.)

Chapter 3

CONVERSION TABLES

Table 18-3A.   Conversion Factors

Length

1 inch = 0.08333 foot, 1,000 mils, 25.40 millimetres.
1 foot = 0.3333 yard, 12 inches, 0.3048 metre, 304.8 millimetres.
1 yard = 3 feet, 36 inches, 0.9144 metre.
1 rod = 16.5 feet, 5.5 yards, 5.029 metres.
1 mile (U.S. and British) = 5,280 feet, 1.609 kilometres, 0.8684 nautical mile.
1 millimeter = 0.03937 inch, 39.37 mils, 0.001 metre, 0.1 centimetre, 100 microns.
1 meter = 1.094 yards, 3.281 feet, 39.37 inches, 1,000 millimetres.
1 kilometer = 0.6214 mile, 1.094 yards, 3,281 feet, 1,000 metres.
1 nautical mile = 1.152 miles (statute), 1.853 kilometres.
1 micron = 0.03937 mil, 0.00003937 inch.
1 mil = 0.001 inch, 0.0254 millimetres, 25.40 microns.
1 degree = 1/360 circumference of a circle, 60 minutes, 3,600 seconds.
1 minute = 1/60 degree, 60 seconds.
1 second = 1/60 minute, 1/3600 degree.

Area

1 square inch = 0.006944 square foot, 1,273,000 circular mils, 645.2 square millimetres.
1 square foot = 0.1111 square yard, 144 square inches, 0.09290 square metre, 92,900 square millimetres.
1 square yard = 9 square feet, 1,296 square inches, 0.8361 square metre.
1 acre = 43,560 square feet, 4,840 square yards, 0.001563 square mile, 4,047 square metres, 160 square rods.
1 square mile = 640 acres, 102,400 square rods, 3,097,600 square yards, 2.590 square kilometres.
1 square millimeter = 0.001550 square inch, 1,974 circular mils.
1 square meter = 1.196 square yards, 10.76 square feet, 1,550 square inches, 1,000,000 square millimetres.
1 square kilometer = 0.3861 square mile, 247.1 acres, 1,196,000 square yards, 1,000,000 square metres.
1 circular mil = 0.7854 square mil, 0.0005067 square millimetre, 0.0000007854 square inch.

Volume (Capacity)

1 fluid ounce = 1.805 cubic inches, 29.57 millilitres, 0.03125 quarts (U.S.) liquid measure.
1 cubic inch = 0.5541 fluid ounce, 16.39 millilitres.
1 cubic foot = 7.481 gallons (U.S.), 6.229 gallons (British), 1,728 cubic inches, 0.02832 cubic metre, 28.32 litres.
1 cubic yard = 27 cubic feet, 46,656 cubic inches, 0.7646 cubic metre, 746.6 litres, 202.2 gallons (U.S.), 168.4 gallons (British).
1 gill = 0.03125 gallon, 0.125 quart, 4 ounces, 7.219 cubic inches, 118.3 millilitres.
1 pint = 0.01671 cubic foot, 28.88 cubic inches, 0.125 gallon, 4 gills, 16 fluid ounces, 473.2 millilitres.
1 quart = 2 pints, 32 fluid ounces, 0.9464 litre, 946.4 millilitres, 8 gills, 57.75 cubic inches.
1 U.S. gallon = 4 quarts, 128 fluid ounces, 231.0 cubic inches, 0.1337 cubic foot, 3.785 litres (cubic decimetres), 3,785 millilitres, 0.8327 Imperial gallon.
1 Imperial (British and Canadian) gallon = 1.201 U.S. gallons, 0.1605 cubic foot, 277.3 cubic inches, 4.546 litres (cubic decimetres), 4,546 millilitres.
1 U.S. bushel = 2,150 cubic inches, 0.9694 British bushel, 35.24 litres.
1 barrel (U.S. liquid) = 31.5 gallons (various industries have special definitions of a barrel).
1 barrel (petroleum) = 42.0 gallons.
1 millimeter = 0.03381 fluid ounce, 0.06102 cubic inch, 0.001 litre.

1 litre (cubic decimeter) = 0.2642 gallon, 0.03532 cubic foot, 1.057 quarts, 33.81 fluid ounces, 61.03 cubic inches, 1,000 millilitres.
1 cubic meter (kiloliter) = 1.308 cubic yards, 35.32 cubic feet, 264.2 gallons, 1,000 litres.
1 cord = 128 cubic feet, 8 feet × 4 feet × 4 feet, 3.625 cubic metres.

Weight

1 grain = 0.0001428 pound.
1 ounce (avoirdupois) = 0.06250 pound (avoirdupois), 28.35 grams, 437.5 grains.
1 pound (avoirdupois) = the mass of 27.69 cubic inches of water weighed in air at 4°C (39.2°F) and 760 millimetres of mercury (atmospheric pressure), 16 ounces (avoirdupois), 0.4536 kilogram, 453.6 grams, 7,000 grains.
1 long ton (U.S. and British) = 1.120 short tons, 2,240 pounds, 1.016 metric tons, 1016 kilograms.
1 short ton (U.S. and British) = 0.8929 long ton, 2,000 pounds, 0.9072 metric ton, 907.2 kilograms.
1 milligram = 0.001 gram, 0.000002205 pound (avoirdupois).
1 gram = 0.002205 pound (avoirdupois), 0.03527 ounce, 0.001 kilogram, 15.43 grains.
1 kilogram = the mass of 1 litre of water in air at 4°C and 760 millimetres of mercury (atmospheric pressure), 2.205 pounds (avoirdupois), 35.27 ounces (avoirdupois), 1,000 grams.
1 metric ton = 0.9842 long ton, 1.1023 short tons, 2,205 pounds, 1,000 kilograms.

Velocity

1 foot per second = 0.6818 mile per hour, 18.29 metres per minute, 0.3048 metres per second.
1 mile per hour = 1.467 feet per second, 1.609 kilometres per hour, 26.82 metres per minute, 0.4470 metres per second.
1 kilometer per hour = 0.2778 metre per second, 0.5396 knot per hour, 0.6214 mile per hour, 54.68 feet per minute.
1 meter per minute = 0.03728 mile per hour, 0.05468 foot per second, 0.06 kilometre per hour, 16.67 millimetres per second, 3.281 feet per minute.
1 knot per hour = 1.152 miles per hour, 1.689 feet per second, 1.853 kilometres per hour.
1 revolution per minute = 0.01667 revolution per second, 6 degrees per second.
1 revolution per second = 60 revolutions per minute, 360 degrees per second.

Acceleration

Standard gravity = 32.17 feet per second per second, 9.807 metres per second per second.

Density

1 gram per millimeter = 0.03613 pound per cubic inch, 8.345 pounds per gallon, 62.43 pounds per cubic foot, 998.9 ounces per cubic foot.
Mercury at 0°C = 0.1360 grams per millimetre, basic value used in expressing pressures in terms of columns of mercury.
1 pound per cubic foot = 16.02 kilograms per cubic metre.
1 pound per gallon = 0.1198 gram per millilitre.

Flow

1 cubic foot per minute = 0.1247 gallon per second, 0.4720 litre per second, 472.0 millilitres per second.

Table 18-3A. Conversion Factors (Cont.)

1 gallon per minute = 0.06308 litre per second, 1,440 gallons per day, 0.002228 cubic foot per second.

1 litre per second = 2.119 cubic feet per minute, 15.85 gallons (U.S.) per minute.

1 litre per minute = 0.0005885 cubic foot per second, 0.004403 gallon per second.

Pressure

1 atmosphere = pressure exerted by 760 millimetres of mercury of standard density at 0°C, 14.70 pounds per square inch, 29.92 inches of mercury at 32°F, 33.90 feet of water at 39.2°F, 101.3 kilopascal.

1 millimeter of mercury (at 0°C) = 0.001316 atmosphere, 0.01934 pound per square inch, 0.04460 foot of water (4°C or 39.2°F), 0.0193 pound per square inch, 0.1333 kilopascal.

1 inch of water (at 39.2°F) = 0.00246 atmosphere, 0.0361 pound per square inch, 0.0736 inch of mercury (at 32°F), 0.2491 kilopascal.

1 foot of water (at 39.2°F) = 0.02950 atmosphere, 0.4335 pound per square inch, 0.8827 inch of mercury (at 32°F), 22.42 millimetres of mercury, 2.989 kilopascal.

1 inch of mercury (at 32°F) = 0.03342 atmosphere, 0.4912 pound per square inch, 1.133 feet of water, 13.60 inches of water (at 39.2°F), 3.386 kilopascal.

1 millibar (1/1000 bar) = 0.02953 inch of mercury. A bar is the pressure exerted by a force of one million dynes on a square centimetre of surface.

1 pound per square inch = 0.06805 atmosphere, 2.036 inches of mercury, 2.307 feet of water, 51.72 millimetres of mercury, 27.67 inches of water (at 39.2°F), 144 pounds per square foot, 2,304 ounces per square foot, 6.895 kilopascal.

1 pound per square foot = 0.00047 atmosphere, 0.00694 pound per square inch, 0.0160 foot of water, 0.391 millimetre of mercury, 0.04788 kilopascal.

Absolute pressure = the sum of the gage pressure and the barometric pressure.

1 ton (short) per square foot = 0.9451 atmosphere, 13.89 pounds per square inch, 9,765 kilograms per square metre.

Power

1 horse power = 746 watts, 1.014 metric horse power, 10.69 kilograms-calories per minute, 42.42 British thermal units per minute, 550 pound-feet per second, 33,000 pound-feet per minute.

1 kilowatt = 1.341 horse power, 1.360 metric horse power, 14.33 kilogram-calories per minute, 56.90 British thermal units per minute, 1,000 watts.

Heat (Mean Values)

1 British thermal unit = 0.2520 kilogram-calorie, 1,055 joules (absolute).

1 kilogram-calorie = 3.969 British thermal units, 4,187 joules.

1 British thermal unit per pound = 0.5556 kilogram-calorie per kilogram, 2.325 joules per gram.

1 gram-calorie per gram = 1.8 British thermal units per pound, 4.187 joules per gram.

Electrical

1 volt = potential required to produce current flow of 1 ampere through a resistance or impedance of 1 ohm, or current flow of 2 amperes through resistance of ½ ohm, etc.

1 ampere = current flow through a resistance or impedance of 1 ohm produced by a potential of 1 volt, or current flow through a resistance of 100 ohms produced by a potential of 100 volts, etc.

1 milliampere = 0.001 ampere.

1 ohm = resistance or impedance through which current of 1 ampere will flow under a potential of 1 volt.

1 microhm = 0.000001 ohm.

mho = Unit of conductance. In a direct current, circuit conductance in mhos is the reciprocal of number of ohms resistance.

1 watt = power developed by current flow of 1 ampere under potential of 1 volt. (DC, or AC with power factor unity.) See also Power.

1 joule = 1 watt second. A flow of 1 ampere through a resistance of 1 ohm for 1 second (see also Heat).

1 millijoule = 0.001 joule.

Radiation

1 curie = the emission of 3.70×10^{10} beta particles per second (the particles emitted per second from 1 gram of radium).

1 roentgen = the quantity of X-rays which will produce 2.08×10^{9} ion pairs in 1 cubic centimetre of dry air at 0°C and standard atmospheric pressure.

SI Units

Included in the conversion tables are the appropriate SI units. SI is an abbreviation for the International System of Units. Most of the industrialized nations of the world have already adopted this system. In all probability, the United States will adopt this system in the near future. SI units consist of seven base units and two supplementary units. Some of the units are derivations of these base and supplementary units.

Base Units

Quantity	Unit	SI Symbol
length	metre	m
mass	kilogram	kg
time	second	s
electric current	ampere	A
thermodynamic temperature	kelvin	K
amount of substance	mole	mol
luminous intensity	candela	cd

Supplementary Units

Quantity	Unit	SI Symbol
plane angle	radian	rad
solid angle	steradian	sr

Number Grouping

To facilitate the reading of numbers having four or more digits, the digits should be placed in groups of three separated by a space instead of commas—counting both to the left and to the right of the decimal point. In the case of four digits, the spacing is optional.

Prefixes

The usual practice is to use not more than four digits and then use the next higher prefix.

Name	Symbol	Multiplication Factor
tera	T	10^{12}
giga	G	10^{9}
mega	M	10^{6}
kilo	k	10^{3}
milli	m	10^{-3}
micro	μ	10^{-6}
nano	n	10^{-9}
pico	p	10^{-12}
femto	f	10^{-15}
atto	a	10^{-18}

Table 18-3B. Temperature Conversion, Celsius—Fahrenheit

Temp. Celsius = 5/9 (Temp. F − 32 deg.)   Temp. Fahrenheit = 9/5 × Temp. C + 32 deg.
Rankine (Fahrenheit Absolute) = Temp. F + 459.67 deg.   kelvin (Celsius Absolute) = Temp. C + 273.15 deg.
Freezing point of water: Celsius = 0 deg.; Fahr. = 32 deg.   Boiling point of water: Celsius = 100 deg.; Fahr. = 212 deg.
Absolute zero: Celsius = −273.15 deg.; Fahr. = −459.67 deg.

Celsius	Fahrenheit	Celsius	Fahrenheit	Celsius	Fahrenheit	Celsius	Fahrenheit
−273.15	−459.67	21	69.8	48.9	120	98	208.4
−200	−328	21.1	70	49	120.2	98.9	210
−100	−148	21.7	71	50	122	99	210.2
0	32	22	71.6	51	123.8	100	212
0.56	33	22.2	72	52	125.6	120	248
1	33.8	22.8	73	53	127.4	121.1	250
1.11	34	23	73.4	54	129.2	140	284
1.67	35	23.3	74	54.4	130	148.9	300
2	35.6	23.9	75	55	131	160	320
2.22	36	24	75.2	56	132.8	176.7	350
2.78	37	24.4	76	57	134.6	180	356
3	37.4	25	77	58	136.4	200	392
3.33	38	25.6	78	59	138.2	204.4	400
3.89	39	26	78.8	60	140	250	482
4	39.2	26.1	79	61	141.8	260	500
4.44	40	26.7	80	62	143.6	300	572
5	41	27	80.6	63	145.4	315.8	600
5.56	42	27.2	81	64	147.2	350	662
6	42.8	27.8	82	65	149	371.1	700
6.11	43	28	82.4	65.6	150	400	752
6.67	44	28.3	83	66	150.8	426.7	800
7	44.6	28.9	84	67	152.6	450	842
7.22	45	29	84.2	68	154.4	482.2	900
7.78	46	29.4	85	69	156.2	500	932
8	46.4	30	86	70	158	537.8	1000
8.33	47	30.6	87	71	159.8	600	1112
8.89	48	31	87.8	71.1	160	648.9	1200
9	48.2	31.1	88	72	161.6	700	1292
9.44	49	31.7	89	73	163.4	760	1400
10	50	32	89.6	74	165.2	800	1472
10.6	51	32.2	90	75	167	871.1	1600
11	51.8	32.8	91	76	168.8	900	1652
11.1	52	33	91.4	76.7	170	982.2	1800
11.7	53	33.3	92	77	171.6	1000	1832
12	53.6	33.9	93	78	172.4	1093.3	2000
12.2	54	34	93.2	79	174.2	1100	2012
12.8	55	34.4	94	80	176	1200	2192
13	55.4	35	95	81	177.8	1204.4	2200
13.3	56	35.6	96	82	179.6	1300	2372
13.9	57	36	96.8	82.2	180	1315.6	2400
14	57.2	36.1	97	83	181.4	1400	2552
14.4	58	36.7	98	84	183.2	1428	2600
15	59	37	98.6	85	185	1500	2732
15.6	60	37.2	99	86	186.8	1537.8	2800
16	60.8	37.8	100	87	188.6	1600	2912
16.1	61	38	100.4	87.8	190	1648.9	3000
16.7	62	39	102.2	88	190.4	1700	3092
17	62.6	40	104	89	192.2	1760	3200
17.2	63	41	105.8	90	194	1800	3272
17.8	64	42	107.6	91	195.8	1871.1	3400
18	64.4	43	109.4	92	197.6	1900	3452
18.3	65	43.3	110	93	199.4	1982	3600
18.9	66	44	111.2	93.3	200	2000	3632
19	66.2	45	113	94	201.2	2204.4	4000
19.4	67	46	114.8	95	203	2500	4532
20	68	47	116.6	96	204.8	2760	5000
20.6	69	48	118.4	97	206.6	3000	5432

Chapter 4

STRENGTH AND SIZE OF MATERIALS

Table 18-4A. Ultimate Strength of Common Metals

American Institute of Steel Construction, Inc.

Material	Stress in Kips per Square Inch					Modulus of Elasticity (psi)	Elongation (percent)
	Tension Ultimate	Elastic Limit	Compression Ultimate	Bending Ultimate	Shearing Ultimate		
Aluminum, Alloy 2014	62–70	42–60			38–42	10,600,000	†20–13
Aluminum, Alloy 6061	35–41	21–40			24–30	10,000,000	†22–12
Brass, 50% Zn	31	17·9	117	33.5	....	....	5.0
Brass, cast, common	18–24	6	30	20	36	9,000,000	
Brass, wire, hard	80						
Brass, wire, annealed	50	16	....	....	....	14,000,000	
Bronze, aluminum 5 to 7½%	75	40	120				
Bronze, Tobin, cast (38% Zn, 1½% Sn, ⅓% Pb)	66						
Bronze, Tobin, rolled (38% Zn, 1½% Sn, ⅓% Pb)	80	40	....	....	....	14,500,000	
Bronze, Tobin, c. rolled (38% Zn, 1½% Sn, ⅓% Pb)	100						
Copper, plates, rods, bolts	32–35	10	32				
Iron, cast, gray	18–24	....	....	25–33			
Iron, cast, malleable	27–35	15–20	46	30	40		
Iron, wrought, shapes	48	26	Tensile	Tensile	⅚ Tens.	28,000,000	
Steel, plates for cold pressing	48–58	½ Tens.	Tensile	Tensile	¾ Tens.	29,000,000	*1,500,000 / Tensile Strength
Steel, cars	50–65	½ Tens.	Tensile	Tensile	¾ Tens.	29,000,000	
Steel, locos., stat. boilers	55–65	½ Tens.	Tensile	Tensile	¾ Tens.	29,000,000	
Steel, bridges and bldgs., ships	60–72	33	Tensile	Tensile	¾ Tens.	29,000,000	
Steel, structural silicon	80–95	45	Tensile	Tensile	¾ Tens.	29,000,000	
Steel, struc. nickel (3.25% Ni)	85–100	50	Tensile	Tensile	¾ Tens.	29,000,000	
Steel, rivet, boiler	45–55	½ Tens.	Tensile	Tensile	¾ Tens.	29,000,000	
Steel, rivet, br., bldg., loco., cars	52–62	28	Tensile	Tensile	¾ Tens.	29,000,000	
Steel, rivet, ships	55–65	30	Tensile	Tensile	¾ Tens.	29,000,000	
Steel, rivet, high-tensile	70–85	38	Tensile	Tensile	¾ Tens.	29,000,000	
Steel, cast, soft	60	27	Tensile	Tensile	¾ Tens.	29,000,000	
Steel, cast, medium	70	31.5	Tensile	Tensile	¾ Tens.	29,000,000	
Steel, cast, hard	80	36	Tensile	Tensile	¾ Tens.	29,000,000	
Steel wire, unannealed	120	60					†24
Steel wire, annealed	80	40					†20
Steel wire, bridge cable	215	95					†17

* 8-in. gage length.
† 2-in. gage length.

Table 18-4B. Ultimate Strength PSI (Average) of Common Materials Other Than Metals

American Institute of Steel Construction, Inc.

Material	Average Ultimate Stress (psi)			Safe Working Stress (psi)			Modulus of Elasticity (psi)
	Compression	Tension	Bending	Compression	Bearing	Shearing	
Masonry, granite	....	....	....	420	600		
Masonry, limestone, bluestone	....	....	....	350	500		
Masonry, sandstone	....	....	....	280	400		
Masonry, rubble	....	....	....	140	250		
Masonry, brick, common	10,000	200	600				
Ropes, cast steel hoisting	....	80,000					
Rope, standing, derrick	....	70,000					
Rope, manila	....	8000					
Stone, bluestone	12,000	1200	2500	1200	1200	200	7,000,000
Stone, granite, gneiss	12,000	1200	1600	1200	1200	200	7,000,000
Stone, limestone, marble	8000	800	1500	800	800	150	7,000,000
Stone, sandstone	5000	150	1200	500	500	150	3,000,000
Stone, slate	10,000	3000	5000	1000	1000	175	14,000,000

Table 18-4C.   Standard Gages for Sheet Metal and Wire
American Institute of Steel Construction, Inc.

Name of Gage	United States Standard Gage*		The United States Steel Wire Gage	American or Brown & Sharpe Wire Gage	New Birmingham Standard Sheet & Hoop Gage	British Imperial or English Legal Standard Wire Gage	Birmingham or Stubs Iron Wire Gage
Principal Use	Uncoated Steel Sheets and Light Plates		Steel Wire except Music Wire	Nonferrous Sheets and Wire	Iron and Steel Sheets and Hoops		Strips, Bands, Hoops and Wire
Gage No.	Weight (oz per sq ft)	Approx. Thickness (inches)			Thickness (inches)		Wire
7/0's			0.4900		0.6666	0.500	
6/0's			0.4615	0.5800	0.6250	0.464	
5/0's			0.4305	0.5165	0.5883	0.432	0.500
4/0's			0.3938	0.4600	0.5416	0.400	0.454
3/0's			0.3625	0.4096	0.5000	0.372	0.425
2/0's			0.3310	0.3648	0.4452	0.348	0.380
0			0.3065	·0.3249	0.3964	0.324	0.340
1			0.2830	0.2893	0.3532	0.300	0.300
2			0.2625	0.2576	0.3147	0.276	0.284
3	160	0.2391	0.2437	0.2294	0.2804	0.252	0.259
4	150	0.2242	0.2253	0.2043	0.2500	0.232	0.238
5	140	0.2092	0.2070	0.1819	0.2225	0.212	0.220
6	130	0.1943	0.1920	0.1620	0.1981	0.192	0.203
7	120	0.1793	0.1770	0.1443	0.1764	0.176	0.180
8	110	0.1644	0.1620	0.1285	0.1570	0.160	0.165
9	100	0.1495	0.1483	0.1144	0.1398	0.144	0.148
10	90	0.1345	0.1350	0.1019	0.1250	0.128	0.134
11	80	0.1196	0.1205	0.0907	0.1113	0.116	0.120
12	70	0.1046	0.1055	0.0808	0.0991	0.104	0.109
13	60	0.0897	0.0915	0.0720	0.0882	0.092	0.095
14	50	0.0747	0.0800	0.0641	0.0785	0.080	0.083
15	45	0.0673	0.0720	0.0571	0.0699	0.072	0.072
16	40	0.0598	0.0625	0.0508	0.0625	0.064	0.065
17	36	0.0538	0.0540	0.0453	0.0556	0.056	0.058
18	32	0.0478	0.0475	0.0403	0.0495	0.048	0.049
19	28	0.0418	0.0410	0.0359	0.0440	0.040	0.042
20	24	0.0359	0.0348	0.0320	0.0392	0.036	0.035
21	22	0.0329	0.0318	0.0285	0.0349	0.032	0.032
22	20	0.0299	0.0286	0.0253	0.0313	0.028	0.028
23	18	0.0269	0.0258	0.0226	0.0278	0.024	0.025
24	16	0.0239	0.0230	0.0201	0.0248	0.022	0.022
25	14	0.0209	0.0204	0.0179	0.0220	0.020	0.020
26	12	0.0179	0.0181	0.0159	0.0196	0.018	0.018
27	11	0.0164	0.0173	0.0142	0.0175	0.0164	0.016
28	10	0.0149	0.0162	0.0126	0.0156	0.0148	0.014
29	9	0.0135	0.0150	0.0113	0.0139	0.0136	0.013
30	8	0.0120	0.0140	0.0100	0.0123	0.0124	0.012
31	7	0.0105	0.0132	0.0089	0.0110	0.0116	0.010
32	6.5	0.0097	0.0128	0.0080	0.0098	0.0108	0.009
33	6	0.0090	0.0118	0.0071	0.0087	0.0100	0.008
34	5.5	0.0082	0.0104	0.0063	0.0077	0.0092	0.007
35	5	0.0075	0.0095	0.0056	0.0069	0.0084	0.005
36	4.5	0.0067	0.0090	0.0050	0.0061	0.0076	0.004
37	4.25	0.0064	0.0085	0.0045	0.0054	0.0068	
38	4	0.0060	0.0080	0.0040	0.0048	0.0060	
39			0.0075	0.0035	0.0043	0.0052	
40			0.0070	0.0031	0.0039	0.0048	

* U.S. Standard Gage is officially a weight gage, in oz per sq ft as tabulated. The Approx. Thickness shown is the "Manufacturers' Standard" of the American Iron and Steel Institute, based on steel as weighing 501.81 lbs per cu ft (489.6 true weight plus 2.5 percent for average over-run in area and thickness). The A.I.S.I. standard nomenclature for flat rolled carbon steel is as follows:

Widths, Inches	Thicknesses, Inch							
	0.2500 and thicker	0.2499 to 0.2031	0.2030 to 0.1875	0.1874 to 0.0568	0.0567 to 0.0344	0.0343 to 0.0255	0.0254 to 0.0142	0.0141 and thinner
To 3½ incl.	Bar	Bar	Strip	Strip	Strip	Strip	Sheet	Sheet
Over 3½ to 6 incl.	Bar	Bar	Strip	Strip	Strip	Sheet	Sheet	Sheet
Over 6 to 12 incl.	Plate	Strip	Strip	Strip	Sheet	Sheet	Sheet	Sheet
Over 12 to 32 incl.	Plate	Sheet	Sheet	Sheet	Sheet	Sheet	Sheet	Black Plate
Over 32 to 48 incl.	Plate	Sheet	Sheet	Sheet	Sheet	Sheet	Sheet	Sheet
Over 48	Plate	Plate	Plate	Sheet	Sheet	Sheet	Sheet	—

Table 18-4D. Coefficients of Expansion

American Institute of Steel Construction, Inc.

The coefficient of linear expansion (ε) is the change in length, per unit of length, for a change of one degree of temperature. The coefficient of surface expansion is approximately two times the linear coefficient, and the coefficient of volume expansion, for solids, is approximately three times the linear coefficient.

A bar, free to move, will increase in length with an increase in temperature and will decrease in length with a decrease in temperature. The change in length will be $\varepsilon t l$, where ε is the coefficient of linear expansion, t the change in temperature, and l the length. If the ends of a bar are fixed, a change in temperature (t) will cause a change in the unit stress of $E\varepsilon t$, and in the total stress of $AE\varepsilon t$, where A is the cross sectional area of the bar and E the modulus of elasticity.

The following table gives the coefficient of linear expansion for 100°, or 100 times the value indicated above.

Example: A piece of medium steel is exactly 40 ft long at 60°F. Find the length at 90°F assuming the ends free to move.

$$\text{Change of length} = \varepsilon t l = \frac{0.00065 \times 30 \times 40}{100} = 0.0078 \text{ ft.}$$

The length at 90°F is 40.0078 ft.

Example: A piece of medium steel is exactly 40 ft long and the ends are fixed. If the temperature increases 30°F, what is the resulting change in the unit stress?

$$\text{Change in unit stress} = E\varepsilon t = \frac{29,000,000 \times 0.00065 \times 30}{100} = 5655 \text{ psi.}$$

Coefficients of Expansion for 100 Degrees = 100ε

Materials	Linear Expansion		Materials	Linear Expansion	
	Celsius	Fahrenheit		Celsius	Fahrenheit
Metals and Alloys			Stone and Masonry		
Aluminum, wrought	0.00231	0.00128	Ashlar masonry	0.00063	0.00035
Brass	0.00188	0.00104	Brick masonry	0.00061	0.00034
Bronze	0.00181	0.00101	Cement, portland	0.00126	0.00070
Copper	0.00168	0.00093	Concrete	0.00099	0.00055
Iron, cast, gray	0.00106	0.00059	Granite	0.00080	0.00044
Iron, wrought	0.00120	0.00067	Limestone	0.00076	0.00042
Iron, wire	0.00124	0.00069	Marble	0.00081	0.00045
Lead	0.00286	0.00159	Plaster	0.00166	0.00092
Magnesium, various alloys	0.00290	0.00160	Rubble masonry	0.00063	0.00035
Nickel	0.00126	0.00070	Sandstone	0.00097	0.00054
Steel, mild	0.00117	0.00065	Slate	0.00080	0.00044
Steel, stainless, 18-8	0.00178	0.00099			
Zinc, rolled	0.00311	0.00173			
Timber			Timber		
Fir ⎫	0.00037	0.00021	Fir ⎫	0.0058	0.0032
Maple ⎬ parallel to fiber	0.00064	0.00036	Maple ⎬ perpendicular to fiber	0.0048	0.0027
Oak ⎬	0.00049	0.00027	Oak ⎬	0.0054	0.0030
Pine ⎭	0.00054	0.00030	Pine ⎭	0.0034	0.0019

Expansion of Water
Maximum Density = 1

°C	Volume	°C	Volume	°C	Volume	°C	Volume	°C	Volume	°C	Volume
0	1.000126	10	1.000257	30	1.004234	50	1.011877	70	1.022384	90	1.035829
4	1.000000	20	1.001732	40	1.007627	60	1.016954	80	1.029003	100	1.043116

Table 18-4E. Sizes and Capacity of Steel Pipe

Nominal Pipe Size (inches)	Outside Diameter (inches)	Inside Diameter (inches)	Capacity of One Foot Length of Pipe		Nominal Pipe Size (inches)	Outside Diameter (inches)	Inside Diameter (inches)	Capacity of One Foot Length of Pipe	
			Cubic Feet	Gallons				Cubic Feet	Gallons
Schedule 40 Pipe					Schedule 80 Pipe				
½	0.840	0.622	0.0021	0.0158	½	0.840	0.546	0.0016	0.012
¾	1.050	0.824	0.0037	0.0276	¾	1.050	0.742	0.0030	0.022
1	1.315	1.049	0.0060	0.0449	1	1.315	0.957	0.0050	0.037
1¼	1.660	1.380	0.0104	0.0774	1¼	1.660	1.278	0.0089	0.066
1½	1.900	1.610	0.0142	0.106	1½	1.900	1.500	0.0123	0.092
2	2.375	2.067	0.0233	0.174	2	2.375	1.939	0.0205	0.153
2½	2.875	2.469	0.0332	0.248	2½	2.875	2.323	0.0294	0.220
3	3.500	3.068	0.0513	0.383	3	3.500	2.900	0.0548	0.344
3½	4.000	3.548	0.0686	0.513	3½	4.000	3.364	0.0617	0.458
4	4.500	4.026	0.0883	0.660	4	4.500	3.826	0.0798	0.597
5	5.563	5.047	0.139	1.04	5	5.563	4.813	0.126	0.947
6	6.625	6.065	0.200	1.50	6	6.625	5.761	0.181	1.35
8	8.625	7.981	0.3474	2.60	8	8.625	7.625	0.3171	2.38
10	10.75	10.020	0.5475	4.10	10	10.75	9.564	0.4989	3.74
12	12.75	11.938	0.7773	5.82	12	12.75	11.376	0.7058	5.28
14	14.0	13.126	0.9397	7.03	14	14.0	12.500	0.8522	6.38
16	16.0	15.000	1.2272	9.16	16	16.0	14.314	1.1175	8.36
18	18.0	16.876	1.5533	11.61	18	18.0	16.126	1.4183	10.61
20	20.0	18.814	1.9305	14.44	20	20.0	17.938	1.7550	13.13
24	24.0	22.626	2.7920	20.87	24	24.0	21.564	2.536	19.0

MISCELLANEOUS DATA

Table 18-4F. Capacity of Cylinders or Cylindrical Tanks
U.S. Gallons and Barrels (Petroleum) per Foot of Length or Height

$$\text{Capacity per foot, U.S. gallons} = \frac{\pi D^2}{4} \times 7.481$$

D = Inside diameter in feet

For capacity in barrels (petroleum), divide by 42

Diameter, ft	Capacity per ft Gals	Bbls	Diameter, ft	Capacity per ft Gals	Bbls	Diameter, ft	Capacity per ft Gals	Bbls
1	5.8751	0.13989	51	15277.3	363.826	101	59932.6	1426.91
2	23.5007	0.55981	52	15883.9	378.235	102	61125.3	1455.30
3	52.8766	1.258	53	16503.3	392.921	103	62329.7	1483.98
4	94.0029	2.2389	54	17131.9	407.888	104	63549.5	1512.94
5	146.879	3.49699	55	17792.4	423.135	105	64773.7	1542.17
6	211.506	5.03565	56	18424.5	438.662	106	66013.4	1571.68
7	287.883	6.85409	57	19088.4	454.468	107	67264.8	1601.48
8	376.011	8.95228	58	19764.1	470.554	108	68528.0	1631.55
9	475.889	11.3302	59	20451.5	486.920	109	69802.9	1661.90
10	587.517	13.9879	60	21150.6	503.565	110	71089.5	1692.54
11	710.892	16.9254	61	21861.5	520.491	111	72387.9	1723.45
12	846.022	20.1425	62	22584.2	537.696	112	73698.1	1754.64
13	992.902	23.6396	63	23318.6	555.182	113	75019.7	1786.12
14	1151.53	27.4164	64	24064.7	572.946	114	76353.5	1817.87
15	1321.92	31.4729	65	24822.6	590.991	115	77699.2	1849.90
16	1504.04	35.8091	66	25592.2	609.314	116	79056.2	1882.21
17	1697.92	40.425	67	26373.6	627.918	117	80425.1	1914.80
18	1903.56	45.3209	68	27166.8	646.802	118	81805.9	1947.68
19	2120.94	50.4965	69	27971.7	665.966	119	83198.1	1980.83
20	2350.07	55.9517	70	28788.3	685.409	120	84602.2	2014.26
21	2590.95	61.6868	71	29616.7	705.132	121	86018.3	2047.97
22	2843.58	67.7016	72	30456.9	725.134	122	87438.8	2081.97
23	3107.89	73.9963	73	31308.8	745.418	123	88885.5	2116.24
24	3384.02	80.5704	74	32172.4	765.980	124	90261.9	2150.79
25	3671.98	87.4247	75	33047.8	786.821	125	91799.2	2185.61
26	3971.69	94.5584	76	33935.0	807.944	126	93274.4	2220.73
27	4283.00	101.972	77	34833.9	829.346	127	94760.7	2256.12
28	4606.13	109.665	78	35744.5	851.026	128	96259.1	2291.79
29	4941.02	117.638	79	36666.9	872.987	129	97768.6	2327.73
30	5286.36	125.891	80	37601.1	895.228	130	99290.2	2363.96
31	5646.04	134.424	81	38547.0	917.749	131	100824	2400.45
32	6016.18	143.237	82	39504.6	940.549	132	102369	2437.26
33	6398.06	152.328	83	40474.1	963.630	133	103927	2474.33
34	6791.70	161.701	84	41455.2	986.989	134	105495	2511.67
35	7197.09	171.352	85	42448.1	1010.63	135	107075	2549.31
36	7614.25	181.284	86	43452.7	1034.55	136	108667	2587.21
37	8043.11	191.494	87	44469.2	1058.75	137	110271	2625.39
38	8483.71	201.984	88	45497.3	1083.23	138	111887	2663.86
39	8936.13	212.756	89	46537.2	1107.99	139	113514	2702.61
40	9400.30	223.807	90	47588.9	1133.02	140	115513	2741.64
41	9876.13	235.136	91	48652.3	1158.34	141	116804	2780.94
42	10363.8	246.747	92	49727.4	1183.94	142	118467	2820.53
43	10863.2	258.636	93	50814.4	1209.82	143	120141	2860.39
44	11374.3	270.806	94	51913.1	1235.79	144	121827	2900.53
45	11897.2	283.256	95	53023.4	1262.41	145	123525	2940.97
46	12431.8	295.984	96	54145.6	1289.13	146	125235	2981.66
47	12978.2	308.992	97	55280.1	1316.14	147	126957	3022.66
48	13536.4	322.283	98	56425.1	1343.40	148	128690	3063.93
49	14106.3	335.850	99	57582.6	1370.96	149	130434	3105.46
50	14688.0	349.699	100	58751.7	1398.79	150	132192	3147.29

Appendices

Appendix A

ORGANIZATIONS WITH FIRE PROTECTION INTERESTS IN THE UNITED STATES OF AMERICA AND OTHER COUNTRIES

Part A of this Appendix tells of the work of the National Fire Protection Association, publishers of this HANDBOOK. As fire is a universal threat, it is natural that a large number of other organizations take active interest in fire prevention and control. The degree of interest and activity varies widely. Parts B through E of this Appendix provide information on other organizations having demonstrated interest in fire prevention and control. Parts A through E are titled as follows:

A. National Fire Protection Association.

B. National Property Insurance Organizations in the United States of America with Fire Protection Interests.

C. National Fire Service Organizations in the United States of America.

D. National Noncommercial, Trade, Professional, and Labor Associations or Organizations in the United States of America with Fire Protection Interests.

E. International and Fire Organizations in Other Countries.

A.   National Fire Protection Association

The National Fire Protection Association (NFPA) is a scientific and educational membership organization concerned with the causes, prevention, and control of destructive fire. Organized in 1896 and incorporated in 1930 under the Laws of Massachusetts, NFPA is a private, voluntary, charitable, and tax-exempt association.

NFPA views the subjects of fire, fire prevention, and fire protection in an objective, business-like manner and accomplishes its purposes through the action and interaction of its membership, the Board of Directors, the staff, and numerous committees. The Association's activities may be summarized as follows: (1) fire safety technical standards development, (2) information exchange, (3) technical advisory services, (4) public education, (5) fire safety research, and (6) services to public protection agencies.

Activities

1. Fire safety technical standards are developed by more than 150 committees of the Association, each of which provides a balanced representation of the affected interests, including the public. Members of committees serve voluntarily and without compensation, and are not necessarily members of the NFPA. More than 2,400 expert individuals participate in these activities. Once approved by the membership at either one of two meetings, held annually standards are published and made available for voluntary adoption by any organization or jurisdiction with power to enforce. The Association views standards development by way of consensus agreements as the fairest and best method available to achieve standardization of safety requirements.

NFPA standards are published in individual pamphlet form as well as in a fifteen-volume compilation set called *National Fire Codes*.

2. Information exchange is accomplished through various services to members. These include the provision of timely and factual information on significant fires and fire-related developments and the dissemination of information relating to the latest techniques in fire prevention, protection, and suppression. The media for these activities are:

Fire Journal, a bimonthly technical journal published by NFPA and distributed as part of its services to members.

Fire News, a monthly newsletter for members.

Technical Committee Reports are compilations of the recommendations of technical committees on proposed new standards or amendments for action at the Association's upcoming regular meeting. Together with the *Technical Committee Documentation*, containing comments and committee action on comments, they afford members and the concerned public an opportunity to review standards proposals in advance of the meeting and encourage meaningful participation.

The NFPA regularly meets and transacts business twice a year; at the *Annual Meeting* in May, and at the *Fall Meeting* in November. Both meetings are open to the general public, and all interested persons are urged to attend. Reports of committees are discussed and acted upon, and papers of both general and technical nature are presented. Both regular meetings are appropriately recorded, and a summary of actions is published in *Fire Journal*.

Yearbook and Committee List is a guide to NFPA committees and activities. It contains all relevant information on Association operations, membership sections, committees, and the external relations of the Association.

3. Technical advisory services are provided on both formal and informal bases to anyone having a legitimate concern. Special services are established in certain areas of fire safety to promote the use of and provide guidance to the application of the respective standards. These include Electrical Safety, Flammable Liquids, Gases, and Marine Fire Safety.

A host of technical books, pamphlets and periodicals support the advisory services program. *Fire Command!* magazine is of interest to the fire service. *Fire Technology*, a quarterly journal, covers topics in the field of fire protection engineering. This FIRE PROTECTION HANDBOOK, now in its 14th Edition, is recognized throughout the world as the authoritative reference on fire protection. Several hundred other publications cover a wide range of topics. The NFPA Library functions as a significant resource of literature and technical data on fire collected from international sources, open to all interested persons.

4. Within its public education program the NFPA develops, produces, and distributes fire safety educational materials containing guidance and instructions for the general public. Some of the nationally known features are Sparky the Fire Dog, Fire Prevention Week and the Spring Clean-up Campaign. Television, film, and print media are used to carry the Association's fire safety messages.

5. Data collection and analysis as well as a number of applied research programs make up NFPA's fire safety research activities. Reports on fires are analyzed and then classified by type of property, hazard and cause, and fire service-related information. Fire data is used by members of standards committees in formulating informed judgments, and in virtually all other activities of the Association. Others relying on NFPA fire data include agencies of the federal and state governments and educational and research institutions.

Many of the NFPA applied research programs are funded by agencies of government. They range from the development and implementation of training programs and seminars, through design of management models and including the design and implementation of data systems. The research team is composed of "talent pools," providing that unit a truly multidisciplinary dimension.

6. Services to public protection agencies include provision of information and advice to fire departments, fire marshal's departments, municipal, state, and federal authorities, and other agencies and individuals involved in public fire protection. Informational records and data related to fire service operations, management, and fire prevention inspection and enforcement are developed. Education, training, and professional advancement in the field of public fire protection is encouraged and promoted.

Membership

The purpose of NFPA membership is two-fold: (1) to facilitate and encourage information exchange; and (2) to enhance the standards development process by providing the broadest possible democratic forum for the consideration of proposed fire safety standards.

The Association's Bylaws in 1975 authorize four membership categories: (1) Member, (2) Organization Member, (3) Sustaining Member, and (4) Honorary Member. The first two types have the broadest application.

A "Member" may be any individual, firm, corporation, institution, fire department, fire brigade, or other public or private agency interested in the Association's work. Through membership none is pledged to any course of action. Each Member has one vote at the regular meetings. Membership dues are intentionally kept at a modest level to allow and encourage the broadest possible participation.

An "Organization Member" may be a national or international institute, society, or association, or a regional, state, provincial, or local institute, societies, or associations whose principal purpose or function is related to the reduction of fire loss. Each Organization Member has six votes in the affairs of the Association at the NFPA regular meetings.

Special interest groups coordinate their activities within "Sections" of the membership which, in 1975, include representation of the industrial, railroad, electrical, chief electrical inspector, fire marshal, and fire service interests.

Administration

The NFPA Board of Directors has general charge of the affairs of the Association. Eighteen directors elected by the membership serve in three staggered three-year terms, and no elected director may serve for more than two successive three-year terms. Six elected officers, the two last living past chairmen of the Board, and the President and Vice President (members of the paid staff) complete the Board of Directors.

The NFPA Staff consists of over 200 professional and secretarial/clerical personnel.

The Association is headquartered in Boston, Massachusetts, U.S.A., and maintains a staff in Washington, D.C., for the purpose of liaison with the federal government and its Washington area organization membership.

External Relationships

The NFPA participates in the activities of the International Standards Organization, a unit of the United Nations Organization in Geneva, Switzerland, and is a member of the Joint Council of National Fire Service Organizations. The Association also participates in the activities of the American National Standards Institute and the several consensus standard and testing organizations in the United States.

Articles of Organization
Adopted May 17, 1971; Effective May 15, 1972.

ARTICLE 1 — NAME. The name of this corporation is NATIONAL FIRE PROTECTION ASSOCIATION, INC.

ARTICLE 2 — PURPOSES. The purposes of the corporation (hereinafter referred to as the Association) shall be to promote the science and improve the methods of fire protection and prevention; to obtain and circulate information on these subjects, and to secure the cooperation of its members and the public in establishing proper safeguards against loss of life and property by fire.

ARTICLE 3 — NATURE OF ORGANIZATION. The Association is a membership corporation not organized for the purposes of realizing pecuniary profit or gain to its members, but the Association may pay reasonable compensation for services rendered and may indemnify the directors, officers, employees, and agents of the Association from certain unexpected consequences of their actions or omissions in the affairs of the Association, to the extent provided from time to time by action of the Board of Directors. Through membership no member is pledged to any course of action.

ARTICLE 4 — MEMBERSHIP. The membership of the Association shall consist of such class or classes with such qualifications, rights, and obligations as shall be set forth in the Bylaws of the Association as the same may from time to time be amended.

ARTICLE 5 — OFFICERS AND DIRECTORS. The officers of the Association shall be a President, Treasurer, Secretary, Chairman, First Vice Chairman, and Second Vice Chairman of the Board of Directors, and such additional officers as shall from time to time be designated by the Board of Directors. There shall be a Board of Directors consisting of not less than fifteen nor more than thirty Directors.

The powers and duties of the President, Treasurer, and Secretary shall be such as usually pertain to the Chief Executive, Financial, and Recording Officers of a corporation respectively. Said Officers shall have such additional powers and duties, and all other Officers shall have such powers and duties, as may from time to time be assigned by the Board of Directors.

The Board of Directors shall have general charge of the affairs of the Association, and the Board shall conduct those affairs through the Officers of the Association and such Committee or Committees as shall from time to time be formed pursuant to the Bylaws of the Association.

ARTICLE 6 — ANNUAL MEETING. The membership of the Association shall meet annually within or without the Commonwealth of Massachusetts to elect such Officers, Directors of the Association, and others in accordance with the Bylaws, and to act on such other business as may properly come before the meeting.

ARTICLE 7 — AMENDMENT. These Articles may be amended at any meeting of the Association members, duly called and held, by a vote of two-thirds of the votes represented at the meeting, notice of the proposed amendment having been given to all members at least sixty days previous.

B. National Property Insurance Organizations in the United States of America with Fire Protection Interests

American Insurance Association, 85 Johns St., New York, NY 10038

A trade association servicing a large number of companies operating in the property and casualty insurance fields, it is a multiline organization designed to help its member and subscriber companies meet the diverse problems confronting the insurance business. It was created in September 1964 by merging the National Board of Fire Underwriters (organized 1866), the Association of Casualty and Surety Companies (organized 1926), and the former American Insurance Association (founded 1953).

The basic objectives of the Association are to promote the economic, legislative, and public standing of its participating insurance companies. In recognition of the historical bond between the insurance industry's social need, the Association makes its services available, where appropriate, to noninsurance interests, such as government agencies.

Operating through headquarters in New York (with regional offices in San Francisco, Chicago, and Washington, D.C.), it provides a range of services to its member companies including legislative services; engineering and safety services; and research and review of claim and loss adjustment functions. In 1971 the Municipal Survey Service of the American Insurance Association was transferred to the Insurance Services Office.

The Engineering and Safety Service of the American Insurance Association has more (member) subscribers than the Association itself. As of 1975 there were 230 subscriber companies to this Service (including foreign and international insurance companies). The Service offers guidance in total loss control, including fire protection, environmental protection, industrial hygiene, product safety, building code requirements, and accident prevention. There are about 7,000 loss prevention engineers working for their subscriber insurance companies, and thus they have direct impact on the extremely important loss prevention activities of these companies. The AIA's Engineering and Safety Service issues 18 separate series of Bulletins for subscribers, including "Chemical Hazards," "Special Hazards," "Occupational Safety and Health," and "Product Liability." One series, known as "Special Interest Bulletins," is of value and is available to all fire protection interests. They also issue a wide range of Accident Prevention Publications, Craft Safety Cards, Supervisor's Safety Memos, Catastrophe Reports, Suggested Codes and Standards (including the National Building Code and a Fire Prevention Code), Fire Resistance Ratings (of building assemblies), Research Publications, and a host of fire prevention and natural hazard guides, folders, and forms.

American Mutual Insurance Alliance, 20 North Wacker Dr., Chicago, IL 60606

The Alliance, organized in 1922, is a national organization of a large number (about 100 in 1975) of mutual fire and casualty insurance companies providing engineering, legal, legislative, educational, and public relations services for its member companies. Its staff is oriented, in part, to fire loss prevention studies, and this work is carried out through the Alliance's Accident and Fire Prevention Department with advice from a Loss Control Committee and its Fire Safety Subcommittee composed of engineers and other technically qualified persons in its member companies.

The Alliance serves its members by organizing technical training sessions on various aspects of fire protection engineering, and maintains training aid materials for instructing new company inspection and engineering personnel. Its fire safety educational material and its "Journal," issued quarterly, are widely distributed and used. It also has a most effective public service program dedicated to promoting home fire safety.

Factory Mutual System, 1151 Boston-Providence Turnpike, Norwood, MA 02062

The Factory Mutual System is composed of four large mutual property insurance companies (Allendale Insurance; Arkwright-Boston Insurance; Philadelphia Manufacturers Insurance; Protection Mutual Insurance) and two System associates (Factory Mutual International and Factory Mutual Engineering and Research). It was founded in 1835 to provide mutual fire insurance coverage for large industrial and commercial properties in the United States and Canada, but is now multi-international in scope. It functions to minimize fire and extended coverage losses, interruption of production, and to provide insurance at cost through loss prevention inspections of plants, research, and consultation services to its insureds.

It is well known for its testing and approval services. Two general classes of products are listed in FM's Approval Guide (issued annually): those used for the control or prevention of property damage, and those that in themselves would present serious hazards if not properly designed. Factory Mutual System "approval" refers to a product which has been tested according to Factory Mutual Standards and found suitable for general application, subject to any limitations stated in the approval and usually in the listing. "Acceptance" refers to a specific installation or arrangement of equipment or materials. Devices included in the FM's Approval Guide are "approved"; installations incorporating these devices, if found satisfactory following review of plans and inspection of completed work, are "accepted."

An exceptional service available from the Factory Mutual System since 1973 is the multivolume, loose leaf *Loss Prevention Data* books (with an updating service) which is available to all interested persons for a fee. They contain information and recommendations for the prevention of fire, explosions, wind damage, electrical breakdowns, and boiler and machinery accidents. The Factory Mutual System also produces training films on fire and explosion hazards. It publishes numerous loss prevention materials, among them "The Handbook of Property Conservation," a 264-page, pocket-size manual directed to Property Conservation Directors and maintaining active plant emergency organizations (P.E.O.). The Factory Mutual "Record," covering property conservation engineering and management, published bimonthly and sent free to Factory Mutual members, is also available on a subscription basis.

Industrial Risk Insurers, 85 Woodland St., Hartford CT 06102

This group, representing a merger of the **Factory Insurance Association** and the **Oil Insurance Association**, is a combined pool of industrial risk underwriters with high loss prevention expertise. The merger became effective on December 1, 1975. The group services risks in the United States and for foreign properties of United States-domiciled insureds. The Association writes property damage and business interruption insurance against fire and allied perils. It also provides substantial engineering, underwriting, and reinsurance support for the Canadian Industrial Risks Insurers, which underwrites Canadian accounts under terms and conditions similar to those in the United States.

The headquarters of the Association are in Hartford, Connecticut, with regional offices in Hartford, Chicago, and San Francisco. There are twenty-eight field offices in major cities, and over five hundred fire protection engineers serving its policyholders.

Surveys of insured properties are conducted on a scheduled basis to review and to recommend improvements in selected areas of loss prevention and control which include: (1) extension of protection systems to new buildings and processes, (2) application of new protection methods resulting from research and development, (3) preplanning for emergencies, (4) proper maintenance and testing of equipment and administration of procedures.

Other visits are made for loss investigations, for consultation regarding changes occurring between surveys, and, when repairs or modifications of protective equipment are necessary, to suggest temporary expedients to maintain adequate protection and means to reduce the duration of the impairment. A training laboratory is maintained to enhance the capabilities of its engineers and to familiarize representatives of its policyholders with fire protection equipment. The association publishes the "SENTINEL," a bimonthly magazine, and other literature in the interest of protecting American industry in general and especially for the benefit of its policyholders.

A headquarters engineering group cooperates with industrial organizations in research. The burning properties of materials and the capabilities of protective devices and systems are analyzed in full-scale tests. The test results are used in the development of recommended good practice guidelines and, for the use of its staff, interpretive guides to NFPA Standards.

Insurance Services Office, 160 Water St., New York, NY 10038

A voluntary, nonprofit, unincorporated association of insurers engaged in casualty and property insurance (founded: 1971). It makes available to any insurer rating, statistical, actuarial, policy form, and related services. The ISO functions, as provided by law, as an insurance rating organization; as an insurance service or advisory organization; and as a statistical agent. In 1975 it served approximately 1,200 affiliated insurance companies and employees, and had a country-wide staff of 4,500.

It was formed in 1971 through the consolidation of several national insurance industry service organizations including the Fire Insurance Research and Actuarial Association, the Inland Marine Insurance Bureau, the Insurance Rating Board, the Multi-Line Insurance Rating Bureau, and the National Insurance Actuarial and Statistical Association. Most of the former state and regional fire rating organizations in the United States are now a part of ISO. ISO operates through regional and state field offices, includes seven major regional offices in Atlanta, Boston, Chicago, Denver, New York, Philadelphia, and San Francisco.

ISO services 13 kinds of insurance including commercial fire and allied lines, and dwelling fire and allied lines. The other 11 are: boiler and machinery; commercial automobile; commercial multiple line; crime; general liability; glass; homeowners; inland marine; nuclear energy liability and property; private passenger automobile; and workmen's compensation and employers' liability.

The municipal grading function for the larger cities was transferred to ISO from the American Insurance Association in 1971. The "Grading Schedule for Municipal Fire Protection," the "Guide for Determination of Required Fire Flow," the "Fire Flow Tests-Discharge Tables for Circular Outlets — Function Losses in Pipes," and the "Fire Department Pumper Tests and Fire Stream Tables" are important publications available from the ISO.

Other Insurance Organizations

There are many other important groups performing varied fire protection and inspection services on behalf of the insurance industry and their insureds. Among these are:

American Hull Insurance Syndicate, 99 John St., New York, NY   10038

An insurance syndicate created to insure vessels of high value.

American Institute of Marine Underwriters, 99 John St., New York, NY   10038

Organized to serve the marine underwriters and to promote, advance, and protect their interests.

Association of Mill and Elevator Mutual Insurance Companies, 2 North Riverside Plaza, Chicago, IL   60606

A group of mutual insurance companies serving the mill and elevator industry's insurance needs.

Assurex International, P. O. Box 1270, Wheeling, WV 26003

Formed to provide a national chain of local agents and brokers for solicitation and servicing of national accounts (formerly Insurance Service Associates).

Conference of Special Risk Underwriters, c/o Insurance Services Office, 160 Water St., New York, NY   10038

Organized to serve as a medium for the exchange of information and to suggest safeguards and protection from the perils insured against for the benefit of its members and the public.

Cotton Fire and Marine Underwriters (A Division of Marine Office — Appleton & Cox Corp.), 1810 Commerce St., P. O. Box 1849, Dallas, TX   75221

A group of the cotton departments of insurance carriers which underwrites insurance against fire, marine, and other risks on cotton warehouses, gins, compresses, and other buildings and facilities for the storage, processing, and handling of cotton.

General Adjustment Bureau, Inc, 123 William St., New York, NY   10038 (a Division of UAL, Inc.)

A loss and claims adjusting organization with over 600 offices in the 50 states, the Caribbean, London (England), Brussels (Belgium), and Madrid (Spain).

Improved Risk Mutuals, 15 North Broadway, White Plains, NY   10601

A voluntary arrangement of 17 mutual companies to furnish greater insurance underwriting capacity than each company can offer. Coverages include fire and allied lines, commercial inland marine, and excess lines. Provides inspection and risk improvement services to help reduce the number and severity of fires.

Insurance Information Institute, 110 William St., New York, NY   10038

Created to attain public understanding and acceptance of all lines of the insurance business (except life, accident, and health) on behalf of the over 160 companies who are its members.

Insurance Institute for Highway Safety (The), Watergate 600, Washington, DC   20037

An independent, nonprofit, scientific and educational organization dedicated to reducing losses (deaths, injuries and property damage) resulting from motor vehicle accidents on the nation's highways. It is supported by the American Insurance Association, the National Association of Automotive Mutual Insurance Companies, the National Association of Independent Insurers, and several independent insurance companies.

Mill Mutual Fire Prevention Bureau, 2 North Riverside Plaza, Chicago, IL   60606

A group of insurance companies have established the Bureau to investigate loss/cause of mill and elevator fires and explosions and to provide engineering technology in the interest of prevention of such fires and explosions for the benefit of their members.

Mutual Atomic Energy Reinsurance Pool (administered by the American Mutual Reinsurance Company), One East Wacker Dr., Chicago, IL   60601

A Pool which has the capacity to insure in excess of $24 million per occurrence on any one nuclear reactor installation or any other operation involving the radiation hazard that meets the requirements of an Underwriting Committee of the Pool.

Mutual Reinsurance Bureau, 1550 Pearl St., P. O. Box 188, Belvidere, IL   61008

An organization to provide property and casualty reinsurance for a large segment of the mutual insurance industry, plus statistical services to member companies.

National Association of Insurance Agents, Inc., 85 John St., New York, NY   10038

An association to uphold the principle of capital stock insurance as well as the "American Agency System."

National Association of Insurance Brokers, Inc. (The), 1511 K St., N.W., Suite 316, Washington, DC   20005

An association to keep track of proposed and current state and national legislation supporting what is in the best interests of brokers and the insurance-buying public.

National Association of Insurance Commissioners, 633 W. Wisconsin Ave., Suite 1015, Milwaukee, WI.   53203

A voluntary association of the chief insurance regulatory officials of the 50 states, the District of Columbia, Guam, Puerto Rico, and the Virgin Islands to promote legislative uniformity and provide a means for protecting the insurance-consuming public.

National Association of Mutual Insurance Agents, 640 Investment Bldg., Washington, DC   20005

An association to promote the public benefits of mutual insurance sold and serviced by local independent mutual agents.

National Association of Mutual Insurance Companies, 2511 E. 46th St., Suite H, Indianapolis, IN   46205

An association of over 1,000 mutual fire and casualty insurance companies, about 75 percent of which are farm, county, or township mutuals, and 25 percent are large and small advance-premium automobile, casualty, and general-writing fire mutuals.

National Automobile Theft Bureau, 30 E. 42nd St., New York, NY   10017

Organized to promote public safety and welfare in the ownership, use, maintenance, and operation of motor vehicles, and the prevention and reduction of theft and fire losses arising from the use of motor vehicles.

National Cargo Bureau, Inc., Suite 2757, One World Trade Center, NY   10048

A nonprofit membership organization to formulate recommendations to government on regulations for the safe stowage of dangerous goods and other cargos and ancilliary cargo handling techniques for water transportation. Offers cargo loading inspection services to promote security of life and property on the seas.

Nuclear Energy Property Insurance Association, 85 Woodland St., Hartford, CT   06102

A voluntary, nonprofit, unincorporated association of stock company insurers to aid in providing insurance protection against hazards arising out of or pertaining to nuclear reactor installations or operations or facilities related thereto. (The day-to-day activities of the NEPIA are managed by the Industrial Risk Insurers at the same address.)

Oil Insurance Association, merged with **Factory Insurance Association** to become the **Industrial Risk Insurers** on Dec. 1, 1975.

Property Loss Research Bureau (formerly Mutual Loss Research Bureau), 20 North Wacker Dr., Chicago, IL 60606

The Bureau is affiliated with the American Mutual Insurance Alliance as an unincorporated association of more than 100, mostly mutual, insurance companies which support the activity through assessments. Its overall effort is to deal with property loss adjustment problems of the member companies and their adjusters. The Bureau operates in five principal areas: (1) educational service, (2) adjuster information service, (3) publications service, (4) catastrophe service, and (5) investigations service. The latter is aimed to determine cause and origin of losses and to collect evidence for the companies to use to defend themselves against fraudulent claims under civil actions (not criminal), mostly as a result of arson.

Transportation Insurance Rating Bureau, 175 W. Jackson Blvd., Chicago, IL   60604

A rating and statistical organization licensed in all states, the District of Columbia, and Puerto Rico for inland marine, aircraft, and multiple-line insurance, including fire and allied lines. Includes mutual fire and casualty insurance companies and some stock and reciprocal companies.

C. National Fire Service Organizations in the United States of America

The following national and international associations are

the most prominent groups which serve the needs of the fire service in the United States of America.

Fire Marshals Association of North America (FMANA)
(a Section of the National Fire Protection Association), 470 Atlantic Ave., Boston, MA   02210

A body of the Fire Marshals (heads of Fire Prevention Bureaus, Fire Investigators and their Staffs), organized in 1906, who work for a state, a province, a county, a town, a city, a municipality, or a fire protection district and to whom the responsibility for fire prevention or investigation has been assigned by law or delegated by the Chief of the Fire Department. Members are the statutory officials and the full-time salaried deputies and assistants to such officials. Associate Members are nonsalaried or part-time legally designated officials who enjoy all the privileges of membership except that of elective office. The Fire Marshals Association of North America publishes a Bulletin and a Yearbook and holds two meetings annually at the time and place of the national meetings of the National Fire Protection Association. Its objectives and purposes are: (1) to unite for mutual benefit those public officials engaged primarily in the control of arson or the prevention of fire, or both, (2) to act as a central agency for exchange of professional information among its members, (3) to assist Fire Marshals in the conduct of their professional activities, and (4) to correlate the activities of Fire Marshals toward the reduction of fire waste. There are no dues beyond that of membership in the NFPA.

Fire Service Section (a Section of the National Fire Protection Association), 470 Atlantic Ave., Boston, MA 02210

Organized in 1973, this organization is open to any member of the National Fire Protection Association who: (1) is a member of a fire department providing public fire prevention and fire suppression services to a state, county, municipality, or organized fire district, (2) is a member of a fire department providing fire prevention and fire suppression services to airfields or military bases, (3) is principally engaged in the training and education of fire department members. Its objectives are: (1) to unite for mutual professional benefit those members of NFPA who are members of the fire service, (2) to act as a vehicle for the exchange of information among its members, (3) to advance the interests of the profession in the fields of fire protection, prevention, and suppression, (4) to stimulate awareness of the need for continually improving programs in management, training, and education, (5) to encourage and assist its members in conducting meetings, conferences, seminars, and such other forums as may be practicable for the exchange of information and the encouragement of professionalism, (6) to encourage participation of its members on the Technical Committees of the NFPA, (7) to advance and encourage the development of improved fire suppression equipment, apparatus, and all related facilities together with methods and practices used by the fire service by pooling experience and correlating the recommendations of its members, (8) to encourage public authorities to specify and purchase fire protection equipment on the basis of performance standards, (9) to bring to the attention of its members such matters of legislation and regulations as would be of interest, (10) to promote cooperation within the fire service and between the fire service and other fire protection practioners, (11) to help the fire service achieve its primary goal of protection of life and property, and (12)

to provide for the establishment, within the Section, of a fire service professional society. There are no dues beyond that of membership in the NFPA.

International Association of Arson Investigators (IAAI),
P. O. Box 1208, Springfield, IL   62705

Active membership in the IAAI is open to any representative (21 years of age or over) of government or of a governmental agency, and any representative of a business or industrial concern who is actively engaged in some phase of the suppression of arson and whose qualifications meet the requirements of the Membership Committee of the Association. Associate Membership is open to persons not qualified for Active Membership after determination of their qualification by the Membership Committee. The IAAI publishes a quarterly Bulletin entitled "The Fire and Arson Investigator" and conducts an annual meeting in conjunction with a conference on arson, normally in conjunction with a State Arson Seminar. Various Committees are organized to assist the Association in its attack on the arson problem, such as the Fire Marshal Advisory Committee; the Fraud Fires and Organized Crime Committee; the Insurance Advisory Committee; the Legislative Committee; the Photography Committee; the Police Advisory Committee; the Riots and Civil Disorders Committee; and the Technical Advisory and Training Committee.

International Association of Black Professional Fire Fighters (IABPFF), Office of the President, c/o New York Fire Department, 24 Humboldt St., Brooklyn, New York, NY 11206

Organized in 1970 to: (1) create a liaison between black fire fighters across the nation, (2) compile information concerning injustices that exist in the working conditions in the fire service and to implement action to correct them, (3) collect and evaluate data on all deleterious conditions where minorities exist, (4) to see that competent blacks are recruited and employed as fire fighters where they reside, (5) promote interracial progress throughout the fire service, and (6) aid in motivating black brothers to seek advancement to elevated ranks. The organization is a Life Member of the National Association for the Advancement of Colored People.

International Association of Fire Chiefs (IAFC), 1725 K St., N.W., Suite 1108, Washington, DC   20006

The IAFC was organized in 1873 to further the professional advancement of the fire service and to insure and maintain greater protection of life and property from fire. Its purposes are fulfilled by: (1) conducting research and studies of major problems affecting the fire service at community, state, provincial, regional, national, and international levels, (2) developing and effectuating an active program vital to the continued well-being of the fire service, (3) serving as the recognized organization for the exchange of ideas, information, knowledge, and experience in areas affecting the safety of life and property from fire, (4) encouraging and developing public education in fire prevention to preserve human life and material resources, and (5) promoting educational programs in the best interests of the fire service. Active Members include the Chief of Department and all Chief Officers of regularly organized public, governmental, or industrial fire departments; State and Provincial Fire Marshals; Fire Commissioners and/or Fire Directors who devote full time to administration and fire fighting operations. Associate Members include Fire Commissioners and/or Fire Directors not responsible for administration or for fire fighting operations; Directors of Public Safety, public officials, officers and members of fire departments; individuals interested in the protection of life and property from fire; and officers of recognized fire prevention organizations. Sustaining Members include individuals and/or concerns engaged in the manufacture of fire apparatus or equipment and/or individuals or concerns otherwise interested in the field of fire protection upon payment of an annual fee determined by the Board of Directors. Other membership categories are: Active Life Members, Associate Life Members, and Honorary Life Members. There are several Divisional Associations (Canadian Division; Eastern Association of Fire Chiefs; Great Lakes Association of Fire Chiefs; Missouri Valley Association of Fire Chiefs; New England Division of International Association of Fire Chiefs; Southeastern Association of Fire Chiefs; Southwestern Association of Fire Chiefs; and the Western Association of Fire Chiefs) which serve the regions in which they are located. The IAFC also has a group of 21 permanent Committees which function for the organization including the Metropolitan Committee (Chiefs of the major cities) who serve the Association in the special areas of their concern. The IAFC holds an Annual Conference each year and offers a series of publications on fire service matters to all interested persons. It has a membership in the range of 7,500 to 8,000 and a headquarters staff of 11 to 15.

International Association of Fire Fighters (IAFF) (affiliated with the American Federation of Labor and Congress of Industrial Organizations in the U.S.A. and the Canadian Labour Congress), 1750 New York Ave., N.W., Washington, DC 20006

Organized in 1918, the IAFF serves all persons engaged in fire fighting or fire prevention who are permanent and paid employees of fire departments. Any person of good moral character engaged in this activity is eligible for active membership through its chartered locals, state or provincial associations, and joint councils. Conventions of the Association are biannual. Local unions with a membership of 100 or less are entitled to one delegate; locals with greater membership are entitled to progressively larger numbers of delegates—up to 10 for unions having 2,001 or more members. There are 15 Districts presently established on a geographical basis covering the U.S. and Canada with District No. 16 covering all federal fire fighters in the U.S. and Canada. The Association's official publication "The International Fire Fighter" is published monthly under the direction of the International President. The IAFF also publishes a series of publications to promote the service, to guide union fire fighters in their public relations, and makes special studies of concern to the fire fighter such as their Annual Death and Injury Survey. It has a total membership in the range of 160,000 to 170,000 and a headquarters staff of 40 to 50.

International Fire Service Training Association (IFSTA), Oklahoma State University, Stillwater, OK 74074

An educational alliance organized to develop training material for the fire service, formed in November 1943. The organization meets each July at Oklahoma State University, and the Fire Protection Publications division at the University publishes all IFSTA training manuals and texts once approved by the Executive Board of the Association. IFSTA's objectives are: (1) to develop training material for

publication, (2) to validate such training material, (3) to check rough drafts for errors, (4) to add new techniques and developments, (5) to delete obsolete and outmoded methods, and (6) to upgrade the fire service through training. The adopting agencies serve as a voluntary group of individuals who govern policies, recommend procedures, and validate material before it is published. Currently some 35 states in the U.S.A., five Canadian provinces, a number of federal governmental agencies, and some agencies outside the U.S.A. adopt the IFSTA Manuals.

International Municipal Signal Association, P. O. Box 187, San Juan Capistrano, CA 92675

The IMSA was organized in 1896 and currently has 3,000 to 3,500 members. It is an educational, nonprofit organization dedicated to imparting knowledge, technical information, and guidance to its membership which consists of municipal signal and communication department heads and their first assistants. The range of communications covered include traffic control, fire alarm, and police alarm. There are 16 Sections of the IMSA (based on geographical areas in the U.S.A. and Canada) and a Sustaining Section. The former serve the regional needs of its members. It publishes the "IMSA Signal Magazine" bimonthly.

International Society of Fire Service Instructors, Fire Service Extension Department, University of Maryland, College Park, MD 20742

Organized in 1960, the ISFSI provides for continuing exchange of ideas and discussion of training techniques between persons concerned with fire service training and education. The goal is to develop uniform professional standards for fire service instructors; to assist in the development of fire service instructors through better training and educational opportunities; to provide the means for continuous upgrading of such instructors through in-service training; and to actively promote the role of the fire service instructor in the total fire service organization. It has a membership of over 600, and through 14 state chapters reaches an additional 2,000 instructors at the local level.

Joint Council of National Fire Service Organizations

The Joint Council is an alliance of the principal national fire service organizations (including the FMANA, IAAI, IABPFF, IAFC, IAFF, IFSTA, IMSA, ISFSI, Metropolitan Committee of the IAFC, and the National Fire Protection Association) formed to identify problems common to each organization, to review current developments of concern to all, and to establish areas of common interest where cooperative efforts of member organizations can be used for maximum results. One area of common interest in which national collective action is deemed desirable is the establishment of standards upon which the levels of competency of personnel within the fire service could be determined. Such a system was approved and established by the Joint Council on October 25, 1972. This lead to establishing Committees for the development of standards of professional competency. The Committees are made up of peer-group representation, with an independent Board to oversee and validate the standards developed and implement same in a nationally coordinated, continuing professional development program for the fire service. The Secretariat for these Committees and the Board is provided by the Staff of the NFPA. The four Committees established in 1975 were charged to develop recommended minimum standards of professional competence required of: (1) fire fighters, (2) fire inspectors and investigators, (3) fire service instructors, and (4) fire service officers. Also established is a National Professional Qualifications Board for the Fire Service with the following specific duties: (1) to supervise the national professional development program. (2) to be responsive to the needs and opinions of all groups involved with the Fire Service and others who have related interests, (3) to identify and define levels of professional progression, (4) to correlate, review, and validate draft standards prepared by the Committees established to produce the professional standards for each level of fire service responsibility, (5) to approve all draft standards before such are submitted for final adoption procedures (as used by NFPA), and (6) be responsible for the accreditation and supervision of national programs of certification, including coordination with implementing agencies to ensure the validity and reliability of the evaluation criteria.

D. National Noncommercial, Trade, Professional, and Labor Associations in the United States of America With Fire Protection Interests

There are a large number of noncommercial, trade, professional, and labor associations (one estimate is over 5,000) in the U.S.A., and a great number of them have a degree of fire protection concerns related to their activities. Among those having considerable identified such interests are the following:

Acoustical and Insulation Materials Association, 205 West Touhy Ave., Park Ridge, IL   60068

Aerospace Industries Association of America, 1725 DeSales Street, N.W., Washington, DC   20036

Airconditioning and Refrigeration Institute, 1815 N. Fort Myer Dr., Arlington, VA   22209

Air Line Pilots Association International, 1625 Massachusetts Ave., N.W., Washington, DC   20036

Air Moving and Conditioning Association, 30 West University Dr., Arlington Heights, IL   60004

Airport Operators Council International, 1700 K St., N.W., Washington, DC   20006

Air Transport Association of America, 1709 New York Ave., N.W., Washington, DC   20006

Aluminum Association, 750 Third Ave., New York, NY 10017

American Analgesia Society, 9 West 67th St., New York, NY   10023

American Association of Airport Executives, 2029 K St., N.W., Washington, DC   20006

American Association of Hospital Consultants, 1700 K St., N.W., Washington, DC   20006

American Association of Nurse Anesthetists, 111 E. Wacker Dr., Chicago, IL   60601

American Association of Port Authorities, 1612 K St., N.W., Washington, DC   20006

American Association for Respiratory Therapy, 7411 Hines Pl., Dallas, TX   75235

American Association of Retired Persons, 1909 K St., N.W., Washington, D.C.   20006

American Automobile Association, 8111 Gatehouse Rd., Falls Church, VA   22042

American Boat and Yacht Council, 15 East 26th St., New York, NY   10010

American Boiler Manufacturers Association, Suite 317, 1500 Wilson Blvd., Arlington, VA   22209

American Chemical Society, 1155 16th St., N.W., Washington, DC   20036

American College of Chest Physicians, 911 Busse Highway, Park Ridge, IL   60068

American College of Surgeons, 55 East Erie, Chicago, IL   60611

American Concrete Institute, Box 19150, Redford Station, Detroit, MI   48219

American Conference of Governmental Industrial Hygienists, P. O. Box 1937, Cincinnati, OH   45201

American Dental Association, 211 East Chicago Ave., Chicago, IL   60611

American Feed Manufacturers Association, Inc., 1701 N. Ft. Myer Dr., Arlington, VA   22209

American Foundrymen's Society, Golf & Wolf Rds., Des Plaines, IL   60016

American Gas Association, Inc., 1515 Wilson Blvd., Arlington, VA   22209

American Health Care Association, 1200 15th Street, N.W., Washington, D.C.   20005

American Hospital Association, 840 North Lake Shore Dr., Chicago, IL   60611

American Hotel and Motel Association, 888 Seventh Ave., New York, NY   10019

American Industrial Hygiene Association, 66 S. Miller Rd., Akron, OH   44313

American Institute of Architects, 1735 New York Ave., N.W., Washington, DC   20006

American Institute of Merchant Shipping, 1625 K Street, N.W., Washington, DC   20006

American Institute of Planners, 1776 Massachusetts Ave., N.W., Washington, DC   20036

American Institute of Steel Construction, Inc., 1221 Ave. of the Americas, New York, NY   10020

American Institute of Timber Construction, 333 W. Hampden Ave., Englewood, CO   80110

American Iron and Steel Institute, 1000 16th Street, N.W., Washington, DC   20036

American Management Associations, 135 West 50th St., New York, NY   10020

American Medical Association, 535 North Dearborn St., Chicago, IL   60610

American National Red Cross, National Headquarters, Washington, DC   20006

American National Standards Institute, 1430 Broadway, New York, NY   10018

American Nurses' Association, 1200 15th St., N.W., Washington, DC   20005

American Oil Chemists Society, 508 S. Sixth St., Champaign, IL   61820

American Petroleum Institute, 1801 K St., N.W., Washington, DC   20006

American Public Health Association, 1015 18th St., N.W., Washington, DC   20036

American Pyrotechnics Association, 407 Campus Ave., Chestertown, MD   21620

American Records Management Association, 24 N. Wabash Ave., Chicago, IL   60602

American Society of Agricultural Engineers, 2950 Niles Rd., P. O. Box 410, St. Joseph, MI   49085

American Society of Anesthesiologists, 515 Busse Highway, Park Ridge, IL   60068

American Society of Architectural Hardware Consultants, Box 3476, San Rafael, CA   94902

American Society of Civil Engineers, 345 East 47th St., New York, NY   10017

American Society of Clinical Pathologists, 2100 W. Harrison St., Chicago, IL   60612

American Society of Heating, Refrigerating, and Air Conditioning Engineers, Inc., 345 East 47th St., New York, NY   10017

American Society for Industrial Security, 2000 K Street, N.W., Washington, DC   20006

American Society of Mechanical Engineers, 345 East 47th St., New York, NY   10017

American Society for Medical Technology, 5555 West Loop S., Bellaire, TX   77401

American Society of Safety Engineers, 850 Busse Highway, Park Ridge, IL   60068

American Society for Testing and Materials, 1916 Race St., Philadelphia, PA   19103

American Transit Association, 465 L'Enfant Plaza West, S.W., Washington, DC   20024

American Trucking Associations, Inc., 1616 P Street, N.W., Washington, DC   20036

American Warehousemen's Association, 222 W. Adams St., Chicago, IL   60606

American Waterways Operators, 1250 Connecticut Ave., Washington, DC   20036

American Water Works Association, Inc., 6666 W. Quincy Ave., Denver, CO   80235

American Welding Society, 2501 N.W. 7th St., Miami, FL   33125

American Wood-Preservers' Association, 1625 Eye St., N.W., Washington, DC   20006

American Wood Preservers Institute, 1651 Old Meadow Rd., McLean, VA   22101

Asbestos Cement Products Association, 325 Delaware Ave., Buffalo, NY   14202

Asphalt Roofing Manufacturers Association, Room 1717, 757 3rd Ave., New York, NY   10017

Association of American Railroads, 1920 L Street, N.W., Washington, DC   20036

Association of Edison Illuminating Companies, 51 East 42nd St., New York, NY   10017

Association of Home Appliance Manufacturers, 20 North Wacker Dr., Chicago, IL   60606

Association of Iron and Steel Engineers, Three Gateway Center, Suite 2350, Pittsburgh, PA   15222

Association of Motion Picture and Television Producers, 8480 Beverly Blvd., Los Angeles, CA   90048

Association of Records Executives and Administrators, P. O. Box 4259, Grand Central P. O., New York, NY   10017

Automatic Fire Alarm Association, 1271 Virginia Ave., Mountainside, NJ   07092

Boating Industry Associations, 401 N. Michigan Ave., Chicago, IL   60611

Brick Institute of America, 1750 Old Meadow Rd., McLean, VA   22101

Bricklayers, Masons and Plasterers' International Union of America, 815 15th Street, N.W., Washington, DC   20005

Builders' Hardware Manufacturers Association, 60 E. 42nd St., New York, NY   10017

Building Officials and Code Administrators International, Inc., 1313 East 60th St., Chicago, IL   60637

Building Owners and Managers Association International, 224 South Michigan Ave., Chicago, IL   60604

Canvas Products Association International, 600 Endicott Bldg., St. Paul, MN   55101

Cast Iron Pipe Research Association, Suite 509, 1301 West 22nd St., Oak Brook, IL   60521

Cast Iron Soil Pipe Institute, 2029 K St., N.W., Washington, DC   20006

Central Station Electrical Protection Association, 1000 Vermont Ave., N.W., Washington, DC   20005

Chamber of Commerce of the United States, 1615 H St., N.W., Washington, DC   20062

Chemical Specialties Manufacturers Association Inc., 1001 Connecticut Ave., N.W., Washington, DC   20036

Chlorine Institute, Inc., 342 Madison Ave., New York, NY   10017

The Combustion Institute, Union Trust Bldg., Pittsburgh, PA   15219

Compressed Gas Association, 500 5th Ave., New York, NY   10036

Computer and Business Equipment Manufacturers Association, 1828 L St., N.W., Washington, DC   20036

Concrete Pipe Association, 1501 Wilson Blvd., Arlington, VA   22209

The Construction Specifications Institute, 1150 17th St., N.W., Washington, DC   20036

Coordinating Research Council Inc., 30 Rockefeller Plaza, New York, NY   10020

Copper Development Association Inc., 405 Lexington Ave., New York, NY   10017

Corn Refiners Association, Inc., 1001 Connecticut Ave., Washington, DC   20006

Council of American Building Officials, Secretariat, c/o International Conference of Building Officials, 5360 South Workman Mill Rd., Whittier, CA   90601

Council of Better Business Bureaus, Inc., 1150 17th St., N.W., Washington, DC   20036

Edison Electric Institute, 90 Park Ave., New York, NY   10016

Electric Energy Association, Inc., 90 Park Ave., New York, NY   10016

Electric Fuse Manufacturers Guild, 331 Madison Ave., New York, NY   10017

Electronic Industries Association, 2001 Eye St., N.W., Washington, DC   20006

Engine Manufacturers Association, 111 E. Wacker Dr., Chicago, IL   60601

Envelope Manufacturers Association, 1 Rockefeller Plaza, New York, NY   10020

Facing Tile Institute, 111 E. Wacker Dr., Chicago, IL   60601

The Fertilizer Institute, 1015 18th St., N.W., Washington, DC   20036

Fire Apparatus Manufacturers Division, Truck Body and Equipment Association, 5530 Wisconsin Ave., Washington, DC   20015

Fire Detection Institute, c/o F. C. Evans, Chairman, 155 Sixth Ave., New York, NY   10013

Fire Equipment Manufacturers Association, 605 East Algonquin Rd., Arlington Heights, IL   60005

Fire Retardant Chemicals Association, 475 Walnut St., Norwood, NJ   07648

Food Facilities Consultants Society, 135 Glenlawn Ave., Sea Cliff, NY   11579

Forging Industry Association, 55 Public Square, Suite 1121, Cleveland, OH   44113

Gas Appliance Manufacturers Association, 1901 N. Fort Myer Dr., Arlington, VA   22209

Gasoline Pump Manufacturers Association, 331 Madison Ave., New York, NY   10017

Gas Vent Institute, 111 East Wacker Dr., Chicago, IL   60601

General Aviation Manufacturers Association, 1025 Connecticut Ave., N.W., Washington, DC   20036

Grain Elevator and Processing Society, Box 15024, Commerce Station, Minneapolis, MN   55415

Gypsum Association, 1603 Orrington Ave., Evanston, IL   60201

Hardwood Plywood Manufacturers Association, 2310 South Walter Reed Dr., Arlington, VA   22206

Helicopter Association of America, Inc., 1156 15th St., N.W., Washington, DC   20005

Human Factors Society, P. O. Box 1369, Santa Monica, CA   90406

The Hydraulics Institute, 2130 Keith Bldg., Cleveland, OH   44115

Incinerator Institute of America, Sumwalt Associates, 105 N. Virginia Ave., Falls Church, VA   22046

Industrial Heating Equipment Association, Inc., 2000 K St., N.W., Washington, DC   20006

Industrial Safety Equipment Association, Inc., 1901 N. Moore St., Arlington, VA   22209

Industrial Truck Association, 1326 Freeport Rd., Pittsburgh, PA   15238

Institute of Electrical and Electronics Engineers, Inc., 345 East 47th St., New York, NY   10017

Institute of Industrial Launderers, 1730 M St., N.W., Washington, DC   20036

Institute of Makers of Explosives, 420 Lexington Ave., New York, NY   10017

Instrument Society of America, 400 Stanwix St., Pittsburgh, PA   15222

International Association of Electrical Inspectors, 802 Busse Highway, Park Ridge, IL   60068

International Association of Fairs and Expositions, 500 Ashland Ave., Chicago Heights, IL   60411

International Association of Plumbing and Mechanical Officials, 5032 Alhambra Ave., Los Angeles, CA   90032

International Association of Refrigerated Warehouses, 7315 Wisconsin Ave., Washington, DC   20014

International Bridge, Tunnel, and Turnpike Association, 1225 Connecticut Ave., N.W., Washington, DC   20036

International Brotherhood of Electrical Workers, 1125 15th St., N.W., Washington, DC   20005

International City Management Association, 1140 Connecticut Ave., N.W., Washington, DC   20036

International Conference of Building Officials, 5360 South Workman Mill Rd., Whittier, CA   90601

International Fabricare Institute, Doris & S. Chicago Sts., Joliet, IL   60434

International Magnesium Association, 1406 Third National Building, Dayton, OH   45402

International Nonwovens and Disposables Association, 10 E. 40th St., New York, NY   10016

Lake Carriers' Association, 614 Superior Ave., N.W., Cleveland, OH   44113

Laundry and Cleaners Allied Trades Association, 543 Valley Rd., Upper Montclair, NJ   07043

Lightning Protection Institute, 122 W. Washington, Madison, WI   53703

Manufactured Housing Institute, 14650 Lee Road, Box 201, Chantilly, VA   22021

Manufacturers Standardization Society of the Valve and Fittings Industry, 1815 North Fort Myer Dr., Arlington, VA   22209

Manufacturing Chemists' Association, Inc., 1825 Connecticut Ave., N.W., Washington, DC   20009

Marine Chemists Association, D. W. Smith, Secretary, 6252 Falls Rd., Baltimore, MD   21209

Materials Handling Institute, Inc., 1326 Freeport Rd., Pittsburgh, PA   15238

Mechanical Contractors Association of America, Inc., 5530 Wisconsin Ave., N.W., Suite 750, Washington, D.C. 20015

Medical-Surgical Manufacturers Association, 1666 K St., N.W., Washington, DC   20006

Metal Building Manufacturers Association, 2130 Keith Building, Cleveland, OH   44115

Metal Lath Association, 221 North LaSalle St., Chicago, IL   60601

Metal Treating Institute, Inc., 1800 N. Central Ave., Phoenix, AZ   85004

Millers' National Federation, 14 East Jackson Blvd., Chicago, IL   50504

Model Code Standardization Council, c/o Chairman, MCSC, Building Officials and Code Administrators International, 1313 East 60th St., Chicago IL   60637

Motor Vehicle Manufacturers Association of the United States, Inc., 320 New Center Bldg., Detroit, MI   48202

Munitions Carriers Conference, Inc., 1616 P St., N.W., Washington, DC   20036

National American Wholesale Grocers Association, 51 Madison Ave., New York, NY   10010

National Association of Architectural Metal Manufacturers, 1033 S. Blvd., Oak Park, IL   60302

National Association of Building Manufacturers, 1619 Massachusetts Ave., N.W., Washington, DC   20036

National Association of Engine and Boat Manufacturers, Inc., 537 Steamboat Rd., Greenwich, CT   06830

National Association of Fire Equipment Distributors, Inc., 111 E. Wacker Dr., Chicago, IL   60601

National Association of Food Equipment Manufacturers, 111 E. Wacker Dr., Chicago, IL   60601

National Association of Home Builders, 15th and M Sts., N.W., Washington, DC   20005

National Association of Insurance Agents, 85 John St., New York, NY   10038

National Association of Manufacturers, 1776 F St., N.W., Washington, DC   20006

National Association of Plumbing-Heating-Cooling Contractors, 1016 20th St., N.W., Washington, DC   20036

National Automatic Laundry and Cleaning Council, 7 S. Dearborn St., Chicago, IL   60603

National Automatic Sprinkler and Fire Control Association, P. O. Box 719, 45 Kensico Dr., Mt. Kisco, NY   10549

National Builders' Hardware Association, 1815 N. Ft. Myer Dr., Suite 412, Arlington, VA   22209

National Burglar and Fire Alarm Association, Inc., 1730 Pennsylvania Ave., N.W., Washington, DC   20006

National Business Aircraft Association, Inc., 401 Pennsylvania Ave., N.W., Washington, D.C.   20004

National Clean-up, Paint-up, Fix-up Bureau, 1500 Rhode Island Ave., N.W., Washington, DC   20005

National Commission on Safety Education, National Education Association of the U. S., 1201 16th St., N.W., Washington, DC   20036

National Concrete Masonry Association, 1800 N. Kent St., Arlington, VA   22209

National Conference of States on Building Codes and Standards, c/o National Bureau of Standards, Washington, DC 20234

National Cottonseed Products Association, Inc., P. O. Box 12023, Memphis, TN   38112

National Electrical Contractors Association, 7315 Wisconsin Ave., Washington, DC   20014

National Electrical Manufacturers Association, 155 E. 44th St., New York, NY   10017

National Elevator Industry, Inc., 600 Third Ave., New York, NY   10016

National Environmental Systems Contractors Association, 1501 Wilson Blvd., Arlington, VA   22209

National Forest Products Association, 1619 Massachusetts Ave., N.W., Washington, DC   20036

National Furniture Warehousemen's Association, 222 West Adams St., Chicago, IL   60606

National League of Cities, 1620 Eye St., N.W., Washington, DC   20006

National LP-Gas Association, 79 W. Monroe St., Chicago, IL   60603

National Lumber and Building Material Dealers Association, 1990 M St., N.W., Washington, DC   20036

National Machine Tool Builders' Association, 7901 Westpark Dr., McLean, VA   22101

National Mineral Wool Insulation Association, Inc., 211 E. 51st St., New York, NY   10022

National Oil Fuel Institute, 60 E. 42nd St., New York, NY 10017

National Paint and Coatings Association, 1500 Rhode Island Ave., N.W., Washington, DC   20005

National Parking Association, 1101 17th St., N.W., Washington, DC   20036

National Particleboard Association, 2306 Perkins Pl., Silver Spring, MD   20910

National Petroleum Refiners Association, 1725 DeSales St., N.W., Washington, DC   20006

National Pilots Association, 806 15th St., N.W., Washington, DC   20005

National Recreation and Park Association, 1601 North Kent St., Arlington, VA   22209

National Restaurant Association, One IBM Plaza, Suite 2600, Chicago, IL   60611

National Rural Electric Cooperative Association, 2000 Florida Ave., N.W., Washington, DC   20009

National Safety Council, 425 N. Michigan Ave., Chicago, IL   60611

National Sanitation Foundation, P. O. Box 1468, Ann Arbor, MI   48105

National School Supply and Equipment Association, 1500 Wilson Blvd., Arlington, VA   22209

National Self-Service Gasoline Association, 134 Francis St., Providence, RI   02903

National Soybean Processors Association, 1730 Pennsylvania Ave., N.W., Washington, DC   20006

National Tank Truck Carriers, Inc., 1616 P Street, N.W., Washington, DC   20036

National Woodwork Manufacturers Association, Inc., 400 W. Madison Ave., Chicago, IL   60606

Perlite Institute, 45 W. 45th St., New York, NY   10036

Petroleum Equipment Institute, 1579 E. 21st St., Tulsa, OK   74114

Portland Cement Association, Old Orchard Rd., Skokie, IL   60076

Power Tool Institute, Inc., 1803 South Busse Rd., Mt. Prospect, IL   60056

Recreation Vehicle Industry Association, Box 204, 14650 Lee Rd., Chantilly, VA   22021

Red Cedar Shingle and Handsplit Shake Bureau, 5510 White Bldg., Seattle, WA   98101

Rubber Manufacturers Association, Inc., 1901 Pennsylvania Ave., N.W., Washington, DC   20006

Safe Manufacturers National Association, 366 Madison Ave., New York, NY   10017

Sheet Metal and Air Conditioning Contractors' National Association, Inc., 1611 N. Kent St., Arlington, VA 22209

Shipbuilders Council of America, Watergate Six Hundred, Washington, DC   20037

Smoke, Fire, and Burn Foundation, Inc., The, 53 State St., Boston, MA   02109

Society of American Archivists, P. O. Box 8198, University of Illinois, Chicago, IL   60680

Society of Automotive Engineers, 400 Commonwealth Dr., Pittsburgh, PA   15096

Society of Fire Protection Engineers, 60 Batterymarch St., Boston, MA   02110

Society of the Plastics Industry, 250 Park Ave., New York, NY   10017

Southern Building Code Congress, 1116 Brown-Marx Bldg., Birmingham, AL   35203

Sporting Arms and Ammunition Manufacturers' Institute, 420 Lexington Ave., New York, NY   10017

Standards Engineers Society, 2617 E. Hennepin Ave., Minneapolis, MN   55413

Steel Bar Mills Association, 188 West Randolph St., Chicago, IL   60601

Steel Deck Institute, Box 270, Westchester, IL   60153

Steel Door Institute, 2130 Keith Bldg., Cleveland, OH 44115

Steel Plate Fabricators Association, Inc., 15 Spinning Wheel Rd., Hinsdale, IL   60521

Steel Tank Institute, 111 E. Wacker Dr., Chicago, IL 60601

Steel Window Institute, 2130 Keith Bldg., Cleveland, OH 44115

Structural Clay Products Institute, 1750 Old Meadow Rd., McLean, VA   22101

Technical Association of the Graphic Arts, Box 3064, Federal Station, Rochester, NY   14614

Technical Association of the Pulp and Paper Industry, One Dunwoody Pk., Atlanta, GA   30341

Terminal Elevator Grain Merchants Association, Box 15004, Commerce Station, Minneapolis, MN   55415

Thermal Insulation Manufacturing Association, 7 Kirby Plaza, Mt. Kisco, NY   10549

Truck Body and Equipment Association, Fire Apparatus Manufacturers Division, 5530 Wisconsin Ave., Washington, DC   20015

Truck Trailer Manufacturers Association, 2430 Pennsylvania Ave., N.W., Washington, DC   20037

Truss Plate Institute, Suite 200, Baltimore Ave., College Park, MD   20740

Underwriters Laboratories, Inc., 207 E. Ohio St., Chicago, IL   60611

Underwriters Service Association, 222 W. Adams, Room 1375, Chicago, IL   60606

United Association of Journeymen and Apprentices of the Plumbing and Pipe Fitting Industry of the United States and Canada, 901 Massachusetts Ave., N.W., Washington, DC   20001

United Lightning Protection Association, Webster, NY 14580

Western Oil and Gas Association, 609 S. Grand Ave., Los Angeles, CA   90017

Western Wood Products Association, 1500 Yeon Bldg., Portland, OR   97204

Woodworking Machinery Manufacturers of America, 1900 Arch St., Philadelphia, PA   19103

E. International and Fire Organizations in Other Countries

The following information about international and fire organizations in other countries than the United States of America is offered as being *representative* of activities known at the time this Appendix was prepared (1975). The intent is to show the scope of interest in fire safety throughout the world.

The **National Fire Protection Association** (NFPA) in 1975 had an international membership (outside of the U.S.A.) of 3,330 with 1,930 in Canada and the balance (1,400) in 67 countries.

The **Society of Fire Protection Engineers** (SFPE) also had (in 1975) an international membership with over 100 members in Canada and in about 20 other countries.

Other prominent international organizations with fire protection related interests include:

Comité Technique International de Prévention et d'Extinction de Feu (International Technical Committee for Fire Prevention and Extinction) (CTIF)

This organization has headquarters in Paris (27 rue de Dunkerque, Paris 10e). It has a "Praesidium" composed of a general secretariat, a "Permanent Council" (to which each member country sends one representative to an annual meeting) and a "General Assembly" composed of three delegates from each member nation which meets at least once every four years and elects the members of the Praesidium. An Annual International Symposium is organized by one of the CTIF's "National Committees." An international fire brigade tournament is held every three years. Every four years a congress is held in conjunction with the CTIF General Assembly.

The following 27 countries made up the CTIF's membership in 1975: Argentina, Austria, Belgium, Brazil, Bulgaria, Czechoslovakia, Denmark, Finland, France, Germany, Great Britain, Hungary, Israel, Italy, Japan, Luxembourg, The Netherlands, Norway, Poland, Portugal, Rumania, Spain, Sweden, Switzerland, Turkey, USSR, and Yugoslavia.

Conference of Fire Protection Associations (CFPA)

This Conference is made up of the administrative heads of various national fire protection associations around the world. It was proposed and organized at a meeting of 10 managers of such associations in London in July of 1965 and the first formal meeting was held in Wiesbaden, Germany in 1966. Meetings have been held about every 2 years since. The Conference is informal in character and designed primarily to facilitate exchange of information on fire matters between the participating members. Presently (1975) the Conference represents 17 fire protection associations headquartered in Australia, Austria, Belgium, Denmark, Finland, France, Germany, Great Britain, Japan, The Netherlands, New Zealand, Norway, South Africa, Spain, Switzerland, Sweden, and the United States of America. The Chairman of the CFPA in 1975 is Charles S. Morgan, President of the National Fire Protection Association, 470 Atlantic Avenue, Boston, MA 02210, U.S.A.

A CFPA Europe has been formed to assist those CFPA member countries in that area to deal with common problems and to initiate similar solutions. It includes the 11 countries of Europe who are CFPA members. The Chairman in 1975 is N. C. Strother Smith, Director, Fire Protection Association, Aldermary House, Queen Street, London EC4N 1TJ, England.

Comité Europeén des Assurances, Groupe de Travail Incendie (CEA-Incendie)

This is a technical fire insurance working party operation within the CEA which is an organization of the national property insurance companies of Western Europe. The headquarters for correspondence with this Group is 11 Rue Pillet-Will, 75009 Paris, France.

Eurofeu (European Committee of the Manufacturers of Fire Engines and Apparatus)

This is a European affiliation of producers of fire protection equipment. The address of the President in 1975 is: 45 Route des Acacias, 1211 Geneva, Switzerland.

Euroalarme

This organization is composed of producers of fire alarm manufacturers. Its 1975 address is D-7000 Stuttgart, Kriegerstr. 17, Germany.

International Civil Aviation Organization

This organization, located at 1080 University Street, Montreal 101, P.Q., Canada, issues in English, French, Spanish, and Russian, publications to promote the aims of the Convention of International Civil Aviation so that the contracting States (Nations) and others may be governed by the agreements and procedures applicable to international civil aviation. Included are recommendations on aerodrome fire and rescue services.

International Civil Defence Organization

This organization (28 av. Pictet de Rochemont, Geneva, Switzerland) conducts International World Civil Defence Conferences. It concentrates currently on improving international rescue efforts, medical assistance, and disaster relief. Fifty-seven countries now participate in the organization. They issue a monthly Bulletin.

International Electrotechnical Commission (Commission Electrotechnique Internationale) — Affiliated with the International Organization for Standardization (ISO)

This organization, headquartered at 1 rue de Varembé, Geneva, Switzerland, operates to coordinate electrical requirements internationally. U.S.A. contacts are through the Secretary, USNC/IEC at the American National Standards Institute, 1430 Broadway, New York, N.Y. 10018. The work of the ISO Technical Committee No. 64 (Electrical Installations of Buildings) is coordinated through the IEC.

International Fire Chiefs' Association of Asia (IFCAA)

An organization of the fire service leaders of the various countries in Asia. The IFCAA can be contacted through the Chief Officer, Tokyo Metropolitan Fire Board, 11-35, 1-Chome, Nagato-cho Chiyoda-ku, Tokyo, Japan.

International Labour Office, International Occupational Safety and Health Information Center (CIS)

This organization (address: Bureau International du Travail CH 1211 Geneva 22, Switzerland) provides a systematic information service covering methods and media of interest from the standpoint of occupational safety and health. At established subscription rates, they issue "CIS cards" containing abstracts of documents on occupational safety and health, issue information sheets, and publish a Bulletin 12 times a year.

International Organization for Standardization (ISO) — L'Organisation Internationale de Normalisation

The ISO's headquarter's address is Case Postale 56, 1211 Geneva 20, Switzerland. It had, in 1974, 73 member countries, made up of 58 national member bodies and 15 correspondent members. Approximately half of the ISO member bodies are governmental institutions; the others are semi- or non-governmental bodies, most of the latter receiving some form of government subsidy. In the USA, the American National Standards Institute (ANSI) — nongovernmental — is the official "member body." The NFPA is active, through ANSI, in ISO Technical Committee TC-21 (which is one of the about 150 technical committees of the organization) responsible for fire protection and fire fighting equipment, including extinguishing agents.

The following descriptions of national programs in the fire protection field are representative of activities in progress in 1975 outside of the United States of America.

Algeria

In 1973 a project was started by the managing director of an insurance company for the founding of an Algerian Loss Prevention Committee whose foremost emphasis would be fire protection. Without doubt there will be a permanent body to promote and advise on fire protection in Algeria in the near future.

Argentina

The Comité Permanente de Lucha contra el Fuego (Permanent Committee for Protection against Fire) was organized in 1960, Headquarters are at Belgrano 1547, Buenos Aires. Members are the paid and volunteer fire departments. A journal is published three times a year.

A group of people concerned with the problems of fire protection and safety founded the Instituto Argentino de Prevencion de Accidentes y Siniestros (IAPAS) in 1974 and they plan to organize a symposium in 1976.

A journal entitled "Revista de Seguridad" is published by the Instituto Argentino de Seguridad (Tucuman 834, 3 piso, Capital Federal).

Australia

The Australian Fire Protection Association was organized in 1960. Headquarters are at 40 Chetwynd Street, Melbourne, Victoria, 3003. This Association was patterned after the National Fire Protection Association. Its membership is open to any company or individual. It holds national and regional conferences, publishes a newsletter, makes reports on fires, collects statistics in fire losses, and sponsors fire prevention campaigns.

There is an Australasian Chapter of the Society of Fire Protection Engineers with headquarters at 54 Nancy Street, Bondi, N.S.W., 2026.

The Standards Association of Australia (Science House, 157 Gloucester Street, Sydney) has standards on some types of fire protection equipment.

The Commonwealth Experimental Building Station of the Australian Dept. of Works (North Ryde, N.S.W., 2113, Australia) conducts fire studies and issues "Technical Records" on their work. It assists other bodies in the preparation of codes, specifications, and building regulations and undertakes research for nongovernment bodies and individuals at appropriate fees.

The Australian Department of Civil Aviation issues Airways Operations Instructions covering aerodrome fire safety matters which are directed by the Department.

Austria

The Zentralstelle für Brandverhütung (Central Fire Protection Department) was founded by the Austrian insurance companies in the 1930s and reestablished in 1948. Headquarters are at A-1030 Wien, Schwarzenbergpl. 7/4. Most of the provinces of Austria have a Fire Protection Department, the cost of which is shared by the government and the insurance companies. They provide information to fire brigades and other local authorities, make inspections of industrial plants and give technical advice. The Central Fire Protection Department coordinates this activity.

Belgium

The Association Nationale pour la Protection contre l'Incendie (Belgium Fire Protection Association) was founded in 1957. Headquarters are at 4 rue de l'Autonomie, B-1070 Brussels. It is supported by the insurance companies of Belgium. Its scope covers fire prevention and control, standards, and public education. It publishes "Revue Belge du Feu" on a bimonthly basis.

A journal entitled "Protection Civile" is published in Belgium periodically. The Secretariat is located at Avenue Julien Hanssens 32, 1020 Brussels, Belgium.

The Fédération Royale des Corps de Sapeurs-Pompiers de Belgique publishes a journal entitled "Le Sapeur-Pompier Belge" (Rue Perdue — 7500 Tournai).

Brazil

A Brazilian Society of Safety Engineering (Sociedade Brasileira de Engenharia de Segurança [SOBES], Edificio Edison, Passos Avenida Rio Branco 124, 2-21 20,000 Rio de Janeiro, GB) has been recently formed. The *Clube de Engenharia* (Engineering club) has a Specialized Technical Department on Safety. The *Associaçao Brasileira de Normas Tecnicas* (Brazilian Association of Technical Norms) has a Permanent Committee on Fire Protection.

Canada

The Canadian Fire Safety Association (Association Canadienne de Securité Incendie). This Association (headquartered at 1750 Finch Avenue East, Willowdale, Ontario, Canada) was granted a Canadian Charter (Letter Patent), effective May 6, 1971. It is organized "to promote the science and improve the methods of fire protection and fire prevention, to obtain and circulate information on these subjects, and to secure the understanding and cooperation of the Canadian public in establishing proper safeguards against loss of life and property by fire."

The Canadian Standards Association (Association Canadienne de Normalisation), located at 178 Rexdale Blvd., Rexdale, Ontario M9W 1R3 was chartered in 1919 and is a national, nonprofit, nongovernmental Association dedicated to providing services in support of standardization in Canada. It operates hundreds of committees that produce national consensus standards. The Committees have balanced national representation from manufacturers, consumers, and scientific, technical and professional organizations, plus governmental agencies. Through the CSA

Testing Laboratories for electrical appliances, devices and materials as well as oil- and gas-fired equipment, it is able to test, examine, and report on products in relation to pertinent CSA Specifications. Production of approved equipment is subject to factory re-inspection. Equipment bearing the appropriate registered CSA Marks indicate conformity with a CSA Standard. The CSA sponsors the Canadian Electrical Code, Part 1 (CSA C22.1-1972) plus a number of other Standards directly related to fire safety. They issue annually a List of Publications.

The Canadian Underwriters Association (Association Canadienne des Assureurs), located at 36 Toronto Street, Toronto, Ontario M5C 2E2, handles matters of fire insurance rating and inspection for many property insurance companies operating in Canada. It adapts a number of NFPA Standards for Canada and publishes them in English and French for their members and others interested. Branch offices of the CUA are located in Calgary, Alberta; Charlottetown, Prince Edward Island; Halifax, Nova Scotia; Montreal, Quebec; Saint John, New Brunswick; St. John's, Newfoundland; Vancouver, British Columbia; and Winnipeg, Manitoba.

Dominion Fire Commissioner (Commissaire Fédéral des Incendies), Department of Public Works (Ministère des Travaux Publics). This office coordinates the work of the Provincial Fire Marshals and Fire Commissioners, the Fire Marshal of the Yukon and Northwest Territories, the Canadian Forces Fire Marshal, Department of National Defence, the Federal Department of the Environment, the Provincial Departments of Forestry and Resources, and the Health and Welfare Division of Statistics Canada. The Office issues an Annual Report of Fire Losses in Canada (Pertes causées par l'incendie au Canada) available from the Dominion Fire Commissioner, Department of Public Works, Ottawa, Ontario K1A OM2.

The National Research Council Canada (Conseil National de Recherches Canada), located in Ottawa, Ontario K1A OR6, has done extensive work in fire safety matters, mostly through its Division of Building Research (Division des Recherches sur le Bâtiment). It publishes annually a List of Publications of the Division (plus Supplements) indicating their Research and Technical Papers, Canadian Building Digests, Bibliographies, Fire Studies, Building Research Notes, Technical Translations, and Miscellaneous Publications. The NRCC has an Associate Committee on National Fire Codes and an Associate Committee on the National Building Code of Canada. The most recent edition (sixth) of the National Building Code of Canada (1975) is NRCC Publication No. 13982. It was prepared by the Associate Committee of 24 individual members with the NRCC providing technical and secretarial support. It has nine parts: 1) Scope and Definitions; 2) Administration; 3) Use and Occupancy; 4) Design; 5) Materials; 6) Building Services; 7) Plumbing; 8) Construction Safety Measures — Public Safety at Construction Sites; and 9) Housing and Small Buildings. There are 5 Supplements (not a legal part of the Code) covering: 1) Climatic Information for Building Design in Canada; 2) Fire Performance Ratings; 3) Commentary on Part 3; 4) Commentaries on Part 4; and 5) Building Standards for the Handicapped. Associated Documents are the: Canadian Heating, Ventilating and Air-conditioning Code 1975; Canadian Plumbing Code 1975; Canadian Construction Safety Code 1975; Residential Standards 1975; Canadian Farm Building Code 1975; Span Tables for Wood Joists, Rafters, Trusses and Beams 1975; List of Standards Referenced in the National Building Code 1975; and Measures for Fire Safety in High Buildings.

Underwriters Laboratories of Canada is a nonprofit organization (incorporated in 1920) located at 7 Crouse Road, Scarborough, Ontario M1R 3A9. It is sponsored by the Canadian Underwriters Association. It maintains and operates laboratories and a certification service for the examination, testing, and classification of devices, constructions, materials, and methods to determine their relation to life, fire and casualty hazards, or their value in the prevention of crime. The ULC also develops and publishes standards, classifications and specifications for products having a bearing on fire or accident hazards or crime prevention. It has no financial, legal, or other connection with Underwriters Laboratories, Inc. in the United States, although there is some technical liaison on matters of mutual interests. The ULC's Scarborough establishment has some 45,000 sq ft of office and laboratory space with a staff of 55. The results of their work appear in their List of Equipment and Materials which is published in two volumes. Volume I contains listings of all products falling under the general categories of accident, hazard, automotive, burglary, electrical, fire protection equipment, and equipment for the handling and utilization of fuel oils and gases. Volume II covers all listings of building materials and serves as a complementary document to Supplement No. 2 to the National Building Code of Canada. There are two Advisory Engineering Councils serving the ULC. One is the Fire Council of Underwriters Laboratories of Canada (composed of representatives of the Laboratories, Provincial Fire Marshals, Building Commissioners, Governmental Agencies, CUA officials, and Fire Commissioners) and the other is the Interprovincial Gas Advisory Council. The Laboratories have a Label Service program, an Integral Marker Service, a Reexamination Service (involving periodic visits to the factory by a representative of the Laboratories for the most recent production of a listed product), and a Certificate Service. They issue a ULC News to aid in communicating current activities of the Laboratories to interested persons.

Other organizations in Canada having fire-related interests include

Association of Canadian Fire Marshals and Fire Commissioners, c/o Fire Prevention Branch, 1305 Chemin Ste. Foy, Quebec, Quebec G1S 2N3 (Organized by Canadian Members of the Fire Marshals Association of North America)

Canadian Association of Fire Chiefs, 2848 Bloor Street, West, Toronto, Ontario M8X 1A9

Canadian Automatic Sprinkler Association, Ste. 72, 1 Sparks Ave., Willowdale, Ontario M2H 2W1

Canadian Forestry Association, 185 Sommerset St., West, Ottawa, Ontario K2P 0J2

Canadian Forestry Service, Environment Canada, (Service des Forêts), Forest Fire Research Institute, Nicol Building, 331 Cooper St., Ottawa, Ontario K1A OH3

Canadian Gas Association, 55 Scarsdale Road, Don Mills, Ontario

Canadian Institute of Steel Construction, Consumers Road, Willowdale, Ontario M2J 4G8

Canadian Institute of Timber Construction, 200 Cooper St., Ottawa, Ontario K2P 0G1

Canada Safety Council, 1765 St. Laurent Blvd., Ottawa, Ontario, K1G 3V4

Canadian Steel Industries Construction Council, 201 Consumers Road, Suite 300, Willowdale, Ont. M2J 4G8

Canadian Wood Council, Ste. 701, 170 Laurier Ave., West, Ottawa, Ontario K1P 5Y5

Industrial Accident Prevention Association, 2 Bloor Street East, 9th Floor, Toronto, Ontario M4W 3C2

Labour Canada, Accident Prevention and Compensation Branch, Ottawa, Ontario K1A 0J3

Maritime Fire Chiefs Association, Box 757, St. John, New Brunswick E2L 4B7

Colombia

El Consejo Colombiano de Seguridad publishes a journal entitled "Proteccion y Seguridad." The address of the publisher is Calle 13 No. 8-23, Piso 8, Apartado Aereo 6839, Bogota, Colombia.

Denmark

The Dansk Brandvaerns-Komité (Danish Fire Protection Association) was established in 1920. Headquarters are at Nygaards Plads 9, 2610 Kφbenhavn-Rφdovre. The Association, which is nonprofit, is financed by fees for its inspection services to industries, and contributions from the Danish government, local governments, and from companies and individuals. It prepares standards, does consulting work, and carries on educational activities. It published a monthly journal entitled "Brandvaern" (Fire Protection) in Danish (includes English summary of the contents).

A Danish fire service journal entitled "Brandmanden" is published monthly and is available from the publisher, Landskronagade 76, 2100 Kφbenhavn.

Finland

The Suomen Palontorjuntalütto (Finnish Fire Protection Association) was founded in 1922. Headquarters are at Iso Roobertinkatu 7 A 4, Helsinki 12. It is supported by municipalities, insurance companies, industries and individuals. It carries on technical, investigative, and educational activities and maintains a consultation bureau for fire fighting techniques known as the Fire Protection Center.

Two fire journals are published in Finland. One is "Palontorjunta-Brandvärn" (which had its 25th anniversary in 1974) and the other is "Palontorjunta-Tekniikka." The latter concentrates on technical material important in the field. Both journals are available on subscription. The publisher's address is Neitsytpolku 3A, 00140 Helsinki 14, Finland. Brief English (and Swedish) translations of the contents are given.

A quarterly journal, "Industribrand Meddelanden," is published in Finland by Omsesidiga Bolaget Industriforsakring, Hallonnäsgränd 8, 00210 Helsingfors 21.

France

Le Centre National de Prevention et de Protection (National Center for Prevention and Protection) has headquarters at 5 rue Daunou, 75002, Paris. Founded in 1956 by the leading fire insurance associations in France, the CNPP is a nonprofit organization to reduce the frequency and seriousness of fires. It publishes a journal entitled "Face au Risque" in French (with briefs available in English).

The fire services in France have a *Fédération Nationale des Sapeurs-Pompiers Français* (27 rue de Dunkerque, Paris 10e, France). They issue a quarterly journal entitled "Le Sapeur-Pompier."

Le Centre Scientifique et Technique du Bâtiment (Scientific and Technical Building Center) in Paris undertakes fire research and testing.

Le Federation Française du Materiel d'Incendie (FFMI) is headquartered at 10 Avenue Hoche, 75382 Paris Cedex 08. They publish a Bulletin d'Information de la Federation.

The fire insurance companies in France have as their trade and technical group the *Assemblée Plénière des Sociétés d'Assurances Contre l'Incendie* (11 Rue Pillet-Will, 75009 Paris).

Germany (Republic of)

The Vereinigung zur Förderung des Deutschen Brandschutzes e. V. (German Fire Protection Association) was founded in 1950. Headquarters are at 2 Hamburg 1 Westphalenswegl. Membership is primarily made up of German fire chiefs, but others concerned with fire protection and prevention are included. A technical journal, the *VFBD Zeitschrift*, is published.

Fire research is carried on by the Institute of Building Materials of the Technical University at Braunschiveig and by the Technical University at Karlsruhe.

A German fire service journal entitled "Brandschutz" is published monthly and available from Deutsche Feuerwehr-Zeitung, Blumenstrasse 34, 8 Munchen 2, Germany.

The Munich Reinsurance Company issues (not on a regular basis) an excellent publication entitled "Schaden Spiegel" (Losses and Loss Prevention) compiled to inform their business associates concerned with fire protection insurance matters. It is bilingual in German and English. The home office of the Munchener Ruckoersicherungs-Gesellschaft is at D-8000 Munchen 40, Koniginstrasse 107, Bundesrepublick Deutschland. The U.S. Offices are at 410 Park Avenue, New York, NY 10022.

Great Britain

The Fire Protection Association (FPA) is the central advisory organization, largely financed by insurance companies and Lloyd's, providing technical and general advice on all aspects of fire protection. It is headquartered at Aldermary House, Queen Street, London EC4N 1TJ. It publishes the FPA Journal "Fire Prevention" six times a year. The FPA has a large number of publications and visual aids in the form of Booklets, Leaflets, Fire Safety Sheets, Planning Guides and Studies, Information Sheets on Hazardous Materials, Fire Safety Data Sheets, Posters, Notices, Slides, Films, and Film-strips. A comprehensive guide to fire publications and films issued by government departments and outside bodies in Great Britain, as well as by the FPA, is available from the Association.

The Home Office (Horseferry House, Dean Ryle St., London SW1 2AW) is the government department primarily concerned with fire service matters. The Fire Services Act 1947 made provision for a permanent staff of Her Majesty's Inspectors of Fire Services together with Assistant Inspectors of Fire Services. The main functions of the Inspectorate are carried out under the direction of HM Chief Inspector of Fire Services. Although the fire service is a local authority service and recruitment and training are the responsibility of the local fire authorities, the Home Office maintains a Fire Service Staff College near Dorking (Surrey) and a Fire Service Technical College at Moreton-in-Marsh (Gloucestershire).

The *Fire Research Station* at Borehamwood, Herts, England WD6 2BL is part of the Building Research Establishment and is operated under the Department of the Environment. The Building Research Station is at Garston, Watford WD2 7JR. The Building Research Establishment is responsible for matters relating to multiple occupancy residences, dock and harbor installations, public service vehicles, and other means of transport. The Department is also responsible for fire precautions in government buildings. The Department publishes BRE News which includes listings of recent publications available from the BRE including those on fire subjects. Many technical publications are issued by the Fire Research Station.

The control of dangerous substances is the responsibility of the *Health and Safety Commission* and its Executive as a result of the Health and Safety at Work etc. Act 1974. Precautions in schools are the responsibility of the *Department of Education and Science* and the *Department of Health and Social Security* is concerned with fire precautions in hospitals, nursing homes and other similar types of residential homes. Other Departments with fire protection responsibilities include the *Department of Energy* (nuclear installations), *Ministry of Agriculture, Fisheries and Food* (farming), *Forestry Commission* (forests and woodlands), *Department of Trade* (ships and aircraft) and *Ministry of Defence* (armed services). The *Civil Aviation Authority* has a Fire Service Training School at Stansted Airport.

Other principal fire safety organizations in the United Kingdom are:

British Fire Protection Systems Associations, Ltd., 37 New Broad Street, London EC2M 1NX

British Fire Services Association, 86 London Road, Leicester LE2 0QR

Chief and Assistant Chief Fire Officers' Association, Fire Brigade HQ., Pirehill, Stone ST15 0BS

Fire Fighting Vehicle Manufacturers Association, Forbes House, Halken Street, London SW1X 7DS

Fire Surveyors Section, Incorporated Association of Architects and Surveyors, 29 Belgrave Square, London SW1X 8QF

Industrial Fire Protection Association of Great Britian, 140 Sloane St., London SW1X 9AY

Institution of Fire Engineers, 148 New Walk, Leicester LE1 7QB

The Institution of Fire Engineers publishes a quarterly journal entitled "Fire Engineers Journal."

The Fire Surveyors Section of the Incorporated Association of Architects and Surveyors publishes a journal entitled "Fire Surveyor" which is available on subscription. The Publisher is Victor Green Publications Ltd., 44 Bedford Row, London WC1R 4LL.

The British Chemical Industry Safety Council of the Chemical Industries Association (Alembic House, 93 Albert Embankment, London SE1 7TU issues a Quarterly Safety Summary containing information of interest to those concerned with chemical plant fire safety.

India

The National Fire Service College (280 Palm Road, Civil Lines, Nagpur 1, India) publishes semiannually a journal entitled "Fire Technology" which is available on a subscription basis.

Regional Committees of the Tariff Advisory Committee inspect industrial properties from the fire insurance and fire protection engineering viewpoints.

Iraq

A fire protection week was held in Baghdad in May of 1972 on the initiative of the National Fire Insurance Institution. Afterwards, a group of interested persons from the Ministries of Civil Defense, Economics, and Planning, and from insurance, industry, and fire departments, decided to organize an *Iraq Fire Protection Association* by Presidential decree. The organization is in its formative stages.

Israel

The *Association of Fire Insurance Companies* organized a two-day fire protection seminar in June 1973 and there is scheduled another meeting on safety in the latter part of 1975.

Italy

Direzione Generale Servizi Antincendio (General Direction of Fire Services) is a section of the Internal Affairs Ministry of the Italian Government. This section operates the National Fire College, publishes and enforces fire safety regulations, and operates a research and test center in Rome.

A magazine entitled "Antincendio e Protezione Civil" is published in Italy and available on subscription from the publisher Edizioni di Protezione Civil S.r.l., 00187 Roma, Via Flavia 72.

Korea

The *Korean Fire Protection Association* has over 100 employees, mainly engineers with various specializations. Its main purpose is to inspect properties and advise on compliance with safety requirements. The work of the KFPA is closely linked with the insurance of privately owned property and the operation is financed, in part, by a tax on fire insurance premiums. Government property is not insured but is inspected. The KFPA also motivates the public at large in the interest of fire prevention. (The address of the KFPA is Jabo Building, 21-9 Chodong, Jungku, Seoul 100, Korea.

Lebanon

At the Beirut International Airport, Beirut, Lebanon, the International Civil Aviation Organization operates a *Civil Aviation Safety Centre*. This Centre conducts courses in aircraft fire, search and rescue activity as well as in other aviation safety subjects.

Japan

The *Japan Fire Protection Association* is located at Kenchiku-Kaikan 19-23 Chome Ginza, Chuo-ku, Tokyo. It publishes a monthly bulletin entitled "Building Fire and Loss Prevention." The JFPA is sponsored by the Japanese Ministry of Building Construction.

The *Building Research Institute* of the Ministry of Construction of the Japanese Government publishes significant "BRI Research Papers" on fire safety and earthquake protection subjects, as well as on other construction techniques. The BRI is located at 4 Chome Hyakunin-cho, Shinjuku-ku, Tokyo, Japan.

The *Fire and Marine Insurance Association of Japan*, (Non-life Insurance Building, 9 Kanda Awajicho 2 Chome, Chiyoda-ku, Tokyo, Japan) publishes installation standards on such fire safety equipment as sprinkler systems, foam extinguishing systems and carbon dioxide systems.

The *Yasuda Fire and Marine Insurance Co., Ltd.* (5-4 Otemachi Itchome, Chiyoda-ku, Tokyo) published in 1974 a "Handbook of Factory Fire Protection."

The National Electrical Code (NFPA No. 70-1975; ANSI C1-1975) has been published in Japanese by the *Japan Electric Association* (3.1 Chome Yuraku-cho, Chiyoda-ku, Tokyo).

A trade association of fire equipment manufacturers in Japan (*National Association of Manufacturers of Fire Prevention Equipment*) is located at Shokaki Kaikan 3-25-7 Asakusabashi Taito-ku, Tokyo.

There are a number of other organizations in Japan concerned with fire related subjects such as the Institute of Fire Administration and Engineering of Japan, the Japan

Society of Safety Engineering, and the Fire Prevention Society of Japan.

Mexico

The Asociación Mexicana de Instituciónes de Seguros (AMIS), Londers No. 4, Mexico 6 D.F., has taken leadership in this country on fire safety matters. A seminar on Fire and Damage Prevention Engineering was held in 1975. Proposals are going to the Mexican government for "Reglamento de Protecciones Contra Incendio" from this group as this HANDBOOK material is being prepared.

The Netherlands

There are two Associations in The Netherlands that do effective fire prevention and protection work. One is the *Nationaal Brandpreventie Instituut* (National Fire Prevention Institute), Laan van Meerdervoot 478, Den Haag, The Netherlands. The other is *Technisch Bureau ter Bevordering van Schadepreventie* (Technical Bureau for Loss Prevention), P. O. Box 54, Baarn, The Netherlands. The former includes members from government departments, municipalities, fire brigades, industry, insurance, and architects and the NBI concentrates on fire prevention educational campaigns using all forms of media, including television. The TBBS serves the insurance industry and concentrates on loss prevention activities for industry and commerce. The TBBS has organized with the University of Maryland College of Engineering in the U.S.A. two international fire protection engineering institutes with the NFPA's planning and administrative assistance.

The fire services in The Netherlands are entrusted (under the Municipal and Fire Service Laws) to local authorities. Of the 842 municipalities, eight have professional, full-time fire brigades; 67 of the brigades are partly professional and partly volunteer; and 702 have volunteer departments only. There is a *Fire Service Inspectorate in the Ministry of Interior* who advises on all fire protection matters and maintains a testing station at The Hague to test appliances, pumps, and extinguishers. A Fire Council advises the Minister of Interior on general problems related to the Fire Service. The TNO (*Toegepast Natuurwetenschappelijk Onderzoek*), a national institution, has a Center for Fire Research at Delft. There are a number of fire service associations and about 1,000 large industrial plants have their own fire brigades.

New Zealand

The *New Zealand Fire Protection Association, Inc.* (P. O. Box 2561, Wellington) is a nonprofit, technical, and educational organization to safeguard life and property against fire. It is a member of the Conference of Fire Protection Associations.

The *New Zealand Department of Scientific and Industrial Research* has done some extensive research in their Chemistry Division related to spontaneous ignition of solids.

The *Standards Association of New Zealand*, World Trade Center, 15-23 Sturdee Street, Wellington 1, has a number of standards on fire protection equipment as well as on many other subjects.

Norway

The *Norsk Brannvern Forening* (Norwegian Fire Protection Association) was founded in 1923. Headquarters are at Oscargate 28B, Boks 7132, Homansbyen, Oslo 3. Membership includes fire brigades, industrial firms, insurance companies, and interested individuals. The Association publishes the Journal, *Mot Brann*.

Philippines

A *Philippines Fire Protection Association* was organized in 1964 under the name of Philippines Underwriters Investigative Association by fire insurance interests. They have organized public fire protection seminars in 1973 and 1975. Risk inspections and advice to industry are included in their activities.

South Africa

The *Fire Protection Association of Southern Africa* (Brand-Beskermings-Vereniging van Suider-Afrika) is located at 520 Maritime House, Loveday Street, Johannesburg, Transvaal 2001 (P. O. Box 61697). It publishes a journal entitled "Fire Protection." It serves as a central advisory organization, largely financed by insurance companies and Lloyd's, providing technical and general advice on all aspects of fire protection.

Spain

The *Asociacion Espanola de Lucha contra el Fuego* (Spanish Association for the Fight against Fire) was founded in 1961. Its headquarters are at Sepulveda 162, Barcelona 11. Active membership comes from the personnel of fire brigades. Associate membership includes all others interested. The Association is nonprofit. It publishes a bimonthly journal for the benefit of its members entitled "ASELF" (in Spanish).

A fire service magazine entitled "Alarma!" is published by the Organo de la A.C.D. del Cuerpo de Bomberos which is available (in Spanish) from Provenza 178, Barcelona 11, Spain.

Sweden

Svenska Brandförsvarsföreningen (Swedish Fire Protection Association), Kungsholms, Hamnplan 3, 112 20 Stockholm, was established through an amalgamation of the Swedish Fire Prevention Association (founded: 1918) and the National Organization of Swedish Fire Brigades (founded: 1912). It is a voluntary membership association supported by member dues, insurance companies, and from government grants. It publishes a monthly journal in Swedish (with English summaries) entitled "Brand Försvar."

The *Royal Institute of Technology*, Division of Building Construction in Stockholm, and the *Lund Institute of Technology*, Division of Structural Mechanics and Concrete Construction, have both done considerable research on fire safety matters affecting building construction.

The Swedish National Board of Rescue and Fire Services (*Statens Brandnamnd*) publishes Informative Bulletins to aid the fire service in the fulfillment of their fire suppression duties. This organization replaced, in 1974, the previous National Inspectorate of Fire Services. The Statens Brandnamnd is located at Observatoriegatan 20, Box 6029, 102 31 Stockholm.

Switzerland

The *Brand-Verhütungsdienst fur Industrie und Gewerbe* (Swiss Fire Prevention Service for Industry and Trade) is located at Nüschelerstrasse 45, CH-8001 Zurich. The service was established in 1944 by the Association of Swiss Fire Insurance Companies, the Central Office of the Swiss Union of Trade and Industry, and the Industrial Federation of Swiss employer organizations. Another supporting institution, the Union of the Cantonal Fire Insurance Establishments, joined in 1958.

Service is provided to some 1,700 industrial and trade enterprises of all kinds and sizes. The service covers all matters of fire protection, such as planning of buildings, fire protection equipment, and organization of employees. Extensive educational leaflets and posters are provided subscribers to the service. Financial support comes from the insurance companies and from the member companies.

The *Vereinigung kantonaler Feuerversicherungsanstalten* (Catonal Association of Fire Insurance Institutions — Association des Establissements Cantonaux d'Assurance Contre l'Indendie), Bundegasse 20, 3011 Bern, issues annual reports and statistics on fire losses and publishes standards for the installation of sprinklers. They also issue a Bulletin available on subscription.

A Centre d' Etudes de la Commission Permanente du Risque Atomique of the Comite Européen des Assurances is headquartered in Switzerland (Schutzenweg 2, CH-8700 Küsnacht [Zurich]).

The "Schweizerische Feuerwehr-Zeitung" (Journal des Sapeurs-Pompiers Suisses; Giornale die Pompieri Svizzeri) is the official organ of the Swiss Fire Brigades and is published quarterly (Ensingerstr. 37, 3006 Bern, Switzerland).

Union of Soviet Socialist Republics

Central Scientific Research Institute for Fire Protection, Moscow. Founded in 1937. This Institute undertakes fire research, consultation, standardization, and testing. Liaison is maintained with 20 fire testing stations in cities in the U.S.S.R.

The *All-Russian Voluntary Fire Protection Association.* The aims of this Association are to prevent fires, to extinguish fires where there is no professional brigade (as on farms), to form industrial fire brigades, and to carry on fire prevention education. It is reported that the Association has four million members.

A magazine Noжaphoe geno ("Fire Affairs") is published monthly in Russian and is available from the U.S.S.R. State Library, 3 Kalinin Street, Moscow G19, U.S.S.R.

Venezuela

The National Electrical Code has been translated in Spanish by the Comite de Electricidad, Edif. Alemo piso 3, Av. Venezuela Esquina Alameda, El Rosal 106, Caracas.

Appendix B

FIRE TESTING AND RESEARCH LABORATORIES IN THE UNITED STATES OF AMERICA

There are many laboratories in the United States of America capable of performing, in varying degrees, fire tests of materials and/or equipment, and many of the same and different laboratories have facilities to conduct fire related research work.

Broadly speaking, these laboratories can be classified in three general categories: (1) private and industrial laboratories, (2) university laboratories, and (3) government laboratories. This chapter deals initially and separately with Underwriters Laboratories, Inc. and Factory Mutual Research since their activities are preeminent in the fire protection field in the United States; great reliance is placed on their fire testing activities by fire protection authorities both nationally and internationally.

No effort is made in this Appendix to tell of specific work currently being done by any of the laboratories mentioned herein since such a cataloging would be quickly outdated. In some cases the activities of private, industrial, and governmental laboratories are indicated by their sponsors or by their names. For some of those included, fire-related testing and research is just one of a number of capabilities possessed by the laboratories named and for many, fire testing may be a small part of their work. Other laboratories not mentioned may have similar capabilities, and no claim is made that the list of those mentioned is all-inclusive. In fact, there has been a marked increase in this type of activity in recent and current years as a result of a national increase in fire safety as well as other safety and health related issues.

A *Directory of Fire Research in the United States* has been published periodically by the Committee on Fire Research of the Division of Engineering, National Research Council, National Academy of Sciences (2101 Constitution Avenue, Washington, D.C. 20418). The latest (Seventh) Edition at the time of preparation of this Appendix was dated 1971-1973 and released in 1975.

A. Underwriters Laboratories, Inc.

Underwriters Laboratories, Inc. (headquarters, 207 East Ohio St., Chicago, Ill. 60611) is a nonprofit corporation having as its sole objective the promotion of public safety through conduct of "—scientific investigation, study, experiments, and tests, to determine the relation of various materials, devices, products, equipment, constructions, methods, and systems to hazards appurtenant thereto or to the use thereof affecting life and property and to ascertain, define, and publish standards, classifications, and specifications for materials, devices, products, equipment, constructions, methods, and systems affecting such hazards, and other information tending to reduce or prevent bodily injury, loss of life, and property damage from such hazards."

The organization was founded in 1894 by the Fire Insurance Industry under whose sponsorship it operated until 1968 when it became an independent, public service type corporation. It has no capital stock, nor shareholders, and exists solely for the service it renders in the fields of fire, crime, and casualty prevention. None of its property, assets, or income accrues for the benefit of any individual or concern. Its current corporate membership is drawn from the following categories: consumer interest, public safety body or agency (responsible primarily for enforcement in the field of public safety), governmental body or agency (not responsible primarily for enforcement in the field of public safety), insurance, safety expert, standardization expert, public utility, education, and officer of the corporation. UL is managed by a Board of Trustees drawn from the aforementioned categories, plus an additional "at large" category. Only one officer of the corporation is included on its Board of Trustees.

UL testing laboratories are located in Melville, New York; Santa Clara, Calif.; Chicago and Northbrook, Ill.; and Tampa, Fla. In addition, UL has inspection centers in approximately 200 cities throughout the United States and in over 35 foreign countries.

Underwriters Laboratories Inc. publishes annually lists of manufacturers whose products, when tested, have proved acceptable under appropriate standards, and which are subjected to one of the forms of follow-up service provided by the Laboratories as a countercheck. These are:

1. Electrical Appliance and Utlization Equipment List
2. Electrical Construction Materials List
3. Hazardous Location Equipment List
4. Fire Protection Equipment List
5. Building Materials Directory
6. Fire Resistance Index
7. Gas and Oil Equipment List
8. Accident, Automotive and Burglary Protection Equipment Lists
9. Marine Products Directory
10. Classified Products Index

In addition, supplements to the above annual lists are published during the year. These listings, subject to appropriate recorded limitations for each of the categories, are affirmative. No negative findings or reports of criticisms are published, except to the submitter manufacturers. The fees for this work are based upon the materials and time spent in examination, testing, and conference, according to payroll cost.

The titles of the various departments in Underwriters Laboratories are indicative of the products handled by them:

1. Burglary Protection and Signaling Department
2. Casualty and Chemical Hazards Department
3. Electrical Department
4. Fire Protection Department
5. Heating, Air-Conditioning and Refrigeration Department
6. Marine Department

The promulgation of a Listing or Classification is contingent upon the establishment of the Laboratories' Follow-Up Service. The nature of the service to be applied to a particular category of products rests with the Laboratories. The Follow-Up Service is designed to serve as a check on the means which the manufacturer exercises to determine compliance of the product with the requirements of the Laboratories. Under the Follow-Up Service, the manufacturer attaches labels, markers, or other authorized evidences of Listing ("Listing Marks") or Classification ("Classification Markings") to those products that are found to be in compliance with the Laboratories' requirements.

Representatives of the Laboratories make periodic

examinations or tests of the products at the factory and may, from time-to-time, select samples from the factory, the open market, or elsewhere to be sent to a Laboratories' testing station for examination and/or test to determine compliance with the Laboratories' requirements.

Should examination or test by the Laboratories' representative disclose features not in compliance with the requirements, the manufacturer is required either to correct such items or to remove the Listing Mark or Classification Marking from the product.

B. Factory Mutual Laboratory Facilities

The Factory Mutual Research staff (headquarters, 1151 Boston-Providence Turnpike, Norwood, Mass. 02062) of the Factory Mutual System consists of the Standards, Research, and Approvals Groups.

The Standards Group is made up of engineers in many fields who develop information and recommendations based on research and loss experience, and also are available to offer advice to Factory Mutual System members on specific loss prevention matters.

The Research Group consists of two groups of scientists: One group is a basic research group whose object is to secure information pertaining to the initial phases of fire, its detection, and growth patterns. The theories that they develop are expected to lead to new method of loss prevention and control. The other group, an applied research group, is concerned with improvement in effectiveness of fire protection systems, fire modeling studies, rack storage and plastics storage fire tests, new suppression agents and systems, ignition and flammability of materials, and design and cost evaluation of effective fire protection systems.

The Approvals Group subjects equipment and materials to rigid tests to determine that devices submitted by manufacturers will operate dependably, and that materials can pass fire tests that indicate an acceptable low flammability. An approval guide is issued annually.

Factory Mutual testing facilities in Norwood, Mass. include fuel, extinguisher, hydraulics, chemical, electrical, and miscellaneous research laboratories. A metallurgical laboratory is equipped with ultrasonic and radiographic equipment to determine causes of failures in boilers, pressure vessels, and machinery; also to perform tests to check quality of workmanship, such as welding. In a chemical section of the laboratory, metals, water, and boiler scale are analyzed to determine the acceptability of equipment and to determine the causes of metal failures.

Large-scale applied research is carried out in the one-acre, 60-ft-high FM Test Center in West Glocester, R.I. During a test, electronic equipment measures and records sprinkler water distribution, water-flow rate and pressure, temperatures of the building atmosphere and steelwork that is exposed to fire, loss of weight of materials while burning, and airflow rates. Typical applied research projects of recent years include the determination of protection needed for

Fig. A-B1. Representative labels of Underwriters Laboratories, Inc.

rack storage, plastics storage, aircraft, hangars, and a great variety of other tests.

Factory Mutual laboratory facilities, operated primarily for Factory Mutual System members, are available to others on a contract basis through Factory Mutual Research.

Fig. A-B2. Representative labels of Factory Mutual System.

C. Other Private and Industrial Laboratories

Following is a listing of other private and industrial laboratories in the United States whose work is known at the time of publication of this HANDBOOK.

Ambric Testing and Engineering Associates of New Jersey, 4041 Ridge Ave., Philadelphia, PA 19129

American Gas Association Laboratories, 8501 E. Pleasant Valley Road, Cleveland, OH 44131

The Ansul Company, One Stanton St., Marinette, WI 54143

Armstrong Cork Company, Research and Development Center, Lancaster, PA 17604

Arthur D. Little, Inc., Acorn Park, Cambridge, MA 02140

Atlantic Research Corporation, Division of the Susquehanna Corporation, Shirley Highway at Edsall Rd, Alexandria, VA 22314

"Automatic" Sprinkler Corporation of America, Division of A-T-O Inc., P. O. Box 180, Cleveland, OH 44147

AVCO Corporation, Systems Division, Fire and Thermal Testing Laboratory, Lowell Industrial Park, Lowell, MA 01851

Battelle Memorial Institute, Columbus Laboratories, 505 King Avenue, Columbus, OH 43201

Battelle Memorial Institute, Pacific Northwest Laboratories, P. O. Box 999, Richland, WA 99352

Bell Helicopter Company, Fort Worth, TX 76101

Calspan Corporation, 4455 Genesee, Buffalo, NY 14225

Copper Development Association, Inc., 1011 High Ridge Road, Stamford, CT 06905

Cornell Aeronautical Laboratory, Inc., P. O. Box 235, Buffalo, NY 14221

Dikewood Corporation, Subsidiary of TRACOR, Inc., 1009 Bradbury Drive, S. E., Albuquerque, NM 87106

E. I. du Pont de Nemours & Company, Savannah River Laboratory, Aiken, SC 29801

E. I. du Pont de Nemours & Company, Elastomer Chemicals Department, Wilmington, DE 19898

E. I. du Pont de Nemours & Company, Haskell Laboratory for Toxicology and Industrial Medicine, Wilmington, DE 19898

Electrical Testing Laboratories, Inc., 2 East End Ave., New York, NY 10021

Dynamic Science, AvSer Facility, 1800 West Deer Valley Dr., Phoenix, AZ 85027

Dynamic Science, Division of Marshall Industries, 2400 Michelson Dr., Irvine, CA 92664

Fenwal Incorporated, 400 Main St., Ashland, MA 01721

Firestone Coated Fabrics Company, P. O. Box 887, Magnolia, AR 71753

Franklin Institute Research Laboratories, 20th and Race Streets, Philadelphia, PA 19103

General Electric Company, Research and Development Center, P. O. Box 8, Schenectady, NY 12301

Gillette Research Company Institute, Harris Research Laboratories Department, 1413 Research Blvd., Rockville, MD 20850

B. F. Goodrich Chemical Company, P. O. Box 122, Avon Lake, OH 44012

Grinnell Fire Protection Systems Company, 10 Dorrance St., Providence, RI 02903

Hardwood Plywood Manufacturers' Association, 2310 South Walter Reed Dr., Arlington, VA 22206

Hooker Chemicals and Plastics Corporation, Research Laboratories, 345 3rd Avenue, Niagara Falls, NY 14303

Horizons Research Inc., 23800 Mercantile, Cleveland, OH 44122

Hough Laboratories, 708 Rice, Springfield, OH 45505

International Business Machines Corporation, Federal Systems Division, Gaithersburg, MD 20760

IIT Research Institute, 10 West 35th St., Chicago, IL 60616

Walter Kidde and Company, Inc., 675 Main St., Belleville NJ 07109

Lockheed Aircraft Corporation, Rye Canyon Research Laboratory, P. O. Box 551, Burbank, CA 91593

McGraw-Edison Company, 2 Babcock Place, West Orange, NJ 07052

Meteorology Research, Inc., 464 West Woodbury Rd., Altadena, CA 91001

Midwest Research Institute, 425 Volker, Kansas City, MO 64110

National Foam System, Inc., Union and Adams St., West Chester, PA 19380

National Gypsum Company, Research Center, 325 Delaware Ave., Buffalo, NY 14202

The New York City-Rand Institute, 545 Madison Ave., New York, NY 10022

Ocean Systems, Inc., Saw Mill River Rd., at Rt., 100C, Tarrytown, NY 10591

Owens-Corning Fiberglas Technical Center, Granville, OH 43023

Pacific Northwest Laboratory, Battelle Blvd., Richland, WA 99352

Petrolite Corporation, 369 Marshall Ave., St. Louis, MO 63119

Philip Carey Company, Division of Panacon Corporation, 320 South Wayne, Cincinnati, OH 45215

Pittsburgh Testing Laboratory, P. O. Box 1646, Pittsburgh, PA 15230

Portland Cement Association, 5420 Old Orchard Rd., Skokie, IL 60076

Smithers Scientific Service, Inc., 425 W. Market St., Akron, OH 44303

Southwest Research Institute, 8500 Culebra Rd., San Antonio, TX 78228

Stanford Research Institute, 333 Ravenswood Ave., Menlo Park, CA 94025

Thomas A. Edison Industries, Instrument Division Laboratory, 61 Alden St., West Orange, NJ 07051

TSI Inc., 3260 Brannon Ave., St. Louis, MO 63139

TRW Systems Group, Fluid Mechanics Laboratory, One Space Pk., Redondo Beach, CA   90278

Union Carbide Corporation, Union Carbide Technical Center, South Charleston, WV   25303

University Engineers, Inc., 1215 Westheimer Dr., Norman, OK   73069

United States Testing Company, Inc., 1415 Park Ave., Hoboken, NJ   07030

URS Research Company, 155 Bovet Rd., San Mateo, CA   94402

Weyerhauser Company, Longview, WA   98632

Universities

Arizona State University, Mechanical Engineering Laboratory, Tempe, AZ   85281

Brown University, Division of Engineering, Providence, RI   02912

University of California, Berkeley, CA   94720

University of California, Department of Agricultural Engineering, Davis, CA   95616

University of California, Hazards Control Department, Livermore, CA   94550

University of California, Department of Applied Mechanics and Engineering Sciences, San Diego (La Jolla), CA   92037

University of California, Department of Mechanical Engineering, Santa Barbara, CA   93106

California Institute of Technology, Pasadena, CA   91109

California State University, Chico, CA   95926

Carnegie-Mellon University, Pittsburgh, PA   15213

University of Cincinnati Medical Center and Shriners Burn Institute, Cincinnati, OH   45221

Cornell University, Sibley School of Mechanical and Aerospace Engineering, Ithaca, NY   14850

Drexel University, Department of Chemical Engineering, Philadelphia, PA   19104

University of Florida, Department of Mechanical Engineering, Gainesville, FL   32601

Georgia Institute of Technology, Fire Hazard and Combustion Research Laboratory, Atlanta, GA   30332

Harvard University, Engineering Sciences Laboratory, Cambridge, MA   02138

University of Illinois, Chicago, IL   60680

University of Illinois, Urbana, IL   61801

The Johns Hopkins University, Applied Physics Laboratory, Silver Spring, MD   20910

Louisiana State University, Baton Rouge, LA   70803

University of Maine, Department of Mechanical Engineering, Orono, ME   04473

University of Maryland, Fire Protection Curriculum, College Park, MD   20740

Massachusetts Institute of Technology, Department of Chemical Engineering, Cambridge, MA   02139

University of Michigan, Department of Aerospace Engineering, Ann Arbor, MI   48105

University of Minnesota, Minneapolis, MN   55455

Mississippi State University, Department of Sociology and Rural Life, State College, MS   39762

University of Montana, Wood Chemistry Laboratory, Missoula, MT   59801

New York University, School of Engineering and Science, New York, NY   10003

State University of New York, Stony Brook, NY   11790

Ohio State University, Building Research Laboratory, Columbus, OH   43210

Ohio State University, Department of Chemical Engineering, Columbus, OH   43210

University of Oklahoma, Office of Research Administration, Norman, OK   73069

Pennsylvania State University, State College, PA   16801

Polytechnic Institute of Brooklyn, Brooklyn, NY   11201

Princeton University, Combustion Laboratory, Princeton, NJ   08450

Rutgers University, Department of Mechanical and Aerospace Engineering, New Brunswick, NJ   08903

University of Tennessee Medical Units, Materials Science Toxicology, Memphis, TN   38103

Texas Tech University, Department of Range and Wildlife Management, Lubbock, TX   79409

University of Utah, Flammability Center, Salt Lake City, UT   84112

University of Virginia, Charlottesville, VA   22901

Washington State University, Fire Laboratory, Department of Materials Science, Pullman, WA   99163

University of Wisconsin, Department of Chemical Engineering, Madison, WI   53706

Worcester Polytechnic Institute, Worcester, MA   01609

D. Federal Government

Department of Agriculture

Agricultural Research Service, Southern Regional Research Laboratory, 1100 Robert E. Lee Blvd., New Orleans, LA   70124

Agricultural Research Service, Western Regional Research Laboratory, Riverside, CA   92500

Forest Service, Forest Products Laboratory, Box 5130, Madison, WI   53705

Intermountain Forest and Range Experiment Station, Missoula, MT   59801

North Central Forest Experiment Station, East Lansing, MI   48823

Pacific Southwest Forest and Range Experiment Station, 2850 Telegraph Ave., Berkeley, CA   94705

Rocky Mountain Forest and Range Experiment Station, Macon, GA

Department of the Air Force

Aero Propulsion Laboratory, Hazards Branch, Wright-Patterson Air Force Base, OH   45433

Department of the Army

U.S. Army Fuels and Lubricants Research Laboratory, Southwest Research Institute, San Antonio, TX   78228

U.S. Army Institute of Surgical Research, Brooks Army Medical Center, Fort Sam Houston, TX   78234

U.S. Army Mobility Equipment Research and Development Center, Fort Belvoir, VA   22060

U.S. Army Natick Laboratories, Natick, MA   01760

U.S. Army Tank Automotive Command, Warren, MI   48090

Department of Commerce

Weather Bureau, Techniques Development Laboratory, 8060 13th St., Silver Spring, MD   20910

National Bureau of Standards, Fire Research and Safety Section, Washington, DC   20234

Department of the Interior

Bureau of Mines, Pittsburgh Mining and Safety Research Center, 4800 Forbes Avenue, Pittsburgh, PA   15213

Department of the Navy

National Naval Medical Center, Bethesda, MD   20014
Naval Air Development Center, Warminister, PA 18974
Naval Air Propulsion Test Center, Trenton, NJ 08628
Naval Civil Engineering Laboratory, Port Hueneme, CA 93043
Naval Ordinance Laboratory, White Oak, Silver Spring, MD   20910
Naval Research Laboratory, Washington, DC   20390
Naval Ship Research and Development Center, Annapolis, MD   21402

Naval Weapons Laboratory, Dahlgren, VA   22448

Department of Transportation

U.S. Coast Guard, Shipboard Fire and Safety Testing Facility, Brookley Aerospace and Industrial Complex, Mobile, AL   36615
Federal Aviation Administration, National Aviation Facilities Experimental Center, Atlantic City, NJ   08405

Independent Agencies

National Aeronautics and Space Administration, Ames Research Center, Moffett Field, CA   94035
National Aeronautics and Space Administration, Lewis Research Center, 2100 Brookpark Rd., Cleveland, OH 44135
U.S. Energy Research and Development Administration, Oak Ridge National Laboratory, P. O. Box X, Oak Ridge, TN   37830

Appendix C

UNITED STATES FEDERAL AGENCIES INVOLVED IN FIRE SAFETY

Federal agencies have been active in fire protection for many years, generally in nonregulatory roles providing for protection of federal property, employees, and the public while on federal property. While federal property is generally exempt from local building codes and regulations, federal agencies usually meet or exceed local requirements by their own requirements and by extensive involvement in the development and use of national consensus standards for fire safety. Federal fire research generally directed to the mission of the sponsoring agency was estimated at $27 million per year during the early 1970s by the National Commission on Fire Prevention and Control. The contributions of these activities in generally advancing the state-of-the-art have been many.

In recent years, federal regulatory authority for safety has been greatly increased. There has also been significant expansion of assistance programs which require compliance with regulations as a condition of participation in these programs. While general revenue sharing continues to be a major source of federal funds to fire departments and for various state and local fire safety programs, there are many other federal grant, contract, and loan programs available to improve fire protection. New federal authority designed to protect the public-at-large, such as the Consumer Product Safety Act of 1973, or to protect major segments of society, such as the Occupational Safety and Health Act of 1970, which applies to employees in the workplace, are having major impact.

Table C-1 lists the various federal agencies directly involved with fire safety during 1975. It can be expected that some of these roles will change over the next 5 to 10 years, but it is likely that the basic federal programs will remain the same or be expanded. All of the agencies have headquarters in the Washington, D.C. area with most having eight to ten regional offices in major cities and field offices throughout the country. The descriptions of the agencies that follow generally avoid mention of specific research activities and laboratories, although nearly every agency has its own laboratories and conducts extensive research in its own laboratories, in other federal labs, or through contracts and grants.

A. Agencies

Department of Agriculture

The Department of Agriculture's fire protection programs are carried out mainly by the U.S. Forest Service and the Farmers Home Administration. Both agencies are active in fire prevention education programs in rural areas; the Forest Service primarily through use of its familiar symbol, "Smokey the Bear."

Farmers Homes Administration: The Farmers Homes Administration makes loans in rural areas for home improvement and purchase provided minimum standards, often the Minimum Property Standards of HUD, are met. Under the Rural Development Act of 1972, the Farmers Home Administration provides for long-term, low-interest loans and matching grants for improving necessary community facilities in communities of up to 10,000 people. These can be applied to improving water supplies, building fire stations, and purchasing apparatus and equipment.

U.S. Forest Service (USFS): This service provides protection for over 200 million acres of national forests, grasslands, and nearby private lands. The Forest Service provides technical and financial assistance to all states for protecting federal and nonfederal land, including training of personnel, inspections, development and procurement of equipment, and provision of surplus federal equipment. Salaries and expenses are paid for actual fire fighting. Fire danger weather forecasting is done cooperatively with the Department of Interior and the National Oceanic and Atmospheric Administration in Commerce. The Forest Service conducts research in its own laboratories and sponsors research elsewhere in fire prevention, suppression, fuel management and modification, and weather modification. Research is conducted on wood and wood products at the Service's Forest Products Laboratory, including fire properties and fire test methods. An extensive information system on all aspects of wildland fire control is run by the USFS.

Civil Service Commission

The Civil Service Commission's role in establishing regulations covering employees under authority of various federal laws has been increasing not just in federal agency employment but in nonfederal employment supported by federal funds and where federal wage, employment opportunities, and civil rights laws apply. The CSC conducts personnel research programs, both in-house and through contracts and grants.

Department of Commerce (DOC)

Based on the recommendations of the National Commission on Fire Prevention and Control (Report, "America Burning", dated May 1973) the Federal Fire Prevention and Control Act of 1974 established within DOC the first major federal program aimed at fire safety for the general public, with direct concern for fire departments. Major programs of the *National Fire Prevention and Control Administration (NFPCA)* are fire service education and training, including establishment of a national fire academy and support to state and local training programs, operation of a National Fire Data System, increased fire technology research and development, and a program of public education.

The Act also provides for the reimbursement to communities and local fire departments of expenses incurred in fighting fires on federal property. The NFPCA includes the operation of the Federal Fire Council which for many years has provided a focal point for data collection, information dissemination, and cooperation among federal agencies in reducing losses on federal property.

Since the early 1900s, DOCs *National Bureau of Standards (NBS)* has been engaged in fire research aimed mainly at building technology and fire tests of materials. The fire prevention and control act provided for greater emphasis by establishment of the NBS Fire Research Center which conducts research in a broad range of basic and applied fire technology both with in-house funds and through contracts from other government agencies and industry. The NBS Center for Building Technology and the Programatic Center for Product Safety also conduct research in various aspects of fire safety. NBS also serves as the Secretariat for

Table C-1.   Federal Agencies Involved in Fire Protection

Department or Industrial Agency	Key Organizational Elements
Department of Agriculture	Farmers Home Administration U.S. Forest Service (USFS)
Civil Service Commission (CSC)	
Department of Commerce (DOC)	Maritime Administration (MARAD) National Bureau of Standards (NBS) National Fire Prevention and Control Administration (NFPCA) Economic Development Administration (EDA)
Consumer Product Safety Commission (CPSC)	
Department of Defense (DOD)	Defense Civil Preparedness Agency (DCPA) Military Departments (Air Force, Army, Marine, Navy)
Environmental Protection Agency (EPA)	
Federal Communications Commission (FCC)	
Federal Trade Commission (FTC)	
General Services Administration (GSA)	Federal Supply Service Public Buildings Service
Department of Health, Education, and Welfare (HEW)	National Institutes of Health (NIH) National Institute of Occupational Safety and Health (NIOSH) Office of Education Public Health Service (PHS) Social Security Administration (SSA)
Department of Housing and Urban Development (HUD)	Federal Housing Administration (FHA) Federal Disaster Assistance Administration
Department of the Interior	Bureau of Indian Affairs Bureau of Land Management (BLM) Bureau of Mines (BUMINES) Mining Enforcement and Safety Administration (MESA) National Park Service (NPS)
Department of Justice	Law Enforcement Assistance Administration (LEAA)
Department of Labor (DOL)	Bureau of Labor Statistics (BLS) Wage and Manpower Division Occupational Safety and Health Administration (OSHA)
National Academy of Sciences (NAS) (Quasi-government)	
National Academy of Engineering (NAE) (Quasi-government)	
National Research Council (Quasi-government)	
National Aeronautics and Space Administration (NASA)	
National Science Foundation (NSF)	
National Transportation Safety Board (NTSB)	
Nuclear Regularoty Commission (NRC) and Energy Research and Development Administration (ERDA)	
Small Business Administration (SBA)	
Department of Transportation (DOT)	Federal Aviation Administration (FAA) Federal Highway Administration (FHWA) Federal Railroad Administration (FRA) Materials Transportation Bureau (MTB) National Highway Traffic Safety Administration (NHTSA) U.S. Coast Guard (USCG) Urban Mass Transportation Administration (UMTA)
Department of the Treasury	Bureau of Alcohol, Tobacco, and Firearms
Veterans Administration (VA)	

the National Conference of States on Building Codes and Standards in promoting adoption and enforcement of uniform standards.

Maritime Administration (MARAD): The Maritime Administration is charged with the responsibility of assisting U.S. merchant shipping interests. MARAD sponsors research in shipboard fire hazards and is working with port cities in improving fire fighting capabilities available for shipboard fires. MARAD operates two fire fighting schools in cooperation with the Military Sealift Command (MSC).

Economic Development Administration (EDA): The Economic Development Administration provides funds under the Economic Development Act to stimulate growth and create jobs in areas of high unemployment. Grants and loans are provided to help construct or improve public facilities including water supply systems and fire stations.

Consumer Product Safety Commission (CPSC)

The Consumer Product Safety Commission has broad regulatory authority over safety and health aspects of products sold to consumers. It may prescribe and enforce mandatory product standards, collect injury data from hospitals through the National Electronic Injury Surveillance System (NEISS), and engage in public information and education programs. The CPSC also administers the Federal Hazardous Substances Act, the Flammable Fabrics Act, and the Poison Prevention Packaging Act. The Commission can ban hazardous products from the marketplace and may seize products determined to possess an "imminent" hazard. CPSC also conducts research in support of its standards and education efforts. The Commission's decision to conduct its business open to public scrutiny was refreshing and welcome.

Department of Defense (DOD)

All of the military departments (*Air Force, Army, Marine Corps, and Navy*) provide for fire protection of DOD facilities, including vehicles, ships, aircraft, and personnel. Regulations of each department make extensive use of national consensus standards. The military operates a variety of fire training schools and has made major contributions to fire protection through in-house and contract research programs.

Defense Civil Preparedness Agency (DCPA): This DOD agency (formerly Civil Defense) has also made substantial contributions through fire research programs. DCPA operates a Staff College at Battle Creek, Mich., where courses are offered to business, industry, and government officials in planning for natural disasters, accidents, and the effects of nuclear attack. It develops standards for fire equipment, provides assistance to communities in improving fire services, and is a major source of surplus equipment (vehicles, communications equipment, etc.). DCPA, at the request of state and local officials, conducts on-site assistance surveys to help communities prepare for disaster emergencies (peacetime or nuclear attack) often in cooperation with other federal agencies.

Environmental Protection Agency (EPA)

This agency has broad regulatory, standards-making, enforcement, and research authority relative to reducing air and water pollution. Some aspects of EPA work have an impact on fire safety. For example, the use of some fire extinguishing agents might be limited; EPA proposed standards for reducing the release of hydrocarbon vapors to the atmosphere conflicted with time-tested fire standards for fuel storage tanks, and EPA limitations on burning for fire research and training purposes.

Federal Communications Commission (FCC)

The FCC exercises federal regulatory authority over assignment of frequencies and operation of all broadcasting equipment and facilities including fire, rescue, and medical services communications. Qualifications and licensing of operators is an FCC responsibility. The Safety and Special Radio Services Bureau generally administers regulations covering public safety facilities and programs.

Federal Trade Commission (FTC)

The FTC has federal regulatory authority over deceptive or misleading advertising covering not only characteristics of products but provisions of warrantees to consumers as well. Health and safety claims for products have received special attention. In 1974, major action was taken against the plastics industry over claims regarding the fire hazards of plastics. FTC, in 1975, began an investigation of standards-making in the U.S. and has authority to assist the Consumer Product Safety Commission against violators of packaging and labelling standards.

General Services Administration (GSA)

This agency is the major provider of supplies and buildings to federal agencies. Through purchase specification, GSA could have major influence not only on the safety of products that it buys but of those available to the general public. GSA has made major advances in developing and adopting a systems approach to firesafety in buildings. Its standards and experience will likely be a major factor in fire protection features of buildings in the future.

Department of Health, Education, and Welfare (HEW)

Firesafety standards for health care facilities are prescribed by at least two major HEW agencies: (1) the Public Health Service and (2) Social Security Administration.

Public Health Service (PHS): This agency imposes standards as a condition of grants and loans for building and improving public and private nonprofit hospitals, nursing homes, and other health care facilities. This program, commonly called the Hill-Burton Program, functions under authority of the Hill-Burton Act which is Title VI of the Public Health Service Act and the National Health Planning and Resources Development Act of 1974 (Titles 15 and 16 of the PHS Act). PHS operates nine Public Health Service Hospitals.

PHS also assists in the establishment and operation of emergency medical services rendered both within and without hospitals under the Emergency Medical Services Systems Act of 1973. Grants, contracts, and technical assistance are available for establishment and initial operation of EMSs and for improvement of existing EMSs. Federal funds of up to 75 percent of total cost are available to government units and certain private organizations. Program development requires centralized communications and implementation of the "911" emergency telephone number.

The Social Security Administration (SSA): This agency administers the Medicare and Medicaid programs (Titles 18 and 19 of the Social Security Act Amendments of 1965) which require compliance with fire safety standards by hospitals and nursing homes participating in the programs. Both the Medicare and Medicaid programs provide for low-interest loans for compliance with fire safety requirements in existing facilities.

Office of Education (OE): The Office of Education provides financial assistance to educational institutions under the Higher Education Act of 1965 and the Vocational Education Act of 1968. Fire protection may benefit from these programs under provisions for students for public service and continuing education projects. Amendments to the latter Act make it clear that fire fighters, both paid and volunteer, can benefit from the Act.

National Institute of Health (NIH): The National Institute of Health is authorized under the Federal Fire Prevention and Control Act of 1974 to conduct burn injury research and to assist in the establishment of burn treatment centers; however, funds were not provided for early implementation of the Act due to concern for duplication of effort. The National Institute of General Medical Sciences (within NIH) does, in fact, conduct limited burn injury and rehabilitation research in cooperation with burn hospitals.

National Institute of Occupational Safety and Health (NIOSH): The NIOSH was established within HEW by the Occupational Safety and Health Act of 1970 to conduct research, evaluate occupational hazards, and to recommend standards and standards criteria in support of the Occupational Safety and Health Administration.

Department of Housing and Urban Development (HUD)

This department promulgates and enforces minimum property standards for one- and two-family dwellings, multi-family housing, and care type housing. HUD insurance on mortgages and loans and direct assistance programs are conditioned in compliance with these standards. Extensive referencing of consensus standards is made in the Minimum Property Standards. HUD has sponsored extensive research in support of its standard making activities, in seeking cost-effective building systems and equipment, and in improving community services such as development of fire station location models and the Uniform Fire Incident Reporting System (UFIRS) in conjunction with NFPA.

Federal Housing Administration (FHA): Currently, HUD's authority is through the Housing and Community Development Act of 1974 which sets the stage for federal housing programs well into the 1980s. New provisions of the Act provide for establishment and enforcement of federal mobile home standards and for establishment of a quasi-government National Institute of Building Sciences to be initiated by HUD and to deal with building codes and standards problems. (See National Research Council later in this Appendix.) HUD's Federal Insurance Administration (FIA), under authority of the Urban Property Protection Reinsurance Act of 1968, has cooperated with the insurance industry to provide fire insurance, particularly in riot prone areas where commercial insurance was not available. FAIR Plans (Fair Access to Insurance Requirements) are in effect in many states with insurers eligible to purchase reinsurance from the FIA.

Federal Disaster Assistance Administration (FDAA): The FDAA provides assistance to public agencies and individuals who have property damaged in emergencies and major disasters, including fires and explosions, if so declared by the President. While declared fire emergencies or disasters are relatively rare and usually related to wildland fires, Chelsea, Mass., received substantial assistance after the 1973 conflagration.

Department of Interior

Fire protection for a total of 545 million acres of land is under the jurisdiction of the Department of the Interior's *Bureau of Land Management (BLM), Bureau of Indian Affairs,* and *National Park Service.* Additional state and private lands are protected under contract by the BLM. On these lands, the majority of which are in remote areas in western states, the Department of the Interior provides for all management, surveillance, and suppression services.

Interior also has major responsibilities in regulating and providing for safety in all mineral mines in the United States. The *Bureau of Mines (BUMINES)* provides grants for controlling mine fires and conducts research through grants and contracts at its Pittsburgh Research Center. The results of BUMINES research have made substantial contributions not only to mine safety but to fire safety in many fields. Interior's *Mining Enforcement and Safety Administration (MESA)* develops and enforces health and safety standards for the mining industry, and also provides grants for mine safety research. MESA trains and maintains its own enforcement personnel, and provides training for state and industry personnel at the National Academy of Mine Health and Safety in West Virginia. Both BUMINES and MESA are involved in testing and approving safety equipment for use in mines, including electrical equipment, breathing apparatus, gas detectors, and fire extinguishing equipment.

Department of Justice

Law Enforcement Assistance Administration (LEAA): The LEAA was established to provide a national strategy, financial support, and technical assistance to help state and local governments achieve important improvements in public safety and crime control programs. LEAA conducts major research programs, demonstration projects, and training programs (including the Law Enforcement Training Academy at Quantico, Virginia), data collection, information services to local law enforcement officials, and grants for equipment purchase (including vehicles, communications equipment, and alarm services). Fire service agencies have received manpower development funds, arson investigation operating funds, research contracts relative to arson investigation, equipment for bomb disposal, communications equipment, planning grants for implementing the "911" emergency telephone number, vehicles, and training in arson investigation, disaster planning, and explosive ordinance disposal.

Department of Labor

Occupational Safety and Health Administration (OSHA): This administration was established in 1970 to adopt, develop, promulgate, and enforce mandatory standards providing for the safety and health of employees in the workplace. Fifty NFPA standards were adopted by reference as mandatory fire safety provisions under early authority of the Act. Unfortunately, requirements for updating to later editions of standards were laborious, and available improvements were slow in being permitted by OSHA. State enforcement of OSHA standards is financially supported by OSHA, and by 1975 emphasis was shifting from punitive measures to consultation and prevention.

OSHA provisions do not cover public employees, but most state plans do. Federal agencies, by executive order (of the President), are required to provide at least equal protection to federal workers as that required in private industry. OSHA has engaged in a wide variety of education and training programs for federal and state compliance officers and industry personnel through the OSHA Training Institute near Chicago, and through field training programs and short courses at colleges and universities. Injury and deaths are required to be reported. Labor's *Bureau of Labor Statistics (BLS)* collects and publishes this data. Research, standards criteria, and standards development are conducted through the National Institute of Occupational Safety and Health (in HEW) and through contracts and grants.

Wage and Manpower Division: This division administers major programs affecting public service employment, particularly the Comprehensive Employment and Training Act of 1973 (CETA). CETA's major purpose is to provide economically disadvantaged, unemployed, and underemployed persons with training and skills needed to secure and hold jobs consistent with their capabilities. CETA consolidates many earlier manpower programs under one. Units of local government are prime sponsors of local programs for funds distribution and establishment of recruiting, training, counseling, and assistance programs. Contracts for recruitment and training have also been led directly by DOL. The Department also establishes regulations under the Fair Labor Standards Act (minimum wage) which is having significant impact upon the fire service.

National Academy of Sciences/National Academy of Engineering/National Research Council

These quasi-government organizations, operating under charters from Congress, provide a focal point and stimulus for research and problems in several aspects of the fire problem. The Committee on Fire Research conducts seminars, publishes pertinent research reviews, and seeks to stimulate necessary fire research. The Committee on Fire Safety Aspects of Polymeric Materials is studying the scope of that problem and compiling pertinent information.

Committee on Hazardous Materials: For some years this committee stimulated research, conducted seminars, and published papers on the subject for the U.S. Coast Guard, and apparently will continue under sponsorship of the Occupational Safety and Health Administration.

Building Research Advisory Board (BRAB): This group has worked closely with the building materials industry on fire hazards in buildings and special projects such as barrier-free designs for the handicapped.

National Institute of Building Sciences (NIBS): The Housing and Community Development Act of 1974, Title VIII, Section 809, established an independent quasi-government National Institute of Building Sciences (NIBS) to establish performance criteria and test methods, and to promote uniformity in building codes and standards. At the time of the writing, few, if any, steps had been taken to implement NIBS, but it appeared that it might operate under the aegis of the NAS.

National Aeronautics and Space Administration (NASA):

The extensive research and development programs dictated by NASA operations are finding application in other areas through the NASA Technology Utilization program by which it seeks to apply space age technology that has been developed to more routine applications. Work in detection devices, fire retardant and fire resistive materials, studies of fire and explosion growth, and research or insulating materials and personnel protective equipment are being adapted to everyday life. NASA continues to conduct in-house and contract research to reach this end.

Nuclear Regulatory Commission and Energy Research and Development Administration (NRC and ERDA)

These two groups resulted from splitting the regulatory and nonregulatory operations of the former Atomic Energy Commission. NRC establishes and enforces standards for construction and operation of all nuclear facilities, including fire protection features. With billions of dollars being devoted by ERDA to developing new sources of energy, it is sincerely hoped that the fire problem inherent with any energy source will receive adequate recognition and attention.

National Science Foundation (NSF)

In 1971 the NSF established a basic and applied fire research program under the broader Research Applied to National Needs (RANN) program. The majority of work is carried out through grants and contracts to universities and government and private research organizations. Responsibility for this program was being transferred to the National Fire Prevention and Control Administration of the Department of Commerce when established in 1975. Other NSF programs, such as those dealing with the delivery of community services, are investigating some practical aspects of fire departments and local fire protection.

National Transportation Safety Board (NTSB)

Originally a part of the Department of Transportation, the NTSB became an independent agency during 1975 under Title III of the Transportation Safety Act of 1974. The Board is charged with investigating and determining the cause of accidents in all modes of transportation (air, highway, rail, marine), accidents in natural gas pipelines, and accidents involving hazardous materials. NTSB conducts special studies and collects certain accident data.

Small Business Administration (SBA)

The SBA can declare disasters under authority of the SBA Administrator and, when disaster areas are declared by the President, must assist in providing relief loans to individuals and small business. Any natural disaster, including fire, applies. SBA also provides loans to certain small businesses for complying with federal safety standards.

Department of Transportation (DOT)

DOT has major regulatory authority for all modes of transportation under the Department of Transportation Act of 1966 and the Transportation Safety Act of 1974. Numerous other laws (for example, the Federal Aviation Act of 1958, the Airport Development Acceleration Act of 1973, and the Natural Gas Pipeline Safety Act of 1968) establish the authority and programs within the various operating elements of DOT. Authority to regulate the construction of private and commercial vehicles, the operation of commercial vehicles and transportation facilities, collecting accident data, establishing and enforcing standards and regulations, conducting research, making grants to states and other bodies for training, equipment, and facility construction and maintenance, and regulating the transportation of hazardous materials is common to all modes.

Federal Aviation Administration (FAA): This agency establishes construction and safety standards for aircraft and airports and provides grants for fire fighting equipment at airports.

Federal Highway Administration: This agency regulates the operation of commercial vehicles and establishes standards for highway construction and safety.

National Highway Traffic Safety Administration (NHTSA): This agency establishes and enforces safety standards for automobiles, trucks, and buses. NHTSA also administers the DOT Emergency Medical Services Program which provides grants for planning, training, equipping, and in some cases, operating emergency medical services primarily to serve highway accident victims.

Federal Railroad Administration (FRA): This agency establishes and enforces safety standards for rolling stock, rail facilities, and equipment and operation of railroads.

U.S. Coast Guard (USCG): The Coast Guard establishes and enforces safety standards and operating regulations for

U.S. merchant ships and conducts regular inspections of such vessels. It also establishes standards for construction and operation of pleasure craft and for offshore platforms and oil drilling rigs, and regulates port facilities. The Coast Guard provides assistance in fighting shipboard fires and fires in port facilities.

Materials Transportation Bureau (MTB): The MTB, a relatively new bureau in the DOT, has regulatory authority, in cooperation with the various modal administrations, for the transportation, storage, and labeling of hazardous materials. The MTB also regulates the transportation of hazardous materials in pipelines.

Urban Mass Transportation Administration (UMTA): This agency conducts research projects and provides financial assistance in establishing mass transit systems. Numerous training courses are conducted for industry and local, state, and federal personnel at DOT's Transportation Safety Institute.

Department of the Treasury

General revenue-sharing funds are distributed directly to units of state and local government by the U.S. Treasury under authority of the State and Local Fiscal Assistance Act of 1972. One of the priority categories in which funds may be spent is public safety, which includes operation and equipment for fire protection and for building and code inspection. Revenue-sharing funds may be given by local government units to volunteer fire departments for equipment purchases. Obviously, fire and code enforcement organizations must learn to compete successfully for the much-in-demand funds.

Bureau of Alcohol, Tobacco, and Firearms (ATF): Treasury's ATF regulates interstate transportation and sale of explosives, certain storage of explosives, and investigates accidents and criminal acts involving explosives. The ATF laboratory in Washington, D.C. tests suspected arson related materials upon request from any local law enforcement agency, and will testify in court. Similar laboratory investigations are conducted by the Federal Bureau of Investigation crime laboratory.

Veterans Administration (VA)

The VA guarantees mortgage loans for veterans to purchase homes meeting requirements of HUD minimum property standards. VA also operates 171 hospitals for veterans which must by law be of fire resistive construction (a requirement that may change after 1975 studies are concluded). VA has sponsored research in the flammability of materials, fire test methods, and in treatment of burn victims. VA requirements for fire resistive furnishings, garments, and interior finishes in its hospitals are among the most stringent.

B. Sources of Information on United States Federal Agencies

One observer has stated that trying to understand federal agency fire programs is like trying to "put socks on an octopus." The sources of information, technical assistance, and funds are incredible, but details are often hard to uncover and follow. Most federal agencies are cooperative and helpful and want the public to know about their programs. If there were ever any doubt, Congress removed it by enacting the Freedom of Information Act of 1974. All agencies have headquarters in the Washington, D.C. area, and preliminary inquiries will probably be successful by writing the agency name, Public Information Office, Washington, D.C. Most agencies have 8 to 10 regional offices in the major cities also. Many agencies will gladly add names to their mailing lists, and will supply routine announcements, press releases, and minor publications free.

Publications

Publications that are good sources of information are:

Congressional Record: The record of hearings, bills introduced, laws passed, and other action by the Congress. It is available by subscription from the Government Printing Office (GPO), Washington, DC 20402.

Federal Register: The official government organ for announcing meetings, proposed rulemaking, final rulemaking, etc. by federal agencies. It is available by subscription from the GPO.

Commerce Business Daily: Daily announcements of agencies' intentions to let contracts, etc. for potential bidders. Available by subscription from the GPO.

Catalog of Federal Domestic Assistance: Catalog of federal agency programs. Available by subscription from the GPO.

Other, more general publications are: Agency publications that are available on a subscription basis from the federal agency involved.

Research Reports that are available by request (with or without charge) from the sponsoring agency or possibly from the Department of Commerce, National Technical Information Service (NTIS), Defense Documentation Center, or the Smithsonian Institute Science Information Exchange.

Commercial Publications of which many are available on a subscription basis (daily, weekly, monthly) from commercial publishers on activities of individual agencies or on subjects of special interest.

Association newsletters, etc.

NFPA publications, particularly its *Fire Journal* magazine and monthly *Fire News*.

Many of the preceding publications may be available in public libraries, in the offices of state and local government agencies, and, for federal publications, in the local offices of members of Congress or field offices of federal agencies.

Appendices

Appendix D

FIRE PROTECTION LAWS AND STANDARDS

Laws, or parts of laws, pertaining to firesafety, are primarily creations of legislative bodies. Administrative agencies of government, be it federal, state, or local, are the instruments through which laws are implemented or specified and enforced.

For the purposes of this discussion the term "fire law" means laws and legal provisions pertaining to firesafety. The term "law" is also used in the broad context of referring to all laws, statutes, ordinances, or similar documents created by legislative entities as well as the resulting rules, regulations, administrative orders, or other documents issued by administrative agencies of government.

The term "Standard," as used in this text, means any standard developed or processed by a voluntary consensus standard-setting organization that lends itself for adoption by public authorities.

Traditionally, firesafety was recognized as a local concern. The history of codified fire protection shows that it has grown in direct proportion to the clustering of people together in little communities, villages, towns, and cities. Fire protection became necessary for survival; consequently, this is where rules in fire prevention started and fire laws began. With increased recognition of the breadth and magnitude of the fire problem, a trend toward more centralized governmental action developed.

Today the limit where legislative responsibility for fire laws ends and executive responsibility begins varies between jurisdictions and between the various levels of government. At some levels of government, most prominently in the federal regulatory area, the practice of the legislature providing an enabling law and the administrative agencies spelling out the actual implementative provisions (often relying on consensus firesafety standards) has become a pattern. In other jurisdictions, however, the legislative body leaves little or no discretion for administrative agencies in implementing the intent of legislation.

A. State and Local Legislation

Firesafety as a recognized and legitimate concern of government dates back only to the second half of the 19th century. Known legal problems and judicial decisions relating to firesafety occurred as early as 1648. During colonial times laws imposed penalties on individuals for suffering fire loss and directed citizens to observe basic measures of fire protection. This, however, did not represent an organized effort for regulation.

Present day state and local laws affecting public firesafety represent an exercise of powers that are "reserved to the states" according to the Tenth Amendment to the federal Constitution. The reasonable exercise of the states' police powers (generally understood to mean concerns affecting the public health, welfare, and safety) traditionally have been interpreted by federal courts as having their source in these "reserved powers."

Having no sovereignty, local governments have no original powers, except as delegated in the constitution and laws of each state to its political subdivisions. The degree to which states delegate regulatory powers to their subdivisions varies according to the extent and scope of municipal home rule prevalent in each state. The general trend in the United States suggests a shift toward increased municipal home rule; this trend, however, is coupled with an increased federal concern for public safety, resulting in federal preemption of certain areas of state-local regulatory authority.

State Fire Laws

The principal instruments for implementing regulatory authority for fire laws at the state level is often the office of state fire marshal. In most states enabling legislation gives the fire marshal the power to make regulations covering various hazards and, in many cases, such regulations have the effect of law.

A state fire marshal, often with an extensive staff, has the general duty of enforcing laws covering such areas as: prevention of fires; storage, use, and sale of combustibles and explosives; installation and maintenance of automatic and other fire alarm systems and fire extinguishing equipment; construction, maintenance, and regulation of fire escapes; means and adequacy of fire exits in factories, asylums, hospitals, churches, schools, halls, theaters, nursing homes, and all other places in which numbers of persons live, work, or congregate from time to time for any purpose; suppression of arson; the investigation of the cause, origin, and circumstances of fires; and the provision of built-in fire protection features in "high-rise" buildings.

An actual function of the fire marshal's office in almost every case is to serve as a central agency for sponsoring and promoting all kinds of fire prevention activities. Fire marshals also have the responsibility for investigating fires and performing fire prevention inspection work. Many also have the responsibility of reviewing construction or remodeling plans of schools, nursing homes, and hospitals.

Local Fire Laws

"Fire laws" developed on a local basis usually more narrowly defines state laws or deals with a specific problem of the locality. Agencies are usually established to administer and enforce these laws. These agencies normally do not have lawmaking powers but are encouraged to submit all recommendations for laws through legislative channels for action. Most localities use nationally recognized standards as the basis for their "fire law," modifying them to fit local circumstances and needs.

A locality may have problems that are unique to its area. For example, not too many jurisdictions have major waterfront facilities nor do many have oil refinery installations. Neither would one expect to find grain elevators and milling properties in every locality. All of these occupancies and operations present possible fire problems that must be controlled. "Fire laws" must be established to adequately deal with the fire and life safety problems presented by these special hazards.

The scope of local fire legislation is limited to that which is considered reasonable and in the general public interest, balanced against the interest of the individual wherever there may be conflict. This is particularly true where fire protection in the public interest may call for expenditures beyond those which a property owner considers essential to his own interests. All "fire laws" still must recognize the right of the individual.

Local "fire laws" generally fall into two classes: (1) those which relate to buildings, and (2) those which relate to hazardous materials, processes, or equipment used in buildings.

The enforcement of local "fire laws" is frequently divided among different local agencies. In general the fire department and building department, which may be independent from each other, handle matters in their respective fields. Laws on electrical installation may be enforced by electrical inspectors who are either attached to the fire department, the building department, are independent, or are part of an integrated local department responsible for building, fire, health, plumbing, electrical and similar inspections. Certain fire matters may also be handled by the police or some other similar local departments.

In a number of states there is a local fire marshal's office which has been established to administer "fire laws" and to promote fire prevention practices at the local level. They generally act in a manner similar to state fire marshals.

Fire Prevention Codes and Building Codes

Historically each community developed its fire prevention code as it saw its particular needs. Whatever the community and its residents thought they required for adequate protection became their fire prevention code. Fire prevention codes were often developed as an after-the-fact solution to a particular problem, and were quite often used to prevent the recurrence of disastrous situations. This history of code development accounts for the great proliferation of local codes and for the great differences in codes.

Currently there are five "model" fire prevention codes available in the United States. They are: American Insurance Association's *Fire Prevention Code* The Uniform Fire Code (published by the International Conference of Building Officials in cooperation with Western Fire Chiefs Association), *The BOCA Basic Fire Prevention Code* (published by the Building Officials and Code Administrators International), the *Southern Standard Fire Prevention Code* (published by the Southern Code Congress), and the NFPA *Fire Prevention Code*. All of these "model" codes utilize NFPA technical standards as the basis for the technical details of their fire prevention and fire control measures. Of these model codes only the NFPA *Fire Prevention Code* is developed through a broad national consensus representing all concerned interests. The basic intent of these documents is to set forth general firesafety regulations and code enforcement and code administration procedures. Each of these codes is flexible enough so that it can be modified by the local jurisdiction to suit local needs. In using these codes, each jurisdiction must develop an ordinance or some other legal document which will specify and make that particular code (as amended) the particular law for that jurisdiction.

There are also four model building codes that complement the fire prevention codes. See Section 6, Chapter 11, for information on the model building codes.

To decide which items go into a fire prevention code and what should be included in the building code is a difficult task. In general, all construction requirements should be part of the building code and administered by the building department. The equipment and machinery incidental to a process or hazard in a building should be part of the fire prevention code and regulated by the fire department. Original requirements for exits and fire extinguishing equipment are usually found in building code provisions, but the maintenance of such items are covered in a fire prevention code.

A principal use of a fire prevention code is as a guide, since a code cannot be specific enough to cover all circumstances in all situations. Fire prevention codes are concerned with hazards and provide for fire control or fire prevention measures that will minimize and possibly eliminate the hazards. Unfortunately, since the presence of hazards is often times brought to the notice of the public in connection with specific occupancies, the measures for controlling or eliminating the hazards are generally tied to the occupancy. Codes address themselves to hazards that may apply to more than one occupancy or process but which are linked to specific occupancies because of the prevalence of the problem in that occupancy.

B. Federal Legislation

The source of the federal government's power to regulate firesafety is an implied power based on Article 1, Section 8, Clause 3 of the Constitution, which gives Congress the power to regulate commerce among the states (interstate commerce).

The logic that leads from the power to regulate interstate commerce to the promulgation of firesafety regulations goes like this: if a certain activity though strictly local (as, for example, mining might be) is not carried out safely, then a fire or other disaster could seriously cripple production; a shortage of ore would mean that railroads would be idle (no ore to carry), the steel industry would slow down (no ore to smelt), the construction industry would slow down (no girders), and the stock market would slump due to slow commercial activity.

The obvious intent of federal safety reguraltions is to protect the general public, and this they accomplish by regulating interstate commerce as a whole. So, from time to time, as Congress sees a need for uniform regulations in a given activity (one that affects interstate commerce), laws are passed regulating that activity. These laws may porvide either: (1) that all state laws on the same subject are superseded by the federal law; or (2) that state laws not conflicting with the federal law remain valid; or (3) that any state law will control if it is more stringent than the federal law (more common in the area of safety standards).

Congress has delegated to various departments and agencies of the federal government the duty and power to promulgate regulations in certain specific areas. Thus the Secretary of Agriculture promulgates fire protection and other regulations relative to federal forests; the Secretary of Health, Education and Welfare is responsible for certain medical facilities; the Secretary of the Interior for mines; the Secretary of Labor for occupational health and safety, and so on. (The more specific regulatory functions of each department and agency are listed in Part E of this Appendix.) Congress has also created independent regulatory agencies to govern certain specific areas of concern, a notable example being the Consumer Product Safety Commission which can promulgate safety standards and regulations for consumer goods.

Each department or agency promulgates regulations pursuant to authority granted to it by a specific act of Congress. While the regulations thus promulgated are not in fact congressional legislation, they have the binding force of law and violation of those regulations that can result in serious criminal penalties. It was heatedly argued in the courts years ago that nobody except the Congress could pass laws *or regulations* that could result in a criminal penalty because Article 1, Section 1 of the Constitution provides: "All legislative powers herein granted shall be vested in a Congress of the United States." But the U.S. Supreme Court, recognizing the practical impossibility of requiring Congress to promulgate all regulations and recognizing the necessity for such regulations, decided that it is constitutional for Congress to require a subordinate federal body to promulgate binding regulations.

Any and all federal regulations of general public effect and interest must be published in the *Federal Register* before they leave the force of law. This requirement of publication stems from the Federal Administrative Procedure Act. General federal regulations are published in the *Federal Register* as they are established, and they are later published in codified and indexed form in the *Code of Federal Regulations*, which is revised and updated annually. Both of these are official publications printed by the National Archives and Records Service of the General Services Administration. Part E (Digest of Federal Laws) of this Appendix is an attempt to alert the reader to many of those federal laws that relate to fire protection, to the federal departments and agencies that administer or enforce those laws, and to those departments and agencies that promulgate and enforce regulations relative to fire protection.

The reader should keep in mind that Congress has the power to create and abolish federal agencies as it sees fit, and it distributes and redistributes responsibilities for the administration of certain laws, often with little or no notice to the public.

C.   Sources of Fire Protection Standards

Standardization of firesafety requirements and safety testing in the United States dates back to the end of the 19th century, coinciding roughly with the widespread introduction of electricity. Concerns expressed by the insurance industry, the need for governmental regulations, and the prospect of substantial variations in requirements that may be set independently by regulatory authorities suggested the need for reasonable, fair, and objective safety standards that would be uniform nationally and would be applied by any jurisdiction. The private sector responded to this need with safety standards that are based on a balanced consensus of all relevant interests.

NFPA Codes and Standards

The NFPA is a principal source of consensus fire protection standards and codes which have been woven into the body of law at all levels of government. NFPA codes and standards are written by voluntary technical committees, balanced to fairly represent all points of view, and charged with preparing firesafety standards that are equitable without prohibitive expense, interference with established processes and methods, and without undue inconvenience. The NFPA technical committees are comprised of individuals who have the technical knowledge and competence in the areas in which the various committees develop standards. The diligent observance and enforcement of consensus procedures at NFPA leaves no room for special interest domination or for the disregard of any legitimate interest.

When a committee has compiled a proposed standard or revision to an existing standard, it is published in advance of the NFPA meeting at which it is intended to submit the document for official approval. Public review and comments are encouraged. Comments received on the standard or revision during the comment review period are in turn reviewed by the committee which developed the original standard or revision. The committee's response to the comments is published for public review. The original document and the committee's response are then submitted to the NFPA membership for official action and approval at either one of two meetings held annually.

Once a code or standard has been adopted by NFPA it is available for adoption by enforcing authorities, both governmental and nongovernmental.

Standards developed by NFPA technical committees range over the entire field of fire protection and fire prevention. More than 200 separate standards and codes have been published by NFPA. They are codified annually in the volumes of the *National Fire Codes*.

Other Consensus Codes and Standards

Other nongovernment agencies have developed consensus standards and codes which are used as guidelines in enforcing fire protection standards and laws. Two other recognized organizations involved in certain fire protection areas are: *American National Standards Institute:* 1430 Broadway, New York, NY 10018

ANSI identifies public requirements for national standards, develops, and publishes them on a broad range of subjects. It coordinates voluntary standardization activities of concerned organizations in order to achieve uniformity in voluntary and mandatory, state, and federal standards. *American Society for Testing and Materials:* 1916 Race Street, Philadelphia, PA 19103

ASTM develops and publishes standards on finished products and on materials used in manufacturing and construction.

Other Standard-writing Groups

In addition, several other types of organizations, such as testing laboratories, trade associations and institutions, develop safety standards. These organizations, however, either do not operate under consensus procedures or the span of representation of interests is so narrow that the resultant standards do not lend themselves for adoption by public regulatory authorities.

Several of the standards developed by these organizations, however, are subsequently subjected to the consensus processes of ANSI; this in effect means that fire safety standards so submitted will be processed through the NFPA standards system.

D.   Adopting Standards into Law

Consensus safety standards are developed so that they can be adopted by jurisdictions that have the power to enforce them. In most cases these jurisdictions are public authorities; however, certain private organizations, such as trade associations which have the means to "enforce" by one way or another, cannot be ignored.

The legal procedures for the adoption of a standard as law may vary from one enforcing jurisdiction to another. It is not possible to state one definitive method which can be universally applied. Generally, the body which has the responsibility for establishing codes takes advantage of NFPA codes and standards, in whole or in part, to suit its needs. NFPA recognizes that its codes and standards are not legalistic, but rather technical documents. Enforcing officials desirous of using NFPA codes and standards therefore must establish the adequacy and appropriateness of each document to be adopted, in achieving the desired purposes within the framework of the legislative prerogatives in their jurisdictions.

NFPA standards are available free of charge for adoption by public authorities. Adoption may be accomplished in two ways: (1) by reference, and (2) by transcription.

Adoption by Reference: This means that the adopting

authority merely cites the title and publishing information of the NFPA standard in the law.

Adoption by Transcription: This means that the text of the adopted standard, with or without certain changes is transcribed into the law.

In adopting a standard by transcription:

1. Deletion of existing materials and addition of new materials can be made only to the extent that they do not change meaning and intent of the existing or remaining materials, whichever is the case.

2. Rewriting the standard (e.g., changing the wording or sentence structure, combining or breaking up editorial units) is not permitted; however, changes can be made for administrative provisions.

3. Changing the strength of requirements and recommendations is permitted only if the changed requirements are stronger than those specified in the NFPA standard under consideration.

Short of outright adoption, a standard can be utilized by an authority in the sense that compliance with provisions of a particular edition of that standard is *prima facie* evidence of a reasonable degree of protection.

The process by which an NFPA Standard becomes a law or rule is called "adoption". NFPA recognizes two methods of adoption: (1) by reference, and (2) by transcription.

Adoption by Reference: This method (applicable to both public authorities and private entities) requires that the text of the "law" or "rule" cite the standard by its title, and by sufficient publishing information to permit exact identification of the standard. The standard is not reprinted in the law or rule. Any deletions, additions or changes made by the adopting authority are noted separately in the text of the law.

Adoption by Transcription: This method (applicable to public authorities only) requires that the text of the law be a printed copy of all or part of the standard with or without deletions, additions, or changes but with due notice of NFPA's copyright.

NFPA's preferred method is the "adoption by reference" method. However, certain governmental jurisdictions are barred by superior legislation from outright "adoption" of anything created outside the government. An established practice in such jurisdictions is to express in the regulatory law a broad intent or need and to then cite the appropriate NFPA Standard as one that carries out the mandate or fills the need. From NFPA's point of view, this practice is acceptable since it amounts to "adoption by reference."

On the other hand "adoption by transcription" is allowed to public authorities only in recognition of the fact that there are a variety of laws affecting the ability of certain governmental jurisdictions to adopt NFPA Standards "by reference" and a variety of provisions requiring public notice by public authorities. NFPA, therefore, permits printing and publishing of individual NFPA codes and standards in numbers reasonably sufficient to satisfy the jurisdiction's lawmaking or rule-making requirements provided (a) due notice of NFPA's copyright is contained therein and (b) that the printing is limited. In case of adoption by a federal governmental agency this may mean publication in the *Federal Register*, while in local jurisdictions it is likely to mean public notice on a much smaller scale; however that term is defined by the adopting authority. Accordingly, public authorities with law making or rule making powers only which wish to adopt an NFPA standard by transcription should contact NFPA for specific guidance.

In adopting a standard by transcription, public authorities should consider the following:

1. Deletion of existing materials and addition of new materials should not change the meaning and intent of the existing or remaining materials.

2. Rewriting the standard (e.g., changing the wording or sentence structure, combining or breaking up editorial units) is not permitted.

The integrity of content and form of NFPA's standards is a vital aspect of the standardization effort. One of the purposes for which NFPA copyrights its standards is to prevent "misuse" of their contents. "Misuse" by NFPA's definition includes but is not limited to: (1) concealing the fact of NFPA's authorship or copyright, (2) use of text out of context, (3) change in the title, text, or format, or (4) weakening the technical specifications or requirements. The only way NFPA can effectively protect the integrity of the content and form of its standards is by continuous attention to and protection of its copyrights therein.

E. Digest of Federal Laws

The following is a brief survey of those federal government departments and agencies that promulgate or enforce regulations, or both, relative to fire protection. Functions of these bodies not related to fire protection regulations have not been mentioned. (See Appendix C for a summary of the general fire protection interests and activities of the various federal departments and agencies aside from their direct regulatory functions.)

Each listing includes, where applicable, a citation referencing the particular Title from the *United States Code* (USC) that is the basis for the creation and scope of fire related activities of a department or agency. Each listing also includes reference to parts of the *Code of Federal Regulations* (CFR) (see Part B, this appendix) where pertinent regulations for a particular department or agency are published.

For a more precise index of the applicable parts of the CFR as they apply to a particular department or agency, the reader should consult the general index to the current CFR. The index references the departments or agencies as well as the particular subjects discussed.

A note of caution: The identities and functions of federal government bodies can change quickly and often without notice. The following list was prepared as of August 1975.

Department of Agriculture

U. S. Forest Service (Title 16, USC, Sec. 551 and following Sections): Provides for the Secretary of Agriculture to promulgate regulations which are pertinent to prevention of forest fires. *Vol. 36, CFR, Parts 200–295*

Department of Health, Education and Welfare

Public Health Service
Vol. 42, CFR, Parts 1–101
Social Security Administration
Vol. 20, CFR, Parts 401–422
Both of the above bodies enforce provisions of the Hill-Burton Act (Title 42, USC, Sec. 29 and following Sections) which provides that the Secretary of HEW can promulgate fire protection standards pertaining to federally-assisted medical and health care facilities.
National Institute for Occupational Safety and Health (Title 29, USC, Sec. 651 and following Section): Directs research into health and safety standards and makes recommendations on standards to the Labor Department's Occupational Safety and Health Administration.
Vol. 29, CFR, Parts 1901–1999

Department of Housing and Urban Development (HUD)

The Secretary of HUD had adopted certain NFPA standards and prescribes Minimum Property Standards relative to specific occupancies receiving mortgage assistance. Similar provisions related to nursing homes and medical facilities receiving mortgage insurance. Under Title VI (Mobile Home Construction Safety Standards) of the Housing and Community Development Act, the Secretary has also published safety standards and regulations relative to mobile home construction.

Vol. 24, CFR, Parts 0–2201 (generally)
Vol. 24, CFR, Parts 200–279 (FHA)

Department of the Interior

Public Lands Administration Act (Title 43, USC, Sec. 1362): The Secretary of the Interior may conduct investigations and promote regulations for the protection of public lands from fire.

Vol. 43, CFR, Parts 2230; 2890; 3560; 3820.

Mining Enforcement & Safety Administration

Federal Coal Mine Health and Safety Act of 1969 (Title 30, USC, Sec. 801 and following Sections): This Act provides for the creation of fire protection regulations relative to coal mines, the violation of which may occasion civil and criminal penalties.

Federal Metal and Nonmetallic Mine Safety Act (Title 30, USC, Sec. 721 and following Sections): This Act is to the same effect as Sec. 801 above relative to all mines other than coal mines.

Vol. 30, CFR, Parts 1–100.

Department of Labor

Occupational Safety and Health Administration: OSHA was created to adopt, promulgate, and enforce regulations governing the protection and safety of workers. (See HEW above for the role of the National Institute for Occupational Safety and Health and for CFR citations.)

Department of Transportation

United States Coast Guard: The Coast Guard promulgates and, under applicable statutes, enforces regulations dealing with fire protection and safety on all classes of boats. Among the acts it enforces are:

Dangerous Cargo Act (Title 46, USC, Sec. 170 and following Sections):
Under this Act, any commercial vessel carrying flammable cargo is subject to USCG regulations and standards.
Motorboat Act of 1940 (Title 46, USC, Sec. 526): This Act prescribes USCG firesafety regulations for noncommercial motorboats.
Steamboat Inspection Act (Title 46, USC, Sec. 361 and following Sections): This Act requires inspection of all commercial steam vessels by the USCG to insure compliance with USCG fire protection and flammable cargo safety standards.

Vol. 33, CFR, Parts 1–199.
Vol. 46, CFR, Parts 1–390; 401–403.
Vol. 49, CFR, Parts 420–424.

Federal Railroad Administration: This agency administers and enforces federal laws and regulations designed to promote railroad safety.

Railroad Safety Act (Title 45, USC, Sec. 421 and following Sections): This Act provides for the promulgation of any necessary safety regulations plus monetary penalties for the violation of such regulations.

Vol. 49, CFR, Parts 211–254.

Federal Aviation Administration: This agency promulgates and enforces regulations concerning firesafety in the conduct of air commerce, including regulations on the handling and transportation of flammable or hazardous materials and standards for the safe construction of aircraft.

Vol. 14, CFR, Parts 1–199.

National Highway Traffic Safety Administration: This agency in general carries out programs relating to the safety performance of motor vehicles and related equipment.

Traffic and Motor Vehicle Safety Act of 1966 (Title 15, USC, Sec. 1381 and following Sections): This Act provides for the promulgation of safety standards relative to the transportation of explosives and flammables.

Vol. 23, CFR, Parts 1204; 1230.
Vol. 49, CFR, Parts 501–580.
Material Transportation Bureau:

Office of Pipeline Safety Operations: Among its functions, this Office administers the Natural Gas Pipeline Safety Act of 1968 (Title 49, USC, Sec. 1671 and following Sections). This Act provides for the promulgation of safety standards for gas pipelines and provides for inspections and civil penalties.

Vol. 49, CFR, Parts 191–195.

Office of Hazardous Materials Operations: Among its functions, this Office administers the Hazardous Materials Transportation Act of 1974 (Title 49, USC, Sec. 1901 and following Sections). Under this Act, the Secretary of Transportation promulgates regulations for the safe transportation of hazardous materials. The regulations may affect any safety aspect of any phase of the handling and production of hazardous materials and containers thereof bound for or affecting interstate commerce. The Act provides both civil and criminal penalties for violation of regulations. The Act does not apply to pipelines (see above), and does not apply where a specific department or agency promulgates such regulations governing transportation exclusively within their particular sphere of interest (e.g., USCG, FAA, NHTSA, FRA).

Vol. 49, CFR, Parts 170–179.

Department of Treasury

Bureau of Alcohol, Tobacco and Firearms: This Bureau promulgates and enforces regulations relating to alcohol, tobacco, firearms and explosives.

Explosives Transportation Act (Title 18, USC, Sec. 831 and following Sections): This Act provides criminal penalties for violation of regulations as to the interstate transport of explosives.

Vol. 26, CFR, Parts 170–296.
Vol. 27, CFR, Parts 1–72.

Agencies (Independent of the Departments Above)

Consumer Product Safety Commission (Title 15, USC, Sec. 2051 and following Sections): This Commission is established to promulgate uniform safety standards for consumer products, enforce those standards with civil and criminal penalties, and disseminate information on consumer-related injuries through the Injury Information Clearinghouse.

Federal Hazardous Substances Act (Title 15, USC, Sec. 1261 and following Sections): This Act provides for the promulgation of regulations to eliminate misbranded or banned hazardous (flammable, explosive) materials from interstate commerce.

Flammable Fabrics Act (Title 15, USC, Sec. 1191 and following Sections): This Act provides for the promulgation of regulations as to flammability of fabrics and related materials.

Packaging for Children Act (Title 15, USC, Sec. 1471 and following Sections): This Act provides for the promulgation of regulations as to the packaging of flammable materials hazardous in the hands of children under five years of age.

Vol. 16, CFR, Parts 1001–1750.

Environmental Protection Agency: This body promulgates regulations relative to the storage and labeling of pesticides including decontamination and disposal of pesticides involved in fires under the Federal Insecticide, Fungicide and Rodenticide Act of 1945 as amended by the Federal Economic Poison Control Act of 1972. Also air and water pollution controls affect fire protection standards.

Federal Communications Commission: This body regulates fire protection inasmuch as it regulates the use of emergency air frequencies.

Vol. 47, CFR, Parts 0–99.

General Services Administration: This body adopts and enforces building and fire safety codes for design, construction, alteration, and maintenance of government buildings.

Vol. 41, CFR, Parts 1; 5; 5A; 5B; 5C; 101; 105.

National Aeronautics and Space Administration: This body adopts and enforces its own firesafety regulations pertinent to its own peculiar hazards and problems.

Vol. 14, CFR, Parts 12–1–1260; 18–1 to 18–52.

Nuclear Regulatory Commission: This is an independent regulatory commission that grew out of the Atomic Energy Commission. It promulgates safety regulations relative to the development and use of nuclear energy.

Vol. 10, CFR, Parts 0–170 (old AEC parts).

Vol. 41, CFR, Parts 9–1 to 9–59; 109–1 to 109–40 (old AEC parts).

Veterans Administration: This body enforces building and firesafety standards relative to VA-supported facilities.

Vol. 38, CFR, Parts 0–36.

Vol. 41, CFR, Parts 8–1 to 8–95.

F. Digest of State Laws and Regulations

A brief description of the enforcement agencies in each of the fifty states and the District of Columbia in the United States of America having jurisdiction in fire related matters, and a brief summary of the general nature of the laws and regulations in effect in 1975 are included in the following part of this Appendix D.

(NOTE: Due to pending local legislation and other difficulties, the following states have not been updated by NFPA since 1968: California, Idaho, Indiana, Montana, and New Jersey.)

ALABAMA: The Office of the State Fire Marshal is organized as a division of the Department of Insurance. The fire marshal enforces regulations covering: arson, fireworks, exits, places of public assembly, mobile homes, schools, hospitals, and other fire prevention laws. LP-Gas regulations are enforced by the Alabama LP-Gas Commission. State owned buildings are inspected by the State Insurance Fund. The Fire Marshal's Office adopted the Southern Standard Building Code and Gas Code, and a majority of NFPA Codes and Standards.

ALASKA: The Office of State Fire Marshal is organized in the Division of Fire Prevention of the Department of Public Safety. The fire marshal enforces the arson law, the Alaska Fire Safety Code governing conditions hazardous to life and property from fire and explosion, and the Uniform Building Code; but local codes are adopted and enforced locally. The National Electrical Code is administered by the Department of Labor. Mobile home regulations are adopted and enforced by the Department of Commerce.

ARIZONA: The state fire marshal operates under the Industrial Commission. The fire marshal adopts and enforces minimum fire prevention and fire safety rules and regulations and has adopted the Uniform Fire Code and Life Safety Code. The fire marshal also assists cities and counties in regulation enforcement, maintains a statewide reporting system, and provides fire prevention and fire fighting training to fire departments statewide.

ARKANSAS: The Director of State Police is the state fire marshal. The Fire Marshal Law covers: arson, exits, fire escapes, fire equipment, fireworks, combustibles, and explosives. LP-Gas is regulated by the LP-Gas Board. There is a State Fire Prevention Code which is substantially the Fire Prevention Code promulgated by the American Insurance Association.

CALIFORNIA: The Office of the State Fire Marshal is a governmental department administered by the state fire marshal who is appointed by the governor. Title 19 of the California Administrative Code contains regulations and standards relative to buildings and public places, fabrics and tents, fire extinguishers and alarms, fireworks, explosives and flammable liquids. The fire marshal maintains a fire research laboratory.

The State Division of Industrial Safety establishes fire safety and exit arrangements for commercial and industrial occupancies; it also adopts electrical, pressure vessel, and LP-Gas standards. The State Division of Housing administers the Housing Act covering hotels, apartment houses, dwellings, trailer parks, and mobile homes.

COLORADO: There is no state fire marshal. Rather, the state is divided into fire protection districts; the fire chief of each such district is responsible for enforcement of state and local fire protection laws. The Industrial Commission of Colorado is empowered by statute to adopt and enforce certain recognized fire and safety codes and standards. The commission has jurisdiction over commercial and industrial occupancies, hotels, schools, theaters, and places of public assembly. It also enforces the Uniform Building Code. The State Department of Health is responsible for hospitals and nursing homes. The State Inspector of Oils enforces LP-Gas Laws. There are also state laws covering arson and fireworks.

CONNECTICUT: The Commissioner of State Police is ex-officio the state fire marshal. The Office of State Fire Marshal is commanded by a deputy state fire marshal, designated as such by the commissioner. The law contains provisions for a fire safety code covering all occupancies other than one- and two-family dwellings and places used for manufacturing purposes. The code covers schools, hospitals, convalescent homes; homes for the aged, places of public assembly, hotels, rooming houses, and child day-care centers. Other regulations of the state fire marshal cover circuses and carnivals; storage and transportation of flammable liquids and liquified petroleum gas; storage and transportation of hazardous chemicals; the operation of motion picture theaters; and other fire hazards. There is a Fireworks Law and an Arson Law. The State Labor Department is responsible for fire safety in factories. A State Building Code is available for towns that wish to adopt it.

DELAWARE: There is a state fire marshal. He enforces laws covering arson, fireworks, explosives, fire escapes and fire prevention standards. There is also a State Fire Prevention Commission which has adopted fire regulations under the Delaware Code, Fire Protection Rules and Regulations.

DISTRICT OF COLUMBIA: The chief of the fire department is responsible for supervising the enforcement of the D.C. Fire Prevention Code. This responsibility is delegated to the deputy fire chief, Fire Prevention Division. The division is responsible for the investigation of fires and the inspection of all buildings, except private dwellings and public buildings or premises owned or under the exclusive control of the United States, relative to LP-Gas installations, hazardous operations, storage, and other common fire hazards. Natural gas, LP-Gas piping, electrical regulations and the D.C. Building Code are enforced by the Bureau of Building, Housing and Zoning.

FLORIDA: The Treasurer-Insurance Commissioner serves as the state fire marshal. He has the authority to carry firearms and to make arrests, searches, and seizures. He is responsible for fire protection, arson investigation, and regulations covering fire extinguishers, explosives, flammable liquids, LP-Gas, fireworks, and common hazards. The state fire marshal is responsible for setting uniform minimum standards for the employment and training of fire fighters. The State Fire Marshal's Office maintains a State Fire College for training members of the fire services and a laboratory facility for testing fire equipment and evidence obtained in fire investigations.

GEORGIA: The Office of State Fire Marshal is under the comptroller general. The Georgia Safety Fire Law contains comprehensive provisions covering the control of flammable liquids and explosives, and it provides for fire investigations and enforcement of arson statutes. The Safety Fire Commissioner promulgates fire safety regulations pertaining to certain buildings and to schools, hospitals, nursing and old age homes, hotels, motels, places of assembly, jails, prisons, and certain other uses. The state has adopted the NFPA Life Safety Code and many NFPA standards relating to construction and hazardous materials. The commissioner promulgates rules and regulations for mobile homes. Georgia has adopted NFPA Standard 501B, Mobile Homes. The State Fire Marshal promulgates rules and regulations pertaining to LP-Gas and mobile homes.

HAWAII: The Director of the State Department of Regulatory Agencies is ex-officio State Fire Marshal. The county fire chiefs are ex-officio deputy fire marshals and are responsible for investigation of fires, inspection of property, and enforcement of fire regulations. The Fire Marshal Law covers investigation of fires; inspection of property; review of construction plans for schools, hospitals, institutions, hotels, places of assembly, and office and industrial occupancies; and review of construction plans for flammable liquid and gas installations. The four counties in the State have adopted the Uniform Building Code for regulation of the various types of construction. Regulation of explosives and blasting agents is the responsibility of the State Department of Labor & Industrial Relations.

IDAHO: There is no state fire marshal. The Department of Labor enforces regulations covering building exits and fire safety in state occupied buildings, as well as paint spraying, gas welding and cutting, air conditioning, ventilation, blower and exhaust systems in industries, and fireworks. The Commissioner of Law Enforcement is responsible for regulations concerning electrical wiring and LP-Gas in industrial establishments, public buildings, schools, hospitals. and institutions. Idaho is hoping to acquire funding for a state fire marshal.

ILLINOIS: The Office of State Fire Marshal is organized as a division of the Department of Law Enforcement. The Fire Prevention Statute covers arson investigations; control of dangerous conditions in and near buildings; fire escapes; school fire drills; flammable fabrics and toys; control of the sale, manufacture, and storage of fireworks; storage and sale of gasoline and volatile oils; and storage and sale of LP-Gas. The state has enacted legislation authorizing the establishment of fire protection districts and the necessary procedures therefor. The Department of Public Welfare has a fire marshal for state institutions. The Department of Public Health issues standards for nursing homes.

INDIANA: The state fire marshal is responsible for enforcing laws relative to arson, exits, places of public assembly, schools, hospitals, and institutions. There are regulations controlling flammable liquids, LP-Gas, fireworks, and other common fire hazards. There is also a State Building Code enforced by the Administrative Building Council.

IOWA: The state fire marshal is in the Department of Public Safety. The Fire Marshal Law contains comprehensive provisions covering arson, places of public assembly, hospitals, institutions, nursing homes, and fire prevention education in schools. Regulations cover flammable liquids, LP-Gas, building exits, electrical wiring, and other common hazards. The Labor Department regulates industrial processes and electrical wiring in industrial occupancies.

KANSAS: The Office of State Fire Marshal is a separate governmental department reporting directly to the Governor. The office is responsible for arson investigation, control of fireworks and explosives, and the promulgation and enforcement of regulations governing dry cleaning establishments, bulk oil stations, LP-Gas, retail gasoline stations, and gasoline transport trucks. The fire marshal is also responsible for the inspection of schools, health care facilities, places of assembly, mercantile, office, industrial, storage and miscellaneous structures. Special inspections of hazardous conditions or buildings are made upon request of fire chiefs or other city officials.

KENTUCKY: The Office of State Fire Marshal is organized under the Department of Insurance and is a part of the Consumer Protection and Regulation Cabinet. The office administers the Kentucky Standards of Safety which include, by adoption, the latest editions of the National Building Code and the NFPA National Fire Codes. These standards contain comprehensive provisions governing factories, schools, apartments, places of public assembly, offices, hotels, motels, and such hazards as electrical wiring, flammable liquids, LP-Gas, fireworks, and other hazardous materials. There is also an arson section under the Division of State Police, Department of Justice, which is not a part of the Office of State Fire Marshal.

LOUISIANA: The Office of State Fire Marshal is a separate governmental department reporting directly to the governor. The Fire Marshal Law covers investigation of fires, arson, inspection of buildings, exits, air conditioning systems, and other common hazards. LP-Gas is under the jurisdiction of the LP-Gas Commission.

MAINE: The Office of State Fire Marshal was established in 1973 as a bureau of the Department of Public Safety. The fire marshal or his deputies investigate suspicious fires and inspect public buildings including schools, hospitals, and nursing homes. They also enforce laws and regulations covering arson, fireworks, dance halls, theaters, explosives, LP-Gas, flammable

liquids, and other common hazards. Oil burners are regulated by the Burner Men's Licensing Board and electrical installations by the Electricians Examining Board, both under the Department of Business Regulations.

MARYLAND: The Office of the State Fire Marshal is an Agency of the Department of Public Safety and Correctional Services. The marshal is responsible for enforcing regulations which are promulgated by a State Fire Prevention Commission covering life safety in all structures and installations, flammable liquids, LP-Gas, fire protection equipment, and for enforcement of State statutes covering explosives, electrical safety, fireworks, and arson. The State Building Code applies to state properties only. The Division of Labor and Industry enforces safety and health standards for places of employment.

MASSACHUSETTS: The Office of State Fire Marshal is organized as a Division of the Department of Public Safety. Fire prevention regulations are promulgated by the Board of Fire Prevention. These include regulations on fireworks, dry cleaning, oil burning equipment, garages, LP-Gas, plastics, tank trucks, explosives, and flammable liquids. Chapter 148 of the Mass. General Laws grants comprehensive powers to the fire marshal. The fire marshal is chairman of the State Board of Examiners of Electricians, a member ex-officio of the Board of Fire Prevention Regulations, and a member ex-officio of the State Building Code Commission. There is a State Arson Law. There is also a Division of Building Inspection in the Department of Public Safety which enforces laws and regulations covering safety in places of public assembly and schools. The Electrical Code is administered by the State Examiners of Electricians. Heating and air conditioning regulations are administered by both the Building Division and the Division of Boiler Inspections. Control of gas piping and installers is under the Gas Regulatory Board.

MICHIGAN: The state fire marshal is also the Director of the Department of State Police. The State Police Fire Marshal Division administers the State Fire Prevention Act which provides for safety to life and property and empowers the fire marshal to promulgate rules governing flammable liquids, liquefied petroleum gases, explosives and fireworks storage. A State Fire Safety Board promulgates rules for life safety in schools, colleges, hospitals and nursing homes. There are state laws that provide enforcement provisions for arson, fireworks, motion picture theaters and dry cleaning plants. A State Construction Code is administered by a Construction Code Commission and encompasses the enforcement of the State Electrical Code through a State Electrical Administrative Board.

MINNESOTA: The State Commissioner of Public Safety is ex-officio state fire marshal and the functions of this office are handled by an appointed state fire marshal. State statutes cover control of arson, exits, places of public assembly, schools, theaters, dry cleaning plants, institutions, and fireworks. There are regulations covering nursing homes, petroleum products and LP-Gas products, natural gas and other common fire hazards. The state adopted by reference the latest edition of the National Electrical Code which is administered by the State Board of Electricians. The state has adopted amended versions of the Uniform Building Code which is administered by the State Building Code Division. The National Fire Codes are utilized by the state fire marshal in conjunction with the Uniform Fire Code as recommended standards of good practice.

MISSISSIPPI: The State Insurance Commissioner is ex-officio state fire marshal. The fire marshal is responsible for arson investigation. LP-Gas regulations are enforced by the Motor Vehicle Commission. State laws cover arson, fire escapes, places of public assembly, and multiple dwellings. These are generally the responsibility of local officials.

MISSOURI: There is an Office of State Fire Marshal in the Department of Public Safety which investigates all fires, including suspected arson. The State Department of Public Health and Welfare, Division of Safety and Fire Prevention, is responsible for fire safety regulations in state operated institutions. The Division of Health regulates hospitals and licensed institutions. The State Inspector of Oils, Department of Revenue, enforces LP-Gas regulations. There are state laws covering fireworks and arson. All fire safety inspections, including mental health and day care facilities, are the responsibility of the fire marshal.

MONTANA: The Office of State Fire Marshal is organized under the State Attorney General. The fire marshal is authorized by statute to adopt and promulgate fire safety regulations with the advice of the State Fire Prevention Advisory Commission, which is appointed by the State Insurance Commissioner. State laws cover arson, fire escapes, exits, explosives, fireworks, fire department organization, fire wardens, and fire districts. The State Electrical Board administers the electrical code and the Industrial Accident Board administers fire safety regulations concerning tank vehicles and LP-Gas. The State Building Code Director enforces only the Building Code Council-adopted codes.

NEBRASKA: The Office of State Fire Marshal is under the direction and supervision of the Director of the Department of Insurance. The fire marshal is responsible for enforcing state laws relating to arson and for promulgating rules and regulations covering fire prevention, flammable liquids, explosives, electrical wiring, exits in places of public assembly, LP-Gas, plastics, chemicals and other common hazards. The fire marshal has adopted a code of building fire safety regulations. State laws also cover waterworks, fire departments, fire fighters, fire training schools, fireworks, fire districts, fire insurance, schools, hotels, apartments, electrical installations, building condemnation, natural gas and pipeline safety and other subjects.

NEVADA: The Nevada State Fire Marshal Division is in the Department of Commerce. The fire marshal is empowered by statute to promulgate regulations relative to arson, fire prevention, fire extinguishers and systems, sprinkler and alarm systems, flammables, fireworks, explosives, adequacy of exits. He also approves licensing for the safety of patients in all state licensed health care facilities. He is also empowered to promulgate or adopt construction standards for mobile homes, factory-built housing and manufactured buildings, and is required by statute to license fire extinguisher service agencies and servicemen, and mobile home dealers, rebuilders, manufacturers and salesmen. LP-Gas regulations are enforced by the State LP-Gas Board. Tank vehicle regulations are enforced by the Public Service Commission.

NEW HAMPSHIRE: The state fire marshal is under the supervision of the Director of Safety Services. The state fire laws cover control of arson, fireworks, exits, construction of buildings, places of public assembly, hospitals, institutions, and nursing homes. There are standards covering flammable liquids, explosives, LP-Gas, and other common hazards.

NEW JERSEY: There is no Office of State Fire Marshal. Fire legislation is largely left to local fire officials. The Department of Labor and Industry has jurisdiction over fire hazards in industrial establishments and places of public assembly. Hospitals and institutions are the responsibility of the Department of Institutions and Agencies. Fire regulations for schools are enforced by the Department of Education. Motor vehicles are controlled by the Division of Motor Vehicles. Multiple dwellings come under the Bureau of Tenement House Supervision. There are laws covering fireworks and arson. LP-Gas installation standards are enforced by the state police. There is a State Forest Fire Service in the Department of Environmental Protection.

NEW MEXICO: The Superintendent of Insurance is also state fire marshal. The Fire Marshal Law covers investigation of fire hazards, fire prevention education in the schools, and training of fire fighters. The fire marshal is also responsible for the investigation of all fires of suspicious origin, and for promulgating rules and regulations relating to life safety in public occupancies. Flammable liquid regulations are enforced by the fire marshal. The electrical code is enforced by the Electrical Administration Board, fire safety in hospitals and institutions by the Department of Public Health, the building code by the Contractor's License Board, dry cleaning regulations by the Dry Cleaning Board, and LP-Gas fire safety regulations by the LP-Gas Commission. The Fireworks Law is enforced on the local level.

NEW YORK: There is no Office of State Fire Marshal. The State Labor Department has jurisdiction over fire safety requirements for business and industrial establishments and certain places of public assembly. The transportation of explosives is controlled, to some degree, by the Labor Department. The State Commissioner of Education has some jurisdiction over public school buildings and, to some degree, over buildings of private schools licensed by him. The responsibility for fire training, mutual aid operations, civil defense fire mobilization, and related state fire responsibilities rests with the Bureau of Fire Training and Advisory Services, Division of Community Affairs, Department of State. The State Commissioners of Health and of Mental Hygiene are responsible for fire safety in state hospitals under their respective jurisdictions. The State Commissioner of Social Services is responsible for fire safety in certain institutions which fall within his area of operation. Nursing home and hospital fire safety is the responsibility of the Department of Health. There is a uniform State Building Code drafted and revised from time to time by a unit in the State Division of Housing and Community Renewal, which local municipalities may adopt and enforce, but there is no separate uniform fire prevention ordinance which may be similarly adopted and enforced on the local level. The state has not adopted the Uniform Arson Law but has adopted a State Fireworks Law.

NORTH CAROLINA: The Commissioner of Insurance is the state fire marshal. The use of fireworks is banned except that permission for use of fireworks at public displays may be obtained from the Board of County Commissioners. The Commissioner of Insurance has the responsibility for administration and enforcement of a statewide building code which applies to all types of buildings throughout the state including assemblies, schools, hospitals and institutional buildings. A Deputy Commissioner of Insurance serves as Director of the Division and also serves as secretary to the Statewide Building Code Council. The Department of Insurance is also responsible for regulations for mobile home construction and the Commissioner of Agriculture is responsible for LP-Gas Regulations. The state fire laws cover control of arson and are enforced by the State Bureau of Investigation.

NORTH DAKOTA: The state fire marshal is head of the Fire Marshal Department, which is organized under the Attorney General. Fire laws cover arson, fireworks, explosives, construction of schools, fire escapes and exits, electrical wiring, and other common hazards. Regulations of the fire marshal cover fire extinguishers, LP-Gas, nursing homes, and hospitals.

OHIO: The Office of State Fire Marshal is organized as a division of the Department of Commerce. The state fire marshal has statutory responsibility for inspection of and issuing corrective orders for maintaining fire safety in all occupancies, with particular emphasis on places of public assembly, and has promulgated and adopted the Ohio Fire Code. There are laws covering flammable liquids, hotels, motels, dry cleaning establishments, investigation and control of arson and of malicious destruction of property, and for the development of fire prevention programs. The National Electrical Code is adopted by reference (latest edition). The state fire marshal is also charged with the establishment and operation of a Fire Training Academy that is scheduled to begin operation in mid-1976. The Division of Factory and Building Inspection of the Department of Industrial Relations is responsible for administering the Ohio State Building Code. Regulations have been issued by this department covering building standards and fire safety devices, theaters, assembly halls, school buildings, churches, hospitals and nursing homes, hotels and apartments, public garages, workshops, factories, mercantile and office buildings, fireworks, and explosives.

OKLAHOMA: The State Fire Marshal Agency is a separate and independent agency in the State Government. A five-member Fire Marshal Commission appoints the state fire marshal and also is empowered by law to adopt and promulgate reasonable rules and regulations relative to fire safety. The Fire Laws cover arson, exits, places of public assembly, schools, hospitals, institutions, and explosives. LP-Gas regulations are administered by the LP-Gas Administration.

OREGON: The Office of State Fire Marshal is organized as a division of the Department of Commerce. Fire laws contain provisions covering arson, fire investigation and reporting, exits, places of public assembly, schools, hospitals and institutions including medicare-medicaid surveys, storage and handling of flammable and combustible liquids, liquefied petroleum gases, liquefied natural gas, storage and handling of explosives and blasting agents, and all other buildings except private one- and two-family dwellings. Laws provide for rural fire protection districts, mutual aid agreements, and fire fighter training. The National Electrical Code is enforced by the State Building Codes Division of the Department of Commerce. The transportation of flammable liquids is the responsibility of the Public Utilities Commission.

PENNSYLVANIA: The officer in charge of the Bureau of Fire Protection of the State Police is the state fire marshal. The Fire Prevention Act provides for the investigation of fires and arson, regulations for flammable liquids, and the removal of certain fire hazards. There is a Fireworks Law, as well as an Arson Law. The Department of Labor and Industry is charged with the enforcement of building regulations for protection from fire and panic; comprehensive regulations are issued. The Hazardous Substances Transportation Board issues regulations covering the transportation of hazardous substances.

RHODE ISLAND: The Office of State Fire Marshal operates within the Division of Fire Safety which is part of the State Executive Department. The state fire laws contain provisions covering control of arson, fireworks, exits, places of public assembly, schools, hospitals, institutions, theaters, and garages. There are regulations covering flammable liquids, LP-Gas, and other common fire hazards. The fire marshal's office enforces the fire safety laws, promulgates and enforces regulations, investigates arson and conducts fire safety inspections of buildings.

SOUTH CAROLINA: The Office of State Fire Marshal functions within the Division of General Services. The fire marshal is appointed by the Budget and Control Board. Rules and regulations covering common hazards are formulated by an Advisory Committee to the State Fire Marshal. LP-Gas and anhydrous ammonia are also controlled within the Division of General Services under the direction of a duly established Licensing Board. Hospital and nursing home facilities are inspected and licensed by the State Department of Health and Environmental Control. Arson Laws are enforced by the South Carolina Law Enforcement Division.

SOUTH DAKOTA: The state fire marshal operates within the Department of Public Safety. The fire marshal's powers include investigation of fire and arson, annual inspection of schools, inspection of state owned buildings, LP-Gas bulk plants and flammable liquids plants, regulation of explosives, licensing of the sale or issuance of fireworks, and administration of pipeline safety and boiler safety programs.

TENNESSEE: The Division of Fire Prevention, also known as the State Fire Marshal's Office, is administered through the director for the Commissioner of Insurance, State of Tennessee. The laws and regulations enforced by the State Fire Marshal's Office cover arson and fraud as related to arson, LP-Gas, explosives and other common hazardous materials, the mobile home industry (both manufacturers and dealers) and the licensing and registration of all electricians in the state. The fire marshal also inspects all health care and educational facilities and reviews construction drawings on related buildings. The Electrical Inspection Section inspects all electrical installations in the state.

TEXAS: The State Board of Insurance appoints the state fire marshal. The Texas Fire Marshal Department issues regulations covering control of arson, exits, flammable liquids, and other common fire hazards. The department supervises the teaching of fire prevention in the public schools. The control of LP-Gas is the responsibility of the Railroad Commission of Texas. Fire protection guidelines for hospitals and nursing homes are created by the State Department of Health. There is no state building code.

UTAH: An appointed State Fire Prevention Board oversees the activities of the State Fire Marshal's Office, which is a separate agency reporting dirctly to the governor. The Board

has authority to adopt rules and regulations pertaining to fire and life safety in all public assembly, educational, institutional, and state-owned occupancies. The fire marshal has code enforcing authority in all public schools and state-owned buildings throughout the state, and all occupancies listed above in unincorporated areas. The Fire Prevention Board is also responsible for drafting for recommendation to political subdivisions throughout the state, codes and regulations relating to fire and life safety in all buildings, and in the use and handling of chemical, gaseous, explosive, radioactive, and other hazardous substances. State laws, rules, and regulations have been adopted pertaining to fire extinguisher servicing, fireworks, explosives, arson, and foamed plastic insulation.

VERMONT: The Office of State Fire Marshal is part of the Bureau of Criminal Investigation of the Vermont State Police. The fire marshal only investigates arson and other criminal burnings. The fire safety codes are mostly NFPA standards and are enforcd by the fire authority official of the Department of Labor and Industry. Regulations cover fire alarm systems, oil burners, electrical wiring, hotels, lighting protection systems, nursing homes, heating equipment, exits, LP-Gas, chimneys, flammable liquids, and other fire hazards.

VIRGINIA: The Office of State Fire Marshal is organized as a division of the State Corporation Commission. The laws cover control of arson and bombing, LP-gas, fireworks, manufactured buildings and mobile homes, and safety to life in existing places of public assembly, schools, hospitals, hotels, institutions, and other public buildings. The fire marshal also investigates complaints of dangerous conditions such as the storage and handling of flammable liquids and has authority to require such alterations as he may deem necessary. The Department of Labor and Industry regulates explosives.

WASHINGTON: The State Insurance Commissioner is ex-officio state fire marshal. The fire marshal is responsible for enforcing state laws and regulations covering arson and fireworks. He is also responsible for fire safety and fire protection equipment in places of public assembly, nursing and boarding homes, hospitals; institutions, in cities and towns without codes; and schools, colleges, and universities. There is a state building code enforced by local governments. The Department of Labor and Industry regulates LP-Gas, electrical installations, and explosives storage and handling. The State Police regulate transportation of explosives.

WEST VIRGINIA: The state fire marshal is selected under civil service rules and is under the direct supervision of the State Insurance Commissioner. The fire marshal is empowered to issue regulations to control fire hazards. Primary fire safety responsibilities include hospitals, nursing homes, educational, and day care facilities. Fire Prevention laws and regulations cover explosives, fireworks, LP-Gas, flammable liquids and the control of arson. Licensing of electricians is the responsibility of the fire marshal.

WISCONSIN: The Arson Bureau is in the Department of Justice. The administrator of the Division of Criminal Investigation is ex-officio state fire marshal. Duties and functions of the office are carried out by the director of the Arson Bureau. The principle duty of the state fire marshal is the investigation of arson fires and criminal explosions. There is an Arson Law. Fire prevention laws and regulations are administered by the Fire Prevention Division of the Department of Industry, Labor, and Human Relations, which has jurisdiction over public buildings, schools, hospitals, factories, stores, apartments, etc. There is a Fireworks Law, a State Building Code, and a Heating and Ventilating Code.

WYOMING: The state fire marshal is appointed by the governor and operates within the Department of Fire Prevention and Electrical Safety. The fire marshal appoints the head of the Fire Prevention Division and the Electrical Safety Division. The duties of the fire marshal include inspecting public, business, and industrial buildings; enforcing the arson laws; condemning unsafe buildings; overseeing the licensing of electricians; and reviewing construction plans for compliance with the Life Safety Code and the Public Handicapped Law. Fireworks laws are enforced by local authorities.

Appendices

Appendix E
EXPLANATION OF TERMS

The terms in this HANDBOOK are in accordance with general usage and dictionary definitions. Those listed below are used in this HANDBOOK with the meanings indicated. A number of special terms are individually defined in the text. See the Index for the location of these definitions.

Combustible is used to refer to a material or structure which can burn. *Combustible* is a relative term; many materials which will burn under one set of conditions will not burn under others, e.g., structural steel is noncombustible, but fine steel wool is combustible. The term *combustible* does not usually indicate ease of ignition, burning intensity, or rate of burning, except when modified by a word such as *highly,* as in *highly combustible interior finish.*

Fire prevention refers primarily to measures directed towards avoiding the inception of fire. *Fire prevention,* as used in the HANDBOOK, is not synonymous with *fire protection.*

Fireproof has been officially discontinued in NFPA publications as misleading, as no material is immune to the effects of fire of sufficient intensity and duration, although *fireproof* as popularly used is synonymous with *fire resistive* as defined here. *Fireproof* is also used in quotation marks in some references to popular misconceptions of the fire resistive properties of buildings.

Fire load refers to the amount of combustibles present in a given situation, usually expressed in terms of weight of combustible material per square foot. This measure is employed frequently to calculate the degree of fire resistance required to withstand a fire or to judge the rate of application and quantity of extinguishing agent needed to control or extinguish a fire.

Fire protection is used in two senses. The general sense, typified by the use of the term in the National Fire Protection Association name, includes everything relating to the prevention, detection, and extinguishment of fire; the reduction of losses and other matters covered in the HANDBOOK; as well as both the safeguarding of human life and the preservation of property. In its specific sense, *fire protection* refers to the methods of providing for fire control or fire extinguishment.

Fire resistance is a relative term, used with a numerical rating or modifying adjective to indicate the extent to which a material or structure resists the effect of fire, e.g., "*fire resistance* of 2 hours as measured on the Standard Time-Temperature Curve."

Fire resistive refers to properties or designs to resist the effects of any fire to which a material or structure may be expected to be subjected. *Fire resistive* materials or assemblies of materials are noncombustible, but noncombustible materials are not necessarily *fire resistive; fire resistive* implies a higher degree of fire resistance than noncombustible. *Fire-resistive* construction is defined in Section 6, Chapter 5 in terms of specified fire resistance as measured by the Standard Time-Temperature Curve.

Fire retardant, in general, denotes a substantially lower degree of fire resistance than fire resistive and is often used to refer to materials or structures which are combustible in whole or in part, but have been subjected to treatments or have surface coverings to prevent or retard ignition or the spread of fire under the conditions for which they are designed.

Flameproof, flameproofing are misleading terms and their use is discouraged in favor of *flame retardant* or *flame resistant.*

Flame resistant is a term that may be used more or less interchangeably with *flame retardant* (see below).

Flame retardant refers to materials, usually decorative, which due to chemical treatment or inherent properties do not ignite readily or propagate flaming under small to moderate exposure. It is the preferable term to denote chemicals, processes, paints, or coatings used for the treatment of such materials as fabrics, foliage, Christmas trees and similar items in the class of decorations or furnishings. Flame retardant denotes a lower degree of resistance than fire retardant.

Flammable is used to describe a combustible material that ignites very easily, burns intensely, or has a rapid rate of flamespread. *Flammable* is used in a general sense without reference to specific limits of ignition temperature, rate of burning, or other property. Where exact differentiations are necessary, numerical divisions are made, such as Class I and Class II *flammable* liquids. *Flammable* and *inflammable* are identical in meaning. *Flammable* is used in preference to *inflammable* to avoid possible confusion due to the prefix *in-* which indicates the negative in many words, e.g., *incombustible.*

Flashover refers to the phenomenon of a slowly developing fire (or radiant heat source) producing radiant energy at wall and ceiling surfaces. The radiant feedback from those surfaces gradually heats the contents of the fire area, and when all the combustibles in the space have become heated to their ignition temperature, simultaneous ignition occurs as from a pilot ignition source.

Hazard (hazardous) is used in different senses. One is to indicate materials of more than average combustibility or materials that are dangerous because of their explosibility, instability, or toxicity, e.g., cellulose nitrate which is *hazardous* because of ease of ignition and intensity of burning, or a combustible dust which presents a *hazardous* condition when in suspension. A second use of *hazardous* is to describe the over-all degree of fire vulnerability of a property, thinking in terms of its fire load. For example, sprinklers require closer spacing in an extra *hazard* occupancy than in an ordinary *hazard* occupancy. A third use of *hazard* is to describe rate of burning, e.g., wood in the form of shavings is more h*azardous* than in the form of solid timber. Then, too, the term *hazard* is used to describe the nature of the fire problem, e.g., common *hazards* are ignition sources encountered in almost every class of property (smoking, heating, electrical, etc.) while special *hazards* are those considered peculiar to an individual property, e.g., dip tanks, spray booths, drying ovens in a metalworking plant. There is no sharp line of demarcation between common and special *hazards* as the same potential fire cause may be considered a common *hazard* in one occupancy and a special *hazard* in another.

Incombustible has the same meaning as *noncombustible,* but may be subject to misunderstanding due to the prefix *in-.*

Inflammable. See Flammable.

Noncombustible means *not combustible.*

Nonflammable means *not flammable.*

GREEK ALPHABET

A	α	alpha	N	ν	nu
B	β	beta	Ξ	ξ	xi
Γ	γ	gamma	O	o	omicron
Δ	δ	delta	Π	π	pi
E	ϵ	epsilon	P	ρ	rho
Z	ζ	zeta	Σ	σ ς	sigma
H	η	eta	T	τ	tau
Θ	θ	theta	Υ	υ	upsilon
I	ι	iota	Φ	ϕ	phi
K	κ	kappa	X	χ	chi
Λ	λ	lambda	Ψ	ψ	psi
M	μ	mu	Ω	ω	omega

Appendix F

ABBREVIATIONS

abs	absolute
ac	alternating current
ACLM	American College of Legal Medicine
ACS	American Chemical Society
AGA	American Gas Association
AIA	American Insurance Association
AIAA	American Institute of Aeronautics & Astronautics
AIC	American Institute of Chemists
AIChE	American Institute of Chemical Engineers
AISC	American Institute of Steel Construction
a.m.	ante meridian
amp	ampere(s)
ANSI	American National Standards Institute
antilog	antilogarithm of
API	American Petroleum Institute
ASA	American Society of Anesthesiologists
ASME	American Society of Mechanical Engineers
ASSE	American Society of Safety Engineers
ASTM	American Society for Testing and Materials
atm	atmosphere(s)
avg	average
AWG	American wire gage
AWWA	American Water Works Association
bbl	barrel(s) (42 gallons)
Bé, Be	Baumé
bhp	brake horsepower
BOCA	Building Officials Conference of America
bp	boiling point
BS	British Standard
B&S	Brown & Sharp gage
BTC	Board of Transport Commissioners for Canada
Btu	British thermal unit(s)
C	Centigrade
CAB	Civil Aeronautics Board
cal	calorie(s)
cal/g	calorie(s) per gram
CC	closed cup
cc	cubic centimeter(s)
cfh	cubic foot (feet) per hour
cfm	cubic foot (feet) per minute
CFR	Code of Federal Regulations
cfs	cubic foot (feet) per second
cm	centimeter(s)
C.P.	chemically pure
CRC	Canadian Railway Commission
CSP	Certified Safety Professional
cu ft	cubic foot (feet)
cu in.	cubic inch (inches)
°Bé, °Be	degree Baumé
°C	degree(s) Celsius (Centigrade)
°F	degree(s) Fahrenheit
°K	degree(s) Kelvin
°R	degree(s) Rankine
db	decibel
dc	direct current
deg., Deg.	degree(s)
diam	diameter
DOT	Department of Transportation
DSIR	Department of Scientific and Industrial Research (British)
DTA	differential thermal analysis

e.g.	for example
emf	electromotive force
ERDA	Energy Research and Development Administration
ESA	Entomological Society of America
etc.	et cetera (and so forth)
F	Fahrenheit
FAA	Federal Aviation Administration
FM	Factory Mutual (system)
fpm	foot (feet) per minute
fps	foot (feet) per second
ft	foot (feet)
ft lb	foot pound(s)
g	gram(s)
gal	gallon(s) (gallons U.S. unless otherwise indicated)
GLA	gross leasable area
gpd	gallon(s) per day
gpm	gallon(s) per minute
HAD	heat-actuated device (thermostat)
hp	horsepower
hr, hrs	hour, hours
Hz	Hertz
IAFC	International Association of Fire Chiefs
IAFF	International Association of Fire Fighters
IATA	International Air Transport Association
IBS	Institute of Biological Science
ICAO	International Civil Aviation Organization
ID	inside diameter
i.e.	that is
IES	Institute of Environmental Sciences
Imp	imperial
in.	inch, inches
ipm	inch(es) per minute
ips	inch(es) per second
ISFI	International Society of Fire Service Instructors
ISO	Insurance Services Office
iso	isometric
J	Joule(s)
kg	kilogram
kJ	kilojoule
kJ/kg	kilojoule(s) per kilogram
kJ/m³	kilojoule(s) per cubic meter
km	kilometre(s)
kPa	kilopaseal(s)
kV	kilovolt(s)
kVa	kilovolt ampere(s)
kW	kilowatt(s)
kWh	kilowatt-hour(s)
l	litre(s)
lb, lbs	pound, pounds
LEL	lower explosive limit
LFL	lower flammable limit
l/min.	litre(s) per minute
l/min.m²	litre(s) per minute per square meter
LOI	limiting oxygen index
log	common log of
LP-Gas	liquified petroleum gas
m	metre, metre(s)
m²	square metre(s)
m³	cubic metre(s)

mA	milliampere(s)	**psi**	pounds per square inch
MAC	maximum allowable concentration	**psia**	pounds per square inch absolute
max	maximum	**psig**	pounds per square inch gage
MCA	Manufacturing Chemists' Association, Inc.	**pt**	pint(s)
MEV	million electron-volts	**qt**	quart(s)
mfd	microfarad(s)	**R**	Reynolds number
mmfd	micromicrofarad(s)	**r**	Roentgen(s)
mgd	million gallons per day	**rad**	radius
min	minimum; minute(s)	**rad**	radiation absorbed dose
ml	millilitre(s)	**RBE**	relative biological effectiveness
mm	millimetre(s)	**rem**	Roentgen equivalent man
mm²	square millimetre(s)	**rep**	Roentgen equivalent physical
mp	melting point	**rev**	revolution(s)
MPC	maximum permissible concentration	**rpm**	revolutions per minute
MPD	maximum permissible dose	**sec**	second(s), secondary
mph	miles per hour	**SFPE**	Society of Fire Protection Engineers
n	normal	**SPE**	Society of Plastics Engineers
NASA	National Aeronautics and Space Administration	**sp gr**	specific gravity
NASFCA	National Automatic Sprinkler and Fire Control Association	**sp ht**	specific heat
		sq ft	square foot (feet)
NBFU	National Board of Fire Underwriters (now American Insurance Association)	**sq in.**	square inch (inches)
		std	standard
NBS	National Bureau of Standards	**sym**	symmetrical
NEC	National Electrical Code	**temp**	temperature
NFPA	National Fire Protection Association	**ter**	tertiary
NPSH	net positive suction head	**TGA**	thermogravimetric
NTSB	National Transportation Safety Board	**UEL**	upper explosive limit
No.	number	**UFL**	upper flammable limit
NSC	National Safety Council	**UL**	Underwriters Laboratories Inc.
O	ohms	**ULC**	Underwriters' Laboratories of Canada
o	ortho	**U.S.**	United States
NSPE	National Society of Professional Engineers	**USCG**	United States Coast Guard
oc	open cup	**USDA**	U.S. Department of Agriculture
OD	outside diameter	**USFPL**	U.S. Forest Products Laboratory
OEA	oxygen enriched atmosphere(s)	**v**	volt(s)
OSHA	Occupational Safety and Health Act	**vad**	vapor-air density
oz	ounce(s)	**vd**	vapor density
p	para	**vel**	velocity
Pa	Pascal	**viz.**	namely
pcf	pound(s) per cubic foot	**vol**	volume
P.E.	professional engineer	**VP**	velocity pressure
p.m.	post meridian	**vs**	versus
ppg	pounds per gallon	**w**	watt(s)
ppm	parts per million	**W & M**	Washburn & Moen wire gage
press	pressure	**wt**	weight(s)
prim	primary	**yd**	yard(s)
psf	pounds per square feet		

Subject Index

This subject index has been compiled as an aid to HANDBOOK users in locating information on specific subjects of interest. Because of space limitations, it was not possible to list in the index all materials on which there is information in the HANDBOOK. As an example, Table 3-11A, Fire Hazard Properties of Flammable Liquids, Gases, and Volatile Solids, contains data on fire hazard properties of more than 1,700 individual entries. Listing in the index each liquid, gas, and solid found in Table 3-11A as well as entries from many other tables would increase the HANDBOOK's bulk to beyond manageable proportions.

HANDBOOK users are urged to consult the listings of tabular material found on page 3-137 (tables on fire hazard properties of materials), and the tables in Section 18, Chapters 2 and 4 (mathematical data and physical properties of certain materials) for guidance in locating subjects not found in the index. In addition, the editor calls attention of HANDBOOK users to the following tables which, because of the extent of their contents, are valuable reference sources. Titles of the tables are self-explanatory.

A

Abbreviations, A-41
Aboveground subway stations, fire hazards of, 17-34
ABS plastic, 3-98, *see also Styrene polymers*
Acceleration, conversion factors for, Table 18-3A
Accelerators, dry-pipe sprinkler systems, 14-21
Acetal resins, 3-82
Acetaldehyde
  ethyl acrylate, 3-60
  methyl acrylate, 3-60
  methyl methacrylate, 3-60
  vinylidene chloride, 3-60
Acetone vapor,
  flammable range in air, 3-22
Acetylene/air mixtures, static electricity, hazards of, 5-37
Acetylene gas
  chemical properties of, 3-47
  classifications of, 3-47
  emergency control of, 3-48
  hazards of, 3-48
  physical properties of, 3-48
  usage of, 3-48
Acid anhydrides, 3-62
Acids, inorganic, 3-65
Acoustical tiles, fire retardant treatments of, 5-73
Acrolien, toxic effects of, 2-18
Acrylics, in plastic manufacturing, 3-94
Acrylonitrile, as a fumigant, Table 5-8B
Acrylonitrile-butadrine-styrene (ABS), 3-98, *see also Styrene polymers*
Actuating devices, fire control systems, 12-21
Additives, wetting agent, 13-7
Adhesives, interior finish, affect on hazard of, 6-46
Adiabatic compression, as an ignition source for vapors, 3-24
Adsorbers, in chemical processes, 4-52
Aerial ladder trucks, 9-49
Aerial ladders, common sizes of, 9-49
Aerial tower trucks, 9-49
Aerosol spray containers, fire retardant solutions in, 5-70

Aerospace Industries Association of America, Inc., 17-15
AFFF, *see Aqueous film forming foam solution*
After-burner incineration, 4-24
Aggregates, in plaster, influence on fire resistance, 6-58
Agricultural dehydrators, 4-25
Agricultural dryers
  construction of, 4-27
  controls for, 4-27
  methods of heating, 4-26
  types of, 4-26
Agricultural products
  dusts, explosion hazards, Table 3-8A
  grinding processes for, 4-58
  solvent extraction for, 4-60
  spontaneous heating in, 2-10
  storage of, 3-64
Air
  extinguishing agent, use as, 15-65
  pressurized, as oxygen-enriched atmosphere, 5-54
Air agitation, oil tank fire control by, 15-65
Air atomizing oil burners, 7-40
Air-break switches, electrical, 7-19
Air classifiers, grinding processes, 4-54
Air cleaners, fire protection for, 7-68, *see also Air filters*
Air compressors, for hospitals, 5-55
Air conditioners
  household use, 7-19
  unit type, 7-70
Air conditioning systems, *see also Ventilating systems*
  controls for, 7-70
  cooling equipment, 7-67
  ducts for, 7-68, *see also Ducts*
  fan units for, 7-70
  filters for, 7-67
  fire dampers in, 7-69
  fresh-air intakes for, 7-66
  general information, 7-2
  heating equipment for, 7-67
  location of equipment, 7-66
  maintenance of, 7-70
  smoke dampers in, 7-69
  smoke detection in, 7-69
  types of, 7-66

Air conveying systems, 5-23
Aircraft, *see also Airports*
  aviation fire safety organizations, 17-15
  brake and tire fires, 17-7
  cabins, interior finish of, 17-7
  cargoes, hazards of, 17-8
  design problems of, 17-2
  electrical systems for, 17-7
  emergencies involving, types of, 9-28
  estimated fire losses in, 1-16
  evacuation devices for, 17-11
  exit facilities from, 17-10
  fire control techniques, 17-12
  fire detection systems in
    installation of, 17-8, 17-9
    location of detectors, 17-9
    zones requiring detectors, 17-9
  fire extinguishers for, 17-10
  fire extinguishing systems in
    design of, 17-8
    installation of, 17-9
  firesafety in
    principles of, 17-2
    regulations for, 17-15
  for forest fire fighting, 13-9, 5-82
  fuel distribution systems for, 17-5
  fueling ramp drainage, 17-14
  fuels for, *see Aviation fuels*
  fuel servicing, 17-4, 17-15
  fuel tanks, 17-5
  fuselage compartments
    air flows in, 17-7
    hazards in, 17-7
  hangars, types of, 17-13
  hydraulic systems, 17-7
  inherent hazards in, 17-7
  large loss fires in, 1-17
  loading walkways, 17-15
  loss of life in, reasons for, 17-2
  lubricating systems for, 17-7
  military type
    armament, 17-11
    bombs, 17-11
    ejection devices, 17-11
    hazards of, 17-11
    missile launch sites, 17-12
    missile propellants, 17-11
    overrun prevention measures, 17-13
    pyrotechnics, 17-11
    rockets, 17-11, 17-12